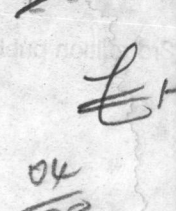

MUSICMASTER
PRICE GUIDE FOR
RECORD COLLECTORS
3rd EDITION

Edited by

Nick Hamlyn

Retail Entertainment Data

Retail Entertainment Data Publishing Ltd,
Paulton House, 8 Shepherdess Walk, London N1 7LB

3rd edition published by **Retail Entertainment Data Publishing Ltd.** 1994

2nd edition published 1992
1st edition published 1991

All enquiries:
Retail Entertainment Data Publishing Ltd.
Paulton House, 8 Shepherdess Walk, London N1 7LB
Tel: +44 (0)171 490 0049 Fax: +44 (0)171 253 1308

Editor: Matthew Garbutt, **Editorial Assistant:** Gary Ford
Editorial Team: Jane Scarratt, Bruno MacDonald, Howard Richardson
Product Manager: Chris Spalding
Sales Manager: Marie-Clare Murray
Senior Sales Executive: Anna Sperni, **Sales Executive:** Adrian Pope
Publisher: Brenda Daly.

Cover artwork and design by: IIIi, London

Database typeset, printed and bound in Great Britain by: Unwin Bros, Surrey.

ISBN 0 904520 87 0

DPA
DIRECTORY PUBLISHERS
ASSOCIATION

CONTENTS

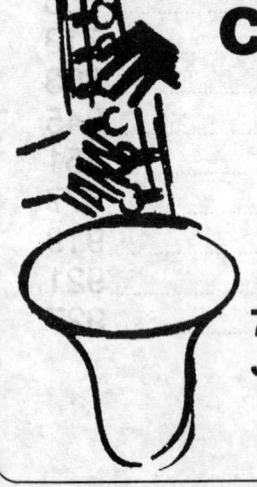

INTRODUCTION

As I write these words, I am sitting behind a stall at a record fair in the Midlands. From the right, the characteristic whine of late-period Bob Dylan can be heard - carelessly destroying one of the classic songs of his youth. Opposite, there is a repeated loop of sustained guitar notes. This has to be Robert Fripp, with one of his exercises in 'Frippertronics'. The collision between Dylan and Fripp is interesting - neither musician is ever likely to work with the other in reality, yet the combination has possibilities!

Everywhere I look, I can see records - the boxed arrays of seven and twelve inch sleeves (so effective for making a display) hiding their curious circular slabs of etched plastic. We are continually told that there is no longer any demand for these anachronistic pieces of vinyl - but the crowds of people pushing past each other to have a close look at what is on offer today obviously have not been listening. The fair has CDs as well, of course, but the stalls selling these are easily outnumbered by those dealing in old-fashioned vinyl. It is likely that all the stall-holders will return home tonight with a feeling of satisfaction over a profitable day's trading.

Four years ago, the first edition of the Music Master Price Guide was published as the first comprehensive record collectors' price guide in the UK. At the time it was possible for die-hard vinyl enthusiasts (amongst whom I numbered myself) to imagine that the outcome of the format battle was still in doubt. Today, as far as the shops selling new releases are concerned, the battle has been won by the compact disc, with vinyl either ousted altogether or else in a state of not very dignified retreat (and the victor, according to several sources, already casting its blood-lustful eyes in the direction of the humble cassette).

The collectors' market has not been unaffected by these developments. A few compact discs are selling for collectors' prices, although, perhaps surprisingly, there are not many more of these than there were four years ago. The market for collectable vinyl, however, has undoubtedly shrunk a little - even if the evidence of the record fairs is that a large number of people - of all ages and tastes - still consider vinyl to be of interest. The general upwards trend in values that has been apparent over the last decade has largely halted (with the notable exception of original fifties rock'n'roll and R&B) - and in some areas, prices are now beginning to fall. The records' condition has become more critical than ever before, with collectors being increasingly reluctant to buy anything in less than pristine condition - especially at the lower end of the value scale. All these changes are reflected in this new, third edition of the Music Master Price Guide, which, for the first time, lists values in two condition categories - 'near mint' (excellent) and the significantly lower 'very good'.

At the same time, this third edition of the Price Guide is actually quite a bit larger than its predecessors. On the one hand, the collectors' interest in specialised areas like jazz and folk is widening - so that it seemed appropriate to add a large number of jazz and folk records to the listings (some would say that this move was long overdue!). On the other hand, many rock collectors delight in discovering previously overlooked 'classics' (or even unknown records that they quite like!), so that new names are becoming collectable all the time.

It would be extremely rash to try and predict the long-term future of record collecting. It is certain, however, that whether the tenth edition of the Music Master Price Guide will prove to be full of listings for (doubtless obsolete) CDs, or will still list a large number of increasingly aged vinyl recordings (or will have quantities of both), it will nevertheless document some kind of flourishing collectors' market for music. As long as people are interested in listening to music, then there will be people wishing to make collections of the artefacts that enable that music to be heard.

Meanwhile, this third edition of the Music Master Price Guide presents the record collectors' market as it is now. Like its predecessors, it is an essential work of reference for collectors, dealers, and researchers alike.

How accurate are the values listed in the guide?

The title of this book means what it says: it is a guide to the values of collectable records. Within any collectors' field, an item is essentially worth whatever a collector is prepared to pay for it. When considering items of which several copies are potentially available, however, as s the case with collectors' records, then a few points need to be kept in mind. Let us suppose that Steve Crick, a collector of extraordinary tastes, is desperate to obtain a copy of 'My Old Killarney Hat' by Sister Mary Gertrude. This is not a record that features very often in dealers' lists, so Steve advertises that he is prepared to pay fifty pounds for a copy. Four dealers eventually manage to come across the elusive record: one is delighted to receive fifty pounds from an equally delighted Steve Crick, but the other three find that they are unable to interest anyone at all in the record, at any price. So what is the value of 'My Old Killarney Hat'?

At the other end of the scale, there must be numerous collectors who would like to obtain a copy of the Beatles fan club album, 'From Then To You'. This is a record with a listed value of £250 - it is scarce, but copies do turn up, and most dealers will have had at least one passing through their hands. Dave Conroy is a keen Beatles collector and he does not have a copy of 'From Then To You'. On the other hand, he does have the actual music in his collection, as he was able to buy an American counterfeit of the record quite cheaply a few years ago. When he sees the real thing in his local collectors' record shop with a price tag of £250, he argues that he has waited twenty years for the record, so he might as well wait a little longer for a copy that is more 'reasonably' priced. In the event, the shop is unable to find a customer for the record. The manager reduces the price to £225, and after a few weeks, with the record still unsold, Dave Conroy offers £200, which is accepted. So again, what is the value of 'From Then To You'?

A junk shop, selling all kinds of second-hand goods from shabby premises, and with a box of old records in the corner, would find in all probability that the records would remain unsold if priced according to the values given in this guide. An efficient specialist mail-order company, on the other hand, with a large number of customers in Scandinavia, Germany, and Japan, could well be regularly managing to obtain prices in excess of those listed in the guide. The above arguments apply equally well in the case of known rarities being sold at auction. As every rare record dealer is aware, offers made on these occasions can often climb way above the 'book values' of the records in question. There are a number of collectors who, like Steve Crick, are prepared to pay well over the odds to gain the rare records they need. There are also a much larger number of collectors who are of the Dave Conroy persuasion and prepared to temper their enthusiasm. It is important, therefore, to resist the temptation to assume that, simply because one copy of, for example, 'Say Those Magic Words' by Bird's Birds has successfully been auctioned for £250, then all subsequent copies of the record will also sell for that figure.

To these considerations must be added the fact that the collectors' market is a volatile one. The success of a new group in the charts can send the values of their back catalogue shooting upwards (although a later fall from favour can just as easily send then tumbling back down again); an influential disc jockey can create a collectors' item out of an obscurity simply by deciding to play it (particularly in the case of soul records); or else the reissue of a scarce album can increase the value of the original by making more people aware of its existence. On the other hand, the discovery of a warehouse full of copies of a previously rare record is likely to make the price fall dramatically; or a similar effect can simply result from several people deciding to sell their cherished copies of the same record at the same time. It happens!

To repeat, therefore, this book is a guide to the values of collectable records. A large amount of research, however, has gone into making it as accurate as possible, much of it being first-hand - the result of actually selling the records through a successful collectors' record shop to both the home and the international market over a period of several years. The values are based on actual sales and, within the constraints detailed above, the margin of error is not likely to be large. Comments and corrections are always welcome, however.

To qualify as collectable, a lower price limit was set. All the LPs included in the guide are valued at ten pounds or over; double LPs are twelve pounds or over. 7" singles are four pounds or over; 7" EPs are five pounds and over; 12", cassette, and CD singles start at six pounds; CD albums start at fifteen pounds.

How is the price guide organised?

The artists are listed alphabetically, and for each one the collectable records are also listed alphabetically. Where more than one listing appears under the same name, then these are actually the recordings of different artists. It must be remembered that the listings are not complete discographies, but only a catalogue of those items that are valuable enough to be considered collectable. As far as possible, it is the A side that is listed in the case of singles, but if a certain title cannot be found, it is always worth checking to see if the B side has been listed instead. Similarly, where a record has a different artist on each side (a common practice with sixties reggae and ska singles), it will only be listed under one of them. Records featuring several different artists are usually listed under the 'Various' heading. A small number of abbreviations have been used. These are as follows:

cass: Cassette
cass-s: Cassingle
CD-s: Compact Disc single
PS: Picture Sleeve
r-reel: reel to reel tape

As a finale to this introduction I would like to offer my grateful thanks to the various dealers and collectors who have helped with information, advice, and record sleeves for photographing. An enormous number of people have contacted me after reading the first and second editions of the price guide and I have talked with a large number of dealers and collectors at different record fairs. I hope that they will have the satisfaction of seeing some of their information included, even if there are far too many names for me to list here! Particular thanks are due, however, to Del Burgess, Geoffrey Burton, Terry Chubb, Andy and Heather Crosskey, Steve Gardner, Michael Gerzon, Stuart Hall, Andrew Hawkey, Mark Hawkins, Natalie Hill, Jo and Steve Horne, Lynda Kerr, Peter Loughran, Rob Lythall, Jane and Tim McMellon, Steve Moulin, Bob Newton, Mick Nightingale, Tony Prince, Chris Savory (author of 'UK Black Music 45s'), Richard Sefton, Pete Sen, Pete Smith, Ron Tabor, John and Carol Talbot, Chris Talbot, Jon Taylor, John Wagstaff (author of 'The International Record & CD Price Guide'), Phil Walker; and my family - Liz, David and Eileen, Catherine, Fred, and Sarah.

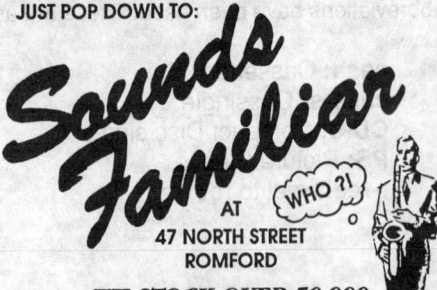

x

INDEX OF COLOUR PLATES

PLATE 6

PLATE 7

PLATE 8

PLATE 9

PLATE 10

PLATE 11

PLATE 12

Rare Amber: .... Rare Amber
Raw Material: .... Time Is
Max Roach And Clifford Brown: .... In Concert Vol. 2
Rockin' Berries: .... In Town
Rolling Stones: .... Flowers
Rolling Stones: .... Get Off My Cloud
Ronettes: .... Ronettes
Samson: .... Are You Samson

PLATE 13

Sandrose: .... Sandrose
Robin Scott: .... Woman From The Warm Grass
Seastone: .... Mirrored Dreams
Second Hand: .... Death May Be Your Santa Claus
Silver Birch: .... Silver Birch
Alan Skidmore: .... Once Upon A Time
Skip Bifferty: .... Skip Bifferty
Bob B. Sox And The Blue Jeans: .... Zip-A-Dee Doo Dah

PLATE 14

Spacemen 3: .... Transparent radiation
Spirogyra: .... St. Radigunds
Bruce Springsteen: .... Darkness On The Edge Of Town
Ringo Starr: .... Scouse The Mouse
Still Life: .... Still Life
Sundown Playboys: .... Saturday Night Special
Tea And Symphony: .... An Asylum For The Musically Insane
Teddy Bears: .... Sing

PLATE 15

Top Topham: .... Ascension Heights
Twistin' Kings: .... Twistin' The World Around
Tyrannosaurus Rex: .... My People Were Fair
Hilton Valentine: .... All In Your Head
Various: .... The Sound Of The R&B Hits
Gene Vincent: .... Crazy Times
Vipers Skiffle Group: .... Coffee Bar Session
Waiting For The Sun: .... Waiting For The Sun

PLATE 16

Way We Live: .... A Candle For Judith
Houston Wells: .... Western Style
Mike Westbrook: .... Release
Westwood One: .... US Radio Transcription Disc
Who: .... Who Did It
Wooden O: .... A Handful Of Pleasant Delites
Writing On The Wall: .... The Power Of The Picts
Zombies: .... Odessey And Oracle

GLOSSARY

ACETATES

Acetates are records made either of hard, brittle plastic or else of metal with a thin vinyl coating. There are two sources of these. Song pluggers in the early sixties would often operate acetate disc-cutters to enable them to easily produce convenient demonstration recordings at a time when cassettes did not exist. Within recording studios, meanwhile, similar quickly produced acetates would be made in order to give the artist or some other interested party some idea of how the finished recording would sound. Where such acetates feature artists whose regular records are collectable, they can also acquire a considerable collectors' interest, especially bearing in mind the fact that, at most, only a handful of copies of any one recording are likely to be in existence. Many commercially released records can be found in acetate form, but values for these tend to be modest, apart from those made by the most collected artists. Examples that have been sold at some of the London rock auctions include the following:

BEATLES:	All My Loving £260 (1991)
	Penny Lane/Strawberry Fields Forever £400 (1990)
MARC BOLAN:	Hot Love £120 (1990)
DAVID BOWIE:	Up The Hill Backwards £35 (1990)
CREAM:	Wrapping Paper £125 (1994)
JIMI HENDRIX:	The Wind Cries Mary £50 (1986)
BUDDY HOLLY:	Peggy Sue £380 (1987)
MICHAEL JACKSON:	Bad £220 (1989)
MADONNA:	True Blue £65 (1989)
BOB MARLEY:	Jamming £90 (1988)
PINK FLOYD:	See Emily Play £154 (1989)
ELVIS PRESLEY:	Heartbreak Hotel 78 £380 (1994)
ROLLING STONES:	The Last Time £330 (1990)
SEX PISTOLS:	Pretty Vacant £200 (1987)

Inevitably, the acetates that are of most interest to collectors are those that contain songs or versions of songs that did not end up as a commercial release. It is in this area that the highest prices have been reached, as the following auction examples make clear:

BEATLES:	Hey Little Girl/Like Dreamers Do £2500 (1986)
	Twelve Bar Original 13.12.65 £1300 (1988)
	Yesterday (alternate take) £770 (1989)
CLIFF RICHARD:	Breathless/Lawdy Miss Clawdy £2800 (1985)
	Breathless/Lawdy Miss Clawdy £1000 (1986)
ROLLING STONES:	Road Runner/Diddley Daddy £1500 (1988)
	Soon Forgotten/Close Together/Can't Judge A Book £6000 (1988)
	Soon Forgotten/Close Together/Can't Judge A Book £4000 (1989)

It is interesting to see how different acetates of the same recordings can realise quite different prices on different occasions. While some of this discrepancy may be explicable in terms of different playing surface conditions, it also highlights the extent to which the demands of just one or two individual collectors can produce a result that confounds general expectations. A third copy of 'Soon Forgotten' (predating the Rolling Stones' earliest Decca recordings) was subsequently auctioned and failed to reach its reserve price. Perhaps there were, after all, only two collectors prepared to pay substantial four figure sums for this small chunk of rock music history.

ACTION

Action was a specialist soul label, whose singles issued in 1968 and 1969 (with a distinctive red and black label bearing a shooting star logo) are all very much in demand. Soul collectors, more than those in other fields, tend to prefer demo copies of singles, arguing that these are the true first pressings. This is particularly true of the Action label, where demos typically have a value of three times that of the standard issues.

APPLE

The label set up and run by the Beatles is viewed as a legitimate area of interest by Beatles collectors. Quite apart from the records of the Beatles themselves, there are a few considerable rarities on the label, by such names as the Iveys, Delaney and Bonnie, Richard Brautigan, and John Taverner. The enormous musical range represented by these and the other names on the label reflects the fact that, of course, the Beatles were wealthy enough to issue whatever music took their individual fancies, without commercial success being a particular consideration. The records issued by the Beatles themselves from 1968 onwards were on the Apple label as far as label design was concerned, but the catalogue numbers were actually part of the main Parlophone series.

ATLANTIC

The Atlantic label's status as one of the most successful independents (until its incorporation within the Kinney organisation in 1971) depended on the skill with its founders, the Ertegun brothers, were able to identify the key developments in jazz and R&B. In the UK, Atlantic releases were originally distributed via the London label, but om 1964 the Atlantic label was issued in its own right. Identification of original pressings is not a problem, since Atlantic obligingly used new catalogue numbers to whenever a reissue was made. In particular, the Kinney take-ver resulted in the use of a 'K' as prefix to all UK catalogue numbers - so that, 'Led Zeppelin IV', for example, hanged from 2401012 to K50008. (There was also a label design change at this time, with the red and plum LP labels becoming green and orange).

AUCTIONS

For some time now, rock music auctions have been held once or twice a year by all the major London auction houses. These have tended to concentrate on memorabilia rather than records as such, and they have become the foremost market place for star instruments, stage clothing, star autographs, gold disc awards, and the like. A number of scarce acetate recordings have also been sold at auction, but commercial recordings, even when very rare, have played a very limited part on such occasions. At a more private level, however, record auctions are often the most appropriate means of sale for the rarest records. While there is little point in asking for offers on an item whose twenty pound value is well established and which is relatively often offered for sale, there are a number of more valuable items (notably the rarest rock-'n-roll and R&B singles from the fifties) where the demand by individual collectors can be such as to make them prepared to offer considerably more than the Guide value on occasion.

AUDIOPHILE PRESSINGS

Hi-fi enthusiasts will always maintain that a vinyl record played on a quality system will always sound better than a compact disc. A better sound still is intended to be obtainable from the 'super-stereo', audiophile albums that were issued in the late seventies and eighties. These are mastered at half the usual speed from a tape playing at half the usual speed, which is supposed to create a superior sound quality when played back normally. The records are also pressed on to virgin vinyl, with a high degree of quality control. Despite this, it is actually quite difficult to distinguish most audiophile recordings from their ordinary stereo equivalents on a blindfold test.

AUTOGRAPHS

Autographs are inevitably the easiest collecting feature to counterfeit, for which reason autographed records will often attract no more than a slight premium over the normal value of the item, particularly in the case of a modern artist who is still touring and is not of the first stellar magnitude. The situation is different in the case of star or historic names, where the value of an artist's rarest records provides an indication of the likely value of a genuine autograph. The most valuable - by artists like the Beatles and Elvis Presley - are regular features of the London rock auctions, where the authenticity of the autographs will have been verified by experts with experience of what the star signatures actually look like. Other dealers will require some kind of provenance, which may comprise nothing more complicated than a convincing story as to how the autograph was obtained, if the estimated value is not too high. It should be realised, to mention just one area of possible confusion, that signed photographs issued by the Beatles fanclub had often never actually been in contact with the pen of a real Beatle, although Ringo Starr apparently quite enjoyed this aspect of fame and would sometimes sign all four names himself! There are, of course, a number of limited edition releases bearing autographs, and these are listed in the Guide where appropriate.

AVENGERS

The cult TV programme is represented on vinyl by recordings of its theme tunes. The first series with Patrick McNee and Honor Blackman had a theme by Johnny Dankworth. The second and third series with McNee and Diana Rigg, followed by McNee and Linda Thorson had a theme by Laurie Johnson, and since these series were the ones that achieved the biggest cult following, it is Johnson's music that is most readily associated with the programme. The New Avengers revival in the seventies was rather less popular, but its theme was also by Laurie Johnson. Details of all these records can be found in the Guide under the appropriate artist headings.

BATMAN

In 1966 the Batman TV series started, complete with its catchy double-note riff theme. A large number of different artists recorded it, entries in this Guide being found under the following names: Neal Hefti, Jan And Dean, The Marketts, Nelson Riddle, The Riddlers, The Spacemen, The Spotlights, The Ventures, Link Wray (a latecomer from 1978), and The Who (on their 'Ready Steady Who' EP). The stars of the show, Adam West and Burt Ward, made an LP themselves, while Ward followed this up with a single the next year (masterminded by Frank Zappa). A reggae tribute was issued in 1970 by the Sydney All Stars, while the 1989 Batman film also turns up in the Guide, represented by Prince's LP picture disc.

BBC TRANSCRIPTION DISCS

These records are not listed within the Guide, although they are actually highly collectable. In order to sell its programmes to radio stations abroad, the BBC records them on to LPs (CDs in recent times), which can be easily used for broadcast purposes. The records of interest to rock music collectors consist of live recordings from programmes like Radio One's 'In Concert'. Essentially, anyone who is anyone in the eighties and nineties has at least one side of one of these records devoted to their music, while a large number of seventies artists are also represented. Unfortunately, the BBC itself does not approve of the sale of its transcription discs. It will not provide any kind of discography and indeed it actively operates to prevent such records being advertised for sale. Copies do change hands on the collectors' market notwithstanding, although values are kept relatively low by the existence of bootlegs and counterfeits, the average being around £50 to £60. Exceptions to this average are the artists one would expect - 'The Beatles At The Beeb' set would be likely to sell for around £500, for example. Any BBC record with a black and white label is definitely a counterfeit, as original labels are green and white (early issues are green and yellow). Also counterfeit are the records that apparently have correct labels, but have hand-scratched matrix numbers on the vinyl.

BLUE HORIZON

Producer Mike Vernon formed the Blue Horizon label as an outlet for his beloved blues music and the entire catalogue is now collectable (even the label's one sore thumb, an album by the group Focus, manages to sneak in). The very earliest records to make use of the Blue Horizon name were ten singles and a pair of albums (one by Dr. Ross and one a various artists collection) that were sold by mail order in 1965-6. The albums in particular are now extremely rare. In 1967 the signing of Peter Green's new group, Fleetwood Mac, prompted a distribution deal with CBS. The first single releases by Fleetwood Mac and Aynsley Dunbar bore a Blue Horizon logo on an orange CBS label, but by the start of 1968 the familiar light blue label was in use.

BLUE NOTE

Blue Note is the most collected jazz label in the UK, with every sixties release being of value (and listed in the Guide). The label was founded in 1939 in the US, and the earliest album releases now command high prices. A mint copy of 'Genius Of Modern Music Vol.1' by Thelonious Monk (Blue Note BLP5002 1951) sells for £250, for example. Starting in 1961, records released on the label became available in the UK as direct imports. Within this Guide, the issue date given often refers to the date of import rather than to the actual release date in the US, which may well have been a few years earlier (this is true for all of the LPs in the BLP15 series). These original US pressings will be worth significantly more than the values listed, which apply to the import copies. Original Blue Note records issued during 1961-66 have a blue and white label design with the legend 'Blue Note Records Inc * New York USA'; from 1966 to 1970 the legend 'A Division Of Liberty Records' appears. The same label design reappeared in 1985, but apart from the fact that the reissues from this time have a generally newer appearance, they also cary the new wording 'The Finest In Jazz Since 1939'.

BOND, JAMES

Records associated with the James Bond films are widely collected and are listed in the Price Guide under the names of the relevant artists. Much of the sound-track music has been written and recorded by John Barry. Other relevant entries are as follows: Monty Norman (Dr. No); Matt Monro (From Russia With Love); Shirley Bassey (Goldfinger and Diamonds Are Forever); Tom Jones (Thunderball); Burt Bacharach (Casino Royale); Dusty Springfield ('The Look Of Love', from Casino Royale, is the B side of 'Give Me Time'); Nancy Sinatra (You Only Live Twice); Louis Armstrong ('We Have All The Time In The World' from On Her Majesty's Secret Service); Lulu (The Man With The Golden Gun); Michel Legrand (Never Say Never Again); and A-Ha (The Living Daylights). A large number of other artists have also issued cover versions of the various Bond theme songs and other songs associated with, or inspired by James Bond.

BOOTLEGS

A bootleg recording is one that consists of either a live performance or else a set of studio out-takes. Such recordings do not duplicate any official record-company release and, unlike the situation with regard to counterfeits, the issue of whether or not they are genuine does not arise. They are illegal because of the lack of record company involvement, although occasionally the artist is involved and may even get some royalty payment. Lowell George, for example, is known to have mixed two Little Feat live bootlegs himself. Bootlegs are, nevertheless, often keenly sought by collectors for the sake of the otherwise unavailable music they contain. Popular titles are constantly reissued by different manufacturers and there is little interest in 'originals' - any pressing will normally satisfy a collector. In so far, therefore, as the value of bootleg records stays at around the ten to fifteen pound figure they fetch when new, they are outside the scope of this Guide.

CAPITOL

Capitol singles had purple labels in the fifties and black in the sixties. The LPs had turquoise labels in the fifties and black labels with a rainbow border in the sixties. In 1968, the rainbow border was dropped for a short time, before the company switched to a lime green label, with a new deep pink logo.

CASSETTES

Cassettes are not very well favoured by collectors. Many of the highly priced progressive albums from the early seventies were also issued on cassette, and these are at least as rare as their vinyl equivalents. Despite this, the cassettes do not have a significant collectors' value at all. To illustrate the point, only one such cassette is actually listed in this Guide. David Bowie's 'The Man Who Sold The World' with the dress cover is listed at £170 for the LP, but a mere £15 for the cassette that was issued at the same time. In the case of modern releases, too, cassette-singles have noticeably failed to maintain an initial interest from collectors, while even the limited privately produced items from early in the careers of subsequently successful groups have much lower values than would vinyl versions if these existed.

CBS

The label that is called Columbia in the US became abbreviated to CBS in the UK (standing for Columbia Broadcasting Systems) to avoid conflict with the UK Columbia label, whose links with its American ancestor became severed during the fifties. The plain orange labels used by CBS on both its singles and LPs in 1962, when the first UK records were released, remained essentially unchanged until 1975, when a new label on which orange shaded into yellow was introduced. As a result, the label design is of limited use in identifying original pressings of records by the likes of Bob Dylan. The BPG prefix used for LPs (SBPG for stereo), however, was dropped at the start of 1968 and reissues from that date onwards have their catalogue numbers amended accordingly.

CHARISMA

The Charisma label began in 1969 as something of a progressive rock specialist label. Most of the early albums are collectable, although the label lacked the sureness of touch of Island or Vertigo, and a few releases are hardly sought after at all. Until 1972, the label design featured a large scroll logo on a deep pink background and first pressings of early albums by the likes of Audience, Van Der Graaf Generator, and Genesis have this label. A new design, featuring a cartoon mad hatter on a pale pink label began with the album 'Foxtrot' by Genesis (CAS1058). Albums bearing this label but with lower catalogue numbers are therefore second issues and are worth no more than 50% of the first issue values.

CLASSICAL MUSIC

Although considerations of time and space prevent their inclusion in this edition of the Price Guide, collectors and dealers generally should be aware of the high prices being demanded and paid for certain classical records. Realistically, a complete listing of all the collectable classical records would fill a second volume as large as this one. The market as a whole, however, is smaller at present than the rock collectors' market, with many fewer specialist dealers serving the appetites of a small but active body of enthusiasts. The most sought after are the early stereo recordings made by Decca, the company that pioneered the LP in Britain. Decca were always very concerned to deliver the highest sound quality possible and the stereo records in the SXL2000 and SXL6000 series, together with the boxed sets in the SET200 series, are collected as being among the finest classical recordings ever made. Also in demand are the later Decca issues on the Phase Four label (PFS series) and on all the Argo subsidiary series. The Decca labels, Eclipse (ECS series), Ace Of Diamonds (SDD and GOS series), and World Of (SPA series), reissued the early Decca recordings at a bargain price, but the sound quality is as good as the originals. These records are therefore collected as well, although the values are inevitably rather lower. (Anything in 'electronic stereo', however, is immediately shunned, as such recordings do not have the high sound quality that collectors demand). The Decca company were also responsible for pressing records on certain other labels, which have again become collectable. These are Capitol (CTL series), Lyrita (SRCS series, until as late as 1980), London (American CS, OS, OSA, and STS series), and RCA (SB2000, SB6500, and SER4000 series until 1970, together with the 'bargain' Victrola releases bearing a ruby label, VICS1000 series) Mercury 'Living Presence' recordings are also renowned for their impressive sound quality, many of them being the result of recordings on to 35mm magnetic film. The American SR series is very collectable in consequence, as is the British AMS series, whose records were made by EMI, using American masters and machine parts. Other collectable early stereo recordings are to be found on the Angel (SAN and American 35000 series), Columbia SAX series until 1967; SCX3000 series; TWO series), HMV (ASD series until 1969; CSD series; SLS series of boxed sets), Philips (SABL series), and RCA (LSC 'Living Stereo' series) labels. Some early mono recordings on all these labels are also sought after by some collectors, although in general the demand for mono records is quite limited, other than for key items that never were issued in stereo. A few of the most collectable records are listed below. It should be stressed, however, that these represent the merest tip of a considerable ice-berg. (It should also be stressed that the small number of dealers working in this area, together with the lack of literature on the subject, results in considerable price variation. The values given here must be viewed as being highly approximate).

ERNEST ANSERMET + Suisse Romande Orchestra: .... Tchaikovsky Sleeping Beauty Decca stereo SXL2160-2 1959 £400 (3 records)
ATAULFO ARGENTA + London Symphony Orchestra: .... Concert (Espana!) Decca stereo SXL2020 1958 £400
ATAULFO ARGENTA + National Orchestra Of Spain: .... De Falla Master Peter's Puppet Show/El Amor Brujo Decca stereo SXL2260 1961 £400
ANDRE CLUYTENS + Paris Conservatoire Orchestra: .... Ravel Concert Columbia stereo SAX2476-9 1963 £400 (4 records)
ANDRE CLUYTENS + Philharmonia Orchestra: .... Concert Columbia stereo SAX2355 1960 £250
GIOCONDA DE VITO: .... Bach Violin Concerto in E/Mozart Violin Concerto No.3 HMV stereo ASD429 1961 £1200 .... HMV mono ALP1856 1961 £200
GIOCONDA DE VITO: .... Beethoven Violin Sonata No.9 (Kreutzer) HMV mono ALP1319 1956 £300
GIOCONDA DE VITO: .... Beethoven Violin Sonata No.7/Brahms Violin Sonata No.2 HMV mono ALP1521 1958 £30
GIOCONDA DE VITO: .... Brahms Violin Sonatas Nos.1 & 3 HMV mono ALP1282 1955 £200
OIVIN FJELDSTAD + London Symphony Orchestra: .... Grieg Peer Gynt Incidental Music Decca stereo SXL2012 1958 £400
WILHELM FURTWANGLER + Vienna Philharmonic Orchestra: .... Wagner Die Walkure HMV mono ALP1257-61 1955 £500 (5 records)
VITTORIO GUI + Glyndebourne Festival Orchestra: .... Mozart Le Nozze Di Figaro HMV stereo ASD274-7 1959 £400 (4 records)
ARAM KHACHATURIAN + Vienna Philharmonic Orchestra: .... Khachaturian Spartacus and Gayaneh excerpts Decca stereo SXL6000 1963 £250
ERICH KLEIBER + Vienna Philharmonic Orchestra: .... Mozart Le Nozze Di Figaro Decca stereo SXL2087-90 1959 £800 (4 records)
OTTO KLEMPERER + Philharmonia Orchestra: .... Mahler Symphony No.2 Columbia stereo SAX2473-4 1963 £200 (2 records)
LEONID KOGAN + Constantin Silvestri + Paris Conservatoire Orchestra: .... Beethoven Violin Concerto Columbia stereo SAX2386 1961 £200
LEONID KOGAN + Kyril Kondrashin + Philharmonia Orchestra: .... Brahms Violin Concerto Columbia stereo SAX2307 1960 £200
LEONID KOGAN + Kyril Kondrashin + Philharmonia Orchestra: .... Lalo Symphonie Espagnole/Tchaikovsky Serenade Melancholique Columbia stereo SAX2329 1960 £200
JOSEF KRIPS + Vienna Philharmonic Orchestra: .... Mozart Don Giovanni Decca stereo SXL2117-20 1959 £800 (4 records)
RAFAEL KUBELIK + Royal Philharmonic Orchestra: .... Beethoven Symphony No.6 HMV stereo ASD349 1960 £250

RAFAEL KUBELIK + Vienna Philharmonic Orchestra: ....
.... Mozart Symphonies Nos.36 & 38 HMV stereo ASD451 1962 £200
RAFAEL KUBELIK + Vienna Philharmonic Orchestra: ....
.... Schubert Symphonies Nos.3 & 4 HMV stereo ASD418 1961 £200
PETER MAAG + London Symphony Orchestra: ....
.... Mendelssohn Midsummer Night's Dream Decca stereo SXL2060 1959 £200
JOHANNA MARTZY: ....
.. Bach Violin Sonatas Nos.1-3/Violin Partitas Nos.1-3 Columbia mono 33CX1286-8 1955 £1200 (3 records)
JOHANNA MARTZY: ....
.... Schubert Rondeau Brilliant in Bmin/Fantaisie in C Columbia mono 33CX1372 1957 £400
JOHANNA MARTZY + Paul Kletzki + Philharmonia Orchestra: ....
.... Brahms Violin Concerto Columbia mono 33CX1165 1954 £600 (first thick pressing)
JOHANNA MARTZY + Paul Kletzki + Philharmonia Orchestra: ....
.... Beethoven Romances/Mendelssohn Violin Concerto Columbia mono 33CX1479 1958 £400
GINETTE NEVEU: ....
.... Chausson Poeme/Debussy Violin Sonata No.3/Ravel Tzigane HMV mono ALP1520 1957 £200
GINETTE NEVEU + Walter Susskind + Philharmonia Orchestra: ....
.... Sibelius Violin Concerto/Suk Four Pieces For Violin & Piano HMV mono ALP1479 1957 £200
CARL SCHURICHT + Vienna Philharmonic Orchestra: ....
.... Bruckner Symphony No.8 HMV stereo ASD602-3 1963 £400 (2 records)
TULLIO SERAFIN + Maria Callas + Orchestra Of La Scala: ....
.... Cherubini Medea Columbia stereo SAX2290-2 1959 £300 (3 records)

COLOURED VINYL

Records made of plastic in colours other than black are considerably older than many collectors appreciate. Though not particularly common, there are 78's made of various different colours. In the rock era, coloured vinyl issues were an occasional occurrence during the fifties and sixties and all of the coloured records with a rock or blues content are now collectable. (A large number of singles and EPs aimed at children were also issued on coloured vinyl - usually red - but these are of no more than novelty value). During the late seventies the use of coloured vinyl became something of an epidemic, to the extent that it ceases to be any guarantee of a record's collectability - a situation that remains true through the eighties, although coloured vinyl had become fairly unusual again by the end of the decade. It remains the case, however, that if an artist's records are collectable anyway, then their coloured vinyl releases are likely to be worth a little more than the equivalent black vinyl issues. With CDs, coloration seems to be so far restricted to the plastic packaging rather than being used for the CDs themselves.

COLUMBIA

LP labels for the main Columbia SX series were green with gold print until 1963, then changed to match the style of EMI's sister label, Parlophone. From 1963-9, this resulted in a black label with silver print and a blue 'Columbia' logo; from 1969 the 'EMI' logo was added to a redesigned black and silver label, with a silver 'Columbia' logo now appearing in a box. Singles also changed from a green to a black label in 1963, with some earlier singles being given later, black label, reissues. Much later reissues using a very similar design to the original green label are easily identifiable by the references to EMI, which are not present on the early labels.

COMPACT DISCS

Research into the feasibility of the compact disc format began as early as the sixties, but it was not until March 1979 that the first public demonstration took place. In June 1981 a European press conference was held at which some specially produced CDs of opera extracts were on show. These, therefore, are the likely candidates for the first CDs to be made. The first generally available CDs, however, were issued by Sony in Japan in October 1982, following which, March 1983 saw the simultaneous release of some two hundred different titles in the UK by all the major record companies. The contrast between this and the situation over two decades earlier, when the LP was adopted by different companies at quite different times (some showing a marked reluctance to invest in a medium with what appeared to be an uncertain future) is quite remarkable. Thus far, the penetration of the collectors' market by compact discs has actually been very limited, although the unaccustomed fall in vinyl prices that has become noticeable in many areas is likely to be directly attributable to the general shrinking of the market for vinyl, caused by the success of the CD format. CD singles crept on to the market much more surreptitiously than the albums. The first was 'If You're Ready' by Ruby Turner (Jive JIVEX109 1986), although the disc's historical position would appear to have had no effect on its value, which is low.

CONDITION

As a description of the condition of a record, the word 'mint' tends to be one of the most mis-used of all. A record with a light surface mark or two is not mint, even if the marks produce no audible effect. A record whose cover is slightly creased at the corners is not mint - and neither is one where the cover has torn slightly along the top or bottom edge (a condition that is actually suffered by some records bought new from regular record shops). Some collectors would argue that a record ceases to be mint the moment it is played; others would merely insist on a completely blemish-free playing surface and cover. For records with conditions lower than mint, a scale of descriptions operates. The higher values quoted in this Guide are for records in excellent (or NM = near mint) condition. Such a record has no scratches or any other mark producing an audible effect that should not be there. The cover is free from tearing and has no more than very slight scuffing or creasing. For a record in worse condition than this, the value will be substantially less than the figure listed. This cannot be stressed too strongly. A record whose music is interrupted by a click that repeats thirty-three or forty-five times every minute is likely to be of interest to a collector only as a stop-gap until he can obtain a better copy. He will certainly not pay a price anywhere approaching the near mint value for such a record. A record whose music is accompanied by what sounds like a frying breakfast is practically worthless. Nor is it possible to use a record's age as an excuse. In many cases, hundreds of thousands of copies of a record may have been sold originally, but a relatively high value is given in the Guide precisely because copies in excellent condition are scarce. At the other end of the scale, a ecord in truly mint condition may sometimes fetch a little more than the listed value. The term VG (very good) is used by dealers to indicate a record that, in practice, has a large number of marks on its surface, some of which are audible. The lower values listed in the Guide are for VG records. Typically, these are 50% of the near mint values, although the figure is lower than this for the relatively common records at the lower end of the value scale, and higher for the more valuable records, where an appearance on the market in any condition at all is a relatively unusual occurrence. The terms G (good) and F (fair) are seldom used - in most cases they refer to a record from which few collectors would gain much listening pleasure. Exactly the same condition grades are applicable to CDs. It is unfortunate that many CD purchasers have been too ready to take at face value the original company claims with regard to the indestructibility of the discs. Scratches do not always cause problems, but they often do make the music on CDs stick or jump.

COUNTERFEITS

It is a sad fact that some of the rarer records have been counterfeited by unscrupulous individuals wishing to pass off their copies as the real thing. Recognising a counterfeit can sometimes be a problem. Often the label or the cover simply look 'too new', or the colour or some feature of the design simply do not look quite right. This is no help, however, where one has no idea what the original record should look like. In the case of UK pressings, a good indication is provided by the matrix number, which is to be found on the vinyl in the space occupied by the run-out groove, next to the label. If this is machine printed, then the record is likely to be genuine. If, however, the number is hand scratched, then the record is likely to be a counterfeit. One should also always be suspicious of a record offered for sale far too cheaply, especially if the record is a well-known collectors' item and the dealer is not one with a reputable name. (Although genuine bargains can always be found, of course, amongst the stock of dealers who are simply unaware of its value. It is a matter of judgement). High value collectors' items from the eighties are a particular target for the counterfeiters, as age discrepancies are less likely to arise. 'Mutant Moments' by Soft Cell, 'Damage Done' by the Sisters Of Mercy, and 'So Young' by the Stone Roses are three rarities of which counterfeits are definitely in circulation, but there are undoubtedly others. In the last few years, a large number of unofficial reissues of scarce albums from the sixties and early seventies have appeared on the market, but the manufacturers of these take care to remove the original record company names from the cover and identification is not a problem.

DANDELION

The Dandelion label was set up and co-financed by disc jockey John Peel in 1969 to enable him to promote the work of artists he felt were worthy of wider exposure, but who may have found some difficulty in gaining record contracts with anyone else! None of the records sold particularly well and the entire catalogue is now collectable. Initially the label was distributed by CBS - the labels for these issues are crimson overlaid with dandelion seed parachutes. In 1971, distribution was taken over by Warner Brothers, whose new label design featured a multi-coloured picture of dandelion flowers on a beige background. None of the CBS records were reissued by Warner Brothers.

DAWN

Dawn was the specialist progressive label set up by Pye. The label's list of signings somehow lacked the class of rival concerns like Vertigo and Harvest, but the majority of the albums released from 1969 to 1975 are collectable, even if only a handful have managed to reach high values.

DEALERS

The values of the records listed in this Guide are the prices that a collector might be expected to pay for a copy of the record concerned in NM (near mint) or VG (very good) condition. The price that a dealer might pay for the record is another matter altogether. A dealer has to cover the cost of his overheads (which include the rent, rates, and other running expenses of the shop; staff salaries; advertising expenses; and the time and effort spent acquiring the knowledge that he must have) before he can even begin to make a profit. A ten or twenty per cent slice of the record's value is too little to justify the outlay involved. In general, dealers expect to pay around half the anticipated selling price for a record, but this figure may be increased in the case of an item for which there is a waiting customer and decreased for an item whose appeal is rather specialised. It is also likely to be decreased too (considerably in these days of falling vinyl appeal) for items at the bottom of the collectors' price scale.

DECCA

Until 1970, Decca used a red label for its mono LPs (LK series) and a blue label for its stereo LPs (SKL series). A few of the mono LPs from the early sixties were still in the catalogue a the end of the decade, but although these later pressings have the same label design as the originals, they no longer use the cover construction in which the edges of the front sheet are folded over the back. From 1970, a blue label is used, but with significantly changed details as compared with the earlier stereo label. The earlier label has a circular 'ffss' logo at the top and a relatively wide 'full frequency stereophonic sound' band immediately adjacent to the centre hole. The later label has a narrow band, with a gap between itself and the hole; there is no circular logo, and the 'Decca' logo is now inside a box. The sleeves for albums released during 1968-70 have a small hole on the back, at the top right corner. The inner sleeves have a red (for mono) or blue (for stereo) coloured band which can be seen through the hole to immediately identify which kind of record it is! Decca singles have a blue label from the early fifties - switching from a tri-centre to a round centre at the end of the decade, and starting to use the boxed Decca logo during 1966.

DEMONSTRATION RECORDS

Demonstration records, or 'demos', are the earliest pressings of a record, used as samples and often made available in advance of the regular commercial copies. Review copies tend to be demos, as do the records sent to radio stations, and collectors' interest centres on those examples where a distinct label design is used. At its most boring, the design simply adds a few printed words to the normal label - something along the lines of

'Demonstration sample. Not for sale'. More excitingly, however, record companies in the sixties, particularly, used demo labels that were striking variations of the issue labels. The EMI group of companies, for example, favoured a white label for their singles, dominated by a big red 'A' on the side that was intended to be the hit. During 1966, this was changed to a green label with a big white 'A'. Pye also favoured a white label, with a black 'A' across the record's centre. The Decca group of companies liked to use a pattern of short radial lines around the edge of the label, and sometimes a colour change - Brunswick from black to red, and London from black to orange or yellow, although the Decca label itself retained its blue colour for both issues and demos. Deram kept the same label lay-out, but replaced its brown colour with light blue. The value and collectability of demos varies considerably. Soul collectors prefer demo copies and will pay double the listed price for them (but see the entries for the Action and Tamla Motown labels). This doubling formula works well for other kinds of single too, but only where the artist is generally collectable. A demo copy of 'Hear Me Calling' by Ten Years After, for example, would be worth £10, rather than the £5 figure that applies to an issue copy. In the case of one-off or genre singles, however, where the song rather than the singer is important, a demo copy is likely to attract only a modest premium. A copy of 'War Machine' by Leviathan is valued at £20: a demo copy of the record would, perhaps, push the price up to £25. This rule is even more relevant in the case of particularly rare singles, which may originally have sold so poorly that demo copies are actually more common than issue copies. 'She Just Satisfies' by Jimmy Page seldom turns up at all - both demo and issue copies are worth the listed value of £220. To collectors of singles from the fifties, demos are actually inferior to issue copies, so that demonstration copies of rare London singles are worth considerably less than the listed values - probably no more than 50%. Note that fifties demos are often one-sided, a pair of such records being made to demonstrate the A and B sides of the commercial single. (This format is prevalent later in the case of demos of LP releases). In all periods, demo copies of common singles by star artists defy all the usual rules. The values of Beatle demos are listed separately in the guide - hit single demos by the likes of Billy Fury, the Kinks, and the Who would fetch around £100 each. Where demos are specifically indicated in the Guide, then this is either to draw attention a value that departs significantly from the guidelines given above, or else it is a reference to a record that was withdrawn from issue, with the demonstration copies, therefore, being the only kind in existence. Demonstration albums are less common, but where they do occur, the general guidelines above apply once more. Often, the demonstration copies are marked by a label stuck on the sleeve, with the cover and record label being in every other respect identical to those on the issue copies. This procedure is the one followed today in the case of demonstration CDs. Such labels could, of course, be mass-produced by a counterfeiter and stuck on to quantities of regular releases, for which reason demonstration items of this kind do not attract any kind of premium.

DERAM

Decca was the first company to start a specialist progressive label with the release of the first Deram records towards the end of 1966. Of course, in 1966 it was by no means clear what music should actually be included in the definition, with the result that some fairly odd records were given Deram releases (such as those by Whistling Jack Smith and Lionel Bart). Nevertheless, the proportion of musically adventurous releases is high and the label's sixties records are widely collected. Both singles and LPs had a brown and white label - albums bearing a 1970 or 1971 release date with red and white labels are later pressings.

DISCO MIX CLUB

The Disco Mix Club, run by disc jockey Tony Prince, has issued a series of special LPs (now CDs) to accredited DJs who pay to join the club, at the rate of two albums per month from the early eighties. The first of these monthly issues is of no interest to collectors, being merely a compilation of recently issued tracks. The second, however, contains various remixes and megamixes of previously released material, much of it being unavailable in this form anywhere else. Although the individual albums are not listed in the Guide, they sell for prices in the range of ten to fifty pounds, depending on the artists involved, on the rare occasions when they come on to the open market.

ELEKTRA

From its beginnings as a US folk and roots specialist company, Elektra was held in high regard as a label that could be relied on to only issue artistically worthwhile records. Even when the company began to branch out into the developing rock market, it still seemed to have the knack of finding artists whose role in the development was destined to be a key one - such as the Butterfield Blues Band, the Doors, Love, and the Incredible String Band. The earliest Elektra records have gold labels, changing briefly to white in 1966, and then orange to the end of the decade. In 1970, a red label was used, then, following the absorption of the label into the Kinney group in 1971, a mottled green label featuring a butterfly logo was introduced.

EMBASSY

Embassy was the record label sold by Woolworths during the late fifties and early sixties. Its policy was to issue sound-alike cover versions of the hits of the day, with the result that the label scarcely features in the collectors' market today. A handful of Embassy artists eventually made it on to 'proper' labels - Johnny Worth, Hal Munro, and, most notably, Maureen Evans.

EXPORTS

The major British record companies have, from time to time, pressed up special editions of selected domestic records for release overseas. Such records are inevitably scarce in their home country and tend to be sought after by collectors. Usually identifiable by their catalogue numbers, such records are distinguishable from releases made by the actual overseas branches of the record companies concerned, by being marked as 'manufactured in Great Britain'.

EXTENDED PLAY RECORDS

As far as most record collectors are concerned, 'EP' is a technical term. It refers to the 7' records that were issued during the fifties and sixties with a playing time around twice that of the standard single. In most cases these had four tracks (though some, like 'The Spotnicks On The Air', had six), played at 45rpm (though some, like 'Something Else By The Move', played at 33rpm), and had picture sleeves constructed out of thin card, with the front cover edges folded over the back, like the LP sleeves of the time (though many of the early fifties EPs have company covers without pictures). These mini-LPs are widely collected for their own sake, with the result that these listings include many EPs by artists who are otherwise only marginally collectable. During the late seventies, many of the tiny independent labels that emerged in the wake of punk released records containing four or more tracks, often using the 12' format. Sometimes, these too are described as EPs, but they are not collected as such by EP specialists, and they do not serve the mini-LP function of the earlier records.

FACTORY

The label that provided a home for the music of Joy Division and New Order is one of the few modern labels to attract collectors trying to put together a complete run. In practice, however, it is impossible for anyone to collect every Factory catalogue item, due to the label's eccentric habit of giving numbers to assorted items other than music releases. The very first Factory item, in fact, is a concert poster (FAC1). Later catalogue oddities include a badge (FAC21), a computer programme (FAC91), the Hacienda club's first birthday party (FAC83), and, indeed, the Hacienda club itself (FAC51)

FLEXI DISCS

Flexi discs are 7' singles pressed on to plastic so thin that it is extremely bendy - and extremely easy to damage! Two companies are primarily responsible for making these discs - Lyntone and Sound For Industry - but these are essentially manufacturers and not record companies as such. A variety of sources are responsible for commissioning the flexi discs in the first place. Record companies use them as promotional devices, typically advertising a forthcoming boxed album set, or else including them as a free extra within the packaging of another record. Magazines, too, use them as a free extra, either on an occasional basis, or with every issue (as in the case of the eighties Flexipop magazine). Fan clubs issue them as an exclusive product for their members (the most famous examples of these being the Beatles Christmas flexi-discs). Occasionally, independent record companies will use the flexi disc format for a cheap, limited edition run. A few of these different flexi discs are collectable and are listed in the Guide. In many cases, test pressings are made on ordinary hard vinyl and these records are typically worth around three to four times the value of the flexi disc.

FOAM EDGE COVERS

For a few months in 1970-1, one manufacturer of album sleeves decided that it would be a good idea to employ a design in which a cardboard cover like a book cover housed the record in a clear plastic sleeve, along the edge of which was fastened a strip of plastic foam. 'Colosseum Live' was one album given such a sleeve; the Pentangle's 'Basket Of Light' was another. Sensible purchasers of these records immediately placed a standard paper sleeve inside the plastic one, because although the strip of foam was intended to clean the record as it was pulled out of the sleeve, in practice the foam used was so coarse that it actually damaged the vinyl surface. A similar problem is sometimes found in the case of LPs using polythene-lined inner sleeves. Where the record has not been removed from its sleeve for a period of years, a reaction can take place between the polythene and the vinyl, leaving a thin but visible deposit on the surface of the record. Unlike the foam edge marking, however, this deposit normally wipes clean and causes minimal effect to the record's sound quality.

FOLK

Folk music is a collectors' area that tends to get ignored by many people, but there are a large number of valuable albums to be found on the specialist labels. As always, the records issued during the sixties and early seventies are the ones in which there is most interest (a tiny number of folk records dating from the fifties also exist), with anything issued on the Topic label being worth investigating. Other key labels are Acorn, Argo (Decca's home for non-commercial music of various kinds - classical and some jazz as well as folk, and also some spoken word material), Broadside, Cottage, Claddagh (from Ireland), Dolphin (also from Ireland), Folkways (from the US), Free Reed, Leader, Rubber, Saydisc, Tradition, Trailer, Transatlantic (most collectors and dealers do know about that one), and Village Thing. For a proportion of the folk information used in this Guide, credit is due to Peter Loughran, who operates a busy mail order business in Consett, County Durham. His catalogue is a real labour of love, including very helpful passages giving information about some of the less well-known artists and records.

FOREIGN RELEASES

The majority of items listed in the Guide are UK issues. A few releases from other countries have also been included where it is felt that these are of particular interest to the UK collector. The majority of these consist of recordings by British artists (by birth or by adoption) that were not actually released in Britain. The rest are a selection of records by artists from other countries that are of particular appeal to collectors in the UK. In particular, a large number of US albums have been included. American LPs have always been imported into Britain in quite large numbers so that they frequently turn up for sale in the collectors' market. Moreover, with so much rock music being American in origin, the first pressing of a large number of releases is actually an American record. As a general rule, US albums have been included in this Guide either if they have no exact UK equivalent, or if the American pressing has a higher value than its British counterpart. American pressings of many UK original albums are actually less valuable in the UK, especially where the label is a key factor in the collectability of the British record.

FREAKBEAT

During their brief career, the Beatles presided over a rock music scene that was growing and developing so fast that it was able to move from British Beat to Psychedelia to Progressive Rock in the space of just seven years. Of course, rock analysts love categories, and not content with these three to cover the major sixties trends, some have sought to define yet another. 'Freakbeat' attempts to find a genre in the space between British Beat and Psychedelia - a space that hardly seems big enough to accommodate it. The term is a recent one - no-one in the sixties thought it necessary to modify the 'Beat' idea until the sounds heard on such records as the Yardbirds' 'Shapes Of Things' and Jimi Hendrix' 'Purple Haze' made it clear that the description had become inadequate. There is also much disagreement over which records should properly be described as freakbeat, which only goes to highlight the artificial nature of the term.

FRENCH EP'S

France has always been highly resistant to Anglo-American cultural imports and it was not until 1962 that the local record industry paid any attention to the rock music phenomenon. Even then, the French response was typically idiosyncratic. Spurning singles entirely (until 1967), the French record companies decided to concentrate instead on four track extended play records. Between 1962 and 1968 a large number of these 7' EP's were issued, featuring both French and some well-known (and not so well-known) English and American artists. The consequence of this was that groups like the Beatles, the Animals, and the Rolling Stones had many more EP releases than they did in the UK, and the novelty of both the cover art and the availability of UK album tracks in a unique 7' format has made these records extremely collectable today. Even more sought after are the EP's by groups like the Creation, the Tony Jackson Group, and the Primitives, who had no picture cover releases at all in the UK. The majority of the French EP catalogue is therefore included within this Guide - information will be gratefully received from collectors who are in a position to make the listing more nearly complete!

GATEFOLD SLEEVES

Single record LP sleeves that open out like a book cover were occasionally used in the fifties and sixties to give a touch of extra class to the records of the biggest stars. Elvis Presley's 'Golden Records' and 'Elvis Is Back', Frank Sinatra's 'Sinatra-Basie', and 'Beatles For Sale' are notable examples. For ten years from the mid-sixties, these double sleeves became a common feature and help to make the albums of the period into attractive artefacts in their own right. With the declining influence of progressive rock in the later seventies, however, gatefold sleeves fell out of use and returned to their role of highlighting certain star issues.

GOLD DISCS

Although there are more copies made of the average gold disc award (or silver or platinum) than many people realise, they are still comparatively uncommon items in the collectors' market-place. Most often, therefore, they tend to be auctioned rather than offered for a fixed price. In most cases, the value reached are actually quite modest (for items in much shorter supply than the average valuable collectors' record), as the following list of recent auction house sales indicates:

BRYAN ADAMS:	Waking Up (platinum) £200
BEATLES:	Abbey Road (gold) £850
	Get Back (gold) £580
	Hey Jude (gold) £780
BOOMTOWN RATS:	A Tonic For The Troops (gold) £130
CARPENTERS:	Please Mr. Postman (platinum) £280
DEF LEPPARD:	Hysteria (platinum) £200
DIRE STRAITS:	Brothers In Arms (platinum) £320
FRANKIE GOES TO HOLLYWOOD:	Relax (gold) £130
GUNS 'N' ROSES:	Appetite For Destruction (platinum) £350
HOUSE OF LOVE:	House Of Love (silver) £100
JANET JACKSON:	Control (gold) £400
JAMES:	Gold Mother (gold) £100
ELTON JOHN:	The Very Best Of Elton John (platinum) £350
PAUL McCARTNEY:	Tripping The Live Fantastic (platinum) £320
METALLICA:	Metallica (gold) £350
SINEAD O'CONNOR:	The Lion And The Cobra (gold) £140
PET SHOP BOYS:	Heart (platinum) £90
PINK FLOYD:	Dark Side Of The Moon (platinum) £280
PRINCE:	Batdance (gold) £400
TEARS FOR FEARS:	Seeds Of Love (platinum) £110

Most valuable are those awards presented to the artist themselves, but these are very seldom offered for sale. The products of those companies that offer to make a 'gold disc from your favourite record' are not the same thing at all, of course, and have no value to collectors.

GOLD LABEL

Just as in the case of the London label, the earliest pressings of singles issued by Columbia, HMV, and Parlophone are described as being 'gold label' copies. It is actually the print on the label that is coloured gold, rather than the label itself, but its presence is a good indication of likely value. If the original issue of a single should have a gold label, then this is indicated in the listings if later pressings bearing the same catalogue number exist. In such cases, the later pressing will have a value of only half the value given.

GRANZ, NORMAN

Norman Granz was a major force within fifties jazz without playing a note himself. His Clef label (issued in the UK on the Columbia 33CX100 series) was an important showcase for a large number of artists. All the records on the label are now sought after by jazz collectors. Alongside this, Granz organised a series of concerts in which he encouraged various well-known musicians from different areas of jazz to play together. The recorded evidence of these concerts is listed in this Guide under the heading Jazz At The Philharmonic.

HARVEST

Harvest was set up as EMI's specialist progressive rock label in 1969. Many of the original releases on each of the two number series (SHSP and SHVL) are now collectable, although EMI's high success rate means that there are fewer high value items than are found on many of the other progressive labels. Unfortunately for collectors, Harvest retained its distinctive lime green label throughout the seventies, so that the first pressings of albums selling well enough to stay in the catalogue cannot easily be identified. This is the reason for the omission from the listings of such well-known albums as Pink Floyd's 'Umma Gumma' and 'Atom Heart Mother' and Deep Purple's 'Deep Purple', 'Concerto For Group And Orchestra' and 'In Rock', original copies of all of which might be expected to be sought after.

HMV

HMV's turquoise-blue labels are a welcome sight on Elvis Presley singles from the fifties, indicating an early release of some value. Sixties HMV labels were black. The LP labels changed from crimson in 1963, acquiring the EMI house-style shown in the Columbia and Parlophone labels of the period. In the case of HMV, this meant a black label with a red 'His Masters Voice' logo. There is no problem with regard to later reissues, since in 1967 HMV became a classical label only.

INTERVIEW RECORDS

As far as copyright law in the UK and US in concerned, the rules that apply to recordings of music do not apply to the spoken word. Accordingly, anyone can issue records containing interviews with the famous, without worrying about the fact that the artists in question have contracts elsewhere. Companies like Baktabak capitalise on this by producing attractive interview picture discs, which can appear to the unwary to be highly desirable collectors' items. In fact, however, few collectors are actually much interested in these items and their values never rise above the cost when new. A small exception to this rule occurs in the case of interview material issued by the artist's record company as a promotional device, although even here interview recordings seldom reach the values of promotional releases containing music.

ISLAND

The Island record company was formed in 1962 as an outlet for Caribbean music in the UK - the catalogue number prefix used for singles being 'WI', standing for 'West Indies'. These singles, with their white and red labels, are all very collectable. During 1967, Island began issuing rock LPs, gaining a significant boost by their successful signing of Stevie Winwood's new group, Traffic. The change in musical emphasis was matched by a change in label design. From 1967 until 1970, Island labels were pink, a fact which easily enables the identification of first pressings. Collectors are not often concerned about the fine differences, but there are actually three different pink label designs. From 1967 until 1969 (beginning with ILP952 by John Martyn), the labels have a distinctive red and black 'eye' logo on the left-hand side. The last album to be issued with this label was ILPS9106 by Dr. Strangely Strange. During 1969 a few issues used a pink label on which an enlarged black-only version of the 'eye' logo appeared at the centre. A few singles, plus copies of 'Five Leaves Left' by Nick Drake, 'Unhalfbricking' by Fairport Convention and 'This Was' by Jethro Tull have been spotted with this label design. The albums are therefore second pressings, although the latter two are rarer than the slightly earlier issues. From 1969 to 1970 the pink labels have a large white 'i' logo below the centre. The last album to be issued with this label was ILPS9131 by The Alan Bown. From 1970 to 1974, the pink colour was relegated to a circular border for a multi-coloured label bearing a stylised picture of an island in the sun. Many of the earlier albums were reissued with this label, but the values of these later pressings are seldom more than 50% of the original pink label copies. Some albums appear with even later label designs, but unless stated otherwise in the listings, these late issues are of no interest to collectors.

JAZZ

For the first time in this edition of the Price Guide, a large number of collectable jazz albums by American artists have been included. This does not reflect a new development within the realm of record collecting, but is rather a belated acknowledgement of a collectors' market that has actually been in existence for some time. The emphasis has been deliberately placed on UK issues via labels such as Esquire, Vogue, and London Jazz, although the highest prices are actually paid for the original American albums that these British labels merely re-packaged.

JAZZ IN BRITAIN

British jazz is a somewhat different animal to its American cousin. From the outset, the restricted market for the music, together with a typically British myopia with regard to the position of jazz's cutting edge, led to a much more intimate relationship between jazz and rock than was ever the case in America. The popularity of traditional jazz was a piece of British idiosyncrasy, for music that was inclined to view jazz as a kind of Music Hall entertainment could have little in common with what had been going on in New York's 52nd Street (the difference between Acker Bilk and Charlie Parker being as great as the difference between Brotherhood Of Man and Kurt Cobain's Nirvana). But it was out of trad that the success of Lonnie Donegan was made; out of trad too that Alexis Korner was able to form his launching pad for much of the British R&B and beat boom that followed. During the sixties, musicians like Jack Bruce, Dick Heckstall-Smith, Jon Hiseman, and Henry Lowther proved themselves to be equally at home playing both jazz and rock - partly out of necessity, but partly too because they were able to make worthwhile musical statements in both areas. Records by people like Neil Ardley, Mike Westbrook, and Ian Carr on the one hand, and Colosseum, Soft Machine, and the Battered Ornaments on the other, contain so many overlapping personnel (who feel little need to compromise their playing styles in either, that it hardly makes sense to differentiate between the two kinds of music. As far as the collectors' market is concerned, it is the overlapping of musical styles and personnel that makes some of the late sixties/early seventies British jazz albums so desirable. Most of these are rare and prices remain high - especially since little in this field has ever been reissued.

KEY

Records issued on the Key label during the early seventies were all Christian in content, but many have become collectable as a by-product of the interest in progressive rock and folk music of the period. Most notable in this respect is the album by Out Of Darkness, which continues to be one of the more sought after progressive rarities.

KING BEES

The rare single 'Liza Jane' is listed in the Guide under the name later used by the group's lead singer - David Bowie.

KINNEY

In 1971, three major US record labels, Elektra, Reprise, and Warner Brothers, amalgamated under the Kinney company name - Atlantic joined the fold in early 1972. Records still in the catalogue at that time were immediately given new numbers beginning with a 'K', a change which is immensely useful to collectors in that it enables the easy identification of original pressings - those without the K numbers. Today the company continues under the name W.E.A.

LASER-ETCHED RECORDS

In 1980 the first records appeared with laser-etched surfaces. As it happens, neither 'True Colours' by Split Enz nor 'Paradise Theatre' by Styx is of much more than novelty value these days, despite the attractive designs visible on the playing surface when the records are tilted towards the light. (Neither record was a limited edition, incidentally - all copies have the surface pictures). The technique has been used very infrequently since 1980, possibly because, although the effect is undoubtedly interesting, it is nevertheless a lot less spectacular than one would imagine.

LITTLE WILBUR

Records credited to Little Wilbur are listed in this Guide under the name Wilbur Whitfield.

LONDON

London was the first label to receive serious attention from collectors due to its policy of issuing in the UK the best of American rock-'n'-roll and rhythm and blues records. Many collectors try to obtain complete runs of London singles at least up until the mid sixties, when the rise of British beat effectively put an end to the label's importance. Their task in this respect is hindered by the extreme rarity of some of the issues, but they are also safe in the knowledge that a complete collection will contain remarkably few dud recordings. The earliest London singles have gold writing on a black label and these 'gold label' singles are the most highly prized and the most valuable. Where gold label singles have been reissued as later 'silver label' pressings (i.e. they have silver writing on a black label), these are generally only worth around half the value of the first issues. Unfortunately, the London label did not appear to be particularly systematic in its procedures, so that during the early months of 1957 some records were issued on gold labels and some on silver. There are, however, no gold label issues after HLP8420 (which happens to be by Slim Whitman). Within these listings, London singles with gold labels are specifically indicated where it might not be clear whether the first issue is gold or silver. A further design change occurs at the end of the decade, when the original triangular single centres were replaced by a round centre. As before, a round centre issue of a record that was first issued with a tri- centre is only worth about half the value of the original. The first round centre issue was HLU8903 (Gloria Smith), but the last tri centre was HLW9050 (Duane Eddy). There is a period of some five months between these two, during which both kinds of centre were being used for new releases. Again, where it would not otherwise be clear in these listings, the existence of a tri-centre is indicated. London EPs have the same label design changes as the singles, but complications with regard to London LPs are restricted to the fact that a few were reissued after 1967 with black labels replacing the original plum coloured labels.

LONG PLAY RECORDS

The first LPs were issued in the United States in early 1949 by the Columbia (CBS) record company. In the UK, however, EMI, which was responsible for distributing the Columbia label, prevaricated - and it was Decca which issued the first LPs in June 1950. The company's initial release sheet comprised fifty-three records, the majority of which were classical, with a sprinkling of light orchestral items, together with gems by such popular artists as Edmundo Ros, The Galloway-Ruault Old Time Dance Orchestra, and Troise And His Banjoliers. The claims made on behalf of the new format by advertisers at the time make interesting reading. Superb sound quality, with 'almost silent' playing surfaces; negligible wear during play; unbreakability; and ease of storage are all cited as reasons for purchasing LPs - and all of these will sound very familiar to those who remember the promotion of CDs nearly three and a half decades later.

MAN FROM UNCLE

Music associated with the sixties cult TV series, The Man From UNCLE, can be found in the Guide under the names of Hugo Montenegro (who was responsible for the main theme), the Challengers, and the Gallants - with a late entry from 1982 by Moskow. Meanwhile, David McCallum, who starred as agent Ilya Kuryakin in the programmes, took the opportunity to record a pair of moderately collectable albums.

MANISH BOYS

The rare single by the Manish Boys, 'I Pity The Fool', is listed in the Guide under the name later used by the group's lead singer - David Bowie.

MARMALADE

The short-lived and collectable Marmalade label was set up and run by impresario Giorgio Gomelsky, who was the original manager of the Yardbirds amongst other things. The company found some interesting artists to record - Blossom Toes, Julie Driscoll and Brian Auger, and John McLaughlin among them - but the label never really recovered from the failure (or refusal) of Julie Driscoll to become the huge star she could have been.

MATRIX NUMBERS

The matrix numbers that are to be found on the vinyl surface of a record in between the playing area and the label are sometimes of considerable help in providing information about the record itself. Much of the number will consist of the record's catalogue number, which is itself a piece of vital information in the case of test pressings issued with nothing useful written on the labels themselves. Extra digits, however, provide information about the stampers used to press the records (the 'matrix' being the mould from which the stampers were made). On some occasions, the recorded version of a song has been changed during an extended pressing run, and the corresponding change in the matrix number enables identification of the different versions without the record having to be played (collectable examples of this appear in the listings - see, for example, the Frankie Goes To Hollywood variations where the relevant matrix number differences are given in brackets after the catalogue numbers). In principle, the matrix number can be used to distinguish first and later pressings where the catalogue number is the same, although only classical record collectors seem to be much interested in these fine distinctions. In the case of UK releases, matrix numbers are generally machine stamped. There may also be one or more slogans or messages hand-scratched in the vinyl. A random inspection reveals the words 'Everything's Jelly' on a Spiritualised 12' test pressing, 'Bilbo' on a copy of the Who's 'Live At Leeds' album, and both 'Loosely From The Stiff Beach' and 'With Pink Warmth' on a copy of 'Psonic Psunspot' by the Dukes Of Stratosphere. The ubiquitous 'Townhouse' refers to one of the major studios, while 'A Porky Prime Cut' indicates that the master has been made by the most highly respected cutting engineer, George Peckham.

MISPRESSED RECORDS

Whenever a record plays music that is not what the label or cover would lead the listener to expect, then this record is said to be a mispress. When pressing plants are producing several different records at the same time, it is an unfortunate but easily understood error if the occasional batch of vinyl is passed under the wrong stamper. Accordingly, records where one side plays what it should, but the other plays something quite different do turn up from time to time. In general, such records are of novelty but little monetary value. The exceptions are those records involving the major collectable artists - a number of Beatles mispressings, for instance, are listed in the Guide, as are a few other interesting examples. In the CD age, incidentally, mispressings continue - discs where the musical content bears no relation to what is printed on the disc are in circulation. Errors involving labels on otherwise correctly pressed records are comparatively common. A record may have a side one (or side two) label on both sides; or else the labels for the two sides may be interchanged; or one or both labels may be missing altogether. None of these occurrences create any increase in value, however, if only because they could be easily reproduced by a counterfeiter. Records where the label is displaced on to the playing surface, preventing play, are virtually worthless, of course.

MUSHROOM

Three companies have adopted the Mushroom name. A late seventies US label released albums by the group Heart, and a long-lived Australian Mushroom label is still going. The Mushroom of most interest to collectors, however, is a tiny concern that issued a handful of LPs during 1970-2. The label's varied catalogue of progressive rock, Indian music, and jazz was never available in ordinary record shops, but was advertised in the underground press (notably Oz magazine) for sale by mail order. The original asking price of a pound for the albums is now multiplied many times over!

MUSHROOM SOUP

In the first (1991) edition of this Price Guide, an album was listed by a group called Mushroom Soup. For long a feature within the wants lists of a few dealers, the record's details were so delightful (Mushroom Soup: 'And Other Recipes' on the Roll and Butter label, catalogue number PAT1) that one longed for it to be real, despite the almost certain knowledge that it was not! (As was said in the first edition). Of course, the record was a fiction - but as such, it joins a fairly long catalogue of imaginary records, some of which have had collectors scouring the specialist shops and record fairs far and wide in an increasingly frantic and fruitless quest. One collectors' shop always used to head its wants list with an intriguing reference to an album called 'Where's Mutley?'; others are more mischievous, slipping in a tantalising reference to a twelve inch version of a record one was certain only existed as a seven inch, or else advertising a previously undiscovered picture disc (such records have always 'just been sold', of course). It was Greil Marcus who started a tradition of joke references within otherwise sensible discographies, with the 'Zurvans: Close The Book (End)' entry at the end of his desert island anthology, 'Stranded'. It is not Marcus' fault if his quiet wit has been worn a little thin in the work of other authors who have repeated the joke to the point of exhaustion! From time to time, the rock press has put its own slant on the process by reviewing records of its own invention - some of which have subsequently turned out to be real after all! Examples can be found in this Guide under the headings 'Heavy Jelly' and 'Masked Marauders'. As for Mushroom Soup, their discography has miraculously expanded of late, if we are to believe the entry in a limited edition 'Rare Record Guide' published in 1994. An imaginary band that has managed to produce nine separate collectors' items (including three made by some kind of spin-off unit) is clearly a force to reckoned with. Perhaps the band could be persuaded to reform or some kind of imaginary tour - the support slot to the Beatles reunion is still vacant, so far as we know!

NADIR, RIKKI

The records credited to Rikki Nadir are actually by Peter Hammill, in a back to basics mood, are listed in this Guide along with his other solo work.

NEON

Neon was the specialist progressive label set up by RCA at a time when all the majors were doing something similar. RCA was actually a little slow off the mark - the first Neon album was released in 1971 - and although some of the records are rather fine (and have the attractive gatefold sleeves typical of the genre), they sold poorly. All the Neon albums are now collectable - there being just eleven of them in the series.

NEPENTHA

The short-lived Nepentha label is often described as being a subsidiary to Vertigo, with whom it shared a house-style. In reality, of course, Vertigo is itself a subsidiary of Phonogram, who presumably felt that if one specialist progressive label could prove to be a success, then it was worth trying a second one. In fact, Nepentha never managed to achieve the strong corporate image that Vertigo did (its label design featured a blue quill, whose link with the music's powers of making the listener forget all grief - for such is the label name's arcane meaning - is not a striking one) and it was abandoned after just five album releases. In fact, the label was lucky to even last that long. After minimal sales of the first three Nepentha albums, the cancelled matrix number visible on the fourth, 'Earth And Fire', shows that the record was originally intended for the Mercury label.

NEW JAZZ ORCHESTRA

The LPs credited to the New Jazz Orchestra are listed under the name of the orchestra's leader, Neil Ardley.

NM CONDITION

NM, standing for Near Mint, is used in this Guide, synonymously with Excellent, to indicate a record in played, but aurally perfect, condition. Further details are given under the heading 'Condition'.

NOVA

Although Deram had originally been conceived as something of a progressive offshoot for Decca records, the flowering of the music in 1969, accompanied by the birth of several specialist labels to feature it, encouraged Decca to try the tactic for a second time. The link with the parent company was made explicit from the outset, and records were issued on labels described either as 'Decca Nova' or 'Deram Nova', although there was only one catalogue number series. Unfortunately, the albums always seemed to convey the impression that Decca's heart was not really in the exercise. Few of the artists were particularly inspiring, and the elaborate gatefold sleeves that were so much a part of the package in the case of rival labels like Vertigo, Harvest, and Island were never used. The label was abandoned at the start of 1971.

OAK

Of the many small private recording studios, catering mainly to young bands without a record contract, that run by R.G. Jones in South London has become the subject of considerable cult interest. Part of this interest derives from the studio's association with the Rolling Stones and the Yardbirds, both of which groups made early recordings there. More, however, is due to the current fascination with any records from the sixties or early seventies that are sufficiently obscure to be suitable candidates for high-priced collectors' items. Oak was the label name given to the small number of records actually pressed up by the R.G. Jones studio. These were paid for by the artists concerned for use as demos - in the same way as modern groups will produce cassettes of their songs in order to obtain a record contract or gigs (or just to sell at those gigs). The small number of collectable Oak records of this kind are listed in the Guide. The Bo Street Runners and the Thyrds found some very limited success via the TV rock group contest organised by the Ready Steady Go programme, but the majority of the Oak artists were never heard of again. There were also a larger number of Oak label acetates, which occasionally come on the market at upwards of £25 each (one featuring two unreleased songs by a youthful David Bowie is worth nearer a hundred times this value!). Although many of the Oak recordings are decent beat group performances, there is a considerable danger in assuming that everything on the label is worthwhile (and collectable). A recent discovery of a complete Oak album may have whetted a few appetites, but the MOR pop selection that makes up 'Wilf Todd And His Music' is not the kind of thing to normally set collectors' pulses racing - a fact which nevertheless proved to be no curb on the hyperbole of one specialist dealer, who managed to describe the record as a 'monster rare Oak label 60s private LP - £400' with a straight face. The R.G. Jones studio is still in operation, incidentally, one of its recent success being the number one single recorded by Mr. Blobby.

ORIGINAL PRESSINGS

The date of publication or the copyright date given on a record usually relates to the original release date, which is not necessarily the date of issue of the particular piece of vinyl in question. Where a record is given a reissue, after having been unavailable for a time, it is usually (though not always, unfortunately) given a new catalogue number. Catalogue numbers are therefore a considerable aid in identifying original pressings, and these are given in the Guide wherever possible. Where a record remains in a company's catalogue over an extended period of time, changes in label design can make the first issues distinctive. Some of the most important of these are described under the appropriate record company headings within this Guide. Values given in this Guide are for original pressings. Later pressings may not be collectable at all, although if the record in question is not easily available in any form, then a later pressing may still command some kind of collectors' value. This, however, will obviously be rather less than for the original.

PARLOPHONE

The changes in Parlophone label designs are of particular importance with regard to records by Beatles. In early 1963, the label used for singles was changed from red to black, so that early pressings of 'Please Please Me' are found with the earlier design and later pressings with the later design. The black label singles, incidentally, all carry the message 'Made In Gt. Britain', which is not present on reissue copies from the seventies. Parlophone LPs were also given a label change in 1963. The original labels are black, with all the print being in gold ink. The

'Parlophone' logo is written in gold 3-D effect capitals. The replacement labels were still black, but the print was now silver. 'Parlophone', now in simple flat capitals, was a bright canary yellow, as was the company's pound-sign logo. Again, the change took place at just the right time for the earliest copies of the Beatles LP 'Please Please Me' to have the original label, while most have the newer one. In 1969, the LP labels were changed again, with the yellow 'Parlophone' now being replaced by a silver one in a box.

PICTURE DISCS

The first picture disc, a 10' 78 rpm recording of 'Cowhand's Last Ride' by Jimmie Rodgers, was issued in America in 1933. At various times after that, further picture discs were issued, but all suffered from the fundamental problem of having poor sound quality, which prevented them from achieving much commercial success. The first rock picture discs (and the earliest to be listed in this Guide) date from 1969-70 and comprise two compilation albums alongside LPs by Curved Air and Saturnalia. The sound quality of these was also poor, due to the fact that they are essentially thin, clear flexi-discs glued to a piece of card on which the actual pictures are printed. From the late seventies, picture discs became very much more common and although the sound quality is still inferior compared to the conventional black vinyl equivalents, it is good enough to allow the inherent attractiveness of the discs to become the major consideration. There tends to be a natural bias towards picturediscs within the collectors' market, to the extent that for artists who are collected anyway, their picture discs are all sought after. The first shaped picture discs were a series of singles by the Police issued in the US (and widely available on import, albeit at quite high prices). These were cut into the shapes of police badges and were issued within special cardboard folders. For some reason, shaped picture discs did not really catch on in a big way until 1982-3, but they are a common record company gimmick throughout the rest of the eighties. Some of these explicitly recognise their primary function as display items, rather than serious sources of music, by including pieces of cardboard within the packaging that are intended to be folded into stands ('plynths') for the records. Uncut shaped picture discs consist of the twelve inch record (with seven inch grooves), from which the shaped disc is cut. They are collected rather in the same way as demonstration copies of regular singles are collected and typically sell for around three times the value of the finished shaped discs.

PRIVATE PRESSINGS

When a group is unable to gain a recording contract with any established record company and decides to finance the production and distribution of a record itself, then the result is a private pressing. Many singles issued in the post-punk era conform with this description, but the term is most generally used in connection with a fairly large number of more-or-less progressive albums issued during the seventies. Many of these albums have been sold or exchanged for extraordinarily high amounts in the past and although the values of such items have started to fall, prices are still high, as reference to the entries for such groups as the Dark, Ithaca, Toby Jug, and Complex will confirm. Arguably, the high values of these records are entirely the result of a skilful exercise in hype on the part of a few specialist dealers, but there have at least been a few transactions now to confirm these as genuine market values. The collector should beware, however, of recent 'discoveries' in this area, where the high prices currently being mentioned in some quarters for albums that were unknown two years ago are largely the product of wishful thinking. The following items come into this category - all have been quoted as being worth upwards of fifty pounds elsewhere, but all are in fact too recently arrived in the collectors' market for these values to be properly established.

ACHOR:	End Of My Day (Cedar 1976)
AWAY FROM THE SAND:	same (Beaujangle 197-)
	B's: In Your Bonnet (1974)
BLUEBEARD:	same (Ember 197-)
BREADWINNER:	Give Us A Light You Bastard (Ninth Band 1990)
BRINDLEY BRAE:	Village Music (Harmony 197-)
BROTHERS AND SISTERS:	Are Watching You (197-)
CANDLE FACTORY:	Nightshift (CAVS 197-)
CASTLE ROCK:	Nottingham Castle Festival Fringe (1973)
C.M.J.:	same (196-)
CRACKED MIRROR:	same (1983)
CRISIS:	Another Fine Mess (197-)
DOGWATCH:	Penfriend (Bridgehouse 1979)
PAULINE FILBY:	Show Me A Rainbow (Herald 1969)
FINN MACCUILL:	Sink Ye Sink Ye (1977)
FIVE DAY RAIN:	same (1970)
GAGS:	Death In Buzzard's Gulch (Look 1979)
GASLIGHT:	same (197-)
STOCKER GREENWOOD & FRIENDS:	Billy And Nine (Changes 1979)
GUGGENHEIM:	same (Indigo 197-)
HOBBIT:	First And Last (Deroy 197-)
HUTCH HUTCHINS:	Feels Like Rain (Goodwood 197-)
ISOLATION:	same (197-)
JONATHAN & CHARLES:	Another Week To Go (Herald 1969)
JANET JONES:	Sing To Me Lady (Midas 1974)
KILLER EXPLODING WAR KING:	Wrong Telescope (Swordfish 1989)
LEMON DIPS:	Who's Gonna Buy? (De Wolfe 1969)
LETTERMEN:	First Class (Stag 1974)
LIFE AFTER LIFE:	same (1984)
MAGUS:	Breezin' Away (Northern Sound 1980)
MILES MARTIN FOLK GROUP:	same (Amber 1971)
MELTON CONSTABLE:	same (SIS 197-)
MODE:	same (198-)
MOTHS:	same (Deroy 1969)

PROMOTIONAL RECORDS

The term 'promo' is often used interchangeably with the term 'demo', even by the record companies themselves. Within this Guide, however, the terms have specific, and different, meanings. A demo is a regular commercial release given a special label for the purposes of radio play or review. A promo, on the other hand, is a record (or other item) specially manufactured for advertising or promotional purposes. While being clearly related to a commercial release, the promo will be different in some major way from any version of the release that could be bought in a shop. Such items have long been a feature of the record industry and in the eighties and nineties in particular, a large number have been issued. Sometimes they consist of mixes not available to the general public, to enable radio stations to present something to their listeners that seems exclusive. It is also common for sampler recordings to be issued containing a small number of tracks from a forthcoming album, while the albums themselves may be provided with special packaging as a promotional device. This may range from a simple box containing one of each of the available formats, to the more elaborate affair typified by Talk Talk's 'Laughing Stock', where a picture CD is housed in a wooden box, along with pencils, rubber, ruler, and other items of stationery, most stamped with the group's name. The majority of such releases have not been included in this Guide, although the intention has been to include collectable items containing music that is not otherwise available, providing that they have values greater than twice any equivalent regular release.

PYE

Pye was the third major British record company (after EMI and Decca) and by the early sixties it was issuing singles on a number of related labels - Pye, Pye International, Pye Jazz, and Piccadilly (as well as a large number of subsidiary labels licensed from US originals, including Cameo Parkway, Colpix, Red Bird, Chess, and Kama Sutra). Only the main Pye and Pye International labels cause much trouble with regard to reissues. Pye labels are purple until 1962; then deep pink until the end of 1967 (with a change of layout at the beginning of 1965, when the 'Pye' moved from the left to the top of the label and gained a wide black band); then sky blue into the seventies. Pye International labels change in tandem: from a greenish-blue, to red and yellow, to red, to sky blue. In both cases, LPs follow through the same label design changes as the corresponding singles. Records by the likes of the Kinks with labels coloured pink shading to mauve, or grey shading to white, or any records mentioning the PRT company, are later pressings from the seventies or eighties and are not collectable.

QUADRAPHONIC RECORDINGS

During the early seventies a number of quadraphonic LPs were issued. When played on a suitable system, incorporating a special decoder, such records enable sounds to be heard from each of four speakers. These are intended to be arranged with two in front of the listener, as in stereo, and a further two behind the listener. The extra two speakers deliver ambient sound in the case of recordings designed to recreate the sound of a live performance; otherwise they can be essential ingredients in a surround-sound experience. Few collectors possess a quadraphonic system - nevertheless, the records are often sought after, since they were designed to be playable on conventional stereo systems and although they do not then provide a quadraphonic effect, they often do contain mixes that sound noticeably different from their stereo equivalents.

R.G.M.

The initials 'R.G.M' on a sixties record (whether in a Triumph record catalogue number or a reference to production by R.G.M. Sound) are indicative of the guiding hand of producer Robert George (Joe) Meek. Beginning as an engineer in the fifties, Joe Meek worked on numerous records by the likes of Frankie Vaughan, Shirley Bassey, Petula Clark, and Lonnie Donegan, before setting himself up as an independent producer. His concern with creating unusual and distinctive sounds led him continually to push the primitive sound equipment of the time to its limits and it is his reputation as an innovator that is responsible for the considerable interest in his records today. Meeks' experiments with speeded-up tape, distortion, close miking, echo, and even multi-tracking were certainly some years before his time, but the fact that all this imagination and inventiveness was directed towards the production of what was, for the most part, crassly commercial material, tends to blunt the impact, for modern listeners, of what Meek was achieving. As it happens, Joe Meek did score some considerable commercial successes, including 'Johnny Remember Me' by John Leyton, 'Don't You Think It's Time' by Mike Berry, 'Have I The Right' by the Honeycombs, 'Just Like Eddie' by Heinz, and, of course, 'Telstar' by the Tornados.

RADIO TRANSCRIPTION DISCS

The American equivalents of the BBC transcription discs, used to syndicate rock music programmes across a large number of radio stations, are mostly the products of two companies: Westwood One and King Biscuit Flour Hour. Originally issued as two and three LP sets, they are now coming out as compact discs. Either way, the values are on a par with the BBC discs, at around fifty to sixty pounds for the average album set or CD (with the same obvious exceptions). These recordings consist of live concerts interspersed with advertisements, ready for broadcast in the US. Other radio show albums contain a mixture of music (some of it previously issued studio material) and interviews. These have lower values than the all-live sets, going down to as little as ten pounds, depending on the amount of unreleased live material they contain.

RCA
RCA was the company that launched the 45rpm single in the United States in 1949, as an initial response to its rival, Columbia's invention of the LP. During the 1950's, the company's records were issued by HMV in the UK (both labels used the distinctive dog and gramophone logo), but in 1957 RCA set up its own UK company. Both singles and LPs used a black label until late 1968, when this was replaced by an orange label.

REGAL ZONOPHONE
The label that was used for Salvation Army records during the fifties was revived by EMI in 1967 as something of a specialist progressive label. The majority of the records released on the label, until its demise in early 1975, are collectable. It is not generally realised that a handful of singles were actually issued on Regal Zonophone during 1964-7. Only one of these is listed in the Guide (that by the Innocents and the Leroys) - the others continued the label's earlier tradition by featuring the Salvation Army's pop group, the Joystrings.

REGGAE
Reggae (or Ska or Rock Steady) from the sixties is very collectable and every record released is of value. Listing the records is in some cases quite problematic due to the chaotic nature of the specialist record labels involved. It is common practice for different artists to appear on either side of a single, but it is not always apparent which is intended to be the A side. Artists' names are frequently mis-spelt or simply change from record to record. Lloyd Charmers, Lloyd Chalmers, Lloyd Tyrell, and Lloyd Terrel, for example, are all the same person; so are Roland Alphonso and Rolando Al; so are Jackie, Jackie Edwards, Wilfred, Wilfred Edwards, and Wilfred Jackie Edwards! Sometimes the B side of a record changes during the lifetime of a single; sometimes a song is re-attributed to a different artist; and there are numerous examples where the name that appears on the record is simply wrong. It would even appear to be the case that, on occasion, more than one single has been issued with the same catalogue number. The reggae listings in this Guide represent the best attempt at making sense of these various difficulties. In practice, sixties reggae collectors are interested in the entire output of the relevant labels and, apart from the special case of records by Bob Marley, which are worth considerably more than their fellows, all the records issued on any particular label have the same value. Singles on the Studio One label sell for £12 each. Other key labels are Black Swan, Blue Beat, Coxsone, Dice, Doctor Bird, Island, Port-O-Jam, R&B, Rio (from 1963-5), Ska Beat, and Treasure Isle (from 1967-8), all of whose singles sell for £10. The small number of albums on these labels range from expensive to very expensive - typically £50 to £100. Sixties reggae labels also worth looking out for, with singles in the price range £5-8, are: Aladdin, Amalgamated, Bamboo, Big Shot, Blue Cat, Caltone, Camel, Clan Disc, Columbia Bluebeat (a unique example of a major label taking an interest in the music), Crab, Double D, Duke, Duke Reid, Escort, Gas, Giant, High Note, Jackpot, Jolly, Jump Up, Nu Beat, Pama, Pressure Beat, Punch, Pyramid, Rainbow, Randys, Rio (from 1966), Treasure Isle (1969), Unity, and Upsetter. Many of these labels continued into the seventies, but collectors' interest falls off dramatically

REMIXES
Ever since Trevor Horn and Frankie Goes To Hollywood hit upon the idea of using multiple remixes as a marketing device, it has been standard practice for modern artists to release several slightly different versions of the same song. A cynic might suggest that the reason for this is primarily to avoid the creative energy necessary in writing more songs and point to the nadir of the practice as being Prince's decision to issue an album-length collection of alternative arrangements of a song that only really consists of a single repeated line in the first place ('The Beautiful Experience'). Collectors, on the other hand, presumably delight in seeking out different mixes, as some of these can reach quite high prices.

REPRISE
Frank Sinatra's Reprise was one of the labels becoming part of the Kinney company in 1971. In addition to its catalogue numbers changing from the RSLP series to the new K series, the label design also changed from yellow and pale green, with a distinctive drawing of a steam-boat, to a plain tawny or orange-yellow.

SEVENTY-EIGHTS
To most collectors, 78 rpm recordings are of little interest. They break much too easily for one thing; and hardly anyone has the means to play them these days for another. The age of these records is of no consequence in this respect - indeed it is actually part of the problem, for most 78's contain music from before the rock-'n-roll era, which is itself subject to only slight collectors' interest. Even within the rock-'n-roll era, the 45 rpm singles are much more collectable than their 78 rpm equivalents, despite what is sometimes suggested by the (non-specialist) media. A small number can be found listed within the pages of this Guide, these being either records by particularly collectable artists, like Elvis Presley and Cliff Richard, or else the handful of significant rock-'n-roll and R&B songs that were not given a 45 rpm release in the fifties. Apart from these, the general rule is that 78's have a value of about one quarter of their seven-inch equivalent. It is suggested elsewhere that there is a growing market for 78's from 1959-60, when the format was rapidly dying out. These records are not actually as rare as is sometimes suggested and neither is it true that many were available by special mail order only. It should be realised that many parts of Scotland, for example, were still without mains electricity at this time, so that demand for 78's in these areas was still high.

SLEEVES
LPs and EPs are supposed to be in sleeves and it should go without saying that a damaged or missing sleeve has a serious effect on the value of a record. As a general rule, the cover should be considered as being responsible for half the value of an item, while the disc is responsible for the other half. An exception to this principle is where a particular sleeve variation is the major factor in a record's rarity - such cases are mentioned explicitly in the

listings. Picture sleeves for singles were a comparative rarity prior to the late seventies and were often reserved for promotional issues. In these cases, the effect of the sleeve on the value of a record can be dramatic (see, for example, the Pink Floyd and Tyrannosaurus Rex discographies). Increasingly from about 1978 onwards, it became standard practice for the first several thousand copies of a single to be issued with a picture sleeve. For these, therefore, collectors expect to find such a sleeve and are not very interested in copies without one. Within these listings, singles from 1980 onwards are presumed to come with picture sleeves and no explicit mention is made of the fact. Collectors like to see a company sleeve on singles from the fifties, sixties, or seventies, where a picture sleeve is not appropriate, but the absence of a company sleeve has a very minor effect on a single's value. It is possible to obtain very good reproductions of many of the major fifties and sixties company sleeves and many collectors are happy to accept these as an alternative to the real thing. It is worth noting that the construction of LP and EP sleeves made in the UK is a considerable aid in the identification of original issues. During the fifties and sixties, the cardboard edges of the front cover were turned over the outside of the back cover; from the late sixties the edges were glued inside the back cover. In addition, LP covers from the fifties seem to be made of a much thinner, flimsier cardboard than used subsequently.

STEREO

At the annual Audio Fair held in New York in October 1957, Decca demonstrated the results of its research into the reproduction of stereo sound by records. EMI had, in fact, been recording many of its artists in stereo for over two years previously and was issuing the results on what it called 'stereosonic' tapes. One company in America had issued twin track stereo discs, which had to be played with two pickups. The first stereo LPs to be issued commercially in the UK were intended to demonstrate the system - Pye CSCL70007, EMI SDD1, and Decca SKL4001 all appearing in mid 1958 and all comprising extracts from various light and classical pieces, together with assorted sound effect recordings. In August, a large number of stereo records, covering various kinds of music, were given a simultaneous release by several different companies, with the first UK stereo LPs appearing a month later (courtesy of EMI and Decca). As a general rule, stereo records from the early years of the medium are worth a little more to collectors than their mono equivalents, due to the rather smaller numbers of them sold at the time. (It should be noted, however, that many jazz collectors prefer the mono versions, as being more faithful to the intentions of the musicians in the studio, so that stereo jazz LPs from the early years are worth a little less than their mono equivalents). Towards the end of the sixties, when stereo recordings were rapidly becoming the norm, it is the mono versions that are scarcer and in consequence worth a little more to collectors. Mono recordings (other than reissues of earlier material) died out altogether after 1970. There tend to be many differences of detail between mono and stereo versions of the same LP - sometimes different takes are used and on occasion, the artist went back to the studio and re-recorded all the music for stereo. With the advent of multi-track recording, musicians began to take increasing liberties with the technology at their disposal. In order, for example, to record more than four parts on a four track machine, the technique of mixing tracks and bouncing them down to create free tape was invented. The final overdubs would be added at the final mixing stage, so that these would inevitably be different in the case of separately prepared mono and stereo mixes. Well-known examples of different mono and stereo versions resulting from this include the Beatles' 'White Album' (the two recordings of 'Don't Pass Me By' are completely different takes; the mono 'Helter Skelter' lacks Ringo's shouted complaint at the end); Jimi Hendrix's 'Axis: Bold As Love' (the stereo 'EXP' is twice as long as the mono); Traffic's 'Mr. Fantasy' (Steve Winwood plays wildly divergent guitar solos at the ends of 'Heaven Is In Your Mind'); and Pink Floyd's 'Saucerful Of Secrets' (the instrumental texture of the two versions of 'Let There Be More Light' is markedly different).

STIFF

The Stiff label made an enviable start with its best-selling releases by Elvis Costello, Ian Dury, and the Damned and looked set to become one of the most successful of the new breed of record companies to emerge along with punk. The company's unconventional, irreverent approach served as a role model for many later record labels and helped to endear itself to the collectors who tried to amass complete runs of Stiff releases a few years ago. Unfortunately, the label lost much of its prominence when its original stars moved elsewhere and only the Pogues have succeeded in providing much of a boost since. One result is that Stiff is now much less collected than it was and the values of its records have fallen across the board.

SUE

The British Sue label was formed in 1963 as a subsidiary of Island Records, with a policy of leasing US soul records, in contrast to the parent labels's West Indian bias. Initially, the label concentrated on records from the American Sue company, but it soon began to cast its net wider. With a label manager, Guy Stevens, who was himself very much a soul fan, the Sue catalogue soon became one of the most impressive of all - and is collected as such by soul enthusiasts today.

TAMLA MOTOWN

The consistency of Tamla Motown's single release policy during the sixties means that, today, every one of those records is a collectors' item. As with many other specialist soul labels, the most sought after items are the demonstration copies of the singles. Collectors take the not unreasonable attitude that only these can really be considered to be the first pressings. The consequence for the value of these is that the usual formula of doubling the value of the standard issue no longer applies. Instead a tripling of the value is more realistic, but only where this takes the value above the following minimum values for demonstration singles: Stateside singles by Motown artists - £50; TMG501-599 - £50; TMG600-635 - £30; TMG636-680 - £20.

TEST PRESSINGS

A test pressing is an earlier stage in the production of a record than even the advance demonstration discs. It is made on ordinary vinyl literally to test the fidelity of each component involved, from the master tape itself, through to the setting of the cutting equipment. Alternatively, a test pressing may represent a try-out for a proposed record release, the most collectable of these being records that did not, after all, become finished commercial releases.

Where these pressings are albums, they may have proof or even finished covers; test pressings generally, however, are distinguished by their plain (usually white) labels. Apart from certain test pressings that are particularly collectable, and are listed as such in the Guide, the values for these records are on a par with the values for demonstration records.

TOPIC

Topic is the oldest specialist folk label, with its first releases appearing on 78rpm recordings in the mid-fifties, and it is by far the most successful. All the fifties and sixties issues are collectable to a greater or lesser extent, and many of the later issues are of interest too. Although the vinyl catalogue has now been deleted in favour of CDs, many of the records remained available for many years. Topic used a plain dark blue label until the mid seventies, however, and the listed values refer to this label design.

TRI-CENTRES

The earliest singles have triangular centres, which identify original pressings in the case of fifties singles that were reissued with the same catalogue numbers. For most companies, tri-centres were used until the end of 1959, at which time round centres replaced them (the precise situation with regard to London singles is described under the London heading). Capitol, however, were using round centres from as early as 1956.

TWELVE INCH SINGLES

The first twelve inch single was conceived very much as a gimmick. This was a 1976 reissue of the Who's 'Substitute', using exactly the same version as on the original 7' single. The popularity of late seventies disco music, however, turned the twelve inch single into a staple format, since the lengthy playing times possible were ideal for coping with extended dance mixes. The early releases did not often have picture sleeves (RCA used what was essentially a company sleeve for its disco records, with a small picture of the artist at the top). From 1980, however, the majority of twelve inch singles did have picture sleeves, which form an essential part of the collectors' package.

VERTIGO

The Vertigo label has been of interest to collectors for several years, with many enthusiasts trying to put together a complete run of the original album releases. These are all characterised by a black and white label design intended to induce vertigo when watched spinning round on a turntable! This design is commonly referred to as a 'spiral', although it is actually nothing of the kind - the alternative 'swirl' description is marginally more accurate for a design made up of overlapping circles. Most albums used the 'spiral' design as the entire side one label, with all the track information being included on the side two label, although a few albums have conventional labels on both sides, with the spiral reduced to the status of a logo. The spiral label albums were nearly all housed in extravagantly designed gatefold sleeves (those by Dr. Z and Mike Absalom are more elaborate opening-out creations), which play an essential part in giving these records the special appeal that they have. Vertigo was set up in 1969 as a specialist progressive label for Phonogram (Philips/Fontana) and from the outset, the high proportion of albums by musically interesting artists was a strong indication that the label was destined for long-term success. In fact, it continues today, although inevitably no longer linked to music that might be described as 'progressive'.

VG CONDITION

VG, standing for Very Good, is a description of a record's condition that is actually less complimentary than it sounds. Further details are given under the heading 'Condition'.

VINYL

Any dealer will tell you that during the last couple of years, the public demand for vinyl records has plummeted. The collectors' market has actually been less affected than the general second-hand market in records, but it is definitely the case that collectable records sell more reluctantly than they used to. The spiralling upward rise in the values of progressive albums has halted and, in some cases, prices have begun to fall. In many other areas too, values in this third edition of the Guide are lower than those in the second edition. In the case of fifties and sixties records, however, demand is still high and in these areas there are a number of trend-bucking price rises. Rock-'n-roll and R&B singles, in particular, are becoming increasingly difficult to find in any condition and several collectors are deciding that they had better buy them now while they still can. As a result, the values are climbing, most noticeably in the case of the more valuable, rarer items.

WARNER BROTHERS

The record division of the well-known American film company was begun in 1958, but despite early success with the Everley Brothers and Peter, Paul And Mary, the label did not really start to become a significant force within the industry until its incorporation within the Kinney company in 1971. The green labels in use at the time were not changed until after several months, with the result that some early K series albums can be easily distinguished from the later pressings bearing the 'tree-lined avenue' label.

YOUNG RASCALS

The group that scored early hits with such songs as 'Groovin', 'Good Lovin' and 'Too Many Fish In The Sea', decided in 1967 that they could no longer credibly be described as 'young'. For the sake of continuity, all the group's collectable releases are listed in this Guide under their adult name, the Rascals.

ZTT

Both the fortunes and the collectability of the Zang Tumb Tuum label were inextricably linked with the popularity of the company's major asset, Frankie Goes To Hollywood. Whereas at the height of Frankie-mania, it was possible to point to a breed of collector that was interested in the dull music of Andrew Poppy purely because it was to be found on the same label as the star group, this would no longer seem to be the case.

A

A - AUSTR

It is appropriate that the first record listed in this guide should be one that typifies exactly what collecting rare records is all about. Produced as a labour of love on an independent label created for the purpose, the record came complete with lavish packaging and sold hardly at all! The music, which is thoughtful and pastoral, is interesting enough to give the record a cult reputation, and the mystique is enhanced for record collectors today by the album being reissued in a very limited facimile edition, itself being sold at something of a collectors' price.

A - Austr	LP	Holyground	HG113	1970	£210	£350	
A - Austr	LP	Magic Mixture	MM1	1989	£8	£20	

A B SKHY

Ramblin' On	LP	MGM	SE4676	1970	£4	£10	US
A B Skhy	LP	MGM	SE4628	1969	£4	£10	US

A CERTAIN RATIO

All Night Party	7"	Factory	FAC5	1979	£2	£5	
Do The Du	12"	Factory	FACUS4	1981	£2.50	£6	US
Double 12'	12"	Factory	FAC42	1981	£2.50	£6	export, double

A HOUSE

Kick Me Again Jesus	12"	Rip	ARIPT1	1987	£2.50	£6	

A II Z

I'm The One Who Loves You	7"	Polydor	POSP314	1981	£1.50	£4	
No Fun After Midnight	7"	Polydor	POSP243	1981	£1.50	£4	
No Fun After Midnight	12"	Polydor	POSPX243	1981	£3	£8	red vinyl

AARDVARK

Aardvark	LP	Nova	SDN17	1970	£25	£50	

ABACUS

Abacus	LP	Polydor	2371215	1971	£15	£30	
Everything You Need	LP	Zebra	2949002	1972	£15	£30	German
Indian Dancer	7"	York	YR207	1973	£4	£8	
Just A Day's Journey Away	LP	Polydor	2371270	1972	£15	£30	
Midway	LP	Zebra	2949013	1974	£15	£30	German

ABBA

Anniversary Boxed Set	7"	Epic	ABBA26	1984	£45	£90	26 blue vinyl singles
Arrival	LP	Nautilus	NR20	1981	£5	£12	US audiophile
Best Of Abba	LP	Readers Digest	GABA112	1986	£10	£25	5 LP set
Chiquitita (Spanish version)	7"	Vogue	45X1188	1978	£2	£5	French
Estoy Sonando	7"	Vogue	101235	1979	£2	£5	French
I Have A Dream	7"	Epic	EPC8088	1979	£1.50	£4	gatefold PS
I Have A Dream (Shakin' Stevens B side)	7"	Kelloggs	KELL1	1984	£2.50	£6	
Ring Ring	LP	Polar	POLS242	1973	£5	£12	Swedish
Ring Ring	7"	Epic	EPC1793	1973	£10	£20	
Ring Ring	7"	Polar	POS1171	1973	£5	£10	Swedish label & language
Ring Ring	7"	Polydor	2040105	1973	£10	£20	sung in German
Singles, The First Ten Years	LP	Epic	ABBOX2	1983	£20	£40	2 pic discs, boxed
Slipping Through My Fingers	7"	Discomate	PD105	1981	£15	£30	Japanese Coca-Cola pic disc
Slipping Through My Fingers	12"	Discomate	PD1005	1981	£30	£60	Japanese, red vinyl
So Long	7"	Epic	EPC2848	1974	£4	£8	
Super Trouper	LP	Epic	ABBOX1	1980	£10	£25	boxed, book, poster
Thank You For The Music	7"	Epic	WA3894	1983	£5	£10	shaped pic disc
Under Attack	7"	Epic	EPCA112971	1982	£1.50	£4	pic disc
Voulez Vous	LP	Epic	EPC86086	1979	£25	£50	pic disc
Waterloo	7"	Polar	POS1186	1974	£5	£10	Swedish label & language
Waterloo	7"	Polydor	2040116	1974	£10	£20	sung in German
Waterloo	7"	Vogue	103104	1974	£10	£20	sung in French
Winner Takes It All	12"	Epic	EPC128835	1980	£8	£20	gatefold PS

ABBEY ROAD

Clunk Click	7"	Parlophone	R5989	1973	£2.50	£6	

ABBEY TAVERN SINGERS

Collectors of records on a particular label often find themselves buying albums or singles that are not at all to their taste! "We're Off To Dublin In The Green" by the Abbey Tavern Singers is an LP of Irish pub songs that just happens to have been released on a subsidiary of Tamla Motown.

We're Off To Dublin In The Green	LP	VIP	VS402	1966	£6	£15	US

ABBOTT, BILL & THE JEWELS

Groovy Baby	7"	Cameo Parkway	P874	1963	£4	£8	

ABICAIR, SHIRLEY

In the quest to find increasingly rare grooves, some very strange artists become included within the domain of Northern Soul. Hence the unlikely inclusion here of Shirley Abicair, a lady who used to sing rather twee songs on Children's Television, to the accompaniment of a strummed autoharp.

Am I Losing You	7"	Piccadilly	7N35364	1967	£2	£5	
Willie Can	7"	Parlophone	MSP6224	1956	£2	£5	

ABRAHAMS, MICK

At Last	LP	Chrysalis	CHR1005	1972	£10	£25	round cover
Learning To Play Guitar With	LP	SRT	SRT73313	1975	£6	£15	
Mick Abrahams	LP	Chrysalis	ILPS9147	1971	£5	£12	

ABSALOM, MIKE

Hector And Other Peccadillos	LP	Philips	6308131	1972	£10	£25	
Mighty Absalom Sings Bathroom Ballads	LP	Sportsdisc	ILP1081	196-	£5	£12	
Mike Absalom	LP	Vertigo	6360053	1971	£30	£60	spiral label
Save The Last Gherkin For Me	LP	Saydisc	SDL162	1969	£8	£20	

ABYSSINIAN BAPTIST CHOIR

Abyssinian Baptist Choir	LP	Philips	847095BY	1963	£15	£30	

AC DONNCA, SEAN

An Aill Bain The White Rock	LP	Claddagh	CC9	1971	£6	£15	Irish

ACADEMY

Pop Lore According To	LP	Morgan Blue Town	BT5001	1969	£35	£70	sleeve pictured in Guide
Rachel's Dream	7"	Morgan Blue Town	BTS2	1969	£4	£8	

ACCENT

Red Sky At Night	7"	Decca	F12679	1967	£25	£50	

ACCENTS

Wiggle Wiggle	7"	Coral	Q72351	1959	£5	£10	

ACCIDENTS

Blood Spattered With Guitars	7"	Hook, Line & Sinker	HOOK1	1980	£1.50	£4	
Kiss Me On The Apocalypse	LP	Hook Line 'n Sinker		1980	£30	£60	test pressing

ACCOLADE

Accolade	LP	Columbia	SCX6405	1970	£8	£20	
Accolade 2	LP	Regal Zonophone	SLRZ1024	1971	£20	£40	
Natural Day	7"	Columbia	DB8688	1970	£2	£5	

AC/DC

Albert Archives	LP	Albert	APLP037	1979	£6	£15	Australian
Can I Sit Next To You Girl	7"	Albert	AP10551	197-	£10		Australian
Danger	7"	Atlantic	A9532P	1985	£7.50	£15	shaped pic disc
Danger	7"	Atlantic	A9532W	1985	£1.50	£4	poster sleeve
Dirty Deeds Done Dirt Cheap	7"	Atlantic	K10899	1977	£10	£20	cartoon schoolboy PS
Flick Of The Switch Interview Album	LP	Atlantic	PR562	1983	£6	£15	US promo
Girl's Got Rhythm	7"	Atlantic	K11406E	1979	£2	£5	envelope sleeve
Guns For Hire	7"	Atlantic	A9774P	1983	£6	£12	shaped pic disc
Heat Seeker	12"	Atlantic	A9136TP	1988	£2.50	£6	pic disc
High Voltage	7"	Atlantic	K10860	1976	£12.50	£25	PS
Highway To Hell	LP	Atlantic	ATL50628		£50	£100	German, yellow vinyl
Highway To Hell	LP	Atlantic	K50628	1979	£6	£15	test pressing different cover
If You Want Blood	LP	Atlantic	ATL50532		£75	£150	red or white vinyl
It's A Long Way To The Top	7"	Atlantic	K10745	1976	£4	£8	
Jailbreak	7"	Atlantic	K10805	1980	£2.50	£6	
Japan Tour '81	LP	Atlantic	SAM155	1981	£45	£90	promo pic disc
Let There Be Rock	7"	Atlantic	K11018	1977	£1.50	£4	US promo
Live From The Atlantic Studios	LP	Atlantic	LAAS001	1978	£40	£80	
Nervous Shakedown	7"	Atlantic	A9651P	1984	£6	£12	shaped pic disc
Powerage	LP	Atlantic	KSD19180	1978	£20	£40	Canadian red vinyl
Rock'n'Roll Ain't Noise Pollution	12"	Atlantic	K11630T	1980	£2.50	£6	with badge
Rock'n'Roll Damnation	12"	Atlantic	K11142T	1978	£2.50	£6	
Shake A Leg	7"	Atlantic	K11600	1979	£15	£30	wrong A side
Shake Your Foundations	7"	Atlantic	A9474P	1986	£6	£12	shaped pic disc
Touch Too Much	7"	Atlantic	K11435	1980	£1.50	£4	back to front sleeve
Who Made Who	7"	Atlantic	A9425P	1986	£5	£10	shaped pic disc
Who Made Who (Collectors Mix)	12"	Atlantic	A9425T	1986	£2.50	£6	with poster
Whole Lotta Rosie	12"	Atlantic	K11207T	1978	£2.50	£6	
You Shook Me All Night Long	7"	Atlantic	A9377P	1986	£5	£10	shaped pic disc

ACE, BUDDY

Buddy Ace	7" EP	Vocalion	VEP170164	1965	£15	£30	
Got To Get Myself Together	7"	Action	ACT4504	1968	£2	£5	

ACE, CHARLIE

Creeper	7"	Upsetter	US359	1971	£1.50	£4	Upsetters B side

ACE, JOHNNY

Johnny Ace	7" EP	Vogue	VE170150	1962	£20	£40	
Memorial Album	LP	Duke	DLP71	1956	£37.50	£75	US
Memorial Album	LP	Vocalion	VA160177	1961	£20	£40	
Memorial Album	10" LP	Duke	DLP70	1955	£100	£200	US, sleeve pictured in Guide
My Song	7"	Vogue	V9200	1962	£12.50	£25	demo only

Pledging My Love .... 7" ...... Vogue .... V9180 .... 1961 ... £12.50 ....£25

ACE, RICHARD
Don't Let The Sun Catch You Crying .... 7" ... Coxsone .... CS7031 ...... 1967 ... £5 ....£10 .... Viceroys B side
Hang 'Em High .... 7" ...... Trojan .... TR654 .... 1969 ... £2.50 ......£6 Black & George B side
I Need You .... 7" ...... Studio One ..... SO2022 ...... 1967 ... £6 ....£12 .. Soul Vendors B side
More Reggae .... 7" ...... Studio One ..... SO2072 ...... 1969 ... £6 ....£12 .... Gladiators B side

ACES
But Say It Isn't So .... 7" ...... Parlophone..... R5108 .... 1964 ... £2.50 ......£6
Wait Till Tomorrow .... 7" ...... Parlophone..... R5094 .... 1963 ... £2.50 ......£6

ACES (2)
One Way Street .... 7" ...... Etc.............. ETC1 .... 1982 ... £5 ....£10

ACHE
Bla Som Altid .... LP .... KHF .... ROLP6570 .... 1977 ... £5 ....£12 .... Danish
De Homine Urbano .... LP .... Philips .... 841906 .... 1970 ... £5 ....£12 .... German
Green Man .... LP .... Philips .... 6318005 ...... 1971 ... £5 ....£12 .... German
Pictures From Cyclus 7 .... LP .... CBS .... 81216 .... 1974 ... £5 ....£12 .... Dutch

ACHES & PAINS
Again And Again .... 7" ...... Page One ...... POF008 .... 1966 ... £1.50 ......£4

ACID GALLERY
Dance Around The Maypole .... 7" ...... CBS .... 4608 .... 1969 ... £12.50 ....£25

ACKLES, DAVID
If the musical worth of a record had any bearing on its value as a collectors' item, then "American Gothic" by David Ackles would be one of the most valuable records of all. Ackles is a singer-songwriter, but he is also an arranger of skill and considerable imagination. Every track on "American Gothic" is memorable, while the lengthy "Montana", with its echoes of Aaron Copland, is little short of a masterpiece. The album is produced by Bernie Taupin.
American Gothic .... LP .... Elektra.......... K42112 .... 1972 ... £4 ....£10
David Ackles .... LP .... Elektra.......... EKL4022/ ..... 1968 ... £8 ....£20
                                                              EKS74022
Down River .... 7" ...... Elektra.......... EKSN45039 ... 1968 ... £1.50 ......£4
Five and Dime .... LP .... CBS .... 32464 .... 1973 ... £6 ....£15 .... US
Laissez Faire .... 7" ...... Elektra.......... EKSN45054 ... 1969 ... £1.50 ......£4
Subway To The Country .... LP .... Elektra.......... EKS74060 ..... 1970 ... £8 ....£20
Subway To The Country .... 7" ...... Elektra.......... EKSN45079 ... 1969 ... £1.50 ......£4

ACKLIN, BARBARA
Am I The Same Girl .... 7" ...... MCA .... MU1071 .... 1969 ... £1.50 ......£4
Love Makes A Woman .... 7" ...... MCA .... MU1038 .... 1968 ... £1.50 ......£4

ACKLIN, BARBARA & GENE CHANDLER
Little Green Apples .... 7" ...... MCA/Soul Bag.. BAG1 .... 1969 ... £1.50 ......£4

ACQUA FRAGILE
Acqua Fragile .... LP .... Numero Uno ... DZSLN55656... 1973 ... £15 ....£30 .... Italian
Mass Media Stars .... LP .... Dischi .... 6150 .... 1974 ... £6 ....£15 .... Italian

ACRE, SEPH & THE PETS
Rock And Roll Cha Cha .... 7" ...... Pye .... 7N25001 ...... 1958 ... £1.50 ......£4

ACT
Absolutely Immune .... 12" .... ZTT .... VIMM1 .... 1987 ... £6 ....£15
Chance .... CD-s .. ZTT .... CDBET1 .... 1988 ... £50 ....£100
Chance .... 7" ...... ZTT .... BET1 .... 1988 ... £20 ....£40
Chance .... 12" .... ZTT .... BETT1 .... 1988 ... £35 ....£70
I Can't Escape From You .... CD-s .. ZTT .... CDIMM2 .... 1987 ... £4 ....£10
Laughter, Tears And Rage .... CD ..... ZTT .... ZQCD1 .... 1988 ... £6 ....£15
Snobbery And Decay .... CD-s .. ZTT .... ZCID28 .... 1987 ... £4 ....£10
Snobbery And Decay .... 12" .... ZTT .... 12XACT28 ..... 1987 ... £5 ....£12
Snobbery And Decay .... 12" .... ZTT .... 12ZTAS28 ..... 1987 ... £2.50 ......£6
Snobbery And Decay .... 12" .... ZTT .... CT01 .... 1987 ... £10 ....£25 .... promo

ACT (2)
Act .... 7" EP.. Oak............ no number .... 1967 ... £30 ....£60
Cobbled Streets .... 7" ...... Columbia .... DB8179 .... 1967 ... £6 ....£12
Here Come Those Tears .... 7" ...... Columbia .... DB8261 .... 1967 ... £6 ....£12
Just A Little Bit .... 7" ...... Columbia .... DB8331 .... 1968 ... £10 ....£20

ACTION
The Action were a mod group with a similar soul/R&B sound to the Who, except that, according to those who saw the group live, the Action were better. Not that this is particularly apparent from the group's records, which are, for the most part, worthy cover versions, but lacking the extra spark of star quality. Sadly, the Action never did get to make an album, although a later incarnation of the group made two, as Mighty Baby.
Baby You've Got It .... 7" ...... Parlophone..... R5474 .... 1966 ... £7.50 ......£15
Harlem Shuffle .... 7" ...... Hansa .... 14321AT ...... 1968 ... £10 ....£20 .... German
I'll Keep On Holding On .... 7" ...... Parlophone..... R5410 .... 1966 ... £7.50 ......£15
Land Of 1000 Dances .... 7" ...... Parlophone..... R5354 .... 1965 ... £7.50 ......£15
Never Ever .... 7" ...... Parlophone..... R5572 .... 1967 ... £7.50 ......£15
Shadows And Reflections .... 7" ...... Parlophone..... R5610 .... 1967 ... £10 ....£20
Shadows And Reflections .... 7" EP.. Odeon.......... MOE149 .... 1967 ... £80 ....£160 .... French

ACTIONS
Wepp .... 7" ...... Studio One ..... SO2065 ...... 1968 ... £6 ....£12 ... Larry & Alvin B side

ACTIVE RESTRAINT
Terror In My Home .... 7" ...... Sticky .... PEELOFF3 ..... 1983 ... £2.50 ......£6

3

ACTRESS
Good Job With Prospects	7"	CBS	4016	1969	£15	£30

ACUFF, ROY
Favorite Hymns	LP	MGM	E3707	1958	£5	£12	US
I Like Mountain Music	7"	Brunswick	05635	1957	£1.50	£4	US
Old Time Barn Music	10" LP	Columbia	CL9010	195-	£8	£20	US
Songs Of The Smokey Mountains	LP	Capitol	T617	1955	£5	£12	US
Songs Of The Smokey Mountains	10" LP	Columbia	CL9004	195-	£8	£20	US

AD CONSPIRACY
Ad Conspiracy	LP	Diamond Age		1979	£6	£15

ADAM & THE ANTS
Goody Two Shoes	7"	CBS	A112367	1982	£5	£10	
Zerox	7"	Do-It	DUN8	1979	£2	£5	mispressed B side - plays 'Physical'

ADAM, MIKE & TIM
Flowers On The Wall	7"	Columbia	DB7836	1966	£1.50	£4
Little Baby	7"	Decca	F12040	1964	£1.50	£4
Little Pictures	7"	Decca	F12221	1965	£1.50	£4
Most Peculiar Man	7"	Columbia	DB7902	1966	£1.50	£4
That's How I Feel	7"	Decca	F12112	1965	£1.50	£4

ADAMS, ARTHUR K.
She Drives Me Out Of My Mind	7"	Blue Horizon	573136	1968	£5	£10

ADAMS, BILLY
Count Every Star	7"	Capitol	CL15107	1959	£5	£10

ADAMS, BRYAN
Hidin' From Love	7"	A&M	AMS7520	1980	£7.50	£15	PS
It's Only Love (with Tina Turner)	7"	A&M	AM285	1985	£2	£5	double
Let Me Take You Dancing	7"	A&M	AMS7460	1979	£4	£8	
Let Me Take You Dancing	12"	A&M	AMSP7460	1979	£8	£20	
One Good Reason	7"	A&M	AM170	1984	£25	£50	
Somebody	7"	A&M	AMP236	1985	£1.50	£4	pic disc

ADAMS, FAYE
I'll Be True	7"	London	HLU8339	1956	£180	£300	
Shake A Hand	LP	Warwick	2031	1961	£25	£50	US

ADAMS, GLADSTON
Dollars And Cents	7"	Trojan	TR659	1969	£2.50	£6

ADAMS, GLEN
Cool Cool Rocksteady	7"	Collins Downbeat	CR006	1968	£4	£8	Owen Gray B side
Hold Down Miss Winey	7"	Island	WI3100	1967	£5	£10	Vincent Gordon B side
My Girl	7"	Duke	DU58	1969	£2.50	£6	Gladiators B side
Rent Too High	7"	Trojan	TR621	1968	£4	£8	
She	7"	Island	WI3083	1967	£5	£10	Sonny Burke B side
She Is Leaving	7"	Blue Cat	BS126	1968	£4	£8	Uniques B side
She Is So Fine	7"	Island	WI3120	1967	£5	£10	Roy Shirley B side
She's So Fine	7"	Amalgamated	AMG837	1969	£4	£8	Ernest Wilson B side
Silent Lover	7"	Island	WI3072	1967	£5	£10	

ADAMS, JOHNNY
Come On	7"	Top Rank	JAR192	1959	£2	£5	
Heart And Soul	LP	SSS	SSS5	196-	£6	£15	US
Reconsider Me	7"	Polydor	56775	1969	£4	£8	

ADAMS, LLOYD
I Wish Your Picture Was You	7"	Blue Beat	BB366	1965	£5	£10	Creepers B side

ADAMS, MARIE
What Do You Want To Make Those Eyes At Me For	7"	Capitol	CL14963	1958	£7.50	£15

ADAMS, MIKE & THE REDJACKETS
Surfers Beat	LP	Crown	CST312	1963	£10	£25	US

ADAMS, PEPPER
Cool Sound	LP	Pye	NPL28007	1959	£10	£25
Critics' Choice	LP	Vogue	LAE12134	1958	£8	£20

ADAMS, RITCHIE
Back To School	7"	London	HLU9200	1960	£6	£12

ADAMS, SUZIE & HELEN WATSON
Songbird	LP	Dingles	DIN327	1983	£5	£12

ADAMS, WOODROW
Baby You Just Don't Know	7"	Blue Horizon	451001	1965	£12.50	£25

ADDERLEY, CANNONBALL
African Waltz	LP	Riverside	RLP377	1961	£6	£15
At The Lighthouse	LP	Riverside	RLP344	1960	£6	£15
Cannonball	LP	London	LTZC15015	1956	£8	£20

Title	Format	Label	Catalogue	Year	Price	Price	Notes
Cannonball Adderley	LP	Emarcy	EJL1261	1957	£8	£20	
Cannonball Adderley And The Pollwinners	LP	Riverside	RLP355	1961	£6	£15	
Cannonball Adderley Quintet Plus	LP	Riverside	RLP388	1961	£6	£15	
Cannonball In Europe	LP	Riverside	RLP499	1963	£5	£12	
Cannonball Plays Bossa Nova	LP	Riverside	RM455	1963	£5	£12	
Cannonball Takers Charge	LP	Riverside	RLP12303	1959	£6	£15	
Cannonball's Sharpshooters	LP	Mercury	MMB12008	1959	£5	£12	
In New York	LP	Riverside	RLP(9)404	1962	£6	£15	
In San Francisco	LP	Riverside	RLP12311	1962	£6	£15	
Know What I Mean?	LP	Riverside	RLP433	1962	£5	£12	
Mercy Mercy Mercy	7"	Capitol	CL15489	1967	£1.50	£4	
Mercy Mercy Mercy!	LP	Capitol	ST2663	1967	£4	£10	
Portrait Of Cannonball	LP	Riverside	RLP12269	1958	£6	£15	
San Francisco Revisited	LP	Riverside	RM444	1963	£5	£12	
Somethin' Else	LP	Blue Note	BLP/BST81595	196-	£10	£25	with Miles Davis
Them Dirty Blues	LP	Riverside	RLP12322	1960	£6	£15	
Things Are Getting Better	LP	Riverside	RLP12286	1958	£6	£15	
Why (Am I Treated So Bad)	7"	Capitol	CL15500	1967	£1.50	£4	
Wow!	LP	Fontana	FJL107	1965	£5	£12	

ADDERLEY, NAT

Title	Format	Label	Catalogue	Year	Price	Price	Notes
Nat Adderley	LP	London	LTZC15018	1956	£10	£25	
That's Right	LP	Riverside	RLP330	1960	£6	£15	
Work Song	LP	Riverside	RLP12318	1960	£6	£15	

ADDICTS

Title	Format	Label	Catalogue	Year	Price	Price	Notes
Here She Comes	7"	Decca	F11902	1964	£4	£8	

ADDICTS (2)

Title	Format	Label	Catalogue	Year	Price	Price	Notes
Lunch With The Addicts	7"	Dining Out	TUX1	1981	£5	£10	

ADDRISSI BROTHERS

Title	Format	Label	Catalogue	Year	Price	Price	Notes
Cherry Stone	7"	London	HL8922	1959	£2	£5	
It's Love	7"	Columbia	DB4370	1959	£2	£5	
Saving My Kisses	7"	London	HL8973	1959	£2	£5	

ADENO, BOBBY

Title	Format	Label	Catalogue	Year	Price	Price	Notes
Hands Of Time	7"	Vocalion	VP9279	1966	£7.50	£15	

ADLAM, BETH

Title	Format	Label	Catalogue	Year	Price	Price	Notes
Seventeen	7"	Starlite	ST45024	1960	£1.50	£4	

ADLIBS

Title	Format	Label	Catalogue	Year	Price	Price	Notes
Boy From New York City	7"	Red Bird	RB10102	1966	£7.50	£15	
Giving Up	7"	Deep Soul	DS9102	1970	£4	£8	

ADLIBS (2)

Title	Format	Label	Catalogue	Year	Price	Price	Notes
Neighbour Neighbour	7"	Fontana	TF584	1965	£10	£20	

ADMIRALS

Title	Format	Label	Catalogue	Year	Price	Price	Notes
Promised Land	7"	Fontana	TF597	1965	£12.50	£25	

ADRIAN & THE SUNSETS

Title	Format	Label	Catalogue	Year	Price	Price	Notes
Breakthrough	LP	Sunset	(SE)63601	1963	£15	£30	US
Breakthrough	LP	Sunset	(SE)63601	1963	£25	£50	US, multi-coloured vinyl

ADVANCEMENT

Title	Format	Label	Catalogue	Year	Price	Price	Notes
Advancement	LP	Philips	PHS600328	1969	£8	£20	US

ADVENTURERS

Title	Format	Label	Catalogue	Year	Price	Price	Notes
Can't Stop Twisting	LP	Columbia	CL2147/CS8547	1961	£6	£15	US

ADVERTS

Title	Format	Label	Catalogue	Year	Price	Price	Notes
Crossing the Red Sea	LP	Bright	BRL201	1978	£6	£15	red vinyl
Crossing The Red Sea	LP	Butt	ALSO002	1981	£4	£10	red vinyl
One Chord Wonders	7"	Stiff	BUY13	1977	£1.50	£4	push-out centre

ADVOCATES

Title	Format	Label	Catalogue	Year	Price	Price	Notes
Advocates	LP	Dovetail	DOVE1	1973	£15	£30	

AERA

Title	Format	Label	Catalogue	Year	Price	Price	Notes
Aera Humanum Est	LP	Erikonig	ERL2001	1974	£6	£15	German
Hand Und Fuss	LP	Erikonig	ERL2002	1976	£5	£12	German

AEROSMITH

Title	Format	Label	Catalogue	Year	Price	Price	Notes
Angel	12"	Geffen	GEF34TP	1988	£2.50	£6	pic disc
Dream On	7"	CBS	1898	1973	£2	£5	
Dude Looks Like A Lady	12"	Geffen	GEF29TP	1987	£2.50	£6	pic disc
Get Your Wings	LP	Columbia	KCQ32847	1974	£6	£15	US quad
Janie's Got A Gun	7"	Geffen	GEF68P	1989	£1.50	£4	shaped pic disc
Rats In The Cellar	7"	CBS	AS1	1976	£4	£8	promo
Rocks	LP	Columbia	PCQ34165	1976	£6	£15	US quad
Toys In The Attic	LP	Columbia	JCQ33479	1975	£6	£15	US quad

AFEX

Title	Format	Label	Catalogue	Year	Price	Price	Notes
She Got The Time	7"	King	KG1058	1967	£10	£20	

AFFINITY

Title	Format	Label	Catalogue	Year	Price	Price	Notes
Affinity	LP	Vertigo	6360004	1970	£30	£60	spiral label
Eli's Comin'	7"	Vertigo	6059018	1970	£4	£8	

I Wonder If I Care As Much .... 7" ...... Vertigo .... 6059007 .... 1970 ... £5 .... £10 ....

AFFLICTED
All Right Boy	7"	Bonk	AFF2	1982	£2.50	£6
I'm Afflicted	7"	Bonk	AFF1	1981	£2.50	£6
untitled	7"	Bonk	AFF4	1982	£2	£5

AFO EXECUTIVES
Compendium	LP	AFO	LP0002		£37.50	£75	US

AFRICAN BEAVERS
Find My Baby	7"	RCA	RCA1447	1965	£1.50	£4

AFRICAN MESSENGERS
High Life Piccadilly	7"	Page One	POF043	1967	£1.50	£4
Niger Blues	7"	Carnival	CV7021	1965	£1.50	£4

AFRICAN MUSIC MACHINE
Black Water Gold	7"	Mojo	2092046	1972	£1.50	£4

AFROTONES
Freedom Sound	7"	Duke	DU19	1969	£2.50	£6	Boys B side
Things I Love	7"	Trojan	TR655	1969	£2.50	£6	Eric Fratter B side

AFTER DARK
Evil Woman	7"	After Dark	AD001	1981	£7.50	£15

AFTER TEA
After Tea	LP	Ace Of Clubs	ACL/SCL1251	1967	£6	£15

AFTER THE FIRE
80-F	cass	Epic	EPC84545	1980	£5	£12	test pressing
80F	7"	Epic	XPR104	1980	£2.50	£6	promo
Love Will Always Make You Cry	7"	Epic	EPC8394	1980	£2.50	£6	
Signs Of Change	LP	Rapid	RR001	1978	£15	£30	

AFTERGLOW
Afterglow	LP	MTA	5010	1967	£6	£15	US

AFTERSHAVE
Skin Deep	LP	Splendid	SLP50106	1972	£60	£120	gatefold sleeve

AGAPE
Gospel Hard Rock	LP	Mark	2170	1966	£20	£40	US

AGGREGATION
Mind Odyssey	LP	L.H.I.	12008	1967	£20	£40	US

AGINCOURT (ITHACA)
Fly Away	LP	Merlin	HF3	1970	£250	£400

AGITATION FREE
At Last	LP	Barclay	XBLY80612	1976	£15	£30	French
Malesch	LP	Vertigo	6360607	1972	£6	£15	
Second Album	LP	Vertigo	6360615	1973	£6	£15	

AGNES STRANGE
Clever Fool	7"	Birdsnest	BN1	1975	£12.50	£25
Strange Flavour	LP	Birdsnest	BRL9000	1975	£50	£100

A-HA
Cry Wolf	12"	Warner Bros	W8500TP	1986	£2.50	£6	pic disc
Hunting High And Low	12"	Warner Bros	W8663T	1986	£2.50	£6	with poster
Hunting High And Low	12"	Warner Bros	W6663TP	1986	£2.50	£6	pic disc
I've Been Losing You	12"	Warner Bros	W8594T	1986	£2.50	£6	with poster
Living Daylights	12"	Warner Bros	W8305TP	1987	£2.50	£6	pic disc
Manhattan Skyline	12"	Warner Bros	W8405T	1987	£3	£8	with poster
Manhattan Skyline	12"	Warner Bros	W8405TP	1987	£3	£8	pic disc
Sun Always Shines On TV	7"	Warner Bros	W8846P	1986	£4	£8	shaped pic disc
Take On Me	7"	Warner Bros	W9006	1985	£2	£5	2 different PS's
Take On Me	7"	Warner Bros	W9146	1984	£12.50	£25	
Take On Me	12"	Warner Bros	W9006T	1985	£3	£8	black & white PS
Take On Me	12"	Warner Bros	W9146T	1984	£20	£40	
Take On Me	12"	Warner Bros	W9146T	1984	£30	£60	with poster
Train Of Thought	7"	Warner Bros	W8736P	1986	£4	£8	shaped pic disc

AHAB
Party Girl	7"	Chicken Jazz	JAZZ5	1982	£2	£5

AILEACH
Ard Ri	LP	Leaf	7014	1977	£6	£15	Irish

AINIGMA
Diluvium	LP	Arc	ALPS151715	1973	£5	£12	German

AIRFORCE
Airforce was put together by Ginger Baker as the archetypal supergroup. Graham Bond, Denny Laine, Steve Winwood, Harold McNair, Rick Grech, and Chris Wood rubbed shoulders within a big band - and achieved very much less than their talents might suggest they should have.
Airforce	LP	Polydor	2662001	1970	£8	£20	double
Airforce 2	LP	Polydor	2383029	1970	£5	£12	chart LP
Man Of Constant Sorrow	7"	Polydor	56380	1970	£1.50	£4	

AIRTO

Airto Moreira is a Brazilian percussionist who was a vital part of the Miles Davis band that virtually invented fusion music in 1969-70. His own records present an immensely appealing, danceable form of jazz, in which many of the key names of the genre are also involved - most notably Airto's singing wife, Flora Purim.

Fingers	LP	CTI	CTI18	1973	£4	£10	
Free	LP	CTI	6020	1972	£5	£12	US
In Concert	LP	CTI	CTI21	1974	£4	£10	
Seeds On The Ground	LP	Polydor	2310040	1972	£5	£12	
Virgin Land	LP	CTI	CTI23	1974	£4	£10	

AITKEN, BOBBY

Baby Baby	7"	Island	WI028	1962	£5	£10	
Don't Leave Me	7"	Blue Beat	BB146	1962	£5	£10	
Garden Of Eden	7"	Rio	R40	1964	£5	£10	
It Takes A Friend	7"	Rio	R15	1963	£5	£10	Laurel Aitken B side
I've Told You	7"	Rio	R14	1963	£5	£10	
Jericho	7"	Black Swan	WI441	1965	£5	£10	Lester Sterling B side
Kiss Bam Bam	7"	Island	WI3028	1967	£5	£10	Cynthia Richards B side
Let Them Have A Home	7"	Doctor Bird	DB1072	1967	£5	£10	
Little Girl	7"	Rio	R50	1964	£5	£10	
Mr.Judge	7"	Rio	R64	1965	£5	£10	
Never Never	7"	Blue Beat	BB93	1962	£5	£10	
Rain Came Tumbling Down	7"	Rio	R52	1965	£5	£10	Shenley Lunan B side
Rolling Stone	7"	Rio	R34	1964	£5	£10	Lester Sterling B side
Shame And Scandal	7"	Blue Beat	BB369	1965	£5	£10	
Sweets For My Sweet	7"	Doctor Bird	DB1077	1967	£5	£10	
Thunderball	7"	Ska Beat	JB252	1966	£5	£10	Originators B side
What A Fool	7"	Giant	GN11	1967	£4	£8	

AITKEN, LAUREL

Adam And Eve	7"	Rio	R11	1963	£5	£10	Bobby Aitken B side
Aitken's Boogie	7"	Kalypso	XX16	1960	£4	£8	
Baby Don't Do It	7"	Rio	R92	1966	£4	£8	
Bachelor Life	7"	R&B	JB171	1964	£5	£10	
Bad Minded Woman	7"	Rio	R13	1963	£5	£10	
Be Mine	7"	Columbia	DB7280	1964	£4	£8	
Bewildered And Blue	7"	Rainbow	RAI106	1966	£4	£8	
Boogie In My Bones	7"	Island	WI198	1965	£5	£10	
Boogie In My Bones	7"	Starlite	ST45011	1960	£5	£10	
Boogie Rock	7"	Blue Beat	BB1	1960	£5	£10	
Bossa Nova Hop	7"	Dice	CC13	1963	£5	£10	
Brother David	7"	Blue Beat	BB84	1961	£5	£10	
Carolina	7"	Doctor Bird	DB1203	1969	£5	£10	
Clementine	7"	Blue Beat	BB340	1965	£5	£10	
Daniel Saw The Stone	7"	Blue Beat	BB194	1963	£5	£10	
Devil Or Angel	7"	Rio	R17	1963	£5	£10	
Don't Be Cruel	7"	Nu Beat	NB040	1969	£2.50	£6	
Drinking Whisky	7"	Starlite	ST45014	1960	£5	£10	
Fire	LP	Doctor Bird	DLM5012	1967	£40	£80	
Fire In Your Wire	7"	Doctor Bird	DB1187	1969	£5	£10	
For Sentimental Reasons	7"	Fab	FAB45	1968	£4	£8	
Freedom Train	7"	Rio	R18	1963	£5	£10	
Green Banana	7"	Ska Beat	JB239	1966	£5	£10	
Haile Haile (The Lion)	7"	Doctor Bird	DB1202	1969	£5	£10	Seven Letters B side
Hailie Selasie	7"	Nu Beat	NB032	1969	£4	£8	
High Priest Of Reggae	LP	Pama	PSP1012	1969	£10	£25	
How Can I Forget You	7"	Rio	R91	1966	£4	£8	
I Shall Remove	7"	Island	WI092	1963	£5	£10	
I'm Still In Love With You Girl	7"	Columbia	DB106	1967	£4	£8	
In My Soul	7"	Island	WI099	1963	£5	£10	
Jamaica	7"	Dice	CC28	1964	£5	£10	
Jamboree	7"	Ska Beat	JB232	1966	£5	£10	
Jeannie Is Back	7"	Blue Beat	BB10	1961	£5	£10	
Jesse James	7"	Nu Beat	NB045	1969	£2.50	£6	
John Saw Them Coming	7"	Rio	R37	1964	£5	£10	
Judgement Day	7"	Blue Beat	BB14	1961	£5	£10	
La La La	7"	Doctor Bird	DB1161	1968	£5	£10	Detours B side
Landlords And Tenants	7"	Nu Beat	NB044	1969	£4	£8	
Last Night	7"	Rainbow	RAI101	1966	£4	£8	
Lawd Doctor	7"	Nu Beat	NB033	1969	£4	£8	
Let's Be Lovers	7"	Rio	R65	1965	£5	£10	
Love Me Baby	7"	Starlite	ST45034	1961	£5	£10	
Low Down Dirty Girl	7"	Duke	DK1002	1963	£4	£8	Duke Reid B side
Lucille	7"	Blue Beat	BB109	1962	£5	£10	
Mabel	7"	Dice	CC1	1962	£5	£10	
Mary	7"	Rio	R12	1963	£5	£10	
Mary Don't You Weep	7"	Rio	R53	1965	£5	£10	
Mary Lee	7"	Melodisc	1570	1960	£5	£10	
Mary Lou	7"	Rio	R54	1965	£5	£10	
Mash Potato Boogie	7"	Blue Beat	BB40	1961	£5	£10	
Mighty Redeemer	7"	Blue Beat	BB70	1961	£5	£10	
Moon Rock	7"	Bamboo	BAM16	1970	£2	£5	
More Whiskey	7"	Blue Beat	BB25	1961	£5	£10	Lloyd Clarke B side
Mr.Lee	7"	Doctor Bird	DB1160	1968	£5	£10	
Nebuchnezer	7"	Kalypso	XX15	1960	£4	£8	
Never You Hurt	7"	Fab	FAB5	1967	£4	£8	
Nursery Rhyme Boogie	7"	Blue Beat	BB52	1961	£5	£10	
One More Time	7"	Rio	R56	1965	£5	£10	
Pick Up Your Bundle And Go	7"	R&B	JB170	1964	£5	£10	

7

Title	Format	Label	Cat. No.	Year	Price	Price	Notes
Propaganda	7"	Ska Beat	JB236	1966	£5	£10	
Pussy Got Thirteen Life	7"	Ackee	ACK104	1970	£1.50	£4	
Pussy Price	7"	Nu Beat	NB046	1969	£4	£8	
Railroad Track	7"	Blue Beat	BB22	1961	£5	£10	
Reggae Prayer	7"	Doctor Bird	DB1196	1969	£5	£10	
Remember My Darling	7"	Black Swan	WI401	1964	£5	£10	
Revival	7"	Rio	R99	1966	£4	£8	
Rice And Peas	7"	Doctor Bird	DB1190	1969	£5	£10	Classics B side
Rise And Fall	LP	J.J.		1969	£40	£80	
Rise And Fall	7"	Doctor Bird	DB1197	1969	£5	£10	
Rock Of Ages	7"	Rio	R35	1964	£5	£10	
Rock Steady	7"	Columbia	DB102	1967	£4	£8	
Run Powell Run	7"	Nu Beat	NB035	1969	£4	£8	Rico B side
Saint	7"	Black Swan	WI411	1964	£5	£10	
Save The Last Dance	7"	Nu Beat	NB039	1969	£2.50	£6	
Scandal In Brixton Market	LP	Pama	ECO8	1969	£8	£20	
Seven Lonely Nights	7"	Rio	R60	1965	£5	£10	
Shoo Be Doo	7"	Nu Beat	NB043	1969	£2.50	£6	
Sin Pon You	7"	Ackee	ACK106	1970	£1.50	£4	
Sixty Days Sixty Nights	7"	Blue Beat	BB120	1962	£5	£10	
Ska With Laurel	LP	Rio	LR1	1966	£40	£80	
Skinhead Invasion	7"	Nu Beat	NB048	1970	£4	£8	test pressing
Skinhead Train	7"	Nu Beat	NB047	1969	£2.50	£6	
Suffering Still	7"	Nu Beat	NB025	1969	£4	£8	
Sweet Precious Love	7"	Rainbow	RAI111	1966	£4	£8	
Think Me No Know	7"	Junior	JR105	1969	£4	£8	Rico B side
This Great Day	7"	Blue Beat	BB249	1964	£5	£10	
Tribute To Collie Smith	7"	Kalypso	XX19	1960	£4	£8	
We Shall Overcome	7"	Rio	R97	1966	£4	£8	
Weary Wanderer	7"	Blue Beat	BB142	1962	£5	£10	Bandits B side
What A Weeping	7"	Island	WI095	1963	£5	£10	
Woppi King	7"	Nu Beat	NB024	1969	£4	£8	
You Can't Stop Me From Loving You	7"	R&B	JB167	1964	£5	£10	
You Left Me Standing	7"	Dice	CC31	1965	£5	£10	
You Left Me Standing	7"	Rio	R36	1964	£5	£10	
Zion	7"	Blue Beat	BB164	1962	£5	£10	

A-JAES

| I'm Leaving You | 7" | Oak | RGJ132 | 1964 | £75 | £150 | |

AKA & THE CHARLATANS

| Heroes Are Losers | 12" | Vanity | VANE1 | 1978 | £3 | £8 | |

AKENS, JEWEL

Birds And The Bees	LP	London	HAN8234	1965	£4	£10	
Birds And The Bees	7"	London	HLN9954	1965	£1.50	£4	chart single
Birds And The Bees	7" EP	London	RE10170	1965	£4	£10	French
Dancing Jenny	7"	Ember	EMBS219	1966	£2.50	£6	
Georgie Porgie	7"	London	HLN9969	1965	£1.50	£4	

AKIYOSHI, TOSHIKO

| Newport Jazz Festival 1957 | LP | Columbia | 33CX10101 | 1958 | £6 | £15 | Side 2 by Leon Sash |

AKRYLYKZ

| Spyderman | 7" | Red Rhino | RED2 | 1980 | £1.50 | £4 | |

AL & THE VIBRATORS

Check Up	7"	High Note	HS005	1969	£2.50	£6	
Move Up	7"	Doctor Bird	DB1085	1967	£5	£10	
Move Up Calypso	7"	High Note	HS007	1969	£2.50	£6	Patsy Todd B side

AL, ROLANDO & THE SOUL BROTHERS

Doctor Ring A Ding	7"	Doctor Bird	DB1023	1966	£5	£10	Freddie & The Heartaches B side
From Russia With Love	7"	Doctor Bird	DB1010	1966	£5	£10	
I Love You	7"	Doctor Bird	DB1035	1966	£5	£10	
Phoenix City	7"	Doctor Bird	DB1020	1966	£5	£10	Deacons B side
Sufferer's Choice	7"	Doctor Bird	DB1011	1966	£5	£10	Soulettes B side
Sugar And Spice	7"	Doctor Bird	DB1017	1966	£5	£10	
VC10	7"	Doctor Bird	DB1008	1966	£5	£10	Larry Marshall B side

ALABAMA JUG BAND

| Alabama Jug Band | 7" EP | Brunswick | OE9161 | 1955 | £4 | £8 | |

ALABAMA STATE TROUPERS

| Alabama State Troupers | LP | Elektra | EKS75022 | 1972 | £6 | £15 | US |

ALAIMO, STEVE

Every Day I Have To Cry	LP	Checker	LP2986	1963	£8	£20	US
Everyday I Have To Cry	7"	Pye	7N25174	1963	£7.50	£15	
It's A Long Long Way To Happiness	7"	Pye	7N25199	1963	£2	£5	
Mashed Potatoes	LP	Checker	LP2983	1962	£8	£20	US
My Friends	7"	Pye	7N25161	1962	£2	£5	
Sings And Swings	LP	ABC	(S)551	1966	£6	£15	US
So Much Love	7"	HMV	POP1531	1966	£2	£5	
Starring Steve Alaimo	LP	ABC	(S)501	1965	£6	£15	US
Steve Alaimo	LP	Crown	CLP5382	1963	£5	£12	US
Twist With Steve Alaimo	LP	Checker	LP2981	1961	£8	£20	US
Where The Action Is	LP	ABC	(S)531	1965	£6	£15	US

ALAMO
Alamo	LP	Atlantic	SD8279	1971	£5 £12	US

ALARM
68 Guns	7"	IRS	PFPC1023	1983	£2 £5	with cassette (CS70504)
Deceiver	7"	IRS	IRS103	1984	£2 £5	clear vinyl
Deceiver	7"	IRS	IRS103	1984	£25 £50	mustard vinyl
Deceiver	7"	IRS	IRSD103	1984	£5 £10	double
Marching On	7"	IRS	ILS0032	1982	£7.50 £15	
Unsafe Buildings	7"	White Cross	001	1981	£25 £50	gatefold PS

ALBA
Alba	LP	Rubber	RUB021	1977	£6 £15

ALBAM, MANNY
And The Jazz Greats Of Our Time Vol.1	LP	Coral	LVA9064	1958	£5 £12
West Side Story	LP	Coral	LVA9097	1959	£5 £12

ALBAM, MANNY & ERNIE WILKINS
Drum Suite	LP	HMV	CLP1107	1957	£5 £12

ALBERT, EDDIE
Come Pretty Little Girl	7"	London	HL8136	1955	£10 £20
Jenny Kissed Me (with Sandra Lee)	7"	London	HLU8241	1956	£7.50 £15

ALBERTO Y LOS TRIOS PARANOIAS
Snuff Rock	12"	Stiff	LAST2	1977	£3 £8	promo

ALBION BAND
Battle Of The Field	LP	Island	HELP25	1976	£6 £15
Prospect Before Us	LP	Harvest	SHSP4059	1976	£6 £15

ALCAPONE, DENNIS
Alpha And Omega	7"	Upsetter	US377	1971	£1.50 £4	Junior Byles B side
Duppy Serenade	7"	Banana	BA328	1971	£1.50 £4	
Fine Style	7"	Attack	ATT8027	1972	£1.50 £4	Winston Scotland B side
Forever Version	7"	Banana	BA341	1971	£2 £5	
Great Woggie	7"	Treasure Isle	TI7069	1971	£2 £5	
Guns Don't Argue	LP	Trojan	TRL187	1971	£5 £12	
King Of The Track	LP	Magnet	MGT001	1973	£5 £12	
Let It Roll	7"	Prince Buster	PB12	1971	£1.50 £4	test pressing, Ansell Collins B side
Master Key	7"	Upsetter	US388	1972	£1.50 £4	
Power Version	7"	Ackee	ACK146	1971	£1.50 £4	Bluesblasters B side
Rasta Dub	7"	Grape	GR3035	1972	£1.50 £4	Upsetters B side
Shades Of Hudson	7"	Big Shot	BI565	1971	£1.50 £4	
Wake Up Jamaica	7"	Treasure Isle	TI7074	1971	£2 £5	Tommy McCook B side
Well Dread	7"	Upsetter	US373	1971	£1.50 £4	
Wonderman	7"	Upsetter	US381	1972	£1.50 £4	Upsetters B side

ALDO, STEVE
Can I Get A Witness	7"	Decca	F12041	1964	£10 £20
Everybody Has To Cry	7"	Parlophone	R5432	1966	£17.50 £35

ALDRICH, RONNIE
Big Band Beat	7"	Columbia	DB3945	1957	£2 £5
Coach Call Boogie	7"	Decca	F10248	1954	£2 £5
Ko Ko Mo	7"	Decca	F10494	1955	£4 £8
Rhythm 'n Blues	7"	Decca	F10564	1955	£4 £8
Right Now, Right Now	7"	Columbia	DB3882	1957	£6 £12
Rock Candy	7"	Decca	F10544	1955	£4 £8
Wolf On The Prowl	7"	Decca	F10274	1954	£2 £5

ALEANNA
Aleanna	LP	Inchecronin	INC7421	1978	£30 £60

ALEONG, AKI & THE NOBLES
C'mon Baby Let's Dance	LP	Reprise	R(9)6020	1962	£5 £12	US
Come Surf With Me	LP	Vee Jay	LP/SR1060	1963	£6 £15	US
Twistin' The Hits	LP	Reprise	R(9)6011	1962	£5 £12	US

ALEX
Alex	LP	Pan	87305	1974	£8 £20	German
That's The Deal	LP	Pan	88831	1976	£6 £15	German

ALEXANDER, ARTHUR
Alexander The Great	7" EP	London	RED1364	1963	£25 £50
Anna	7"	London	HLD9641	1962	£10 £20
Black Night	7"	London	HLD9899	1964	£6 £12
For You	7"	London	HLU10023	1966	£4 £8
Go Home Girl	7"	London	HLD9667	1963	£7.50 £15
Soldier Of Love	7" EP	London	RED1401	1963	£25 £50
Soldiers Of Love	7"	London	HLD9566	1962	£7.50 £15
You Better Move On	LP	London	HAD2457	1962	£40 £80
You Better Move On	7"	London	HLD9523	1962	£7.50 £15

ALEXANDER'S TIMELESS BLOOZBAND
Alexander's Timeless Bloozband .... LP .... Smack .... 1001 .... 1967 ... £32.50 ..... £65 .... US

ALEXANDRIA, LOREZ
Lorez Sings Pres .... 10" LP Parlophone...... PMD1062 .... 1958 ... £10 .... £25

ALFIE & HARRY
Closing Time .... 7" .... London .... HLU8494 .... 1957 ... £2.50 ...... £6
Trouble With Harry .... 7" .... London .... HLU8242 .... 1956 ... £7.50 ..... £15 .... chart single

ALFONSO, CARLTON
I Have Changed .... 7" .... Nu Beat .... NB004 .... 1968 ... £4 .... £8

ALFORD, CLEM
Mirror Image .... LP ...... Columbia .... SCX6571 .... 1974 ... £30 .... £60

ALFRED & MELMOTH
I Want Someone .... 7" .... Island .... WI3130 .... 1967 ... £5 .... £10

ALFRED, SANDRA
Rocket And Roll .... 7" .... Oriole .... CB1408 .... 1958 ... £10 .... £20

ALICE
Alice .... LP ...... Byg .... 529016 .... 1970 ... £5 .... £12 .... French
Arretez Le Monde .... LP ...... Polydor .... 2393043 .... 1972 ... £4 .... £10 .... French

ALICE THROUGH THE LOOKING GLASS (ITHACA)
Alice Through The Looking Glass .... LP ...... private .... SNP .... 1969 ... £250 ..... £400

ALIEN SEX FIEND
ASF Box .... 12" ..... Windsong .... 02 .... 1990 ... £8 .... £20 .... 3 coloured
                                                                                                                                                              vinyl singles, boxed
Dead And Buried .... 7" .... Anagram .... EANA23 .... 1984 ... £1.50 ...... £4 .... pic disc
E.S.T. .... 11" ..... Anagram .... 11ANA25 .... 1984 ... £2.50 ...... £6
Ignore The Machine .... 7" .... Anagram .... PANA11 .... 1985 ... £1.50 ...... £4 .... pic disc

ALL ABOUT EVE
A comparison between the present edition of the Price Guide and the earlier versions will reveal that many bands from the eighties have passed out of fashion, with a corresponding drop in the values of their rarest records. Most dramatic in this respect is perhaps All About Eve, whose list of collector's items is now only a third as long as it used to be.

D For Desire .... 12" .... Eden .... EDEN1 .... 1985 ... £20 .... £40
Flowers In Our Hair .... 12" .... Eden .... EVENX4 .... 1987 ... £3 .... £8
In The Clouds .... cass ... Mercury .... EVCX13 .... 1991 ... £3 .... £8 .... 6 tracks
In The Clouds .... 7" .... Mercury .... EVENP5 .... 1987 ... £1.50 ...... £4 .... with poster
In The Clouds .... 12" .... Eden .... EDEN2 .... 1986 ... £8 .... £20
In The Clouds .... 12" .... Eden .... EDEN2222 .... 1986 ... £10 .... £25 .... with poster
Martha's Harbour .... CDV ... Mercury .... 0805222 .... 1988 ... £3 .... £8
Martha's Harbour .... 12" .... Mercury .... EVNXB8 .... 1988 ... £2.50 ...... £6 .... boxed with
                                                                                                                                                              poster, autographed
Our Summer .... 7" .... Eden .... EVEN3 .... 1987 ... £1.50 ...... £4
Our Summer .... 12" .... Eden .... EVENX3 .... 1987 ... £4 .... £10
What Kind Of Fool .... CDV ... Mercury .... 0806182 .... 1988 ... £8 .... £20

ALL DAY
York Pop Music Project .... LP ...... private .... 1973 ... £180 ..... £300

ALL STARS
All Stars .... LP ...... Capitol .... LCT6110 .... 1956 ... £6 .... £15
Season At Riverside .... LP ...... Capitol .... T761 .... 1957 ... £5 .... £12

ALLAN, RICHARD
As Time Goes By .... 7" .... Parlophone...... R4634 .... 1960 ... £1.50 ...... £4 .... chart single

ALLEN & MILTON
It Is I .... 7" .... Blue Beat .... BB348 .... 1965 ... £5 .... £10
Someone Like You .... 7" .... Blue Beat .... BB353 .... 1965 ... £5 .... £10

ALLEN, ANNISTEEN
Don't Nobody Move .... 7" .... Brunswick .... 05639 .... 1957 ... £4 .... £8
Fujiyama Mama .... 7" .... Capitol .... CL14264 .... 1955 ... £15 .... £30

ALLEN, CHAD & THE EXPRESSIONS
Chad Allen And The Expressions .... LP ...... Scepter .... SP(S)533 .... 1966 ... £6 .... £15 .... US

ALLEN, CLAY
Crazy Crazy World .... 7" .... Starlite .... ST45106 .... 1963 ... £2.50 ...... £6
I Can't Stop The Blues From Moving .... 7" .... Starlite .... ST45096 .... 1963 ... £2.50 ...... £6
This Time It's Really Goodbye .... 7" .... Starlite .... ST45086 .... 1962 ... £2.50 ...... £6

ALLEN, DAEVID
Good Morning .... LP ...... Virgin .... V2054 .... 1976 ... £6 .... £15
It's The Time Of Your Life .... 7" .... Virgin .... VS123 .... 1975 ... £5 .... £10 .... promo

ALLEN, DAVE
Color Blind .... LP ...... International .... IALP11 .... 1969 ... £8 .... £20 .... US
                                                              Artists ....
Good Earth .... 7" .... Philips .... BF1748 .... 1969 ... £1.50 ...... £4

ALLEN, DAVIE & THE ARROWS
Apache '65 .... LP ...... Tower .... (D)T5002 .... 1965 ... £6 .... £15 .... US
Blues Theme .... LP ...... Tower .... (D)T5078 .... 1967 ... £6 .... £15 .... US
Cycledelic Sounds .... LP ...... Tower .... DT5094 .... 1968 ... £6 .... £15 .... US

| Wild In The Streets | LP | Tower | DT5099 | 1968 | £6 | £15 | US |

ALLEN, DEAN
| Ooh Ooh Baby Baby | 7" | London | HLM8698 | 1958 | £7.50 | £15 | |

ALLEN, HENRY RED
| Newport Jazz Festival 1957 | LP | Columbia | 33CX10106 | 1958 | £6 | £15 | with Jack Teagarden & Kid Ory |
| Ride, Red, Ride In Hi Fi | LP | RCA | RD27045 | 1958 | £8 | £20 | |

ALLEN, LEE
Cat Walk	7"	Top Rank	JAR265	1960	£2.50	£6	
Walking With Mr.Lee	LP	Ember	ELP200	1958	£37.50	£75	US
Walking With Mr.Lee	7"	HMV	POP452	1958	£10	£20	
Walking With Mr.Lee	7" EP	Top Rank	JKR8020	1959	£7.50	£15	

ALLEN, MAURICE
| Oooh Baby | 7" | Pye | 7N15128 | 1958 | £2.50 | £6 | |

ALLEN, RAY & THE UPBEATS
| Tribute To Six | LP | Blast | BLP6804 | | £15 | £30 | US |

ALLEN, REX
| Country And Western Aces | 7" EP | Mercury | 10011MCE | 1964 | £2 | £5 | |
| Westward Ho The Wagons | 7" EP | Brunswick | OE9317 | 1957 | £2 | £5 | |

ALLEN, RITCHIE
Rising Surf	LP	Imperial	LP9229/LP12229	1963	£10	£25	US
Stranger From Durango	LP	Imperial	LP9212/LP12212	1963	£10	£25	US
Surfer's Slide	LP	Imperial	LP9243/LP12243	1963	£10	£25	US

ALLEN, STEVE
| Ballad Of Davy Crockett | 7" | Vogue Coral | Q72118 | 1956 | £2 | £5 | |
| Memories Of You | 7" | Vogue Coral | Q72126 | 1956 | £1.50 | £4 | |

ALLEN, TONY
| Rock And Roll With Tony Allen | LP | Crown | CLP5231 | 1960 | £10 | £25 | US |
| Time To Swing | 7" EP | Philips | BBE12522 | 1962 | £2 | £5 | |

ALLEN, VERNON
| Babylon | 7" | R&B | JB169 | 1964 | £5 | £10 | |

ALLEN, WOODY
Spot Floyd	7"	Colpix	PX775	1964	£1.50	£4	
Third Woody Allen Album	LP	Capitol	T2986	1968	£5	£12	US
Wonderful Wacky World	LP	Bell	6008	1968	£4	£10	US
Woody Allen	LP	Colpix	(S)CP488	1964	£5	£12	US
Woody Allen 2	LP	Colpix	(S)CP518	1965	£5	£12	US

ALLENS, ARVIE
| Fast Freight | 7" | Del Fi | 4111 | 1958 | £7.50 | £15 | US |

ALLEY CATS
| Snap Crackle And Pop | 7" | Vogue | V9155 | 1959 | £7.50 | £15 | |

ALLISON, GENE
| Gene Allison | LP | Vee Jay | VJLP1009 | 1959 | £25 | £50 | US |
| Hey Hey I Love You | 7" | London | HLU8605 | 1958 | £25 | £50 | |

ALLISON, KEITH
| In Action | LP | Columbia | CL2641/CS9441 | 1967 | £5 | £12 | US |

ALLISON, LUTHER
| Luther Allison | LP | Delmark | DS625 | 1971 | £6 | £15 | |

ALLISON, MOSE
Autumn Song	LP	Transatlantic	PR7189	1967	£5	£12	
Baby Please Don't Go	7" EP	Fontana	H292	1961	£4	£8	
Back Country Suite	7" EP	Esquire	EP221	1959	£4	£8	
Blueberry Hill	7" EP	Esquire	EP224	1960	£4	£8	
Creek Bank	LP	Esquire	32094	1960	£6	£15	
I Love The Life I Live	LP	Realm	RM52318	1966	£5	£12	
I Love The Life I Live	7"	Columbia	DB7330	1964	£4	£8	
Local Color	LP	Esquire	32071	1959	£6	£15	
Mose Alive!	LP	Atlantic	587/588007	1966	£5	£12	
Parchman Farm	7" EP	Esquire	EP214	1959	£4	£8	
Seventh Son	LP	Transatlantic	PR7279	1966	£5	£12	
Sings	LP	Stateside	SL10106	1964	£6	£15	
Sings The Blues	7" EP	Columbia	SEG8353	1964	£4	£8	
Swingin' Machine	LP	London	HAK8083	1963	£6	£15	
That Man Mose Again	7" EP	Esquire	EP231	1960	£4	£8	
V8 Ford	LP	Columbia	SX6058	1964	£6	£15	
Wild Man On The Loose	LP	Atlantic	587/588031	1966	£5	£12	

ALLISONS
Allisons	7" EP	Fontana	TFE17339	1961	£5	£10	
Are You Sure	LP	Fontana	TFL5135/STFL558	1961	£8	£20	
Are You Sure	7"	Fontana	H294	1961	£1.50	£4	chart single
I'll Cross My Fingers	7"	Fontana	267255TF	1962	£1.50	£4	
Lessons In Love	7"	Fontana	H362	1962	£1.50	£4	
Sweet And Lovely	7"	Fontana	267231TF	1962	£1.50	£4	chart single
What A Mess	7"	Fontana	H336	1961	£1.50	£4	

Words	7"	Fontana	H304	1961 ...	£1.50	£4	chart single

ALLISONS (2)

Surfer Street	7"	Stateside	SS289	1964 ...	£2	£5	

ALLMAN BROTHERS BAND

Allman Brothers Band	LP	Capricorn	228033	1969 ...	£4	£10	
At Fillmore East	LP	Atlantic	2659005...........	1971 ...	£6	£15	double
Eat A Peach	LP	Capricorn	CP40102	1972 ...	£8	£20	US quad
Eat A Peach	LP	Capricorn	K67501	1972 ...	£6	£15	double
Eat A Peach	LP	Mobile Fidelity	MFSL2157	1983 ...	£8	£20	US audiophile
Idlewild South	LP	Capricorn	2400032...........	1970 ...	£4	£10	

ALLMAN, DUANE

Anthology	LP	Capricorn	K67502	1972 ...	£6	£15	double
Anthology Vol.2	LP	Capricorn	2659037...........	1974 ...	£5	£12	double

ALLMAN JOYS

Allman Joys	LP	Mercury	6398005...........	1973 ...	£6	£15	

ALLSUP, TOMMY

Buddy Holly Songbook	LP	Reprise	R(S)6182	1965 ...	£10	£25	US

ALMEIDA, LAURINDO

Laurindo Almeida Quartet	LP	Brunswick........	LAE12019	1956 ...	£10	£25	

ALMIGHTY

Destroyed	12"	Polydor	PZP60	1989 ...	£2.50	£6	pic disc

ALMOND, JOHNNY

Hollywood Blues	LP	Deram	SML1057	1970 ...	£8	£20	
Patent Pending	LP	Deram	DML/SML1043 ...	1969 ...	£8	£20	
Solar Level	7"	Deram	DM266	1969 ...	£2	£5	

ALMOND LETTUCE

Magic Circle	7"	Philips	BF1764	1969 ...	£4	£8	
Tree Dog Song	7"	Columbia	DB8442	1968 ...	£1.50	£4	

ALMOND, MARC

Boy Who Came Back	10"	Some Bizarre...	BZS2310	1984 ...	£3	£8	
Days Of Pearly Spencer	12"	Some Bizarre...	YZ638T	1992 ...	£3	£8	promo
House Is Haunted	7"	Some Bizarre...	GLOW1	1985 ...	£2.50	£6	promo
Kept Boy	7"	Parlophone......	PSR500	1988 ...	£4	£8	1 side etched
Love Letter	10"	Some Bizarre...	BONK210	1985 ...	£3	£8	
Mother Fist	7"	Some Bizarre...	GLOW5	1987 ...	£2.50	£8	promo
My Death	7"	Gutterhearts	LYN14210	198- ...	£4	£8	flexi
Stories Of Johnny	10"	Some Bizarre...	BONK110	1985 ...	£3	£8	
Tenderness Is A Weakness	7"	Some Bizarre...	BZS2510	1984 ...	£3	£8	
Woman's Story	10"	Some Bizarre...	GLOW210	1986 ...	£3	£8	
You Have	10"	Some Bizarre...	BZS2410	1984 ...	£3	£8	
Your Aura	7"	Gutterhearts	....	198- ...	£4	£8	flexi

ALONE AGAIN OR

Drum The Beat	7"	All One.............	ALG1	1984 ...	£4	£8	

ALOVE & PAXTON

Wickeder	7"	Blue Cat	BS168	1969 ...	£4	£8	

ALPERT, TRIGGER

Trigger Happy	LP	London	LTZU15096	1957 ...	£10	£25	

ALPHONSO, CARLTON

Belittle Me	7"	Grape	GR3000	1969 ...	£1.50	£4	
Where In This World	7"	Pama	PM700	1967 ...	£4	£8	

ALPHONSO, CLYDE

Good Enough	7"	Studio One	SO2076	1969 ...	£6	£12	

ALPHONSO, ORVILLE

Belly Lick	7"	Caribou	CRC1	1965 ...	£4	£8	

ALPHONSO, ROLAND

Blackberry Brandy	7"	Blue Beat	BB58..................	1961 ...	£5	£10	
Cat	7"	Pyramid	PYR6008............	1967 ...	£4	£8	Desmond Dekker B side
Crime Wave	7"	R&B	JB164	1964 ...	£5	£10	
Devoted To You	7"	Island	WI264	1966 ...	£5	£10	Jackie Opel B side
El Pussy Cat	7"	Island	WI217	1965 ...	£5	£10 ...	Lord Brynner B side
Federal Special	7"	R&B	JB122	1963 ...	£5	£10	
Feeling Fine	7"	Island	WI146	1964 ...	£5	£10 ..	Leon & Owen B side
Four Corners Of The World	7"	Blue Beat	BB112	1962 ...	£5	£10	Shiners B side
Green Door	7"	Blue Beat	BB63..................	1961 ...	£5	£10 ...	Monty & Roy B side
Guantanamera Ska	7"	Pyramid	PYR6009............	1967 ...	£4	£8	Spanishtonians B side
Jazz Ska	7"	Rio	R58	1965 ...	£5	£10	Hyacinth B side
Jericho Chain	7"	Blue Beat	BB356................	1965 ...	£5	£10	
Jungle Bit	7"	Pyramid	PYR6007............	1967 ...	£4	£8	.Norman Grant B side
Middle East	7"	Pyramid	PYR6003............	1967 ...	£4	£8	Desmond Dekker B side
Never To Be Mine	7"	Trojan	TR001	1967 ...	£5	£10	Duke Reid B side
Nimblefoot	7"	Ska Beat	JB210	1965 ...	£5	£10	Andy And Joey B side

Title	Format	Label	Cat. No.	Year			Notes
Nothing For Nothing	7"	Pyramid	PYR6011	1967	£4	£8	Desmond Dekker B side
Nuclear Weapon	7"	Ska Beat	JB216	1965	£5	£10	Stranger Cole B side
On The Move	7"	Pyramid	PYR6006	1967	£4	£8	Desmond Dekker B side
Peace And Love	7"	Pyramid	PYR6023	1968	£4	£8	
Phoenix City	7"	Trojan	TRM9010	1974	£1.50	£4	
Reggae In The Grass	7"	Coxsone	CS7077	1968	£5	£10	Roy Richards B side
Rinky Dink	7"	Ska Beat	JB231	1966	£5	£10	Scratch & The Dynamites B side
Roland Plays The Prince	7"	Blue Beat	BB286	1964	£5	£10	Gaynor & Errol B side
Roll On	7"	Punch	PH39	1970	£2	£5	
Shanty Town Curfew	7"	Island	WI3055	1967	£5	£10	Hopeton Lewis B side
Ska Au Go-Go	LP	Coxsone	CSL8003	1967	£50	£100	
Sock It To Me	7"	Pyramid	PYR6018	1967	£4	£8	Spanishtonians B side
Stream Of Life	7"	Pyramid	PYR6016	1967	£4	£8	Austin Faithful B side
Thousand Tons Of Megaton	7"	Gas	GAS112	1969	£4	£8	
Whiter Shade Of Pale	7"	Pyramid	PYR6022	1968	£4	£8	
Woman Of The World	7"	Pyramid	PYR6005	1967	£4	£8	Spanishtonians B side
Yard Broom	7"	Ska Beat	JB183	1965	£5	£10	Dotty & Bonnie B side

ALTECS
| Easy | 7" | London | HLU9387 | 1961 | £2 | £5 | |

ALTERNATIVE TV
| Live At The Rat Club | LP | Crystal | CLP01 | 1979 | £5 | £12 | |

ALTERNATIVE TV & HERE AND NOW
| What You See Is What You Are | LP | Deptford Fun City | DLP02 | 1978 | £4 | £10 | |

ALTON & EDDY
| Muriel | 7" | Blue Beat | BB17 | 1961 | £5 | £10 | |
| My Love Divine | 7" | Island | WI009 | 1962 | £5 | £10 | |

ALTON & PHYLLIS
| Love Letters | 7" | Trojan | TR622 | 1968 | £4 | £8 | |

ALTONA
| Altona | LP | RCA | PPL11049 | 1974 | £5 | £12 | German |
| Chicken Farm | LP | RCA | PPL14129 | 1975 | £5 | £12 | German |

ALVARO
Drinking My Own Sperm	LP	Squeaky Shoes	SSRM1	1977	£6	£15	
Mum's Milk Not Powder	LP	Squeaky Shoes	SSRM2	1979	£5	£12	
Working Class	LP	Squeaky Shoes	SSRM3	1981	£5	£12	

ALVYN
| You've Gotta Have An Image | 7" | Morgan Bluetown | MR18 | 1969 | £1.50 | £4 | |

AMALGAM
| Play Blackwell And Higgins | LP | A Records | A002 | 1973 | £8 | £20 | |
| Prayer For Peace | LP | Transatlantic | TRA196 | 1969 | £15 | £30 | |

AMAZIAH
| Straight Talker | LP | Sunrise | SR001 | 1973 | £75 | £150 | |

AMAZING BLONDEL
Alleluia	7"	Island	WIP6153	1972	£1.50	£4	
Amazing Blondel	LP	Bell	SBLL131	1970	£60	£120	sleeve pictured in Guide
Blondel	LP	Island	ILPS9257	1973	£4	£10	
England	LP	Island	ILPS9205	1972	£4	£10	
Evensong	LP	Island	ILPS9136	1970	£4	£10	
Fantasia Lindum	LP	Island	ILPS9156	1971	£4	£10	
Mulgrave Street	LP	DJM	DJF20442	1974	£4	£10	
Mulgrave Street	7"	DJM	DJX503	1974	£5	£10	promo

AMAZING CATSFIELD STEAMERS
| United Friends | LP | Fat Hen | FH002LP | 1983 | £5 | £12 | |

AMAZING DANCE BAND
| Deep Blue Train | 7" | Verve | VS567 | 1968 | £5 | £10 | |

AMAZING FRIENDLY APPLE
| Water Woman | 7" | Decca | F12887 | 1969 | £10 | £20 | |

AMBER SQUAD
| Can We Go Dancing? | 7" | Deadgood | DEAD17 | 1980 | £2.50 | £6 | |
| Put My Finger On You | 7" | Sound Of Leicester | ST1 | 1980 | £4 | £8 | |

AMBOY DUKES
In order to appreciate the Amboy Dukes' tendency to overdo everything, one need look no further than the seminal punk (sixties style) compilation, "Nuggets". Here the group turns "Tobacco Road" into a totally unsuitable vehicle for guitar excess. Lead guitarist Ted Nugent has followed more or less the same approach ever since.
| All I Need | 7" | Polydor | 56172 | 1967 | £4 | £8 | |

He Came To Me Yesterday	7"	Polydor	56281	1968	£4	£8
High Life In Whitley Wood	7"	Polydor	56190	1967	£4	£8
Judy In Disguise	7"	Polydor	56228	1968	£4	£8
Marriage On The Rocks	LP	Polydor	244012	1970	£8	£20 ..... US
Simon Says	7"	Polydor	56243	1968	£4	£8
Turn Back To Me	7"	Polydor	56149	1966	£4	£8

AMBOY DUKES (2)

Amboy Dukes	LP	Fontana	(S)TL5468	1968	£15	£30
Journey To The Centre Of The Mind	LP	London	HAT/SHT8378	1968	£10	£25
Let's Go Get Stoned	7"	Fontana	TF971	1968	£5	£10
Migration	LP	London	HAT/SHT8392	1969	£8	£20

AMBROSE, SAM

Monkey See Monkey Do	7"	Stateside	SS399	1965	£25	£50
This Diamond Ring	7"	Stateside	SS385	1965	£15	£30

AMBROSE SLADE

Ambrose Slade was the original name of Slade, back in the days when they were being marketed as the first skinhead group (despite the fact that the group's music had nothing in common with the likes of 'Skinhead Moonstomp'). The reissue of the group's LP, on Contour, is as rare as the original - it was withdrawn shortly after release - but the US version of the record, retitled "Ballzy" and given an appropriate cover, is rather more common.

Ballzy	LP	Fontana	SRF67598	1969	£30	£60 ..... US
Beginnings	LP	Contour	6870678	1975	£20	£40
Beginnings	LP	Fontana	STL5492	1969	£100	£200 ..... sleeve pictured in Guide
Genesis	7"	Fontana	TF1015	1969	£50	£100

AMBROSIA

Ambrosia	LP	20th Century	BT434	1975	£4	£10
Somewhere I've Never Travelled	LP	20th Century	BT510	1976	£4	£10

AME SON

Ame Son	LP	Byg	529325	1970	£5	£12 ..... French

AMECHE, LOLA

Rock The Joint	78	Oriole	CB1143	1953	£2	£5

AMEN CORNER

Bend Me Shape Me	7"	Deram	DM172	1968	£1.50	£4 ..... chart single
Farewell Magnificent Seven	LP	Immediate	IMSP028	1969	£4	£10
Get Back	7"	Immediate	IM083	1969	£1.50	£4
Gin House Blues	7"	Deram	DM136	1967	£1.50	£4 ..... chart single
Half As Nice	7"	Immediate	IM073	1969	£1.50	£4 ..... chart single
Hello Suzie	7"	Immediate	IM081	1969	£1.50	£4 ..... chart single
High In The Sky	7"	Deram	DM197	1968	£1.50	£4 ..... chart single
National Welsh Coast Live	LP	Immediate	IMSP023	1969	£4	£10 ..... chart LP
Return Of The Magnificent Seven	LP	Immediate	IML1004	1976	£4	£10
Round Amen Corner	LP	Deram	DML/SML1021	1968	£4	£10 ..... chart LP
So Fine	7"	Immediate	AS3	1969	£10	£20 ..... promo
World Of Broken Hearts	7"	Deram	DM151	1967	£1.50	£4 ..... chart single

AMENDS

Making Up	7"	Uni	UN511	1969	£1.50	£4

AMERICAN BLUES

The only UK release of the second American Blues album is a 1987 reissue on the See For Miles label. Although the record is a typically inventive chunk of psychedelia, its real interest, and the reason for the collectibility of the original, lies in the fact that two thirds of American Blues later became two thirds of ZZ Top.

American Blues Is Here	LP	Karma	KLP1001	1967	£37.50	£75 ..... US
Do Their Thing	LP	Uni	73044	1969	£15	£30 ..... US

AMERICAN BREED

American Breed	LP	Dot	DOLP255	1967	£4	£10
Bend Me Shape Me	LP	Dot	(S)LPD502	1968	£4	£10
Bend Me Shape Me	7"	Stateside	SS2078	1968	£1.50	£4 ..... chart single
Green Light	7"	Dot	DOT101	1968	£1.50	£4
Lonely Side Of The City	LP	Dot	(S)LPD526	1969	£4	£10
Pumpkin Powder,Scarlet & Green	LP	Dot	(S)LPD518	1968	£4	£10
Ready Willing And Able	7"	Dot	DOT106	1968	£1.50	£4
Step Out Of Your Mind	7"	CBS	2888	1967	£4	£8
Step Out Of Your Mind	7"	CBS	2972	1967	£2	£5

AMERICAN DREAM

American Dream	LP	Ampex	A10101	1968	£10	£25 ..... US

AMERICAN EAGLE

American Eagle	LP	Decca	DL75258	1970	£5	£12 ..... US

AMERICAN FOUR

Both Arthur Lee and fellow Love guitarist were members of the American Four, which stayed together just long enough to make this rare single.

Luci Baines	7"	Selma	2001	1964	£12.50	£25 ..... US

AMERICAN GYPSY

American Gypsy	LP	BTM	BTM1001GG	1975	£4	£10
Anithesis	LP	RCA	LSP4775	1972	£4	£10 ..... US
Gypsy	LP	CBS	66270	1971	£4	£10 ..... US
In The Garden	LP	Metromedia	1044	1972	£4	£10 ..... US
Unlock The Dead Gates	LP	RCA	APL10093	1973	£4	£10 ..... US

14

AMERICAN POETS
She Blew A Good Thing	7"	London	HLC10037	1966	£12.50	£25	

AMERICAN REVOLUTION
American Revolution	LP	Flick	45002	1968	£6	£15	US

AMERICAN SPRING
American Spring	LP	United Artists	UAS29363	1972	£8	£20	
Good Time	7"	United Artists	UP35376	1972	£5	£10	
Mama Said	7"	United Artists	UP35421	1972	£5	£10	
Now That Everything's Been Said	7"	United Artists	50848	1971	£7.50	£15	US
Shyin' Away	7"	CBS	1590	1973	£5	£10	

AMERICAN TEARS
Branded Bad	LP	CBS	33038	1974	£8	£20	US
Powerhouse	LP	CBS	34676	1977	£8	£20	US
Teargas	LP	CBS	33847	1975	£8	£20	US

AMERICAN YOUTH CHOIR
Together We Can Make It	7"	Polydor	2066013	1971	£6	£12	

AMES BROTHERS
Best Of The Ames Brothers	7" EP	RCA	RCX1047	1959	£4	£8	
Boogie Woogie Maxine	7"	HMV	7M179	1954	£2	£5	
Exactly Like You	7" EP	HMV	7EG8237	1957	£4	£8	
Hopelessly	7"	HMV	7M253	1954	£1.50	£4	
If You Wanna See Mamie Tonight	7"	HMV	7M410	1956	£1.50	£4	
If You Wanna See Mamie Tonight	7"	HMV	7MC46	1956	£1.50	£4	export
I'm Gonna Love You	7"	HMV	POP242	1956	£2	£5	
Man With The Banjo	7"	HMV	7M209	1954	£1.50	£4	
Merci Beaucoup	7"	HMV	7M322	1955	£1.50	£4	
My Bonnie Lassie	7"	HMV	7M331	1955	£1.50	£4	
Naughty Lady Of Shady Lane	7"	HMV	7M281	1955	£5	£10	chart single
Rockin' Shoes	7"	RCA	RCA1015	1957	£2	£5	
Sweet Brown-Eyed Baby	7"	HMV	7M310	1955	£1.50	£4	
You You You	7"	HMV	7M153	1953	£2	£4	

AMES, NANCY
Cry Softly	7"	Columbia	DB8039	1966	£20	£40	
Friends And Lovers Forever	7"	Columbia	DB7809	1966	£2	£5	

AMM
AMM are probably the only group to have received mention in books on Rock, Jazz, Classical, and Avant Garde musics. In truth, they are all of these - and none, playing in a unique free improvised style, incorporating both instrumental and found sounds. Cornelius Cardew went on to form the Scratch Orchestra, which featured musicians performing on instruments that they had never learnt to play!
AMM Music	LP	Elektra	EUKS7256	1967	£30	£60	
At The Roundhouse	7"	Incus	EP1	197-	£25	£50	

AMM & MEV
Live Electronic Music Improvised	LP	Mainstream	MS5002	1968	£15	£30	US

AMMONS, ALBERT
Albert Ammons	7" EP	Vogue	EPV1071	1955	£20	£40	
And His Rhythm Kings	LP	Mercury	MG25012	1954	£10	£25	
Boogie Woogie Stomp	7" EP	Brunswick	OE9325	1957	£6	£12	

AMMONS, ALBERT, PETE JOHNSON & MEADE LUX LEWIS
Giants Of Boogie Woogie	LP	Riverside	RLP12106	1963	£6	£15	
Boogie Woogie Trio	LP	Storyville	SLP184	1966	£5	£12	
Shout For Joy	7" EP	Columbia	SEG7528	1954	£7.50	£15	

AMMONS, GENE
Ammons Boogie	7"	Starlite	ST45017	1960	£10	£20	
Anna	7"	Starlite	ST45097	1963	£2.50	£6	
Bossa Nova By The Boss	7" EP	Esquire	EP249	1962	£2.50	£6	
Hi Fidelity Jam Session	LP	Esquire	32047	1958	£15	£30	
Jammin' With Gene	LP	Esquire	32097	1960	£6	£15	

AMON DUUL
Amon Duul	LP	Prophesy	1003	1969	£8	£20	
Collapsing	LP	Metronome	SMLP012	1969	£8	£20	
Disaster	LP	BASF	2929079	1971	£8	£20	German
Minnelied	LP	Brain	0040149	1975	£6	£15	German
Paradieswarts Duul	LP	Ohr	56068	1969	£8	£20	German
This Is Amon Duul	LP	Brain	200146	1973	£6	£15	German

AMON DUUL II
Amon Duul II were originally a splinter group away from Amon Duul, following an ideological disagreement, but they rapidly became rather better known than the parent group. Essentially, the group is a German version of Hawkwind, with a similar mystical outlook and fascination with spacey noises. Equally, the music is at root very simply constructed, with single chords being worried half to death for minutes at a time.
Almost Live	LP	Nova	623305	1977	£4	£10	German
Carnival In Babylon	LP	United Artists	UAG29327	1972	£4	£10	
Dance Of The Lemmings	LP	United Artists	60003/4	1971	£5	£12	double
Hi Jack	LP	Atlantic	K50136	1974	£4	£10	
Lemmingmania	LP	United Artists	UAS29723	1975	£4	£10	
Live In London	LP	United Artists	USP102	1973	£4	£10	
Made In Germany	LP	Atlantic	K50182	1975	£4	£10	
Made In Germany	LP	Nova	628350	1975	£6	£15	German, double
Only Human	LP	Vinyl	LV1004	1978	£4	£10	
Phallus Dei	LP	Liberty	LBS83279	1969	£8	£20	
Pyragony	LP	Nova	622890	1976	£4	£10	German

15

Viva La Trance	LP	United Artists	UAS29504	1973	£4	£10	
Wolf City	LP	United Artists	UAG29406	1972	£4	£10	
Yeti	LP	Liberty	LSP101/2	1970	£5	£12	double

AMOR VIVI
Dirty Dog	7"	Big Shot	BI534	1969	£2.50	£6	

AMOS, TORI
Five years before releasing her acclaimed "Little Earthquakes" album, Tori Amos signed a contract with Atlantic, but only made one record with them. "Y Tori Kant Read" presents a startlingly different Tori Amos, casting her in the same mould as Pat Benatar. The record is extremely scarce, however, and Tori Amos herself disowns it. Even scarcer is the US single "Baltimore", recorded when Ms.Amos was just seventeen. The listed value has to be viewed as highly approximate, since few copies are ever likely to appear on the market.

Baltimore	7"	MEA	5290	1980	£75	£150	US, credited to Ellen Amos
Cornflake Girl	CD-s	East West	A7281CDX	1994	£4	£10	digipak
Crucify Live EP	CD-s	East West	A7479CDX	1992	£6	£15	
Little Drummer Boy	CD-s	East West	no number	1992	£37.50	£75	promo
Me And A Gun EP (Silent All These Years)	CD-s	East West	YZ618CD	1991	£8	£20	
Me And A Gun EP (Silent All These Years)	12"	East West	YZ618T	1991	£4	£10	
Silent All These Years	CD-s	East West	YZ618CD	1991	£5	£12	
Silent All These Years	7"	East West	YZ618	1991	£2.50	£6	
Silent All These Years	12"	East West	YZ618T	1991	£4	£10	
Winter	CD-s	East West	A7504CDX	1992	£6	£15	
Y Kant Tori Read	LP	Atlantic	81845	1988	£30	£60	US
Y Kant Tori Read	CD	Atlantic	81845	1988	£35	£70	US

AMRAM-BARROW QUARTET
Jazz Studio Six	LP	Brunswick	LAT8239	1958	£8	£20	

AMY, CURTIS
Katanga	LP	Fontana	688136ZL	1966	£5	£12	

ANAN
Haze Woman	7"	Pye	7N17571	1968	£7.50	£15	
Madena	7"	Pye	7N17642	1968	£6	£12	

ANCIENT GREASE
Women And Children First	LP	Mercury	6338033	1970	£15	£30	

AND ALSO THE TREES
Secret Sea	7"	Reflex	RE6	1984	£4	£8	
Secret Sea	12"	Reflex	12RE6	1984	£2.50	£6	
Shantell	7"	Reflex	FS9	1984	£4	£8	

ANDERSEN, ERIC
Avalanche	LP	Warner Bros	WS1748	1970	£5	£12	US
Best Of Eric Andersen	LP	Vanguard	VSD7/8	1973	£6	£15	US, double
Blue River	LP	CBS	65145	1973	£5	£12	
'Bout Changes & Things	LP	Fontana	STFL6068	1968	£6	£15	
'Bout Changes And Things	LP	Vanguard	VSD79206	1966	£6	£15	US
Country Dream	LP	Vanguard	VSD6540	1969	£6	£15	US
Eric Andersen	LP	Warner Bros	WS1806	1970	£5	£12	US
More Hits From Tin Can Alley	LP	Vanguard	VSD79271	1968	£6	£15	US
Stage	LP	CBS	65571	1974	£5	£12	US
Today Is The Highway	LP	Fontana	TFL6061	1965	£6	£15	

ANDERSON, ALISTAIR
Concertina Workshop	LP	Free Reed	FRS501	1974	£5	£12	
Plays English Concertina	LP	Trailer	LER2074	1972	£5	£12	
Traditional Tunes	LP	Front Hall	FHR08	1976	£8	£20	US

ANDERSON, CASEY
Bag I'm In	LP	Atco	(SD)33149	1962	£5	£12	US
Blues Is A Woman Gone	LP	Atco	(SD)33176	1965	£5	£12	US
Goin' Places	LP	Elektra	EKL/EKS7192	1960	£5	£12	US
Live At The Ice House	LP	Atco	(SD)33172	1965	£5	£12	US
More Pretty Girls Than One	LP	Atco	(SD)33166	1964	£5	£12	US

ANDERSON, CAT
Cat On A Hot Tin Horn	LP	Mercury	MMB12006	1959	£6	£15	

ANDERSON, ERNESTINE
Azure-Te	7" EP	Mercury	ZEP10105	1961	£2	£5	
By Special Request	LP	Pye	NPT19025	1958	£5	£12	
Ernestine Anderson	LP	Columbia	SX/SCX6145	1967	£4	£10	
Ernestine Anderson	7" EP	Mercury	10007MCE	1964	£2.50	£6	
Fascinating Ernestine	LP	Mercury	MMC14037	1960	£5	£12	
Jerk And Twine	7" EP	Mercury	MF912	1965	£2	£5	
Just A Swinging	7" EP	Mercury	ZEP10124	1962	£2	£5	
Keep An Eye On Love	7"	Sue	WI309	1964	£6	£12	
Lover's Question	7"	Mercury	AMT1137	1961	£1.50	£4	
Moanin'	LP	Mercury	MMC14062	1961	£5	£12	
New Sound Of Ernestine Anderson	LP	Sue	ILP914	1964	£25	£50	
Runnin' Wild	LP	Mercury	MMC14016	1959	£6	£15	
Running Wild	7" EP	Mercury	ZEP10057	1960	£2.50	£6	
Somebody Told You	7"	Stateside	SS455	1965	£2	£5	
Welcome To The Club	7" EP	Mercury	ZEP10089	1960	£2.50	£6	

16

ANDERSON, GLADSTONE
Judas	7"	Blue Cat	BS172	1969	£4	£8

ANDERSON, IAN A.
Almost The Country Blues	7" EP.	Saydisc	EPSD134	1969	£6	£12	
Book Of Changes	LP	Fontana	STL5542	1970	£6	£15	
One More Chance	7"	Village Thing	VTSX1002	1971	£5	£10	
Royal York Crescent	LP	Village Thing	VTS3	1970	£6	£15	
Singer Sleeps On As Blaze Rages	LP	Village Thing	VTS18	1972	£5	£12	
Stereo Death Breakdown	LP	Liberty	LBS83242	1969	£15	£30	
Vulture Is Not A Bird You Can Trust	LP	Village Thing	VTS9	1971	£5	£12	

ANDERSON, IAN A. & MIKE COOPER
Inverted World	LP	Matchbox	SDM159	1968	£15	£30

ANDERSON, JON
Evening With Jon Anderson	LP	Atlantic	PR285	1976	£6	£15	US promo

ANDERSON, JONES, JACKSON
Anderson, Jones, Jackson	7" EP.	Saydisc	EPSD125	1968	£7.50	£15

ANDERSON, LEROY
Anderson Compositions	7" EP.	Brunswick	OE9021	1954	£2	£5	
Forgotten Dreams	7"	Brunswick	05485	1955	£1.50	£4	chart single
Pops Concert Pt.1	7" EP.	Brunswick	OE9356	1958	£2	£5	
Pops Concert Pt.2	7" EP.	Brunswick	OE9357	1958	£2	£5	

ANDERSON, MILLER
Miller Anderson was the lead guitarist and singer with the Keef Hartley Band. His solo LP uses the band musicians (but not Hartley himself) to rather less effect than on "Little Big Band", which was released at the same time.
Bright City	LP	Deram	SDL3	1971	£15	£30
Bright City	7"	Deram	DM337	1971	£1.50	£4

ANDERSON, PINK
Ballad And Folk Singer	LP	Bluesville	BV1071	1963	£6	£15	US
Carolina Blues Man	LP	Bluesville	BV1038	1961	£6	£15	US
Medicine Show Man	LP	Bluesville	BV1051	1962	£6	£15	US

ANDERSON, REUBEN
Christmas Time Again	7"	Doctor Bird	DB1045	1966	£5	£10

ANDERSON, SONNY
Lonely Lonely Train	7"	London	HLP9036	1960	£15	£30

ANDERSON, UDELL T.
Don't Go Away	7"	Direction	584645	1969	£1.50	£4
Keep On Loving Me	7"	Direction	584459	1969	£1.50	£4
Love Ain't Love	7"	Direction	584212	1969	£1.50	£4

ANDERSON, VICKI
I'm Too Tough For Mr.Big Stuff	7"	Mojo	2093005	1973	£1.50	£4
Super Good	7"	Polydor	2001150	1971	£1.50	£4

ANDERSON'S ALL STARS
Intensified Girls	7"	Blue Cat	BS132	1968	£4	£8
Intensified Girls	7"	Blue Cat	BS133	1968	£4	£8

ANDREWS, CHRIS
Hold On	7"	Decca	F22668	1967	£1.50	£4	
I'll Walk To You	7"	Decca	F22597	1967	£1.50	£4	
Man With The Red Balloon	7"	Pye	7N17617	1968	£1.50	£4	
Pretty Belinda	7"	Pye	7N17727	1969	£1.50	£4	
Something On My Mind	7"	Decca	F22365	1966	£1.50	£4	chart single
Stop That Girl	7"	Decca	F22472	1966	£1.50	£4	chart single
That's What She Said	7"	Decca	F22521	1966	£1.50	£4	
To Whom It Concerns	7"	Decca	F22285	1965	£1.50	£4	chart single
Whatcha Gonna Do Now	7"	Decca	F22404	1966	£1.50	£4	chart single
Yesterday Man	7"	Decca	F12236	1965	£1.50	£4	chart single

ANDREWS, ERNIE
In The Dark	LP	Vogue	VA160147	1959	£5	£12
Round Midnight	7"	Vogue	V9166	1960	£2.50	£6
Where Were you	7"	Capitol	CL15407	1965	£6	£12

ANDREWS, HARVEY
Brand New Day	LP	Polydor	2383595	1980	£5	£12
Fantasies From A Corner Seat	LP	Transatlantic	TRA298	1975	£5	£12
Friends Of Mine	LP	Fly	HIFLY15	1973	£5	£12
Harvey Andrews	7" EP.	Transatlantic	TRAEP133	1965	£10	£20
Places And Faces	LP	Nova	DN/SND9	1969	£10	£25
Soldier	7"	Cube	BUG20	1971	£1.50	£4
Someday	LP	Transatlantic	TRA329	1976	£4	£10
Writer Of Songs	LP	Cube	HIFLY10	1972	£5	£12

ANDREWS, INEZ & THE ANDREWETTES
Inex Andrews And The Andrewettes	7" EP.	Vogue	EDVP1283	1965	£7.50	£15

ANDREWS, JOHN & THE LONELY ONES
Rose Grows In The Ruins	7"	Parlophone	R5455	1966	£7.50	£15

ANDREWS, LEE & THE HEARTS

Teardrops	7"	London	HL7031	1957	£25	£50 .... export
Teardrops	7"	London	HLM8546	1958	£75	£150
Try The Impossible	7"	London	HLU8661	1958	£100	£200

ANDREWS, PATTY

Suddenly There's A Valley	7"	Capitol	CL14374	1955	£2.50	£6
Where To My Love?	7"	Capitol	CL14324	1955	£2.50	£6

ANDREWS SISTERS

Rum And Coca-Cola	7"	Capitol	CL14705	1957	£1.50	£4

ANDREWS, TIM

Sad Simon Lives Again	7"	Parlophone	R5656	1967	£2	£5
Tiny Goddess	7"	Parlophone	R5824	1970	£1.50	£4
Your Tea Is Strong	7"	Parlophone	R5695	1968	£1.50	£4

ANDREWS, TIM & PAUL KORDA

Angel Face	7"	Parlophone	R5746	1968	£1.50	£4
Discovery	7"	Parlophone	R5769	1969	£1.50	£4
Makin' Love To Him	7"	Parlophone	R5714	1968	£1.50	£4

ANDREWS, WILLIAM & LIAM WALSH

Classics Of Irish Piping Vol.2	LP	Topic	12T262	1976	£6	£15

ANDROMEDA

Andromeda	LP	RCA	SF8031	1969	£60	£120 .... sleeve pictured in Guide
Go Your Way	7"	RCA	RCA1854	1969	£5	£10

ANDWELLA

Are You Ready	7"	Reflection	RS6	1970	£2.50	£6
Peoples People	LP	Reflection	REFL10	1971	£6	£15
World's End	LP	Reflection	REF1010	1970	£6	£15

ANDWELLA'S DREAM

Every Little Minute	7"	Reflection	RS1	1970	£2.50	£6
Love And Poetry	LP	CBS	63673	1969	£150	£250 .... sleeve pictured in Guide
Midday Sun	7"	CBS	4301	1969	£10	£20
Mrs.Man	7"	CBS	4469	1969	£5	£10
Mr.Sunshine	7"	CBS	4634	1969	£5	£10

ANDY & CLYDE

I'm So Lonesome	7"	Rio	R69	1965	£5	£10
Never Be A Slave	7"	Rio	R62	1965	£5	£10
We All Have To Part	7"	Rio	R71	1965	£5	£10

ANDY & JOEY

Have You Ever	7"	Island	WI056	1962	£5	£10
I Want To Know	7"	Port-O-Jam	PJ4009	1964	£5	£10
You'll Never	7"	R&B	JB162	1964	£5	£10

ANDY, BOB

Born A Man	7"	Coxsone	CS7074	1968	£5	£10 Marcia Griffiths B side
Experience	7"	Studio One	SO2063	1968	£6	£12
Going Home	7"	Studio One	SO2075	1969	£6	£12 .... Sound Dimension B side
Way I Feel	7"	Doctor Bird	DB1183	1969	£5	£10 Ethiopians B side

ANDY, HORACE

You Are My Angel	LP	Trojan	TBL197	1972	£6	£15

ANGEL

Angel's claim to fame lies not so much in their status as the poor man's Kiss, but rather in being home to Punky Meadows, the guitarist who took exception to being lampooned in Frank Zappa's song, "Punky's Whips"

Angel	LP	Casablanca	CBC4007	1976	£8	£20
Helluva Band	LP	Casablanca	CBC4010	1976	£6	£15
Live Without A Net	LP	Casablanca	CALH2703	1980	£6	£15 .... double
On Earth As It Is In Heaven	LP	Casablanca	CAL2002	1977	£6	£15
Sinful	LP	Casablanca	CAL2046	1979	£5	£12
White Hot	LP	Casablanca	CSL2023	1978	£5	£12

ANGEL (2)

Good Time Fanny	7"	Cube	BUG41	1974	£1.50	£4
Little Boy Blue	7"	Cube	BUG51	1974	£2.50	£6

ANGEL, MARION

It's Gonna Be Alright	7"	Columbia	DB7537	1965	£2.50	£6

ANGEL PAVEMENT

Baby You've Gotta Stay	7"	Fontana	TF1059	1969	£4	£8
Tell Me What I've Got To Do	7"	Fontana	TF1072	1970	£4	£8

ANGELA & THE FANS

This tribute/cash-in song in praise of Illya Kuryakin, the character played by David McCallum in TV's "The Man From UNCLE", was actually performed by Alma Cogan.

Love Ya Illya	7"	Pye	7N17108	1966	£5	£10

ANGELIC UPSTARTS

Brighton Bomb	12"	Gas	GM3010	1985	£2.50	£6 .... Thatcher sleeve

Title	Format	Label	Catalogue	Year	Price1	Price2	Notes
England	7"	Regal Zonophone	Z12	1980	£2.50	£6	
Murder Of Liddle Towers	7"	Angelic Upstarts	AU1024	1978	£7.50	£15	

ANGELO, BOBBY & THE TUXEDOS
Baby Sitting	7"	HMV	POP892	1961	£5	£10	chart single
Don't Stop	7"	HMV	POP982	1961	£5	£10	

ANGELO, MICHAEL
Tears	7"	Columbia	DB4800	1962	£2	£5	

ANGELOU, MAYA
Miss Calypso	LP	London	HAU2062	1957	£4	£10	

ANGELS
And The Angels Sing	LP	Caprice	(S)LP1001	1962	£10	£25	US
Everybody Loves A Lover	7"	Pye	7N25150	1962	£2	£5	
Greatest Hits	LP	Ascot	AM13009/ALS6009	1964	£6	£15	US
Halo To You	LP	Smash	MGS27048/SRS67048	1964	£8	£20	US
I Adore Him	7"	Mercury	AMT1215	1963	£2	£5	
My Boyfriend's Back	LP	Smash	MGS27039/SRS67039	1963	£10	£25	US
My Boyfriend's Back	7"	Mercury	AMT1211	1963	£2	£5	chart single
Wow Wow Wee	7"	Philips	BF1312	1964	£1.50	£4	

ANGELWITCH
Angel Witch	7"	Bronze	BRO108	1980	£2	£5	
Loser	7"	Bronze	BRO121	1981	£2	£5	
Sweet Danger	7"	EMI	EMI5064	1980	£2	£5	chart single
Sweet Danger	12"	EMI	125064	1980	£4	£10	

ANGLIANS
Friend Of Mine	7"	CBS	202489	1967	£2	£5	

ANGLOS
The marvelous "Incense" by the Anglos was issued several times during the sixties and by some means still managed to avoid becoming a hit. The group, however, was purely a studio creation, the intensely soulful singer being Steve Winwood, and the musicians probably the members of the Spencer Davis Group.

Incense	7"	Brit	WI1004	1965	£7.50	£15	
Incense	7"	Fontana	TF561	1965	£15	£30	demo only
Incense	7"	Fontana	TF589	1965	£6	£12	
Incense	7"	Island	WIP6061	1969	£2.50	£6	
Incense	7"	Sue	WI4033	1967	£10	£20	

ANIMA
Anima	LP	Pilz	20290972	1972	£6	£15	German
Sturmischer Himmel	LP	Ohr	OMM58011	1974	£6	£15	German

ANIMALS
As with the Beatles and the Rolling Stones, the British and American LPs by the Animals have numerous differences, even where the titles are the same. Five tracks on the first UK album were replaced in the US by the songs from the first two singles, together with a track, "Blue Feeling", that never did get a British release. The second album, called "Animal Tracks" in the UK, had three of its songs removed and four different ones added for the US version, which was retitled "The Animals On Tour". An American LP called "Animal Tracks" was also issued, but this was a different record altogether, being a compilation of various singles and LP tracks not already released in the US. The two hits anthologies are inevitably different - the British "Most Of The Animals" (not to be confused with a later Music For Pleasure release with a greatly inferior selection) has fourteen tracks, while the American "Best Of The Animals" has only eleven - and only nine are to be found on both records. "Animalisms" and "Animalization" have four differences in their running orders; the American "Animalism" LP has no British equivalent at all. Of its eleven tracks, nine were not released in the UK, while a tenth, "Outcast", is a different take to the version found on "Animalisms".

Animal Tracks	LP	Columbia	33SX1708	1965	£8	£20	chart LP
Animal Tracks	LP	MGM	(S)E4305	1965	£10	£25	US
Animal Tracks	7" EP	Columbia	SEG8499	1966	£7.50	£15	
Animalism	LP	MGM	(S)E4414	1966	£10	£25	US
Animalisms	LP	Decca	LK4797	1966	£8	£20	chart LP
Animalization	LP	MGM	(S)E4384	1966	£10	£25	US
Animals	LP	Columbia	33SX1669	1964	£8	£20	chart LP
Animals	LP	MGM	(S)E4264	1964	£10	£25	US
Animals	LP	Regal	SREG104	196-	£5	£12	export
Animals Are Back	7" EP	Columbia	SEG8400	1965	£6	£12	
Animals Is Here	7" EP	Columbia	SEG8452	1965	£5	£10	
Animals No.2	7" EP	Columbia	SEG8374	1964	£6	£12	
Animals On Tour	LP	MGM	(S)E4281	1965	£10	£25	US
Baby Let Me Take You Home	7"	Columbia	DB7247	1964	£1.50	£4	chart single
Best Of The Animals	LP	MGM	(S)E4324	1966	£6	£15	US
Best Of The Animals Vol.2	LP	MGM	(S)E4454	1967	£6	£15	US
Boom Boom	7" EP	Columbia	ESRF1632	1964	£7.50	£15	French
Bring It On Home To Me	7"	Columbia	DB7539	1965	£1.50	£4	chart single
Bring It On Home To Me	7" EP	Columbia	ESRF1671	1965	£7.50	£15	French
Don't Bring Me Down	7"	Decca	F12407	1966	£2	£5	chart single
Don't Bring Me Down	7" EP	Barclay	071043	1966	£7.50	£15	French
Don't Let Me Be Misunderstood	7"	Columbia	DB7445	1965	£1.50	£4	chart single
Don't Let Me Be Misunderstood	7"	Columbia	DB7445	1965	£25	£50	demo A side - matrix 1N
Help Me Girl	7"	Decca	F12502	1966	£2	£5	chart single
House Of The Rising Sun	7"	Columbia	DB7301	1964	£1.50	£4	chart single
House Of The Rising Sun	7" EP	Columbia	ESRF1571	1964	£7.50	£15	French
I Just Want To Make Love To You	7" EP	Graphic Sound	ALO10867	1963	£100	£200	

19

I'm Crying	7"	Columbia	DB7354	1964	£1.50	£4	chart single
I'm Crying	7" EP	Columbia	ESRF1593	1964	£7.50	£15	French
In The Beginning There Was Early Animals	7" EP	Decca	DFE8643	1965	£10	£20	
Inside Looking Out	7"	Decca	F12332	1966	£2	£5	chart single
It's My Life	7"	Columbia	DB7741	1965	£1.50	£4	chart single
It's My Life	7" EP	Columbia	ESRF1717	1965	£7.50	£15	French
Mama Told Me Not To Come	7"	Decca	F12502	1966	£20	£40	
Most Of The Animals	LP	Columbia	SX6035	1966	£8	£20	chart LP
Outcast	7" EP	Barclay	070970	1966	£7.50	£15	French
We've Gotta Get Out Of This Place	7"	Columbia	DB7639	1965	£1.50	£4	chart single
We've Gotta Get Out This Place	7" EP	Columbia	ESRF1692	1965	£7.50	£15	French

ANIMALS & OTHERS

Get Yourself A College Girl	LP	MGM	(S)E4273	1964	£6	£15	US

ANIMATED EGG

Animated Egg	LP	Marble Arch	MAL890	1969	£5	£12	

ANKA, PAUL

Alive	LP	RCA	LPM/LSP3875	1967	£5	£12	US
Anka Again	7" EP	Columbia	SEG7801	1958	£5	£10	
At The Copa	LP	ABC	(S)353	1960	£8	£20	US
Bells At My Wedding	7"	Columbia	DB4772	1962	£1.50	£4	
Can't Get You Out Of My Mind	7"	RCA	RCA1676	1968	£12.50	£25	
Cinderella	7"	Columbia	DB4702	1961	£1.50	£4	
Crazy Love	7"	Columbia	DB4110	1958	£1.50	£4	chart single
Diana	LP	ABC	(S)420	1962	£8	£20	US
Diana	7"	Columbia	DB3980	1957	£2	£5	chart single
Diana	7" EP	Columbia	SEG7747	1957	£6	£12	
Eso Beso	7"	RCA	RCA1318	1962	£1.50	£4	
Excitement On Park Avenue	LP	RCA	RD7700	1964	£5	£12	
Fly Me To The Moon	7" EP	RCA	RCX7127	1964	£4	£8	
Four Golden Hits	7" EP	RCA	RCX7152	1964	£4	£8	
Hello Young Lovers	7"	Columbia	DB4504	1960	£1.50	£4	chart single
I Confess	7"	RPM	472	1956	£15	£30	US
I Don't Wanna Catch Him Round You Any More	7"	RCA	RCA1567	1967	£1.50	£4	
I Love You Baby	7"	Columbia	DB4022	1957	£1.50	£4	chart single
I Miss You So	7"	Columbia	DB4286	1959	£1.50	£4	
I Talked To You	7"	Columbia	DB4669	1961	£1.50	£4	
It's Christmas Everywhere	LP	Columbia	33SX1287	1960	£8	£20	
It's Time To Cry	7"	Columbia	DB4390	1960	£1.50	£4	chart single
Just Young	7"	Columbia	DB4199	1958	£1.50	£4	
Let's Sit This One Out	LP	RCA	RD/SF7533	1962	£5	£12	
Lonely Boy	7"	Columbia	DB4324	1959	£1.50	£4	chart single
Love Me Warm And Tender	7"	RCA	RCA1276	1962	£1.50	£4	
Midnight	7"	Columbia	DB4172	1958	£1.50	£4	chart single
My Heart Sings	LP	Columbia	33SX1196	1959	£8	£20	
My Heart Sings	7"	Columbia	DB4241	1959	£1.50	£4	
My Home Town	7"	Columbia	DB4472	1960	£1.50	£4	
Our Man Around The World	LP	RCA	RD/SF7547	1963	£5	£12	
Paul Anka	LP	Columbia	33SX1092	1958	£8	£20	
Puppy Love	7"	Columbia	DB4434	1960	£1.50	£4	chart single
Put Your Head On My Shoulder	7"	Columbia	DB4355	1959	£1.50	£4	chart single
Sing Sing Sing	7" EP	Columbia	SEG7890	1959	£5	£10	
Sings His Big 15	LP	Columbia	33SX1282	1960	£6	£15	
Sings His Big 15 Vol.2	LP	Columbia	33SX1395	1961	£6	£15	
Sings His Big 15 Vol.3	LP	Columbia	33SX1432	1962	£6	£15	
Sings Songs From Girls Town	7" EP	Columbia	SEG7985	1960	£5	£10	
Songs I Wish I'd Written	LP	RCA	RD/SF7613	1963	£5	£12	
Story Of My Love	7"	Columbia	DB4582	1961	£1.50	£4	
Strictly Instrumental	LP	ABC	(S)371	1961	£8	£20	US
Strictly Nashville	LP	RCA	LPM/LSP3580	1966	£5	£12	US
Summer's Gone	7"	Columbia	DB4524	1960	£1.50	£4	
Swings For Young Lovers	LP	Columbia	33SX1268	1960	£6	£15	
Sylvia	7" EP	RCA	RCX7170	1964	£4	£8	
Timeless	LP	RCA	RD/SF7956	1968	£4	£10	
To Wait For Love	7"	RCA	RCA1434	1965	£1.50	£4	PS
Tonight My Love, Tonight	7"	Columbia	DB4629	1961	£1.50	£4	
Twenty-One Golden Hits	LP	RCA	RD/SF7573	1963	£5	£12	
You Are My Destiny	7"	Columbia	DB4063	1958	£1.50	£4	chart single
Young Alive And In Love	7"	RCA	RD27257/SF5129	1962	£5	£12	

ANKA, PAUL, SAM COOKE & NEIL SEDAKA

Three Great Guys	LP	RCA	RD/SF7608	1963	£5	£12	

ANN, BARBARA

You've Lost That Loving Feeling	7"	Piccadilly	7N35221	1965	£1.50	£4	

ANNETTE

Annette	LP	Buena Vista	BV3301	1959	£15	£30	US
Annette And Hayley Mills	LP	Buena Vista	BV3508	196-	£25	£50	US
Annette At Bikini Beach	LP	Buena Vista	BV/STER3324	1964	£10	£25	US
Annette Funicello	LP	Buena Vista	BV4037	1962	£15	£30	US
Annette On Campus	LP	Buena Vista	BV/STER3320	1964	£10	£25	US
Annette Sings Anka	LP	Buena Vista	BV3302	1960	£15	£30	US
Annette Sings Golden Surfin' Hits	LP	Buena Vista	BV/STER3327	1964	£10	£25	US
Annette's Beach Party	LP	HMV	CLP1782	1963	£10	£25	
Annette's Pajama Party	LP	Buena Vista	BV/STER3325	1964	£10	£25	US

Title	Format	Label	Catalogue	Year			Notes
Babes In Toyland	LP	Buena Vista	BV(S)4022	1961	£8	£20	US
Best Of Broadway	LP	Disneyland	DQ1267	1965	£8	£20	US
Dance Annette	LP	Buena Vista	BV3305	1961	£10	£25	US
First Name Initial	7"	Top Rank	JAR233	1959	£2.50	£6	
Hawaiiannette	LP	Buena Vista	BV3303	1960	£10	£25	US
How To Stuff A Wild Bikini	LP	Wand	(S)671	1965	£6	£15	US
Italiannette	LP	Buena Vista	BV3304	1960	£10	£25	US
Lonely Guitar	7"	Top Rank	JAR137	1959	£2.50	£6	
Merlin Jones	7"	HMV	POP1322	1964	£2	£5	
Monkey's Uncle	7"	HMV	POP1447	1965	£6	£12	
Muscle Beach Party	LP	Buena Vista	BV/STER3314	1963	£10	£25	US
Muscle Beach Party	7"	HMV	POP1270	1964	£2.50	£6	
O Dio Mio	7"	Top Rank	JAR343	1960	£2.50	£6	
Parent Trap	LP	Buena Vista	BV(S)3309	1961	£8	£20	US
Pineapple Princess	7"	Pye	7N25061	1960	£2	£5	
Something Borrowed, Something Blue	LP	Buena Vista	BV3328	1964	£10	£25	US
Songs From Annette	LP	Mickey Mouse	MM24	196-	£15	£30	US
State And College Songs	LP	Disneyland	DQ(S)1293	1967	£8	£20	US
Story Of My Teens	LP	Buena Vista	BV3312	1962	£15	£30	US
Tall Paul	7" EP.	Gala	45XP1046	196-	£6	£12	
Teen Street	LP	Buena Vista	BV3313	1962	£10	£25	US
Thunder Alley	LP	Sidewalk	(S)T5902	1967	£5	£12	US
Tubby The Tuba	LP	Disneyland	DQ(S)1287	1966	£6	£15	US
Walt Disney's Wonderful World Of Color	LP	Disneyland	DQ(S)1245	1964	£6	£15	US

ANNETTE & THE KEYMEN
Look Who's Blue	7"	King	KG1006	1964	£1.50	£4	

ANNEXUS QUAM
Beziehungen	LP	Ohr	OMM56028	1972	£8	£20	German
Osmose	LP	Ohr	OMM56007	1970	£15	£30	German

ANNIS
Don't Play Your Games	7"	GTO	266	1979	£4	£8	

ANNO DOMINI
On The New Day	LP	Deram	SLM1085	1971	£50	£100	

ANONYMOUSLY YOURS
Get Back	7"	Trojan	TR680	1969	£2.50	£6	
It's Your Thing	7"	Trojan	TR681	1969	£2.50	£6	
Organism	7"	Duke	DU40	1969	£2.50	£6	

ANOTHER DREAM
Forever In Darkness	7"	Sticky	PEELOFF2	198-	£2	£5	

ANOTHER PRETTY FACE
All The Boys Love Carrie	7"	New Pleasures	Z1	1979	£10	£20	green & white sleeve
All The Boys Love Carrie	7"	New Pleasures	Z1	1979	£6	£12	red & white sleeve
Heaven Gets Closer Every Day	7"	Chicken Jazz	JAZZ1	1980	£7.50	£15	
I'm Sorry That I Beat You	cass	Chicken Jazz	JAZZ2	1981	£20	£40	with badge & book
Soul To Soul	7"	Chicken Jazz	JAZZ3	1981	£10	£20	gatefold PS
Whatever Happened To The West	7"	Virgin	VS320	1980	£2.50	£6	

ANOTHER SUNNY DAY
Anorak City	7"	Sarah	SARAH4	1988	£5	£10	flexi
I'm In Love With A Girl	7"	Sarah	SARAH7	1988	£1.50	£4	

ANSWERS
It's Just A Fear	7"	Columbia	DB7847	1966	£20	£40	
That's What You're Doing To Me	7"	Columbia	DB7953	1966	£15	£30	

ANT, ADAM
Apollo 9	12"	CBS	TA4719	1984	£4	£10	
Desperate But Not Serious	7"	CBS	A2892	1982	£7.50	£15	single sleeve

ANT TRIP CEREMONY
Twenty-Four Hours	LP	C.R.C.	2129	1967	£50	£100	US

ANTEEKS
Don't Want You	7"	Philips	BF1471	1966	£20	£40	

ANTELL, PETER
Times They Are A-Changin'	7"	Pye	7N25329	1965	£2	£5	

ANTHEM
Anthem	LP	Buddah	BDS5071	1970	£6	£15	US

ANTHONY, BILLIE
Banjo's Back In Town	7"	Columbia	SCM5191	1955	£2	£5	
Bring Me A Bluebird	7"	Columbia	SCM5210	1955	£2	£5	
Dreamed	7"	Columbia	DB3874	1957	£1.50	£4	
Lay Down Your Arms	7"	Columbia	DB3818	1956	£2	£5	
No More	7"	Columbia	SCM5164	1955	£2.50	£6	
Rock A Billy	7"	Columbia	DB3935	1957	£5	£10	
Something's Gotta Give	7"	Columbia	SCM5184	1955	£2.50	£6	
Sweet Old Fashioned Girl	7"	Columbia	SCM5286	1956	£2.50	£6	
Teach Me Tonight	7"	Columbia	SCM5155	1954	£5	£10	
This Ole House	7"	Columbia	SCM5143	1954	£7.50	£15	chart single

Title	Size	Label	Catalogue	Year	Price	Price	Notes
Tweedle Dee	7"	Columbia	SCM5174	1955	£4	£8	

ANTHONY, DAVE

All Night	7"	Island	WI3148	1968	£5	£10	
Race With The Wind	7"	Mercury	MF1031	1968	£4	£8	

ANTHONY, DAVE MOODS

New Directions	7"	Parlophone	R5438	1966	£6	£12	

ANTHONY, RAY

Arthur Murray Swing Foxtrots	10" LP	Capitol	LC6692	1955	£5	£12	
Baby You	7"	Capitol	CL14275	1955	£2	£5	
Bunny Hop	7"	Capitol	CL14769	1957	£1.50	£4	
Flip Flop	7"	Capitol	CL14525	1956	£4	£8	
Girl Can't Help It	7" EP.	Capitol	EAP1823	1957	£10	£20	
Heat Wave	7"	Capitol	CL14243	1955	£4	£8	
Hernando's Hideaway	7"	Capitol	CL14354	1955	£4	£8	
House Party	10" LP	Capitol	LC6617	1953	£5	£12	
I Remember Glen Miller	10" LP	Capitol	LC6653	1954	£4	£10	
Learning The Blues	7"	Capitol	CL14321	1955	£2.50	£6	
Pete Kelly's Blues	7"	Capitol	CL14345	1955	£2	£5	
Peter Gunn	7" EP.	Capitol	EAP11181	1959	£2.50	£6	
Plymouth Rock	7"	Capitol	CL14703	1957	£1.50	£4	
Ray Anthony's Orchestra	10" LP	Capitol	LC6570	1953	£5	£12	
Rock And Roll With Ray Anthony	7" EP.	Capitol	EAP1958	1957	£10	£20	
Rock Around The Rockpile	7"	Capitol	CL14689	1957	£4	£8	
Rockin' Through Dixie	7"	Capitol	CL14567	1956	£1.50	£4	
Sluefoot	7"	Capitol	CL14306	1955	£2	£5	
Sweet And Lovely	10" LP	Capitol	LC6615	1953	£4	£10	
Woman's World	7"	Capitol	CL14205	1954	£2	£5	

ANTHONY, RAYBURN

There's No Tomorrow	7"	London	HLS9167	1960	£4	£8	

ANTHRAX

Armed And Dangerous	12"	Megaforce	MRS05P	1987	£4	£10	pic disc
I'm The Man	7"	Island	ISP338	1987	£2	£5	shaped pic disc
Indians	7"	Island	ISP325	1987	£1.50	£4	pic disc

ANTI GROUP

Big Sex	7"	Sweatbox	OX011	1987	£2	£5	
Big Sex	12"	Sweatbox	SOX011	1987	£2.50	£6	
Ha	12"	Sweatbox	SOX009	1985	£2.50	£6	with booklet
ShT	7"	Sweatbox	SOX010	1986	£2	£5	

ANTI-NOWHERE LEAGUE

Streets Of London	7"	WXYZ	ABCD1	1982	£2	£5	chart single

ANTISOCIAL

Traffic Lights	7"	Dynamite	DRO1	1978	£2	£5	

ANTOINETTE

Lullaby Of Love	7"	Piccadilly	7N35310	1966	£2	£5	
Why Don't I Run Away From You	7"	Piccadilly	7N35293	1966	£1.50	£4	

ANTON, REY

Don't Worry Boy	7"	Parlophone	R5420	1966	£4	£8	
Girl You Don't Know Me	7"	Parlophone	R5274	1965	£4	£8	
Heard It All Before	7"	Parlophone	R5172	1964	£4	£8	
Hey Good Looking	7"	Oriole	CB1771	1962	£2.50	£6	
Nothing Comes Easy	7"	Parlophone	R5310	1965	£4	£8	
Peppermint Man	7"	Oriole	CB1811	1963	£2.50	£6	
Premeditation	7"	Parlophone	R5358	1965	£4	£8	
Things Get Better	7"	Parlophone	R5487	1966	£4	£8	
Wishbone	7"	Parlophone	R5245	1965	£4	£8	
You Can't Judge A Book By The Cover	7"	Parlophone	R5132	1964	£7.50	£15	

ANTS

Christmas Star	7"	Parlophone	R5082	1963	£1.50	£4	

ANVIL FLUTES & CAPRICORN VOICES

April Showers	7"	Deram	DM208	1968	£1.50	£4	
Something New Is Coming	LP	Deram	DML/SML1026	1968	£5	£12	

ANY TROUBLE

Any Trouble's first LP was released to a fanfare of critical acclaim. It was as though after bravely withstanding the onslaught of punk for three years or so, the rock weeklies were delighted to find a new group that actually played "real tunes". Unfortunately, Any Trouble's material was not really strong enough to take the weight of the praise heaped on it, and although the group carried on for a few years, it was with diminishing success. Clive Gregson, the group's leader, has since established himself in the folk circuit as half a duo with Christine Collister - the pair also finding useful employment as part of the Richard Thompson band.

Live At The Venue	LP	Stiff	TRUBZ1	1980	£6	£15	
Nice Girls	7"	Pennine	PSS165	1979	£5	£10	

AORTA

Aorta	LP	Columbia	CS9785	1968	£5	£12	US
Aorta 2	LP	Happy Tiger	HT1010	1970	£8	£20	US

APARTMENT ONE

Open House	LP	Pink Elephant		1970	£6	£15	

APEX GROUP

Caravan	7"	John Lever	AP100	1959	£10	£20	

APEX RHYTHM & BLUES ALL STARS

Title	Format	Label	Cat No	Year	Low	High	Notes
Tall Girl	7" EP..	John Lever	JLEP1	1963	£100	£200	

APHRODITE'S CHILD

To choose a name taken from Greek mythology was rather par for the course in the late sixties - but since the members of Aphrodite's Child did actually come from Greece, they were more entitled than most. Best known for the pop hit, "Rain And Tears", the group was perhaps an unlikely signing to the progressive Vertigo label. But the group was always something of a compromise between the diverse interests of the singer and the keyboards player - the pop sensibilities of Demis Roussos versus the ambition of Vangelis. Both, of course, became rather better known after the group split up.

Title	Format	Label	Cat No	Year	Low	High	Notes
666, Apocalypse Of John	LP	Vertigo	6641581	1972	£8	£20	spiral label, double, German
666, Apocalypse Of John	LP	Vertigo	6673001	1972	£10	£25	spiral label, double
Break	7"	Vertigo	6032900	1972	£2	£5	
End Of The World	LP	Mercury	SMCL20140	1969	£5	£12	
End Of The World	7"	Mercury	MF1075	1969	£1.50	£4	
I Want To Live	7"	Polydor	56789	1969	£2	£5	
It's Five O'Clock	7"	Polydor	56791	1970	£1.50	£4	
Let Me Love Let Me Live	7"	Polydor	56785	1969	£2	£5	
Rain And Tears	7"	Mercury	MF1039	1968	£1.50	£4	chart single

APOLLOS

Title	Format	Label	Cat No	Year	Low	High	Notes
Rocking Horse	7"	Mercury	AMT1096	1960	£2.50	£6	

APOSTLES

Title	Format	Label	Cat No	Year	Low	High	Notes
Hour Of Prayer	LP	Sound Recording	1245		£37.50	£75	US

APOSTOLIC INTERVENTION

Title	Format	Label	Cat No	Year	Low	High	Notes
Have You Ever Seen Me	7"	Immediate	IM043	1967	£25	£50	

APPALACHIANS

Title	Format	Label	Cat No	Year	Low	High	Notes
Bony Moronie	7"	HMV	POP1158	1963	£2	£5	
Look Away	7"	Mercury	MF930	1965	£1.50	£4	

APPALOOSA

Title	Format	Label	Cat No	Year	Low	High	Notes
Appaloosa	LP	Columbia	CS9819	1971	£6	£15	US

APPELL, DAVE

Title	Format	Label	Cat No	Year	Low	High	Notes
Alone Together	LP	Cameo	C1004	1959	£8	£20	US
Happy Jose	7"	Columbia	DB4763	1962	£2	£5	

APPELL, DAVE & APPLEJACKS

Title	Format	Label	Cat No	Year	Low	High	Notes
Smarter	7"	Brunswick	05396	1955	£7.50	£15	

APPLE

Title	Format	Label	Cat No	Year	Low	High	Notes
Apple A Day	LP	Page One	POLS016	1968	£330	£500	
Dr.Rock	7"	Page One	POF110	1968	£20	£40	
Let's Take A Trip Down The Rhine	7"	Page One	POF101	1968	£15	£30	
Thank U Very Much	7"	Smash	2143	1968	£15	£30	US

APPLEJACKS

Title	Format	Label	Cat No	Year	Low	High	Notes
Applejacks	LP	Decca	LK4635	1964	£40	£80	
Chim Chim Cheree	7"	Decca	F12050	1965	£10	£20	
I Go To Sleep	7"	Decca	F12216	1965	£7.50	£15	
I'm Through	7"	Decca	F12301	1965	£4	£8	
It's Not A Game	7"	Decca	F12106	1965	£5	£10	
Like Dreamers Do	7"	Decca	F11916	1964	£1.50	£4	chart single
Tell Me When	7"	Decca	F11833	1964	£1.50	£4	chart single
Three Little Words	7"	Decca	F11981	1964	£1.50	£4	chart single
You've Been Cheatin'	7"	CBS	202615	1967	£5	£10	

APPLEJACKS (2)

Title	Format	Label	Cat No	Year	Low	High	Notes
Applejack	7"	Columbia	DB3894	1957	£10	£20	
Circle Dance	7"	Top Rank	JAR273	1960	£1.50	£4	
Mexican Hat Rock	7"	London	HL7063	1958	£2	£5	export
Mexican Hat Rock	7"	London	HLU8753	1958	£6	£12	
Rock A Conga	7"	London	HLU8806	1959	£6	£12	

APPLETREE THEATRE

Title	Format	Label	Cat No	Year	Low	High	Notes
Playback	LP	Polydor	2353051	1968	£6	£15	

APPLEWHITE, CHARLIE

Title	Format	Label	Cat No	Year	Low	High	Notes
Blue Star	7"	Brunswick	05416	1955	£2.50	£6	chart single

APRYL FOOL

Title	Format	Label	Cat No	Year	Low	High	Notes
	LP				£50	£100	Japanese

AQUARIAN AGE

Title	Format	Label	Cat No	Year	Low	High	Notes
Ten Thousand Words In A Cardboard Box	7"	Parlophone	R5700	1968	£20	£40	

AQUATONES

Title	Format	Label	Cat No	Year	Low	High	Notes
Aquatones Sing	LP	Fargo	3001	1964	£50	£100	US
You	7"	London	HLO8631	1958	£12.50	£25	

AQUILA

Title	Format	Label	Cat No	Year	Low	High	Notes
Aquila	LP	RCA	SF8126	1970	£15	£30	

ARANBEE POP SYMPHONY ORCHESTRA

Title	Format	Label	Cat No	Year	Low	High	Notes
Today's Pop Symphony	LP	Immediate	IMLP/IMSP003	1966	£40	£80	

ARBORS

I Can't Quit Her	7"	CBS	4379	1969	£1.50	£4	
Letter	7"	CBS	4137	1969	£1.50	£4	
Motet Overture	7"	CBS	4640	1969	£1.50	£4	
Symphony For Susan	7"	CBS	202410	1966	£1.50	£4	
Valley Of The Dolls	7"	CBS	3221	1968	£1.50	£4	

ARC

Arc At This	LP	Decca	SKLR5077	1971	£15	£30	

ARC ANGEL

Arc Angel	LP	Portrait	BFR38247	1983	£8	£20	US

ARCADIA

Election Day	12"	EMI	12NSR1	1985	£6	£15	promo in foil PS
Election Day (Cryptic Cut)	12"	EMI	12NSRA1	1985	£5	£12	1 sided promo
Election Day (Re-election Day)	12"	EMI	PSLP393	1985	£15	£30	1 sided promo
Promise	12"	EMI	12NSR2	1986	£2.50	£6	with poster

ARCADIUM

Breathe Awhile	LP	Middle Earth	MDLS302	1969	£150	£250	sleeve pictured in Guide
Sing My Song	7"	Middle Earth	MDS102	1969	£12.50	£25	

ARCHIES

Sugar Sugar	LP	RCA	RD/SF8073	1969	£4	£10	
Sugar Sugar	7"	RCA	RCA1872	1969	£1.50	£4	chart single

ARCHITECTS OF DISASTER

Cucumber Sandwich	7"	Neuter	NEU1	1982	£2	£5	with insert, polythene bag

ARCOCHA, JUAN & LESLIE MACKENZIE

Book Of Am: Part One	LP	Labo Lab	LTM1016	1978	£40	£80	French

ARDEN, TONI

Little By Little	7"	Brunswick	05645	1957	£1.50	£4	

ARDLEY, NEIL

The high prices being fetched by British jazz albums from the sixties and early seventies reflects the fact that, with many of the same musicians being involved in both jazz and rock recordings, LPs like those of Neil Ardley are very much part of the progressive rock scene. Certainly, drummer Jon Hiseman viewed his role within Neil Ardley's big band as being no different from that in his own group, Colosseum (most of whose members also played with Neil Ardley). Side two of 'Symphony of Amaranths' includes, by way of a contrast, the delightfully eccentric Ivor Cutler reciting Edward Lear's "The Dong With The Luminous Nose", with Ardley's band performing a suitable accompaniment.

Dejeuner Sur L'Herbe	LP	Verve	SVLP9236	1969	£50	£100	
Symphony Of Amaranths	LP	Regal Zonophone	SLRZ1028	1972	£50	£100	sleeve pictured in Guide
Western Reunion London 1965	LP	Decca	LK/SKL4690	1965	£50	£100	

ARDLEY, NEIL, IAN CARR & DON RENDELL

Greek Variations	LP	Columbia	SCX6414	1970	£50	£100	

ARDLEY, NEIL, IAN CARR & MIKE GIBBS

Will Power	LP	Argo	ZDA164/5	1974	£75	£150	double

ARDO DOMBEC

Ardo Dombec	LP	BASF	2021095	1971	£8	£20	German

AREA

Arbeit Macht Frei	LP	Cramps	5205101	1973	£8	£20	Italian
Areazione	LP	Cramps	5205104	1975	£5	£12	Italian
Caution Nacht Frei	LP	Cramps	5205102	1974	£5	£12	Italian
Crac	LP	Cramps	5205103	1975	£5	£12	Italian
Maledetti	LP	Cramps	5205105	1976	£5	£12	Italian

ARENA TWINS

Mama, Care Mama	7"	London	HL7071	1959	£2.50	£6	export

ARGENT

Argent was formed by the Zombies' keyboard player, Rod Argent, and the group's first LP takes the earlier group's posthumous hit, "Time Of The Season", as a stylistic jumping-off point. "Argent" emerges, in effect, as the follow up to the Zombies excellent "Odessey and Oracle". Subsequent Argent releases were less distinctive, although the group was quite successful in sales terms. Rod Argent's colleagues included Russ Ballard and Bob Henrit, both of whom had been members of the Roulettes.

Argent	LP	CBS	63781	1970	£4	£10	
In Deep	LP	Epic	Q65475	1974	£5	£12	quad

ARGONAUTS

Apeman	7"	Lyntone	LYN18249/50	1986	£2.50	£6	

ARIZONA SWAMP COMPANY

Train Keeps Rollin'	7"	Parlophone	R5841	1970	£6	£12	

ARKTIS

Arktis	LP	Bonnbons	BBR4040	1974	£20	£40	German
Arktis Tapes	LP	Bonnbons	BBR7502	1975	£20	£40	German

ARLEN, STEVE

That's Love	7"	Melodisc	1458	1958	£4	£8	

ARLON, DEKE

Can't Make Up My Mind	7"	Columbia	DB7194	1964	£7.50	£15	
Hard Times For Young Lovers	7"	Columbia	DB7841	1966	£2	£5	

I Need You	7"	HMV	POP1340	1964	£7.50	£15	
If I Didn't Have A Dime	7"	Columbia	DB7487	1965	£4	£8	
Little Piece Of Paper	7"	Columbia	DB7753	1965	£2	£5	

ARMAGEDDON

Armageddon	LP	A&M	AMLH64513	1975	£10	£25	

ARMAGEDDON (2)

Armageddon	LP	Amos	AAS7009	1969	£5	£12	US

ARMAGEDDON (3)

Armageddon	LP	Kuckuck	2375003	1970	£20	£40	German

ARMATRADING, JOAN

Live At The Bijou, Philadelphia	LP	A&M	SP8414	1977	£8	£20	US promo
Talk Under Ladders	LP	A&M	SAMP12	1981	£5	£12	promo

ARMENIAN JAZZ QUARTET

Harem Dance	7"	London	HLR8454	1957	£2	£5	

ARMS & LEGS

Heat Of The Night	7"	MAM	MAM147	1976	£4	£8	
Is There Any More Wine	7"	MAM	MAM156	1977	£4	£8	
Janice	7"	MAM	MAM140	1976	£4	£8	

ARMS, RUSSELL

Cinco Robles	7"	London	HLB8406	1957	£2	£5	

ARMSTRONG, FRANKIE

And The Music Plays So Grand	LP	Briar	SBR4211	1980	£5	£12	US
Lovely On The Water	LP	Topic	12TS216	1972	£5	£12	

ARMSTRONG, FRANKIE, KATHY HENDERSON, SANDRA KERR, ALISON MCMORLA

My Song Is My Own	LP	Plane	TPL0001	1979	£6	£15	

ARMSTRONG, JACK

Celebrated Minstrel	LP	Saydisc	SDL252	1974	£6	£15	
Northumbrian Pipe Music	7" EP	Beltona	SEP43	1957	£15	£30	

ARMSTRONG, JACK & PATRICIA JENNINGS

Northumbrian Small Pipes	LP	Morton	MTN3073	1969	£5	£12	

ARMSTRONG, LOUIS

Ambassador Satch	LP	Philips	BBL7091	1956	£4	£10	
At Pasadena	LP	Brunswick	LAT8019	1952	£5	£12	
At Symphony Hall Vol.1	LP	Brunswick	LAT8017	1952	£5	£12	
At Symphony Hall Vol.2	LP	Brunswick	LAT8018	1952	£5	£12	
At The Crescendo Vol.1	LP	Brunswick	LAT8084	1956	£6	£15	
At The Crescendo Vol.2	LP	Brunswick	LAT8085	1956	£6	£15	
Basin Street Blues	10" LP	Brunswick	LA8691	1954	£5	£12	
Blueberry Hill	10" LP	Brunswick	LA8700	1955	£5	£12	
Classics	10" LP	Brunswick	LA8528	1951	£5	£12	
I've Got The World On A String	LP	HMV	CLP1388/CSD1317	1960	£6	£15	
Jazz Classics	10" LP	Brunswick	LA8597	1953	£5	£12	
Jazz Concert	10" LP	Brunswick	LA8534	1951	£5	£12	
Jazzin' With Armstrong	10" LP	Columbia	33S1007	1953	£5	£12	
Laughin' Louis	10" LP	HMV	DLP1036	1954	£5	£12	
Louis And The Good Book	LP	Brunswick	LAT8270	1958	£5	£12	
Louis Armstrong	10" LP	Columbia	33S1069	1955	£5	£12	
Louis Armstrong And Earl Hines	LP	Philips	BBL7046	1955	£4	£10	
Louis Armstrong And His Hot Five	LP	Columbia	33SX1029	1954	£5	£12	
Louis Armstrong And His Hot Five	10" LP	Fontana	TFR6003	1958	£4	£10	
Louis Armstrong Andf His Hot Seven	10" LP	Columbia	33S1041	1954	£5	£12	
Louis Armstrong Story Vol.1	LP	Philips	BBL7134	1957	£5	£12	
Louis Armstrong Story Vol.2	LP	Philips	BBL7189	1958	£5	£12	
Louis Under The Stars	LP	HMV	CLP1247	1959	£6	£15	
Meets Oscar Peterson	LP	HMV	CLP1328	1960	£6	£15	
Musical Autobiography	LP	Brunswick	LAT8211-14	1958	£20	£40	4 LPs boxed
New Orleans Days	10" LP	Brunswick	LA8537	1952	£5	£12	
New York Town Hall Concert 1947	10" LP	HMV	DLP1015	1953	£5	£12	
Plays The Blues	10" LP	London	AL3501	1953	£6	£15	
Plays W.C.Handy	LP	Philips	BBL7017	1955	£4	£10	
Rendezvous At The Sunset Cafe	10" LP	Columbia	33S1058	1955	£5	£12	
Satch Plays Fats	LP	Philips	BBL7007	1956	£4	£10	
Satchmo Plays King Oliver	LP	Audio Fidelity	AFLP1930/ AFSD5930	1960	£4	£10	
Satchmo Serenades	10" LP	Brunswick	LA8679	1954	£5	£12	
Satchmo Session	10" LP	HMV	DLP1105	1955	£5	£12	
Satchmo Sings	LP	Brunswick	LAT8243	1958	£6	£15	
Satchmo The Great	LP	Philips	BBL7216	1958	£4	£10	
We Have All The Time In The World	7"	United Artists	JB001	1969	£7.50	£15	1 sided promo
We Have All The Time In The World	7"	United Artists	UA3172	1969	£12.50	£25	PS
We Have All The Time In The World	7"	United Artists	UP35059	1969	£7.50	£15	

ARMY OF LOVERS

Love Me LIke A Loaded Gun	7"	Ton Son Ton	SON7	1988	£1.50	£4	
Love Me LIke A Loaded Gun	12"	Ton Son Ton	SONL7	1988	£3	£8	

ARNAU, B.J.

Live And Let Die	7"	RCA	RCA2365	1973	£2	£5	

ARNEZ, CHICO
Yashmak .... 7" ...... Pye .... 7N15196 .... 1959 ... £7.50 ......£15 ....

ARNOLD, CALVIN
Funky Way .... 7" ...... MGM .... MGM1378 .... 1968 ... £1.50 ......£4
Mama In Law .... 7" ...... MGM .... MGM1449 .... 1968 ... £1.50 ......£4

ARNOLD, EDDIE
All-Time Favorites .... LP ...... RCA .... LPM1223 .... 1955 ... £6 ....£15 ....US
All-Time Favorites .... 10" LP RCA .... LPM3117 .... 1953 ... £8 ....£20 ....US
All-Time Hits From The Hills ...... 10" LP RCA .... LPM3031 .... 1952 ... £8 ....£20 ....US
American Institution .... 10" LP RCA .... LPM3230 .... 1954 ... £8 ....£20 ....US
Anytime .... LP ...... RCA .... LPM1224 .... 1955 ... £6 ....£15 ....US
Anytime .... 10" LP RCA .... LPM3027 .... 1952 ... £8 ....£20 ....US
Chapel On The Hill .... LP ...... RCA .... LPM1225 .... 1955 ... £6 ....£15 ....US
Chapel On The Hill .... 7" EP.. HMV .... 7EG8080 .... 1955 ... £2 ....£5
Chapel On The Hill .... 10" LP RCA .... LPM3219 .... 1954 ... £8 ....£20 ....US
Dozen Hits .... LP ...... RCA .... LPM1293 .... 1956 ... £6 ....£15 ....US
Eddie Arnold .... 7" EP.. HMV .... 7EG8020 .... 1954 ... £2 ....£5
Free Home Demonstrations ...... 7" ...... HMV .... 7MC16 .... 1954 ... £2.50 .....£6 ....export
Gonna Find Me A Bluebird .... 7" ...... RCA .... RCA1008 .... 1957 ... £1.50 .....£4
Have Guitar, Will Travel .... LP ...... RCA .... LPM/LSP1928 ... 1959 ... £4 ....£10 ....US
Hep Cat Baby .... 7" ...... HMV .... 7MC22 .... 1954 ... £2.50 .....£6 ....export
In Time .... 7" ...... HMV .... 7MC32 .... 1955 ... £2.50 .....£6 ....export
Little On The Lonely Side .... LP ...... RCA .... LPM1377 .... 1956 ... £6 ....£15 ....US
Make The World Go Away .... 7" ...... RCA .... RCA1496 .... 1966 ... £1.50 .....£4 ....chart single
My Darling, My Darling .... LP ...... RCA .... LPM1575 .... 1957 ... £6 ....£15 ....US
Praise Him, Praise Him .... LP ...... RCA .... LPM1733 .... 1958 ... £5 ....£12 ....US
Prayer .... 7" ...... HMV .... 7MC10 .... 1954 ... £2.50 .....£6 ....export
Richest Man .... 7" ...... HMV .... 7M339 .... 1955 ... £1.50 .....£4
Second Fling .... 7" ...... HMV .... 7MC19 .... 1954 ... £2.50 .....£6 ....export
Tennessee Stud .... 7" ...... RCA .... RCA1138 .... 1959 ... £1.50 .....£4
Thereby Hangs A Tale .... LP ...... RCA .... RD27155 .... 1959 ... £5 ....£12
Wanderin' .... LP ...... RCA .... LPM1111 .... 1955 ... £6 ....£15 ....US
When They Were Young .... LP ...... RCA .... LPM1484 .... 1957 ... £6 ....£15 ....US

ARNOLD, KOKOMO
Kokomo Arnold .... LP ...... Saydisc .... SDR163 .... 1969 ... £5 ....£12

ARNOLD, P.P.
Pat Arnold tried hard for solo success with a number of releases on the Immediate label. Despite producing several fondly remembered tracks, however, it was her backing group, the Nice, that achieved the most success. P.P.Arnold returned to session work, although she achieved a brief revival at the end of the eighties. She had originally been a member of Ike and Tina Turner's backing group, the Ikettes.
Angel Of The Morning .... 7" ...... Immediate ...... IM067 .... 1968 ... £2 ....£5 ....chart single
Everything's Gonna Be Alright ... 7" ...... Immediate ...... IM040 .... 1966 ... £25 ....£50 ....chart single
First Cut Is The Deepest .... 7" ...... Immediate ...... IM047 .... 1967 ... £2 ....£5 ....chart single
First Cut Is The Deepest .... 7" ...... Immediate ...... IM079 .... 1969 ... £1.50 .....£4
First Cut Is The Deepest .... 7" EP.. Columbia .... ESRF1877 .... 1967 ... £5 ....£10 ....French
First Lady Of Immediate .... LP ...... Immediate ...... IMLP/IMSP11 .... 1967 ... £6 ....£10
If You Think You're Groovy .... 7" ...... Immediate ...... IM061 .... 1968 ... £2 ....£5 ....chart single
Kafunta .... LP ...... Immediate ...... IMSP17 .... 1968 ... £5 ....£12
Time Has Come .... 7" ...... Immediate ...... IM055 .... 1967 ... £1.50 .....£4 ....chart single

ARRIVAL
Friends .... 7" ...... Decca .... F12986 .... 1969 ... £1.50 .....£4 ....chart single

ARRIVALS
Scooby Doo .... 7" ...... Pye .... 7N17761 .... 1969 ... £1.50 .....£4

ARROWS
Apache '65 .... 7" ...... Capitol .... CL15386 .... 1965 ... £2 ....£5
Apache '65 .... 7" EP.. Capitol .... EAP60000 .... 1965 ... £6 ....£12 ....French

ARROWS (2)
Mercy .... 7" ...... Pye .... 7N17756 .... 1969 ... £1.50 .....£4

ARS NOVA
Ars Nova .... LP ...... Elektra .... EKS74020 .... 1968 ... £4 ....£10
Fields Of People .... 7" ...... Elektra .... EKSN45034 .... 1968 ... £1.50 .....£4
Sunshine And Shadows .... LP ...... Atlantic .... 588196 .... 1969 ... £4 ....£10
Zoroaster .... 7" ...... Elektra .... EKSN45029 .... 1968 ... £1.50 .....£4

ART
When Chris Blackwell of Island records decided to expand his sphere of operations by entering the rock market place, he demonstrated from the start a remarkable sureness of touch in his decisions regarding which artists to sign. If Island albums seldom reach the high prices regularly achieved by Vertigo and Deram releases, then that is not because their music is uninteresting, but because the company was rather more successful at selling it. The Art LP is a relative obscurity, however, perhaps because the group itself immediately added an extra member and mutated into the rather better known Spooky Tooth.
Supernatural Fairy Tales .... LP ...... Island .... ILP967 .... 1975 ... £6 ....£15 ....pink rim label
Supernatural Fairytales .... LP ...... Island .... ILP967 .... 1968 ... £15 ....£30
What's That Sound .... 7" ...... Island .... WIP6019 .... 1967 ... £7.50 ......£15
What's That Sound .... 7" ...... Island .... WIP6224 .... 1975 ... £1.50 .....£4

ART ATTACKS
I Am A Dalek .... 7" ...... Albatross .... TIT1 .... 1978 ... £2.50 .....£6
Punk Rock Stars .... 7" ...... Fresh .... FRESH3 .... 1979 ... £2 ....£5

ART BEARS
Coda To Man And Boy .... 7" ...... Re .... RE6622 .... 1981 ... £2.50 .....£6 ....pic disc

Coda To Man And Boy	7"	Re	RE6622	1981	£4	£8	pic disc, signed and numbered
Hopes And Fears	LP	Recommended	REC2188	1978	£4	£10	
Winter Songs	LP	Recommended	RECO618	1979	£4	£10	

ART MOVEMENT

For As Long As You Need Me	7"	Columbia	DB8651	1970	£1.50	£4	
Game Of Love	7"	Decca	F12768	1968	£1.50	£4	
Loving Touch	7"	Decca	F12836	1968	£2	£5	
Sooner I Get You	7"	Columbia	DB8697	1970	£1.50	£4	
Yes Sir No Sir	7"	Columbia	DB8602	1969	£1.50	£4	

ART NOUVEAUX

Extra Terrestrial Visitations	7"	Fontana	TF483	1964	£4	£8	

ART OF LOVIN'

Art Of Lovin'	LP	Mainstream	6613	1968	£5	£12	US

ART OF NOISE

Into Battle With the Art Of Noise	cass-s	ZTT	CTIS100	1983	£2.50	£6	
Moments In Love	7"	ZTT	PZTPS02	1985	£1.50	£4	shaped pic disc

ARTERY

Mother Moon	7"	Limited Edition	TAKE1	1979	£5	£10	
Unbalanced	7"	Aardvark	STEAL3	1980	£2	£5	double

ARTHUR, DAVE & TONI

Bushes And Briars	7"	Trailer	LER1	1970	£1.50	£4	
Hearken To The Witches' Rune	LP	Trailer	LER2017	1970	£15	£30	
Lark In The Morning	LP	Topic	12T190	1969	£10	£25	
Morning Stands On Tiptoe	LP	Transatlantic	TRA154	1967	£15	£30	
Sing A Story	LP	Decca	SPA509	1977	£5	£12	

ARTHURS, ANDY

I Can Detect You For A Million Miles	7"	Radar	ADA7	1978	£4	£8	

ARTI & MESTIERI

Tilt	LP	Cramps	5501	1974	£6	£15	Italian

ARTISTICS

Girl I Need you	7"	Coral	Q72492	1967	£7.50	£15	
I'm Gonna Miss You	7"	Coral	Q72488	1966	£5	£10	

ARTWOODS

The Artwoods were typical of the many R&B and beat groups that spent years slogging round the British club circuit without ever really gaining much success. Unlike many, however, two of the group's members did achieve success later - drummer Keef Hartley, who used his stint with John Mayall's Bluesbreakers as a springboard to forming his own band; and organist Jon Lord, the founder member of Deep Purple and Whitesnake. As for poor Art Wood himself, he has been rather eclipsed by his more famous brother, Ron Wood.

Art Gallery	LP	Decca	LK4830	1966	£60	£120	
Art Gallery	LP	Eclipse	ECS2025	1974	£20	£40	
Artwoods	LP	Spark	SRLM2006	1973	£15	£30	
Goodbye Sisters	7"	Decca	F12206	1965	£12.50	£25	
I Feel Good	7"	Decca	F12465	1966	£12.50	£25	
I Take What I Want	7"	Decca	F12384	1966	£12.50	£25	
Jazz In Jeans	7" EP	Decca	DFE8654	1966	£100	£200	
Oh My Love	7"	Decca	F12091	1965	£12.50	£25	
Oh My Love	7" EP	Decca	457076	1965	£100	£200	French
Sweet Mary	7"	Decca	F12015	1964	£12.50	£25	
What Shall I Do	7"	Parlophone	R5590	1967	£25	£50	

ARZACHEL

The Arzachel LP only received a limited release, but it is a fine and innovative recording. As would be expected from the musicians involved - guitarist Steve Hillage and keyboard wizard Dave Stewart, with Clive Brooks and Hugh Montgomery-Campbell in support. In other words, this is Egg, augmented by guitar.

Arzachel	LP	Evolution	Z1003	1969	£180	£300	

ASGARD

Children Of A New Born Age	7"	Threshold	TH10	1972	£1.50	£4	
In The Realm Of Asgard	LP	Threshold	THS6	1972	£15	£30	
In The Realm Of Asgard	7"	Threshold	TH15	1973	£1.50	£4	

ASH, MARVIN

New Orleans At Midnight	LP	Brunswick	LAT8191	1957	£5	£12	

ASH RA TEMPLE

Ash Ra Temple	LP	Ohr	OMM556013	1971	£8	£20	German
Inventions For Electric Guitar	LP	Komische	KM58015	1975	£6	£15	German
Join In	LP	Ohr	OMM556032	1973	£6	£15	German
Schwingungen	LP	Ohr	OMM556020	1972	£8	£20	German
Seven Up	LP	Komische	KM58001	1973	£6	£15	German
Starring Rosi	LP	Komische	KM58007	1973	£6	£15	German

ASHBY, HAROLD

Born To Swing	LP	Columbia	33SX1257	1960	£4	£10	

ASHBY, IRVING

Big Guitar	7"	London	HLP8578	1958	£6	£12	

ASHES

Ashes	LP	Vault	125	1968	£8	£20	US

27

ASHKAN
In From The Cold .... LP ..... Nova .... (S)RNR1 .... 1970 ... £20 ..... £40 ....

ASHLEY, DEL
Little Miss Stuck-Up .... 7" ...... Planetary .... 103 .... 1965 ... £5 ..... £10 .... US
She Don't Cry .... 7" ...... Manchester ..... 101 .... 1965 ... £6 ..... £12 .... US

ASHLEY, STEVE
Stroll On .... LP ..... Gull .... GULP1003 .... 1974 ... £5 ..... £12

ASIA
Don't Cry .... 7" ...... Geffen .... WA3580 .... 1982 ... £1.50 ..... £4 .... shaped pic disc
Only Time Will Tell .... 7" ...... Geffen .... GEFA112228 ...... 1982 ... £2 ..... £5 .... pic disc

ASMUSSEN, SVEND
Hot Fiddle .... 10" LP Parlophone...... CPMD1 .... 1955 ... £8 ..... £20

ASPEY, GARY & VERA
From The North .... LP ..... Topic .... 12TS255 .... 1975 ... £5 ..... £12
Taste Of Hotpot .... LP ..... Topic .... 12TS299 .... 1976 ... £5 ..... £12

ASPEY, VERA
Blackbird .... LP ..... Topic .... 12TS356 .... 1977 ... £5 ..... £12

ASSAGAI
.... LP ..... Vertigo .... 6360058 .... 1971 ... £20 ..... £40 .... test pressing
Assagai .... LP ..... Vertigo .... 6360030 .... 1971 ... £8 ..... £20 .... spiral label
Telephone Girl .... 7" ...... Vertigo .... 6059034 .... 1971 ... £1.50 ..... £4
Zimbabwe .... LP ..... Philips .... 6308079 .... 1972 ... £5 ..... £12

ASSOCIATES
Affectionate Punch .... 7" ...... Fiction .... FICS11 .... 1980 ... £1.50 ..... £4
Boys Keep Swinging .... 7" ...... Double Hip ..... DHR1 .... 1980 ... £20 ..... £40
Boys Keep Swinging .... 7" ...... MCA .... MCA537 .... 1980 ... £10 ..... £20
Country Boy .... CD-s .. WEA .... YZ329CD .... 1988 ... £20 ..... £40
Country Boy .... 12" .... WEA .... YZ329T .... 1988 ... £25 ..... £50 .... test pressing
Heart Of Glass .... 12" .... WEA .... YZ310TX .... 1988 ... £4 ..... £10 .... with 3D glasses
Tell Me Easter's On Friday ..... 7" ...... Beggars .... BEG86 .... 1984 ... £7.50 ..... £15 .... test pressing
                                          Banquet ....

ASSOCIATION
Most of the successful Californian groups that emerged during the late sixties had backgrounds rooted in folk music and naturally tended to favour melodic material and close harmony singing. The Association were very much a case in point, sustaining a six year career on the back of four tuneful singles, which if not exactly classics, are at any rate fondly remembered. "Along Comes Mary", "Cherish", "Windy", and "Never My Love" are to be found scattered through their LP releases alongside similar fare, although, the vagueries of the pop charts being what they are, it was the much less well known "Time For Living" that scored in a small way in the UK.
Along Comes Mary .... 7" ...... London .... HLT10054 .... 1966 ... £2 ..... £5
And Then...Along Came Association ... LP ..... London .... HAT8305 .... 1966 ... £5 ..... £12
Association .... LP ..... Warner Bros.... W(S)1800 .... 1969 ... £4 ..... £10
Birthday .... LP ..... Warner Bros.... W(S)1733 .... 1968 ... £4 ..... £10
Cherish .... 7" ...... London .... HLT10074 .... 1966 ... £1.50 ..... £4
Cherish .... 7" EP. Riviera .... 231209 .... 1966 ... £5 ..... £10 .... French
Everything That Touches You ... 7" ...... Warner Bros.... WB7163 .... 1968 ... £1.50 ..... £4
Goodbye Columbus .... LP ..... Warner Bros.... W(S)1786 .... 1969 ... £4 ..... £10
Goodbye Columbus .... 7" ...... Warner Bros.... WB7267 .... 1969 ... £1.50 ..... £4
Greatest Hits .... LP ..... Warner Bros.... W(S)1767 .... 1969 ... £4 ..... £10
Insight Out .... LP ..... London .... HAT/SHT8342 .... 1967 ... £5 ..... £12
Just About The Same .... 7" ...... Warner Bros.... WB7372 .... 1970 ... £1.50 ..... £4
Live .... LP ..... Warner Bros.... 2WS1868 .... 1970 ... £8 ..... £20 .... US
Never My Love .... 7" ...... London .... HLT10157 .... 1967 ... £1.50 ..... £4
No Fair At All .... 7" ...... London .... HLT10118 .... 1967 ... £1.50 ..... £4
No Fair At All .... 7" EP. Riviera .... 231241 .... 1967 ... £5 ..... £10 .... French
Pandora's Golden Heebie Jeebies . 7" ...... London .... HLT10098 .... 1966 ... £2.50 ..... £6
Renaissance .... LP ..... London .... HAT8313 .... 1967 ... £5 ..... £12
Six Man Band .... 7" ...... Warner Bros.... WB7229 .... 1968 ... £1.50 ..... £4
Stop The Motor .... LP ..... Warner Bros.... WS1927 .... 1971 ... £4 ..... £10 .... US
Time For Livin' .... 7" ...... Warner Bros.... WB7195 .... 1968 ... £1.50 ..... £4 .... chart single
Windy .... 7" ...... London .... HLT10140 .... 1967 ... £1.50 ..... £4
Windy .... 7" ...... Warner Bros.... WB7119 .... 1969 ... £1.50 ..... £4
Windy .... 7" EP. Riviera .... 231243 .... 1967 ... £5 ..... £10 .... French

ASTAIRE, FRED
Funny Face .... 7" ...... HMV .... POP337 .... 1957 ... £2 ..... £5 .... Audrey
                                                                                                          Hepburn B side
Ritz Roll And Rock .... 7" ...... MGM .... MGM964 .... 1957 ... £4 ..... £8

ASTERIX
Asterix .... LP ..... Decca .... SLK16695P .... 1970 ... £5 ..... £12 .... German

ASTLEY, EDWIN
Saint .... LP ..... RCA .... LSP3631 .... 1966 ... £8 ..... £20 .... US
Secret Agent (Danger Man) ..... LP ..... RCA .... LSP3630 .... 1966 ... £8 ..... £20 .... US
Secret Agent Meets The Saint ... LP ..... RCA .... LSP3467 .... 1965 ... £8 ..... £20 .... US

ASTLEY, EDWIN ORCHESTRA
Danger Man Theme .... 7" ...... RCA .... RCA1492 .... 1965 ... £6 ..... £12

ASTLEY, VIRGINIA
A Bao A Qu .... 10" ..... Why Fi........... WHYD8 .... 1982 ... £2.50 ..... £6

ASTORS
Candy	7"	Atlantic	584245	1969	£4	£8
Candy	7"	Atlantic	AT4037	1965	£10	£20

ASTRAL NAVIGATION
Astral Navigation	LP	Holyground	HG114	1971	£100	£200
Astral Navigation	LP	Magic Mixture	MM2	1989	£8	£20

ASTRONAUTS
Banana	7"	Hala Gala	HG14	196-	£5	£10
Before You Leave	7"	Hala Gala	HG9	1966	£5	£10
Before You Leave	7"	Island	WI3065	1967	£5	£10
I'll Be There	7"	Hala Gala	HG13	196-	£5	£10
Oh Why I Still Love You	7"	Hala Gala	HG12	196-	£5	£10

ASTRONAUTS (2)
Astronauts Go Go Go	LP	RCA	LPM/LSP3307	1965	£6	£15	US
Astronauts Orbit Campus	LP	RCA	LPM/LSP2903	1964	£6	£15	US
Baja	7" EP.	RCA	86328	1963	£7.50	£15	French
Baju	7"	RCA	RCA1349	1963	£2	£5	
Big Boss Man	7" EP.	RCA	86367	1963	£7.50	£15	French
Competition Coupe	LP	RCA	LPM/LSP2858	1964	£6	£15	US
Down The Line	LP	RCA	LPM/LSP3454	1965	£6	£15	US
Everything Is A-OK	LP	RCA	LPM/LSP2782	1964	£6	£15	US
Favorites For You, Our Fans, From Us	LP	RCA	LPM/LSP3359	1965	£6	£15	US
I'm A Rollin' Stone	7" EP.	RCA	86457	1964	£7.50	£15	French
Kuk	7" EP.	RCA	86334	1963	£7.50	£15	French
Rockin' With The Astronauts	LP	RCA	PRM183	1964	£6	£15	US
Surf Party	LP	20th Century	TFM3131/ TFS4131	1964	£6	£15	US
Surfin' With The Astronauts	LP	RCA	LPM/LSP2760	1963	£8	£20	US
Travelin' Men	LP	RCA	LPM/LSP3733	1967	£5	£12	US
Wild On The Beach	LP	RCA	LPM/LSP3441	1965	£6	£15	US
Wild Wild Winter	LP	Decca	DL(7)4699	1966	£5	£12	US

ASTRONAUTS (3)
All Night Party	7"	Bugle	BLAST1	1979	£4	£8
Peter Pan Hits The Suburbs	LP	Bugle	GENIUS001	1981	£15	£30
We Were Talking	7"	Bugle	BLAST5	1979	£2	£5

AT LAST THE 1958 ROCK'N'ROLL SHOW
I Can't Drive	7"	CBS	3349	1968	£4	£8

ATACAMA
Atacama	LP	Charisma	CAS1039	1971	£4	£10
Sun Burns Up Above	LP	Charisma	CAS1060	1972	£4	£10

ATHENIANS
I've Got Love If You Want It	7"	Waverley	SLP532	1964	£12.50	£25	
I've Got Love If You Want It	7"	Waverley	SLP532	1964	£25	£50	PS
Thinking Of Our Love	7"	Waverley	SLP533	1965	£15	£30	PS
Thinking Of Your Love	7"	Waverley	SLP533	1965	£7.50	£15	
You Tell Me	7"	Edinburgh Students Charity	ESC1	1964	£10	£20	
You Tell Me	7"	Edinburgh Students Charity	ESC1	1964	£20	£40	PS

ATHENS, GLENN & THE TROJANS
Glen Athens And The Trojans	7" EP.	Spot	7E1018	1965	£100	£200

ATILA
Intencion	LP	BASF		1976	£70	£140	Spanish
Revlure	LP	Odeon		1978	£70	£140	Spanish

ATKIN, PETE
Pete Atkin was the author of some half dozen LPs, whose stylish and intelligent singer-songwriting was somehow never as popular as it should have been. In the collectors' market too this remains the case, as such classics of the genre as "A King At Nightfall" and "The Road Of Silk" steadfastly refuse to fetch even moderate collectors' prices, despite being long deleted. Not that Atkin himself should worry, having forged a satisfying career as a television producer. The lyricist on the records has done rather well for himself too - his name is Clive James - yes, it is the same one!
Be Careful When They Offer You	7"	Philips	6006050	1970	£1.50	£4
Beware Of The Beautiful Stranger	LP	Fontana	6309011	1970	£6	£15
Beware Of The Beautiful Stranger	LP	RCA	SF8387	1974	£4	£10
Driving Through Mythical America	LP	Philips	6308070	1971	£5	£12
Driving Through Mythical America	LP	RCA	SF8386	1974	£4	£10
King At Nightfall	LP	RCA	SF8336	1973	£4	£10
Live Libel	LP	RCA	RS1013	1975	£4	£10
Master Of The Revels	LP	RCA	PL25041	1977	£4	£10
Road Of Silk	LP	RCA	LPL15014	1974	£4	£10
Secret Drinker	LP	RCA	LPL15062	1974	£4	£10

ATKINS, BENNY
Lipstick On Your Lips	7"	Mercury	AMT1113	1960	£1.50	£4

ATKINS, CHET
At Home	LP	RCA	LPM1544	1957	£6	£15	US
Boo Boo Stick Beat	7"	RCA	RCA1153	1959	£1.50	£4	
Chet Atkins' Gallopin' Guitar	10" LP	RCA	LPM3079	1952	£15	£30	US
Chet Atkins' Workshop	LP	RCA	RD27214	1960	£4	£10	

Title	Format	Label	Cat. No.	Year			Notes
Finger Style Guitar	LP	RCA	LPM1383	1956	£6	£15	US
Guitar Genius	7" EP	RCA	RCX7118	1963	£2.50	£6	
Hi Fi In Focus	LP	RCA	LPM1577	1957	£6	£15	US
In Three Dimensions	LP	RCA	LPM1197	1956	£6	£15	US
Other Chet Atkins	LP	RCA	RD27194	1960	£4	£10	
Picks On The Beatles	LP	RCA	RD/SF7813	1966	£5	£12	
Session With Chet Atkins	LP	RCA	LPM1090	1955	£6	£15	US
String Dustin'	10" LP	RCA	LPM3167	1953	£10	£25	US
Stringin' Along	LP	RCA	LPM1236	1956	£6	£15	US
Stringin' Along	10" LP	RCA	LPM3169	1953	£10	£25	US
Teensville	LP	RCA	RD27168	1960	£5	£12	
Teensville	7"	RCA	RCA1174	1960	£1.50	£4	chart single

ATLANTA RHYTHM SECTION

Title	Format	Label	Cat. No.	Year			Notes
Champagne Jam	LP	Mobile Fidelity	MFSL1038	1979	£4	£10	US audiophile

ATLANTIC BRIDGE

Title	Format	Label	Cat. No.	Year			Notes
Atlantic Bridge	LP	Dawn	DNLS3014	1970	£4	£10	

ATLANTIC OCEAN

Title	Format	Label	Cat. No.	Year			Notes
Tranquility Bay	LP	Love		1970	£30	£60	Swedish

ATLANTICS

Title	Format	Label	Cat. No.	Year			Notes
Bomborra	7"	Oriole	CB1963	1964	£1.50	£4	

ATLANTIS

Title	Format	Label	Cat. No.	Year			Notes
Atlantis	LP	Vertigo	6360609	1973	£6	£15	spiral label

ATLAS

Title	Format	Label	Cat. No.	Year			Notes
Against All The Odds	LP	Atlas	WIL001	1978	£6	£15	

ATMOSFEAR

Title	Format	Label	Cat. No.	Year			Notes
Dancing In Outer Space	12"	Elite	DAZZ47	1986	£3	£8	
Dancing In Outer Space	12"	MCA	MCA543	1979	£2.50	£6	
Entrance	LP	MCA	MCF3110	1981	£5	£12	

ATMOSPHERES

Title	Format	Label	Cat. No.	Year			Notes
Fickle Chicken	7"	London	HLW8977	1959	£6	£12	
Telegraph	7"	London	HLW9091	1960	£6	£12	

ATOLL

Title	Format	Label	Cat. No.	Year			Notes
L'araignee Mal	LP	Eurodisc	913002	1975	£4	£10	French
Musiciens Et Magiciens	LP	Eurodisc	87008	1974	£4	£10	French

ATOMIC ROOSTER

Title	Format	Label	Cat. No.	Year			Notes
Atomic Rooster	LP	B&C	CAS1010	1970	£6	£15	chart LP
Death Walks Behind You	LP	B&C	CAS1026	1970	£6	£15	chart LP
Friday The 13th	7"	B&C	CB121	1970	£2.50	£6	PS
In Hearing Of	LP	Pegasus	PEG1	1971	£6	£15	chart LP
Made In England	LP	Dawn	DNLS3038	1972	£5	£12	
Made In England	LP	Dawn	DNLS3038	1972	£10	£25	denim cover
Nice And Greasy	LP	Dawn	DNLS3049	1973	£10	£25	
Tell Your Story - Sing Your Song	7"	Decca	FR13503	1974	£2.50	£6	export

ATTACK

The Attack were best known as the performers of the other version of "Hi Ho Silver Lining", but unfortunately for them, despite receiving fairly extensive radio play, they lost out to Jeff Beck. The guitarist with the Attack was David O'List, who subsequently became a member of the Nice.

Title	Format	Label	Cat. No.	Year			Notes
Created By Clive	7"	Decca	F12631	1967	£7.50	£15	
Hi Ho Silver Lining	7"	Decca	F12578	1967	£7.50	£15	
Neville Thumbcatch	7"	Decca	F12725	1968	£12.50	£25	
Try It	7"	Decca	F12550	1967	£12.50	£25	

ATTACK (2)

Title	Format	Label	Cat. No.	Year			Notes
Please Mr.Phil Spector	7"	Philips	BF1585	1967	£7.50	£15	

ATTILA

Title	Format	Label	Cat. No.	Year			Notes
Attila	LP	Epic	E30030	1970	£8	£20	US

ATTRACTIONS

Title	Format	Label	Cat. No.	Year			Notes
Party Line	7"	Columbia	DB8010	1966	£10	£20	
Stupid Girl	7"	Columbia	DB7936	1966	£10	£20	

ATTRITION

Title	Format	Label	Cat. No.	Year			Notes
Fear	7"	Sound For Industry	SFI671	1981	£2	£5	flexi
Monkey In A Bin	12"	Uniton	19841	1984	£4	£10	
Shrinkwrap	12"	Third Mind	TMS04	1985	£3	£8	
Two Traces	7"	Adventures In Reality	AINR2	1982	£4	£8	flexi
Voice Of God	12"	Third Mind	TMS03	1984	£3	£8	

ATWELL, WINIFRED

Title	Format	Label	Cat. No.	Year			Notes
Big Ben Boogie	7"	Decca	F10476	1955	£1.50	£4	
Boogie With Winifred Atwell	7" EP	Decca	DFE6099	1955	£2	£5	
Bumble Boogie	7"	Decca	F10785	1956	£1.50	£4	
Let's Rock'n'Roll	7"	Decca	F10852	1957	£2.50	£6	
Poor People Of Paris	7"	Decca	F10681	1956	£2.50	£6	
Seventeenth Century Boogie	7"	Decca	F10496	1955	£1.50	£4	
Spaceship Boogie	7"	Decca	F10886	1957	£2	£5	
Winifred Atwell Plays Gershwin	LP	Decca	LK214	1958	£4	£10	

AU GO-GO SINGERS

San Francisco Bay Blues	7"	Columbia	DB7493	1965	£4	£8	
They Call Us The Au Go-Go Singers	LP	Columbia	33SX1696	1964	£20	£40	

AUBREY SMALL

Aubrey Small	LP	Polydor	2383048	1971	£20	£40	

AUDIENCE

As label-mates of Genesis and Van Der Graaf Generator, Audience played very much the same kind of complex structured but essentially melodic material, although with rather less commercial success. The real Audience rarity, however, is the first LP, recorded for Polydor. The scarcity of this record has led some dealers to conclude that the record was withdrawn soon after its release, although the truth is that it was simply deleted after a short time, due to its sales being rather poor.

Audience	LP	Polydor	583065	1969	£35	£70	
Friends Friends Friends	LP	Charisma	CAS1012	1970	£5	£12	
House On The Hill	LP	Charisma	CAS1032	1971	£4	£10	
Indian Summer	7"	Charisma	CB141	1971	£1.50	£4	PS
Lunch	LP	Charisma	CAS1054	1972	£4	£10	

AUDREY

Love Me Tonight	7"	Downtown	DT414	1969	£1.50	£4	Brother Dan Allstars B side
Lovers' Concerto	7"	Downtown	DT418	1969	£1.50	£4	Brother Dan Allstars B side
Oh I Was Wrong	7"	Downtown	DT454	1969	£1.50	£4	
Someday We'll Be Together	7"	Downtown	DT457	1969	£1.50	£4	Music Doctors B side
Sweeter Than Sugar	7"	Downtown	DT452	1969	£1.50	£4	
You'll Lose A Good Thing	7"	Downtown	DT436	1969	£1.50	£4	Desmond Riley B side

AUGER, BRIAN

Brian Auger's long career as a jazz-rock organist peaked on the recordings made jointly with singer Julie Driscoll. For just a short while, Auger was more than just the skilled craftsman of his recordings before and since, becoming part of a group with real innovative power. Nothing Julie Driscoll and the Brian Auger Trinity recorded together could quite match the brilliance of "This Wheel's On Fire", but all the Marmalade recordings contain much worthwhile and memorable music.

Befour	LP	RCA	SF8101	1970	£4	£10	
Definitely What	LP	Marmalade	607003	1968	£8	£20	
Fool Killer	7"	Columbia	DB7590	1965	£5	£10	
Green Onions '65	7"	Columbia	DB7715	1965	£4	£8	
I Don't Know Where You Are	7"	Marmalade	598006	1968	£2	£5	
Oblivion Express	LP	RCA	SF8170	1971	£4	£10	
Red Beans And Rice	7"	Marmalade	598003	1967	£2	£5	
Tiger	7"	Columbia	DB8163	1967	£7.50	£15	
What You Gonna Do	7"	Marmalade	598015	1969	£1.50	£4	

AUGER, BRIAN, JIMMY PAGE & SONNY BOY WILLIAMSON

Don't Send Me No Flowers	LP	Marmalade	607/608004	1968	£15	£30	

AULD, GEORGIE

Dancing In The Land Of Hi-Fi	LP	Emarcy	EJL1266	1958	£5	£12	
Georgie Auld	LP	Vogue Coral	LVA9023	1956	£5	£12	
In The Land Of Hi-Fi	LP	Emarcy	EJL1251	1957	£5	£12	with Sarah McLawler
Manhattan	7"	Vogue Coral	Q2002	1954	£1.50	£4	
With The Andre Previn Orchestra	LP	Vogue Coral	LVA9012	1956	£5	£12	

AULDRIDGE, MIKE

Blues And Bluegrass	LP	Sonet	SNTF673	1974	£5	£12	

AUM

Bluesvibes	LP	London	HAK/SHK8401	1969	£6	£15	
Resurrection	LP	Fillmore	30002	1969	£6	£15	US

AUNT MARY

Aunt Mary	LP	Polydor	2380002	1971	£40	£80	
Best Of Vol.1	LP	Polydor	6478009	1974	£25	£50	
Best Of Vol.2	LP	Polydor	6478055	1975	£25	£50	
Janus	LP	Vertigo	6317750	1973	£60	£120	
Loaded	LP	Philips	6317010	1971	£75	£150	
Whispering Farewell	LP	Polydor	2499083	1974	£25	£50	German

AURA

Aura	LP	Mercury	SRM1620	1971	£6	£15	

AUSTIN, CLAIRE

Claire Austin Sings The Blues	10" LP	Good Time Jazz	LDG185	1956	£20	£40	
When Your Lover Has Gone	LP	Contemporary	LAC12139	1959	£8	£20	

AUSTIN, PATTI

Are You Ready For Love	7"	CBS	7180	1971	£1.50	£4	
Your Love Made The Difference In Me	7"	United Artists	UP35097	1970	£1.50	£4	

AUSTIN, PETER

Your Love	7"	Caltone	TONE125	1968	£4	£8	

AUSTIN, REG

My Saddest Day	7"	Pye	7N15885	1965	£10	£20	

AUSTIN, SIL

Band With The Beat	7" EP	Mercury	MEP9540	1958	£7.50	£15	
Don't You Just Know It	7"	Mercury	7MT220	1958	£5	£10	
Go Sil Go	7" EP	Mercury	MEP9541	1958	£7.50	£15	
Hey Eula	7"	Mercury	7MT225	1958	£5	£10	

AUSTRALIAN JAZZ QUARTET

Australian Jazz Quartet	LP	London	LTZN15054	1957	£5	£12	
Australian Jazz Quartet	LP	London	LTZN15065	1957	£5	£12	

AUSTRALIAN JAZZ QUINTET

Australian Jazz Quintet Plus One	LP	London	LTZN15089	1957	£5	£12	

AUSTRALIAN PLAYBOYS

Black Sheep	7"	Immediate	IM054	1967	£50	£100	

AUTOSALVAGE

The one LP recorded by Autosalvage is a little like Jefferson Airplane and a little like The Lovin' Spoonful, but with more ambitious arranging than either (including the use of Medieval instruments, though not a Medieval sound). Unfortunately, the songs are not as strong as they might be, but the record is still very interesting. Frank Zappa is supposed to have had a hand in the group's discovery.

Autosalvage	LP	RCA	LSP3940	1968	£6	£15	US

AUTRY, GENE

At The Rodeo	10" LP	Columbia	JL8001	1949	£10	£25	US
Champion Western Adventures	LP	Columbia	CL677	1955	£6	£15	US
Christmas With Gene Autry	LP	Challenge	CHL600	1958	£6	£15	US
Gene Autry Sings Peter Cottontail	10" LP	Columbia	CL2568	1955	£10	£25	US
Golden Hits	LP	RCA	LPM/LSP2623	1962	£5	£12	US
Greatest Hits	LP	Columbia	CL1575	1961	£6	£15	US
Little Johnny Pilgrim	10" LP	Columbia	MJV83	195-	£10	£25	US
Merry Christmas	10" LP	Columbia	CL2547	1955	£10	£25	US
Rusty The Rocking Horse	10" LP	Columbia	MJV94	195-	£10	£25	US
Stampede	10" LP	Columbia	JL8009	195-	£10	£25	US
Story Of The Nativity	10" LP	Columbia	MJV82	195-	£10	£25	US
Western Classic, Vol.1	10" LP	Columbia	HL9001	195-	£10	£25	US
Western Classic, Vol.2	10" LP	Columbia	HL9002	195-	£10	£25	US

AUTUMN VINE

He Ain't Superman	7"	Evolution	E2447	1969	£1.50	£4	

AVALANCHES

Ski Surfin'	LP	Warner Bros	1525	1963	£6	£15	US

AVALON

Voice Of Life	LP	London		1977	£8	£20	US

AVALON, FRANKIE

And Now About Mr.Avalon	LP	Chancellor	CHL(S)5022	1961	£5	£12	US
Bobby Sox To Stockings	7"	HMV	POP636	1959	£1.50	£4	
Christmas Album	LP	Chancellor	CHL(S)5031	1962	£6	£15	US
Cleopatra	LP	Chancellor	CHL(S)5032	1963	£6	£15	US
Darling	7"	London	HL8636	1958	£10	£20	
Dede Dinah	7"	HMV	POP453	1958	£5	£10	
Don't Throw Away All Those Teardrops	7"	HMV	POP727	1960	£1.50	£4	chart single
Fifteen Greatest Hits	LP	United Artists	UAL3382/ UAS6382	1964	£5	£12	US
Frankie Avalon	LP	Chancellor	CHL5001	1958	£8	£20	US
Frankie Avalon	7" EP	HMV	7EG8471	1958	£5	£10	
Frankie Avalon No.2	7" EP	HMV	7EG8482	1958	£5	£10	
Frankie Avalon No.3	7" EP	HMV	7EG8507	1958	£5	£10	
Gingerbread	7"	HMV	POP517	1958	£2.50	£6	chart single
I'll Wait For You	7"	HMV	POP569	1959	£1.50	£4	
Italiano	LP	Chancellor	CHL(S)5025	1962	£5	£12	US
Just Ask Your Heart	7"	HMV	POP658	1959	£1.50	£4	
Songs From Muscle Beach Party	LP	United Artists	ULP1078	1964	£5	£12	
Songs Of The Alamo	7" EP	HMV	7EG8632	1960	£2.50	£6	
Summer Scene	LP	HMV	CLP1423	1960	£5	£12	
Swingin' On A Rainbow	LP	HMV	CLP1346	1959	£6	£15	
Trumpet Sorrento	7"	X	0006	1954	£12.50	£25	US
Trumpet Tarantella	7"	X	0026	1954	£12.50	£25	US
Venus	7"	HMV	POP603	1959	£1.50	£4	chart single
Very Young Man With A Horn	7" EP	X	EXA20	1955	£30	£60	US
Whole Lot Of Frankie	LP	Chancellor	CHL5018	1961	£6	£15	US
Why	7"	HMV	POP688	1960	£1.50	£4	chart single
You Are Mine	LP	Chancellor	CHL(S)5027	1962	£5	£12	US
Young And In Love	LP	HMV	CLP1440/CSD1358	1960	£6	£15	
Young Frankie Avalon	LP	Chancellor	CHL5002	1959	£6	£15	US

AVALONS

Every Day	7"	Island	WI263	1966	£5	£10	

AVANT-GARDE

Naturally Stoned	7"	CBS	1333160	1975	£1.50	£4	
Naturally Stoned	7"	CBS	3704	1968	£2.50	£6	

AVENGERS

Everyone's Gonna Wonder	7"	Parlophone	R5661	1968	£2.50	£6	

AVENGERS (2)

American In Me	12"	White Noise	WNR002	1979/ 81	£5	£12	different PS's
We Are The One	7"	Dangerhouse	SFD400	1977	£12.50	£25	PS in plastic bag, red vinyl

AVENGERS VI

Real Cool Hits	LP	Mark 56 Records		1965	£30	£60	US

AVON, ALAN & THE TOY SHOP

Night To Remember	7"	Concord	CONC005	1974	£4	£8	

AVON CITIES JAZZ BAND

Avon Cities Jazz Band	10" LP	Tempo	LAP10	1956	£4	£10	

AVON CITIES SKIFFLE GROUP

Hey Hey Daddy Blues	7"	Tempo	A146	1956	£1.50	£4	
How Long Blues	7"	Tempo	A156	1957	£1.50	£4	
Lonesome Day Blues	7"	Tempo	A157	1957	£1.50	£4	
Ray Bush & The Avon Cities Skiffle Group	7" EP	Tempo	EXA40	1957	£4	£8	
Ray Bush & The Avon Cities Skiffle Group No.2	7" EP	Tempo	EXA50	1957	£4	£8	
This Little Light Of Mine	7"	Tempo	A149	1956	£1.50	£4	

AVONS

Four Little Heels	7"	Columbia	DB4522	1960	£1.50	£4	
Jerri-Lee	7"	Columbia	DB4236	1959	£1.50	£4	chart single
Pickin' Petals	7"	Columbia	DB4413	1960	£1.50	£4	
Seven Little Girls Sitting In The Back Seat	7"	Columbia	DB4363	1959	£1.50	£4	chart single
We're Only Young Once	7"	Columbia	DB4461	1960	£1.50	£4	chart single

AVONS (2)

Avons	LP	Hull	HLP1000	1960	£75	£150	US

AXELROD, DAVID

Earth Rot	LP	Capitol	SKAO456	1970	£4	£10	US
Rock Messiah	LP	RCA	4636	1972	£4	£10	US
Songs Of Experience	LP	Capitol	SKAP338	1969	£4	£10	US
Songs Of Innocence	LP	Capitol	ST2982	1968	£4	£10	US

AXIS

Axis	LP	Riviera	421088	1973	£5	£12	French
Axis	LP	Riviera	95010	1971	£5	£12	French
Ela Ela	LP	Riviera	521192	1971	£5	£12	French

AXTON, HOYT

Apart from being quite well known as a folk and country singer in his own right, Hoyt Axton is also the son of the woman who wrote "Heartbreak Hotel". Intending the song as a smooth, sentimental ballad, Mrs.Axton was apparently quite upset when she heard what Elvis Presley had done to the song - although she cheered up considerably when the royalties started to arrive!

Best Of Hoyt Axton	LP	London	HAF/SHF8276	1966	£5	£12	
Country Anthem	LP	Capitol	SMAS850	1971	£4	£10	US
Explodes	LP	Vee Jay	VJS1098	1964	£6	£15	US
Greenback Dollar	LP	Stateside	SL10082	1964	£6	£15	
Joy To The World	LP	Capitol	EST788	1970	£4	£10	US
Less Than A Song	LP	A&M	AMLH64376	1973	£4	£10	
Saturday's Child	LP	Vee Jay	VJS1127	1965	£6	£15	US
Sings Betty Smith	LP	Exodus	301	1965	£5	£12	US
Thunder And Lightnin'	LP	Stateside	SL10096	1964	£6	£15	

AYERS, KEVIN

As one of the founders of the "English eccentric" school of rock music, Kevin Ayers still makes records for the loyal army of fans who have followed his activities since his days as bass player for the Soft Machine. The two earliest albums contain what is arguably his most interesting music, with telling contributions from the supporting musicians, who include Soft Machine on "Joy Of A Toy", and on 'Shooting At The Moon", saxophonist Lol Coxhill, composer/arranger David Bedford (here playing keyboards), and the youthful Mike Oldfield.

As Close As You Think	LP	Illuminated	AMA25	1986	£5	£12	
Bananamour	LP	Harvest	SHVL807	1973	£5	£12	
Bananamour	LP	Harvest	SHVL807	1973	£8	£20	with booklet
Caribbean Moon	7"	Harvest	HAR5071	1973	£4	£8	PS
Caribbean Moon	7"	Harvest	HAR5109	1976	£4	£8	PS
Joy Of A Toy	LP	Harvest	SHVL763	1970	£6	£15	
Joy Of A Toy/Shooting At The Moon	LP	Harvest	SHDW407	1975	£5	£12	double
Puis-Je?	7"	Harvest	HAR5027	1970	£2	£5	
Shooting At The Moon	LP	Harvest	SHSP4005	1971	£6	£15	
Singing A Song In The Morning	7"	Harvest	HAR5011	1970	£4	£8	
Stepping Out	7"	Illuminated	LEV71	1986	£1.50	£4	
Whatevershebringswesing	LP	Harvest	SHVL800	1973	£4	£10	

AYERS, ROY

Africa Centre Of The World	LP	Polydor	2391157	1981	£4	£10	
Best Of Roy Ayers	LP	Polydor	2391429	1979	£4	£10	
Crystal Reflection	LP	Muse	MR5101	1977	£5	£12	
Daddy Bug And Friend	LP	Atco	SD1692	1973	£6	£15	US
Everybody Loves The Sunshine	LP	Polydor	PD16070	1976	£4	£10	US
Evolution	7"	Polydor	2066671	1976	£1.50	£4	
Feelin' Good	LP	Polydor	2391539	1982	£8	£20	
Fever	LP	Polydor	2391396	1979	£4	£10	
Let's Do It	LP	Polydor	2490145	1978	£4	£10	
Lifeline	LP	Polydor	2391292	1977	£4	£10	
Mystic Voyage	LP	Polydor	PD6057	1975	£5	£12	
Red, Black And Green	LP	Polydor	PD16078	1976	£4	£10	US
Running Away	12"	Polydor	POSPX135	1980	£2.50	£6	
Step Into Our Life	LP	Polydor	2391380	1978	£4	£10	
Ubiquity	LP	Polydor	PD6046	1975	£5	£12	US
Vibrations	LP	Polydor	2391256	1976	£4	£10	

Virgo Vibes	LP	Atlantic	SD1488	1967	£8	£20	US
You Send Me	LP	Polydor	2391365	1978	£4	£10	

AYLER, ALBERT

Ghosts	LP	Fontana	SFJL925	1969	£6	£15	
Spiritual Unity	LP	Fontana	SFJL933	1969	£6	£15	

AYSHEA

Another Night	7"	Polydor	56302	1969	£1.50	£4	
Lift Off With Ayshea	LP	DJM	DJLPS445	1974	£5	£12	
Only Your Love Can Save Me	7"	Polydor	56276	1968	£4	£8	
Peep My Love	7"	Fontana	TF627	1965	£1.50	£4	

AZTEC CAMERA

Just Like Gold	7"	Postcard	81-3	1981	£6	£12	
Just Like Gold	7"	Postcard	81-3	1981	£7.50	£15	lyric postcard
Mattress Of Wire	7"	Postcard	81-8	1981	£7.50	£15	PS
Oblivious (Langer/Winstanley remix)	7"	Rainhill	ACFC1	1983	£5	£10	
Pillar To Post	7"	Rough Trade	RT112P	1982	£2.50	£6	pic disc
Still On Fire	7"	WEA	AC2P	1984	£2	£5	shaped pic disc

AZTECS

Live At The Ad-Lib Club	LP	World Artists	WAM2001	1964	£25	£50	US

AZZAM, BOB

Mustapha	7"	Decca	F21235	1960	£1.50	£4	chart single

B

B-52'S
Future Generation	7"	Island	ISD107	1983	£2.50	£6	double
Planet Claire	7"	Island	WIP6551	1980	£1.50	£4	pic disc
Rock Lobster	7"	Boofant	DB52	1978	£5	£10	US
Rock Lobster	7"	Island	BFTP1/BFTL1/ BFTR1	1986	£6	£12	set of 3 rectangular pic discs
Rock Lobster	7"	Island	PSR438	1979	£2	£5	
Strobe Light	7"	Island	WIP6665	1980	£1.50	£4	plastic sleeve
Wild Planet	LP	Island	ILPS9622	1980	£5	£12	with carrying bag, badge

BABASIN, HARRY
For Moderns Only	LP	Emarcy	EJL1265	1958	£8	£20	

BABE RUTH
Amar Caballero	LP	Harvest	SHVL812	1973	£4	£10	
Babe Ruth	LP	Harvest	SHSP4038	1975	£4	£10	

BABY
Baby	LP	Lone Star	6264	1974	£5	£12	US

BABY HUEY
Living Legend	LP	Curtom	CRS8007	1970	£10	£25	US

BABY LEMONADE
Secret Goldfish	7"	Narodnik	NRK004	1987	£1.50	£4	

BABY RAY & THE FERNS
The single by Baby Ray And The Ferns is one of the early steps in the career of Frank Zappa, who wrote the songs on both sides.
How's Your Bird?	7"	Donna	1378	1963	£50	£100	US

BABY SUNSHINE
Baby Sunshine	LP	Deroy	DER1301	1975	£30	£60	

BACH TWO BACH
Bach Two Bach	LP	Mushroom	100MR10	1971	£50	£100	

BACHARACH, BURT
Alfie	7"	A&M	AMS702	1969	£5	£10	
Casino Royale	LP	RCA	RD/SF7874	1967	£10	£25	

BACHDENKEL
Lemmings	LP	Initial	IRL001	1977	£4	£10	
Lemmings	LP	Initial	IRL001	1977	£8	£20	with 7'
Stalingrad	LP	Initial	IRL002	1977	£4	£10	

BACHELOR, JOHNNY
Mumbles	7"	London	HLN9074	1960	£15	£30	

BACHELORS
Ding Ding	7"	Parlophone	R4547	1959	£4	£8	
Platter Party	7"	Parlophone	R4454	1958	£4	£8	

BACHELORS (2)
Lovin' Babe	7"	Decca	F11300	1960	£1.50	£4	

BACHMAN-TURNER OVERDRIVE
You Ain't Seen Nothin' Yet	7"	Phonogram	DJ013	1974	£2	£5	promo with spoken intro

BACK ALLEY CHOIR
Back Alley Choir	LP	York	FYK406	1972	£75	£150	
Nursery Rhyme Song	7"	York	SYK547	1973	£7.50	£15	
Smile Born Of Courtesy	7"	York	SYK517	1972	£7.50	£15	

BACK DOOR
Back Door	LP	Blakey	BLP5989	1972	£8	£20	

BACK PORCH MAJORITY
Ramblin' Man	7"	Columbia	DB7627	1965	£1.50	£4	

BACKBEAT PHILHARMONIC
Rock And Roll Symphony	7"	Top Rank	JAR576	1961	£2	£5	

BACKUS, JIM
Delicious	7"	London	HLJ8674	1958	£2.50	£6	

BACON FAT
Evil	7"	Blue Horizon	573181	1971	£2.50	£6	
Grease One For Me	LP	Blue Horizon	763858	1970	£15	£30	
Nobody But You	7"	Blue Horizon	573171	1970	£2.50	£6	
Tough Dude	LP	Blue Horizon	2431001	1971	£20	£40	

BACON, GAR

Chains Of Love	7"	Felsted	AF107	1958	£4	£8	
Marshall Marshall	7"	Fontana	H196	1959	£10	£20	

BAD COMPANY

Deal With The Preacher	7"	Island	BCDJ1	1976	£12.50	£25	1 sided promo

BADFINGER

Apple Of My Eye	7"	Apple	49	1974	£4	£8	
Ass	LP	Apple	SAPCOR27	1974	£8	£20	
Badfinger	LP	Warner Bros	K56023	1974	£4	£10	
Come And Get It	7"	Apple	20	1969	£4	£8	PS
Day After Day	7"	Apple	40	1972	£5	£10	PS
Magic Christian Music	LP	Apple	SAPCOR12	1970	£15	£30	
No Dice	LP	Apple	SAPCOR16	1970	£10	£25	
No Matter What	7"	Apple	31	1970	£5	£10	PS
Straight Up	LP	Apple	SAPCOR19	1972	£15	£30	
Wish You Were Here	LP	Warner Bros	K56076	1974	£10	£25	

BADGE

Silver Woman	7"	Metal Minded	MM2	1981	£7.50	£15	

BADGER

Badger was the group formed by Tony Kaye after his departure from Yes. "One Live Badger" has a pop-up cover - a badger (naturally) stands up when the gatefold sleeve is opened.

One Live Badger	LP	Atlantic	K40473	1973	£6	£15	

BADGER'S MATE

Brighter Than Usual	LP	Cottage	COT521	197-	£8	£20	

BAEZ, JOAN

Any Day Now	LP	Vanguard	VSD79306/7	1968	£5	£12	double
Baptism	LP	Vanguard	SVRL19000	1968	£4	£10	
Blessed Are	LP	Vanguard	VSD6570/1	1971	£5	£12	double
Carry It On	LP	Vanguard	VSD519042	1972	£4	£10	
Come From The Shadows	LP	A&M	AMLH64339	1972	£4	£10	
David's Album	LP	Vanguard	SVRL19050	1969	£4	£10	
Don't Think Twice	7" EP	Fontana	TFE18007	1964	£2	£5	
Farewell Angelina	LP	Fontana	(S)TFL6058	1965	£4	£10	chart LP
Farewell Angelina	7"	Fontana	TF639	1965	£1.50	£4	chart single
First Ten Years	LP	Vanguard	VSD6560	1970	£5	£12	double
Gracias A La Vida	LP	A&M	AMLH63614	1974	£4	£10	
Hard Rain's Gonna Fall	7" EP	Fontana	TFE18013	1966	£2	£5	
In Concert	LP	Fontana	(S)TFL6033	1962	£4	£10	
In Concert 2	LP	Fontana	(S)TFL6035	1963	£4	£10	chart LP
It's All Over Now Baby Blue	7"	Fontana	TF604	1965	£1.50	£4	chart single
Joan	LP	Fontana	(S)TFL6082	1967	£4	£10	
Joan Baez	LP	Fontana	(S)TFL6002	1960	£4	£10	chart LP
Joan Baez 2	LP	Fontana	(S)TFL6025	1961	£4	£10	
Joan Baez 5	LP	Fontana	(S)TFL6043	1964	£4	£10	chart LP
Joan Baez No.1	7" EP	Fontana	TFE18000	1964	£2	£5	
Joan Baez No.2	7" EP	Fontana	TFE18001	1964	£2	£5	
Joan Sings Silver Dagger	7" EP	Fontana	TFE18005	1964	£2	£5	
Noel	LP	Fontana	(S)TFL6078	1966	£4	£10	
Once I Had A Sweetheart	7" EP	Fontana	TFE18006	1964	£2	£5	
One Day At A Time	LP	Vanguard	VSD23010	1970	£4	£10	
Portrait	LP	Fontana	(S)TFL6077	1966	£4	£10	
Pretty Boy Floyd	7" EP	Fontana	TFE18008	1965	£2	£5	
There But For Fortune	7"	Fontana	TF587	1965	£1.50	£4	chart single
We Shall Overcome	7"	Fontana	TF564	1965	£1.50	£4	chart single
Where Are You Now My Son	LP	A&M	AMLH64390	1973	£4	£10	
With God On Our Side	7" EP	Fontana	TFE18012	1965	£2	£5	

BAGDASARIAN, ROSS

Crazy, Mixed-Up World	LP	Liberty	LRP3451/LST7451	1966	£6	£15	US

BAGLEY, DON

Jazz On The Rocks	LP	Pye	NPL28008	1959	£8	£20	

BAILEY, BURR

San Francisco Bay	7"	Decca	F11686	1963	£2.50	£6	
You Made Me Cry	7"	Decca	F11846	1964	£5	£10	

BAILEY, BUSTER

All About Memphis	LP	Felsted	FAJ7003	1959	£6	£15	

BAILEY, CLIVE & RICO

Evening Train	7"	Blue Beat	BB92	1961	£5	£10	

BAILEY, DEREK

Duo (with Tristan Hosinger)	LP	Incus	INCUS2	197-	£8	£20	

BAILEY, MILDRED

Mildred Bailey And Her Alley Cats	7" EP	Parlophone	GEP8600	1957	£4	£8	
Rockin' Chair Lady	10" LP	Brunswick	LA8692	1954	£8	£20	

BAILEY, PEARL

She's Something Spanish	7"	Vogue Coral	Q2026	1954	£1.50	£4	
That Certain Feeling	7"	London	HLN8354	1956	£7.50	£15	
That Certain Feeling	7" EP	London	REU1104	1957	£2.50	£6	
Tired	7"	HMV	POP244	1956	£1.50	£4	

BAILEY, ROY

New Bell Wake	LP	Fuse	AC262	1976	£5	£12	
Roy Bailey	LP	Trailer	LER3021	1971	£6	£15	

BAILEY, ROY & LEON ROSSELSON

Love, Loneliness, Laundry	LP	Acorn	CF271	1976	£5	£12	

BAILEY, ROY & VAL & LEON ROSSELSON

Oats And Beans And Kangaroos	LP	Fontana	SFL13061	1968	£10	£25	

BAIN, ALY & MIKE WHELLANS

Aly Bain And Mike Whellans	LP	Trailer	LER2022	1971	£6	£15	

BAIN, ALY & TOM ANDERSON

Shetland Folk Fiddling Vol.1	LP	Topic	12TS281	1976	£5	£12	
Shetland Folk Fiddling Vol.2	LP	Topic	12TS379	1978	£5	£12	

BAIN, BOB

Rockin', Rollin'	LP	Capitol	T965	1958	£15	£30	US

BAIRD, ARTHUR SKIFFLE GROUP

Union Train	7"	Beltona	BL2669	1956	£1.50	£4	

BAKER, CHET

At Ann Arbor	LP	Vogue	LAE12044	1957	£10	£25	
Chet Baker And Crew	LP	Vogue	LAE12076	1958	£8	£20	
Chet Baker And His Crew	LP	Vogue	LAE12076/SEA5005	1958	£10	£25	
Chet Baker And His Crew	7" EP	Vogue	EPV1186	1957	£2	£5	
Chet Baker And Strings	10" LP	Philips	BBL7022	1955	£8	£20	
Chet Baker Ensemble	10" LP	Vogue	LDE163	1956	£15	£30	
Chet Baker Ensemble Vol.1	7" EP	Vogue	EPV1131	1956	£2	£5	
Chet Baker Ensemble Vol.2	7" EP	Vogue	EPV1132	1956	£2	£5	
Chet Baker Plays Standards	7" EP	Felsted	ESD3069	1959	£2	£5	
Chet Baker Quartet	7" EP	Vogue	EPV1007	1954	£2	£5	
Chet Baker Quartet	10" LP	Vogue	LDE045	1954	£15	£30	
Chet Baker Quartet	10" LP	Vogue	LDE116	1955	£15	£30	
Chet Baker Quartet Vol.1	LP	Felsted	PDL85008	1956	£10	£25	
Chet Baker Quartet Vol.2	LP	Felsted	PDL85013	1956	£10	£25	
Chet Baker Sextet	7" EP	Vogue	EPV1121	1956	£2	£5	
Chet Baker Sextet	10" LP	Vogue	LDE159	1955	£15	£30	
Chet Baker Sings	LP	Vogue	LAE12018	1956	£10	£25	
Chet Baker Sings	LP	Vogue	LAE12164	1959	£8	£20	
Chet Baker Sings	10" LP	Vogue	LDE182	1956	£15	£30	
Chet Baker Sings And Plays Vol.1	7" EP	Vogue	EPV1137	1956	£2	£5	
Chet Baker Sings And Plays Vol.2	7" EP	Vogue	EPV1138	1956	£2	£5	
Fabulous Chet Baker Quartet	7" EP	Vogue	EPV1032	1955	£2	£5	
I Get Chet	LP	Felsted	PDL85036	1957	£10	£25	
Michelle	LP	Fontana	TL5326	1966	£5	£12	
Myth	7" EP	Felsted	ESD3034	1957	£2	£5	
Phil's Blues	LP	Vogue	LAE12109	1958	£8	£20	
Playboys	LP	Vogue	LAE12183	1959	£8	£20	with Art Pepper

BAKER, DESMOND

Rude Boy Gone Jail	7"	Island	WI295	1966	£5	£10	Sharks B side

BAKER, GINGER

Eleven Sides Of Baker	LP	Mountain	5005	1977	£4	£10	
Fela Ransome Kuti with Ginger Baker	LP	Regal Zonophone	SLRZ1023	1972	£5	£12	
Stratavarious	LP	Polydor	2383133	1972	£5	£12	

BAKER, JEANETTE

Crazy With You	7"	Vogue	V9143	1959	£30	£60	

BAKER, KENNY

Baker Plays McHugh	10" LP	Pye	NJT517	1959	£5	£12	
Blowin' Up A Storm	10" LP	Columbia	33S1140	1959	£6	£15	
Kenny Baker Half Dozen	LP	Nixa	NJL10	1957	£5	£12	

BAKER, LAVERN

Best Of Lavern	7" EP	Atlantic	AET6009	1965	£12.50	£25	
Best Of Lavern Baker	LP	Atlantic	ATL5002	1964	£25	£50	
Blues Ballads	LP	Atlantic	8030	1959	£20	£40	US
Bumble Bee	7"	London	HLK9252	1960	£7.50	£15	
Game Of Love	7"	London	HLE8442	1957	£40	£80	
Get Up Get Up	7"	London	HLE8260	1956	£40	£80	
Humpty Dumpty Heart	7"	London	HLE8524	1957	£20	£40	
Can't Love You Enough	7"	London	HLE8396	1957	£30	£60	
Cried A Tear	7"	London	HLE8790	1959	£12.50	£25	
I've Waited Too Long	7"	London	HLE8871	1959	£12.50	£25	
Jim Dandy	7"	Columbia	DB3879	1957	£50	£100	
Lavern	LP	Atlantic	8002	1956	£40	£80	US
Lavern Baker	LP	Atlantic	8007	1957	£25	£50	US
Learning To Love	7"	London	HLE8638	1958	£15	£30	
Precious Memories	LP	Atlantic	8036	1959	£20	£40	US
Rock And Roll With Lavern Baker	LP	London	HAE2107	1958	£75	£150	
Saved	LP	London	HAE2422	1961	£25	£50	
Saved	7"	London	HLK9343	1961	£7.50	£15	
See See Rider	LP	Atlantic	587/588133	1968	£6	£15	
See See Rider	LP	London	HAK8074	1963	£20	£40	

See See Rider	7"	London	HLK9649	1963	£7.50	£15	
Sings Bessie Smith	LP	London	LTZK15139	1958	£20	£40	
So High So Low	7"	London	HLE8945	1959	£10	£20	
That Lucky Old Sun	7"	London	HLA8199	1955	£50	£100	
Tiny Tim	7"	London	HLE9023	1960	£10	£20	
Tweedle Dee	7"	Columbia	SCM5172	1955	£50	£100	
Voodoo Voodoo	7"	London	HLK9468	1961	£15	£30	
Whipper Snapper	7"	London	HLE8672	1958	£15	£30	
You're The Boss	7"	London	HLK9300	1961	£6	£12	with Jimmy Ricks

BAKER, MICKEY

But Wild	LP	King	K(S)839	1963	£15	£30	US
In Blunderland	LP	Major Minor	SMLP67	1970	£4	£10	
Wildest Guitar	LP	Atlantic	(SD)8035	1959	£30	£60	US

BAKER, ROBERT

Pardon Me For Being So Friendly	LP	GNP	2027	1966	£6	£15	US

BAKER, SAM

I Believe In You	7"	Monument	MON1009	1968	£4	£8

BAKER, TWO TON

Clink Clank	7"	London	HL8121	1955	£25	£50

BAKERLOO

Bakerloo (originally Bakerloo Blues Line) were one of the many guitarist-led blues groups to surface in the wake of the pioneering work carried out by the various editions of John Mayall's Bluesbreakers. This one featured Dave "Clem" Clempson, whose name has graced many album sleeves since - most notably during his time as a member of Humble Pie.

Bakerloo	LP	Harvest	SHVL762	1969	£30	£60
Driving Backwards	7"	Harvest	HAR5004	1969	£12.50	£25

BAKERLOO JUNCTION

Emigrant's Return	LP	Emerald	GES1187	1978	£5	£12
Next Stop	LP	Emerald	GES1156	1976	£5	£12

BALANCE

Balance	LP	Incus	INCUS11	1973	£10	£25

BALANCE (2)

Balance	LP	Portrait	FTR37357	1981	£8	£20	US
In For The Count	LP	Portrait	PRT85787	1982	£8	£20	US

BALDHEAD GROWLER

Sausage	7"	Jump Up	JU531	1967	£4	£8

BALDO, CHRIS

Living For Your Love	7"	Vogue	VRS7029	1968	£5	£10

BALDRY, LONG JOHN

John Baldry, known as "long" because he is indeed something like six foot six tall, has for most of his career sung the blues, for which his distinctive, smokey voice is an ideal instrument. He is featured on Alexis Korner's "R&B At The Marquee" album, and was a member of Cyril Davies' group. When Davies died, Baldry became the leader of the group, which now became called the Hoochie Coochie Men. The earliest recordings in Baldry's name are by this group. With the switch to Pye, Baldry made what was probably a wrong-career move when he decided to start singing middle-of-the-road ballad material. Four hits followed, but then nothing, and his attempts to recapture his blues audience in the seventies were not very successful.

Cuckoo	7"	United Artists	UP1158	1966	£2	£5	
Cuckoo	7" EP	United Artists	36108	1966	£7.50	£15	French
Drifter	7"	United Artists	UP1136	1966	£7.50	£15	
How Long Will It Last	7"	United Artists	UP1107	1965	£10	£20	
Iko Iko	7"	Warner Bros	K16175	1972	£1.50	£4	
I'm On To You Baby	7"	United Artists	UP1078	1965	£2.50	£6	
Let Him Go	7"	United Artists	UP1204	1967	£2	£5	
Long John Baldry And The Hoochie Coochie Men	LP	Hallmark	HM560	1970	£8	£20	
Long John's Blues	LP	United Artists	ULP1081	1964	£20	£40	
Long John's Blues	7" EP	United Artists	UEP1013	1965	£6	£12	
Looking At Long John	LP	United Artists	(S)ULP1146	1966	£15	£30	
Unseen Hands	7"	United Artists	UP1124	1966	£2.50	£6	
Up Above My Head	7"	United Artists	UP1056	1964	£7.50	£15	

BALDWIN

Land At Rainbow's End	7"	Decca	F22624	1967	£1.50	£4

BALES, BURT

Burt Bales	10" LP	Good Time Jazz	LDG136	1955	£5	£12
Jazz From The San Francisco Waterfront	LP	HMV	CLP1218	1958	£6	£15

BALFOUR, KEITH

Dreaming	7"	Studio One	SO2079	1969	£6	£12

BALIN, MARTY

I Specialize In Love	7"	Challenge	9156	1962	£10	£20	US
Nobody But You	7"	Challenge	9146	1962	£10	£20	US

BALL, KENNY

Waterloo	7"	Collector	JDN101	1959	£5	£10

BALLARD, FLORENCE

Doesn't Matter How I Say It	7"	Stateside	SS2113	1968	£7.50	£15

BALLARD, FRANK

Rhythm And Blues Party	LP	Philips		1985	1962	£150	£250	US

BALLARD, HANK & THE MIDNIGHTERS

1963 Sound Of Hank Ballard	LP	King	815	1963	£10	£25	US
Biggest Hits	LP	King	867	1963	£10	£25	US
Continental Walk	7"	Parlophone	R4771	1961	£5	£10	
Finger Popping Time	7"	Parlophone	R4682	1960	£6	£12	
Glad Songs, Sad Songs	LP	King	927	1966	£8	£20	US
Hoochi Coochi Coo	7"	Parlophone	R4728	1961	£6	£12	Little Willie John B side
Jumpin' Hank Ballard	LP	London	HA8101	1963	£10	£25	
Let's Go Again	LP	King	748	1961	£15	£30	US
Let's Go Again	7"	Parlophone	R4762	1961	£5	£10	
Let's Go Let's Go Let's Go	7"	Parlophone	R4707	1960	£6	£12	
Midnighters	LP	Federal	395541	1956	£75	£150	US
Midnighters	LP	King	395541	1958	£30	£60	US
Midnighters	10" LP	Federal	29590	1954	£180	£300	US
Midnighters Vol.2	LP	Federal	395581	1957	£50	£100	US
Midnighters Vol.2	LP	King	395581	1958	£30	£60	US
Mr.Rhythm And Blues	LP	King	700	1960	£210	£350	US
One And Only Hank Ballard	LP	King	674	1960	£15	£30	US
Sing Along	LP	King	759	1961	£15	£30	US
Singin' And Swingin'	LP	King	618	1959	£15	£30	US
Spotlight On Hank Ballard	LP	Parlophone	PMC1158	1961	£10	£25	
Star In Your Eyes	LP	King	896	1964	£10	£25	US
Those Lazy Lazy Days	LP	King	913	1965	£8	£20	US
Twenty-Four Great Songs	LP	King	981	1968	£6	£15	US
Twenty-Four Hit Tunes	LP	King	950	1966	£8	£20	US
Twist	7"	Parlophone	R4558	1959	£12.50	£25	
Twist	7"	Parlophone	R4688	1960	£7.50	£15	
Twistin' Fools	LP	King	781	1962	£10	£25	US
You Can't Keep A Good Man Down	LP	King	KSD1052	1969	£6	£15	US

BALLOON FARM

Question Of Temperature	7"	London	HLP10185	1968	£20	£40	

BALLS

Much was expected of the alliance between Denny Laine and the Move's Trevor Burton, but in the end, Balls could only manage one single. This was later reissued under Burton's name.

Fight For My Country	7"	Wizard	WIZ101	1971	£5	£10	

BALTIK

Baltik	LP	CBS	65581	1973	£15	£30	Swedish

BALTIMORE & OHIO MARCHING BAND

Lapland	LP	Stateside	SL/SSL10231	1968	£10	£25	
Lapland	7"	Stateside	SS2065	1967	£30	£60	

BAMA WINDS

Windy	LP	Island	ILPS9096	1969	£5	£12	

BAMBIS

Baby Blue	7"	CBS	201778	1965	£5	£10	
Not Wrong	7"	Oriole	CB1965	1964	£6	£12	

BAMBOO SHOOTS

Fox Has Gone To Ground	7"	Columbia	DB8370	1968	£35	£70	

BANANAMEN (CRAMPS)

Crusher	7"	Big Beat	NS88	1983	£1.50	£4	

BANANARAMA

Aie A Mwana	7"	Demon	D1010	1981	£4	£8	
Aie A Mwana	7"	Deram	DM446	1981	£2	£5	
Aie A Mwana	12"	Deram	DMX446	1981	£3	£8	

BANCO

Banco Del Mutuo Soccorso	LP	Orizzonte	ORL8041	1972	£5	£12	Italian
Carofano Rosso	LP	Orizzonte	ORL8334	1976	£5	£12	Italian
Come In Un Ultima Cena	LP	Manticore	28004	1976	£10	£25	
Darwin	LP	Orizzonte	ORL8094	1972	£8	£20	Italian
Lo Sono Nato Libero	LP	Orizzonte	ORL8202	1973	£10	£25	Italian

BAND

Band	LP	Capitol	EST132	1969	£4	£10	chart LP
Cahoots	LP	Capitol	EAST651	1971	£4	£10	chart LP
Islands	LP	Capitol	EST11602	1977	£4	£10	
Jabberwocky	7"	Capitol	2041	1968	£5	£10	US
Moondog Matinee	LP	Capitol	ESW11241	1973	£6	£15	
Music From Big Pink	LP	Capitol	(S)T2955	1968	£4	£10	
Northern Lights Southern Cross	LP	Capitol	EST11440	1975	£4	£10	
Rag Mama Rag	7"	Capitol	CL15629	1970	£1.50	£4	chart single
Rock Of Ages	LP	Capitol	ESTSP1	1972	£6	£15	double
Stage Fright	LP	Capitol	EASW425	1970	£4	£10	chart LP
Up On Cripple Creek	7"	Capitol	CL15613	1969	£1.50	£4	
Weight	7"	Capitol	CL15559	1968	£1.50	£4	chart single

BAND AID

Do They Know It's Christmas?	7"	Mercury	FEEDP1	1985	£2	£5	shaped pic disc

BAND OF ANGELS

A Band Of Angels wore straw boaters to emphasise their Harrow origins, and it would have been surprising if at least some of them had not achieved success. First up was singer Mike D'Abo, who became the lead singer with Manfred Mann after the departure of Paul Jones. Later, however, the group's guitarist and manager founded EG management, amongst whose signings were King Crimson and Roxy Music.

Gonna Make A Woman Of You	7"	United Artists	UP1066	1964	£6	£12
Invitation	7"	Piccadilly	7N35292	1966	£7.50	£15
Invitation	7" EP	Pye	PNV24162	1966	£15	£30 ...... French
Leave It To Me	7"	Piccadilly	7N35279	1966	£6	£12
Not True As Yet	7"	United Artists	UP1049	1964	£6	£12
She'll Never Be You	7" EP	United Artists	36050	1964	£15	£30 ...... French

BAND OF MERCY & SALVATION

Suffering Stink	7"	Duke	DU20	1969	£2.50	£6

BANDOGGS

Bandoggs	LP	Transatlantic	LTRA504	1978	£6	£15

BANGOR FLYING CIRCUS

Bangor Flying Circus	LP	Stateside	SSL5022	1969	£4	£10

BANGS

Debbi and Vicki Peterson and Susanna Hoffs first recorded as the Bangs, before expanding both the size of the group and its name - becoming the Bangles.

Getting Out Of Hand	7"	Downkiddie	001	1981	£12.50	£25 ...... US

BANJO BOYS

Hey Mr.Banjo	7"	Capitol	CL14298	1955	£1.50	£4

BANJO KINGS

Nostalgia Revisited	LP	Good Time Jazz	LAG12174	1959	£5	£12

BANKS, BESSIE

Go Now	7"	Red Bird	BC106	1964	£10	£20
Go Now	7"	Soul City	SC105	1968	£4	£8
I Can't Make It	7"	Verve	VS563	1967	£10	£20

BANKS, DARRELL

Angel Baby	7"	Atlantic	584120	1967	£7.50	£15
Here To Stay	LP	Stax	SXATS1011	1969	£5	£12
Just Because Your Love Is Gone	7"	Stax	STAX124	1969	£10	£20
Open The Door To Your Heart	7"	London	HL10070	1966	£100	£200 ...... demo only
Open The Door To Your Heart	7"	Stateside	SS536	1966	£6	£12

BANKS, HOMER

Hooked By Love	7"	Liberty	LIB12060	1967	£6	£12
Lot Of Love	7"	Liberty	LIB12028	1966	£7.50	£15
Me Or Your Mama	7"	Minit	MLF11015	1969	£2	£5
Round The Clock Lover Man	7"	Minit	MLF11004	1968	£2	£5
Sixty Minutes Of Your Love	7"	Liberty	LBF15392	1970	£2	£5
Sixty Minutes Of Your Love	7"	Liberty	LIB12047	1967	£6	£12
Sixty Minutes Of Your Love	7"	Minit	MLF11007	1968	£2	£5

BANKS, LARRY

I Don't Wanna Do It	7"	Stateside	SS579	1967	£4	£8

BANKS, LLOYD

We'll Meet Again	7"	Reaction	591008	1966	£2.50	£6

BANKS, PETER

Peter Banks	LP	Sovereign	SVNA7256	1973	£8	£20
Peter Banks & Jan Akkerman	LP	Sovereign	SVNA7250	1972	£8	£20

BANKS, ROSE

Darling Baby	7"	Tamla Motown	TMG1037	1976	£1.50	£4

BANNED

Little Girl	7"	Can't Eat	EAT1UP	1977	£4	£8

BANSHEES

The Banshees' "I Got A Woman" is one of a number of classic beat singles that somehow failed to achieve chart success, although the group's singer re-emerged for a very successful career throughout the seventies. His name was Bryan Ferry.

Big Buildin'	7"	Columbia	DB7530	1965	£7.50	£15
I Got A Woman	7"	Columbia	DB7361	1964	£12.50	£25
Yes Indeed	7"	Columbia	DB7752	1965	£10	£20

BANTAMS

Beware The Bantams	LP	Warner Bros	W(S)1625	1966	£6	£15 ...... US
Over You	7" EP	Warner Bros	WEP1448	1966	£7.50	£15 ...... French

BARA MENYN

Bara Menyn	7" EP	Wren	WRE1065	1969	£7.50	£15
Rhagor O'r Bara Menyn	7" EP	Wren	WRE1072	1969	£7.50	£15

BARBARA & BRENDA

Never Love A Robin	7"	Direction	583799	1968	£4	£8

BARBARIANS

Are You A Boy Or Are You A Girl	7"	Stateside	SS449	1965	£6	£12
Are You A Boy Or Are You A Girl	7" EP	Vogue	INT18027	1965	£50	£100 ...... French
Are You A Boy Or Are You A Girl?	LP	Laurie	LLP/SLP2033	1966	£25	£50 ...... US
Moulty	7"	Stateside	SS497	1966	£5	£10

BARBARIN, PAUL

New Orleans Band	10" LP	Vogue	LDE013	1952	£8	£20
New Orleans Jazz	LP	London	LTZK15032	1957	£6	£15

BARBARIN, PAUL & PUNCH MILLER

Jazz At Preservation Hall Vol.4	LP	London	HAK/SHK8164	1964	£4	£10

BARBECUE BOB

Georgia Blues No.1	LP	Kokomo	K1002	1967	£20	£40

BARBEE, JOHN HENRY

Portraits In Blues Vol.9	LP	Storyville	670171	1967	£5	£12

BARBER, CHRIS

American Jazz Band	LP	Columbia	33SX1321/ SCX3376	1961	£4	£10	
Band Box Vol.1	LP	Columbia	33SX1158	1959	£4	£10	
Band Box Vol.2	LP	Columbia	33SX1245/ SCX3319	1960	£4	£10	
Barber's Best	LP	Decca	LK4246	1958	£4	£10	
Battersea Rain Dance	LP	Marmalade	608009	1969	£8	£20	
Battersea Rain Dance	LP	Polydor	2384020	197-	£5	£12	
Battersea Rain Dance	7"	Marmalade	598013	1969	£1.50	£4	
Best Of Chris Barber	LP	Ace Of Clubs	ACL1037	1960	£4	£10	
Blues Book	LP	Columbia	33SX1333/ SCX3384	1961	£4	£10	
Bobby Shafto	7"	Decca	F10492	1955	£1.50	£4	
Can't You Line 'Em	7"	Pye	7NJ2017	1958	£1.50	£4	
Catcall	7"	Marmalade	598005	1967	£15	£30	
Chimes Blues	7"	Decca	F10417	1954	£1.50	£4	
Chris Barber Plays Vol.1	10" LP	Nixa	NJT500	1956	£5	£12	
Chris Barber Plays Vol.1	10" LP	Polygon	JTL3	1955	£8	£20	
Chris Barber Plays Vol.2	10" LP	Nixa	NJT502	1956	£5	£12	
Chris Barber Plays Vol.3	10" LP	Nixa	NJT505	1957	£5	£12	
Chris Barber Plays Vol.4	10" LP	Nixa	NJT508	1957	£5	£12	
Chris Barber Skiffle Group	7" EP	Pye	NJE1025	1957	£6	£12	
Doin' My Time	7"	Pye	7NJ2014	1958	£1.50	£4	
Echoes Of Harlem	LP	Nixa	NJL1	1955	£5	£12	
Everybody Loves My Baby	78	Esquire	10180	1951	£1.50	£4	
Finishing Straight	7"	Columbia	DB7461	1965	£7.50	£15	
High Society	7"	Pye	7NJ2007	1958	£1.50	£4	
I Never Knew Just What A Girl Could Do	7"	Decca	FJ10790	1956	£1.50	£4	
Ice Cream	7"	Tempo		1957	£1.50	£4	
In Berlin Vol.1	LP	Columbia	33SX1189	1959	£4	£10	
In Berlin Vol.2	LP	Columbia		1959	£4	£10	
In Concert	LP	Nixa	NJL6	1957	£4	£10	
In Concert Vol.2	LP	Pye	NJL15	1958	£4	£10	
In Concert Vol.3	LP	Pye	NJL17	1958	£4	£10	
In Copenhagen	LP	Columbia	33SX1274/ SCX3342	1961	£4	£10	
It's Tight Like That	7"	Decca	F10666	1955	£1.50	£4	
Jazz Sacred And Secular	10" LP	Columbia	33S1112	1957	£8	£20	
Lonesome	7"	Columbia	DB4333	1959	£1.50	£4	chart single
New Orleans Joys	10" LP	Decca	LF1198	1954	£8	£20	
Oh Didn't He Ramble	78	Esquire	12013	1951	£1.50	£4	
Petite Fleur	7"	Pye	7NJ2026	1959	£1.50	£4	chart single
Plus/Minus One	7" EP	Polygon	JTE103	1956	£2.50	£6	
Saratoga Swing	7"	Tempo	A132	1956	£1.50	£4	
Tiger Rag	7"	Tempo	A116	1956	£1.50	£4	
Tuxedo Rag	7"	Pye	7NJ2004	1958	£1.50	£4	
When The Saints Go Marching In	7"	Pye	7NJ2023	1958	£1.50	£4	
Whistlin' Rufus	7"	Pye	7NJ2011	1958	£1.50	£4	
World Is Waiting For The Sunrise	7"	Decca	FJ10724	1956	£1.50	£4	

BARBER, FRANK

Flyover	7"	Ember	JBS709	1962	£1.50	£4

BARBOUR, DAVE

Tough	7"	Oriole	CB1507	1959	£1.50	£4

BARCLAY, EDDIE

Eddie And Quincy	LP	Felsted	PDL85056	1959	£4	£10	with Quincy Jones
James Dean - Music From His Films	7" EP	Felsted	ESD3041	1957	£2.50	£6	

BARCLAY JAMES HARVEST

Barclay James Harvest	LP	Harvest	SHVL770	1970	£4	£10	
Breathless	7"	Harvest	HAR5095	1975	£1.50	£4	
Brother Thrush	7"	Harvest	HAR5003	1969	£4	£8	
Early Morning	7"	Parlophone	R5693	1968	£6	£12	
I'm Over You	7"	Harvest	HAR5051	1972	£2	£5	
Just A Day Away	7"	Polydor	POPPX585	1983	£2.50	£6	shaped pic disc
Mocking Bird	7"	Harvest	HAR5034	1971	£2	£5	
Once Again	LP	Harvest	Q4SHVL0788	1971	£6	£15	quad
Rock And Roll Woman	7"	Harvest	HAR5068	1973	£2	£5	PS
Taking Some Time On	7"	Harvest	HAR5025	1970	£2	£5	
Thank You	7"	Harvest	HAR5058	1972	£2	£5	
Victims Of Circumstance	7"	Polydor	POSPP674	1984	£2.50	£6	pic disc

BARCLAY, RUE & PEGGY DUNCAN
Tongue Tied Boy	7"	London	HL8033	1954	£7.50	£15	

BARDENS, PETER
Answer	LP	Transatlantic	TRA222	1970	£6	£15	
Peter Bardens	LP	Transatlantic	TRA243	1971	£6	£15	

BARDOT, BRIGITTE
Harley Davidson	7"	Pye	7N25450	1968	£2	£5	
Mr.Sun	7"	Vogue	VRS7018	1966	£2	£5	
Mr.Sun	7"	Vogue	VRS7018	1966	£4	£8	PS

BARE, BOBBY
Above And Beyond	7"	RCA	RCA1302	1962	£1.50	£4	
Detroit City	7"	RCA	RCA1352	1963	£1.50	£4	
Detroit City	7" EP.	RCA	RCX7139	1964	£2	£5	
Five Hundred Miles Away From Home	LP	RCA	LPM/LSP2835	1963	£4	£10	US
Five Hundred Miles Away From Home	7"	RCA	RCA1366	1963	£1.50	£4	
I'm Hanging Up My Rifle	7"	Top Rank	JAR310	1960	£2.50	£6	
Jeannie's Last Kiss	7"	RCA	RCA1387	1964	£1.50	£4	

BARGE, GENE
Dance With Daddy G	LP	Checker	2994	1965	£8	£20	US

BARHAM, TINY
Tiny Barham	10" LP	Audubon		195-	£8	£20	

BARKAN, MARK
Pity The Woman	7"	Stateside	SS2064	1967	£4	£8	

BARKAYS
Black Rock	LP	Polydor	2362003	1971	£5	£12	
Cold Blooded	LP	Stax	STX1033	1976	£4	£10	
Do You See What I See?	LP	Polydor	2325087	1972	£4	£10	
Give Everybody Some	7"	Stax	601025	1967	£1.50	£4	
Gotta Groove	LP	Stax	STATS1009	1969	£5	£12	
Hard Day's Night	7"	Stax	601036	1968	£1.50	£4	
Soul Finger	LP	Atco	228030	1969	£5	£12	
Soul Finger	LP	Atlantic	K40184	1972	£4	£10	
Soul Finger	7"	Atlantic	584244	1969	£1.50	£4	
Soul Finger	7"	Stax	601014	1967	£2	£5	chart single

BARKER, DAVE
Prisoner Of Love	LP	Trojan	TRL127	1976	£6	£15	
Prisoner Of Love	7"	Punch	PH20	1970	£1.50	£4	Busty & Upsetters B side
Shock Of Might	7"	Punch	PH25	1970	£1.50	£4	
Shocks Of Mighty	7"	Upsetter	US331	1970	£2	£5	
Some Sympathy	7"	Upsetter	US344	1970	£2	£5	Untouchables B side
You Betray Me	7"	Punch	PH22	1970	£1.50	£4	

BARNES, BARNEY J. & THE INTRO
It Must Be Love	7"	Decca	F12662	1967	£1.50	£4	

BARNES, J.J.
Baby Please Come Back Home	7"	Stax	STAX130	1969	£4	£8	
Daytripper	7"	Polydor	56722	1967	£5	£10	
Real Humdinger	7"	Tamla Motown	TMG870	1973	£1.50	£4	

BARNES, J.J. & STEVE MANCHA
Rare Stamps	LP	Stax	SXATS1012	1969	£8	£20	

BARNES, LLOYD
Time Is Hard	7"	Blue Beat	BB235	1963	£5	£10	Buster's Allstars B side

BARNES, MAE
Songs By Mae Barnes	10" LP	Atlantic	ALS404	195-	£37.50	£75	US

BARNES, MYRA
Message For The Soul Sisters	12"	Urban		1988	£2.50	£6	

BARNET, CHARLIE
Cherokee	LP	Top Rank	35037	1960	£4	£10	
Classics In Jazz	LP	Capitol	LCT6018	1955	£8	£20	
Dance Session	10" LP	Columbia	33C9024	1956	£8	£20	
Hop On The Skyliner	LP	Brunswick	LAT8094	1956	£8	£20	

BARNET, ERIC
Horse	7"	Gas	GAS100	1969	£2.50	£6	
Quaker City	7"	Crab	CRAB37	1969	£2.50	£6	
Te Ta Toe	7"	Gas	GAS106	1969	£2.50	£6	Milton Boothe B side

BARNETT, BARRY
All I Have To Do Is Dream	7"	HMV	POP487	1958	£1.50	£4	
My Lucky Love	7"	HMV	POP521	1958	£1.50	£4	
Susie Darlin'	7"	HMV	POP532	1958	£1.50	£4	
When	7"	HMV	POP511	1958	£1.50	£4	

BARNUM, H.B.
Big Voice Of Barnum	LP	RCA	RD/SF7500	1962	£5	£12	

Everybody Loves H.B.	LP	RCA	RD/SF7543	1963	£5	£12
Great	7" EP	RCA	RCX7147	1964	£10	£20
Lost Love	7"	Fontana	H299	1961	£2	£5
Record	7"	Capitol	CL15391	1965	£5	£10

BAROCK & ROLL ENSEMBLE

"Eine Kleine Beatlemusik" by the Barock and Roll Ensemble consists of tunes written by the Beatles arranged for a small group of strings a though the music was by Mozart. The joke - perpetrated by musicologist Fritz Spiegl - is a good one, and the record works as music too. Th B side is less successful, however; Spiegl knows his Mozart but not his rock music and his arrangements of themes by Wagner as if they we pieces by the Shadows are simply feeble.

Eine Kleine Beatlemusik	7" EP	HMV	7EG8887	1965	£2.50	£6

BARON & HIS POUNDING PIANO

Is A Bluebird Blue	7"	Sue	WI398	1965	£10	£20	with the V.I.P.'

BARON, CARL & THE CHEETAHS

Beg Borrow Or Steal	7"	Columbia	DB7162	1963	£2.50	£6

BARONS

Don't Walk Out	7"	London	HLP8391	1957	£250	£400

BARONS (2)

Cossack	7"	Oriole	CB1608	1961	£4	£8
Samurai	7"	Oriole	CB1620	1961	£4	£8

BAROQUES

Baroques	LP	Chess	(S)1516	1967	£8	£20	US

BARRACUDAS

Plane View	LP	Justice	143	1968	£37.50	£75	US

BARRACUDAS (2)

1965 Again	7"	Zonophone	Z11	1980	£2.50	£6	
His Last Summer	7"	Zonophone	Z8	1980	£2.50	£6	
I Can't Pretend	7"	Zonophone	Z17	1981	£2.50	£6	
I Want My Woody Back	7"	Cells	CELLOUT1	1979	£4	£8	
Inside Mind	7"	Flicknife	FLS207	1982	£1.50	£4	
Summer Fun	7"	Zonophone	Z5	1980	£2.50	£6	with sticker sheet

BARRETT, RICHARD

Come Softly To Me	7"	HMV	POP609	1959	£2.50	£6

BARRETT, RITCHIE

Some Other Guy	7"	London	HLK9552	1962	£10	£20

BARRETT, SYD

Syd Barrett was eased out of the Pink Floyd due to his increasingly unreliable behaviour - a guitarist with a tendency to stand still on stage without actually playing anything was something of a liability. Nevertheless, the rest of the Floyd bore him no malice and were happy to turn up to lend support to Barrett's solo recordings (as did Soft Machine too). Whether these records are the work of a brilliant eccentric or merely the last gasp of semi-coherency from an unmitigated loony probably depends on the listener's point of view.

Barrett	LP	Harvest	SHSP4007	1970	£6	£15	chart LP
Madcap Laughs	LP	Harvest	SHVL765	1970	£6	£15	chart LP
Octopus	7"	Harvest	HAR5009	1969	£30	£60	

BARRETTO, RAY

Acid	LP	London	HA/SH8383	1969	£6	£15
Acid	7"	London	HL10262	1969	£2	£5
El Watusi	LP	Island	ILP946	1967	£20	£40
El Watusi	7"	Columbia	DB7051	1963	£4	£8
El Watusi	7"	Columbia	DB7684	1965	£2	£5

BARRIER

Georgie Brown	7"	Eyemark	EMS1013	1968	£20	£40
Spot The Lights	7"	Philips	BF1731	1968	£7.50	£15
Tide Is Turning	7"	Philips	BF1692	1968	£4	£8

BARRINO BROTHERS

I Shall Not Be Moved	7"	Invictus	INV523	1972	£2.50	£6

BARRON KNIGHTS

Barron Knights	LP	Columbia	SX6007	1966	£5	£12	
Call Up The Groups	LP	Columbia	33SX1648	1964	£6	£15	
Call Up The Groups	7"	Columbia	DB7317	1964	£1.50	£4	chart single
Come To The Dance	7"	Columbia	DB7375	1964	£1.50	£4	chart single
Coming Home Baby	7"	Columbia	DB7188	1964	£1.50	£4	
Guying The Top Pops	7" EP	Columbia	SEG8424	1965	£2.50	£6	
House Of Johann Strauss	7"	Columbia	DB7427	1964	£1.50	£4	
Jo Anne	7"	Columbia	DB7108	1963	£1.50	£4	
Lazy Fat People	7" EP	Festival	FX1537	196-	£7.50	£15	French
Merry Gentle Pops	7"	Columbia	DB7780	1965	£1.50	£4	chart single
Never Miss A Chance	7"	Fontana	H368	1962	£1.50	£4	
Olympic Record	7"	Columbia	DB8485	1968	£1.50	£4	chart single
Pop Go The Workers	7"	Columbia	DB7525	1965	£1.50	£4	chart single
Popumentary '71	7"	Penny Farthing	PEN777	1971	£1.50	£4	
Scribed	LP	Columbia	SX/SCX6176	1967	£4	£10	
Those Versatile Barron Knights	7" EP	Columbia	SEG8526	1966	£2.50	£6	
Under New Management	7"	Columbia	DB8071	1966	£1.50	£4	chart single

BARROW POETS

The Barrow Poets were a poetry and music group, a little like the Liverpool Scene, but with much less of a rock sound. Where the Liverpool Scene played on the John Peel programme, the Barrow Poets would have turned up on Radio Four. Essentially the records are an extension of the fifties and sixties jazz-and-poetry experiments, in which the words are by far the most important element. Fortunately, they are always well worth hearing.

Title	Format	Label	Cat. No.	Year			Notes
At The Printer's Devil	7" EP	Barrow	BR1	1967	£12.50	£25	
Entertainment Of Poetry And Music	LP	Argo	PLP1072	197-	£8	£20	
Folk Rhymes Tunes And Verses	LP	Fontana	STL5479	1968	£10	£25	
Joker	LP	RCA	SF8110	1970	£8	£20	
Letter In A Bottle	7"	Fontana	TF939	1968	£2	£5	
Magic Egg	LP	Argo	ZSW511	1972	£8	£20	
Outpatients	LP	Argo	ZSW508	1972	£8	£20	

BARRY & THE TAMERLANES

Title	Format	Label	Cat. No.	Year			Notes
Butterfly	7"	Warner Bros	WB124	1964	£1.50	£4	
Don't Go	7"	Warner Bros	WB116	1963	£1.50	£4	
Wonder What She's Doing Tonight	LP	A&M	W406	1963	£20	£40	US
What She's Doing Tonight	7" EP	Warner Bros	WEP1429	1964	£7.50	£15	French

BARRY, DAVE & SARAH BERNER

Title	Format	Label	Cat. No.	Year			Notes
Out Of This World With Flying Saucers	7"	London	HLU8324	1956	£20	£40	

BARRY, JOE

Title	Format	Label	Cat. No.	Year			Notes
Fool To Care	7" EP	Mercury	ZEP10130	1962	£12.50	£25	
I Started Loving You Again	7"	Stateside	SS2127	1969	£2.50	£6	
I'm A Fool To Care	7"	Mercury	AMT1149	1961	£2	£5	chart single

BARRY, JOHN

Title	Format	Label	Cat. No.	Year			Notes
007	7"	Ember	EMBS243	1967	£2	£5	
007	7"	Ember	EMBS243	1967	£4	£8	PS
Adventurer	7"	Polydor	2058275	1972	£1.50	£4	
Americans	LP	Polydor	2383405	1976	£6	£15	
Barry Theme Successes	7" EP	Columbia	SEG8255	1963	£5	£10	
Beat For Beatniks	7"	Columbia	DB4446	1960	£1.50	£4	chart single
Big Beat	7" EP	Parlophone	GEP8737	1958	£10	£20	
Big Guitar	7"	Parlophone	R4418	1958	£7.50	£15	
Black Stockings	7"	Columbia	DB4554	1960	£1.50	£4	chart single
Boom	LP	MCA	MUPS360	1969	£37.50	£75	
Chase	LP	CBS	(S)BPG62665	1966	£5	£12	
Concert John Barry	LP	Polydor	2383156	1971	£5	£12	
Cutty Sark	LP	Columbia	DB4806	1962	£1.50	£4	chart single
Deadfall	LP	Stateside	(S)SL10263	1968	£5	£12	
Diamonds Are For Ever	LP	United Artists	UAS29216	1971	£5	£12	
Diamonds Are For Ever	7"	Polydor	2058216	1972	£2.50	£6	
Every Which Way	7"	Parlophone	R4394	1958	£7.50	£15	
Farrago	7"	Parlophone	R4488	1958	£1.50	£4	
From Russia With Love	LP	United Artists	(S)ULP1052	1963	£6	£15	
From Russia With Love	7"	Ember	EMBS181	1963	£1.50	£4	chart single
From Russia With Love	7"	Ember	EMBS181	1963	£4	£8	PS
From Russia With Love	7" EP	United Artists	UEP1011	1965	£7.50	£15	
Goldfinger	LP	United Artists	(S)ULP1076	1964	£5	£12	
Goldfinger	7"	United Artists	UP1068	1964	£1.50	£4	
Goldfinger	7" EP	United Artists	UEP1012	1965	£7.50	£15	
Hit And Miss	7"	Columbia	DB4414	1960	£2	£5	chart single
Human Jungle	7"	Columbia	DB7003	1963	£1.50	£4	
Human Jungle	7"	Columbia	DB7003	1963	£5	£10	PS
Ingersoll Trendsetters	7"	Lyntone	LYN378	196-	£5	£10	flexi
Ipcress File	LP	CBS	BPG62530	1966	£8	£20	
James Bond Collection	LP	United Artists	UAD60027/8	1973	£6	£15	Double
James Bond Is Back	7" EP	Ember	EMBEP4551	1964	£5	£10	
James Bond Theme	7"	CBS	WB730	1968	£2	£5	Ray Conniff B side
James Bond Theme	7"	Columbia	DB4898	1962	£1.50	£4	chart single
John Barry Sound	7" EP	Columbia	SEG8069	1961	£7.50	£15	
Kinky	7"	Ember	EMBS178	1963	£1.50	£4	
Last Valley	LP	Probe	SPB1027	1971	£10	£25	
Lion In Winter	LP	CBS	70049	1968	£5	£12	
Lion In Winter	7"	CBS	3935	1969	£6	£12	
Little John	7"	Parlophone	R4560	1959	£2	£5	
London Theme	7"	Ember	EMBS183	1963	£1.50	£4	
Loneliness Of Autumn	7" EP	Ember	EMBEP4544	1964	£5	£10	
Long John	7"	Parlophone	R4530	1959	£1.50	£4	
Magnificent Seven	7"	Columbia	DB4598	1961	£1.50	£4	chart single
Man Alone	7"	CBS	201747	1965	£2.50	£6	
Man In The Middle	LP	Stateside	(S)SL10087	1964	£10	£25	
Man In The Middle	7"	Stateside	SS296	1964	£5	£10	
March Of The Manderins	7"	Columbia	DB4941	1962	£2	£5	
Meets Chad And Jeremy	LP	Ember	NR5032	1965	£6	£15	
Menace	7"	Columbia	DB4659	1961	£1.50	£4	
Midnight Cowboy	7"	CBS	4468	1969	£1.50	£4	
Music Of John Barry	LP	CBS	22014	1976	£6	£15	Double
Never Let Go	7"	Columbia	DB4480	1960	£1.50	£4	chart single
On Her Majesty's Secret Service	LP	United Artists	UAS29020	1969	£6	£15	
On Her Majesty's Secret Service	7"	CBS	4680	1969	£4	£8	
Pancho	7"	Parlophone	R4453	1958	£2.50	£6	
Play It Again	LP	Polydor	2383300	1974	£5	£12	
Plays 007	LP	Ember	NR5025	1964	£8	£20	
Ready When You Are JB	LP	CBS	63952	1970	£5	£12	
Revisited	LP	Ember	SE8008	1971	£6	£15	
Seance On A Wet Afternoon	7"	United Artists	UP1060	1964	£6	£12	

Title	Format	Label	Catalogue	Year			Notes
Seven Faces	7"	Columbia	DB7414	1964	£6	£12	
Starfire	7"	Columbia	DB4699	1961	£1.50	£4	
Stringbeat	LP	Columbia	33SX1358/ SCX3401	1961	£15	£30	
Syndicate	7"	CBS	201822	1965	£5	£10	
Thunderball	LP	United Artists	(S)ULP1110	1965	£6	£15	
Thunderball	7" EP	United Artists	UEP1015	1966	£6	£12	
Twelfth Street Rag	7"	Parlophone	R4582	1959	£5	£10	
Vendetta	7"	CBS	202390	1966	£1.50	£4	
Walk Don't Run	7"	Columbia	DB4505	1960	£1.50	£4	chart single
Watch Your Step	7"	Columbia	DB4746	1961	£1.50	£4	
Wednesday's Child	7"	CBS	202451	1967	£2.50	£6	
You Only Live Twice	LP	United Artists	(S)ULP1171	1967	£5	£12	
You Only Live Twice	7"	CBS	2825	1967	£2.50	£6	
Zip Zip	7"	Parlophone	R4363	1957	£10	£20	
Zulu	LP	Ember	NR5012	1964	£5	£12	
Zulu Stamp	7"	Ember	EMBS185	1963	£1.50	£4	
Zulu Stamp	7"	Ember	EMBS185	1963	£4	£8	PS

BARRY, LEN

Title	Format	Label	Catalogue	Year			Notes
1-2-3	LP	Brunswick	LAT8637	1965	£6	£15	
1-2-3	7"	Brunswick	05942	1965	£1.50	£4	chart single
1-2-3	7" EP	Brunswick	10672	1965	£6	£12	French
1-2-3	7" EP	Decca	60001	1965	£6	£12	French
4-5-6 Now I'm Alone	7"	Bell	BLL1022	1968	£1.50	£4	
Hearts Are Trumps	7"	Cameo Parkway	P969	1965	£5	£10	
I Struck It Rich	7"	Brunswick	05966	1966	£1.50	£4	
It's A Crying Shame	7" EP	Decca	60005	1966	£5	£10	French
It's That Time Of The Year	7"	Brunswick	05962	1966	£2.50	£6	
Like A Baby	7"	Brunswick	05949	1966	£1.50	£4	chart single
Moving Finger Writes	7"	RCA	RCA1588	1967	£2.50	£6	
My Kind Of Soul	LP	RCA	LSP/LSP3823	1967	£5	£12	US
Sings With The Dovells	LP	Cameo Parkway	C1082	1966	£6	£15	
Somewhere	7"	Brunswick	05955	1966	£1.50	£4	

BARRY, LEN & THE DOVELLS

Title	Format	Label	Catalogue	Year			Notes
Having A Good Time	7" EP	Cameo Parkway	CPE556	1966	£5	£10	

BARRY, MARGARET & MICHAEL GORMAN

Title	Format	Label	Catalogue	Year			Notes
Blarney Stone	LP	XTRA	XTRA5037	1967	£6	£15	
Her Mantle So Green	LP	Topic	12T123	1965	£5	£12	reissue with different sleeve
Her Mantle So Green	LP	Topic		1958	£8	£20	
Ireland's Queen Of The Tinkers Sings	LP	Top Rank	25020	1960	£10	£25	
Margaret Barry And Michael Gorman	LP	Folkways	FW8729	1975	£6	£15	US

BARRY, SANDRA

Title	Format	Label	Catalogue	Year			Notes
End Of The Line	7"	Pye	7N15753	1965	£2	£5	
Question	7"	Pye	7N15840	1965	£2	£5	
Really Gonna Shake	7"	Decca	F11851	1964	£7.50	£15	with The Boys
Stop Thief	7"	Pye	7N17102	1966	£2.50	£6	

BARRY, SANDRA, & THE BOYS

"Really Gonna Shake" by Sandra Barry And The Boys represents the first recording by the group that became (without Ms.Barry) the Action.

BARRY SISTERS

Title	Format	Label	Catalogue	Year			Notes
Baby Come A Little Closer	7"	London	HLA8248	1956	£7.50	£15	
Intrigue	7"	London	HLA8304	1956	£7.50	£15	

BARRY SISTERS (2)

Title	Format	Label	Catalogue	Year			Notes
Jo Jo	7"	Decca	F11141	1959	£1.50	£4	
Tall Paul	7"	Decca	F11118	1959	£1.50	£4	

BART, LIONEL

Title	Format	Label	Catalogue	Year			Notes
Isn't This Where We Came In	LP	Deram	DML/SML1028	1967	£5	£12	

BARTHOLOMEW, DAVE

Title	Format	Label	Catalogue	Year			Notes
Fats Domino Presents Dave Bartholomew	LP	Imperial	LP9162/LP12076	1961	£10	£25	US
New Orleans House Party	LP	Imperial	LP9217/LP12217	1963	£10	£25	US

BARTLEY, CHRIS

Title	Format	Label	Catalogue	Year			Notes
I Found A Goodie	7"	Bell	BLL1031	1968	£4	£8	
Sweetest Thing This Side Of Heaven	7"	Cameo Parkway	P101	1962	£20	£40	

BARTOK

Title	Format	Label	Catalogue	Year			Notes
Insanity	7"	On	ON1	1982	£2	£5	

BARTON, EILEEN

Title	Format	Label	Catalogue	Year			Notes
Cry Me A River	7"	Vogue Coral	Q72122	1956	£4	£8	
Fujiyama Mama	7"	Vogue Coral	Q72075	1955	£7.50	£15	
Spring It Was	7"	Vogue Coral	Q72205	1956	£1.50	£4	
Teenage Heart	7"	Vogue Coral	Q72148	1956	£1.50	£4	
Too Close For Comfort	7"	Vogue Coral	Q72250	1957	£1.50	£4	
Without Love	7"	Vogue Coral	Q72270	1957	£1.50	£4	
Year We Fell In Love	7"	Vogue Coral	Q72060	1955	£2	£5	

45

BARTY, ALAN
Barty's Bow .... LP ..... Kettle .... KOP4 .... 1980 ... £5 ....£12 ....

BASES
Home Sweet Home .... 7" ...... Coxsone .... CS7062 .... 1968 ... £5 ....£10 Marcia Griffiths B side
Don't Mind .... 7" .... Studio One ...... SO2056 .... 1968 ... £6 ....£12 ...Jackie Mittoo B side

BASHO, ROBBIE
Falconer's Arm 1 .... LP ..... Takoma............ 1017 .... 1967 ... £4 ....£10 .... US
Falconer's Arm 2 .... LP ..... Takoma............ 1018 .... 1968 ... £4 ....£10 .... US
Song Of The Stallion .... LP ..... Takoma............ 1031 .... 1972 ... £4 ....£10 .... US
Venus In Cancer .... LP ..... Blue Thumb .... BTS10 .... 1969 ... £4 ....£10 .... US
Zarthus .... LP ..... Vanguard......... VSD79339 .... 1972 ... £4 ....£10 .... US

BASIC BLACK & PEARL
There'll Come A Time .... 7" .... Bus Stop .... BUS1030 .... 1975 ... £4 ....£8

BASIE, COUNT
April In Paris .... LP ..... Columbia........ 33CX10088 ...... 1957 ... £6 ....£15
At Newport .... LP ..... Columbia........ 33CX10110 ...... 1958 ... £6 ....£15
Atomic Mr.Basie .... LP ..... Columbia........ 33SX1084/ ...... 1958 ... £5 ....£12
                                                                                      SCX3265 ....
Atomic Mr.Basie .... LP ..... Columbia........ 33SX1084......... 1958 ... £6 ....£15
Band Of Distinction .... LP ..... HMV .... CLP1428 .... 1961 ... £4 ....£10
Basie .... LP ..... Columbia........ 33CX10065 ...... 1957 ... £6 ....£15
Basie At Birdland .... LP ..... Columbia........ 33SX1404 .... 1961 ... £4 ....£10
Basie Plays Hefti .... LP ..... Columbia........ 33SX1135 .... 1958 ... £4 ....£10
Basie's Back In Town .... LP ..... Philips .... BBL7141 .... 1957 ... £6 ....£15
Basie's Best .... 10" LP Brunswick..... LA8589 .... 1953 ... £8 ....£20
Blues By Basie .... LP ..... Philips .... BBL7190 .... 1957 ... £6 ....£15
Breakfast Dance And Barbecue ...... LP ..... Columbia........ 33SX1209/ ...... 1959 ... £4 ....£10
                                                                                      SCX3294 ....
Chairman Of The Board .... LP ..... Columbia........ 33SX1224/ ...... 1960 ... £4 ....£10
                                                                                      SCX3304 ....
Count .... 10" LP Columbia....... 33S1054 .... 1955 ... £8 ....£20
Count Basie .... LP ..... Brunswick..... LAT8028 .... 1954 ... £10 ....£25
Count Basie Classics .... LP ..... Fontana .... TFL5077 .... 1960 ... £4 ....£10
Count Basie Sextet .... 10" LP Columbia....... 33C9010 .... 1955 ... £8 ....£20
Count Basie Story Vol.1 .... LP ..... Columbia........ 33SX1316/ ...... 1961 ... £4 ....£10
                                                                                      SCX3372 ....
Count Basie Story Vol.2 .... LP ..... Columbia........ 33SX1317/ ...... 1961 ... £4 ....£10
                                                                                      SCX3373 ....
Count Basie Swings And Joe Williams LP ..... Columbia........ 33CX10026 ...... 1956 ... £6 ....£15
Sings
Count Basie Swings, Tony Bennett ... LP ..... Columbia........ 33SX1174 .... 1959 ... £4 ....£10
Sings
Count Basie/Lester Young .... 10" LP Mercury .... MG25015 .... 1954 ... £8 ....£20
Dance Along With Basie .... LP ..... Columbia........ 33SX1264/ ...... 1960 ... £4 ....£10
                                                                                      SCX3333 ....
Dance Session .... LP ..... Columbia........ 33CX10007 ...... 1955 ... £6 ....£15
Dance Session No.2 .... LP ..... Columbia........ 33CX10044 ...... 1956 ... £6 ....£15
Just The Blues .... LP ..... Columbia........ 33SX1326/ ...... 1961 ... £4 ....£10
                                                                                      SCX3380 ....
Memories Ad-Lib .... LP ..... Columbia........ 33SX1175/ ...... 1959 ... £4 ....£10
                                                                                      SCX3280 ....
Night At Count Basie's .... LP ..... Vanguard......... PPL11005 .... 1957 ... £6 ....£15
Not Now - I'll Tell You When .... LP ..... Columbia........ 33SX1293/ ...... 1961 ... £4 ....£10
                                                                                      SCX3356 ....
Old Count And The New Count .... 10" LP Philips .... BBR8036 .... 1955 ... £8 ....£20
One More Time .... LP ..... Columbia........ 33SX1183/ ...... 1959 ... £4 ....£10
                                                                                      SCX3284 ....
One O'Clock Jump .... LP ..... Fontana .... TFL5046 .... 1959 ... £4 ....£10
String Along With Basie .... LP ..... Columbia........ 33SX1151 .... 1959 ... £4 ....£10

BASS, BILLY
I'm Coming Too .... 7" .... Pama.............. PM761 .... 1969 ... £4 ....£8

BASS, FONTELLA
Don't Mess Up A Good Thing .... 7" .... Chess .... CRS8007 .... 1965 ... £5 ....£10 .... with Bobby
                                                                                                                                McClure, 2 different B
                                                                                                                                sides
Fontella Bass & Bobby McClure ...... 7" EP.. Chess .... CRE6025 .... 1966 ... £5 ....£10
Fontella's Hits .... 7" EP.. Chess .... CRE6015 .... 1966 ... £5 ....£10
I Can't Rest .... 7" .... Chess .... CRS8032 .... 1966 ... £2.50 .....£6
I Can't Rest .... 7" EP.. Chess .... CRE6020 .... 1966 ... £5 ....£10
New Look .... LP ..... Chess .... CRL4517 .... 1966 ... £5 ....£12
Recovery .... 7" .... Chess .... CRS8027 .... 1966 ... £2 ....£5 .... chart single
Rescue Me .... 7" .... Chess .... CRS8023 .... 1965 ... £2 ....£5 .... chart single
Safe And Sound .... 7" .... Chess .... CRS8042 .... 1966 ... £2 ....£5

BASSES
River Jordan .... 7" .... Coxsone .... CS7030.............. 1967 ... £5 ....£10

BASSEY, SHIRLEY
Banana Boat Song .... 7" .... Philips............ JK1006 .... 1957 ... £4 ....£8 .... chart single
Big Spender .... 7" .... United Artists.. UP1192 .... 1967 ... £1.50 ......£4
Born To Sing The Blues .... 10" LP Philips .... BBR8130 .... 1957 ... £5 ....£12
Diamonds Are Forever .... 7" .... United Artists.. UP35293............ 1972 ... £1.50 ......£4
Don't Take The Lovers From The ...... 7" .... United Artists.. UP1134.............. 1966 ... £2 ....£5
World

Goldfinger	7"	Columbia	DB7360	1964	£1.50	£4	chart sing
If I Had A Needle And Thread	7"	Philips	JK1018	1957	£2.50	£6	
Kiss Me, Honey Honey, Kiss Me	7"	Philips	PB860	1958	£1.50	£4	chart sing
Puh-leeze Mister Brown	7"	Philips	JK1034	1957	£2.50	£6	
To Give	7"	United Artists	UP2254	1968	£2.50	£6	

BAS-SHEVA

| Flame Of Love | 7" | Capitol | CL14218 | 1955 | £1.50 | £4 | |

BATAAN, JOE

| Riot! | LP | London | HA/SH8386 | 1969 | £5 | £12 | |

BATES, COLIN

| Brew | LP | Fontana | SFJL913 | 1968 | £5 | £12 | |

BATORS, STIV

| It's Cold Outside | 7" | London | HLZ10575 | 1979 | £2.50 | £6 | |

BATS

Accept It	7"	Columbia	DB7429	1964	£2	£5	
Listen To My Heart	7"	Decca	F22534	1966	£2	£5	
Take Me As I Am	7"	Decca	F22616	1967	£1.50	£4	
You Will Won't You	7"	Decca	F22568	1967	£1.50	£4	

BATT, MIKE

I See Wonderful Things In You	7"	Liberty	LBF15122	1968	£1.50	£4	
Mr.Poem	7"	Liberty	LBF15093	1968	£1.50	£4	
Your Mother Should Know	7"	Liberty	LBF15210	1969	£1.50	£4	

BATTERED ORNAMENTS

The Battered Ornaments was the group originally brought together by poet Pete Brown. Without him, they still did not have an effective vocalist, but the "Mantle Piece" LP is an interesting and worthwhile addition to the Harvest catalogue.

| Mantle Piece | LP | Harvest | SHVL758 | 1969 | £30 | £60 | |

BATTIN, SKIP

| Skip | LP | Signpost | SG4255 | 1972 | £6 | £15 | |

BATTLEFIELD BAND

| Scottish Folk | LP | Arfolk | SB349 | 1976 | £6 | £15 | French |

BAUHAUS

Bela Lugosi's Dead	12"	Small Wonder	TEENY2	1979	£4	£10	white vinyl
Burning From The Inside	LP	Beggars Banquet	BEGA45P	1983	£5	£12	pic disc
Dark Entries	7"	4AD	AD3	1980	£1.50	£4	blue label
Dark Entries	7"	4AD	BEG37	1980	£2.50	£6	
Dark Entries	7"	Axis	AXIS3	1980	£4	£8	
Dark Entries	7"	Beggars Banquet	BEG37	1980	£4	£8	
Kick In The Eye	12"	Beggars Banquet	BEG54T	1981	£2.50	£6	
Kick In The Eye	12"	Beggars Banquet	BEG54T	1981	£4	£10	white label, stamped sleeve
Kick In The Eye	12"	Beggars Banquet	BEG74TA1	1983	£8	£20	mispress with 'Poison Pen'
Sanity Assassin	7"	Fan Club		1983	£60	£120	
She's In Parties	7"	Beggars Banquet	BEG91P	1983	£2	£5	pic disc
Spirit	7"	Beggars Banquet	BEG79P	1982	£2	£5	pic disc
Telegram Sam	12"	4AD	AD17T	1980	£2.50	£6	
Terror Couple Kill Colonel	7"	4AD	AD7	1980	£1.50	£4	
Terror Couple Kill Colonel (remix)	7"	4AD	AD7	1980	£4	£8	

BAUMSTAM

| On Tour | LP | private | | 1974 | £60 | £120 | German |

BAXTER, ART

Don't Knock The Rock	78	Philips	PB666	1957	£2.50	£6	
Jingle Rock	78	Philips	PB652	1956	£2.50	£6	
Rock You Sinners	10" LP	Philips	BBR8107	1957	£30	£60	

BAXTER, DAVID

| Goodbye Dave | LP | Reflection | REFL9 | 1970 | £20 | £40 | |

BAXTER, LES

Cherry Pink And Apple Blossom White	7"	Capitol	CL14337	1955	£2	£5	
Earth Angel	7"	Capitol	CL14239	1955	£5	£10	
I Ain't Mad At You	7"	Capitol	CL14249	1955	£2	£5	
I Love Paris	7"	Capitol	CL14166	1954	£2	£5	
Midnight On The Cliffs	7"	Capitol	CL14173	1954	£2	£5	
Poor John	7"	Capitol	CL14533	1956	£1.50	£4	
Strike	7"	Capitol	CL14351	1955	£1.50	£4	
Take My Love	7"	Capitol	CL14358	1955	£1.50	£4	
Unchained Melody	7"	Capitol	CL14257	1955	£4	£8	chart single
Wake The Town And Tell The People	7"	Capitol	CL14344	1955	£2	£5	
When You're In Love	7"	Capitol	CL14217	1954	£2	£5	

BAXTER, RONNIE

| I Finally Found You | 7" | Top Rank | JAR293 | 1960 | £1.50 | £4 | |

BAY CITY JAZZ BAND

Bay City Jazz Band	LP	Vogue	LAG12093	1958	£5	£12	

BAYSIDERS

Over The Rainbow	LP	Everest	LPBR/BRST5124	1961	£15	£30	US

BAYTOWN SINGERS

Walkin' Down The Line	7"	Decca	F12160	1965	£2.50	£6	

B.B.BLUNDER

"Worker's Playtime" is the often overlooked third LP by the Blossom Toes, and shares many of the inventive qualities of its predecessors. The cover is a delight, being a parody of the Radio Times, with all the song lyrics and credits disguised as programme information.

Sticky Living	7"	United Artists	UP5203	1971	£1.50	£4	
Workers Playtime	LP	United Artists	UAS29156	1971	£5	£12	

BBC RADIOPHONIC WORKSHOP

Dr.Who	7"	BBC	RESL11	1974	£1.50	£4	
Dr.Who	7"	Decca	F11837	1964	£4	£8	

BEACH BOYS

For a group as long-lived and as popular as the Beach Boys, there are surprisingly few hard-core rarities, although all their original issues from the sixties are inevitably collectable. The ultimate Beach Boys rarity has still not been released in full - the LP 'Smile' was cancelled by Brian Wilson and would perhaps have included tracks to rival the masterworks "Good Vibrations", "Heroes and Villains", and 'Surf's Up', which were all destined for inclusion on the lost album. For collectors who do not actually feel the need to own every note that the group has produced, it should be noted that the World Record Club boxed set "The Capitol Years" is a particularly well assembled compilation of the group's sixties work, with no major omissions. A bonus LP, moreover, assembles a number of Brian Wilson productions which are otherwise rather difficult to find.

20 Golden Greats	LP	EMI	EMTV1	1977	£4	£10	blue vinyl
20 Golden Greats Promo	LP	EMI	PSR402	1976	£5	£10	promo
20/20	LP	Capitol	ET133	1969	£4	£10	chart LP, mono
All Summer Long	LP	Capitol	(S)T2110	1964	£6	£15	
All Summer Long	7"	Capitol	CL15384	1965	£2	£5	
Ballad Of An Old Car	7" EP	Capitol	EAP120576	1964	£10	£20	French
Barbara Ann	7"	Capitol	CL15432	1966	£1.50	£4	chart single
Barbara Ann	7"	Capitol	CMS2	1972	£1.50	£4	
Barbara Ann	7" EP	Capitol	EAP120762	1965	£7.50	£15	French
Beach Boy Interviews	LP	Caribou	XPR1204	1980	£8	£20	promo
Beach Boys Concert	LP	Capitol	(S)T2198	1964	£6	£15	
Beach Boys Concert	7" EP	Capitol	EAP42198	1964	£5	£10	
Beach Boys' Hits	7" EP	Capitol	EAP120781	1964	£4	£8	
Beach Boys Party	LP	Capitol	(S)T2398	1965	£5	£12	chart LP
Beach Boys Today	LP	Capitol	(S)T2269	1965	£5	£12	chart LP
Bluebirds Over The Mountain	7"	Capitol	CL15572	1968	£1.50	£4	chart single
Break Away	7"	Capitol	CL15598	1969	£1.50	£4	chart single
California Girls	7"	Capitol	CL15409	1965	£1.50	£4	chart single
California Girls	7" EP	Capitol	EAP42354	1965	£7.50	£15	French
California Saga - California	7"	Reprise	K14232	1973	£1.50	£4	chart single
California/Sail On Sailor	7"	Reprise	K14346	1974	£1.50	£4	
Capitol Years	LP	World Record Club	SM651-7	1981	£25	£50	7 LPs, boxed
Christmas Album	LP	Capitol	(S)T2164	1964	£8	£20	
Cottonfields	7"	Capitol	CL15640	1970	£1.50	£4	chart single
Dance Dance Dance	7"	Capitol	CL15370	1965	£1.50	£4	chart single
Dance Dance Dance	7" EP	Capitol	EAP120648	1965	£7.50	£15	French
Darlin'	7"	Capitol	CL15527	1968	£1.50	£4	chart single
Deluxe Set	LP	Capitol	DTCL2813	1967	£20	£40	US, triple, stereo
Deluxe Set	LP	Capitol	TCL2813	1967	£30	£60	US, triple, mono
Do It Again	7"	Capitol	CL15554	1968	£1.50	£4	chart single
Don't Go Near The Water	7"	Stateside	SS2194	1971	£1.50	£4	
Don't Go Near The Water	7"	Stateside	SS2194	1971	£6	£12	demo, PS
Driving Cars	7" EP	Capitol	EAP41998	1964	£10	£20	French
Four By The Beach Boys	7" EP	Capitol	EAP15267	1964	£4	£8	
Friends	LP	Capitol	T2895	1968	£4	£10	chart LP, mono
Friends	7"	Capitol	CL15545	1968	£1.50	£4	chart single
Fun Fun Fun	7"	Capitol	CL15339	1964	£2	£5	
Fun Fun Fun	7" EP	Capitol	EAP120603	1964	£5	£10	
God Only Knows	7"	Capitol	CL15459	1966	£1.50	£4	chart single
God Only Knows	7" EP	Capitol	EAP62458	1967	£4	£8	
Good Vibrations	7"	Capitol	CL15475	1966	£1.50	£4	chart single
Help Me Rhonda	7"	Capitol	CL15392	1965	£1.50	£4	chart single
Help Me Ronda	7" EP	Capitol	EAP42269	1965	£7.50	£15	French
Here Comes The Night	12"	Caribou	127204	1979	£2.50	£6	blue vinyl
Heroes And Villains	7"	Capitol	CL15510	1967	£1.50	£4	chart single
Holland	LP	Reprise	K54008	1973	£4	£10	with 7',chart LP
Holland	LP	Reprise	MS2118	1973	£75	£150	US test pressing with 'We Got Love'
I Can Hear Music	7"	Capitol	CL15584	1969	£1.50	£4	chart single
I Get Around	7"	Capitol	CL15350	1964	£1.50	£4	chart single
I Get Around	7" EP	Capitol	EAP120620	1964	£7.50	£15	French, 2 different sleeves
L.A. (Light Album)	LP	Caribou	CRB1186081	1979	£5	£12	pic disc
Little Deuce Coupe	LP	Capitol	(S)T1998	1963	£6	£15	
Little Girl I Once Knew	7"	Capitol	CL15425	1965	£2	£5	chart single
Long Promised Road	7"	Stateside	SS2190	1971	£1.50	£4	
Louie Louie	7" EP	Capitol	EAP120658	1965	£7.50	£15	French
Pet Sounds	LP	Capitol	(S)T2458	1966	£4	£10	chart LP
Shut Down Vol.2	LP	Capitol	(S)T2027	1964	£6	£15	
Singles Collection	7"	Capitol	BBP26	1979	£30	£60	26 singles, boxed
Sloop John B	7"	Capitol	CL15441	1966	£1.50	£4	chart single
Sloop John B	7" EP	Capitol	EAP120812	1966	£7.50	£15	French

Title		Format	Label	Catalogue	Year	Price	Price	Notes
Smiley Smile		LP	Capitol	(S)T9001	1967	£4	£10	chart LP
Smiley Smile		LP	Capitol	ST82891	1968	£37.50	£75	US, record club issue
Stack-O-Tracks		LP	Capitol	DKAO2893	1968	£30	£60	US, with booklet
Summer Days & Summer Nights		LP	Capitol	(S)T2354	1965	£5	£12	chart LP
Summertime Blues		LP	Sears	SPS609	1970	£25	£50	US
Sunflower		LP	Capitol	SKAO93352	1970	£8	£20	US, record club issue
Surfer Girl		LP	Capitol	(S)T1981	1963	£6	£15	chart LP
Surfer Party		7" EP	Capitol	EAP120561	1963	£10	£20	French
Surfin'		7"	Candix	301	1961	£75	£150	US
Surfin'		7"	Candix	331	1961	£60	£120	US
Surfin'		7"	X	301	1961	£100	£200	US
Surfin' Safari		LP	Capitol	T1808	1962	£8	£20	
Surfin' Safari		7"	Capitol	CL15273	1962	£4	£8	
Surfin' Safari		7" EP	Capitol	EAP51808	1962	£10	£20	French
Surfin' USA		LP	Capitol	(S)T1890	1963	£6	£15	chart LP
Surfin' USA		7"	Capitol	CL15305	1963	£2.50	£6	chart single
Surfin' USA		7" EP	Capitol	EAP120504	1963	£10	£20	French
Surfin' USA		7" EP	Capitol	EAP120540	1963	£5	£10	
Surf's Up		LP	Asylum	R113793	1971	£25	£50	US, record club issue
Susie Cincinnatti		7"	Reprise	K14411	1976	£15	£30	demo
Tears In The Morning		7"	Stateside	SS2181	1970	£1.50	£4	
Ten Little Indians		7"	Capitol	CL15285	1963	£7.50	£15	
Then I Kissed Her		7"	Capitol	CL15502	1967	£1.50	£4	chart single
When I Grow Up		7"	Capitol	CL15361	1964	£1.50	£4	chart single
Wild Honey		LP	Capitol	T2859	1968	£4	£10	chart LP, mono
Wild Honey		7"	Capitol	CL15517	1967	£30	£60	
Wild Honey		7"	Capitol	CL15521	1967	£1.50	£4	chart single
Wouldn't It Be Nice		7"	Capitol	CMS1	1972	£1.50	£4	
Wouldn't It Be Nice		7" EP	Capitol	EAP502458	1967	£7.50	£15	French
You Need A Mess of Help		7"	Reprise	K14173	1972	£1.50	£4	PS

BEACH NUTS

Out In The Sun	7"	London	HL9988	1965	£2	£5	

BEACHCOMBERS

An instrumental group whose drummer was Keith Moon, who left to join the High Numbers just as the latter decided to revert to their earlier name of the Who.

Mad Goose	7"	Columbia	DB7124	1963	£5	£10	
Night Train	7"	Columbia	DB7200	1964	£5	£10	

BEACON STREET UNION

Blue Suede Shoes	7"	MGM	MGM1416	1968	£2.50	£6	
Clown Died In Marvin Gardens	LP	MGM	SE4568	1968	£6	£15	US
Eyes Of The Beacon Street Union	LP	MGM	8069	1968	£6	£15	

BEAN & LOOPY'S LOT

Haywire	7"	Parlophone	R5458	1966	£4	£8	

BEAN, GEORGE

Privilege	7" EP	Vogue	INT18137	1967	£4	£8	French, B side by Mike Leander Orchestra
Sad Story	7"	Decca	F11922	1964	£2.50	£6	
Secret Love	7"	Decca	F11762	1963	£2	£4	
She Belongs To Me	7"	Decca	F12228	1965	£1.50	£4	
Will You Be My Lover Tonight	7"	Decca	F11808	1964	£2.50	£6	

BEANS

Hey Janey	7"	Starlite	ST45075	1962	£2	£5	
Jumping Beans	7"	Starlite	ST45071	1962	£2	£5	

BEAR

Greetings Children Of Paradise	LP	Verve	FTS3059	1968	£6	£15	

BEARCATS

Beatlemania	LP	Somerset	P20800	1964	£8	£20	US

BEARD, DEAN & THE CREWCUTS

On My Mind Again	7"	London	HLE8463	1957	£75	£150	

BEARZ

She's My Girl	7"	Axis	AXIS2	1980	£2.50	£6	

BEAS

Dr.Goodfoot And His Bikini Machine	7"	Pama	PM744	1968	£6	£12	

BEASLEY, JIMMY

Fabulous Jimmy Beasley	LP	Crown	CLP5014	1957	£15	£30	US
Fabulous Jimmy Beasley	LP	Modern	LMP1214	1956	£25	£50	US
Twist With Jimmy Beasley	LP	Crown	CLP5247	1961	£8	£20	US

BEASTIE BOYS

Polly Wog Stew	12"	Rat Cage	MOTR21	1982	£2.50	£6	

BEAT BOYS

That's My Plan	7"	Decca	F11730	1963	£6	£12	

BEAT BROTHERS

Nick Nack Hully Gully	7"	Polydor	NH52185	1963	£12.50	£25	

BEAT CHICS

| Skinny Minny | 7" | Decca | F12016 | 1964 | £2.50 | £6 | |

BEAT MERCHANTS

| Pretty Face | 7" | Columbia | DB7367 | 1964 | £10 | £20 | |
| So Fine | 7" | Columbia | DB7492 | 1965 | £10 | £20 | |

BEAT SIX

| Bernadine | 7" | Decca | F12011 | 1964 | £2.50 | £6 | |

BEATLES

The Beatles sold so many copies of their singles that it should come as no surprise that few of them have aquired much of a value in the collectors' market. It is a different matter with their LPs, however, especially as so many original copies have been extremely well played over the years! There are also a number of rarer items. The Polydor singles and LP are the first pressings of the material that the Beatles recorded in Germany in 1962 - mainly as a backing group to singer Tony Sheridan, although "Ain't She Sweet" features a typically gritty John Lennon vocal, and "Cry For A Shadow" is George Harrison's instrumental tribute to Hank Marvin and company. This material has been reissued on a number of occasions, along with live recordings by the Beatles in Hamburg without Sheridan, but few of these records fetch any kind of collectors' prices, despite the historical importance of the music they present. The Christmas flexi-disc singles were issued each year to members of the fan-club and feature specially recorded material not otherwise available, although not very much of this is actually musical! "From Then To You" gathers all these singles together on a highly sought-after LP - inevitably this has been frequently bootlegged, but the copies in current circulation do not have the Apple label of the original. The US version of the LP has a different cover and title ("The Beatles

Title	Format	Label	Catalog#	Year	Price1	Price2	Notes
1962-1970	7"	Lyntone		1977	£5	£10	promo flex
1962-66	LP	Apple	PCSPR717	1978	£8	£20	red vinyl, double
1967-70	LP	Apple	PCSPR718	1978	£6	£15	blue vinyl, double
4 Garcons Dans Le Vent	7" EP	Odeon	SOE3756	1964	£7.50	£15	French
4 Garcons Dans Le Vent	7" EP	Odeon	SOE3757	1964	£7.50	£15	French
Abbey Road	r-reel	Apple	TAPMC7088	1970	£25	£50	mono
Abbey Road	r-reel	Apple	TDPCS7088	1970	£15	£30	stereo
Abbey Road	LP	Apple	PCS7088	1969	£4	£10	chart LP, dark green labe
Abbey Road	LP	Apple	PCS7088	1978	£32.50	£65	green viny
Abbey Road	LP	Apple	PHO7088	197-	£150	£250	pic disc
Abbey Road	LP	Apple	SO383	1969	£4	£10	US
Abbey Road	LP	Capitol	SEAX11900	1978	£6	£15	US pic disc
Abbey Road	LP	EMI	5CP06204243	1979	£5	£12	German pic disc
Abbey Road	LP	Mobile Fidelity	MFSL1023	1978	£17.50	£35	US audiophile
Abbey Road	LP	Parlophone	PPCS7088	1969	£100	£200	export silver & black labe
Abbey Road	LP	Parlophone	PPCS7088	1969	£250	£400	export yellow & black labe
Abbey Road	CD	EMI	BEACD25/7	1987	£8	£20	HMV box, badge booklet, 2 posters
Abbey Road	CD	Odeon	CP353016	1986	£40	£80	Japanese
All My Loving	7" EP	Odeon	SOE3751	1964	£7.50	£15	French
All My Loving	7" EP	Parlophone	GEP8891	1964	£2.50	£6	
All You Need Is Love	7"	Parlophone	R5620	1967	£1.50	£4	chart single
All You Need Is Love	7"	Parlophone	R5620	1967	£150	£250	demo
All You Need Is Love	7"	Parlophone	R5620	1967	£6	£12	no reference to TV transmission
All You Need Is Love	7"	Parlophone	RP5620	1987	£5	£10	pic disc
Amazing Beatles	LP	Clarion	601	1966	£20	£40	US, mono
Amazing Beatles	LP	Clarion	S601	1966	£30	£60	US, stereo
Another Beatles Christmas Record	7"	Lyntone	LYN757	1964	£20	£40	PS, flex
Another Beatles Christmas Record	7"	Lyntone	LYN757	1964	£25	£50	PS, flexi, newsletter
Ballad Of John And Yoko	7"	Apple	R5786	1969	£1.50	£4	chart single
Ballad Of John And Yoko	7"	Apple	R5786	1969	£150	£250	demo
Ballad Of John And Yoko	7"	Apple	RP5786	1989	£5	£10	pic disc
Beatles	LP	Parlophone	PPCS7067/8	1968	£400	£600	export yellow & black labe
Beatles & Frank Ifield On Stage	LP	Vee Jay	LP1085	1964	£530	£800	US, Beatles on cove
Beatles & Frank Ifield On Stage	LP	Vee Jay	LP1085	1964	£25	£50	US, old man on cover, mono
Beatles & Frank Ifield On Stage	LP	Vee Jay	LPS1085	1964	£75	£150	US, old man on cover, stereo
Beatles 1962	7"	Baktabak	TABOKS1001	1988	£25	£50	15 singles, boxed
Beatles '65	LP	Capitol	ST2228	1964	£6	£15	US, stereo
Beatles '65	LP	Capitol	T2228	1964	£8	£20	US, mono
Beatles At The Beeb	LP	BBC	CN3970	1982	£330	£500	transcription disc
Beatles At The Hollywood Bowl	7"	Parlophone	EMTV4	1977	£25	£50	promo boxed se
Beatles Box	LP	World Record Club	SM701-8	1980	£25	£50	8 LPs, boxed
Beatles' Christmas Album	LP	Apple	SBC100	1970	£100	£200	US, sleeve pictured in Guide
Beatles' Christmas Record	7"	Lyntone	LYN492	1963	£37.50	£75	PS, flex
Beatles Collection	LP	Mobile Fidelity		1982	£150	£250	US audiophile, 14 LPs boxed
Beatles Collection	LP	Parlophone	BC13	1978	£55	£110	13 LPs (double), boxed
Beatles Collection	7"	Lyntone	LYN9657	1978	£1.50	£4	flex
Beatles Collection	7"	Lyntone	LYNSF165	1978	£5	£10	promo flexi, poster
Beatles Collection	7"	World Record Club		1977	£20	£40	24 singles, boxed
Beatles Collection	7"	World Record Club		1978	£22.50	£45	25 singles, boxed
Beatles Conquer America	7"	Baktabak	BAKPAK1004	1989	£6	£12	4 single pac
Beatles EP Collection	7" EP	Parlophone	BEP14	1981	£20	£40	14 EP
Beatles Fifth Christmas Record	7"	Lyntone	LYN1360	1967	£20	£40	PS, flex
Beatles Fifth Christmas Record	7"	Lyntone	LYN1360	1967	£25	£50	PS, flexi, newsletter

Title	Format	Label	Cat. No.	Year	Price	Price	Notes
Beatles For Sale	r-reel	Parlophone	TAPMC1240/ TDPCS3062	1965	£10	£25	
Beatles For Sale	LP	Mobile Fidelity	MFSL1104	1984	£6	£15	US audiophile
Beatles For Sale	LP	Parlophone	PCS3062	1964	£10	£25	stereo, chart LP
Beatles For Sale	LP	Parlophone	PMC1240	1964	£8	£20	mono, chart LP
Beatles For Sale	7" EP	Parlophone	GEP8931	1965	£4	£8	
Beatles For Sale No.2	7" EP	Parlophone	GEP8938	1965	£6	£12	
Beatles Fourth Christmas Record	7"	Lyntone	LYN1145	1966	£20	£40	PS, flexi
Beatles Fourth Christmas Record	7"	Lyntone	LYN1145	1966	£25	£50	PS, flexi, newsletter
Beatles Greatest Hits	LP	Parlophone	EMTVS34	1982	£25	£50	double, test pressing
Beatles Hits	7" EP	Parlophone	GEP8880	1963	£2.50	£6	
Beatles Million Sellers	7" EP	Parlophone	GEP8946	1965	£5	£10	
Beatles Mono Collection	LP	Parlophone	BMC10	1982	£60	£120	10 LPs, boxed
Beatles No.1	7" EP	Parlophone	GEP8883	1963	£2.50	£6	
Beatles' Rock'n'Roll Medley	7"	EMI	PSR401	1976	£10	£20	1 sided promo
Beatles Second Album	LP	Capitol	ST2080	1964	£6	£15	US, stereo
Beatles Second Album	LP	Capitol	ST82080	1964	£25	£50	US, Record Club issue
Beatles Second Album	LP	Capitol	T2080	1964	£8	£20	US, mono
Beatles Second Album	LP	Parlophone	CPCS103	1969	£100	£200	export, silver & black label
Beatles' Second Album	LP	Parlophone	CPCS103	1966	£250	£400	export
Beatles Seventh Christmas Record	7"	Lyntone	LYN1970/1	1969	£20	£40	PS, flexi
Beatles Seventh Christmas Record	7"	Lyntone	LYN1970/1	1969	£25	£50	PS, flexi, newsletter
Beatles Singles Collection	7"	EMI	BSC1	1982	£20	£40	26 singles, boxed
Beatles Singles Collection	7"	EMI	BSCP1	1982	£25	£50	27 singles, boxed, export
Beatles Singles Collection	7"	Lyntone	LYNSF1291	1977	£5	£10	promo flexi, poster
Beatles Singles Collection	7"	Parlophone/ Apple	BS24	1976	£25	£50	24 singles, boxed
Beatles Singles Collection	7"	Parlophone	BSCP1	1982	£35	£70	box set with mispressed pic disc - Love Me Do both sides
Beatles Sixth Christmas Record	7"	Lyntone	LYN1743/4	1968	£20	£40	PS, flexi
Beatles Sixth Christmas Record	7"	Lyntone	LYN1743/4	1968	£25	£50	PS, flexi, newsletter
Beatles Story	LP	Capitol	STBO2222	1964	£8	£20	US, stereo
Beatles Story	LP	Capitol	TBO2222	1964	£10	£25	US, mono
Beatles Tapes (David Wigg Interviews)	LP	Polydor	2683068	1976	£6	£15	double
Beatles Third Christmas Record	7"	Lyntone	LYN948	1965	£20	£40	PS, flexi
Beatles Third Christmas Record	7"	Lyntone	LYN948	1965	£25	£50	PS, flexi, newsletter
Beatles VI	LP	Capitol	ST2358	1965	£6	£15	US, stereo
Beatles VI	LP	Capitol	ST82358	1965	£25	£50	US, Record Club issue
Beatles VI	LP	Capitol	T2358	1965	£8	£20	US, mono
Beatles VI	LP	Parlophone	CPCS104	1966	£250	£400	export
Beatles VI	LP	Parlophone	CPCS104	1969	£100	£200	export, black & silver label
Beatles Vs. The Four Seasons	LP	Vee Jay	DX30	1964	£840	£1200	US double
Beatles (White Album)	r-reel	Apple	DTAPMC/ DTDPCS7067/8	1969	£15	£30	
Beatles (White Album)	LP	Apple	PCS7067/8	1968	£17.50	£35	stereo, chart LP
Beatles (White Album)	LP	Apple	PCS7067/8	1978	£35	£70	white vinyl
Beatles (White Album)	LP	Apple	PMC7067/8	1968	£25	£50	mono, chart LP
Beatles (White Album)	LP	Apple	SWBO101	1968	£8	£20	US, double
Beatles (White Album)	LP	Mobile Fidelity	MFSL2072	1982	£10	£25	US audiophile
Beatles (White Album)	LP	Parlophone	PCSJ7067/8	1969	£250	£400	double export
Beatles (White Album)	LP	Parlophone	PPCS7067/8	1969	£250	£400	double export, silver & black label
Beatles (White Album)	CD	EMI	BEACD25/4	1987	£17.50	£35	HMV box, badge, booklet
Beatles With Tony Sheridan	LP	MGM	E4215	1964	£20	£40	US, mono
Beatles With Tony Sheridan	LP	MGM	SE4215	1964	£45	£90	US, stereo
Can't Buy Me Love	7"	Parlophone	R5114	1964	£1.50	£4	chart single
Can't Buy Me Love	7"	Parlophone	R5114	1964	£210	£350	demo
Can't Buy Me Love	7"	Parlophone	RP5114	1984	£5	£10	pic disc
Can't Buy Me Love	7" EP	Odeon	SOE3750	1964	£7.50	£15	French
Chansons Du Film Help	7" EP	Odeon	SOE3771	1965	£7.50	£15	French
Collection Of Beatles Oldies	r-reel	Parlophone	TAPMC/ TDPCS7016	1967	£10	£25	
Collection Of Beatles Oldies	LP	Parlophone	PMC/PCS7016	1967	£8	£20	chart LP
Day Tripper	78	Parlophone	R5389	196-	£150	£250	Indian
Day Tripper	7"	Parlophone	R5389	1965	£1.50	£4	chart single
Day Tripper	7"	Parlophone	R5389	1965	£210	£350	demo
Day Tripper	7"	Parlophone	RP5389	1985	£5	£10	pic disc
Devil In Her Heart	7" EP	Odeon	SOE3777	1964	£12.50	£25	French
Dizzy Miss Lizzy	78	Odeon	DPE183	196-	£150	£250	Indian
Do You Want To Know A Secret	7"	Odeon	22710	1964	£6	£12	German import
Early Beatles	LP	Capitol	ST2309	1965	£6	£15	US, stereo
Early Beatles	LP	Capitol	T2309	1965	£8	£20	US, mono
Eight Days A Week	7" EP	Odeon	SOE3764	1965	£7.50	£15	French
From Me To You	7"	Parlophone	R5015	1963	£1.50	£4	chart single
From Me To You	7"	Parlophone	R5015	1963	£210	£350	demo
From Me To You	7"	Parlophone	RP5015	1983	£7.50	£15	pic disc
From Me To You	7" EP	Odeon	SOE3739	1963	£7.50	£15	French
From Me To You	7" EP	Odeon	SOE3739	1963	£50	£100	French, Beatles in French costume on PS
From Then To You	LP	Apple	LYN2153/4	1970	£150	£250	green Apple label
Get Back	7"	Apple	R5777	1969	£1.50	£4	chart single

Title	Format	Label	Catalogue	Year	Price	Price	Notes
Get Back	7"	Apple	R5777	1978	£7.50	£15	mispress - B side plays 'I've Had Enough' by Wings
Get Back	7"	Apple	R5779	1969	£150	£250	demo
Get Back	7"	Apple	RP5777	1989	£5	£10	pic disc
Girl	78	Parlophone	DPE188	196-	£150	£250	Indian
Hard Day's Night	r-reel	Parlophone	TAPMC1230/ TDPCS3058	1964	£10	£25	
Hard Day's Night	LP	Mobile Fidelity	MFSL1103	1984	£6	£15	US audiophile
Hard Day's Night	LP	Parlophone	PCS3058	1964	£10	£25	stereo, chart LP
Hard Day's Night	LP	Parlophone	PMC1230	1964	£8	£20	mono, chart LP
Hard Day's Night	LP	United Artists	SP2359	1964	£100	£200	US promo with script
Hard Day's Night	LP	United Artists	UAL3366	1964	£10	£25	US, mono
Hard Day's Night	LP	United Artists	UAS6366	1964	£8	£20	US, stereo
Hard Day's Night	7"	Parlophone	R5160	1964	£1.50	£4	chart single
Hard Day's Night	7"	Parlophone	R5160	1964	£210	£350	demo
Hard Day's Night	7"	Parlophone	RP5160	1984	£5	£10	pic disc
Hard Day's Night	7" EP	Parlophone	GEP8920	1964	£4	£8	
Hard Day's Night No.2	7" EP	Parlophone	GEP8924	1964	£6	£12	
Hello Goodbye	7"	Parlophone	R5655	1967	£1.50	£4	chart single
Hello Goodbye	7"	Parlophone	R5655	1967	£150	£250	demo
Hello Goodbye	7"	Parlophone	RP5655	1987	£5	£10	pic disc
Help	r-reel	Parlophone	TAPMC1255/ TDPCS3071	1965	£10	£25	
Help	LP	Capitol	MAS2386	1965	£8	£20	US, mono
Help	LP	Capitol	SMAS2386	1965	£6	£15	US, stereo
Help	LP	Capitol	SMAS82386	1965	£25	£50	US, Record Club issue
Help	LP	Mobile Fidelity	MFSL1105	1984	£6	£15	US audiophile
Help	LP	Parlophone	PMC1255/ PCS3071	1965	£8	£20	chart LP
Help	78	Parlophone	R5305	196-	£150	£250	Indian
Help	7"	Parlophone	RP5305	1985	£5	£10	pic disc
Help	7" EP	Odeon	SOE3769	1965	£7.50	£15	French
Help	7"	Parlophone	R5305	1965	£1.50	£4	chart single
Help!	7"	Parlophone	R5305	1965	£210	£350	demo
Help,Rubber Soul,Revolver	CD			198-	£50	£100	export
Help/Rubber Soul/Revolver	CD	EMI	BEACD25/2	1987	£37.50	£75	HMV red box, magazine
Here, There And Everywhere	78	Parlophone	DPE189	196-	£150	£250	Indian
Hey Jude	LP	Apple	CPCS106	197-	£8	£20	export
Hey Jude	LP	Apple	CPCS106	1970	£30	£60	dark green Apple label
Hey Jude	LP	Parlophone	CPCS106	1970	£100	£200	export, silver & black label
Hey Jude	LP	Parlophone	PCSJ149	1970	£8	£20	export
Hey Jude	78	Parlophone	DPE190	196-	£150	£250	Indian
Hey Jude	7"	Apple	R5722	1968	£1.50	£4	chart single
Hey Jude	7"	Apple	RP5722	1988	£5	£10	pic disc
Hey Jude	7"	Parlophone	DP570	1968	£30	£60	export
Hey Jude	7"	Parlophone	R5722	1968	£150	£250	demo
Hey Jude	12"	Apple	12RP5722	1988	£4	£10	pic disc
Hey Jude/The Beatles Again	LP	Apple	SO/SW385	1970	£5	£12	US
History Of Rock Vol.26	LP	Orbis	HRL026	1984	£6	£15	double
Honey Don't	7" EP	Odeon	SOE3779	1965	£12.50	£25	French
I Feel Fine	78	Parlophone	R5200	196-	£150	£250	Indian
I Feel Fine	7"	Parlophone	R5200	1964	£1.50	£4	chart single
I Feel Fine	7"	Parlophone	R5200	1964	£210	£350	demo
I Feel Fine	7"	Parlophone	RP5200	1984	£5	£10	pic disc
I Feel Fine	7" EP	Odeon	SOE3760	1964	£7.50	£15	French
I Saw Her Standing There	78	Parlophone	DPE159	196-	£150	£250	Indian
I Should Have Known Better	78	Parlophone	DPE168	196-	£150	£250	Indian
I Wanna Be Your Man	7"	Odeon	22681	1964	£6	£12	German import
I Want To Hold Your Hand	7"	Odeon	22623	1964	£6	£12	German import
I Want To Hold Your Hand	7"	Parlophone	R5084	1963	£1.50	£4	chart single
I Want To Hold Your Hand	7"	Parlophone	R5084	1963	£210	£350	demo
I Want To Hold Your Hand	7"	Parlophone	RP5084	1983	£5	£10	pic disc
I Want To Hold Your Hand	7" EP	Odeon	SOE3745	1963	£7.50	£15	French
If I Fell	78	Parlophone	DPE167	196-	£150	£250	Indian
If I Fell	78	Parlophone	DP562	1964	£20	£40	export
I'm A Loser	78	Parlophone	DPE178	196-	£150	£250	Indian
I'm A Loser	7"	HMV	MQ20007	1964	£6	£12	Italian import
I'm Looking Through You	78	Parlophone	DPE193	196-	£150	£250	Indian
In The Beginning	LP	Polydor	244504	1970	£5	£12	US, red label
Introducing The Beatles	LP	Vee Jay	LP1062	1963	£180	£300	US, with Love Me Do, blank back cover, mono
Introducing The Beatles	LP	Vee Jay	LP1062	1963	£50	£100	US, with Love Me Do, songs listed on back
Introducing The Beatles	LP	Vee Jay	LP1062	1964	£25	£50	US, with Please Please Me, mono
Introducing The Beatles	LP	Vee Jay	LPS1062	1963	£400	£600	US, with Love Me Do, blank back cover, stereo
Introducing The Beatles	LP	Vee Jay	LPS1062	1964	£180	£300	US, with Please Please Me, stereo
Kansas City	7" EP	Odeon	SOE3776	1965	£12.50	£25	French
Komm Gib Mir Deine Hand	7"	Odeon	22671	1964	£25	£50	German import, PS
Lady Madonna	7"	Parlophone	R5675	1968	£1.50	£4	chart single

Title	Format	Label	Catalogue	Year			Notes
Lady Madonna	7"	Parlophone	R5675	1968	£150	£250	demo
Lady Madonna	7"	Parlophone	RP5675	1988	£5	£10	pic disc
Let It Be	r-reel	Apple	TAPMC7096	1970	£25	£50	mono
Let It Be	r-reel	Apple	TDPCS7096	1970	£15	£30	stereo
Let It Be	LP	Apple	AR34001	1970	£4	£10	US, 'a subsidiary of Capitol'
Let It Be	LP	Apple	PCS7096	1970	£4	£10	chart LP, orange Apple on back cover
Let It Be	LP	Apple	PCS7096	1978	£25	£50	white vinyl
Let It Be	LP	Apple	PPCS7096	1970	£8	£20	export
Let It Be	LP	Apple	PXS1/PCS7096	1970	£90	£180	boxed with book
Let It Be	LP	Mobile Fidelity	MFSL1109	1984	£6	£15	US audiophile
Let It Be	LP	Parlophone	PPCS7096	1970	£100	£200	export, silver & black label
Let It Be	LP	Parlophone	PPCS7096	1970	£250	£400	export, yellow & black label
Let It Be	CD			1988	£60	£120	promo, pic label, boxed
Let It Be	CD	EMI	BEACD25/8	1987	£10	£25	HMV boxed set, poster, booklet, badge
Let It Be	7"	Apple	PR5833	1970	£37.50	£75	export
Let It Be	7"	Apple	R5833	1970	£1.50	£4	chart single
Let It Be	7"	Apple	R5833	1970	£150	£250	demo
Let It Be	7"	Apple	R5833	1970	£4	£8	PS
Let It Be	7"	Apple	RP5833	1990	£5	£10	pic disc
Let It Be	7"	Parlophone	PR5833	1970	£25	£50	export
Long Tall Sally	78	Parlophone	DPE164	196-	£150	£250	Indian
Long Tall Sally	7"	Odeon	22745	1964	£7.50	£15	German import
Long Tall Sally	7" EP	Odeon	SOE3755	1964	£6	£12	French
Long Tall Sally	7" EP	Parlophone	GEP8913	1964	£4	£8	
Love Me Do	7"	Parlophone	R4949	1962	£700	£1000	demo, pictured in Guide
Love Me Do	7"	Parlophone	R4949	1962	£17.50	£35	red label, chart single
Love Me Do	7"	Parlophone	R4949	1963	£25	£50	black label
Love Me Do	7"	Parlophone	R4949	1982	£10	£20	Ardmore & Beechwood credit
Love Me Do	7"	Parlophone	RP4949	1982	£12.50	£25	Ardmore & Beechwood credit, pic disc
Love Me Do	7"	Parlophone	RP4949	1982	£12.50	£25	pic disc mispress - 2 A sides
Love Me Do	12"	Parlophone	12R4949	1982	£2.50	£6	
Magical Mystery Tour	LP	Capitol	MAL2835	1967	£25	£50	US, mono
Magical Mystery Tour	LP	Capitol	SMAL2835	1967	£5	£12	US, stereo, chart LP
Magical Mystery Tour	LP	Mobile Fidelity	MFSL1047	1981	£8	£20	US audiophile
Magical Mystery Tour	LP	Parlophone	PCTC255	1978	£20	£40	yellow vinyl
Magical Mystery Tour	CD	EMI	BEACD25/6	1987	£15	£30	HMV box, badge, booklet, poster
Magical Mystery Tour	7" EP	Odeon	MEOHS39501/2	1967	£7.50	£15	French double
Magical Mystery Tour	7" EP	Parlophone	MMT1	1967	£7.50	£15	double, mono
Magical Mystery Tour	7" EP	Parlophone	MMT1	1967	£15	£30	mispress with Beach Boys Darlin' on B side of Walrus
Magical Mystery Tour	7" EP	Parlophone	SMMT1	1967	£6	£12	double, stereo
Magical Mystery Tour	7" EP	Parlophone	SMMT1	197-	£2.50	£6	yellow lyric sheet
Meet The Beatles	LP	Capitol	ST2047	1964	£8	£20	US, brown title, stereo
Meet The Beatles	LP	Capitol	ST2047	1964	£6	£15	US, green title, stereo
Meet The Beatles	LP	Capitol	ST82047	1964	£25	£50	US, Record Club issue
Meet The Beatles	LP	Capitol	T2047	1964	£10	£25	US, brown title, mono
Meet The Beatles	LP	Capitol	T2047	1964	£8	£20	US, green title, mono
Michelle	78	Parlophone	DPE186	196-	£150	£250	Indian
Michelle	78	Parlophone	DPE187	196-	£150	£250	Indian
Michelle	7"	Parlophone	DP564	1966	£30	£60	export
Michelle	7" EP	Odeon	MEO102	1965	£5	£10	French
Misery	7" EP	Odeon	SOE3778	1965	£12.50	£25	French
Money	7"	Odeon	22638	1964	£6	£12	German import
No Reply	7"	Odeon	22893	1964	£6	£12	German import
Nowhere Man	7" EP	Parlophone	GEP8952	1966	£10	£20	
Ob-La-Di, Ob-La-Da	78	Parlophone	DPE192	196-	£150	£250	Indian
Only The Beatles	cass	EMI	SMMC151	1986	£6	£15	Heineken promotion
Paperback Writer	7"	Parlophone	R5452	1966	£1.50	£4	chart single
Paperback Writer	7"	Parlophone	R5452	1966	£210	£350	demo
Paperback Writer	7"	Parlophone	RP5452	1986	£5	£10	pic disc
Paperback Writer	7"	Parlophone	RP5452	1986	£12.50	£25	pic disc mispress - A side plays 'Friends Will Be Friends' by Queen
Paperback Writer	7" EP	Odeon	MEO119	1966	£5	£10	French
Past Masters Vol.1	CD	EMI	BEACD25/9	1987	£8	£20	HMV box, booklet, badge
Past Masters Vol.2	CD	EMI	BEACD25/10	1987	£8	£20	HMV box, booklet, badge
Penny Lane	7"	Parlophone	R5570	1967	£1.50	£4	chart single
Penny Lane	7"	Parlophone	R5570	1967	£180	£300	demo
Penny Lane	7"	Parlophone	R5570	1967	£10	£20	PS
Penny Lane	7"	Parlophone	RP5570	1987	£5	£10	pic disc

Title	Format	Label	Cat. No.	Year	Price	Price	Notes
Please Please Me	r-reel	Parlophone	TAPMC1202/ TDPCS3042	1963	£10	£25	
Please Please Me	LP	Mobile Fidelity	MFSL1101	1984	£6	£15	US audiophile
Please Please Me	LP	Parlophone	PCS3042	1963	£700	£1000	gold label stereo
Please Please Me	LP	Parlophone	PCS3042	1963	£10	£25	stereo, chart LP
Please Please Me	LP	Parlophone	PMC1202	1963	£8	£20	mono, chart LP
Please Please Me	LP	Parlophone	PMC1202	1963	£100	£200	mono, gold labe
Please Please Me	78	Parlophone		196-	£150	£250	Indian
Please Please Me	7"	Parlophone	R4983	1963	£2	£5	black label, chart single
Please Please Me	7"	Parlophone	R4983	1963	£400	£600	demo
Please Please Me	7"	Parlophone	R4983	1963	£17.50	£35	red labe
Please Please Me	7"	Parlophone	RP4983	1982	£10	£20	pic disc mispress, plays 'From Me To You
Please Please Me	7"	Parlophone	RP4983	1983	£5	£10	pic disc
Please Please Me/With.../Hard Day's Night/For Sale	CD	EMI	BEACD25	1987	£100	£200	HMV black box, book, leafle
Rarities	LP	Capitol	SN12009	1978	£17.50	£35	US green labe
Reel Music	LP	Capitol	SV12199	1982	£5	£12	US gold viny
Reel Music	LP	Capitol	SV12199	1982	£10	£25	US gold vinyl, numbered
Revolver	r-reel	Parlophone	TAPMC/ TDPCS7009	1966	£10	£25	
Revolver	LP	Capitol	ST2576	1966	£6	£15	US, stereo
Revolver	LP	Capitol	ST82576	1966	£25	£50	US, Record Club issue
Revolver	LP	Capitol	T2576	1966	£8	£20	US, mono
Revolver	LP	Mobile Fidelity	MFSL1107	1984	£6	£15	US audiophile
Revolver	LP	Parlophone	PMC/PCS7009	1966	£8	£20	chart LP
Rock And Roll Music	78	Parlophone	DPE179	196-	£150	£250	Indian
Roll Over Beethoven	7" EP	Odeon	SOE3746	1963	£7.50	£15	French
Rubber Soul	r-reel	Parlophone	TAPMC1267/ TDPCS3075	1966	£10	£25	
Rubber Soul	LP	Capitol	ST2442	1965	£6	£15	US, stereo
Rubber Soul	LP	Capitol	ST82442	1965	£25	£50	US, Record Club issue
Rubber Soul	LP	Capitol	T2442	1965	£8	£20	US, mono
Rubber Soul	LP	Mobile Fidelity	MFSL1106	1984	£6	£15	US audiophile
Rubber Soul	LP	Parlophone	PMC1267/ PCS3075	1966	£8	£20	chart LP
Searchin'	7"	AFE	AFS1	1982	£5	£10	
Sgt.Pepper	r-reel	Parlophone	TAPMC7027	1967	£10	£25	mono
Sgt.Pepper	r-reel	Parlophone	TDPCS7027	1967	£15	£30	stereo
Sgt.Pepper	LP	Capitol	MAS2653	1967	£15	£30	US, mono
Sgt.Pepper	LP	Capitol	SEAX11840	1978	£6	£15	US pic disc
Sgt.Pepper	LP	Capitol	SMAS2653	1967	£5	£12	US, stereo
Sgt.Pepper	LP	Mobile Fidelity	MFSL1100	1982	£6	£15	US audiophile
Sgt.Pepper	LP	Mobile Fidelity	UHQR1100	1982	£100	£200	US audiophile, quarter inch thick vinyl
Sgt.Pepper	LP	Parlophone	PCS7027	1967	£8	£20	stereo, chart L
Sgt.Pepper	LP	Parlophone	PHO7027	1979	£5	£12	pic disc
Sgt.Pepper	LP	Parlophone	PMC7027	1967	£15	£30	mono, chart L
Sgt.Pepper	LP	Parlophone	PMC7027	1982	£6	£15	from BMC10, but with stereo B sid
Sgt.Pepper	CD	EMI	BEACD25/3	1987	£10	£25	HMV box, badge booklet, cutout
She Loves You	7"	Parlophone	R5055	1963	£1.50	£4	chart sing.
She Loves You	7"	Parlophone	R5055	1963	£210	£350	demo
She Loves You	7"	Parlophone	RP5055	1983	£7.50	£15	pic disc
She Loves You	7" EP	Odeon	SOE3741	1963	£7.50	£15	French, slightly different sleeve
Something	7"	Apple	R5814	1969	£1.50	£4	chart single
Something	7"	Apple	R5814	1969	£150	£250	demo
Something	7"	Apple	RP5814	1989	£5	£10	pic disc
Something New	LP	Capitol	ST2108	1964	£6	£15	US, stereo
Something New	LP	Capitol	ST82108	1964	£25	£50	US, Record Club issu
Something New	LP	Capitol	T2108	1964	£8	£20	US, mono
Something New	LP	Parlophone	CPCS101	1965	£250	£400	export
Something New	LP	Parlophone	CPCS101	1969	£100	£200	export silver & black lab
Songs, Pictures And Stories	LP	Vee Jay	LP1092	1964	£37.50	£75	US, fold-open cove
Strawberry Fields Forever	7" EP	Odeon	MEO134	1967	£5	£10	Frenc
Tell Me What You See	7" EP	Odeon	SOE3775	1965	£7.50	£15	Frenc
Tell Me Why	78	Parlophone	DPE172	196-	£150	£250	Indian
Their Greatest Hits	cass	St.Michael	13615701	1984	£8	£20	with boo
Ticket To Ride	7"	Parlophone	R5265	1965	£1.50	£4	chart sing
Ticket To Ride	7"	Parlophone	R5265	1965	£210	£350	demo
Ticket To Ride	7"	Parlophone	RP5265	1985	£5	£10	pic di
Ticket To Ride	7"	Parlophone	RP5265	1985	£10	£20	pic di mispress, B sid plays 'Some Like Hot' by Power Static
Ticket To Ride	7" EP	Odeon	SOE3766	1965	£7.50	£15	Frenc
Twist And Shout	7"	Lingasong	NB1	1977	£7.50	£15	
Twist And Shout	7"	Odeon	22581	1964	£6	£12	German impo
Twist And Shout	7" EP	Parlophone	GEP8882	1963	£2.50	£6	
Volume 1	7" EP	Odeon	MOE21001	1965	£25	£50	Frenc
Volume 2	7" EP	Odeon	MOE21002	1965	£25	£50	Frenc
Volume 3	7" EP	Odeon	MOE21003	1965	£40	£80	Frenc

Title	Format	Label	Catalogue	Year	Low	High	Notes
Volume 4	7" EP	Odeon	MOE21004	1965	£25	£50	French
We Can Work It Out	7" EP	Odeon	MEO107	1965	£5	£10	French
With The Beatles	r-reel	Parlophone	TAPMC1206/ TDPCS3045	1964	£10	£25	
With The Beatles	LP	Mobile Fidelity	MFSL1102	1984	£20	£40	US audiophile
With The Beatles	LP	Parlophone	PCS3045	1963	£10	£25	stereo, chart LP
With The Beatles	LP	Parlophone	PMC1206	1963	£8	£20	mono, chart LP
Words Of Love	78	Parlophone	DPE180	196-	£150	£250	Indian
World Records Presents The Music Of The Beatles	7"	Lyntone	LYN8982	1980	£5	£10	promo flexi
Yellow Submarine	r-reel	Apple	TAPMC/ TDPCS7070	1969	£15	£30	
Yellow Submarine	LP	Apple	PCS7070	1969	£6	£15	stereo, chart LP
Yellow Submarine	LP	Apple	PMC7070	1969	£17.50	£35	mono, chart LP
Yellow Submarine	LP	Apple	SW153	1968	£4	£10	US
Yellow Submarine	LP	Mobile Fidelity	MFSL1108	1984	£6	£15	US audiophile
Yellow Submarine	LP	Odeon	PPCS7070	1969	£180	£300	export
Yellow Submarine	LP	Parlophone	PPCS7070	1969	£100	£200	export, silver & black label
Yellow Submarine	LP	Parlophone	PPCS7070	1969	£250	£400	export, yellow & black label
Yellow Submarine	CD	EMI	BEACD25/5	1987	£25	£50	HMV box, badge, cutout, leaflet
Yellow Submarine	7"	Parlophone	R5493	1966	£1.50	£4	chart single
Yellow Submarine	7"	Parlophone	R5493	1966	£180	£300	demo
Yellow Submarine	7"	Parlophone	RP5493	1986	£5	£10	pic disc
Yellow Submarine	7" EP	Odeon	MEO126	1966	£5	£10	French
Yesterday	78	Parlophone	DPE184	196-	£150	£250	Indian
Yesterday	7"	Parlophone	DP563	1965	£30	£60	export
Yesterday	7" EP	Odeon	MEO105	1965	£5	£10	French
Yesterday	7" EP	Odeon	SOE3772	1965	£7.50	£15	French
Yesterday	7" EP	Parlophone	GEP8948	1966	£7.50	£15	
Yesterday And Today	LP	Capitol	ST2553	1966	£2100	£3000	US, peeled butcher sleeve, stereo, sleeve pictured in Guide
Yesterday And Today	LP	Capitol	ST2553	1966	£6	£15	US, stereo
Yesterday And Today	LP	Capitol	ST2553	1966	£400	£600	US, unpeeled butcher sleeve, stereo
Yesterday And Today	LP	Capitol	ST82553	1966	£25	£50	US, Record Club issue
Yesterday And Today	LP	Capitol	T2553	1966	£530	£800	US peeled butcher sleeve
Yesterday And Today	LP	Capitol	T2553	1966	£100	£200	US unpeeled butcher sleeve
Yesterday And Today	LP	Capitol	T2553	1966	£8	£20	US, mono
You Like Me Too Much	78	Parlophone	DPE185	196-	£150	£250	Indian
You've Got To Hide Your Love Away	7" EP	Odeon	SOE3772	1965	£12.50	£25	French

BEATLES & OTHERS

Title	Format	Label	Catalogue	Year	Low	High	Notes
Our First Four	7"	Apple		1968	£530	£800	promo, pack with 4 x 7'

BEATLES & TONY SHERIDAN

Title	Format	Label	Catalogue	Year	Low	High	Notes
Early Years	LP	Contour	2870111	1971	£4	£10	
Ain't She Sweet	LP	Atco	33169	1964	£30	£60	US, mono
Ain't She Sweet	LP	Atco	SD33169	1964	£37.50	£75	US, stereo
Ain't She Sweet	7"	Polydor	NH52317	1964	£17.50	£35	chart single, orange label
Ain't She Sweet	7"	Polydor	NH52317	1967	£6	£12	red label
Ain't She Sweet	7" EP	Polydor	21965	1964	£15	£30	French
Beatles First	CD	Polydor	8237012	1985	£27.50	£55	withdrawn sleeve with wrong line-up
Beatles' First	LP	Polydor	236201	1964	£25	£50	rough red label
Beatles' First	LP	Polydor	236201	1967	£17.50	£35	smooth red label
Beatles' First	LP	Polydor	POLD666	197-	£15	£30	
Cry For A Shadow	7"	Polydor	NH52275	1964	£20	£40	orange label
Cry For A Shadow	7"	Polydor	NH52275	1967	£6	£12	red label
Mister Twist	7" EP	Polydor	21914	1962	£20	£40	French
My Bonnie	7"	Polydor	NH66833	1962	£30	£60	chart single, orange label
My Bonnie	7"	Polydor	NH66833	1967	£6	£12	red label
Sweet Georgia Brown	7"	Polydor	NH52906	1964	£40	£80	orange label
Sweet Georgia Brown	7"	Polydor	NH52906	1967	£12.50	£25	red label
Tony Sheridan With The Beatles	7" EP	Polydor	EPH21610	1963	£25	£50	sleeve pictured in Guide
When The Saints	7" EP	Polydor	21914	1963	£15	£30	French, 2 different sleeves

BEATMEN

Title	Format	Label	Catalogue	Year	Low	High	Notes
Now The Sun Has Gone	7"	Pye	7N15792	1965	£2	£5	
You Can't Sit Down	7"	Pye	7N15659	1964	£2.50	£6	

BEATSTALKERS

Title	Format	Label	Catalogue	Year	Low	High	Notes
Everybody's Talkin' About My Baby	7"	Decca	F12259	1965	£4	£8	
Everything Is You	7"	CBS	3557	1968	£6	£12	
Left Right Left	7"	Decca	F12352	1966	£5	£10	
Love Like Yours	7"	Decca	F12460	1966	£6	£12	
My One Chance	7"	CBS	2732	1967	£7.50	£15	
Silver Tree Top School For Boys	7"	CBS	3105	1967	£10	£20	
When I'm Five	7"	CBS	3936	1969	£6	£12	

You'd Better Get A Better Hold On .... 7" EP.. Decca .... 457112.................... 1966 ... £50 ....£100 ....Frenc

BEATTIE, PAUL
I'm Comin' Home .... 7"........ Parlophone...... R4385 .... 1957 ... £1.50 ....£4

BEATTY, E.C.
Ski King .... 7"....... Felsted .... AF127 .... 1959 ... £4 ....£8

BEAU
C.J.T.Midgley (Beau) was a singer songwriter whose songs would have benefitted from more fully worked out arrangements than the actually get. No doubt John Peel's Dandelion label could not afford the expense of a cast of session musicians. Nevertheless, "191 Revolution" with its taut strummed twelve string guitar echoing across the sound-stage is quite wonderful.

1917 Revolution	7"	Dandelion	K4403	1970	£1.50	£4	
Beau	LP	Dandelion	63751	1969	£8	£20	
Creation	LP	Dandelion	DAN8006	1971	£8	£20	

BEAU BRUMMELS
The natural response of America to the initial furore surrounding the Beatles was for the record-buying public to embrace a number of hom grown talents, whose sound and style owed everything to their Liverpudlian rivals. The Beau Brummels were probably the most successf of these, although they inevitably meant little in Britain. As a result, one of the classic albums of the late sixties has been largely ignored - f "Triangle" is an immaculate collection of imaginatively arranged songs to rival Love's "Forever Changes".

Beau Brummels	LP	Pye	NPL28062	1965	£10	£25	
Beau Brummels 66	LP	Warner Bros	W(S)1644	1966	£8	£20	U
Beau Brummels Vol.2	LP	Autumn	(S)LP104	1966	£8	£20	U
Best Of The Beau Brummels	LP	Vault	LPS114	1967	£6	£15	U
Bradley's Barn	LP	Warner Bros	WS1760	1968	£8	£20	U
Don't Talk To Strangers	7"	Pye	7N25333	1965	£2	£5	
Good Time Music	7"	Pye	7N25342	1966	£2	£5	
Here We Are Again	7" EP..	Warner Bros	WB112	1966	£12.50	£25	Frenc
Just A Little	7"	Pye	7N25306	1965	£2	£5	
Just A Little	7" EP..	Vogue	INT18010	1965	£12.50	£25	Frenc
Laugh Laugh	7"	Pye	7N25293	1965	£2.50	£6	
Laugh Laugh	7" EP..	Vogue	INT18002	1965	£12.50	£25	Frenc
Triangle	LP	Warner Bros	W(S)1692	1967	£8	£20	U!
Vol.44	LP	Vault	LPS121	1967	£8	£20	U!
You Tell Me Why	7"	Pye	7N25318	1965	£2	£5	

BEAUMARKS
Clap Your Hands .... 7"........ Top Rank .... JAR377 .... 1960 ... £4 ....£8

BEAUMONT, JIMMY
You Got Too Much Going For You .... 7"........ London .... HLZ10059 .... 1966 ... £15 ....£30

BEAVER, PAUL
Perchance To Dream .... LP ...... Rapture .... 11111 .... £6 ....£15 ....U

BEAVER-KRAUSE
Paul Beaver and Bernie Krause were the other pair of synthesiser pioneers, but, unlike the records by Tonto's Expanding Headband, their mix the electronics with conventional instruments. The "Guide To Electronic Music" is by way of being an aural handbook, recorded for a avant-garde classical label.

All Good Men	LP	Warner Bros	K46184	1972	£5	£12	
Gandharva	LP	Warner Bros	K46130	1971	£5	£12	
In A Wild Sanctuary	LP	Warner Bros	WS1850	1970	£5	£12	U
Nonesuch Guide To Electronic Music	LP	Nonesuch	HC73018	1968	£6	£15	
Ragnarok Electronic Funk	LP	Limelight	86069	1969	£6	£15	U!

BEAZERS (CHRIS FARLOWE)
Blue Beat .... 7"........ Decca .... F11827 .... 1964 ... £7.50 ....£15

BEBOP DELUXE
Between Two Worlds	7"	Harvest	HAR5091	1975	£15	£30	
Jet Silver And The Dolls Of Venus	7"	Harvest	HAR5081	1974	£1.50	£4	
Teenage Archangel	7"	Smile	LAFS001	1973	£7.50	£15	

BEBOP PRESERVATION SOCIETY
Bebop Preservation Society .... LP ...... Dawn .... DNLS3027 .... 1971 ... £5 ....£12

BECHET, SIDNEY
At Storyville	10" LP	Vogue	LDE132	1955	£20	£40	
At Storyville	10" LP	Vogue	LDE149	1955	£20	£40	
Blue Note Jazz Men	10" LP	Vogue	LDE025	1953	£25	£50	
Blue Note Jazzmen	10" LP	Vogue	LDE127	1955	£20	£40	
Blue Note Jazzmen Vol.2	10" LP	Vogue	LDE086	1954	£20	£40	
Fabulous	LP	Blue Note	BLP/BST81207	196-	£8	£20	
Festival de Jazz 1958	LP	Vogue	LAE12168	1959	£6	£15	
Giant Of Jazz Vol.1	LP	Blue Note	BLP/BST81203	196-	£8	£20	
Giant Of Jazz Vol.2	LP	Blue Note	BLP/BST81204	196-	£8	£20	
Golden Disc Concert	LP	Vogue	LAE12010	1956	£10	£25	
Golden Disc Concert	LP	Vogue	LAE12011	1956	£10	£25	
Hot Six	10" LP	Vogue	LDE138	1955	£20	£40	
Jazz Classics Vol.1	LP	Blue Note	BLP/BST81201	196-	£8	£20	
Jazz Classics Vol.2	LP	Blue Note	BLP/BST81202	196-	£8	£20	
Jazz Concert Vol.1	10" LP	Vogue	LDE018	1953	£20	£40	
Jazz Concert Vol.2	10" LP	Vogue	LDE019	1953	£20	£40	
Jazz Concert Vol.3	10" LP	Vogue	LDE027	1953	£20	£40	
Last Show	LP	Pye	NPL28006	1959	£6	£15	
New Orleans In Paris	10" LP	Vogue	LDE069	1954	£20	£40	
Shake It And Break It	10" LP	HMV	DLP1042	1954	£20	£40	
Sidney Bechet	10" LP	Columbia	33S1042	1954	£20	£40	
Sidney Bechet	10" LP	Vogue	LDE001	1952	£20	£40	
Vogue Jazzmen	10" LP	Vogue	LDE119	1955	£20	£40	

With Sammy Price's Bluesicians	LP	Vogue	LAE12037	1957	£10	£25
With The Claude Luter Orchestra	LP	Vogue	LAE12003	1955	£10	£25
With The Claude Luter Orchestra	LP	Vogue	LAE12024	1956	£10	£25

BECK, BOGERT & APPICE

Beck, Bogert & Appice	LP	CBS	Q65455	1975	£5	£12	quad
Live In Japan	LP	CBS/Sony	ECPJ11/12	1973	£8	£20	Japanese double

BECK, ELDER CHARLES

RCA Victor Race Series Vol.5	7" EP	RCA	RCX7176	1965	£2	£5

BECK, GORDON

Beck-Matthewson-Humair Trio	LP	Dire	FO341	1972	£15	£30
Experiments With Pops	LP	Major Minor	MMLP/SMLP21	1969	£15	£30
Gyroscope	LP	Morgan	MJ1	1968	£20	£40
Plays Dr.Doolittle	LP	Major Minor	SML88	1968	£15	£30
Plays Half A Jazz Sixpence	LP	Major Minor	MMLP/SMLP22	1968	£15	£30

BECK, JEFF

When the Observer surveyed a number of well-known rock guitarists to discover who the "guitarists' guitarist" was, the consensus of opinion chose Jeff Beck. Notoriously difficult to work with, Beck's career has been notable for the instability of his group line-ups and also for his apparent difficulty in deciding on the best music style to display his talents. He has, nevertheless, managed to create the occasional masterpiece along the way, of which the most obvious examples are the electric jazz album "Blow By Blow" (too common to be valuable, unfortunately) and the blues-rock "Truth". This record, which included Rod Stewart and Ron Wood as members of a fine band, was a direct influence on Led Zeppelin, whose guitarist Jimmy Page used to very much model his guitar playing on that of Jeff Beck.

Beck-ola	LP	Columbia	SCX6351	1969	£5	£12	chart LP
Blow By Blow	LP	Epic	PEQ33409	1975	£6	£15	US quad
Hi Ho Silver Lining	7"	Columbia	DB8151	1967	£2.50	£6	chart single
Hi Ho Silver Lining	7"	RAK	RRP3	1982	£2.50	£6	pic disc
Jeff Beck Group	LP	Epic	EQ31331	1974	£6	£15	US quad
Live	LP	Epic	PEQ34433	1977	£6	£15	US quad
Love Is Blue	7"	Columbia	DB8359	1968	£2.50	£6	chart single
Plinth	7"	Columbia	DB8590	1968	£20	£40	promo only
Rough And Ready	LP	Epic	Q64619	1974	£6	£15	quad
Tallyman	7"	Columbia	DB8227	1967	£5	£10	chart single
Truth	LP	Columbia	SCX6293	1968	£6	£15	
Truth	7"	Columbia	PSR317	1968	£10	£20	promo
Wired	LP	Epic	PEQ33849	1976	£6	£15	US quad

BECKETT, HAROLD

Harold Beckett is a jazz trumpeter whose playing seems to be included somewhere on most British rock LPs made in the early seventies! His own records, which feature the usual familiar jazz faces of the period, are actually remarkably free from rock influence, which is the reason for their relatively low collectors' values today.

Flare Up	LP	Philips	6308026	1971	£8	£20
Joy Unlimited	LP	Cadillac	SGC1004	1975	£6	£15
Theme For Fega	LP	RCA	SF8264	1973	£8	£20
Warm Smiles	LP	RCA	SF8225	1972	£8	£20

BECKFORD, KEITH

Suzy Wong	7"	Big Shot	BI521	1969	£2.50	£6

BECKFORD, LYN

Kiss Me Quick	7"	Jackpot	JP707	1969	£2.50	£6	Mr.Miller B side

BECKFORD, LYNN

Combination	7"	Island	WI3144	1968	£5	£10

BECKFORD, THEO

Bollerman	7"	Island	WI106	1963	£5	£10
Bringing In The Sheep	7"	Blue Beat	BB132	1962	£5	£10
Brother Ram Goat	7"	Crab	CRAB25	1969	£2.50	£6	Starlights B side
Dig The Dig	7"	Blue Beat	BB303	1964	£5	£10
Don't Worry To Cry	7"	Blue Beat	BB257	1964	£5	£10
Easy Snappin'	7"	Nu Beat	NB009	1968	£4	£8	Eric Morris B side
Easy Snapping	7"	Blue Beat	BB15	1961	£5	£10
Georgie And The Old Shoes	7"	Blue Beat	BB50	1961	£5	£10
I Don't Want You	7"	Island	WI026	1962	£5	£10
If Life Was A Thing	7"	Island	WI246	1965	£5	£10	Lloyd Clarke B side
Jack And Jill Shuffle	7"	Blue Beat	BB33	1961	£5	£10
On Your Knees	7"	Blue Beat	BB287	1964	£5	£10
She's Gone	7"	Blue Beat	BB250	1964	£5	£10
Take Your Time	7"	Black Swan	WI452	1965	£5	£10	Stranger Cole B side
Trench Town People	7"	Island	WI238	1965	£5	£10	Pioneers B side
Walking Down King Street	7"	Blue Beat	BB87	1961	£5	£10	Sir Dee's Group B side
What A Woe	7"	Island	WI248	1965	£5	£10
You Are The One	7"	Island	WI243	1965	£5	£10

BEDFORD, DAVID

David Bedford is an avant-garde composer whose sympathy for rock music has led to his gaining much employment as an arranger. In particular, he has worked extensively with Mike Oldfield, producing an orchestral version of "Tubular Bells" and writing a guitar concerto for him (the superb 'Star's End'', which should be required listening for Jon Lord, Keith Emerson, and other rock-classical fusionists whose ideas of how classical music is constructed are still rooted in the nineteenth century). "Nurses Song With Elephants" is less accessible than later Bedford works, but is still crammed with original ideas.

Music For Albion Moonlight	LP	Argo	ZRG638	1970	£8	£20	other side Elizabeth Lutyens
Nurses Song With Elephants	LP	Dandelion	2310165	1972	£8	£20

BEDLAM

Bedlam	LP	Chrysalis	CHR1048	1973	£5	£12

BEDROCKS
Ob La Di Ob La Da .... 7" ...... Columbia .... DB8516 .... 1968 ... £1.50 ....£4 .... chart single

BEE, EDWIN
I've Been Loving You .... 7" .... Decca .... F12781 .... 1968 ... £2.50 ....£6 ....

BEE GEES
Title		Label	Cat No	Year			
Bee Gees First	LP	Polydor	582/583012	1967 ...	£4	.....£10	.... chart LP
Boogie Child	7"	RSO	2090224	1977 ...	£5	.....£10	.... promo only
Cucumber Castle	LP	Polydor	2383010	1970 ...	£4	.....£10	.... chart LP
Don't Forget To Remember	7"	Polydor	56343	1969 ...	£1.50	.....£4	...... chart single
First Of May	7"	Polydor	56304	1969 ...	£1.50	.....£4	...... chart single
Horizontal	LP	Polydor	582/583020	1968 ...	£4	.....£10	.... chart LP
Idea	LP	Polydor	582/583036	1968 ...	£4	.....£10	.... chart LP
Inception	LP	Karussell	2674002	1973 ...	£30	.....£60	.... German
I.O.I.O.	7"	Polydor	56377	1970 ...	£1.50	.....£4	...... chart single
I've Gotta Get A Message To You	7"	Polydor	56273	1968 ...	£1.50	.....£4	...... chart single
Jumbo	7"	Polydor	56242	1968 ...	£1.50	.....£4	...... chart single
Life In A Tin Can	LP	RSO	2394102	1973 ...	£4	.....£10	....
Lonely Days	7"	Polydor	2001104	1970 ...	£1.50	.....£4	...... chart single
Massachusetts	7"	Polydor	56192	1967 ...	£1.50	.....£4	...... chart single
Mr.Natural	LP	RSO	2394132	1974 ...	£4	.....£10	....
New York Mining Disaster 1941	7"	Polydor	56161	1967 ...	£1.50	.....£4	...... chart single
New York Mining Disaster 1941	7" EP..	Polydor	27806	1967 ...	£6	.....£12	.... French
Odessa	LP	Polydor	583049/050	1969 ...	£6	.....£15	... felt sleeve, chart LP
Odessa	7"	Polydor	56304	1969 ...	£10	.....£20	....
Rare Precious & Beautiful Vol.1	LP	Polydor	236221	1968 ...	£4	.....£10	....
Rare Precious & Beautiful Vol.2	LP	Polydor	236513	1968 ...	£4	.....£10	....
Rare Precious & Beautiful Vol.3	LP	Polydor	236556	1969 ...	£4	.....£10	....
Short Cuts	LP	RSO	BGPLP1	1979 ...	£4	.....£10	.... promo
Sing & Play 14 Barry Gibb Songs	LP	Calendar	R66241	1968 ...	£20	.....£40	... Australian reissue
Sing & Play 14 Barry Gibb Songs	LP	Leedon	LL31801	1965 ...	£60	.....£120	.... Australian
Spicks And Specks	LP	Spin	EL32031	1966 ...	£8	.....£20	.... Australian
Spicks And Specks	7"	Polydor	56727	1967 ...	£4	.....£8	....
Spirits Having Flown	LP	Nautilus	NR17	1981 ...	£5	.....£12	... US audiophile
Spirits Having Flown	LP	RSO	13041	1979 ...	£4	.....£10	...US pic disc
To Love Somebody	7"	Polydor	56178	1967 ...	£1.50	.....£4	...... chart single
To Love Somebody	7" EP..	Polydor	27811	1967 ...	£6	.....£12	.... French
To Whom It May Concern	LP	Polydor	2383139	1972 ...	£4	.....£10	....
Tomorrow Tomorrow	7"	Polydor	56331	1969 ...	£1.50	.....£4	...... chart single
Trafalgar	LP	Polydor	2383052	1971 ...	£4	.....£10	....
Two Years On	LP	Polydor	2310069	1970 ...	£4	.....£10	....
Words	7"	Polydor	56229	1968 ...	£1.50	.....£4	...... chart single
World	7"	Polydor	56220	1967 ...	£1.50	.....£4	...... chart single

BEE, MOLLY
Title		Label	Cat No	Year		
Five Points Of A Star	7"	Capitol	CL14949	1958 ...	£1.50	.....£4
Going Steady	7"	Capitol	CL14849	1958 ...	£1.50	.....£4
Please Don't Talk About Me	7"	Capitol	CL14880	1958 ...	£1.50	.....£4
Since I Met You Baby	7"	London	HLD8400	1957 ...	£4	.....£8
Single Girl Again	7"	MGM	MGM1280	1965 ...	£1.50	.....£4

BEEFEATERS
Please Let Me Love You .... 7" ...... Elektra .... 2101007 .... 1970 ... £6 .....£12
Please Let Me Love You .... 7" ...... Pye .... 7N25277 .... 1964 ... £37.50 ....£75

BEEFEATERS (2)
Meet You There .... LP ...... Sonet .... SPLP1509 .... 1969 ... £8 .....£20

BEER, MARK
Dust On The Road .... LP ...... My China .... TAO001 .... 1981 ... £8 .....£20

BEES
Jesse James Rides Again .... 7" ...... Columbia .... DB101 .... 1967 ... £4 .....£8
Prisoner From Alcatraz .... 7" ...... Columbia .... DB111 .... 1968 ... £4 .....£8

BEES MAKE HONEY
Music Every Night .... LP ...... EMI .... EMC3013 .... 1972 ... £8 .....£20

BEGGARS FARM
Depth Of A Dream .... LP ...... White Rabbit ... WR1001 .... 1984 ... £15 ....£30

BEGGAR'S HILL
Beggar's Hill .... LP ...... Moonshine ...... MS60 .... 1976 ... £100 .....£200

BEGGARS OPERA
Title		Label	Cat No	Year			
Act One	LP	Vertigo	6360018	1970 ...	£10	.....£25	...... spiral label
Get Your Dog Off Me	LP	Vertigo	6360090	1973 ...	£4	.....£10	....
Pathfinder	LP	Vertigo	6360073	1972 ...	£8	.....£20	...... spiral label
Sagittary	LP	Jupiter	88907	1974 ...	£6	.....£15	.... German
Sarabande	7"	Vertigo	6059026	1970 ...	£4	.....£8	....
Waters Of Change	LP	Vertigo	6360054	1971 ...	£8	.....£20	...... spiral label

BEGINNING OF THE END
Funky Nassau .... LP ...... Atlantic .... K40304 .... 1971 ... £6 .....£15
Funky Nassau .... 7" ...... Atlantic .... 2091097 .... 1971 ... £1.50 .....£4

BEHAN, BRENDAN
Hostage .... LP ...... Argo .... RG239 .... 1960 ... £8 ....£20

BEHAN, DOMINIC

Arkle	7"	Piccadilly	7N35238	1965	£1.50	£4
Bells Of Hell	7"	Decca	F11147	1959	£1.50	£4
Cosmopolitan Man	LP	Folklore	FLEUT4	1962	£20	£40
Down By The Liffeyside	LP	Topic	12T35	1960	£15	£30
Easter Week And After	LP	Topic	12T44	1961	£15	£30
Finnegan's Wake	7" EP	Collector	JEI4	1960	£12.50	£25
Ireland Sings	LP	Pye	NPL18134	1965	£10	£25
Irish Rover	LP	Folklore	FLEUT2	1961	£20	£40
Liverpool Lou	7"	Piccadilly	7N35172	1964	£1.50	£4
Lots Of Fun At Finnegan's Wake	7" EP	Collector	JEI1	1959	£12.50	£25
McCafferty	7" EP	Collector	JEI2	1959	£12.50	£25
Patriot Game	7"	Topic	STOP115	1964	£2	£5
Rifles Of The IRA	7"	Major Minor	MM575	1968	£1.50	£4
Songs Of The Streets	7" EP	Collector	JEI3	1959	£12.50	£25

BEIDERBECKE, BIX

Bix Beiderbecke	7" EP	Columbia	SEG7577	1956	£4	£8
Bix Beiderbecke And His Orchestra	7" EP	Columbia	SEG7523	1955	£4	£8
Bix Beiderbecke And The Wolverines	10" LP	London	AL3532	1954	£10	£25
Great Bix	10" LP	Columbia	33S1035	1954	£6	£15

BEL CANTOS

Feel Alright	7"	R&B	MRB5003	1965	£4	£8

BELAFONTE, HARRY

Banana Boat Song	7"	HMV	POP308	1957	£2	£5	chart single
Calypso	7" EP	HMV	7EG8211	1957	£2	£5	
Close Your Eyes	7"	Capitol	CL14312	1955	£1.50	£4	
Close Your Eyes	7" EP	Capitol	EAP1619	1956	£2	£5	
Hold 'Em Joe	7"	HMV	7M202	1954	£1.50	£4	
I'm Just A Country Boy	7"	HMV	7M242	1954	£1.50	£4	
Island In The Sun	7"	RCA	RCA1007	1957	£1.50	£4	chart single
Mary's Boy Child	7"	RCA	RCA1022	1957	£1.50	£4	chart single
Mathilda Mathilda	7" EP	HMV	7EG8259	1957	£2	£5	
Scarlet Ribbons	7"	HMV	POP360	1957	£1.50	£4	chart single
Versatile Mr.Belafonte	10" LP	HMV	DLP1147	1957	£4	£10	

BELFAST GYPSIES

Gloria's Dream	7"	Island	WI3007	1966	£6	£12	
Gloria's Dream	7" EP	Vogue	INT18079	1966	£25	£50	French

BELIEVERS

Money In The Rock	7"	Masters Time	MT001	196-	£2.50	£6

BELIN, ED TEX

Ed Tex Belin	7" EP	Starlite	GRK509	1966	£2	£5
Ed Tex Belin	7" EP	Starlite	STEP39	1963	£4	£8

BELL, ALEXANDER

Alexander Bell Believes	7"	CBS	2977	1967	£4	£8

BELL, ARCHIE & THE DRELLS

I Can't Stop Dancing	7"	Atlantic	584217	1968	£1.50	£4
Tighten Up	LP	Atlantic		1968	£6	£15
Tighten Up	7"	Atlantic	2091156	1971	£1.50	£4
Tighten Up	7"	Atlantic	584185	1968	£2	£5

BELL, BENNY & THE BLOCKBUSTERS

Sack Dress	7"	Parlophone	R4372	1957	£2	£5

BELL BROTHERS

Tell Him No	7"	Action	ACT4510	1968	£2	£5

BELL, CAREY

Carey Bell	LP	Delmark	DS622	1971	£6	£15

BELL, FREDDY & THE BELL BOYS

Bells Are Swinging	LP	20th Century	(S)4146	1964	£5	£12	US
Big Bad Wolf	78	Mercury	MT149	1957	£2.50	£6	
Giddy-Up-A-Ding-Dong	78	Mercury	MT122	1956	£2.50	£6	chart single
Hucklebuck	78	Mercury	MT141	1957	£2.50	£6	
Rock And Roll - All Flavors	LP	Mercury	MG20289	1958	£25	£50	US
Rock With The Bell Boys	7" EP	Mercury	MEP9508	1956	£15	£30	
Rock With The Bell Boys Vol.2	7" EP	Mercury	MEP9512	1957	£20	£40	
Rockin' Is My Business	78	Mercury	MT159	1957	£2.50	£6	
Teach You To Rock	78	Mercury	MT146	1957	£2.50	£6	

BELL, FREDERICK

Rocksteady Cool	7"	Nu Beat	NB004	1968	£4	£8

BELL, GRAHAM

Graham Bell	LP	Charisma	CAS1061	1972	£6	£15
How Can You Say I Don't Love You	7"	Polydor	56067	1966	£4	£8

BELL, MADELINE

Because You Didn't Care	7"	HMV	POP1215	1963	£2.50	£6
Bells A-Poppin'	LP	Philips	(S)BL7818	1967	£5	£12
Climb Every Mountain	7"	Philips	BF1596	1967	£1.50	£4
Daytime	7"	Columbia	DB7512	1965	£1.50	£4
Doin' Things	LP	Philips	SBL7865	1969	£4	£10

Don't Come Running To Me	7"	Philips	BF1501	1966	£4	£8	
Hold It	7"	Philips	BF1726	1968	£1.50	£4	
If You Didn't Hear Me The First Time	7"	Philips	6006082	1970	£1.50	£4	
I'm Gonna Make You Love Me	7"	Philips	BF1656	1968	£1.50	£4	
One Step At A Time	7"	Philips	BF1526	1966	£1.50	£4	
Picture Me Gone	7"	Philips	BF1611	1967	£7.50	£15	
Thinkin'	7"	Philips	BF1688	1968	£1.50	£4	
We're So Much In Love	7"	Philips	BF1799	1969	£1.50	£4	
What The World Needs Now	7"	Philips	BF1448	1965	£4	£8	
You Don't Love Me No More	7"	Columbia	DB7257	1964	£1.50	£4	

BELL, MAGGIE

Queen Of The Night	LP	Polydor	2383239	1973	£5	£12	
Suicide Sal	LP	Polydor	2383313	1975	£5	£12	

BELL SOUNDS

Marching Guitars	7"	HMV	POP685	1959	£1.50	£4	

BELL, WILLIAM

Bound To Happen	LP	Stax	SXATS1016	1970	£4	£10	
Eloise	7"	Stax	601019	1967	£1.50	£4	
Every Day Will Be Like A Holiday	7"	Atlantic	584259	1969	£1.50	£4	
Happy	7"	Stax	STAX128	1969	£2	£5	
I Forgot How To Be Your Lover	7"	Stax	STAX110	1969	£1.50	£4	
My Whole World Is Falling Down	7"	Stax	STAX121	1969	£1.50	£4	
Never Like This Before	7"	Atlantic	584076	1967	£1.50	£4	
Tribute To A King	LP	Atco	228003	1969	£4	£10	
Tribute To A King	7"	Stax	601038	1968	£1.50	£4	chart single

BELLA & ME

Help Me Break The Habit	7"	Columbia	DB8243	1967	£1.50	£4	

BELLAMY, GEORGE

Where I'm Bound	7"	Parlophone	R5282	1965	£2.50	£6	

BELLAMY, PETER

Barrack Room Ballads	LP	Free Reed	FRR014	1977	£6	£15	
Both Sides Then	LP	Topic	12TS400	1979	£5	£12	
Fair England's Shore	LP	XTRA	XTRA1075	1969	£10	£25	
Fox Jumps Over The Parson's Gate	LP	Topic	12T200	1970	£10	£25	
Keep On Kipling	LP	Fellside	FE032	1982	£6	£15	
Mainly Norfolk	LP	XTRA	XTRA1060	1968	£8	£20	
Merlin's Isle Of Gramarye	LP	Argo	ZFB81	1972	£10	£25	
Oak, Ash And Thorn	LP	Argo	ZFB11	1970	£8	£20	
Peter Bellamy	LP	Green Linnet	SIF1001	1975	£6	£15	US
Rudyard Kipling Made Exceedingly Good Songs	LP	Dambuster	DAM019	1989	£5	£12	
Second Wind	LP	EFDSS	ES002	1985	£5	£12	
Tell It Like It Was	LP	Trailer	LER2089	1975	£6	£15	
Transports	LP	Free Reed	FRR021/2	1977	£8	£20	Double
Won't You Go My Way	LP	Argo	ZFB37	1970	£8	£20	with Louis Killen

BELLES

Don't Pretend	7"	President	PT311	1970	£1.50	£4	

BELLETTO, AL

Half And Half	LP	Capitol	T751	1957	£6	£15	

BELLINE, DENNY & THE RICH KIDS

Denny Belline And The Rich Kids	LP	RCA	LPM/LSP3655	1966	£5	£12	US

BELLNOTES

I've Had It	7"	Top Rank	JAR102	1959	£1.50	£4	
She Went Thataway	7"	Top Rank	JAR147	1959	£1.50	£4	
That's Right	7"	Top Rank	JAR201	1959	£1.50	£4	

BELLSON, LOUIS

At The Flamingo	LP	Columbia	33CX10142	1959	£6	£15	
Brilliant Bellson Sound	LP	HMV	CLP1343	1960	£6	£15	
Louis Bellson	LP	Columbia	33CX10083	1957	£6	£15	
Louis Bellson	10" LP	Columbia	33C9017	1956	£20	£40	

BELLUS, TONY

Robbing The Cradle	LP	NRC	LPA8	1960	£25	£50	US
Robbing The Cradle	7"	London	HL8933	1959	£10	£20	

BELMONTS

Carnival Of Hits	LP	Sabina	SALP5001	1962	£37.50	£75	US
Cigars, Acappella, Candy	LP	Buddah	BDS5123	1972	£6	£15	US
Come On Little Angel	7"	Stateside	SS128	1962	£1.50	£4	
Summer Love	LP	Dot	DLP25949	1969	£6	£15	US
Tell Me Why	7"	Pye	7N25094	1961	£2.50	£6	

BELOVED

Forever Dancing	12"	Flim Flam	HARP7T	1987	£3	£8	
Hundred Words	12"	Flim Flam	HARP2T	1986	£2.50	£6	
Loving Feeling	CD-s	WEA	YZ311CD	1989	£4	£10	
Time After Time	7"	WEA	YZ482X	1990	£1.50	£4	pic disc

BELTONES

Broken Heart	7"	High Note	HS023	1969	£2.50	£6	Afrotones B side

Title	Format	Label	Catalogue	Year	Price	Price	Notes
Home Without You	7"	Duke	DU17	1969	£2.50	£6	
Mary Mary	7"	High Note	HS017	1969	£2.50	£6	
No More Heartaches	7"	Blue Cat	BS142	1968	£4	£8	
No More Heartaches	7"	Trojan	TR628	1968	£4	£8	

BELVIN, JESSE

Title	Format	Label	Catalogue	Year	Price	Price	Notes
Best Of Jesse Belvin	LP	Camden	CAS960	1966	£6	£15	US
But Not Forgotten	LP	United	7220	1968	£5	£12	US
Casual	LP	Crown	CLP5145	1960	£6	£15	US
Funny	7"	RCA	RCA1119	1959	£4	£8	US
Just Jesse Belvin	LP	RCA	LPM/LSP2089	1959	£10	£25	US
Mr.Easy	LP	RCA	LPM/LSP2105	1960	£10	£25	US
Unforgettable	LP	Crown	CLP5187	1960	£6	£15	US

BEN

Title	Format	Label	Catalogue	Year	Price	Price	Notes
Ben	LP	Vertigo	6360052	1971	£80	£160	spiral label

BENATAR, PAT

Title	Format	Label	Catalogue	Year	Price	Price	Notes
If You Think You Know How To Love Me	7"	Chrysalis	CHS2373	1979	£1.50	£4	
In The Heat Of The Night	LP	Mobile Fidelity	MFSL1057	1981	£6	£15	US audiophile
Shadows Of The Night	7"	Chrysalis	CHSP2662	1983	£2	£5	shaped pic disc
Treat Me Right	7"	Chrysalis	CHS2511	1981	£2	£5	clear vinyl

BENBOW, STEVE

Title	Format	Label	Catalogue	Year	Price	Price	Notes
Captain Kidd	7" EP	Collector	JEB2	1960	£2	£5	
Of Situations And Predicaments	7"	Decca	LK4881	1967	£6	£15	
Whaling In Greenland	7" EP	Collector	JEB1	1959	£2	£5	

BENDIX, RALF & LITTLE ELIZABETH

Title	Format	Label	Catalogue	Year	Price	Price	Notes
Sag Mir Deine Sorgen	7"	Columbia	DB7774	1965	£1.50	£4	

BENNETT, BOBBY

Title	Format	Label	Catalogue	Year	Price	Price	Notes
All My Life Is You	7"	Columbia	DB8435	1968	£2	£5	
Just Say Goodbye	7"	CBS	202511	1967	£2.50	£5	
You're Ready Now	7"	Columbia	DB8532	1969	£10	£20	

BENNETT, BOBBY (2)

Title	Format	Label	Catalogue	Year	Price	Price	Notes
Big New York	7"	London	HLZ10274	1969	£2	£5	

BENNETT, BOYD & HIS ROCKETS

Title	Format	Label	Catalogue	Year	Price	Price	Notes
Banjo Rock And Roll	7"	Parlophone	MSP6203	1956	£60	£120	
Blue Suede Shoes	7"	Parlophone	MSP6233	1956	£50	£100	
Boogie At Midnight	7"	Parlophone	MSP6161	1955	£60	£120	
Boyd Bennett	LP	King	594	1957	£400	£600	US
Hi That Jive Jack	7"	Parlophone	R4214	1956	£50	£100	with Big Moe
Move	7"	Parlophone	R4423	1958	£40	£80	
Rocking Up A Storm	7"	Parlophone	R4252	1957	£40	£80	with Big Moe
Seventeen	7"	Parlophone	MSP6180	1955	£60	£120	chart single
Tight Tights	7"	Mercury	AMT1031	1959	£15	£30	

BENNETT, BRIAN

Title	Format	Label	Catalogue	Year	Price	Price	Notes
Canvas	7"	Columbia	DB8294	1967	£6	£12	
Change Of Direction	LP	Columbia	SX/SCX6144	1968	£15	£30	
Chase Side Shoot Up	7"	Fontana	6007040	1974	£2	£5	
Illustrated London Noise	LP	Studio Two	TWO268	1969	£25	£50	

BENNETT, CLIFF

Title	Format	Label	Catalogue	Year	Price	Price	Notes
Back In The USSR	7"	Parlophone	R5749	1968	£1.50	£4	
Branches Out	LP	Parlophone	PMC/PCS7054	1968	£10	£25	
Good Times	7"	Parlophone	R5711	1968	£1.50	£4	
House Of A Thousand Dolls	7"	Parlophone	R5666	1968	£1.50	£4	
I'll Take Good Care Of You	7" EP	Odeon	MEO149	1967	£12.50	£25	French
Memphis Streets	7"	Parlophone	R5792	1969	£1.50	£4	
Nobody Runs Forever	7"	Parlophone	R5728	1968	£1.50	£4	
You're Breaking Me Up	7"	Parlophone	R5691	1968	£1.50	£4	

BENNETT, CLIFF & REBEL ROUSERS

Title	Format	Label	Catalogue	Year	Price	Price	Notes
Cliff Bennett & The Rebel Rousers	LP	Parlophone	PMC1242	1964	£15	£30	
Cliff Bennett & The Rebel Rousers	7" EP	Parlophone	GEP8923	1964	£10	£20	
Don't Help Me Out	7"	Parlophone	R5534	1966	£1.50	£4	
Everybody Loves A Lover	7"	Parlophone	R5046	1963	£2	£5	
Got My Mojo Working	7"	Parlophone	R5119	1964	£2	£5	
Got To Get You into My Life	7"	Parlophone	R5489	1966	£1.50	£4	chart single
Got To Get You Into Our Lives	LP	Parlophone	PMC/PCS7017	1967	£15	£30	
Hold On I'm Coming	7"	Parlophone	R5466	1966	£1.50	£4	
Have Cried My Last Tear	7"	Parlophone	R5317	1965	£1.50	£4	
I'll Take Good Care Of You	7"	Parlophone	R5565	1967	£1.50	£4	
I'll Take You Home	7"	Parlophone	R5229	1965	£1.50	£4	chart single
One Way Love	7"	Parlophone	R5173	1964	£1.50	£4	chart single
Poor Joe	7"	Parlophone	R4895	1962	£6	£12	
Three Rooms With Running Water	7" EP	Parlophone	R5259	1965	£2	£5	
Try It Baby	7" EP	Parlophone	GEP8936	1965	£10	£20	
Use Me	7"	Parlophone	R5598	1967	£1.50	£4	
We're Gonna Make It	7" EP	Parlophone	GEP8955	1966	£20	£40	
When I Get Paid	7"	Parlophone	R4836	1961	£6	£12	
You Can't Love 'Em All	7"	Parlophone	R5406	1966	£1.50	£4	
You Got What I Like	7"	Parlophone	R4793	1961	£6	£12	
You Really Got A Hold On Me	7"	Parlophone	R5406	1963	£1.50	£4	
Cliff Bennett	LP	Regal	REG1039	1966	£5	£12	export

BENNETT, DICKIE
Dungaree Doll .... 7" .... Decca .... F10697 .... 1956 ... £1.50 ....£4 ....

BENNETT, DUSTER
Using his nickname to avoid an obvious confusion, Tony Bennett was a one man band who played the blues, and played it rather well. Although a few supporting musicians are used in places on his records, what one hears is essentially Duster Bennett's voice and harmonica, his guitar, and his bass drum. If the format sounds limited, then Bennett proves that it need not be. He was an unlikely addition to John Mayall's band in the early seventies, but this facet of his career was never recorded.

12 dBs	LP	Blue Horizon...	763868......	1970 ...	£15 ....£30	
Act Nice And Gentle	7"	Blue Horizon...	573179.......	1970 ...	£4 ....£8	
Bright Lights	LP	Blue Horizon....	763221.......	1969 ...	£20 ....£40	
Bright Lights, Big City	7"	Blue Horizon...	573154.......	1969 ...	£4 ....£8	
Comin' Home	7"	RAK	RAK177.......	1974 ...	£4 ....£8	
Fingertips	LP	Toadstool	L35436........	1974 ...	£15 ....£30	...........Australian
I Chose To Sing The Blues	7"	Blue Horizon...	573173.......	1970 ...	£4 ....£8	
I'm Gonna Wind Up Endin' Up	7"	Blue Horizon...	573164.......	1969 ...	£6 ....£12	
It's A Man Down There	7"	Blue Horizon...	573141.......	1967 ...	£4 ....£8	
Raining In My Heart	7"	Blue Horizon...	573148.......	1967 ...	£5 ....£10	
Smiling Like I'm Happy	LP	Blue Horizon...	763208.......	1968 ...	£15 ....£30	

BENNETT, JO JO

Groovy Jo Jo	LP	Trojan	TBL133	1970 ...	£6 ....£15	
Leaving Rome	7"	Trojan	TR7774	1970 ...	£1.50 ....£4	
Lecture	7"	Doctor Bird	DB1097.......	1967 ...	£5 ....£10	
Rocksteady	7"	Doctor Bird	DB1117.......	1967 ...	£5 ....£10	

BENNETT, JOE & THE SPARKLETONES

Black Slacks	7"	HMV	POP399	1957 ...	£40 ....£80	
Rocket	7"	HMV	POP445	1958 ...	£30 ....£60	

BENNETT, LEE
Poor Bachelor Boy .... 7" .... Decca .... F12024 .... 1964 ... £2 ....£5

BENNETT, RAY

Introducing Ray Bennett	7" EP..	Decca	DFE8516	1962 ...	£4 ....£8	
Twisting To The Blues	7"	Decca	F11550..........	1962 ...	£1.50 ....£4	

BENNETT, TONY

Congratulations To Someone	7"	Columbia........	SCM5048	1953 ...	£1.50 ....£4	
Stranger In Paradise	7" EP..	Philips..............	BBE12009.....	1955 ...	£2.50 ....£6	
Whatever Lola Wants	7"	Philips.............	JK1008	1957 ...	£2 ....£5	

BENNETT, VAL

All In The Game	7"	Trojan	TR625	1968 ...	£4 ....£8 . George Penny B side
Any More	7"	Fab	FAB131	1970 ...	£2.50 ....£6
Baby Baby	7"	Trojan	TR640	1968 ...	£4 ....£8
Jumping With Mr.Lee	7"	Island	WI3113	1967 ...	£5 ....£10 ......Roy Shirley B side
Midnight Spin	7"	Camel	CA24	1969 ...	£2.50 ....£6 ....Soul Cats B side
My Girl	7"	Trojan	TR649	1969 ...	£2.50 ....£6 .. Clancy Eccles B side
Reggae City	7"	Crab	CRAB6...........	1969 ...	£4 ....£8 ... Cannon King B side
Russians Are Coming	7"	Island	WI3146	1968 ...	£5 ....£10 ....Lester Stirling B side
Soul Survivor	7"	Island	WI3116	1967 ...	£5 ....£10 ... Lloyd Clarke B side
South Parkway Rock	7"	Trojan	TR626	1968 ...	£4 ....£8 Derrick Morgan B side
Spanish Harlem	7"	Trojan	TR611	1968 ...	£4 ....£8 ......Roy Shirley B side

BENNINGS, JOHN & HIS RHYTHM & BLUES BAND
Timber .... 78 ...... Esquire .... 10376.................... 1954 ... £7.50 ....£15 ....

BENNY & TINA
This Love Is Real .... 7" .... Mercury .... MF1133 .... 1969 ... £2 ....£5

BENSON, BARRY

Always Waitin'	7"	Parlophone......	R5544	1966 ...	£1.50 ....£4	
Cousin Jane	7"	Parlophone......	R5578	1967 ...	£1.50 ....£4	
I Can't Wait	7"	Page One	POF034	1967 ...	£2 ....£5	
Stay A Little While	7"	Parlophone......	R5446	1966 ...	£7.50 ....£15	
Sunshine Child	7"	Parlophone......	R5484	1966 ...	£1.50 ....£4	

BENSON, HOAGY
Kangaroo .... 7" .... Ember .... CBM003 .... 1968 ... £1.50 ....£4

BENSON, MARIE
Mambo Italiano .... 7" .... Decca .... F10452 .... 1955 ... £1.50 ....£4 ....

BENSUSAN, PIERRE
Solilai .... LP ..... Rounder........... 3068 .... 1982 ... £10 ....£25 ....US

BENT WIND
Sussex .... LP ..... Trend .... 1972 ... £840 ....£1200 ....Canadian

BENTINE, MICHAEL

It's A Square World	LP	Parlophone......	PMC1179/ PCS3031...............	1962 ...	£5 ....£12	
Square Bashing	LP	RCA	RD7885..........	1967 ...	£4 ....£10	

BENTLEY, BRIAN & THE BACHELORS

Caramba	7"	Salvo................	SLO1813	1962 ...	£2.50 ....£6	
First Flight East	7"	Philips..............	PB1086	1960 ...	£1.50 ....£4	
Wishing Well	7"	Philips..............	PB1085	1960 ...	£1.50 ....£4	

BENTLEY, JAY & THE JET SET

Watusi '64	7"	Vocalion	VN9230	1964	£4	£8	
Watusi 64	7" EP..	Vogue	18006	1964	£12.50	£25	French

BENTON, BROOK

Boll Weevil Song	LP	Mercury	MMC14090/ CMS18060	1961	£4	£10	
Boll Weevil Song	7"	Mercury	AMT1148	1961	£1.50	£4	
Brook Benton & Jesse Belvin	LP	Crown	CST350	1963	£6	£15	US
Caressing Voice Of Brook Benton	7" EP..	Mercury	ZEP10023	1959	£2	£5	
Do Your Own Thing	7"	Atlantic	584222	1968	£1.50	£4	
Endlessly	LP	Mercury	MMC14022	1959	£4	£10	
Endlessly	7"	Mercury	AMT1043	1959	£1.50	£4	chart single
Fools Rush In	7"	Mercury	AMT1121	1960	£1.50	£4	chart single
I Love You In So Many Ways	LP	Mercury	MMC14042	1960	£4	£10	
It's Just A Matter Of Time	LP	Mercury	MMC14015	1958	£4	£10	
It's Just A Matter Of Time	7"	Mercury	AMT1014	1958	£1.50	£4	
Kiddio	7"	Mercury	AMT1109	1960	£1.50	£4	chart single
Make A Date With Brook Benton	7" EP..	Mercury	ZEP10046	1959	£2	£5	
Million Miles From Nowhere	7"	RCA	RCA1044	1958	£1.50	£4	
Rainy Night In Georgia	7"	Atlantic	584315	1970	£1.50	£4	
Rockin' Good Way	7"	Mercury	MF1100	1969	£1.50	£4	
So Warm	7" EP..	Mercury	SEZ19024	1962	£2	£5	stereo
Songs I Love To Sing	LP	Mercury	MMC14060/ CMS18041	1960	£4	£10	
There Goes That Song Again	LP	Mercury	MMC14108/ CMS18068	1961	£4	£10	
Walk On The Wild Side	7"	Mercury	AMT1172	1962	£1.50	£4	
When I Fall In Love	7" EP..	Mercury	SEZ19009	1961	£2	£5	stereo
When You're In Love	7" EP..	Mercury	SEZ19019	1961	£2	£5	stereo

BENTON, BROOK & DINAH WASHINGTON

Baby	7"	Mercury	AMT1083	1960	£2	£5	
Rockin' Good Way	7"	Mercury	AMT1099	1960	£4	£8	
Rockin' Good Way	7" EP..	Mercury	SEZ19022	1961	£7.50	£15	stereo
Rockin' Good Way	7" EP..	Mercury	ZEP10120	1961	£4	£8	

BENTON, OSCAR BLUES BAND

Benton '71	LP	Decca	641900	1971	£4	£10	Dutch
Blues Is Gonna Wreck My Life	LP	Decca	XBY846521	1969	£5	£12	Dutch
Feel So Good	LP	Decca	XBY846510	1969	£4	£10	Dutch

BENTON, WALTER

Out Of This World	LP	Jazzland	JLP28	1960	£8	£20	with Freddie Hubbard

BERGIN, MARY

Feadoga Stain	LP	Gael-Linn	CEF071	1979	£5	£12	

BERIGAN, BUNNY

Bunny Berigan	LP	Philips	BBL7086	1956	£8	£20	
Plays Again	10" LP	HMV	DLP1018	1953	£8	£20	

BERKELEY KITES

Alice In Wonderland	7"	Polydor	56770	1969	£2	£5	
Hang Up City	7"	Polydor	56742	1968	£1.50	£4	

BERLE, MILTON

In The Middle Of The House	7"	Vogue Coral	Q72197	1956	£4	£8	

BERMUDAS

Donnie	7"	London	HLN9894	1964	£2.50	£6	

BERNARD, KENNY

Ain't No Sole Left In These Old Shoes	7"	Pye	7N17233	1967	£7.50	£15	
I Do	7"	Pye	7N17284	1967	£1.50	£4	
Nothing Can Change That Love	7"	Pye	7N17131	1966	£10	£20	
Somebody	7"	CBS	2936	1967	£17.50	£35	
Tracker	7"	Pye	7N15920	1965	£2.50	£6	
Victim Of Perfume And Lace	7"	CBS	3860	1968	£15	£30	

BERNARD, ROD

One More Chance	7"	Mercury	AMT1070	1959	£2.50	£6	
This Should Go On Forever	7"	London	HLM8849	1959	£10	£20	

BERNIE & THE BUZZ BAND

House That Jack Built	7"	Decca	F22829	1968	£5	£10	B side by Pete Kelly's Soulution
When Something's Wrong With My Baby	7"	Deram	DM181	1968	£2	£5	

BERNSTEIN, ELMER

Rat Race	7"	MGM	MGM1238	1963	£2.50	£6	
Staccato	7" EP..	Capitol	EAP11287	1960	£2	£5	
Staccato's Theme	7"	Capitol	CL15101	1960	£1.50	£4	chart single
Walk On The Wild Side	7"	MGM	MGM1164	1962	£1.50	£4	

BERNSTEIN, LEONARD

What Is Jazz?	LP	Philips	BBL7149	1957	£6	£15	

BERRY, CHU

Stompy Stevedores	LP	Philips	BBL7054	1955	£10	£25	

BERRY, CHUCK

Although Elvis Presley defined the rock 'n' roll image, it was Chuck Berry

Title	Format	Label	Cat No	Year	Price	Price	Notes
After School Session	LP	Chess	LP1426	1958	£25	£50	US
Back To Memphis	7"	Mercury	MF994	1967	£1.50	£4	
Beautiful Delilah	7"	London	HL8677	1958	£10	£20	
Berry Is On Top	LP	Chess	LP1435	1959	£20	£40	US
Best Of Chuck Berry	7" EP	Pye	NEP44018	1964	£4	£8	
Blue Mood	7" EP	Pye	NEP44033	1964	£4	£8	
Bye Bye Johnny	7"	London	HLM9159	1960	£6	£12	
Carol	7"	London	HL8712	1958	£12.50	£25	
Chuck Berry	LP	Golden Guinea	GGL0352	1965	£4	£10	
Chuck Berry	LP	Pye	NPL28024	1963	£6	£15	chart LP
Chuck Berry	7" EP	Pye	NEP44011	1963	£4	£8	
Chuck Berry Hits	7" EP	Pye	NEP44028	1964	£4	£8	
Chuck In London	LP	Chess	CRL4005	1965	£5	£12	
Club Nitty Gritty	7"	Mercury	MF958	1966	£1.50	£4	
Come On	7" EP	Chess	CRE6005	1965	£7.50	£15	
Concerto In B.Goode	LP	Mercury	20162SMCL	1969	£4	£10	
Dear Dad	7"	Chess	CRS8012	1965	£2	£5	
Fresh Berrys	LP	Chess	CRL4506	1965	£5	£12	
Go Go Go	7"	Pye	7N25209	1963	£2	£5	chart single
Golden Decade	LP	Chess	6641018	1972	£5	£12	double
I Got A Booking	7" EP	Chess	CRE6012	1966	£7.50	£15	
I'm Talking About You	7"	Pye	7N25100	1961	£5	£10	
In Memphis	LP	Mercury	(S)MCL20110	1967	£4	£10	
It Wasn't Me	7"	Chess	CRS8022	1965	£2	£5	
Johnny B Goode	7"	London	HLM8629	1958	£7.50	£15	
Johnny B.Goode	7"	Chess	CRS8075	1968	£2.50	£6	
Latest And The Greatest	LP	Pye	NPL28031	1964	£6	£15	chart LP
Let It Rock	7"	London	HLM9069	1960	£6	£12	
Little Marie	7"	Pye	7N25271	1964	£2	£5	
Little Queenie	7"	London	HLM8853	1959	£7.50	£15	
Live At The Fillmore	LP	Mercury	(S)MCL20112	1967	£4	£10	
Lonely School Days	7"	Chess	CRS8006	1965	£2	£5	
Memphis Tennessee	7"	London	HLM8921	1959	£6	£12	
Memphis Tennessee	7"	Pye	7N25218	1963	£2	£5	chart single
More Chuck Berry	LP	Pye	NPL28028	1963	£6	£15	chart LP
Nadine	7"	Pye	7N25236	1964	£2	£5	chart single
New Juke Box Hits	LP	Pye	NPL28019	1962	£8	£20	
No Money Down	7"	London	HLU8275	1956	£90	£180	gold label
No Particular Place To Go	7"	Chess	CRS8089	1969	£2	£5	
No Particular Place To Go	7"	Pye	7N25242	1964	£2	£5	chart single
On Stage	LP	Pye	NPL28027	1963	£6	£15	chart LP
One Dozen Berrys	LP	London	HAM2132	1958	£30	£60	
Promised Land	7"	Pye	7N25285	1965	£1.50	£4	chart single
Promised Land	7" EP	Chess	CRE6002	1965	£7.50	£15	
Ramona Say Yes	7"	Chess	CRS8037	1966	£2	£5	
Reeling And Rocking	7" EP	London	REM1188	1960	£30	£60	
Rhythm And Blues With Chuck Berry	7" EP	London	REU1053	1956	£20	£40	gold label
Rock & Roll Music	7"	London	HLM8531	1957	£20	£40	
Rockin' At The Hops	LP	Chess	LP1448	1960	£20	£40	US
Roll Over Beethoven	7"	London	HLU8428	1957	£30	£60	
Roll Over Beethoven	7"	Mercury	MF1102	1969	£1.50	£4	
Run Rudolph Run	7"	Pye	7N25228	1963	£2	£5	chart single
Saint Louis To Frisco	7"	Mercury	MF1057	1968	£1.50	£4	
Schooldays	7"	Columbia	DB3951	1957	£50	£100	chart single
Sweet Little Rock and Roller	7"	London	HLM8767	1958	£7.50	£15	
Sweet Little Sixteen	7"	London	HLM8585	1958	£10	£20	chart single
This Is Chuck Berry	7" EP	Pye	NEP44013	1963	£4	£8	
You Came A Long Way From Saint Louis	7" EP	Chess	CRE6016	1966	£7.50	£15	
You Can't Catch Me	7"	London	HLN8375	1957	£75	£150	gold labe
You Never Can Tell	LP	Marble Arch	MALS702	1967	£4	£10	stereo, 12 tracks
You Never Can Tell	LP	Pye	NPL28039	1964	£6	£15	chart LP
You Never Can Tell	7"	Pye	7N25257	1964	£2	£5	chart single

BERRY, CHUCK & BO DIDDLEY

Title	Format	Label	Cat No	Year	Price	Price	Notes
Chuck And Bo Vol.1	7" EP	Pye	NEP44009	1963	£4	£8	
Chuck And Bo Vol.2	7" EP	Pye	NEP44014	1963	£4	£8	
Chuck And Bo Vol.3	7" EP	Pye	NEP44017	1964	£4	£8	
Two Great Guitars	LP	Pye	NPL28047	1964	£6	£15	

BERRY, DAVE

Title	Format	Label	Cat No	Year	Price	Price	Notes
Baby It's You	7"	Decca	F11876	1964	£1.50	£4	chart single
Can I Get It From You	7" EP	Decca	DFE8625	1965	£4	£8	
Chaplin House	7"	Decca	F13080	1970	£2	£5	
Crying Game	7"	Decca	F11937	1964	£1.50	£4	chart single
Dave Berry	LP	Decca	LK4653	1964	£10	£25	
Dave Berry	7" EP	Decca	DFE8601	1964	£5	£10	
Dave Berry '68	LP	Decca	LK/SKL4932	1968	£6	£15	
Dozen Berrys	LP	Ace Of Clubs	ACL/SCL1218	1966	£5	£12	
Forever	7"	Decca	F12651	1967	£1.50	£4	
Huma Luma	7"	Decca	F12905	1969	£1.50	£4	
If You Wait For Love	7"	Decca	F12337	1966	£1.50	£4	
I'm Gonna Take You There	7"	Decca	F12258	1965	£1.50	£4	
In Your Life	7"	Decca	F12771	1968	£1.50	£4	
Just As Much As Ever	7"	Decca	F12739	1968	£1.50	£4	
Little Things	7"	Decca	F12103	1965	£1.50	£4	chart single
Little Things	7" EP	Decca	457071	1965	£7.50	£15	French
Mama	7"	Decca	F12435	1966	£1.50	£4	chart single

Mama	7" EP	Decca	457124	1966	£7.50 £15	French
Memphis Tennessee	7"	Decca	F11734	1963	£1.50 £4	chart single
My Baby Left Me	7"	Decca	F11803	1963	£1.50 £4	chart single
One Heart Between Two	7"	Decca	F12020	1964	£1.50 £4	chart single
Picture Me Gone	7"	Decca	F12513	1966	£1.50 £4	chart single
Special Sound Of Dave Berry	LP	Decca	LK4823	1966	£8 £20	
Stranger	7"	Decca	F12579	1967	£1.50 £4	
This Strange Effect	7"	Decca	F12188	1965	£1.50 £4	chart single

BERRY, EMMETT

Beauty And The Blues	LP	Columbia	33SX1246	1960	£5 £12	side 2 by Buddy Tate
Emmett Berry Orchestra	10" LP	Columbia	33S1107	1957	£4 £10	

BERRY, MIKE

Don't Try To Stand In My Way	7"	HMV	POP1362	1964	£1.50 £4	
Don't You Think It's Time	7"	HMV	POP1105	1962	£2 £5	chart single
Every Little Kiss	7"	HMV	POP1042	1962	£2.50 £6	
It Comes And Goes	7"	HMV	POP1494	1965	£1.50 £4	
It Really Doesn't Matter	7"	HMV	POP1194	1963	£2.50 £6	
It's Just A Matter Of Time	7"	HMV	POP979	1962	£2.50 £6	
It's Time For Mike Berry	7" EP	HMV	7EG8793	1963	£7.50 £15	
Lovesick	7"	HMV	POP1284	1964	£2.50 £6	
My Little Baby	7"	HMV	POP1142	1963	£2.50 £6	chart single
Raining In My Heart	7"	Polydor	56182	1967	£1.50 £4	
Talk	7"	HMV	POP1314	1964	£2.50 £6	
That's All I Ever Want From You	7"	HMV	POP1449	1965	£1.50 £4	
This Little Girl	7"	HMV	POP1257	1964	£2.50 £6	
Tribute To Buddy Holly	7"	HMV	POP912	1961	£2.50 £6	chart single
Tribute To Buddy Holly	7" EP	HMV	7EG8808	1963	£10 £20	
Warm Baby	7"	HMV	POP1530	1966	£1.50 £4	
Will You Love Me Tomorrow	7"	Decca	F11314	1961	£5 £10	

BERRY, RICHARD

Live At The Century Club	LP	Pam	1001		£15 £30	US
Rhythm And Blues Vol.3	7" EP	Ember	EMBEP4527	1964	£50 £100	US
Richard Berry And The Dreamers	LP	Crown	CLP5371	1963	£6 £15	US
Wild Berry	LP	Pam	1002		£15 £30	US

BERRYMAN, PETE

Pete Berryman And Guitar	LP	Autogram	FLLP509	1978	£6 £15	German

BERT, EDDIE

Encore	LP	London	LTZC15060	1957	£8 £20	
Musician Of The Year	LP	London	LTZC15040	1957	£8 £20	

BEST, JON

Young Boy Blues	7"	Decca	F12077	1965	£2.50 £6	

BEST, PETE

Pete Best was the original drummer with the Beatles, who is still understandably bitter at the way he was sacked to make way for Ringo Starr just as the group was about to make its first record for Parlophone. The American LP was given a deliberately misleading title - these are not Beatles recordings.

Anyway	7"	Beatles	800	1964	£25 £50	US
Best Of The Beatles	LP	Savage	BM71	1965	£37.50 £75	US
Boys	7"	Cameo	391	1966	£12.50 £25	US
Casting My Spell	7"	Mr.Maestro	712	1965	£12.50 £25	US
I Can't Do Without You Now	7"	Mr.Maestro	711	1964	£25 £50	US
If You Can't Get Her	7"	Happening	117/8	1964	£25 £50	US
If You Can't Get Her	7"	Happening	405	1964	£25 £50	US
I'm Gonna Knock On Your Door	7"	Decca	F11929	1964	£12.50 £25	

BETHNAL

Fiddler	7"	Bethnal	VIOL1	1977	£1.50 £4	

BETTERDAYS

Don't Want That	7"	Polydor	56024	1965	£40 £80	
Down On The Waterfront	7" EP	NTB	1002	1992	£2 £5	
Howl Of The Streets	7" EP	NTB	001	1991	£2 £5	

BETTERS, HAROLD

Do Anything You Wanna	7"	Sue	WI378	1965	£5 £10	

BEVERLEY

Beverley became Beverley Martyn when she married John Martyn. The pair recorded two fine albums together.

Happy New Year	7"	Deram	DM101	1966	£7.50 £15	
Museum	7"	Deram	DM137	1967	£2.50 £6	

BEVERLEY SISTERS

Beverley Sisters	7" EP	Decca	DFE6307	1956	£2.50 £6	
Beverley Sisters No.2	7" EP	Decca	DFE6401	1957	£4 £8	
Beverley Sisters No.3	7" EP	Decca	DFE6402	1957	£2 £5	
Beverley Sisters No.4	7" EP	Decca	DFE6512	1958	£2.50 £6	
Bevs For Christmas	7" EP	Decca	DFE6611	1959	£2 £5	
Born To Be With You	7"	Decca	F10770	1956	£1.50 £4	
Bye Bye Love	7"	Decca	F10909	1957	£1.50 £4	
Date With The Bevs	10" LP	Philips	BBR8052	1955	£5 £12	
Enchanting Beverley Sisters	LP	Columbia	33SX1285	1960	£4 £10	
Humming Bird	7"	Decca	F10603	1955	£1.50 £4	
I Dreamed	7"	Decca	F10832	1957	£1.50 £4	chart single
I Remember Mama	7"	Decca	F10539	1955	£1.50 £4	
Long Black Nylons	7"	Decca	F10971	1958	£2.50 £6	

My Heart Goes A-Sailing	7"	Decca	F10641	1955	£1.50	£4	
Those Beverley Sisters	LP	Ace Of Clubs	ACL1048	1960	£4	£10	
Three's Company	7" EP.	Columbia	SEG7602	1956	£2.50	£6	
Willie Can	7"	Decca	F10705	1956	£2.50	£6	chart single

BEVERLEY'S ALL STARS

| Double Shot | 7" | Trojan | TR683 | 1969 | £2.50 | £6 | |
| Go Home | 7" | Black Swan | WI449 | 1965 | £5 | £10 | |

BEVERLEY'S ALLSTARS

| Busy Bee | 7" | Trojan | TR7714 | 1970 | £2 | £5 | |

BEVIS FROND

Nick Salomon knows about record collecting from two different sides. Starting as a dealer, he was able to put his love and knowlege of psychedelic music to good use. As an artist, demonstrating that love by playing the same style himself, he has seen his limited edition record releases aquiring a cult reputation and hence an increase in value. Woronzow is Salomon's own label, which he uses to issue recordings by several like-minded groups as well as his own efforts, which appear under the name of The Bevis Frond.

Bevis Through The Looking Glass	LP	Woronzow	WOO51/2	1987	£25	£50	double, booklet
Inner Marshland	LP	Woronzow	WOO4	1987	£5	£12	
Miasma	LP	Woronzow	WOO3	1987	£5	£12	
Triptych	LP	Woronzow	WOO8	1988	£5	£12	

BEWES, RODNEY

| Dear Mother Love Albert | 7" | Revolution | REVP1001 | 1970 | £1.50 | £4 | |
| Remember When | 7" | Revolution | REV1003 | 1969 | £1.50 | £4 | |

BIANCHI, MAURICIO

| Sympathy For A Genocide | LP | Sterile | SR2 | 1981 | £25 | £50 | |

BIANCO, GENE

| Alarm Clock Boogie | LP | Vogue | V9167 | 1960 | £6 | £12 | |

BIBBY

| Rub It Down | 7" | Blue Beat | BB289 | 1964 | £5 | £10 | |

BIBLE

Graceland	7"	Backs	NCH109	1986	£1.50	£4	
Mahalia	7"	Backs	NCH111	1986	£1.50	£4	
Mahalia	12"	Backs	NCH12111	1986	£2.50	£6	

BIDDU

| Daughter Of Love | 7" | Regal Zonophone | RZ3002 | 1967 | £1.50 | £4 | |

BIFF BANG POW

Creation is that true rarity - a record label with a player-manager. For Alan McGee, when not keeping an eye on the likes of Teenage Fanclub and Ride, plays guitar and sings for his own group, Biff Bang Pow.

BIFF BANG POW!

Fifty Years Of Fun	7"	Creation	CRE003	1984	£2	£5	
Sleep	7"	Caff	CAFF13	1991	£6	£12	Times B side
There Must Be A Better Life	7"	Creation	CRE007	1984	£5	£10	

BIG AUDIO DYNAMITE

| Ally Pally Paradiso | LP | CBS | BIG11 | 1990 | £4 | £10 | promo |
| Medicine Show | 12" | CBS | DTA7181 | 1985 | £2.50 | £6 | double |

BIG BEATS

| Live | LP | Liberty | LRP/LST7407 | 1965 | £5 | £12 | US |

BIG BEN ACCORDION BAND

| Rock'n'Roll Medley No.1 | 7" | Columbia | DB3835 | 1956 | £2 | £5 | |
| Rock'n'Roll Medley No.2 | 7" | Columbia | DB3856 | 1957 | £2 | £5 | |

BIG BERTHA

This group was formed by the original Move bass-player, Ace Kefford, as the Ace Kefford Stand, becoming Big Bertha when Kefford himself left. The drummer for a short while was Cozy Powell. The single would appear to have been withdrawn - or else never given a full release in the first place, as it bears the same catalogue number as a single by Yes.

| World's An Apple | 7" | Atlantic | 584298 | 1969 | £7.50 | £15 | |

BIG BLACK

Headache	12"	Blast First	BFFP14T	1987	£20	£40	red vinyl, with booklet, poster, 7'
Pigpile	LP	Touch & Go	TG81	1992	£6	£15	with video & T shirt, boxed
Sound Of Impact	LP		NOT2(BUT1)	1986	£25	£50	nos 1-1000
Sound Of Impact	LP		NOT2(BUT1)	1987	£15	£30	nos 1001-1500

BIG BOB

| Your Line Was Busy | 7" | Top Rank | JAR185 | 1959 | £7.50 | £15 | |

BIG BOPPER

Big Bopper	7" EP.	Mercury	ZEP10004	1959	£40	£80	
Big Bopper's Wedding	7"	Mercury	AMT1017	1958	£7.50	£15	
Chantilly Lace	LP	Contour	6870531	1974	£4	£10	
Chantilly Lace	LP	Mercury	MMC14008	1958	£75	£150	
Chantilly Lace	7"	Mercury	AMT1002	1958	£5	£10	chart single
It's The Truth Ruth	7"	Mercury	AMT1046	1959	£7.50	£15	
Pink Petticoats	7" EP.	Mercury	ZEP10027	1959	£40	£80	

BIG BORIS

| Big Country | 7" | RCA | RCA2187 | 1972 | £1.50 | £4 | |

BIG BOY PETE
Cold Turkey .... 7" .... Camp .... 602005 .... 1968 ... £25 .... £50

BIG BOYS
Frat Cars .... 7" .... Big Boys .... BB42480 .... 1980 ... £35 .... £70

BIG BROTHER
Confusion .... LP ..... All American ... 5770 .... 1970 ... £25 .... £50 .... US

BIG BROTHER & THE HOLDING CO.
Big Brother & The Holding Co. had Janis Joplin as their lead singer, but were far from being just her backing group. The first LP, recorded before Cream toured America with their amplifiers turned up to maximum, sounds weak. The partly live "Cheap Thrills", however, is an exciting and vital recording. Janis Joplin without the Holding Co. failed to achieve this power, but equally, the Holding Co. without Janis Joplin (as on the 1971 recordings) lacked distinction.
Be A Brother .... LP ..... CBS .... 64118 .... 1971 ... £4 .... £10
Big Brother & The Holding Co. .... LP ..... Fontana .... (S)TL5457 .... 1967 ... £8 .... £20
Big Brother & The Holding Co. .... LP ..... London .... HAT/SHT8377 ...... 1968 ... £6 .... £15
Bye Bye Baby .... 7" .... Fontana .... TF881 .... 1967 ... £6 .... £12
Cheap Thrills .... LP ..... CBS .... 63392 .... 1968 ... £4 .... £10
Down On Me .... 7" .... London .... HLT10226 .... 1969 ... £4 .... £8
How Hard It Is .... LP ..... CBS .... 30738 .... 1971 ... £5 .... £12 .... US
Light Is Faster Than Sound .... 7" EP ... Vogue .... INT18147 .... 1967 ... £12.50 ... £25 .... French
Piece Of My Heart .... 7" .... CBS .... 3683 .... 1968 ... £2 .... £5
Piece Of My Heart .... 7" .... CBS .... 3683 .... 1968 ... £6 .... £12 .... PS

BIG CARROT
The single credited to Big Carrot is actually the work of T Rex, being designed as a showcase for Marc Bolan's increasing desire to be taken seriously as a lead guitarist.
Blackjack .... 7" .... EMI .... EMI2047 .... 1973 ... £7.50 ... £15

BIG CHARLIE
Red Sea .... 7" .... Blue Beat .... BB241 .... 1963 ... £5 .... £10

BIG COUNTRY
Chance .... 12" ..... Mercury .... COUP4 .... 1983 ... £5 .... £12 .... pic disc
Crossing .... LP ..... Mercury .... MERS27 .... 1983 ... £6 .... £15 .... white sleeve
Fields Of Fire .... 7" .... Mercury .... COUP2 .... 1983 ... £4 .... £8 .... shaped pic disc
Fields Of Fire .... 12" ..... Mercury .... COUNX2 .... 1983 ... £4 .... £10 .... clear vinyl
Harvest Home .... 12" ..... Mercury .... COUNX1 .... 1982 ... £4 .... £10 .... clear vinyl
In A Big Country .... 12" ..... Mercury .... COUNT313 .... 1983 ... £3 .... £8 .... red sleeve
Look Away .... 7" .... Mercury .... BIGCP1 .... 1986 ... £2.50 ... £6 .... shaped pic disc
Twelve Inch Singles .... 12" ..... Mercury .... £35 .... £70 .... box set
Where The Rose Is Sown .... 7" .... Mercury .... MERD185 .... 1984 ... £4 .... £8 .... double

BIG DADDY
Big Daddy's Blues .... LP ..... Gee .... (S)G704 .... 1960 ... £8 .... £20 .... US
Twist Party .... LP ..... Regent .... 6106 .... 1962 ... £6 .... £15 .... US

BIG DAVE & HIS ORCHESTRA
Cat From Coos Bay .... 7" .... Capitol .... CL14195 .... 1954 ... £5 .... £10
Rock And Roll Party .... 7" .... Capitol .... CL14245 .... 1955 ... £7.50 ... £15
Rock, Roll, Ball And Wail .... 78 .... Capitol .... CL14156 .... 1954 ... £3 .... £8

BIG FLAME
Rigour .... 7" .... Ron Johnson ... ZRON3 .... 1985 ... £2 .... £5
Sink .... 7" .... Plaque .... 001 .... 1984 ... £5 .... £10
Tough .... 7" .... Ron Johnson ... ZRON4 .... 1985 ... £1.50 ... £4
Why Pop Stars Can't Dance .... 7" .... Ron Johnson ... ZRON7 .... 1986 ... £1.50 ... £4

BIG FOOT
Big Foot .... LP ..... Winro .... 1004 .... 1968 ... £5 .... £12 .... US

BIG GROUP
Big Hammer .... LP ..... Peer
                                                         International
                                                         Library .... PIL9009 .... 1971 ... £50 .... £100

BIG IN JAPAN
Various people passing through the ranks of Big In Japan went on to be fairly big in lots of places - most notably Budgie (Siouxsie and the Banshees) and David Balfe (Teardrop Explodes). The main reason for the collectability of the group's singles, however, is the presence of Holly Johnson on bass, some time before emerging as front man with Frankie Goes To Hollywood.
Big In Japan .... 7" .... Erics .... ERICS001 .... 1977 ... £5 .... £10
From Y To Z And Never Again .... 7" .... Zoo .... CAGE001 .... 1978 ... £5 .... £10

BIG MAYBELLE
All Of Me .... 7" .... London .... HLC8447 .... 1957 ... £12.50 ... £25
Baby Won't You Please Come Home ... 7" .... London .... HLC8854 .... 1959 ... £10 .... £20
Blues, Candy And Big Maybelle .... LP ..... Savoy .... MG14011 .... 1958 ... £15 .... £30 .... US
Careless Love .... 7" .... London .... HL9941 .... 1965 ... £4 .... £8
Gospel Soul .... LP ..... Brunswick .... BL754142 .... 1968 ... £5 .... £12 .... US
Got A Brand New Bag .... LP ..... Rajac .... (S)S122 .... 1967 ... £5 .... £12 .... US
Mama He Treats Your Daughter Mean ... 7" .... CBS .... 2926 .... 1967 ... £2.50 ... £6
Pure Soul Of Big Maybelle .... LP ..... CBS .... 62999 .... 1967 ... £6 .... £15
Quittin' Time .... 7" .... Direction .... 583312 .... 1968 ... £6 .... £12
Sings .... LP ..... Savoy .... MG14005 .... 1958 ... £15 .... £30 .... US
Soul Of Big Maybelle .... LP ..... Scepter .... (S)S522 .... 1964 ... £6 .... £15 .... US
Turn The World Around .... 7" .... CBS .... 2735 .... 1967 ... £7.50 ... £15
What More Can A Woman Do .... LP ..... Brunswick .... BL(7)54107 .... 1962 ... £8 .... £20 .... US

BIG MOOSE
Puppy Howl Blues .... 7" .... Python .... PKM1 .... 1968 ... £7.50 ... £15

BIG SLEEP
Bluebell Wood .... LP ...... Pegasus .... PEG4 .... 1971 ... £20 ....£40 ....

BIG STAR
Big Star, the group led by Alex Chilton following the disbanding of the Box Tops, has aquired a formidable cult reputation wholly unjustified by the actual music to be found on the records. The songs are rather ordinary and Big Star's lack of success is not at all surprising.

Big Star	LP	Ardent.............	ADS1501	1971 ... £6	£15	.... US
Radio City	LP	Ardent.............	ADS2803	1971 ... £6	£15	.... US
Radio City/Big Star	LP	Stax.................	SXSP302	1978 ... £6	£15	.........double
Third Album	LP	Aura	AUL703	1978 ... £4	£10	....

BIG THREE
By all accounts, the Big Three were, on stage, the most impressive Liverpool group of them all. Their records, however, never did them justice - even with the live "At The Cavern" EP, it is clearly a case of "you had to be there". Bass player Johnny Gustafson has been ubiquitous ever since, however, playing, among others, with Quatermass, Hard Stuff, Gillan, and Roxy Music.

At The Cavern	7" EP..	Decca	DFE8552	1963 ... £7.50	£15	
By The Way	7"	Decca	F11689	1963 ... £2.50	£6	..........chart single
If You Ever Change Your Mind ...	7"	Decca	F11927	1964 ... £4	£8	
I'm With You	7"	Decca	F11752	1963 ... £4	£8	
Resurrection	LP	Polydor	2383199	1973 ... £6	£15	
Some Other Guy	7"	Decca	F11614	1963 ... £4	£8	..........chart single
Some Other Guy	7"	Polydor	2058343	1973 ... £1.50	£4	
What'd I Say	7" EP..	Decca	457029	1964 ... £12.50 .....£25		..........French

BIG THREE (CASS ELLIOTT,JIM HENDRICKS,TIM ROSE)

Big Three	LP	FM	(FS)307	1963 ... £6	£15	.... US
Big Three Featuring Cass Elliott	LP	Roulette	RCP1003	1967 ... £4	£10	
Live At The Recording Studio	LP	FM	(FS)311	1964 ... £6	£15	.... US

BIG YOUTH
Of the many toasting DJs to emerge in the wake of U Roy's first successes, Big Youth was the most idiosyncratic and the most spectacular. His "Ace 90 Skank" set the pattern - a roaring motor bike engine is overlaid by thickly accented Jamaican voices; then a lanky bass guitar begins its deep descent as Big Youth unleashes a stream of words that manage to sound lazy even while tumbling over each other.

A So We Say	7"	Summit	SUM8542	1973 ... £1.50 ....£4		.............Winston Scotland B side
Ace 90 Skank	7"	Downtown.......	DT492	1972 ... £2	£5	
Cane And Abel	7"	Prince Buster ...	PB50	1973 ... £1.50	£4	
Chi Chi Run	LP	Fab	MS8	1972 ... £8	£20	
Chi Chi Run	7"	Blue Beat	BB424	1972 ... £2	£5	.....John Holt B side
Chi Chi Run	7"	Prince Buster ...	PB46	1972 ... £1.50	£4	
Concrete Jungle	7"	Grape..............	GR3061	1973 ... £1.50	£4	
Cool Breeze	7"	Green Door.....	GD4051	1973 ... £1.50	£4	.....Crystalites B side
Dock Of The Bay	7"	Downtown.......	DT497	1972 ... £1.50	£4	.....Crystalites B side
Foreman v. Frazier	LP	Grape..............	GR3040	1973 ... £1.50	£4	
Hit The Road Jack	LP	Trojan..............	TRLS137	1976 ... £4	£10	
JA To UK	7"	Grape..............	GR3044	1973 ... £1.50	£4	
Leggo Beast	7"	Prince Buster ...	PB48	1973 ... £1.50	£4	
Medicine Doctor	7"	Gayfeet	CS206	1969 ... £2.50	£6	
Natty Cultural Dread	LP	Trojan..............	TRLS123	1976 ... £4	£10	
Opportunity Rock	7"	Grape..............	GR3051	1973 ... £1.50	£4	
Screaming Target	LP	Trojan..............	TRLS61	1973 ... £5	£12	

BIG YOUTH & KEITH HUDSON
Can You Keep A Secret .... 7" ...... Pyramid .... PYR7015.......... 1974 ... £1.50 ....£4

BIGGUN, IVOR
Winker's Song (Misprint) .... 7" ...... Beggars .... BOP1 .... 1978 ... £1.50 ....£4 ....chart single
Banquet ....

BIKINIS
Bikini .... 7" ...... Columbia......... DB4149.............. 1958 ... £4 ....£8

BILLIE & EDDIE
King Is Coming Back .... 7" ...... Top Rank .... JAR249.............. 1959 ... £4 ....£8 ....

BILLIE & LILLIE

Bells Bells Bells	7"	Top Rank	JAR157	1959 ... £1.50	£4	
Creeping Crawling Crying	7"	London	HLU8630	1958 ... £10	£20	
Hanging On To You	7"	London	HLU8689	1958 ... £6	£12	
La Dee Dah	7"	London	HLU8564	1958 ... £10	£20	
Lucky Ladybug	7"	London	HLU8795	1959 ... £6	£12	

BILLIE & THE ESSENTIALS
Maybe You'll be There .... 7" ...... London .... HLW9657 .... 1963 ... £7.50 ....£15

BILLMUSS, TREVOR
Family Apology .... LP ... Charisma .... CAS1017 .... 1970 ... £6 ....£15

BINDI, UMBERTO
Il Nostro Concerto .... 7" ...... Oriole .... CB1577 .... 1960 ... £1.50 ....£4 ....chart single

BINNS, SONNY & THE RUDIES
Untouchables .... 7" ...... Downtown....... DT420.............. 1969 ... £2.50 ....£6
Wheels .... 7" ...... Downtown....... DT424.............. 1969 ... £2.50 ....£6

BINTANGS

Blues On The Ceiling	LP	Decca	6440676	1969 ... £5	£12	.............Dutch
Genuine Bull	LP	RCA	YHPL10982	1975 ... £4	£10	.............Dutch
Ridin' On The L&N	7"	Decca	F22995	1970 ... £1.50	£4	
Ridin' With The Bintangs	LP	Decca		1970 ... £6	£15	.............Dutch

BIRD, IVOR
Over The Wall We Go	7"	RSO	2090270	1978	£1.50	£4	

BIRD, RONNIE
Adieu A Un Ami	7" EP	Decca	460844	196-	£12.50	£25	French
Chante	7" EP	Philips	437220	196-	£7.50	£15	French
Elle M'Attend	LP	Decca	154134	196-	£25	£50	French
Elle M'Attend	7" EP	Decca	460918	196-	£7.50	£15	French
La Surprise	7" EP	Philips	437353	196-	£7.50	£15	French
L'Amour Nous Rend Fou	7" EP	Decca	460889	196-	£7.50	£15	French
Le Pivert	7"	Philips	370601	196-	£5	£10	French, PS
Le Pivert	7" EP	Philips	437403	196-	£7.50	£15	French
N'Ecoute Pas Ton Coeur	7" EP	Philips	437239	196-	£7.50	£15	French
Ou Va-T-Elle	7" EP	Decca	460946	196-	£7.50	£15	French
Sad Soul	7"	Philips	370768	196-	£6	£12	French, PS
Tu En Dis Trop	7" EP	Philips	437327	196-	£7.50	£15	French

BIRD, STANLEY & JEFFREY
Johnny At The Crossroads	7"	HMV	POP702	1960	£1.50	£4	

BIRDLEGS & PAULINE
Spring	7"	Sue	WI4014	1966	£6	£12	

BIRDS
Leavin' Here	7"	Decca	F12140	1965	£15	£30	chart single
No Good Without You Baby	7"	Decca	F12257	1965	£15	£30	
No Good Without You Baby	7" EP	Decca	457114	1966	£80	£160	French
You're On My Mind	7"	Decca	F12031	1964	£25	£50	

BIRD'S BIRDS
Say Those Magic Words	7"	Reaction	591005	1966	£60	£120	

BIRDS OF A FEATHER
All God's Children	7"	Page One	POF179	1970	£1.50	£4	
Birds Of A Feather	LP	Page One	POLS027	1970	£30	£60	
Blacksmith Blues	7"	Page One	POF156	1969	£1.50	£4	

BIRKIN, JANE & SERGE GAINSBOURG
Jane Birkin And Serge Gainsbourg	LP	Fontana	STL5493	1969	£4	£10	
Je T'Aime Moi Non Plus	7"	Antic	K11511	1974	£2	£5	PS
Je T'Aime...Moi Non Plus	7"	Fontana	TF1042	1969	£1.50	£4	chart single
Je T'Aime...Moi Non Plus	7"	Major Minor	MM645	1969	£1.50	£4	chart single

BIRMINGHAM
Birmingham	LP	Grosvenor	GRS1011	1971	£60	£120	

BIRTH CONTROL
Birth Control	LP	Charisma	CAS1036	1971	£6	£15	
Hoodoo Man	LP	CBS	65316	1972	£4	£10	German
Live	LP	CBS	88088	1974	£6	£15	German, double
Operation	LP	Ohr	OMM556015	1971	£5	£12	German
Plastic People	LP	CBS	80921	1975	£4	£10	German
Re-birth	LP	CBS	65963	1974	£4	£10	German

BIRTHDAY PARTY
Friend Catcher	7"	4AD	AD12	1980	£2	£5	
Mr.Clarinet	7"	4AD	AD114	1981	£2	£5	
Release The Bats	7"	4AD	AD111	1981	£1.50	£4	

BISCAYNES
The recordings by the Biscaynes are the first by the group that found success when they changed their name to the Walker Brothers.
Church Key	7"	Northridge	1001	1963	£10	£20	US
Church Key	7"	Reprise	2047	1963	£7.50	£15	US
Midnight In Montevideo	7"	Co-En	01	196-	£10	£20	US

BISHOP, DICKIE & HIS SIDEKICKS
Cumberland Gap	7"	Decca	F10869	1957	£2.50	£6	
Jumping Judy	7"	Decca	F11028	1958	£2	£5	
No Other Baby	7"	Decca	F10981	1958	£2	£5	
Prisoners Song	7"	Decca	F10959	1957	£1.50	£4	

BISHOP, ELVIN
Elvin Bishop	LP	Fillmore	30001	1969	£6	£15	US
Feel It	LP	Epic	EPC64180	1970	£4	£10	
Rock My Soul	LP	Epic	31563	1972	£4	£10	US

BISHOP, JOHN
Plays His Guitar (Doesn't He?)	LP	Tangerine	6495002	1971	£5	£12	

BISHOP, TOMMY RICOCHETS
Should Have Known	7"	Decca	F12238	1965	£2	£5	

BITCHES SIN
Predator	LP	Heavy Metal	HMRLP4	1982	£5	£12	

BITTER END SINGERS
Taste Of Your Love	7"	Atlantic	584075	1967	£1.50	£4	

BJORK

Bjork	LP	Falkinn	FA006	1977	£75	£150	Icelandic, credited to Bjork Gudmundsdottir

BLACK

Human Features	7"	Rox	ROX17	1981	£12.50	£25	
More Than The Sun	7"	Wonderful World Of	WW3	1982	£2	£5	

BLACK ABBOTTS

Everybody Needs A Little Sunshine	7"	Evolution	E3001	1971	£1.50	£4	
Love Is Alive	7"	Evolution	E3004	1971	£5	£10	
She Looked Away	7"	Chapter One	123	1970	£1.50	£4	

BLACK ACE

Black Ace	LP	Heritage	HLP1006	1962	£10	£25	
Black Ace	7" EP	XX	MIN701	1961	£4	£8	

BLACK AXE

Red Lights	7"	Metal	MELT1	1980	£1.50	£4	

BLACK, BILL COMBO

All Timers	LP	Hi	HLP32032	1966	£4	£10	US
Beat Goes On	LP	London	HAU/SHU8367	1968	£4	£10	
Bill Black's Combo	7" EP	London	REU1277	1960	£5	£10	
Black Lace	LP	Hi	HLP32033	1967	£4	£10	US
Blue Tango	7"	London	HLU9267	1961	£1.50	£4	
Coming On	7"	London	HLU9855	1964	£1.50	£4	
Do It Rat Now	7"	London	HLU9721	1963	£1.50	£4	
Don't Be Cruel	7"	London	HLU9212	1960	£2	£5	chart single
Goes Big Band	LP	Hi	HLP32020	1964	£4	£10	US
Greatest Hits	LP	London	HAU8113	1963	£4	£10	
Hearts Of Stone	7"	London	HLU9306	1961	£1.50	£4	
Hot Taco	7"	London	HLU9645	1962	£1.50	£4	
Josephine	7"	London	HLU9156	1960	£2	£5	
King Of The Road	LP	Hi	HLP32036	1967	£4	£10	US
Let's Twist	7"	London	HAU2427/ SAHU6222	1962	£6	£15	
Little Queenie	7"	London	HLU9925	1964	£6	£12	
Long Gone	7"	London	HLU9788	1963	£1.50	£4	
More Solid And Raunchy	LP	Hi	HLP32023	1965	£5	£12	US
Movin'	LP	London	HAU2433	1962	£6	£15	
Moving	7"	London	HLU9436	1961	£2	£5	
Mr.Beat	LP	Hi	HLP32027	1965	£5	£12	US
My Girl Josephine	7"	London	HLU9479	1961	£1.50	£4	
Ole Buttermilk Sky	7"	London	HLU9383	1961	£1.50	£4	
Plays Chuck Berry	LP	London	HAU8187	1964	£6	£15	
Plays The Blues	LP	Hi	HLP32015	1964	£6	£15	US
Record Hop	LP	Hi	HLP32006	1961	£8	£20	US
Saxy Jazz	LP	Hi	HLP32002	1960	£8	£20	US
Smokie	LP	Hi	HLP12001	1960	£8	£20	US
Smokie	7"	Felsted	AF129	1959	£4	£8	
So What	7"	London	HLU9594	1962	£1.50	£4	
Solid & Raunchy	LP	London	HAU2310	1962	£8	£20	
Solid And Raunchy 3	LP	Hi	HLP32052	1969	£4	£10	US
Tequila	7"	London	HLU9903	1964	£1.50	£4	
That Wonderful Feeling	LP	Hi	HLP32004	1962	£5	£12	US
Turn On Your Love Light	7"	London	HLU10216	1968	£1.50	£4	
Untouchable Sound	7" EP	London	REU1369	1963	£5	£10	
Untouchable Sound Of Bill Black	LP	London	HAU8080	1963	£5	£12	
White Silver Sands	7"	London	HLU9090	1960	£2	£5	chart single

BLACK CAT BONES

Barbed Wire Sandwich	LP	Nova	SDN15	1970	£30	£60	

BLACK, CILLA

Nothing detracts from an artist's collectability as much as their becoming a popular entertainer and interest in Cilla Black's recordings ha plummeted since her emergence as a television personality. She was, however, an integral part of the Merseybeat phenomenon and her firs LP, in particular, stands up well.

Alfie	7" EP	Odeon	MEO114	1966	£5	£10	Frencl
Anyone Who Had A Heart	7" EP	Odeon	SOE3747	1963	£5	£10	Frencl
Anyone Who Had A Heart	7" EP	Parlophone	GEP8901	1964	£2.50	£6	
Cilla	LP	Parlophone	PCS3063	1965	£6	£15	stereo, chart LI
Cilla	LP	Parlophone	PMC1243	1965	£6	£12	mono, chart LI
Cilla	LP	World Record Club	STP1036	1966	£6	£15	
Cilla Sings A Rainbow	LP	Parlophone	PMC/PCS7004	1966	£4	£10	chart LI
Cilla's Hits	7" EP	Parlophone	GEP8954	1966	£2.50	£6	
It's For You	7" EP	Parlophone	GEP8916	1964	£2.50	£6	
Love Of The Loved	7"	Parlophone	R5065	1963	£1.50	£4	
Sheroo!	LP	Parlophone	PMC/PCS7041	1968	£4	£10	chart L
Surround Yourself With Cilla	LP	Parlophone	PMC/PCS7079	1969	£4	£10	
Time For Cilla	7" EP	Parlophone	GEP8967	1967	£2.50	£6	
You're My World	7" EP	Odeon	SOE3758	1964	£5	£10	Frenc
You've Lost That Lovin' Feelin'	7" EP	Odeon	SOE3765	1965	£5	£10	Frenc

BLACK COUNTRY THREE

Black Country Three	LP	Transatlantic	TRA140	1966	£15	£30	

BLACK CROWES

Hard To Handle		7"	Def American ..	DEFAP10	1991	£1.50	£4	shaped pic disc
Hard To Handle		12"	Def American ..	DEFAP612	1990	£2.50	£6	shaped pic disc
Jealous Again		12"	Def American ..	DEFAP412	1990	£3	£8	pic disc
Twice As Hard		12"	Def American ..	DEFA712	1991	£2.50	£6	
Twice As Hard		12"	Def American ..	DEFAP712	1991	£2.50	£6	pic disc

BLACK DYKE MILLS BAND

| Thingumybob | | 7" | Apple | 4 | 1968 | £12.50 | £25 | |

BLACK DYNAMITES

| Brush Those Tears | | 7" | Top Rank | JAR319 | 1960 | £7.50 | £15 | |

BLACK, JEANNE

| He'll Have To Stay | | 7" | Capitol | CL15131 | 1960 | £1.50 | £4 | chart single |

BLACK KNIGHTS

| I Got A Woman | | 7" | Columbia | DB7443 | 1965 | £4 | £8 | |

BLACK MARKET BABY

| Potential Suicide | | 7" | Limp | | 1981 | £10 | £20 | |

BLACK MERDA

| Black Merda | | LP | Chess | 569517 | 1970 | £10 | £25 | US |
| Long Burn The Fire | | LP | Janus | JLS3042 | 1971 | £6 | £15 | US |

BLACK OAK ARKANSAS

Black Oak Arkansas		LP	Atlantic	2400180	1971	£4	£10	
High On A Hog		LP	Atlantic	K40538	1974	£4	£10	
If An Angel Came To See You		LP	Atco	7008	1972	£4	£10	US
Keep The Faith		LP	Atco	SD33381	1972	£4	£10	US
Raunch & Roll		LP	Atlantic	K40451	1973	£4	£10	
Street Party		LP	Atlantic	K50057	1974	£4	£10	

BLACK PEARL

| Live | | LP | Prophesy | PRS1001 | 1970 | £5 | £12 | US |

BLACK SABBATH

Black Sabbath were hated by the critics in the early days, who were discomfitted to see the group's first LP release climb high into the album charts. The achievement was based on the group's sheer hard work in building up a large and loyal following through live performance. Essentially, the group also invented the heavy metal genre, or at any rate solidified the style into the riff-based music that it has remained ever since.

Black Sabbath		LP	Vertigo	VO6	1970	£4	£10	spiral label, chart LP
Black Sabbath 4		LP	Vertigo	6360071	1972	£4	£10	spiral label, booklet, chart LP
Children Of The Grave		7"	Phonogram	DJ005	1974	£12.50	£25	promo, Status Quo B side
Evil Woman		7"	Fontana	TF1067	1970	£20	£40	
Evil Woman		7"	Vertigo	V2	1970	£7.50	£15	
Hard Road		7"	Vertigo	SAB002	1978	£1.50	£4	purple vinyl
Master Of Reality		LP	Vertigo	6360050	1971	£4	£10	spiral label, poster
Paranoid		LP	Nems	NEP6003	1977	£4	£10	pic disc
Paranoid		LP	Vertigo	6360011	1970	£4	£10	spiral label, chart LP
Paranoid		LP	Warner Bros	K3104	1970	£6	£15	US quad
Paranoid		LP	NEMS	NEP1	1982	£2	£5	pic disc
Tomorrow's Dream		7"	Vertigo	6059061	1972	£2.50	£6	
Turn Up The Night		7"	Vertigo	SABP6	1982	£1.50	£4	pic disc
Turn Up The Night		12"	Vertigo	SABP612	1982	£2.50	£6	pic disc

BLACK SHEEP

| Black Sheep | | LP | Capitol | 11369 | 1975 | £6 | £15 | US |

BLACK VELVET

African Velvet		7"	Beacon	BEA129	1969	£1.50	£4	
Can You Feel It		LP	Seven Sun	SUNLP1	1973	£20	£40	
People Of The World		LP	Pye	NSPL18392	1972	£15	£30	
This Is Black Velvet		LP	Beacon	BEAS16	1971	£10	£25	

BLACK WIDOW

Black Widow		LP	CBS	64133	1970	£8	£20	
Come To The Sabbat		7"	CBS	5031	1970	£10	£20	
Sacrifice		LP	CBS	63948	1970	£8	£20	chart LP
Three		LP	CBS	64562	1971	£8	£20	
Wish You Would		7"	CBS	7596	1971	£1.50	£4	

BLACKBIRDS

No Destination		LP	Saga	FID2113	1968	£20	£40	
No Destination		7"	Saga	OPP3	1968	£7.50	£15	
Touch Of Music		LP	Opp	534	1971	£20	£40	German

BLACKBURDS

| Play The Bugaloo | | 7" EP.. | Philips | 437323 | 196- | £4 | £8 | French |

BLACKBURN, BRYAN & PETER REEVES

| We'll Not Twist Again | | 7" | Philips | 326534BF | 1962 | £1.50 | £4 | |

BLACKBURN, TONY

Blessed Are The Lonely		7"	Polydor	56360	1969	£1.50	£4	
Don't Get Off That Train		7"	Fontana	TF562	1965	£1.50	£4	
Green Light		7"	Fontana	TF729	1966	£1.50	£4	
Is There Another Way To Love You		7"	Fontana	TF601	1965	£1.50	£4	

It's Only Love	7"	MGM	MGM1467	1969	£1.50	£4	chart single
Meets Matt Monro	LP	Fontana	SFL13161	1966	£4	£10	
She's My Girl	7"	MGM	MGM1394	1968	£1.50	£4	
So Much Love	7"	MGM	MGM1375	1968	£1.50	£4	chart single
Tony Blackburn Sings	LP	MGM	C(S)8062	1968	£4	£10	

BLACKBYRDS

Action	LP	Fantasy	FT534	1977	£5	£12	
Blackbyrds	LP	Fantasy	FT9444	1975	£5	£12	
City Life	LP	Fantasy	FTA3003	1976	£5	£12	
Do It Fluid	7"	Fantasy	FTC113	1974	£1.50	£4	
Flying Start	LP	Fantasy	FT522	1974	£5	£12	
Night Grooves	LP	Fantasy	FT555	1979	£4	£10	
Walking In Rhythm	7"	Fantasy	FTC114	1975	£1.50	£4	

BLACKFEATHER

At The Mountains Of Madness	LP	Festival	37159	1974	£35	£70	Australian
Boppin' The Blues	LP	Infinity	34731	1972	£35	£70	Australian
Live	LP	Festival	25095	197-	£35	£70	Australian

BLACKFOOT, J.D.

Song Of Crazy Horse	LP	Fantasy	9468	1974	£6	£15	US
Southbound And Gone	LP	Fantasy	9487	1975	£5	£12	US
Ultimate Prophecy	LP	Mercury	6338031	1970	£10	£25	

BLACKFOOT SUE

Gun Running	LP	DJM	DJLPS455	1975	£15	£30	

BLACKJACK

The lead singer of this otherwise obscure American AOR group was Michael Bolton.

Blackjack	LP	Polydor	2391411	1979	£6	£15	
Worlds Apart	LP	Polydor	PD16279	1980	£8	£20	US

BLACKJACKS

Woo Hoo	7"	Pye	7N15586	1963	£4	£8	
Woo Hoo	7" EP	Pye	PNV24117	1964	£6	£12	French

BLACKMAN, HONOR

Before Today	7"	CBS	3896	1968	£4	£8	
Everything I've Got	LP	Decca	LK4642	1964	£6	£15	

BLACKMORE, RITCHIE

Getaway	7"	Oriole	CB314	1965	£180	£300	

BLACKTHORN

Blackthorn	LP	WHM	1921	1977	£8	£20	
Blackthorn II	LP	WHM	1923	1978	£8	£20	

BLACKTHORN (2)

Blackthorn	LP	Homespun	HRL118	1976	£5	£12	Irish

BLACKWATER PARK

Blackwater Park	LP	BASF	20212386	1971	£30	£60	German

BLACKWELL, CHARLES

Freight Train	7"	Columbia	DB4919	1962	£2	£5	
Hawaiian War Chant	7"	Columbia	DB7066	1963	£1.50	£4	
High Noon	7"	Columbia	DB4994	1963	£1.50	£4	
Lost Patrol	7"	Columbia	DB7139	1963	£1.50	£4	
Meditation	7"	Columbia	DB7501	1965	£1.50	£4	
Supercar	7"	Columbia	DB4839	1962	£5	£10	
Taboo	7"	HMV	POP977	1962	£6	£12	

BLACKWELL, OTIS

Make Ready For Love	7"	London	HLE8616	1958	£12.50	£25	
Singin' The Blues	LP	Davis	109	1956	£40	£80	US

BLACKWELL, RORY & THE BLACKJACKS

Bye Bye love	7"	Parlophone	R4326	1957	£6	£12	

BLACKWELL, SCRAPPER

Blues Before Sunrise	LP	77	LA124	1961	£6	£15	
Longtime Blues	7" EP	Collector	JEN7	1962	£2.50	£6	
Mr.Scrapper's Blues	LP	XTRA	XTRA5011	1966	£5	£12	

BLACKWELLS

Love Or Money	7"	London	HLW9334	1961	£2.50	£6	
Unchained Melody	7"	London	HLW9135	1960	£2.50	£6	

BLACKWELLS (2)

Why Don't You Love Me	7"	Columbia	DB7442	1965	£10	£20	

BLADES OF GRASS

Charlie And Fred	7"	Stateside	SS2101	1968	£1.50	£4	
Happy	7"	Stateside	SS2040	1967	£1.50	£4	

BLAH BLAH BLAH

Blah Blah Blah	LP	Some Bizarre		1981	£15	£30	test pressing

BLAINE, HAL

Deuces, T's, Roadsters And Drums	LP	RCA	RD7624	1964	£8	£20	
Gear Stripper	7"	RCA	RCA1379	1963	£4	£8	

BLAIR
Night Life .... 12" ..... Miracle .... M4 .... 1979 ... £2.50 ....£6

BLAIR, SALLIE
Squeeze Me .... LP ...... Parlophone..... PMC1083 .... 1959 ... £6 ....£15

BLAKE, ERIC
Sin City .... 7" ..... Carrere .... CAR141 .... 1980 ... £2 ....£5

BLAKE, KEITH
Musically .... 7" ..... Blue Cat .... BS102 .... 1968 ... £4 ....£8
Woo Oh Oh .... 7" ..... Amalgamated . AMG809 .... 1968 ... £4 ....£8 .... Overtakers B side

BLAKE, RALPH
High Blood Pressure .... 7" ..... Coxsone .... CS7063 .... 1968 ... £5 ....£10

BLAKE, SONNY
Harmonica Blues .... 7" EP.. Rooster .... R706 .... 1980 ... £2 ....£5

BLAKE, TIM
Going under the name of Hi-T Moonweed when a member of Gong, Tim Blake contributed greatly to that group's science fiction ambience with his arsenal of synthesizer sounds. For his solo recordings, the synthesizer takes over completely, with Blake covering similar territory to that explored by Tangerine Dream.
Blake's New Jerusalem .... LP ..... Barclay .... CLAY7005 .... 1978 ... £6 ....£15
Crystal Machine .... LP ..... Egg.................. 900545 .... 1977 ... £6 ....£15 .... French

BLAKEY, ART
African Beat .... LP ..... Blue Note.. ...... BLP/BST84097 ..... 196- ... £8 ....£20
Are You Real .... 7" EP.. Fontana .... TFE17364 .... 1961 ... £2.50 ....£6
Art Blakey Jazz Messengers ... LP ..... HMV .... CLP1532/CSD1423 1962 ... £6 ....£15
Art Blakey's Big Band .... LP ..... Parlophone...... PMC1099 .... 1959 ... £10 ....£25
At The Cafe Bohemia Vol.1 .... LP ..... Blue Note........ BLP/BST81507 ..... 196- ... £10 ....£25
At The Cafe Bohemia Vol.2 .... LP ..... Blue Note........ BLP/BST81508 ..... 196- ... £10 ....£25
At The Jazz Corner Of The World Vol.1 LP ..... Blue Note........ BLP/BST84015 ..... 196- ... £10 ....£25
At The Jazz Corner Of The World Vol.2 LP ..... Blue Note........ BLP/BST84016 ..... 196- ... £10 ....£25
Big Beat .... LP ..... Blue Note........ BLP/BST84029 ..... 196- ... £10 ....£25
Blue Monk .... LP ..... Atlantic .... 590009 .... 1967 ... £5 ....£12 with Thelonious Monk
Blues March .... 7" EP.. Fontana .... TFE17257 .... 1960 ... £2.50 ....£6
Buhaina's Delight .... LP ..... Blue Note........ BLP/BST84104 ..... 1963 ... £8 ....£20
Buttercorn Lady .... LP ..... Mercury .... (S)LML4021 .... 1966 ... £5 ....£12
Caravan .... LP ..... Riverside .... RLP438 .... 1964 ... £6 ....£15
Cu-Bop .... LP ..... London .... LTZJ15110 .... 1958 ... £6 ....£20
Drum Suite .... LP ..... Philips .... BBL7196 .... 1958 ... £6 ....£15
Free For All .... LP ..... Blue Note........ BLP/BST84170 ..... 1966 ... £8 ....£20
Freedom Rider .... LP ..... Blue Note........ BLP/BST84156 ..... 1964 ... £8 ....£20
Hard Bop .... LP ..... Philips .... BBL7212 .... 1958 ... £8 ....£20
Hard Bop .... LP ..... Philips .... BBL7220 .... 1958 ... £8 ....£20
Hard Drive .... LP ..... Parlophone...... PMC1084 .... 1959 ... £8 ....£20
Hold On, I'm Comin' .... LP ..... Mercury .... (S)LML4023 .... 1967 ... £5 ....£12
Holiday For Skins Vol.1 .... LP ..... Blue Note........ BLP/BST84004 ..... 196- ... £10 ....£25
Holiday For Skins Vol.2 .... LP ..... Blue Note........ BLP/BST84005 ..... 196- ... £10 ....£25
I Remember Clifford .... 7" EP.. Fontana .... TFE17337 .... 1961 ... £2.50 ....£6
Indestructable .... LP ..... Blue Note........ BLP/BST84193 ..... 1965 ... £8 ....£20
Jazz Message .... LP ..... HMV .... CLP1760 .... 1964 ... £6 ....£15
Jazz Messengers .... LP ..... Philips .... BBL7121 .... 1957 ... £8 ....£20
Jazz Messengers With Thelonious Monk ... LP ..... London .... LTZK15157/ .... 1959 ... £8 ....£20
                                                                              SAHK6017...........
Kyoto .... LP ..... Storyville .... 673013................ 1969 ... £4 ....£10
Les Liaisons Dangereuses .... LP ..... Fontana .... TFL5184 .... 1962 ... £6 ....£15
Like Someone In Love .... LP ..... Blue Note........ BLP/BST84245 ..... 1967 ... £6 ....£15
Meet You At The Jazz Corner Of The World Vol.1 LP ..... Blue Note........ BLP/BST84054 ..... 196- ... £8 ....£20
Meet You At The Jazz Corner Of The World Vol.2 LP ..... Blue Note........ BLP/BST84055 ..... 196- ... £8 ....£20
Message From Kenya .... 7" ..... Blue Note........ 451626................ 1964 ... £1.50 ....£4
Moanin' .... LP ..... Blue Note........ BLP/BST84003 ..... 1963 ... £10 ....£25
Moanin' .... 7" ..... Blue Note........ 451735................ 1962 ... £1.50 ....£4
Mosaic .... LP ..... Blue Note........ BLP/BST84090 ..... 1962 ... £8 ....£20
Night At Birdland Vol.1 .... LP ..... Blue Note........ BLP/BST81521 ..... 1964 ... £10 ....£25
Night At Birdland Vol.2 .... LP ..... Blue Note........ BLP/BST81522 ..... 1964 ... £10 ....£25
Night In Tunisia .... LP ..... Blue Note........ BLP/BST84049 ..... 1962 ... £10 ....£25
Night In Tunisia .... 7" ..... Blue Note........ 451796................ 1961 ... £1.50 ....£4
Olympia Concert .... LP ..... Fontana .... TFL5116 .... 1961 ... £6 ....£15
Orgy In Rhythm Vol.1 .... LP ..... Blue Note........ BLP/BST81554 ..... 1962 ... £10 ....£25
Orgy In Rhythm Vol.2 .... LP ..... Blue Note........ BLP/BST81555 ..... 1965 ... £10 ....£25
Ritual .... LP ..... Vogue .... LAE12096 .... 1958 ... £10 ....£25
Roots And Herbs .... LP ..... Blue Note........ BST84347 .... 1969 ... £5 ....£12
'S Make It .... LP ..... Mercury .... (S)LML4000 .... 1965 ... £5 ....£12
Soul Finger .... LP ..... Mercury .... (S)LML4012 .... 1966 ... £5 ....£12
Three Blind Mice .... LP ..... United Artists .. (S)ULP1017 .... 1963 ... £8 ....£20
Ugetsu .... LP ..... Riverside .... RLP464 .... 1964 ... £6 ....£15
Witch Doctor .... LP ..... Blue Note........ BLP/BST84258 ..... 1967 ... £6 ....£15

BLANC, MEL
Bugs Bunny .... 7" EP.. Capitol .... EAP56 .... 1958 ... £2 ....£5
I Taut I Taw A Puddy Tat .... 7" EP.. Capitol .... CL14950 .... 1958 ... £2 ....£5
Tweety Pie .... 7" EP.. Capitol .... EAP57 .... 1958 ... £2 ....£5
Tweety Pie .... 7" EP.. Capitol .... EAP59 .... 1958 ... £2 ....£5
Woody Woodpecker .... 7" EP.. Capitol .... EAP58 .... 1958 ... £2 ....£5

Woody Woodpecker's Family Album No.1	7" EP..	Brunswick........	OE9397	1959 ... £2 ....£5	
Woody Woodpecker's Family Album No.2	7" EP..	Brunswick........	OE9398	1959 ... £2 ....£5	
Woody Woodpecker's Family Album No.3	7" EP..	Brunswick........	OE9399	1959 ... £2 ....£5	

BLANCA, BURT
Texas Rider	7"....	Zodiac	ZR004	1960 ... £4 ....£8

BLANCMANGE
Irene And Mavis	7"....	Blahh	no number	1979 ... £4 ....£8

BLAND, BILLY
Let The Little Girl Dance	7"....	London	HL9096	1960 ... £4 ....£8	............chart single

BLAND, BOBBY
Ain't Doing Too Bad	7" EP..	Vocalion	VEP170157	1964 ... £15 ....£30	
Ain't No Love In The Heart Of The City	7"....	ABC	4014	1974 ... £2.50 ....£6	
Ain't Nothin' You Can Do	LP	Vocalion	VAP8027	1964 ... £25 ....£50	
Best Of Bobby Bland	LP	Duke	DLP(S)84	1967 ... £5 ....£12	US
Best Of Bobby Bland Vol.2	LP	Duke	DLP(S)86	1968 ... £6 ....£12	US
Blue Moon	7"....	Vogue	V9192	1962 ... £6 ....£12	
Call On Me	LP	Vocalion	VAP8034	1965 ... £25 ....£50	
Chains Of Love	7"....	Action	ACT4553	1969 ... £4 ....£8	
Cry Cry Cry	7"....	Vogue	V9178	1961 ... £7.50 ....£15	
Don't Cry No More	7"....	Vogue	V9188	1961 ... £6 ....£12	
Good Time Charlie	7"....	Vocalion	VP9273	1966 ... £5 ....£10	
Gotta Get To Know You	7"....	Action	ACT4538	1969 ... £6 ....£12	
Here's The Man	LP	Vocalion	VAP8041	1962 ... £25 ....£50	
His California Album	LP	ABC	ABCL5044	1973 ... £6 ....£15	
His California Album	LP	Probe	SPB1088	1973 ... £5 ....£12	
Honey Child	7"....	Vocalion	VP9222	1964 ... £5 ....£10	
I Wouldn't Treat A Dog	7"....	ABC	ABC4030	1975 ... £2 ....£5	
If Loving You Is Wrong	LP	Duke	X90	1970 ... £5 ....£12	US
I'm Too Far Gone	7"....	Vocalion	VP9262	1966 ... £5 ....£10	
Lead Me On	7"....	Vogue	V9182	1961 ... £7.50 ....£15	
Piece Of Gold	LP	Action	ACLP6006	1969 ... £8 ....£20	
Rockin' In The Same Old Boat	7"....	Action	ACT4524	1969 ... £4 ....£8	
Share Your Love With Me	7"....	Action	ACT4548	1969 ... £4 ....£8	
Share Your Love With Me	7"....	Vocalion	VP9229	1964 ... £5 ....£10	
Soul Of The Man	LP	Duke	DLP(S)79	1966 ... £8 ....£20	US
Spotlighting The Man	LP	Duke	DLPS89	1969 ... £8 ....£20	US
These Hands	7"....	Vocalion	VP9251	1965 ... £5 ....£10	
Touch Of The Blues	LP	Island	ILP974	1968 ... £10 ....£25	
Touch Of The Blues	7"....	Sue	WI4044	1968 ... £7.50 ....£15	
Two Steps From The Blues	LP	Vogue	VAP160183	1961 ... £15 ....£30	
Yield Not To Temptation	7"....	Vocalion	VP9232	1965 ... £5 ....£10	
Yield Not To Temptation	7" EP.	Vocalion	VEP170153	1963 ... £15 ....£30	
You're The One That I Need	7"....	Vogue	V9190	1962 ... £6 ....£12	

BLANE, MARCIE
Bobby's Girl	7"....	London	HLU9599	1962 ... £4 ....£8
How Can I Tell Him	7"....	London	HLU9673	1963 ... £1.50 ....£4
Little Miss Fool	7"....	London	HLU9744	1963 ... £1.50 ....£4
Marcie Blane	7" EP.	London	REU1413	1964 ... £12.50 ...£25
You Gave My Number To Billy	7"....	London	HLU9787	1963 ... £1.50 ....£4

BLANKS
Northern Ripper	7"....	Void	SRTS79CUS560....	1979 ... £5 ....£10

BLASTERS
American Music	LP	Rollin' Rock	021	1980 ... £10 ....£25	US

BLAZERS
Rock And Roll	10" LP	Fontana	TFR6010	1958 ... £10 ....£25

BLAZING SONS
Chant Down The National Front	7"....	Cool Ghoul	COOL002	1983 ... £2.50 ....£6

BLEAK HOUSE
Chase The Wind	7"....	Buzzard	BUZZ2	1982 ... £12.50 ...£25

BLEECHERS
Come Into My Parlour	7"....	Upsetter..........	US314	1969 ... £2.50 ....£6	...... Melotones B side
Ease Up	7"....	Trojan	TR679	1969 ... £2.50 ....£6	
Send Me The Pillow	7"....	Columbia	DB118	1970 ... £4 ....£8	

BLENDELLS
Dance With Me	7"....	Reprise	R20340	1964 ... £4 ....£8
Lalalalalala	7"....	Reprise	R20291	1964 ... £4 ....£8

BLESSING, MICHAEL
Before becoming a Monkee, Mike Nesmith recorded as Michael Blessing.
New Recruit	7"....	Colpix	787	1965 ... £12.50 ...£25	US, probably promo only
Until It's Time For You To Go	7"....	Colpix	792	1965 ... £12.50 ...£25	US, probably promo only

74

BLEY, CARLA

Carla Bley's "Escalator Over The Hill" is a jazz opera, covering a range of musical styles, and bringing together some unlikely combinations of musicians. Linda Ronstadt and John McLaughlin, Don Cherry and Jack Bruce, Paul Jones and Gato Barbieri all have key roles in a work that continues to grow in stature. Carla Bley has never achieved this greatness again, and few other composers have either.

Escalator Over The Hill	LP	JCOA	EOTH3	1972	£8	£20	triple, boxed

BLEY, PAUL

Paul Bley	10" LP	Vogue	LDE171	1956	£25	£50	
Touching	LP	Fontana	SFJL929	1969	£10	£25	

BLEYER, ARCHIE

Amber	7"	London	HL8035	1954	£7.50	£15	
Bridge Of Happiness	7"	London	HLA8263	1956	£6	£12	
Hernando's Hideaway	7"	London	HLA8176	1955	£7.50	£15	
Naughty Lady Of Shady Lane	7"	London	HL8111	1954	£7.50	£15	
Nothin' To Do	7"	London	HLA8243	1956	£6	£12	

BLIND BLAKE

Blind Blake	10" LP	Collector	JFL2001	1960	£8	£20	
Blind Blake 1927-30	LP	Whoopee	101	196-	£5	£12	
Blues In Chicago	LP	Riverside	RLP8804	1967	£6	£15	
Hey Hey Daddy Blues	78	Tempo	R23	1950	£2	£5	
Legendary Blind Blake	10" LP	Ristic	LP18	1958	£15	£30	

BLIND BLAKE & CHARLIE JACKSON

Blind Blake And Charlie Jackson	LP	Heritage	HLP1011	1960	£10	£25	

BLIND FAITH

Blind Faith	LP	Polydor	583059	1969	£4	£10	chart LP, gatefold sleeve
untitled instrumental	7"	Island	no number	1969	£20	£40	promo

BLIND JAKE & RAMBLING THOMAS

Male Blues Vol.3	7" EP	Collector	JEL4	1959	£4	£8	

BLINKERS

Original Sin	7"	Pye	7N17752	1969	£15	£30	

BLISS

Castles In Castille	7"	Chapter One	CH107	1969	£1.50	£4	

BLITZ

All Out Attack	7"	No Future	OI1	1982	£1.50	£4	

BLITZ BOYS

Eddy's New Shoes	12"	Told You So	TYS001	1981	£3	£8	

BLITZKRIEG BOP

Let's Go	7"	Mortonsound	MTN3172/3	1977	£5	£10	

BLODWYN PIG

The natural successor to the bluesy, jazzy music to be found on Jethro Tull's first LP, "This Was", is Blodwyn Pig's "Ahead Rings Out", rather than the later recordings of Ian Anderson and his cohorts. The common factor, of course, is guitarist Mick Abrahams, whose distinctive playing style dominates both records. For Blodwyn Pig, he found an ideal foil in Jack Lancaster, whose fluent work on saxophones and flute is far more noteworthy than Ian Anderson's flautistry!

Ahead Rings Out	LP	Island	ILPS9101	1969	£6	£15	chart LP
Dear Jill	7"	Island	WIP6059	1969	£2	£5	
Getting To This	LP	Chrysalis	ILPS9122	1970	£5	£12	chart LP
Same Old Story	7"	Island	WIP6078	1969	£2	£5	
Walk On The Water	7"	Island	WIP6069	1969	£2	£5	

BLOND

Blond	LP	Fontana	SRF67607	1969	£8	£20	US
Lilac Years	LP	Fontana	STL5515	1969	£50	£100	
Wake Up And Call	7"	Fontana	TF1040	1969	£4	£8	

BLONDE ON BLONDE

All Day All Night	7"	Pye	7N17637	1968	£12.50	£25	
Blonde On Blonde	LP	Ember	NR50--	1972	£10	£25	
Castles In The Sky	7"	Ember	EMBS279	1970	£2.50	£6	
Contrasts	LP	Pye	NSPL18288	1969	£15	£30	
Rebirth	LP	Ember	NR5049	1970	£10	£25	
Reflections On A Life	LP	Ember	NR5058	1971	£10	£25	

BLONDIE

Auto-American Interview	7"	Fan Club	FLX146	1980	£2	£5	flexi
Blondie	LP	Private Stock	PVLP1017	1976	£4	£10	double
Encounters With Blondie	LP	Chrysalis	CDMR1		£30	£60	double
Hunter	LP	Chrysalis	PCDL1384	1982	£4	£10	pic disc
In The Flesh	7"	Private Stock	PVT105	1977	£6	£12	no PS
On The Road	LP	Private Stock	PSPRO8059	1980	£50	£100	pic disc
Parallel Lines	LP	Chrysalis	PCDL1192	1978	£4	£10	US pic disc
Parallel Lines	LP	Mobile Fidelity	MFSL1050	1981	£6	£15	US audiophile
Rip Her To Shreds	7"	Chrysalis	CHS2180	1977	£2.50	£6	
X Offender	7"	Private Stock	PVT90	1977	£50	£100	

BLOOD

Se Parare Nex	LP	Conquest	QUEST3	1985	£6	£15	

BLOOD, SWEAT & TEARS

Blood, Sweat & Tears	LP	Columbia	CQ30994	1973	£5	£12	US quad

Child Is Father To The Man	LP	CBS	63296	1968	£4	£10	chart LP
Child Is Father To The Man	LP	Columbia	HC49619	1981	£5	£12	US audiophile
Greatest Hits	LP	Columbia	CQ31170	1973	£4	£10	US quad
I Can't Quit Her	7"	CBS	3563	1968	£1.50	£4	

BLOODROCK
Bloodrock	LP	Capitol	ST435	1969	£5	£12	US

BLOODY MARY
Bloody Mary	LP	Family	2707	1972	£8	£20	US

BLOOM, ROGER HAMMER
Out Of The Blue	7"	CBS	202654	1967	£2.50	£6	
Polly Pan	7"	CBS	2848	1967	£2	£5	

BLOOMFIELD, MIKE
Analine	LP	Sonet	SNTF749	1977	£4	£10	
Between The Hard Place	LP	Takoma	TAK7070	1979	£4	£10	US
Count Talent And The Originals	LP	Clouds		1978	£4	£10	US
Cruisin' For A Bruisin'	LP	Sonet	SNTF860	1981	£4	£10	
Gospel Duets	LP	Sonet	SNTF164	1981	£4	£10	
If You Love Those Blues	LP	Sonet	SNTF726	1977	£4	£10	
It's Not Killing Me	LP	CBS	63652	1969	£4	£10	
Live At Bill Graham's Fillmore West	LP	CBS	63816	1969	£4	£10	
Living In The Fast Lane	LP	Waterhouse	11	1980	£4	£10	US
Michael Bloomfield	LP	Takoma	1063	1978	£4	£10	US
Red Hot And Blues	LP	UN	2328	1981	£4	£10	US
Try It Before You Buy It	LP	Columbia	PC33173	1973	£4	£10	US

BLOOMFIELD, MIKE & AL KOOPER
Live Adventures	LP	CBS	66216	1969	£6	£15	double
Weight	7"	CBS	4094	1969	£2.50	£6	

BLOOMFIELD, MIKE, DR.JOHN, JOHN HAMMOND
Triumvirate	LP	CBS	65659	1973	£4	£10	

BLOSSOM TOES
Blossom Toes were one of the most interesting groups to emerge out of the psychedelic period, but failed to find the success they deserved. All the members managed to sustain subsequent careers, however, especially guitarists Jim Cregan and Brian Godding - the former playing for Family and Rod Stewart amongst others, while the latter has placed his increasingly finely honed technique and imagination at the disposal of such diverse employers as Keith Tippett, Mike Westbrook, and Kevin Coyne, before recording an impressive solo album in 1988. What is in effect a third Blossom Toes LP, incidentally, was issued under the name of BB Blunder in 1971.

If Only For A Moment	LP	Marmalade	608010	1969	£35	£70	sleeve pictured in Guide
I'll Be Your Baby Tonight	7"	Marmalade	598009	1968	£7.50	£15	
New Day	7"	Marmalade	598022	1969	£15	£30	test pressing only
Peace Loving Man	7"	Marmalade	598014	1969	£5	£10	
Postcard	7"	Marmalade	598012	1969	£5	£10	
We Are Ever So Clean	LP	Marmalade	607/608001	1967	£25	£50	
What On Earth	7"	Marmalade	598002	1967	£6	£12	
What On Earth	7"	Marmalade	598002	1967	£12.50	£25	PS

BLOSSOMS
Led by Darlene Love, the Blossoms provided backing vocals for a vast number of other artists, including Elvis Presley. The high value of "Things Are Changing", however, derives from the fact that it is a rare collaboration between Phil Spector, who produced, and Brian Wilson, who played piano.

Baby Daddy-o	7"	Capitol	CL14947	1958	£6	£12	
Blossoms	LP	MGM	LN1007	1972	£5	£12	US
Little Louie	7"	Capitol	CL14856	1958	£6	£12	
Move On	7"	Capitol	CL14833	1958	£6	£12	
Things Are Changing	7"	EOEOC		1965	£60	£120	US

BLOSSOMS (2)
Stand By	7"	Pama	PM814	1971	£5	£10	

BLOUNT, MICHAEL
Fantasies	LP	York	FYK414	1973	£6	£15	
Patchwork	LP	CBS	64230	1970	£6	£15	
Souvenirs	LP	York	FYK401	1972	£6	£15	

BLOW MONKEYS
Forbidden Fruit	12"	RCA	PT40334	1985	£2.50	£6	double
It Pays To Be Twelve	12"	RCA	PT42232R	1988	£3	£8	
Live Today Love Tomorrow	7"	Parasol	PAR1	1980	£4	£8	

BLUE & FERRIS
You Stole My Money	7"	Blue Cat	BS147	1968	£4	£8	

BLUE ACES
All I Want	7"	Columbia	DB7755	1965	£7.50	£15	
Land Of Love	7"	Pye	7N15672	1964	£2	£5	
That's All I Want	7"	Columbia	DB7954	1966	£20	£40	
You Don't Care	7"	Pye	7N15821	1965	£1.50	£4	

BLUE ANGEL
Blue Angel made an album and two singles, but the group's lead singer only found success once she had decided to go solo. Her name - Cyndi Lauper.

Blue Angel	LP	Polydor	2391486	1980	£8	£20	
I Had A Love	7"	Polydor	POSP241	1981	£6	£12	
I'm Gonna Be Strong	7"	Polydor	POSP212	1980	£7.50	£15	
I'm Gonna Be Strong	7"	Polydor	POSP212	1984	£2.50	£6	reissue with PS

BLUE, BABBITY
Don't Hurt Me	7"	Decca	F12149	1965	£1.50	£4
Don't Make Me	7"	Decca	F12053	1965	£1.50	£4 .... chart single

BLUE BARONS
Twist To The Great Blues Hits	LP	Philips	PHM2/PHS600017	1962	£5	£12 .... US

BLUE BEATS
Beatle Beat	LP	A.A.	133	1964	£10	£25 .... US

BLUE BLOOD
Blue Blood	LP	Sonet	SNTF615	1970	£5	£12

BLUE CHEER
Blue Cheer	LP	Philips	6336001	1969	£6	£15
Feathers From Your Tree	7"	Philips	BF1711	1968	£2	£5
Just A Little Bit	7"	Philips	BF1684	1968	£2	£5
New Improved	LP	Philips	SBL7896	1969	£6	£15
Oh Pleasant Hope	LP	Philips	PHS600350	1971	£8	£20 .... US
Original Human Being	LP	Philips	6336004	1970	£8	£20
Outside Inside	LP	Philips	SBL7860	1968	£6	£15
Pilot	7"	Philips	6051010	1971	£1.50	£4
Summertime Blues	7"	Philips	BF1646	1968	£2.50	£6
Vincebus Eruptum	LP	Philips	(S)BL7839	1967	£6	£15
West Coast Child Of Sunshine	7"	Philips	BF1778	1969	£2.50	£6

BLUE CHIPS
I'm On The Right Side	7"	Pye	7N15970	1965	£7.50	£15
Some Kind Of Lovin'	7"	Pye	7N17111	1966	£7.50	£15
Tell Her	7"	Pye	7N17155	1966	£7.50	£15

BLUE, DAVID
23 Days In September	LP	Reprise	RS6293	1968	£5	£12 .... US
David Blue	LP	Elektra	EKS74003	1966	£5	£12 .... US
Me	LP	Reprise	RS6375	1970	£5	£12 .... US

BLUE DIAMONDS
I'm Forever Blowing Bubbles	7" EP..	Decca	DFE6675	1960	£2	£5

BLUE EPITAPH
Ode	LP	Holyground	HG117	1974	£210	£350

BLUE FLAMES
The two instrumental singles credited to the Blue Flames are the earliest recordings made by Georgie Fame's band, with Fame himself on the organ.
J.A.Blues	7"	R&B	JB114	1963	£15	£30
Stop Right Here	7"	R&B	JB126	1963	£15	£30

BLUE JEANS
Hey Mrs.Housewife	7"	Columbia	DB8555	1969	£6	£12

BLUE MEN
I Hear A New World	LP	Triumph	TRXST9000	1960	£400	£600
I Hear A New World	7" EP..	Triumph	RGXST5000	1960	£100	£200

BLUE MOUNTAIN BOYS
Drop Me Gently	7"	Oriole	CB1774	1962	£1.50	£4

BLUE MOUNTAIN EAGLE
Blue Mountain Eagle	LP	Atco	SD33324	1970	£5	£12 .... US

BLUE NILE
I Love This Life	7"	RSO	RSO84	1981	£5	£10

BLUE OYSTER CULT
Don't Fear The Reaper/Tattoo Vampire	7"	CBS	4483	1976	£2.50	£6 .... demo
Live Bootleg	10" LP	Columbia	AS40	1973	£6	£15 ... US promo
Secret Treaties	LP	CBS	PCQ32858	1974	£5	£12 ...... US quad
Tyranny and Mutation	LP	CBS	PCQ32017	1973	£5	£12 ...... US quad

BLUE, PAMELA
My Friend Bobby	7"	Decca	F11761	1963	£10	£20

BLUE PHANTOM
Distortions	LP	Kaleidoscope	KAL101	1972	£30	£60

BLUE RONDOS
Don't Want Your Lovin'	7"	Pye	7N15833	1965	£10	£20
Little Baby	7"	Pye	7N15734	1964	£15	£30

BLUE STARS
I Can Take It	7"	Decca	F12303	1965	£30	£60

BLUE THINGS
Blue Things	LP	RCA	LPM/LSP3603	1966	£30	£60 .... US

BLUE VELVET BAND
Hitch Hiker	7"	Warner Bros.	WB7320	1969	£1.50	£4
Sweet Moments	LP	Warner Bros.	WS1802	1969	£6	£15 .... US

BLUEBEATS
Fabulous Bluebeats Vol.1	7" EP..	Ember	EMBEP4525	1962	£15	£30

Fabulous Bluebeats Vol.2	7" EP	Ember	EMBEP4526	1962	£15	£30	

BLUEBELLS
Young At Heart	7"	London	LON49	1984	£1.50	£4	shaped pic disc

BLUEBERRIES
It's Gonna Work Out Fine	7"	Mercury	MF894	1965	£10	£20	

BLUES BAND
Official Bootleg Album	LP	Arista	BBBP101	1980	£6	£15	autographed

BLUES BLENDERS
Girl Next Door	7"	Rio	R93	1966	£4	£8	

BLUES BUSTERS
Behold!	LP	Island	ILP923	1965	£40	£80	
Blues Busters	LP	Doctor Bird	DLM5008	1966	£40	£80	
Donna	7"	Blue Beat	BB55	1961	£5	£10	
How Sweet It Is	7"	Island	WI214	1965	£5	£10	
I've Been Trying	7"	Doctor Bird	DB1030	1966	£5	£10	
Little Vilma	7"	Limbo	XL101	1960	£5	£10	
Oh Baby	7"	Island	WI023	1962	£5	£10	
Philip And Lloyd	LP	Dynamic	DYLP3007	1976	£5	£12	
Spiritual	7"	Starlite	ST45031	1961	£5	£10	
Tell Me Why	7"	Blue Beat	BB102	1962	£5	£10	
There's Always A Sunshine	7"	Doctor Bird	DB1078	1967	£5	£10	
There's Always Sunshine	7"	Blue Beat	BB73	1961	£5	£10	
Wings Of A Dove	7"	Island	WI222	1965	£5	£10	Byron Lee B side
Your Love	7"	Starlite	ST45072	1962	£4	£8	

BLUES BY FIVE
Boom Boom	7"	Decca	F12029	1964	£15	£30	

BLUES COUNCIL
Baby Don't Look Down	7"	Parlophone	R5264	1965	£20	£40	

BLUES DIMENSION
Blues Dimension	LP	Decca	ND254	1969	£6	£15	German

BLUES IMAGE
Blues Image	LP	Atco	SD33300	1969	£5	£12	US
Open	LP	Atco	33317	1970	£5	£12	US
Red,White,& Blues Image	LP	Atlantic	2400120	1971	£5	£12	

BLUES MAGOOS
Basic Blues Magoos	LP	Mercury	MG2/SR61167	1968	£8	£20	US
Blues Magoos	LP	Fontana	(S)TL5402	1966	£10	£25	
Electric Comic Book	LP	Mercury	MG2/SR61104	1967	£15	£30	US, with comic
Gulf Coast Bound	LP	ABC	ABCS710	1970	£8	£20	US
Never Going Back To Georgia	LP	ABC	S697	1969	£8	£20	US
One By One	7"	Fontana	TF848	1967	£6	£12	
Psychedelic Lollipop	LP	Mercury	MG2/SR61096	1966	£10	£25	US
We Ain't Got Nothin' Yet	7"	Mercury	MF954	1966	£10	£20	
We Ain't Got Nothin' Yet	7" EP	Mercury	126221	1967	£25	£50	French

BLUES PROJECT
The Blues Project had an important role within the growing maturity of rock music during the sixties, which the loss of credibility of leading member Al Kooper in the succeeding years should do nothing to diminish. The group had a loose, improvisational approach to the blues, in which Andy Kulberg's flute playing was an effective element. "Lazarus" and "Blues Project" represent an attempt to revive the group in the seventies, but by then the spark had inevitably gone.

Blues Project	LP	Capitol	EST11017	1972	£5	£12	US
Flanders, Kalb, Katz...	LP	Verve	FTS3069	1969	£6	£15	US
I Can't Keep From Crying	7"	Verve	VS1505	1967	£6	£12	
Lazarus	LP	Capitol	ST872	1971	£5	£12	US
Live At The Cafe Au Go-Go	LP	Verve	FT(S)3000	1966	£8	£20	US
Live At Town Hall	LP	Verve	FT(S)3025	1967	£8	£20	US
No Time Like The Right Time	7" EP	Verve	519905	1967	£25	£50	French
Planned Obsolescence	LP	Verve	FTS3046	1968	£8	£20	US
Projections	LP	Verve	(S)VLP6009	1967	£8	£20	US
Reunion In Central Park	LP	MCA	8003	1973	£5	£12	US

BLUESBREAKERS
Curly	7"	Decca	F12588	1967	£4	£8	

BLUESOLOGY
Bluesology worked as the backing group for Long John Baldry when the singer was still performing rhythm and blues. The group's pianist was Reg Dwight - or rather Elton John, as he subsequently chose to be known.

Come Back Baby	7"	Fontana	TF594	1965	£150	£250	
Mr.Frantic	7"	Fontana	TF668	1966	£150	£250	
Since I Found You Baby	7"	Polydor	56195	1967	£150	£250	with Stu Brown

BLUEWATER FOLK
Bluewater Folk	LP	Folk Heritage		197-	£15	£30	

BLUR
High Cool	12"	Food	12BLUR4	1991	£2.50	£6	promo
She's So High	CD-s	Food	CDFOOD26	1990	£2.50	£6	
Wassailing Song	7"	Food	BLUR6	1992	£5	£10	1 sided promo

BLYTHE, JIMMY
South Side Blues Piano	10" LP	London	AL3527	1954	£8	£20	
South Side Chicago Jazz	10" LP	London	AL3529	1954	£8	£20	

B-MOVIE
Nowhere Girl	12"	Dead Good	BIGDEAD9	1980	£6	£15	
Nowhere Girl	12"	Wax	12WAX3	1988	£3	£8	orange vinyl
Nowhere Girl	12"	Wax	12WAX3	1988	£2.50	£6	pink vinyl
Take Three	7"	Dead Good	DEAD9	1980	£10	£20	
Volume 1 - Remembrance Days	LP	Dead Good	GOOD3	1991	£5	£12	with 7'

BO & PEEP
Young Love	7"	Decca	F11968	1964	£7.50	£15

BO, EDDIE
Check Your Bucket	7"	Action	ACT4609	1973	£2	£5

BO STREET RUNNERS
When the cult TV show "Ready Steady Go" organised a beat group talent contest in 1964, the Bo Street Runners were the winners. (The various artists' LP "Ready Steady Win" documents the affair). As is usually the case with talent contests, however, the win yielded nothing in terms of subsequent success for the Bo Street Runners. The group was led by organist Tim Hinkley, while both Mick Fleetwood and Mike Patto were members for a time.

Baby Never Say Goodbye	7"	Columbia	DB7640	1965	£10	£20
Bo Street Runner	7"	Decca	F11986	1964	£12.50	£25
Bo Street Runners	7" EP.	Oak	RGJ131	1964	£250	£400
Drive My Car	7"	Columbia	DB7901	1966	£10	£20
Tell Me What You're Gonna Do	7"	Columbia	DB7488	1965	£20	£40

BOARDMAN, HARRY
Lancashire Mon	LP	Topic	12TS236	1974	£5	£12

BOARDMAN, HARRY & DAVE HILLERY
Trans Pennine	LP	Topic	12TS215	1971	£5	£12

BOB
Esmerelda Brooklyn	7"	House Of Teeth	HOT003	1989	£2.50	£6	
Prune	7"	House Of Teeth		1988	£2	£5	flexi

BOB & BOBBY
The single by Bob And Bobby is one of the small number of outside productions undertaken by Beach Boy Brian Wilson in the sixties.

Twelve-O-Four	7"	Tower	154	1965	£12.50	£25	US

BOB & EARL
Baby I'm Satisfied	7"	Sue	WI393	1965	£6	£12	
Bob And Earl	LP	B&C	BSB1	1969	£4	£10	
Dancin' Everywhere	7"	B&C	CB102	1969	£1.50	£4	
Don't Ever Leave Me	7"	Sue	WI4030	1967	£6	£12	
Everybody Jerk	7"	Warner Bros	WB6059	1969	£1.50	£4	
Harlem Shuffle	LP	Sue	ILP951	1967	£15	£30	
Harlem Shuffle	7"	Island	WIP6053	1969	£1.50	£4	chart single
Harlem Shuffle	7"	Sue	WI374	1965	£5	£10	
Pickin' Up Love's Vibrations	7"	Uni	UN519	1970	£1.50	£4	

BOB & JERRY
Ghost Satellite	7"	Pye	7N25003	1958	£2.50	£6
We're The Guys	7"	Philips	PB1205	1961	£1.50	£4

BOB & MARCIA
Pied Piper	LP	Trojan	TRLS26	1971	£5	£12	
Really Together	7"	Bamboo	BAM40	1970	£2	£5	
Young Gifted And Black	7"	Harry J	HJ6605	1970	£1.50	£4	chart single
Young, Gifted And Black	LP	Trojan	TBL122	1970	£6	£15	

BOB & SHERI
The ultra-rare single by Bob And Sheri is a Brian Wilson production.

Surfer Moon	7"	Safari	101	1962	£400	£600	US, blue label

BOB & TYRONE
I Don't Care	7"	Coxsone	CS7086	1969	£5	£10

BOBBETTES
Come A Come A Come A	7"	London	HLE8597	1958	£15	£30
Have Mercy Baby	7"	London	HLU9248	1960	£10	£20
I Shot Mr.Lee	7"	London	HLK9173	1960	£12.50	£25
I Shot Mr.Lee	7"	Pye	7N25060	1960	£7.50	£15
Mr.Lee	7"	London	HLE8477	1957	£20	£40
That's A Bad Thing To Know	7"	Action	ACT4603	1972	£4	£8

BOBBSEY TWINS
Change Of Heart	7"	London	HLA8474	1957	£4	£8

BOBBY & LAURIE
Hitch Hiker	7"	Parlophone	R5480	1966	£1.50	£4

BOBCATS
Can't See For Looking	7"	Pye	7N17242	1967	£4	£8

BOCKY & THE VISIONS
I Go Crazy	7"	Atlantic	AT4049	1965	£4	£8

BODINES
God Bless	7"	Creation	CRE016	1985	£2	£5

BODKIN
Bodkin .... LP ...... West .... CSA104 .... 1972 ... £180 ......£300 ....

BODY
Body Album .... LP ...... Recession .... REC01 .... 1981 ... £20 ....£40 ....

BODY ELECTRIC
Body Electric .... LP ...... Attic .... LAT1194 .... £8 ....£20 ....Canadian

BOFFALONGO
Beyond Your Head .... LP ...... United Artists .. UAG29130 .... 1970 ... £6 ....£15 ....
Boffalongo .... LP ...... United Artists .. 6726 .... 1969 ... £6 ....£15 .... US

BOGARDE, DIRK
Darling .... 7" ...... Fontana .... TF615 .... 1965 ... £1.50 ....£4 ....
Lyrics For Lovers .... LP ...... Decca .... LK4373 .... 1960 ... £6 ....£15 ....

BOHEMIAN VENDETTA
Bohemian Vendetta .... LP ...... Mainstream ..... (5)6106 .... 1968 ... £8 ....£20 .... US

BOINES, HOUSTON
Superintendant Blues .... 7" .... Blue Horizon.... 451006 .... 1966 ... £20 ....£40 ....

BOKAJ RETSIEM
Psychedelic Underground .... LP ..... Fass .... 1532WY .... 1969 ... £6 ....£15 ....German

BOLAN, MARC
For an artist with an essentially rather limited talent, Marc Bolan has managed to attract an extraordinarily devoted following. Part of this is no doubt the direct consequence of Bolan's premature death. In any event, there are a number of quite valuable recordings to be found scattered through Bolan's catalogue. These include the original issue of his "Zinc Alloy" LP, which has an individually numbered poster sleeve, and the early solo singles (whose lack of chart success is not hard to understand once they are heard; they are somewhat less than inspiring). Records made with John's Children and Tyrannosaurus Rex are listed under those headings.

Beginning Of Doves .... LP ...... Track .... 2410201 .... 1974 ... £6 ....£15 ....
Hippy Gumbo .... 7" ...... Parlophone ...... R5539 .... 1966 ... £120 ....£220 ....
Jasper C.Debussy .... 7" ...... Track .... 2094013 .... 1974 ... £6 ....£12 .... PS
Road I'm On .... 7" ...... Archive Jive ..... TOBY1 .... 1990 ... £5 ....£10 ....as Toby Tyler
Third Degree .... 7" ...... Decca .... F12413 .... 1966 ... £120 ....£220 ....
Wizard .... 7" ...... Decca .... F12288 .... 1965 ... £80 .....£160 ....
You Scare Me To Death .... LP ...... Cherry Red ...... PERED20 .... 1981 ... £4 ....£10 .... pic disc
You Scare Me To Death .... 7" ...... Cherry Red ...... CHERRY29 .... 1981 ... £2 ....£5 .with flexi (LYN10086)
You Scare Me To Death .... 7" ...... Cherry Red ...... CHERRYP29 .... 1981 ... £1.50 ....£4 .... pic disc

BOLAN, MARC & T REX
Celebrate Summer .... 7" ...... EMI .... MARC18 .... 1977 ... £1.50 ....£4 .... PS
Chariot Choogle .... 7" ...... EMI .... SPSR346 .... 1972 ... £50 .....£100 .... promo
Children Of Rarn .... 10" ...... Marc .... ABOLAN2 .... 1982 ... £6 ....£15 .... with book
Electric Warrior .... LP ...... Fly .... HIFLY6 .... 1971 ... £5 ....£12 ....with inner & poster, chart LP
Get It On .... 7" ...... Fly .... BUG10 .... 1971 ... £5 ....£10 ... PS, silver fly on label, handwritten credits
Great Hits .... LP ...... EMI .... BLN5003 .... 1972 ... £4 ....£10 ... with poster
Hard On Love .... LP ...... Track .... 2406101 .... 1972 ... £100 ....£200 ... test pressing
History Of T Rex .... LP ...... Marc On Wax ... WARRIOR1-4 ..... 1986 ... £8 ....£20 ....4 pic discs, boxed
Jeepster .... 7" ...... Fly .... GRUB1 .... 1971 ... £40 .....£80 .... promo
Jeepster .... 7" ...... Fly .... GRUB1 .... 1971 ... £60 .....£120 ... promo, pink sleeve
Life's A Gas .... 12" ...... Cube .... ANTS001 .... 1979 ... £3 ....£8 ....
Ride A White Swan .... 7" ...... Fly .... BUG1 .... 1970 ... £1.50 ....£4 .... PS, mustard label
Ride A White Swan .... 7" ...... Fly .... BUG1 .... 1970 ... £6 ....£12 .... PS, purple label
Ride A White Swan .... 7" ...... Octopus .... OCTO1 .... 1970 ... £400 ....£600 ....test pressing
Sing Me A Song .... 12" ...... Rarn .... MBFS001P .... 1981 ... £6 ....£12 ...... pic disc, black rim
T Rex In Concert .... LP ...... Marc .... ABOLAN1 .... 1981 ... £6 ....£15 ...promo, no applause
Tanx .... LP ...... EMI .... BLN5002 .... 1972 ... £5 ....£12 ....with inner & poster, chart LP
Words And Music Of Marc Bolan .... LP ...... Cube .... HIFLY1 .... 1978 ... £6 ....£15 ....double, with 7' (BINT1)
Zinc Alloy & Hidden Riders Of Tomorrow ... LP ...... EMI .... BLNA7751 .... 1974 ... £5 ....£12 ....with inner, chart LP
Zinc Alloy & Hidden Riders Of Tomorrow ... LP ...... T Rex Wax Co.. BLNA7751 .... 1974 ... £60 .....£120 promo fold-out sleeve
Zip Gun .... LP ...... EMI .... BLN7752 .... 1975 ... £6 ....£15 .... diamond cut sleeve, inner

BOLIVAR, SIMON
Merengue Holiday .... 7" ...... London .... HLG8245 .... 1956 ... £5 ....£10 ....

BOLOTIN, MICHAEL
Bolotin is, of course, Michael Bolton, performing in much the same style as was successful for him several years later.
Every Day Of My Life .... LP ...... RCA .... APL11550 .... 1976 ... £8 ....£20 .... US
Michael Bolotin .... LP ...... RCA .... SF8451 .... 1975 ... £8 ....£20 ....

BOMBAY DUCKS
Dance Music .... LP ...... United Dairies . UP05 .... 198- ... £6 ....£15 ....
Sympathy For The Devil .... 7" ...... Complete Control .... CON1 .... 1980 ... £2 ....£5 ....

BON BONS
Circle .... 7" ...... London .... HLU8262 .... 1956 ... £10 ....£20 ....
That's The Way Love Goes .... 7" ...... London .... HL8139 .... 1955 ... £12.50 ...£25 ....

BON JOVI

Hardest Part Is The Night	7"	Vertigo	VER22	1985	£2	£5	chart single
Hardest Part Is The Night	7"	Vertigo	VERDP22	1985	£4	£8	double
Hardest Part Is The Night	12"	Vertigo	VERX22	1985	£3	£8	
Hardest Part Is The Night	12"	Vertigo	VERXR22	1985	£6	£15	red vinyl
In And Out Of Love	7"	Vertigo	VER19	1985	£2.50	£6	
In And Out Of Love	7"	Vertigo	VERP19	1985	£7.50	£15	pic disc
In And Out Of Love	12"	Vertigo	VERX19	1985	£3	£8	
Living On A Prayer	7"	Vertigo	VERP28	1986	£4	£8	pic disc
Living On A Prayer	7"	Vertigo	VERPA28	1986	£1.50	£4	with patch
Living On A Prayer	12"	Vertigo	VERXG28	1986	£3	£8	double
Living On A Prayer	12"	Vertigo	VERXR28	1986	£3	£8	green vinyl
Runaway	7"	Vertigo	VER14	1984	£5	£10	
Runaway	12"	Vertigo	VERX14	1984	£5	£12	
She Don't Know Me	7"	Vertigo	VER11	1984	£5	£10	
She Don't Know Me	12"	Vertigo	VERX11	1984	£8	£20	
Slippery When Wet	LP	Vertigo	VERHP38	1988	£4	£10	pic disc, poster
Wanted Dead Or Alive	12"	Vertigo	JOVR112	1987	£2.50	£6	silver vinyl
You Give Love A Bad Name	12"	Vertigo	VERX26	1986	£2.50	£6	with poster
You Give Love A Bad Name	12"	Vertigo	VERXR26	1986	£3	£8	blue vinyl
You Give Love A Bad Name	10"	Vertigo	VERP26	1986	£4	£10	shaped pic disc

BONANO, SHARKEY

At The Round Table	LP	Columbia	33SX1255/ SCX3327	1960	£4	£10	

BOND, BOBBY

One More Mile One More Town	7"	Warner Bros	WB7292	1969	£1.50	£4	
Sweet Love	7"	Pye	7N25081	1961	£2.50	£6	

BOND, BRIGITTE

Blue Beat Baby	7"	Blue Beat	BB212	1963	£5	£10	

BOND, EDDIE

Greatest Country Gospel Hits	LP	Philips	1980	1961	£25	£50	US

BOND, GRAHAM

Although he was undoubtedly a major influence within the development of sixties rock, Bond's tragedy was to see his ideas developed more successfully by others. Few of his records really do justice to his undoubted talents, partly because despite being a good alto sax jazz player (as his work on both the Don Rendell Quintet LP of 1962 and on the early Organisation tracks included on 'Solid Bond" prove), he constantly compromised his art in a desperate search for commercial success. He never did find it, however, and yet all his sixties sidemen managed to - Ginger Baker and Jack Bruce with Cream; Jon Hiseman and Dick Heckstall-Smith with Colosseum; and John McLaughlin with Mahavishnu Orchestra. Bond himself stumbled through increasingly marginal musical projects, in which personal and drug problems did not help, until he fell under a train in 1974.

Bond In America	LP	Mercury	6499200/1	1971	£15	£30	double
Holy Magick	LP	Vertigo	6360021	1971	£8	£20	spiral label
Lease On Love	7"	Columbia	DB7647	1965	£10	£20	
Long Tall Shorty	7"	Decca	F11909	1964	£12.50	£25	
Love Is The Law	LP	Pulsar	AR10604	1968	£8	£20	US
Mighty Graham Bond	LP	Pulsar	AR10606	1968	£8	£20	US
Solid Bond	LP	Warner Bros	WS3001	1970	£10	£25	double, chart LP
Sound Of '65	LP	Columbia	33SX1711	1965	£30	£60	
St.James Infirmary	7"	Columbia	DB7838	1966	£10	£20	
Tammy	7"	Columbia	DB7471	1965	£10	£20	
Tell Me	7"	Columbia	DB7528	1965	£10	£20	
There's A Bond Between Us	LP	Columbia	33SX1750	1966	£30	£60	
This Is Graham Bond	LP	Philips	6382010	1972	£6	£15	
Walking In The Park	7"	Warner Bros	WB8004	1970	£5	£10	
We Put Our Magick On You	LP	Vertigo	6360042	1971	£8	£20	spiral label
You've Gotta Have Love Babe	7"	Page One	POF014	1967	£15	£30	

BOND, GRAHAM & PETE BROWN

Lost Tribe	7"	Greenwich	GSS104	1972	£10	£20	
Two Heads Are Better Than One	LP	Chapter One	CHSR813	1972	£30	£60	

BOND, JACKI

He Say	7"	Strike	JH320	1966	£7.50	£15	
Now I Know	7"	Columbia	DB7719	1965	£1.50	£4	
Tell Him To Go Away	7"	Strike	JH302	1966	£1.50	£4	

BOND, JOHNNY

Hot Rod Jalopy	7"	London	HLU9189	1960	£6	£12	
Hot Rod Lincoln	7"	London	HL7100	1960	£4	£8	export
Live It Up	LP	London	HAB8098	1963	£5	£12	
Songs That Made Him Famous	LP	London	HAB8228	1965	£6	£15	
Ten Little Bottles	7"	London	HLB9957	1965	£1.50	£4	
That Wild, Wicked But Wonderful West	LP	Stateside	SL10008	1962	£4	£10	

BOND, JOYCE

Back To School	7"	Pama	PM718	1968	£2.50	£6	
Do The Teasy	7"	Island	WIP6010	1967	£4	£8	
It's Alright	7"	Airborn	NBP0011	1967	£5	£10	
Mr.Pitiful	7"	Pama	PM770	1969	£2.50	£6	
Ob La Di Ob La Da	7"	Island	WIP6051	1968	£4	£8	
Soul And Ska	LP	Island	ILP968	1968	£30	£60	
Tell Me What It's All About	7"	Island	WI3019	1966	£5	£10	
This Train	7"	Island	WIP6018	1967	£4	£8	
Wind Of Change	7"	Upfront	UPF5	1970	£1.50	£4	

BOND, MARGARET
Your Love Is My Love .... 7" ...... Parlophone...... R4283 .... 1957 ... **£2** ....**£5** ....

BOND, OLIVER
Let Me Love You .... 7" ...... Parlophone...... R5476 .... 1966 ... **£4** ....**£8** ....

BOND, RONNIE
Anything For You .... 7" ...... Page One .... POF123 .... 1969 ... **£7.50** ....**£15** ....

BONDS, GARY (U.S.)
Copy Cat	7"	Stateside	SS125	1962	£1.50	£4	
Dance Till Quarter To Three	LP	Legrand	LLP3001	1961	£25	£50	US
Dance Till Quarter To Three	LP	Top Rank	35114	1961	£10	£25	
Dear Lady Twist	7"	Top Rank	JAR602	1962	£1.50	£4	
Do The Limbo With Me	7"	Stateside	SS179	1963	£1.50	£4	
Ella Is Yella	7"	Stateside	SS308	1964	£1.50	£4	
Greatest Hits	LP	Stateside	SL10037	1962	£8	£20	
I Dig This Station	7"	Stateside	SS144	1963	£1.50	£4	
I Don't Wanna Wait	7"	Stateside	SS219	1963	£1.50	£4	
New Orleans	7"	Top Rank	JAR527	1961	£1.50	£4	chart single
Not Me	7"	Top Rank	JAR566	1961	£1.50	£4	
Quarter To Three	7"	Stateside	SS271	1964	£1.50	£4	
Quarter To Three	7"	Top Rank	JAR575	1961	£1.50	£4	chart single
School Is In	7"	Top Rank	JAR595	1961	£1.50	£4	
School Is Out	7"	Top Rank	JAR581	1961	£1.50	£4	
Send Her To Me	7"	Stateside	SS2025	1967	£4	£8	
Seven Day Weekend	7"	Stateside	SS111	1962	£1.50	£4	
Twist Twist Senora	7"	Top Rank	JAR615	1962	£1.50	£4	
Twist Up Calypso	LP	Stateside	SL10001	1962	£8	£20	

BONE, OLIVER
Knock On Wood .... 7" ...... Parlophone...... R5527 .... 1966 ... **£2.50** ....**£6** ....

BONFIRE, MARS
Faster Than The Speed Of Life	LP	Columbia	CS9834	1969	£5	£12	US
Mars Bonfire	LP	UNI	73027	1968	£5	£12	US

BONNER, JUKE BOY
One Man Trio	LP	Flyright	LP3501	1968	£8	£20	
Runnin' Shoes	7"	Blue Horizon	573163	1969	£6	£12	
Things Ain't Right	LP	Liberty	LBS83319	1969	£5	£12	

BONNET, GRAHAM
Graham Bonnet .... LP ...... Ring O' .... 2320103 .... 1977 ... **£5** ....**£12** ....

BONNEVILLES
Meet The Bonnevilles .... LP ...... Drum Boy .... DLM/LS1001 ...... 1963 ... **£8** ....**£20** ...... US

BONNEY, GRAHAM
Baby's Gone	7"	Columbia	DB7934	1966	£1.50	£4	
Devil's Child	7"	Columbia	DB8338	1968	£1.50	£4	
Frenzy	7"	Columbia	DB8464	1968	£1.50	£4	
Get Ready	7"	Columbia	DB8531	1969	£2.50	£6	
Happy Together	7"	Columbia	DB8142	1967	£1.50	£4	
I'll Be Your Baby Tonight	7"	Columbia	DB8382	1968	£1.50	£4	
Leander Angeline	7"	Columbia	DB8592	1969	£1.50	£4	
My Little World Is Blue	7"	Columbia	DB7773	1965	£1.50	£4	
No One Knows	7"	Columbia	DB8005	1966	£2	£5	
Poppa Joe	7"	Columbia	DB8283	1967	£1.50	£4	
Sign On The Dotted Line	7"	Columbia	DB8648	1970	£2	£5	
Super Girl	7"	Columbia	DB7843	1966	£2	£5	chart single
Supergirl	LP	Columbia	SX6052	1966	£5	£12	
Thank You Baby	7"	Columbia	DB8111	1967	£1.50	£4	
When Evelyn Was Mine	7"	Columbia	DB8687	1970	£1.50	£4	

BONNIE
Did You Get The Message	7"	Ska Beat	JB270	1967	£5	£10	
Lovin' You	7"	Jolly	JY014	1968	£4	£8	

BONNIE & THE TREASURES
Home Of The Brave .... 7" ...... London .... HLU9998 .... 1965 ... **£7.50** ....**£15** ....

BONNIWELL, T.S.
Close .... LP ...... Capitol .... ST277 .... 1969 ... **£15** ....**£30** ...... US

BONZO DOG (DOO-DAH) BAND
Alley Oop	7"	Parlophone	R5499	1966	£7.50	£15	
Best Of The Bonzos	LP	Liberty	LBS83332	1970	£5	£12	
Doughnut In Granny's Greenhouse	LP	Liberty	LBL/LBS83158	1968	£6	£15	with booklet, chart LP
Equestrian Statue	7"	Liberty	LBF15040	1967	£2.50	£6	
Gorilla	LP	Liberty	LBL/LBS83056	1967	£6	£15	with booklet
History Of The Bonzos	LP	United Artists	UAD60071/2	1974	£8	£20	double
I Want To Be With You	LP	Liberty	LBF15273	1969	£1.50	£4	
Keynsham	LP	Liberty	LBS83290	1969	£6	£15	
Let's Make Up & Be Friendly	LP	United Artists	UAS29288	1972	£6	£15	
Mr.Apollo	7"	Liberty	LBF15201	1969	£2	£5	
My Brother Makes The Noises For The Talkies	7"	Parlophone	R5430	1966	£7.50	£15	
Tadpoles	LP	Liberty	LBS83257	1969	£5	£12	chart LP
Urban Spaceman	7"	Liberty	LBF15144	1968	£1.50	£4	2 versions of B-side, chart single

You Done My Brain In	7"	Liberty	LBF15314	1970	£2	£5

BONZO DOG (DOO-DAH) BAND & OTHERS

Alberts,The Bonzo Dog Band,& The Temperance Seven	LP	Starline	SRS5151	1973	£4	£10

BOO RADLEYS

Ichabod And I	LP	Boo Radleys		199-	£5	£12

BOOGIE KINGS

Blue Eyed Soul	LP	Montel-Michelle	109	1967	£5	£12	US
Boogie Kings	LP	Montel-Michelle	104	1966	£5	£12	US

BOOKER, BERYL

Beryl Booker Trio	10" LP	London	HBA1054	1956	£20	£40

BOOKER, JAMES

Cool Turkey	7"	Vogue	V9177	1961	£5	£10
Gonzo	7" EP	Vocalion	VEP170154	1963	£15	£30

BOOKER T & THE MG'S

And Now	LP	Stax	589002	1966	£4	£10	
Back To Back (with Markeys)	LP	Stax	(STS)720	1967	£4	£10	US
Best Of Booker T And The MG's	LP	Atlantic	228015	1968	£4	£10	
Booker T Set	LP	Stax	SXATS1015	1970	£4	£10	
Bootleg	7"	Atlantic	AT4033	1965	£4	£8	
Chinese Checkers	7"	London	HLK9784	1963	£2.50	£6	
Chinese Checkers	7"	Stax	601026	1967	£1.50	£4	
Doin' Our Thing	LP	Atlantic	2464011	1968	£4	£10	
Get Ready	LP	Atco	228004	1969	£4	£10	
Green Onions	LP	Atlantic	587/588033	1966	£4	£10	
Green Onions	LP	London	HAK8182	1964	£6	£15	chart LP
Green Onions	7"	Atlantic	584088	1967	£2	£5	
Green Onions	7"	London	HLK9595	1962	£4	£8	
Hip Hugger	7"	Stax	601009	1967	£1.50	£4	
Hip Hug-Her	LP	Stax	(STS)717	1967	£4	£10	US
In The Christmas Spirit	LP	Stax	(STS)713	1966	£4	£10	US
Jelly Bread	7"	London	HLK9670	1963	£2.50	£6	
Jingle Bells	7"	Atlantic	584060	1966	£1.50	£4	
McLemore Avenue	LP	Stax	SXATS1031	1970	£4	£10	chart LP
My Sweet Potato	7"	Stax	584044	1966	£1.50	£4	
R&B With Booker T Vol.1	7" EP	London	REK1367	1963	£7.50	£15	
R&B With Booker T Vol.2	7" EP	Atlantic	AET6002	1964	£7.50	£15	
Red Beans And Rice	7"	Atlantic	AT4063	1966	£2	£5	
Slim Jenkins' Place	7"	Stax	601018	1967	£2	£5	
Soul Christmas	LP	Stax	589013	1967	£4	£10	
Soul Clap '69	7"	Stax	STAX127	1969	£1.50	£4	chart single
Soul Dressing	LP	Atlantic	587047	1967	£4	£10	
Soul Dressing	LP	Atlantic	ATL5027	1965	£5	£12	
Soul Limbo	LP	Stax	(S)XATS1001	1968	£4	£10	
Soul Limbo	7"	Stax	STAX102	1968	£1.50	£4	chart single
Time Is Tight	7"	Stax	STAX119	1969	£1.50	£4	chart single
Uptight	LP	Stax	(S)XATS1005	1968	£4	£10	

BOOMERANGS

Another Tear Falls	7"	Fontana	TF555	1965	£6	£12
Dream World	7"	Pye	7N17049	1966	£6	£12
Rockin' Robin	7"	Fontana	TF507	1964	£10	£20

BOOMTOWN RATS

Rat Pack	7"	Ensign		1978	£6	£12	6 singles in plastic wallet

BOONE, PAT

Ain't That A Shame	7"	London	HLD8172	1955	£10	£20	chart single
All Hands On Deck	7" EP	London	RED1294	1961	£2	£5	
Always You And Me	7" EP	London	RED1384	1963	£2.50	£6	
April Love	LP	London	HAD2078	1958	£4	£10	
April Love	LP	London	HAD2078	1958	£5	£12	
April Love	7"	London	HLD8512	1957	£2	£5	chart single
Beach Girl	7"	Dot	DS16658	1964	£1.50	£4	
Beyond The Sunset	7"	London	HLD9029	1960	£1.50	£4	
Big Hits Vol.2	LP	London	HAD2098	1958	£5	£12	
Boss Beat	LP	Dot	(D)DLP3594	1965	£4	£10	
Candy Sweet	7"	London	HLD9184	1960	£1.50	£4	
Dear John	7"	London	HLD9238	1960	£1.50	£4	
Don't Forbid Me	7"	London	HLD8370	1957	£5	£10	chart single
Down Lovers Lane	7" EP	London	RED1359	1963	£2	£5	
Easy	7"	London	RED1255	1960	£2	£5	
Fool's Hall Of Fame	7"	London	HLD8974	1959	£1.50	£4	
For A Penny	7"	London	HLD8855	1959	£1.50	£4	chart single
For A Penny	7"	London	SLD4002	1959	£7.50	£15	export, stereo
Four By Pat	7" EP	London	RED1109	1957	£2	£5	
Friendly Persuasion	7"	London	HLD8346	1956	£5	£10	chart single
Gee, But It's Lonely	7"	London	HLD8703	1958	£1.50	£4	chart single
Gee Whittakers	7"	London	HLD8233	1956	£7.50	£15	
Golden Hits	LP	London	HAD/SHD8031	1962	£4	£10	
Good Rockin' Tonight	7"	London	HLD8824	1959	£2	£5	chart single
Hey Baby	7" EP	Dot	DEP20008	1966	£2	£5	

Title	Format	Label	Cat. No.	Year	Price 1	Price 2	Notes
Howdy	LP	London	HAD2030	1957	£6	£15	
Howdy Part 1	7" EP	London	RED1081	1957	£2	£5	
Howdy Part 2	7" EP	London	RED1082	1957	£2	£5	
Howdy Part 3	7" EP	London	RED1119	1958	£2	£5	
I Almost Lost My Mind	7"	London	HLD8303	1956	£5	£10	chart single
I Love You Truly	LP	London	HAD/SHD8053	1963	£4	£10	
If Dreams Came True	7"	London	HLD8675	1958	£1.50	£4	chart single
I'll Be Home	7"	London	HLD8253	1956	£6	£12	chart single
I'll Remember Tonight	7"	London	HLD8775	1959	£1.50	£4	chart single
I'll See You In My Dreams	LP	London	HAD2452/ SAHD6240	1962	£5	£12	
I'll See You In My Dreams	7"	London	HLD9504	1962	£1.50	£4	
Johnny Will	7"	London	HLD9461	1961	£1.50	£4	chart single
Just A Closer Walk With Thee	7" EP	London	RED1095	1957	£2	£5	
Latest And Greatest	7" EP	London	RED1281	1961	£2	£5	
Latest And Greatest No.2	7" EP	London	RED1335	1962	£2.50	£6	
Long Tall Sally	7"	London	HLD8291	1956	£5	£10	chart single
Love Letters In The Sand	7"	London	HLD8445	1957	£5	£5	chart single
Make The World Go Away	7" EP	Dot	DEP20012	1966	£2	£5	
Merry Christmas	7" EP	London	RED1128	1958	£2	£5	
Mexican Joe	7"	London	HLD7121	1963	£4	£8	export
Moody River	LP	London	HAD2382/ SAHD6182	1961	£5	£12	
Moody River	7"	London	HLD9350	1961	£1.50	£4	chart single
Moody River	7" EP	London	RED1302	1961	£2	£5	
Moonglow	LP	London	HAD2265/ SAHD6085	1960	£5	£12	
Moonglow Pt.1	7" EP	London	RED1267	1961	£2	£5	
Moonglow Pt.2	7" EP	London	RED1268	1961	£2	£5	
New Lovers	7"	London	HLD9067	1960	£1.50	£4	
No Arms Could Ever Hold You	7"	London	HLD8197	1955	£10	£20	
On Mike	7" EP	London	RED1069	1957	£2	£5	
Pat!	LP	London	HAD2049	1957	£6	£15	
Pat Boone Sings The Hits	7" EP	London	RED1063	1956	£2.50	£6	
Pat Boone Sings The Hits No.2	7" EP	London	RED1086	1957	£2.50	£6	
Pat Boone Sings The Hits No.3	7" EP	London	RED1112	1958	£2.50	£6	
Pat Boone's Hits	7" EP	Dot	DEP20001	1965	£2	£5	
Pat Boone's Hits Vol.2	7" EP	Dot	DEP20005	1965	£2	£5	
Pat Part 1	7" EP	London	RED1132	1958	£5	£10	
Pat Part 2	7" EP	London	RED1133	1958	£2.50	£6	
Pat Sings	LP	London	HAD2161/ SAHD6013	1959	£5	£12	
Pat Sings Movie Themes	7" EP	London	RED1391	1963	£2.50	£6	
Pat's Big Hits	LP	London	HAD2024	1957	£6	£15	
Pat's Big Hits	7" EP	London	RED1118	1958	£2	£5	
Remember You're Mine	7"	London	HLD8479	1957	£2	£5	chart single
Rich In Love	7"	London	HLD8316	1956	£5	£10	
Send Me The Pillow You Dream On	7"	London	HL7118	1963	£2.50	£6	export
Side By Side	LP	London	HAD2210/ SAHD6057	1960	£5	£12	with Shirley Boone
Side By Side	7" EP	London	RED1220	1959	£2	£5	with Shirley Boone
Sings Guess Who?	LP	London	HAD/SHD8109	1963	£8	£20	
Sings Irving Berlin	LP	London	HAD2082/ SAHD6038	1958	£5	£12	
Sings Irving Berlin Pt.1	7" EP	London	RED1164	1958	£2	£5	
Sings Irving Berlin Pt.2	7" EP	London	RED1165	1958	£2	£5	
Sings Irving Berlin Pt.3	7" EP	London	RED1166	1958	£2	£5	
Songs From Friendly Persuasion	7" EP	London	RED1068	1957	£2	£5	
Songs From Mardi Gras	7" EP	London	RED1194	1959	£2	£5	
Speedy Gonzales	7"	London	HLD9573	1962	£1.50	£4	chart single
Stardust	LP	London	HAD2127/ SAHD6001	1958	£5	£12	chart LP
Stardust Part 1	7" EP	London	RED1177	1959	£2	£5	
Stardust Part 2	7" EP	London	RED1178	1959	£2	£5	
Stardust Part 3	7" EP	London	RED1179	1959	£2	£5	
State Fair	LP	London	HAD2453/ SAHD6241	1962	£6	£15	
Sugar Moon	7"	London	HLD8640	1958	£1.50	£4	chart single
Sweet Little Sixteen	7" EP	Dot	DEP20013	1966	£2	£5	
Tenderly	LP	London	HAD2204/ SAHD6053	1960	£5	£12	
This And That	LP	London	HAD2305	1961	£5	£12	
Touch Of Your Lips	LP	London	HAD/SHD8153	1964	£4	£10	
Twixt Twelve And Twenty	7"	London	HLD8910	1959	£1.50	£4	chart single
Walking The Floor Over You	7"	London	HLD9138	1960	£1.50	£4	chart single
White Christmas	7"	London	HLD8520	1957	£2	£5	chart single
Why Baby Why	7"	London	HLD8404	1957	£5	£10	chart single
Wonderful Time Up There	7"	London	HLD8574	1958	£2	£5	chart single
Yes Indeed	LP	London	HAD2144/ SAHD6010	1959	£5	£12	
Yes Indeed Part 1	7" EP	London	RED1190	1959	£2	£5	
Yes Indeed Part 2	7" EP	London	RED1191	1959	£2	£5	
Yes Indeed Part 3	7" EP	London	RED1192	1959	£2	£5	

BOOTH, ANTHONY

Title	Format	Label	Cat. No.	Year	Price 1	Price 2	Notes
Till Death Do Us Part	7"	Tangerine	DP0008	1969	£1.50	£4	

BOOTHE, KEN

Title	Format	Label	Cat. No.	Year	Price 1	Price 2	Notes
Be Yourself	7"	Bamboo	BAM8	1969	£2.50	£6	Sound Dimension B side

Everybody Knows	7"	Coxsone	CS7041	1968	£5	£10	Gaylads B side
Feel Good	7"	Studio One	SO2000	1967	£6	£12	
Girl I Left Behind	7"	Studio One	SO2041	1968	£6	£12	Termites B side
Home Home Home	7"	Coxsone	CS7020	1967	£5	£10	Soul Brothers B side
I Remember Someone	7"	Fab	FAB63	1968	£4	£8	
Lady With The Starlight	7"	High Note	HS003	1969	£2.50	£6	Leslie Butler & Count Ossie B side
Lonely Teardrops	7"	Coxsone	CS7006	1967	£5	£10	
Mr.Rock Steady	LP	Studio One	SOL9001	1967	£50	£100	
One I Love	7"	Caltone	TONE107	1967	£4	£8	
Original Six	7"	Banana	BA352	1971	£2	£5	
Pleading	7"	Bamboo	BAM4	1969	£2.50	£6	Sound Dimension B side
Puppet On A String	7"	Studio One	SO2012	1967	£6	£12	Roland Alphonso B side
Say You	7"	Doctor Bird	DB1110	1967	£5	£10	Lyn Taitt B side
Sherry	7"	Coxsone	CS7094	1969	£5	£10	
Tomorrow	7"	Studio One	SO2053	1968	£6	£12	
Train Is Coming	7"	Island	WI3020	1966	£5	£10	
When I Fall In Love	7"	Studio One	SO2039	1968	£6	£12	Heptones B side
Why Baby Why	7"	Trojan	TR7716	1970	£2	£5	
You Keep Me Hanging On	7"	Coxsone	CS7043	1968	£5	£10	Charmers B side
You're No Good	7"	Ska Beat	JB248	1966	£5	£10	Soulettes B side
You're On My Mind	7"	Studio One	SO2073	1969	£6	£12	Richard Ace B side

BOOTHE, MILTON

Lonely And Blue	7"	Gas	GAS106	1969	£4	£8	

BOOTLES

I'll Let You Hold My Hand	7"	Vocalion	VN9216	1964	£2.50	£6	

BOOTS

Animal In Me	7"	CBS	3550	1968	£4	£8	
Here Are The Boots	LP	Telefunken	SLE14399	1966	£20	£40	German
Keep Your Lovelight Burning	7"	CBS	3833	1968	£6	£12	

BOOTS, DAVE

Green Satin And Gold	LP	Solent	SM013	196-	£50	£100	

BOOZERS

No No No	7" EP	DiscAZ		1967	£5	£10	French

BOP & THE BELTONES

Smile Like An Angel	7"	Coxsone	CS7007	1967	£5	£10	Soul Agents B side

BORDERSONG

Morning	LP	Real Good	1001	1975	£10	£25	US

BOSTIC, EARL

Alto Magic	7" EP	Parlophone	GEP8754	1958	£2	£5	
Alto Magic In Hi-Fi	LP	King	597	1958	£8	£20	US
Alto Sax And Mambo Strings	7" EP	Parlophone	GEP8565	1956	£2	£5	
Alto-Tude	LP	King	515	195-	£8	£20	US
Best Of Bostic	LP	King	500	195-	£8	£20	US
Beyond The Blue Horizon	7"	Parlophone	R4232	1956	£2.50	£6	
Big Bostic Beat	7" EP	Parlophone	GEP8701	1958	£2	£5	
Blue Skies	7"	Parlophone	MSP6119	1954	£4	£8	
Bo Do Rock	7"	Parlophone	R4208	1956	£4	£8	
Bostic In Harlem	7" EP	Parlophone	GEP8637	1957	£2	£5	
Bostic Meets Doggett	10" LP	Parlophone	PMD1054	1958	£8	£20	
Bostic Rocks	LP	King	571	1958	£8	£20	US
Bostic Rocks	10" LP	Parlophone	PMD1068	1958	£8	£20	
Bostic Showcase Of Swinging Dance Hits	LP	King	583	1958	£8	£20	US
Bostic Workshop	LP	King	613	1959	£8	£20	US
Bubbin's Rock	7"	Parlophone	R4278	1957	£4	£8	
C'mon Dance With Earl Bostic	LP	King	558	1958	£8	£20	US
Dance Time	LP	King	525	195-	£8	£20	US
Deep Purple	7"	Parlophone	MSP6089	1954	£5	£10	
Don't You Do It	7"	Parlophone	MSP6105	1954	£4	£8	
Earl Bostic	7" EP	Parlophone	GEP8520	1955	£4	£8	
Earl Bostic	7" EP	Vogue	EPV1010	1955	£5	£10	
Earl Bostic And His Alto Sax No.2	10" LP	Parlophone	PMD1016	1954	£10	£25	
Earl Bostic And His Alto Sax No.2	10" LP	Parlophone	PMD1040	1956	£8	£20	
Earl Bostic And His Orchestra	10" LP	Vogue	LDE100	1954	£8	£20	
Earl's Imagination	7" EP	Parlophone	GEP8548	1956	£2	£5	
Flamingo	7"	Vogue	V2145	1956	£5	£10	
Flamingo	7" EP	Parlophone	GEP8506	1954	£4	£8	
For You	LP	King	503	195-	£8	£20	US
Harlem Nocturne	7"	Parlophone	R4263	1957	£2.50	£6	
Honeymoon Night	7"	Island	WI271	1966	£5	£10	
Invitation To Dance	LP	King	547	1957	£8	£20	US
Jungle Drums	7"	Parlophone	MSP6110	1954	£4	£8	
Let's Dance With Earl Bostic	LP	King	529	195-	£8	£20	US
Linger Awhile	7" EP	Parlophone	GEP8513	1955	£2.50	£6	
Mambostic	7"	Parlophone	MSP6131	1954	£4	£8	
Melody Of love	7"	Parlophone	MSP6162	1955	£4	£8	
Moonglow	7"	Vogue	V2148	1956	£5	£10	
Music A La Bostic No.1	7" EP	Parlophone	GEP8571	1956	£2	£5	
Music A La Bostic No.2	7" EP	Parlophone	GEP8574	1956	£2.50	£6	
Music A La Bostic No.3	7" EP	Parlophone	GEP8603	1957	£2.50	£6	

Off Shore	7"	Parlophone	MSP6075	1954	£5	£10
Over The Waves Rock	7"	Parlophone	R4460	1958	£2.50	£6
Plays The Sweet Side Of The Fantastic 50's	LP	King	602	1959	£8	£20 ... US
Rocking With Bostic	7" EP.	Parlophone	GEP8741	1958	£2.50	£6
Showcase Of Swinging Dance Hits	10" LP	Parlophone	PMD1071	1959	£6	£15
Steamwhistle Jump	78	Parlophone	R4187	1956	£1.50	£4
Sweet Tunes Of The Fantastic Fifties	10" LP	Parlophone	PMD1074	1959	£6	£15
Temptation	7"	Parlophone	R4370	1957	£2	£5
Too Fine For Crying	7"	Parlophone	R4305	1957	£2	£5
Tuxedo Junction	7"	Ember	JBS708	1962	£1.50	£4
Ubangi Stomp	78	Parlophone	R4169	1956	£1.50	£4
Velvet Sunset	7" EP.	Vogue	EPV1111	1956	£2	£5
Wrap It Up	7" EP..	Parlophone	GEP8539	1955	£2.50	£6

BOSTON

Boston	LP	Epic	E99-34188	1978	£5	£12 ... US pic disc
Boston	LP	Epic	EPCH81611	197-	£4	£10 ... audiophile
Don't Look Back	LP	Epic	HE45050	1981	£4	£10 ... US audiophile
Don't Look Back	LP	Epic	PAL35050	1979	£4	£10 ... US pic disc

BOSTON CRABS

In an effort to make themselves stand out from the mass of mid-sixties British beat groups, the Boston Crabs favoured an intriguing assortment of stage costumes - the lead guitarist dressed as a country bumpkin, the drummer wore an asbestos fire-fighting suit, and the lead singer posed as a blind man in a wheel chair! Uniform red shirts and blue jeans for the second half proved the last to be indeed a pose. Not that any of this did the group much good, for even substantial airplay on pirate radio for their cover of the Lovin' Spoonful's "You Didn't Have To Be So Nice" failed to give the Boston Crabs the success they sought.

As Long As I Have You	7"	Columbia	DB7679	1965	£4	£8
Down In Mexico	7"	Columbia	DB7586	1965	£4	£8
You Didn't Have To Be So Nice	7"	Columbia	DB7830	1966	£4	£8

BOSTON DEXTERS

I've Got Something To Tell You	7"	Columbia	DB7498	1965	£7.50	£15
I've Got Troubles Of My Own	7"	Contemporary.	CR103	1964	£10	£20
La Bamba	7"	Contemporary.	CR101	1964	£12.50	£25
Try Hard	7"	Columbia	DB7641	1965	£6	£12
You've Been Talking About Me	7"	Contemporary.	CR102	1964	£10	£20

BOSWELL, CONNIE

How Important Can It Be?	7"	Brunswick	05397	1955	£1.50	£4
If I Give My Heart To You	7"	Brunswick	05319	1954	£2	£5

BOSWELL, EVE

Bobby	7"	Parlophone	R4401	1958	£1.50	£4
Chantez Chantez	7"	Parlophone	R4299	1957	£2.50	£6
Cookie	7"	Parlophone	MSP6220	1956	£5	£10
Enchanting Eve	7" EP.	Parlophone	GEP8601	1957	£5	£10
Following The Sun Around	LP	Parlophone	PMC1105	1959	£5	£12
Gypsy In My Soul	7"	Parlophone	R4341	1957	£2	£5
Keeping Cool With Lemonade	7"	Parlophone	MSP6245	1956	£2.50	£6
Left Right Out Of Your Heart	7"	Parlophone	R4455	1958	£1.50	£4
Love Me Again	7"	Parlophone	R4414	1958	£1.50	£4
Pam-Poo-Dey	7"	Parlophone	MSP6158	1955	£5	£10
Saries Marais	7"	Parlophone	MSP6250	1956	£2.50	£6
Sentimental Eve	LP	Parlophone	PMC1038	1957	£6	£15
Showcase	7" EP.	Parlophone	GEP8690	1958	£5	£10
Showcase No.2	7" EP.	Parlophone	GEP8717	1958	£5	£10
Sugar And Spice	10" LP	Parlophone	PMD1039	1957	£10	£25
Sugar Bush	7"	Parlophone	MSP6006	1953	£6	£12
Swedish Polka	7"	Parlophone	R4362	1957	£1.50	£4
Tika Tika Tok	7"	Parlophone	MSP6160	1955	£5	£10
Tra La La	7"	Parlophone	R4275	1957	£4	£8
True Love	7"	Parlophone	R4230	1956	£2.50	£6
With All My Heart	7"	Parlophone	R4328	1957	£2	£5
Young And Foolish	7"	Parlophone	MSP6208	1956	£5	£10

BOTHY BAND

Afterhours	LP	Polydor	2383530	1979	£5	£12
Bothy Band	LP	Polydor	2383379	1975	£5	£12
Old Hag You Have Killed Me	LP	Polydor	2383417	1976	£5	£12
Out Of The Wind And Into The Sun	LP	Polydor	2383456	1977	£5	£12

BOURBON STREET ALL STAR DIXIELANDERS

Bourbon Street All Star Dixielanders	LP	HMV	CLP1121	1957	£4	£10

BOW BELLS

Belinda	7"	Parlophone	R5520	1966	£2	£5
Not To Be Taken	7"	Polydor	56030	1965	£2	£5

BOW STREET RUNNERS

Bow Street Runners	LP	B.T.Puppy	BTPS1026	1969	£50	£100 ... US

BOW WOW WOW

Mile High Club	7"	Tour D'Eiffel	TE001	1981	£2	£5

BOWEN, JIMMY

Crossover	7"	Columbia	DB4027	1957	£7.50	£15
I'm Sticking With You	7"	Columbia	DB3915	1957	£15	£30
Jimmy Bowen	LP	Roulette	R25004	1957	£25	£50 ... US
Meet Jimmy Bowen	7" EP.	Columbia	SEG7757	1958	£25	£50
Meet Jimmy Bowen No.2	7" EP..	Columbia	SEG7793	1958	£25	£50

Title	Format	Label	Catalogue	Year	Price	Price	Notes
Spanish Cricket	7"	Reprise	RS23043	1965	£15	£30	
Sunday Morning With The Comics	LP	Reprise	R(S)6210	1966	£6	£15	US
Two Step	7"	Columbia	DB4184	1958	£6	£12	
Warm Up To Me Baby	7"	Columbia	DB3984	1957	£12.50	£25	

BOWERS, BEN

Title	Format	Label	Catalogue	Year	Price	Price	Notes
Big Ben Blues	7" EP	Pye	NJE1001	1956	£2	£5	
Country Boy	7"	Parlophone	R4317	1957	£1.50	£4	
Kentuckian Song	7"	Columbia	SCM5192	1955	£2.50	£6	
Kings Of Calypso Vol.4	7" EP	Pye	NEP24069	1958	£2	£5	

BOWIE, DAVID

David Bowie achieved popularity a fairly long time after starting to make records, so that there are a considerable number of rare and expensive records from the early years of his career for the Bowie completist to obtain. Perhaps the most famous of these is the original cover of the LP "The Man Who Sold The World", which portrays Bowie casually attired in a dress - "It's a man's dress," he explained at the time. The uncensored cover of "Diamond Dogs", on which Bowie is painted as a creature half man and half dog, has the dog's genitalia intact - these were airbrushed out on all but the first issues. More recently, Bowie's RCA albums were issued on compact disc and then speedily withdrawn due to a royalty dispute. These have become, in consequence, among the first CDs to aquire collectors' values.

Title	Format	Label	Catalogue	Year	Price	Price	Notes
1980 All Clear	LP	RCA	DJL13545	1980	£8	£20	US promo
Absolute Beginners	7"	Virgin	VSS838	1986	£1.50	£4	square pic disc
Aladdin Sane	LP	RCA	BOPIC1	1984	£6	£15	pic disc
Aladdin Sane	CD	RCA	PD83890	1985	£15	£30	
Beauty And The Beast	7"	RCA	PB1190	1978	£1.50	£4	PS
Can't Help Thinking About Me	7"	Pye	7N17020	1966	£45	£90	
ChangesOneBowie	LP	RCA	RS1055	1976	£8	£20	with sax version of 'John'
ChangesOneBowie	CD	RCA	PD81732	1985	£15	£30	
ChangesTwoBowie	LP & cass	RCA	DF1	1983	£6	£15	LP & cassette in holder
ChangesTwoBowie	CD	RCA	PD84202	1985	£15	£30	
David Bowie	LP	Deram	DML1007	1967	£60	£120	mono
David Bowie	LP	Deram	SML1007	1967	£85	£170	stereo
David Bowie	LP	Philips	SBL7912	1969	£60	£120	
David Bowie	CD	Deram	8000872	1984	£20	£40	white title
David Bowie Now	LP	RCA	DJL12697	1977	£10	£25	US promo
David Bowie Radio Special Vol.1	LP	RCA	DJL13829	1980	£10	£25	US promo
David Live	CD	RCA	PD80771	1985	£15	£30	
Diamond Dogs	LP	RCA	APL10576	1974	£100	£200	uncensored cover
Diamond Dogs	LP	RCA	BOPIC5	1984	£6	£15	pic disc
Diamond Dogs	CD	RCA	PD83859	1985	£15	£30	
DJ	7"	RCA	BOW3	1979	£7.50	£15	PS, green vinyl
Do Anything You Say	7"	Pye	7N17079	1966	£45	£90	
Do Anything You Say	7"	Pye	7NX8002	1972	£4	£8	PS
Evening With David Bowie	LP	RCA	DJL13036	1977	£10	£25	US promo
Fame And Fashion	CD	RCA	PD84919	1985	£20	£40	
Fashions	7"	RCA	BOW100	1982	£20	£40	set of 10 pic discs in folder
Golden Years	CD	RCA	PD84792	1985	£8	£20	
Helden	7"	RCA	PB9168	1978	£2	£5	sung in German
Heroes	CD	RCA	PD83857	1985	£6	£15	
Heros	7"	RCA	PB9167	1978	£2	£5	sung in French
Holy Holy	7"	Mercury	6052049	1971	£40	£80	
Hunky Dory	LP	RCA	BOPIC2	1984	£6	£15	pic disc
Hunky Dory	CD	RCA	PD84623	1985	£15	£30	
I Dig Everything	7"	Pye	7N17157	1966	£45	£90	
Laughing Gnome	7"	Deram	DM123	1967	£20	£40	matrix no. upside down on label
Let's Dance	LP	Mobile Fidelity	MFSL1083	1982	£6	£15	US audiophile
Let's Dance	LP	RCA	UK83	1983	£100	£200	numbered promo
Let's Talk	LP	EMI	SPRO9960/1	1983	£10	£25	US promo
Life On Mars	7"	RCA	RCA2316	1973	£2.50	£6	PS
Lifetimes	LP	RCA	LIFETIMES1	1983	£10	£25	
Lodger	CD	RCA	PD84234	1985	£8	£20	promo
Love You Till Tuesday	7"	Deram	DM135	1967	£40	£80	
Loving The Alien	7"	EMI	EAP195	1984	£1.50	£4	shaped pic disc
Low	CD	RCA	PD83856	1985	£10	£25	
Man Of Words, Man Of Music	LP	Mercury	SR61246	1969	£50	£100	US
Man Who Sold The World	LP	Mercury	61325	1971	£10	£25	US, cartoon cover, stamped matrix no.
Man Who Sold The World	LP	Mercury	6338041	1971	£85	£170	dress cover, sleeve pictured in Guide
Man Who Sold The World	LP	Mercury		1970	£180	£300	German, round sleeve
Man Who Sold The World	LP	RCA	LSP4816	1971	£4	£10	with inner and poster
Man Who Sold The World	CD	RCA	PD84654	1985	£15	£30	
Man Who Sold The World	cass	Mercury	6338041	1971	£6	£15	dress cover
Memory Of A Free Festival	7"	Mercury	6052026	1970	£40	£80	
Narrates Peter And The Wolf	LP	RCA	ARL12743	1978	£4	£10	US green vinyl
Narrates Peter And The Wolf	CD	RCA	PD82743	1985	£15	£30	
Pin-Ups	LP	RCA	BOPIC4	1984	£6	£15	pic disc
Pin-Ups	CD	RCA	PD84653	1985	£6	£15	
Prettiest Star	7"	Mercury	MF1135	1970	£40	£80	
Ragazza Sola, Ragazza Solo	LP	Philips	BW704208	1969	£50	£100	sung in Italian
Ragazza Sola, Ragazza Solo	7"	Philips	BW704208	1969	£75	£150	sung in Italian, PS, black label
Ragazza Sola, Ragazza Solo	7"	Philips	BW704208	1969	£60	£120	sung in Italian, PS, blue label
Rare Bowie	LP	RCA	PL45406	1982	£8	£20	hand stamped edition
Rubber Band	7"	Deram	DM107	1966	£40	£80	

Scary Monsters	LP	RCA	BOWLP2	1980	£100	£200	purple vinyl
Scary Monsters	CD	RCA	PD83647	1985	£6	£15	
Scary Monsters Interview	LP	RCA	DJL13840	1980	£10	£25	US promo
Space Oddity	CD	RCA	PD84813	1985	£15	£30	
Space Oddity	7"	Philips	BF1801	1969	£2	£5	chart single
Space Oddity	7"	Philips	BF1801	1969	£4	£8	stereo
Space Oddity	7"	RCA	RCA2593	1975	£2	£5	PS
Stage	LP	RCA	PL02913	1978	£8	£20	double, green or blue vinyl
Stage	LP	RCA	PL02913	1978	£6	£15	double, yellow vinyl
Stage	CD	RCA	PD89002	1985	£15	£30	
Starman	7"	RCA	RCA2199	1972	£15	£30	PS
Station To Station	LP	RCA	APLI1327	1976	£100	£200	US multicoloured vinyl
Station To Station	CD	RCA	PD81327	1985	£15	£30	
Suffragette City	7"	RCA	RCA2726	1976	£5	£10	PS
Underground	7"	EMI	EAP216	1986	£2	£5	shaped pic disc
World Of David Bowie	LP	Decca	PA58	1970	£6	£15	mono
Young Americans	CD	RCA	PD80998	1985	£15	£30	
Ziggy Stardust	LP	Mobile Fidelity	MFSL1064	1982	£8	£20	US audiophile
Ziggy Stardust	LP	RCA	BOPIC3	1984	£6	£15	pic disc
Ziggy Stardust	CD	RCA	PD84702	1985	£15	£30	
Ziggy Stardust: The Motion Picture	LP	RCA	CPL24862	1983	£30	£60	US clear vinyl
Ziggy Stardust: The Motion Picture	CD	RCA	PD84862	1985	£8	£20	

BOWIE, DAVID (DAVIE JONES & LOWER THIRD)

You've Got A Habit Of Leaving	7"	Parlophone	R5315	1965	£150	£250	

BOWIE, DAVID (KING BEES)

Liza Jane	7"	Vocalion	V9221	1964	£250	£400	

BOWIE, DAVID (MANISH BOYS)

I Pity The Fool	7"	Parlophone	R5250	1965	£150	£250	

BOWN, ALAN

Alan Bown	LP	Deram	DML/SML1049	1970	£5	£12	
Baby Don't Push Me	7"	Pye	7N17084	1966	£5	£10	
Can't Let Her Go	7"	Pye	7N15934	1965	£4	£8	
Emergency	7"	Pye	7N17192	1966	£5	£10	
First Album - Outward Bown	LP	Music Factory	CUBLM/LS1	1968	£6	£15	
Gonna Fix You Good	7"	Pye	7N17256	1967	£6	£12	
Gypsy Girl	7"	Deram	DM278	1969	£2	£5	
Headline News	7"	Pye	7N17148	1966	£2.50	£6	
Jeu De Massacre	7" EP	Vogue	EPL8537	1967	£6	£12	French, with tracks by Jacques Loussier
Listen	LP	Island	ILPS9131	1970	£4	£10	
Outward Bown	LP	Music Factory	MF12000	1967	£8	£20	
Pyramid	7"	Island	WIP6091	1970	£2	£5	
Still As Stone	7"	Deram	DM259	1969	£2	£5	
Story Book	7"	MGM	MGM1387	1968	£2	£5	
Toyland	7"	MGM	MGM1355	1967	£2	£5	
We Can Help You	7"	Music Factory	CUB1	196-	£2.50	£6	

BOWN, ALAN & JIMMY JAMES

London Swings	LP	Pye	N(S)PL18156	1966	£8	£20	1 side each

BOWN, ANDY

Lulli Rides Again	7"	Parlophone	R5856	1970	£1.50	£4	

BOX, DAVID

Little Lonely Summer Girl	7"	London	HLU9924	1964	£2	£5	
Sweet Sweet Day	7"	London	HLU9874	1964	£2	£5	

BOX TOPS

Choo Choo Train	7"	Bell	BLL1017	1968	£1.50	£4	
Cry Like A Baby	LP	Bell	MBLL/SBLL105	1968	£5	£12	
Cry Like A Baby	7"	Bell	BLL1001	1968	£1.50	£4	chart single
Dimensions	LP	Bell	SBLL120	1969	£4	£10	
I Met Her In Church	7"	Bell	BLL1035	1968	£1.50	£4	
I Shall Be Released	7"	Bell	BLL1063	1969	£1.50	£4	
Letter	7"	Stateside	SS2044	1967	£2	£5	chart single
Letter/Neon Rainbow	LP	Stateside	(S)SL10218	1968	£5	£12	
Lifetime Believing	LP	Cotillon	SD057	1971	£4	£10	US
Mi Sento Felice	7"		SIR20072	1967	£5	£10	sung in Italian
Neon Rainbow	7"	Stateside	SS2070	1967	£1.50	£4	
Non Stop	LP	Bell	MBLL/SBLL108	1968	£4	£10	
Soul Deep	7"	Bell	BLL1068	1969	£1.50	£4	chart single
Super Hits	LP	Bell	S6025	1968	£4	£10	US
Sweet Cream Ladies Forward March	7"	Bell	BLL1045	1968	£1.50	£4	
Turn On A Dream	7"	Bell	BLL1084	1969	£1.50	£4	

BOXER

Bloodletting	LP	Virgin	V2073	1976	£30	£60	demo only

BOY HAIRDRESSERS

Golden Shower	12"	53rd & 3rd	AGARR12T	1987	£5	£12	

BOYCE, TOMMY

Pretty Thing	7"	MGM	MGM1287	1965	£1.50	£4	
Twofold Talent	LP	Camden	CAL/CAS2202	1967	£5	£12	US

BOYCE, TOMMY & BOBBY HART

Alice Long	7"	A&M	AMS729	1968	£1.50	£4	
Goodbye Baby	7"	A&M	AMS722	1968	£1.50	£4	
I Wonder What She's Doing Tonight	LP	A&M	SP4143	1968	£5	£12	US
I Wonder What She's Doing Tonight	7"	A&M	AMS714	1968	£1.50	£4	
It's All Happening On The Inside	LP	A&M	SP4162	1968	£5	£12	US
Out And About	7"	A&M	AMS705	1967	£1.50	£4	
Out And About	7" EP	A&M	EAM1001	1967	£4	£8	French
Sometimes She's A Little Girl	7"	A&M	AMS710	1967	£1.50	£4	
Test Patterns	LP	A&M	AML907	1967	£5	£12	

BOYD, EDDIE

7936 South Rhodes	LP	Blue Horizon	763202	1968	£25	£50	
Big Boat	7"	Blue Horizon	573137	1967	£6	£12	
Boyd's Blues	7" EP	Esquire	EP247	1962	£4	£8	
Dust My Broom	LP	London	PS554	1969	£6	£15	US
Eddie Boyd And His Blues Band	LP	Decca	LK/SKL4872	1967	£30	£60	
Five Long Years	LP	Fontana	STJL905	1965	£8	£20	
It's So Miserable To Be Alone	7"	Blue Horizon	451009	1966	£20	£40	

BOYD, EDDIE & BUDDY GUY

With the Blues	7" EP	Chess	CRE6009	1966	£6	£12	

BOYD, JIMMY

I Saw Mommy Kissing Santa Claus	7"	Columbia	SCM5072	1953	£10	£20	chart single

BOYLE, BILLY

Hooting In The Kitchen	7"	Columbia	DB7127	1963	£1.50	£4	
I'm Coming Home	7"	Decca	F11709	1963	£1.50	£4	
Lovers Hill	7"	Columbia	DB7111	1963	£1.50	£4	
My Baby's Crazy About Elvis	7"	Decca	F11503	1962	£6	£12	
Walk Walk Walkin'	7"	Columbia	DB7294	1964	£2.50	£6	

BOYLES BROTHERS

Introducing The Boyles Brothers	LP	International Artists	6801	1968	£8	£20	US

BOYS

The Boys, who released "It Ain't Fair" in 1964, became the Action shortly afterwards.

It Ain't Fair	7"	Pye	7N15726	1964	£15	£30	

BOYS (2)

Kamikaze	7"	Safari	SAFE21	1979	£1.50	£4	with booklet

BOYS (3)

Polaris	7"	Parlophone	R5027	1963	£10	£20	

BOYS BLUE

Take A Heart	7"	HMV	POP1427	1965	£20	£40	

BOYS OF THE LOUGH

Boys Of The Lough	LP	Trailer	LER2086	1973	£5	£12	
Good Friends Good Music	LP	Transatlantic	TRA354	1977	£5	£12	
Piper's Broken Finger	LP	Transatlantic	TRA333	1976	£5	£12	
Recorded Live	LP	Transatlantic	TRA296	1975	£5	£12	
Second Album	LP	Trailer	LER2090	1974	£5	£12	

BOZ

Baby Song	7"	Columbia	DB7972	1966	£2	£5	
I Shall Be Released	7"	Columbia	DB8406	1968	£2	£5	
Isn't That So	7"	Columbia	DB7832	1966	£2.50	£6	
Light My Fire	7"	Columbia	DB8468	1968	£2	£5	
Meeting Time	7"	Columbia	DB7889	1966	£4	£8	
Pinnochio	7"	Columbia	DB7941	1966	£2	£5	

BRACE, JANET

Teach Me Tonight	7"	Brunswick	05272	1955	£1.50	£4	

BRACEY, ISHMAN

RCA Victor Race Series Vol.1	7" EP	RCA	RCX7167	1964	£2	£5	

BRACKEN

Prince Of The Northlands	LP	Look	LKLP6438	1979	£37.50	£75	

BRADFORD, PROFESSOR ALEX

Angel On Vacation	LP	Stateside	SL10083	1964	£4	£10	
One Step	LP	Stateside	SL10047	1963	£4	£10	
Too Close To Heaven	7" EP	London	REU1357	1963	£2.50	£6	

BRADLEY, JAN

Mama Didn't Lie	7"	Pye	7N25182	1963	£7.50	£15	

BRADLEY, OWEN

Big Guitar	7"	Brunswick	05736	1958	£4	£8	
White Silver Sands	7"	Brunswick	05700	1957	£1.50	£4	

BRADSHAW, SONNY

Festival Jump Up	7"	Duke	DK1003	1963	£4	£8	

BRADSHAW, TINY

Breaking Up The House	78	Vogue	V2146	1952	£2	£5	

Great Composer	LP	King	653	1959	£10	£25	US
Off And On	10" LP	King	29574	195-	£50	£100	US
Overflow	7"	Parlophone	MSP6145	1955	£5	£10	
Pompton Turnpike	7" EP	Parlophone	GEP8552	1956	£6	£12	
Selections	LP	King	395501	195-	£20	£40	US
Spider Web	7"	Parlophone	MSP6118	1954	£4	£8	
Train Kept A Rolling	7" EP	Parlophone	GEP8507	1954	£7.50	£15	
Twenty-Four Great Songs	LP	King	953	1966	£5	£12	US

BRADSHAW, TINY & WYNONIE HARRIS

Kings Of Rhythm And Blues	LP	Polydor	623273	1970	£5	£12	

BRADY, BOB & THE CONCHORDS

Everybody Goin' To A Love-In	7"	Bell	BLL1025	1968	£2.50	£6	

BRADY, PAUL

Welcome Here Kind Stranger	LP	Mulligan	LUN024	1974	£6	£15	Irish

BRAFF, RUBY

Hustlin' And Bustlin'	LP	Vogue	LAE12051	1957	£10	£25	
Inventions In Jazz Part 2	10" LP	Vanguard	PPT12022	1958	£10	£25	with Ellis Larkins
Newport Jazz Festival 1957	LP	Columbia	33CX10104	1958	£6	£15	Side 2 by Bobby Henderson
Ruby Braff All Stars	LP	Philips	BBL7130	1957	£5	£12	
Ruby Braff And The Dixie Victors	LP	HMV	CLP1091	1956	£6	£15	
Ruby Braff Orchestra	10" LP	London	LZN14022	1956	£10	£25	
Ruby Braff Sextet	10" LP	London	LZN14028	1956	£10	£25	
Ruby Braff Special	LP	Vanguard	PPL11003	1956	£6	£15	

BRAGGS, AL TNT

Al TNT Braggs	7" EP	Vocalion	VEP170163	1965	£10	£20	
Earthquake	7"	Action	ACT4506	1968	£2.50	£6	
Earthquake	7"	Vocalion	VP9278	1966	£4	£8	
I'm A Good Man	7"	Action	ACT4526	1969	£2	£5	

BRAHAM, ERNEL

Musical Fight	7"	Rio	R79	1966	£4	£8	

BRAIN

The Brain's "Nightmares In Red" is not so much psychedelic as lunatic. It is in fact an early recorded effort by the brothers Giles - prior to them joining forces with guitarist Robert Fripp and beginning the rehearsals that led to the debut of King Crimson.

Nightmares In Red	7"	Parlophone	R5595	1967	£20	£40	

BRAINBOX

Best Of Brainbox	LP	EMI	05424327	1972	£5	£12	German
Brainbox	LP	Parlophone	PCS7094	1970	£8	£20	
Down Man	7"	Parlophone	R5775	1969	£4	£8	
Parts	LP	Harvest	05624551	1972	£5	£12	German
To You	7"	Parlophone	R5842	1970	£2	£5	

BRAINCHILD

Healing Of The Lunatic Owl	LP	A&M	AMLS979	1970	£10	£25	

BRAINIAC FIVE

Mushy Doubt	7"	Roach	RREP5001	1978	£4	£8	
Working	7"	Roach	RR5002	1980	£2.50	£6	

BRAINSTORM

Second Smile	LP	Spiegelei	28596	1974	£4	£10	German
Smile A While	LP	Spiegelei	28505	1972	£4	£10	German

BRAINTICKET

Celestial Ocean	LP	RCA	SF8398	1974	£5	£12	
Cotton Wood Hill	LP	Bellaphon	BLPS19019	1971	£6	£15	German
Psychonaut	LP	Bellaphon	BLPS19104	1972	£8	£20	German

BRAITH, GEORGE

Extension	LP	Blue Note	BLP/BST84171	1964	£15	£30	
Soul Dream	LP	Blue Note	BLP/BST84161	1964	£15	£30	
Two Souls In One	LP	Blue Note	BLP/BST84148	1963	£15	£30	

BRAM STOKER

Hard Rock Spectacular	LP	Windmill	WMD117	1972	£20	£40	

BRAMLETT, DELANEY

Heartbreak Hotel	7"	Vocalion	VN9227	1964	£6	£12	
Liverpool Lou	7"	Vocalion	VN9237	1965	£7.50	£15	

BRAMWELL, BILL

My Old Man	7"	Starlite	ST45004	1958	£1.50	£4	

BRAN

Ail Ddechra	LP	Sain	1038M	1974	£10	£25	
Hedfan	LP	Sain	1070M	1976	£10	£25	

BRAND

I'm A Lover Not A Fighter	7"	Piccadilly	7N35216	1965	£30	£60	2 different B sides

BRAND, DOLLAR

Anatomy Of A South African Village	LP	Fontana	688314ZL	1964	£4	£10	

BRANDON, JOHNNY

Glendora	7"	Decca	F10778	1956	£1.50	£4
Hits	7" EP.	Pye	NEP24003	1955	£6	£12
Rock A Bye Baby	7"	Parlophone	MSP6238	1956	£2	£5
Shim Sham Shuffle	7"	Parlophone	R4207	1956	£2.50	£6
Sort Of Feeling	7"	Decca	F10858	1957	£1.50	£4

BRANDON, TONY

Candy Kisses	7"	MGM	MGM1401	1968	£1.50	£4

BRANDON, VERN

Gotta Know The Reason	7"	Decca	F11472	1962	£2.50	£6

BRANDY BOYS

Gale Winds	7"	Columbia	DB7507	1965	£2.50	£6

BRANDYWINE BRIDGE

English Meadow	LP	Cottage	COT321	1978	£8	£20
Grey Lady	LP	Cottage	COT311	1977	£8	£20

BRANTLEY, JOHNNY

Place	7"	London	HLU8606	1958	£6	£12

BRASS MONKEY

Brass Monkey	LP	Topic	12TS431	1983	£5	£12

BRASS TACKS

I'll Keep Holding On	7"	Transatlantic	BIG110	1968	£1.50	£4

BRASSEUR, ANDRE

Early Birds	7"	Pye	7N25332	1965	£2.50	£6
Holiday	7"	CBS	202557	1967	£2	£5

BRAUN, CHRIS

Both Sides	LP	BASF	20213994	1972	£4	£10	German
Foreign Lady	LP	Pan	87586	1973	£4	£10	German

BRAUTIGAN, RICHARD

Richard Brautigan is an American writer whose whimsically poetic prose-style struck something of a chord in the late sixties and early seventies. "Trout Fishing In America" is perhaps his best known book, but his reading of extracts from it failed to achieve the release on Apple that was intended.

Listening To Richard Brautigan	LP	Apple	ZAPPLE03	1969	£150	£250	test pressing
Listening To Richard Brautigan	LP	Straight	ST424	1969	£6	£15	US

BRAVE NEW WORLD

Impressions On Reading Aldous Huxley	LP	Vertigo	6360606	1972	£10	£25

BRAVO, CEDRIC

Merry Christmas	7"	Ska Beat	JB229	1965	£5	£10

BRAZIER, PRISCILLA

Priscilla Brazier	LP	Dovetail	DOVE9	1974	£8	£20
Something Beautiful	LP	Key		197-	£8	£20

BREAD & BEER BAND

The high value of the Bread and Beer Band's single derives from the fact that the band's pianist was one Reg Dwight (who was shortly to adopt the stage name Elton John). There is an LP by the band, but it is believed that only one copy of this exists. It came up for sale at one of the London rock auctions at the end of the eighties and fetched £1700.

Dick Barton Theme	7"	Decca	F12891	1969	£40	£80
Dick Barton Theme	7"	Decca	F13354	1973	£7.50	£15

BREAD, LOVE & DREAMS

Amarylis	LP	Decca	SKL5081	1971	£80	£160
Bread, Love & Dreams	LP	Decca	SKL5008	1969	£20	£40
Strange Tale Of Captain Shannon	LP	Decca	LK/SKL5048	1970	£20	£40
Switch Out The Sun	7"	Decca	F12958	1969	£2.50	£6

BREAD, LOVE AND DREAMS

Bread, Love and Dreams were a folk trio - a man and two women - whose self-composed acoustic songs are pretty enough without being particularly memorable. The group's name is a good one, however - the perfect ingredients for a happy life.

BREAKAWAYS

Danny Boy	7"	Pye	7N15973	1965	£1.50	£4	
He Doesn't Love Me	7"	Pye	7N15618	1964	£1.50	£4	
Here She Comes	7"	Pye	7N15585	1963	£1.50	£4	
He's A Rebel	7"	Pye	7N15471	1962	£1.50	£4	
That Boy Of Mine	7" EP.	Pye	PNV24119	1964	£10	£20	French

BREAKTHRU

Ice Cream Tree	7"	Mercury	MF1066	1968	£4	£8

BRECKER, RANDY

Score	LP	Solid State	18051	1968	£6	£15	US

BREEDLOVE, JIMMY

Over Somebody Else's Shoulder	7"	London	HLE8490	1957	£20	£40
You're Following Me	7"	Pye	7N25121	1962	£2.50	£6

BREGMAN, BUDDY

Buddy Bregman And His Orchestra	LP	HMV	CLP1154	1958	£6	£15

BREL, JACQUES
A L'Olympia .... LP ..... Fontana .... SFJL967 .... 1968 ... £5 .... £12 ....

BREMERS, BEVERLY
Get Smart Girl .... 7" ...... Wand .... WN18 .... 1972 ... £4 .... £8

BRENDA & THE TABULATIONS
Baby You're So Right For Me .... 7" .... Direction .... 583678 .... 1968 ... £4 .... £8
Dry Your Eyes .... LP ..... Action .... ACLP6003 .... 1969 ... £6 .... £15
Dry Your Eyes .... 7" .... London .... HL10127 .... 1967 ... £5 .... £10
That's In The Past .... 7" .... Action .... ACT4541 .... 1969 ... £7.50 ... £15
When You're Gone .... 7" .... London .... HL10174 .... 1967 ... £6 .... £12

BRENNAN, ROSE
Band Of Gold .... 7" .... HMV .... 7M383 .... 1956 ... £4 .... £8
Courtin' In The Kitchen .... 7" .... HMV .... 7M392 .... 1956 ... £1.50 ... £4
Sincerely .... 7" .... HMV .... 7M299 .... 1955 ... £4 .... £8
Ten Little Kisses .... 7" .... HMV .... 7M328 .... 1955 ... £2.50 ... £6
Tra La La .... 7" .... HMV .... POP302 .... 1957 ... £2 .... £5
You Are My Love .... 7" .... HMV .... 7M360 .... 1956 ... £2.50 ... £6

BRENNAN, WALTER
Dutchman's Gold .... 7" .... London .... HLD9148 .... 1960 ... £1.50 ... £4

BRENT, FRANKIE
Rockin' Shoes .... 78 ...... Pye .... N15102 .... 1957 ... £1.50 ... £4

BRENT, TONY
Amore .... 7" .... Columbia .... DB3884 .... 1957 ... £2.50 ... £6
Big Hits .... LP ..... Columbia .... 33SX5001 .... 195- ... £8 .... £20
Butterfly .... 7" .... Columbia .... DB3918 .... 1957 ... £4 .... £8
Chanson D'Amour .... 7" .... Columbia .... DB4128 .... 1958 ... £1.50 ... £4
Cindy, Oh Cindy .... 7" .... Columbia .... DB3844 .... 1956 ... £4 .... £8 .... chart single
Clouds Will Soon Roll By ...... 7" .... Columbia .... DB4066 .... 1958 ... £1.50 ... £4 .... chart single
Dark Moon .... 7" .... Columbia .... DB3950 .... 1957 ... £2.50 ... £6 .... chart single
Deep Within Me .... 7" .... Columbia .... DB3987 .... 1957 ... £2 .... £5
Ding Dong Boogie .... 7" .... Columbia .... SCM5029 .... 1953 ... £7.50 ... £15
Girl Of My Dreams .... 7" .... Columbia .... DB4177 .... 1958 ... £1.50 ... £4 .... chart single
Have You Heard .... 7" .... Columbia .... SCM5042 .... 1953 ... £7.50 ... £15
I Understand Just How You Feel ... 7" .... Columbia .... SCM5135 .... 1954 ... £6 .... £12
It's A Woman's World .... 7" .... Columbia .... SCM5160 .... 1955 ... £6 .... £12
Love By The Jukebox Light .... 7" .... Columbia .... DB4043 .... 1957 ... £2 .... £5
Mirror Mirror .... 7" .... Columbia .... SCM5188 .... 1955 ... £5 .... £10
My Little Angel .... 7" .... Columbia .... SCM5272 .... 1956 ... £4 .... £8
Nicolette .... 7" .... Columbia .... SCM5146 .... 1954 ... £5 .... £10
Off Stage .... 7" EP.. Columbia .... SEG8019 .... 1960 ... £6 .... £12
Off Stage .... 10" LP . Columbia .... 33S1125 .... 1958 ... £10 ...... £25
Off Stage No.2 .... 7" EP.. Columbia .... SEG8040 .... 1960 ... £6 .... £12
Open Up Your Heart .... 7" .... Columbia .... SCM5170 .... 1955 ... £7.50 ... £15
Sooner Or Later .... 7" .... Columbia .... SCM5245 .... 1956 ... £4 .... £8
Time For Tony .... 7" EP.. Columbia .... SEG7869 .... 1957 ... £6 .... £12
Tony Calls The Tune .... 7" EP.. Columbia .... SEG7824 .... 1958 ... £6 .... £12
Tony Takes Five .... LP ..... Columbia .... 33SX1200/ .... 1960 ... £6 .... £15
.... SCX3288 ....
Which Way The Wind Blows ... 7" .... Columbia .... SCM5057 .... 1953 ... £7.50 ... £15
Why Should I Be Lonely? ...... 7" .... Columbia .... DB4304 .... 1959 ... £1.50 ... £4 .... chart single
With Your Love .... 7" .... Columbia .... SCM5200 .... 1955 ... £4 .... £8

BRENTWOOD ROAD ALL STARS
Love At First Sight .... 7" .... Bamboo .... BAM23 .... 1970 ... £2 .... £5
Soul Shake .... 7" .... Bamboo .... BAM25 .... 1970 ... £2 .... £5

BRESSLAW, BERNARD
Charlie Brown .... 7" .... HMV .... POP599 .... 1959 ... £1.50 ... £4
I Only Arsked .... 7" EP.. HMV .... 7EG8439 .... 1957 ... £2 .... £5
Mad Passionate Love .... 7" .... HMV .... POP522 .... 1958 ... £1.50 ... £4 .... chart single

BRETT, PAUL
Jubilation Foundry .... LP ..... Dawn .... DNLS3021 .... 1971 ... £5 .... £12
Paul Brett .... LP ..... Bradleys .... BRAD1001 .... 1973 ... £5 .... £12
Paul Brett Sage .... LP ..... Pye .... NSPL18347 .... 1970 ... £6 .... £15
Phoenix Future .... LP ..... Phoenix Future . PF001 .... 1975 ... £6 .... £15
Schizophrenia .... LP ..... Dawn .... DNLS3032 .... 1972 ... £5 .... £12
Very Strange Brew .... LP ..... ABC................. 672 .... 1969 ... £6 .... £15 .... US

BRETT, STEVE & THE MAVERICKS
Chains On My Heart .... 7" .... Columbia .... DB7794 .... 1965 ... £30 ...... £60
Sad Lonely And Blue .... 7" .... Columbia .... DB7581 .... 1965 ... £30 ...... £60
Wishing .... 7" .... Columbia .... DB7470 .... 1965 ... £30 ...... £60

BREVETT, LLOYD
Wayward Ska .... 7" .... Ska Beat .... JB213 .... 1965 ... £5 .... £10 .... Winston
.... Samuels B side

BREWER & FARNER
Monumental Funk .... LP ..... Quadico .... QLP7401 .... 1974 ... £6 .... £15 .... US

BREWER & SHIPLEY
Down In L.A. .... LP ..... A&M .... SP4154 .... 1968 ... £4 .... £10 .... US

BREWER, TERESA

Aloha From Teresa	LP	Coral	LVA9152	1962	£6	£15	
And The Dixieland Band	LP	Coral	LVA9107	1959	£6	£15	
And The Dixieland Band Pt.1	7" EP	Coral	FEP2047	1960	£4	£8	
And The Dixieland Band Pt.2	7" EP	Coral	FEP2048	1960	£4	£8	
At Christmas Time	LP	Coral	LVA9091	1958	£6	£15	
Au Revoir	7"	Vogue Coral	Q2029	1954	£5	£10	
Banjo's Back In Town	7"	Vogue Coral	Q72098	1955	£2.50	£6	
Bouquet Of Hits	LP	Coral	CRL56072	1954	£6	£15	US
Bye Bye Baby Goodbye	7"	Coral	Q72375	1959	£1.50	£4	
Crazy With Love	7"	Vogue Coral	Q72213	1956	£2	£5	
Don't Mess Around With Tess	LP	Coral	LVA9204	1962	£6	£15	
Empty Arms	7"	Vogue Coral	Q72251	1957	£2	£5	
For Teenagers In Love	LP	Coral	LVA9075	1957	£6	£15	
Good Man Is Hard To Find	7"	Coral	Q72130	1956	£2.50	£6	
Heavenly Lover	7"	Coral	Q72364	1959	£1.50	£4	
How Do You Know It's Love	7" EP	Coral	FEP2061	1960	£4	£8	
How Important Can It Be?	7"	Vogue Coral	Q72065	1955	£4	£8	
Hula Hoop Song	7"	Coral	Q72340	1958	£1.50	£4	
Hula Hoop Time	7" EP	Coral	FEP2013	1959	£5	£10	
I'm Drowning My Sorrows	7"	Vogue Coral	Q72239	1957	£1.50	£4	
Jilted	78	Vogue Coral	Q2001	1954	£1.50	£4	
Jingle Bell Rock	7"	Coral	Q72349	1958	£1.50	£4	
Keep Your Cotton Pickin' Paddies	7"	Vogue Coral	Q72199	1956	£2	£5	
Let Me Go Lover	7"	Vogue Coral	Q72043	1955	£6	£12	chart single
Lula Rock-a-Hula	7"	Vogue Coral	Q72278	1957	£4	£8	
Music! Music! Music!	LP	Coral	LVA9020	1956	£6	£15	
Mutual Admiration Society	7"	Coral	Q72301	1958	£1.50	£4	
My Golden Favourites	LP	Coral	LVA9131	1960	£5	£12	
Naughty Naughty Naughty	LP	Coral	LVA9138	1960	£6	£15	
Nora Malone	7"	Vogue Coral	Q72224	1957	£2	£5	chart single
Pickle Up A Doodle	7"	Coral	Q72336	1958	£1.50	£4	
Pledging My Love	7"	Vogue Coral	Q72077	1955	£5	£10	
Remembering	7"	Vogue Coral	Q72139	1956	£4	£8	
Ridin' High	LP	Coral	LVA9129	1960	£6	£15	
Rock Love	7"	Vogue Coral	Q72066	1955	£6	£12	
Saturday Dance	7"	Coral	Q72320	1958	£1.50	£4	
Showcase	10" LP	London	HAPB1006	1951	£10	£25	
Skinny Minnie	7"	Vogue Coral	Q2011	1954	£6	£12	
Songs Everybody Knows	LP	Coral	LVA9145	1961	£6	£15	
Sweet Old-Fashioned Girl	7"	Vogue Coral	Q72172	1956	£4	£8	chart single
Tear Fell	7"	Vogue Coral	Q72146	1956	£5	£10	chart single
Till I Waltz Again With You	LP	Coral	CRL56093	1954	£6	£15	US
Time For Teresa Brewer	LP	Coral	LVA9095	1959	£6	£15	
When Your Lover Has Gone	LP	Coral	LVA9100/SVL3003	1959	£6	£15	
When Your Lover Has Gone Pt.1	7" EP	Coral	FEP2036	1959	£4	£8	
When Your Lover Has Gone Pt.2	7" EP	Coral	FEP2037	1959	£4	£8	
When Your Lover Has Gone Pt.3	7" EP	Coral	FEP2038	1959	£4	£8	
You Send Me	7"	Vogue Coral	Q72292	1957	£2	£5	
You're Telling Our Secret	7"	Vogue Coral	Q72083	1955	£4	£8	

BREWERS DROOP

Opening Time	LP	RCA	SF8301	1972	£5	£12	

BRIDES OF FUNKENSTEIN

Funk Or Walk	LP	Atlantic	K50545	1978	£6	£15	

BRIDGES

Fakkeltog	LP	Vakenatt	VN01	1980	£8	£20	Norwegian

BRIERLEY, MARC

Autograph Of Time	7"	CBS	3857	1968	£2.50	£6	
Be My Brother	7"	CBS	5266	1970	£1.50	£4	
Hello	LP	CBS	63835	1969	£6	£15	
Lady Of The Light	7"	CBS	4632	1969	£2	£5	
Stay A Little Longer	7"	CBS	4191	1969	£2	£5	
Welcome To The Citadel	LP	CBS	63478	1967	£8	£20	

BRIGGS, ANNE

Anne Briggs	LP	Topic	12TS207	1971	£50	£100	
Hazards Of Love	7" EP	Topic	TOP94	1963	£30	£60	
Time Has Come	LP	CBS	64612	1971	£50	£100	sleeve pictured in Guide

BRIGGS, BILLY

Chew Tobacco Rag	78	Columbia	DB2938	1951	£2.50	£6	

BRIGGS, LILLIAN

Not A Soul	7"	Coral	Q72408	1960	£1.50	£4	

BRIGHT, RONNELL

Bright Flight	LP	Vanguard	PPL11016	1958	£5	£12	

BRILLIANT, ASHLEIGH

In The Haight-Ashbury	LP	Dorash	1001	1967	£15	£30	US

BRILLIANT CORNERS

Big Hip	7"	SS20	SS22	1984	£2	£5	
My Baby's In Black	12"	SS20	SS23T	1984	£3	£8	
She's Got Fever	7"	SS20	SS21	1984	£7.50	£15	

BRIMSTONE, DEREK

Derek Brimstone	LP	Fontana	STL5478	1969	£5	£12	

BRINSLEY SCHWARZ

Forever damned as the group whose manager virtually invented the concept of hype (when he chartered a plane-load of journalists to watch his clients perform at the bottom of the Fillmore bill), Brinsley Schwarz never quite managed to find the acclaim that their frequently fine material deserved. Bassist Nick Lowe, however, went on to do quite well for himself, while other members of the group, including guitarist Schwarz himself, found employment as members of Graham Parker's Rumour.

Brinsley Schwarz	LP	United Artists	UAS29111	1970	£5	£12	
Country Girl	7"	Liberty	LBY15419	1970	£2	£5	
Despite It All	LP	Liberty	LBG83427	1970	£6	£15	
Nervous On The Road	LP	United Artists	UAS29374	1972	£4	£10	
New Favourites	LP	United Artists	UAS29641	1974	£4	£10	
Please Don't Ever Change	LP	United Artists	UAS29489	1973	£6	£15	
Shining Brightly	7"	United Artists	UP35118	1970	£2	£5	
Silver Pistol	LP	United Artists	UAS29217	1972	£4	£10	

BRITISH WALKERS

I Found You	7"	Pye	7N25298	1965	£7.50	£15	

BRITT

Leave My Baby Alone	7"	Piccadilly	7N35273	1966	£4	£8	

BRITT, ELTON

Wandering Cowboy	LP	ABC-Paramount	(S)293	1959	£4	£10	US
Yodel Songs	LP	RCA	LPM1288	1956	£6	£15	US
Yodel Songs	10" LP	RCA	LPM3222	1954	£10	£25	US

BRITT, TINA

Real Thing	7"	London	HLC9974	1965	£10	£20	

BRITTEN, BUDDY & THE REGENTS

Don't Spread It Around	7"	Decca	F11435	1962	£5	£10	
Hey There	7"	Oriole	CB1839	1963	£5	£10	
I Guess I'm In The Way	7"	Oriole	CB1911	1964	£5	£10	
If You've Gotta Make A Fool Of Somebody	7"	Oriole	CB1827	1963	£5	£10	
Money	7"	Oriole	CB1889	1963	£5	£10	
My Pride And Joy	7"	Piccadilly	7N35075	1962	£5	£10	
My Resistance Is Low	7"	Oriole	CB1859	1963	£5	£10	
Right Now	7"	Piccadilly	7N35257	1965	£5	£10	
She's About A Mover	7"	Piccadilly	7N35241	1965	£5	£10	

BRITTON, CHRIS

As I Am	LP	Page One	POLS022	1969	£40	£80	

BROADSIDE

To Drive The Dark Away	LP	Guildhall	12	1975	£6	£15	

BROCK, B. & THE SULTANS

Do The Beetle	LP	Crown	CST399	1964	£6	£15	US

BROCK, DAVE

Social Alliance	7"	Flicknife	FLS024P	1983	£2	£5	pic disc

BROCKETT, JAIME

Remember The Wind And The Rain	LP	Capitol	ST678	1968	£5	£12	US

BROCKSTEDT, NORAH

Big Boy	7"	Top Rank	JAR353	1960	£2.50	£6	

BROGUES

Greg Elmore and Gary Duncan played as members of the Brogues before helping to form the Quicksilver Messenger Service.

But Now I'm Fine	7"	Challenge		1965	£7.50	£15	US
But Now I'm Fine	7"	Twilight	408	1965	£12.50	£25	US
I Ain't No Miracle Worker	7"	Challenge	59316	1965	£7.50	£15	US

BROMLEY, JOHN

And The Feeling Goes	7"	Polydor	56287	1968	£2	£5	
Hold Me Woman	7"	Polydor	56340	1969	£1.50	£4	
Kick A Tin Can	7"	Atlantic	584289	1969	£2	£5	
Melody Fayre	7"	Polydor	56305	1969	£1.50	£4	
Sing	LP	Polydor	583048	1969	£4	£10	
What A Woman Does	7"	Polydor	56244	1968	£2	£5	

BRONCO

Jess Roden, former singer with Alan Bown, hit on the idea of a group that could rock hard on acoustic guitars. Live, Bronco played sitting down, which was certainly a novelty, and their records, particularly "Country Home", still have a remarkable freshness. Guitarist Robbie Blunt is also an impressive electric player, as he later proved as a member of the Robert Plant band.

Ace Of Sunlight	LP	Island	ILPS9161	1971	£4	£10	
Country Home	LP	Island	ILPS9124	1970	£5	£12	

BRONX CHEER

Greatest Hits	LP	Dawn	DNLS3034	1972	£4	£10	

BROOK BROTHERS

Ain't Gonna Wash For A Week	7"	Pye	7N15369	1961	£1.50	£4	chart single
Brook Brothers	LP	Pye	NPL18067	1961	£15	£30	
Brook Brothers	7" EP	Pye	NEP24155	1962	£5	£10	
Hit Parade	7" EP	Pye	NEP24140	1961	£5	£10	

Title	Format	Label	Cat. No.	Year	Low	High	Notes
Hit Parade Vol.2	7" EP..	Pye	NEP24148	1961	£5	£10	
Little Bitty Tear	7"	Pye	7N15352	1961	£1.50	£4	
Married	7"	Pye	7N15387	1961	£1.50	£4	
Say The Word	7"	Pye	7N15298	1960	£1.50	£4	
Warpaint	7"	Pye	7N15333	1961	£1.50	£4	chart single

BROOK, PATTI

Title	Format	Label	Cat. No.	Year	Low	High	Notes
I Love You, I Need You	7"	Pye	7N15422	1962	£2.50	£6	
Since You've Been Gone	7"	Pye	7N15300	1960	£1.50	£4	
When The Red Red Robin	7"	Pye	7N15339	1961	£1.50	£4	

BROOK, TONY & THE BREAKERS

Title	Format	Label	Cat. No.	Year	Low	High	Notes
Love Dances On	7"	Columbia	DB7444	1965	£4	£8	
Meanie Genie	7"	Columbia	DB7279	1964	£12.50	£25	

BROOKLYN

Title	Format	Label	Cat. No.	Year	Low	High	Notes
Hollywood	7"	Rondelet	ROUND6	1981	£1.50	£4	
I Wanna Be A Detective	7"	Rondelet	ROUND3	1980	£1.50	£4	

BROOKLYN BRIDGE

Title	Format	Label	Cat. No.	Year	Low	High	Notes
Little Red Boat By The River	7"	Pye	7N25473	1968	£1.50	£4	
Worst That Could Happen	7"	Buddah	201029	1969	£1.50	£4	

BROOKMEYER, BOB

Title	Format	Label	Cat. No.	Year	Low	High	Notes
Blues Hot And Cold	LP	HMV	CLP1438/CSD1356	1961	£6	£15	
Bob Brookmeyer Quartet	10" LP	Vogue	LDE131	1955	£20	£40	
Bob Brookmeyer Quartet	10" LP	Vogue	LDE164	1956	£20	£40	

BROOKMEYER. BOB

Title	Format	Label	Cat. No.	Year	Low	High	Notes
Dual Roll	10" LP	Esquire	20084	1957	£10	£25	

BROOKMEYER, BOB

Title	Format	Label	Cat. No.	Year	Low	High	Notes
Portrait Of The Artist	LP	London	LTZK15208/SAHK6125	1961	£6	£15	
Street Swingers	LP	Vogue	LAE12147	1959	£8	£20	
Tonight's Jazz Today	LP	Vogue	LAE12047	1957	£10	£25	with Zoot Sims
Traditionalism Revisited	LP	Vogue	LAE12108	1958	£8	£20	
Whooeeee	LP	Vogue	LAE12053	1957	£10	£25	with Zoot Sims

BROOKS

Title	Format	Label	Cat. No.	Year	Low	High	Notes
Please Help Me, I'm Falling	7"	Top Rank	JAR409	1960	£1.50	£4	chart single

BROOKS & JERRY

Title	Format	Label	Cat. No.	Year	Low	High	Notes
I Got What It Takes	7"	Direction	583267	1968	£1.50	£4	

BROOKS, BABA

Title	Format	Label	Cat. No.	Year	Low	High	Notes
Baby Elephant Walk	7"	Black Swan	WI466	1965	£5	£10	Don Drummond B side
Bank To Bank	7"	Island	WI096	1963	£5	£10	
Catch A Fire	7"	Island	WI150	1964	£5	£10	Eric Morris B side
Clock	7"	Doctor Bird	DB1042	1966	£5	£10	Lyn Taitt B side
Cork Foot	7"	Black Swan	WI438	1964	£5	£10	Hersang Combo B side
Duck Soup	7"	Island	WI235	1965	£5	£10	Zodiacs B side
Eighth Games	7"	Doctor Bird	DB1043	1966	£5	£10	Joe White B side
Ethiopia	7"	Black Swan	WI451	1965	£5	£10	Archibald Trott B side
Faberge	7"	Doctor Bird	DB1081	1967	£5	£10	Monty Morris B side
First Session	7"	Doctor Bird	DB1001	1966	£5	£10	Joe White B side
Girls Town Ska	7"	Ska Beat	JB218	1965	£5	£10	Derrick Morgan B side
Guns Fever	7"	Island	WI229	1965	£5	£10	Dotty & Bonnie B side
Independence Ska	7"	Island	WI233	1965	£5	£10	Strangher & Claudette B side
Jelly Beans	7"	Black Swan	WI412	1964	£5	£10	Eric Morris B side
King Size	7"	Doctor Bird	DB1009	1966	£5	£10	Saints B side
Mattie Rag	7"	Ska Beat	JB217	1965	£5	£10	Lord Tanamo B side
Musical Workshop	7"	Black Swan	WI442	1965	£5	£10	Duke White B side
One Eyed Giant	7"	Ska Beat	JB220	1965	£5	£10	Dynamites B side
One Eyed Giant	7"	Ska Beat	JB268	1967	£5	£10	Dynamites B side
Open The Door	7"	Doctor Bird	DB1067	1966	£5	£10	Monty Morris B side
Our Man Flint	7"	High Note	HS030	1969	£2.50	£6	Hippy Boys B side
Party Time	7"	Doctor Bird	DB1064	1966	£5	£10	Aston & Yen B side
Roll Call	7"	Doctor Bird	DB1062	1966	£5	£10	
Scratch	7"	Doctor Bird	DB1065	1966	£5	£10	Valentines B side
Shock Resistance	7"	Island	WI078	1963	£5	£10	
Skank J.Sheck	7"	Rio	R61	1965	£5	£10	Shenley & Hiacinth B side
Spider	7"	Black Swan	WI434	1964	£5	£10	
Teenage Ska	7"	Island	WI241	1965	£5	£10	Alton Ellis B side
Three Blind Mice	7"	Island	WI127	1963	£5	£10	Billy & Bobby B side
Virginia Ska	7"	Island	WI247	1965	£5	£10	Riots B side
Water Melon Man	7"	R&B	JB125	1963	£5	£10	Stranger Cole B side

BROOKS, CHUCK

Title	Format	Label	Cat. No.	Year	Low	High	Notes
Black Sheep	7"	Soul City	SC116	1969	£2	£5	

BROOKS, DALE

Title	Format	Label	Cat. No.	Year	Low	High	Notes
I Wanna Be Your Girl	7"	Stateside	SS553	1966	£1.50	£4	

BROOKS, DONNIE

Title	Format	Label	Cat. No.	Year	Low	High	Notes
Doll House	7"	London	HLN9253	1960	£1.50	£4	
Happiest	LP	London	HAN2391	1961	£8	£20	

Mission Bell	7"	London	HLN9168	1960	£1.50	£4	
Oh You Beautiful Doll	7"	London	HLN9572	1962	£1.50	£4	
That's Why	7"	London	HLN9361	1961	£1.50	£4	

BROOKS, ELKIE

All Of My Life	7"	HMV	POP1480	1965	£4	£8	
Baby Let Me Love You	7"	HMV	POP1512	1966	£4	£8	
Come September	7"	Nems	564136	1969	£2.50	£6	
He's Gotta Love Me	7"	HMV	POP1431	1965	£4	£8	
Nothing Left To Do But Cry	7"	Decca	F11983	1964	£4	£8	
Something's Got A Hold On Me	7"	Decca	F11928	1964	£4	£8	
Way You Do The Things You do	7"	Decca	F12061	1965	£4	£8	

BROOKS, HADDA

Boogie	LP	Crown	CLP5058	1958	£8	£20	US
Femme Fatale	LP	Crown	CLP5010	1957	£8	£20	US
Femme Fatale	LP	Modern	LMP1210	1956	£30	£60	US
Sings And Swings	LP	Crown	CLP5374	1963	£5	£12	US

BROOKS, JOEY

I Ain't Blamin' You	7"	Decca	F12328	1966	£1.50	£4	

BROOKS, NORMAN

Baby Mine	7" EP	London	REP1021	1955	£6	£12	
Back In Circulation	7"	London	HL8115	1955	£7.50	£15	
Hello Sunshine	7"	London	L1166	1954	£10	£20	
I Can't Give You Anything But Love	7"	London	HL8041	1954	£7.50	£15	
I'd Like To Be In Your Shoes Baby	7"	London	HL8015	1954	£7.50	£15	
My Three D Sweetie	7"	London	HL8051	1954	£7.50	£15	
Skyblue Shirt & A Rainbow Tie	7"	London	L1228	1954	£10	£20	chart single
Vol.1	7" EP	London	REP1004	1954	£6	£12	
You Shouldn't Have Kissed Me	7"	London	L1202	1954	£10	£20	

BROOKS, ROSA LEE

The collaboration between Love's Arthur Lee and Jimi Hendrix, which produced, in the song "The Everlasting First", a particularly noteworthy addition to the careers of both musicians, was not the first time they worked together. "My Diary" was written by Arthur Lee and features Jimi Hendrix's guitar. Like all of Hendrix's early work, it is not exactly essential, but the single has not been reissued and seldom appears in the market-place.

My Diary	7"	Revis	1013	1964	£100	£200	US

BROOKS, TINA

True Blue	LP	Blue Note	BLP/BST84041	196-	£60	£120	

BROONZY, BIG BILL

Back Water Blues	78	Vogue	V2068	1951	£2.50	£6	
Big Bill Blues	LP	Vogue	LAE12009	1956	£8	£20	
Big Bill Blues	78	Vogue	V2075	1951	£2.50	£6	
Big Bill Broonzy	LP	Philips	BBL7113	1957	£15	£30	
Big Bill Broonzy	7" EP	Columbia	SEG7674	1957	£5	£10	
Big Bill Broonzy & Washboard Sam	LP	Chess	LP1468	1962	£8	£20	US
Big Bill Broonzy No.2	7" EP	Columbia	SEG7790	1958	£5	£10	
Big Bill Broonzy Sings	10" LP	Period	1114	195-	£8	£20	US
Big Bill Broonzy, Sonny Terry & Brownie McGhee	LP	Folkways	FA3817	1959	£5	£12	US
Big Bill's Blues	LP	CBS	52648	1969	£4	£10	
Big Bill's Blues	LP	Columbia	WL111	1958	£8	£20	US
Bill Bailey Won't You Please Come Home	7" EP	Tempo	EXA61	1957	£4	£8	
Black, Brown And White	78	Vogue	V2077	1951	£2.50	£6	
Blues	LP	Mercury	MMB12003	1959	£8	£20	
Blues	LP	Vogue	LAE12063	1958	£8	£20	
Blues Anthology Vol.3	7" EP	Storyville	SEP383	1962	£2.50	£6	
Blues By Broonzy	LP	EmArcy	MG26137	1957	£8	£20	US
Country Blues	LP	Folkways	FA2326	195-	£6	£15	US
Country Blues	LP	XTRA	XTRA1093	1970	£4	£10	
Do You Remember Big Bill Broonzy	7" EP	Emarcy	YEP9508	1959	£2.50	£6	
Evening With Big Bill Broonzy	LP	Storyville	SLP114	1964	£5	£12	
Evening With Big Bill Broonzy	LP	Tempo	TAP23	1959	£10	£25	
Five Foot Seven	78	Melodisc	1203	1952	£2.50	£6	
Folk Blues	LP	EmArcy	MG26034	1957	£8	£20	US
Guitar Shuffle	7"	Vogue	V2351	1958	£4	£8	
Guitar Shuffle	7" EP	Vogue	EPV1107	1956	£5	£10	
Hey Bud Blues	7" EP	Vogue	EPV1024	1955	£4	£8	
His Songs And Story	LP	Folkways	FA3586	195-	£6	£15	US
Hollering Blues	7" EP	Mercury	ZEP10093	1960	£4	£8	
House Rent Stomp	78	Vogue	V2076	1951	£2.50	£6	
In Concert	LP	Verve	VLP5006/SVLP506	1966	£5	£12	with Pete Seeger
In Concert	LP	XTRA	XTRA1006	1964	£6	£15	with Pete Seeger US
In Paris	LP	Vogue	LO60530	1956	£8	£20	
In The Evenin'	78	Vogue	V2073	1951	£2.50	£6	
John Henry	78	Vogue	V2074	1951	£2.50	£6	
Keep Your Hands Off	78	Melodisc	1191	1951	£2.50	£6	
Keep Your Hands Off	7" EP	Melodisc	EPM765	1956	£4	£8	
Last Session Part 1	LP	HMV	CLP1544	1961	£5	£12	
Last Session Part 2	LP	HMV	CLP1551	1961	£5	£12	
Last Session Part 3	LP	HMV	CLP1562	1961	£5	£12	
Make My Getaway	78	Vogue	V2078	1952	£2.50	£6	
Memorial	LP	Mercury	MG2/SR60822	1963	£5	£12	US
Midnight Special	7"	Storyville	A45053	1961	£2.50	£6	
Mississippi Blues Vol.1	7" EP	Pye	NJE1005	1956	£4	£8	
Mississippi Blues Vol.2	7" EP	Pye	NJE1015	1956	£4	£8	

Portraits In Blues Vol.2	LP	Storyville	670154	1967	£5	£12	
Remembering Big Bill Broonzy	LP	Mercury	MG2/SR60905	1964	£5	£12	
Remembering Broonzy	LP	Mercury	20044MCL	1966	£4	£10	US
Sings The Blues	7" EP	Vogue	EPV1074	1956	£4	£8	
South Bound Train	78	Pye	NJ2016	1957	£2	£5	
Southern Saga	7" EP	Pye	NJE1047	1957	£4	£8	
Tribute To Big Bill	LP	Nixa	NJL16	1958	£8	£20	
Trouble In Mind	LP	Fontana	688206ZL	1965	£6	£15	
Walking Down A Lonesome Road	7" EP	Mercury	10003MCE	1964	£2.50	£6	
Walking Down A Lonesome Road	7" EP	Mercury	ZEP10065	1960	£4	£8	
When Do I Get To Be Called A Man	78	Pye	NJ2012	1957	£2	£5	

BROONZY, BIG BILL & JOSH WHITE

Blues	7" EP	Pieces Of 8	PEP605	1961	£2.50	£6

BROONZY, BIG BILL & SONNY BOY WILLIAMSON

Big Bill And Sonny Boy	LP	RCA	RD7685	1965	£6	£15

BROTH

Broth	LP	Mercury	6338032	1970	£6	£15

BROTHER DAN ALL STARS

Another Saturday Night	7"	Trojan	TR608	1968	£4	£8
Donkey Returns	7"	Trojan	TR601	1968	£4	£8
Eastern Organ	7"	Trojan	TR602	1968	£4	£8
Follow That Donkey	LP	Trojan	TRL1	1969	£6	£15
Hold Pon Them	7"	Trojan	TR603	1968	£4	£8
Let's Catch The Beat	LP	Trojan	TBL101	1968	£8	£20
Read Up	7"	Trojan	TR607	1968	£4	£8

BROTHER FOX & THE TAR BABY

Brother Fox And The Tar Baby	LP	Capitol	ST544	1969	£6	£15	US

BROTHERHOOD

Brotherhood	LP	RCA	LSP4092	1968	£5	£12	US
Brotherhood Brotherhood	LP	RCA	LSP4228	1969	£5	£12	US
Paper Man	7"	Philips	BF1766	1969	£2.50	£6	

BROTHERHOOD OF BREATH

Brotherhood Of Breath was a big band formed by South African exile Chris McGregor, in which the cream of British jazz musicians (including McGregor's contingent of mixed race compatriots) could be heard playing together. The music is an exciting blend of swing and kwela and the Neon LP in particular is something of a landmark recording.

Brotherhood	LP	RCA	SF8269	1972	£15	£30
Brotherhood Of Breath	LP	Neon	NE2	1971	£20	£40
Live At Willisau	LP	Ogun	OG100	1974	£8	£20

BROTHERS

Love Story	7"	London	HLU10158	1967	£1.50	£4

BROTHERS (2)

Disco Soul	LP	People	PLEO25	1975	£8	£20

BROTHERS FOUR

Green Leaves Of Summer	7"	Philips	PB1072	1960	£1.50	£4	
Greenfields	7"	Philips	PB1009	1959	£1.50	£4	chart single
Sing Bob Dylan	7" EP	CBS	EP6063	1965	£2	£5	

BROTHERS GRIMM

Looky Looky	7"	Ember	EMBS222	1966	£50	£100
Lost Love	7"	Decca	F12224	1965	£1.50	£4

BROTHERS TWO

Here I Am In Love Again	7"	Action	ACT4513	1968	£2.50	£6

BROTHERS WILLIAM

Honey Love	7"	Parlophone	R5293	1965	£2	£5

BROUGHTON, EDGAR, BAND

The Edgar Broughton Band were a staple feature of the open-air festivals and free concerts of 1969-70. They were supremely good at giving an audience a good time, but on record their musical limitations become rather glaringly obvious. The crowd-pleasing chant, "Out Demons Out", with which they always ended their stage act, sounds rather weak on cold vinyl, while the fusion of Captain Beefheart with the Shadows on "Apache Drop Out" sounds silly. Nevertheless, the track "Love In The Rain", on the first LP, provides for an exhilarating three minutes or so, and would do Motorhead proud.

BROUGHTON, EDGAR BAND

Apache Drop Out	7"	Harvest	HAR5032	1970	£1.50	£4	chart single
Bandages	LP	Nems	NEL6006	1975	£4	£10	
Edgar Broughton Band	LP	Harvest	SHVL791	1971	£6	£15	chart LP
Evil	7"	Harvest	HAR5001	1969	£2	£5	
Inside Out	LP	Harvest	SHTC252	1972	£6	£15	
Legendary	LP	Babylon	DB80073	1984	£6	£15	German double
Live Hits Harder	LP	BB	BB201009	1979	£6	£15	
Oora	LP	Harvest	SHVL810	1973	£6	£15	
Out Demons Out	7"	Harvest	HAR5015	1970	£1.50	£4	chart single
Parlez Vous English	LP	EMI	INS3027	1979	£4	£10	
Sing Brother Sing	LP	Harvest	SHVL772	1970	£6	£15	chart LP
Super Chip	LP	Sheet	SHEET2	1982	£6	£15	
Wasa Wasa	LP	Harvest	SHVL757	1969	£6	£15	

BROWN, AL & HIS TUNE TOPPERS

Madison Dance Party	LP	Amy	A(S)1	1960	£8	£20	US

BROWN, ARTHUR

Arthur Brown's stage act, which began with his being lowered on to the stage with his head-dress on fire, was legendary during 1967-8. His album, "The Crazy World Of Arthur Brown" (which was actually the name of his group) easily matches the visual bombast, emerging as one of the classic recordings of the period. The music is guitar-free, which is often a recipe for dullness, but Vincent Crane's organ playing is so full of imagination, and Arthur Brown's singing so powerful, that guitars are not missed. The non-album "Devil's Grip" is in the same league, although the jokey B-side, "Give Him A Flower", is a bit of a throwaway. Brown's contribution to the soundtrack records of the Roger Vadim film "The Game Is Over/La Curee" is uncredited, but consists of two songs in a style close to that of the Crazy World.

Chisholm In My Bosom	LP	Gull	GULP1023	1978	£4	£10	
Crazy World Of Arthur Brown	LP	Track	612/613005	1968	£6	£15	chart LP
Devil's Grip	7"	Track	604008	1967	£2.50	£6	
Faster Then The Speed Of Sound	LP	WEA	58088	1980	£4	£10	Dutch
Fire	7"	Track	604022	1968	£1.50	£4	chart single
Game Is Over (La Curee)	LP	Atco	33205	1966	£30	£60	US
La Curee	7" EP	Barclay	71026	1966	£30	£60	French
Nightmare	LP	Track	604026	1968	£2	£5	
Requiem	LP	Remote	REM101	1982	£4	£10	
You Don't Know	7"	Reading Rag Record	LYN771	1965	£30	£60	flexi, with The Diamonds

BROWN, B. & BUSTER

B. & Buster Brown	7" EP	XX	MIN713	196-	£4	£8	

BROWN, BEN

Ask The Lonely	7"	Polydor	56198	1967	£12.50	£25	

BROWN, BOBBY

Enlightening Beam Of Axonda	LP	Destiny	4002	1972	£6	£15	US

BROWN, BOOTS

Cerveza	7"	RCA	RCA1078	1958	£1.50	£4	
Jim Twangy	7"	RCA	RCA1102	1959	£1.50	£4	
Rock That Beat	LP	RCA	LG1000	1958	£8	£20	US

BROWN BROTHERS

Let The Good Times Roll	7"	Vogue	V9131	1959	£30	£60	

BROWN, BUSTER

Fannie Mae	7"	Melodisc	1559	1960	£20	£40	
Fannie Mae	7"	Sue	WI368	1965	£6	£12	
My Blue Heaven	7"	Island	WI3031	1967	£7.50	£15	
New King Of The Blues	LP	Fire	FLP102	1960	£37.50	£75	US
Sugar Babe	7"	Blue Horizon	573147	1969	£6	£12	

BROWN, BUSTY

Broken Heart	7"	Punch	PH10	1969	£2	£5	
Here Comes The Night	7"	Doctor Bird	DB1158	1968	£5	£10	
To Love Somebody	7"	Upsetter	US308	1969	£2.50	£6	Bleechers B side
What A Price	7"	Upsetter	US304	1969	£2.50	£6	

BROWN, CHARLES

Ballads My Way	LP	Mainstream	6035	1965	£5	£12	US
Christmas Question	7"	Parlophone	R4848	1961	£10	£20	
Confidential	7"	Vogue	V9065	1957	£40	£80	
Driftin' Blues	LP	Score	SLP4011	1957	£30	£60	US
Great Charles Brown	LP	King	878	1963	£10	£25	US
Legend	LP	Bluesway	6039	1970	£5	£12	US
Million Sellers	LP	Imperial	A9178	1961	£20	£40	US
Mood Music	LP	Aladdin	809	1956	£50	£100	US
Mood Music	10" LP	Aladdin	702	1954	£75	£150	US
Mood Music	10" LP	Aladdin	702	1954	£180	£300	US, red vinyl
Sings Christmas Songs	LP	King	775	1961	£15	£30	US
Soothe Me	7"	Vogue	V9061	1956	£50	£100	

BROWN, CLARENCE GATEMOUTH

Clarence Gatemouth Brown	7" EP	Vocalion	VE170161	1965	£25	£50	
Vol 1: 1948-1953	LP	Python	PLP26	1972	£8	£20	
Vol 2: 1956-1965	LP	Python	PLP27	1972	£8	£20	

BROWN, CLIFFORD

At Basin Street	LP	Emarcy	EJL1253	1957	£15	£30	with Max Roach
Clifford Brown - Gigi Gryce Orchestra	7" EP	Vogue	EPV1027	1955	£2	£5	
Clifford Brown And Art Farmer Vol.1	7" EP	Esquire	EP3	1954	£2	£5	
Clifford Brown And Art Farmer Vol.2	7" EP	Esquire	EP4	1954	£2	£5	
Clifford Brown And Max Roach	7" EP	Emarcy	ERE1572	1958	£2	£5	
Clifford Brown And Tadd Dameron	7" EP	Esquire	EP71	1955	£2	£5	
Clifford Brown Ensemble	7" EP	Vogue	EPV1119	1956	£2	£5	
Clifford Brown Ensemble	10" LP	Vogue	LDE158	1955	£20	£40	
Clifford Brown Quartet	10" LP	Vogue	LDE042	1954	£10	£25	
Clifford Brown Sextet	10" LP	Vogue	LDE121	1955	£10	£25	
Conception	7" EP	Vogue	EPV1041	1955	£2	£5	
Memorial Album	LP	Blue Note	BLP/BST81526	1963	£10	£25	
Remember Clifford	LP	Mercury	20022MCL	1964	£6	£15	
Study In Brown	LP	Emarcy	EJL1278	1958	£8	£20	
Sudy In Brown Vol.1	7" EP	Emarcy	ERE1565	1958	£2	£5	
Sudy In Brown Vol.2	7" EP	Emarcy	ERE1566	1958	£2	£5	
Sweet Clifford	7" EP	Emarcy	ERE1501	1956	£2	£5	

BROWN, DAVID

All My Life	7"	Island	WI3112	1967	£5	£10	B side Ron Wilson

BROWN, DENNIS

Title	Format	Label	Cat No	Year	Price1	Price2	Notes
Black Magic Woman	7"	Explosion	EX2068	1972	£1.50	£4	
Little Green Apples	7"	Ocean	OC001	1971	£2	£5	Sound Dimension B side
Love Grows	7"	Bamboo	BAM56	1970	£2	£5	Sound Dimension B side
Money In My Pocket	7"	Pressure Beat	PB5513	1972	£1.50	£4	Joe Gibbs B side
Never Fall In Love	7"	Banana	BA336	1971	£2	£5	
No Man Is An Island	7"	Banana	BA309	1970	£2	£5	Soul Sisters B side
Super Reggae And Soul Hits	LP	Trojan	TRLS57	1973	£4	£10	

BROWN, DUSTY

Title	Format	Label	Cat No	Year	Price1	Price2
Please Don't Go	7"	Starlite	ST45058	1961	£10	£20

BROWN, FAY

Title	Format	Label	Cat No	Year	Price1	Price2
Unchained Melody	7"	Columbia	SCM5185	1955	£6	£12

BROWN, FRANK

Title	Format	Label	Cat No	Year	Price1	Price2
Some Come Some Go	7"	Island	WI3103	1967	£5	£10

BROWN, GERRY

Title	Format	Label	Cat No	Year	Price1	Price2
It's Trad Time	LP	Fontana	TFL5165	1961	£6	£15

BROWN, GLEN, JOE WHITE & TREVOR

Title	Format	Label	Cat No	Year	Price1	Price2	Notes
Way Of Life	7"	Blue Cat	BS131	1968	£4	£8	Carl Bryan & Lyn Taitt B side

BROWN, GLENMORE & HOPETON LEWIS

Title	Format	Label	Cat No	Year	Price1	Price2
Girl You're Cold	7"	Fab	FAB42	1968	£4	£8

BROWN, HENRY

Title	Format	Label	Cat No	Year	Price1	Price2
Blues	LP	77	LA125	1961	£6	£15

BROWN, IRVING

Title	Format	Label	Cat No	Year	Price1	Price2
I'm Still Around	7"	Bamboo	BAM58	1970	£2	£5
Now I'm Alone	7"	Bamboo Now	BN1003	1971	£2	£5
Today	7"	Bamboo	BAM36	1970	£2	£5

BROWN, JAMES

Title	Format	Label	Cat No	Year	Price1	Price2	Notes
Ain't It Funky	LP	Polydor	2343010	1970	£8	£20	
Ain't It Funky Now	7"	Polydor	56793	1970	£1.50	£4	
Ain't That A Groove	7"	Pye	7N25367	1966	£2	£5	
Always Amazing James Brown	LP	King	LP743	1961	£15	£30	US
At The Apollo	LP	London	HA8184	1964	£15	£30	
At The Apollo	LP	Polydor	582703	1967	£6	£15	
At The Apollo Vol.2	LP	Polydor	583729/730	1969	£8	£20	
Best Of James Brown	LP	Polydor	583765	1969	£4	£10	
Black Caesar	LP	Polydor	2490117	1974	£10	£25	
Bodyheat	LP	Polydor	2391258	1977	£4	£10	
Bodyheat	7"	Polydor	2066763	1977	£1.50	£4	
Bring It Up	7"	Pye	7N25411	1967	£2	£5	
Bring It Up	7" EP	Pye	NEP44088	1967	£5	£10	
Christmas Album	LP	Pye	NPL28097	1966	£10	£25	
Cold Sweat	7"	Pye	7N25430	1967	£2.50	£6	
Don't Be A Drop-Out	7"	Pye	7N25394	1966	£2.50	£6	
Everybody's Doin' The Hustle	LP	Polydor	2391197	1975	£5	£12	
Exciting James Brown	LP	King	LP780	1962	£15	£30	US
Eyesight	7"	Polydor	2066915	1978	£1.50	£4	
Funky President	7"	Polydor	2066520	1975	£1.50	£4	
Get Involved	7"	Polydor	2001190	1971	£1.50	£4	
Get It Together	7"	Pye	7N25441	1967	£2	£5	
Get On The Good Foot	LP	Polydor	2659018	1973	£10	£25	double
Get On The Good Foot	7"	Polydor	2066231	1972	£1.50	£4	
Get Up Offa That Thing	LP	Polydor	2391244	1976	£4	£10	
Get Up Offa That Thing	7"	Polydor	2066687	1976	£1.50	£4	
Gettin' Down To It	LP	Polydor	583742	1970	£8	£20	
Greatest Hits	LP	Polydor	623017	1968	£4	£10	
Grits And Soul	LP	Philips	BL7664	1965	£10	£25	
Handful Of Soul	LP	Philips	(S)BL7761	1967	£8	£20	
Have Mercy Baby	7"	London	HL9945	1965	£5	£10	
Hell	LP	Polydor	2659036	1974	£15	£30	double
Hey America	7"	Mojo	2093046	1971	£1.50	£4	
Honky Tonk	7"	Polydor	2066216	1972	£1.50	£4	
Honky Tonk	7"	Polydor	2066834	1977	£1.50	£4	
Hot	LP	Polydor	2391214	1976	£5	£12	
Hot	7"	Polydor	2066642	1976	£1.50	£4	
Hot Pants	LP	Polydor	2425086	1971	£5	£12	
Hot Pants	7"	Polydor	2001213	1971	£1.50	£4	
How Long Darling	7" EP	Pye	NEP44076	1967	£5	£10	
I Can't Stand Myself	LP	Polydor	184136	1968	£10	£25	
I Can't Stand Myself	7"	Polydor	56787	1970	£2	£5	
I Do Just What I Want	7" EP	Ember	EMBEP4549	1964	£6	£12	
I Got A Bag Of My Own	7"	Polydor	2066285	1973	£1.50	£4	
I Got A Feeling	7"	Polydor	56743	1968	£2.50	£6	
I Got Ants In My Pants	7"	Polydor	2066296	1973	£1.50	£4	
I Got You	7"	Pye	7N25350	1966	£4	£8	chart single
I Got You	7" EP	Pye	NEP44059	1966	£5	£10	
I Got You (I Feel Good)	LP	Pye	NPL28074	1966	£10	£25	
I'll Go Crazy	7" EP	Pye	NEP44068	1966	£5	£10	
I'm A Greedy Man	7"	Polydor	2066153	1971	£1.50	£4	

Title	Format	Label	Catalogue	Year	Price	Price	Notes
In The Jungle Groove	LP	Urban	URBLP11	1988	£6	£15	double
It's A Man's Man's Man's World	LP	Pye	NPL28079	1966	£8	£20	
It's A Man's Man's Man's World	7"	Pye	7N25371	1966	£4	£8	chart single
It's A Mother	LP	Polydor	583768	1969	£10	£25	
It's A New Day	LP	Polydor	2310029	1971	£8	£20	
It's A New Day	7"	Polydor	2001018	1970	£1.50	£4	
It's Hell	7"	Polydor	2066513	1974	£1.50	£4	
Jump Around	LP	King	LP/KS771	1962	£15	£30	US
Kansas City	7"	Pye	7N25418	1967	£2.50	£6	
King Heroin	7"	Polydor	2066185	1972	£1.50	£4	
King Of Soul	LP	Polydor	184159	1969	£6	£15	
Let A Man Come In	7"	Polydor	56783	1969	£2	£5	
Let Yourself Go	7"	Pye	7N25423	1967	£2.50	£6	
Licking Stick	7"	Polydor	56744	1968	£2	£5	
Live At The Apollo	LP	Polydor	2482184	1975	£4	£10	
Live At The Apollo Vol.2	LP	Polydor	2612005	1970	£6	£15	
Live At The Garden	LP	Pye	NPL28104	1967	£10	£25	
Make It Funky	7"	Polydor	2001223	1971	£1.50	£4	
Mighty Instrumentals	LP	Pye	NPL28093	1967	£8	£20	
Money Won't Change You	7"	Pye	7N25379	1966	£2.50	£6	
Mother Popcorn	7"	Polydor	56776	1969	£1.50	£4	
Mr.Dynamite	LP	Polydor	623032	1968	£6	£15	
Mr.Excitement	LP	Pye	NPL28100	1967	£6	£15	
Mr.Soul	LP	Polydor	184100	1968	£6	£15	
Mutha Nature	LP	Polydor	2391300	1977	£5	£12	
My Thing	7"	Polydor	2066485	1974	£1.50	£4	
Nature	7"	Polydor	2066984	1978	£1.50	£4	
New Breed	7"	Philips	BF1481	1966	£2.50	£6	
Night Train	7"	Parlophone	R4922	1962	£10	£20	
Night Train	7"	Sue	WI360	1964	£10	£20	
Out Of Sight	LP	Mercury	SMCL20133	1969	£6	£15	
Out Of Sight	7"	Philips	BF1368	1964	£5	£10	
Papa's Got A Brand New Bag	LP	London	HA8262	1966	£10	£25	
Papa's Got A Brand New Bag	LP	Polydor	2334009	1970	£5	£12	
Papa's Got A Brand New Bag	LP	Pye	NPL28099	1967	£8	£20	
Papa's Got A Brand New Bag	7"	London	HL9990	1965	£4	£8	chart single
Papa's Got A Brand New Bag	7"	Polydor	2141008	1973	£1.50	£4	
Payback	LP	Polydor	2659030	1974	£20	£40	double
Plays James Brown Today & Yesterday	LP	Philips	BL7697	1966	£8	£20	
Plays New Breed	LP	Philips	BL7718	1966	£8	£20	
Plays The Real Thing	LP	Philips	(S)BL7823	1967	£8	£20	
Please Please Please	LP	King	395610	1959	£25	£50	US
Please Please Please	LP	London	HA8231	1965	£10	£25	
Popcorn	LP	Polydor	184319	1970	£15	£30	
Prisoner Of Love	LP	King	LP/KS851	1963	£15	£30	US
Prisoner Of Love	7"	London	HL9730	1963	£7.50	£15	
Prisoner Of Love	7" EP	London	RE1410	1964	£7.50	£15	
Prisoner Of Love	7" EP	Pye	NEP44072	1967	£5	£10	
Pure Dynamite	LP	London	HA8177	1964	£10	£25	
Raw Soul	LP	Pye	NPL28103	1967	£6	£15	
Reality	LP	Polydor	2391164	1975	£6	£15	
Revolution Of The Mind	LP	Polydor	2659011	1972	£10	£25	double
Say It Loud I'm Black & I'm Proud	LP	Polydor	583741	1969	£10	£25	
Say It Loud, I'm Black And I'm Proud	7"	Polydor	56752	1968	£2.50	£6	
Sex Machine	LP	Polydor	2625004	1971	£8	£20	double
Sex Machine	7"	Polydor	2001071	1970	£1.50	£4	chart single
Sex Machine Today	LP	Polydor	2391175	1975	£5	£12	
Shout And Shimmy	7"	Parlophone	R4952	1962	£7.50	£15	
Showtime	LP	Philips	BL7630	1964	£10	£25	
Slaughter's Big Rip-Off	LP	Polydor	2391084	1973	£8	£20	
Soul Brother No.1	LP	Polydor	2343036	1971	£5	£12	
Soul Classics	LP	Polydor	2391057	1973	£5	£12	
Soul Classics Vol.2	LP	Polydor	2391116	1974	£5	£12	
Soul Classics Vol.3	LP	Polydor	2391166	1975	£6	£15	
Soul Fire	LP	Polydor	184148	1969	£8	£20	
Soul On Top	LP	Polydor	2310022	1971	£8	£20	
Soul Power	7"	Polydor	2001163	1971	£1.50	£4	
Stone To The Bone	7"	Polydor	2066411	1974	£1.50	£4	
Super Bad	LP	Polydor	2310089	1971	£6	£15	
Super Bad	7"	Polydor	2001097	1970	£1.50	£4	
Tell Me What You're Gonna Do	LP	Ember	EMB3357	1964	£10	£25	Sleeve pictured in Guide
Tell Me What You're Gonna Do	7"	Ember	EMBS216	1965	£5	£10	
That's Life	7"	Polydor	56540	1970	£1.50	£4	
There It Is	LP	Polydor	2391033	1972	£10	£25	
There It Is	7"	Polydor	2066210	1972	£1.50	£4	
There Was A Time	7"	Polydor	56740	1968	£2.50	£6	
These Foolish Things	7"	London	HL9775	1963	£6	£12	
Think	LP	King	LP683	1960	£25	£50	US
Think	7"	Parlophone	R4667	1960	£10	£20	
Think	7"	Polydor	2066329	1973	£1.50	£4	
This Is James Brown	LP	Philips	6336201	1972	£4	£10	
This Is James Brown	LP	Philips	643317	1969	£5	£12	
This Old Heart	7"	Fontana	H273	1960	£10	£20	
Tours The USA	LP	London	HA8240	1965	£10	£25	
Try Me	LP	King	395635	1959	£25	£50	US
Try Me	7"	Philips	BF1458	1965	£2.50	£6	
Turn It Loose	LP	Polydor	580701	1970	£8	£20	
Unbeatable Sixteen Hits	LP	London	HA8203	1965	£10	£25	

What My Baby Needs Now	7"	Polydor	2066283	1972	£1.50	£4	
Woman	7"	Polydor	2066370	1973	£1.50	£4	
World	7"	Polydor	56780	1969	£1.50	£4	

BROWN, JERICHO

Look For A Star	7"	Warner Bros	WB14	1960	£1.50	£4	

BROWN, JIM EDWARD

Introducing	7" EP	RCA	RCX7179	1965	£2	£5	

BROWN, JIM EDWARD & MAXINE

Country Songs	7" EP	London	REP1024	1955	£7.50	£15	
Country Songs Vol.3	7" EP	London	REU1044	1955	£7.50	£15	
Here Today And Gone Tomorrow	7"	London	HLU8200	1955	£7.50	£15	
Itsy Witsy Bitsy Me	7"	London	HL8123	1955	£12.50	£25	
Your Love Is Wild As The West Wind	7"	London	HLU8166	1955	£12.50	£25	

BROWN, JOE

As the guitarist on Billy Fury's highly regarded "Sound Of Fury" album, Joe Brown had considerable credibility, yet his own records are wildly variable in quality. The problem was that Brown seemed to be determined to prove his versatility, but when this included the performance of old music hall songs and an instrumental version of "All Things Bright And Beautiful", then the effort did not seem to be particularly worthwhile. At his best, however, such as on the succession of hit singles begun with "A Picture Of You", Brown created an effective form of robust pop-country that could, perhaps, have become a significant influence if only he had developed it further.

All Things Bright And Beautiful	7" EP	Piccadilly	NEP34026	1962	£2.50	£6	
Charlie Girl	7"	Pye	7N15983	1965	£1.50	£4	
Crazy Mixed-Up Kid	7"	Piccadilly	7N35000	1961	£1.50	£4	
Darktown Strutters Ball	7"	Decca	F11207	1960	£4	£8	chart single
Don't	7"	Piccadilly	7N35194	1964	£1.50	£4	
Here Comes Joe Brown	LP	Golden Guinea	GGL0231	1963	£4	£10	
Hit Parade	7" EP	Piccadilly	NEP34025	1962	£2.50	£6	
I'm Henry The Eighth I Am	7"	Piccadilly	7N35005	1961	£1.50	£4	
It Only Took A Minute	7"	Piccadilly	7N35082	1962	£1.50	£4	chart single
Jellied Eels	7"	Decca	F11246	1960	£2.50	£6	
Little Ray Of Sunshine	7"	Pye	7N17135	1966	£1.50	£4	
Little Ukelele	7"	Piccadilly	7N35150	1963	£1.50	£4	
Live	LP	Piccadilly	NPL38006	1963	£5	£12	chart LP
Mrs O's Theme	7" EP	Pye	PNV24195	1967	£6	£12	French
Nature's Time For Love	7"	Piccadilly	7N35129	1963	£1.50	£4	chart single
People Gotta Talk	7"	Decca	F11185	1959	£4	£8	
People Gotta Talk	7"	Decca	F11496	1962	£1.50	£4	
Picture Of Joe Brown	LP	Ace Of Clubs	ACL1127	1962	£5	£12	
Picture Of Joe Brown	7" EP	Decca	DFE8500	1962	£4	£8	
Picture Of You	LP	Golden Guinea	GGL0146	1962	£4	£10	chart LP
Picture Of You	7"	Piccadilly	7N35047	1962	£1.50	£4	chart single
Sally Ann	7"	Piccadilly	7N35138	1963	£1.50	£4	chart single
Satisfied Mind	7"	Pye	7N17184	1966	£2	£5	
Sea Of Heartbreak	7"	Pye	7N17074	1966	£1.50	£4	
Shine	7"	Pye	7N15322	1960	£2	£5	chart single
Sicilian Tarantella	7"	Pye	7N15888	1965	£1.50	£4	
Teardrops In The Rain	7"	Pye	7N15784	1965	£1.50	£4	
That's What Love Will Do	7"	Piccadilly	7N35106	1963	£1.50	£4	chart single
What A Crazy World	7"	Piccadilly	7N35024	1962	£1.50	£4	chart single
With A Little Help From My Friends	7"	Pye	7N17339	1967	£1.50	£4	
You Do Things To Me	7"	Piccadilly	7N35163	1964	£1.50	£4	
Your Tender Look	7"	Piccadilly	7N35058	1962	£1.50	£4	chart single

BROWN, JOE & MARK WYNTER

Big Hits	7" EP	Golden Guinea	WO1	1963	£2	£5	
Joe Brown Mark Wynter	LP	Golden Guinea	GGL0179	1963	£4	£10	
Just For Fun	7" EP	Pye	NEP24167	1963	£2.50	£6	

BROWN, JOHNNY

Walking Talking Kissing Doll	7"	Philips	PB1119	1961	£1.50	£4	

BROWN, K.

Pocket Money	7"	Blue Beat	BB66	1961	£5	£10	

BROWN, KENT & THE RAINBOWS

Come Ya Come Ya	7"	Fab	FAB53	1968	£4	£8	

BROWN, LAWRENCE

Slide Trombone	LP	Columbia	33CX10046	1956	£6	£15	

BROWN, LES

Forty Cups Of Coffee	7"	Vogue Coral	Q72242	1957	£2.50	£6	
Frenesi	7"	Capitol	CL14331	1955	£1.50	£4	
He Needs Me	7"	Capitol	CL14350	1955	£1.50	£4	
Les Brown Band	10" LP	Vogue Coral	LVC10017	1955	£5	£12	
Les Brown Band	10" LP	Vogue Coral	LVC10033	1956	£5	£12	
Les Brown Orchestra	10" LP	Vogue Coral	LVC10002	1955	£5	£12	

BROWN, MARION

Porto Novo	LP	Polydor	583724	1969	£8	£20	

BROWN, MARK

Brown Low Special	7"	Island	WI3097	1967	£5	£10	Dawn Penn B side

BROWN, MAXINE

All In My Mind	7"	London	HLU9286	1961	£5	£10	
Fabulous Sound Of Maxine Brown	LP	Wand	WD656	1963	£6	£15	US
Greatest Hits	LP	Wand	WD(S)684	1967	£5	£12	US

I Can't Get Along Without You	7"	Major Minor	MM709	1970	£1.50	£4	
It's Gonna Be Alright	7"	Pye	7N25299	1965	£4	£8	
I've Got A Lot Of Love Left In Me	7"	Pye	7N25410	1967	£2.50	£6	
Oh No Not My Baby	7"	Pye	7N25272	1964	£4	£8	
One Step At A Time	7"	Pye	7N25317	1965	£2.50	£6	
Promise Me Anything	7"	HMV	POP1102	1962	£7.50	£15	
Since I Found You	7"	Pye	7N25434	1967	£2.50	£6	
Spotlight On Maxine Brown	LP	Wand	WD(S)663	1965	£5	£12	US
Yesterday's Kisses	7"	Stateside	SS188	1963	£5	£10	

BROWN, NAPPY

Don't Be Angry	7"	London	HL8145	1955	£180	£300	
It Don't Hurt No More	7"	London	HLC8760	1958	£20	£40	
Little By Little	7"	London	HLC8384	1957	£60	£120	
Nappy Brown Sings	LP	Savoy	MG14002	1958	£30	£60	US
Pitter Patter	7"	London	HLC8182	1955	£90	£180	
Right Time	LP	Savoy	MG14025	1960	£25	£50	US

BROWN, NOEL

Man's Temptation	7"	Island	WI3149	1968	£5	£10	

BROWN, OSCAR JR.

But I Was Cool	7"	Philips	PB1097	1961	£1.50	£4	

BROWN, PETE

Pete Brown was one of the first poets to attempt to make a living by giving performances of his work, but achieved his greatest success as lyricist for Cream and for Jack Bruce solo. His own rock groups - Battered Ornaments and Piblokto - were interesting and featured strong contributions from musicians with their feet in both the jazz and rock camps, such as Chris Spedding, Jim Mullen, and George Khan. They were ultimately handicapped, however, by their vocalist's (Brown himself) inability to sing.

Art School Dance Goes On Forever	LP	Harvest	SHVL768	1970	£25	£50	
Can't Get Off The Planet	7"	Harvest	HAR5023	1970	£4	£8	
Flying Hero Sandwich	7"	Harvest	HAR5028	1970	£4	£8	
Living Life Backwards	7"	Harvest	HAR5008	1970	£4	£8	
Meal You Can Shake Hands With In The Dark	LP	Harvest	SHVL752	1969	£25	£50	
My Last Band	LP	Harvest	SHSM2017	1977	£8	£20	
Not Forgotten Association	LP	Deram	SML1103	1973	£25	£50	
Pete Brown Sextet	10" LP	London	LZN14002	1955	£15	£30	
Thousands On A Raft	LP	Harvest	SHVL782	1970	£25	£50	
Week Looked Good On Paper	7"	Parlophone	R5767	1969	£7.50	£15	
Week Looked Good On Paper	7"	Parlophone	R5767	1969	£15	£30	demo, PS

BROWN, PETE & IAN LYNN

Party In The Rain	LP	Discs International	INTLP1	1982	£20	£40	

BROWN, RAY

Bass Hit	10" LP	Columbia	33C9037	1957	£8	£20	

BROWN, ROY

Blues Are All Brown	LP	Bluesway	BLS6019	1968	£5	£12	US
Hard Luck Blues	LP	King	KS1130	1971	£5	£12	US
Hard Times	LP	Bluesway	BLS6056	1973	£5	£12	US
Live At Monterey	LP	Epic	BG30473	1971	£5	£12	US
Party Doll	7"	London	HLP8398	1957	£75	£150	
Saturday Night	7"	London	HLP8448	1957	£180	£300	
Sings 24 Hits	LP	King	(KS)956	1966	£8	£20	US

BROWN, ROY & WYNONIE HARRIS

Battle Of The Blues Vol.1	LP	King	607	1958	£75	£150	US
Battle Of The Blues Vol.2	LP	King	627	1959	£75	£150	US

BROWN, ROY, WYNONIE HARRIS & EDDIE VINSON

Battle Of The Blues Vol.4	LP	King	668	1960	£180	£300	US

BROWN, RUTH

Along Comes Ruth	LP	Philips	652012BL	1962	£8	£20	
As Long As I'm Moving	7"	London	HLE8210	1955	£50	£100	
Best Of Ruth Brown	LP	Atlantic	ATL5007	1964	£25	£50	
Don't Deceive Me	7"	London	HLE9093	1960	£10	£20	
Gospel Time	LP	Philips	652020BL	1963	£8	£20	
Gospel Time	7" EP	Philips	BE12537	1963	£5	£10	
I Don't Know	7"	London	HLE8946	1959	£10	£20	
I Want To Do More	7"	London	HLE8310	1956	£37.50	£75	
Jack Of Diamonds	7"	London	HLE8887	1959	£12.50	£25	
Just Too Much	7"	London	HLE8645	1958	£15	£30	
Late Date	LP	Atlantic	(S)1308	1959	£25	£50	US
Late Date	LP	London	LTZK15187	1960	£10	£25	
Lucky Lips	7"	Columbia	DB3913	1957	£40	£80	
Mambo Baby	7"	London	HL8153	1955	£50	£100	
Miss Rhythm	LP	Atlantic	8026	1959	£25	£50	US
Mom Oh Mom	7"	London	HLE8401	1957	£30	£60	
New Love	7"	London	HLE8552	1958	£15	£30	
One More Time	7"	London	HLE8483	1957	£20	£40	
Queen Of R&B	7" EP	London	REE1038	1955	£35	£70	
Rockin' With Ruth	LP	London	HAE2106	1958	£30	£60	
Ruth Brown	LP	Atlantic	8004	1957	£30	£60	US
Ruth Brown '65	LP	Mainstream	1/S6044	1965	£6	£15	US
Ruth Brown Sings	10" LP	Atlantic	115	1956	£400	£600	US
Sure Nuff	7"	London	HLK9304	1961	£7.50	£15	
This Little Girl's Gone Rocking	7"	London	HLE8757	1958	£25	£50	

Yes Sir That's My Baby	7"	Brunswick	05904	1964	£10	£20	

BROWN, RUTH & JOE TURNER
King And Queen Of R&B	7" EP	London	REE1047	1956	£50	£100	

BROWN, SANDY
Doctor McJazz	LP	Columbia	33SX1306/ SCX3367	1961	£5	£12	...with Al Fairweather
McJazz	LP	Nixa	NJL9	1957	£6	£15	
Playing Compositions By Al Fairweather	LP	Tempo	TAP3	1956	£6	£15	
Traditional Jazz Vol.2	10" LP	Esquire	20022	1953	£8	£20	

BROWN, TINY
No More Blues	78	Capitol	CL13306	1950	£6	£12	

BROWNE, DUNCAN
Duncan Browne	LP	Rak	SRKA6754	1973	£6	£15	
Give Me Take You	LP	Immediate	IMSP018	1968	£10	£25	
On The Bombsite	7"	Immediate	IM070	1968	£4	£8	

BROWNE, FRIDAY
Getting Nowhere	7"	Parlophone	R5396	1966	£1.50	£4	

BROWNE, JACKSON
Jackson Browne	LP	Asylum	SD5051	1972	£6	£15	canvas cover, US
Late For The Sky	LP	Asylum	K243007	1974	£6	£15	quad
Pretender	LP	Mobile Fidelity	MFSL1055	1981	£6	£15	US audiophile

BROWNE, SANDRA
Johnny Boy	7"	Columbia	DB4998	1963	£1.50	£4	
Knock On Any Door	7"	Columbia	DB7465	1965	£2	£5	
You'd Think He Didn't Know Me	7"	Columbia	DB7109	1963	£1.50	£4	

BROWNE, TEDDY
Pretty Little Baby	7"	Starlite	ST45033	1961	£2	£5	

BROWNE, THOMAS F.
Wednesday's Child	LP	Vertigo	6343700	1972	£20	£40	spiral label

BROWNE, WATSON T.
Some Lovin'	7"	President	PT207	1968	£1.50	£4	

BROWNHILL'S STAMP DUTY
Maxwell's Silver Hammer	7"	Columbia	DB8625	1969	£2	£5	

BROWNS
In The Country	7" EP	RCA	RCX187	1960	£4	£8	
Margo	7"	RCA	RCA1193	1960	£1.50	£4	
Scarlet Ribbons	7"	RCA	RCA1157	1959	£1.50	£4	
Send Me The Pillow You Dream On	7"	RCA	RCA1218	1960	£1.50	£4	
Sweet Sounds By The Browns	LP	RCA	RD27153/SF5052	1959	£5	£12	
Teen Ex	7"	RCA	RCA1176	1960	£1.50	£4	
Three Bells	7"	RCA	RCA1140	1959	£1.50	£4	chart single

BROWNSVILLE STATION
Brownsville Station	LP	Palladium	P1004	1970	£6	£15	US

BROX, VICTOR & ANNETTE
Rollin' Back	LP	Sonet	SNTF663	1974	£6	£15	
Wake Me And Shake Me	7"	Fontana	TF536	1965	£2.50	£6	

BRUBECK, DAVE
At Storyville	LP	Philips	BBL7018	1955	£6	£15	
Bernstein Plays Brubeck Plays Bernstein	LP	Fontana	TFL5114/STFL542	1960	£4	£10	
Best Of Brubeck	LP	Fontana	TFL5136	1961	£4	£10	
Brubeck And Rushing	LP	Fontana	TFL5126/STFL550	1961	£4	£10	
Dave Brubeck	LP	Philips	BBL7116	1957	£5	£12	
Dave Brubeck And Jay And Kai At Newport	LP	Philips	BBL7147	1957	£6	£15	with J.J.Johnson & Kai Winding
Dave Brubeck Quartet	LP	Philips	BBL7041	1955	£6	£15	
Dave Brubeck Quartet	LP	Philips	BBL7060	1956	£6	£15	
Dave Brubeck Quartet	LP	Vogue	LAE12105	1959	£4	£10	
Dave Brubeck Quartet	10" LP	Vogue	LDE095	1954	£10	£25	
Dave Brubeck Quartet Featuring Paul Desmond	LP	Vogue	LAE12114	1959	£6	£15	
Dave Brubeck Quartet Vol.2	10" LP	Vogue	LDE104	1954	£10	£25	
Dave Brubeck Quartet Vol.3	10" LP	Vogue	LDE114	1955	£10	£25	
Dave Brubeck Trio	10" LP	Vogue	LDE090	1954	£10	£25	
Dave Digs Disney	LP	Fontana	TFL5017	1957	£5	£12	
Fabulous Trio And Octet	LP	Vogue	LAE12008	1956	£8	£20	
Gone With The Wind	LP	Fontana	TFL5071/STFL501	1959	£5	£12	
Gone With The Wind	LP	Fontana	TFL5071	1960	£4	£10	
In Europe	LP	Fontana	TFL5034	1959	£4	£10	
Jazz At Oberlin	LP	Vogue	LAE12048	1957	£8	£20	
Jazz At The Black Hawk	LP	Vogue	LAE12094	1958	£5	£12	
Jazz At The College Of The Pacific	LP	Vogue	LAE12110	1960	£5	£12	
Jazz Goes To College	LP	Philips	BBL7447	1960	£4	£10	
Jazz Goes To Junior College	LP	Fontana	TFL5002	1958	£5	£12	

MUSIC MASTER PRICE GUIDE

Title	Format	Label	Catalogue	Year	Price1	Price2	Notes
Jazz Impressions Of Eurasia	LP	Fontana	TFL5051	1959	£4	£10	
Jazz Impressions Of The USA	LP	Philips	BBL7171	1957	£5	£12	
Newport 1958	LP	Fontana	TFL5059	1959	£4	£10	
Riddle	LP	Fontana	TFL5101/STFL532.	1960	£4	£10	
Southern Scene	LP	Fontana	TFL5099/STFL530.	1960	£4	£10	
Take Five	7"	Fontana	H339	1961	£1.50	£4	
Time Further Out	LP	CBS	BPG62078	1962	£4	£10	
Time In	LP	CBS	62757	1966	£4	£10	
Time Out	LP	Fontana	TFL5085/STFL523.	1960	£5	£12	
Tonight Only!	LP	Fontana	STFL566	1961	£4	£10	.. with Carmen McRae

BRUCE, JACK

As a member of the Graham Bond Organisation, John Mayall's Bluesbreakers (briefly), and Cream, Jack Bruce was perhaps the first rock bass player to attract notice for the excellence of his musicianship. At the same time, he was playing jazz with the likes of Mike Taylor, Mike Gibbs, and John McLaughlin, as well as developing a fruitful song-writing partnership with poet Pete Brown. The solo albums from 1969 and 1971 (as well as the impressive "Out Of The Storm" from 1974) combine all these talents in magnificent manner and make it all the more a matter of regret that Bruce's career since then has largely consisted of a catalogue of lost opportunities.

Title	Format	Label	Catalogue	Year	Price1	Price2	Notes
Consul At Sunset	7"	Polydor	2058153	1971	£2	£5	
Harmony Row	LP	Polydor	2310107	1971	£4	£10	
I'm Gettin' Tired	7"	Polydor	56036	1965	£15	£30	
Songs For A Tailor	LP	Polydor	583058	1969	£5	£12	chart LP
Things We Like	LP	Polydor	2343033	1970	£5	£12	

BRUCE, LENNY

Title	Format	Label	Catalogue	Year	Price1	Price2	Notes
Berkeley Concert	LP	Transatlantic	TRA195	1969	£10	£25	double
Best Of Lenny Bruce	LP	Fantasy	7012	1962	£8	£20	US
Essential Lenny Bruce	LP	Douglas	SD788	1968	£6	£15	US
I Am Not A Nut, Elect Me	LP	Fantasy	7007	1960	£8	£20	US
Interviews Of Our Times	LP	Fantasy	7001	1959	£8	£20	US
Law, Language And Lenny Bruce	LP	Spector	SP9101	1974	£6	£15	US
Lenny Bruce	LP	United Artists	UAL3580	1967	£6	£15	US
Lenny Bruce, American	LP	Fantasy	7011	1962	£8	£20	US
Lenny Bruce Is Out Again	LP	Philles	PHLP4010	1966	£30	£60	US
Live At The Curran Theatre	LP	Fantasy	34201	1972	£6	£15	US
Midnight Concert	LP	United Artists	UAS6794	197-	£6	£15	US
Sick Humor Of Lenny Bruce	LP	Fantasy	7003	1959	£8	£20	US
Thank You, Masked Man	LP	Fantasy	7017	1972	£6	£15	US

BRUCE, TOMMY

Title	Format	Label	Catalogue	Year	Price1	Price2	Notes
Ain't Misbehaving	7"	Columbia	DB4453	1960	£1.50	£4	chart single
Babette	7"	Columbia	DB4776	1962	£1.50	£4	
Boom Boom	7"	Polydor	BM56006	1965	£2	£8	
Broken Doll	7"	Columbia	DB4498	1960	£2	£5	chart single
Buttons And Bows	7"	Columbia	DB4927	1962	£1.50	£4	
Horror Movies	7"	Columbia	DB4850	1962	£1.50	£4	
I'm Crazy About My Baby	7"	Columbia	DB4581	1961	£1.50	£4	
Knockout	7" EP	Columbia	SEG8077	1961	£15	£30	
Lavender Blue	7"	Columbia	DB7132	1963	£1.50	£4	
Let It Be Me	7"	Columbia	DB7241	1964	£1.50	£4	
Let's Do It, Let's Fall In Love	7"	Columbia	DB7025	1963	£1.50	£4	
Love, Honour And Oh Baby!	7"	Columbia	DB4682	1961	£1.50	£4	
Monster Gonzales	7"	RCA	RCA1535	1966	£1.50	£4	
My Little Girl	7"	Columbia	DB4532	1960	£1.50	£4	
Over Suzanne	7"	Columbia	DB7387	1964	£1.50	£4	

BRUFORD, BILL

Title	Format	Label	Catalogue	Year	Price1	Price2
Bruford Tapes	LP	Canadian Imps	BRUBOOT28	1980	£4	£10
Feels Good To Me	LP	Polydor	2302075	1978	£4	£10
Gradually Going Tornado	LP	EG	EGLP104	1980	£4	£10
One Of A Kind	LP	Polydor	POLD5020	1979	£4	£10

BRUISERS

Title	Format	Label	Catalogue	Year	Price1	Price2	Notes
Blue Girl	7"	Parlophone	R5042	1963	£2	£5	chart single
Your Turn To Cry	7"	Parlophone	R5092	1963	£2	£5	

BRUMBEATS

Title	Format	Label	Catalogue	Year	Price1	Price2
Cry Little Girl, Cry	7"	Decca	F11834	1964	£6	£12

BRUMMELL, BEAU

Title	Format	Label	Catalogue	Year	Price1	Price2
Better Man Than I	7"	Columbia	DB7675	1965	£4	£8
I Know Know Know	7"	Columbia	DB7447	1965	£4	£8
Next Kiss	7"	Columbia	DB7538	1965	£4	£8
Take Me Like I Am	7"	Columbia	DB7878	1966	£2	£5

BRUNNING HALL SUNFLOWER BLUES BAND

Saga was a bargain-priced label, specialising in cheaply produced cash-ins of the prevailing trends. The Brunning Hall Band was Saga's blues band, and by having their records released on the label, the group was fighting a losing battle from the outset with regard to being taken as serious rivals for the likes of Fleetwood Mac or Savoy Brown. In fact, Bob Brunning had been the original bass player with Fleetwood Mac (and plays on one track on the group's debut LP), while Bob Hall played piano on all Savoy Brown's early records, albeit without ever being counted as a member of the group.

Title	Format	Label	Catalogue	Year	Price1	Price2
Bullen Street Blues	LP	Boulevard	4032	1971	£4	£10
Bullen Street Blues	LP	Saga	FID2118	1968	£6	£15
I Wish You Would	LP	Saga	SAGA8150	1970	£20	£40
Sunflower Blues Band	LP	Gemini	GM2010	1969	£25	£50
Trackside Blues	LP	Saga	EROS8132	1969	£10	£25

BRUTE FORCE

Title	Format	Label	Catalogue	Year	Price1	Price2
King Of Fuh	7"	Apple	8	1969	£250	£400

BRYAN & THE BRUNELLES

Title	Format	Label	Catalogue	Year	Price1	Price2
Jacqueline	7"	HMV	POP1394	1965	£12.50	£25

104

BRYAN, CANNONBALL
Man About The Town	7"	Amalgamated	AMG829	1968	£4	£8	Hugh Malcolm B side
Red Ash	7"	Trojan	TR673	1969	£2	£5	Silvertones B side

BRYAN, CARL
Run For Your Life	7"	Camel	CA22	1969	£1.50	£4	Two Sparks B side

BRYAN, DORA
All I Want For Christmas Is A Beatle	7"	Fontana	TF427	1963	£1.50	£4	chart single

BRYAN, FITZVAUGHN ORCHESTRA
Evening News	7"	Melodisc	1560	1960	£2.50	£6

BRYAN, WES
Honey Baby	7"	London	HLU8978	1959	£12.50	£25
Lonesome Lover	7"	London	HLU8607	1958	£6	£12

BRYANT, ANITA
Do Re Mi	7"	London	HLL9353	1961	£1.50	£4	
In My Little Corner Of The World	LP	London	HAL2381	1961	£8	£20	
Kisses Sweeter Than Wine	7" EP	CBS	AGG20005	1962	£2	£5	
Little George	7"	London	HLL9075	1960	£1.50	£4	
My Little Corner Of The World	7"	London	HLL9171	1960	£1.50	£4	chart single
My Mind's Playing Tricks On Me Again	7"	CBS	202026	1966	£12.50	£25	
One Of The Lucky Ones	7"	London	HLL9219	1960	£1.50	£4	
Paper Roses	7"	London	HLL9114	1960	£1.50	£4	chart single
Six Boys And Seven Girls	7"	London	HLL8983	1959	£1.50	£4	
Till There Was You	7"	London	HLL9281	1961	£1.50	£4	
Wonderland By Night	7"	London	HLL9247	1960	£1.50	£4	

BRYANT, DENIS
Soul Man	7"	Discreet	K19204	1975	£1.50	£4

BRYANT, LAURA K.
Bobby	7"	London	HLU8551	1958	£4	£8

BRYANT, MARIE
Calypso's Too Hot To Handle	7" EP	Kalypso	XXEP7	1963	£4	£8
Don't Touch Me Nylons	LP	Melodisc	MLP132	196-	£6	£15
Don't Touch My Nylon	7"	Kalypso	XX28	1961	£1.50	£4
Water Melon	7"	Kalypso	XX27	1961	£1.50	£4

BRYANT, RAY
Alone With The Blues	LP	Esquire	32106	1960	£8	£20
Ray Bryant Trio	LP	Esquire	32066	1958	£10	£25

BRYANT, RUSTY
All Night Long	LP	Dot	DLP3006	1956	£8	£20	US
Rock'n'Roll With Rusty Bryant	10" LP	London	HBD1066	1956	£15	£30	

BRYANT, SANDRA
Girl With Money	7"	Major Minor	MM523	1967	£1.50	£4
Out To Get You	7"	Major Minor	MM553	1968	£4	£8

BRYARS, GAVIN
Sinking Of The Titanic/Jesus Blood	LP	Obscure	OBS1	1975	£5	£12

BRYCE, CALUM
Love Maker	7"	Condor	PS1001	1968	£15	£30

BRYDEN, BERYL
Casey Jones	7"	Decca	F10823	1956	£4	£8
I'm Movin' On	7"	Columbia	DB4860	1962	£1.50	£4
I've Been Living With The Blues	7"	Columbia	DB7010	1963	£1.50	£4

BRYE, BETSY
Sleep Walk	7"	Columbia	DB4350	1959	£1.50	£4

BUBBLE PUPPY
Gathering Of Promises	LP	International Artists	IALP10	1969	£15	£30	US

BUBBLEGUM
Little Red Bucket	7"	Philips	BF1677	1968	£2	£5

BUBBLES
Bopping In The Barnyard	7"	Duke	DK1001	1963	£4	£8

BUCHANAN BROTHERS
Medicine Man	LP	Event	ES101	1969	£5	£12	US
Son Of A Lovin' Man	7"	Page One	POF154	1969	£1.50	£4	

BUCHANAN, ROY
In The Beginning	LP	Polydor	PD6035	1975	£4	£10	US
Live Stock	LP	Polydor	2391192	1975	£4	£10	
Loading Zone	LP	Polydor	2391295	1977	£4	£10	
Rescue Me	LP	Polydor	2391152	1975	£4	£10	
Roy Buchanan	LP	Polydor	2391042	1972	£5	£12	
Roy Buchanan	LP	Polydor	2482275	1976	£4	£10	
Second Album	LP	Polydor	2391062	1973	£5	£12	

Street Called Straight	LP	Polydor	2391233	1976	£4	£10	
That's What I'm Here For	LP	Polydor	2391114	1974	£4	£10	
You're Not Alone	LP	Atlantic	SD19170	1978	£4	£10	US

BUCKINGHAM-NICKS

Lindsey Buckingham and Stevie Nicks achieved little success with their LP, yet its sound is almost exactly that of the LPs "Fleetwood Mac" and "Rumours", with which the Buckingham-Nicks team managed so spectacularly to restore Fleetwood Mac's fortunes. The earlier LP was reissued in 1981, when it might have been expected to do very well, and yet once again the record sank without a trace.

Buckingham-Nicks	LP	Polydor	2391093	1973	£17.50	£35	
Buckingham-Nicks	LP	Polydor	2482378	1981	£10	£25	
Don't Let Me Down Again	7"	Polydor	2066398	1974	£2.50	£6	
Don't Let Me Down Again	7"	Polydor	2066700	1976	£1.50	£4	

BUCKINGHAMS

Back In Love Again	7"	CBS	3559	1968	£1.50	£4	
Don't You Care	7"	CBS	2640	1968	£6	£12	
Greatest Hits	LP	Columbia	CS9812	1969	£5	£12	US
Hey Baby	7"	CBS	2995	1967	£1.50	£4	
I Call Your Name	7"	Stateside	SS529	1966	£1.50	£4	
In One Ear And Gone Tomorrow	LP	Columbia	CS9703	1968	£5	£12	US
Kind Of A Drag	LP	USA	107	1967	£6	£15	US
Kind Of A Drag	LP	USA	107	1967	£8	£20	US, with 'I'm A Man'
Kind Of A Drag	7"	Stateside	SS588	1967	£1.50	£4	
Kind Of A Drag	7" EP	Columbia	ESRF1841	1967	£7.50	£15	French
Making Up And Breaking Up	7"	Stateside	SS2011	1967	£1.50	£4	
Mercy Mercy Mercy	7"	CBS	2859	1967	£2	£5	
Portraits	LP	Columbia	CL2798/CS9598	1968	£5	£12	US
Susan	7"	CBS	3195	1967	£1.50	£4	
Time And Charges	LP	Columbia	CL2669/CS9469	1967	£5	£12	US

BUCKINGHAMS (2)

I'll Never Hurt You No More	7"	Pye	7N15848	1965	£2.50	£6	
To Be Or Not To Be	7"	Pye	7N15921	1965	£2.50	£6	

BUCKLE, BOB

Come Listen To Bob Buckle	LP	Ash	ALP1075	1973	£5	£12	

BUCKLEY, SEAN & THE BREADCRUMBS

It Hurts Me When I Cry	7"	Stateside	SS421	1965	£20	£40	

BUCKLEY, TIM

Aren't You The Girl	7"	Elektra	EKSN45008	1967	£2	£5	
Blue Afternoon	LP	Straight	STS1060	1969	£10	£25	
Goodbye And Hello	LP	Elektra	EKL/EKS318	1967	£6	£15	
Greetings From L.A.	LP	Warner Bros	K46176	1972	£4	£10	
Happy Sad	LP	Elektra	EKS74045	1968	£8	£20	
Happy Time	7"	Straight	4799	1970	£1.50	£4	
Look At The Fool	LP	Discreet	K59204	1974	£4	£10	
Lorca	LP	Elektra	2410005	1970	£8	£20	
Morning Glory	7"	Elektra	EKSN45018	1967	£2	£5	
Once I Was	7"	Elektra	EKSN45023	1968	£2	£5	
Pleasant Street	7"	Elektra	EKSN45041	1968	£2	£5	
Sefronia	LP	Discreet	K49201	1973	£4	£10	
Starsailor	LP	Straight	STS1064	1970	£8	£20	
Tim Buckley	LP	Elektra	EKL/EKS4004	1966	£8	£20	
Wings	7"	Elektra	EKSN45031	1968	£2	£5	

BUCKNER, MILT

Rockin' Hammond	10" LP	Capitol	T722	1956	£5	£12	
Rocking With Milt	7" EP	Capitol	EAP1000	1956	£2	£5	

BUCKNER, TEDDY

Dixieland Jubilee	10" LP	Vogue	LDE175	1956	£4	£10	
Salute To Louis Armstrong	LP	Vogue	LAE12129	1958	£4	£10	
Teddy Buckner	LP	Vogue	LAE12026	1957	£4	£10	

BUCKY & THE STRINGS

Lolitas On The Loose	7"	Salvo	SLO1807	1962	£2	£5	

BUDD, BILLY

Why Can't It Rain	7"	Page One	POF099	1968	£1.50	£4	

BUDD, HAROLD

Pavilion Of Dreams	LP	Obscure	OBS10	1978	£4	£10	

BUDD, ROY

Birth Of The Budd	7"	Pye	7N15807	1965	£1.50	£4	

BUDDIES

Buddies And The Compacts	LP	Wing	MGW12293/SRW16293	1965	£8	£20	US
Go Go	LP	Wing	MGW12306/SRW16306	1965	£6	£15	US

BUDGIE

Bandolier	LP	MCA	MCF2723	1975	£4	£10	chart LP
Budgie	LP	MCA	MCF2506	1974	£4	£10	
Budgie	LP	MCA	MKPS2018	1971	£10	£25	
Crash Course In Brain Surgery	7"	MCA	MK5072	1971	£2.50	£6	
If I Was Britannia I'd Waive The Rules	LP	A&M	AMLH68377	1976	£4	£10	
If Swallowed Do Not Induce Vomiting	12"	Active	BUDGIE1	1980	£2.50	£6	

Impeckable	LP	A&M	AMLH64675	1978	£4	£10	
In For The Kill	LP	MCA	MCF2546	1974	£4	£10	chart L
Never Turn Your Back On A Friend	LP	MCA	MCG3513	1974	£4	£10	
Never Turn Your Back On A Friend	LP	MCA	MDKS8010	1973	£5	£12	
Squawk	LP	MCA	MCF2502	1974	£5	£12	
Squawk	LP	MCA	MKPS2023	1972	£6	£15	
Whisky River	7"	MCA	MK5085	1972	£1.50	£4	

BUENA VISTAS

Hot Shot	7"	Stateside	SS525	1966	£6	£12	

BUFFALO

Dead Forever	LP	Vertigo		1974	£30	£60	
Mother's Choice	LP	Vertigo		197-	£30	£60	
Only Want You For Your Body	LP			197-	£30	£60	
Volcanic Rock	LP			197-	£30	£60	

BUFFALO (2)

Battle Torn Heroes	7"	Heavy Metal	HEAVY3	1981	£2	£5	
Mean Machine	7"	Heavy Metal	HEAVY15	1982	£2.50	£6	

BUFFALO NICKEL JUGBAND

Buffalo Nickel Jugband	LP	Happy Tiger	1018	1971	£6	£15	US

BUFFALO SPRINGFIELD

The uneasy alliance that existed between Buffalo Springfield's three major talents - Neil Young, Steve Stills, and Ritchie Furay - meant that the group was never destined to last very long. The competition, however, inspired the three into producing some particularly inventive material, which turns "Buffalo Springfield Again" into one of the key albums of the late sixties. By comparison, the eponymous first album is strictly formative, while "Last Time Around", released when the group had already split apart, suffers from being compiled from the material that the three song-writers did not particularly want to keep for their next projects.

Beginning	LP	Atlantic	K30028	1973	£4	£10	
Best Of/Retrospective	LP	Atlantic	K40071	1972	£4	£10	
Bluebird	7"	Atlantic	K10237	1972	£2	£5	PS
Buffalo Springfield	LP	Atlantic	587/588070	1967	£10	£25	
Buffalo Springfield	LP	Atlantic	587/588070	1967	£20	£40	with 'Baby Don't Scold Me'
Buffalo Springfield	LP	Atlantic	K70001	1973	£6	£15	double
Buffalo Springfield Again	LP	Atlantic	587/588091	1968	£6	£15	
Buffalo Springfield Again	LP	Atlantic	K40014	1971	£4	£10	
Expecting To Fly	LP	Atlantic	2462012	1970	£4	£10	
Expecting To Fly	7"	Atlantic	584165	1968	£2	£5	
For What It's Worth	7"	Atlantic	584077	1967	£2	£5	
For What It's Worth	7" EP.	Atco	123	1967	£12.50	£25	French
Last Time Around	LP	Atco	228024	1969	£8	£20	
Last Time Around	LP	Atlantic	K40077	1971	£6	£15	
Pretty Girl Why	7"	Atco	226006	1969	£2	£5	
Retrospective	LP	Atco	228012	1969	£5	£12	
Rock'n'Roll Woman	7"	Atlantic	584145	1967	£2	£5	
Uno Mundo	7"	Atlantic	584189	1968	£2	£5	

BUFFOONS

My World Fell Down	7"	Columbia	DB8317	1967	£2.50	£6	

BUGGS

Beetle Beat	LP	Coronet	212	1964	£6	£15	US

BULAWAYO SWEET RHYTHMS BAND

Skokiaan	7"	Decca	F10350	1954	£1.50	£4	

BULL

This Is Bull	LP	Paramount	PAS5028	1970	£15	£30	US

BULL, SANDY

Like a one-man Incredible String Band, Sandy Bull gathers together an impressive collection of exotic instruments for his records. He then proceeds, however, to make some rather prosaic music with them - very simple and very long blues-based instrumentals. They are pleasant enough, but the lack of imagination displayed, given the potential of the resources, is frustrating.

E Pluribus Unum	LP	Vanguard	SVRL19040	1969	£5	£12	
Inventions	LP	Vanguard	VSD79191	1965	£6	£15	US

BULLDOG BREED

Made In England	LP	Nova	(S)DN5	1970	£10	£25	
Portcullis Gate	7"	Deram	DM270	1969	£10	£20	

BULLDOGS

John, Paul, George, and Ringo	7"	Mercury	MF808	1964	£4	£8	

BULLET

Hobo	7"	Purple	PUR101	1971	£1.50	£4	

BULLY WEE BAND

Bully Wee	LP	Folksound	FS102AB	1975	£10	£25	
Enchanted Lady	LP	Red Rag	RRR007	1976	£6	£15	
Madmen Of Gotham	LP	Red Rag		1981	£8	£20	
Silvermines	LP	Red Rag	RRR017	1978	£6	£15	

BUMBLE, B. & THE STINGERS

Apple Knocker	7"	Stateside	SS113	1962	£1.50	£4	
Baby Mash	7"	Stateside	SS192	1963	£1.50	£4	
Bumble Boogie	7"	Top Rank	JAR561	1961	£1.50	£4	
Dawn Cracker	7"	Stateside	SS131	1962	£1.50	£4	
Nut Rocker	7"	Top Rank	JAR611	1962	£1.50	£4	chart single
Nut Rocker	7" EP.	Pathe	EMF316	1962	£7.50	£15	French

Piano Stylings Of B.Bumble	7" EP..	Stateside	SE1001	1962	£7.50	£15	
Silent Movies	7"	Mercury	MF977	1967	£2	£5	

BUNCH
The Bunch was not a real group as such, but rather members and friends of Fairport Convention on holiday. "Rock On" contains their versions of a number of rock'n'roll classics - and it has to be admitted that once the novelty of hearing these particular musicians tackling this kind of material has worn off, the results are not especially impressive.

Rock On	LP	Island	ILPS9189	1972	£10	£25	with flexi

BUNCH (2)

Birthday	7"	CBS	3692	1968	£5	£10
Birthday	7"	CBS	3709	1968	£2.50	£6
Spare A Shilling	7"	CBS	3060	1967	£20	£40
You Can't Do This	7"	CBS	2740	1967	£4	£8
You Never Came Home	7"	CBS	202506	1967	£15	£30

BUNCH OF FIVES

Go Home Baby	7"	Parlophone	R5494	1966	£7.50	£15

BUNN, ROGER

Piece Of Mind	LP	Major Minor	SMLP70	1971	£6	£15

BUNNIES

Thumper	7"	Decca	F12350	1966	£2.50	£6

BUNNY & RUDDY

On The Town	7"	Nu Beat	NB011	1968	£4	£8	.. Monty Morris B side
True Romance	7"	Nu Beat	NB007	1968	£4	£8	Bobby Kalphat B side

BUNTING, BOB

You've Got To Go Down This Way	LP	Transatlantic	TRA166	1968	£8	£20

BUNYAN, VASHTI

Just Another Diamond Day	LP	Philips	6308019	1971	£150	£250

BURCHETTE, WILBURN

Guitar Grimoire	LP	Burchette		1973	£50	£100	US
Mind Storm	LP	Burchette		1977	£50	£100	US
Music Of The Godhead	LP	Burchette		1975	£50	£100	US
Occult Concert	LP	Ames		1971	£50	£100	US
Opens The Seven Gates	LP	Ebos		1972	£50	£100	US
Psychic Meditation Music	LP	Burchette		1974	£50	£100	US
Transcendental Music	LP	Burchette		1976	£50	£100	US

BURDON, ERIC

Guilty	LP	United Artists ..	UAG29251	1971	£5	£12	with Jimmy Witherspoon

BURDON, ERIC & THE ANIMALS

Eric Is Here	LP	MGM	(S)E4433	1967	£8	£20	US
Everyone Of Us	LP	MGM	(S)E4553	1968	£6	£15	US
Good Times	7"	MGM	MGM1344	1967	£1.50	£4	chart single
Hey Gyp	7" EP..	Barclay	071121	1967	£6	£12	French
Love Is	LP	MGM	2619002	1971	£8	£20	double
Love Is	LP	MGM	CS8105	1968	£5	£12	
Love Is	LP	MGM	SE4591/2	1968	£10	£25	US double
Monterey	7"	MGM	MGM1412	1968	£1.50	£4	
Ring Of Fire	7"	MGM	MGM1461	1969	£1.50	£4	chart single
River Deep Mountain High	7"	MGM	MGM1481	1969	£1.50	£4	
San Franciscan Nights	7"	MGM	MGM1359	1967	£1.50	£4	chart single
See See Rider	7" EP..	Barclay	071081	1966	£6	£12	French
Sky Pilot	7"	MGM	MGM1373	1968	£1.50	£4	chart single
Twain Shall Meet	LP	MGM	CS8074	1968	£6	£15	
When I Was Young	7"	MGM	MGM1340	1967	£1.50	£4	chart single
Winds Of Change	LP	MGM	2354001	1971	£4	£10	
Winds Of Change	LP	MGM	C(S)8052	1967	£6	£15	

BURDON, ERIC & WAR

Blackman's Burdon	LP	Liberty	LDS8400	1970	£6	£15	double
Eric Burdon Declares War	LP	Polydor	2310041	1970	£4	£10	

BURGESS, DAVE

I Love Paris	7"	London	HLB8175	1955	£7.50	£15
I'm Available	7"	Oriole	CB1413	1957	£25	£50

BURGESS, JOHN

King Of Highland Pipers	LP	Topic	12T199	1969	£6	£15

BURGESS, SONNY

Sadie's Back In Town	7"	London	HLS9064	1960	£50	£100

BURKE, JOE, ANDY MCGANN & FELIX DOLAN

Tribute To Michael Coleman	LP	Shaskeen	05360	1970	£8	£20

BURKE, KEVIN & JACKIE DALY

Eavesdropper	LP	Mulligan	LUN039	1981	£6	£15	Irish

BURKE, KEVIN & MICHAEL O DOMHNAILL

Promenade	LP	Mulligan	LUN028	1979	£6	£15	Irish

BURKE, SOLOMON

Baby Come On Home	7"	Atlantic	AT4073	1966	£2	£5

Best Of Solomon Burke	LP	Atlantic	587/588016	1966	£6	£15	
Can't Nobody Love You	7"	London	HLK9763	1963	£4	£8	
Cry To Me	7"	London	HLK9512	1962	£5	£10	
Down In The Valley	7"	London	HLK9560	1962	£4	£8	
Everybody Needs Somebody To Love	7"	Atlantic	AT4004	1964	£4	£8	
Greatest	LP	London	HAK8018	1963	£8	£20	
He'll Have To Go	7"	London	HLK9849	1964	£4	£8	
I Feel A Sin Comin' On	7"	Atlantic	584005	1966	£1.50	£4	
I Wish I Knew	LP	Atlantic	587/588117	1968	£6	£15	
I Wish I Knew	7"	Atlantic	584191	1968	£2	£5	
If You Need Me	LP	Atlantic	(SD)8085	1963	£10	£25	US
If You Need Me	7"	London	HLK9715	1963	£4	£8	
Just Out Of Reach	7"	London	HLK9454	1961	£7.50	£15	
Keep A Light In The Window	7"	Atlantic	584100	1967	£1.50	£4	
Keep Lookin'	7"	Atlantic	584026	1966	£1.50	£4	
King Of Rock'n'Soul	LP	Atlantic	590004	1966	£6	£15	
King Solomon	LP	Atlantic	587105	1968	£6	£15	
Maggie's Farm	7"	Atlantic	AT4030	1965	£2.50	£6	
More Rocking Soul	7"	Atlantic	AT4014	1964	£4	£8	
Only Love	7"	Atlantic	AT4061	1965	£2.50	£6	
Peepin'	7"	Atlantic	AT4022	1965	£2.50	£6	
Proud Mary	LP	Bell	MBLL/SBLL118	1969	£5	£12	
Proud Mary	7"	Bell	BLL1062	1969	£1.50	£4	
Rock'n'Soul	LP	Atlantic	ATL5009	1964	£10	£25	
Rock'n'Soul	7" EP	Atlantic	AET6008	1965	£7.50	£15	
Save It	7"	Atlantic	584204	1968	£1.50	£4	
Solomon Burke	LP	Apollo	ALP498	1962	£20	£40	US
Someone Is Watching	7"	Atlantic	AT4044	1965	£2.50	£6	
Someone To Love	7"	London	HLK9887	1964	£4	£8	
Take Me	7"	Atlantic	584122	1967	£1.50	£4	
Tonight My Heart She Is Crying	7" EP	London	REK1379	1963	£10	£20	
Uptight Good Woman	7"	Bell	BLL1047	1968	£1.50	£4	

BURKE, SONNY

Auntie Mame Theme	7"	Brunswick	05781	1959	£1.50	£4	
Phffft Mambo	7"	Brunswick	05361	1955	£1.50	£4	
Pride And The Passion	7"	Brunswick	05706	1957	£1.50	£4	

BURKE, SONNY (2)

Blue Island	7"	Blue Beat	BB363	1965	£5	£10	
Choo Choo Train	7"	Island	WI3082	1967	£5	£10	Ken Parker B side
Dance With Me	7"	Black Swan	WI470	1965	£5	£10	
Glad	7"	Black Swan	WI469	1965	£5	£10	
Grandpa	7"	Island	WI221	1965	£5	£10	
Have Faith	7"	Ska Beat	JB272	1967	£5	£10	
Life Without Fun	7"	Island	WI134	1963	£5	£10	
Rudy Girl	7"	Island	WI3040	1967	£5	£10	Bob Andy B side
Sounds Of Sonny Burke	LP	Island	ILP972	1968	£25	£50	
Wicked People	7"	Black Swan	WI471	1965	£5	£10	
You Rule My Heart	7"	Island	WI3022	1966	£5	£10	Gaylads B side

BURKE, VINNIE

String Jazz Quartet	LP	HMV	CLP1163	1958	£6	£15	
Vinnie Burke All Stars	LP	HMV	CLP1217	1958	£6	£15	

BURLAND, DAVE

Dalesman's Litany	LP	Trailer	LER2029	1971	£6	£15	
Dave Burland	LP	Trailer	LER2082	1972	£6	£15	
Double Take	LP	Rubber	RUB012/036	1980	£10	£25	double
Rollin'	LP	Moonraker	MOO6	1985		£12	
Songs And Buttered Haycocks	LP	Rubber	RUB012	1975	£6	£15	
You Can't Fool The Fat Man	LP	Rubber	RUB036	1979	£6	£15	

BURLAND, DAVE, TONY CAPSTICK & DICK GAUGHAN

Songs Of Ewan MacColl	LP	Rubber	RUB027	1978	£5	£12	

BURLAND, SACHA

Hole In My Soul	7"	Philips	PB1152	1961	£1.50	£4	

BURMOE BROTHERS

Skin	12"	Some Bizarre	WBY121	1985	£2.50	£6	

BURNEL, JEAN-JACQUES

Euroman Cometh	LP	Mau Mau	PMAU601	1988	£4	£10	pic disc

BURNEL, J.J.

Girl From The Snow Country	7"	United Artists	BP361	1980	£100	£200	

BURNETTE, DORSEY

Dorsey Burnette	LP	London	HAD8050	1963	£20	£40	
Dorsey Burnette Sings	7" EP	London	RED1402	1963	£12.50	£25	
Greatest Hits	LP	Era	ES800	1969	£6	£15	US
Greatest Love	7"	Liberty	LIB15190	1969	£2.50	£6	
Hey Little One	7"	London	HLN9160	1960	£5	£10	
It's No Sin	7"	London	HLN9365	1961	£4	£8	
Jimmy Brown	7"	Tamla Motown	TMG534	1965	£20	£40	
Tall Oak Tree	LP	Era	EL(S)102	1960	£37.50	£75	US
Tall Oak Tree	7"	London	HLN9047	1960	£5	£10	

BURNETTE, JAN

All At Once	7"	Oriole	CB1742	1962	£1.50	£4	

Boy I Used To Know	7"	Oriole	CB1807	1963	£1.50	£4	
Could Have Loved You So Well	7"	Oriole	CB1716	1962	£1.50	£4	
Let Me Make You Smile Again	7"	Oriole	CB1905	1964	£1.50	£4	
Love, Let Me Not Hunger	7"	Oriole	CB1949	1964	£1.50	£4	
Teddy	7"	Oriole	CB1761	1962	£1.50	£4	
Till I Hear The Truth From You	7"	Oriole	CB1841	1963	£1.50	£4	
Too Young	7"	Oriole	CB1920	1964	£1.50	£4	

BURNETTE, JOHNNY

Johnny Burnette's original rock 'n' roll trio played rockabilly to rival that of Elvis Presley's. Like Presley, however, Burnette rapidly descended into trite pop music - there is simply no comparison between "You're Sixteen" and "Train Kept A-Rollin". Not for nothing has the latter song inspired furious cover versions by the Yardbirds and Motorhead.

All Week Long	7"	Capitol	CL15322	1963	£4	£8	
Big Big World	7" EP	London	REG1309	1961	£20	£40	
Clown Shoes	7"	Liberty	LIB55416	1962	£1.50	£4	chart single
Damn The Defiant	7"	Liberty	LIB55489	1962	£1.50	£4	
Dreamin'	LP	London	HAG2306	1961	£25	£50	
Dreamin'	LP	Sunset	SLS50007	1969	£4	£10	
Dreamin'	7"	Liberty	LIB10235	1966	£1.50	£4	
Dreamin'	7"	London	HLG9172	1960	£2.50	£6	chart single
Dreamin'	7" EP	London	REG1263	1960	£20	£40	
Eager Beaver Baby	7"	Vogue Coral	Q72283	1957	£75	£150	
Fool	7"	London	HLG9473	1961	£2.50	£6	
Four By Johnny Burnette	7" EP	Capitol	EAP120645	1964	£15	£30	
Girls	7"	London	HLG9388	1961	£1.50	£4	chart single
God, Country And My Baby	7"	London	HLG9453	1961	£1.50	£4	
Hit After Hit	7" EP	Liberty	LEP2091	1963	£7.50	£15	
Hits And Other Favourites	LP	Liberty	LBY1006	1961	£10	£25	
I Wanna Thank Your Folks	7"	Pye	7N25158	1962	£1.50	£4	
I'm The One Who Loves You	7"	Pye	7N25187	1963	£1.50	£4	
Johnny Burnette	7" EP	London	REG1327	1961	£20	£40	
Johnny Burnette Sings	LP	London	HAG2375	1961	£25	£50	
Johnny Burnette Sings	LP	London	SAHG6175	1961	£30	£60	stereo
Johnny Burnette Story	LP	Liberty	LBY1231	1964	£20	£40	
Johnny Burnette/You're 16	LP	London	HAG2349	1961	£25	£50	
Little Boy Sad	7"	London	HLG9315	1961	£1.50	£4	chart single
Little Boy Sad	7" EP	London	REG1291	1961	£20	£40	
Lonesome Train	7"	Vogue Coral	Q72227	1957	£75	£150	
Rock'n'Roll Trio	LP	Ace Of Hearts	AH120	1966	£10	£25	
Rock'n'Roll Trio	LP	Coral	CP61	1971	£5	£12	
Rock'n'Roll Trio	LP	Coral	CRL57080	1956	£400	£600	US
Rock'n'Roll Trio	10" LP	Coral	LVC10041	1956	£180	£300	
Roses Are Red	LP	Liberty	LRP3255/LST7255	1962	£10	£25	US
Setting The Woods On Fire	7"	London	HLG9458	1961	£2	£5	
Tear It Up	LP	Coral	CP15	1969	£5	£12	
Tear It Up	7"	Vogue Coral	Q72177	1956	£100	£200	
Walking Talking Doll	7"	Capitol	CL15347	1964	£4	£8	
You're Sixteen	7"	London	HLG9254	1960	£2	£5	chart single
You're Undecided	7"	Von	1006	1954	£330	£500	US

BURNETTE, JOHNNY & DORSEY

Hey Sue	7"	Reprise	R20153	1963	£7.50	£15	

BURNETTE, SMILEY

Chugging On Down Sixty-Six	7"	London	HL8085	1954	£20	£40	
Lazy Locomotive	7"	London	HL8071	1954	£20	£40	
Rudolph The Red-Nosed Reindeer	78	Capitol	CL13388	1950	£2	£5	

BURNIN' RED IVANHOE

6 Elefantskovcikadeviser	LP	Sonet	SLSP1528	1971	£6	£15	Danish
Burnin' Red Ivanhoe	LP	Warner Bros	K44062	1970	£4	£10	
M144	LP	Sonet	SLPS1512/3	1969	£10	£25	Danish
Miley Smile	LP	Sonet	SLSP1540	1972	£6	£15	Danish
Right On	LP	Sonet	SLSP1549	1974	£8	£20	Danish
WWW	LP	Dandelion	2310145	1971	£6	£15	

BURNS, EDDIE 'GUITAR'

Bottle Up And Go	LP	Action	ACMP100	1972	£20	£40	

BURNS, JACKIE & THE BELLS

He's My Guy	7"	MGM	MGM1226	1963	£25	£50	

BURNS, RALPH

Jazz Studio Five	LP	Brunswick	LAT8121	1956	£10	£25	
Ralph Burns Group	LP	Columbia	33CX10017	1955	£10	£25	
Very Warm For Jazz	LP	Brunswick	LAT8289	1959	£6	£15	

BURNS, RAY

Condemned For Life	7"	Columbia	DB3811	1956	£2	£5	
Helpless	7"	Columbia	SCM5115	1954	£1.50	£4	
I Can't Tell A Waltz From A Tango	7"	Columbia	SCM5153	1954	£1.50	£4	
Rags To Riches	7"	Columbia	SCM5077	1953	£1.50	£4	
Ray Burns	7" EP	Columbia	SEG7594	1955	£5	£10	
Spring, Spring, Spring	7"	Columbia	SCM5165	1955	£2.50	£6	
Stealin'	7"	Columbia	SCM5224	1956	£1.50	£4	
Why?	7"	Columbia	SCM5179	1955	£1.50	£4	
Wild Cherry	7"	Columbia	SCM5263	1956	£1.50	£4	

BURNT SUITE

Burnt Suite	LP	B.J.W.	9	1967	£20	£40	US

BURRAGE, HAROLD
I'll Take One .... 7" ...... Sue .... WI353 .... 1965 ... £5 ....£10
You Made Me So Happy .... 7" ...... President .... PT130 .... 1968 ... £1.50 ....£4

BURRELL, KENNY
All Day Long .... LP ..... Esquire .... 32107 .... 1960 ... £10 ....£25
All Night Long .... LP ..... Esquire .... 32140 .... 1961 ... £6 ....£15
Blue Bash .... LP ..... Verve .... VLP9058 .... 1964 ... £5 ....£12 ...... with Jimmy Smith
Blue Nights Vol.1 .... LP ..... Blue Note .... BLP/BST81596 .... 196- ... £10 ....£25
Blue Nights Vol.2 .... LP ..... Blue Note .... BLP/BST81597 .... 196- ... £10 ....£25
Blues, The Common Ground .... LP ..... Verve .... (S)VLP9217 .... 1968 ... £5 ....£12
Crash .... LP ..... Stateside .... SL10163 .... 1966 ... £6 ....£15 ...... with Jack McDuff
Guitar Forms .... LP ..... Verve .... VLP9099 .... 1965 ... £5 ....£12
Introducing .... LP ..... Blue Note .... BLP/BST81523 .... 196- ... £10 ....£25
Kenny Burrell Vol.2 .... LP ..... Blue Note .... BLP/BST81543 .... 196- ... £10 ....£25
Midnight Blue .... LP ..... Blue Note .... BLP/BST84123 .... 1964 ... £8 ....£20
On View At The Five Spot Cafe .... LP ..... Blue Note .... BLP/BST84021 .... 1961 ... £10 ....£25

BURROUGHS, WILLIAM
Call Me Burroughs .... LP ..... ESP .... 1050 .... 1968 ... £10 ....£25 ...... US
Nothing Here Now But The Recordings LP ..... Industrial .... IR0016 .... 1980 ... £6 ....£15
....

BURTON, GARY
The track "General Mojo Cuts Up" on the album "Lofty Fake Anagram" has the dubious distinction of featuring the first burst of guitar feedback on a jazz record. Courtesy of Larry Coryell, the sound is actually a fairly modest one, more reminiscent of what the Beatles had pioneered some years earlier on "I Feel Fine" than of the extravagances of the contemporary Jimi Hendrix.
Genuine Tong Funeral .... LP ..... RCA .... SF8015 .... 1969 ... £5 ....£12 ...... with Carla Bley
Lofty Fake Anagram .... LP ..... RCA .... RD/SF7923 .... 1968 ... £4 ....£10

BURTON, JAMES
James Burton's legendary reputation as an ace guitarist is entirely justified by his playing on record. Largely content to work for others - most notably Rick Nelson and Elvis Presley - his two solo LPs are quite scarce (and undervalued).
Corn Pickin' And Slick Slidin' .... LP ..... Capitol .... ST2822 .... 1968 ... £10 ....£25 ...... US
Guitar Sounds Of James Burton .... LP ..... A&M .... AMLS64293 .... 1971 ... £15 ....£30

BURTON, LORI
Breakout .... LP ..... Mercury .... SR61136 .... 1967 ... £10 ....£25 ...... US

BURTON, TOMMY
I'm Walking .... 7" ...... Blue Beat .... BB237 .... 1963 ... £5 ....£10

BURTON, TREVOR
Fight For My Country .... 7" ...... Wizard .... WIZ103 .... 1971 ... £1.50 ....£4

BUSCH, LOU
Wild Ones .... 7" ...... Capitol .... CL14730 .... 1957 ... £1.50 ....£4
Zambesi .... 7" ...... Capitol .... CL14504 .... 1956 ... £4 ....£8 .... chart single

BUSH, KATE
When Kate Bush first appeared on TV's "Top Of The Pops" wailing to Heathcliffe in that extraordinary high voice, it seemed impossible that she could ever turn out to be more than a one-hit-wonder novelty act. Instead, of course, it turned out that she was possessed of a rare talent - as a singer, as a dancer, as a performance artist, and above all as a composer and musician. Each of her album releases has been more impressive than the one before it and she is without doubt one of the most important rock artists of the eighties and nineties. Many of her records have become collectable, with picture sleeve copies of all her early singles rising steadily in value. The sought after picture disc version of Kate Bush's first LP exists in two closely similar pressings. The second can be identified by looking at the copyright clause on side two: it has the words "manufactured in the UK by EMI Records Ltd.". These are not to be found on the original pressing.
Amiga .... LP ..... EMI .... 856072 .... 1984 ... £15 ....£30 ...... German
Big Sky .... 7" ...... EMI .... KB4P .... 1986 ... £5 ....£10 ...... pic disc
Dreaming .... 7" ...... EMI .... EMI5296 .... 1982 ... £1.50 ....£4 .... chart single, PS
Hammer Horror .... 7" ...... EMI .... EMI2887 .... 1978 ... £1.50 ....£4 .... PS
Hounds Of Love .... LP ..... EMI .... ST17171 .... 1985 ... £8 ....£20 ...... US, coloured vinyl
Interview With Kate Bush .... LP ..... EMI .... SPRO282 .... 1985 ... £100 ....£200 .... Canadian promo
Kate Bush .... LP ..... EMI .... MLP19004 .... 1984 ... £30 ....£60 ...... Canadian 6 track LP, brown or clear vinyl
Kate Bush .... LP ..... EMI .... MLP19004 .... 1984 ... £15 ....£30 ...... Canadian 6 track LP, green, yellow, blue, or white vinyl
Kick Inside .... LP ..... EMI/ Harvest.... EMC3223/ SW11761 .. 1978 ... £6 ....£15 ...... different US sleeve on UK record
Kick Inside .... LP ..... EMI .... 5C06206603 .... 1978 ... £25 ....£50 ...... coloured vinyl, Dutch
Kick Inside .... LP ..... EMI .... EMCP3223 .... 1978 ... £50 ....£100 .... pic disc with same pic on both sides
Kick Inside .... LP ..... EMI .... EMCP3223 .... 1979 ... £25 ....£50 ...... pic disc
Kick Inside .... LP ..... EMI .... EMCP3223 .... 1979 ... £20 ....£40 ...... pic disc, 2nd pressing
Man With The Child In His Eyes .... 7" ...... EMI .... EMI2806 .... 1978 ... £5 ....£10 ...... PS
Ne T'En Fui Pas .... 7" ...... EMI .... PM102 .... 1983 ... £5 ....£10 ...... sung in French
Never For Ever .... LP ..... EMI .... SFI562 .... 1980 ... £7.50 ....£15 ...... promo, flexi
On Stage .... 7" ...... EMI .... PSR442/443 .... 1979 ... £25 ....£50 ...... promo, double
Self Portrait .... LP ..... EMI .... SSA3020 .... 1979 ... £100 ....£200 .... US promo
Single File .... 7" ...... EMI .... KBS1 .... 1984 ... £50 ....£100 .... boxed with booklet, box pictured in Guide
There Goes A Tenner .... 7" ...... EMI .... EMI5350 .... 1982 ... £1.50 ....£4 .... PS
This Woman's Work .... LP ..... EMI .... KBBX1 .... 1990 ... £40 ....£80 ...... box set
This Woman's Work .... CD ..... EMI .... CDKBBX1 .... 1990 ... £50 ....£100 .... box set
This Woman's Work .... 7" ...... EMI .... EMPD119 .... 1989 ... £1.50 ....£4 .... pic disc
Wow .... 7" ...... EMI .... EMI2911 .... 1979 ... £1.50 ....£4 .... PS
Wuthering Heights .... 7" ...... EMI .... EMI2719 .... 1978 ... £12.50 ....£25 ...... PS

BUSHKIN, JOE
Joe Bushkin Orchestra	LP	Capitol	LCT6126	1957	£4	£10	
Piano After Midnight	LP	Fontana	TFL5014	1958	£4	£10	

BUSKERS
Buskers	LP	Hawk	HALPX142	1975	£6	£15	
Life Of A Man	LP	Rubber	RUB007	1973	£6	£15	

BUSTERS
Bust Out	7"	Stateside	SS231	1963	£2	£5	

BUTALA, TONY
Long Black Stockings	7"	Salvo	SLO1801	1962	£5	£10	

BUTCHER, EDDIE
Once Was A Daysman	LP	Free Reed	FRR003	1976	£6	£15	
Shamrock, Rose And Thistle	LP	Leader	LED2070	1976	£5	£12	

BUTERA, SAM & THE WITNESSES
Big Horn	LP	Capitol	T1098	1959	£8	£20	
Bim Bam	7"	Capitol	CL14913	1958	£25	£50	
Good Gracious Baby	7"	HMV	POP476	1958	£10	£20	
Handle With Care	7"	Capitol	CL14988	1959	£6	£12	
Rat Race	LP	London	HAD2288	1960	£8	£20	
Sax Serenade	7" EP	HMV	7EG8087	1955	£10	£20	
Skinnie Minnie	7"	Prima	PR1003	1964	£1.50	£4	

BUTLER, BILLY
Right Track	LP	Soul City		196-	£8	£20	
Right Track	7"	Soul City	SC113	1969	£4	£8	

BUTLER, CHAMP
Joshua Tree	7"	Vogue Coral	Q72163	1956	£1.50	£4	
Someone On Your Mind	7"	Vogue Coral	Q72119	1956	£1.50	£4	

BUTLER, JERRY
Are You Happy	7"	Mercury	MF1078	1969	£1.50	£4	
Aware Of Love	LP	Vee Jay	LP/SR1038	1961	£8	£20	US
Best Of Jerry Butler	LP	Vee Jay	LP/SR1048	1962	£6	£15	US
Brand New Me	LP	Mercury	MF1132	1969	£2	£5	
Cooling Out	7"	Philadelphia	PIR6790	1978	£1.50	£4	demo only
Folk Songs	LP	Stateside	SL10050	1963	£6	£15	
For Your Precious Love	LP	Vee Jay	LP/VJS1075	1963	£6	£15	US
For Your Precious Love	7"	London	HL8697	1958	£40	£80	
Give Me Your Love	7"	Stateside	SS252	1964	£4	£8	
Giving Up On Love	LP	Vee Jay	LP/VJS1076	1963	£6	£15	US
Good Times	7"	Fontana	TF553	1965	£4	£8	
He Will Break Your Heart	LP	Stateside	SL10032	1963	£8	£20	
He Will Break Your Heart	7"	Top Rank	JAR531	1961	£12.50	£25	
Hey Mr.Western Union Man	7"	Mercury	MF1058	1968	£2.50	£6	
I Can't Stand To See You Cry	7"	Fontana	TF588	1965	£2.50	£6	
I Dig You Baby	7"	Mercury	MF964	1967	£2.50	£6	
I Found A Love	7"	Top Rank	JAR389	1960	£7.50	£15	
I Stand Accused	7"	Sue	WI4003	1966	£7.50	£15	
Ice Man Cometh	LP	Mercury	20154SML	1969	£5	£12	
I've Been Trying	7"	Stateside	SS300	1964	£4	£8	
Jerry Butler Esquire	LP	Abner	R2001	1959	£37.50	£75	US
Jerry Butler Esquire	LP	Vee Jay	LP1027	1961	£10	£25	US
Just For You	7"	Sue	WI4009	1966	£5	£10	
Love	7"	Mercury	MF932	1965	£1.50	£4	
Love Me	LP	Fontana	(S)TL5264	1968	£5	£12	
Make It Easy On Yourself	7"	President	PT299	1970	£1.50	£4	
Make It Easy On Yourself	7"	Stateside	SS121	1962	£5	£10	
Moody Woman	7"	Mercury	MF1122	1969	£2.50	£6	
Moon River	LP	Vee Jay	LP/SR1046	1962	£8	£20	US
Moon River	7"	Columbia	DB4743	1961	£5	£10	
More Of The Best Of Jerry Butler	LP	Vee Jay	(VJS)1119	1965	£5	£12	US
Mr.Dream Merchant	7"	Mercury	MF1005	1967	£1.50	£4	
Never Give You up	7"	Mercury	MF1035	1968	£1.50	£4	
Only The Strong Survive	7"	Mercury	MF1094	1969	£2	£5	
Send A Telegram	7"	Mercury	MF1058	1968	£2.50	£6	
Spice Of Life	LP	Mercury	6338102	1972	£4	£10	
When Trouble Calls	7"	Top Rank	JAR562	1961	£7.50	£15	
You Can Run	7"	Stateside	SS158	1963	£4	£8	
You Go Right Through Me	7"	Stateside	SS170	1963	£4	£8	
You Won't Be Sorry	7"	Stateside	SS195	1963	£4	£8	

BUTLER, LESLIE
Ramona	7"	Doctor Bird	DB1083	1967	£5	£10	
Revival	7"	High Note	HS009	1969	£2.50	£6	
Soul Drums	7"	High Note	HS001	1969	£2.50	£6	Gaylads B side
Top Cat	7"	High Note	HS008	1969	£2.50	£6	
You Don't Have To Say You Love Me	7"	Island	WI3069	1967	£5	£10	

BUTTERCUPS
Come Put My Life In Order	7"	Pama	PM760	1969	£4	£8	
If I Love You	7"	Pama	PM742	1968	£6	£12	

BUTTERFIELD, BILLY
Ballads For Sweethearts	10" LP	Nixa	WLPY6729	1955	£5	£12	
Billy Butterfield Orchestra	10" LP	London	HBF1043	1956	£5	£12	

Title	Format	Label	Catalogue	Year			Notes
Classics In Jazz	10" LP	Capitol	LC6684	1955	£6	£15	
Magnificent Matador	7"	London	HLF8181	1955	£7.50	£15	
That Butterfield Bounce	10" LP	Nixa	WLPY6720	1955	£5	£12	

BUTTERFIELD, PAUL BLUES BAND

Title	Format	Label	Catalogue	Year			Notes
All These Blues	7"	Elektra	EKSN45007	1967	£2	£5	
Butterfield Blues Band	LP	Elektra	K42004	1971	£4	£10	
Come On In	7"	London	HLZ10100	1966	£5	£10	
East West	LP	Elektra	EKL/EKS315	1966	£8	£20	
East West	7"	Elektra	EKSN45047	1968	£2	£5	
Get Yourself Together	7"	Elektra	EKSN45047	1968	£2	£5	
Golden Butter	LP	Elektra	K62011	1972	£5	£12	double
I Got My Mojo Working	7" EP	Vogue	INT18063	1965	£12.50	£25	French
In My Own Dream	LP	Elektra	EKL/EKS74025	1968	£5	£12	
In My Own Dream	LP	Elektra	K42042	1971	£4	£10	
Keep On Moving	LP	Elektra	EKS74053	1969	£5	£12	
Keep On Moving	LP	Elektra	K42033	1971	£4	£10	
Live	LP	Elektra	EKS2001	1970	£6	£15	double
Live	LP	Elektra	K62001	1971	£5	£12	double
Offer You Can't Refuse	LP	Red Lightnin'	R008	1972	£4	£10	
Paul Butterfield Blues Band	LP	Elektra	EKL/EKS7294	1965	£8	£20	
Resurrection Of Pigboy Crabshaw	LP	Elektra	EKL/EKS74015	1967	£5	£12	
Resurrection Of Pigboy Crabshaw	LP	Elektra	K42017	1971	£4	£10	
Run Out Of Time	7"	Elektra	EKSN45020	1967	£2	£5	
Where Did My Baby Go	7"	Elektra	EKSN45069	1968	£2	£5	

BUTTERFLYS

Title	Format	Label	Catalogue	Year			Notes
Goodnight Baby	7"	Red Bird	RB10009	1964	£6	£12	

BUTTHOLE SURFERS

Title	Format	Label	Catalogue	Year			Notes
Double Live	LP	LBV		198-	£6	£15	double

BUX

Title	Format	Label	Catalogue	Year			Notes
We Came To Play	LP	Capitol	11459	1976	£8	£20	US

BUXTON, SHEILA

Title	Format	Label	Catalogue	Year			Notes
Charm	7"	Columbia	DB4051	1957	£1.50	£4	
Perfect Love	7"	Columbia	DB3887	1957	£1.50	£4	
Thank You For The Waltz	7"	Columbia	SCM5193	1955	£1.50	£4	

BUZZ

Title	Format	Label	Catalogue	Year			Notes
You're Holding Me Down	7"	Columbia	DB7887	1966	£50	£100	

BUZZ & BUCKY

Title	Format	Label	Catalogue	Year			Notes
Tiger A-Go-Go	7"	Stateside	SS428	1965	£6	£12	

BUZZCOCKS

The Buzzcocks' "Spiral Scratch" EP was the first self-produced record to emerge out of punk and was an early collectors' item. A reissue brought the record's value down to its current level, although the two issues are easily distinguished by the original making no specific reference to Howard Devoto on the front cover.

Title	Format	Label	Catalogue	Year			Notes
Another Music In A Different Kitchen	LP	United Artists	UAG30159	1978	£8	£20	with printed carrier bag
Moving Away From The Pulsebeat	12"	United Artists	UALP15	1978	£6	£15	1 sided promo
Spiral Scratch	7" EP	Document	DPRO1	1991	£2.50	£6	promo
Spiral Scratch	7" EP	New Hormones	ORG1	1977	£5	£10	no Devoto reference on sleeve

BYAS, DON

Title	Format	Label	Catalogue	Year			Notes
Don Byas	10" LP	Esquire	20005	1953	£20	£40	
Don Byas	10" LP	Felsted	EDL87004	1954	£20	£40	

BYE LAWS

Title	Format	Label	Catalogue	Year			Notes
Run Baby Run	7"	Pye	7N17701	1969	£2	£5	
Then You Tell Me Goodbye	7"	Pye	7N17481	1968	£2	£5	

BYLES, JUNIOR

Title	Format	Label	Catalogue	Year			Notes
Beat Down Babylon	LP	Trojan	TRL52	1972	£5	£12	
Beat Down Babylon	7"	Bullet	BU499	1971	£2	£5	Upsetters B side
Festival Da Da	7"	Upsetter	US387	1971	£1.50	£4	Upsetters B side
Fever	7"	Pama	PM857	1972	£2	£5	Groovers B side

BYRD, BOBBY

Title	Format	Label	Catalogue	Year			Notes
Back From The Dead	7"	Seville	SEV1003	1975	£1.50	£4	
Headquarters	7"	Seville	SEV1005	1975	£1.50	£4	
Hot Pants I'm Coming I'm Coming	7"	Mojo	2093004	1973	£1.50	£4	
Know You Got Soul	7"	Mojo	2027003	1971	£2	£5	
Know You Got Soul	12"	Urban	URBX8	1987	£2.50	£6	
Need Help	7"	Polydor	2001118	1971	£2	£5	
Need Help - Live	LP	Mojo	2918002	1972	£25	£50	
If You Got A Love	7"	Mojo	2093017	1974	£1.50	£4	
Keep On Doin' What You're Doin'	7"	Mojo	2093013	1974	£1.50	£4	
Never Get Enough	7"	Mojo	2093020	1974	£1.50	£4	
Sayin' It Aint Doin' It	7"	Mojo	2093028	1975	£1.50	£4	
Try It Again	7"	Warner Bros	K16291	1973	£1.50	£4	

BYRD, CHARLIE

Title	Format	Label	Catalogue	Year			Notes
Blues Sonata	LP	Riverside	OLP(9)3009	1963	£4	£10	
Guitar Artistry	LP	Riverside	OLP(9)3007	1963	£4	£10	

BYRD, DONALD

Title	Format	Label	Catalogue	Year			Notes
And Then Some	LP	Eros	ERL50067	1962	£4	£10	

Title	Format	Label	Catalogue	Year	Price	Price	Notes
At The Half Note Cafe	LP	Blue Note	BLP/BST84060	1961	£10	£25	
At The Half Note Cafe Vol.2	LP	Blue Note	BLP/BST84061	1961	£15	£30	
Black Byrd	7"	Blue Note	BNXW7001	1975	£1.50	£4	
Black Byrd	7"	United Artists	UP35564	1973	£1.50	£4	
Black Jack	LP	Blue Note	BLP/BST84259	1967	£6	£15	
Boom Boom	7"	Verve	VS532	1966	£2	£5	
Byrd In Flight	LP	Blue Note	BLP/BST84048	196-	£10	£25	
Cat Walk	LP	Blue Note	BLP/BST84075	1961	£8	£20	
Changes Make You Want To Hustle	7"	Blue Note	BNXW7003	1976	£1.50	£4	
Child's Play	LP	Polydor	423/623224	1967	£4	£10	
Donald Byrd And Gigi Gryce	7" EP	Philips	BBE12274	1959	£2	£5	
Donald Byrd Group	LP	Esquire	32013	1956	£15	£30	
Donald Byrd Group	LP	London	LTZC15039	1957	£15	£30	
Donald Byrd Sextet	LP	Esquire	32019	1956	£15	£30	
Donald Byrd's Jazz Group	7" EP	Esquire	EP139	1957	£2	£5	
Donald Byrd's Jazz Group	7" EP	Esquire	EP149	1957	£2	£5	
Electric Byrd	LP	Blue Note	BST84349	1970	£6	£15	
Ethiopian Nights	LP	Blue Note	BST84380	1970	£6	£15	
Fancy Free	LP	Blue Note	BST84319	1969	£6	£15	
Flight Time	7"	Blue Note	BNXW623	1974	£1.50	£4	
Free Form	LP	Blue Note	BLP/BST84118	1962	£8	£20	
Fuego	LP	Blue Note	BLP/BST84026	1961	£10	£25	
Fuego	7"	Blue Note	451764	1962	£1.50	£4	
I'm Trying To Get Home	LP	Blue Note	BLP/BST84188	1965	£8	£20	
Jazz Lab	LP	Philips	BBL7210	1958	£10	£25	with Gigi Gryc
Modern Jazz Perspective	LP	Philips	BBL7244	1958	£8	£20	with Gigi Gryc
Mustang	LP	Blue Note	BLP/BST84238	1966	£8	£20	
New Perspective	LP	Blue Note	BLP/BST84124	1963	£10	£25	
Places And Spaces	LP	United Artists	UAG20001	197-	£8	£20	
Royal Flush	LP	Blue Note	BLP/BST84101	1962	£8	£20	
Slow Drag	LP	Blue Note	BST84292	1968	£6	£15	
Three Trumpets	LP	Esquire	32093	1960	£6	£15	with Art Farme & Idrees Suliema
Up With Donald Byrd	LP	Verve	VLP9104	1965	£6	£15	

BYRD, JOE & THE FIELD HIPPIES

"American Metaphysical Circus" is, in effect, the follow-up to the innovative LP made by The United States Of America. With only Joe Byr remaining from the original line-up, however, a change of name was clearly appropriate.

Title	Format	Label	Catalogue	Year	Price	Price	Notes
American Metaphysical Circus	LP	CBS	7317	1969	£10	£25	U

BYRD, RUSSELL

Title	Format	Label	Catalogue	Year	Price	Price	Notes
Hitch Hike	7"	Sue	WI305	1964	£7.50	£15	

BYRDS

Title	Format	Label	Catalogue	Year	Price	Price	Notes
All I Really Want To Do	7"	CBS	201796	1965	£1.50	£4	chart singl
Bad Night At The Whisky	7"	CBS	4055	1969	£1.50	£4	
Ballad Of Easy Rider	LP	CBS	63795	1970	£4	£10	chart L
Byrdmaniax	LP	CBS	64389	1971	£4	£10	
Byrds	LP	Asylum	SYLA8754	1973	£4	£10	chart L
Chestnut Mare	7"	CBS	5322	1971	£1.50	£4	chart singl
Dr.Byrds & Mr.Hyde	LP	CBS	63545	1969	£4	£10	chart L
Early Flight	LP	Together	ST1014	1969	£8	£20	U
Eight Miles High	7"	CBS	202067	1966	£2	£5	chart singl
Eight Miles High	7" EP	CBS	EP6077	1966	£6	£12	
Farther Along	LP	CBS	64676	1972	£4	£10	
Fifth Dimension	LP	CBS	(S)BPG62783	1966	£6	£15	chart L
Fifth Dimension	7"	CBS	202259	1966	£1.50	£4	
Goin' Back	7"	CBS	3093	1967	£1.50	£4	
I Am A Pilgrim	7"	CBS	3752	1968	£1.50	£4	
It Won't Be Wrong	7" EP	CBS	5668	1966	£7.50	£15	Frenc
Jesus Is Just Alright	7"	CBS	4753	1970	£1.50	£4	
Lady Friend	7"	CBS	2924	1967	£5	£10	
Lay Lady Lay	7"	CBS	4284	1969	£1.50	£4	
Mr.Spaceman	7"	CBS	202295	1966	£2	£5	
Mr.Tambourine Man	LP	CBS	(S)BPG62571	1965	£6	£15	chart L
Mr.Tambourine Man	7"	CBS	201765	1965	£1.50	£4	chart singl
Mr.Tambourine Man	7" EP	CBS	6100	1965	£7.50	£15	French, different track listing
My Back Pages	7"	CBS	2648	1967	£1.50	£4	
Notorious Byrd Brothers	LP	CBS	(S)BPG63169	1968	£6	£15	chart L
Preflyte	LP	Bumble	GEXP8001	196-	£8	£20	U
Preflyte	LP	CBS	KC32183		£8	£20	
Preflyte	LP	Together	ST1001	1969	£8	£20	U
Set You Free This Time	7"	CBS	202037	1966	£4	£8	
So You Want To Be A Rock'n'Roll Star	7"	CBS	202559	1967	£1.50	£4	
Sweetheart Of The Rodeo	LP	CBS	63353	1968	£6	£15	chart L
Things Will Be Better	7"	Asylum	AYM516	1973	£5	£10	demo, P
Times They Are A Changing	7" EP	CBS	EP6069	1966	£5	£10	
Turn Turn Turn	LP	CBS	(S)BPG62652	1966	£6	£15	chart L
Turn Turn Turn	7" EP	CBS	6521	1965	£7.50	£15	Frenc
Turn! Turn! Turn!	7"	CBS	202008	1965	£1.50	£4	chart singl
Untitled	LP	CBS	66253	1970	£6	£15	double, chart L
Wasn't Born To Follow	7"	CBS	4572	1969	£1.50	£4	
You Ain't Goin' Nowhere	7"	CBS	3411	1968	£1.50	£4	chart singl
Younger Than Yesterday	LP	CBS	(S)BPG62988	1967	£6	£15	chart L

BYRNE, BRIAN

Title	Format	Label	Catalogue	Year	Price	Price	Notes
Brian Byrne	LP	Hawk	HALP105	1976	£6	£15	Iris

BYRNE, JERRY
Lights Out .... 7" .... Speciality .... SON5011 .... 1976 ... £2 ....£5 ....

BYRNE, PACKIE
Packie Byrne .... LP ...... EFDSS .... LP1009 .... 1969 ... £6 ....£15 ....
Songs Of A Donegal Man .... LP ...... Topic .... 12TS257 .... 1975 ... £6 ....£15 ....

BYRNE, PACKIE & BONNIE SHALJEAN
Half Door .... LP ..... Dingles .... DIN302 .... 1977 ... £5 ....£12 ....
Roundtower .... LP ..... Dingles .... DIN311 .... 1981 ... £5 ....£12 ....

BYRNES, EDDIE
Kookie .... LP ...... Warner Bros .... W(S)1309 .... 1959 ... £6 ....£15 .... US
Kookie .... 7" EP.. Warner Bros .... WEP6010............. 1960 ... £4 ....£8
Kookie, Kookie, Lend Me Your Comb ... 7" .... Warner Bros .... WB5.................. 1960 ... £1.50 ....£4 ....chart single
Kookie Vol.2 .... 7" EP.. Warner Bros .... WEP6108............. 1963 ... £4 ....£8 ....

BYRNES, MARTIN
Martin Byrnes .... LP ...... Leader............. LEA2004 .... 1969 ... £10 ....£25 ....

BYRON, PAUL
Pale Moon .... 7" .... Decca .... F11210.................. 1960 ... £2.50 ....£6 ....

BYSTANDERS
There were a number of sixties groups who eventually achieved some measure of success in the seventies by effecting a dramatic change of style. Status Quo are the obvious example, yet the Bystanders are another good one. In their case, the change from their original harmony vocal approach was so great that they found it necessary to change their name too - to Man.
98.6 .... 7" .... Piccadilly .... 7N35363 .... 1967 ... £4 ....£8 ....chart single
My Love Come Home .... 7" .... Piccadilly .... 7N35351 .... 1966 ... £7.50 ....£15 ....
Pattern People .... 7" .... Piccadilly .... 7N35399 .... 1967 ... £5 ....£10 ....
Royal Blue Summer Sunshine Day ...... 7" .... Piccadilly .... 7N35382 .... 1967 ... £7.50 ....£15 ....
That's The End .... 7" .... Pylot .... 501 .... 1965 ... £30 ....£60 ....
This World Is My World .... 7" .... Pye .... 7N17540 .... 1968 ... £6 ....£12 ....
When Jezamine Goes .... 7" .... Pye .... 7N17476 .... 1968 ... £10 ....£20 ....
You're Gonna Hurt Yourself .... 7" .... Piccadilly .... 7N35330 .... 1966 ... £6 ....£12 ....

BYZANTIUM
Byzantium .... LP ..... A&M .... AMLS68104 .... 1972 ... £6 ....£15 ....
Live and Studio .... LP ..... private .... 1972 ... £60 ....£120 ....
Seasons Changing .... LP ..... A&M .... AMLH68163 .... 1972 ... £10 ....£25 ....
What A Coincidence .... 7" .... A&M .... AMS7064 .... 1973 ... £1.50 ....£4 ....

C & THE SHELLS

Good Morning Starshine	7"	Atlantic	584271	1969	£1.50	£4	

C, FANTASTIC JOHNNY

Boogaloo Down Broadway	LP	Action	ACLP6001	1969	£6	£15	
Boogaloo Down Broadway	7"	London	HL10169	1967	£2.50	£6	
Don't Depend On Me	7"	Island	USA008	1975	£2	£5	
Hitch It To The Horse	7"	London	HL10212	1968	£2.50	£6	
New Love	7"	Action	ACT4543	1969	£2	£5	

C JAM BLUES

Candy	7"	Columbia	DB8064	1966	£7.50	£15	

C, ROY

Sex And Soul	LP	Mercury	9100017	1975	£4	£10	
Shotgun Wedding	7"	Island	WI273	1966	£4	£8	chart single, 2 different B sides
Shotgun Wedding	7"	UK	UK19	1972	£1.50	£4	chart single
That Shotgun Wedding Man	LP	Ember	NR5055	1966	£5	£12	
Twistin' Pneumonia	7"	Ember	EMBS230	1967	£2.50	£6	

C.A. QUINTET

Trip Through Hell	LP	Psycho	PSYCHO12	1983	£6	£15	

CABAL, BRELLO

Margarine Flavoured Pineapple Chunk	7"	CBS	3214	1967	£1.50	£4	

CABARET VOLTAIRE

Eddie's Out	12"	Rough Trade	RT096T	1981	£2.50	£6	with pink vinyl 7' (RT095)
Limited Edition	cass	private		1976	£20	£40	

CABLES

Be A Man	7"	Studio One	SO2060	1968	£6	£12	
Got To Find Someone	7"	Studio One	SO2085	1969	£6	£12	
How Can I Trust You?	7"	Bamboo	BAM19	1970	£2	£5	
Love Is A Pleasure	7"	Studio One	SO2071	1968	£6	£12	
So Long	7"	Bamboo	BAM12	1969	£2.50	£6	
What Kind Of World	7"	Coxsone	CS7072	1968	£5	£10	

CACTUS

Cactus	LP	Atlantic	2400020	1970	£5	£12	

CADDICK, BILL

Duck On His Head	LP	Highway	SHY7012	1980	£5	£12	
Rough Music	LP	Park	SHP102	1976	£5	£12	
Sunny Memories	LP	Trailer	LER2097	1977	£5	£12	

CADDY, ALAN

Workout	7"	HMV	POP1286	1964	£7.50	£15	

CADETS

Cadets	LP	Crown	CLP5370/CST370	1963	£10	£25	US
Rockin' 'N' Reelin'	LP	Crown	CLP5015	1957	£30	£60	US
Stranded In The Jungle	7"	London	HLU8313	1956	£75	£150	

CADETS (2)

Are You Teasing Me	7"	Pye	7N15769	1965	£1.50	£4	
At The Close Of A Long Long Day	7"	Pye	7N17167	1966	£1.50	£4	
Baby Roo	7"	Pye	7N15947	1965	£1.50	£4	
Chapel Of Love	7"	Pye	7N15693	1964	£1.50	£4	
Crying Ranger	7"	Pye	7N17762	1969	£1.50	£4	
If I Had My Life To Live Over	7"	Pye	7N17024	1966	£1.50	£4	
Our First Quarrel	7"	Decca	F11677	1963	£1.50	£4	
Right Or Wrong	7"	Pye	7N15852	1965	£1.50	£4	

CADILLAC

Valentino	7"	CBS	A7180	1986	£2	£5	

CADILLACS

Cadillacs Meet The Orioles	LP	Jubilee	JGM1117	1961	£30	£60	US
Crazy Cadillacs	LP	Jubilee	JGM1089	1959	£40	£80	US
Fabulous Cadillacs	LP	Jubilee	JGM1045	1957	£60	£120	US
Peek A Boo	7"	London	HLJ8786	1959	£10	£20	US
Twisting With The Cadillacs	LP	Jubilee	JGM5009	1962	£25	£50	US

CAEDMON

Caedmon	LP	private		1978	£180	£300	with 7'

CAESAR & CLEO

Letter	7"	Vocalion	VP9247	1965	£2	£5	
Love Is Strange	7"	Reprise	R20419	1965	£2	£5	

CAESARS
Five In The Morning	7"	Decca	F12462	1966	£6	£12	
On The Outside Looking In	7"	Decca	F12251	1965	£5	£10	

CAFE SOCIETY
*Cafe Society included Tom Robinson in its line-up, but the collectability of the group's records has more to do with the fact that they we...
among the few releases on the label founded by the Kinks' Ray Davies.*
Cafe Society	LP	Konk	KONK102	1975	£8	£20	

CAGE, BUTCH & MABEL LEE WILLIAMS
Country Blues	LP	Storyville	SLP129	1964	£5	£12	

CAGE, JOHN
Cartridge Music	LP	Deutsche Grammophon	137009	1969	£6	£15	
Concerto For Piano & Orchestra	LP	EMI	C165289547		£6	£15	
Concerto For Prepared Piano & Orchestra	LP	Nonesuch	H71202	1968	£6	£15	other side Lukas Fos...
Fontana Mix	LP	Turnabout	TV34046	196-	£6	£15	
HPSCHD	LP	Nonesuch	H71224	1970	£6	£15	...other sid... Ben Johnsto...
Sonatas & Interludes For Prepared Piano	LP	Decca	HEAD9	1976	£6	£15	
Variations	LP	Everest	3132		£6	£15	
Variations II	LP	Columbia	MS7051		£6	£15	U...

CAGLE, AUBREY
Come Along Little Girl	7"	Starlite	ST45082	1962	£60	£120	

CAHILL, PATRICIA
Summer's Daughter	LP	Nova	SDN22	1970	£6	£15	

CAIN
Her Emotion	7"	Page One	POF054	1968	£2.50	£6	

CAIN, JACKIE & ROY KRAL
Bits And Pieces	LP	HMV	CLP1187	1958	£6	£15	
Free And Easy	LP	HMV	CLP1232	1959	£6	£15	
Glory Of Love	LP	HMV	CLP1219	1958	£6	£15	
Jackie And Roy	LP	Vogue	VA160111	1958	£4	£10	

CAIN, JONATHAN BAND
Windy City Breakdown	LP	Bearsville	6969	1977	£6	£15	U

CAIOLA, AL
Bonanza	7"	London	HLT9325	1961	£4	£8	
Deep In A Dream	LP	London	HAC2017	1956	£4	£10	
Flamenco Love	7"	London	HLC8285	1956	£7.50	£15	
Hit TV Themes	7" EP	United Artists	UEP1018	1966	£4	£8	
Serenade In Blue	LP	London	HAC2022	1957	£4	£10	
Tuff Guitar	LP	United Artists	ULP1090	1964	£4	£10	

CAKE
Cake	LP	MCA	MUPS303	1968	£4	£10	
Slice Of Cake	LP	MCA	MUPS390	1969	£4	£10	

CALDWELL, LOUISE HARRISON
All About The Beatles	LP	Recar	2012	1964	£30	£60	U

CALE, J.J.
J.J.Cale	LP	Shelter	ISADJ1	1976	£5	£12	prom...
Outside Looking In	7"	Liberty	LBY55881	1966	£4	£8	

CALE, JOHN
Academy In Peril	LP	Reprise	K44212	1972	£4	£10	
Hear Fear	LP	Island	IXP2	1976	£5	£12	US prom...
Jack The Ripper	7"	Illegal	IL006	1977	£4	£8	...dem...
Paris 1919	LP	Reprise	K44239	1973	£4	£10	
Vintage Violence	LP	CBS	64256	1970	£4	£10	

CALE, JOHN & TERRY RILEY
Church Of Anthrax	LP	CBS	64259	1971	£8	£20	

CALEB
Woman Of Distinction	7"	Philips	BF1588	1967	£50	£100	

CALEDONIANS
Funny Way Of Laughing	7"	Fab	FAB103	1969	£4	£8	

CALIFORNIA IN CROWD
Questions And Answers	7"	Fontana	TF779	1966	£12.50	£25	

CALIFORNIANS
Congratulations	7"	Decca	F12758	1968	£1.50	£4	
Cooks Of Cake And Kindness	7"	Fontana	TF991	1969	£12.50	£25	
Follow Me	7"	Decca	F12678	1967	£4	£8	
Golden Apples	7"	CBS	202263	1967	£7.50	£15	
Out In The Sun	7"	Decca	F12802	1968	£2	£5	
Sad Old Song	7"	Fontana	TF1052	1969	£2.50	£6	
Sunday Will Never Be The Same	7"	Decca	F12712	1967	£2	£5	

CALL GIRLS
Primal World .... 7" ...... 53rd and 3rd .... AGAR001 .... 1988 ... £2.50 .....£6

CALLAN & JOHN
House Of Delight .... 7" ...... CBS .... 4447 .... 1969 ... £2.50 .....£6

CALLICOTT, MISSISSIPPI JOE
Deal Gone Down .... LP ...... Revival .... RVS1002 .... 1972 ... £6 ....£15
Presenting The Country Blues .... LP ...... Blue Horizon.... 763227 .... 1968 ... £15 ....£30

CALLINAN FLYNN
Freedom's Lament .... LP ...... Mushroom ...... 150MR18 .... 1972 ... £100 .....£200

CALLIOPE
Steamed .... LP ...... Buddah .... 203016 .... 1968 ... £5 ....£12

CALLOWAY, CAB
Cab Calloway .... 7" EP .. Fontana .... TFE17216 .... 1960 ... £10 .....£20
Cab Calloway .... 7" EP .. Gala .... 45XP1016 .... 1958 ... £2 ....£5
Cabulous Calloway .... 7" EP .. Vintage Jazz .... VEP22 .... 196- ... £5 ....£10
Cabulous Calloway Vol.2 .... 7" EP .. Vintage Jazz .... VEP35 .... 196- ... £5 ....£10
History Repeats Itself .... 7" ...... Stateside .... SS509 .... 1966 ... £1.50 ...£4
Minnie The Moocher .... 78 ...... Brunswick ...... 05022 .... 1952 ... £1.50 ...£4

CALVERT, EDDIE
Ave Maria .... 7" ...... Columbia........ SCM5004 .... 1953 ... £1.50 ...£4
Cherry Pink And Apple Blossom White 7" ...... Columbia........ SCM5168 .... 1955 ... £4 ....£8 ....chart single
Man With The Golden Arm .... 7" ...... Columbia........ SCM5237 .... 1956 ... £1.50 ...£4
Mandy .... 7" ...... Columbia........ DB3956 .... 1957 ... £1.50 ...£4 ....chart single
My Son, My Son .... 7" ...... Columbia........ SCM5129 .... 1954 ... £1.50 ...£4
My Yiddishe Momma .... 7" ...... Columbia........ SCM5003 .... 1953 ... £1.50 ...£4

CALVERT, ROBERT
At The Queen Elizabeth Hall .... LP ...... Clear .... BLACK1 .... 1989 ... £8 ....£20 .. with badge & T shirt
Captain Lockheed & The Starfighters ... LP ...... United Artists.. UAG29507 .... 1974 ... £8 ....£20
Captain Lockheed And The .... LP ...... United Artists.. UAG29507 .... 1974 ... £15 ....£30 ....with booklet
Starfighters
Catch A Falling Starfighter .... 7" ...... United Artists.. UP35543 .... 1973 ... £4 ....£8 ....different mix
Catch A Falling Starfighter .... 7" ...... United Artists.. UP35543 .... 1973 ... £7.50 ...£15 ....PS
Hype .... LP ...... A Side .... IFO311 .... 1980 ... £4 ....£10
Lucky Leif & The Longships .... LP ...... United Artists.. UAG29852 .... 1975 ... £15 ....£30

CALVIN, TABBY & THE ROUNDERS
False Alarm .... 7" ...... Capitol .... CL14640 .... 1956 ... £1.50 ...£4

CALYPSO QUINTET
Chambolina .... 7" ...... Kalypso .... XX02 .... 1960 ... £1.50 ...£4
Night Food .... 7" ...... Kalypso .... XX01 .... 1960 ... £1.50 ...£4

CAMARATA
Velvet Gentleman .... LP ...... Deram .... SML1101 .... 1973 ... £25 ....£50

CAMEL
Never Let Go .... 7" ...... MCA.............. MU1177 .... 1973 ... £2 ....£5

CAMEL DRIVERS
Sunday Morning Six O'Clock .... 7" ...... Pye .... 7N25471 .... 1968 ... £1.50 ...£4

CAMEO
Cardiac Arrest .... LP ...... Casablanca ...... CAL2015 .... 1977 ... £5 ....£12
We All Know Who We Are .... LP ...... Casablanca ...... CAL2026 .... 1978 ... £4 ....£10

CAMEOS
My Baby's Coming Home .... 7" ...... Columbia........ DB7201 .... 1964 ... £6 ....£12
Powercut .... 7" ...... Columbia........ DB7092.......... 1963 ... £7.50 ...£15

CAMEOS (2)
On The Good Ship Lollipop .... 7" ...... Toast .... TT508 .... 1968 ... £4 ....£8
Pretty Shade Of Blue .... 7" ...... Toast .... TT503 .... 1967 ... £5 ....£10

CAMERON, DEBBIE & TOMMY SEEBACH
Lord Have Mercy .... 7" ...... EMI............... EMI5173 .... 1981 ... £1.50 ...£4

CAMERON, DION
Get Ready .... 7" ...... Rio .... R111 .... 1966 ... £4 ....£8
Miserable Friday .... 7" ...... Doctor Bird .... DB1101 .... 1967 ... £5 ....£10

CAMERON, G.C.
Me And My Life .... 7" ...... Tamla Motown TMG1033 .... 1976 ... £1.50 ...£4

CAMERON, ISLA
Lost Love .... 7" EP.. Transatlantic ... TRAEP109 .... 1964 ... £4 ....£8

CAMERON, ISLA, GUY CARAWAN, PEGGY SEEGER
Origins Of Skiffle .... 7" EP.. Pye .... NJE1043 .... 1957 ... £5 ....£10

CAMERON, JOHN
Lover Lover .... LP ...... Columbia........ SCX6116 .... 1967 ... £8 ....£20
Off Centre .... LP ...... Deram .... DML/SML1044 .... 1969 ... £20 ....£40
Troublemaker .... 7" ...... Deram .... DM256.......... 1969 ... £2 ....£5
Walk Small .... 7" ...... Columbia........ DB8120.......... 1967 ... £2 ....£5

CAMERON, RAY
Doin' My Time .... 7" ...... Island .... WIP6003 .... 1967 ... £2 ....£5 ....

CAMERON, TED & THE DEEJAYS
Early In The Morning .... 7" ...... Pye .... 7N15292 .... 1960 ... £5 ....£10 ....

CAMPBELL, AL & THE THRILLERS
Heart For Sale .... 7" .... Blue Cat .... BS118 .... 1968 ... £4 ....£8 .... Zoot Sims B side

CAMPBELL, ALEX
Alex Campbell	LP	XTRA	XTRA1041 ...	1966 ...	£5	£12	
Alex Campbell And Friends	LP	Saga............	EROS8021 ...	1967 ...	£15	£30	......with Sandy Denny
At His Best	LP	Boulevard	4073	1972 ...	£5	£12	
Been On The Road So Long	7"	Transatlantic .	TRASP4	1965 ...	£1.50	£4	
Big Daddy Of Folk Music	LP	Antagon........	LP3206	1976 ...	£6	£15	.......German
Folk Session	LP	Society.........	SOC960	1963 ...	£5	£12	
In Copenhagen	LP	Polydor	623035.........	1965 ...	£10	£25	
No Regrets	LP	Look	LKLP6043 ...	1976 ...	£8	£20	
Out West	7"	Arc	ARC36	196- ...	£1.50	£4	
This Is Alex Campbell 1	LP	Ad Rhythm-Tepee	ARPS1	1971 ...	£20	£40	
This Is Alex Campbell 2	LP	Ad Rhythm-Tepee	ARPS2	1971 ...	£20	£40	
Victoria Dines Alone	7"	Saga............	OPP2	1968 ...	£1.50	£4	
With The Greatest Respect	LP	Sundown........	SDLP2048 ...	1987 ...	£6	£15	............double

CAMPBELL, ALEX, ALAN ROBERTS, DOUGIE MACLEAN
Alex Campbell, Alan Roberts, Dougie .. LP ...... Burlington .... BURL002 .... 1979 ... £6 ....£15 ....
Maclean ....

CAMPBELL, ALEX, COLIN WILKIE & SHIRLEY HART
Sing Folk .... LP ..... Presto .... PRE648 .... 1965 ... £6 ....£15 ....

CAMPBELL, CHOKER
Hits Of The Sixties .... LP ..... Tamla Motown TML11011 .... 1965 ... £50 ......£100 ....sleeve
pictured in Guide
Mickey's Monkey .... 7" ..... Tamla Motown TMG517 .... 1965 ... £22.50 ....£45 ....

CAMPBELL, CORNELL
Cornell Campbell	LP	Trojan	TBL199	1972 ...	£6	£15	
Each Lonely Night	7"	Island	WI083	1963 ...	£5	£10	
Gloria	7"	Rio	R38	1964 ...	£5	£10	
Jericho Road	7"	Port-O-Jam......	PJ4008	1964 ...	£5	£10	
Rosahelle	7"	Island	WI039	1962 ...	£5	£10	

CAMPBELL, DAVID
Young Blood .... LP ..... Transatlantic ... . 1967 ... £10 ....£25 ....

CAMPBELL, DICK
Sings Where It's At .... LP ..... Mercury .... MG2/SR61060 ...... 1965 ... £5 ....£12 ....US

CAMPBELL, DOREEN
Rude Girls .... 7" ...... Rainbow .... RAI117 .... 1967 ... £4 ....£8 ....

CAMPBELL, DUGGIE
Enough To Make You Mine .... 7" ...... DinDisc .... DIN3 .... 1979 ... £1.50 ....£4 ....

CAMPBELL, ETHNA
What's Easy For Two .... 7" ...... Mercury .... MF804 .... 1964 ... £5 ....£10 ....

CAMPBELL FAMILY
Singing Campbells .... LP ..... Topic .... 12T120 .... 1965 ... £10 ....£25 ....

CAMPBELL, GLEN
Glen Campbell is dismissed as unredeemably middle-of-the-road by rock music collectors, yet his versions of songs by Jimmy Webb ar
always worth hearing and include at least one genuine classic in "Wichita Lineman". In 1965 he turned down the chance to become a full-tim
Beach Boy, but did record Brian Wilson's "Guess I'm Dumb" with the writer in the producer's chair.
Guess I'm Dumb	7"	Capitol	5441............	1965 ...	£15	£30	...............U
Turn Around, Look At Me	7"	Top Rank	JAR596.........	1961 ...	£2	£5	
Wichita Lineman	7"	Ember	EMBS261	1969 ...	£1.50	£4	

CAMPBELL, IAN
Across The Hills	LP	Transatlantic ...	TRA118	1964 ...	£10	£25	
Break My Mind	7"	Major Minor ...	MM639	1969 ...	£2	£5	
Ceilidh At The Crown	7" EP..	Topic	TOP76	1962 ...	£12.50	£25	
Circle Game	LP	Transatlantic ...	TRA163	1968 ...	£8	£20	
Coaldust Ballads	LP	Transatlantic ...	TRA123	1965 ...	£10	£25	
Cock Doth Craw	LP	XTRA	XTRA1061 ...	1968 ...	£8	£20	
Come Kiss Me	7"	Transatlantic ...	TRASP6	1966 ...	£1.50	£4	
Contemporary Campbells	LP	Transatlantic ...	TRA137	1965 ...	£10	£25	
Guantanamera	7"	Transatlantic ...	TRASP7	1966 ...	£1.50	£4	
Ian Campbell Folk Group	LP	MFP	MFP1349	1969 ...	£5	£12	
Ian Campbell Folk Group	7" EP..	Decca	DFE8592	1964 ...	£4	£8	
Kelly From Killane	7"	Transatlantic ...	TRASP2	1965 ...	£1.50	£4	
Lover Let Me In	7"	Transatlantic ...	BIG103	1968 ...	£2	£5	
Marilyn Monroe	7"	Decca	F11802	1964 ...	£2	£5	
New Impressions	LP	Transatlantic ...	TRA151	1967 ...	£8	£20	
One Eyed Reilly	7"	Transatlantic ...	TRASP10	1966 ...	£1.50	£4	
Presenting The Ian Campbell Folk	LP	Contour	2870314	197- ...	£5	£12	
Group							
Sampler	LP	Transatlantic ...	TRASAM4	1969 ...	£6	£15	

Sampler	7" EP	Transatlantic	TRAEP128	1965	£2.50	£6	
Sampler 2	LP	Transatlantic	TRASAM12	1969	£6	£15	
Something To Sing About	LP	Pye	PKL5506	1972	£10	£25	
Sun Is Burning	LP	Argo	ZFB13	1971	£10	£25	
Sun Is Burning	7"	Topic	STOP102	1964	£2	£5	
Tam O'Shanter	LP	XTRA	XTRA1074	1968	£8	£20	
This Is The Ian Campbell Folk Group	LP	Transatlantic	TRA110	1963	£10	£25	
Times They Are A-Changin'	7"	Transatlantic	TRASP5	1965	£2	£5	chart single

CAMPBELL, JIMMY

Album	LP	Philips	6308100	1972	£5	£12	
Half Baked	LP	Vertigo	6360010	1970	£5	£12	with Merseybeats
Songs Of Anastasia	LP	Fontana	STL5508	1969	£4	£10	

CAMPBELL, JO ANN

All The Hits	LP	Cameo	(S)C1026	1962	£8	£20	US
I Changed My Mind Jack	7"	HMV	POP1003	1962	£1.50	£4	
I'm Nobody's Baby	LP	End	LP306	1959	£15	£30	US
I'm The Girl From Wolverton Mountain	7"	Columbia	DB4889	1962	£1.50	£4	
Kookie Little Paradise	7"	HMV	POP776	1960	£1.50	£4	
Mister Fixit Man	7"	Cameo Parkway	C237	1962	£1.50	£4	
Mother Please	7"	Cameo Parkway	C249	1963	£2	£5	
Motorcycle Michael	7"	HMV	POP873	1961	£1.50	£4	chart single
Starring	LP	Coronet	CX(S)199	1964	£6	£15	US
Twistin' And Listenin'	LP	ABC	(S)393	1962	£8	£20	US
Wait A Minute	7"	London	HLU8536	1958	£12.50	£25	

CAMPBELL, NOLA

Pictures Of You	7"	Gas	GAS107	1969	£4	£8	

CAMPBELL, ROY

Another Saturday Night	7"	Giant	GN41	1968	£4	£8	
Engine Number Nine	7"	Jolly	JY003	1968	£4	£8	

CAMPBELL-LYONS, PATRICK

Electric Plough	LP	Public	PUBL1	1981	£5	£12	
Everybody Should Fly A Kite	7"	Sovereign	SOV115	1973	£4	£8	
Me And My Friend	LP	Sovereign	SVNA7258	1973	£50	£100	
Out On The Road	7"	Sovereign	SOV119	1973	£4	£8	

CAN

Cannibalisms	LP	United Artists	UDM105/6	1978	£5	£12	double
Deep End (Soundtracks)	LP	United Artists	UAS29283	1970	£6	£15	
Ege Bamyasi	LP	United Artists	UAS29414	1972	£6	£15	
Flow Motion	LP	Virgin	V2071	1976	£4	£10	
Future Days	LP	United Artists	UAS29505	1973	£6	£15	
Landed	LP	Virgin	V2041	1975	£5	£12	
Limited Edition	LP	United Artists	USP103	1974	£5	£12	
Monster Movie	LP	United Artists	UAS29094	1969	£6	£15	
Onlyou	cass	Pure Freude	PF23	1982	£15	£30	tin container
Opener	LP	Sunset	SLS50400	1976	£4	£10	
Saw Delight	LP	Virgin	V2079	1977	£4	£10	
Soon Over Babaluma	LP	United Artists	UAG29673	1974	£6	£15	
Tago Mago	LP	United Artists	UAD60009/10	1971	£8	£20	double
Unlimited Edition	LP	Caroline	CAD3001	1976	£6	£15	double

CANAAN

Canaan	LP	Dovetail	DOVE3	1973	£25	£50	
Out Of The Wilderness	LP	Myrrh		197-	£15	£30	

CANADIAN BEATLES

Three Faces North	LP	Tide	2005	1964	£15	£30	US

CANADIAN SQUIRES

Levon and the Hawks - later to become the Band - recorded as the Canadian Squires for one single.

Uh Uh Uh	7"	Ware	6002	1965	£7.50	£15	US

CANARIES

Flying High	LP	B.T.Puppy	BTPS1007	1970	£6	£15	US

CANDIDO

Beautiful	LP	Blue Note	BST84357	1970	£5	£12	
Candido In Indigo	LP	HMV	CLP1265	1959	£6	£15	
Candido The Volcanic	10" LP	HMV	DLP1182	1958	£6	£15	

CANDOLI, CONTE

Sincerely, Conte	10" LP	London	LZN14010	1956	£8	£20	
Toots Sweet	LP	London	LTZN15036	1957	£6	£15	

CANDOLI, PETE

St.Louis Blues Boogie	7"	Capitol	CL14615	1956	£2	£5	

CANDY & THE KISSES

Do The 81	7"	Cameo Parkway	C336	1965	£20	£40	
Mr.Creator	7"	Kent	TOWN104	1985	£5	£10	Chuck Jackson B side

CANDY CHOIR

Title	Format	Label	Cat No	Year	Price	Price	Notes
Alexander's Ragtime Band	7"	CBS	3305	1968	£1.50	£4	
Children And Flowers	7"	CBS	3061	1967	£1.50	£4	
Shake Hands And Come Out Crying	7"	Parlophone	R5472	1966	£2	£5	

CANDYMEN

Title	Format	Label	Cat No	Year	Price	Price	Notes
De Manchester A Paris	7" EP	Barclay	70806	1965	£7.50	£15	French
Georgia Pines	7"	HMV	POP1612	1967	£2	£5	

CANE

Title	Format	Label	Cat No	Year	Price	Price
3 X 3	7"	Lightning	GIL531	1978	£2	£5

CANNED HEAT

At their best ("Boogie With Canned Heat"), Canned Heat were one of the most convincing white blues groups. Bob Hite and Henry Vestine had a collection of blues records of legendary proportions, so they were not short of good examples to follow. They did have a liking, however, for what they called "boogie", by which they meant a string of extremely long and extremely tedious instrumental solos played over an elemental riff. Both extremes can be found on the double "Living The Blues": a boogie of record-breaking length, but also some short experimental tracks that take interesting liberties with the blues format. The record made with John Lee Hooker also shows Canned Heat's abilities well. They let Hooker run the show, but by virtue of their telling support, they push him into making one of his very best records.

Title	Format	Label	Cat No	Year	Price	Price	Notes
Boogie With Canned Heat	LP	Liberty	LBL/LBS83103	1968	£5	£12	chart LP
Canned Heat	LP	Liberty	LBL/LBS83059	1967	£6	£15	chart LP
Canned Heat '70: Concert	LP	Liberty	LBS83333	1970	£5	£12	chart LP
Cookbook	LP	Liberty	LBS83303	1970	£4	£10	chart LP
Future Blues	LP	Liberty	LBS83364	1970	£5	£12	chart LP
Going Up The Country	7"	Liberty	LBF15169	1968	£1.50	£4	chart single
Hallelujah	LP	Liberty	LBS83239	1969	£5	£12	
Let's Work Together	7"	Liberty	LBF15302	1969	£1.50	£4	chart single
Live At Topanga Canyon	LP	Wand	WDS693	1970	£6	£15	US
Living The Blues	LP	Liberty	LDS84001	1969	£8	£20	double
Living The Blues	LP	United Artists	UAS29258/9	1972	£6	£15	double
On The Road Again	7"	Liberty	LBS15090	1968	£1.50	£4	chart single
Rockin' With The King	7"	United Artists	UP35248	1972	£1.50	£4	with Little Richard
Spoonful	7"	Pye	7N25513	1970	£1.50	£4	
Vintage Heat	LP	Pye	NSPL28129	1970	£5	£12	

CANNED HEAT & CLARENCE GATEMOUTH BROWN

Title	Format	Label	Cat No	Year	Price	Price	Notes
Gate's On Heat	LP	Barclay	80603	1973	£6	£15	French

CANNED HEAT & MEMPHIS SLIM

Title	Format	Label	Cat No	Year	Price	Price	Notes
Memphis Heat	LP	Barclay	80607	1975	£6	£15	French

CANNED ROCK

Title	Format	Label	Cat No	Year	Price	Price
Kinetic Energy	LP	Canned Rock	CAN002	1978	£4	£10
Live	LP	Canned Rock	CAN003	1979	£4	£10

CANNIBAL & THE HEADHUNTERS

Title	Format	Label	Cat No	Year	Price	Price
Land Of 1000 Dances	LP	CBS	62942	1967	£6	£15
Land Of 1000 Dances	7"	Stateside	SS403	1965	£6	£12

CANNIBALS

Title	Format	Label	Cat No	Year	Price	Price
Good Guys	7"	Big Cock	FUK1	1978	£2	£5

CANNON, ACE

Title	Format	Label	Cat No	Year	Price	Price	Notes
Blues Stay Away From Me	7"	London	HLU9546	1962	£1.50	£4	
Cottonfields	7"	London	HLU9745	1963	£1.50	£4	
Searching	7"	London	HLU9866	1964	£1.50	£4	
Tuff	LP	Hi	HLP32007	1961	£4	£10	US
Tuff	7"	London	HLU9498	1962	£1.50	£4	
Wonderland By Night	7"	London	HLU10105	1967	£1.50	£4	

CANNON BROTHERS

Title	Format	Label	Cat No	Year	Price	Price
Turn Your Eyes To Me	7"	Brit	WI1003	1965	£5	£10

CANNON, FREDDIE

Title	Format	Label	Cat No	Year	Price	Price	Notes
Abigail Beecher	7"	Warner Bros	WB123	1964	£1.50	£4	
Action	LP	Warner Bros	W(S)1612	1965	£6	£15	US
Action	7"	Warner Bros	WB5645	1965	£1.50	£4	
Bang On	LP	Stateside	SL10013	1963	£10	£25	
Beautiful Downtown Burbank	7"	London	HLK10252	1969	£1.50	£4	
Blast Off	7" EP	Stateside	SE1002	1962	£6	£12	
Buzz Buzz A Diddle It	7"	Top Rank	JAR568	1961	£6	£12	chart single
California Here I Come	7"	Top Rank	JAR309	1960	£1.50	£4	
Chattanooga Shoeshine Boy	7"	Top Rank	JAR334	1960	£1.50	£4	
Come On And Love Me	7"	Stateside	SS155	1963	£1.50	£4	
Dedication Song	7"	Warner Bros	WB5693	1966	£1.50	£4	
Everybody Monkey	7"	Stateside	SS220	1963	£1.50	£4	
Explosive Freddie Cannon	LP	Top Rank	25018	1960	£8	£20	
Explosive Freddie Cannon	7" EP	Top Rank	JKP2058	1960	£7.50	£15	
Four Direct Hits	7" EP	Top Rank	JKP2066	1960	£6	£12	
Freddie Cannon	LP	Warner Bros	WM/WS8153	1964	£8	£20	
Freddie Cannon Favourites	LP	Top Rank	35113	1961	£10	£25	
From Me And My Gal	7"	Top Rank	JAR592	1961	£1.50	£4	
Greatest Hits	LP	Warner Bros	W(S)1628	1966	£6	£15	US
Happy Shades Of Blue	LP	Top Rank	35106	1961	£10	£25	
Happy Shades Of Blue	7"	Top Rank	JAR407	1960	£1.50	£4	
Humdinger	7"	Top Rank	JAR518	1960	£1.50	£4	
If You Were A Rock And Roll Record	7"	Stateside	SS134	1962	£1.50	£4	
Muskrat Ramble	7"	Top Rank	JAR548	1961	£1.50	£4	chart single
Okefenokee	7"	Top Rank	JAR207	1959	£2	£5	
On Target	7" EP	Top Rank	JKP3010	1961	£7.50	£15	
Palisades Park	7"	Stateside	SS101	1962	£1.50	£4	chart single

Title	Format	Label	Cat No	Year			Notes
Patty Baby	7"	Stateside	SS201	1963	£1.50	£4	
Steps Out	LP	Stateside	SL10062	1964	£15	£30	
Sweet Georgia Brown	7"	Stateside	SS298	1964	£1.50	£4	
Tallahassee Lassie	7"	Top Rank	JAR135	1959	£1.50	£4	chart single
Teen Queen Of The Week	7"	Top Rank	JAR609	1962	£1.50	£4	
That's The Way Girls Are	7"	Stateside	SS260	1964	£1.50	£4	
Transistor Sister	7"	Top Rank	JAR579	1961	£1.50	£4	
Ups And Downs Of Love	7"	Stateside	SS183	1963	£1.50	£4	
Urge	7"	Top Rank	JAR369	1960	£1.50	£4	chart single
Way Down Yonder In New Orleans	7"	Top Rank	JAR247	1959	£1.50	£4	chart single
What's Gonna Happen When Summer's Done	7"	Stateside	SS118	1962	£1.50	£4	

CANNON, GUS

Title	Format	Label	Cat No	Year			Notes
Cannon's Jug Stompers/Clifford's Louisville Jug Band	LP	Tax	LP2	1966	£6	£15	
Walk Right In	LP	Stax	702	1962	£8	£20	US

CANNON, JUDY

Title	Format	Label	Cat No	Year			Notes
Very First Day I Met You	7"	Pye	7N15900	1965	£7.50	£15	

CANNON, SEAN

Title	Format	Label	Cat No	Year			Notes
Erin The Green	LP	Ogham	BLB5004	1979	£5	£12	Irish
Roving Journey Man	LP	Cottage	COT411	1977	£5	£12	

CANNONBALL & JOHNNY MELODY

Title	Format	Label	Cat No	Year			Notes
Cool Hand Luke	7"	Big Shot	BI518	1969	£2.50	£6	

CANNONBALLS

Title	Format	Label	Cat No	Year			Notes
Calliope Boogie	7"	Coral	Q72431	1961	£4	£8	
New Orleans Beat	7"	Coral	Q72428	1961	£4	£8	

CANNONS

Title	Format	Label	Cat No	Year			Notes
Bush Fire	7"	Columbia	DB4724	1961	£4	£8	
I Didn't Know The Gun Was Loaded	7"	Decca	F11269	1960	£4	£8	

CANNY FETTLE

Title	Format	Label	Cat No	Year			Notes
Varry Canny	LP	Tradition	TSR023	1975	£6	£15	

CANTELON, WILLARD

Title	Format	Label	Cat No	Year			Notes
LSD Battle For The Mind	LP	Supreme	M/S113	1966	£5	£12	US

CANTOR, EDDIE

Title	Format	Label	Cat No	Year			Notes
Ma He's Making Eyes At Me	7" EP	Capitol	EAP120113	1961	£2.50	£6	

CAPE KENNEDY CONSTRUCTION CO.

Title	Format	Label	Cat No	Year			Notes
First Step On The Moon	7"	President	PT265	1969	£1.50	£4	

CAPEHART, JERRY

Title	Format	Label	Cat No	Year			Notes
Song Of New Orleans	7"	Crest	1101	1962	£7.50	£15	US
Walkin' Stick Boogie	7"	Cash	1021	1956	£45	£90	US

CAPITOLS

Title	Format	Label	Cat No	Year			Notes
Cool Jerk	7"	Atlantic	2091105	1971	£2	£5	
Cool Jerk	7"	Atlantic	584004	1966	£2.50	£6	
Cool Jerk	7"	Atlantic	584251	1969	£2	£5	
Dance The Cool Jerk	LP	Atco	(SD33)190	1966	£6	£15	US
Dance The Cool Jerk	LP	Atlantic	587/588019	1966	£6	£15	
I Got To Handle It	7"	Atlantic	584043	1966	£1.50	£4	
We Got A Thing	LP	Atco	(SD33)201	1966	£5	£12	US

CAPITOLS (2)

Title	Format	Label	Cat No	Year			Notes
Honey And Wine	7"	Pye	7N17025	1966	£2	£5	

CAPP, ANDY

Title	Format	Label	Cat No	Year			Notes
Law	7"	Duke	DU69	1970	£2	£5	

CAPRI, DANNY

Title	Format	Label	Cat No	Year			Notes
Desirable	7"	Capitol	CL14265	1955	£1.50	£4	
Don't Make A Liar Out Of Me	7"	Capitol	CL14302	1955	£1.50	£4	

CAPRIS

Title	Format	Label	Cat No	Year			Notes
There's A Moon Out Tonight	7"	Columbia	DB4605	1961	£20	£40	

CAPSTICK, TONY

Title	Format	Label	Cat No	Year			Notes
Punch And Judy Man	LP	Rubber	RUB008	1974	£5	£12	

CAPTAIN BEEFHEART

Title	Format	Label	Cat No	Year			Notes
Bluejeans And Moonbeams	LP	Virgin	V2123	1974	£4	£10	
Clear Spot	LP	Reprise	K54007	1972	£4	£10	
Diddy Wah Diddy	7" EP	A&M	AME600	1971	£90	£180	
Legendary A&M Sessions	12"	A&M	AMY226	1984	£2.50	£6	
Lick My Decals Off	LP	Reprise	K44244	1973	£4	£10	
Lick My Decals Off	LP	Straight	STS1063	1970	£6	£15	chart LP
Light Reflected Off The Oceans Of The Moon	12"	Virgin	VS53412	1982	£2.50	£6	
Mirror Man	LP	Buddah	2365022	1971	£4	£10	chart LP
Moonchild	7"	A&M	AMS726	1968	£7.50	£15	
Safe As Milk	LP	Buddah	623171	1969	£4	£10	
Safe As Milk	LP	Marble Arch	MAL1117	1969	£4	£10	
Safe As Milk	LP	Pye	NPL28110	1968	£8	£20	
Sixpack	7"	Virgin	SIXPACK1	1979	£7.50	£15	pic disc

Spotlight Kid	LP	Reprise	K44162	1972	£4	£10	chart LP
Strictly Personal	LP	Liberty	LBL/LBS83172	1968	£8	£20	
Too Much Time	7"	Reprise	K14233	1973	£2.50	£6	
Trout Mask Replica	LP	Straight	STS1053	1969	£8	£20	double, chart LP
Unconditionally Guaranteed	LP	Virgin	V2015	1974	£4	£10	
Upon The My-Oh-My	7"	Virgin	VS110	1974	£2.50	£6	
Yellow Brick Road	7"	Pye	7N25443	1968	£7.50	£15	
Ice Cream For Crow	7"	Virgin	VS534	1982	£1.50	£4	
Sure 'Nuff 'N Yes I Do	7"	Buddah	BDS466	1978	£1.50	£4	

CAPTAIN BEYOND

Captain Beyond	LP	Capricorn	K47503	1972	£4	£10	3-D cover

CAPTAIN NOAH & HIS FLOATING ZOO

Captain Noah & His Floating Zoo	LP	Argo		1972	£6	£15	
Holy Moses	LP	Argo	ZDA149	1972	£6	£15	

C.A.QUINTET

Trip Through Hell	LP	Candy Floss	7764	1969	£700	£1000	US

CARAVAN

Caravan	LP	MGM	2353058	1972	£5	£12	
Caravan	LP	Verve	SVLP6011	1968	£25	£50	sleeve pictured in Guide
Caravan	LP	Verve	VLP6011	1969	£35	£70	Mono
For Girls Who Grow Plump In The Night	LP	Deram	SDL12	1973	£4	£10	
If I Could Do It All Over Again	7"	Decca	F13063	1970	£4	£8	
If I Could Do It All Over Again	LP	Decca	SKL5052	1970	£5	£12	
In The Land Of Grey And Pink	LP	Deram	SDL1	1971	£4	£10	
Love To Love You	7"	Decca	F23125	1971	£2.50	£6	
Place Of My Own	7"	Verve	VS1518	1968	£7.50	£15	
Waterloo Lily	LP	Deram	SDL8	1972	£4	£10	

CARAVELLES

Caravelles	LP	Decca	LK4565	1963	£8	£20	
Have You Ever Been Lonely	7"	Decca	F11816	1964	£1.50	£4	
Hey Mama You've Been On My Mind	7"	Polydor	BM56137	1966	£1.50	£4	
I Don't Care If The Sun Don't Shine	7"	Fontana	TF509	1964	£1.50	£4	
I Really Don't Want To Know	7"	Decca	F11758	1963	£1.50	£4	
I Want To Love You Again	7"	Polydor	BM56164	1967	£1.50	£4	
Other Side Of Love	7"	Pye	7N17654	1968	£1.50	£4	
True Love Never Runs Smooth	7"	Polydor	NH59034	1964	£1.50	£4	
You Are Here	7"	Fontana	TF466	1964	£1.50	£4	
You Don't Have to Be A Baby To Cry	7"	Decca	F11697	1963	£1.50	£4	chart single

CARAWAN, GUY

Guy Carawan Sings	LP	Folkways	3548	1959	£5	£12	US
Old Man Atom	7"	Pye	7N15132	1958	£1.50	£4	
Songs From The South	7" EP	Collector	JEA4	1961	£2	£5	

CARDIAC ARREST

Bus For A Bus On A Bus	7"	Tortch	TOR002	1979	£4	£8	
Running In The Street	7"	Another Record	AN1	1981	£2	£5	

CARDIACS

Seaside Treats	12"	Alphabet	ALPH002	1986	£2.50	£5	
Toy World	cass	Cardiacs		1981	£4	£10	

CARDIGANS

Poor Boy	7"	Mercury	AMT1007	1958	£2	£5	

CAREFREES

We Love You All	LP	London	LL3/PS379	1964	£8	£20	US
We Love You Beatles	7"	Oriole	CB1916	1964	£4	£8	

CAREY, DAVE

Broken Wings	7"	Columbia	SCM5030	1953	£1.50	£4	

CARGO

Cargo	LP	Harvest	5C05224582	1971	£60	£120	Dutch

CARIBBEANS

Let Me Walk By	7"	Doctor Bird	DB1181	1969	£5	£10	Amblings B side
Please Please	7"	Crab	CRAB14	1969	£2	£5	Matadors B side

CARIBBEATS

Bells Of Saint Mary's Ska	7"	Ska Beat	JB246	1966	£5	£10	Winston Richards B side
Highway 300	7"	Double D	DD101	1967	£4	£8	
I'll Try	7"	Double D	DD103	1967	£4	£8	

CARIBS

Taboo	7"	Starlite	ST45012	1960	£2	£5	

CARL & THE CHEETAHS

Beg Borrow And Steal	7"	Columbia	DB7162	1963	£1.50	£4	

CARL & THE COMMANDERS

Farmer John	7"	Columbia	DB4719	1961	£2.50	£6	

CARLEW CHOIR
Huma Lama	7"	Spark	SRL1028	1971	£1.50	£4	

CARLISLE, BELINDA
Circle In The Sand	CD-s	Virgin	VSCD1074	1987	£4	£10	
Circle In The Sand	12"	Virgin	VSTY1074	1988	£10	£25	pic disc
Heaven Is A Place On Earth	CD-s	Virgin	VSCD1036	1987	£4	£10	
I Get Weak	CD-s	Virgin	VSCD1046	1988	£6	£15	pic disc
Leave A Light On	CD-s	Virgin	VSCD1210	1989	£2.50	£6	
Leave A Light On	7"	Virgin	VSP1210	1989	£1.50	£4	poster PS
Love Never Dies	CD-s	Virgin	VSCD1150	1988	£2.50	£6	
Mad About You	CD-s	IRS	DIRM118	1988	£15	£30	
Runaway Horses	CD-s	Virgin	VSCD1244	1990	£2.50	£6	
Summer Rain	CD-s	Virgin	VSCDT1323	1990	£2.50	£6	
Vision Of You	CD-s	Virgin	VSCDT1264	1990	£2.50	£6	
World Without You	CD-s	Virgin	VSCD1114	1988	£4	£10	
World Without You	7"	Virgin	VSX1114	1988	£4	£8	boxed
World Without You	12"	Virgin	VST1114	1988	£3	£8	poster sleeve

CARLISLE, BILLY
Down Boy	7"	Mercury	AMT1063	1959	£7.50	£15	

CARLISLE BROTHERS
Fresh From The Country	7" EP	Parlophone	GEP8799	1959	£7.50	£15	

CARLSEN, DAVE
Pale Horse	LP	Spark	SRLP110	1973	£5	£12	

CARLTON & HIS SHOES
Love Me Forever	LP	Studio One	PSOL003	197-	£6	£15	
Love Me Forever	7"	Coxsone	CS7065	1968	£5	£10	
This Feeling	7"	Studio One	SO2062	1968	£6	£12	

CARLTON, EDDIE
It Will Be Done	7"	Cream	5001	1976	£2	£5	

CARLTON, LARRY
Singing Playing	LP	Blue Thumb	BTS46	1973	£5	£12	US

CARLTON, LITTLE CARL
46 Drums 1 Guitar	7"	Action	ACT4514	1968	£1.50	£4	
Competition Ain't Nothing	7"	Action	ACT4501	1968	£7.50	£15	
Look At Mary Wonder	7"	Action	ACT4537	1969	£4	£8	

CARMEN
Dancing On A Cold Wind	LP	Regal Zonophone	SLRZ1040	1975	£8	£20	
Fandangos In Space	LP	Regal Zonophone	SRZA8518	1973	£8	£20	

CARMICHAEL, HOAGY
Crazy Otto Rag	7"	Vogue Coral	Q72078	1955	£1.50	£4	
Flight To Hong Kong	7"	Vogue Coral	Q72206	1956	£1.50	£4	
Hoagy Carmichael	7" EP	Vogue	VE170113	1958	£4	£8	
Hong Kong Blues	7"	Vogue Coral	Q72123	1956	£1.50	£4	
Lazy River	7"	Vogue Coral	Q72095	1955	£1.50	£4	
Stardust	7" EP	HMV	7EG8037	1954	£2	£5	
Stardust Road	7" EP	Brunswick	OE9023	1954	£2.50	£6	

CARN, JEAN
Free Love	7"	Philadelphia	PIR5051	1977	£1.50	£4	

CARNABY
Jump And Dance	7"	Piccadilly	7N35272	1965	£12.50	£25	

CARNABY STREET POP
Carnaby Street Pop	LP	Carnaby	CNLS6003	1969	£25	£50	

CARNATIONS
Mighty Man	7"	Blue Beat	BB285	1964	£5	£10	

CARNE, JUDY
Sock It To Me	7"	Reprise	RS20680	1968	£1.50	£4	

CARNEGY HALL
Bells Of San Francisco	7"	Polydor	56224	1968	£5	£10	

CARNES, KIM
Mistaken Identity	LP	Mobile Fidelity	MFSL1073	1982	£5	£12	US audiophile
Rest On Me	LP	Amos	7016	1970	£5	£12	US

CARNIVAL
Big Bright Green Pleasure Machine	7"	Columbia	DB8255	1967	£2	£5	
Son Of A Preacher Man	7"	Liberty	LBF15252	1969	£1.50	£4	

CAROL & THE MEMORIES
Tears On My Pillow	7"	CBS	202086	1966	£2	£5	

CAROL, BOBBI
Will You Love Me Tomorrow	7"	Fontana	267260TF	1963	£1.50	£4	

CAROLINA SLIM
Carolina Blues And Boogie .... LP ...... Flyright .... LP4702 .... 1972 ... £6 ....£15 ....

CAROLINES
Love Made A Fool Of Me .... 7" ...... Polydor .... 56027 .... 1965 ... £1.50 ....£4 ....

CAROSONE, RENATO
Torero Cha Cha Cha .... 7" .... Parlophone ...... R4433 .... 1958 ... £1.50 ....£4 ....chart single

CARPENTER, IKE
Lights Out .... LP ...... Aladdin .... LP811 .... 1956 ... £50 ....£100 .... US
Lights Out .... LP ...... Score .... SLP4010 .... 1957 ... £30 ....£60 .... US

CARPENTER, KAREN
I'll Be Yours .... 7" .... Magic Lamp .... 704 .... 196- ... £150 ....£250 .... US

CARPENTER, THELMA
Back Street .... 7" ...... Coral .... Q72442 .... 1961 ... £1.50 ....£4 ....
Yes I'm Lonesome Tonight .... 7" ...... Coral .... Q72422 .... 1961 ... £1.50 ....£4 ....

CARPENTERS
Carpenters .... LP ...... A&M .... QU53502 .... 1971 ... £4 ....£10 ....US quad
Close To You .... LP ...... A&M .... QU54271 .... 1970 ... £4 ....£10 ....US quad
Horizon .... LP ...... A&M .... QU54530 .... 1975 ... £4 ....£10 ....US quad
Now And Then .... LP ...... A&M .... QU53519 .... 1973 ... £4 ....£10 ....US quad
Singles 1969-1973 .... LP ...... A&M .... QU53601 .... 1973 ... £4 ....£10 ....US quad
Song For You .... LP ...... A&M .... QU53511 .... 1972 ... £4 ....£10 ....US quad

CARPET BAGGERS
Flea Teacher .... 7" .... Spin .... SP2006 .... 1967 ... £2 ....£5 ....

CARR, CATHY
Heartbroken .... 7" ...... Vogue Coral .... Q72175 .... 1956 ... £1.50 ....£4 ....
Ivory Tower .... 7" ...... London .... HLH8274 .... 1956 ... £12.50 .....£25 ....

CARR, GEORGIA
Rocks In My Bed .... LP ...... Vee Jay .... LP/VJS1105 .... 1964 ... £5 ....£12 .... US
Shy .... LP ...... Roulette .... (S)R25077 .... 196- ... £5 ....£12 .... US
Songs By A Moody Miss .... LP ...... Tops .... 1617 .... 1958 ... £6 ....£15 .... US

CARR, HELEN
Why Do I Love You? .... LP ...... London .... HAN2065 .... 1957 ... £5 ....£12 ....

CARR, JAMES
Baby You've Got My Mind Messed Up 7" ...... Stateside .... SS507 .... 1966 ... £12.50 .....£25 ....
Dark End Of The Street .... 7" ...... Stateside .... SS2001 .... 1967 ... £2.50 ....£6 ....
Freedom Train .... 7" ...... B&C .... CB101 .... 1969 ... £1.50 ....£4 ....
I'm A Fool For You .... 7" ...... Stateside .... SS2052 .... 1967 ... £2 ....£5 ....
Let It Happen .... 7" ...... Stateside .... SS2038 .... 1967 ... £4 ....£8 ....
Love Attack .... 7" ...... Stateside .... SS535 .... 1966 ... £5 ....£10 ....
Man Needs A Woman .... LP ...... Bell .... MBLL/SBLL113 ..... 1968 ... £8 ....£20 ....
Man Needs A Woman .... LP ...... Bell .... BLL1004 .... 1968 ... £1.50 ....£4 ....
Pouring Water On A Drowning Man .... 7" ...... Stateside .... SS545 .... 1966 ... £4 ....£8 ....
You Got My Mind Messed Up .... LP ...... Stateside .... SL10205 .... 1967 ... £20 ....£40 ....

CARR, JOE 'FINGERS'
Barky-Roll Stomp .... 7" ...... Capitol .... CL14359 .... 1955 ... £2 ....£5 ....
Give Me A Band And My Baby .... 7" ...... Capitol .... CL14372 .... 1955 ... £1.50 ....£4 ....
Let Me Be Your Honey, Honey .... 7" ...... Capitol .... CL14535 .... 1956 ... £1.50 ....£4 ....
Memories Of You .... 7" ...... Capitol .... CL14520 .... 1956 ... £1.50 ....£4 ....
Piccadilly Rag .... 7" ...... Capitol .... CL14169 .... 1954 ... £2.50 ....£6 ....
Portuguese Washerwoman .... 7" ...... Capitol .... CL14587 .... 1956 ... £1.50 ....£4 ....chart single

CARR, JOHNNY
Do You Love That Girl .... 7" ...... Fontana .... TF600 .... 1965 ... £2.50 ....£6 ....
Respectable .... 7" ...... Decca .... F11854 .... 1964 ... £5 ....£10 ....
Then So Do I .... 7" ...... Fontana .... TF681 .... 1966 ... £2.50 ....£6 ....
Things Get Better .... 7" ...... Fontana .... TF823 .... 1967 ... £6 ....£12 ....

CARR, LEROY
Blues Before Sunrise .... LP ...... CBS .... BPG62206 .... 1963 ... £8 ....£20 ....
RCA Victor Race Series Vol.2 .... 7" EP. RCA .... RCX7168 .... 1964 ... £5 ....£10 ....
Singin' The Blues .... LP ...... Biograph.......... C9 .... 1973 ... £4 ....£10 .... US
Treasures Of North American Negro   7" EP.. Fontana .... TFE17051 .... 1958 ... £6 ....£12 ....
Music ....

CARR, LINDA
Everytime .... 7" ...... Stateside .... SS2058 .... 1967 ... £5 ....£10 ....

CARR, ROMEY
These Things Will Keep Me Loving   7" ...... Columbia.......... DB8710 .... 1970 ... £7.50 ....£15 ....
You ....

CARR, VALERIE
When The Boys Talk About The Girls ... 7" ...... Columbia.......... DB4131 .... 1958 ... £1.50 ....£4 ....chart single

CARR, WYNONA
I Gotta Stand Tall .... 7" ...... Reprise .... R20033 .... 1961 ... £5 ....£10 ....

CARROLL, ANDREA
It Hurts To Be Sixteen .... 7" ...... London .... HLX9772 .... 1963 ... £1.50 ....£4 ....

CARROLL, BARBARA
North By Northwest .... 7" .... London .... HLR8981 .... 1959 ... £1.50 ....£4

CARROLL, BERNADETTE
Party Girl .... 7" .... Stateside .... SS311 .... 1964 ... £1.50 ....£4

CARROLL, BOB
Hi Ho Silver .... 7" .... London .... HLT8724 .... 1958 ... £4 ....£8
I Can't Get You Out Of My Life .... 7" .... London .... HLT8888 .... 1959 ... £2 ....£5
I Love You So Much It Hurts .... 7" .... MGM .... SP1132 .... 1955 ... £1.50 ....£4
Red Confetti,Pink Balloons,& .... 7" .... London .... HLU8299 .... 1956 ... £7.50 ....£15
Tambourines ....

CARROLL, DIAHANN
Big Country .... 7" .... London .... HLT8788 .... 1959 ... £2 ....£5
Sings Harold Arlen .... LP ...... RCA .... LPM1467 .... 1956 ... £8 ....£20 .... US

CARROLL, JOHNNY & THE HOT ROCKS
Hot Rock .... 7" .... Brunswick....... 05603 .... 1956 ... £150 ......£250
Wild Wild Women .... 7" .... Brunswick....... 05580 .... 1956 ... £150 ......£250

CARROLL, PAT
To The Sun .... 7" .... Pye .... 7N25592 .... 1972 ... £5 ....£10

CARROLL, RONNIE
Mr. And Mrs. Is The Name .... LP ...... Philips .... (S)BL7591 .... 1964 ... £4 ....£10 ..with Millicent Martin
Ring-A-Ding Girl .... 7" .... Philips .... PB1222 .... 1962 ... £1.50 ....£4
Sometimes I'm Happy, Sometimes I'm . LP ...... Philips .... BL7563 .... 1963 ... £4 ....£10
Blue
Walk Hand In Hand .... 7" EP.. Philips .... BBE12074 .... 1956 ... £4 ....£8
Wonderful Things And Other .... LP ...... Wing .... WL1108 .... 1965 ... £4 ....£10
Favourites

CARROLLS
Come On .... 7" .... CBS .... 3710 .... 1968 ... £2 ....£5
Surrender Your Love .... 7" .... Polydor .... 2058152 .... 1971 ... £1.50 ....£4
Surrender Your Love .... 7" .... Polydor .... BM56081 .... 1966 ... £2 ....£5

CARRUTHERS, BEN
The "Jack O'Diamonds" single is of special interest to Bob Dylan collectors, as the song consists of a setting of part of the poetry written by Bob Dylan as sleeve notes for his "Another Side" album. An effective version of the song was also recorded by Fairport Convention on their debut LP.
Jack O'Diamonds .... 7" .... Parlophone...... R5295 .... 1965 ... £12.50 ......£25

CARS
Candy O .... LP ...... Nautilus .... 1981 ... £6 ....£15 .... US audiophile
Cars .... LP ...... Nautilus .... 1981 ... £6 ....£15 .... US audiophile
Double Life .... 7" .... Elektra .... K12385P .... 1979 ... £1.50 ....£4 .... pic disc
Just What I Needed .... 7" .... Elektra .... K12301 .... 1978 ... £2.50 ....£6

CARSON, CHAD
Don't Pick On Me .... 7" .... HMV .... POP1156 .... 1963 ... £5 ....£10

CARSON, KEN
Daniel Boone .... 7" .... London .... HLF8237 .... 1956 ... £12.50 ......£25
Hawkeye .... 7" .... London .... HLF8213 .... 1955 ... £12.50 ......£25

CARSON, KIT
Band Of Gold .... 7" .... Capitol .... CL14524 .... 1956 ... £2 ....£5

CARTER, ANITA
Blue Doll .... 7" .... London .... HLA8693 .... 1958 ... £2 ....£5
Moon Girl .... 7" .... London .... HLW9102 .... 1960 ... £1.50 ....£4

CARTER, BENNY
Aspects .... LP ...... London .... LTZT15169 .... 1959 ... £6 ....£15
Benny Carter Orchestra .... 10" LP Columbia........ 33C9002 .... 1955 ... £20 ....£40
Jazz Giant .... LP ...... Contemporary. LAC12188 .... 1959 ... £6 ....£15
Swingin' The Twenties .... LP ...... Contemporary. LAC12225 .... 1959 ... £6 ....£15

CARTER, BETTY
Good Life .... 7" .... London .... HLK9748 .... 1963 ... £2 ....£5

CARTER, CALVIN
Twist Along .... LP ...... Vee Jay .... LP/SR1041 .... 1962 ... £6 ....£15 .... US

CARTER, CAROLYN
I'm Thru .... 7" .... London .... HL9959 .... 1965 ... £6 ....£12

CARTER, CLARENCE
Dynamic .... LP ...... Atlantic .... 588172 .... 1968 ... £5 ....£12
Feeling Is Right .... 7" .... Atlantic .... 584272 .... 1969 ... £1.50 ....£4
It's All In Your Mind .... 7" .... Atlantic .... 2091045 .... 1971 ... £1.50 ....£4
Looking For A Fox .... 7" .... Atlantic .... 584176 .... 1968 ... £2.50 ....£6
Patches .... 7" .... Atlantic .... 2091030 .... 1970 ... £1.50 ....£4 .... chart single
Slip Away .... 7" .... Atlantic .... 584187 .... 1968 ... £1.50 ....£4
Slipped, Tripped And Fell In Love .... 7" .... Atlantic .... 2091139 .... 1971 ... £1.50 ....£4
Snatchin' It Back .... 7" .... Atlantic .... 584248 .... 1969 ... £1.50 ....£4
Take It Off Him And Put It On Me .... 7" .... Atlantic .... 584309 .... 1970 ... £1.50 ....£4
Testifyin' .... LP ...... Atlantic .... 588191 .... 1969 ... £5 ....£12
This Is Clarence Carter .... LP ...... Atlantic .... 588152 .... 1968 ... £5 ....£12

Thread The Needle	7"	Atlantic	584154	1968	£2	£5	
Too Weak To Fight	7"	Atlantic	584223	1968	£1.50	£4	

CARTER FAMILY

Mean As Hell	7" EP..	CBS	EP6073	1966	£4	£8	
Mountain Music Vol.2	7" EP..	Brunswick	OE9168	1955	£4	£8	
Original And Great Carter Family Vol.1	7" EP..	RCA	RCX7100	1962	£4	£8	
Original And Great Carter Family Vol.2	7" EP..	RCA	RCX7101	1962	£4	£8	
Original And Great Carter Family Vol.3	7" EP..	RCA	RCX7102	1962	£4	£8	
Original And Great Carter Family Vol.4	7" EP..	RCA	RCX7109	1963	£4	£8	
Original And Great Carter Family Vol.5	7" EP..	RCA	RCX7110	1963	£4	£8	
Original And Great Carter Family Vol.6	7" EP..	RCA	RCX7111	1963	£4	£8	

CARTER, HAL

Twisting Time Is Here	7"	Oriole	CB1709	1962	£1.50	£4	

CARTER, HERBIE

Happy Time	7"	Duke	DU4	1968	£4	£8	

CARTER, JEAN

No Good Jim	7"	Stateside	SS2114	1968	£1.50	£4	

CARTER LEWIS & THE SOUTHERNERS

Poor Joe	7"	Piccadilly	7N35085	1962	£10	£20	
Skinnie Minnie	7"	Oriole	CB1919	1964	£6	£12	
So Much in Love	7"	Piccadilly	7N35004	1961	£7.50	£15	
Sweet And Tender Romance	7"	Oriole	CB1835	1963	£6	£12	
Tell Me	7"	Ember	EMBS165	1962	£12.50	£25	
Two Timing Baby	7"	Ember	EMBS145	1961	£12.50	£25	
Your Mama's Out Of Town	7"	Oriole	CB1868	1963	£10	£20	

CARTER, MARTIN

Ups And Downs	LP	Tradition	TSR012	1972	£6	£15	

CARTER, MEL

Easy Listening	LP	Imperial	12319	1966	£5	£12	US
Hold Me, Thrill Me, Kiss Me	LP	Imperial	12289	1965	£5	£12	US
My Heart Sings	LP	Imperial	12300	1965	£5	£12	US
When A Boy Falls In Love	LP	Derby	LPM702	1963	£25	£50	US
When A Boy Falls In Love	7"	Pye	7N25212	1963	£2	£5	

CARTER, SONNY

There Is No Greater Love	7"	Parlophone	MSP6167	1955	£2.50	£6	with Earl Bostic

CARTER, SYDNEY

Lord Of The Dance	7" EP.	Elektra	EPK801	1966	£6	£12	

CARTER THE UNSTOPPABLE SEX MACHINE

Christmas Shoppers Paradise	7"	Rough Trade	GIFT1	1990	£10	£20	
Handbuilt For Perverts	LP	Big Cat	ABB103X	1990	£5	£12	export

CARTHY, MARTIN

Bonny Lass Of Anglesey	7"	Topic	STOP7002	196-	£2	£5	
Brigg Fair	LP	Fontana	6857010	1967	£6	£15	Same LP as Byker Hil
But Two Came By	LP	Fontana	STL5477	1968	£15	£30	
Byker Hill	LP	Fontana	(S)TL5434	1967	£10	£25	
Landfall	LP	Philips	6309049	1971	£6	£15	
Martin Carthy	LP	Fontana	(S)TL5269	1965	£10	£25	
Prince Heathen	LP	Fontana	STL5529	1969	£8	£20	
Second Album	LP	Fontana	(S)TL5362	1966	£10	£25	
Selections	LP	Pegasus	PEG6	1971	£6	£15	
Shearwater	LP	Mooncrest	CREST25	1974	£5	£12	
Shearwater	LP	Pegasus	PEG12	1972	£6	£15	
Sweet Wivelsfield	LP	Deram	SML1111	1974	£6	£15	
This Is Martin Carthy	LP	Philips	6282022	1972	£4	£10	

CARTHY, MARTIN & DAVE SWARBRICK

No Songs	7" EP..	Fontana		196-	£6	£12	

CARTOONE

Cartoone	LP	Atlantic	588174	1969	£15	£30	
Penny for The Sun	7"	Atlantic	584240	1969	£4	£8	

CARTWRIGHT, DAVE

In The Middle Of The Road	LP	Harmony	DB0001	1970	£6	£15	

CARTY, PADDY & MICK O'CONNOR

Traditional Music of Ireland	LP	Morning Star	1	1974	£6	£15	U

CASCADES

Cheryl's Going Home	7"	Stateside	SS515	1966	£1.50	£4	
Cinderella	7"	RCA	RCA1358	1963	£1.50	£4	
I Bet You Won't Stay	7"	Liberty	LIB55822	1965	£1.50	£4	
I Wanna Be Your Lover	7"	Warner Bros	WB103	1963	£1.50	£4	
Jeannie	7"	RCA	RCA1378	1964	£1.50	£4	
Maybe The Rain Will Fall	LP	Uni	73069	1969	£5	£12	U
Rhythm Of The Rain	LP	Warner Bros	WM8127	1963	£8	£20	
Rhythm Of The Rain	7"	Warner Bros	WB88	1963	£1.50	£4	chart singl
Rhythm Of The Rain	7" EP.	Warner Bros	WEP1419	1963	£7.50	£15	Frenc
Rhythm Of The Rain	7" EP.	Warner Bros	WEP6106	1963	£6	£12	
Shy Girl	7"	Warner Bros	WB98	1963	£1.50	£4	

Vol.2	7" EP	Warner Bros	WEP1421	1963	£7.50	£15	French
What Goes On	LP	Cascade	681001	1968	£10	£25	US

CASEY, AL & THE K.C.ETTES

Surfing Hootenanny	7"	Pye	7N25215	1963	£2	£5	

CASEY, HOWIE & THE SENIORS

Bony Moronie	7"	Fontana	TF403	1963	£5	£10	
Double Twist	7"	Fontana	H364	1962	£6	£12	
I Ain't Mad At You	7"	Fontana	H381	1962	£5	£10	
Let's Twist	LP	Wing	WL1022	1965	£8	£20	
Twist At The Top	LP	Fontana	TFL5180	1962	£20	£40	

CASH, ALVIN

Alvin's Boogaloo	7"	President	PT119	1968	£1.50	£4	
Charge	7"	President	PT147	1968	£1.50	£4	
Doin' The Ali Shuffle	7"	President	PT129	1968	£1.50	£4	
Philly Freeze	LP	President	PTL1000	1966	£6	£15	
Philly Freeze	7"	President	PT115	1968	£1.50	£4	
Philly Freeze	7"	Stateside	SS543	1966	£5	£10	
Twine Time	7"	Stateside	SS386	1965	£6	£12	

CASH, JOHNNY

All Aboard the Blue Train	LP	Sun	1270	1963	£6	£15	US
All Over Again	7"	Philips	PB874	1958	£2	£5	
Ballad Of A Teenage Queen	7"	London	HL7032	1958	£4	£8	export
Ballad Of A Teenage Queen	7"	London	HLS8586	1958	£7.50	£15	
Bitter Tears	LP	CBS	(S)BPG62463	1964		£10	
Blood, Sweat And Tears	LP	CBS	BPG62119	1963	£5	£12	
Christmas Spirit	LP	CBS	(S)BPG62284	1963	£4	£10	
Country Boy	7" EP	London	RES1212	1959	£10	£20	
Don't Take Your Guns To Town	7"	Philips	PB897	1959	£2.50	£6	
Down The Street To 301	7"	London	HLS9182	1960	£4	£8	
Fabulous Johnny Cash	LP	CBS	(S)BPG62042	1961	£4	£10	
Fabulous Johnny Cash	LP	Philips	BBL7298/SBBL554	1959	£6	£15	
Folsom Prison Blues	7" EP	CBS	EP6601	1969	£5	£10	
Forty Shades Of Green	7"	Philips	PB1148	1961	£1.50	£4	
Forty Shades Of Green	7" EP	CBS	AGG20050	1964	£6	£12	
Frankie's Man, Johnny	7"	Philips	PB928	1959	£2	£5	
Going To Memphis	7"	Philips	PB1075	1960	£1.50	£4	
Guess Things Happen That Way	7"	London	HLS8656	1958	£4	£8	
Holy Land	LP	CBS	63428	1968	£5	£12	
Holy Land	LP	Columbia	CS9726	1969	£6	£15	US, 3D cover
Home Of The Blues	7"	London	HL7023	1957	£5	£10	export
Home Of The Blues	7"	London	HLS8514	1957	£7.50	£15	
Hymns By Johnny Cash	LP	Philips	BBL7373	1960	£4	£10	
I Got Stripes	7"	Philips	PB953	1959	£2	£5	
I Walk The Line	LP	CBS	(S)BPG62371	1964	£4	£10	
I Walk The Line	7"	London	HL8358	1957	£30	£60	gold label
It Ain't Me Babe	7" EP	CBS	EP6061	1965	£5	£10	
It's Just About Time	7"	London	HLS8789	1959	£4	£8	
Johnny Cash	7" EP	London	RES1120	1958	£12.50	£25	tri centre
Johnny Cash No.2	7" EP	London	RES1230	1959	£10	£20	tri centre
Johnny Cash Sings Hank Williams	LP	Sun	1245	1960	£8	£20	US
Johnny Cash Sings Hank Williams	7" EP	Sun	RES1193	1959	£10	£20	tri centre
Johnny Cash With His Hot And Blue Guitar	LP	Sun	1220	1956	£20	£40	US
Johnny Cash's Greatest	LP	Sun	1240	1959	£15	£30	US
Katy Too	7"	London	HLS8928	1959	£4	£8	
Little Drummer Boy	7"	Philips	PB979	1959	£1.50	£4	
Little Fauss And Big Halsey	7" EP	CBS	EP9155	1972	£2	£5	
Live At San Quentin	LP	CBS	Q63629	1973	£4	£10	quad
Lonesome Me	LP	London	HAS8253	1966	£6	£15	
Lure Of The Grand Canyon	LP	Columbia	CL1622/CS8422	1961	£6	£15	US
Luther Played The Boogie	7"	London	HLS8847	1959	£7.50	£15	
Mean As Hell	7" EP	CBS	EP6073	1966	£5	£10	
Next In Line	7"	London	HL7020	1957	£5	£10	export
Next In Line	7"	London	HLS8461	1957	£12.50	£25	
Now Here's Johnny Cash	LP	Sun	1255	1961	£8	£20	US
Now There Was A Song	LP	Philips	BBL7358/SBBL580	1960	£5	£12	
Oh Lonesome Me	7"	London	HLS9314	1961	£1.50	£4	
Original Sun Sound Of Johnny Cash	LP	London	HAS8220	1965	£6	£15	
Ride This Train	LP	Philips	BBL7417	1960	£5	£12	
Ring Of Fire	LP	CBS	(S)BPG62171	1963	£4	£10	
Ring Of Fire	7"	CBS	AAG159	1963	£1.50	£4	
Rock Island Line	7"	London	HAS2179	1959	£6	£15	
Seasons Of My Heart	7"	Philips	PB1017	1960	£1.50	£4	
Songs Of Our Soil	LP	Philips	BBL7353	1959	£5	£12	
Songs Of Our Soil	7" EP	Philips	BBE12395	1960	£6	£12	
Songs That Made Him Famous	LP	London	HAS2157	1959	£8	£20	
Songs That Made Him Famous	LP	Sun	1235	1958	£15	£30	US
Sound Of Johnny Cash	LP	CBS	(S)BPG62073	1962	£4	£10	
Straight A's In Love	7"	London	HLS9070	1960	£5	£10	
Strictly Cash	7" EP	Philips	BBE12494	1961	£6	£12	
Tennessee Flat Top Box	7"	Philips	PB1200	1961	£1.50	£4	
Train Of Love	7"	London	HLS8427	1957	£20	£40	
Troubadour	7" EP	Philips	BBE12377	1960	£6	£12	
Ways Of A Woman In Love	7"	London	HL70533	1958	£2.50	£6	export
Ways Of A Woman In Love	7"	London	HLS8709	1958	£6	£12	
You Tell Me	7"	London	HLS8979	1959	£4	£8	

CASINO ROYALES

When I Tell You That I Love You	7"	London	HLU10122	1967	£1.50	£4	

CASINOS

That's The Way	7"	Ember	EMBS241	1967	£10	£20	
Then You Can Tell Me Goodbye	LP	President	PTL1007	1967	£6	£15	
Then You Can Tell Me Goodbye	7"	President	PT123	1968	£2.50	£6	chart single
To Be Loved	7"	President	PT140	1968	£1.50	£4	
When I Stop Dreaming	7"	President	PT156	1968	£1.50	£4	

CASSIDY, STEVE

Ecstasy	7"	Ember	EMBS177	1963	£1.50	£4	

CASSIDY, TED

Lurch	7"	Capitol	CL15423	1965	£6	£12	

CAST OF THOUSANDS

My Jeannie Wears A Mini	7"	Stateside	SS546	1966	£4	£8	

CASTANARC

Journey To The East	LP	Peninsula	PENCIL010	1986	£15	£30	

CASTAWAYS

Liar Liar	7"	London	HL10003	1965	£6	£12	

CASTE

Don't Cast Aside	7"	President	PT211	1968	£2	£5	

CASTELL, JOEY

I'm Left,You're Right,She's Gone	7"	Decca	F10966	1957	£20	£40	

CASTELLS

Sacred	7"	London	HLN9392	1961	£5	£10	
So This Is Love	LP	Era	EL/ES109	1962	£20	£40	US
So This Is Love	7"	London	HLN9551	1962	£5	£10	
Two Lovers	7"	Masquerade	MA5000	196-	£1.50	£4	

CASTLE JAZZ BAND

Famous Castle Jazz Band In Hi Fi	LP	Good Time Jazz	LAG12176	1959	£5	£12	
Five Pennies	LP	Good Time Jazz	LAG12207	1960	£5	£12	

CASTLE, LEE & THE BARONS

Love She Can Count On	7"	Parlophone	R5151	1964	£4	£8	

CASTLE SISTERS

Stop Your Lying	7"	Ska Beat	JB257	1966	£5	£10	

CASTOR, JIMMY

Hey Leroy	LP	Smash	MGS2/SRW67091	1967	£5	£12	US
Hey Leroy	7"	Philips	BF1543	1967	£1.50	£4	
Magic Saxophone	7"	Philips	BF1590	1967	£7.50	£15	

CASUALS

Adios Amor	7"	Decca	F12737	1968	£1.50	£4	
Caroline	7"	Decca	F22969	1969	£1.50	£4	
Hour World	LP	Decca	SKL5001	1969	£6	£15	
If You Walk Out	7"	Fontana	TF635	1965	£1.50	£4	
Jesamine	7"	Decca	F22784	1968	£1.50	£4	chart single
Sunflower Eyes	7"	Decca	F22943	1969	£1.50	£4	
Toy	7"	Decca	F22852	1968	£1.50	£4	chart single

CAT

Run Run Run	7"	Reaction		196-	£60	£120	

CAT IRON

Cat Iron	LP	XTRA	XTRA1087	1969	£20	£40	

CAT MOTHER & ALL NIGHT NEWSBOYS

The first LP by Cat Mother And The All Night Newsboys was produced by Jimi Hendrix, a fact which once gave the record a higher collectors' value than it now has. The problem is that the group sound extremely ordinary. Hendrix does not play on the record and the production wizardry that he brought to his own records is nowhere in evidence.

Albion Doowah	LP	Polydor	2425021	1970	£4	£10	
Good Old Rock'n'Roll	7"	Polydor	56543	1970	£2	£5	
Street Giveth	LP	Polydor	184300	1969	£5	£12	

CATALINAS

Fun Fun Fun	LP	Ric	M1006	1964	£10	£25	US

CATAPILLA

Catapilla	LP	Vertigo	6360029	1971	£20	£40	spiral label
Changes	LP	Vertigo	6360074	1972	£75	£150	spiral label

CATCH

Borderline	7"	Logo	GO103	1977	£30	£60	

CATHARSIS

Catharsis	LP	Explosive	558004	1971	£5	£12	
Et S'aimer Et Mourir	LP	Festival	678	1978	£4	£10	French
Illuminations	LP	Festival	655	1974	£4	£10	French
Le Bolero	LP	Festival	676	1976	£4	£10	French

Les Chevrons	LP	Festival	651	1972	£5	£12	French
Mars	LP	Festival	652	1973	£4	£10	French
Masq	LP	Festival	650	1971	£5	£12	French

CATHODE, RAY
Time Beat	7"	Parlophone	R4901	1962	£1.50	£4

CATHY JEAN & THE ROOMATES
At The Hop!	LP	Valmor	789	1961	£37.50	£75	US

CATS
What A Crazy Life	7"	Parlophone	R5558	1967	£1.50	£4
What Is The World Coming To	7"	Parlophone	R5663	1968	£1.50	£4

CATS (2)
Falling In Love	7"	Baf	BAF5	1969	£2.50	£6
Hig	7"	Baf	BAF3	1968	£2.50	£6
My Girl	7"	Baf	BAF2	1968	£2.50	£6
Swan Lake	7"	Baf	BAF1	1968	£2.50	£6
William Tell	7"	Baf	BAF4	1968	£2.50	£6

CATS EYES
Come Away Melinda	7"	MCA	MK5043	1970	£1.50	£4
I Thank You Marianne	7"	Deram	DM209	1968	£1.50	£4
Loser	7"	MCA	MK5028	1970	£1.50	£4
Smile Girl For Me	7"	Deram	DM190	1968	£1.50	£4
Where Is She Now	7"	Deram	DM251	1969	£5	£10
Wizard	7"	MCA	MK5056	1970	£1.50	£4

CATS PYJAMAS
Camera Man	7"	Direction	583482	1968	£5	£10
Virginia Waters	7"	Direction	583235	1968	£5	£10

CATTINI, CLEM
No Time To Think	7"	Decca	F12135	1965	£6	£12

CATTOUSE, NADIA
Beautiful Barbados	7"	Reality	RE503	1966	£2.50	£6
Earth Mother	LP	RCA	SF8070	1969	£6	£15
Nadia Cattouse	LP	Reality	RY1001	1966	£30	£60
Port Mahon	7"	Parlophone	R5240	1965	£2	£5

CAVALLI, PIERRE
Strictly Guitar	7" EP	HMV	7EG8817	1963	£2	£5

CAVE, EDDIE & THE FIX
Fresh Out Of Tears	7"	Pye	7N17161	1966	£10	£20

CAVELL, ANDY
Always On Saturday	7"	HMV	POP1080	1962	£7.50	£15
Andy	7"	Pye	7N15539	1963	£7.50	£15
Hey There Cruel Heart	7"	HMV	POP1024	1962	£7.50	£15
Tell The Truth	7"	Pye	7N15610	1964	£7.50	£15

CAVELLO, JIMMY & THE HOUSE ROCKERS
Footstomping	7"	Vogue Coral	Q72240	1957	£60	£120
Rock Rock Rock	7"	Vogue Coral	Q72226	1957	£60	£120

CAZAZZA, MONTE
Something For Nobody	7"	Industrial	IR0010	1980	£2	£5
To Mom On Mother's Day	7"	Industrial	IR0005	1979	£4	£8

CCS
CCS was a big band assembled round Alexis Korner, in which some impressive musicians, including Korner himself, woefully under-used their talents. The band's version of "Whole Lotta Love" was adopted as the theme tune for TV's "Top Of The Pops", a somewhat ironical development in view of the fact that the song's originator, Led Zeppelin, refused to issue singles.
CCS	LP	RAK	SRKA6751	1970	£4	£10

CEDARS
Cedars	7" EP	Decca		1968	£50	£100
For Your Information	7"	Decca	F22720	1968	£10	£20
I Like The Way	7"	Decca	F22772	1968	£10	£20

CELESTIN, OSCAR 'PAPA'
New Orleans Band	10" LP	Melodisc	MLP506	1956	£6	£15

CELIA & THE MUTATIONS
You Better Believe Me	7"	United Artists	UP36318	1977	£2	£5

CELTIC FISHERMAN
Celtic Fisherman	LP	Mushroom		197-	£20	£40

CELTIC FOLKWEAVE
Celtic Folkweave	LP	Polydor		197-	£15	£30

CENOTAPH CORNER
Every Day But Wednesday	LP	Cottage	COT031	1979	£8	£20
Ups And Downs	LP	Cottage		1976	£8	£20

CENTAURUS
Centaurus	LP	Azra	61549	1978	£20	£40	US pic disc

CENTIPEDE

Centipede was so named because of its huge line-up – fifty-five people play on the record, not including Robert Fripp, who played guitar with the band on stage, but who remains in the producer's chair here. Centipede was the inspiration of jazz pianist Keith Tippett, as a piece of mad indulgence that would be unlikely to make anyone's fortune. "Septober Energy" is a single piece of music spread over four sides of vinyl, but it falls naturally into sections, which enable different combinations of musicians to be highlighted.

Septober Energy	LP	Neon	NE9	1971	£25	£50	double
Septober Energy	LP	RCA	DPS2054	1974	£20	£40	different cover

CENTURY 21

Alias Mister Hackenbacker	7" EP	Century 21	MA123	1967	£10	£20	
Atlantic Inferno	7" EP	Century 21	MA125	1967	£10	£20	
Brink Of Disaster	7" EP	Century 21	MA124	1967	£10	£20	
Captain Scarlet & The Mysterons	7" EP	Century 21	MA132	1967	£7.50	£15	
Captain Scarlet Is Indestructable	7" EP	Century 21	MA133	1967	£7.50	£15	
Captain Scarlet Of Spectrum	7" EP	Century 21	MA134	1967	£7.50	£15	
Captain Scarlet Vs Captain Black	7" EP	Century 21	MA135	1967	£7.50	£15	
Chain Chain	7" EP	Century 21	MA122	1967	£10	£20	
Daleks	7" EP	Century 21	MA106	1966	£15	£30	
Day Of Disaster	7" EP	Century 21	MA121	1967	£10	£20	
Desperate Intruder	7" EP	Century 21	MA119	1966	£7.50	£15	
Fab	7" EP	Century 21	MA107	1966	£6	£12	
Favourite Television Themes	LP	Century 21	LA6	1966	£10	£25	
Great Themes From Thunderbirds	7" EP	Century 21	MA116	1966	£6	£12	
Imposters	7" EP	Century 21	MA120	1966	£7.50	£15	
Into Action With Troy Tempest	7" EP	Century 21	MA101	1965	£5	£10	
Introducing Captain Scarlet	7" EP	Century 21	MA131	1967	£7.50	£15	
Introducing Thunderbirds	7" EP	Century 21	MA103	1965	£5	£10	
Jeff Tracy Introduces International Rescue	LP	Century 21	LA3	1966	£15	£30	
Journey To The Moon	LP	Century 21	LA100	1965	£20	£40	
Journey To The Moon	7" EP	Century 21	MA100	1965	£5	£10	
Lady Penelope & Other TV Themes	7" EP	Century 21	MA111	1966	£6	£12	
Lady Penelope Investigates	LP	Century 21	LA4	1966	£15	£30	
Lady Penelope Presents	LP	Century 21	LA2	1966	£15	£30	
Marina Speaks	7" EP	Century 21	MA104	1965	£5	£10	
One Move And You're Dead	7" EP	Century 21	MA128	1967	£10	£20	
Perils Of Penelope	7" EP	Century 21	MA114	1966	£6	£12	
Ricochet	7" EP	Century 21	MA126	1967	£10	£20	
Space Age Nursery Rhymes	7"	Century 21	MA117	1966	£7.50	£15	
Stately Home Robberies	7" EP	Century 21	MA110	1966	£6	£12	
Thirty Minutes After Noon	7" EP	Century 21	MA129	1967	£10	£20	
Thunderbird Four	7" EP	Century 21	MA113	1966	£6	£12	
Thunderbird One	7" EP	Century 21	MA108	1966	£6	£12	
Thunderbird Three	7" EP	Century 21	MA112	1966	£6	£12	
Thunderbird Two	7" EP	Century 21	MA109	1966	£6	£12	
Thunderbirds And Captain Scarlet	LP	Hallmark	HMA227	1973	£10	£25	
Tingha And Tucker And The Wombaville Band	7" EP	Century 21	MA127	1967	£10	£20	
Tingha And Tucker Club Song Book	LP	Century 21	LA5	1966	£6	£15	
Tingha And Tucker In Nursery Rhyme Time	7" EP	Century 21	MA130	1967	£7.50	£15	
Top Gigio In London	7" EP	Century 21	MA115	1966	£6	£12	
Trip To Marineville	7" EP	Century 21	MA102	1965	£5	£10	
TV Favourites Vol.1	LP	Marble Arch	MAL770	1968	£10	£25	
TV Favourites Vol.2	LP	Marble Arch	MAL771	1968	£10	£25	
TV Themes	7" EP	Century 21	MA136	1967	£7.50	£15	
TV21 Themes	7" EP	Century 21	MA105	1965	£5	£10	
Vault Of Death	7" EP	Century 21	MA118	1966	£10	£20	
World Of Tomorrow	LP	Century 21	LA1	1965	£10	£25	

CESANA

Tender Emotions	LP	Modern	M100	1964	£5	£12	US

CEYLIB PEOPLE

Tanyet	LP	Vault	LP117	1968	£10	£25	US

CHACKSFIELD, FRANK

Donkey Cart	7"	Decca	F10743	1956	£1.50	£4	chart single
Fiddler's Boogie	7"	Decca	F10284	1954	£1.50	£4	
In Old Lisbon	7"	Decca	F10689	1956	£1.50	£4	chart single
Quiet Rhythm Blues	7"	Parlophone	MSP6018	1953	£1.50	£4	

CHAFFIN, ERNIE

Lonesome For My Baby	7"	London	HLS8409	1957	£30	£60	

CHAIRMEN OF THE BOARD

Bittersweet	LP	Invictus	SVT1006	1972	£4	£10	
Chairmen Of The Board	LP	Invictus	SVT1002	1970	£6	£15	
Give Me Just A Little More Time	7"	Invictus	INV501	1970	£1.50	£4	chart single
Greatest Hits	LP	Invictus	SVT1009	1973	£4	£10	
In Session	LP	Invictus	SVT1003	1971	£6	£15	
Skin I'm In	LP	Invictus	65868	1974	£4	£10	

CHAKACHAS

Jungle Fever	LP	Polydor	2489050	1972	£5	£12	

CHAKIRIS, GEORGE

Cool	7"	Saga	SAG452905	1959	£2	£5	
I'm Always Chasing Rainbows	7"	Triumph	RGM1010	1960	£7.50	£15	

CHALKER, BRYAN

Bryan Chalker	LP	Chapter One	CMS1017	1973	£5	£12	
Daddy Sing Me A Song	LP	Chapter One	CMS1020	1974	£4	£10	
New Frontier	LP	Chapter One	CMS1010	1972	£10	£25	

CHALLENGERS

At The Teenage Fair	LP	GNP-Crescendo	(S)2010	1965	£6	£15	US
Billy Strange And The Challengers	LP	GNP-Crescendo	(S)2030	1966	£6	£15	US
Bulldog	7"	Stateside	SS177	1963	£2	£5	
California Kicks	LP	GNP-Crescendo	(S)2025	1966	£6	£15	US
Challengers Au Go-Go	LP	Vault	LP/VS110	1966	£8	£20	US
Greatest Hits	LP	Vault	LP/VS111	1967	£6	£15	US
K-39	LP	Vault	LP107	1964	£10	£25	US
Light My Fire	LP	GNP-Crescendo	S2045	1968	£5	£12	US
Man From UNCLE	LP	GNP-Crescendo	(S)2018	1965	£6	£15	US
Man From UNCLE	7"	Vocalion	VN9253	1965	£5	£10	
On The Move	LP	Vault	LP/VS102	1963	£8	£20	US
Sidewalk Surfing	LP	Triumph	(TR)100	1965	£6	£15	US
Surfbeat	LP	Stateside	SL10030	1963	£8	£20	
Surfing	LP	Vault	LP/VS101	1963	£8	£20	US
Surf's Up	LP	Vault	LP/VS109	1965	£8	£20	US
Twenty-Five Great Instrumental Hits	LP	GNP-Crescendo	(S)609	1967	£6	£15	US
Vanilla Funk	LP	GNP-Crescendo	S2056	1970	£4	£10	US
Walk With Me	7"	Vocalion	VN9270	1966	£2	£5	
Wipe Out	LP	Vocalion	VAN/SAVN8069	1967	£8	£20	
Wipe Out	7" EP	Vogue	INT18094	1966	£7.50	£15	French

CHALLENGERS (2)

Cry Of The Wild Goose	7"	Parlophone	R4773	1961	£2	£5	

CHALMERS, LLOYD

Cooyah	7"	Duke	DU15	1969	£2.50	£6	Uniques B side
Death A Come	7"	Explosion	EX2001	1969	£2	£6	
Duckey Luckey	7"	Songbird	SB1007	1969	£2.50	£6	
Five To Five	7"	Duke	DU25	1969	£2.50	£6	
Follow This Sound	7"	Duke	DU16	1969	£2.50	£6	
For The Good Times	7"	Duke	DU162	1973	£1.50	£4	
I'm Gonna Love You Just A Little	7"	Trojan	MJ6662	1974	£1.50	£4	
Reggae Charm	LP	Trojan	TTL30	1970	£6	£15	
Reggae Is Tight	LP	Trojan	TTL25	1970	£6	£15	
Safari	7"	Duke	DU36	1969	£2.50	£6	
Time Is Getting Hard	7"	Coxsone	CS7023	1967	£5	£10	Tony Gregory B side
Why Baby	7"	Gas	GAS114	1969	£4	£8	

CHALOFF, SERGE

Blue Serge	LP	Capitol	T742	1956	£8	£20	
Fable Of Mabel	LP	Vogue	LAE12052	1957	£20	£40	
Lestorian Mode	LP	Realm	RM113	1963	£5	£12	with tracks by Stan Getz & Brew Moore

CHAMBER POP ENSEMBLE

Chamber Pop Ensemble	LP	Decca	SKL4933	1968	£6	£15	
Walk Away Renee	7"	Decca	F12789	1968	£1.50	£4	

CHAMBERLAIN, RICHARD

Love Me Tender	7"	MGM	MGM1173	1962	£1.50	£4	chart single
Richard Chamberlain Hits	7" EP	MGM	MGMEP776	1963	£2	£5	
Richard Chamberlain Sings	LP	MGM	C923	1963	£5	£12	chart LP
Theme From Dr.Kildare	7"	MGM	MGM1160	1962	£1.50	£4	chart single

CHAMBERS BROTHERS

All Strung Out Over You	7"	CBS	202565	1967	£1.50	£4	
Are You Ready	7"	Direction	584098	1969	£1.50	£4	
Call Me	7"	Vocalion	VP9276	1966	£4	£8	
Feelin' The Blues	LP	Liberty	LBS83276	1970	£4	£10	
Greatest Hits	LP	Vault	135	1970	£5	£12	US
I Can't Turn You Loose	7"	Direction	583865	1968	£1.50	£4	
Let's Do It	7"	Direction	585033	1970	£1.50	£4	
Love Me Like The Rain	7"	Vocalion	VP9267	1966	£2.50	£6	
Love, Peace And Happiness	LP	CBS	66228	1970	£5	£12	double
Love, Peace And Happiness	7"	Direction	584846	1970	£1.50	£4	
New Generation	LP	CBS	64136	1971	£4	£10	
New Time - A New Day	LP	Direction	863451	1969	£5	£12	
Now	LP	Vault	115	1967	£6	£15	US
Oh My God	LP	Columbia	KC31158	1972	£6	£15	US
People Get Ready	LP	Vocalion	VAL/SAVL8058	1966	£10	£25	
People Get Ready	7"	Direction	584318	1969	£1.50	£4	
Shout	LP	Vault	120	1968	£5	£12	US
Time Has Come Today	LP	Direction	863407	1968	£5	£12	
Time Has Come Today	7"	Direction	583671	1968	£1.50	£4	
Time Has Come Today (extended)	7"	Direction	583760	1968	£1.50	£4	

CHAMBERS, JACK & RALPH HODGE
Country & Western Express Vol.2	7" EP..	Top Rank	JKP2056	1960	£4	£8	

CHAMBERS, PAUL
Bass On Top	LP	Blue Note	BLP/BST81569	196-	£10	£25	
Whims Of Chambers	LP	Blue Note	BLP/BST81534	196-	£10	£25	

CHAMBLEE, EDDIE
Blues For Eddie	78	Esquire	10330	1953	£3	£8	
Chamblee Music	LP	Emarcy	EJL1281	1958	£6	£15	
Cradle Rock	78	Esquire	10340	1953	£3	£8	

CHAMELEONS
As High As You Can Go	7"	Statik	STAT30	1983	£2.50	£6	
As High As You Can Go	12"	Statik	STAT3012	1983	£4	£10	
In Shreds	7"	Epic	EPCA2210	1982	£7.50	£15	
In Shreds	7"	Statik	TAK29	1985	£4	£8	double
In Shreds	12"	Statik	TAK2912	1985	£5	£12	
Person Isn't Safe Anywhere These Days	7"	Statik	TAK6	1983	£2.50	£6	
Person Isn't Safe Anywhere These Days	12"	Statik	TAK612	1983	£4	£10	
Script Of The Bridge	LP	Statik	STATP17	1985	£6	£15	pic disc
Singing Rule Britannia	12"	Statik	TAK1235	1985	£2.50	£6	
Tears	7"	Geffen	GEF4/SAM287	1986	£4	£8	double
Tony Fletcher Walked On Water	CD-s..	Glass Pyramid.	EMCD1	1990	£10	£25	
Tony Fletcher Walked On Water	12"	Glass Pyramid.	EMC1	1990	£10	£25	

CHAMPIONS
Circlorama	7"	Oriole	CB1854	1963	£2	£5	

CHAMPS
All American Music	LP	Challenge	CHL/CHS614	1962	£8	£20	US
Another Four By The Champs	7" EP.	London	REH1209	1959	£10	£20	
Beatnick	7"	London	HLH8811	1959	£4	£8	
Cantina	7"	London	HLH9430	1961	£1.50	£4	
Caramba	7"	London	HLH8864	1959	£4	£8	
Chariot Rock	7"	London	HL8715	1958	£6	£12	
El Rancho Rock	7"	London	HL8655	1958	£6	£12	
Everybody's Rockin'	LP	London	HAH2184	1959	£10	£25	
Experiment In Terror	7"	London	HLH9539	1962	£1.50	£4	
Four By The Champs	7" EP.	London	RE1176	1959	£7.50	£15	
Go Champs Go	LP	London	HAH2152	1958	£10	£25	
Great Dance Hits	LP	London	HAH2451	1962	£6	£15	
Knockouts	7" EP.	London	REH1250	1961	£10	£20	
Latin Limbo	7"	London	HLH9604	1962	£1.50	£4	
Limbo Rock	7"	London	HLH9506	1962	£1.50	£4	
Still More By The Champs	7" EP.	London	REH1223	1959	£10	£20	
Tequila	7"	London	HLU8580	1958	£4	£8	chart single
Too Much Tequila	7"	London	HL9052	1960	£2	£5	chart single

CHAMPS (2)
Walk Between Your Enemies	7"	Blue Beat	BB267	1964	£5	£10	

CHANCE, ROB & CHANCES R
At The End Of The Day	7"	CBS	3130	1967	£2	£5	

CHANCES ARE
Fragile Child	7"	Columbia	DB8144	1967	£7.50	£15	

CHANCES R
Do It Yourself	7"	CBS	2940	1967	£2	£5	
Talking Out The Back Of My Head	7"	CBS	202614	1967	£2	£5	

CHANDELLE, DANY
Lying Awake	7"	Columbia	DB7540	1965	£5	£10	

CHANDLER, BARBARA
Do You Really Love Me Too	7"	London	HLR9823	1963	£1.50	£4	
Lonely New Year	7"	London	HLR9861	1964	£1.50	£4	

CHANDLER, GENE
Bless Our Love	7"	Stateside	SS364	1964	£2.50	£6	
Duke Of Earl	LP	Fontana	TL5247	1962	£10	£25	
Duke Of Earl	7"	Columbia	DB4793	1962	£10	£20	
Duke Of Earl	7"	President	PT234	1969	£1.50	£4	
Duke Of Soul	LP	Checker	LP(S)3003	1967	£5	£12	US
Fool For You	7"	Stateside	SS500	1966	£4	£8	
Girl Don't Care	7"	Coral	Q72490	1967	£4	£8	
Good Times	7"	Stateside	SS458	1965	£4	£8	
Greatest Hits	LP	Constellation	LP1421	1964	£6	£15	US
I Can't Save It	7"	Action	ACT4551	1969	£7.50	£15	
Just Be True	LP	Constellation	LP1423	1964	£6	£15	US
Live On Stage	LP	Action	ACLP6010	1969	£6	£15	
Nothing Can Stop Me	7"	Soul City	SC102	1968	£4	£8	chart single
Nothing Can Stop Me	7"	Stateside	SS425	1965	£12.50	£25	
Song Called Soul	7"	Stateside	SS331	1964	£5	£10	
Such A Pretty Thing	7"	Chess	CRS8047	1966	£7.50	£15	
There Was A Time	LP	MCA	MUPS367	1968	£5	£12	
What Now	7"	Stateside	SS388	1965	£4	£8	
You Can't Hurt Me No More	7"	Stateside	SS401	1965	£4	£8	

You Threw A Lucky Punch	7"	Stateside	SS185	1963	£5	£10	
You're A Lady	7"	Mercury	6052098	1971	£5	£10	

CHANDLER, GENE & JERRY BUTLER

One And One	LP	Mercury	6338051	1971	£5	£12	

CHANDLER, JEFF

Everything Happens To Me	7"	Brunswick	05380	1955	£2.50	£6	
Half Of My Heart	7"	London	HLU8484	1957	£4	£8	
I Should Care	7"	Brunswick	05264	1954	£2.50	£6	
My Prayer	7"	Brunswick	05417	1955	£2	£5	
Sings To You	LP	London	HAU2100	1958	£5	£12	

CHANDLER, KAREN

My Own True Love	7"	Salvo	SLO1803	1962	£1.50	£4	
Tonight You Belong To Me	7"	Brunswick	05596	1956	£1.50	£4	... with Jimmy Wakely

CHANDLER, KENNY

Beyond Love	7"	Stateside	SS2110	1968	£20	£40	
Heart	7"	Stateside	SS166	1963	£2	£5	

CHANDONS

Timber	7"	RCA	RCA1704	1968	£1.50	£4	

CHANNEL, BRUCE

Blue And Lonesome	7"	London	HLU9776	1963	£1.50	£4	
Going Back To Louisiana	7"	London	HLU9841	1964	£1.50	£4	
Hey Baby	7"	Mercury	AMT1171	1962	£2	£5	chart single
Hey Baby!	LP	Mercury	MMC14104	1962	£8	£20	
Keep On	LP	Bell	MBLL/SBLL111	1969	£6	£15	
Keep On	7"	Bell	BLL1010	1968	£1.50	£4	chart single
Mr.Bus Driver	7"	Bell	BLL1038	1968	£1.50	£4	
Mr.Bus Man	7"	Stateside	SS2066	1967	£1.50	£4	
Number One Man	7"	Mercury	AMT1177	1962	£1.50	£4	
Run Romance Run	7"	Pye	7N25137	1962	£1.50	£4	
Try Me	7"	Bell	BLL1030	1968	£1.50	£4	

CHANTAYS

Beyond	7"	King	KG1018	1965	£2	£5	
Pipeline	LP	Downey	DLP1002	1963	£37.50	£75	US
Pipeline	LP	London	HAD/SHD8087	1963	£10	£25	
Pipeline	7"	Dot	DS26757	1967	£1.50	£4	
Pipeline	7"	London	HLD9696	1963	£2.50	£6	chart single
Pipeline	7" EP	London	RED1397	1963	£7.50	£15	
Two Sides Of The Chantays	LP	Dot	DLP3771/25771	1966	£6	£15	US

CHANTELLES

Blue Moon	7"	CBS	2777	1967	£2	£5	
Gonna Get Burned	7"	Parlophone	R5350	1965	£2.50	£6	
I Think Of You	7"	Parlophone	R5431	1966	£1.50	£4	
I Want That Boy	7"	Parlophone	R5271	1965	£2.50	£6	
Secret Of Success	7"	Parlophone	R5303	1965	£1.50	£4	
There's Something About You	7"	Polydor	56119	1966	£2.50	£6	

CHANTELS

Eternally	7"	Capitol	CL15297	1963	£2.50	£6	
Look In My Eyes	7"	London	HLL9428	1961	£7.50	£15	
Maybe	7"	London	HLU8561	1958	£30	£60	
Maybe	7"	Roulette	RO514	1969	£1.50	£4	
On Tour	LP	Carlton	(ST)LP144	1961	£30	£60	US
Still	7"	London	HLL9480	1962	£6	£12	
Summertime	7"	London	HLL9532	1962	£6	£12	
There's Our Song Again	LP	End	LP312	1962	£10	£25	US
We're The Chantels	LP	End	LP301	1958	£180	£300	US, group photo cover
We're The Chantels	LP	End	LP301	1959	£50	£100	US, jukebox cover

CHANTER SISTERS

Birds Of A Feather	LP	Page One	POLS027	1970	£4	£10	

CHANTERS

Every Night I Sit And Cry	7"	CBS	202454	1966	£2	£5	
My Love Is For You	7"	CBS	3668	1968	£2.50	£6	
What's Wrong With You	7"	CBS	3400	1968	£2	£5	
You Can't Fool Me	7"	CBS	202616	1967	£2.50	£6	

CHANTS

Ain't Nobody Home	7"	Page One	POF016	1967	£2.50	£6	
Come Back & Get This Loving Boy	7"	Fontana	TF716	1966	£2	£5	
I Could Write A Book	7"	Pye	7N15591	1964	£2.50	£6	
I Don't Care	7"	Pye	7N15557	1963	£4	£8	
I Get The Sweetest Feeling	7"	RCA	RCA1823	1969	£6	£12	
I've Been Trying	7"	Chipping Norton	CHIP2	1976	£15	£30	
Lover's Story	7"	Decca	F12650	1967	£2	£5	
Man Without A Face	7"	RCA	RCA1754	1968	£10	£20	
She's Mine	7"	Pye	7N15643	1964	£2.50	£6	
Sweet Was The Wine	7"	Pye	7N15691	1964	£4	£8	

CHANTS (2)

Close Friends	7"	Capitol	CL14876	1958	£2.50	£6	

CHAPIN BROTHERS
Chapin Music	LP	Rockland	66	1967	£17.50	£35	US

CHAPIN, HARRY
Dance Band On The Titanic	LP	Elektra	K62021	1977	£4	£10
Greatest Stories Live	LP	Elektra	K62017	1976	£4	£10
Heads And Tales	LP	Elektra	K42107	1971	£4	£10
Legends Of The Lost And Found	LP	Elektra	K62026	1979	£4	£10
Living Room Suite	LP	Elektra	K52089	1978	£4	£10
On The Road To Kingdom Come	LP	Elektra	K52040	1976	£4	£10
Portrait Gallery	LP	Elektra	K52023	1975	£4	£10
Sequel	LP	CBS	84996	1980	£4	£10
Short Stories	LP	Elektra	K42115	1973	£4	£10
Sniper And Other Love Songs	LP	Elektra	K42125	1972	£4	£10
Verities And Balderdash	LP	Elektra	K52007	1974	£4	£10

CHAPLAIN, PAUL & THE EMERALDS
Shortning Bread	7"	London	HLU9205	1960	£10	£20

CHAPMAN, GENE
Oklahoma Blues	7"	Starlite	ST45102	1963	£37.50	£75

CHAPMAN, MICHAEL
Almost Alone	LP	Black Crow	CRO202	1981	£4	£10	
Deal Gone Down	LP	Deram	SML1114	1974	£4	£10	
Fully Qualified Survivor	LP	Harvest	SHVL764	1969	£5	£12	chart LP
Guitars	LP	Standard	ESL146	197-	£25	£50	
It Didn't Work Out	7"	Harvest	HAR5002	1969	£1.50	£4	
Lady On The Rocks	LP	Intercord	126309	197-	£4	£10	German
Life On The Ceiling	LP	Criminal	STEAL5	1978	£4	£10	
Lived Here	LP	Cube	GNAT1	1977	£4	£10	
Looking For Eleven	LP	Criminal	STEAL9	1980	£4	£10	
Man Who Hated Mornings	LP	Decca	SKLR5290	1977	£5	£12	
Millstone Grit	LP	Deram	SML1105	1973	£5	£12	
Playing Guitar The Easy Way	LP	Criminal	STEAL2	1978	£4	£10	
Pleasures Of The Street	LP	Nova	622321	1975	£6	£15	German
Rainmaker	LP	Harvest	SHVL755	1969	£5	£12	
Savage Amusement	LP	Decca	SKLR5242	1976	£5	£12	
Window	LP	Harvest	SHVL786	1971	£5	£12	
Wrecked Again	LP	Harvest	SHVL798	1971	£5	£12	

CHAPS
Popping Medley	7"	Parlophone	R4979	1962	£5	£10

CHAPTER FIVE
Anything That You Do	7"	CBS	202395	1966	£60	£120
One In A Million	7"	CBS	2696	1967	£40	£80

CHAPTER FOUR
In My Life	7"	United Artists	UP1143	1966	£30	£60

CHAPTERHOUSE
Free Fall	CD-s	Dedicated	STONE001CD	1990	£3	£8
Free Fall	12"	Dedicated	STONE001T	1990	£2.50	£6

CHAPTERS
Can't Stop Thinking About Her	7"	Pye	7N15815	1965	£12.50	£25

CHARIG, MARC
Pipedream	LP	Ogun	OG710	1977	£5	£12

CHARLATANS
The original Charlatans were one of the great, pioneering San Franciso groups, but only the Kapp single comes anywhere near to capturing them at their peak. By the time the Charlatans got to make an album, several of the founder members had departed and the moment had passed.
32:20	7"	Kapp	779	1966	£10	£20	US
Charlatans	LP	Philips	SBL7903	1969	£20	£40	

CHARLATANS (2)
Indian Rope	12"	Dead Dead Good	GOOD ONE	1990	£3	£8

CHARLES, BOBBY
"See You Later Alligator" by Bobby Charles has the distinction of being the most valuable single issued commercially in the UK. One of the few copies to appear on the market has sold for two thousand pounds and one London dealer maintains that this copy is the only surviving one, having changed hands on a number of occasions, with the price climbing steadily each time. Another dealer, however, insists with equal certainty that he has personally handled six different copies!
Bobby Charles	LP	Bearsville	K45516	1972	£4	£10	
See You Later Alligator	7"	Chess	6145024	1973	£1.50	£4	Dixie Cups B side
See You Later Alligator	7"	London	HLU8247	1956	£700	£1000	

CHARLES, DON
Angel Of Love	7"	Decca	F11602	1963	£5	£10
Don Charles	7" EP	Decca	DFE8530	1963	£12.50	£25
Drifter	7"	Parlophone	R5688	1968	£10	£20
Heart's Ice Cold	7"	Decca	F11645	1963	£7.50	£15
Hermit Of Misty Mountain	7"	Decca	F11464	1962	£4	£8
If You Don't Know	7"	HMV	POP1307	1964	£1.50	£4
It's My Way Of Loving You	7"	Decca	F11528	1962	£4	£8
Look Before You Love	7"	HMV	POP1271	1963	£1.50	£4
She's Mine	7"	HMV	POP1332	1964	£4	£8

Title	Format	Label	Catalogue	Year	Price	Price	Notes
Walk With Me My Angel	7"	Decca	F11424	1962	£4	£8	chart single

CHARLES, JIMMY

Title	Format	Label	Catalogue	Year	Price	Price	Notes
Million To One	7"	London	HLU9206	1960	£2	£5	
Pitter Patter	7"	Windsor	WPS120	1964	£1.50	£4	

CHARLES, RAY

Title	Format	Label	Catalogue	Year	Price	Price	Notes
Baby Don't You Cry	7"	HMV	POP1272	1964	£1.50	£4	
Baby It's Cold Outside	7" EP	HMV	7EG8807	1963	£4	£8	
Ballad Style Of Ray Charles	7" EP	HMV	7EG8783	1963	£2.50	£8	
Busted	7"	HMV	POP1221	1963	£2	£5	chart single
Busted	7" EP	HMV	7EG8841	1964	£2.50	£6	
Cincinnati Kid	LP	MGM	(S)E4313	1965	£5	£12	US
Cincinnati Kid	7"	HMV	POP1484	1965	£1.50	£4	
Come Rain Or Come Shine	7"	London	HLK9251	1960	£2	£5	
Cry	7"	HMV	POP1392	1965	£1.50	£4	
Cryin' Time	7"	HMV	POP1502	1966	£1.50	£4	chart single
Crying Time	LP	HMV	CLP/CSD3533	1966	£4	£10	
C&W Meets R&B	LP	HMV	CLP1914/CSD1630	1965	£5	£12	
Dedicated To You	LP	HMV	CLP1449/CSD1362	1961	£5	£12	
Don't Set Me Free	7"	HMV	POP1133	1963	£1.50	£4	chart single
Early In The Mornin'	7"	London	HLK9364	1961	£2	£5	
Eleanor Rigby	7"	Stateside	SS2120	1968	£1.50	£4	chart single
Genius After Hours	LP	HMV	HAK8035	1963	£5	£12	
Genius Hits The Road	LP	HMV	CLP1387/CSD1320	1960	£5	£12	
Genius Of Ray Charles	LP	London	LTZK15190	1960	£8	£20	
Genius Sings The Blues	LP	London	LTZK15238	1960	£6	£15	
Genius&Soul=Jazz	LP	HMV	CLP1475/CSD1384	1961	£5	£12	
Georgia On My Mind	7"	HMV	POP792	1960	£1.50	£4	
Great Ray Charles	LP	London	LTZK15134	1958	£10	£25	
Great Ray Charles	7" EP	London	EZK19043	1959	£5	£10	
Greatest Hits	LP	HMV	CLP1626/CSD1482	1962	£5	£12	chart LP
Have A Smile With Me	LP	HMV	CLP1795/CSD1566	1964	£5	£12	
Here We Go Again	7"	HMV	POP1595	1967	£1.50	£4	
Hide Nor Hair	7"	HMV	POP1017	1962	£1.50	£4	
Hit The Road Jack	7"	HMV	POP935	1961	£2	£5	chart single
Hit the Road Jack	7" EP	HMV	7EG8729	1962	£4	£8	
I Can't Stop Loving You	7"	HMV	POP1034	1962	£1.50	£4	chart single
I Can't Stop Loving You	7" EP	HMV	7EG8781	1962	£4	£8	
I Chose To Sing The Blues	7"	HMV	POP1551	1966	£2	£5	
I Gotta Woman	7"	HMV	POP1437	1965	£2	£5	
I Wonder Who	7"	London	HLK9435	1961	£2	£5	
I'm Movin' On	7"	London	HLE9009	1959	£4	£8	
In Person	LP	London	HAK2284	1960	£6	£15	
In The Heat Of The Night	LP	United Artists	5160	1967	£4	£10	US
In The Heat Of The Night	7"	HMV	POP1607	1967	£1.50	£4	
Ingredients In A Recipe For Soul	LP	HMV	CLP1678	1963	£5	£12	
Let The Good Times Roll	7"	London	HLE9058	1960	£4	£8	
Let's Go Get Stoned	7"	HMV	POP1537	1966	£1.50	£4	
Light Out Of Darkness	7"	HMV	POP1414	1965	£1.50	£4	
Listen	LP	HMV	CLP/CSD3630	1967	£4	£10	
Live In Concert	LP	HMV	CLP1872/CSD1606	1965	£5	£12	
Love's Gonna Live Here	7"	HMV	POP1457	1965	£1.50	£4	
Makin' Whoopee	7"	HMV	POP1383	1965	£1.50	£4	chart single
Man And His Soul	LP	ABC	(S)590	1967	£4	£10	US
Memories Of A Middle-Aged Man	LP	Atlantic	SD263	1968	£4	£10	US
Modern Sounds In C&W	LP	HMV	CLP1580/CSD1451	1961	£5	£12	chart LP
Modern Sounds In C&W 2	LP	HMV	CLP1613/CSD1477	1962	£5	£12	chart LP
My Baby Don't Dig Me	7"	HMV	POP1315	1964	£1.50	£4	
No One	7"	HMV	POP1202	1963	£1.50	£4	chart single
No One To Cry To	7"	HMV	POP1333	1964	£1.50	£4	chart single
One Mint Julep	7"	HMV	POP862	1961	£1.50	£4	
Original Ray Charles	LP	London	HAK8022	1962	£6	£15	
Original Ray Charles Vol.1	7" EP	London	REB1407	1963	£5	£10	
Original Ray Charles Vol.2	7" EP	London	REB1408	1963	£5	£10	
Original Ray Charles Vol.3	7" EP	London	REB1409	1963	£5	£10	
Please Say You're Fooling	7"	HMV	POP1566	1966	£7.50	£15	
Ray Charles & Betty Carter	LP	HMV	CLP1520/CSD1414	1961	£5	£12	
Ray Charles At Newport	LP	London	LTZK15149/ SAHK6008	1959	£6	£15	
Ray Charles At Newport	7" EP	London	REK1317	1961	£4	£8	
Ray Charles Live	7" EP	HMV	7EG8932	1966	£2.50	£6	
Ray Charles Sextet	LP	London	LTZK15178	1960	£6	£15	
Ray Charles Sings	7" EP	HMV	7EG8861	1964	£2.50	£6	
Ray Charles Story Vol.1	LP	London	HAK8023	1962	£5	£12	
Ray Charles Story Vol.2	LP	London	HAK8024	1962	£5	£12	
Ray Charles Story Vol.3	LP	Atlantic	(SD)8083	1963	£5	£12	US
Ray Charles Story Vol.4	LP	Atlantic	(SD)8094	1964	£5	£12	US
Ray Charles/Rock And Roll	LP	Atlantic	8006	1957	£10	£25	US
Ray's Moods	LP	HMV	CLP/CSD3574	1966	£5	£12	
Rockhouse	7"	London	HLE8768	1958	£7.50	£15	
Ruby	7"	HMV	POP825	1961	£1.50	£4	
Sings Songs Of Buck Owens	7" EP	HMV	7EG8951	1966	£2.50	£6	
Smack Dab In The Middle	7"	HMV	POP1350	1964	£1.50	£4	
Soul Brothers	LP	London	LTZK15146/ SAHK6030	1959	£6	£15	
Soul Brothers	7" EP	London	EZK19048	1959	£5	£10	
Soul Meeting	LP	London	HAK/SHK8045	1963	£5	£12	with Milt Jackson
Sticks And Stones	7"	HMV	POP774	1960	£1.50	£4	
Sweet & Sour Tears	LP	HMV	CLP1728/CSD1537	1963	£5	£12	

137

Swinging Style Of Ray Charles	7" EP	HMV	7EG8801	1963	£2.50	£6	
Take These Chains From My Heart	7"	HMV	POP1161	1963	£1.50	£4	chart single
Take These Chains From My Heart	7" EP	HMV	7EG8812	1963	£2.50	£6	
Tell The Truth	7"	London	HLK9181	1960	£4	£8	
That Lucky Old Sun	7"	HMV	POP1251	1964	£1.50	£4	
Them That Got	7"	HMV	POP838	1961	£1.50	£4	
Together Again	LP	ABC	(S)520	1966	£4	£10	US
Together Again	7"	HMV	POP1519	1966	£1.50	£4	chart single
Unchain My Heart	7"	HMV	POP969	1962	£1.50	£4	
What I Say	7"	Atlantic	584093	1967	£2	£5	
What I Say	7"	London	HLE8917	1959	£6	£12	
What'd I Say	LP	London	HAK2226	1959	£6	£15	
What'd I Say	7" EP	London	REK1306	1961	£4	£8	
Yes Indeed	LP	London	HAE2168	1958	£6	£15	
Yesterday	7"	Stateside	SS2071	1967	£1.50	£4	chart single
You Don't Know Me	7"	HMV	POP1064	1962	£1.50	£4	chart single
You Win Again	7"	HMV	POP1589	1967	£1.50	£4	
Young Ray Charles	7" EP	Realm	REP4001	1964	£4	£8	
Your Cheating Heart	7"	HMV	POP1099	1962	£1.50	£4	chart single

CHARLES, SONNY

Black Pearl	7"	A&M	AMS752	1969	£2	£5	
Mastered The Art Of Love	7"	Ember	EMBS240	1967	£5	£10	

CHARLES, TEDDY

New Directions	10" LP	Esquire	20034	1954	£20	£40	
New Directions Quartet	10" LP	Esquire	20043	1955	£20	£40	
Teddy Charles Quartet	10" LP	Atlantic	ATLLP3	1955	£25	£50	
Teddy Charles Tentet	LP	London	LTZK15034	1957	£6	£15	
Three For Duke	LP	London	LTZJ15119	1958	£6	£15	with Hal Overton & Oscar Pettiford

CHARLIE PARKAS

Ballad Of Robin Hood	7"	Paranoid Plastics	PPS1	1980	£2	£5	

CHARMERS

Oh Yes	7"	Vogue	V9095	1958	£60	£120	

CHARMERS (2)

Angel Love	7"	R&B	JB118	1963	£5	£10	
Back To Back	7"	Melodisc	CAL9	1963	£4	£8	
Dig Them Prince	7"	Blue Beat	BB251	1964	£5	£10	
Done Me Wrong	7"	Blue Beat	BB157	1962	£5	£10	
Glamour Girl	7"	Blue Beat	BB256	1964	£5	£10	Prince Buster B side
I Am Through	7"	R&B	JB151	1964	£5	£10	
I'm Back	7"	Blue Beat	BB204	1963	£5	£10	
In My Soul	7"	R&B	JB156	1964	£5	£10	
Keep On Going	7"	Treasure Isle	TI7036	1968	£5	£10	
Lonely Boy	7"	Blue Beat	BB42	1961	£5	£10	
Now You Want To Cry	7"	Blue Beat	BB114	1962	£5	£10	
Oh My Baby	7"	Blue Beat	BB315	1964	£5	£10	Spanishtonians B side
Oh Why Baby	7"	R&B	JB121	1963	£5	£10	Roland Alphonso B side
Skinhead Train	7"	Explosion	EX2045	1970	£2	£5	
Stone Cold Man	7"	Melodisc	CAL8	1963	£4	£8	
Waiting For You	7"	Blue Beat	BB238	1963	£5	£10	
You Don't Know	7"	Rio	R78	1966	£4	£8	

CHARMETTES

Please Don't Kiss Me Again	7"	London	HLR9820	1963	£2.50	£6	

CHARMS

Carry, Go, Bring, Come	7"	Island	WI154	1964	£5	£10	
Everybody Say Yeah	7"	Rio	R98	1966	£4	£8	

CHARMS (2)

The rare single, "Hearts Of Stone", is listed in the Guide under the name used on other singles by the group - Otis Williams And The Charms.

CHARMS, TEDDY

I Want It Girl	7"	Blue Cat	BS141	1968	£4	£8	

CHARTBUSTERS

She's The One	7"	London	HLU9906	1964	£1.50	£4	
Why	7"	London	HLU9934	1964	£1.50	£4	

CHASE

Chase	LP	Epic	EQ30472	1971	£5	£12	US quad

CHASE, LINCOLN

Explosive	LP	Liberty	LRP3076	1958	£6	£15	US
Johnny Klingeringding	7"	London	HLU8495	1957	£4	£8	
Miss Orangutang	7"	Philips	PB1103	1961	£1.50	£4	

CHASERS

Hey Little Girl	7"	Decca	F12302	1965	£12.50	£25	
Hey Little Girl	7"	Decca	F12302	1965	£20	£40	PS
Inspiration	7"	Parlophone	R5451	1966	£25	£50	
Ways Of A Man	7"	Philips	BF1546	1967	£5	£10	

138

CHEAP TRICK

Title	Format	Label	Cat No	Year	Price	Price	Notes
So Good To See You	7"	Epic	EPC6199	1978	£2.50	£6	
Voices	7"	Epic	EPC7144	1979	£1.50	£4	

CHEATIN' HEARTS

Title	Format	Label	Cat No	Year	Price	Price	Notes
Bad Kind	7"	Columbia	DB8048	1966	£4	£8	

CHECKER, CHUBBY

Title	Format	Label	Cat No	Year	Price	Price	Notes
All The Hits	LP	Cameo Parkway	P7014	1963	£6	£15	
Beach Party	LP	Parkway	(S)P7030	1963	£6	£15	US
Biggest Hits	LP	Parkway	(S)P7022	1962	£6	£15	US
Black Cloud	7"	Cameo Parkway	P873	1963	£1.50	£4	
Chubby Checker	LP	Cameo Parkway	P7036	1963	£6	£15	
Chubby Checker	LP	Parkway	5001	1960	£15	£30	US
Class	7"	Top Rank	JAR154	1959	£10	£20	
Dancing Party	7"	Columbia	DB4876	1962	£1.50	£4	chart single
Dancing Party	7" EP.	Cameo Parkway	CPE550	1963	£2.50	£6	
Discotheque	LP	Parkway	(S)P7045	1965	£6	£15	US
Discotheque	7"	Cameo Parkway	P949	1965	£7.50	£15	
Don't Knock The Twist	LP	Parkway	P7011	1962	£6	£15	US
Eighteen Golden Hits	LP	Parkway	(S)P7048	1966	£5	£12	US
Everything's Wrong	7"	Cameo Parkway	P959	1965	£7.50	£15	
Fly	7"	Columbia	DB4728	1961	£1.50	£4	
Folk Album	LP	Parkway	(S)P7040	1963	£6	£15	US
For Twisters Only	LP	Columbia	33SX1341	1961	£6	£15	chart LP
Good Good Loving	7"	Columbia	DB4652	1961	£1.50	£4	
Gotta Get Myself Together	7"	Pye	7N25160	1962	£1.50	£4	
Hey Bobba Needle	7"	Cameo Parkway	P907	1964	£1.50	£4	
Hey You Little Boogaloo	7"	Cameo Parkway	P989	1965	£5	£10	
Hucklebuck	7"	Columbia	DB4541	1960	£2	£5	
In Person	LP	Parkway	(S)P7026	1963	£6	£15	US
It's Pony Time	LP	Columbia	33SX1365	1961	£6	£15	
King Of The Twist	7" EP.	Columbia	SEG8155	1962	£4	£8	
Lazy Elsie Molly	7"	Cameo Parkway	P920	1964	£1.50	£4	
Let's Limbo Some More	LP	Parkway	(S)P7027	1963	£6	£15	US
Let's Limbo Some More	7"	Cameo Parkway	P862	1963	£2	£5	
Let's Twist Again	LP	Columbia	33SX1411	1961	£6	£15	
Let's Twist Again	7"	Cameo Parkway	P824	1961	£2	£5	
Let's Twist Again	7"	Columbia	DB4691	1961	£1.50	£4	chart single
Limbo Party	LP	Cameo Parkway	P7020	1963	£6	£15	
Limbo Rock	7"	Cameo Parkway	P849	1962	£2	£5	chart single
Loddy Lo	7"	Cameo Parkway	P890	1964	£1.50	£4	
Lovely Lovely	7"	Cameo Parkway	P936	1965	£2	£5	
Pony Time	7"	Columbia	DB4591	1961	£1.50	£4	chart single
She Wants To Swim	7"	Cameo Parkway	P923	1964	£1.50	£4	
Slow Twisting	7"	Columbia	DB4808	1962	£1.50	£4	chart single
Twist	7"	Columbia	DB4503	1960	£2	£5	chart single
Twist Along With Chubby Checker	LP	Columbia	33SX1445	1962	£6	£15	
Twist It Up	7"	Cameo Parkway	P879	1963	£2	£5	
Twist With Chubby Checker	LP	Columbia	33SX1315	1961	£6	£15	chart LP
Twistin' Around The World	LP	Golden Guinea	GGL0236	1962	£5	£12	
Twistin' Around The World	LP	Parkway	P7008	1962	£6	£15	US
Two Hearts Make One Love	7"	Cameo Parkway	P965	1965	£40	£80	
What Do You Say	7"	Cameo Parkway	P806	1963	£1.50	£4	chart single
Your Twist Party	LP	Parkway	P7007	1961	£6	£15	US

CHECKER, CHUBBY & BOBBY RYDELL

Title	Format	Label	Cat No	Year	Price	Price	Notes
Bobby Rydell/Chubby Checker	LP	Cameo	C1013	1961	£6	£15	US
Chubby Checker & Bobby Rydell In London	7" EP.	Cameo Parkway	CPE554	1964	£4	£8	
Chubby Checker And Bobby Rydell	LP	Columbia	33SX1424	1962	£6	£15	
Jingle Bell Rock	7"	Cameo Parkway	C205	1962	£1.50	£4	chart single
Teach Me To Twist	7"	Columbia	DB4802	1962	£1.50	£4	chart single

CHECKER, CHUBBY & DEE DEE SHARP

Title	Format	Label	Cat No	Year	Price	Price	Notes
Down To Earth	LP	Cameo Parkway	C1029	1963	£6	£15	

CHECKMATES

Title	Format	Label	Cat No	Year	Price	Price	Notes
Around	7"	Decca	F12114	1965	£5	£10	

Checkmates	LP	Pye	NPL18061	1961	£6	£15
Every Day Is Just The Same	7"	Parlophone	R5495	1966	£7.50	£15
Rocking Minstrel	7"	Piccadilly	7N35010	1961	£4	£8
Sticks And Stones	7"	Decca	F11844	1964	£2.50	£6
Stop That Music	7"	Parlophone	R5337	1965	£6	£12
You Got The Gamma Goochie	7"	Parlophone	R5402	1966	£10	£20
You've Gotta Have A Gimick Today	7"	Decca	F11603	1963	£4	£8

CHECKMATES (2)

Invisible Ska	7"	Ska Beat	JB225	1965	£5	£10	Winston Richards B side

CHECKMATES LTD.

Do The Walk	7"	Ember	EMBS235	1967	£2	£5	
I Keep Forgettin'	7"	A&M	AMS780	1970	£1.50	£4	
Live At Caesar's Palace	LP	Capitol	ST2840	1967	£6	£15	US
Love Is All I Have To Give	7"	A&M	AMS747	1969	£1.50	£4	
Love Is All We Have To Give	LP	A&M	AMLS943	1969	£6	£15	
Proud Mary	7"	A&M	AMS769	1969	£1.50	£4	chart single

CHEERS

Bazoom I Need Your Loving	7"	Capitol	CL14189	1954	£15	£30	
Black Denim Trousers	7"	Capitol	CL14377	1955	£15	£30	
Blueberries	7"	Capitol	CL14280	1955	£10	£20	
Cheers	7" EP	Capitol	EAP1584	1956	£12.50	£25	
Chicken	7"	Capitol	CL14561	1956	£10	£20	
I Must Be Dreaming	7"	Capitol	CL14337	1955	£10	£20	
Que Pasa Muchacha	7"	Capitol	CL14601	1956	£5	£10	Bert Convy B side
Whadya Want	7"	Capitol	CL14248	1955	£10	£20	

CHEETAHS

Goodbye Baby	7"	Philips	BF1412	1965	£4	£8	chart single
Mecca	7"	Philips	BF1362	1964	£4	£8	
Russian Boat Song	7"	Philips	BF1499	1966	£4	£8	chart single
Soldier Boy	7"	Philips	BF1383	1965	£4	£8	
Whole Lotta Love	7"	Philips	BF1453	1965	£4	£8	

CHELSEA

Alternative Hits	LP	Step Forward	SFLP5	1981	£5	£12
Chelsea	LP	Step Forward	SFLP2	1979	£5	£12
Evacuate	LP	Step Forward	SFLP7	1982	£4	£10

CHENIER, CLIFTON

Bayou Blues	LP	Sonet	SNTF5012	1970	£5	£12
Black Girl	7"	Action	ACT4550	1969	£2	£5
Very Best	LP	Harvest	SHSP4002	1970	£6	£15

CHER

3614 Jackson Highway	LP	Atlantic	226026	1969	£4	£10	French
Alfie	7" EP	Polydor	27788	1966	£5	£10	chart LP
All I Really Want To Do	LP	Liberty	LBY3058	1965	£4	£10	chart single
All I Really Want To Do	7"	Liberty	LIB66114	1965	£1.50	£4	
All I Really Want To Do	7" EP	Polydor	27771	1965	£5	£10	French
Backstage	LP	Liberty	LBL/LBS83156	1968	£4	£10	
Bang Bang	7"	Liberty	LIB66160	1966	£1.50	£4	chart single
Bang Bang	7" EP	Polydor	27782	1966	£6	£12	French, 2 different sleeves
Bittersweet White Light	LP	MCA	MUPS484	1973	£4	£10	
Cher	LP	Liberty	(S)LBY3081	1967	£4	£10	
Cher	LP	MCA	MUPS438	1971	£4	£10	
Cherished	LP	Warner Bros	K56401	1977	£4	£10	
Dark Lady	LP	MCA	MCF2559	1974	£4	£10	
Foxy Lady	LP	MCA	MUPS459	1972	£4	£10	
Golden Greats	LP	Liberty	LBL/LBS83105	1968	£4	£10	
Half Breed	LP	MCA	MCF2501	1974	£4	£10	
Hits Of Cher	7" EP	Liberty	LEP4047	1966	£2.50	£6	
I Paralyze	LP	CBS	85850	1982	£4	£10	
I'd Rather Believe In You	LP	Warner Bros	K56292	1977	£4	£10	
Mama	7" EP	Polydor	27797	1966	£4	£8	French
Prisoner	LP	Casablanca	NBLP7184	1980	£4	£10	
Sonny Side Of Cher	LP	Liberty	(S)LBY3072	1966	£4	£10	chart LP
Stars	LP	Warner Bros	K56111	1975	£4	£10	
Sunny	7"	Liberty	LIB12083	1966	£1.50	£4	chart single
Take Me Home	LP	Casablanca	CAL2047	1979	£4	£10	
Take Me Home	LP	Casablanca	NBPIX7133	1979	£5	£12	pic disc
Walk On Gilded Splinters	7"	Atlantic	584278	1969	£1.50	£4	
Where Do You Go	7"	Liberty	LIB66136	1966	£1.50	£4	
With Love	LP	Liberty	LBL/LBS83051	1967	£4	£10	

CHEROKEES

Dig A Little Deeper	7"	Columbia	DB7704	1965	£2	£5	
Land Of A Thousand Dances	7"	Columbia	DB7822	1966	£2	£5	
Seven Daffodils	7"	Columbia	DB7341	1964	£2	£5	chart single
Wondrous Place	7"	Columbia	DB7473	1965	£2	£5	
You've Done It Again Little Girl	7"	Decca	F11915	1964	£2.50	£6	

CHEROKEES (2)

Cherokee	7"	Pye	7N25066	1961	£1.50	£4

CHERRY, DON

Complete Communion	LP	Blue Note	BLP/BST84226	1966	£8	£20

Last Dance	7"	Philips	JK1013	1957	£1.50	£4	
Symphony For Improvisors	LP	Blue Note	BLP/BST84247	1966	£8	£20	
Wanted Someone To Love	7"	Brunswick	05538	1956	£1.50	£4	
Where Is Brooklyn?	LP	Blue Note	BST84311	1969	£6	£15	

CHERRY PEOPLE
And Suddenly	7"	MGM	MGM1438	1968	£10	£20	
Cherry People	LP	Heritage	HTS35000	1968	£6	£15	US
Gotta Get Back	7"	MGM	MGM1472	1969	£2.50	£6	
Light Of Love	7"	MGM	MGM1489	1969	£2.50	£6	

CHERRY SMASH
Fade Away Maureen	7"	Decca	F12884	1969	£4	£8	
Goodtime Sunshine	7"	Decca	F12838	1968	£2	£5	
Sing Songs Of Love	7"	Track	604017	1967	£4	£8	

CHESTER, GARY
| Yeah Yeah Yeah | LP | DCP | D(S)6803 | 1964 | £4 | £10 | US |

CHESTER, PETE
| Forest Fire | 7" | Pye | 7N25074 | 1961 | £6 | £12 | |
| Ten Swinging Bottles | 7" | Pye | 7N15305 | 1960 | £6 | £12 | |

CHESTER, VIC
| Rock A Billy | 7" | Decca | F10882 | 1957 | £4 | £8 | |

CHESTERFIELDS
| A Guitar In Your Bath | 7" | Subway | SUBWAY3 | 1986 | £1.50 | £4 | |

CHESTNUT, MORRIS
| Too Darn Soulful | 7" | Grapevine | GRP127 | 1979 | £1.50 | £4 | |

CHEVIOT RANTERS
Cheviot Barn Dance	LP	Topic	12TS245	1974	£6	£15	
Cheviot Hills	LP	Topic	12TS222	1973	£6	£15	
Sound Of The Cheviots	LP	Topic	12T214	1972	£6	£15	

CHEVLONS
| Too Long Alone | 7" | Pye | 7N17145 | 1966 | £1.50 | £4 | |

CHEVRONS
| Lullaby | 7" | Top Rank | JAR308 | 1960 | £2 | £5 | |
| Sing Along Rock And Roll | LP | Time | T10008 | 1961 | £8 | £20 | US |

CHEVY
| Taker | 7" | Avatar | AAA107 | 1980 | £2.50 | £6 | |
| Too Much Loving | 7" | Avatar | AAA104 | 1980 | £1.50 | £4 | |

CHEYNES
A well respected, but ultimately unsuccessful R&B group, the Cheynes included Peter Bardens and Mick Fleetwood, whose next project was the Peter B's, and Phil Sawyer, who later turned up as a member of the second Spencer Davis Group.
Down And Out	7"	Columbia	DB7464	1965	£15	£30	
Going To The River	7"	Columbia	DB7368	1964	£15	£30	
Respectable	7"	Columbia	DB7153	1963	£15	£30	

CHICAGO
Chicago have fallen into almost as much disfavour as have Blood, Sweat And Tears, but many of their records are actually rather fine. The presence of brass instruments, however, does not make the group's music jazz-rock. The primary function of the brass is to give the music power, in the manner of the Atlantic recordings by Otis Redding and Wilson Pickett. Meanwhile, the most dominant solo voice is that of Terry Kath's guitar, which is fluent and exciting, though without, perhaps, being particularly individual.
Chicago At Carnegie Hall	LP	Columbia	CQ30865	1974	£10	£25	US quad, 4 LPs
Chicago II	LP	Columbia	GQ33258	1975	£6	£15	US quad, double
Chicago III	LP	Columbia	C2Q30110	1974	£6	£15	US quad, double
Chicago Transit Authority	LP	Columbia	GQ33255	1975	£6	£15	US quad, double
Chicago Transit Authority	LP	Mobile Fidelity	MFSL2218	1983	£6	£15	US audiophile, double
I'm A Man	7"	CBS	4503	1969	£4	£8	
I'm A Man	7"	CBS	4715	1969	£1.50	£4	chart single
Live In Japan 1972	LP	CBS/Sony	SCPS31	1975	£5	£12	Japanese

CHICAGO LINE
| Shimmy Shimmy Ko Ko Bop | 7" | Philips | BF1488 | 1966 | £25 | £50 | |

CHICAGO LOOP
| She Comes To Me | 7" | Stateside | SS564 | 1966 | £1.50 | £4 | |

CHICKEN BONES
| Hard Rock In Concert | LP | Procom | | 1973 | £150 | £250 | |

CHICKEN SHACK
As the second most successful group signed to Blue Horizon (behind Fleetwood Mac), Chicken Shack relied heavily on the blues guitar of Stan Webb. He was not, however, as talented as he thought he was, as his embarrassing attempts to prove his versatility via live versions of Davy Graham's tricky instrumental, "Angie", showed only too clearly. The real talent in the group was singer and pianist Christine Perfect (later Christine McVie), but she defected to Fleetwood Mac after the first two LPs.
100 Ton Chicken	LP	Blue Horizon	763218	1969	£10	£25	
40 Blue Fingers Freshly Packed And Ready To Serve	LP	Blue Horizon	763203	1968	£15	£30	chart LP
Accept	LP	Blue Horizon	763861	1970	£10	£25	
Goodbye (Live)	LP	Nova	621579	1974	£5	£12	
I'd Rather Go Blind	7"	Blue Horizon	573153	1969	£2	£5	chart single
Imagination Lady	LP	Deram	SDL5	1971	£10	£25	
It's OK With Me Baby	7"	Blue Horizon	573135	1967	£4	£8	

Maudie	7"	Blue Horizon	573168	1970	£2.50	£6	
O.K. Ken?	LP	Blue Horizon	763209	1968	£10	£25	chart LP
Sad Clown	7"	Blue Horizon	573176	1970	£2.50	£6	
Tears In The Wind	7"	Blue Horizon	573160	1969	£2.50	£6	chart single
Unlucky Boy	LP	Deram	SML1100	1973	£5	£12	
When The Train Comes Back	7"	Blue Horizon	573146	1968	£2.50	£6	
Worried About My Woman	7"	Blue Horizon	573143	1968	£2.50	£6	

CHICKEN SHED

Alice	LP	Colby	AJ370	1977	£25	£50	
Rock	LP	Colby	AJ371	1978	£6	£15	

CHIEFS

Apache	7"	London	HLU8624	1958	£10	£20	
Enchiladas	7"	London	HLU8720	1958	£6	£12	

CHIEFTAINS

Chieftains	LP	Claddagh	CC2	1965	£8	£20	
Chieftains Vol.2	LP	Claddagh	CC7	1969	£6	£15	
Chieftains Vol.3	LP	Claddagh	CC10	1971	£6	£15	
Chieftains Vol.4	LP	Claddagh	CC14	1973	£6	£15	

CHIFFONS

Chiffons	LP	Stateside	SL10040	1963	£15	£30	
He's So Fine	LP	Laurie	LLP2018	1963	£15	£30	US
He's So Fine	7"	Stateside	SS172	1963	£2	£5	chart single
I Have A Boyfriend	7"	Stateside	SS254	1964	£1.50	£4	
Love So Fine	7"	Stateside	SS230	1963	£1.50	£4	
My Boyfriend's Back	7"	Stateside	SS578	1967	£4	£8	
My Secret Love	LP	B.T.Puppy	S1011	1970	£8	£20	US
Nobody Knows What's Goin' On	7"	Stateside	SS437	1965	£7.50	£15	
One Fine Day	LP	Laurie	LLP2020	1963	£15	£30	US
One Fine Day	7"	Stateside	SS202	1963	£1.50	£4	chart single
Out Of This World	7"	Stateside	SS533	1966	£2	£5	
Sailor Boy	7"	Stateside	SS332	1964	£1.50	£4	
Stop,Look,& Listen	7"	Stateside	SS559	1966	£2	£5	
Sweet Talkin' Guy	LP	Stateside	(S)SL10190	1966	£15	£30	
Sweet Talkin' Guy	7"	Stateside	SS512	1966	£4	£8	chart single
They're So Fine	7" EP.	Stateside	SE1012	1964	£12.50	£25	

CHILDE, SONNY

Giving Up On Love	7"	Decca	F12218	1965	£4	£8	
Heartbreak	7"	Polydor	56141	1966	£5	£10	
To Be Continued	LP	Polydor	582003	1966	£5	£12	
Two Lovers	7"	Polydor	56108	1966	£12.50	£25	

CHILDREN

Rebirth	LP	Atco	SD33271	1968	£6	£15	US
Rebirth	LP	Cinema	CLP1	1967	£10	£25	US

CHILDREN OF ONE

Children Of One	LP	Real	101	1970	£20	£40	US

CHILDREN OF THE NIGHT

Dinner With Drac	LP	Pip	PIP6822	1977	£8	£20	US

CHILDS, DR.A.A.

Healing Prayer	7"	Starlite	ST45009	1960	£1.50	£4	

CHI-LITES

Give It Away	LP	MCA	MUPS397	1968	£4	£10	
Give More Power To The People	LP	MCA	MUPS437	1971	£4	£10	
I Like Your Lovin'	LP	Brunswick	754153	1969	£4	£10	US
Lonely Man	LP	MCA	MUPS457	1972	£4	£10	
Pretty Girl	7"	Beacon	BEA119	1968	£5	£10	

CHILLI WILLI & RED HOT PEPPERS

Kings Of The Robot Rhythm	LP	Revelation	REV002	1972	£5	£12	

CHILLIWACK

All Over You	LP	A&M	4375	1972	£6	£15	US
Chilliwack	LP	London	SHU8418	1971	£6	£15	

CHILLUM

Chillum	LP	Mushroom	100MR11	1971	£10	£25	

CHIMES

Once In A While	7"	London	HLU9283	1961	£10	£20	

CHIMES (2)

I'll Be Waiting, I'll Be There	7"	Decca	F11885	1964	£1.50	£4	
Say It Again	7"	Decca	F11783	1963	£1.50	£4	

CHINA DOLLS

One Hit Wonder	7"	Speed	FIRED001	1982	£5	£10	

CHINATOWN

Short And Sweet	7"	Airship	AP138	1981	£10	£20	

CHIN'S CALYPSO SEXTET

Adam And Eve	7"	Kalypso	C1010	196-	£1.50	£4	
Come Back To Me	7"	Kalypso	C1006	196-	£1.50	£4	

Industrial Fair	7"	Kalypso	C1003	196-	£1.50	£4	
Night Food Recipe	7"	Kalypso	C1005	196-	£1.50	£4	
Red Tomato	7"	Kalypso	C1008	196-	£1.50	£4	

CHINS, KES

Annie	7"	Starlite	ST45089	1962	£1.50	£4	

CHIPMUNKS

All My Loving	7"	Liberty	LIB10170	1964	£1.50	£4	
Chipmunk Song	7"	London	HLU8762	1958	£1.50	£4	
Sing The Beatles Hits	7" EP	Liberty	LEP2188	1964	£4	£8	French

CHISHOLM, GEORGE

George Chisholm Sextet	LP	Decca	LK4147	1956	£5	£12	
Honky Tonk	7"	Beltona	BL2671	1956	£2	£5	

CHITINOUS ENSEMBLE

Chitinous Ensemble	LP	Deram	SML1093	1971	£30	£60	

CHOCOLATE FROG

Butchers And Bakers	7"	Atlantic	584207	1968	£5	£10	

CHOCOLATE MILK

Actions Speak Louder Than Words	7"	RCA	RCA2592	1975	£2.50	£6	
Comin'	LP	RCA	PL11830	1977	£8	£20	

CHOCOLATE WATCH BAND

Inner Mystique	LP	Tower	ST5106	1968	£50	£100	US
No Way Out	LP	Tower	(S)T5096	1967	£50	£100	US
One Step Beyond	LP	Tower	ST5153	1969	£25	£50	US
Requiem	7"	Decca	F12704	1967	£7.50	£15	
Sound Of The Summer	7"	Decca	F12649	1967	£7.50	£15	

CHOIR

It's Cold Outside	7"	Major Minor	MM537	1968	£12.50	£25	
When You Were With Me	7"	Major Minor	MM557	1968	£10	£20	

CHOPYN

Grand Slam	LP	Jet	LP08	1975	£6	£15	

CHORDETTES

Baby Of Mine	7"	London	HLA8566	1958	£6	£12	
Born To Be With You	7"	London	HA7011	1956	£6	£12	export
Born To Be With You	7"	London	HLA8302	1956	£12.50	£25	chart single
Chordettes	LP	London	HAA2088	1958	£10	£25	
Chordettes	7" EP	London	REA1228	1960	£10	£20	
Chordettes Sing	LP	London	HAA2441	1962	£8	£20	
Close Harmony	LP	Cadence	CLP3002	1957	£10	£25	US
Duddlesack Polka	7"	London	HLA8217	1956	£10	£20	
Girl's Work Is Never Done	7"	London	HLA8926	1959	£5	£10	
Harmony Encores	10" LP	Columbia	CL6218	1953	£15	£30	US
Harmony Time	10" LP	Columbia	CL6111	1950	£15	£30	US
Harmony Time Vol.2	10" LP	Columbia	CL6170	1951	£15	£30	US
Hummingbird	7"	London	HLA8169	1955	£12.50	£25	
Just Between You And Me	7"	London	HLA8473	1957	£6	£12	
Lay Down Your Arms	7"	London	HLA8323	1956	£10	£20	
Like A Baby	7"	London	HLA8497	1957	£6	£12	
Listen	LP	Columbia	CL956	1954	£15	£30	US
Lollipop	7"	London	HLA8584	1958	£6	£12	chart single
Love Is A Two Way Street	7"	London	HLA8654	1958	£5	£10	
Mister Sandman	7"	Columbia	SCM5158	1954	£30	£60	chart single
Never On Sunday	LP	Cadence	CLP3062/25062	1962	£8	£20	US
Never On Sunday	7"	London	HLA8400	1961	£1.50	£4	
No Other Arms No Other Lips	7"	London	HLA8809	1959	£4	£8	
Our Melody	7"	London	HLA8264	1956	£12.50	£25	
Your Requests	10" LP	Columbia	CL6285	1953	£15	£30	US

CHORDS

Sh'boom	7"	Columbia	SCM5133	1954	£180	£300	

CHORDS FIVE

I'm Only Dreaming	7"	Island	WI3044	1967	£7.50	£15	
Same Old Fat Man	7"	Polydor	56261	1968	£12.50	£25	

CHORDS FIVE (2)

Some People	7"	Jayboy	BOY6	1968	£6	£12	

CHOSEN FEW

Hit After Hit	LP	Trojan	TRLS56	1973	£4	£10	

CHOSEN FEW (2)

I Can Make Your Dreams Come True	7"	Polydor	2058721	1976	£2.50	£6	
You Mean Everything To Me	7"	Polydor	2058975	1978	£2.50	£6	

CHRIS & COSEY

Heartbeat	LP	Rough Trade	ROUGH34	1981	£4	£10	
Sweet Surprise	cass	Electronic Soundmaker		198-	£6	£15	with magazine
Sweet Surprise	12"	Rough Trade	RTT148	1985	£2.50	£6	with The Eurythmics

CHRIS & STUDENTS
Lass Of Richmond Hill .... 7" ..... Parlophone...... R4806 .... 1961 ... **£5** ....**£10** ....

CHRIS, PETER & THE OUTCASTS
Over The Hill .... 7" ..... Columbia .... DB7923........... 1966 ... **£7.50** ....**£15** ....

CHRISTIAN, BOBBY
Crickets On Parade .... 7" ..... Oriole .... CB1384 .... 1957 ... **£4** ....**£8** ....

CHRISTIAN, CHARLIE
Profoundly Blue .... 7" ..... Blue Note...... 451634........ 1964 ... **£1.50** ....**£4** .....Ike Quebec B side
With The Benny Goodman Sextet And LP ...... Philips............. BBL7172....... 1957 ... **£5** ....**£12** ....
Orchestra ....

CHRISTIAN DEATH
Official Anthology Of Live Bootlegs ..... LP ..... Jungle............. NOS006 .... 1986 ... **£8** ....**£20** ..black & yellow cover
Only Theatre Of Pain .... LP ..... No Future .... FL2 .... 1983 ... **£8** ....**£20** ....

CHRISTIAN, HANS
This was, for a short time, the stage name of the future lead singer of Yes, Jon Anderson.
Mississippi Hobo .... 7" ..... Parlophone...... R5698 .... 1968 ... **£15** ....**£30** ....
Never My Love .... 7" ..... Parlophone...... R5676 .... 1968 ... **£15** ....**£30** ....

CHRISTIAN, LIZ
Suddenly You Find Love .... 7" ..... CBS .... 202520............ 1967 ... **£15** ....**£30** ....

CHRISTIAN, NEIL & THE CRUSADERS
Lead guitarist with this group for a time was the young Jimmy Page, although he does not play on many of the singles.
All Things Bright And Beautiful .... 7" ..... Pye .... 7N17372........ 1967 ... **£2.50** ....**£6** ....
Big Beat Drum .... 7" ..... Columbia........ DB4938........... 1962 ... **£5** ....**£10** ....
Get A Load Of This .... 7" ..... Columbia........ DB7075........... 1963 ... **£5** ....**£10** ....
Honey Hush .... 7" ..... Columbia........ DB7289........... 1964 ... **£5** ....**£10** ....
Little Bit Of Something Else ..... 7" EP.. Columbia........ SEG8492 .... 1966 ... **£15** ....**£30** ....
Oops .... 7" ..... Strike .... JH313 .... 1966 ... **£4** ....**£8** ....
That's Nice .... 7" ..... Strike .... JH301 .... 1966 ... **£4** ....**£8** .....chart single
That's Nice .... 7" EP.. Riviera .... 231161........... 1966 ... **£15** ....**£30** .....French
Two At A Time .... 7" ..... Strike .... JH319 .... 1966 ... **£4** ....**£8** ....

CHRISTIE, JOHN
Fourth Of July .... 7" ..... Polydor .... 2058496........ 1974 ... **£2.50** ....**£6** ....
Fourth Of July .... 7" ..... Polydor .... 2058496........ 1974 ... **£6** ....**£12** .....PS

CHRISTIE, KEITH
Homage To The Duke .... 10" LP Esquire .... 20047............ 1955 ... **£6** ....**£15** ....

CHRISTIE, LOU
All That Glitters Isn't Gold .... 7" ..... King .... KG1036 .... 1966 ... **£1.50** ....**£4** ....
Guitars And Bongos .... 7" ..... Colpix .... PX735 .... 1964 ... **£1.50** ....**£4** ....
Gypsy Cried .... 7" ..... Columbia........ DB4983........... 1963 ... **£1.50** ....**£4** ....
How Many Teardrops .... 7" ..... Columbia........ DB7096........... 1963 ... **£1.50** ....**£4** ....
Lightnin' Strikes .... LP ..... MGM............. C(S)8008 .... 1966 ... **£4** ....**£10** ....
Lightnin' Strikes .... 7" ..... MGM............. MGM1297....... 1966 ... **£1.50** ....**£4** .....chart single
Lou Christie .... LP ..... Roulette .... (S)R25208 ...... 1963 ... **£5** ....**£12** .....US
Lou Christie Strikes Back .... LP ..... Co & Ce........ LP1231 .... 1966 ... **£5** ....**£12** .....US
Strikes Again .... LP ..... Colpix .... PXL551 .... 1966 ... **£4** ....**£10** ....
Two Faces Have I .... 7" ..... Columbia........ DB7031........... 1963 ... **£1.50** ....**£4** ....

CHRISTMAS, JOHNNY & THE SUNSPOTS
I'm Gonna Sing Sing Sing .... 7" EP.. Starlite............ STEP5............ 1958 ... **£2** ....**£5** ....

CHRISTMAS, KEITH
Fable Of The Wings .... LP ..... B&C.............. CAS1015 .... 1971 ... **£5** ....**£12** ....
Pigmy .... LP ..... B&C.............. CAS1041 .... 1971 ... **£5** ....**£12** ....
Stimulus .... LP ..... RCA.............. SF8059 .... 1969 ... **£15** ....**£30** ....

CHRISTOPHER
Christopher .... LP ..... Metromedia .... 1024............. 1970 ... **£25** ....**£50** .....US

CHRISTY, JUNE
Duet .... LP ..... Capitol .... T656 .... 1955 ... **£6** ....**£15** .....US
Gone For The Day .... LP ..... Capitol .... T902 .... 1957 ... **£6** ....**£15** ....
June Fair And Warmer .... LP ..... Capitol .... T833 .... 1957 ... **£6** ....**£15** .....US
June's Got Rhythm .... LP ..... Capitol .... T1076 .... 1959 ... **£4** ....**£10** ....
Misty Miss Christy .... LP ..... Capitol .... T725 .... 1956 ... **£6** ....**£15** .....US
Pete Kelly's Blues .... 7" ..... Capitol .... CL14355 .... 1955 ... **£1.50** ....**£4** ....
Something Cool .... LP ..... Capitol .... T516 .... 1955 ... **£6** ....**£15** .....US
Something Cool .... 7" EP.. Capitol .... EAP1516 .... 1955 ... **£2.50** ....**£6** ....
Something Cool .... 10" LP Capitol .... LC6682 .... 1954 ... **£8** ....**£20** ....
This Is June Christy .... LP ..... Capitol .... T1006 .... 1959 ... **£6** ....**£15** ....

CHROME
Alien Soundtracks .... LP ..... Siren .... DE2100 .... 1978 ... **£6** ....**£15** ....
Blood On The Moon .... LP ..... Don't Fall Off ... X6 .... 1981 ... **£4** ....**£10** ....
                                              The Mountain..
Firebomb .... 7" ..... Don't Fall Off ... Z17 .... 1982 ... **£2** ....**£5** ....
                                              The Mountain..
Half Lip Machine Moves .... LP ..... Beggars .... BEGA18........... 1980 ... **£4** ....**£10** ....
                                              Banquet ....
Inworlds .... 12" .... Don't Fall Off ... Y3 .... 1981 ... **£3** ....**£8** ....
                                              The Mountain..

New Age	7"	Beggars Banquet	BEG36	1980	£1.50	£4	
No Humans Allowed	LP	Siren		1981	£6	£15	US
Read Only Memory	12"	Siren	RS12007	1980	£3	£8	with poster
Red Exposure	LP	Beggars Banquet	BEGA15	1980	£4	£10	
Third From The Sun	LP	Don't Fall Off The Mountain..	X18	1982	£4	£10	
Visitation	LP	Siren	DE1000	1977	£6	£15	

CHRYSTAL BAND

Chrystal Band	LP	Carole			£20	£40	

CHUBBY & THE HONEYSUCKERS

Emergency Ward	7"	Rio	R75	1966	£4	£8	

CHUCK & BETTY

Sissy Britches	7"	Brunswick	05815	1959	£7.50	£15	

CHUCK & DOBBY

Cool School	7"	Blue Beat	BB23	1961	£5	£10	
Do Du Wap	7"	Blue Beat	BB39	1961	£5	£10	
Lovey Dovey	7"	Starlite	ST45044	1961	£5	£10	
Oh Fanny	7"	Blue Beat	BB59	1961	£5	£10	
Sweeter Than Honey	7"	Starlite	ST45043	1961	£5	£10	
Till The End Of Time	7"	Blue Beat	BB19	1961	£5	£10	

CHUCK & GARY

Teenie Weenie Jeannie	7"	HMV	POP466	1958	£10	£20	

CHUCK & GIDEON

Cherry Berry Lips	7"	Parlophone	R5011	1963	£1.50	£4	

CHUCKS

Chucks	7" EP	Decca	DFE8562	1964	£4	£8	
Hitch Hiker	7"	Decca	F11777	1963	£2	£5	
Loo Be Loo	7"	Decca	F11569	1963	£2	£5	chart single
Mulberry Bush	7"	Decca	F11617	1963	£2	£5	

CHURCH

Almost With You	7"	Carrere	CAR247	1982	£2.50	£6	
Blurred Crusade	LP	Carrere	CAL140	1982	£5	£12	gatefold sleeve
Different Man	7"	Carrere	CHURCHR5A	1983	£5	£10	No PS
It's No Reason	7"	Carrere	CAR336	1984	£1.50	£4	
It's No Reason	12"	Carrere	CART336	1984	£2.50	£6	
She Never Said	7"	Parlophone	A367	1981	£20	£40	Australian
Sing Songs	12"	Carrere	CHURCH5	1983	£8	£20	
Starfish	LP	Arista	208895	1988	£6	£15	with bonus 12'
Too Fast For You	7"	Parlophone	A536/525	1981	£20	£40	Australian double
Unguarded Moment	7"	Carrere	CAR212	1982	£2.50	£6	
Unguarded Moment	7"	Carrere	CAR257	1982	£1.50	£4	
Unguarded Moment	10"	Carrere	CAREP257	1982	£5	£12	

CHURCH, EUGENE

Miami	7"	London	HL8940	1959	£12.50	£25	

CHURCHILL, SAVANNAH

I Want To Be Loved	7"	London	HLW9273	1961	£1.50	£4	

CHURLS

Churls	LP	A&M	SP4169	1969	£5	£12	US

CHWYS

Gwr Bonheddig Hael	7"	Afon	RAS001	1975	£2.50	£6	

CIGARETTES

Can't Sleep At Night	7"	Dead Good	DEAD10	1980	£2.50	£6	
They're Back Again, Here They Come	7"	Company	CIGCO008	1979	£5	£10	

CIMARONS

Bad Day At Black Rock	7"	Reggae	REG3003	1970	£2	£5	
In Time	LP	Trojan	TRLS87	1974	£4	£10	

CINDERELLAS

Baby Baby I Still Love You	7"	Colpix	PX11126	1964	£15	£30	
Mr.Dee-Jay	7"	Brunswick	05794	1959	£6	£12	
Trouble With Boys	7"	Philips	PB1012	1960	£5	£10	

CINDERS

Cinnamon Cinder	7"	Warner Bros	WB86	1963	£1.50	£4	

CINDY & BERT

Our Summer Song Of Love	7"	BASF	BA1004	1974	£2	£5	

CINDY & LINDY

Saturday Night In Tiajuana	7"	Coral	Q72368	1959	£1.50	£4	

CINEMA FACE

Cinema Face	LP		RS2		£10	£25	Canadian

CINNAMOND, ROBERT

You Rambling Boys Of Pleasure	LP	Topic	12T269	1976	£5	£12	

CIRCLES
Take Your Time .... 7" ...... Island .... WI279 .... 1966 ... £12.50 ....£25 ....

CIRCLES (2)
Circles .... 7" ...... Graduate .... GRAD17 .... 1985 ... £1.50 ....£4 ....

CIRCUS
Circus played a serviceable rock style with jazz overtones and were chiefly notable for launcing the career of Mel Collins, whose saxophone and flute have been used to spice literally dozens of records since.
Circus .... LP .... Transatlantic ... TRA207 .... 1969 ... £15 ....£30 ....
Do You Dream .... 7" ...... Parlophone...... R5672 .... 1968 ... £12.50 ....£25 ....
Sink Or Swim .... 7" ...... Parlophone...... R5633 .... 1967 ... £4 ....£8 ....

CIRCUS 2000
Circus 2000 .... LP ..... Rifi .... 1969 ... £75 ....£150 ....
Escape From A Box .... LP ..... Rifi .... 1970 ... £50 ....£100 ....

CIRCUS MAXIMUS
Circus Maximus .... LP ..... Vanguard........ VSD79260 .... 1967 ... £8 ....£20 .... US
Neverland Revisited .... LP ..... Vanguard........ VSD79274 .... 1968 ... £8 ....£20 .... US

CIRKUS
Future Shock .... LP ..... Shock............... SHOCK1 .... 1977 ... £75 ....£150 ....
Melissa .... 7" ...... Guardian .... GRCA4 .... 197- ... £20 ....£40 ....
One .... LP ..... RCB .... RCB1 .... 1973 ... £50 ....£100 ....

CITATIONS
Moon Race .... 7" ...... Columbia......... DB7068 .... 1963 ... £5 ....£10 ....

CITY
Carole King's first LP was issued under the name of a group, City, but the sound is the same as on its successors. Following her success with "Tapestry", the City album was counterfeited - copies with black and white covers are the unofficial ones.
Now That Everything's Been Said .... LP ..... Ode .... Z1244012 .... 1969 ... £8 ....£20 .... colour cover

CITY OF WESTMINSTER STRING BAND
Touch Of Velvet A Sting Of Brass .... 7" ...... Pye .... 7N17620 .... 1968 ... £2 ....£5 ....

CITY RAMBLERS SKIFFLE GROUP
Delia's Gone .... 7" ...... Tempo .... A165 .... 1957 ... £1.50 ....£4 ....
Delia's Gone .... 7" EP.. Tempo .... EXA77 .... 1958 ... £4 ....£8 ....
Ella Speed .... 7" ...... Tempo .... A158 .... 1957 ... £1.50 ....£4 ....
Good Morning Blues .... 7" EP.. Tempo .... EXA71 .... 1957 ... £4 ....£8 ....
I Shall Not Be Moved .... 7" EP.. Storyville .... SEP345 .... 195- ... £4 ....£8 ....
I Want A Girl .... 7" EP.. Storyville .... SEP327 .... 195- ... £4 ....£8 ....
I Want A Girl .... 7" EP.. Tempo .... EXA59 .... 1957 ... £4 ....£8 ....
Mama Don't Allow .... 7" ...... Tempo .... A161 .... 1957 ... £1.50 ....£4 ....

CITY SMOKE
Sunday Morning .... 7" ...... Mercury .... MF971 .... 1967 ... £1.50 ....£4 ....

CITY WAITES
City Waites .... LP ..... Decca .... SKL5264 .... 1976 ... £40 ....£80 ....
Fox .... 7" ...... EMI................... EMI2149 .... 1974 ... £1.50 ....£4 ....
Gorgeous Gallery Of Gallant .... LP ...... EMI................... EMC3017 .... 1974 ... £40 ....£80 .... sleeve
Inventions .... pictured in Guide

CLAGUE
The two singles credited to Clague were the work of the same band that played on John Peel's radio show as Coyne-Clague and then made two LPs as Siren.
Bottle Up And Go .... 7" ...... Dandelion .... K4493 .... 1970 ... £2.50 ....£6 ....
Stride .... 7" ...... Dandelion .... K4494 .... 1970 ... £2.50 ....£6 ....

CLAIRE, ALISDAIR
Adam And The Beasts .... LP ...... Acorn .... 197- ... £10 ....£25 ....

CLANCY, WILLIE
Minstrel From Clare .... LP ...... Topic................ 12T175 .... 1967 ... £8 ....£20 ....

CLANCY, WILLY & MICHAEL GORMAN
Irish Jigs, Reels And Hornpipes .... 10" LP Folkways .... FW6819 .... 1956 ... £15 ....£30 .... US

CLANNAD
Clannad .... LP ...... Philips .... 6392013 .... 1973 ... £6 ....£15 .... Irish
Clannad 2 .... LP ...... Gael-Linn .... CEF041 .... 1974 ... £6 ....£15 .... Irish
Dulaman .... LP ...... Gael Linn .... CEF058 .... 1976 ... £5 ....£12 .... Irish
In Concert .... LP ...... Ogham .... BLB5001 .... 1978 ... £5 ....£12 .... Irish

CLANTON, JIMMY
Another Sleepless Night .... 7" ...... Top Rank .... JAR382............. 1960 ... £1.50 ....£4 .... chart single
Best Of Jimmy Clanton .... LP ...... Philips.............. PHM2/PHS600154 .. 1964 ... £8 ....£20 .... US
Come Back .... 7" ...... Top Rank .... JAR509............. 1960 ... £1.50 ....£4 ....
Darkest Street In Town .... 7" ...... Stateside .... SS159 .... 1963 ... £1.50 ....£4 ....
Go Jimmy Go .... 7" ...... Top Rank .... JAR269............. 1960 ... £1.50 ....£4 ....
Hurting Each Other .... 7" ...... Stateside .... SS410 .... 1965 ... £1.50 ....£4 ....
Jimmy's Blue .... LP ...... Ace .... 1008 .... 1960 ... £10 ....£25 .... US
Jimmy's Blue .... LP ...... Ace .... 1008 .... 1960 ... £20 ....£40 .... US, blue viny
Jimmy's Happy .... LP ...... Ace .... 1007 .... 1960 ... £10 ....£25 .... US
Jimmy's Happy .... LP ...... Ace .... 1007 .... 1960 ... £20 ....£40 .... US, red viny
Just A Dream .... LP ...... Ace .... 1001 .... 1959 ... £15 ....£30 .... US
Just A Dream .... 7" ...... London .... HLS8699 .... 1958 ... £6 ....£12 ....
Just A Dream .... 7" EP.. London .... RES1224 .... 1959 ... £15 ....£30 ....

Title	Format	Label	Cat. No.	Year	Price	Price	Notes
Letter To An Angel	7"	London	HL7066	1958	£5	£10	export
Letter To An Angel	7"	London	HLS8779	1959	£10	£20	
My Best To You	LP	Ace	1011	1961	£15	£30	US
My Own True Love	7"	Top Rank	JAR189	1959	£2	£5	
Teenage Millionaire	LP	Ace	1014	1961	£15	£30	US
Venus In Blue Jeans	LP	Ace	1026	1962	£15	£30	US
Venus In Blue Jeans	7"	Stateside	SS120	1962	£1.50	£4	
What Am I Gonna Do	7"	Top Rank	JAR544	1961	£1.50	£4	

CLAP

Title	Format	Label	Cat. No.	Year	Price	Price	Notes
Have You Reached Yet?	LP	Nova Sol	1001		£50	£100	US

CLAPTON, ERIC

Anyone attempting to collect a complete set of the records with which Eric Clapton has been involved is facing an extremely difficult task. For Clapton probably holds the prize for the highest number of guest appearances, including some on records that have become extremely rare. The compilation album "Clapton" was withdrawn and supposedly only four copies were left undestroyed. In fact many more than this have appeared on the market and the value of the record remains stubbornly low.

Title	Format	Label	Cat. No.	Year	Price	Price	Notes
461 Ocean Boulevard	LP	RSO	QD4801	1974	£6	£15	US quad
Clapton	LP	RSO	2479702	1978	£10	£25	
Just One Night	LP	Nautilus		1981	£6	£15	US audiophile
Slowhand	LP	Mobile Fidelity	MFSL1030	1979	£6	£15	US audiophile
There's One In Every Crowd	LP	RSO	QD4806	1974	£6	£15	US quad
Wonderful Tonight	12"	RSO	JONX001	1979	£3	£8	promo

CLARE, ALAN

Title	Format	Label	Cat. No.	Year	Price	Price	Notes
Jazz Around The Clock	LP	Decca	LK4260	1959	£6	£15	

CLARENDONIANS

Title	Format	Label	Cat. No.	Year	Price	Price	Notes
Baby Baby	7"	Caltone	TONE114	1968	£4	£8	
Baby Don't Do It	7"	Trojan	TR7719	1970	£1.50	£4	
Come Along	7"	Duke	DU97	1970	£2	£5	
Goodbye Forever	7"	Island	WI3041	1967	£5	£10	
He Who Laughs Last	7"	Studio One	SO2007	1967	£6	£12	
I Can't Go On	7"	Studio One	SO2004	1967	£6	£12	Gaylads B side
I'll Never Change	7"	Island	WI3005	1966	£5	£10	
Jerk	7"	Ska Beat	JB261	1966	£5	£10	
Little Girl	7"	Island	WI180	1965	£5	£10	
Ma Bien	7"	Ska Beat	JB219	1965	£5	£10	
Musical Train	7"	Rio	R115	1967	£4	£8	
Rudie Bam Bam	7"	Rio	R112	1966	£4	£8	
Sweetheart Of Beauty	7"	Island	WI3032	1967	£5	£10	
Try Me One More Time	7"	Island	WI284	1966	£5	£10	

CLARK, CHRIS

Title	Format	Label	Cat. No.	Year	Price	Price	Notes
C C Rides Again	LP	Weed	WS801		£15	£30	US
From Head To Toe	7"	Tamla Motown	TMG624	1967	£10	£20	
I Want To Go Back There Again	7"	Tamla Motown	TMG638	1968	£7.50	£15	
Love's Gone Bad	7"	Tamla Motown	TMG591	1967	£15	£30	
Soul Sounds	LP	Tamla Motown	(S)TML11069	1968	£15	£30	

CLARK, CLAUDINE

Title	Format	Label	Cat. No.	Year	Price	Price	Notes
Party Lights	LP	Chancellor	CHL5029	1962	£15	£30	US
Party Lights	7"	Pye	7N25157	1962	£2	£5	
Strength To Be Strong	7"	Sue	WI4039	1967	£5	£10	
Walk Me Home From The Party	7"	Pye	7N25186	1963	£1.50	£4	

CLARK, DAVE

Title	Format	Label	Cat. No.	Year	Price	Price	Notes
Dave Clark And Friends	LP	Columbia	SCX6494	1972	£6	£15	
Draggin' The Line	7"	Columbia	DB8834	1971	£1.50	£4	
Rub It In	7"	Columbia	DB8907	1972	£1.50	£4	
Sha-Na-Na-Na	7"	EMI	EMI2082	1973	£1.50	£4	
Sweet City Woman	7"	EMI	EMI2013	1973	£1.50	£4	
Think Of Me	7"	Columbia	DB8862	1972	£1.50	£4	

CLARK, DAVE FIVE

Title	Format	Label	Cat. No.	Year	Price	Price	Notes
5 By 5 - Go!	LP	Epic	LN24/BN26236	1967	£8	£20	US
5 By 5 - Go! (14 Titles By Dave Clark)	LP	Columbia	SCX6309	1968	£8	£20	
All Time Greats	7"	Columbia	DB8963	1972	£1.50	£4	PS
American Tour	LP	Epic	LN24/BN26117	1964	£8	£20	US
Anyway You Want It	7"	Columbia	DB7377	1964	£1.50	£4	chart single
Best Of The Dave Clark Five	LP	Starline	SRS5037	1970	£4	£10	
Bits And Pieces	7"	Columbia	DB7210	1964	£1.50	£4	chart single
Bits And Pieces	7" EP	Columbia	ESRF1525	1964	£7.50	£15	French
Can't You See That She's Mine	7"	Columbia	DB7291	1964	£1.50	£4	chart single
Catch Us If You Can	LP	Columbia	SX1756	1965	£8	£20	chart LP
Catch Us If You Can	7"	Columbia	DB7625	1965	£1.50	£4	chart single
Catch Us If You Can	7" EP	Columbia	ESRF1699	1965	£7.50	£15	French
Chaquita	7"	Ember	EMBS156	1962	£12.50	£25	
Coast To Coast	LP	Epic	LN24/BN26128	1965	£8	£20	US
Come Home	7"	Columbia	DB7580	1965	£1.50	£4	chart single
Dave Clark 5 & Washington DCs	LP	Ember	FA2003	1965	£10	£25	
Dave Clark Five	LP	Epic	EG30434	1971	£8	£20	US double
Dave Clark Five	7" EP	Columbia	SEG8289	1964	£5	£10	
Do You Love Me	7"	Columbia	DB7112	1963	£1.50	£4	chart single
Everybody Get Together	7"	Columbia	DB8660	1970	£1.50	£4	chart single
Everybody Knows	LP	Columbia	SX6207	1968	£8	£20	
Everybody Knows	7"	Columbia	DB7453	1965	£1.50	£4	chart single
Everybody Knows	7"	Columbia	DB8286	1967	£1.50	£4	chart single
Everybody Knows	7"	Polydor	2058953	1977	£4	£8	PS
First Love	7"	Piccadilly	7N35088	1962	£12.50	£25	
Get It On Now	7"	Columbia	DB8591	1969	£40	£80	test pressing

Title	Format	Label	Catalogue	Year	Price	Price	Notes
Glad All Over	LP	Epic	LN24/BN26093	1964	£8	£20	US
Glad All Over	7"	Columbia	DB7154	1963	£1.50	£4	chart single
Glad All Over	7" EP	Columbia	ESRF1489	1964	£7.50	£15	French
Good Old Rock'n'Roll	7"	Columbia	DB8638	1969	£1.50	£4	PS, chart single
Greatest Hits	LP	Columbia	SX6105	1966	£6	£15	
Having A Wild Weekend	LP	Epic	LN24/BN26162	1965	£8	£20	US
Here Comes Summer	7"	Columbia	DB8689	1970	£1.50	£4	chart single
Hits Of The Dave Clark Five	7" EP	Columbia	SEG8381	1965	£6	£12	
I Knew It All The Time	7"	Piccadilly	7N35500	1962	£12.50	£25	
I Like It Like That	LP	Epic	LN24/BN26178	1966	£8	£20	US
If Somebody Loves You	LP	Columbia	SCX6437	1971	£6	£15	
In Session	LP	Regal	REG2017	1965	£10	£25	export
Julia	7"	Columbia	DB8681	1970	£1.50	£4	
Live In The Sky	7"	Columbia	DB8505	1968	£1.50	£4	chart single
Look Before You Leap	7"	Columbia	DB7909	1966	£1.50	£4	chart single
More Good Old Rock'n'Roll	7"	Columbia	DB8724	1970	£1.50	£4	chart single
More Greatest Hits	LP	Epic	LN24/BN26221	1966	£6	£15	US
Mulberry Bush	7"	Columbia	DB7011	1963	£7.50	£15	
Mulberry Tree	7"	Columbia	DB8545	1969	£1.50	£4	
Nineteen Days	7"	Columbia	DB8028	1966	£1.50	£4	
No One Can Break A Heart Like You	7"	Columbia	DB8342	1968	£1.50	£4	chart single
Over And Over	7"	Columbia	DB7744	1965	£1.50	£4	chart single
Over And Over	7" EP	Columbia	ESRF1727	1965	£7.50	£15	French
Play Good Old Rock & Roll	LP	Starline	SRS5090	1971	£6	£15	
Please Tell Me Why	7" EP	Columbia	ESRF1795	1966	£7.50	£15	French
Put A Little Love In Your Heart	7"	Columbia	DB8624	1969	£1.50	£4	chart single
Red Balloon	7"	Columbia	DB8465	1968	£1.50	£4	chart single
Reelin' And Rockin'	7"	Columbia	DB7503	1965	£1.50	£4	chart single
Reelin' And Rockin'	7" EP	Columbia	ESRF1647	1964	£7.50	£15	French
Return	LP	Epic	LN24/BN26104	1964	£8	£20	US
Satisfied With You	LP	Epic	LN24/BN26212	1966	£8	£20	US
Session With The Dave Clark Five	LP	Columbia	33SX1598	1964	£8	£20	chart LP
Session With The Dave Clark Five	LP	MFP	MFP1260	1968	£4	£10	
Southern Man	7"	Columbia	DB8749	1971	£1.50	£4	
Tabatha Twitchit	7"	Columbia	DB8194	1967	£1.50	£4	
Thinking Of You Baby	7"	Columbia	DB7335	1964	£1.50	£4	chart single
Thinking Of You Baby	7" EP	Columbia	ESRF1581	1964	£7.50	£15	French
Try Too Hard	LP	Epic	LN24/BN26198	1966	£8	£20	US
Try Too Hard	7"	Columbia	DB7863	1966	£1.50	£4	
Weekend In London	LP	Epic	LN24/BN26139	1965	£8	£20	US
Wild Weekend	7" EP	Columbia	SEG8447	1965	£5	£10	
Won't You Be My Lady	7"	Columbia	DB8791	1971	£1.50	£4	
You Got What It Takes	LP	Epic	LN24/BN26312	1967	£8	£20	US
You Got What It Takes	7" EP	Columbia	ESRF1871	1967	£7.50	£15	French
You Knew It All The Time	7" EP	Palette	22009	1963	£7.50	£15	French, B side by the Ravens
You've Got What It Takes	7"	Columbia	DB8152	1967	£1.50	£4	chart single

CLARK, DEE

Title	Format	Label	Catalogue	Year	Price	Price	Notes
At My Front Door	7"	Top Rank	JAR373	1960	£6	£12	
Best Of Dee Clark	LP	Vee Jay	LP/SR1047	1964	£6	£15	US
Dee Clark	LP	Abner	LP/SR2000	1959	£10	£25	US
Dee Clark	LP	Vee Jay	LP1028	1961	£8	£20	US
Don't Walk Away From Me	7"	Columbia	DB4768	1962	£2	£5	
Heartbreak	7"	Stateside	SS355	1964	£2	£5	
Hey Little Girl	7"	Top Rank	JAR196	1959	£5	£10	
Hold On, It's Dee Clark	LP	Vee Jay	LP/SR1037	1961	£8	£20	US
How About That	LP	Top Rank	BUY044	1960	£8	£20	
How About That	7"	Top Rank	JAR284	1960	£4	£8	
I'm A Soldier Boy	7"	Stateside	SS180	1963	£10	£20	
Just Keep It Up	7"	London	HL8915	1959	£5	£10	chart single
Raindrops	7"	Top Rank	JAR570	1961	£2	£5	
T.C.B.	7"	Stateside	SS400	1965	£5	£10	
When I Call On You	7"	London	HL8802	1959	£5	£10	
Where Did All The Good Times Go	7"	Liberty	LBF15334	1970	£2	£4	
Your Friends	7"	Top Rank	JAR551	1961	£2.50	£6	
You're Looking Good	LP	Vee Jay	LP1019	1960	£8	£20	US
You're Looking Good	7"	Top Rank	JAR501	1960	£2	£5	

CLARK, GENE

Title	Format	Label	Catalogue	Year	Price	Price	Notes
Early L.A. Sessions	LP	CBS	31123	1972	£6	£15	US
Echoes	7"	CBS	202523	1967	£2.50	£6	
Gene Clark And The Gosdin Brothers	LP	CBS	62934	1967	£6	£15	
No Other	LP	Asylum	SYL9020	1974	£4	£10	
Road Master	LP	Ariola	87584	1973	£6	£15	Dutch
White Light	LP	A&M	AMLS64297	1972	£5	£12	

CLARK, MICHAEL

Title	Format	Label	Catalogue	Year	Price	Price	Notes
None Of These Girls	7"	Liberty	LIB5893	1966	£2.50	£6	

CLARK, PETULA

Title	Format	Label	Catalogue	Year	Price	Price	Notes
A Date With Pet	10" LP	Pye	NPT19014	1956	£25	£50	
Adonis	7"	Pye	7N15220	1959	£1.50	£4	
Alone	7"	Pye	7N15112	1957	£1.50	£4	chart single
Baby Lover	7"	Pye	7N15126	1958	£1.50	£4	chart single
Beautiful Sounds	LP	Pet Projects	PP2	1976	£5	£12	
Call Me	7" EP	Pye	NEP24237	1966	£2	£5	
C'Est Ma Chanson	LP	Pye-Vogue	VRL3030	967	£4	£10	
C'Est Ma Chanson	7" EP	Pye-Vogue	VRE5025	1967	£2.50	£6	
Chante En Italian	7" EP	Vogue	VRE5007	1965	£4	£8	

Title	Format	Label	Catalogue	Year	Price	Price	Notes
Chariot	7"	Pye	7N15522	1963	£1.50	£4	
Children's Choice	7" EP	Pye	NEP24006	1956	£10	£20	
Christmas Carol	7" EP	Pye	NEP24094	1958	£4	£8	
Christmas Carol	7" EP	Pye	NSEP85001	1958	£7.50	£15	stereo
Cinderella	7"	Pye	7N15281	1960	£1.50	£4	
Colour My World	LP	Pye	N(S)PL18171	1967	£5	£12	with 'England Swings' & 'Reach Out'
Come On Home	LP	Polydor	2383279	1974	£4	£10	
Dear Daddy	7"	Pye	7N15233	1959	£1.50	£4	
Devotion	7"	Pye	7N15152	1958	£1.50	£4	
Dis Moi Au Revoir	7" EP	Vogue	VRE5028	1968	£2	£5	
Don't Give Up	7" EP	Pye	NEP24301	1968	£4	£8	
Downtown	LP	Pye	NPL18114	1965	£4	£10	
Downtown	7"	Pye	7N15722	1964	£1.50	£4	chart single
Downtown	7" EP	Pye	NEP24206	1965	£2.50	£6	
En Francais	7" EP	Pye	NEP24182	1963	£4	£8	
Encore	7" EP	Pye	NEP24121	1959	£2	£5	
Encore En Francais	7" EP	Pye	NEP24189	1964	£4	£8	
Ever Been In Love	7"	Pye	7N15182	1959	£1.50	£4	
Fibbin'	7"	Pye	7N15168	1958	£1.50	£4	
Finian's Rainbow	LP	Warner Bros	WF(S)2550	1968	£6	£15	
Goodbye Mr.Chips	LP	MGM	CS8113	1969	£6	£15	
Hello Dolly In French	7" EP	Pye	NEP24194	1964	£2	£5	
Hello Mr.Brown	7" EP	Pye-Vogue	VRE5023	1966	£2.50	£6	
Hello Paris Vol.1	LP	Pye-Vogue	VRL3016	1966	£5	£12	
Hello Paris Vol.2	LP	Pye-Vogue	VRL3019	1966	£4	£10	
Hit Parade	7" EP	Pye	NEP24016	1956	£6	£12	
Hit Parade 4	7" EP	Pye	NEP24137	1961	£4	£8	
Hit Parade 5	7" EP	Pye	NEP24150	1961	£2	£5	
Hit Parade No.2	7" EP	Pye	NEP24056	1957	£4	£8	
Hit Parade No.3	7" EP	Pye	NEP24080	1958	£4	£8	
Hits	7" EP	Pye	NEP24163	1962	£2	£5	
I Am Your Song	7"	Polydor	2058560	1975	£2.50	£6	
I Couldn't Live Without Your Love	LP	Pye	N(S)PL18148	1966	£4	£10	
I Couldn't Live Without Your Love	7" EP	Pye	NEP24266	1966	£2.50	£6	
I Couldn't Live Without Your Love ('89 Mix)	CD-s	Legacy	LGYCD100	1989	£2.50	£6	
I Know A Place	7"	Pye	7N15772	1965	£1.50	£4	chart single
I Love A Violin	7"	Pye	7N15244	1960	£1.50	£4	
I Want To Sing With Your Band	7"	Pye	7N17646	1968	£1.50	£4	
I'm The Woman You Need	LP	Polydor	2383324	1975	£6	£15	
In Other Words	LP	Pye	NPL18070	1962	£6	£15	
Jumble Sale	7"	Pye	7N15456	1962	£1.50	£4	
Just Say Goodbye	7" EP	Pye	NEP24259	1966	£2.50	£6	
L'Agent Secret	7" EP	Pye-Vogue	VRE5019	1966	£2.50	£6	
L'Amour Viendra	7" EP	Vogue	VRE5026	1968	£2	£5	
Lead Me On	7"	Polydor	2058413	1973	£5	£10	
Les Disques D'Or De La Chanson	7" EP	Vogue	VRE5034	1965	£2	£5	
Les James Dean	LP	Pye-Vogue	VRL3001	1964	£4	£10	
Let's Sing A Love Song	7"	Polydor	2058519	1974	£2	£5	
Live In London	LP	Polydor	2383303	1974	£5	£12	
Love Me Again	7"	Pye	7N15135	1958	£1.50	£4	
Many Faces	7" EP	Pye	NEP24280	1967	£2.50	£6	
My Friend The Sea	7"	Pye	7N15387	1961	£1.50	£4	chart single
My Love	LP	Pye	NPL18141	1966	£4	£10	
My Love	7" EP	Pye	NEP24246	1966	£2	£5	
New Petula Clark Album	LP	Pye	N(S)PL18118	1965	£4	£10	
Noel	LP	Pet Projects	PP1	1975	£5	£12	
Pet Ooh La La	7" EP	Pye	NEP24157	1962	£2	£5	
Petula	LP	Pye	NPL18089	1962	£4	£10	
Petula '65	LP	Pye-Vogue	VRL3010	1965	£6	£15	
Petula '66	LP	Pye-Vogue	VRL3022	1966	£4	£10	
Petula '71	LP	Pye	NSPL18370	1971	£5	£12	
Petula Clark	7" EP	Pye	NEP24286	1968	£2	£5	
Petula Clark In Hollywood	LP	Pye	NPL18039	1959	£15	£30	
Petula Clark Sings	10" LP	Pye	NPT19002	1956	£25	£50	
Road	7"	Pye	7N15478	1962	£1.50	£4	
Romeo	7"	Pye	7N15361	1961	£1.50	£4	chart single
Sailor	7"	Pye	7N15324	1961	£1.50	£4	chart single
Sign Of The Times	7"	Pye	7N17071	1966	£2.50	£6	
Sings In French	7" EP	Pye	NEP24089	1958	£4	£8	
Sings The International Hits	LP	Pye	NPL18123	1965	£4	£10	
This Is My Song	7" EP	Pye	NEP24279	1967	£2.50	£6	
Today	LP	Pye	PKL5502	1971	£4	£10	
Valentino	7"	Pye	7N15517	1963	£4	£8	
Watch Your Heart	7"	Pye	7N15191	1959	£1.50	£4	
Where Do I Go From Here?	7"	Pye	7N15208	1959	£1.50	£4	
Whistlin' For The Moon	7"	Pye	7N15437	1962	£1.50	£4	
With All My Heart	7"	Pye	7N15096	1957	£5	£10	chart single
Ya Ya Twist	7"	Pye	7N15448	1962	£1.50	£4	chart single
You Are My Lucky Star	LP	Pye	NPL18007	1957	£15	£30	
You Are My Lucky Star Part 1	7" EP	Pye	NEP24060	1957	£5	£10	
You Are My Lucky Star Part 2	7" EP	Pye	NEP24061	1957	£5	£10	
You Are My Lucky Star Part 3	7" EP	Pye	NEP24062	1957	£5	£10	
You're The One	7"	Pye	7N15991	1965	£1.50	£4	
You're the One	7" EP	Pye	NEP24233	1965	£2.50	£6	

CLARK, ROY

Title	Format	Label	Catalogue	Year	Price	Price
Lightning Fingers	LP	Capitol	(S)T1780	1962	£4	£10

Please Mr.Mayor	7"	HMV	POP581	1959	£15	£30	
Texas Twist	7"	Capitol	CL15288	1963	£2	£5	
Tips Of My Fingers	7"	Capitol	CL15317	1963	£1.50	£4	

CLARK, SANFORD

Fool	7"	London	HL7014	1956	£12.50	£25	export
Fool	7"	London	HLD8320	1956	£30	£60	
Lowdown Blues	7" EP..	London	REW1256	1960	£12.50	£25	
Pledging My Love	7"	London	HLW9095	1960	£5	£10	
Presenting Sanford Clark	7" EP..	London	RED1105	1957	£20	£40	
Run Boy Run	7"	London	HLW8959	1959	£7.50	£15	
Shades	7"	Ember	EMBS250	1968	£2	£5	
Son Of A Gun	7"	London	HLW9026	1960	£5	£10	

CLARK SISTERS

Beauty Shop Beat	LP	Coral	CRL(7)57290	1960	£5	£12	US
Chicago	7"	London	HLD8791	1959	£2	£5	
Sing Sing Sing	LP	London	HAD2128	1958	£6	£15	
Sing Sing Sing	7" EP..	London	RED1198	1959	£5	£10	
Swing Again	LP	London	HAD2177/	1959	£6	£15	
			SAHD6025				

CLARK, SONNY

Cool Struttin'	LP	Blue Note	BLP/BST81588	196-	£10	£25	
Leapin' And Lopin'	LP	Blue Note	BLP/BST84091	1961	£15	£30	

CLARK, TREVOR

Sufferer	7"	Studio One	SO2082	1969	£6	£12	Jackie Mittoo B side

CLARKE, ALICE

You Got A Deal	7"	Action	ACT4520	1969	£2	£5	

CLARKE, ALLAN

Allan Clarke	LP	EMI	EMC3041	1974	£4	£10	
Headroom	LP	EMI	EMA752	1973	£4	£10	
I've Got Time	LP	EMI	EMC3130	1976	£4	£10	
Legendary Heroes	LP	Elektra	K52224	1979	£4	£10	
My Real Name Is 'Arold	LP	RCA	SF8283	1972	£4	£10	

CLARKE, JOHN COOPER

Gimmix	7"	Epic	EPC127009	1978	£1.50	£4	orange vinyl, plectrum shaped disc
Snap Crackle & Bop	LP	Epic	EPC84083	1980	£4	£10	with book
Suspended Sentence	7"	Rabid	TOSH103	1977	£1.50	£4	orange PS

CLARKE, KENNY

Jacksonville	LP	Realm	RM124	1963	£5	£12	
Jazz International	LP	Vogue	LAE12029	1957	£10	£25	
Jazz Is Universal	LP	London	HAK8085	1963	£6	£15	
Kenny Clarke	LP	London	LTZC15038	1957	£10	£25	
Kenny Clarke	LP	London	LTZC15047	1957	£10	£25	
Kenny Clarke Quartet	7" EP.	Columbia	SEG7830	1957	£2	£5	
Kenny Clarke Sextet	LP	London	LTZC15004	1956	£10	£25	
Klook's Clique	LP	Realm	RM156	1963	£5	£12	
Plenty For Kenny	LP	London	LTZC15008	1956	£10	£25	with Ernie Wilkins
What's New	LP	Realm	RM115	1963	£5	£12	

CLARKE, KENNY & FRANCY BOLAND

Golden Eight	LP	Blue Note	BLP/BST84092	1961	£15	£30	

CLARKE, LLOYD

Fellow Jamaican	7"	Rio	R24	1964	£5	£10	Patrick & George B side
Fools Day	7"	Blue Beat	BB104	1962	£5	£10	
Good Morning	7"	Blue Beat	BB99	1962	£5	£10	
Japanese Girl	7"	Island	WI045	1962	£5	£10	
Love Is Strange	7"	Blue Beat	BB371	1965	£5	£10	Sonny Burke B side
Love Me	7"	Rio	R16	1963	£5	£10	
Love You The Most	7"	Island	WI007	1962	£5	£10	Lloyd Robinson B side
Stop Your Talking	7"	Rio	R23	1964	£5	£10	
Young Love	7"	Blue Cat	BS136	1968	£4	£8	Untouchables B side

CLARKE, TONY

Ain't Love Good Ain't Love Proud	7"	Pye	7N25251	1964	£5	£10	
Entertainer	7"	Chess	CRS8011	1965	£7.50	£15	
Entertainer	7"	Chess	CRS8091	1969	£2.50	£6	
Entertainer	7"	Janus	6146030	1974	£2	£5	

CLARK-HUTCHINSON

The Clark-Hutchinson LP, "A=MH2", was probably the best selling record on Decca's progressive offshoot, Nova, although as most of the records on the label sank without trace, this is not saying very much. The duo turned themselves into a group by extensive multi-tracking, concentrating on Mick Hutchinson's guitar playing to provide a focus of interest. In truth, he was not that remarkable a player and although Clark-Hutchinson got to make two more LPs, they have not been heard from since.

A=MH2	LP	Nova	(S)DNR2	1970	£6	£15	
Gestalt	LP	Deram	SML1090	1971	£6	£15	
Retribution	LP	Deram	SML1076	1970	£6	£15	

CLASH

Capital Radio	7"	CBS	CL1	1977	£12.50	£25	promo
Combat Rock	LP	Epic	AS991592	1982	£15	£30	US promo pic disc

Combat Rock	LP	Epic	FE37689	1982	£10	£25	US promo
							camoflague vinyl
Give 'Em Enough Rope	LP	CBS	82431	1978	£10	£25	promo with poster
If Music Could Talk	LP	Epic	AS952	1981	£8	£20	US promo
London Calling	12"	CBS	128087	1979	£2.50	£6	
Remote Control	12"	CBS	125293	1978	£6	£15	promo
Sandinista Now!	LP	Epic	AS913	1980	£8	£20	US single LP promo
Should I Stay Or Should I Go	7"	CBS	A112646	1982	£1.50	£4	pic disc
Take A Gamble	12"	CBS		1980	£2.50	£6	promo
World According To The Clash	LP	Epic	AS1574	1982	£20	£40	US promo

CLASSICS

Life Is But A Dream	7"	Mercury	AMT1152	1961	£12.50	£25	
Pollyanna	7"	Capitol	CL15470	1966	£4	£8	
Till Then	7"	Stateside	SS215	1963	£4	£8	

CLASSICS (2)

| History Of Africa | 7" | New Beat | NB071 | 1970 | £2.50 | £6 | |

CLASSICS IV

Everyday With You Girl	7"	Liberty	LBF15231	1969	£2	£5	
Golden Greats	LP	Imperial	16000	1969	£4	£10	US
Mamas And Papas Soul Train	LP	Imperial	12407	1968	£4	£10	US
Spooky	LP	Imperial	12371	1968	£5	£12	US
Spooky	7"	Liberty	LBF15051	1968	£2	£5	chart single
Stormy	7"	Liberty	LBF15177	1969	£1.50	£4	
Traces	7"	Liberty	LBF15196	1969	£1.50	£4	

CLASSMATES

Go Away	7"	Decca	F12047	1964	£2.50	£6	
Go Tell It On The Mountain	7"	Decca	F11779	1963	£1.50	£4	
In Morocco	7"	Decca	F11806	1964	£1.50	£4	
Let's Get Together Tonight	7"	Decca	F11736	1963	£1.50	£4	

CLAUDETTE & THE CORPORATION

| Skinheads A Bash Them | 7" | Grape | GR3020 | 1970 | £2 | £5 | |

CLAY, CASSIUS

If the idea of Cassius Clay (or Mohammed Ali as he became better known) wailing "Stand By Me" seems hard to take, then the single's B side may be more to the point - "I Am The Greatest", it is called.

I Am The Greatest!	LP	Columbia	CL2093/CS8893	1963	£10	£25	US
Stand By Me	7"	CBS	202190	1966	£4	£8	
Stand By Me	7"	CBS	AAG190	1964	£6	£12	

CLAY, JUDY

| You Can't Run Away From Your Heart | 7" | Stax | 601022 | 1967 | £4 | £8 | |

CLAY, JUDY & WILLIAM BELL

| Private Number | 7" | Stax | STAX101 | 1968 | £1.50 | £4 | chart single |

CLAY, OTIS

Baby Jane	7"	Atlantic	584282	1969	£1.50	£4	
It's Easier Said Than Done	7"	President	PT121	1968	£1.50	£4	
Lasting Love	7"	President	PT176	1968	£1.50	£4	

CLAY, TOM

| What The World Needs Now | 7" | Tamla Motown | TMG801 | 1972 | £2.50 | £6 | |

CLAYRE, ALASDAIR

| Alasdair Clayre | LP | Elektra | EUK255 | 1967 | £20 | £40 | |

CLAYTON, BUCK

All The Cats Join In	LP	Philips	BBL7129	1957	£5	£12	
Buck	LP	Vogue	LAE12032	1957	£5	£12	
Buck Clayton	LP	Philips	BBL7068	1956	£6	£15	
Buck Clayton	10" LP	Vogue	LDE140	1955	£8	£20	
Buck Clayton Special	LP	Philips	BBL7217	1958	£5	£12	
Buck Meets Ruby	10" LP	Vanguard	PPT12006	1956	£8	£20	with Ruby Braff
Buckin' The Blues	LP	Vanguard	PPL11010	1958	£5	£12	
Jam Session	LP	Philips	BBL7032	1955	£6	£15	
Jam Session	LP	Philips	BBL7040	1955	£6	£15	
Jam Session	LP	Philips	BBL7446	1961	£4	£10	
Jumpin' At The Woodside	LP	Philips	BBL7087	1956	£5	£12	
Newport Jazz Festival All Stars	LP	London	LTZK15202/ SAHK6116	1961	£4	£10	
Songs For Swingers	LP	Philips	BBL7317	1959	£4	£10	

CLAYTON, PAUL

| Paul Clayton | 7" EP | London | REU1276 | 1960 | £5 | £10 | |
| Wings Of A Dove | 7" | London | HLU9285 | 1961 | £2 | £5 | |

CLAYTON SQUARES

| Come And Get It | 7" | Decca | F12250 | 1965 | £6 | £12 | |
| There She Is | 7" | Decca | F12456 | 1966 | £15 | £30 | |

CLEANLINESS & GODLINESS SKIFFLE BAND

| Greatest Hits | LP | Vanguard | SVRL19043 | 1968 | £5 | £12 | |

CLEAR BLUE SKY

| Clear Blue Sky | LP | Vertigo | 6360013 | 1971 | £30 | £60 | spiral label |

CLEAR LIGHT

Black Roses	7"	Elektra	EKSN45019	1967	£2.50	£6
Clear Light	LP	Elektra	EKL/EKS74011	1967	£8	£20
Night Sounds Loud	7"	Elektra	EKSN45027	1968	£2	£5

CLEARLIGHT

Clearlight Symphony	LP	Virgin	V2029	1975	£6	£15	
Forever Blowing Bubbles	LP	Virgin	V2039	1975	£6	£15	
Les Contes Du Singe Fou	LP	Isadora	ISA9009	1976	£8	£20	French
Visions	LP	LTM	1005	1978	£8	£20	French

CLEARWAYS

I'll Be Here	7"	Columbia	DB7333	1964	£2	£5

CLEESE, JOHN & OTHERS

I'm Sorry, I'll Read That Again	LP	Parlophone	PMC7024	1967	£4	£10

CLEESE, JOHN & THE 1948 CHOIR

Ferret Song	7"	Pye	7N17336	1967	£1.50	£4

CLEFS

Dream Train Special	7"	Salvo	SLO1810	1962	£5	£10

CLEFTONES

For Sentimental Reasons	LP	Gee	(S)GLP707	1962	£40	£80	US
Heart And Soul	LP	Gee	(S)GLP705	1961	£40	£80	US
Heart And Soul	7"	Columbia	DB4678	1961	£15	£30	
I Love You For Sentimental Reasons	7"	Columbia	DB4720	1961	£10	£20	
Little Girl Of Mine	7"	Columbia	DB3801	1956	£75	£150	
Lover Come Back To Me	7"	Columbia	DB4988	1963	£6	£12	

CLEMENT, JACK

Ten Years	7"	London	HLS8691	1958	£15	£30

CLEMENTS, SOUL JOE

Never Never	7"	Plexium	PXM10	1968	£75	£150

CLEMENTS, VASSAR

Bluegrass Session	LP	Sonet	SNTF748	1977	£5	£12

CLEVELAND, JIMMY

Jimmy Cleveland	LP	Mercury	MMB12012	1959	£8	£20	
Map Of Jimmy Cleveland	LP	Mercury	MMC14023	1959	£5	£12	
Trombones	LP	London	LTZC15088	1958	£8	£20	with Henry Coker, Bill Hughes, Benny Powell

CLIFF DWELLERS

Hang On Stupid	7"	Polydor	56707	1966	£1.50	£4

CLIFF, JIMMY

Another Cycle	LP	Island	ILPS9159	1971	£5	£12	
Give And Take	7"	Island	WIP6004	1967	£4	£8	
Hard Road To Travel	LP	Island	ILP962	1968	£30	£60	
Harder They Come	7"	Island	WIP6139	1972	£1.50	£4	
Huricane Hatty	7"	Island	WI012	1962	£5	£10	
I Got A Feeling	7"	Island	WIP6011	1967	£4	£8	
I'm Sorry	7"	Blue Beat	BB78	1961	£5	£10	Red Price B side
Jimmy Cliff	LP	Trojan	TRLS16	1969	£8	£20	
KIng Of Kings	7"	Island	WI070	1963	£5	£10	Sir Percy B side
Man	7"	Black Swan	WI403	1964	£5	£10	
Miss Jamaica	7"	Island	WI016	1962	£5	£10	
Miss Universe	7"	Island	WI112	1963	£5	£10	
My Lucky Day	7"	Island	WI062	1962	£5	£10	
One Eyed Jacks	7"	Stateside	SS342	1964	£4	£8	
Pride And Passion	7"	Fontana	TF641	1966	£5	£10	
Since Lately	7"	Island	WI025	1962	£5	£10	
Struggling Man	LP	Island	ILPS9235	1974	£4	£10	
That's The Way Life Goes	7"	Island	WIP6024	1967	£2.50	£6	
Trapped	7"	Island	WIP6132	1972	£1.50	£4	
Unlimited	LP	EMI	EMA757	1973	£4	£10	
Vietnam	7"	Trojan	TR7722	1970	£2	£5	chart single
Waterfall	7"	Island	WIP6039	1968	£5	£10	
Wild World	7"	Island	WIP6087	1970	£1.50	£4	chart single
Wonderful World	LP	A&M	SP4251	1970	£5	£12	US
Wonderful World Beautiful People	7"	Trojan	TR690	1969	£2	£5	chart single

CLIFFORD, BILLY

Irish Traditional Flute Solos	LP	Topic	12TS312	1977	£5	£12

CLIFFORD, BUZZ

Baby Sittin' Boogie	7"	Fontana	H297	1961	£2.50	£6	chart single
Baby Sittin' With Buzz	LP	Fontana	TFL5147	1961	£10	£25	
Nobody Loves Me Like You	7"	Columbia	DB4903	1962	£1.50	£4	
Three Little Fishes	7"	Fontana	H312	1961	£1.50	£4	

CLIFFORD, LINDA

After Loving You	7"	Paramount	3051	1974	£1.50	£4

CLIFFORD, MIKE

For The Love Of Mike	LP	United Artists	UAL/UAS6409	1965	£4	£10	US

CLIFTERS
Title	Format	Label	Cat. No.	Year			Notes
Amapola	7"	Philips	PB1242	1962	£2	£5	

CLIFTON, BILL
Title	Format	Label	Cat. No.	Year			Notes
Beatle Crazy	7"	Decca	F11793	1963	£4	£8	
Bill Clifton	7" EP	Mercury	MEP9546	1958	£2.50	£6	
You Don't Think About Me	7"	Melodisc	1554	1960	£1.50	£4	

CLIFTON, BILL & GEORGE JONES
Title	Format	Label	Cat. No.	Year			Notes
Country & Western Trailblazers No.2	7" EP	Mercury	ZEP10052	1960	£4	£8	

CLIFTON, BILL & JIM EANES
Title	Format	Label	Cat. No.	Year			Notes
Blue River Hoedown	7" EP	Melodisc	EPM7102	195-	£5	£10	

CLIMACTICS
Title	Format	Label	Cat. No.	Year			Notes
Farewell To The Playground	7"	Pulsebeat	CINE001	198-	£10	£20	

CLIMAX BLUES BAND
Title	Format	Label	Cat. No.	Year			Notes
Climax Chicago Blues Band	LP	Parlophone	PMC/PCS7069	1969	£8	£20	
Like Uncle Charlie	7"	Parlophone	R5809	1969	£2	£5	
Lot Of Bottle	LP	Harvest	SHSP4009	1970	£5	£12	
Plays On	LP	Parlophone	PCS7084	1969	£6	£15	
Rich Man	LP	Harvest	SHSP4024	1972	£4	£10	
Tightly Knit	LP	Harvest	SHSP4015	1971	£5	£12	

CLINE, PATSY
Title	Format	Label	Cat. No.	Year			Notes
Crazy	7"	Brunswick	05861	1961	£4	£8	
Cry Not For Me	7" EP	Ember	EMBEP4552	1964	£2.50	£6	
Heartaches	7"	Brunswick	05878	1962	£2	£5	chart single
I Fall To Pieces	7"	Brunswick	05855	1961	£4	£8	
Leaving On Your Mind	7"	Brunswick	05883	1963	£2	£5	
Patsy Cline	LP	Decca	DL8611	1957	£10	£25	US
Patsy Cline Showcase	LP	Brunswick	LAT8344	1959	£8	£20	
Patsy Cline Story	LP	Decca	D(S)XB(7)176	1963	£6	£15	US, with booklet
Portrait Of Patsy Cline	LP	Brunswick	LAT/STA8589	1964	£6	£15	
Sentimentally Yours	LP	Brunswick	LAT/STA8510	1962	£6	£15	
She's Got You	7"	Brunswick	05866	1962	£2	£5	chart single
So Wrong	7"	Brunswick	05874	1962	£2	£5	
Sweet Dreams	7"	Brunswick	05888	1963	£2	£5	
Sweet Dreams	7" EP	Brunswick	OE9490	1962	£4	£8	
That's How A Heartache Begins	LP	Decca	DL(7)4586	1964	£5	£12	US
Tribute To Patsy Cline	LP	Brunswick	LAT8549	1963	£5	£12	
Walkin' After Midnight	7"	Brunswick	05660	1957	£6	£12	
When I Get Through With You	7"	Brunswick	05869	1962	£2	£5	

CLINTON, LARRY
Title	Format	Label	Cat. No.	Year			Notes
She's Wanted In Three States	7"	Grapevine	GRP120	1979	£1.50	£4	

CLIQUE
Title	Format	Label	Cat. No.	Year			Notes
	7" EP			196-	£250	£400	promo
She Ain't No Good	7"	Pye	7N15786	1965	£20	£40	
We Didn't Kiss	7"	Pye	7N15853	1965	£50	£100	

CLIQUE (2)
Title	Format	Label	Cat. No.	Year			Notes
Love Can Be Wonderful	7"	Unity	UN505	1969	£2.50	£6	Lester Stirling B side

CLIQUE (3)
Title	Format	Label	Cat. No.	Year			Notes
Sugar On Sunday	7"	London	HLU10286	1969	£6	£12	

CLIVE & GLORIA
Title	Format	Label	Cat. No.	Year			Notes
Change Of Plan	7"	R&B	JB113	1963	£5	£10	
Do The Ska	7"	King	KG1004	1964	£5	£10	
Have I Told You Lately That I Love You?	7"	Ska Beat	JB173	1964	£5	£10	

CLIVE & NAOMI
Title	Format	Label	Cat. No.	Year			Notes
Open The Door	7"	Ska Beat	JB181	1965	£5	£10	

CLIVE ALL STARS
Title	Format	Label	Cat. No.	Year			Notes
Donkey Trot	7"	Big Shot	BI501	1968	£4	£8	Tennors B side

CLOCK DVA
Title	Format	Label	Cat. No.	Year			Notes
Four Hours	7"	Fetish	FET008	1981	£2	£5	
Thirst	LP	Fetish	FR2002	1981	£4	£10	
White Souls In Black Suits	cass	Industrial	IRC31	1981	£4	£10	

CLOCKWORK ORANGES
Title	Format	Label	Cat. No.	Year			Notes
Ready Steady	7"	Ember	EMBS227	1966	£2.50	£6	

CLOONEY, BETTY
Title	Format	Label	Cat. No.	Year			Notes
I Love You A Mountain	7"	HMV	7M311	1955	£1.50	£4	

CLOONEY, ROSEMARY
Title	Format	Label	Cat. No.	Year			Notes
At The London Palladium	10" LP	Philips	BBR8073	1956	£6	£15	
Blues In The Night	7"	Columbia	SCM5049	1953	£4	£8	
Children's Favourites	LP	Philips	BBL7191	1957	£5	£12	
Date With The King	10" LP	Columbia	CL2572	195-	£8	£20	US
Half As Much	7"	Columbia	SCM5019	1953	£6	£12	chart single
Hey Baby	LP	Philips	BBL7090	1956	£5	£12	
Still Feel The Same About You	7"	Columbia	SCM5093	1954	£2	£5	
If I Had A Penny	7"	Columbia	SCM5027	1953	£2.50	£6	

I'm The One Who Loves You	7"	Columbia	SCM5040	1953	£2	£5	
Mangos	7"	Philips	JK1010	1957	£5	£10	chart single
On The First Warm Day	7"	Columbia	SCM5028	1953	£4	£8	
Ring Around Rosie	LP	Philips	BBL7156	1957	£5	£12	with The Hi-Lo's
Rosemary Clooney	7" EP	Philips	BBE12004	1955	£6	£12	
Rosemary Clooney	7" EP	Philips	BBE12051	1956	£4	£8	
Rosemary Clooney	10" LP	Philips	BBR8047	1955	£8	£20	
Rosemary Clooney & Benny Goodman	7" EP	Philips	BBE12038	1956	£2	£5	
Rosemary Clooney & Harry James	7" EP	Columbia	SEG7552	1954	£2.50	£6	
Showcase Of Hits	LP	Philips	BBL7301	1958	£5	£12	
Sings For You	7" EP	MGM	MGMEP721	1960	£2	£5	
Swing Around Rosie	LP	Coral	LVA9112	1959	£4	£10	
Swing Around Rosie Vol.1	7" EP	Coral	FEP2045	1960	£2	£5	
Swing Around Rosie Vol.2	7" EP	Coral	FEP2046	1960	£2	£5	
Swings Softly No.1	7" EP	MGM	ES3514	1961	£2.50	£6	stereo
Swings Softly No.1	7" EP	MGM	MGMEP758	1961	£2	£5	
Tenderly	10" LP	Columbia	CL2525	195-	£8	£20	US
Too Old To Cut The Mustard	7"	Columbia	SCM5010	1953	£4	£8	
White Christmas	10" LP	Philips	BBR8022	1954	£10	£25	

CLOUD, CLAUDE

Beat	7"	MGM	MGM946	1957	£2.50	£6	
Let's Get Catstatic No.1	7" EP	MGM	MGMEP517	1955	£10	£20	
Rock'n'Roll Music For Dancing	10" LP	MGM	D142	1956	£15	£30	

CLOUDS

As 1-2-3, the organ trio that became Clouds pioneered a brand of underground music that was unfortunately not properly represented by the records that the group made. To quote organist Billy Ritchie, " The records are a very poor record of a good live group. On a good night, we could kill anybody, and often did, especially in the States". It seems that Clouds suffered from the sadly familiar record company behaviour whereby they were signed on the basis of an exciting live sound and then forced to change style for their records.

Make No Bones About It	7"	Island	WIP6055	1969	£2.50	£6	
Scrapbook	LP	Island	ILPS9100	1969	£6	£15	
Scrapbook	7"	Island	WIP6067	1969	£2.50	£6	
Watercolour Days	LP	Island	ILPS9151	1971	£6	£15	

CLOUGH, TOM, NED PEARSON, BILLY BALLANTINE

Holey Ha'penny	LP	Topic	12T283	1978	£5	£12	

CLOVEN HOOF

Opening Ritual	7"	Cloven Hoof	TOA1402	1982	£4	£8	

CLOVER

Clover	LP	Liberty	LBS83340	1970	£4	£10	
Forty-Niner	LP	Liberty	LBS83487	1971	£4	£10	
Wade In The Water	7"	Liberty	LBF15341	1970	£1.50	£4	

CLOVERLEAFS

Step Right Up And say Howdy	7"	MGM	MGM933	1956	£1.50	£4	

CLOVERS

Clovers	LP	Atlantic	LP1248	1956	£100	£200	US
Clovers	LP	Atlantic	LP8009	1957	£75	£150	US
Dance Party	LP	Atlantic	LP8034	1959	£40	£80	US
Easy Loving	7"	London	HLT9154	1960	£10	£20	
From The Bottom Of My Heart	7"	London	HLE8334	1956	£100	£200	
Honey Dripper	7"	HMV	POP883	1961	£6	£12	
In Clover	LP	Poplar	1001	1958	£40	£80	US
In Clover	LP	United Artists	UAL3033/ UAS6033	1959	£40	£80	US
In The Good Old Summertime	7"	HMV	POP542	1958	£7.50	£15	
Love Bug	LP	Atlantic	587162	1969	£10	£25	
Love Love Love	7"	London	HLE8314	1956	£100	£200	
Love Potion No.9	LP	United Artists	UAL3/UAS6099	1960	£40	£80	US
Love Potion No.9	7"	London	HLT8949	1959	£12.50	£25	
Nip Sip	7"	London	HLE8229	1956	£150	£250	gold labe
One Mint Julep	7"	London	HLT9122	1960	£12.50	£25	
Original Love Potion No.9	LP	Grand Prix	K428	1964	£8	£20	US
Wishing For Your Love	7"	London	HL7048	1958	£30	£60	expor
Your Cash Ain't Nothin' But Trash	7"	Atlantic	584160	1968	£4	£8	

CLUE J & HIS BLUES BUSTERS

Little Willie	7"	Blue Beat	BB60	1961	£5	£10	
Lovers' Jive	7"	Blue Beat	BB37	1961	£5	£10	

CLUSTER

After The Heat	LP	Sky	SKY021	1979	£4	£10	German
Cluster	LP	Philips	6305074	1971	£6	£15	German
Cluster 2	LP	Brain	0001006	1972	£6	£15	German
Cluster And Eno	LP	Sky	SKY010	1977	£4	£10	German
Curiosum	LP	Sky	SKY063	1981	£4	£10	German
Grosses Wasser	LP	Sky	SKY027	1979	£4	£10	German
Klopfzeichen	LP	Schwann	STUDIO511	1970	£8	£20	German
Sowieso	LP	Sky	SKY005	1976	£4	£10	German
Stimmungen	LP	Sky	SKY093	1984	£4	£10	German
Zuckerzeit	LP	Brain	0001065	1974	£5	£12	German
Zwei Osterie	LP	Schwann	STUDIO512	1970	£8	£20	German

CLUTHA

Bonnie Mill Dams	LP	Topic	12TS330	1977	£5	£12	
Scotia!	LP	Argo	ZFB18	1971	£8	£20	

CLYDE, JEREMY
| I Love My Love | 7" | CBS | 201823 | 1965 | £1.50 | £4 | |

CLYDE VALLEY STOMPERS
| Clyde Valley Stompers | 10" LP | Beltona | ABL524 | 1958 | £4 | £10 | |

CLYNE, JEFF & OTHERS
| Springboard | LP | Polydor | 545007 | 1966 | £20 | £40 | |

CMU
Heart Of The Sun	7"	Transatlantic	BIG508	1972	£5	£10	
Open Spaces	LP	Transatlantic	TRA237	1971	£20	£40	
Space Cabaret	LP	Transatlantic	TRA259	1972	£20	£40	

COACHMEN
Here Come The Coachmen	LP	Vogue	VA16062	1960	£5	£12	
Here Come The Coachmen	7" EP	Vogue	VE170149	1962	£4	£8	
Those Brown Eyes	7"	Vogue	V9154	1959	£2.50	£6	

COACHMEN (2)
| Seasons In The Sun | 7" | Columbia | DB8057 | 1966 | £2 | £5 | |

COAST ROAD DRIVE
| Delicious And Refreshing | LP | Deram | SML1113 | 1974 | £15 | £30 | |

COASTERS
Ain't That Just Like Me	7"	London	HLK9493	1962	£4	£8	
All Time Great Hits	LP	Atlantic	590015	1967	£6	£15	
Along Came Jones	7"	London	HLE8882	1959	£5	£10	
Besame Mucho	7"	London	HLK9111	1960	£4	£8	
Charlie Brown	7"	London	HL7073	1959	£2	£5	
Charlie Brown	7"	London	HLE8819	1959	£4	£8	chart single
Coasters	LP	Atco	33101	1958	£50	£100	US
Coasters	7" EP	London	REE1203	1959	£20	£40	
Coastin' Along	LP	Atlantic	587134	1968	£6	£15	
Coastin' Along	LP	London	HAK8033	1963	£15	£30	
Cool Jerk	7"	Stateside	SS2201	1972	£2.50	£6	
Girls Girls Girls	7"	London	HLK9413	1961	£4	£8	
Greatest Hits	LP	Atco	33111	1959	£25	£50	US
Greatest Hits	LP	London	HAE2237	1960	£10	£25	
Hungry	LP	Joy	JOYS189	1971	£5	£12	
Little Egypt	7"	London	HLK9349	1961	£4	£8	
On Broadway	LP	London	SHZ8460	1974	£4	£10	
One By One	LP	Atco	(SD)33123	1960	£8	£20	US
Poison Ivy	7"	London	HLE8938	1959	£4	£8	chart single
Searchin'	7"	Atlantic	584087	1967	£1.50	£4	
Searchin'	7"	London	HL7021	1957	£6	£12	export
Searchin'	7"	London	HLE8450	1957	£12.50	£25	chart single
Shadow Knows	7"	London	HLE8729	1958	£7.50	£15	
She Can	7"	Direction	583701	1968	£1.50	£4	
She's A Yum Yum	7"	Atlantic	584033	1966	£1.50	£4	
Shopping For Clothes	7"	London	HLK9208	1960	£4	£8	
Soul Pad	7"	CBS	2749	1967	£1.50	£4	
Stewball	7"	London	HLK9151	1960	£4	£8	
T'ain't Nothing To Me	7"	London	HLK9863	1964	£4	£8	
Thumbin' A Ride	7"	London	HLK9293	1961	£4	£8	
What About Us	7"	London	HLE9020	1960	£4	£8	
Yakety Yak	7"	London	HLE8665	1958	£6	£12	chart single

C.O.B. (CLIVE'S OWN BAND)
Singer and banjo-player Clive Palmer seemed to be a man who was scared of success. As a founder member of the Incredible String Band, he played on their first album, yet left just as they began to gain a following. He then formed the Famous Jug Band, recorded a promising LP, but again left when it began to seem as though the band might actually live up to its name. Finally, he formed COB, and was no doubt highly gratified when neither of the group's albums sold more than a handful of copies.
Blue Morning	7"	Polydor	2058260	1972	£10	£20	
Moyshe McStiff	LP	Polydor	2383161	1972	£75	£150	
Spirit Of Love	LP	CBS	69010	1971	£30	£60	

COBB, ARNETT
| Blow Arnett, Blow | LP | Esquire | 32114 | 1961 | £8 | £20 | with Eddie 'Lockjaw' Davis |

COBB, JUNIE HOMETOWN BAND
| Chicago Buzz | 7" | Collector | JDL38 | 1959 | £1.50 | £4 | |

COBBLERS LAST
| Boot In The Door | LP | Banshee | BAN1012 | 197- | £30 | £60 | |

COBBS
| Hot Buttered Corn | 7" | Amalgamated | AMG845 | 1969 | £4 | £8 | |
| Space Doctor | 7" | Amalgamated | AMG849 | 1969 | £4 | £8 | |

COBHAM, BILLY
Crosswinds	LP	Atlantic	K50037	1974	£4	£10	
Spectrum	LP	Atlantic	K40406	1973	£4	£10	
Total Eclipse	LP	Atlantic	K50098	1974	£4	£10	

COCHISE
| Cochise | LP | United Artists | UAS29117 | 1970 | £4 | £10 | |

COCHRAN BROTHERS
Though sharing a surname, Hank and Eddie Cochran were not actually related at all.

Guilty Conscience	7"	Ekko	1005	1955	£60	£120		US
Mr.Fiddle	7"	Ekko	1003	1955	£60	£120		US
Tired And Sleepy	7"	Ekko	3001	1956	£75	£150		US

COCHRAN, DIB & THE EARWIGS
This mysterious pseudonym actually hides the identities of Tyrannosaurus Rex, having fun with Rick Wakeman and Tony Visconti. It has often been thought that David Bowie appears on the record too, but this would seem not to be the case.

Oh Baby	7"	Bell	BLL1121	1970	£60	£120	

COCHRAN, EDDIE

Cherished Memories	LP	Liberty	LBL/LBS83072	1967	£4	£10	
Cherished Memories	LP	Liberty	LBY1109	1962	£6	£15	chart LP
Cherished Memories Of Eddie Cochran	7" EP	Liberty	LEP2123	1963	£12.50	£25	
Cherished Memories Of Eddie Cochran	7" EP	London	REG1301	1961	£25	£50	
Cherished Memories Vol.1	7" EP	Liberty	LEP2090	1963	£12.50	£25	
C'mon Again	7" EP	Liberty	LEP2165	1964	£15	£30	
C'mon Everybody	7"	Liberty	LBF15366	1970	£2.50	£6	
C'mon Everybody	7"	Liberty	LIB10233	1966	£5	£10	
C'mon Everybody	7"	London	HLU8792	1959	£6	£12	chart single
C'mon Everybody	7"	Liberty	LEP2111	1963	£10	£20	
C'mon Everybody	7" EP	London	REU1214	1959	£25	£50	tri centre
C'mon Everybody/Summertime Blues	7"	Liberty	LIB10233	1966	£7.50	£15	demo
Drive In Show	7"	Liberty	LIB10108	1963	£7.50	£15	
Eddie's Hits	7" EP	Liberty	LEP2124	1963	£10	£20	
Eddie's Hits	7" EP	London	REG1262	1960	£25	£50	
Hallelujah I Love Her So	7"	London	HLW9022	1960	£5	£10	chart single
Jeannie Jeannie Jeannie	7"	London	HLG9460	1961	£7.50	£15	chart single
Legendary Masters	LP	United Artists	UAD60017/8	1972	£6	£15	double
Memorial Album	LP	Liberty	LBL/LBS83009	1967	£4	£10	
Memorial Album	LP	Liberty	LBY1127	1963	£6	£15	chart LP
Memorial Album	LP	London	HAG2267	1960	£20	£40	chart LP
My Way	LP	Liberty	LBL83104	1968	£4	£10	
My Way	LP	Liberty	LBY1205	1964	£15	£30	
My Way	7"	Liberty	LIB10088	1963	£5	£10	chart single
Never To Be Forgotten	LP	Liberty	LRP3220	1962	£15	£30	US
Never To Be Forgotten	7" EP	Liberty	LEP2052	1962	£10	£20	
On The Air	LP	United Artists	UAS29380	1972	£5	£12	
Pretty Girl	7"	London	HLG9464	1961	£10	£20	
Singing To My Baby	LP	Liberty	LBL/LBS83152	1968	£4	£10	
Singing To My Baby	LP	Liberty	LBY1158	1963	£8	£20	chart LP
Singing To My Baby	LP	Liberty	LRP3061	1958	£60	£120	US
Singing To My Baby	LP	London	HAG2093	1958	£37.50	£75	chart LP
Singles Album	LP	United Artists	UAK30244	1979	£5	£12	with FREE 12"
Sitting In The Balcony	7"	London	HLU8433	1957	£75	£150	US
Skinny Jim	7"	Crest	1026	1956	£75	£150	US
Skinny Jim	7"	Crest	1026	1956	£330	£500	US, red vinyl
Skinny Jim	7"	Liberty	LIB10151	1964	£12.50	£25	
Somethin' Else	7"	Liberty	LBF15109	1968	£4	£8	
Somethin' Else	7"	London	HLU8944	1959	£17.50	£35	chart single, tri-centre
Somethin' Else	7" EP	Liberty	LEP2122	1963	£10	£20	
Somethin' Else	7" EP	London	REU1239	1960	£25	£50	
Stockings And Shoes	7"	London	HLG9467	1961	£10	£20	
Stockings And Shoes	7" EP	Liberty	LEP2180	1964	£10	£20	
Summertime Blues	7"	Liberty	LBF15071	1968	£4	£8	chart single
Summertime Blues	7"	London	HLU8702	1958	£7.50	£15	chart single
Sweetie Pie	7"	London	HLG9196	1960	£6	£12	chart single
Teenage Heaven	7"	London	HL7082	1959	£30	£60	export
Teenage Heaven	7"	London	HLU8880	1959	£10	£20	
Think Of Me	7"	Liberty	LIB10049	1962	£6	£12	
Three Stars	7"	Liberty	LIB10249	1966	£15	£30	
Three Steps To Heaven	7"	Liberty	LIB10276	1967	£12.50	£25	
Three Steps To Heaven	7"	London	HLG9115	1960	£5	£10	chart single
Twentieth Anniversary Album	LP	United Artists	ECSP20	1980	£17.50	£35	4 LPs, boxed
Twenty Flight Rock	7"	London	HLU8386	1957	£40	£80	
Weekend	7"	London	HLG9362	1961	£5	£10	chart single

COCHRAN, JACKIE LEE

Mama Don't You Think I Know	7"	Brunswick	05669	1957	£250	£400	

COCHRAN, WAYNE

Wayne Cochran	LP	Chess	LP(S)1519	1967	£5	£12	US

COCK SPARRER

England Belongs To Me	7"	Carrere	CAR255	1982	£2.50	£6	
Running Riot	7"	Decca	FR13710	1977	£2.50	£6	
Running Riot	7"	Decca	FR13710	1977	£12.50	£25	PS
We Love You	7"	Decca	FR13732	1977	£2	£5	
We Love You	12"	Decca	FR13732	1977	£3	£8	

COCKBURN, BRUCE
Bruce Cockburn is a Canadian singer-songwriter who, since first issuing LPs on his own True North label at the start of the seventies, seems to have grown in stature with each passing year. His most impressive recordings are the most recent ones, the earliest records being interesting mainly for the glimpses they afford of a great artist in the making. This, of course, is the exact reverse of the usual state of affairs where rock performers are concerned.

Bruce Cockburn	LP	True North	TN1	1970	£6	£15	Canadian
Circles In The Stream	LP	Island	ILTA9475	1977	£6	£15	US double

Further Adventures	LP	True North	TN33	1976	£6	£15	Canadian
Hand Dancing	LP	True North	TN13	1974	£6	£15	Canadian
High Winds White Sky	LP	True North	TN3	1971	£6	£15	Canadian
In The Falling Dark	LP	True North	TN26	1976	£6	£15	Canadian
Joy Will Find A Way	LP	True North	TN23	1975	£6	£15	Canadian
Night Vision	LP	True North	TN11	1973	£6	£15	Canadian
Salt, Sun And Time	LP	True North	TN16	1974	£6	£15	Canadian
Sunwheel Dance	LP	Epic	65187	1972	£6	£15	

COCKER, JOE

Cry Me A River	7"	Fly	BUG3	1970	£2	£5	PS
Delta Lady	7"	Regal Zonophone	RZ3024	1969	£1.50	£4	chart single
I'll Cry Instead	7"	Decca	F11974	1964	£12.50	£25	
Joe Cocker	LP	Regal Zonophone	SLRZ1011	1969	£5	£12	
Joe Cocker	7" EP	Oak		196-	£75	£150	
Letter	7"	Regal Zonophone	RZ3027	1970	£1.50	£4	chart single
Luxury You Can Afford	LP	Asylum	DP400	1978	£6	£15	US promo pic disc
Mad Dogs And Englishmen	LP	A&M	AMLD6002	1970	£5	£12	fold-out cover, double, chart LP
Marjorine	7"	Regal Zonophone	RZ3006	1968	£2	£5	chart single
Rag Goes Mad At The Mojo	7"	Action	ACT002	1967	£20	£40	with other artists
Ruby Lee	7"	Island	WIP6818	1983	£1.50	£4	export
With A Little Help From My Friends	LP	Regal Zonophone	SLRZ1006	1969	£6	£15	
With A Little Help From My Friends	7"	MagniFly	ECHO103	1972	£2.50	£6	PS
With A Little Help From My Friends	7"	Regal Zonophone	RZ3013	1968	£1.50	£4	chart single
With A Little Help/Joe Cocker	LP	Fly	TOOFA1/2	1972	£5	£12	double, chart LP

COCKNEY REBEL

Best Years Of Our Lives	7"	EMI	EMI2673	1977	£2.50	£6	PS
Human Menagerie	LP	EMI	EMA759	1973	£10	£25	with booklet
Psychomodo	7"	EMI	EMI2191	1974	£25	£50	demo

COCKNEYS

After Tomorrow	7"	Philips	BF1303	1964	£2.50	£6	
After Tomorrow	7"	Philips	BF1338	1964	£5	£10	
I Know You're Gonna Be Mine	7"	Philips	BF1360	1964	£5	£10	

COCKTAIL CABINET

Puppet On A String	7"	Page One	POF23046	1967	£5	£10	

COCTEAU TWINS

Peppermint Pig	7"	4AD	AD303	1983	£6	£12	
Sugar Hiccup	7"	4AD	AD314	1984	£5	£10	1 sided promo

C.O.D.'S

Michael	7"	Stateside	SS489	1966	£7.50	£15	

COE, DAVID ALAN

Penitentiary Blues	LP	SSS	9	1968	£5	£12	US
Requiem For A Harlequin	LP	SSS	31	1969	£5	£12	US

COE, JAMIE

Fool	7"	London	HLX9713	1963	£5	£10	
How Low Is Low	7"	HMV	POP991	1961	£5	£10	
Schoolday Blues	7"	Parlophone	R4621	1960	£12.50	£25	
Summertime Symphony	7"	Parlophone	R4600	1959	£40	£80	

COE, PETE & CHRIS

Game Of All Fours	LP	Highway	SHY7007	1979	£5	£12	
Open The Door And Let Us In	LP	Leader	LER2077	1972	£6	£15	
Out Of Season Out Of Rhyme	LP	Trailer	LER2098	1976	£6	£15	

COE, TONY

Pop Makes Progress	LP	Chapter One	CHS804	1970	£15	£30	with Robert Farnon
Swingin' Till The Girls Come Home	LP	Philips	B10784L	196-	£8	£20	
Tony Coe And The Brian Lemon Trio	LP	77	SEU1241	1968	£15	£30	

COEUR MAGIQUE

Wankan Tanka	LP	Byg	529018	1971	£6	£15	French

COFFEE SET

Dicky Boy	7"	Mercury	MF1076	1969	£1.50	£4	
Happy Birthday	7"	Mercury	MF1113	1969	£1.50	£4	

COGAN, ALMA

All Alone	7"	Columbia	DB4749	1961	£1.50	£4	
Alma	LP	Columbia	SX6130	1967	£15	£30	
Alma Sings With You In Mind	LP	Columbia	33SX1345	1961	£20	£40	
Bell Bottom Blues	7"	HMV	7M188	1954	£10	£20	chart single
Birds And The Bees	7"	HMV	7M415	1956	£7.50	£15	chart single
Chantez Chantez	7"	HMV	POP336	1957	£5	£10	
Chee Chee Oo Chee	7"	HMV	7M293	1955	£7.50	£15	
Cowboy Jimmy Joe	7"	Columbia	DB4607	1961	£1.50	£4	chart single
Do Do Do Do Do Do Do It Again	7"	HMV	7M226	1954	£6	£12	with Frankie Vaughan
Eight Days A Week	7"	Columbia	DB7786	1965	£2	£5	

Fabulous	7"	HMV	POP367	1957	£6	£12	
Fly Away Lovers	7"	HMV	POP500	1958	£2.50	£6	
Girl With The Laugh In Her Voice	LP	MFP	MFP1377	1970	£4	£10	
Girl With The Laugh In Her Voice	7" EP	HMV	7EG8122	1955	£7.50	£15	
Girl With The Laugh In Her Voice No.2	7" EP	HMV	7EG8151	1955	£6	£12	
Girl With The Laugh In Her Voice No.3	7" EP	HMV	7EG8169	1956	£6	£12	
Goodbye Joe	7"	Columbia	DB4912	1962	£1.50	£4	
Got 'n Idea	7"	HMV	7M316	1955	£7.50	£15	chart single
Hits From My Fair Lady	7" EP	HMV	7EG8352	1957	£2.50	£6	with Ronnie Hilton
How About Love	LP	Columbia	33SX1465	1962	£20	£40	
I Can't Tell A Waltz From A Tango	7"	HMV	7M271	1954	£7.50	£15	chart single
I Love To Sing	LP	HMV	CLP1152	1958	£20	£40	
I Went To Your Wedding	7"	HMV	7M106	1953	£10	£20	
In The Middle Of The House	7"	HMV	POP261	1956	£10	£20	chart single
It's All Been Done Before	7"	HMV	7M390	1956	£10	£20	chart single, with Ronnie Hilton
It's You	7"	Columbia	DB7390	1964	£1.50	£4	
Just Once More	7"	Columbia	DB7059	1963	£1.50	£4	
Last Night On The Back Porch	7"	HMV	POP573	1959	£4	£8	chart single
Little Shoemaker	7"	HMV	7M219	1954	£10	£20	
Little Things Mean A Lot	7"	HMV	7M228	1954	£7.50	£15	chart single
Love And Marriage	7"	HMV	7M367	1956	£7.50	£15	
Love Is A Word	7"	Columbia	DB7619	1965	£1.50	£4	
Make Love To Me	7"	HMV	7M196	1954	£7.50	£15	
Mama Teach Me To Dance	7"	HMV	POP239	1956	£12.50	£25	
More Than Ever Now	7"	HMV	7M301	1955	£7.50	£15	
Must Be Santa	7"	HMV	POP815	1960	£1.50	£4	
Never Do A Tango With An Eskimo	7"	HMV	7M337	1955	£7.50	£15	chart single
Now That I've Found You	7"	Columbia	DB8088	1966	£1.50	£4	
O Dio Mio	7"	HMV	POP728	1960	£1.50	£4	
Oliver	LP	HMV	CLP1459	1961	£15	£30	mono
Oliver	LP	HMV	CSD1370	1961	£20	£40	stereo
Over And Over Again	7"	HMV	7M166	1953	£7.50	£15	with Les Howard
Paper Kisses	7"	HMV	7M286	1955	£7.50	£15	
Party Time	7"	HMV	POP415	1957	£4	£8	
Pink Shoelaces	7"	HMV	POP608	1959	£4	£8	
Ricochet	7"	HMV	7M173	1954	£10	£20	
She Loves To Sing	7" EP	HMV	7EG8437	1957	£6	£12	
She's Got You	7"	Columbia	DB4794	1962	£1.50	£4	
Snakes And Snails	7"	Columbia	DB7652	1965	£1.50	£4	
Stairway Of Love	7"	HMV	POP482	1958	£5	£10	
Story Of My Life	7"	HMV	POP433	1958	£5	£10	chart single
Sugartime	7"	HMV	POP450	1958	£6	£12	chart single
Tell Him	7"	Columbia	DB4965	1963	£1.50	£4	
Tennessee Waltz	7"	Columbia	DB7233	1964	£1.50	£4	
That's Happiness	7"	HMV	POP392	1957	£4	£8	
There's Never Been A Night	7"	HMV	POP531	1958	£4	£8	
This Ole House	7"	HMV	7M269	1954	£10	£20	
To Be Loved By You	7"	HMV	7M107	1953	£10	£20	
Train Of Love	7"	HMV	POP760	1960	£2	£5	chart single
We Got Love	7"	HMV	POP670	1959	£2	£5	chart single
What Am I Gonna Do, Ma?	7"	HMV	7M239	1954	£12.50	£25	
Whatever Lola Wants	7"	HMV	POP317	1957	£6	£12	
With You In Mind	7"	Columbia	DB4679	1961	£1.50	£4	
You Me And Us	7"	HMV	POP284	1957	£6	£12	chart single

COGAN, SHAYE

Mean To Me	7"	MGM	MGM1063	1960	£1.50	£4	chart single

COHEN, LEONARD

Bird On The Wire	7"	CBS	2494	1974	£1.50	£4	
Bird On The Wire	7"	CBS	4245	1969	£2	£5	
Joan Of Arc	7"	CBS	7292	1971	£1.50	£4	
Lover Lover Lover	7"	CBS	2699	1974	£1.50	£4	
McCabe & Mrs.Miller	7" EP	CBS	7684	1972	£2.50	£6	chart LP
Songs From A Room	LP	CBS	63587	1968	£4	£10	chart LP
Songs Of Leonard Cohen	LP	CBS	63241	1968	£4	£10	chart LP
Songs Of Leonard Cohen	LP	Columbia	CL2733	1968	£50	£100	US, mono
Songs Of Love And Hate	LP	CBS	69004	1970	£4	£10	with booklet, chart LP
Suzanne	7"	CBS	3337	1968	£2	£5	
Suzanne	7"	CBS	4306	1976	£1.50	£4	
Suzanne	7"	CBS	8353	1973	£2	£5	

COHEN, LEONARD & OTHERS

Canadian Poets 1	LP	CBC		1966	£15	£30	Canadian
Six Montreal Poets	LP	Folkways	FL9805	1957	£20	£40	US

COHN, AL

Al Cohn Orchestra	10" LP	HMV	DLP1107	1955	£20	£40	

COIL

Anal Staircase	12"	Force & Form	ROTA121	1986	£2.50	£6	
Anal Staircase	12"	Force & Form	ROTA121	1986	£4	£10	clear vinyl
Gold Is The Metal	LP	Threshold House	LOCI1	1988	£20	£40	boxed
Gold Is The Metal	LP	Threshold House	LOCI1	1988	£100	£200	boxed with 7", poster, booklet, liner, folder
Gold Is The Metal	LP	Threshold House	LOCI1	1988	£6	£15	red or clear vinyl

158

Title	Format	Label	Catalog	Year	Price1	Price2	Notes
Gold Is The Metal	LP	Threshold House	LOCI1	1988	£8	£20	red or clear vinyl, with bonus 7'
Hellraiser	10"	Solar Lodge	COIL001	198-	£2.50	£6	clear or pink vinyl
Horse Rotorvator	LP	Threshold	ROTA1	1987	£4	£10	clear vinyl
Panic	12"	Force & Form	FFK512	1985	£2.50	£6	
Panic	12"	Force & Form	FFK512	1985	£4	£10	red vinyl
Wrong Eye	7"	Shock	SX002	1989	£10	£20	individually lettered
Wrong Eye	7"	Shock	SX002	1989	£4	£8	individually numbered

COIL (2)

Title	Format	Label	Catalog	Year	Price1	Price2	Notes
Motor Industry	7"	Northampton Wood Hill	HAV1	1979	£2	£5	

COIT, JAMES

Title	Format	Label	Catalog	Year	Price1	Price2
Black Power	7"	Destiny	DS1004	1979	£1.50	£4

COKER, ALVADEAN

Title	Format	Label	Catalog	Year	Price1	Price2
We're Gonna Bop	7"	London	HLU8191	1955	£90	£180

COKER, SANDY

Title	Format	Label	Catalog	Year	Price1	Price2
Meadowlark Melody	7"	London	HL8109	1954	£12.50	£25

COLBECK, RIC

Title	Format	Label	Catalog	Year	Price1	Price2
Sun Is Coming Up	LP	Fontana	63883001	1970	£8	£20

COLD BLOOD

Title	Format	Label	Catalog	Year	Price1	Price2	Notes
First Blood	LP	Atlantic	588218	1970	£5	£12	
First Taste Of Sin	LP	Reprise	2074	1972	£5	£12	US
Lydia	LP	Warner Bros	K56047	1974	£5	£12	
Sisyphus	LP	Atlantic	2400102	1971	£5	£12	
You Got Me Hummin'	7"	Atlantic	584319	1970	£1.50	£4	

COLD STEEL

Title	Format	Label	Catalog	Year	Price1	Price2	Notes
Cold Steel	LP	Ariola	87736	1974	£4	£10	Dutch

COLDER, BEN

Title	Format	Label	Catalog	Year	Price1	Price2
Make The World Go Away	7" EP	MGM	MGMEP791	1964	£4	£8

COLE, B.J.

Title	Format	Label	Catalog	Year	Price1	Price2
New Hovering Dog	LP	United Artists	UAS29418	1972	£6	£15

COLE, CINDY

Title	Format	Label	Catalog	Year	Price1	Price2
Just Being Your Baby	7"	Columbia	DB7973	1966	£4	£8
Love Like Yours	7"	Columbia	DB7519	1965	£1.50	£4

COLE, CLAY

Title	Format	Label	Catalog	Year	Price1	Price2
Twist Around The Clock	7"	London	HLP9499	1962	£1.50	£4

COLE, COZY

Title	Format	Label	Catalog	Year	Price1	Price2	Notes
Big Noise From Winnetka	7"	Coral	Q72457	1962	£1.50	£4	
Cozy Cole All Stars	7" EP	MGM	MGMEP622	1957	£4	£8	
Father Cooperates	7"	Mercury	AMT1015	1958	£1.50	£4	
Topsy	7"	London	HL7065	1958	£1.50	£4	export
Topsy	7"	London	HL8750	1958	£4	£8	chart single
Turvy	7"	London	HL8843	1959	£2	£5	

COLE, JERRY

Title	Format	Label	Catalog	Year	Price1	Price2	Notes
Hot Rod Dance Party	LP	Capitol	(S)T2061	1964	£5	£12	US
Outer Limits	LP	Capitol	(S)T2044	1963	£5	£12	US
Surf Age	LP	Capitol	(S)T2112	1964	£8	£20	US, with bonus Dick Dale 7'

COLE, LLOYD & THE COMMOTIONS

Title	Format	Label	Catalog	Year	Price1	Price2
Are You Ready To Be Heartbroken?	7"	Welcome To Las Vegas	LC1	1984	£20	£40

COLE, NAT 'KING'

Title	Format	Label	Catalog	Year	Price1	Price2	Notes
After Midnight	LP	Capitol	LCT6133	1957	£6	£15	
After Midnight Part 1	7" EP	Capitol	EAP1782	1957	£2.50	£6	
After Midnight Part 2	7" EP	Capitol	EAP2782	1957	£2.50	£6	
After Midnight Part 3	7" EP	Capitol	EAP3782	1957	£2.50	£6	
After Midnight Part 4	7" EP	Capitol	EAP4782	1958	£2.50	£6	
Annabelle	7"	Capitol	CL14317	1955	£2.50	£6	
Around The World	7" EP	Capitol	EAP1813	1957	£2.50	£6	
At The Piano	10" LP	Capitol	H156	1952	£8	£20	US
Ballads Of The Day	LP	Capitol	T680	1956	£5	£12	US
Ballads Of The Day	10" LP	Capitol	LC6818	1956	£6	£15	
Blossom Fell	7"	Capitol	CL14235	1955	£5	£10	chart single
Capitol Presents Nat King Cole	10" LP	Capitol	LC6569	1953	£8	£20	
Capitol Presents Nat King Cole & His Trio Vol.1	10" LP	Capitol	LC6587	1953	£6	£15	
Capitol Presents Nat King Cole & His Trio Vol.2	10" LP	Capitol	LC6594	1953	£6	£15	
Capitol Presents Nat King Cole At The Piano	10" LP	Capitol	LC6593	1953	£6	£15	
Christmas Song	7" EP	Capitol	EAP1036	1956	£2.50	£6	
Cole Espanol	LP	Capitol	LCT6166	1958	£5	£12	
Cole Espanol Part 1	7" EP	Capitol	EAP11031	1959	£2	£5	
Cole Espanol Part 2	7" EP	Capitol	EAP21031	1959	£2	£5	

Dreams Can Tell A Lie	7"	Capitol	CL14513	1956	£4	£8		chart single
Every Time I Feel The Spirit	LP	Capitol	LCT6187	1959	£5	£12		
I Am In Love	7"	Capitol	CL14172	1954	£2.50	£6		
If I Give My Heart To You	7"	Capitol	CL14203	1954	£2.50	£6		
If I May	7"	Capitol	CL14295	1955	£2.50	£6		
In The Beginning	LP	Brunswick	LAT8123	1956	£8	£20		
Instrumental Classics	LP	Capitol	T592	1955	£5	£12	US	
Just One Of Those Things	LP	Capitol	(S)LCT6149	1958	£6	£15		
King Cole Trio	10" LP	Capitol	H8	1950	£8	£20	US	
King Cole Trio	10" LP	Score	SLP4019	1950	£30	£60	US	
King Cole Trio Vol.2	10" LP	Capitol	H29	1950	£8	£20	US	
King Cole Trio Vol.3	10" LP	Capitol	H59	1950	£8	£20	US	
King Cole Trio Vol.4	10" LP	Capitol	H139	1951	£8	£20	US	
Long Long Ago	7"	Capitol	CL14215	1955	£4	£8		
Looking Back	7" EP	Capitol	EAP1960	1958	£2.50	£6		
Love Is A Many Splendoured Thing	7"	Capitol	CL14364	1955	£2.50	£6		
Love Is A Many Splendoured Thing	7" EP	Capitol	EAP1010	1956	£2.50	£6		
Love Is Here To Stay	7" EP	Capitol	EAP120151	1961	£2	£5		
Love Is The Thing	LP	Capitol	(S)LCT6129	1957	£6	£15		
Love Is The Thing Part 1	7" EP	Capitol	EAP1824	1957	£2.50	£6		
Love Is The Thing Part 2	7" EP	Capitol	EAP2824	1957	£2.50	£6		
Love Is The Thing Part 3	7" EP	Capitol	EAP3824	1957	£2.50	£6		
Love Me As Though There Were No Tomorrow	7"	Capitol	CL14621	1956	£2.50	£6		chart single
Midnight Flyer	7" EP	Capitol	EAP11317	1960	£2	£5		
Moods In Song	7" EP	Capitol	EAP1633	1956	£4	£8		
My One Sin	7"	Capitol	CL14327	1955	£5	£10		chart single
My Personal Possession	7"	Capitol	CL14765	1957	£1.50	£4		chart single
Nat King Cole And George Shearing Part 1	7" EP	Capitol	EAP41675	1961	£2	£5		
Nat King Cole And George Shearing Part 2	7" EP	Capitol	EAP51675	1963	£2	£5		
Nat King Cole Trio	10" LP	Capitol	H177	1952	£8	£20	US	
Nat King Cole Trio	10" LP	Capitol	H220	1952	£8	£20	US	
Night Lights	7" EP	Capitol	EAP1801	1957	£2.50	£6		
Night Of The Quarter Moon	7" EP	Capitol	EAP11211	1959	£2	£5		
Non Domenticar	7" EP	Capitol	EAP11138	1959	£2	£5		
Nothing Ever Changes My Love For You	7"	Capitol	CL14529	1956	£1.50	£4		
Penthouse Serenade	LP	Capitol	T332	1953	£5	£12	US	
Penthouse Serenade	10" LP	Capitol	H332	1953	£8	£20	US	
Piano Style Of Nat King Cole	LP	Capitol	W689	1956	£5	£12	US	
Piano Style Of Nat King Cole	10" LP	Capitol	LC6830	1956	£6	£15		
Ramblin' Rose	7" EP	Capitol	EAP51793	1963	£2	£5		
Sand And The Sea	7"	Capitol	CL14251	1955	£2.50	£6		
Sings For Two In Love	LP	Capitol	T420	1954	£5	£12	US	
Sings For Two In Love	10" LP	Capitol	LC6627	1953	£6	£15		
Smile	7"	Capitol	CL14149	1954	£5	£10		chart single
Someone You Love	7"	Capitol	CL14378	1955	£2.50	£6		
Stardust	7"	Capitol	CL14787	1957	£1.50	£4		chart single
St.Louis Blues	LP	Capitol	(S)LCT6156	1958	£6	£15		
St.Louis Blues Part 1	7" EP	Capitol	EAP1993	1958	£2.50	£6		
St.Louis Blues Part 2	7" EP	Capitol	EAP2993	1958	£2.50	£6		
St.Louis Blues Part 3	7" EP	Capitol	EAP3993	1958	£2.50	£6		
Strip For Action	7" EP	Capitol	EAP1040	1956	£2.50	£6		
Teach Me Tonight	7"	Capitol	CL14207	1954	£4	£8		
Tenderly	7" EP	Capitol	EAP120108	1961	£2	£5		
Tenth Anniversary Album	LP	Capitol	LCT6003	1954	£8	£20		
Tenth Anniversary Album Part 1	7" EP	Capitol	EAP1514	1955	£4	£8		
Tenth Anniversary Album Part 2	7" EP	Capitol	EAP2514	1955	£4	£8		
Tenth Anniversary Album Part 3	7" EP	Capitol	EAP3514	1955	£4	£8		
Tenth Anniversary Album Part 4	7" EP	Capitol	EAP4514	1955	£4	£8		
This Is Nat King Cole	LP	Capitol	LCT6142	1957	£6	£15		
To Whom It May Concern	LP	Capitol	(S)LCT6182	1959	£5	£12		
To Whom It May Concern Part 1	7" EP	Capitol	EAP11190	1959	£2	£5		
To Whom It May Concern Part 2	7" EP	Capitol	EAP21190	1959	£2	£5		
To Whom It May Concern Part 3	7" EP	Capitol	EAP31190	1959	£2	£5		
Too Young To Go Steady	7"	Capitol	CL14573	1956	£2.50	£6		chart single
Unbelievable	7"	Capitol	CL14155	1954	£2.50	£6		
Unforgettable	LP	Capitol	T357	1953	£5	£12	US	
Unforgettable	7" EP	Capitol	EAP120053	1961	£2	£5		
Unforgettable	10" LP	Capitol	H357	1953	£8	£20	US	
Very Thought Of You	LP	Capitol	(S)LCT6173	1959	£5	£12		
Very Thought Of You Part 1	7" EP	Capitol	EAP11084	1959	£2	£5		
Very Thought Of You Part 2	7" EP	Capitol	EAP21084	1959	£2	£5		
Vocal Classics	LP	Capitol	T591	1955	£5	£12	US	
Welcome To The Club	LP	Capitol	(S)LCT6176	1959	£5	£12		
Welcome To The Club	7" EP	Capitol	EAP11120	1959	£2.50	£6		
When I Fall In Love	7"	Capitol	CL14709	1957	£1.50	£4		chart single
When Rock And Roll Came To Trinidad	7"	Capitol	CL14733	1957	£2.50	£6		chart single

COLE, NATALIE

Party Lights	7"	Capitol	CL15929	1977	£2.50	£6		demo only

COLE, STRANGER

All Your Friends	7"	R&B	JB120	1963	£5	£10		with Ken
Cherry May	7"	Island	WI162	1964	£5	£10		Do...
								Drummond B side

Academy: Pop Lore According To The Academy
£70

Johnny Ace: Memorial US 10" LP £200

Amazing Blondel £120

Ambrose Slade: Beginnings £200

Andromeda £120

Andwella's Dream: Love And Poetry £250

Arcadium: Breathe Awhile £250

Neil Ardley: A Symphony Of Amaranths £100

BBC Transcription Disc

Beatles Love Me Do 7" Demo £100 (Signed)

Beatles: Christmas Album US LP £250

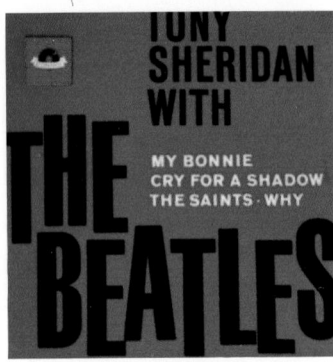

Beatles with Tony Sheridan 7" EP £50

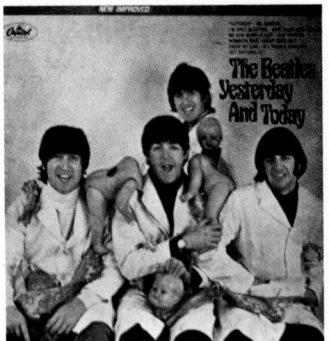

Beatles: Yesterday And Today (Peeled Butcher
Sleeve) US Stereo LP £3000

Blossom Toes: If Only For A Moment £70

David Bowie: The Man Who Sold The World

Anne Briggs: The Time Has Come £100

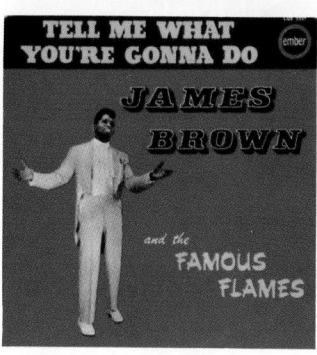

James Brown: Tell Me What You're Gonna Do
£25

Kate Bush: Single File 7" Boxed Set £100

Choker Campbell: Hits Of The Sixties £100

Caravan Mono £70 / Stereo £50

City Waites: A Gorgeous Gallery Of Gallant
Inventions £80

Elvis Costello: My Aim Is True / This Year's Model
US Promo Pic Disc £150

Crystals He's a Rebel £100

Czar: Tread Softly On My Dreams £180

Dark: Round The Edges £1200

Deep Purple: Hush 7" Promo £40

Downliners Sect: Nite In Great Newport Street
7" EP £120

John Dummer: Oobleedooblee Jubilee £30

Earth And Fire £160

Elias Hulk: Unchained £150

Eno: Music For Films (1976 Issue) £200

Eyes: The Arrival Of The Eyes 7" EP £150

Fire: The Magic Shoemaker £250

Four Pennies: Mixed Bag £60

Fourmost: First And Fourmost £70

Fox: For Fox Sake £60

Ghost: When You're Dead – One Second £100

Gnidrolog: Lady Lake £60

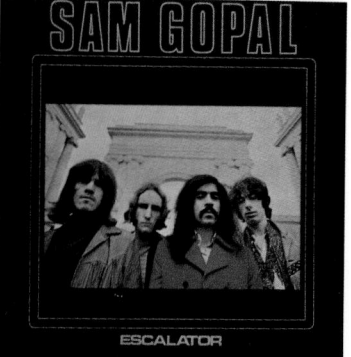

Sam Gopal: Escalator £60

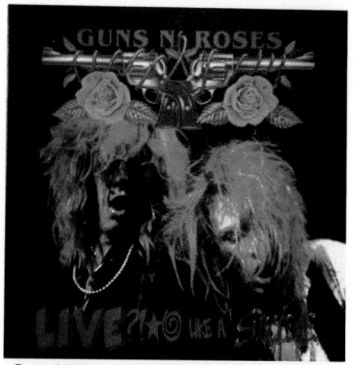

Guns 'N' Roses: Live ?!@ Like A Suicide US LP

H.P. Lovecraft: H.P. Lovecraft II £25

Hair: Hair Piece £100

Ron Hargrave: Latch On 7" £750

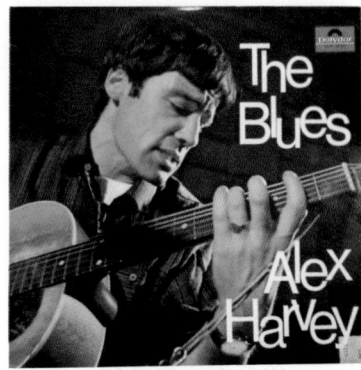

Alex Harvey: The Blues £60

Head Machine: Orgasm £120

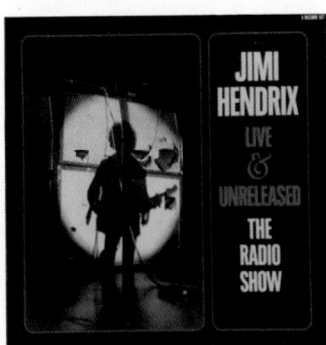

Jimi Hendrix: Live And Unreleased - The Radio Show Boxed Set £40

High Tide £30

Horse £120

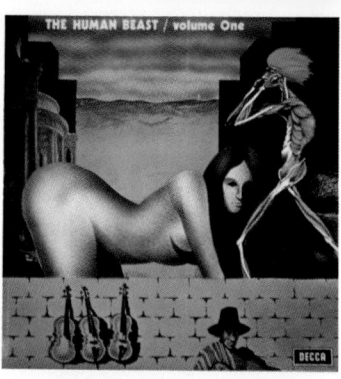

Human Beast Volume One £120

Ice: Saga Of The Ice King £100

Idle Race: Time Is £70

Jawbone £60

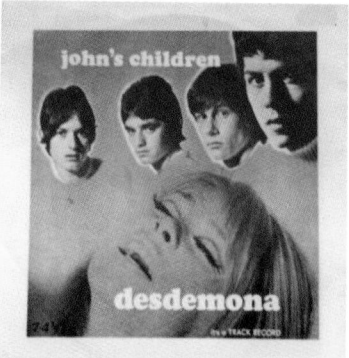

John's Children: Desdemona 7" £50

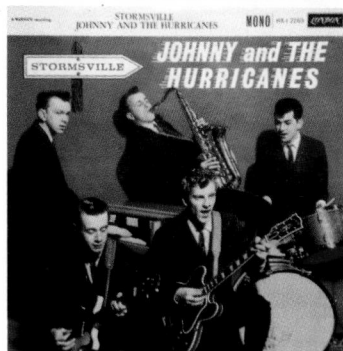

Johnny And The Hurricanes: Stormsville £25

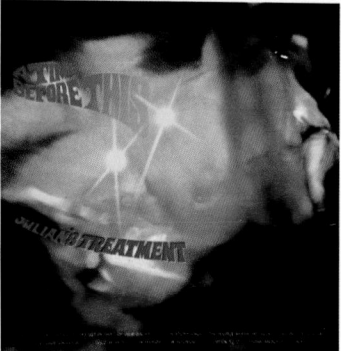

Julian's Treatment A Time Before This £100

Kaleidoscope: Faintly Blowing £100

Kaleidoscope (U.S.): Side Trips £30

Killing Floor: Original Killing Floor £80

B.B. King: Take A Swing With Me £35

Koobas £250

Kraftwerk: Kraftwerk 2 £50

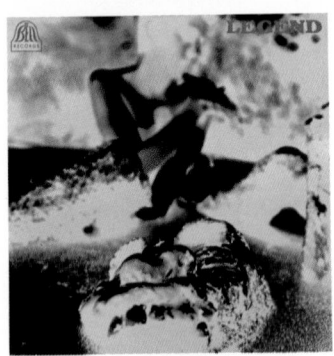

Legend £50

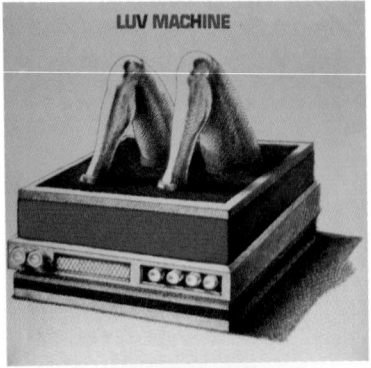

Luv Machine £100

Madonna: Crazy For You Shaped Pic Disc £50

Cow In A Pasture	7"	Island	WI169	1965	£5	£10	Gloris & Dreamletts B side
Darling Please	7"	Songbird	SB1008	1969	£2.50	£6	
Down The Train Line	7"	Doctor Bird	DB1087	1967	£5	£10	with Patsy Todd
Drop The Rachet	7"	Doctor Bird	DB1040	1966	£5	£10	
Give Me One More Chance	7"	Rio	R81	1966	£4	£8	with Patsy Cole
Give Me The Right	7"	Doctor Bird	DB1050	1966	£5	£10	with Patsy Todd
Glad You're Living	7"	Duke	DU27	1969	£2.50	£6	
Hey Little Girl	7"	Black Swan	WI462	1965	£5	£10	with Patsy Todd, Cornell Campbell B side
I Want To Go Home	7"	Black Swan	WI465	1965	£5	£10	
Jeboza Macod	7"	Island	WI3154	1968	£5	£10	
Just Like A River	7"	Amalgamated	AMG801	1968	£4	£8	Leaders B side
Last Love	7"	Island	WI114	1963	£5	£10	Stranger & Ken B side
Leana Leana	7"	Escort	ES819	1969	£2.50	£6	
Little Boy Blue	7"	Black Swan	WI435	1964	£5	£10	Eric Morris B side
Morning Star	7"	R&B	JB129	1963	£5	£10	
Night After Night	7"	Black Swan	WI461	1965	£5	£10	
Oh Oh I Need You	7"	Island	WI141	1964	£5	£10	Don Drummond B side
Out Of Many	7"	R&B	JB133	1963	£5	£10	
Over And Over Again	7"	Island	WI3128	1967	£5	£10	
Pretty Cottage	7"	Escort	ES810	1969	£2.50	£6	
Pussy Cat	7"	Ska Beat	JB192	1965	£5	£10	Maytals B side
Remember	7"	Escort	ES826	1969	£2.50	£6	
Rolling On	7"	Island	WI126	1963	£5	£10	
Run Joe	7"	Island	WI177	1965	£5	£10	
Seeing Is Knowing	7"	Amalgamated	AMG806	1968	£4	£8	Roy Shirley B side
Senor Senorita	7"	Island	WI113	1963	£5	£10	with Patsy Todd, Don Drummond B side
Stranger At The Door	7"	Island	WI110	1963	£5	£10	
Summer Day	7"	Black Swan	WI415	1964	£5	£10	
Tell It To Me	7"	Doctor Bird	DB1084	1967	£5	£10	with Patsy Todd
Things Come To Those Who Wait	7"	Island	WI160	1964	£5	£10	with Patsy Todd
Till My Dying Days	7"	Island	WI133	1963	£5	£10	Stranger & Patsy B side
Tom Dick And Harry	7"	Island	WI144	1964	£5	£10	with Patsy Todd
Uno-Dos-Tres	7"	Black Swan	WI413	1964	£5	£10	
We Shall Overcome	7"	Doctor Bird	DB1025	1966	£5	£10	
What Moma No Want She Get	7"	Amalgamated	AMG838	1969	£4	£8	
When I Get My Freedom	7"	Unity	UN514	1969	£2.50	£6	
When The Party Is Over	7"	Blue Beat	BB345	1965	£5	£10	Charmers B side
Yea Yea Baby	7"	Island	WI152	1964	£5	£10	with Patsy Todd, Baba Brooks B side
You Took My Love	7"	Doctor Bird	DB1066	1966	£5	£10	

COLEMAN, BOBBY

You Don't Have To Tell Me	7"	Pye	7N25365	1966	£25	£50	

COLEMAN, FITZROY

Lucille	7"	Starlite	ST45064	1961	£2	£5	

COLEMAN, LONNIE & JESSE ROBERTSON

Dolores Diana	7"	London	HLU8335	1956	£12.50	£25	

COLEMAN, MICHAEL

Irish Jigs And Reels	LP	Ace Of Hearts	AH56	1963	£10	£25	
Legacy Of Michael Coleman	LP	Shanachie	33002	1976	£5	£12	US

COLEMAN, ORNETTE

Art Of The Improvisors	LP	Atlantic	2400109	1971	£5	£12	
At The Golden Circle, Stockholm, Vol.1	LP	Blue Note	BLP/BST84224	1966	£8	£20	
At The Golden Circle, Stockholm, Vol.2	LP	Blue Note	BLP/BST84225	1966	£8	£20	
Change Of The Century	LP	London	LTZK15199/ SAHK6099	1961	£8	£20	
Chappaqua Suite	LP	CBS	66203	1967	£10	£25	double
Empty Foxhole	LP	Blue Note	BLP/BST84246	1967	£8	£20	
Evening With Ornette Coleman	LP	Polydor	623246/7	1968	£10	£25	boxed double
Free Jazz	LP	Atlantic	(SD)1364	1961	£6	£15	US
Love Call	LP	Blue Note	BST84356	1970	£8	£20	
Music Of Ornette Coleman	LP	RCA	RD/SF7944	1970	£6	£15	
New York Is Now	LP	Blue Note	BST84287	1968	£8	£20	
Ornette	LP	London	LTZK15241/ SAHK6235	1962	£8	£20	
Ornette At Twelve	LP	Impulse	M/SIPL518	1969	£5	£12	
Ornette On Tenor	LP	Atlantic	588121	1968	£6	£15	
Science Fiction	LP	CBS	64774	1972	£5	£12	
Shape Of Jazz To Come	LP	Atlantic	587/588022	1966	£6	£15	
Skies Of America	LP	CBS	65147	1972	£5	£12	
Something Else	LP	Contemporary	LAC12170	1959	£10	£25	
This Is Our Music	LP	London	LTZK15228/ SAHK6181	1961	£8	£20	
Tomorrow Is The Question	LP	Contemporary	LAC12228	1960	£8	£20	
Town Hall 1962	LP	Fontana	SFJL923	1969	£5	£12	
Twins	LP	Atlantic	K40278	1972	£5	£12	

COLEMAN TRADITIONAL SOCIETY
Music From The Coleman Country .... LP ...... Leader .... LEA2044 .... 1972 ... £5 ....£12 ....

COLES, JOHNNY
Little Johnny C .... LP ...... Blue Note........ BLP/BST84144 ...... 1963 ... £20 ....£40 ....

COLETTE & THE BANDITS
Ladies Man .... 7" .... Stateside .... SS416 .... 1965 ... £1.50 ....£4 ....

COLLAGE
Misty .... LP ...... Studio Two ...... TWO410 .... 1973 ... £5 ....£12 ....

COLLECTORS
Collectors .... LP ...... Warner Bros .... WS1746................ 1968 ... £6 ....£15
Grass And Wild Strawberries .... LP ...... Warner Bros .... WS1774................ 1968 ... £6 ....£15
I Must Have Been Blind .... 7" ...... London .... HLU10304 .... 1970 ... £1.50 ....£4

COLLEGE BOYS
Someone Will Be There .... 7" ...... Blue Beat .... BB202 .... 1963 ... £5 ....£10

COLLETTE, BUDDY
Man Of Many Parts .... LP ...... Contemporary. LAC12090............. 1958 ... £6 ....£15
Nice Day With Buddy Collette .... LP ...... Contemporary. LAC12092............. 1958 ... £6 ....£15
Porgy And Bess .... LP ...... Top Rank .... 25003................... 1960 ... £5 ....£12
Swinging Shepherds .... LP ...... Mercury .... MMB12001 .... 1959 ... £5 ....£12

COLLIER, GRAHAM
Deep Dark Blue Centre .... LP ...... Deram .... DML/SML1005.... 1967 ... £15 ....£30
Down Another Road .... LP ...... Fontana .... SFJL922 .... 1969 ... £15 ....£30
Mosaics .... LP ...... Philips .... 6308051............... 1971 ... £15 ....£30
Portraits .... LP ...... Saydisc .... SDL244................ 1972 ... £15 ....£30
Songs For My Father .... LP ...... Polydor .... 6309006............... 1970 ... £15 ....£30

COLLIER, MITTY
I Had A Talk With My Man .... 7" ...... Pye .... 7N25275 .... 1964 ... £10 ....£20

COLLINS, AL JAZZBO
East Coast Jazz Scene .... LP ...... Vogue Coral .... LVA9030.............. 1956 ... £15 ....£30

COLLINS, ALBERT
Compleat Albert Collins .... LP ...... Imperial .... 12445 .... 1969 ... £8 ....£20 .... US
Cool Sound Of Albert Collins .... LP ...... TCF Hall .... 8002 .... 1965 ... £8 ....£20 .... US
Love Can Be Found Anywhere .... LP ...... Liberty .... LBS83238 .... 1969 ... £8 ....£20
There's Gotta Be A Change .... LP ...... Tumbleweed .... TW3501 .... 1971 ... £8 ....£20
Trash Talkin' .... LP ...... Imperial .... 12438................. 1969 ... £8 ....£20 .... US
Truckin' .... LP ...... Blue Thumb.... 8758................... 197- ... £8 ....£20 .... US

COLLINS, ANSELL
Cock Robin .... 7" ...... J-Dan .... JDN4401 .... 1970 ... £2 ....£5
My Last Waltz .... 7" ...... Amalgamated . AMG851 .... 1969 ... £4 ....£8 ....Immortals B side
Night Of Love .... 7" ...... Trojan .... TR699 .... 1969 ... £2.50 ....£6

COLLINS, DAVE & ANSELL
Double Barrel .... LP ...... Trojan .... TBL162 .... 1971 ... £6 ....£15
Double Barrel .... 7" ...... Technique .... TE901 .... 1971 ... £1.50 ....£4 ....chart single
Monkey Spanner .... 7" ...... Technique .... TE914 .... 1971 ... £1.50 ....£4 ....chart single

COLLINS, DONNIE SHOW BAND
Get Down With It .... 7" ...... Pye .... 7N17628 .... 1968 ... £4 ....£8

COLLINS, DOROTHY
At Home With Dorothy And Raymond . LP ...... Coral .... LVA9058.............. 1957 ... £5 ....£12
Baby Can Rock .... 7" ...... Vogue Coral .... Q72232................ 1957 ... £4 ....£8
Cool It Baby .... 7" ...... Vogue Coral .... Q72198................ 1956 ... £10 ....£20
Dorothy Collins Sings .... 7" EP.. London .... REP1025.............. 1955 ... £5 ....£10
Four Walls .... 7" ...... Vogue Coral .... Q72262................ 1957 ... £1.50 ....£4
Moments To Remember .... 7" ...... Vogue Coral .... Q72116................ 1956 ... £2.50 ....£6
Mr.Wonderful .... 7" ...... Vogue Coral .... Q72252................ 1957 ... £1.50 ....£4
My Boy Flat Top .... 7" ...... Vogue Coral .... Q72111................ 1955 ... £10 ....£20
Rock And Roll Train .... 7" ...... Vogue Coral .... Q72193................ 1956 ... £10 ....£20
Seven Days .... 7" ...... Vogue Coral .... Q72137................ 1956 ... £4 ....£8
Soft Sands .... 7" ...... Vogue Coral .... Q72287................ 1957 ... £1.50 ....£4
Treasure Of Love .... 7" ...... Vogue Coral .... Q72173................ 1956 ... £6 ....£12
Twelve Gifts Of Christmas .... 7" ...... Vogue Coral .... Q72208................ 1956 ... £1.50 ....£4

COLLINS, EDWYN
Don't Shilly Shally .... 12" ..... Creation........... CRE047T .... 1987 ... £8 ....£20 ....test pressing

COLLINS, GLENDA
Age For Love .... 7" ...... Decca .... F11321 .... 1961 ... £1.50 ....£4
Baby It Hurts .... 7" ...... HMV .... POP1283 .... 1964 ... £6 ....£12
Head Over Heels In Love .... 7" ...... Decca .... F11417 .... 1961 ... £1.50 ....£4
I Lost My Heart In The Fairground .... 7" ...... HMV .... POP1163 .... 1963 ... £30 ....£60
If You've Got To Pick A Baby .... 7" ...... HMV .... POP1233 .... 1963 ... £6 ....£12
It's Hard To Believe It .... 7" ...... Pye .... 7N17150 .... 1966 ... £6 ....£12
Johnny Loves Me .... 7" ...... HMV .... POP1439 .... 1965 ... £7.50 ....£15
Lollipop .... 7" ...... HMV .... POP1323 .... 1964 ... £6 ....£12
Something I've Got To Tell You .... 7" ...... Pye .... 7N17044 .... 1966 ... £6 ....£12
Take A Chance .... 7" ...... Decca .... F11280 .... 1960 ... £1.50 ....£4
Thou Shalt Not Steal .... 7" ...... HMV .... POP1475 .... 1965 ... £5 ....£10

COLLINS, JOHNNY

Johnny's Private Army	LP	Tradition	TSR020	1975	£5	£12	
Traveller's Rest	LP	Tradition	TSR014	1973	£5	£12	

COLLINS, JUDY

Both Sides Now	7"	Elektra	EKSN45043	1970	£1.50	£4	chart single
Concert	LP	Elektra	EKL/EKS7280	1964	£4	£10	
Fifth Album	LP	Elektra	EKL/EKS7300	1965	£4	£10	
Golden Apples Of The Sun	LP	Elektra	EKL/EKS7222	1962	£4	£10	
I'll Keep It With Mine	7"	London	HLZ10029	1966	£1.50	£4	
In My Life	LP	Elektra	EKL/EKS7320	1967	£4	£10	
In My Life	7"	Elektra	EKSN45011	1967	£1.50	£4	
Maid Of Constant Sorrow	LP	Elektra	EKL/EKS7209	1962	£4	£10	
Pretty Polly	7"	Elektra	EKSN45073	1969	£1.50	£4	
Someday Soon	7"	Elektra	EKSN45053	1969	£1.50	£4	
Third Album	LP	Elektra	EKL/EKS7243	1964	£4	£10	
Turn Turn Turn	7"	Elektra	EKSN45077	1969	£1.50	£4	
Who Knows Where The Time Goes	LP	Elektra	EKL/EKS74033	1969	£4	£10	
Wild Flowers	LP	Elektra	EKL/EKS74012	1968	£4	£10	

COLLINS, LYN

Check Me Out If You Don't Know Me By Now	LP	People	PE6605	1975	£15	£30	US
Female Preacher	LP	Urban	URBLP7	1988	£5	£12	
Rock Me Again And Again	LP	Polydor	2066490	1974	£4	£8	
Rock Me Again And Again And Again	12"	Urban	URBX15	1988	£2.50	£6	
Think	LP	Polydor	2918006	1972	£15	£30	
Think	7"	Mojo	2093029	1974	£2.50	£6	

COLLINS, PETER

First Album	LP	Nova	SDN21	1970	£5	£12	

COLLINS, PHIL

In The Air Tonight	7"	Virgin	VSK102	1981	£2	£5	with booklet
One More Night	7"	Virgin	VSS755	1985	£2	£5	shaped pic disc
Separate Lives	7"	Virgin	VSSD818	1985	£5	£10	2 pic discs
Sussudio	7"	Virgin	VSY73612	1985	£2	£5	shaped pic disc
Thru' These Walls	7"	Virgin	VSY524	1982	£1.50	£4	pic disc
You Can't Hurry Love	7"	Virgin	VSY531	1982	£2.50	£6	pic disc

COLLINS, ROGER

She's Looking Good	7"	Vocalion	VP9285	1967	£4	£8	

COLLINS, SHIRLEY

Adieu To Old England	LP	Topic	12T238	1974	£10	£25	
Amaranth	LP	Harvest	SHSM2008	1976	£10	£25	
Anthems In Eden	LP	Harvest	SHVL754	1969	£30	£60	with Dolly Collins
English Songs Vol.2	7" EP	Collector	JEB9	1964	£20	£40	
False True Lovers	LP	Folkways	FG3564	1959	£75	£150	US
Favourite Garland	LP	Deram	SML1117	1975	£8	£20	
Foggy Dew	7" EP	Collector	JEB3	1960	£20	£40	
For As Many As Will	LP	Topic	12T380	1979	£5	£12	
Heroes In Love	7" EP	Topic	TOP95	1963	£20	£40	
Love, Death And The Lady	LP	Harvest	SHVL771	1970	£25	£50	with Dolly Collins
No Roses	LP	Mooncrest	CREST11	1974	£6	£15	with Dolly collins
No Roses	LP	Pegasus	PEG7	1971	£10	£25	with Dolly Collins
Power Of The True Love Knot	LP	Hannibal	HNBL1327	198-	£5	£12	
Power Of The True Love Knot	LP	Polydor	583025	1968	£30	£60	
Sweet England	LP	Argo	RG150	1960	£30	£60	
Sweet Primroses	LP	Topic	12TS170	1967	£20	£40	
Unquiet Grave	7" EP	Collector	JEB5	1961	£20	£40	

COLLINS, TOMMY

Dynamic Tommy Collins	LP	Columbia	CL2510/CS9310	1966	£8	£20	US
Let Down	7"	Capitol	CL14894	1958	£1.50	£4	
Let's Live A Little	LP	Tower	(D)T5021	1966	£5	£12	US
Light Of The Lord	LP	Capitol	T1125	1959	£10	£25	US
Little June	7"	Capitol	CL15076	1959	£2	£5	
On Tour	LP	Columbia	CL2778/CS9578	1968	£8	£20	US
Shindig	LP	Tower	(D)T5107	1968	£5	£12	US
Songs I Love To Sing	LP	Capitol	(S)T1436	1961	£8	£20	US
Think It Over Boys	7"	Capitol	CL14838	1958	£1.50	£4	
This Is Tommy Collins	LP	Capitol	T1196	1959	£10	£25	
Words And Music Country Style	LP	Capitol	T776	1957	£15	£30	
Wreck Of The Old '97	7"	Capitol	CL15118	1960	£1.50	£4	

COLONEL

Too Many Cooks In The Kitchen	7"	Virgin	VS380	1980	£2	£5	

COLONNA, JERRY

Chicago Style	7"	London	HL8143	1955	£7.50	£15	
Ebb Tide	7"	Brunswick	05243	1954	£5	£10	
It Might As Well Be Spring	7"	Brunswick	05342	1954	£4	£8	
Let Me Go Lover	7"	Parlophone	MSP6165	1955	£2	£5	
Let's All Sing	LP	London	HAU2190	1959	£6	£15	
Shifting Whispering Sands	7"	HMV	7M369	1956	£1.50	£4	

COLORADOS

Lips Are Redder On You	7"	Oriole	CB1972	1964	£2.50	£6	

COLOSSEUM

Title	Format	Label	Cat No	Year			Notes
Collectors' Colosseum	LP	Bronze	ILPS9173	1971	£4	£10	
Daughter Of Time	LP	Vertigo	6360017	1970	£5	£12	.. spiral label, chart LP
Live	LP	Bronze	ICD1	1971	£5	£12	double, chart LP
Those About To Die Salute You	LP	Fontana	STL5510	1969	£6	£15	chart LP
Those Who Are About To Die	7"	Fontana	TF1029	1969	£2.50	£6	
Valentyne Suite	LP	Vertigo	VO1	1969	£6	£15	.. spiral label, chart LP

COLOURBOX

Title	Format	Label	Cat No	Year			
Breakdown	7"	4AD	AD215	1982	£2.50	£6	
Breakdown	12"	4AD	BAD215	1982	£4	£10	
Breakdown (Version Two)	7"	4AD	AD304	1983	£1.50	£4	

COLOURED RAISINS

Title	Format	Label	Cat No	Year			
One Way Love	7"	Trojan	TR7700	1969	£2.50	£6	

COLOURFUL SEASONS

Title	Format	Label	Cat No	Year			
Out Of The Blue	7"	MGM	MGM1433	1968	£1.50	£4	

COLOURS

Title	Format	Label	Cat No	Year			
Wake Up Wake Up	7"	Parlophone	R5940	1972	£1.50	£4	

COLOURS OF LOVE

Title	Format	Label	Cat No	Year			
I'm A Train	7"	Page One	POF060	1968	£1.50	£4	
Just Another Fly	7"	Page One	POF086	1968	£1.50	£4	
Mother Of Convention	7"	Page One	POF124	1969	£1.50	£4	

COLOURS OUT OF TIME

Title	Format	Label	Cat No	Year			
Rock Section	7"	Monsters In Orbit	TVEYE1	1981	£1.50	£4	

COLT, CHRISTOPHER

Title	Format	Label	Cat No	Year			
Virgin Sunrise	7"	Decca	F12726	1968	£5	£10	

COLTON, TONY

Title	Format	Label	Cat No	Year			
I Stand Accused	7"	Pye	7N15886	1965	£30	£60	
In The World Of Marnie Dreaming	7"	Columbia	DB8385	1968	£4	£8	
I've Laid Some Down In My Time	7"	Pye	7N17117	1966	£7.50	£15	
Lose My Mind	7"	Decca	F11879	1964	£4	£8	
You're Wrong There Baby	7"	Pye	7N17046	1966	£7.50	£15	

COLTRANE, JOHN

In the sixties, John Coltrane's passionate brand of modal improvisation often appealed to rock fans who did not otherwise like jazz. And when rock groups started to introduce long improvised solos, it was invariably the Coltrane style that they adopted. (This was made explicit by Mike Bloomfield and Al Kooper in their Coltrane tribute track "His Holy Modal Majesty"). There is one oddity in the Coltrane discography - some copies of "Kulu Se Mama" actually play the album "Om", which was not otherwise given a UK release. There are likely to be some owners of "Kulu Se Mama" who are unaware that the music they know by that title is actually something totally different!

Title	Format	Label	Cat No	Year			Notes
Africa/Brass	LP	HMV	CLP1548/CSD1431	1962	£6	£15	
Afro Blue	LP	Probe	SPB1025	1971	£5	£12	
Ascension	LP	HMV	CLP/CSD3543	1966	£6	£15	
Atlantic Years	LP	Atlantic	K60052	1974	£5	£12	double
Avant-Garde	LP	Atlantic	587/588004	1966	£6	£15	with Don Cherry
Bags And Trane	LP	London	LTZK15232/ SAHK6192	1962	£10	£25	with Milt Jackson
Bahia	LP	Stateside	SL10162	1966	£6	£15	
Ballads	LP	HMV	CLP1647/CSD1496	1963	£6	£15	
Bass Blues	7" EP.	Esquire	EP239	1961	£2.50	£6	
Black Pearls	LP	Prestige	PR24037	1974	£5	£12	double
Black Pearls	LP	Stateside	SL10124	1965	£6	£15	
Blue Train	LP	Blue Note	BLP/BST81577	1961	£15	£30	
Cattin'	LP	Esquire	32101	1960	£8	£20	
Coltrane	LP	HMV	CLP1629/CSD1483	1963	£6	£15	
Coltrane Jazz	LP	Atlantic	ATL/SAL1354	1967	£4	£10	
Coltrane Jazz	LP	London	LTZK15219/ SAHK6162	1961	£8	£20	
Coltrane Plays The Blues	LP	London	HAK/SHK8017	1963	£8	£20	
Coltrane Time	LP	United Artists	(S)ULP1018	1963	£8	£20	
Coltrane's Sound	LP	Atlantic	587/588039	1966	£6	£15	
Cosmic Music	LP	Impulse	M/SIPL515	1969	£8	£20	with Alice Coltrane
Crescent	LP	HMV	CLP1799/CSD1567	1965	£6	£15	
Dakar	LP	Transatlantic	PR7280	1968	£6	£15	
Duke Ellington And John Coltrane	LP	HMV	CLP1657/CSD1502	1963	£6	£15	
Expression	LP	Impulse	M/SIPL502	1968	£8	£20	
First Trane	LP	Esquire	32079	1958	£10	£25	
Giant Steps	LP	Atlantic	588168	1969	£4	£10	
Giant Steps	LP	Atlantic	ATL1311	1967	£8	£20	
Giant Steps	LP	London	LTZK15197	1960	£8	£20	
Impressions	LP	HMV	CLP1695/CSD1509	1964	£6	£15	
John Coltrane	LP	Prestige	PR24003	1973	£5	£12	double
John Coltrane Quartet Plays	LP	HMV	CLP1897/CSD1619	1965	£6	£15	
John Coltrane With Johnny Hartman	LP	HMV	CLP1700	1964	£8	£20	
Kulu Se Mama	LP	HMV	CLP/CSD3617	1967	£6	£15	
Kulu Se Mama	LP	HMV	CLP/CSD3617	1967	£8	£20	mispress - plays Coltrane's 'Om' LP
Last Trane	LP	Transatlantic	PR7378	1968	£6	£15	
Live At Birdland	LP	HMV	CLP1741/CSD1544	1964	£6	£15	
Live At The Village Vanguard	LP	HMV	CLP1590/CSD1456	1962	£6	£15	
Live At The Village Vanguard Again	LP	HMV	CLP/CSD3599	1967	£6	£15	
Love Supreme	LP	HMV	CLP1869/CSD1605	1965	£6	£15	
Lush Life	LP	Esquire	32129	1961	£10	£25	
Meditation	LP	HMV	CLP/CSD3575	1966	£6	£15	

Title	Format	Label	Catalogue	Year			Notes
Moment's Notice	7"	Blue Note	451718	1964	£2	£5	
More Lasting Than Bronze	LP	Prestige	PR24014	1973	£5	£12	double
My Favourite Things	LP	Atlantic	588146	1969	£4	£10	
My Favourite Things	LP	Atlantic	ATL/SAL5022	1965	£6	£15	
New Thing At Newport	LP	HMV	CLP/CSD3551	1966	£6	£15	with Archie Shepp
Ole Coltrane	LP	London	LTZK15239/ SAHK6223	1962	£8	£20	
On West 42nd Street	LP	Realm	RM157	1964	£5	£12	
Selflessness	LP	Impulse	SIPL522	1969	£6	£15	
Soul Of Trane	7" EP	Esquire	EP229	1960	£2.50	£6	
Soultrane	LP	Esquire	32089	1959	£10	£25	
Standard Coltrane	LP	Esquire	32179	1963	£8	£20	
Tanganyika Strut	LP	Realm	RM52226	1965	£5	£12	
Tenor Conclave	LP	Esquire	32059	1958	£8	£20	
Trane Ride	LP	Realm	RM181	1964	£5	£12	
Traneing In	LP	Esquire	32091	1959	£10	£25	
While My Lady Sleeps	7" EP	Fontana	469203TE	1964	£2.50	£6	

COLTS

Title	Format	Label	Catalogue	Year			
San Miguel	7"	Pye	7N15955	1965	£1.50	£4	

COLUMBIA BOYS

Title	Format	Label	Catalogue	Year			
Baby Come Back	7"	Pye	7N17513	1968	£1.50	£4	
That's My Pa	7"	Pye	7N17763	1969	£1.50	£4	

COLUMBUS

Title	Format	Label	Catalogue	Year			
Everybody Loves The US Marshall	7"	Deram	DM294	1970	£2.50	£6	

COLWELL BROTHERS

Title	Format	Label	Catalogue	Year			
Africa's Got The Answer	7" EP	Philips	NBE11117	1959	£2	£5	
Colwell Brothers	7" EP	Philips	NBE11047	195-	£2	£5	
Colwell Brothers	7" EP	Philips	NBE11048	195-	£2	£5	
There'll Be A New World	7" EP	Philips	NBE11118	1959	£2	£5	

COLWELL-WINFIELD BLUES BAND

Title	Format	Label	Catalogue	Year			Notes
Live Bust	LP	Zazoo	1	1971	£6	£15	US

COLYER, KEN

Title	Format	Label	Catalogue	Year			
And Back To New Orleans Vol.1	7" EP	Decca	DFE6268	1955	£2	£5	
And Back To New Orleans Vol.2	7" EP	Decca	DFE6299	1956	£2	£5	
And His Omega Brass	7" EP	Decca	DFE6435	1957	£2	£5	
Back To The Delta	10" LP	Decca	LF1196	1954	£8	£20	
Club Session	LP	Decca	LK4178	1957	£5	£12	
Dippermouth Blues	7"	Decca	FJ10755	1956	£1.50	£4	
Early Hours	7"	Decca	F10504	1955	£1.50	£4	
If I Ever Cease To Love	7"	Decca	F10519	1955	£1.50	£4	
In Glory Land	10" LP	Decca	LF1301	1958	£6	£15	
In Hamburg	10" LP	Decca	LF1319	1959	£6	£15	
In New Orleans	7" EP	Tempo	EXA53	1957	£2	£5	
In New Orleans	7" EP	Vogue	EPV1102	1956	£2	£5	
In New Orleans	10" LP	Vogue	LDE161	1955	£8	£20	
In New Orleans Pt.2	7" EP	Vogue	EPV1202	1958	£2	£5	
Isle Of Capri	7"	Tempo	A120	1956	£1.50	£4	
Ken Colyer	7" EP	Melodisc	EPM7105	195-	£2.50	£6	
Ken Colyer Jazzmen	7" EP	Storyville	SEP301	196-	£2	£5	
Ken Colyer Jazzmen	7" EP	Tempo	EXA26	1956	£2	£5	
Ken Colyer Jazzmen	7" EP	Tempo	EXA31	1956	£2	£5	
Ken Colyer Jazzmen & Crane River Jazz Band	7" EP	Melodisc	EPM759	1956	£2.50	£6	
Ken Colyer's Jazzmen	7" EP	Storyville	SEP305	196-	£2.50	£6	
Ken Colyer's Jazzmen	7" EP	Storyville	SEP309	196-	£2.50	£6	
Ken Colyer's Jazzmen	10" LP	Tempo	LAP11	1956	£6	£15	
Maryland My Maryland	7"	Tempo	A136	1956	£1.50	£4	
New Orleans To London	10" LP	Decca	LF1152	1954	£8	£20	
Plays Standards	LP	Decca	LK4294	1959	£5	£12	
Red Wing	7"	Decca	F10565	1955	£1.50	£4	
Rum And Coca Cola	7" EP	Esquire	EP233	1960	£2	£5	
Sheik Of Araby	7"	Tempo	A117	1956	£1.50	£4	
Stomping	7" EP	Esquire	EP243	1961	£2	£5	
They All Played Ragtime	7" EP	Decca	DFE6466	1958	£2	£5	
This Is Jazz	LP	Columbia	33SX1220	1960	£4	£10	
This Is Jazz	7" EP	Columbia	SEG8038	1960	£2	£5	
This Is Jazz Vol.1 No.2	7" EP	Columbia	SEG8104	1961	£2	£5	
This Is Jazz Vol.2	LP	Columbia	33SX1297/ SCX3360	1961	£4	£10	
This Is Jazz Vol.2	7" EP	Columbia	SEG8145	1962	£2	£5	
Too Busy	7" EP	Columbia	SEG8180	1962	£2	£5	
Trad Jazz Scene In Europe Vol.2	7" EP	Storyville	SEP392	1961	£2	£5	
Wabash Blues	7"	Tempo	A126	1956	£1.50	£4	
Walking The Blues	7" EP	Decca	DFE6645	1960	£2	£5	
Walking The Blues	7" EP	Decca	STO143	1960	£2.50	£6	
Wildcat Blues	7" EP	Storyville	SEP412	196-	£2	£5	

COLYER, KEN SKIFFLE GROUP

Title	Format	Label	Catalogue	Year			
Downbound Train	7"	Decca	FJ10751	1956	£2.50	£6	
Ella Speed	7"	Decca	FJ10972	1958	£2.50	£6	
Green Corn	7" EP	KC	KCS11EP	195-	£4	£8	
Grey Goose	7"	Decca	FJ10889	1957	£2.50	£6	
House Rent Stomp	7"	Decca	FJ10926	1957	£2.50	£6	
Ken Colyer Skiffle Group In Hamburg	7" EP	Decca	DFE6563	1959	£5	£10	
Ken Colyer's Skiffle Group	7" EP	Decca	DFE6286	1956	£4	£8	

Ken Colyer's Skiffle Group No.2	7" EP	Decca	DFE6444	1957 ... £4 ...... £8	
Ole Riley	7"	Decca	FJ10772	1956 ... £2.50 ...... £6	
Streamline Train	7"	Decca	F10711	1956 ... £2.50 ...... £6	
Take This Hammer	7"	Decca	F10631	1955 ... £2.50 ...... £6	

COMBAT 84
Orders Of The Day	7"	Victory	VIC1	1983 ... £4 ...... £8	
Rapist	7"	Victory	VIC2	1983 ... £2 ...... £5	

COME
Come Sunday	7"	Come Org.	WDC88001	1979 ... £12.50 ...... £25	
I'm Jack	LP	Come Org.	WDC880012	1981 ... £20 ...... £40	orange vinyl
Rampton	LP	Come Org.	WDC88002	1979 ... £25 ...... £50	

COMICS, ARTHUR
Isgodaman?	7"	XS		1977 ... £5 ...... £10	

COMMANCHES
Tomorrow	7"	Pye	7N15609	1964 ... £1.50 ...... £4	

COMMANDERS
Cat From Coos Bay	7"	Brunswick	05433	1955 ... £1.50 ...... £4	
Meet The Commanders	7" EP	Brunswick	OE9037	1955 ... £2 ...... £5	
Monster	7"	Brunswick	05467	1955 ... £1.50 ...... £4	

COMMODORES
Keep On Dancing	7"	Atlantic	584273	1969 ... £2 ...... £5	
Zoo	7"	Tamla Motown	TMG924	1974 ... £1.50 ...... £4	

COMMODORES (2)
Riding On A Train	7"	London	HLD8209	1955 ... £75 ...... £150	
Speedo	7"	London	HLD8251	1956 ... £180 ...... £300	

COMMON PEOPLE
Of The People, By The People, For The People	LP	Capitol	ST266	1969 ... £15 ...... £30	US

COMMON ROUND
Four Pence A Day	LP	Galliard	GAL4015	197- ... £6 ...... £15	

COMO, PERRY
All At Once You Love Her	7"	HMV	POP394	1957 ... £1.50 ...... £4	
Bushel And A Peck	7"	HMV	7M138	1953 ... £5 ...... £10	
Como Sings	7" EP	HMV	7EG8192	1956 ... £2 ...... £5	
Don't Let The Stars Get In Your Eyes	7"	HMV	7M118	1953 ... £6 ...... £12	chart single
Door Of Dreams	7"	HMV	POP305	1955 ... £2.50 ...... £6	
Frosty The Snowman	7"	HMV	7M278	1954 ... £2.50 ...... £6	
Girl With The Golden Braids	7"	RCA	RCA1001	1957 ... £1.50 ...... £4	
Glendora	7"	HMV	7MC49	1956 ... £5 ...... £10	
Hello Young Lovers	7"	HMV	7M155	1953 ... £2.50 ...... £6	
Hot Diggity	7"	HMV	7M404	1956 ... £4 ...... £8	chart single
Idle Gossip	7"	HMV	7M200	1954 ... £4 ...... £8	chart single
If You Were Only Mine	7"	HMV	7M241	1954 ... £4 ...... £8	
Juke Box Baby	7"	HMV	7MC39	1956 ... £12.50 ...... £25	export
Kewpie Doll	7"	RCA	RCA1055	1958 ... £1.50 ...... £4	chart single
Ko Ko Mo	7"	HMV	7M296	1955 ... £4 ...... £8	
Magic Moments	7"	RCA	RCA1036	1958 ... £1.50 ...... £4	chart single
Moonlight Love	7"	HMV	POP271	1956 ... £2 ...... £5	
More	7"	HMV	POP240	1956 ... £4 ...... £8	chart single
Papa Loves Mambo	7"	HMV	7M263	1954 ... £5 ...... £10	chart single
Perry Como	7" EP	HMV	7EG8013	1954 ... £2 ...... £5	
Perry Como Sings	10" LP	HMV	DLP1026	1954 ... £5 ...... £12	
Rose Tattoo	7"	HMV	7M366	1956 ... £2.50 ...... £6	
Round And Round	7"	HMV	POP328	1957 ... £2 ...... £5	
Ruby And The Pearl	7"	HMV	7M102	1953 ... £2.50 ...... £6	
Say You're Mine Again	7"	HMV	7M149	1953 ... £4 ...... £8	
Silk Stockings	7"	HMV	POP369	1957 ... £1.50 ...... £4	
So Smooth	7" EP	HMV	7EG8171	1956 ... £2 ...... £5	
Some Enchanted Evening	7"	HMV	7M110	1953 ... £4 ...... £8	
Somebody Up There Likes Me	7"	HMV	7MC51	1957 ... £4 ...... £8	export
Somebody Up There Likes Me	7"	HMV	POP304	1957 ... £2 ...... £5	
Tina Marie	7"	HMV	7M326	1955 ... £4 ...... £8	chart single
Wanted	7"	HMV	7M215	1954 ... £4 ...... £8	chart single
Why Did You Leave Me?	7"	HMV	7M163	1953 ... £2.50 ...... £6	
Wild Horses	7"	HMV	7M124	1953 ... £4 ...... £8	
With A Song In My Heart	7" EP	HMV	7EG8244	1957 ... £2 ...... £5	
You Alone	7"	HMV	7M175	1954 ... £4 ...... £8	

COMPETITORS
Hits Of The Street And Strip	LP	Dot	DLP3542/25542	1963 ... £10 ...... £25	US

COMPLEX
Complex	LP	Halpix	CLPM001	1970 ... £400 ...... £600	
Way We Feel	LP	Deroy		1971 ... £330 ...... £500	

COMSAT ANGELS
Red Planet	7"	Junta	JUNTA1	1979 ... £2 ...... £5	red viny

COMSTOCK, BOBBY
I'm A Man	7"	United Artists	UP1086	1965 ... £5 ...... £10	
Jambalaya	7"	London	HLE9080	1960 ... £5 ...... £10	

Let's Stomp	7"	Stateside	SS163	1963	£4	£8	
Out Of Sight	LP	Ascot	ALM13/ALS16026.	1966	£6	£15	US
Susie Baby	7"	Stateside	SS221	1963	£1.50	£4	
Tennessee Waltz	7"	Top Rank	JAR223	1959	£1.50	£4	

COMUS
Comus were like a folky version of Family, with the group's singer adopting the same gargling tones as Roger Chapman. The largely acoustic instrumentation, however, gives the vocals a considerable dramatic emphasis, especially when underscored by a female singer. "First Utterance" is not exactly a classic, but it is certainly interesting.

Diana	7"	Dawn	DNX2506	1971	£10	£20	PS
First Utterance	LP	Dawn	DNLS3019	1971	£35	£70	
To Keep From Crying	LP	Virgin	V2018	1974	£6	£15	

CONCHORDS
You Can't Take It Away	7"	Polydor	BM56059	1965	£4	£8	

CONCORDS
I Need Your Loving	7"	Blue Cat	BS170	1969	£4	£8	

CONDON, EDDIE
Dixieland	LP	Philips	BBL7109	1957	£6	£15	
Dixieland Dance Party	LP	London	LTZD15158/ SAHD6014	1959	£5	£12	
Eddie Condon All Stars	LP	Philips	BBL7031	1955	£6	£15	
Eddie Condon Is Uptown Now	LP	MGM	C768	1958	£4	£10	
Eddie Condon Orchestra	10" LP	London	LZC14024	1956	£6	£15	
Eddie Condon Quartet	10" LP	Philips	BBL7061	1956	£6	£15	
Gershwin Jazz	10" LP	Brunswick	LA8518	1951	£8	£20	
Jazz Band Ball Vol.1	10" LP	Brunswick	LA8549	1952	£8	£20	
Jazz Concert	10" LP	Brunswick	LA8577	1953	£8	£20	
Ringside At Condon's Vol.1	10" LP	London	LZC14004	1955	£6	£15	
Roaring Twenties	LP	Philips	BBL7227	1958	£6	£15	
That Toddlin' Town	LP	Warner Bros	WM4009/WS8009.	1960	£5	£12	
Treasury Of Jazz	LP	Philips	BBL7131	1957	£6	£15	
We Called It Music	10" LP	Brunswick	LA8542	1952	£8	£20	

CONDOR, HOWIE G.
Big Noise From Winnetka	7"	Fontana	TF613	1965	£2	£5	

CONEY ISLAND KIDS
Baby Baby You	7"	London	HLJ8207	1955	£7.50	£15	

CONLEY, ARTHUR
All Day Singing	7"	Atlantic	2091025	1970	£1.50	£4	
Aunt Dora's Love Soul Shack	7"	Atlantic	584224	1968	£1.50	£4	
Funky Street	7"	Atlantic	584175	1968	£2	£5	chart single
More Sweet Soul	LP	Atco	228019	1969	£5	£12	
People Sure Act Funny	7"	Atlantic	584197	1968	£1.50	£4	
Shake Rattle And Roll	7"	Atlantic	584121	1967	£2	£5	
Shake, Rattle And Roll	LP	Atlantic	587084	1967	£5	£12	
Soul Directions	LP	Atlantic	587128	1968	£5	£12	
Star Revue	7"	Atco	226004	1969	£1.50	£4	
Sweet Soul Music	LP	Atlantic	587069	1967	£6	£15	
Sweet Soul Music	7"	Atlantic	2091106	1971	£1.50	£4	
Sweet Soul Music	7"	Atlantic	584083	1967	£2	£5	chart single
They Call The Wind Maria	7"	Atco	226011	1970	£1.50	£4	
Whole Lotta Woman	7"	Atlantic	584143	1967	£1.50	£4	

CONN, FRANK COMPANY
My Bonnie	7"	MGM	MGM1055	1959	£1.50	£4	

CONNELL, BRIAN & THE ROUND SOUND
Considerable confusion exists as to whether Brian Connell is the same person as Brian Connolly, the lead singer of the Sweet. Some authorities state that Connell is Connolly, while others are equally certain that he is not. Brian Connolly himself is no help in the matter, unfortunately, having made contrary statements to his Dutch fan club when they tried to determine the facts once and for all!

I Know	7"	Philips	BF1718	1968	£4	£8	
Just My Kind Of Loving	7"	Mercury	MF956	1966	£4	£8	
Same Thing Happened To Me	7"	Mercury	MF991	1966	£5	£10	
What Good Am I	7"	Philips	BF1661	1968	£5	£10	

CONNIFF, RAY & HIS ROCKING RHYTHM BOYS
Piggy Bank Boogie	7"	Vogue Coral	QW5001	1955	£4	£8	

CONNOLLY, BRIAN
Hypnotised	7"	Carrere	CAR231	1981	£2.50	£6	

CONNOR, CHRIS
Ballad Of The Sad Cafe	LP	London	LTZK15183	1960	£4	£10	
Bethlehem Girls	LP	Bethlehem	BCP6006	1956	£6	£15	US
Chris	LP	Bethlehem	BCP56	1956	£6	£15	US
Chris	10" LP	London	HBN1074	1956	£6	£15	
Chris Connor	LP	Atlantic	1228	1957	£6	£15	US
Chris Connor	LP	London	LZN14007	1956	£6	£15	
Chris Craft	LP	London	LTZK15151	1959	£6	£15	
Chris In Person	LP	London	LTZK15195/ SAHK6088.	1960	£4	£10	
George Gershwin Almanac Of Songs	LP	Atlantic	2601	1957	£8	£20	US
Hallelujah I Love Him So	7"	London	HLE8869	1959	£2.50	£6	
He Loves Me, He Loves Me Not	LP	London	HAK2066	1957	£6	£15	
Miss You So	LP	Atlantic	8014	1956	£6	£15	US
Only Want Some	7"	London	HLK9124	1960	£2.50	£6	

Title	Format	Label	Cat No	Year	Price	Price	Notes
Jazz Date	LP	London	LTZK15142	1959	£6	£15	
London's Girl Friends No.2	7" EP	London	REN1093	1957	£2.50	£6	
Lullaby Of Birdland	7" EP	London	EZN19010	1956	£2	£5	
Lullabys For Lovers	LP	Bethlehem	BCP6005	1956	£6	£15	US
Lullabys For Lovers	10" LP	Bethlehem	1002	1954	£8	£20	US
Lullabys Of Birdland	LP	Parlophone	PMC1082	1959	£6	£15	
Lullabys Of Birdland	10" LP	Bethlehem	1001	1954	£8	£20	US
Meets J And Kai	7" EP	Parlophone	GEP8767	1958	£2	£5	
Presenting	LP	London	HAK2020/ SHK6032	1957/ 1959	£6	£15	
This Is Chris	LP	Bethlehem	BCP20	1955	£6	£15	US
This Is Chris	7" EP	Parlophone	GEP8778	1958	£2	£5	
Witchcraft	LP	London	LTZK15185	1960	£4	£10	

CONNOR, KENNETH
| Rail Road Rock | 7" | Top Rank | JAR138 | 1959 | £1.50 | £4 | |

CONNY
| Gino | 7" | Columbia | DB4845 | 1962 | £4 | £8 | |

CONQUERORS
If You Can't Beat Them Join Them	7"	High Note	HS016	1969	£2.50	£6	
Jumpy Jumpy Girl	7"	Amalgamated	AMG832	1968	£4	£8	
Lonely Street	7"	Treasure Isle	TI7035	1968	£5	£10	
Mr.D.J.	7"	High Note	HS025	1969	£2.50	£6	
What A Agony	7"	Doctor Bird	DB1046	1966	£5	£10	Baba Brooks B side
Won't You Come Home Now	7"	Doctor Bird	DB1119	1967	£5	£10	

CONRAD, JESS
Cherry Pie	7"	Decca	F11236	1960	£1.50	£4	chart single
Hey Little Girl	7"	Decca	F11412	1961	£1.50	£4	
Human Jungle	7" EP	Decca	DFE8524	1963	£4	£8	
Hurt Me	7"	Pye	7N15849	1965	£4	£8	
Jess Conrad	7" EP	Decca	DFE6666	1960	£4	£8	
Jess For You	LP	Decca	LK4390	1961	£8	£20	
Mystery Girl	7"	Decca	F11315	1961	£1.50	£4	chart single
Oh You Beautiful Doll	7"	Decca	F11375	1961	£1.50	£4	
Pretty Jenny	7"	Decca	F11511	1962	£1.50	£4	chart single
Pussycat	7"	Columbia	DB7223	1964	£1.50	£4	
Things I'd Like To Say	7"	Columbia	DB7561	1965	£1.50	£4	
This Pullover	7"	Decca	F11348	1961	£1.50	£4	
Twist My Wrist	7" EP	Decca	DFE6702	1962	£2.50	£6	
Unless You Mean It	7"	Decca	F11259	1960	£1.50	£4	
Walk Away	7"	Decca	F11394	1961	£1.50	£4	

CONRAD, TONY & FAUST
| Outside The Dream Syndicate | LP | Caroline | C1501 | 1972 | £6 | £15 | |

CONROY
The value of the once-legendary "London Underground" LP has ben steadily falling since collectors have realised that this is not actually the work of a forgotten progressive group. The "Conroy Recorded Music Library" is not a group at all, in fact, but a series of records produced by anonymous session musicians for use in film and TV work.

Background Action	LP	Berry Music Co.		197-	£25	£50	
Far West/Far East	LP	Berry Music Co.	BMLP155	1976	£5	£12	
Indian Suite	LP	Berry Music Co.		197-	£5	£12	
London's Underground	LP	Berry Music Co.	BMLP092	1972	£25	£50	
London's Underground No.2	LP	Berry Music Co.	BMLP115	1975	£15	£30	
Psychosis Suite	LP	Berry Music Co.		197-	£5	£12	
Way In Way Out	LP	Berry Music Co.		197-	£5	£12	

CONSUMATES
| What Is It | 7" | Coxsone | CS7054 | 1968 | £5 | £10 | |

CONTINENTALS
| Going Crazy | 7" | Island | WI010 | 1962 | £5 | £10 | |

CONTINUUM
| Autumn Grass | LP | RCA | SF8196 | 1971 | £4 | £10 | |
| Continuum | LP | RCA | SF8157 | 1970 | £6 | £15 | |

CONTOURS
Baby Hit And Run	7"	Tamla Motown	TMG886	1974	£1.50	£4	
Can You Do It	7"	Stateside	SS299	1964	£10	£20	
Can You Jerk Like Me	7"	Stateside	SS381	1965	£10	£20	
Contours	7" EP	Tamla Motown	TME2002	1965	£15	£30	
Determination	7"	Tamla Motown	TMG564	1966	£12.50	£25	
Do You Love Me	LP	Oriole	PS40043	1963	£25	£50	
Do You Love Me	7"	Oriole	CBA1763	1962	£25	£50	
Do You Love Me	7"	Tamla Motown	TMG899	1974	£1.50	£4	
Don't Let Her Be Your Baby	7"	Oriole	CBA1831	1963	£25	£50	
First I Look At The Purse	7"	Tamla Motown	TMG531	1965	£12.50	£25	
It's So Hard Being A Loser	7"	Tamla Motown	TMG605	1967	£12.50	£25	
Just A Little Misunderstanding	7"	Tamla Motown	TMG723	1970	£1.50	£4	chart single
Shake Sherry	7"	Oriole	CBA1799	1963	£25	£50	

CONTRABAND
Contraband .... LP ...... Transatlantic ... TRA278 .... 1974 ... £6 ....£15 ....

CONTRASTS
What A Day .... 7" ...... Monument .... MON1018............ 1968 ... £2 ....£5

CONTROLLED BLEEDING
Headcrack .... LP ..... Sterile .... SR11 .... 1986 ... £8 ....£20

CONVAIRS
Mignight Mary .... 7" ...... HMV .... POP1549 .... 1966 ... £4 ....£8

CONVY, BERT & THE THUNDERBIRDS
Come On Back .... 7" ...... London .... HLB8190.............. 1955 ... £30 ....£60

CONWAY, MIKE
I'm Gonna Get Me A Woman .... 7" ...... Plexium .... PXM1 .... 1968 ... £1.50 ....£4

COO-COO RACHAS
Chili Beans .... 7" ...... Capitol .... CL15024 .... 1959 ... £1.50 ....£4

COODER, RY
Borderlive	LP	Warner Bros		1981	£8	£20	US promo
Chicken Skin Music	7"	Reprise	PRO644	1977	£4	£8	promo
Crazy 'Bout An Automobile	12"	Warner Bros	PROA943	1980	£3	£8	promo
How Can A Poor Man Stand Such Times And Live	7"	Reprise	RE23497	1971	£1.50	£4	
Jazz	LP	Mobile Fidelity	MFSL1085	1982	£6	£15	US audiophile
Money Honey	7"	Reprise	K14151	1972	£1.50	£4	
Money Honey	7"	Reprise	PRO514	1973	£1.50	£4	promo
Ry Cooder	LP	Reprise	RSLP6402	1971	£4	£10	
Ry Cooder Radio Show	LP	Reprise	PRO558	1976	£8	£20	US promo

COOK, LITTLE JOE
Don't You Have Feelings .... 7" ...... Sonet .... SON2002 .... 1973 ... £2.50 ....£6

COOK, LITTLE JOE (CHRIS FARLOWE)
Stormy Monday Blues .... 7" ...... Sue................. WI385 .... 1965 ... £17.50 ....£35

COOK, PETER
Ballad Of Spotty Muldoon .... 7" ...... Decca .... F12182................ 1965 ... £1.50 ....£4 ....chart single
Georgia .... 7" ...... Pye .... 7N15847 .... 1965 ... £4 ....£8
Presents Misty Mr.Wisty .... LP ..... Decca .... LK4722 .... 1965 ... £5 ....£12

COOK, PETER & DUDLEY MOORE
The duo's comedy records include a drug culture spoof, "L.S.Bumble Bee", that was given a perfect punch-line by being included on several Beatles bootleg albums in the seventies under the guise of a supposed Sgt.Pepper out-take.
Bedazzled	7"	Decca	F12710	1967	£1.50	£4	
By Appointment	7" EP	Decca	DFE8644	1965	£2.50	£6	
Goodbye-ee	7"	Decca	F12158	1965	£1.50	£4	chart single
Isn't She A Sweetie	7"	Decca	F12380	1966	£1.50	£4	
L.S.Bumble Bee	7"	Decca	F12551	1967	£2.50	£6	
Not Only But Also	LP	Decca	LK4703	1965	£4	£10	
Not Only But Also - TV Excerpts	LP	Decca	LK5080	1971	£4	£10	
Once Moore With Cook	LP	Decca	LK4785	1966	£4	£10	chart LP
Peter Cook & Dudley Moore	7" EP	Parlophone	GEP8940	1965	£2.50	£6	

COOK, PETER & OTHERS
Beyond The Fringe	LP	Parlophone	PMC1145	1961	£5	£12	chart LP
Bridge On The River Wye	LP	Parlophone	PMC1190/ PCS3036	1962	£5	£12	
Peter Cook Presents The Establishment	LP	Parlophone	PMC1198	1963	£5	£12	
Private Eye's Blue Record	LP	Transatlantic	TRA131	1965	£6	£15	
Sitting On The Bench	7"	Parlophone	R4969	1962	£1.50	£4	

COOK, ROGER
Meanwhile Back At The World	LP	Regal Zonophone	SRZA8508	1972	£8	£20	
Minstrel In Flight	LP	Regal Zonophone	SLRZ1035	1973	£10	£25	
Study	LP	Columbia	SCX6388	1970	£4	£10	

COOKE, SAM
Ain't That Good News	LP	RCA	RD/SF7635	1964	£6	£15	
Another Saturday Night	7"	RCA	RCA1341	1963	£1.50	£4	chart single
Another Saturday Night	7"	RCA	RCA1701	1968	£7.50	£15	Duane Eddy B side
At The Copa	LP	RCA	RD/SF7674	1965	£6	£15	
Best Of Sam Cooke	LP	RCA	LPM/LSP2625	1962	£6	£15	US
Best Of Sam Cooke Vol.2	LP	RCA	LPM/LSP3373	1965	£6	£15	US
Bring It On Home To Me	7"	RCA	RCA1296	1962	£2	£5	
Chain Gang	7"	RCA	RCA1202	1960	£2	£5	chart single
Cooke's Tour	LP	RCA	RD27190/SF5076	1961	£10	£25	
Cousin Of Mine	7"	RCA	RCA1420	1964	£1.50	£4	
Cupid	7"	RCA	RCA1242	1961	£1.50	£4	chart single
Cupid	7"	RCA	RCA1817	1969	£1.50	£4	
Encore	LP	HMV	CLP1273	1959	£20	£40	
Feel It	7"	RCA	RCA1260	1961	£1.50	£4	
Frankie And Johnny	7"	RCA	RCA1361	1963	£1.50	£4	chart single
Good News	7"	RCA	RCA1386	1964	£1.50	£4	
Good Times	7"	RCA	RCA1405	1964	£1.50	£4	

Title	Format	Label	Cat No	Year	Price	Price	Notes
Heart And Soul	7" EP	RCA	RCX7117	1963	£6	£12	
Hit Kit	LP	Keen	86101	1959	£15	£30	US
Hits Of The Fifties	LP	RCA	RD27215/SF5098	1961	£10	£25	
I Need You Now	7"	London	HLU9046	1960	£6	£12	
I Thank God	LP	Keen	86103	1960	£10	£25	US
I'll Come Running Back To You	7"	Speciality	SON5010	1976	£2	£5	
It's Got The Whole World Shakin'	7"	RCA	RCA1452	1965	£1.50	£4	
Little Red Rooster	7"	RCA	RCA1367	1963	£1.50	£4	
Little Things You Do	7"	HMV	POP610	1959	£6	£12	
Love Me	7"	RCA	RCA1221	1961	£2	£5	
Love You Most Of All	7"	HMV	POP568	1958	£6	£12	
Man Who Invented Soul	LP	RCA	LSP3991	1968	£6	£15	US
Mr.Soul	LP	RCA	RD/SF7539	1963	£6	£15	
My Kind Of Blues	LP	RCA	RD27245/SF5120	1962	£8	£20	
Night Beat	LP	RCA	RD/SF7583	1963	£10	£25	
Nothing Can Change This Love	7"	RCA	RCA1310	1962	£1.50	£4	
One Hour Ahead	7"	HMV	POP675	1959	£5	£10	
Only Sixteen	7"	HMV	POP642	1959	£6	£12	chart single
Sam Cooke	LP	HMV	CLP1261	1958	£25	£50	
Send Me Some Loving	7"	RCA	RCA1327	1963	£1.50	£4	
Shake	LP	RCA	RD7730	1965	£6	£15	
Shake	7"	RCA	RCA1436	1965	£2	£5	
Sugar Dumpling	7"	RCA	RCA1476	1965	£4	£8	
Swing Low	LP	RCA	RD27222	1960	£8	£20	
Swing Sweetly	7" EP	RCA	RCX7128	1964	£5	£10	
Teenage Sonata	7"	RCA	RCA1184	1960	£2	£5	
That's All I Need To Know	7"	London	HLU8615	1958	£10	£20	
That's Heaven To Me	7"	Immediate		1966	£12.50	£25	demo only
That's It I Quit, I'm Moving On	7"	RCA	RCA1230	1961	£1.50	£4	
Tribute To The Lady	LP	Keen	2004	1959	£15	£30	US
Try A Little Love	LP	RCA	RD/SF7764	1966	£6	£15	
Twistin' The Night Away	LP	RCA	RD27263/SF5133	1962	£6	£15	
Twistin' The Night Away	7"	RCA	RCA1277	1962	£1.50	£4	chart single
Unforgettable Sam Cooke	LP	RCA	LPM/LSP3517	1966	£6	£15	US
Wonderful World	7"	HMV	POP754	1960	£2.50	£6	chart single
Wonderful World Of Sam Cooke	LP	Immediate	IMLP002	1966	£6	£15	
You Send Me	7"	London	HLU8506	1957	£20	£40	chart single

COOKIES

Title	Format	Label	Cat No	Year	Price	Price	Notes
Chains	7"	London	HLU9634	1962	£4	£8	chart single
Don't Say Nothing Bad About My Baby	7"	London	HLU9704	1963	£4	£8	
Girls Grow Up Faster Than Boys	7"	Colpix	PX11120	1964	£2.50	£6	
Willpower	7"	Colpix	PX11112	1963	£2.50	£6	

COOL BREEZE

Title	Format	Label	Cat No	Year	Price	Price	Notes
People Ask What Love Is	7"	Pathway	PAT103	197-	£5	£10	

COOL CATS

Title	Format	Label	Cat No	Year	Price	Price	Notes
Hold Your Love	7"	Jolly	JY009	1968	£4	£8	Helmsley Morris B side
What Kind Of Man	7"	Jolly	JY007	1968	£4	£8	

COOL MEN

Title	Format	Label	Cat No	Year	Price	Price	Notes
Cool For Cats No.1	7" EP	Parlophone	GEP8739	1958	£7.50	£15	
Cool For Cats No.2	7" EP	Parlophone	GEP8752	1958	£7.50	£15	

COOL SPOON

Title	Format	Label	Cat No	Year	Price	Price	Notes
Yakety Yak	7"	Coxsone	CS7032	1967	£5	£10	

COOL STICKY

Title	Format	Label	Cat No	Year	Price	Price	Notes
Train To Soulville	7"	Amalgamated	AMG825	1968	£4	£8	Eric Morris B side

COOLEY, EDDIE & THE DIMPLES

Title	Format	Label	Cat No	Year	Price	Price	Notes
Got A Little Woman	7"	Columbia	DB3873	1957	£37.50	£75	

COOMBES, CHRIS

Title	Format	Label	Cat No	Year	Price	Price	Notes
Where It's At	7" EP	Holyground	HG110	1965	£12.50	£25	

COOPER, ALICE

Title	Format	Label	Cat No	Year	Price	Price	Notes
Be My Lover	7"	Warner Bros	K16154	1972	£1.50	£4	
Billion Dollar Babies	LP	Warner Bros	BS42685	1973	£5	£12	US quad
Clones	7"	Warner Bros	K17598	1980	£1.50	£4	
Easy Action	LP	Straight	STS1061	1969	£10	£25	
Eighteen	7"	Straight	S7209	1971	£4	£8	PS
Elected	7"	Warner Bros	K16214	1972	£4	£8	
Greatest Hits	LP	Warner Bros	W42803	1974	£5	£12	US quad
House Of Fire	7"	Epic	ALICEP4	1989	£1.50	£4	shaped pic disc
I Love America	12"	Warner Bros	ALICE1T	1983	£2.50	£6	
Killer	LP	Warner Bros	K56005	1971	£4	£10	calendar cover, chart LP
Love It To Death	LP	Straight	STS1065	1971	£10	£25	
Love It To Death	LP	Warner Bros	K46177	1971	£4	£10	chart LP
Muscle Of Love	LP	Warner Bros	BS42748	1974	£5	£12	US quad
Poison	CD-s	Epic	6551652	1989	£4	£10	bottle sleeve
Pretties For You	LP	Straight	STS1051	1969	£10	£25	
Reflected	7"	Straight	101	1969	£7.50	£15	US, probably promo only
Schooldays	LP	Warner Bros	K66021	1973	£6	£15	double
School's Out	LP	Warner Bros	K56007	1972	£4	£10	with panties
School's Out	7"	Warner Bros	K16188	1972	£4	£8	PS

Under My Wheels	7"	Warner Bros....	K16127	1971	£2	£5	
Welcome To My Nightmare	LP	Mobile Fidelity	MFSL1063	1980	£6	£15	US audiophile
Welcome To My Nightmare	12"	Anchor	ANE12001	1977	£2.50	£6	
Who Do You Think We Are?	12"	Warner Bros....	K17940T	1982	£3	£8	

COOPER, BOB

Bob Cooper Sextet	10" LP	Capitol	KPL102	1955	£8	£20	
Coop	LP	Contemporary.	LAC12157	1959	£6	£15	

COOPER, GARNELL & KINFOLK

Green Monkey	7"	London	HL9757	1963	£4	£8

COOPER, JIM

Jim Cooper Band	LP	Jim Cooper Band	JCB1	1979	£10	£25

COOPER, JIMMY

Dulcimer Player	LP	Forest Tracks...	FTS3009	1976	£5	£12

COOPER, LES & THE SOUL ROCKERS

Wiggle Wobble	7"	Stateside	SS142	1962	£2	£5

COOPER, MIKE

Do I Know You	LP	Dawn	DNLS3005	1970	£5	£12
Life & Death In Paradise	LP	Fresh Air	6370500	1974	£5	£12
Machine Gun Company	LP	Dawn	DNLS3031	1972	£5	£12
Oh Really	LP	Pye	NSPL18281	1969	£10	£25
Places I Know	LP	Dawn	DNLS3026	1971	£5	£12
Trout Steel	LP	Dawn	DNLS3011	1970	£5	£12
Up The Country Blues	7" EP..	Saydisc	SD137	196-	£7.50	£15

COOPER, TOMMY

Don't Jump Off The Roof Dad	7"	Palette	PG9019	1961	£4	£8	chart single

COPAS, COWBOY

Alabam	7"	Melodisc	1566	1960	£2.50	£6
Best Of American Country Music Vol.3	7" EP.	Ember	EMBEP4547	1964	£2	£5
Country Entertainer No.1	LP	London	HAB8088	1963	£5	£12
Country Hits	7" EP.	Stateside	SE1003	1963	£4	£8
Country Music	7" EP.	Top Rank	JKP3014	1962	£4	£8
Cowboy Copas	LP	Melodisc	MLP12119	1961	£5	£12
Favourite Cowboy Songs	7" EP.	Parlophone.	GEP8527	1955	£4	£8
Heartbreak Ago	7"	Parlophone.	MSP6109	1954	£7.50	£15
Return To Sender	7"	Parlophone.	MSP6164	1955	£7.50	£15
Star Of The Grand Ole Opry	LP	London	HAB8180	1964	£5	£12
Tennessee Senorita	7"	Parlophone.	MSP6079	1954	£7.50	£15
Unforgettable...Vol.1	7" EP.	London	REB1418	1964	£2.50	£6
Unforgettable...Vol.2	7" EP.	London	REB1419	1964	£2.50	£6
Unforgettable...Vol.3	7" EP.	London	REB1420	1964	£2.50	£6
Western Style	7" EP.	Parlophone.	GEP8575	1956	£4	£8

COPE, JULIAN

Droolian	LP	Mofo	MOFOCOLP90	1990	£5	£12	
Droolian	CD	Mofo	MOFOCOCD90	1990	£6	£15	
Safesurfer	7"	Island	JC1	1991	£5	£10	
Saint Julian	LP	Island	ILPS9861	1987	£6	£15	with bonus interview LP
Skellington	LP	Copeco	JULP89	1989	£5	£12	
Skellington	CD	Copeco	JUCD89	1989	£6	£15	
Sunspots	7"	Mercury	MER1822	1985	£2	£5	double

COPE, SUZY

Biggity Big	7"	HMV	POP1167	1963	£1.50	£4
Not Never Not Now	7"	HMV	POP1047	1962	£1.50	£4
Teenage Fool	7"	HMV	POP941	1961	£1.50	£4
You Can't Say I Never Told You	7"	CBS	201792	1965	£1.50	£4

COPELAND, ALAN

Feeling Happy	7"	Vogue Coral ...	Q72237	1957	£2.50	£6
Flip Flop	7"	Pye	7N25007	1959	£1.50	£4
How Will I Know?	7"	Vogue Coral ...	Q72277	1957	£1.50	£4

COPELAND, JOHNNY

Sufferin' City	7"	Atlantic	K10242	1972	£2.50	£6

COPELAND, KEN

Pledge Of Love	7"	London	HLP8423	1957	£75	£150	Mints B side

COPELAND, MARTHA

RCA Victor Race Series Vol.8	7" EP.	RCA	RCX7183	1966	£2	£5

COPPER, BOB

Sweet Rose In June	LP	Topic	12TS328	1977	£5	£12

COPPER FAMILY

Song For Every Season	LP	Leader	LEAB404	1971	£37.50	£75	4 LP box set

COPPERFIELD

Any Old Time	7"	Instant	IN004	1969	£2.50	£6
I'll Hold Out My Hand	7"	Parlophone	R5818	1969	£1.50	£4

COPS & ROBBERS

I Could Have Danced All Night	7"	Pye	7N15870	1965	£7.50	£15	
I Could Have Danced All Night	7" EP.	Pye	PNV24148	1965	£15	£30	French
It's All Over Now Baby Blue	7"	Pye	7N15928	1965	£6	£12	
St.James Infirmary	7"	Decca	F12019	1964	£12.50	£25	

CORBAN

Break In The Clouds	LP	Acorn		1978	£8	£20

CORBETT, HARRY H.

Junk Shop	7"	Pye	7N15468	1962	£1.50	£4

CORBETT, HARRY H. & WILFRED BRAMBELL

Gems From The Steptoe Scrap Heap	LP	Pye	NPL18153	1966	£5	£12
Love And Harold Steptoe	LP	Pye	NPL18135	1965	£5	£12
Steptoe And Son	LP	Pye	NPL18081	1962	£4	£10

CORBETT, RONNIE

Big Man	7"	Columbia	DB8512	1968	£1.50	£4

CORBY & THE CHAMPAGNE

Time Marches On	7"	Pye	7N17203	1966	£1.50	£4

CORDELL, FRANK

Sadie's Shawl	7"	HMV	7M419	1956	£1.50	£4	chart single

CORDELL, PHIL

Chevy Van	7"	Mowest	MW3026	1975	£4	£8	demo

CORDES

Give Her Time	7"	Cavern Sound	IMSTL1	1965	£10	£20

CORDET, LOUISE

Don't Let The Sun Catch You Crying	7"	Decca	F11824	1964	£1.50	£4	
Don't Make Me Over	7"	Decca	F11875	1964	£1.50	£4	
I'm Just A Baby	7"	Decca	F11476	1962	£1.50	£4	chart single
Sweet Beat Of Louise Cordet	7" EP	Decca	DFE8515	1962	£7.50	£15	
Sweet Enough	7"	Decca	F11524	1962	£1.50	£4	
Which Way The Wind Blows	7"	Decca	F11673	1963	£1.50	£4	

CORDUROYS

Tick Tock	7"	Planet	PLF122	1966	£7.50	£15

CORKSCREW

For Openers	LP	Highway	SHY7005	1979	£10	£25

CORNELL, DON

But Love Me	7"	Vogue Coral	Q72164	1956	£2	£5	
Don Cornell	7" EP.	HMV	7EG8105	1955	£2	£5	
For You	10" LP	Vogue Coral	LVC10004	1955	£8	£20	
Heaven Only Knows	7"	Vogue Coral	Q72203	1956	£1.50	£4	
Hold My Hand	7"	Vogue Coral	Q2013	1954	£10	£20	chart single
I've Got Bells On My Heart	7"	Coral	Q72313	1958	£2	£5	
Let's Be Friends	7"	Vogue Coral	Q72234	1957	£1.50	£4	
Let's Get Lost	LP	Coral	LVA9037	1956	£6	£15	
Love Is A Many Splendoured Thing	7"	Vogue Coral	Q72104	1955	£4	£8	
Mailman Bring Me No More Blues	7"	Coral	Q72308	1958	£4	£8	
Mama Guitar	7"	Vogue Coral	Q72276	1957	£5	£10	
No Man Is An Island	7"	Vogue Coral	Q72058	1955	£2	£5	
Rock Island Line	7"	Vogue Coral	Q72152	1956	£4	£8	
See-saw	7"	Vogue Coral	Q72218	1956	£4	£8	
Sempre Amore	7"	Pye	7N25041	1959	£1.50	£4	
Sittin' In The Balcony	7"	Vogue Coral	Q72257	1957	£4	£8	
Size Twelve	7"	Vogue Coral	Q72071	1955	£2	£5	
S'posin'	7"	Vogue Coral	Q2037	1954	£2.50	£6	
Stranger In Paradise	7"	Vogue Coral	Q72073	1955	£4	£8	chart single
Teenage Meeting	7"	Vogue Coral	Q72144	1956	£6	£12	
There Once Was A Beautiful	7"	Vogue Coral	Q72132	1956	£2	£5	
There's Only You	7"	Vogue Coral	Q72291	1957	£2	£5	
This Earth Is Mine	7"	London	HLD8937	1959	£2.50	£6	
Unchained Melody	7"	Vogue Coral	Q72080	1955	£2.50	£6	
When You Are In Love	7"	Vogue Coral	Q72070	1955	£2	£5	

CORNELL, JERRY

Please Don't Talk About Me	7"	London	HL8157	1955	£7.50	£15

CORNS, ARNOLD

The records issued by Arnold Corns are actually song-writing demos recorded by David Bowie (and re-recorded later, of course, for inclusion on his "Ziggy Stardust" album).

Hang On To Yourself	7"	B&C	CB189	1971	£10	£20
Hang On To Yourself	7"	Mooncrest	MOON25	1974	£4	£8
Moonage Daydream	7"	B&C	CB149	1971	£20	£40

CORNUCOPIA

Full Horn	LP	Brain	0001030	1973	£8	£20	German

CORONADOES

Johnny B Goode	7"	Stateside	SS2043	1967	£1.50	£4
Love Me With All Your Heart	7"	London	HL9895	1964	£4	£8

CORONETS

Title	Format	Label	Catalogue	Year	Price	Price	Notes
Do Do Do It Again	7"	Columbia	SCM5117	1954	£4	£8	
Lizzie Borden	7"	Columbia	SCM5235	1956	£4	£8	
Magic Touch	7"	Columbia	SCM5261	1956	£5	£10	
Perfect Combination	7" EP	Columbia	SEG7621	1956	£2.50	£6	
Rhythm And Blues	7" EP	Columbia	SEG7603	1956	£4	£8	
Someone To Love	7"	Columbia	DB3827	1956	£1.50	£4	

CORPORATION

Title	Format	Label	Catalogue	Year	Price	Price	Notes
Corporation	LP	Capitol	ST175	1969	£5	£12	
Get On Our Swing	LP	Age Of Aquarius	4150	1969	£6	£15	US
Hassels In My Mind	LP	Age Of Aquarius	4250	1969	£6	£15	US

CORRIB FOLK

Title	Format	Label	Catalogue	Year	Price	Price	Notes
Corrib Folk	LP	Homespun	HRL107	1975	£5	£12	Irish

CORRIE FOLK TRIO

Title	Format	Label	Catalogue	Year	Price	Price	Notes
Cam Ye By Atholl	LP	Philips	6382083	1973	£5	£12	reissue of Those Wild Corries
Corrie Folk Trio With Paddie Bell	LP	Waverley	(S)ZLP2042	1966	£8	£20	
Those Wild Corries!	LP	Fontana	STL5337	1966	£6	£15	

CORRIE FOLK TRIO AND PADDY BELL

Title	Format	Label	Catalogue	Year	Price	Price	Notes
In Retrospect	LP	Talisman	STAL5005	1970	£6	£15	

CORRIES

Title	Format	Label	Catalogue	Year	Price	Price	Notes
Bonnet, Belt And Sword	LP	Fontana	STL5401	1967	£6	£15	
Bonnet, Belt And Sword	LP	Philips	8220841		£5	£12	
Kishmul's Gallery	LP	Fontana	STL5465	1968	£6	£15	
Live At The Royal Lyceum Theatre Edinburgh	LP	Columbia	SCX6469	1971	£6	£15	
Live At The Royal Lyceum Theatre Edinburgh	LP	EMI	NTS109	197-	£5	£12	
Sound The Pibroch	LP	Columbia	SCX6511	1972	£5	£12	
Spotlight On The Corries	LP	Philips	6625035	1977	£6	£15	double
Strings And Things	LP	Columbia	SCX6442	1970	£5	£12	
These Are The Corries Vol.2	LP	Philips	6382059	1969	£4	£10	

CORSAIRS

Title	Format	Label	Catalogue	Year	Price	Price	Notes
I'll Take You Home	7"	Pye	7N25142	1962	£4	£8	

CORSAIRS (2)

Title	Format	Label	Catalogue	Year	Price	Price	Notes
I'm Gonna Shut You Down	7"	CBS	202624	1967	£4	£8	

CORT, BOB

Title	Format	Label	Catalogue	Year	Price	Price	Notes
Ain't It A Shame	LP	Decca	LK4222	1958	£6	£15	
Ark	7"	Decca	F10989	1958	£1.50	£4	
Ballad Of The Alamo	7"	Decca	F11285	1960	£1.50	£4	
Don't You Rock Me Daddy-O	7"	Decca	FJ10831	1957	£5	£10	
El Paso	7"	Decca	F11197	1960	£1.50	£4	
Eskimo Nell	LP	Decca	LK4301	1959	£6	£15	
Kissin' Time	7"	Decca	F11160	1959	£1.50	£4	
Mule Skinner Blues	7"	Decca	F11256	1960	£1.50	£4	
On Top Of Old Smokey	7"	Decca	F11109	1959	£1.50	£4	
Schoolday	7"	Decca	F10905	1957	£5	£10	
Six Five Special	7"	Decca	F10892	1957	£5	£10	
Skiffle Party	7"	Decca	F10951	1957	£5	£10	
Waterloo	7"	Decca	F11145	1959	£1.50	£4	

CORTEZ, DAVE BABY

Title	Format	Label	Catalogue	Year	Price	Price	Notes
And His Happy Organ	LP	RCA	LPM/LSP2099	1959	£8	£20	US
Countdown	7"	Roulette	RK7001	1966	£2	£5	
Dave Baby Cortez	LP	Clock	C331	1960	£8	£20	US
Dave Baby Cortez	7" EP	London	REU1233	1960	£10	£20	
Deep In The Heart Of Texas	7"	London	HLU9126	1960	£5	£10	
Golden Hits	LP	London	HAU8142	1964	£6	£15	
Happy Organ	7"	London	HLU8852	1959	£5	£10	
In Orbit	LP	Roulette	(S)R25328	1966	£5	£12	US
Organ Shindig	LP	Roulette	(S)R25298	1965	£6	£15	US
Piano Shuffle	7"	Columbia	DB4404	1960	£2.50	£6	
Rinky Dink	LP	Chess	LP1473	1962	£8	£20	US
Rinky Dink	7"	Pye	7N25159	1962	£4	£8	
Tweety Pie	LP	Roulette	(S)R25315	1966	£5	£12	US
Whistling Organ	7"	London	HLU8919	1959	£5	£10	

CORTINAS

Title	Format	Label	Catalogue	Year	Price	Price	Notes
Phoebe's Flower Shop	7"	Polydor	56255	1968	£2	£5	

CORYELL, LARRY

Larry Coryell caused much comment as the first guitarist in a jazz group to employ feedback, but the offending track, Gary Burton's "General Mojo Cuts Up", is actually a very mild-mannered affair. Ever since, Coryell has languished in the shade of John McLaughlin, who is the real innovator where the use of a highly amplified guitar in jazz is concerned. There is a reasonable sampler of his work - the double "Essential Larry Coryell" on Vanguard. Otherwise, he has made a great many records, of which the scarcer, earlier ones listed here are just the start.

Title	Format	Label	Catalogue	Year	Price	Price	Notes
Barefoot Boy	LP	Philips	6369407	1972	£4	£10	
Coryell	LP	Vanguard	SVRL19059	1969	£5	£12	
Fairyland	LP	Philips	6369411	1972	£4	£10	
Introducing The Eleventh House	LP	Vanguard	VSD79342	1974	£5	£12	quad
Lady Coryell	LP	Vanguard	SVRL19051	1969	£5	£12	
Live At The Village Gate	LP	Vanguard	VSD6573	1971	£4	£10	quad

| Offering | LP | Vanguard | VSD79319 | 1972 | £4 | £10 | quad |
| Spaces | LP | Philips | 6359005 | 1970 | £5 | £12 | with John McLaughlin |

COSBY, BILL

| Little Ole Man | 7" | Warner Bros | WB7072 | 1967 | £2 | £5 | |
| Little Ole Man | 7" | Warner Bros | WB7072 | 1967 | £5 | £10 | PS |

COSMIC DEALER

| Crystallization | LP | Negram | | 1970 | £60 | £120 | |

COSMIC EYE

Cosmic Eye represented an attempt on the part of some of the second division of British jazz musicians - basically John Mayer's Indo-jazz group - to break directly into the progressive rock market.

| Dream Sequence | LP | Regal Zonophone | SLRZ1030 | 1972 | £50 | £100 | |

COSMIC JOKERS

| Cosmic Jokers | LP | Metronome | KM58008 | 1974 | £4 | £10 | German |
| Planet Sit In | LP | Metronome | KM58013 | 1974 | £4 | £10 | German |

COSMIC SOUNDS

"The Zodiac" was the first electronic rock record and featured spoken verses, one for each Zodiacal sign, behind which Paul Beaver put his new synthesizer through its paces.

| Zodiac | LP | Elektra | EKL/EKS74009 | 1967 | £8 | £20 | |

COSMO & DENZIL

Bed Of Roses	7"	Blue Beat	BB145	1962	£5	£10	
Come On Come On	7"	Blue Beat	BB312	1964	£5	£10	
Sweet Rosemarie	7"	Blue Beat	BB296	1964	£5	£10	

COSMO, FRANK

Alone	7"	Black Swan	WI446	1965	£5	£10	
Better Get Right	7"	Island	WI135	1964	£5	£10	
Gypsy Woman	7"	Blue Beat	BB175	1963	£5	£10	
I Love You	7"	R&B	JB119	1963	£5	£10	Don Drummond B side
Merry Christmas	7"	Island	WI100	1963	£5	£10	
Revenge	7"	Island	WI058	1963	£5	£10	

COSTA, DON

| I Walk The Line | 7" | London | HLT8992 | 1959 | £2 | £5 | |
| Love Is A Many Splendoured Thing | 7" | London | HLF8186 | 1955 | £7.50 | £15 | |

COSTA, EDDIE

| Eddie Costa Quintet | 10" LP | Top Rank | 25017 | 1960 | £6 | £15 | |
| Newport Jazz Festival 1957 | LP | Columbia | 33CX10108 | 1958 | £6 | £15 | with Mat Matthews & Don Elliott |

COSTANZO, JACK

| Mr.Bongo | LP | Vogue | VA160150 | 1959 | £8 | £20 | |

COSTELLO, DAY

Despite its early date, the Beatles cover credited to "Day Costello" was long thought to have been attributable to the young Declan McManus. It is not, but the guess was not so very wide of the mark, as the name actually hides the identity of Elvis Costello's father, the former singer with the Joe Loss Orchestra, Ross McManus.

| Long And Winding Road | 7" | Spark | SRL1042 | 1970 | £2.50 | £6 | |

COSTELLO, ELVIS

Two of Elvis Costello's limited edition releases are vital additions to any collection of his work. "A Conversation With Elvis Costello" spreads the contents of his "Imperial Bedroom" LP over two records, adding a substantial amount of interview material in which Costello explains the genesis of each of the songs, prior to each one being heard. (The promo version of "Almost Blue" gives the same treatment to that album, but the interview segments are much shorter and much less interesting). "Live At The El Mocambo", meanwhile, contains a brilliant live reworking of some of the songs from Costello's first two LPs. Most copies that appear on the market are actually counterfeits, although this has little effect on their value. (As usual, the counterfeits are readily identified by their hand-written matrix numbers). The US issue of "Alison" is included because the addition of a string synthesiser part to the music makes the song significantly different to the UK version. The original pressing of the "Armed Forces" LP, complete with its opening-out cover and its EP record and postcard inserts, is nothing like as rare as some people seem to imagine. The record just scrapes into this list, but the package was not a limited edition.

Alison	7"	Columbia	310641	1977	£2.50	£6	US
Alison	7"	Stiff	BUY14	1977	£7.50	£15	white vinyl A side
Armed Forces	LP	CBS	JC35709	1979	£4	£10	Canadian, yellow vinyl
Armed Forces	LP	Radar	RAD15	1979	£4	£10	with EP (SAM90) and postcards
Big Sister	7"	F-Beat		1982	£4	£8	1 sided promo
Blood And Chocolate	cass	Demon	XFIENDCASS80	1986	£5	£12	'chocolate bar' package
Conversation With Elvis Costello	LP	F-Beat	ECCHAT2	1982	£25	£50	double promo
Don't Let Me Be Misunderstood (Live)	12"	Columbia	CAS2310	1986	£6	£15	US promo
Excerpts from Almost Blue	7"	F-Beat	EC1	1981	£12.50	£25	promo
Excerpts from Trust	12"	F-Beat	EL2	1981	£17.50	£35	promo
Get Happy	7"	F-Beat	XXPROMO1	1980	£20	£40	double 12' promo
Good Year For The Roses	7"	F-Beat	XX17	1981	£7.50	£15	PS
Highlights From Blood And Chocolate	7"	Imp	CHOC1	1986	£4	£8	red vinyl promo
I Can't Stand Up For Falling Down	7"	2-Tone	CHSTT7	1980	£4	£8	matrix no. XX1
I Can't Stand Up For Falling Down	7"	2-Tone	CHSTT7	1980	£7.50	£15	paper label
I Wanna Be Loved (Radio Version)	7"	F-Beat	XX35DJ	1984	£4	£8	promo
I Wanna Be Loved (Radio Version)	12"	F-Beat	XX35Z	1984	£5	£12	promo
Imperial Bedroom	LP	Columbia	HC48157	1982	£6	£15	US audiophile
Introduces The Tracks From Almost Blue	LP	F-Beat	ECCHAT1	1981	£25	£50	promo

Live At Hollywood High	12"	Columbia	AS529	1979	£6	£15	US promo
Live At The El Mocambo	LP	Columbia	CDN10	1978	£25	£50	Canadian promo
My Aim Is True/This Year's Model	LP	Columbia	no number	1978	£75	£150	US promo pic disc, pictured in Guide
New Amsterdam	7"	F-Beat	XX5P	1980	£4	£8	pic disc, black rim
New Amsterdam	7"	F-Beat	XX5P	1980	£2	£5	pic disc, white rim
Party Party	7"	A&M	PARTY5	1982	£1.50	£4	promo, Bananarama B-side
Punch The Clock	7"	F-Beat		1983	£12.50	£25	2 x 7" in plastic wallet, promo
Radio Radio	12"	Columbia	AS443	1978	£6	£15	US promo, orange vinyl, with other artists
Radio Radio	12"	Radar	ADA24	1978	£6	£15	promo
Red Shoes	7"	Stiff	BUY15	1977	£1.50	£4	Max Wall mispressed B side
Stiff Singles Four Pack	7"	Stiff	GRAB3	1980	£7.50	£15	
Sweet Dreams	7"	F-Beat	XX19	1981	£1.50	£4	mispressed with 2 A sides
Taking Liberties	LP	Columbia	JC36939	1980	£5	£12	US
Taking Liberties	12"	Columbia	AS847	1980	£6	£15	US promo, Costello label
Talking In The Dark	7"	Radar	RG1	1978	£4	£8	
Ten Bloody Marys And Ten How's Your Fathers	cass	F-Beat	XXC6	1980	£4	£10	gold cassette & case
This Year's Model	LP	Radar	RAD3	1978	£4	£10	with 7' (SAM83)
Tom Snyder Interview	12"	Columbia	AS958	1980	£6	£15	US promo

COTTON, BILLY

Friends And Neighbours	7"	Decca	F10299	1954	£1.50	£4	chart single
This Ole House	7"	Decca	F10377	1954	£1.50	£4	

COTTON, JAMES BLUES BAND

Cotton In Your Ears	LP	Verve	FTS3060	1969	£5	£12	US
Cut You Loose	LP	Vanguard	SVRL19035	1968	£5	£12	US
James Cotton Blues Band	LP	Verve	FT(S)3023	1967	£5	£12	US
Pure Cotton	LP	Verve	FTS3038	1968	£5	£12	US
Taking Care Of Business	LP	Capitol	SM814	1970	£5	£12	US

COTTON, JIMMY

Chris Barber Presents Jimmy Cotton	7" EP	Columbia	SEG8141	1962	£4	£8	
Chris Barber Presents Jimmy Cotton No.2	7" EP	Columbia	SEG8189	1962	£4	£8	

COTTON, MIKE JAZZMEN

Ain't Misbehavin'	7"	Columbia	DB4779	1962	£1.50	£4	
Cobbler's Song	7"	Columbia	DB4821	1962	£1.50	£4	
Cotton Picking	7" EP	Columbia	SEG8144	1962	£2	£5	
Senora	7"	Columbia	DB4697	1961	£1.50	£4	
Swing That Hammer	7"	Columbia	DB7029	1963	£4	£8	chart single
Wild And The Willing	7" EP	Columbia	SEG8190	1962	£2	£5	
Zulu Warrior	7"	Columbia	DB4910	1962	£1.50	£4	

COTTON, MIKE SOUND

Harlem Shuffle	7"	Polydor	56096	1966	£7.50	£15	
I Don't Wanna Know	7"	Columbia	DB7267	1964	£10	£20	
Make Up Your Mind	7"	Columbia	DB7623	1965	£7.50	£15	
Make Up Your Mind	7" EP	Festival	452433	1965	£20	£40	French
Midnight Flyer	7"	Columbia	DB7134	1963	£4	£8	
Mike Cotton Sound	LP	Columbia	33SX1647	1964	£180	£300	
Round And Round	7"	Columbia	DB7382	1964	£15	£30	

COUGARS

Caviare And Chips	7"	Parlophone	R5115	1964	£2.50	£6	
Red Square	7"	Parlophone	R5038	1963	£2	£5	
Saturday Night At The Duckpond	7"	Parlophone	R4989	1963	£2	£5	chart single
Saturday Night With The Cougars	7" EP	Parlophone	GEP8886	1963	£10	£20	

COUGHLAN, CATHAL

I'm Long Me Measaim	7"	Caff	CAFF1	198-	£2.50	£6	flexi, East Village B side

COULDRY, DENIS & SMILE

James In The Basement	7"	Decca	F12734	1968	£1.50	£4	
Penny For The Wind	7"	Decca	F12786	1968	£1.50	£4	

COUNCE, CURTIS

Carl's Blues	LP	Contemporary	LAC12263	1961	£8	£20	
Curtis Counce Group	LP	Contemporary	LAC12073	1958	£8	£20	
You Get More Bounce With Curtis Counce	LP	Contemporary	LAC12133	1959	£8	£20	

COUNT DOWN & THE ZEROS

Hello My Angel	7"	Ember	EMBS189	1964	£10	£20	

COUNT FIVE

Psychotic Reaction	LP	Double Shot	DSM1001/ DSS5001	1966	£15	£30	US
Psychotic Reaction	7"	Pye	7N25393	1966	£7.50	£15	
Psychotic Reaction	7" EP	DiscAZ	1058	1966	£15	£30	French

COUNT LASHER

Calabash	7"	Kalypso	106AB	196-	£2	£5	
Calypso Cha Cha Cha	7"	Kalypso	100AB	196-	£2	£5	
Slide Mongoose	7"	Kalypso	105AB	196-	£2	£5	

COUNT OSSIE

Grounation	LP	Ashanti	NTI301	1973	£10	£25	triple
Nyiah Bongo	7"	Doctor Bird	DB1086	1967	£5	£10	
Pure Soul	7"	Doctor Bird	DB1113	1967	£5	£10	Patsy Todd B side
Turn Me On	7"	Doctor Bird	DB1018	1966	£5	£10	

COUNT STICKY

Chico Chico	7"	Kalypso	XX18	1960	£2.50	£6

COUNT VICTORS

Peeping And Hiding	7"	Coral	Q72456	1962	£1.50	£4
Road Runner	7"	Coral	Q72462	1963	£2	£5

COUNT ZEBRA

Bedbug	7"	Kalypso	XX23	196-	£2.50	£6

COUNTRY BOY

I'm A Lonely Boy	7"	Blue Beat	BB236	1963	£5	£10

COUNTRY GENTLEMEN

Greensleeves	7"	Decca	F11766	1963	£10	£20

COUNTRY HAMS

Walking In The Park With Eloise	7"	EMI	EMI2220	1974	£12.50	£25	red & brown label
Walking In The Park With Eloise	7"	EMI	EMI2220	1982	£2	£5	straw label

COUNTRY JOE & THE FISH

Best Of Country Foe And The Fish	LP	Vanguard	SVRL19058	1969	£4	£10	
C.J.Fish	LP	Vanguard	6369002	1970	£4	£10	
Country Joe And The Fish	7" EP.	Rag Baby	1002	1965	£15	£30	US
Electric Music For The Mind & Body	LP	Fontana	(S)TFL6081	1967	£8	£20	
Electric Music For The Mind & Body	LP	Vanguard	SVRL19026	1967	£6	£15	
Electric Music For The Mind And Body	LP	Vanguard	VSD79244	1972	£4	£10	
Here I Go Again	7"	Vanguard	VA3	1969	£4	£8	
Here We Are Again	LP	Vanguard	SVRL19048	1969	£6	£15	
I Feel Like I'm Fixin' To Die	LP	Vanguard	VSD79266	1971	£4	£10	
I Feel Like I'm Fixin' To Die	7"	Vanguard	6076250	1970	£4	£8	
I Feel Like I'm Fixing To Die	LP	Fontana	(S)TFL6087	1967	£8	£20	
I Feel Like I'm Fixing To Die	LP	Vanguard	SVRL19029	1967	£6	£15	
Life And Times Of Country Joe And The Fish	LP	Vanguard	VSD27/28	1973	£8	£20	double
Life And Times Of Country Joe And The Fish	LP	Vanguard	VSQ40004/5	1973	£10	£25	quad, double
Not So Sweet Martha Lorraine	7"	Fontana	TF882	1967	£5	£10	
Talking Issue	7" EP.	Rag Baby	1001	1965	£15	£30	US
Together	LP	Vanguard	SVRL19006	1968	£6	£15	

COUNTRY LANE

Substratum	LP	Splendid		1973	£100	£200	

COUNTY, WAYNE & THE ELECTRIC CHAIRS

Storm The Gates Of Heaven	LP	Safari	GOOD1	1978	£4	£10	multi-coloured vinyl

COURIERS

Take Away	7"	Ember	EMBS218	1966	£10	£20	
Take Away	7"	Ember	EMBS218	1966	£15	£30	PS

COURTENAY, TOM

Mrs.Brown You've Got A Lovely Daughter	7"	Decca	F11729	1963	£1.50	£4

COURTNEY, DEAN

I'll Always Need You	7"	RCA	RCA2534	1975	£1.50	£4

COURTNEY, PETER

Docteur David's Private Papers	7" EP.	Fontana	469210	1967	£4	£8	French

COUSIN EMMY & HER KINFOLK

Kentucky Mountain Ballads Vol.1	7" EP.	Brunswick	OE9258	1956	£4	£8
Kentucky Mountain Ballads Vol.2	7" EP.	Brunswick	OE9259	1956	£4	£8

COUSINS

Anda	7"	Palette	PG9035	1962	£1.50	£4
Buddah	7"	Palette	KG9017	1961	£1.50	£4
Kili Watch	7"	Palette	KG9011	1961	£1.50	£4

COUSINS (2)

Yes Sir That's My Baby	7"	Decca	F11924	1964	£1.50	£4

COUSINS, DAVE

Old School Songs	LP	Slurp	1.	1980	£6	£15
Two Weeks Last Summer	LP	A&M	AMLS68118	1972	£10	£25

COVAY, DON

Different Strokes	LP	Janus	3038	1970	£5	£12	US
Everything I Do Goin' Be Funky	7"	Atlantic	2091018	1970	£1.50	£4	

Forty Days - Forty Nights	7"	Atlantic	584114	1967	£1.50	£4	
House Of Blue Light	LP	Atlantic	K50225	1969	£6	£15	
Mercy	LP	Atlantic	ATL5025	1965	£20	£40	
Mercy Mercy	7"	Atlantic	584094	1967	£1.50	£4	
Mercy Mercy	7"	Atlantic	AT4006	1964	£2.50	£6	
Pony Time	7"	Pye	7N25075	1961	£2.50	£6	
Popeye Waddle	7"	Cameo Parkway	C239	1962	£7.50	£15	
See Saw	7"	Atlantic	2091104	1971	£1.50	£4	
See Saw	7"	Atlantic	584059	1966	£1.50	£4	
See Saw	7"	Atlantic	AT4056	1965	£2.50	£6	
See-Saw	LP	Atlantic	587062	1967	£6	£15	
Shake Wid The Shake	7"	Philips	PB1140	1961	£4	£8	
Shing-A-Ling '67	7"	Atlantic	584082	1967	£1.50	£4	
Sookie Sookie	7"	Atlantic	AT4078	1966	£2	£5	
Take This Hurt Off Me	7"	Atlantic	AT4016	1965	£2.50	£6	
You Put Something On Me	7"	Atlantic	584025	1966	£1.50	£4	

COVEY, JULIAN & THE MACHINE
Little Bit Hurt	7"	Island	WIP6009	1967	£6	£12	

COVINGTON, JULIE
Beautiful Changes	LP	Columbia	SCX6466	1971	£40	£80	
Magic Wasn't There	7"	Columbia	DB8649	1970	£4	£8	
Tonight Your Love Is Over	7"	Columbia	DB8705	1970	£4	£8	

COWSILLS
Captain Sad And His Ship Of Fools	LP	MGM	CS8095	1968	£4	£10	
Cowsills	LP	MGM	C(S)8059	1967	£4	£10	
Cowsills And The Lincoln Park Zoo	LP	Fontana	SFL13055	1968	£4	£10	
Hair	7"	MGM	MGM1469	1969	£1.50	£4	
In Concert	LP	MGM	SE4619	1969	£4	£10	US
In Need Of A Friend	7"	MGM	MGM1400	1968	£1.50	£4	
Love American Style	7"	MGM	MGM1490	1969	£1.50	£4	
Newspaper Blanket	7"	MGM	MGM1424	1968	£1.50	£4	
On My Side	LP	London	SHU8421	1971	£4	£10	
Prophecy Of Daniel & John Devine	7"	MGM	MGM1484	1969	£2	£5	
Rain, The Park And Other Things	7"	MGM	MGM1353	1967	£2	£5	
Two By Two	LP	MGM	SE4639	1970	£4	£10	US
We Can Fly	LP	MGM	CS8077	1968	£4	£10	
We Can Fly	7"	MGM	MGM1383	1968	£1.50	£4	

COX, BILLY
Immediately after the death of his employer, Jimi Hendrix, bassist Billy Cox recorded what amounts to a tribute LP before effectively vanishing from the music scene. For "Nitrofunction", he recruited a rather fine lady guitarist, who manages to convey the spirit of Jimi Hendrix rather better than most, although she too subsequently disappeared. The record cover, incidentally, is a creation by the same man who was responsible for the series of distinctive Yes sleeves - Roger Dean.
Nitro Function	LP	Pye	NSPL28158	1971	£10	£25	

COX, HARRY
Sings English Love Songs	LP	DTS	LFX4	1965	£10	£25	

COX, IDA
Blues For Rampart Street	LP	Riverside	RLP374	196-	£6	£15	
Ida Cox	7" EP	Fontana	TFE17136	1959	£5	£10	
Ida Cox Vol.1	LP	Fountain	FB301	1974	£5	£12	
Ida Cox Vol.2	LP	Fountain	FB304	1975	£5	£12	
Sings The Blues	10" LP	London	AL3517	1954	£8	£20	

COX, IDA & ETHEL WATERS
Ida Cox And Ethel Waters	LP	Poydras	104	195-	£10	£25	

COX, IDA & MA RAINEY
Female Blues Vol.1	7" EP	Collector	JEL12	1960	£5	£10	

COX, KENNY
Introducing	LP	Blue Note	BST84302	1968	£5	£12	
Multidirection	LP	Blue Note	BST84339	1969	£5	£12	

COX, MICHAEL
Along Came Caroline	7"	HMV	POP789	1960	£4	£8	chart single
Angela Jones	7"	Ember	EMBS103	1960	£6	£12	
Angela Jones	7"	Triumph	RGM1011	1960	£5	£10	chart single
Boy Meets Girl	7"	Decca	F11166	1959	£2.50	£6	
Don't You Break My Heart	7"	HMV	POP1137	1963	£4	£8	
Gee What A Party	7"	HMV	POP1220	1963	£4	£8	
Gypsy	7"	HMV	POP1417	1965	£4	£8	
I Hate Getting Up In The Morning	7"	Parlophone	R5436	1966	£1.50	£4	
I'll Always Love You	7"	Parlophone	R5580	1967	£1.50	£4	
Rave On	7"	HMV	POP1293	1964	£5	£10	
Stand Up	7"	HMV	POP1065	1962	£4	£8	
Sweet Little Sixteen	7"	HMV	POP905	1961	£4	£8	
Teenage Love	7"	HMV	POP830	1961	£4	£8	
Too Hot To Handle	7"	Decca	F11182	1959	£2.50	£6	
Young Only Once	7"	HMV	POP972	1962	£4	£8	

COX, WALLY
I Can't Help It	7"	Vogue	V9175	1961	£5	£10	

COXHILL, LOL

Lol Coxhill is as great an eccentric as he is a saxophone player - and his work on that instrument is very fine indeed! The Dandelion double album "Ear Of The Beholder" is the ideal introduction to both the man and the musician. It contains free group improvisation; recordings of Coxhill busking on the streets of London (he is supposed to be the inspiration behind Joni Mitchell's "For Free", although he was apparently mildly insulted by this); Victorian music-hall songs interpreted by the Coxhill-Bedford duo; and a group of school children singing "I Am The Walrus". The later "Murder In The Air" consists of a radio play with all the parts interpreted by a saxophone!

Digwell Duets	LP	Random Radar	RRR005	1979	£4	£10	
Diverse	LP	Ogun	OG510	1976	£4	£10	
Ear Of The Beholder	LP	Dandelion	69001	1971	£20	£40	double
Fleas In The Custard	LP	Caroline	C1515	1975	£6	£15	
Joy Of Paranoia	LP	Ogun	OG525	1978	£4	£10	
Lid	LP	Ictus	0011	1978	£4	£10	
Lol Coxhill & Welfare State	LP	Caroline	C1514	1975	£6	£15	
Moot	LP	Ictus	0008	1978	£4	£10	
Murder In The Air	12"	Chiltern Sound	CS100	1978	£4	£10	
Slow Music	LP	Pipe	PIPE1	1980	£4	£10	
Story So Far	LP	Caroline	C1507	1974	£6	£15	
Toverbal Sweet	LP	Mushroom	150MR23	1972	£40	£80	

COXHILL, LOL & DAVID BEDFORD

Pretty Little Girl	7"	Polydor	2001253	1971	£2	£5	

COXHILL, LOL & STEPHEN MILLER

Coxhill Miller	LP	Caroline	C1503	1973	£6	£15	

COXSONE, LLOYD

Cruising	7"	Pyramid	PYR7003	1973	£1.50	£4	

COYNE, KEVIN

Blame It On The Night	LP	Virgin	V2012	1974	£6	£15	
Case History	LP	Dandelion	2310228	1972	£20	£40	
Cheat Me	7"	Polydor	2001357	1972	£1.50	£4	
Heartburn	LP	Virgin	V2047	1976	£5	£12	
In Living Black And White	LP	Virgin	VD2505	1976	£6	£15	double
Marjory Razorblade	LP	Virgin	VD2501	1973	£6	£15	double
Matching Head And Feet	LP	Virgin	V2033	1975	£6	£15	

CRACKERS

Honey Do	7"	Fontana	TF995	1969	£2	£5	

CRADDOCK, BILLY 'CRASH'

Boom Boom Baby	7"	Philips	PB966	1959	£6	£12	
Goodtime Billy	7"	Philips	PB1092	1961	£5	£10	
I'm Tore Up	LP	King	912	1964	£10	£25	US
Since She Turned Seventeen	7"	Philips	PB1006	1960	£7.50	£15	
Truly True	7"	Mercury	AMT1146	1961	£4	£8	

CRAIG

Ain't That A Shame	7"	King	KG1022	1965	£5	£10	
I Must Be Mad	7"	Fontana	TF715	1966	£50	£100	
Little Bit Of Soap	7"	Fontana	TF665	1966	£15	£30	

CRAMER, FLOYD

Chattanooga Choo Choo	7"	RCA	RCA1275	1962	£1.50	£4	
Fancy Pants	7"	London	HL8012	1954	£10	£20	
Flip Flop And Bop	7"	RCA	RCA1050	1958	£7.50	£15	
Hang On	7"	RCA	RCA1259	1961	£1.50	£4	
Hot Pepper	7"	RCA	RCA1301	1962	£1.50	£4	
Java	7"	RCA	RCA1325	1962	£1.50	£4	
Jolly Cholly	7"	London	HL8062	1954	£10	£20	
Last Date	7"	RCA	RCA1211	1960	£1.50	£4	
Lovesick Blues	7"	RCA	RCA1284	1962	£1.50	£4	
On The Rebound	LP	RCA	RD27221/SF5103	1961	£4	£10	
On The Rebound	7"	RCA	RCA1231	1961	£1.50	£4	chart single
Piano Hayride	7" EP	London	REP1023	1955	£12.50	£25	
Rag A Tag	7"	London	HLU8195	1955	£10	£20	
San Antonio Rose	7"	RCA	RCA1241	1961	£1.50	£4	chart single
Swing Low	7"	RCA	RCA1311	1962	£1.50	£4	
That Handsome Piano	7" EP	RCA	RCX7120	1963	£5	£10	

CRAMPS

Crusher	12"	IRS	PFSX1008	1981	£4	£10	
Drug Train	7"	Illegal	ILS021	1980	£4	£8	
Fever	7"	Illegal	ILS017	1980	£2.50	£6	band PS
Garbageman/Mystery Plane	7"	Illegal	ILS017	1980	£6	£12	demo
Goo Goo Muck	7"	IRS	PFS1003	1981	£2.50	£6	yellow vinyl
Gravest Hits	12"	Illegal	ILS12013	1979	£2.50	£6	
Gravest Hits	12"	Illegal	ILS12013	1979	£4	£10	blue vinyl
Human Fly	7"	Vengeance	668	1978	£10	£20	US, PS
Off The Bone	LP	Illegal	ILP012	1983	£4	£10	pic disc
Smell Of Female	LP	Big Beat	BEDP6	1984	£4	£10	pic disc
Songs The Lord Taught Us	LP	Illegal	ILP005	1980	£30	£60	test pressing with 'Drug Train'
Way I Walk	7"	Vengeance	666	1978	£10	£20	US, PS

CRANE, DON & THE NEW DOWNLINERS SECT

I Can't Get Away From You	7"	Pye	7N17261	1967	£30	£60	

CRANE RIVER JAZZ BAND

Crane River Jazz Band	7" EP	Parlophone	GEP8652	1957	£2	£5	
Lily Of The Valley	7"	Parlophone	MSP6008	1953	£1.50	£4	

CRANE, VINCENT & CHRIS FARLOWE
Can't Find A Reason .... 7" ...... Dawn .... DNS1034.............. 1972 ... £2.50 ....£6 ....

CRANES
Fuse .... cass ... Biteback.......... .... 1987 ... £8 ....£20 ....

CRASHERS
Off Track .... 7" ...... Amalgamated . AMG834 .... 1969 ... £4 ....£8 ....

CRASS
Feeding Of The Five Thousand .... 12" ..... Small Wonder . WEENY2 .... 1978 ... £2.50 ....£6 ....

CRAVINKEL
Cravinkel .... LP ..... Philips............ 6305055.............. 1970 ... £6 ....£15 .... German
Garden Of Loneliness .... LP ..... Philips............ 6305124.............. 1971 ... £5 ....£12 .... German

CRAWFORD BROTHERS
I Ain't Guilty .... 7" ...... Vogue .... V9140 .... 1959 ... £30 ....£60 ....
Midnight Mover Groover .... 7" ...... Vogue .... V9077 .... 1957 ... £30 ....£60 ....

CRAWFORD, CAROLYN
When Someone's Good To You .... 7" ...... Stateside ...... SS384 .... 1965 ... £40 ....£80 ....

CRAWFORD, GLORIA
Sad Movies .... 7" ...... Doctor Bird ..... DB1057 .... 1966 ... £5 ....£10 .Lester Sterling B side

CRAWFORD, JIMMY
Another Of Your Toys .... 7" ...... Columbia ...... DB4975.............. 1963 ... £1.50 ....£4 ....
Don't Worry About Bobby .... 7" ...... Columbia ...... DB7175.............. 1963 ... £1.50 ....£4 ....
I Love How You Love Me .... 7" ...... Columbia ...... DB4717.............. 1961 ... £1.50 ....£4 .... chart single
I Shoulda Listened To Mama .... 7" ...... Columbia ...... DB4841.............. 1962 ... £1.50 ....£4 ....
Long Stringy Baby .... 7" ...... Columbia ...... DB4525.............. 1960 ... £7.50 ....£15 ....
Love Or Money .... 7" ...... Columbia ...... DB4633.............. 1961 ... £1.50 ....£4 .... chart single
There'll Be No Goodbyes .... 7" ...... Columbia ...... DB4895.............. 1962 ... £1.50 ....£4 ....

CRAWFORD, JOHNNY
Captivating Johnny Crawford .... LP .... Del-Fi .... LP1220 .... 1962 ... £8 ....£20 .... US
Cindy's Birthday .... 7" ...... Pye .... 7N25145 .... 1962 ... £1.50 ....£4 ....
Greatest Hits .... LP .... Del-Fi .... LP/ST1229 .... 1963 ... £6 ....£15 .... US
Greatest Hits Vol.2 .... LP .... Del-Fi .... LP/ST1248 .... 1964 ... £6 ....£15 .... US
His Greatest Hits .... LP .... London .... HA8197 .... 1964 ... £6 ....£15 ....
Johnny Crawford .... 7" EP. London .... RE1343 .... 1962 ... £6 ....£12 ....
Judy Loves Me .... 7" ...... London .... HL9836 .... 1964 ... £1.50 ....£4 ....
Proud .... 7" ...... London .... HL9669 .... 1963 ... £1.50 ....£4 ....
Rumors .... LP .... London .... HA8060 .... 1963 ... £6 ....£15 ....
Rumors .... 7" ...... London .... HL9638 .... 1962 ... £1.50 ....£4 ....
When I Fall In Love .... 7" EP. London .... RE1416 .... 1964 ... £5 ....£10 ....
Young Man's Fancy .... LP .... Del-Fi .... LP/ST1223 .... 1963 ... £6 ....£15 .... US
Your Nose Is Gonna Grow .... 7" ...... London .... HL9605 .... 1962 ... £1.50 ....£4 ....

CRAWFORD, MICHAEL
It's Gonna Take A Little Time .... 7" ...... United Artists .. UP1127 .... 1966 ... £1.50 ....£4 ....
Knack .... 7" ...... United Artists .. UP1095 .... 1965 ... £1.50 ....£4 ....

CRAWLER
Crawler .... LP ..... Epic .... PAL34900 .... 1978 ... £4 ....£10 ....US pic disc

CRAYTON, PEE WEE
Pee Wee Crayton .... LP ..... Crown .... CLP5175 .... 1959 ... £10 ....£25 .... US

CRAZY ELEPHANT
Crazy Elephant .... LP ..... Major Minor .... SMLP62 .... 1969 ... £5 ....£12 ....
Gimme Gimme Good Lovin' .... 7" ...... Major Minor .... MM609 .... 1969 ... £1.50 ....£4 .... chart single
Space Buggy .... 7" ...... Major Minor .... MM672 .... 1970 ... £1.50 ....£4 ....
Sunshine Red Wine .... 7" ...... Major Minor .... MM623 .... 1969 ... £1.50 ....£4 ....

CRAZY FEELINGS
Please Lie .... 7" ...... Polydor .... 56723 .... 1967 ... £1.50 ....£4 ....

CRAZY ROCKERS
Third Man Theme .... 7" ...... King .... KG1001 .... 1964 ... £1.50 ....£4 ....

CREAM
Cream are not highly regarded by those who feel that improvisation has no place in rock music, but on a good night the interplay between the three virtuoso musicians, each trying to outplay the others, was thrilling. Of course this approach does not always work, but when it does, the risks are entirely justified. "Crossroads" is an electric blues masterpiece, while the long modal improvisation on 'Spoonful' (also included on "Wheels Of Fire") is as inspirational as the lengthy drum solo on "Toad" is tedious. The other side of Cream was their ability to create intelligent pop music with an attractive blues edge - "Disraeli Gears" was quite rightly hailed as one of the most impressive recordings of 1967 - in a year when the competition was extremely stiff.
Anyone For Tennis .... 7" ...... Polydor .... 56258 .... 1968 ... £2 ....£5 .... chart single
Badge .... 7" ...... Polydor .... 56315 .... 1969 ... £1.50 ....£4 .... chart single
Disraeli Gears .... LP ..... Reaction .... 593003 .... 1967 ... £6 ....£15 .... mono, chart LP
Disraeli Gears .... LP ..... Reaction .... 594003 .... 1967 ... £5 ....£12 ... stereo, chart LP
Fresh Cream .... LP ..... Reaction .... 593001 .... 1966 ... £6 ....£15 .... mono, chart LP
Fresh Cream .... LP ..... Reaction .... 594001 .... 1966 ... £5 ....£12 ... stereo, chart LP
Goodbye .... LP ..... Polydor .... 583053 .... 1969 ... £4 ....£10 .... chart LP
I Feel Free .... 7" ...... Reaction .... 591011 .... 1966 ... £1.50 ....£4 .... chart single
I Feel Free .... 7" EP. Polydor .... 27798 .... 1966 ... £12.50 ....£25 .... French
On Top .... LP ..... Polydor .... 2855002 .... 1969 ... £6 ....£15 ....
Strange Brew .... 7" ...... Reaction .... 591015 .... 1967 ... £1.50 ....£4 .... chart single
Strange Brew .... 7" EP. Polydor .... 27810 .... 1967 ... £12.50 ....£25 .... French

Title	Format	Label	Cat No	Year	Price1	Price2	Notes
Sunshine Of Your Love	7"	Polydor	56286	1968	£1.50	£4	chart single
Wheels Of Fire	LP	Mobile Fidelity	MFSL2066	1982	£8	£20	US audiophile
Wheels Of Fire	LP	Polydor	582031/2	1968	£8	£20	double, mono, chart LP
Wheels Of Fire	LP	Polydor	583031/2	1968	£6	£15	double, stereo, chart LP
Wheels Of Fire In The Studio	LP	Polydor	582033	1968	£5	£12	mono, chart LP
Wheels Of Fire In The Studio	LP	Polydor	583033	1968	£4	£10	stereo, chart LP
Wheels Of Fire Live At Fillmore	LP	Polydor	582040	1968	£5	£12	mono
Wheels Of Fire Live At Fillmore	LP	Polydor	583040	1968	£4	£10	stereo
White Room	7"	Polydor	56300	1968	£1.50	£4	chart single
Wrapping Paper	7"	Reaction	591007	1966	£2	£5	chart single
Wrapping Paper	7" EP	Polydor	27791	1966	£12.50	£25	French

CREAMERS
| Sunday Head | 7" | Fierce | FRIGHT045 | 1989 | £2.50 | £6 | |

CREARY SISTERS
| Oh What A Glory | 7" | High Note | HS020 | 1969 | £2.50 | £6 | |

CREATION
The Creation have aquired the status of one of the great groups of the sixties, with guitarist Eddie Phillips being a pioneer in the use of feedback and violin bow techniques. The group failed to find much success, however, and in all honesty they are not well served by their records, which are much less impressive than those of their rivals, the Who.

1966-67	LP	Charisma	CS8	1973	£10	£25	
Best Of The Creation	LP	Pop Schallplaten	ZS10168	1968	£25	£50	German
How Does It Feel To Feel	7"	Polydor	56230	1968	£7.50	£15	
If I Stay Too Long	7"	Polydor	56177	1967	£7.50	£15	
Making Time	7"	Charisma	CB213	1973	£2	£5	
Making Time	7"	Planet	PLF116	1966	£7.50	£15	chart single
Making Time	7"	Raw	RAW4	1977	£1.50	£4	
Making Time	7" EP	Vogue	INT18098	1966	£150	£250	French
Midway Down	7"	Polydor	56246	1968	£7.50	£15	
Painter Man	7"	Polydor	56207	1967	£10	£20	
Through My Eyes	7"	Planet	PLF119	1966	£7.50	£15	chart single
Tom Tom	7" EP	Vogue	INT18144	1967	£150	£250	French
We Are The Paintermen	LP	Hitton	340037	1967	£50	£100	German
We Are The Paintermen	LP	Sonet	SLPS1251	1967	£50	£100	Danish

CREATION (2)
| I Got The Fever | 7" | Stateside | SS2205 | 1972 | £4 | £8 | |

CREATION OF SUNLIGHT
| Creation Of Sunlight | LP | Windi | 1001 | 1969 | £30 | £60 | US |

CREATIONS
| Get On Up | 7" | Amalgamated | AMG818 | 1968 | £4 | £8 | |
| Meet Me At Eight | 7" | Rio | R133 | 1967 | £4 | £8 | |

CREATIVE ROCK
| Gorilla | LP | Brain | 0001017 | 1973 | £5 | £12 | German |
| Lady Pig | LP | Brain | 0001061 | 1974 | £5 | £12 | German |

CREATURES
| Wild Things | 7" | Polydor | POSPD354 | 1981 | £2 | £5 | double, single PS |
| Wild Things | 7" | Polydor | POSPG354 | 1981 | £2 | £5 | double, gatefold PS |

CREATURES (2)
Looking At Tomorrow	7"	CBS	2666	1967	£1.50	£4	
String Along	7"	CBS	202350	1966	£1.50	£4	
Turn Out The Light	7"	CBS	202048	1966	£1.50	£4	

CREEDENCE CLEARWATER REVIVAL
Bad Moon Rising	7"	Liberty	LBF15230	1969	£1.50	£4	chart single
Bayou Country	LP	Liberty	LBS83261	1969	£4	£10	chart LP
Cosmo's Factory	LP	Liberty	LBS83388	1970	£4	£10	chart LP
Cosmo's Factory	LP	Mobile Fidelity	MFSL1037	1979	£6	£15	US audiophile
Creedence Clearwater Revival	LP	Liberty	LBS83259	1969	£4	£10	
Down On The Corner	7"	Liberty	LBF15283	1970	£1.50	£4	chart single
Green River	LP	Liberty	LBS83273	1969	£4	£10	chart LP
Green River	7"	Liberty	LBF15250	1969	£1.50	£4	chart single
Have You Ever Seen The Rain	7"	Liberty	LBF15440	1971	£1.50	£4	chart single
Hey Tonight	7"	United Artists	UP35210	1971	£1.50	£4	
Long As I Can See The Light	7"	Liberty	LBF15384	1970	£1.50	£4	chart single
Long As I Can See The Light	7"	Liberty	LBF15384	1970	£2.50	£6	PS
Mardi Gras	LP	Fantasy	FAN9404	1972	£4	£10	
Pendulum	LP	Liberty	LBS83400	1971	£4	£10	chart LP
Porterville	7"	Scorpio	412	1967	£12.50	£25	US
Proud Mary	7"	Liberty	LBF15223	1969	£1.50	£4	chart single
Proud Mary/I Put A Spell On You	7"	Liberty	LBF15223	1969	£7.50	£15	
Sweet Hitch-Hiker	7"	United Artists	UP35261	1971	£1.50	£4	chart single
Travellin' Band	7"	Liberty	LBF15310	1970	£1.50	£4	chart single
Up Around The Bend	7"	Liberty	LBF15354	1970	£1.50	£4	chart single
Up Around The Bend	7"	Liberty	LBF15354	1970	£2.50	£6	PS
Willie & The Poor Boys	LP	Liberty	LBS83338	1970	£4	£10	chart LP

CREME CARAMEL
Crying Eyes	7"	Pye	7N25521	1970	£1.50	£4	
My Idea	7"	Pye	7N25495	1969	£1.50	£4	
Your Heart's Not In Your Love	7"	Pye	7N25529	1970	£1.50	£4	

CREME SODA
Title	Fmt	Label	Cat	Year			Notes
Tricky Zingers	LP	Trinity	CST11	1968	£17.50	£35	US

CRESCENDOS
| Oh Julie | LP | Guest Star | G1453 | 196- | £15 | £30 | US |
| Oh Julie | 7" | London | HLU8563 | 1958 | £25 | £50 | |

CRESCENTS
| Baby Baby Baby | 7" | Columbia | DB4093 | 1958 | £12.50 | £25 | |

CRESCENTS (2)
| Pink Dominoes | 7" | London | HLN9851 | 1964 | £5 | £10 | |

CRESSIDA
| Asylum | LP | Vertigo | 6360025 | 1971 | £40 | £80 | spiral label |
| Cressida | LP | Vertigo | VO7 | 1970 | £25 | £50 | spiral label |

CRESTAS
| I Want To Be Loved | 7" | Fontana | TF551 | 1965 | £10 | £20 | |

CRESTERS
| I Just Don't Understand | 7" | HMV | POP1249 | 1964 | £2 | £5 | |
| Put Your Arms Around Me | 7" | HMV | POP1296 | 1964 | £2 | £5 | |

CRESTS
Angels Listened In	7"	London	HL8954	1959	£12.50	£25	
Best Of The Crests	LP	Coed	LPC/LPS904	1961	£50	£100	US
Crests Sing All The Biggies	LP	Coed	LPC901	1960	£60	£120	US
Flower Of Love	7"	Top Rank	JAR150	1959	£4	£8	
Gee	7"	Top Rank	JAR372	1960	£6	£12	
Guilty	7"	London	HLU9671	1963	£4	£8	
Isn't It Amazing	7"	HMV	POP808	1960	£5	£10	
Little Miracles	7"	HMV	POP976	1962	£5	£10	
Model Girl	7"	HMV	POP848	1961	£5	£10	
Paper Crown	7"	Top Rank	JAR302	1960	£6	£12	
Six Nights A Week	7"	Top Rank	JAR168	1959	£6	£12	
Sixteen Candles	7"	London	HL8794	1959	£12.50	£25	
Trouble in Paradise	7"	HMV	POP768	1960	£6	£12	

CREW
| Cecilia | 7" | Decca | F13000 | 1970 | £1.50 | £4 | |
| Marty | 7" | Plexium | PXM12 | 1969 | £2 | £5 | |

CREWCUTS
Angels In The Sky	7"	Mercury	7MT2	1956	£5	£10	export
Crewcut Capers	LP	Mercury	MG20143	1954	£15	£30	US
Crewcuts	LP	Wing	MGW12177	1959	£8	£20	US
Crewcuts	7" EP	Mercury	MEP9002	1956	£12.50	£25	
Crewcuts Go Longhair	LP	Mercury	MG20067	1954	£15	£30	US
Crewcuts On The Campus	LP	Mercury	MG20140	1954	£15	£30	US
Crewcuts Sing	LP	RCA	LPM/LSP2037	1959	£8	£20	US
Crewcuts Sing Folk	LP	Camay	CA1/CA3002	196-	£8	£20	US
Hey Stella	7"	RCA	RCA1075	1958	£12.50	£25	
High School Favorites	LP	Wing	MGW12180	1959	£8	£20	US
Music A La Carte	LP	Mercury	MG20199	1955	£15	£30	US
On Parade	10" LP	Mercury	MPT7501	1956	£20	£40	
Rock And Roll Bash	LP	Mercury	MG21044	1955	£20	£40	US
Surprise Package	LP	RCA	LPM/LSP1933	1958	£8	£20	US
Susie-Q	78	Mercury	MT161	1957	£2.50	£6	
You Must Have Been A Beautiful Baby	LP	RCA	LPM/LSP2067	1960	£8	£20	US

CREWE, BOB
| Barbarella | LP | Stateside | (S)SL10260 | 1968 | £6 | £15 | |
| Maggie Maggie May | 7" | Stateside | SS356 | 1964 | £1.50 | £4 | |

CRIBBINS, BERNARD
Combination Of Cribbins	LP	Parlophone	PMC1186	1962	£4	£10	
Gossip Calypso	7"	Parlophone	R4961	1962	£1.50	£4	chart single
Hole In The Ground	7"	Parlophone	R4869	1962	£1.50	£4	chart single
Hole In The Ground	7" EP	Parlophone	GEP8859	1962	£2	£5	
Right Said Fred	7"	Parlophone	R4923	1962	£1.50	£4	chart single

CRICKETS
April Avenue	7"	Liberty	LIB55603	1966	£1.50	£4	
Baby My Heart	7"	Coral	Q72395	1960	£1.50	£4	
Collection	LP	Liberty	LBY1258	1965	£6	£15	
Come On	7" EP	Liberty	LEP2173	1964	£5	£10	
Crickets	7" EP	Coral	FEP2053	1960	£10	£20	
Crickets Don't Ever Change	7" EP	Coral	FEP2064	1961	£7.50	£15	
Don't Ever Change	7"	Liberty	LIB55441	1962	£1.50	£4	chart single
Don't Try To Change Me	7"	Liberty	LIB10092	1963	£1.50	£4	chart single
He's Old Enough To Know Better	7"	London	HLG9486	1961	£2.50	£6	
I Fought The Law	7"	Coral	Q72440	1961	£2.50	£6	
I Think I've Got The Blues	7"	Liberty	LIB10174	1964	£1.50	£4	
In Style With	LP	Coral	LVA9142	1959	£10	£25	chart LP
La Bamba	7"	Liberty	LIB55696	1964	£1.50	£4	chart single
Little Hollywood Girl	7"	Liberty	LIB55495	1962	£2.50	£6	
Lonely Avenue	7"	Liberty	LIB10145	1964	£1.50	£4	
Long Way From Lubbock	LP	Mercury	6310007	1974	£4	£10	
Love's Made A Fool Of You	7"	Coral	Q72365	1959	£2.50	£6	chart single
My Little Girl	7"	Liberty	LIB10067	1963	£1.50	£4	chart single

Now Hear This	7"	Liberty	LIB10196	1965	£1.50	£4	
Peggy Sue Got Married	7"	Coral	Q72417	1961	£2.50	£6	
Right Or Wrong	7"	Liberty	LIB10113	1963	£1.50	£4	
Something Old Something New	LP	Liberty	(S)LBY1120	1962	£8	£20	
Straight No Strings	7" EP	Liberty	LEP2094	1963	£6	£12	
Straight No Strings	7" EP	Liberty	SLEP2094	1963	£7.50	£15	stereo
When You Ask About Love	7"	Coral	Q72382	1959	£2.50	£6	chart single

CRIMSON BRIDGE

Crimson Bridge	LP	Myrrh	MST6503	1972	£6	£15	

CRISIS

Alienation	7"	Ardkor	CRI004	1981	£2.50	£6	
Holocaust	12"	Dead Russian		1982	£3	£8	
Hymns Of Faith	12"	Ardkor	CRI003	1980	£3	£8	
No Town Hall (Southwark)	7"	Peckham Action Group	NOTH1	1982	£2.50	£6	
UK '79	7"	Ardkor	CRI002	1979	£2	£5	

CRISPY AMBULANCE

Four Minutes From The Frontline	7"	Aural Assault	AAR001	1976	£2.50	£6	

CRISS, GARY

Hands Off Buddy	7"	Stateside	SS427	1965	£1.50	£4	
Long Lonely Nights	7"	Stateside	SS164	1963	£1.50	£4	
My Little Heavenly Angel	7"	Stateside	SS123	1962	£1.50	£4	
Our Favourite Melodies	7"	Stateside	SS104	1962	£1.50	£4	
Sweet Warm And Soft	7"	Stateside	SS265	1964	£1.50	£4	

CRISS, SONNY

Sonny Criss Plays Cole Porter	LP	London	LTZP15094	1957	£25	£50	

CRISTINA

Is That All There Is	12"	Ze	WIP6560T	1980	£2.50	£6	

CRISTO, BOBBY & THE REBELS

Other Side Of The Track	7"	Decca	F11913	1964	£7.50	£15	

CRISTY, MARY

Thank You For Rushing Into My Life	7"	Polydor	2056513	1976	£2.50	£6	

CRITICS & NYAH SHUFFLE

Behold	7"	Joe	JRS1	197-	£1.50	£4	Sexy Frankie B side

CRITICS GROUP

Merry Progress To London	LP	Argo	(Z)DA46	1966	£10	£25	
Sweet Thames Flow Softly	LP	Argo	(Z)DA47	1966	£10	£25	

CRITTERS

Bad Misunderstanding	7"	London	HLR10101	1966	£2	£5	
Don't Let The Rain Fall Down On Me	7"	London	HLR10149	1967	£1.50	£4	
Heart Of Love, Head Of Stone	7" EP	Kapp	KEV13028	1966	£7.50	£15	French
Marrying Kind Of Love	7"	London	HLR10119	1967	£1.50	£4	
Mr.Dieingly Sad	7"	London	HLR10071	1966	£1.50	£4	
Mr.Dieingly Sad	7" EP	Kapp	KEV13031	1966	£7.50	£15	French
Younger Girl	LP	London	HAR8302	1966	£6	£15	
Younger Girl	7"	London	HLR10047	1966	£2	£5	chart single

CROCE, JIM

Croce (with Ingrid Croce)	LP	Capitol	ST315	1969	£8	£20	US
You Don't Mess Around With Jim	LP	Vertigo	6360700	1971	£5	£12	spiral label

CROCHETED DOUGHNUT RING

Havana Anna	7"	Deram	DM169	1967	£10	£20	
Maxine's Parlour	7"	Deram	DM180	1968	£7.50	£15	
Two Little Ladies	7"	Polydor	56204	1967	£10	£20	

CROMBIE, TONY

Atmosphere	LP	Columbia	33SX1119	1958	£6	£15	
Atmosphere	7" EP	Columbia	ESG7753	1959	£2.50	£6	
Atmosphere	7" EP	Columbia	SEG7918	1959	£2	£5	
Brighton Rock	7"	Columbia	DB3921	1957	£7.50	£15	
Drums! Drums! Drums!	LP	Top Rank	BUY027	1960	£6	£15	
Dumplin's	7"	Columbia	DB4076	1958	£2	£5	
Flying Hickory	7"	Decca	F10592	1955	£4	£8	
Flying Home	7"	Decca	F10547	1955	£2.50	£6	
Four Favourite Film Themes	7" EP	Decca	DFE6670	1960	£2	£5	
Gigglin' Gurgleburp	7"	Columbia	DB4189	1958	£1.50	£4	
Gutbucket	7"	Ember	JBS706	1962	£1.50	£4	
I Want You To Be My Baby	7"	Decca	F10637	1955	£4	£8	
Jazz Inc	LP	Tempo	TAP30	1960	£6	£15	
Let's You And I Rock	7"	Columbia	DB3859	1956	£7.50	£15	
Let's You And I Rock	7" EP	Columbia	SEG7686	1957	£15	£30	
Lonesome Train	7"	Columbia	DB3881	1957	£7.50	£15	
Man From Interpol	LP	Top Rank	35043	1959	£6	£15	
Presenting Tony Crombie No.1	7" EP	Decca	DFE6247	1956	£4	£8	
Presenting Tony Crombie No.2	7" EP	Decca	DFE6281	1956	£4	£8	
Rock Rock Rock	7"	Columbia	DB3880	1957	£7.50	£15	
Rock Rock Rock	7" EP	Columbia	SEG7676	1957	£12.50	£25	
Rockin' With The Rockets	10" LP	Columbia	33S1108	1957	£40	£80	
Stop It	7"	Decca	F10424	1954	£2	£5	

Sweet And Rhythmic	7" EP.	Columbia	SEG7769	1958	£2	£5	
Sweet Beat	7"	Columbia	DB4000	1957	£4	£8	
Sweet, Side And Blue!	LP	Decca	SKL4114	1961	£6	£15	
Swinging Dance Beat No.1	7" EP.	Columbia	SEG7882/ ESG7768	1959	£2	£5	
Swinging Dance Beat No.2	7" EP.	Columbia	SEG7896	1959	£2	£5	
Teach You To Rock	7"	Columbia	DB3822	1956	£12.50	£25	chart single
Twelve Favourite Film Themes	LP	Decca	LK4385/SKL4127	1961	£5	£12	
Ungaua	7"	Columbia	DB4145	1958	£2	£5	

CROME CYRCUS

| Love Cycle | LP | Command | 925 | 1968 | £8 | £20 | US |

CROMPTON, BILL

| Hoot An' A Holler | 7" | Fontana | H152 | 1958 | £1.50 | £4 | |

CROMWELL

This pleasant but unexceptional album is undoubtedly rare, but its value has been considerably boosted by claims that the music is like that of the Rolling Stones on "Exile On Main Street". In fact, the resemblance is limited to the fact that both groups play guitars and drums and sing. If a comparison is really required for Cromwell, then a name like Edison Lighthouse would be far more appropriate.

| At The Gallop | LP | private | WELL005 | 1975 | £75 | £150 | |

CROMWELL, LINK

| Crazy Like A Fox | 7" | London | HLB10040 | 1966 | £4 | £8 | |

CRONSHAW, ANDREW

| A Is For Andrew Z Is For Zither | LP | Transatlantic | XTRA1139 | 1974 | £6 | £15 | |

CROOKED OAK

| Foot O'Wor Stairs | LP | Eron | 019 | 1979 | £15 | £30 | |
| From Little Acorns Grow | LP | Folkland | FL0102 | 1976 | £75 | £150 | |

CROOKS

| All The Time In The World | 7" | Blue Print | BLU2006 | 1980 | £2 | £5 | |

CROPPER, STEVE

| Funky Broadway | 7" | Stax | STAX147 | 1970 | £1.50 | £4 | |
| With A Little Help From My Friends | LP | Stax | SXATS1008 | 1971 | £4 | £10 | |

CROPPER, STEVE, ALBERT KING & POP STAPLES

| Jammed Together | LP | Stax | SXATS1020 | 1971 | £4 | £10 | |

CROSBY, BING

Around The World	7"	Brunswick	05674	1957	£1.50	£4	chart single
Bing And Connie	10" LP	Brunswick	LA8558	1953	£4	£10	with Connie Boswell
Bing Crosby And The Dixieland Bands	10" LP	Brunswick	LA8579	1953	£4	£10	
Bing Sings The Hits	10" LP	Brunswick	LA8674	1954	£4	£10	
Blue Of The Night	10" LP	Brunswick	LA8595	1953	£4	£10	
Blue Skies	10" LP	Brunswick	LA8602	1953	£4	£10	with Fred Astaire
Changing Partners	7"	Brunswick	05244	1954	£1.50	£4	chart single
Collectors' Classics Vol.1	10" LP	Brunswick	LA8687	1954	£4	£10	
Collectors' Classics Vol.2	10" LP	Brunswick	LA8723	1955	£4	£10	
Collectors' Classics Vol.3	10" LP	Brunswick	LA8726	1955	£4	£10	
Collectors' Classics Vol.4	10" LP	Brunswick	LA8727	1955	£4	£10	
Count Your Blessings Instead Of Sheep	7"	Brunswick	05339	1954	£1.50	£4	chart single
Country Girl	10" LP	Brunswick	LA8714	1955	£4	£10	
Country Style	10" LP	Brunswick	LA8724	1955	£4	£10	
Crosby Classics	10" LP	Columbia	33S1036	1954	£5	£12	
Don't Bingle	10" LP	Fontana	TFR6000	1958	£4	£10	
Down Memory Lane	10" LP	Brunswick	LA8620	1953	£4	£10	
Down Memory Lane Vol.2	10" LP	Brunswick	LA8624	1953	£4	£10	
Early Thirties Vol.1	10" LP	Brunswick	LA8740	1956	£4	£10	
Early Thirties Vol.2	10" LP	Brunswick	LA8741	1956	£4	£10	
El Bingo	10" LP	Brunswick	LA8529	1951	£5	£12	
Favourite Hawaiian Songs	10" LP	Brunswick	LA8730	1956	£4	£10	
George Gershwin Songs	10" LP	Brunswick	LA8666	1954	£4	£10	
Holiday Inn	10" LP	Brunswick	LA8592	1953	£4	£10	with Fred Astaire
How Lovely Is Christmas	7"	London	HLR8513	1957	£2	£5	
In A Little Spanish Town	7"	Brunswick	05543	1956	£1.50	£4	chart single
Merry Christmas	10" LP	Brunswick	LA8686	1954	£4	£10	
Never Be Afraid	7"	London	HLR8504	1957	£2	£5	
Old Lang Syne	10" LP	Brunswick	LA8585	1953	£4	£10	
Quiet Man	10" LP	Brunswick	LA8584	1953	£4	£10	
Secret Love	7"	Brunswick	05269	1954	£2.50	£6	
Silent Night	7"	Brunswick	03929	1954	£1.50	£4	chart single
Sings Cole Porter Songs	10" LP	Brunswick	LA8513	1951	£5	£12	
Sings Jerome Kern Songs	10" LP	Brunswick	LA8505	1951	£5	£12	
Sings Victor Herbert Songs	10" LP	Brunswick	LA8600	1953	£4	£10	
Some Fine Old Chestnuts	10" LP	Brunswick	LA8673	1954	£4	£10	
Song Hits From Broadway Shows	10" LP	Brunswick	LA8675	1954	£4	£10	
Song Hits Of Paris	10" LP	Brunswick	LA8645	1954	£4	£10	
Stardust	10" LP	Brunswick	LA8514	1951	£5	£12	
Stephen Foster Songs	10" LP	Brunswick	LA8571	1953	£4	£10	
Straight Down The Middle	7"	Philips	PB817	1958	£1.50	£4	
Stranger In Paradise	7"	Brunswick	05410	1955	£1.50	£4	chart single
True Love (with Grace Kelly)	7"	Capitol	CL14645	1956	£1.50	£4	chart single
Way Back Home	10" LP	Brunswick	LA8656	1954	£4	£10	
When Irish Eyes Are Smiling	10" LP	Brunswick	LA8606	1953	£4	£10	
White Christmas	7"	Brunswick	03384	1954	£1.50	£4	

White Christmas	7"	Brunswick	05354	1954	£1.50	£4	with Danny Kaye & others
Young At Heart	7"	Brunswick	05277	1954	£1.50	£4	
Yours Is My Heart Alone	10" LP	Brunswick	LA8684	1954	£4	£10	

CROSBY, BOB

Bob Crosby And His Bobcats	10" LP	Capitol	LC6553	1952	£6	£15	
Bob Crosby's Bobcats	LP	Brunswick	LAT8050	1955	£5	£12	
Dark At The Top Of The Stairs	7"	London	HLD9228	1960	£2	£5	
Great Hits	LP	London	HAD2293/	1960	£4	£10	
			SAHD6105				
In Hi-Fi	LP	Coral	LVA9083	1958	£4	£10	
Petite Fleur	7"	London	HLD8828	1959	£2	£5	

CROSBY, DAVID

If I Could Only Remember My Name	LP	Atlantic	2401005	1971	£4	£10	chart LP

CROSBY, GARY

Ayuh Ayuh	7"	Brunswick	05446	1955	£2	£5	
Gary Crosby	LP	Vogue	VA160118	1957	£5	£12	
Give Me A Band And My Baby	7"	Brunswick	05496	1955	£2	£5	
Happy Bachelor	7"	HMV	POP648	1959	£1.50	£4	
Judy Judy	7"	HMV	POP550	1958	£6	£12	
Ko Ko Mo	7"	Brunswick	05400	1955	£4	£8	with Louis Armstrong
Mambo In The Moonlight	7"	Brunswick	05340	1954	£2	£5	
Palsy Walsy	7"	Brunswick	05365	1955	£2	£5	
Ready, Willing And Able	7"	Brunswick	05378	1955	£4	£8	
Yaller Yaller Gold	7"	Brunswick	05546	1956	£1.50	£4	
Yaller Yaller Gold	7"	Brunswick	05633	1956	£1.50	£4	

CROSBY, STILLS & NASH

Crosby, Stills, & Nash	LP	Atlantic	588189	1969	£4	£10	chart LP
Marrakesh Express	7"	Atlantic	584283	1969	£1.50	£4	chart single
Suite: Judy Blue Eyes	7"	Atlantic	584304	1969	£1.50	£4	

CROSBY, STILLS, NASH & YOUNG

Celebration Record	LP	Atlantic	PR165	1971	£10	£25	US promo
Deja Vu	LP	Atlantic	2401001	1970	£4	£10	chart LP
Deja Vu	LP	Mobile Fidelity	MFSL1088	1982	£5	£12	US audiophile
Deju Vu	LP	Atlantic	SD19118	197-	£6	£15	Dutch, brown vinyl
Four Way Street	LP	Atlantic	2657004	1972	£5	£12	double, chart LP
Ohio	7"	Atlantic	2091023	1970	£1.50	£4	
Our House	7"	Atlantic	2091039	1970	£1.50	£4	
Rap With Crosby, Stills, Nash And Young	LP	Atlantic	18102	1973	£8	£20	US promo
Teach Your Children	7"	Atlantic	2091002	1970	£1.50	£4	
Woodstock	7"	Atlantic	2091010	1970	£1.50	£4	

CROSS

Cowboys And Indians	CD-s	Virgin	CDEP10	1987	£4	£10	
Cowboys And Indians	cass-s	Virgin	VSTC1007	1987	£2.50	£6	
Cowboys And Indians	7"	Virgin	VS1007	1987	£1.50	£4	
Cowboys And Indians	12"	Virgin	VST1007	1987	£2.50	£6	
Heaven For Everyone	7"	Virgin	VS1062	1988	£1.50	£4	
Heaven For Everyone	12"	Virgin	VST1062	1988	£2.50	£6	
Shove It	CD-s	Virgin	CDEP20	1988	£4	£10	
Shove It	7"	Virgin	VS1026	1988	£1.50	£4	
Shove It	12"	Virgin	VST1026	1988	£5	£12	

CROSS, JIMMIE

Super Duper Man	7"	Red Bird	RB10042	1966	£5	£10	

CROSS, KEITH & PETER ROSS

Bored Civilians	LP	Decca	SKL5129	1972	£25	£50	
Can You Believe It?	7"	Decca	F13224	1971	£1.50	£4	
Peace In The End	7"	Decca	F13316	1972	£1.50	£4	

CROSSBEATS

Crazy Mixed Up Generation	LP	Pilgrim	KLP12	197-	£15	£30	

CROWBAR

Hippie Punks	7"	Skinhead	SKIN1	1984	£4	£8	

CROWDED HOUSE

Better Be Home Soon	CD-s	Capitol	CDCL498	1988	£5	£12	
Fall At Your Feet	CD-s	Capitol	CDCL626	1991	£5	£12	double
Four Seasons In One Day	CD-s	Capitol	CDCLS655	1992	£5	£12	double
Live At The Town And Country Club	CD	Capitol	CH1	1992	£20	£40	double promo
Sister Madly	CD-s	Capitol	CDCL509	1988	£6	£15	
Weather With You	CD-s	Capitol	CDCLS643	1992	£5	£12	double
World Where You Live	CD-s	Capitol	CDCL416	1986	£5	£12	
World Where You Live	12"	Capitol	12CL416	1986	£2.50	£6	

CROWNS

I Know It's Alright	7"	Pama	PM725	1968	£2.50	£6	
Jerking The Dog	7"	Pama	PM736	1968	£2.50	£6	
She Ain't Gonna Do Right	7"	Pama	PM745	1968	£2.50	£6	
Since You Been Gone	7"	Pama	PM759	1968	£2.50	£6	

CROWS

Gee	7"	Columbia	SCM5119	1954	£150	£250	

CRUCIFIXION
Green Eyes	12"	Neat	NEAT3712	1984	£2.50	£6	

CRUDUP, ARTHUR
Crudup's Mood	LP	Delmark	DS621	1971	£6	£15	
Father Of Rock'n'Roll	LP	RCA	RD8224	1971	£5	£12	
Look On Yonder's Wall	LP	Delmark	DS614	1970	£6	£15	
Mean Ole Frisco	LP	Blue Horizon	763855	1969	£25	£50	
My Baby Left Me	7"	RCA	RCA1401	1964	£10	£20	
Rhythm And Blues Vol.4	7" EP	RCA	RCX7161	1964	£7.50	£15	

CRUISERS
It Ain't Me Babe	7"	Decca	F12098	1965	£4	£8	

CRUM, SIMON
Enormity In Motion	7"	Capitol	CL15183	1961	£4	£8	
Morgan Poisoned The Waterhole	7"	Capitol	CL15077	1959	£4	£8	
Stand Up Sit Down	7"	Capitol	CL14965	1958	£10	£20	

CRUMB, R.& THE CHEAP SUIT SERENADERS
Cheap Suit Serenaders	LP	Blue Goose	BG2014	1974	£4	£10	
Cheap Suit Serenaders Vol.2	LP	Blue Goose	BG2019	1976	£4	£10	
Elephant Songs And Cow Cow Clubs	LP	Blue Goose	BG2025	1978	£4	£10	

CRUSADERS
Crusaders	LP	Blue Thumb	ILPS9218	1972	£5	£12	double
Hollywood	LP	Mowest	MWS7004	1973	£6	£15	
Old Socks, New Shoes	LP	Rare Earth	SRE3001	1971	£4	£10	

CRYAN SHAMES
Scratch In The Sky	LP	CBS	CL/CS9586	1967	£15	£30	US
Sugar And Spice	LP	CBS	CL2589/CS9389	1966	£15	£30	US
Sugar And Spice	7"	CBS	202344	1966	£7.50	£15	
Synthesis	LP	CBS	CS9719	1968	£15	£30	US

CRYCH, TALCEN
Angharad	7"	Afon	RAS002	1975	£2	£5	

CRYER, BARRY
Angelina	7"	Fontana	H177	1959	£1.50	£4	
Nothin' Shakin'	7"	Fontana	H151	1958	£1.50	£4	
Purple People Eater	7"	Fontana	H139	1958	£1.50	£4	

CRYIN' SHAMES
Nobody Waved Goodbye	7"	Decca	F12425	1966	£6	£12	
Please Stay	7"	Decca	F12340	1966	£5	£10	chart single

CRYSTAL MANSION
Carolina In My Mind	7"	Polydor	2058070	1970	£1.50	£4	
Thought Of Loving You	7"	Capitol	CL15577	1969	£1.50	£4	

CRYSTALITES
Biafra	7"	Big Shot	BI510	1969	£2.50	£6	
Ilya Kuryakin	7"	Island	WI3134	1968	£5	£10	
James Ray	7"	Island	WI3153	1968	£5	£10	Derrick Harriott B side
Splashdown	7"	Nu Beat	NB036	1969	£2.50	£6	
Try A Little Merriness	7"	Island	WI3151	1968	£4	£8	

CRYSTALS
All Grown Up	7"	London	HLU9909	1964	£5	£10	
Da Doo Ron Ron	7"	London	HLU9732	1963	£2	£5	chart single
Da Doo Ron Ron	7" EP	London	REU1381	1963	£25	£50	
Do The Screw	7"	Philles	111	1963	£700	£1000	US, promo only
Greatest Hits	LP	Philles	PHLP4003	1963	£50	£100	US
He Sure Is The Boy I Love	7"	London	HLU9661	1963	£6	£12	
He's A Rebel	LP	London	HAU8120	1963	£50	£100	sleeve pictured in Guide
He's A Rebel	7"	London	HLU9611	1962	£5	£10	chart single
I Wonder	7"	London	HLU9852	1964	£5	£10	chart single
Little Boy	7"	London	HLU9837	1964	£15	£30	
My Place	7"	United Artists	UP1110	1965	£10	£20	
Then He Kissed Me	7"	London	HLU9773	1963	£2	£5	chart single
There's No Other	7"	Parlophone	R4867	1962	£37.50	£75	
Twist Uptown	LP	Philles	PHLP4000	1962	£50	£100	US

CUBA, JOE SEXTET
Bang Bang	7"	Pye	7N25401	1966	£1.50	£4	

CUBY & THE BLIZZARDS
Afscheidsconcert	LP	Philips	6343229	1974	£6	£15	Dutch
Appleknockers Flophouse	LP	Philips	SBL7918	1969	£6	£15	
Appleknockers Flophouse	7"	Philips	BF1827	1969	£2.50	£6	
Best Of 66-68	LP	Philips	6677023	1968	£6	£15	Dutch
Desolation	LP	Philips	SBL7874	1968	£6	£15	
Distant Smile	7"	Philips	BF1638	1968	£4	£8	
King Of The World	LP	Philips	6314002	1970	£6	£15	Dutch
Live	LP	Philips	6440091	1968	£8	£20	Dutch
Praise The Blues	LP	Philips	6440308	1968	£8	£20	Dutch
Simple Man	LP	Philips	6440306	1971	£5	£12	Dutch
Sometimes	LP	Philips	6440311	1972	£5	£12	Dutch
Soul	LP	Philips	044054	1968	£8	£20	Dutch

Too Blind To See	LP	Philips	6413002	1969	£6	£15	Dutch
Trippin' Thru A Midnight Blues	LP	Philips	6343228	1967	£8	£20	Dutch
Windows Of My Eyes	7"	Philips	BF1719	1968	£2.50	£6	
With Regards From Grollo	LP	Philips	6343227	1967	£8	£20	Dutch

CUD

Haywire	12"	Imaginary	MIRAGE18T	1990	£3	£8	signed
Slack Time	12"	Dug	DUGNI001T	1988	£4	£10	
Under My Hat	12"	Ediesta	CALC049	1988	£4	£10	
You're The Boss	12"	Reception	REC007	1987	£5	£12	

CUDDLY DUDLEY

Blarney Blues	7"	Oriole	ICB9	1964	£2.50	£6	
Later	7"	HMV	POP586	1959	£2.50	£6	
Sitting On A Train	7"	Ember	EMBS136	1961	£1.50	£4	
Too Pooped To Pop	7"	HMV	POP725	1960	£2.50	£6	
Way Of Life	7"	Oriole	ICB10	1964	£2.50	£6	

CUES

Burn That Candle	7"	Capitol	CL14501	1956	£40	£80	
Crackerjack	7"	Capitol	CL14651	1956	£40	£80	
Prince Or Pauper	7"	Capitol	CL14682	1957	£37.50	£75	

CUFF LINKS

Tracy	7"	MCA	MU1101	1969	£1.50	£4	chart single
When Julie Comes Around	7"	MCA	MU1112	1970	£1.50	£4	chart single

CULPEPPER'S ORCHARD

All Dressed Up And Nowhere To Go	LP	Sonet	SLP1558	1977	£15	£30	Danish
Culpeper's Orchard	LP	Polydor	2380006	1971	£45	£90	
Second Sight	LP	Polydor	2480123	1972	£30	£60	

CULT

Dreamtime	LP	Beggars Banquet	BEGA57	1984	£5	£12	with live LP
Dreamtime	LP	Beggars Banquet	BEGA57P	1984	£5	£12	pic disc
Electric	LP	Beggars Banquet	BEGA80	1987	£5	£12	gold vinyl
Electric	LP	Beggars Banquet	CULTLP12	1987	£6	£15	interview & music promo
Li'l Devil	CD-s	Beggars Banquet	BEG188CD	1987	£3	£8	
Li'l Devil	12"	Beggars Banquet	BEG188TD	1987	£2.50	£6	double
Sonic Temple	LP	Beggars Banquet	BEGA98	1989	£5	£12	red vinyl

CULT HERO

I'm A Cult Hero	7"	Fiction	FICS006	1979	£20	£40	

CULTURE CLUB

God Thank You Woman	7"	Virgin	VSY861	1986	£2.50	£6	pic disc
War Song	7"	Virgin	VSY694	1984	£17.50	£35	pic disc

CULVER STREET PLAYGROUND

Alley Pond Park	7"	President	PT145	1968	£2	£5	

CUMBERLAND THREE

Prior to joining the Kingston Trio, John Stewart was a member of a rather less well-known folk trio, the Cumberland Three.

Civil War Almanac - The Rebels	LP	Columbia	33SX1325	1961	£4	£10	
Civil War Almanac - The Yankees	LP	Columbia	33SX1318	1961	£4	£10	
Cumberland Crow	7"	Parlophone	R5113	1964	£1.50	£4	
Folk Scene USA	LP	Columbia	33SX1302/ SCX3364	1961	£4	£10	
Johnny Reb	7"	Columbia	DB4460	1960	£1.50	£4	

CUMMINGS, BARBARA

She's The Woman	7"	London	HLU10110	1967	£1.50	£4	

CUPIDS

Lillie Mae	7"	Vogue	V9102	1958	£100	£200	

CUPID'S INSPIRATION

My World	7"	NEMS	563702	1968	£1.50	£4	chart single
Yesterday Has Gone	LP	Nems	63553	1968	£4	£10	
Yesterday Has Gone	7"	NEMS	563500	1968	£1.50	£4	chart single

CUPOL

Like This For Ages	12"	4AD	BAD9	1980	£2.50	£6	

CUPPA T

Miss Pinkerton	7"	Deram	DM144	1967	£6	£12	
Streatham Hippodrome	7"	Deram	DM185	1968	£5	£10	

CUPS

Good As Gold	7"	Polydor	56777	1968	£5	£10	

CURE

Boys Don't Cry	7"	Fiction	FICS002	1979	£5	£10	
Catch	CD-s	Fiction	0801862	1987	£8	£20	CD Video
Catch	7"	Fiction	FICS26	1987	£1.50	£4	

Title	Format	Label	Cat No	Year	Price	Price	Notes
Catch	7"	Fiction	FICSC26	1987	£5	£10	clear vinyl
Catch	12"	Fiction	FICSE26	1987	£2.50	£6	with live tracks
Caterpillar	7"	Fiction	FICSP20	1984	£10	£20	pic disc
Caterpillar	12"	Fiction	FICSX20	1984	£2.50	£6	
Charlotte Sometimes	7"	Fiction	FICS14	1981	£2.50	£6	chart single
Charlotte Sometimes	12"	Fiction	FICSX14	1981	£5	£12	
Close To Me	CD-s	Fiction	FICCD36	1990	£2.50	£6	poster pack
Close To Me	7"	Fiction	FICSG23	1985	£1.50	£4	poster PS
Close To Me	7"	Fiction	FICSP23	1985	£4	£8	poster sleeve, sticker
Close To Me	10"	Fiction	FICST23	1985	£5	£12	
Disintegration	LP	Fiction	FIXHP14	1990	£4	£10	pic disc
Entreat	CD	Fiction	FIXCD17	1990	£6	£15	promo
Forest	7"	Fiction	FICS10	1980	£2.50	£6	'radio' sleeve, silver label
Forest	7"	Fiction	FICS10	1980	£5	£10	PS, blue label, chart single
Forest	12"	Fiction	FICSX10	1980	£8	£20	
Grinding Halt	12"	Fiction	CUR1	1979	£20	£40	promo
Hanging Garden	7"	Fiction	FICG15	1982	£7.50	£15	double
Hanging Garden	7"	Fiction	FICS15	1982	£4	£8	chart single
Hot! Hot! Hot!	CD-s	Fiction	FIXCD28	1988	£3	£8	
Hot! Hot! Hot!	7"	Fiction	FICS28	1988	£4	£8	promo
In Between Days	CD	Polygram	0801822	1988	£8	£20	CD Video
Jumping Someone Else's Train	7"	Fiction	FICS005	1979	£7.50	£15	
Just Like Heaven	CD-s	Fiction	FIXCD27	1987	£5	£12	
Just Like Heaven	7"	Fiction	FICSP27	1987	£5	£10	pic disc
Just Like Heaven	7"	Fiction	FICSW27	1987	£2.50	£6	white vinyl
Killing An Arab	7"	Fiction	FICS001	1979	£5	£10	
Killing An Arab	7"	Small Wonder	SMALL11	1978	£7.50	£15	
Killing An Arab (Peel Sessions)	7"	Strange Fruit	671002	1991	£1.50	£4	shaped pic disc
Kiss Me Kiss Me Kiss Me	LP	Fiction	FIXH13	1987	£8	£20	with orange vinyl disc in cellophane
Kiss Me Kiss Me Kiss Me Interview	LP	Fiction	KSME2	1987	£4	£10	promo
Lament	7"	Lyntone	LYN12011	1982	£2.50	£6	Flexipop green flexi
Lament	7"	Lyntone	LYN12011	1982	£5	£10	Flexipop red flexi
Let's Go To Bed	12"	Fiction	FICSX17	1982	£2.50	£6	
Love Cats	7"	Fiction	FICSP19	1983	£12.50	£25	pic disc
Love Song	CD-s	Fiction	FICCD30	1989	£2.50	£6	
Lovesong	CD-s	Fiction	0813982	1989	£3	£8	CD Video
Lovesong	12"	Fiction	FICSX30	1989	£20	£40	pic disc test pressing
Lullaby	7"	Fiction	FICSP29	1989	£4	£8	clear vinyl
Lullaby	12"	Fiction	FICVX29	1989	£4	£10	pink vinyl
One Hundred Years	12"	Fiction	CURE1	1982	£15	£30	promo
Pictures Of You	CD-s	Fiction	FICDA34	1990	£2.50	£6	
Pictures Of You	CD-s	Fiction	FICDB34	1990	£2.50	£6	
Pictures Of You	7"	Fiction	FICPB34	1990	£2	£5	purple vinyl
Pictures Of You	12"	Fiction	FIXPB34	1990	£3	£8	purple vinyl
Primary	7"	Fiction	FICS12	1981	£5	£10	chart single
Primary	12"	Fiction	FICSX12	1981	£6	£15	
Stranger Than Fiction	CD	Fiction	SCIFCD301	1989	£20	£40	promo sampler
Three Imaginary Boys	LP	Fiction	FIX1	1979	£4	£10	with postcard
Walk	7"	Fiction	FICS18	1983	£5	£10	poster sleeve
Walk	7"	Fiction	FICSP18	1983	£12.50	£25	pic disc
Walk	12"	Fiction	FICSX18	1983	£2.50	£6	
Why Can't I Be You	7"	Fiction	FICSG25	1987	£4	£8	double

CURE, MARTIN & THE PEEPS

Title	Format	Label	Cat No	Year	Price	Price	Notes
It's All Over Now	7"	Philips	BF1605	1967	£7.50	£15	

CURIOSITY SHOPPE

Title	Format	Label	Cat No	Year	Price	Price	Notes
Baby I Need You	7"	Deram	DM220	1968	£7.50	£15	

CURIOUS, JOHNNY & THE STRANGERS

Title	Format	Label	Cat No	Year	Price	Price	Notes
In Tune	7"	Illegal	IL009	1978	£1.50	£4	
Someone Else's Home	7"	Bugle	BLAST2	1979	£4	£8	

CURLY CURVE

Title	Format	Label	Cat No	Year	Price	Price	Notes
Curly Curve	LP	Brain	0001040	1974	£20	£40	German

CURRANT KRAZE

Title	Format	Label	Cat No	Year	Price	Price	Notes
Lady Pearl	7"	Deram	DM292	1970	£2	£5	

CURRENT 93

Title	Format	Label	Cat No	Year	Price	Price	Notes
Christ And The Pale Queen	LP	Maldorer	MAL666	1988	£25	£50	
Crowleymass	12"	Maldorer	MAL108	1987	£2.50	£6	
Faith's Favourites	7"	Yangki	002	1988	£2.50	£6	
Live At Bar Maldorer	LP	Durtro	DURTRO001	1989	£10	£25	
She Is Dead And All Fall Down	7"	Shock	SX003	198-	£4	£8	
She Is Dead And All Fall Down	7"	Shock	SX003	198-	£7.50	£15	individually lettered
This Ain't The Summer Of Love	7"	Cerne	004	198-	£2.50	£6	Sol Invictus B side

CURRY, CLIFFORD

Title	Format	Label	Cat No	Year	Price	Price	Notes
I Can't Get A Hold Of Myself	7"	Pama	PM797	1969	£2.50	£6	
She Shot A Hole In My Soul	7"	Action	ACT4549	1969	£2	£5	
You Turn Out The Light	7"	Pama	PM793	1969	£1.50	£4	

CURSON, TED

Title	Format	Label	Cat No	Year	Price	Price	Notes
Tears For Dolphy	LP	Fontana	688310ZL	1964	£4	£10	

CURTIS, CHRIS

Title	Format	Label	Cat No	Year	Price	Price	Notes
Aggravation	7"	Pye	7N17132	1966	£12.50	£25	

CURTIS, DAVE & THE TREMORS

Summertime Blues	7"	Philips	BF1330	1964	£4	£8	
What Kind of Girl Are You	7"	Philips	BF1285	1963	£4	£8	
You Don't Love Me	7"	Philips	BF1257	1963	£2.50	£6	

CURTIS, JOHNNY

Our Love's Disintegrating	7"	Parlophone	R5529	1966	£7.50	£15	

CURTIS, KING

Arthur Murray's Music For Dancing - The Twist	LP	RCA	RD27252	1962	£6	£15	
Azure	LP	Everest	DBR1121	1961	£8	£20	US
Best Of King Curtis	LP	Atlantic	228002	1968	£5	£12	
Doin' The Dixie Twist	LP	Tru-Sound	(S)TS15009	1962	£6	£15	US
Good To Me	7"	Atlantic	584109	1967	£1.50	£4	
Have Tenor Sax Will Blow	7" EP	London	REK1307	1961	£7.50	£15	
Have Tenor Sax, Will Blow	LP	London	HAK2247	1960	£8	£20	
Hits Made Famous By Sam Cooke	LP	Capitol	(S)T2341	1965	£6	£15	US
Instant Groove	LP	Atlantic	228027	1968	£5	£12	
It's Party Time	LP	Tru-Sound	(S)TS15008	1962	£6	£15	US
Kingsize Soul	LP	Atlantic	587043	1967	£5	£12	
La Jeanne	7"	Atlantic	584287	1969	£1.50	£4	
Live At Small's Paradise	LP	Atco	(SD)33198	1966	£6	£15	US
Memphis Soul Stew	7"	Atlantic	584134	1967	£2	£5	
New Scene	LP	Esquire	32161	1962	£6	£15	
Plays Great Memphis Hits	LP	Atlantic	587067	1967	£5	£12	
Soul Serenade	LP	Capitol	(S)T2095	1964	£6	£15	US
Soul Serenade	LP	Ember	SPE/LP6600	1968	£4	£10	
Soul Serenade	7"	Capitol	CL15346	1964	£4	£8	
Soul Twist	7"	London	HLU9547	1962	£5	£10	
Sweet Soul	LP	Atlantic	587115	1968	£5	£12	
Teasin'	7"	Atlantic	2091012	1970	£2	£5	
That Lovin' Feeling	LP	Atco	(SD)33189	1966	£6	£15	US
Whole Lotta Love	7"	Atlantic	2091158	1971	£1.50	£4	
Wiggle Wobble	7"	Speciality	SPE1000	1967	£2	£5	

CURTIS, KING, OLIVER NELSON, JIMMY FORREST

Soul Battle	LP	Esquire	32189	1963	£8	£20	

CURTIS, LEE & THE ALL STARS

Ecstasy	7"	Philips	BF1385	1964	£6	£12	
Let's Stomp	7"	Decca	F11690	1963	£6	£12	
Little Girl	7"	Decca	F11622	1963	£5	£10	
What About Me	7"	Decca	F11830	1964	£5	£10	

CURTIS, MAC

You Ain't Treating Me Right	7"	Parlophone	R4279	1957	£330	£500	

CURTIS, SONNY

Beatle Hits Flamenco Guitar Style	LP	Imperial	LP9276/LP12276	1964	£6	£15	US
Beatle I Want To Be	7"	Colpix	PX11024	1964	£2	£5	
Bo Diddley Bach	7"	Liberty	LIB55710	1964	£1.50	£4	
Red Headed Stranger	7"	Coral	Q72400	1960	£6	£12	

CURTOLA, BOBBY

Aladdin	7"	London	HL9639	1962	£1.50	£4	
Fortune Teller	7"	London	HL9577	1962	£1.50	£4	
I'm Sorry	7"	Decca	F11670	1963	£1.50	£4	
Indian Giver	7"	Decca	F11725	1963	£1.50	£4	
My Heart's Tongue Tied	7"	Columbia	DB4672	1961	£1.50	£4	

CURVE

Ten Little Girls	7"	Anxious	ANXP27	1991	£1.50	£4	pic disc

CURVED AIR

Curved Air (named after the Terry Riley piece) were more successful than most at integrating elements of classical music within a rock format and both Francis Monkman and Darryl Way have worked extensively with the same approach ever since the group's first release. The first LP, "Air Conditioning", was issued as a limited edition picture disc - probably the first rock record to be released in this form. Its value has been kept low, however, by the fact that a small number of playings causes a drastic deterioration in sound quality.

Air Conditioning	LP	Warner Bros	WSX3012	1970	£6	£15	pic disc
Air Cut	LP	Warner Bros	K46224	1973	£4	£10	
It Happened Today	7"	Warner Bros	WB8023	1971	£1.50	£4	
Live	LP	Deram	SML119	1975	£4	£10	
Phantasmagoria	LP	Warner Bros	K46158	1972	£4	£10	chart LP
Second Album	LP	Warner Bros	K46092	1971	£5	£12	chart LP

CUSHING, JOHN

She's Independent	7"	Carnaby	CNS4002	1969	£1.50	£4	

CUT AND DRY BAND

Cut And Dry Dolly	LP	Topic	12TS278	1976	£5	£12	
Cut And Dry No.2	LP	Topic	12TS413	1980	£5	£12	

CUTLER, IVOR

Get Away From The Wall	7" EP	Decca	DFE6677	1961	£10	£20	
Great Grey Grasshopper	7"	Parlophone	R5624	1967	£2	£5	
Ludo	LP	Parlophone	PCS7040	1967	£15	£30	
Of Y'hup	7" EP	Fontana	TFE17144	1959	£12.50	£25	
Who Tore Your Trousers	LP	Decca	LK4405	1961	£15	£30	

CUTTERS

Title	Format	Label	Cat#	Year			Notes
I've Had It	7"	Decca	F11110	1959	£1.50	£4	

CUTTY, GORDON

Title	Format	Label	Cat#	Year			Notes
Grand Old Fashioned Dance	LP	Free Reed	FRR006	1976	£6	£15	

CWT

Title	Format	Label	Cat#	Year			Notes
Hundredweight	LP	Kuckuck	2375022	1973	£25	£50	German

CYAN THREE

Title	Format	Label	Cat#	Year			Notes
Since I Lost My Baby	7"	Decca	F12371	1966	£6	£12	

CYBERMEN

Title	Format	Label	Cat#	Year			Notes
Cybermen	7"	Rockaway	AERE101	1978	£2	£5	

CYCLONES

Title	Format	Label	Cat#	Year			Notes
Nobody	7"	Oriole	CB1898	1964	£6	£12	

CYKLE

Title	Format	Label	Cat#	Year			Notes
Cykle	LP	Label	9261	1969	£100	£200	US

CYMANDE

Title	Format	Label	Cat#	Year			Notes
Brothers On The Slide	7"	Contempo	CS2019	1974	£1.50	£4	
Cymande	LP	Alaska	ALKA100	1973	£6	£15	
Promised Height	LP	Contempo	CLP508	1974	£6	£15	

CYMBAL, JOHNNY

Title	Format	Label	Cat#	Year			Notes
Cymbal Smashes	7" EP.	London	RER1406	1963	£10	£20	
Dum Dum De Dum	7"	London	HLR9762	1963	£2.50	£6	chart single
Go VW Go	7"	United Artists	UP1093	1965	£6	£12	
It'll Be Me	7"	MGM	MGM1106	1960	£4	£8	
Mister Bass Man	LP	Kapp	KL1324/KS3324	1963	£15	£30	US
Mister Bass Man	7"	London	HLR9682	1963	£2	£5	
Mister Bass Man	7" EP.	London	RER1375	1963	£10	£20	
Robinson Crusoe On Mars	7"	London	HLR9911	1964	£2.50	£6	
Teenage Heaven	7"	London	HLR9731	1963	£4	£8	

CYMBALINE

Title	Format	Label	Cat#	Year			Notes
Down By The Seaside	7"	Philips	BF1681	1968	£1.50	£4	
I Don't Want It	7"	Mercury	MF961	1967	£2.50	£6	
Matrimonial Fears	7"	Philips	BF1624	1967	£10	£20	
Peanuts And Chewy Macs	7"	Mercury	MF975	1967	£2	£5	
Please Little Girl	7"	Pye	7N15916	1965	£7.50	£15	
Top Girl	7"	Mercury	MF918	1965	£2.50	£6	
Turn Around	7"	Philips	BF1749	1969	£2	£5	

CYMERONS

Title	Format	Label	Cat#	Year			Notes
Everyday	7"	Polydor	56098	1966	£4	£8	
I'll Be There	7"	Decca	F11976	1964	£4	£8	

CYRKLE

Title	Format	Label	Cat#	Year			Notes
I Wish You Could Be There	7"	CBS	202577	1967	£2	£5	
Neon	LP	CBS	62977	1967	£6	£15	
Penny Arcade	7"	CBS	2917	1967	£1.50	£4	
Please Don't Leave Me	7"	CBS	202516	1967	£1.50	£4	
Red Rubber Ball	LP	CBS	CL2544/CS9344	1966	£6	£15	US
Red Rubber Ball	7"	CBS	202064	1966	£1.50	£4	
Turn Down Day	7"	CBS	202246	1966	£1.50	£4	
We Had A Good Thing Going	7"	CBS	2790	1967	£1.50	£4	

CZAR

Title	Format	Label	Cat#	Year			Notes
Oh Lord I'm Getting Heavy	7"	Philips	6006071	1970	£12.50	£25	
Tread Softly On My Dreams	LP	Fontana	6309009	1970	£80	£160	sleeve pictured in Guide

CZUKAY, HOLGER & ROLF DAMMERS

Title	Format	Label	Cat#	Year			Notes
Canaxis 5	LP	Music Factory	SRS002	1969	£85	£170	

D

D JUNIOR, DON
Dirty Dozen .... 7" ...... Caltone .... TONE124 .... 1968 ... £4 .... £8 .... Phil Pratt B side

D, KIM
Real Thing .... 7" ...... Pye .... 7N15953 .... 1965 ... £2.50 .... £6

D, TONY & THE SHAKEDOWNS
Is It True .... 7" ...... Piccadilly .... 7N35168 .... 1964 ... £1.50 .... £4

D'ABO, MICHAEL
D'Abo .... LP ..... MCA .... MAPS2040 .... 1970 ... £4 .... £10
Gulliver's Travels .... LP ..... Instant .... INLP003 .... 1968 ... £8 .... £20
Gulliver's Travels .... 7" ...... Immediate ...... IM075 .... 1969 ... £5 .... £10
Let It Roar .... 7" ...... UNI .... UNS525 .... 1970 ... £1.50 .... £4

D'ABO, MIKE
D'Abo .... LP ..... Uni .... UNLS114 .... 1970 ... £4 .... £10

DACOSTA, RITA
Don't Bring Me Down .... 7" ...... Contempo ...... CS2061 .... 1975 ... £1.50 .... £4

DADA
Dada was an ambitious big band that unfortunately found the costs of maintaining a large line-up too great to continue when their LP failed to set the country alight. A slimmed down version of the group continued as Vinegar Joe. The singer in both cases was Elkie Brooks, and at the end, Dada's second singer was Robert Palmer, although he makes no more than a passing appearance on the album.
Dada .... LP ..... Atco .... 2400030 .... 1970 ... £6 .... £15

DADDY LONGLEGS
Daddy Longlegs .... LP ..... Warner Bros ... WS3004 .... 1970 ... £6 .... £15
Oakdown Farm .... LP ..... Vertigo .... 6360038 .... 1971 ... £8 .... £20 .... spiral label
Shifting Sands .... LP ..... Polydor .... 2371323 .... 1972 ... £6 .... £15
Three Musicians .... LP ..... Polydor .... 2371261 .... 1972 ... £6 .... £15

DADDY-O'S
Got A Match? .... 7" ...... Oriole .... CB1454 .... 1958 ... £2 .... £5

DADDY'S ACT
Eight Days A Week .... 7" ...... Columbia .... DB8242 .... 1967 ... £5 .... £10

DAFOS, CALVIN
Brown Sugar .... 7" ...... Blue Beat .... BB347 .... 1965 ... £5 .... £10
Lash Them .... 7" ...... Doctor Bird ..... DB1174 .... 1969 ... £5 .... £10

DAGABAND
Second Time Around .... 7" ...... MHM .... AM094 .... 1983 ... £1.50 .... £4

DAGGERMEN
Introducing The Daggermen .... 7" ...... Empire .... UPW258J .... 1986 ... £1.50 .... £4

DAILY, PETE
Dixie By Daily .... 10" LP Capitol .... LC6603 .... 1953 ... £5 .... £12
Dixieland Band .... 10" LP Capitol .... LC6525 .... 1951 ... £5 .... £12
Pete Daily And Phil Napoleon .... 10" LP Brunswick .... LA8515 .... 1951 ... £6 .... £15

DAINES, TONY
Chapel In The Moonlight .... 7" ...... Fontana .... TF433 .... 1963 ... £1.50 .... £4
Too Late .... 7" ...... Fontana .... TF472 .... 1964 ... £1.50 .... £4

DAINTEES
Roll On Summertime .... 7" ...... Kitchenware ... SK3 .... 1984 ... £2 .... £5

DAISY PLANET
Daisy Planet .... 7" EP.. Oak .... no number .... 196- .... £20 .... £40 .... no PS

DAKOTAS
Cruel Sea .... 7" ...... Parlophone...... R5044 .... 1963 ... £1.50 .... £4 .... chart single
I Can't Break The News To Myself .... 7" ...... Philips .... BF1645 .... 1968 ... £15 .... £30
I'm An 'Ardworkin' Barrow Boy .... 7" ...... Page One .... POF018 .... 1967 ... £6 .... £12
Magic Carpet .... 7" ...... Parlophone...... R5064 .... 1963 ... £2.50 .... £6
Meet The Dakotas .... 7" EP.. Parlophone...... GEP8888 .... 1963 ... £12.50 .... £25
Oyeh .... 7" ...... Parlophone...... R5203 .... 1964 ... £5 .... £10

DAKOTA'S ALL STARS
Call Me Master .... 7" ...... Blue Beat .... BB358 .... 1965 ... £5 .... £10

D'ALBUQUERQUE, MICHAEL
We May Be Cattle But We've All Got .... LP ..... RCA .... SF8383 .... 1974 ... £5 .... £12
Names ....

DALE & GRACE
Dale And Grace No.1 .... 7" EP.. London .... RE1428 .... 1964 ... £6 .... £12
Dale And Grace No.2 .... 7" EP.. London .... RE1429 .... 1964 ... £6 .... £12

Dale And Grace No.3	7" EP..	London	RE1430	1964	£6	£12	
I'm Leaving It Up To You	LP	Montel	LP100	1964	£20	£40	US
I'm Leaving It Up To You	7"	London	HL10249	1969	£1.50	£4	
I'm Leaving It Up To You	7"	London	HL9807	1963	£4	£8	chart single
Stop And Think It Over	7"	London	HL9857	1964	£2.50	£6	

DALE, ALAN

Cherry Pink And Apple Blossom White	7"	Vogue Coral	Q72072	1955	£2.50	£6	
Don't Knock The Rock	7"	Vogue Coral	Q72225	1957	£4	£8	
Lonesome Road	7"	Vogue Coral	Q72231	1957	£4	£8	
Robin Hood	7"	Vogue Coral	Q72121	1956	£7.50	£15	
Rockin' The Cha-Cha	7"	Vogue Coral	Q72105	1955	£2	£5	
Sweet And Gentle	7"	Vogue Coral	Q72089	1955	£2	£5	
Test Of Time	7"	Vogue Coral	Q72194	1956	£1.50	£4	

DALE, DICK & THE DELTONES

Checkered Flag	LP	Capitol	(S)T2002	1963	£6	£15	US
King Of The Surf Guitar	LP	Capitol	(S)T1930	1963	£8	£20	US
Mr.Eliminator	LP	Capitol	(S)T2053	1964	£6	£15	US
Peppermint Man	7"	Capitol	CL15296	1963	£4	£8	
Rock Out	LP	Capitol	(S)T2293	1965	£6	£15	US
Scavenger	7"	Capitol	CL15320	1963	£4	£8	
Summer Surf	LP	Capitol	(S)T2111	1964	£6	£15	US
Surfer's Choice	LP	Capitol	T1886	1963	£8	£20	
Surfer's Choice	LP	Deltone	LPM1001	1962	£10	£25	US

DALE, GLEN

Good Day Sunshine	7"	Decca	F12475	1966	£1.50	£4	

DALE, JIM

Be My Girl	7"	Parlophone	R4343	1957	£2	£5	chart single
Gotta Find A Girl	7"	Parlophone	R4522	1959	£1.50	£4	
Jane Belinda	7"	Parlophone	R4424	1958	£1.50	£4	
Jim	LP	Parlophone	PMD1055	1958	£20	£40	
Jim Dale	7" EP..	Parlophone	GEP8656	1957	£7.50	£15	
Just Born	7"	Parlophone	R4376	1957	£1.50	£4	chart single
One Boy One Girl	7"	Piccadilly	7N35039	1962	£1.50	£4	
Piccadilly Line	7"	Parlophone	R4329	1957	£2.50	£6	
Somewhere There's A Someone	7"	Academy	AD001	196-	£1.50	£4	
Start All Over Again	7"	Piccadilly	7N35100	1962	£1.50	£4	
Sugartime	7"	Parlophone	R4402	1958	£1.50	£4	chart single

DALE, JIM, VIPERS & KING BROTHERS

Top Ten Special	7"	Parlophone	R4356	1957	£2.50	£6	

DALE SISTERS

Kiss	7"	HMV	POP781	1960	£2.50	£6	
My Sunday Baby	7"	Ember	EMBS140	1961	£1.50	£4	
Secrets	7"	Ember	EMBS151	1962	£1.50	£4	

DALEY, BASIL

Born To Love	7"	Studio One	SO2054	1968	£6	£12	

DALEY, JIMMY & THE DING-A-LINGS

Rock Pretty Baby	7"	Brunswick	05648	1957	£37.50	£75	
Rock, Pretty Baby	LP	Brunswick	LAT8162	1957	£25	£50	

DALI, SALVADOR

Dali In Venice	LP	Decca	SET230	1962	£8	£20	

DALLON, MIKI

Cheat And Lie	7"	Strike	JH306	1966	£2.50	£6	
Do You Call That Love?	7"	RCA	RCA1438	1965	£7.50	£15	
I Care About You	7"	RCA	RCA1478	1965	£10	£20	
What Will Your Mama Say	7"	Strike	JH318	1966	£2.50	£6	

DALTON BROTHERS
US copies of the single by Scott Engel (Walker) and John Stewart were credited to the Dalton Brothers.

I Only Came To Dance With You	7"	Martay	2001	1964	£6	£12	US

DALTON, KATHY

Amazing	LP	Discreet	K59202	1973	£5	£12	
Boogie Bands & One Night Stands	LP	Discreet	DS2208	1974	£5	£12	US

DALTONS

Never Kiss You Again	7"	Fab	FAB30	1967	£4	£8	Righteous Flames B side

DALTREY, ROGER

I'm Free	7"	Ode	ODS66302	1972	£2	£5	PS
Say It Ain't So/Satin And Lace	7"	Polydor	2058948	1976	£5	£10	

DALY, JACKIE

Music From Sliabh Luachra Vol.6	LP	Topic	12TS358	1977	£5	£12	

DAMERON, TADD

Fontainebleau	LP	Esquire	32034	1957	£10	£25	
Tadd Dameron Band	10" LP	Esquire	20044	1955	£20	£40	
Tadd's Delight	7" EP..	Capitol	EAP120388	195-	£2	£5	

DAMIAN

Time Warp	7"	Jive	JIVE160	1987	£1.50	£4	

Title	Format	Label	Cat No	Year			Notes
Time Warp	7"	Jive	JIVE182	1988	£1.50	£4	
Time Warp	12"	Jive	JIVET160	1987	£2.50	£6	
Time Warp	12"	Sedition	EDITL3311	1986	£2.50	£6	

DAMNED

Title	Format	Label	Cat No	Year			Notes
Best Of The Damned	LP	Big Beat	DAM1	1981	£4	£10	red or blue vinyl
Black Album	LP	Chiswick	CWK3015	1980	£6	£15	double, chart LP
Captain's Birthday Party	LP	Stiff	GET4	1986	£4	£10	blue vinyl
Damned Damned Damned	LP	Stiff	SEEZ1	1977	£4	£10	chart LP
Damned Damned Damned	LP	Stiff	SEEZ1	1977	£20	£40	Eddie & Hot Rods photo
Damned Damned Damned	LP	Stiff	SEEZ1	1977	£25	£50	Eddie & Hot Rods photo, with red sticker
Damned Damned Damned/Music For Pleasure	LP	Stiff	MAIL2	1986	£5	£12	double, yellow vinyl
Don't Cry Wolf	7"	Stiff	BUY24	1977	£2	£5	pink vinyl
Four Pack	7"	Stiff	GRAB2	1981	£10	£20	BUY6,10,18,24 in plastic wallet
Generals	7"	Bronze	BRO159	1982	£4	£8	
Grimly Fiendish	7"	MCA	GRIM1	1985	£2	£5	gatefold PS, autographed
Grimly Fiendish	7"	MCA	GRIMP1	1985	£1.50	£4	pic disc
Grimly Fiendish	12"	MCA	GRIMT1	1985	£2.50	£6	autographed
Grimly Fiendish	12"	MCA	GRIMX1	1985	£2.50	£6	white vinyl
I Just Can't Be Happy Today	7"	Chiswick	CHIS120	1979	£2	£5	chart single
Live In Newcastle	LP	Damned	DAMU2	1983	£10	£25	
Live In Newcastle	LP	Damned	PDAMU2	1983	£8	£20	pic disc
Lively Arts	7"	Big Beat	NS80	1982	£2	£5	green vinyl
Lively Arts	10"	Big Beat	NST80	1982	£2.50	£6	
Love Song	7"	Dodgy Demo	SGS105	1978	£10	£20	
Lovely Money	7"	Bronze	BROP149	1982	£2	£5	pic disc
Machine Gun Etiquette	LP	Big Beat	DAM2	1982	£4	£10	blue or white vinyl
Neat Neat Neat	7"	Stiff	BUY10	1977	£2	£5	'Damned' in fancy text on label
New Rose	7"	Stiff	BUY6	1976	£2	£5	press-out centre
Phantasmagoria	LP	MCA	MCF3275	1985	£4	£10	white vinyl
Phantasmagoria	LP	MCA	MCF3275	1985	£4	£10	with blue vinyl 12'
Phantasmagoria	LP	MCA	MCFP3275	1985	£4	£10	pic disc
Problem Child	7"	Stiff	BUY18	1977	£1.50	£4	press-out centre
Shadow Of Love	7"	MCA	GRIM2	1985	£2.50	£6	gatefold PS & 7" (GRIMY2)
Stretcher Case Baby	7"	Stiff	DAMNED1	1977	£12.50	£25	
Thanks For The Night	7"	Plus One	DAMNED1P	1986	£12.50	£25	shaped pic disc, plinth
Wait For The Blackout	7"	Big Beat	NS77	1982	£1.50	£4	red/black Damned labels
Wait For The Blackout	7"	Big Beat	NSP77	1982	£2	£5	pic disc
White Rabbit	7"	Chiswick	CHIS130	1980	£20	£40	2 x 1 sided test pressings only

DAMON, RUSS

Title	Format	Label	Cat No	Year			Notes
Hip Huggers	7"	Stateside	SS258	1964	£1.50	£4	

DAMONE, VIC

Title	Format	Label	Cat No	Year			Notes
All-Time Song Hits	10" LP	Mercury	MPT7514	1957	£6	£15	
Closer Than A Kiss	LP	Philips	BBL7259	1958	£4	£10	
That Towering Feeling	LP	Philips	BBL7144	1957	£5	£12	
Walking My Baby Back Home	7" EP	Mercury	EP13121	1954	£4	£8	

DANCE CHAPTER

Title	Format	Label	Cat No	Year			Notes
Anonymity	7"	4AD	AD18	1980	£2	£5	insert

DANCING DID

Title	Format	Label	Cat No	Year			Notes
Dancing Did	7"	Fruit And Veg	F&V1	1979	£2	£5	

DANDO SHAFT

Title	Format	Label	Cat No	Year			Notes
Dando Shaft	LP	Neon	NE5	1971	£25	£50	
Evening With	LP	Youngblood	SSYB6	1970	£25	£50	
Kingdom	LP	Rubber	RUB034	1978	£10	£25	
Lantaloon	LP	RCA	SF8256	1972	£25	£50	with poster
Sun Clog Dance	7"	RCA	RCA2246	1972	£2	£5	

DANDY

Title	Format	Label	Cat No	Year			Notes
Baby Don't Go	7"	Dice	CC21	1963	£5	£10	
Be Natural Be Proud	7"	Downtown	DT434	1969	£1.50	£4	
Charlie Brown	7"	Giant	GN20	1968	£4	£8	
Come On Home	7"	Downtown	DT437	1969	£1.50	£4	
Dandy Livingstone	LP	Trojan	TRL45	1972	£4	£10	
Everybody Loves A Winner	7"	Downtown	DT442	1969	£1.50	£4	
Fight	7"	Ska Beat	JB247	1966	£5	£10	
Games People Play	7"	Downtown	DT421	1969	£1.50	£4	
Hey Boy Hey Girl	7"	Blue Beat	BB319	1964	£5	£10	
I Found Love	7"	Blue Beat	BB336	1965	£5	£10	
I'm Back with A Bang Bang	7"	Giant	GN36	1968	£4	£8	
I'm In The Mood	7"	Giant	GN19	1968	£4	£8	
I'm Looking For Love	7"	Blue Beat	BB308	1964	£5	£10	
I'm Your Puppet	7"	Downtown	DT416	1969	£1.50	£4	
In The Mood	7"	Caltone	TONE103	1967	£4	£8	Honeyboy Martin B side
Let's Go Rocksteady	7"	Giant	GN7	1967	£4	£8	
Little More Ska	7"	Dice	CC29	1964	£5	£10	

193

Move Your Mule	7"	Downtown	DT401	1969	£1.50	£4	
My Babe	7"	Blue Beat	BB327	1965	£5	£10	
My Time Now	7"	Giant	GN3	1967	£4	£8	
Now I Have You	7"	Dice	CC24	1964	£5	£10	
One Scotch, One Bourbon, One Beer	7"	Ska Beat	JB269	1967	£5	£10	
People Get Ready	7"	Downtown	DT429	1969	£1.50	£4	
Play It Cool	7"	Columbia	DB112	1969	£4	£8	
Propogandist	7"	Giant	GN23	1968	£4	£8	
Puppet On A String	7"	Giant	GN5	1967	£4	£8	
Reggae In Your Jeggae	7"	Downtown	DT410	1969	£1.50	£4	
Returns	LP	Trojan	TRL2	1969	£8	£20	
Rocksteady With Dandy	LP	Giant	GNL1000	1967	£25	£50	
Rudy A Message To You	7"	Ska Beat	JB273	1967	£5	£10	
Sentence	7"	Trojan	TR629	1968	£4	£8	Lee Perry B side
Shake Me Wake Me	7"	Downtown	DT402	1969	£1.50	£4	
Somewhere My Love	7"	Giant	GN10	1967	£4	£8	
Sweet Ride	7"	Giant	GN27	1968	£4	£8	
Tears On My Pillow	7"	Giant	GN30	1968	£4	£8	
Tell Me Darling	7"	Downtown	DT404	1969	£1.50	£4	
There Is A Mountain	7"	Giant	GN15	1967	£4	£8	
Toast	7"	Trojan	TR618	1968	£4	£8	
Trier	7"	Downtown	DT411	1969	£1.50	£4	
Vipers	7"	Carnival	CV7020	1965	£4	£8	
Won't You Come Home	7"	Downtown	DT453	1969	£1.50	£4	
Your Musical Doctor	LP	Trojan	TTL26	1970	£6	£15	
You're No Hustler	7"	Ska Beat	JB279	1967	£5	£10	

DANDY & AUDREY

I Need You	LP	Trojan	TRL17	1969	£6	£15
Morning Side Of The Mountain	LP	Trojan	TBL118	1970	£6	£15

DANE, CHRIS

Cynthia's In Love	7"	London	HLA8165	1955	£7.50	£15

DANE, SHELLEY

Hannah Lee	7"	Pye	7N25064	1960	£1.50	£4

DANGER, CAL

Teenage Girlie Blues	7"	Fontana	267225TF	1962	£7.50	£15

DANGERFIELD, A.P.

Conversations	7"	Fontana	TF935	1968	£6	£12

DANGERFIELD, KEITH

The Keith Dangerfield single owes its high value to the once-held belief that the Dangerfield name was a pseudonym for the Yardbirds' vocalist, Keith Relf. This was very much a case of wishful thinking, however. Relf did attempt a solo career while still with the Yardbirds, but his singles have the obvious credit - Keith Relf.

No Life Child	7"	Plexium	P1237	1968	£60	£120

DANGERFIELD, TONY

She's Too Way Out	7"	Pye	7N15695	1964	£12.50	£25

DANI

That Old Familiar Feeling	7"	Pye	7N25667	1974	£4	£8

DANIELS, BILLY

At The Crescendo	LP	Vogue	LAE12021	1956	£5	£12
Best Of Billy Daniels	7" EP.	HMV	7EG8485	1958	£2	£5
Songs At Midnight	10" LP	Mercury	MG25163	1954	£8	£20
Songs At Midnight	7"	Mercury	MPT7505	1956	£6	£15
That Old Black Magic	7"	Vogue	V9172	1960	£4	£8
That Old Black Magic	7" EP.	Mercury	MEP9001	1956	£4	£8
That Old Black Magic	7" EP.	Mercury	ZEP10066	1960	£2	£5
Torch Hour	10" LP	Mercury	MG10003	1953	£8	£20
Torch Hour	10" LP	Mercury	MG25103	1954	£6	£15
Torch Hour	10" LP	Mercury	MPT7006	1956	£5	£12
You Go To My Head	10" LP	HMV	DLP1174	1958	£4	£10

DANIELS, JULIUS

RCA Victor Race Series Vol.4	7" EP..	RCA	RCX7175	1965	£5	£10

DANIELS, ROLY 'YO YO'

Yo Yo Boy	7"	Decca	F11501	1962	£1.50	£4
Yo Yo Boy	7"	Stardisc	SD101	196-	£5	£10

DANIELS, SAM

Tell Me Baby	7"	Sway	SW003	1963	£2.50	£6

DANKWORTH, JOHNNY

African Waltz	7"	Columbia	DB4590	1961	£1.50	£4	chart single
African Waltz	7" EP.	Columbia	SEG8137	1961	£2	£5	
Avengers	7"	Columbia	DB4695	1961	£4	£8	
Avengers	7"	Fontana	TF422	1963	£4	£8	
Criminal	7" EP..	Columbia	SEG8037/ ESG7825	1960	£2	£5	
Dankworth Workshop No.1	7" EP.	Parlophone	GEP8653	1958	£2	£5	
Dankworth Workshop No.2	7" EP.	Parlophone	GEP8697	1958	£2	£5	
Experiments With Mice	7"	Parlophone	MSP6255	1956	£2	£5	chart single
Five Steps To Dankworth	LP	Parlophone	PMC1043	1957	£8	£20	
Jazz Routes	LP	Columbia	33SX1280/ SCX3347	1961	£6	£15	

London To Newport	LP	Top Rank	25019	1960	£6	£15
London To Newport	LP	Top Rank	30019	1960	£5	£12
Million Dollar Collection	LP	Fontana	TL5445	1968	£5	£12
Modesty Blaise Theme	7"	Fontana	TF700	1966	£1.50	£4
Vintage Years	LP	Parlophone	PMC1076	1959	£8	£20
What The Dickens	LP	Fontana	TL/STL5203	1964	£5	£12
Zodiac Variations	LP	Fontana	TL5229	1965	£5	£12

DANLEERS

One Summer Night	7"	Mercury	AMT1003	1958	£20	£40

DANNY & THE JUNIORS

At The Hop	7"	HMV	POP436	1958	£7.50	£15	chart single
Back To The Hop	7"	Top Rank	JAR587	1961	£4	£8	
Dottie	7"	HMV	POP504	1958	£7.50	£15	
Oo-La-La-Limbo	7"	London	HL9666	1963	£2	£5	
Pony Express	7"	Top Rank	JAR552	1961	£4	£8	
Rock And Roll Is Here To Stay	7"	HMV	POP467	1958	£12.50	£25	
Twisting All Night Long	7"	Top Rank	JAR604	1962	£2.50	£6	
Twisting USA	7"	Top Rank	JAR510	1960	£4	£8	

DANSE SOCIETY

2000 Light Years From Home	12"	Arista	SOCV127	1984	£3	£8	
Clock	7"	North	SOC381	1981	£4	£8	blue marble vinyl
There Is No Shame In Death	12"	Pax	PAX2	1981	£2.50	£6	
There Is No Shame In Death	12"	Pax	PAX2	1981	£15	£30	blue vinyl
Woman's Own	7"	Pax	PAX5	1982	£2.50	£6	
Woman's Own	12"	Pax	PAX5	1982	£3	£8	

DANTALIAN'S CHARIOT

With the arrival of psychedelia, Zoot Money was able to indulge his penchant for onstage flamboyance and, with the aid of his latest re-named version of the Big Roll Band, recorded one of the classic singles of the genre. The drummer, Colin Allen, subsequently played with John Mayall and Stone The Crows; bassist Pat Donaldson joined Fotheringay and has been a busy session musician ever since; while guitarist Andy Summers eventually found mega-stardom as a member of the Police.

Madman Running Through The Fields	7"	Columbia	DB8260	1967	£20	£40

DANTE

Bye Bye Baby	7"	Brunswick	05857	1961	£1.50	£4

DANTE & THE EVERGREENS

Alley Oop	7"	Top Rank	JAR402	1960	£6	£12	
Dante & The Evergreens	LP	Madison	MA1002	1961	£75	£150	US

DANTE, TROY & THE INFERNOS

This Little Girl	7"	Fontana	TF477	1964	£2.50	£6

DARIN, BOBBY

25th Day Of December	7" EP	London	REK1321	1961	£10	£20	
At The Copa	LP	London	HAK2291	1960	£8	£20	
At The Copa	LP	London	SAHK6103	1960	£10	£25	stereo
At The Crossroads	7"	Atlantic	584147	1967	£1.50	£4	
Baby Face	7"	London	HLK9624	1962	£1.50	£4	chart single
Be Mad Little Girl	7"	Capitol	CL15328	1963	£1.50	£4	
Beachcomber	7"	London	HLK9197	1960	£1.50	£4	
Best Of Bobby Darin	LP	Capitol	T2571	1966	£5	£12	
Bill Bailey Won't You Please Come Home	7"	London	HLK9142	1960	£1.50	£4	chart single
Blue Monday	7"	Mowest	MW3014	1974	£1.50	£4	
Bobby Darin	LP	London	HAE2140	1958	£20	£40	
Bobby Darin	LP	Motown	M753L	1972	£4	£10	US
Bobby Darin	7" EP	London	REE1173	1959	£15	£30	
Bobby Darin No.2	7" EP	London	REE1225	1959	£12.50	£25	
Born Robert Walden Cassotto	LP	Bell	MBLL/SBLL112	1969	£5	£12	
Change	7"	Bell	BLL1040	1968	£1.50	£4	
Clementine	7"	London	HLK9086	1960	£1.50	£4	chart single
Commitment	LP	Bell	SBLL128	1970	£4	£10	
Dream Lover	7"	London	HLE8867	1959	£2	£5	chart single
Early In The Morning	7"	London	HLE8679	1958	£20	£40	
Earthy	LP	Capitol	T1826	1963	£6	£15	
Eighteen Yellow Roses	LP	Capitol	ST1942	1963	£8	£20	stereo
Eighteen Yellow Roses	LP	Capitol	T1942	1963	£6	£15	
Eighteen Yellow Roses	7"	Capitol	CL15306	1963	£1.50	£4	chart single
For Teenagers Only	LP	Capitol	HAK2311	1960	£8	£20	
For Teenagers Only	7" EP	London	REK1286	1961	£10	£20	
From Hello Dolly To Goodbye Charlie	LP	Capitol	T2194	1964	£4	£10	
Girl That Stood Beside Me	7"	Atlantic	584063	1967	£1.50	£4	
Golden Folk Hits	LP	Capitol	ST2007	1964	£8	£20	stereo
Golden Folk Hits	LP	Capitol	T2007	1964	£6	£15	
Gyp The Cat	7"	Capitol	CL15414	1965	£1.50	£4	
Hear Them Bells	7"	Brunswick	05831	1960	£4	£8	
I Wanna Be Around	LP	Capitol	T2322	1965	£5	£12	
I Wonder Who's Kissing Her Now	7"	Capitol	CL15338	1964	£1.50	£4	
If A Man Answers	7"	Capitol	CL15272	1962	£1.50	£4	chart single
If I Were A Carpenter	LP	Atlantic	587/588051	1966	£5	£12	
If I Were A Carpenter	7"	Atlantic	584051	1966	£1.50	£4	chart single
In A Broadway Bag	LP	Atlantic	587/588020	1966	£5	£12	
Inside Out	LP	Atlantic	587076	1967	£5	£12	
It's You Or No One	LP	London	HAK8102	1963	£6	£15	
It's You Or No One	LP	London	SHK8102	1963	£8	£20	stereo
Keep A Walking	7"	London	HLK9663	1963	£1.50	£4	
La Mer	7"	London	HLK9034	1960	£1.50	£4	chart single

Title	Format	Label	Cat. No.	Year	Price 1	Price 2	Notes
Lady Came From Baltimore	7"	Atlantic	584105	1967	£1.50	£4	
Lazy River	7"	London	HLK9303	1961	£1.50	£4	chart single
Lost Love	7"	London	HL7060	1958	£10	£20	export
Love Swings	LP	London	HAK2394	1961	£6	£15	mono
Love Swings	LP	London	SAHK6194	1961	£8	£20	stereo
Love Swings	7" EP.	London	REK1334	1961	£6	£12	
Lovin' You	7"	Atlantic	584079	1967	£1.50	£4	
Mack The Knife	7"	London	HLE8939	1959	£1.50	£4	chart single
Mame	7"	Atlantic	584014	1966	£1.50	£4	
Maybe We Can Get It Together	7"	Major Minor	MM697	1970	£1.50	£4	
Mighty Mighty Man	7"	London	HLE8793	1959	£12.50	£25	
Milord	7"	Atlantic	AT4002	1964	£1.50	£4	
Milord	7" EP.	Atlantic	AET6013	1965	£5	£10	
Multiplication	7"	London	HLK9474	1961	£1.50	£4	chart single
Nature Boy	7"	London	HLK9375	1961	£1.50	£4	chart single
Oh Look At Me Now	LP	Capitol	T1791	1962	£6	£15	
Plain Jane	7"	London	HL7078	1959	£7.50	£15	export
Plain Jane	7"	London	HLE8815	1959	£10	£20	
Queen Of The Hop	7"	London	HLE8737	1958	£10	£20	chart single
Rock Island Line	7"	Brunswick	05061	1956	£30	£60	
Shadow Of Your Smile	LP	Atlantic	587/588014	1966	£5	£12	
Sings Dr.Doolittle	LP	Atlantic	587089	1968	£4	£10	
Sings Ray Charles	LP	London	HAK2456	1962	£6	£15	
Sings Ray Charles	LP	London	SAHK6243	1962	£8	£20	stereo
Somebody To Love	7"	London	HLK9215	1960	£1.50	£4	
Something Special	LP	Atlantic	587073	1967	£8	£20	
Splish Splash	7"	Atlantic	K10238	1972	£1.50	£4	PS
Splish Splash	7"	London	HLE8666	1958	£10	£20	chart single
Story	LP	Atlantic	587065	1967	£5	£12	
Story	LP	London	HAK2372	1961	£8	£20	
Sugarman	7"	Bell	BLL1090	1969	£1.50	£4	
That's All	LP	London	HAE2172	1959	£8	£20	chart LP
That's All	7" EP.	London	REK1243	1960	£7.50	£15	
Theme From Come September	7"	London	HLK9407	1961	£1.50	£4	chart single
Things	7"	London	HLK9575	1962	£1.50	£4	chart single
Things And Other Things	7" EP.	London	REK1342	1962	£6	£12	
Things	LP	London	HAK8030	1962	£8	£20	
Things In This House	7"	Capitol	CL15360	1964	£1.50	£4	
This Is Bobby Darin	LP	London	HAK2235	1959	£8	£20	chart LP
This Is Bobby Darin	LP	London	SAHK6067	1960	£10	£25	stereo
Twist With Bobby Darin	7" EP.	London	REK1338	1962	£6	£12	
Two Of A Kind	LP	London	HAK2363	1961	£6	£15	with Johnny Mercer
Two Of A Kind	LP	London	SAHK6164	1961	£8	£20	with Johnny Mercer, stereo
Two Of A Kind	7" EP.	London	REK1310	1961	£6	£12	with Johnny Mercer
Up A Lazy River	7" EP.	London	REK1290	1961	£6	£12	
We Didn't Ask To Be Brought Here	7"	Atlantic	AT4046	1965	£1.50	£4	
What'd I Say	7"	London	HLK9540	1962	£1.50	£4	
When I Get Home	7"	Capitol	CL15401	1965	£1.50	£4	
Winners	LP	Atlantic	ATL5014	1965	£5	£12	
You Must Have Been A Beautiful Baby	7"	London	HLK9429	1961	£1.50	£4	chart single
You're The Reason I'm Living	7"	Capitol	CL15286	1963	£1.50	£4	

DARK

The high value attaching to privately pressed progressive albums by groups like the Dark, Forever Amber, and Complex depends in part on the mystique woven around them by collectors and dealers alike. The records are certainly rare and when so few people have actually heard them, it is difficult to gainsay claims that they are masterpieces. Now these records are being reissued, but in tiny limited editions and at prices that are often themselves well into the realm of serious collecting. Thus the mystique continues. Original copies of the Dark album exist in four different forms. The first ten or twelve copies came in a colour gatefold sleeve; the next edition of around thirty copies had a black and white gatefold sleeve; and a final run of about thirty-five copies had a black and white single sleeve. Meanwhile, just one eight-track cartridge was made for a friend who wanted it to play in his car!

Title	Format	Label	Cat. No.	Year	Price 1	Price 2	Notes
Round The Edges	LP	Darkside	001	1991	£25	£50	
Round The Edges	LP	S.I.S.	SR0102S	1972	£840	£1200	sleeve pictured in Guide

DARK (2)

Title	Format	Label	Cat. No.	Year	Price 1	Price 2	Notes
Living End	LP	Fallout	FALLLP005	1982	£4	£10	

DARK STAR

Title	Format	Label	Cat. No.	Year	Price 1	Price 2	Notes
Lady Of Mars	12"	Avatar	AAA105	1981	£3	£8	

DARLING BUDS

Title	Format	Label	Cat. No.	Year	Price 1	Price 2	Notes
If I Said	7"	Darling Buds	DAR1	1987	£5	£10	

DARNELL, BILL

Title	Format	Label	Cat. No.	Year	Price 1	Price 2	Notes
Guilty Lips	7"	London	HLU8267	1956	£7.50	£15	
Last Frontier	7"	London	HLU8234	1956	£12.50	£25	
My Little Mother	7"	London	HLU8204	1955	£7.50	£15	
Tell Me More	7"	London	HLU8292	1956	£7.50	£15	

DARRELL, GUY

Title	Format	Label	Cat. No.	Year	Price 1	Price 2	Notes
Crystal Ball	7"	CBS	202642	1967	£1.50	£4	
Evil Woman	7"	Piccadilly	7N35406	1967	£7.50	£15	
Go Home Girl	7"	Oriole	CB1932	1964	£2	£5	
Guy Darrell	LP	CBS	53364	196-	£4	£10	
Hard Lovin'	7"	CBS	202510	1967	£1.50	£4	
I've Been Hurt	7"	CBS	202082	1966	£5	£10	
My Way Of Thinking	7"	CBS	202296	1966	£1.50	£4	
Somewhere They Can't Find Me	7"	CBS	202033	1966	£1.50	£4	
Sorry	7"	Oriole	CB1964	1964	£1.50	£4	
Stupidity	7"	CBS	201806	1965	£1.50	£4	

DARREN, JAMES

Album No.1	LP	Colpix	CP406	1960	£6	£15	US
All	LP	Warner Bros	WS1688	1967	£5	£12	US
Angel Face	7"	Pye	7N25034	1959	£1.50	£4	
Backstage	7"	Colpix	PX708	1963	£1.50	£4	
Because They're Young	7"	Pye	7N25059	1960	£1.50	£4	chart single
Conscience	7"	Pye	7N25138	1962	£1.50	£4	chart single
Gidget	7"	Pye	7N25019	1959	£1.50	£4	
Goodbye Cruel World	7"	Pye	7N25116	1961	£1.50	£4	chart single
Hail To The Conquering Hero	7"	Pye	7N25168	1962	£1.50	£4	
Her Royal Majesty	7"	Pye	7N25125	1962	£1.50	£4	chart single
James Darren Hit Parade	7" EP	Pye	NEP44008	1962	£5	£10	
Love Among The Young	LP	Pye	NPL28021	1963	£6	£15	
Mary's Little Lamb	7"	Pye	7N25155	1962	£1.50	£4	
Pin A Medal On Joey	7"	Pye	7N25170	1963	£1.50	£4	
P.S. I Love You	7" EP	Pye	NEP44004	1959	£4	£8	
Sings For All Sizes	LP	Colpix	CP424	1962	£6	£15	US
Sings The Movies	LP	Colpix	CP418	1961	£6	£15	US

DARREN, JENNIE

River Deep Mountain High	7"	Major Minor	MM611	1969	£1.50	£4	

DARTELLS

Dartell Stomp	7"	London	HLD9719	1963	£5	£10	
Hot Pastrami	LP	Dot	DLP3522/25522	1963	£6	£15	US

DARTS

Hollywood Drag	LP	Del-Fi	DF(ST)1244	1963	£5	£12	US

DARVELL, BARRY

How Will It End	7"	London	HL9191	1960	£15	£30	

DARWIN'S THEORY

Daytime	7"	Major Minor	MM503	1967	£10	£20	

DASGUPTA, NATAI

Songs Of India	LP	Mushroom	100MR22	1972	£8	£20	

DATE WITH SOUL
This single is a reissue of one originally credited to Hale and the Hushabyes.

Yes Sir That's My Baby	7"	Stateside	SS2062	1967	£2	£5	
Yes Sir, That's My Baby	7"	York	408	1967	£15	£30	US

DAUGHTERS OF THE ALBION

Daughters Of The Albion	LP	Fontana	STL5486	1968	£8	£20	

DAUNER, WOLFGANG

Et Cetera	LP	Intercord	26001	1971	£6	£15	German
Et Cetera Live	LP	MPS	2921754	1973	£6	£15	German
Khirsh	LP	MPS	2121432	1972	£6	£15	German
Rischkas Soul	LP	Brain	0001016	1972	£6	£15	German

DAVANI, DAVE

Don't Fool Around	7"	Columbia	DB7125	1963	£4	£8	
Four Faced	LP	Parlophone		1962	£10	£25	
Fused	LP	Parlophone	PMC1258	1965	£8	£20	
Midnight Special	7"	Decca	F11896	1964	£5	£10	
One Track Mind	7"	Parlophone	R5525	1966	£6	£12	
Top Of The Pops	7"	Parlophone	R5329	1965	£5	£10	
Tossin' And Turnin'	7"	Parlophone	R5490	1966	£5	£10	

DAVE & THE DIAMONDS

I Walk The Lonely Night	7"	Columbia	DB7692	1965	£2.50	£6	

DAVE DEE, DOZY, BEAKY, MICK & TICH

All I Want	7"	Fontana	TF586	1965	£4	£8	
Bend It	7"	Fontana	TF746	1966	£1.50	£4	chart single
Bend It	7" EP	Fontana	465324	1966	£5	£10	French
Dave Dee,Dozy,Beaky,Mick & Tich	LP	Fontana	(S)TL5350	1966	£5	£12	chart LP
DDDBMT	LP	Fontana	SFL13002	1968	£4	£10	
Don Juan	7"	Fontana	TF1000	1969	£1.50	£4	chart single
Golden Hits	LP	Fontana	(S)TL5441	1967	£4	£10	
Hideaway	7"	Fontana	TF711	1966	£1.50	£4	chart single
Hideaway	7" EP	Fontana	465312	1966	£5	£10	French
Hold Tight	7"	Fontana	TF671	1966	£1.50	£4	chart single
If Music Be The Food Of Love	LP	Fontana	(S)TL5388	1966	£4	£10	chart LP
If No One Sang	7"	Fontana	(S)TL5471	1968	£4	£10	
Last Night In Soho	7"	Fontana	TF953	1968	£1.50	£4	chart single
Legend Of	LP	Fontana	SFL13063	1969	£4	£10	
Legend Of Xanadu	7"	Fontana	TF903	1968	£1.50	£4	chart single
Loos Of England	7" EP	Fontana	TE17488	1967	£2.50	£6	
No Time	7"	Fontana	TF531	1965	£6	£12	
Okay	7"	Fontana	TF830	1967	£1.50	£4	chart single
Save Me	7"	Fontana	TF775	1966	£1.50	£4	chart single
Save Me	7" EP	Fontana	465349	1966	£5	£10	French
Snake In The Grass	7"	Fontana	TF1020	1969	£1.50	£4	chart single
Together	LP	Fontana	SFL13173	1969	£4	£10	
Touch Me Touch Me	7"	Fontana	TF798	1967	£1.50	£4	chart single
Touch Me Touch Me	7" EP	Fontana	465372	1966	£5	£10	French
Wreck Of The Antoinette	7"	Fontana	TF971	1968	£1.50	£4	chart single
You Make It Move	7"	Fontana	TF630	1965	£1.50	£4	chart single

Zabadak .... 7" ...... Fontana .... TF873 .... 1967 ... £1.50 ....£4 ....chart single

DAVENPORT, BOB
And The Marsden Rattlers .... LP ..... Trailer .... LER3008 .... 1971 ... £10 ....£25 ....
Bob Davenport And The Rakes .... LP ..... Columbia .... SX1786 .... 1965 ... £10 ....£25 ....
Bob Davenport And The Rakes .... LP ..... Topic .... 12TS350 .... 1977 ... £5 ....£12 ....
Down The Long Road .... LP ..... Topic .... 12TS274 .... 1975 ... £6 ....£15 ....
Geordie Songs .... 7" EP.. Collector .... JEB4 .... 1959 ... £7.50 .....£15 ....
Postcards Home .... LP ..... Topic .... 12TS318 .... 1977 ... £5 ....£12 ....

DAVEY & MORRIS
Davey & Morris .... LP ..... York .... FYK417 .... 1973 ... £10 ....£25 ....

DAVEY & THE BADMEN
Wanted .... LP ..... KRW .... WA63054 .... £17.50 .....£35 .... US

DAVID
Another Day, Another Lifetime .... LP ..... UMC .... 124 .... 1968 ... £8 ....£20 .... US
Please Mr.Postman .... 7" .... Philips .... BF1776 .... 1969 ... £10 ....£20 ....

DAVID & JONATHAN
David & Jonathan .... LP ..... Columbia .... SX/SCX6031 ...... 1967 ... £6 ....£15 ....
Laughing Fit To Cry .... 7" ...... Columbia .... DB7717 .... 1965 ... £1.50 ....£4 ....
Lovers Of The World Unite .... 7" ...... Columbia .... DB7950 .... 1966 ... £1.50 ....£4 ....chart single
Lovers Of The World Unite .... 7" EP.. Columbia .... ESRF1807 .... 1966 ... £4 ....£8 ....French
Michelle .... 7" ...... Columbia .... DB7800 .... 1966 ... £1.50 ....£4 ....chart single
She's Leaving Home .... 7" ...... Columbia .... DB8208 .... 1967 ... £1.50 ....£4 ....
Softly Whispering I Love You .... 7" ...... Columbia .... DB8287 .... 1967 ... £1.50 ....£4 ....
Speak Her Name .... 7" ...... Columbia .... DB7873 .... 1966 ... £1.50 ....£4 ....
Ten Storeys High .... 7" ...... Columbia .... DB8035 .... 1966 ... £1.50 ....£4 ....
You Ought To Meet My Baby .... 7" ...... Columbia .... DB8428 .... 1968 ... £1.50 ....£4 ....

DAVID & ROZAA
Spark That Lights The Flame .... 7" .... Philips .... 6006094 .... 1971 ... £5 ....£10 ....
Time Of Our Life .... 7" .... Philips .... 6006040 .... 1970 ... £5 ....£10 ....

DAVIDSON, DIANE
Ain't Gonna Be Treated This Way .... 7" .... Janus .... 6146021 .... 1974 ... £1.50 ....£4 ....
Sympathy .... 7" .... Janus .... 6146019 .... 1974 ... £1.50 ....£4 ....
Sympathy .... 7" .... Janus .... no number .... 1972 ... £5 ....£10 .... demo, & 2
tracks by other artists

DAVIDSON, FRANKIE
Detour .... 7" .... London .... HL9309 .... 1961 ... £1.50 ....£4 ....
Have You Ever Been To See London .... 7" .... HMV .... POP1224 .... 1963 ... £1.50 ....£4 ....
I Just Love To Shake .... 7" .... HMV .... POP1256 .... 1963 ... £1.50 ....£4 ....
I've Got A Heart .... 7" .... HMV .... POP1458 .... 1965 ... £1.50 ....£4 ....
Love .... 7" .... HMV .... POP1345 .... 1964 ... £1.50 ....£4 ....

DAVIDSON, FRANKIE & THE HI MARKS
You're Driving Me Crazy .... 7" .... Starlite .... ST45037 .... 1961 ... £6 ....£12 ....

DAVIDSON, TOMMY
Half Past Kissing Time .... 7" .... London .... HLU8219 .... 1956 ... £12.50 .....£25 ....

DAVIE, HUTCH & HIS HONKY TONKERS
At The Woodchoppers' Ball .... 7" .... London .... HLE8667 .... 1958 ... £5 ....£10 ....

DAVIES, ALUN
Daydo .... LP ..... CBS .... 65108 .... 1972 ... £5 ....£12 ....

DAVIES, BOB
Rock And Roll Show .... 7" .... London .... HLU9767 .... 1963 ... £7.50 .....£15 ....

DAVIES, CYRIL
Country Line Special .... 7" .... Pye .... 7N17663 .... 1969 ... £4 ....£8 ....
Country Line Special .... 7" .... Pye .... 7N25194 .... 1963 ... £6 ....£12 ....
Legendary Cyril Davies .... LP ..... Folklore .... FLEUT9 .... 1970 ... £20 ....£40 ....
Legendary Cyril Davies .... 10" LP 77 .... LP2 .... 1957 ... £60 ....£120 ....
Preaching The Blues .... 7" .... Pye .... 7N25221 .... 1963 ... £5 ....£10 ....
Sound Of Davies .... 7" EP.. Pye .... NEP44025 .... 1964 ... £15 ....£30 ....

DAVIES, DAVE
Dave Davies Hits .... 7" EP.. Pye .... NEP24289 .... 1968 ... £75 ....£150 ....
Death Of A Clown .... 7" .... Pye .... 7N17356 .... 1967 ... £1.50 ....£4 ....chart single
Death Of A Clown .... 7" EP.. Pye .... PNV24196 .... 1967 ... £12.50 .....£25 ....French, B
side by the Kinks
Hold My Hand .... 7" .... Pye .... 7N17678 .... 1969 ... £4 ....£8 ....
Lincoln County .... 7" .... Pye .... 7N17514 .... 1968 ... £4 ....£8 ....
Susannah's Still Alive .... 7" .... Pye .... 7N17429 .... 1967 ... £1.50 ....£4 ....chart single

DAVIES, IRVING
Method .... 7" .... Decca .... F11456 .... 1962 ... £1.50 ....£4 ....

DAVIES, MIAR
I Hear You Knocking .... 7" .... Decca .... F11894 .... 1964 ... £1.50 ....£4 ....

DAVIS, BETTE & DEBBIE BURTON
Whatever Happened To Baby Jane ...... 7" .... London .... HLU9711 .... 1963 ... £1.50 ....£4 ....

DAVIS, BETTY
Betty Davis .... LP ..... Just Sunshine . JSS5 .... 1973 ... £4 ....£10 .... US

Nasty Gal	LP	Island	ILPS9329	1975	£4	£10	
They Say I'm Different	LP	Polydor	2933402	1974	£4	£10	

DAVIS, BILLIE

Angel Of The Morning	7"	Decca	F12696	1967	£1.50	£4	
Billie Davis	LP	Decca	SKL5029	1970	£6	£15	
Heart And Soul	7"	Piccadilly	7N35308	1966	£2	£5	
He's The One	7"	Decca	F11658	1963	£1.50	£4	chart single
I Can Remember	7"	Decca	F12923	1969	£4	£8	
I Want You To Be My Baby	7"	Decca	F12823	1968	£1.50	£4	
Just Walk In My Shoes	7"	Piccadilly	7N35350	1966	£4	£8	
Last One To Be Loved	7"	Piccadilly	7N35227	1965	£1.50	£4	
Make The Feeling Go Away	7"	Decca	F12870	1969	£1.50	£4	
Nights In White Satin	7"	Decca	F12977	1969	£1.50	£4	
No Other Baby	7"	Piccadilly	7N35266	1965	£1.50	£4	
Say Nothing	7"	Columbia	DB7195	1964	£1.50	£4	
School Is Over	7"	Columbia	DB7246	1964	£1.50	£4	
Tell Him	7"	Decca	F11572	1963	£1.50	£4	chart single
Wasn't It You	7"	Decca	F12620	1967	£1.50	£4	
Whatcha Gonna Do	7"	Columbia	DB7346	1964	£1.50	£4	
You And I	7"	Columbia	DB7115	1963	£1.50	£4	

DAVIS, BOBBY

Hype You Into Selling Your Head	7"	Starlite	ST45056	1961	£10	£20	

DAVIS, BONNIE

Pepperhot Baby	7"	Brunswick	05507	1955	£7.50	£15	

DAVIS, CLIFFORD

Before the Beginning	7"	Reprise	RS27003	1969	£2.50	£6	
Come On Down And Follow Me	7"	Reprise	RS25008	1970	£2.50	£6	
Man Of The World	7"	Reprise	K14282	1973	£2.50	£6	

DAVIS, DANNY

Love Me	7"	Parlophone	R4657	1960	£1.50	£4	
Patches	7"	Pye	7N15470	1962	£1.50	£4	
Rome Wasn't Built In A Day	7"	Pye	7N15427	1962	£2	£5	
Rumours	7"	Pye	7N15391	1961	£1.50	£4	

DAVIS, DANNY ORCHESTRA

Main Theme From The Saint	7"	MGM	MGM1277	1965	£1.50	£4	

DAVIS, EDDIE 'LOCKJAW'

Count Basie Presents The Eddie Davis Trio	LP	Columbia	33SX1117	1959	£6	£15	
Eddie Lockjaw Davis	7" EP	Esquire	EP217	1959	£2	£5	
Eddie 'Lockjaw' Davis Cookbook	LP	Esquire	32104	1960	£6	£15	
Eddie Lockjaw Davis Quartet	7" EP	Esquire	EP237	1961	£2	£5	
Eddie Lockjaw Davis Trio	7" EP	Parlophone	GEP8587	1956	£2	£5	
Eddie Lockjaw Davis Trio	7" EP	Parlophone	GEP8685	1958	£2	£5	
First Set (Live At Minton's)	LP	Stateside	SL10102	1964	£6	£15	
Jaws In Orbit	LP	Esquire	32128	1961	£6	£15	
Lockjaw	7" EP	Parlophone	GEP8678	1957	£2	£5	
Very Saxy	LP	Esquire	32117	1960	£6	£15	

DAVIS, JACKIE

Land Of Make Believe	7"	Pye		196-	£6	£12	

DAVIS, JESSE ED

Jesse Ed Davis	LP	Atco	2400106	1971	£5	£12	
Keep On Coming	LP	CBS	65649	1973	£5	£12	
Ululu	LP	Atlantic	K40329	1972	£5	£12	

DAVIS, JIMMY

Maxwell Street Jimmy Davis	LP	Bounty	BY6009	1966	£6	£15	

DAVIS, KIM

Don't Take Your Lovin' Away	7"	Decca	F12387	1966	£7.50	£15	
Tell It Like It Is	7"	CBS	202568	1967	£2.50	£6	

DAVIS, LARRY & FENTON ROBINSON

Larry Davis And Fenton Robinson	LP	Python	PLP24	1972	£8	£20	

DAVIS, MARTHA & SPOUSE

Tribute To Fats Waller	LP	HMV	CLP1216	1958	£4	£10	

DAVIS, MELVIN

Save It	7"	Action	ACT4531	1969	£5	£10	

DAVIS, MILES

The changing styles of jazz presented by Miles Davis during his four-and-a-half decade career give his many fans a uniquely varied listening experience if they follow it all through. From the late sixties until a serious car crash put a temporary halt to his career in 1975, Miles Davis maintained a remarkable creative run in which he not only invented the fusion genre, but also began to explore most of the possibilities inherent in it. He released an unusually large number of records during this period, and every one is different. Of the rarities listed here, the quadrophonic mix of "Bitches Brew" is significantly different from the stereo, with extra percussion and a frequent doubling up of melodic phrases to create an echo effect. The Japanese double albums are all live recordings - "Black Beauty", with Chick Corea, Jack DeJohnette, and Steve Grossman, is close to the jazz avant-garde in places; "Dark Magus" is a densely rhythmic work-out from a 1974 Carnegie Hall concert; while "Pangaea" is a companion set to the UK released "Agharta" - the second set from the same evening's performance. It is magnificent, powerful music, though not for the faint-hearted. The Session Disc LP, a poorly recorded set from 1971, would qualify as a bootleg if it was a rock album - in the jazz world, however, such live recordings have always been accepted as part of the natural scheme of things.

Bags' Groove	LP	Esquire	32090	1959	£10	£25	
Birth Of The Cool	LP	Capitol	T1974	1966	£5	£12	

Title	Format	Label	Catalogue	Year	Price	Price	Notes
Birth Of The Cool	LP	Capitol	T762	1957	£20	£40	
Bitches Brew	LP	CBS	66236	1970	£5	£12	double
Bitches Brew	LP	CBS	QBL30998/9	1971	£8	£20	quad double
Black Beauty	LP	CBS-Sony	SOPJ39/40	1973	£10	£25	Japanese double
Blue Changes	7" EP	Esquire	EP242	1961	£2	£5	
Blue Haze	LP	Esquire	32088	1960	£15	£30	
Blue Miles	7" EP	Esquire	EP232	1960	£2	£5	
Blue Moods	LP	Vocalion	LAEF584	1964	£8	£20	
Changes	LP	Esquire	32028	1957	£10	£25	
Classics In Jazz	10" LP	Capitol	LC6683	1954	£15	£30	
Collectors' Item	LP	Esquire	32030	1957	£20	£40	
Cookin'	LP	Esquire	32048	1958	£10	£25	
Dark Magus	LP	CBS-Sony	40AP741/2	1977	£10	£25	Japanese double
Davis Cup	7" EP	Philips	BBE12418	1961	£2	£5	
Dig	10" LP	Esquire	20017	1953	£15	£30	
Early Miles	LP	Esquire	32118	1961	£10	£25	
E.S.P.	LP	CBS	(S)BPG62577	1966	£5	£12	
Ezz-thetic	LP	XTRA	XTRA5004	1966	£5	£12	with Lee Konitz, B side by Teddy Charles
Filles De Kilimanjaro	LP	CBS	63551	1969	£4	£10	
Four And More	LP	CBS	(S)BPG62655	1966	£5	£12	
Friday Night At The Blackhawk	LP	CBS	(S)BPG62306	1964	£5	£12	
Friday Night At The Blackhawk	LP	Fontana	TFL5163/STFL580	1961	£8	£20	
HiFi Modern Jazz Jam Session	10" LP	Esquire	20052	1955	£15	£30	
Hooray For Miles Davis	LP	Session Disc.	123	1972	£6	£15	
In A Silent Way	LP	CBS	63630	1970	£4	£10	
Jazz Track	LP	Fontana	TFL5081	1960	£10	£25	
Kind Of Blue	LP	CBS	(S)BPG62066	1966	£4	£10	
Kind Of Blue	LP	Fontana	TFL5072/STFL513	1960	£8	£20	
Live/Evil	LP	CBS	QBL30954	1973	£6	£15	quad double
Miles Ahead	LP	CBS	(S)BPG62496	1966	£4	£10	
Miles Ahead	LP	Fontana	TFL5007	1957	£10	£25	
Miles And Monk At Newport	LP	CBS	(S)BPG62389	1964	£6	£15	with Thelonious Monk
Miles Davis	LP	Esquire	32021	1957	£20	£40	
Miles Davis	7" EP	Esquire	EP152	1957	£2	£5	
Miles Davis	7" EP	Fontana	TFE17119	1959	£2	£5	
Miles Davis	7" EP	Philips	BBE12266	1959	£2	£5	
Miles Davis	7" EP	Philips	BBE12351	1960	£2	£5	
Miles Davis	7" EP	Vogue	EPV1191	1958	£2	£5	
Miles Davis All Stars	10" LP	Esquire	20021	1953	£15	£30	
Miles Davis All Stars	10" LP	Vogue	LDE028	1953	£25	£50	
Miles Davis All Stars Sextet	10" LP	Esquire	20062	1956	£15	£30	
Miles Davis And His Orchestra	10" LP	Vogue	LDE064	1954	£15	£30	
Miles Davis And John Coltrane Play Richard Rogers	LP	Pacific Jazz	688204ZL	1965	£6	£15	
Miles Davis And John Coltrane Play Richard Rogers	LP	Stateside	SL10111	1965	£6	£15	
Miles Davis And John Coltrane Play Richard Rogers	LP	Transatlantic	PR7322	1968	£5	£12	
Miles Davis And The Modern Jazz Giants	LP	Esquire	32100	1960	£10	£25	
Miles Davis At Carnegie Hall	LP	CBS	(S)BPG62081	1962	£6	£15	
Miles Davis In Europe	LP	CBS	(S)BPG62390	1964	£6	£15	
Miles Davis New Quartet	7" EP	Esquire	EP212	1959	£2	£5	
Miles Davis No.2	7" EP	Fontana	TFE17223	1960	£2	£5	
Miles Davis No.3	7" EP	Fontana	TFE17225	1960	£2	£5	
Miles Davis Orchestra	7" EP	Capitol	EAP1459	1954	£2	£5	
Miles Davis Orchestra	7" EP	Capitol	EAP2459	1954	£2	£5	
Miles Davis Plays For Lovers	LP	Stateside	SL10168	1966	£6	£15	
Miles Davis Quartet	7" EP	Esquire	EP12	195-	£2	£5	
Miles Davis Quartet	7" EP	Esquire	EP132	1957	£2	£5	
Miles Davis Quartet	7" EP	Esquire	EP172	1958	£2	£5	
Miles Davis Quartet	7" EP	Fontana	TFE17359	1961	£2	£5	
Miles Davis Quintet	10" LP	Esquire	20041	1955	£15	£30	
Miles Davis Quintet	10" LP	Esquire	20072	1956	£15	£30	
Miles Davis Sextet	7" EP	Vogue	EPV1075	1956	£2	£5	
Miles Davis Vol.1	LP	Blue Note	BLP/BST81501	1961	£10	£25	
Miles Davis Vol.2	LP	Blue Note	BLP/BST81502	1964	£10	£25	
Miles In The Sky	LP	CBS	63352	1969	£4	£10	
Miles Smiles	LP	CBS	(S)BPG62933	1967	£5	£12	
Miles Theme	7" EP	Esquire	EP222	1959	£2	£5	
Milestones	LP	CBS	62308	1967	£4	£10	
Milestones	LP	Fontana	TFL5035	1958	£8	£20	
Modern Jazz Giants	LP	Transatlantic	PR7150	1967	£5	£12	
More Miles	7" EP	Fontana	TFE17195	1959	£2	£5	
Most Of Miles	LP	Fontana	TFL5089	1960	£6	£15	
Musings Of Miles	LP	Esquire	32012	1956	£15	£30	
My Funny Valentine	LP	CBS	(S)BPG62510	1965	£5	£12	
Nature Boy	10" LP	Vogue	LDE191	1957	£20	£40	
Nefertiti	LP	CBS	63248	1968	£4	£10	
Odyssey!	LP	XTRA	XTRA5050	1968	£5	£12	
Pangaea	LP	CBS-Sony	36AP1789/90	1975	£10	£25	Japanese double
Porgy And Bess	LP	CBS	(S)BPG62108	1966	£4	£10	
Porgy And Bess	LP	Fontana	TFL5056	1959	£8	£20	
Porgy And Bess	7" EP	Fontana	TFE17247	1960	£2	£5	
Quiet Nights	LP	CBS	(S)BPG62213	1964	£6	£15	
Relaxin'	LP	Esquire	32068	1958	£10	£25	
Round About Midnight	LP	Philips	BBL7140	1957	£8	£20	
Saturday Night At The Blackhawk	LP	CBS	(S)BPG62307	1964	£5	£12	

Title	Format	Label	Catalogue	Year	Price	Price	Notes
Saturday Night At The Blackhawk	LP	Fontana	TFL5164/STFL581	1961	£8	£20	
Second HiFi Modern Jazz Jam Session	10" LP	Esquire	20056	1955	£15	£30	
Seven Steps To Heaven	LP	CBS	(S)BPG62170	1964	£6	£15	
Sketches Of Spain	LP	CBS	(S)BPG62327	1964	£4	£10	
Sketches Of Spain	LP	Fontana	TFL5100/STFL531	1961	£10	£25	
Someday My Prince Will Come	LP	CBS	(S)BPG62104	1966	£4	£10	
Someday My Prince Will Come	LP	Fontana	TFL5172/STFL587	1962	£8	£20	
Sorcerer	LP	CBS	63097	1968	£4	£10	
Steamin' With The Miles Davis Quintet	LP	Esquire	32138	1961	£10	£25	
Straight No Chaser	7" EP	Fontana	TFE17197	1959	£2	£5	
Walkin'	LP	Esquire	32098	1960	£10	£25	
Workin' With The Miles Davis Quintet	LP	Esquire	32108	1960	£10	£25	

DAVIS, MILES & ART BLAKEY

Title	Format	Label	Catalogue	Year	Price	Price	Notes
Back To Back	LP	Fontana	FJL135	1966	£4	£10	

DAVIS, REV.GARY

Title	Format	Label	Catalogue	Year	Price	Price	Notes
Bring Your Money Honey	LP	Fontana	SFJL914	1969	£5	£12	
Children Of Zion	LP	Transatlantic	TRA249	1971	£4	£10	
Harlem Street Singer	LP	Fontana	688303ZL	1964	£5	£12	
Little More Faith	LP	Prestige	BV1032	1962	£6	£15	US
Little More Faith	LP	XTRA	XTRA5042	1968	£6	£15	
Lo I Be With You Always	LP	Kicking Mule	SNKD1	1974	£5	£12	double
Lord I Wish I Could See	LP	Biograph	BLP12034	1971	£5	£12	US
Pure Religion And Bad Company	LP	77	LA1214	1963	£6	£15	
Ragtime Guitar	LP	Transatlantic	TRA244	1971	£4	£10	
Say No To The Devil	LP	XTRA	XTRA5014	1966	£6	£15	
When I Die, I'll Live Again	LP	Fantasy	F24704	1972	£5	£12	US

DAVIS, SAMMY JR.

Title	Format	Label	Catalogue	Year	Price	Price	Notes
All Of You	7"	Brunswick	05629	1956	£1.50	£4	chart single
And This Is My Beloved	7"	Brunswick	05409	1955	£1.50	£4	
Azure	7"	Capitol	CL14562	1956	£1.50	£4	
Because Of You	7"	Brunswick	05326	1954	£1.50	£4	
Birth Of The Blues	7"	Brunswick	05383	1955	£1.50	£4	
Happy To Make You Acquaintance	7"	Brunswick	05830	1960	£1.50	£4	chart single
Hey There	7"	Brunswick	05469	1955	£4	£8	chart single
In A Persian Market	7"	Brunswick	05518	1956	£2	£5	chart single
Just For Lovers	LP	Brunswick	LAT8088	1956	£4	£10	
Love Me Or Leave Me	7"	Brunswick	05428	1955	£4	£8	chart single
Not For Me	7"	Reprise	R20289	1964	£2	£5	
Shelter Of Your Arms	7"	Reprise	R20227	1964	£1.50	£4	
Six Bridges To Cross	7"	Brunswick	05389	1955	£1.50	£4	
Starring Sammy Davis	LP	Brunswick	LAT8153	1956	£4	£10	
That Old Black Magic	7"	Brunswick	05450	1955	£4	£8	chart single

DAVIS SISTERS

Title	Format	Label	Catalogue	Year	Price	Price	Notes
Rock-a-bye Boogie	78	HMV	B10582	1953	£5	£10	

DAVIS, SKEETER

Title	Format	Label	Catalogue	Year	Price	Price	Notes
Cloudy, With Occasional Tears	LP	RCA	RD/SF7604	1963	£5	£12	
End Of The World	LP	RCA	RD/SF7563	1963	£5	£12	
End Of The World	7"	RCA	RCA1328	1963	£1.50	£4	chart single
Gonna Get Along Without Ya Now	7"	RCA	RCA1398	1964	£1.50	£4	
He Says The Same Things To Me	7"	RCA	RCA1384	1964	£1.50	£4	
Here's The Answer	LP	RCA	LPM2327	1961	£5	£12	US
I Can't Stay Mad At You	7"	RCA	RCA1363	1963	£1.50	£4	
I'll Sing You A Song And Harmonize Too	LP	RCA	LPM2197	1960	£5	£12	US
I'm Falling Too	7"	RCA	RCA1201	1960	£2	£5	
Let Me Get Close To You	LP	RCA	RD7676	1964	£5	£12	
Mary Frances	LP	RCA	SF8068	1969	£4	£10	
My Last Date With You	7"	RCA	RCA1222	1961	£1.50	£4	
Silver Threads And Golden Needles	7" EP	RCA	RCX7153	1964	£4	£8	
Somebody Else On Your Mind	7"	RCA	RCA1345	1963	£1.50	£4	
Sun Glasses	7"	RCA	RCA1474	1965	£1.50	£4	

DAVIS, SKEETER & BOBBY BARE

Title	Format	Label	Catalogue	Year	Price	Price	Notes
Tunes For Two	LP	RCA	RD7711	1965	£4	£10	

DAVIS, SKEETER & PORTER WAGONER

Title	Format	Label	Catalogue	Year	Price	Price	Notes
Duets	LP	RCA	LPM/LSP2529	1962	£5	£12	US

DAVIS, SPENCER, GROUP

Spencer Davis had no dominant role within the group that bore his name, which is probably why his solo career in the seventies and eighties has been such a low-key affair. Originally, the Spencer Davis Group focussed on its dynamic young singer, Stevie Winwood, who was also a talented guitarist and keyboard player. Winwood shines throughout the group's sturdy R&B material and in particular on the impressive series of singles, which include some real classics. Remarkably, when Winwood left to form Traffic, Spencer Davis was able to find a replacement, Eddie Hardin, whose singing and keyboard playing was almost as fine. "Time Seller" and "Mr.Second Class" are a worthy continuation of the singles series, being soulful performances tinged with psychedelia. They are included on the album "With Their New Face On", which is itself a very under-rated recording.

Title	Format	Label	Catalogue	Year	Price	Price	Notes
After Tea	7"	United Artists	UP2213	1968	£1.50	£4	
Autumn 66	LP	Fontana	STL5359	1966	£8	£20	chart LP
Best Of The Spencer Davis Group	LP	Island	ILP970/ILPS9070	1968	£8	£20	
Dimples	7"	Fontana	TF471	1964	£5	£10	
Every Little Bit Hurts	7"	Fontana	TF530	1965	£4	£8	chart single
Every Little Bit Hurts	7" EP	Fontana	TE17450	1965	£5	£10	
Gimme Some Lovin'	LP	United Artists	UAL3578/UAS6578	1967	£6	£15	US

201

Gimme Some Lovin'	7"	Fontana	TF762	1966	£1.50	£4	chart single
Gimme Some Loving	7" EP	Fontana	465337	1966	£6	£12	French
Hits Of The Spencer Davis Group	cass-s	Philips	MCF5003	1968	£4	£10	
I Can't Stand It	7"	Fontana	TF499	1964	£4	£8	chart single
I'm A Man	LP	United Artists	UAL3589/	1967	£6	£15	US
			UAS6589				
I'm A Man	7"	Fontana	TF785	1967	£1.50	£4	chart single
I'm A Man	7" EP	Fontana	465360	1966	£6	£12	French
Keep On Running	7"	Fontana	TF632	1965	£1.50	£4	chart single
Keep On Running	7" EP	Fontana	465297	1965	£6	£12	French
Letters From Edith	LP	CBS	63842	1969	£30	£60	test pressing
Mr.Second Class	7"	United Artists	UP1203	1967	£1.50	£4	chart single
Second Album	LP	Fontana	TL5295	1966	£8	£20	chart LP
Short Change	7"	United Artists	UP2226	1968	£1.50	£4	
Sitting And Thinking	7" EP	Fontana	TE17463	1966	£5	£10	
Somebody Help Me	7"	Fontana	TF679	1966	£1.50	£4	chart single
Somebody Help Me	7" EP	Fontana	465305	1966	£6	£12	French
Strong Love	7"	Fontana	TF571	1965	£2.50	£6	chart single
Their First Album	LP	Fontana	TL5242	1965	£8	£20	chart LP
Their First Album	LP	Wing	WL1165	1968	£4	£10	
Time Seller	7"	Fontana	TF854	1967	£1.50	£4	chart single
When I Come Home	7"	Fontana	TF739	1966	£1.50	£4	chart single
When I Come Home	7" EP	Fontana	465318	1966	£6	£12	French
With Their New Face On	LP	United Artists	SULP1192	1968	£6	£15	
You Put The Hurt On Me	7" EP	Fontana	TE17444	1965	£5	£10	

DAVIS, SPENCER GROUP & TRAFFIC

Here We Go Round The Mulberry Bush	LP	United Artists	SULP1186	1968	£6	£15	

DAVIS, STEVE

Takes Time To Know Her	7"	Fontana	TF922	1968	£12.50	£25	

DAVIS, TYRONE

Can I Change My Mind	7"	Atlantic	584253	1969	£1.50	£4	
Could I Forget You	7"	Atlantic	2091078	1971	£1.50	£4	
If This World Were Mine	7"	Trojan	TR677	1969	£1.50	£4	
Is It Something You've Got	7"	Atlantic	584265	1969	£1.50	£4	
Need Your Lovin' Every Day	7"	Atlantic	584288	1969	£1.50	£4	
One Way Ticket	7"	Atlantic	2091131	1971	£1.50	£4	
Turn Back The Hands Of Time	LP	Atlantic	2465021	1970	£4	£10	
Turn Back The Hands Of Time	LP	Atlantic	2091003	1970	£2	£5	
What If A Man	7"	Stateside	SS2092	1968	£2.50	£6	

DAVIS, WALTER

RCA Victor Race Series Vol.3	7" EP	RCA	RCX7169	1964	£5	£10	
Think You Need A Shot	LP	RCA	INTS1085	1970	£4	£10	

DAVIS, WARREN MONDAY BAND

Love Is A Hurting Thing	7"	Columbia	DB8270	1967	£4	£8	
Wait For Me	7"	Columbia	DB8190	1967	£6	£12	

DAVIS, WILD BILL

Wild Bill Davis	10" LP	Philips	BBR8079	1956	£8	£20	

DAVISON, BRIAN

Brian Davison, previously the drummer with the Nice, formed Every Which Way after that group split up - and probably watched with envy the rise to international stardom of Emerson, Lake, and Palmer.

Every Which Way	LP	Charisma	CAS1021	1970	£4	£10	

DAVISON, WILD BILL

Greatest Of The Greats	LP	Vogue	LAE12217	1960	£4	£10	
Wild Blll Davison	LP	London	LTZU15068	1957	£5	£12	
Wild Bill Davison Band	10" LP	Melodisc	MLP501	1955	£8	£20	
With Strings Attached	LP	Philips	BBL7104	1957	£5	£12	

DAWE, TIM

Penrod	LP	Straight	ST1058	1969	£8	£20	US

DAWKINS, CARL

All Of A Sudden	7"	Rio	R136	1967	£4	£8	
Baby I Love You	7"	Rio	R137	1967	£4	£8	
Hot And Sticky	7"	Rio	R138	1967	£4	£8	Rulers B side
I Love The Way You Are	7"	Blue Cat	BS114	1968	£4	£8	Dermott Lynch B side
I'll Make It Up	7"	Duke	DU3	1968	£4	£8	J.J.Allstars B side
Rodney's History	7"	Nu Beat	NB030	1969	£2.50	£6	Dynamites B side

DAWKINS, HORELL

Butterfly	7"	Ska Beat	JB240	1966	£5	£10	

DAWKINS, JIMMY

Fast Fingers	LP	Delmark	DS623	1971	£6	£15	

DAWKINS, RUSS & THE WAILERS

Picture On The Wall	7"	Upsetter	US368	1971	£6	£12	Upsetters B side

DAWN & THE DEEJAYS

These Are The Things About You	7"	RCA	RCA1470	1965	£1.50	£4	

DAWN, JULIE

Wild Horses	7"	Columbia	SCM5035	1953	£1.50	£4	

DAWNBREAKERS

Let's Live	7"	Decca	F12110	1965	£1.50	£4	

DAWNWIND

Looking Back On The Future	LP	Amron	ARD5003	1976	£25	£50	

DAWSON, LES SYNDICATE

Last Chicken In The Shop	7"	Melodisc	1586	1964	£2	£5	

DAWSON, LESLEY

Just Say Goodbye	7"	Mercury	MF946	1967	£1.50	£4	
Run For Shelter	7"	Mercury	MF965	1967	£4	£8	

DAX, DANIELLE

Pop-Eyes	LP	Initial	IRC009	1983	£10	£25	

DAY, BING

I Can't Help It	7"	Mercury	AMT1047	1959	£20	£40	

DAY BLINDNESS

Day Blindness	LP	Studio 10	DBX101	1968	£10	£25	US

DAY, BOBBY

Bluebird Buzzard And Oriole	7"	London	HL8800	1959	£12.50	£25	
Little Bitty Pretty One	7"	HMV	POP425	1957	£30	£60	
Love Is A One Time Affair	7"	London	HL8964	1959	£7.50	£15	
My Blue Heaven	7"	London	HLY9044	1960	£7.50	£15	
Over And Over	7"	Top Rank	JAR538	1961	£5	£10	
Rockin' Robin	7"	London	HL8726	1958	£10	£20	chart single
Rockin' Robin	7"	Sue	WI388	1965	£6	£12	
Rockin' With Robin	LP	Class	LP5002	1959	£50	£100	US

DAY, DORIS

Annie Get Your Gun	LP	CBS	(S)BPG62129	1963	£5	£12	
April In Paris	7"	Columbia	SCM5038	1953	£2.50	£6	
Boys And Girls Together	10" LP	Columbia	CL2530	195-	£6	£15	US
Bright And Shiny	LP	CBS	(S)BPG62053	1962	£4	£10	
Bright And Shiny	LP	Philips	BBL7471/SBBL619	1961	£6	£15	
Bushel And A Peck	7"	Columbia	SCM5044	1953	£5	£10	
By The Light Of The Silvery Moon	10" LP	Columbia	CL6248	1953	£10	£25	US
Calamity Jane (with Howard Keel)	10" LP	Philips	BBR8104	1956	£6	£15	
Canadian Capers	7" EP.	Columbia	SEG7507	1954	£2.50	£6	
Cherries	7"	Columbia	SCM5059	1953	£2.50	£6	
Christmas Album	LP	CBS	(S)BPG62712	1966	£5	£12	
Cuttin' Capers	LP	Philips	BBL7296/SBBL540	1959	£5	£12	
Day By Day	LP	Philips	BBL7142	1957	£10	£25	
Day By Night	LP	Philips	BBL7211	1958	£10	£25	
Day By Night	LP	Philips	SBBL548	1959	£6	£15	stereo, 1 different track
Day Dreams	LP	Philips	BBL7120	1957	£6	£15	
Day Dreams	7" EP.	Philips	BBE12151	1957	£4	£8	
Day In Hollywood	LP	Philips	BBL7175	1957	£6	£15	
Doris	7" EP.	Philips	BBE12167	1958	£4	£8	
Doris And Frank	LP	Philips	BBL7137	1957	£5	£12	with Frank Sinatra
Doris Day	7" EP.	Philips	BBE12007	1955	£6	£12	
Doris Day No.2	7" EP.	Philips	BBE12089	1956	£4	£8	
Dream A Little Dream Of Me	7" EP.	Philips	BBE12213	1958	£2.50	£6	
Duet	LP	CBS	(S)BPG62010	1962	£5	£12	with Andre Previn
Duet	7" EP.	CBS	AGG20018	1962	£2.50	£6	with Andre Previn
Duet No.2	7" EP.	CBS	AGG20029	1963	£2.50	£6	with Andre Previn
Favourites	10" LP	Philips	BBR8094	1956	£6	£15	
Hooray For Hollywood	LP	Philips	SBBL519	1959	£6	£15	stereo
Hooray For Hollywood Vol.1	LP	Philips	BBL7247	1958	£6	£15	
Hooray For Hollywood Vol.2	LP	Philips	BBL7248	1958	£6	£15	
Hot Canaries	10" LP	Columbia	CL2534	195-	£6	£15	US, with Peggy Lee
I Have Dreamed	LP	CBS	(S)BPG62057	1962	£4	£10	
I Have Dreamed	LP	Philips	BBL7496/SBBL643	1961	£6	£15	
I Have Dreamed	7" EP.	CBS	AGG20009	1962	£2.50	£6	
I'll Never Stop Loving You	7" EP.	Philips	BBE12011	1955	£6	£12	
I'll See You In My Dreams	10" LP	Columbia	CL6198	1951	£10	£25	US
In The Still Of The Night	LP	Philips	SBBL537	1960	£6	£15	
Jumbo	LP	CBS	(S)BPG62118	1962	£5	£12	
Just One Of Those Things	7"	Columbia	SCM5171	1955	£2.50	£6	
Latin For Lovers	LP	CBS	(S)BPG62502	1965	£5	£12	
Let's Fly Away	7" EP.	Philips	BBE12298	1959	£2.50	£6	
Let's Fly Away	7" EP.	Philips	SBBE9006	1960	£5	£10	stereo
Lights, Cameras, Action	10" LP	Columbia	CL2518	195-	£6	£15	US
Load Of Hay	7"	Columbia	SCM5087	1954	£2.50	£6	
Love Him	LP	CBS	(S)BPG62226	1964	£10	£25	
Love Me Or Leave Me	LP	Philips	BBL7047	1955	£10	£25	
Love Me Or Leave Me/Young At Heart	LP	CBS	63528	1969	£10	£25	
Lullaby Of Broadway	10" LP	Columbia	CL6168	1951	£10	£25	US
Lullaby Of Broadway (Doris Day Hits)	10" LP	Columbia	33S1038	1954	£8	£20	
Ma Says, Pa Says	7"	Columbia	SCM5033	1953	£5	£10	chart single
Mister Tap-Toe	7"	Columbia	SCM5062	1953	£2.50	£6	
Move Over Darling	7"	CBS	AAG183	1964	£1.50	£4	chart single
Move Over Darling	7" EP.	CBS	AGG20048	1964	£2.50	£6	
Nobody's Sweetheart	7" EP.	Columbia	SEG7531	1954	£2.50	£6	
On Moonlight Bay	10" LP	Columbia	CL6186	1951	£10	£25	US
Party's Over	7"	Philips	JK1031	1957	£2.50	£6	juke-box issue

Title	Format	Label	Catalogue	Year	Price	Price	Notes
Pillow Talk	7" EP	Philips	BBE12339	1959	£2.50	£6	
Pyjama Game	LP	Philips	BBL7197	1957	£4	£10	
Second Star To The Right	7"	Columbia	SCM5045	1953	£2.50	£6	
Sentimental Journey	LP	CBS	(S)BPG62562	1966	£5	£12	
Show Time	LP	Philips	BBL7392/SBBL577	1960	£5	£12	
Show Time No.1	7" EP	Philips	SBBE9034	1961	£2.50	£6	stereo
Showcase Of Hits	LP	Philips	BBL7297	1959	£5	£12	
Sings Her Great Movie Hits	LP	CBS	BPG62785	1966	£5	£12	
Sings Songs From Calamity Jane & The Pyjama Game	LP	CBS	BPG63032	1967	£4	£10	
Sometimes I'm Happy	7" EP	Columbia	SEG7546	1954	£2.50	£6	
Song Is You	7" EP	Philips	BBE12187	1958	£2.50	£6	
Tea For Two	10" LP	Columbia	CL6149	1950	£10	£25	US
That's The Way He Does It	7"	Columbia	SCM5075	1953	£2.50	£6	
That's What Makes Paris Paree	7"	Columbia	SCM5039	1953	£2.50	£6	
Twelve O'Clock Tonight	7"	Philips	JK1020	1957	£2.50	£6	juke-box issue
Vocal Gems From The Film Young Man Of Music	7" EP	Columbia	SEG7572	1955	£2.50	£6	
Voice Of Your Choice	10" LP	Philips	BBR8026	1954	£6	£15	
We Kiss In A Shadow	7"	Columbia	SCM5067	1953	£2.50	£6	
We Kiss In A Shadow	7" EP	Columbia	SEG7515	1954	£2.50	£6	
What Every Girl Should Know	LP	Philips	BBL7377/SBBL563	1965	£5	£12	
With A Smile And A Song	LP	CBS	(S)BPG62461	1965	£8	£20	
You Can't Have Everything	7" EP	Philips	BBE12388	1960	£2.50	£6	
You Can't Have Everything	7" EP	Philips	SBBE9021	1960	£5	£10	stereo
You'll Never Walk Alone	LP	CBS	(S)BPG62101	1963	£10	£25	
Young At Heart	10" LP	Philips	BBR8040	1955	£6	£15	with Frank Sinatra
Young Man With A Horn	LP	Columbia	CL582	1954	£6	£15	US
Young Man With A Horn	10" LP	Columbia	CL6106	1950	£10	£25	US
You're My Thrill	10" LP	Columbia	CL6071	1949	£8	£20	US

DAY, JACKIE

Title	Format	Label	Catalogue	Year	Price	Price	Notes
Before It's Too Late	7"	Sue	WI4040	1967	£25	£50	

DAY, JILL

Title	Format	Label	Catalogue	Year	Price	Price	Notes
I Hear You Knocking	7"	HMV	7M362	1956	£4	£8	
Mangos	7"	HMV	POP320	1957	£1.50	£4	
Promises	7"	Parlophone	MSP6177	1955	£2	£5	
Sincerely	7"	Parlophone	MSP6169	1955	£2.50	£6	
Tear Fell	7"	HMV	7M391	1956	£2	£5	

DAY, MURIEL

Title	Format	Label	Catalogue	Year	Price	Price	Notes
Nine Times Out Of Ten	7"	Page One	POF151	1969	£12.50	£25	
Wages Of Love	7"	CBS	4115	1969	£2.50	£6	

DAY OF THE PHOENIX

Title	Format	Label	Catalogue	Year	Price	Price	Notes
Neighbour's Son	LP	Chapter One	CNSR812	1972	£20	£40	
Wide Open N Way	LP	Greenwich	GSLPR1002	1970	£15	£30	

DAY, TANYA

Title	Format	Label	Catalogue	Year	Price	Price	Notes
His Lips Get In The Way	7"	Polydor	NH52331	1964	£1.50	£4	

DAY, TERRY

Title	Format	Label	Catalogue	Year	Price	Price	Notes
That's All I Want	7"	CBS	AAG104	1962	£2.50	£6	

DAYE, JOHNNY

Title	Format	Label	Catalogue	Year	Price	Price	Notes
Stay Baby Stay	7"	Stax	STAX111	1969	£1.50	£4	

DAYLIGHT

Title	Format	Label	Catalogue	Year	Price	Price	Notes
Daylight	LP	RCA	SF8194	1971	£15	£30	

DAYLIGHTERS

Title	Format	Label	Catalogue	Year	Price	Price	Notes
Oh Mom Teach Me How	7"	Sue	WI343	1964	£5	£10	

DE BURGH, CHRIS

Title	Format	Label	Catalogue	Year	Price	Price	Notes
Spaceman Came Travelling	7"	A&M	AMS7267	1976	£1.50	£4	PS

DE CARLO, YVONNE

Title	Format	Label	Catalogue	Year	Price	Price	Notes
Take It Or Leave It	7"	Capitol	CL14380	1955	£1.50	£4	

DE CASTRO SISTERS

Title	Format	Label	Catalogue	Year	Price	Price	Notes
Boom Boom Boomerang	7"	London	HL8137	1955	£10	£20	
Christmas Is Coming	7"	London	HLU8212	1955	£7.50	£15	
Give Me Time	7"	London	HLU8228	1956	£7.50	£15	
If I Ever Fall In Love	7"	London	HLU8189	1955	£7.50	£15	
I'm Bewildered	7"	London	HL8158	1955	£10	£20	
No One To Blame But You	7"	London	HLU8296	1956	£7.50	£15	
Red Sails In The Sunset	7"	Capitol	CL15199	1961	£1.50	£4	
Teach Me Tonight	7"	London	HL8104	1954	£12.50	£25	chart single
Teach Me Tonight Cha-Cha	7"	HMV	POP583	1959	£2	£5	
Who Are They To Say	7"	HMV	POP527	1958	£2	£5	

DE DANANN

Title	Format	Label	Catalogue	Year	Price	Price	Notes
De Danann	LP	Decca	SKL5287	1977	£8	£20	
De Danann	LP	Polydor	2904005	1975	£6	£15	Irish
Banks Of The Nile	LP	Decca	SKL5318	1980	£5	£12	

DE FRANCO, BUDDY

Title	Format	Label	Catalogue	Year	Price	Price	Notes
Buddy DeFranco	10" LP	Columbia	33C9022	1956	£10	£25	
Buddy DeFranco Wailers	LP	Columbia	33CX10091	1957	£8	£20	
King Of The Clarinet	10" LP	MGM	D112	1953	£15	£30	

Plays Benny Goodman	LP	HMV	CLP1215	1958	£6	£15	
Takes You To The Stars	10" LP	Vogue	LDE077	1954	£15	£30	
With Oscar Peterson	12"	Columbia	33CX10003	1955	£10	£25	

DE GALLIER, ZION
Dream Dream Dream	7"	Parlophone	R5710	1968	£4	£8	
Winter Will Be Cold	7"	Parlophone	R5686	1968	£4	£8	

DE HAVEN , GLORIA
Red Hot Pepper Pot	7"	Brunswick	05457	1955	£1.50	£4	

DE LORY, AL
Yesterday	7"	London	HLU9999	1965	£5	£10	

DE LUGG, MILTON ORCHESTRA
Addams Family Theme	7"	Columbia	DB7474	1965	£2.50	£6	
Munsters Theme	7"	Columbia	DB7762	1966	£4	£8	

DE MARCO SISTERS
Bouillabasse	7"	MGM	SP1043	1953	£2.50	£6	
Dreamboat	7"	Brunswick	05425	1955	£4	£8	
Hot Barcarolle	7"	Brunswick	05411	1955	£2.50	£6	
Love Me	7"	Brunswick	05349	1954	£2.50	£6	
Romance Me	7"	Brunswick	05526	1956	£2.50	£6	

DE PARIS, SIDNEY
DeParis Dixie	LP	Blue Note	B6501	1969	£4	£10	

DE PARIS, WILBUR
At Symphony Hall	LP	London	LTZK15086/ SAHK6016	1957	£6	£15	
New Orleans Jazz	LP	London	LTZK15024	1957	£6	£15	
Plays Cole Porter	LP	London	LTZK15156	1959	£5	£12	
Something Old, New, Gay Blue	LP	London	LTZK15175/ SAHK6060	1960	£5	£12	
That's A Plenty	LP	London	LTZK15192/ SAHK6079	1960	£5	£12	
Wild Jazz Age	LP	London	LTZK15201/ SAHK6115	1961	£4	£10	

DE ROSA, FRANK
Big Guitar	7"	London	HLD8576	1958	£7.50	£15	

DE VIVRE, JOY
Our Wedding	7"	Crass	ENVY1	1981	£7.50	£15	white flexi

DE VORZON, BARRY
Barbara Jean	7"	RCA	RCA1066	1958	£25	£50	B side by Jimmy Bell
Betty Betty	7"	Philips	PB993	1960	£4	£8	

DEACON BLUE
Chocolate Girl	CD-s	CBS	CDDEAC6	1988	£3	£8	
Chocolate Girl	7" EP	CBS	DEACEP6	1988	£2.50	£6	
Dignity	CD-s	CBS	CDDEAC4	1988	£2.50	£6	
Dignity	7"	CBS	DEAC1	1987	£1.50	£4	with cassette XPC4011
Dignity	7" EP	CBS	DEACEP4	1988	£2	£5	
Dignity	10"	CBS	DEACQ4	1988	£3	£8	
Raintown	cass	CBS	4505498	1988	£6	£15	with Riches cassette
Raintown/Riches	LP	CBS	4505491/XPR1361	1988	£15	£30	double
Real Gone Kid	CD-s	CBS	CDDEAC7	1988	£4	£10	
Real Gone Kid	7" EP	CBS	DEACEP7	1988	£2	£5	
Real Gone Kid	12"	CBS	DEACQT7	1988	£2.50	£6	with poster
Riches	LP	CBS	XPR1361	1988	£6	£15	
Wages Day	7"	CBS	DEACQ8	1989	£1.50	£4	
When Will You Make My Telephone Ring	CD-s	CBS	CDDEAC5	1988	£2.50	£6	
When Will You Make My Telephone Ring	7"	CBS	DEACB5	1988	£1.50	£4	boxed set

DEACON, BOBBY
Fool Was I	7"	Pye	7N15270	1960	£2.50	£6	

DEACON, GEORGE & MARION ROSS
Sweet William's Ghost	LP	XTRA	XTRA1130	1973	£50	£100	

DEAD BOYS
Sonic Reducer	12"	Sire	6078609	1977	£3	£8	
Tell Me	7"	Sire	SRE1029	1978	£1.50	£4	
We Have Come For Your Children	LP	Sire	SRK6054	1978	£5	£12	
Young Loud And Snotty	LP	Sire	9103329	1977	£5	£12	

DEAD OR ALIVE
I'd Do Anything	7"	Epic	A4069	1984	£1.50	£4	
I'd Do Anything	12"	Epic	TA4069	1984	£2.50	£6	
I'd Do Anything	10"	Epic	QA4069	1984	£4	£10	
I'll Save You All My Kisses	12"	Epic	BURNSQ3	1987	£2.50	£6	
I'm Falling	7"	Inevitable	INEV005	1980	£4	£8	
In Too Deep (2 versions)	12"	Epic	QTA6360	1985	£2.50	£6	with poster
Lover Come Back To Me	7"	Epic	A6086	1985	£12.50	£25	
Lover Come Back To Me	7"	Epic	WA6086	1985	£2	£5	shaped pic disc

Title	Format	Label	Cat. No.	Year	Low	High	Notes
Lover Come Back To Me	12"	Epic	QTA6086	1985	£4	£10	poster sleeve
Mighty Mix	12"	Epic	XPR1257	198-	£15	£30	promo
Misty Circles	7"	Epic	A3399	1983	£2	£5	
Misty Circles	12"	Epic	TA3399	1983	£4	£10	
My Heart Goes Bang	7"	Epic	DA6571	1985	£1.50	£4	double
My Heart Goes Bang (American Wipe Out Mix)	12"	Epic	QTA6571	1985	£2.50	£6	
Nowhere To Nowhere	12"	Black Eyes	BE1	1982	£4	£10	
Number Eleven	7"	Inevitable	INEV008	1981	£2	£5	
Something In My House (Clean & Dirty Mix)	12"	Epic	XPR1328	1987	£25	£50	promo
Stranger	7"	Black Eyes	BE2	1982	£2.50	£6	
That's The Way	7"	Epic	WA4271	1984	£1.50	£4	pic disc
Turn Around And Count To Ten	CD-s	Epic	BURNSC4	1988	£6	£15	pic disc
Turn Around And Count To Ten	12"	Epic	BURNSQ4	1988	£8	£20	
What I Want	7"	Epic	A3676	1983	£6	£12	black PS
What I Want	7"	Epic	A3676	1983	£15	£30	floppy hat PS
What I Want	12"	Epic	TA3676	1983	£2.50	£6	
What I Want	12"	Epic	TA3676	1983	£4	£10	with poster
What I Want (Dance Mix)	12"	Epic	TA4510	1984	£2.50	£6	with poster
What I Want (Remix)	7"	Epic	A4510	1984	£2.50	£6	poster sleeve
You Spin Me Round	7"	Epic	DA4861	1984	£1.50	£4	double
You Spin Me Round (Performance Mix)	12"	Epic	QTX4861	1984	£2.50	£6	
Youthquake	CD	Epic	EPC26420	1985	£15	£30	2 extra 12' mixes

DEAD SEA FRUIT

Title	Format	Label	Cat. No.	Year	Low	High	Notes
Dead Sea Fruit	LP	Camp	603001	1967	£20	£40	
Kensington High Street	7"	Camp	602001	1967	£4	£8	
Loulou Put Another Record On	7" EP	DiscAZ	1126	1967	£10	£20	French, 2 different sleeves
Love At The Hippiedrome	7"	Camp	602004	1968	£7.50	£15	

DEADLY ONES

Title	Format	Label	Cat. No.	Year	Low	High	Notes
It's Monster Surfing Time	LP	Vee Jay	LP/VS1090	1964	£5	£12	US

DEAL, BILL & THE RHONDELLS

Title	Format	Label	Cat. No.	Year	Low	High	Notes
I've Been Hurt	7"	MGM	MGM1479	1969	£2.50	£6	

DEAN & JEAN

Title	Format	Label	Cat. No.	Year	Low	High	Notes
Hey Jean Hey Dean	7"	Stateside	SS283	1964	£2.50	£6	
I Love The Summertime	7"	Stateside	SS249	1964	£2.50	£6	
I Wanna Be Loved	7"	Stateside	SS313	1964	£4	£8	

DEAN & MARK

Title	Format	Label	Cat. No.	Year	Low	High	Notes
Kissing Games	7"	Hickory	451227	1964	£1.50	£4	
There Oughta Be A Law	7"	Hickory	451249	1964	£1.50	£4	

DEAN, ALAN

Title	Format	Label	Cat. No.	Year	Low	High	Notes
Rock'n'Roll Tarantella	7"	Columbia	DB3932	1957	£5	£10	

DEAN, ALAN & THE PROBLEMS

Title	Format	Label	Cat. No.	Year	Low	High	Notes
Thunder And Rain	7"	Pye	7N15749	1965	£15	£30	
Time It Takes	7"	Decca	F11947	1964	£6	£12	

DEAN, ELTON

Elton Dean (from whom Reg Dwight pinched half of his stage name) was the saxophonist with Soft Machine during the early seventies. His solo LP is very much a continuation of the same style of music.

Title	Format	Label	Cat. No.	Year	Low	High	Notes
Cheque Is In The Mail	LP	Ogun	OG610	1977	£4	£10	
Elton Dean	LP	CBS	64539	1971	£8	£20	
Ninesense	LP	Ogun	OG900	1977	£4	£10	
They All Be On This Old Road	LP	Ogun	OG410	1977	£4	£10	

DEAN, ELTON, HUGH HOPPER, & ALAN GOWEN

Title	Format	Label	Cat. No.	Year	Low	High	Notes
Rogue Element	LP	Ogun	OG527	1978	£4	£10	

DEAN, JIMMY

Title	Format	Label	Cat. No.	Year	Low	High	Notes
Best Of Jimmy Dean	7" EP	CBS	EP6075	1966	£2.50	£6	
Big Bad John	LP	Columbia	CL1735	1962	£6	£15	US
Big Bad John	7"	Philips	PB1187	1961	£2	£5	chart single
Cajun Queen	7"	Philips	PB1210	1961	£1.50	£4	
Hour Of Prayer	LP	Columbia	CL1025	1957	£6	£12	US
Jimmy Dean	7" EP	Philips	BBE12501	1961	£4	£8	
Little Bitty Big John	7"	CBS	AAG107	1962	£1.50	£4	
Little Black Book	7"	CBS	AAG122	1962	£1.50	£4	chart single
Smoke Smoke That Cigarette	7"	Philips	PB1223	1962	£1.50	£4	
There's Still Time Brother	7"	Philips	PB984	1960	£1.50	£4	
Weekend Blues	7"	Philips	PB940	1959	£1.50	£4	

DEAN, LITTLE BILLY

Title	Format	Label	Cat. No.	Year	Low	High	Notes
That's Always Like You	7"	Strike	JH325	1967	£7.50	£15	

DEAN, NORA

Title	Format	Label	Cat. No.	Year	Low	High	Notes
Same Thing You Gave To Daddy	7"	Upsetter	US322	1969	£2	£5	Upsetter Pilgrims B side

DEAN, PAUL & THE SOUL SAVAGES

Title	Format	Label	Cat. No.	Year	Low	High	Notes
She Can Build A Mountain	7"	Reaction	591002	1966	£5	£10	

DEAN, PAUL & THE THOUGHTS

Title	Format	Label	Cat. No.	Year	Low	High	Notes
You Don't Own Me	7"	Decca	F12136	1965	£5	£10	

DEAN, ROGER

Roger Dean is a painter, whose science-fantasy landscapes were commissioned on several occasions through the seventies for use on LP sleeves. The most well-known of these are the series he produced for Yes, but Dean's sleeves are also to be found on records by the likes of Osibisa, Greenslade, Badger, Keith Tippett, Billy Cox, Paladin, The Gun, Ramases, and, more recently, Asia. All of these are collected by fans of Dean.

DEANE, JASON

Down In The Street	7"	King	KG1060	1967	£15	£30	
Make Believe	7"	King	KG1049	1966	£7.50	£15	

DEARIE, BLOSSOM

Blossom Dearie	LP	Fontana	STL5454	1968	£4	£10	
I'm Hip	7"	Fontana	TF719	1966	£1.50	£4	
Plays For Dancing	10" LP	Felsted	SDL86034	1956	£6	£15	
Sweet Georgie Fame	7"	Fontana	TF788	1967	£1.50	£4	

DEARLY BELOVED

Peep Peep Pop Pop	7"	CBS	202398	1966	£4	£8	

DEATH IN JUNE

And Murder Love	7"	New European	BADVC73	1985	£6	£12	
And Murder Love	12"	New European	BADVC73T	1985	£6	£15	
Born Again	12"	Cenaz	CENAZ09	1988	£3	£8	pic disc
Born Again	12"	New European	BADVC69	1985	£5	£12	
Burial	LP	New European	UBADVC4	199-	£6	£15	brown vinyl
Burial	LP	New European	UBADVC4	199-	£10	£25	white vinyl
Heaven Street	7"	New European	SA29634	1984	£10	£20	
Heaven Street	12"	New European	SA29634	1984	£10	£25	
Heaven Street	12"	Three Circles		1982	£20	£40	
Holy Water	7"	New European	SA30634	1982	£10	£20	
Nada	LP	New European	BADVC13	1985	£8	£20	blue sleeve
Nada	LP	New European	BADVC13	1985	£5	£12	brown sleeve
She Said Destroy	7"	New European	BADVC6	1984	£7.50	£15	
She Said Destroy	12"	New European	BADVC6T	1984	£8	£20	
To Drown A Rose	10"	New European	BADVC10	1987	£5	£12	
Wall Of Sacrifice	LP	New European	BADVC88	1988	£15	£30	green & yellow sleeve
Wall Of Sacrifice	LP	New European	BADVC88	1988	£20	£40	red sleeve
World That Summer	LP	New European	BADVC9	199-	£5	£12	double

DEBONAIRES

Crying Behind Your Smile	7"	Pye	7N17204	1966	£1.50	£4	
Love Of Our Own	7"	Pye	7N17151	1966	£1.50	£4	
That's Right	7"	Parlophone	R5054	1963	£1.50	£4	

DEBONAIRES (2)

I'm In Love Again	7"	Track	604035	1970	£6	£12	

DEBS

Sloopy's Gonna Hang On	7"	Mercury	MF888	1965	£1.50	£4	

DEB-TONES

Knock, Knock, Who's There?	7"	RCA	RCA1137	1959	£4	£8	

DECKER, DIANA

Abracadabra	7"	Columbia	SCM5145	1954	£2.50	£6	
Apples, Peaches And Cherries	7"	Columbia	SCM5173	1955	£1.50	£4	
Happy Wanderer	7"	Columbia	SCM5096	1954	£1.50	£4	
Kitty In The Basket	7"	Columbia	SCM5123	1954	£1.50	£4	
Mama Mia	7"	Columbia	SCM5130	1954	£2	£5	
Man With The Banjo	7"	Columbia	SCM5120	1954	£2	£5	
Oh My Papa	7"	Columbia	SCM5083	1954	£2.50	£6	
Open The Window Of Your Heart	7"	Columbia	SCM5166	1955	£1.50	£4	
Rock-a-Boogie Baby	7"	Columbia	SCM5246	1956	£6	£12	

DEDICATED MEN'S JUG BAND

Boodle Am Shake	7"	Piccadilly	7N35245	1965	£1.50	£4	
Don't Come Knocking	7"	Piccadilly	7N35283	1966	£1.50	£4	

DEE & THE DYNAMITES

South Bound Gasser	7"	Philips	PB1081	1960	£1.50	£4	

DEE DEE

Love Is Always	7"	Palette	PB25579	1968	£10	£20	

DEE, JEANNIE

Don't Come Home My Little Darling	7"	Beacon	BEA142	1969	£2	£5	

DEE, JOEY & THE STARLIGHTERS

All The World Is Twistin'	LP	Columbia	33SX1502	1962	£6	£15	
Back To The Peppermint Lounge Twistin'	LP	Roulette	(S)R25173	1962	£5	£12	US
Dance Dance Dance	7"	Columbia	DB7102	1963	£1.50	£4	
Dance, Dance, Dance	LP	Roulette	(S)R25221	1963	£4	£10	US
Doin' The Twist	LP	Columbia	33SX1406	1961	£6	£15	
Fannie Mae	7"	Columbia	DB4862	1962	£1.50	£4	
Hey Let's Twist	LP	Columbia	33SX1421	1962	£6	£15	
Hey Let's Twist	7"	Columbia	DB4803	1962	£1.50	£4	
Hot Pastrami	7"	Columbia	DB7055	1963	£1.50	£4	
I Lost My Baby	7"	Columbia	DB4955	1963	£1.50	£4	
Joey Dee	LP	Roulette	(S)R25197	1963	£4	£10	US
Peppermint Twist	7"	Columbia	DB4758	1962	£2	£5	chart single

Title	Format	Label	Cat No	Year	Price	Price	Notes
Shout	7"	Columbia	DB4842	1962	£1.50	£4	
Two Tickets To Paris	LP	Roulette	(S)R25182	1962	£4	£10	US
What Kind Of Love Is This	7"	Columbia	DB4905	1962	£1.50	£4	

DEE, JOHNNIE
Frankie's Angel	7"	Columbia	DB7612	1965	£1.50	£4	

DEE, JOHNNY
Sitting In The Balcony	7"	Oriole	CB1367	1957	£30	£60	

DEE, KIKI
Baby I Don't Care	7"	Fontana	TF490	1964	£1.50	£4	
Can't Take My Eyes Off You	7"	Fontana	TF926	1968	£1.50	£4	
Early Night	7"	Fontana	TF394	1963	£2	£5	
En Francais	7" EP	Fontana	465323	1966	£5	£10	French
Excuse Me	7"	Fontana	TF870	1967	£1.50	£4	
Great Expectations	LP	Tamla Motown	STML11158	1970	£10	£25	
I	7"	Fontana	TF833	1967	£1.50	£4	
I Was Only Kidding	7"	Fontana	TF414	1963	£1.50	£4	
I'm Going Out	7"	Fontana	TF792	1967	£1.50	£4	
I'm Kiki Dee	LP	Fontana	(S)TL5455	1968	£5	£12	
Kiki Dee	7" EP	Fontana	TE17443	1965	£4	£8	
Kiki Dee In Clover	7" EP	Fontana	TE17470	1966	£4	£8	
Now The Flowers Cry	7"	Fontana	TF983	1968	£20	£40	
Our Day Will Come Between Monday & Sunday	7"	Tamla Motown	TMG739	1970	£2.50	£6	
Running Out Of Fools	7"	Fontana	TF596	1965	£1.50	£4	
That's Right Walk On By	7"	Fontana	TF443	1964	£1.50	£4	
Why Don't I Run Away From You	7"	Fontana	TF669	1966	£2	£5	

DEE, LENNY
Plantation Boogie	7"	Brunswick	05440	1955	£1.50	£4	

DEE, RICKY & THE EMBERS
Workout	7"	Stateside	SS136	1962	£2.50	£6	

DEE, SANDRA
Tammy Tell Me	7"	Brunswick	05858	1961	£1.50	£4	

DEE SET
I Know A Place	7"	Blue Cat	BS146	1968	£4	£8	

DEE, SIMON
Julie	7"	Chapter One	CH105	1969	£1.50	£4	

DEE, TOMMY & THE TEEN TONES
Three Stars	7"	Melodisc	1516	1959	£15	£30	

DEEJAYS
Black-Eyed Woman	7"	Polydor	56501	1965	£25	£50	
Blackeyed Woman	7" EP	Polydor	27773	1965	£25	£50	French
Dimples	7"	Polydor	56034	1965	£12.50	£25	

DEELEY, ANTHONY
Anytime Man	7"	Pama	PM728	1968	£2.50	£6	

DEENE, CAROL
Dancing In Our Eyes	7"	Columbia	DB7890	1966	£1.50	£4	
Growing Up	7"	HMV	POP1123	1963	£1.50	£4	
He Just Don't Know	7"	Columbia	DB7743	1965	£1.50	£4	
I Can't Forget Someone Like You	7"	HMV	POP1405	1965	£1.50	£4	
I Want To Stay Here	7"	HMV	POP1200	1963	£1.50	£4	
James	7"	HMV	POP1086	1962	£1.50	£4	
Johnny Get Angry	7"	Columbia	DB8107	1967	£1.50	£4	
Love Not Have I	7"	HMV	POP973	1962	£1.50	£4	chart single
Norman	7"	HMV	POP922	1961	£1.50	£4	chart single
Sad Movies	7"	HMV	POP1058	1962	£1.50	£4	chart single
Some People	7"	HMV	POP1337	1964	£1.50	£4	chart single
Very First Kiss	7"	HMV	POP1337	1964	£1.50	£4	
Who's Been Sleeping In My Bed	7"	HMV	POP1275	1964	£1.50	£4	

DEEP
Psychedelic Moods	LP	Parkway	7051	1966	£15	£30	US

DEEP FEELING
Deep Feeling	LP	DJM	DJLPS419	1971	£10	£25	
Do You Love Me	7"	Page One	POF23165	1970	£1.50	£4	chart single
Skyline Pigeon	7"	Page One	POF23177	1970	£1.50	£4	

DEEP FREEZE MICE
Gates Of Lunch	LP	Mole Embalming	MOLE3	1981	£5	£12	
Hang On Constance Let Me Hear The News	7"	Cordelia	ERICAT004	198-	£2	£5	
I Love You Little Bo Bo With Your Delicate Golden Lions	LP	Cordelia	ERICAT001	198-	£5	£12	double
My Geraniums Are Bulletproof	LP	Mole Embalming	MOLE1	1979	£10	£25	
My Geraniums Are Bulletproof	LP	Mole Embalming	MOLE1	1979	£25	£50	various inserts, DIY sleeve
Rain Is When The Earth Is Television	7"	Cordelia	ERICAT013	198-	£1.50	£4	

Title	Format	Label	Cat No	Year			Notes
Saw A Ranch Burning Last Night	LP	Mole Embalming	MOLE4	1983	£5	£12	
Teenage Head In My Refrigerator	LP	Mole Embalming	MOLE2	1981	£20	£40	
These Floors Are Smooth	7"	Cordelia	ERICAT002	198-	£2.50	£6	

DEEP PURPLE

Title	Format	Label	Cat No	Year			Notes
Concerto For Group And Orchestra	7"	Harvest	PSR325	1970	£5	£10	promo
Deep Purple Mark 2 Singles	LP	Purple	TPS3514	1979	£5	£12	purple vinyl
Emmaretta	7"	Parlophone	R5763	1969	£5	£10	
Fireball	LP	EMI	EJ2603440	1984	£4	£10	pic disc with poster
Hallelujah	7"	Harvest	HAR5006	1969	£2	£5	
Hallelujah	7"	Harvest	HAR5006	1969	£10	£20	promo, PS
Hush	7"	Parlophone	R5708	1968	£5	£10	
Hush	7"	Parlophone	R5708	1968	£20	£40	demo, PS, sleeve pictured in Guide
In Rock	LP	EMI	EJ2603430	1984	£4	£10	pic disc with poster
Kentucky Woman	7"	Parlophone	R5745	1968	£10	£20	
Machine Head	LP	EMI	EJ2603450	1984	£4	£10	pic disc with poster
Machine Head	LP	Harvest	Q4SHVL7504	1974	£6	£15	quad
Shades Of Deep Purple	LP	Parlophone	PCS7055	1968	£10	£25	stereo
Shades Of Deep Purple	LP	Parlophone	PMC/PCS7055	1968	£5	£12	black & white label
Shades Of Deep Purple	LP	Parlophone	PMC7055	1968	£20	£40	mono
Singles A's And B's	LP	Harvest	SHSM2026	1978	£5	£12	purple vinyl
Stormbringer	LP	Warner Bros	PR42832	1975	£6	£15	US quad
Woman From Tokyo	7"	Purple	PUR112	1973	£10	£20	

DEEP RIVER BOYS

Title	Format	Label	Cat No	Year			Notes
Deep River Boys	LP	Vik	LXA1019	1956	£25	£50	US
Deep River Boys	7" EP	HMV	7EG8133	1955	£2.50	£6	
Ezikiel Saw The Wheel	7" EP	Nixa	45EP131	1955	£2.50	£6	
Go On Board Little Children	7" EP	Nixa	45EP113	1955	£2.50	£6	
Itchy Twitchy Feeling	7"	HMV	POP537	1958	£6	£12	
Midnight Magic	LP	Que	FLS104	1957	£17.50	£35	US
Negro Spirituals	7" EP	HMV	7EG8445	1957	£2.50	£6	
Nola	7"	Top Rank	JAR172	1959	£1.50	£4	
Not Too Old To Rock And Roll	7"	HMV	POP449	1958	£6	£12	
Presenting The Deep River Boys	LP	Camden	CAL303	1956	£17.50	£35	US
Presenting The Deep River Boys	LP	Capitol	T6050	195-	£8	£20	US
Rock A Beating Boogie	7"	HMV	7M361	1956	£7.50	£15	
Romance A La Mode	7" EP	HMV	7EG8321	1957	£2.50	£6	
Settle Down	7"	HMV	POP1081	1962	£2.50	£6	
Shake Rattle And Roll	7"	HMV	7M280	1954	£10	£20	
Spirituals	10" LP	Nixa	XLPY135	1954	£8	£20	
Spirituals	10" LP	Pye	XLTY138	1954	£6	£15	
Spirituals And Jubilees	10" LP	Waldorf	120	1956	£25	£50	US
Spirituals And Jubilees	10" LP	Waldorf	108	1956	£25	£50	US
Sweet Mama Tree Top Tall	7"	HMV	7M174	1954	£7.50	£15	
Swing Low Sweet Chariot	7" EP	Nixa	45EP114	1955	£2.50	£6	
That's Right	7"	HMV	POP263	1956	£7.50	£15	chart single
Timbers Gotta Roll	7"	Top Rank	JAR174	1959	£1.50	£4	
Walk Together Children	7" EP	Nixa	45EP130	1955	£2.50	£6	
Whole Lotta Shaking Going On	7"	HMV	POP395	1957	£7.50	£15	

DEEP SET

Title	Format	Label	Cat No	Year			
I Started A Joke	7"	Major Minor	MM607	1969	£4	£8	
That's The Way Life Goes	7"	Pye	7N17594	1968	£2	£5	

DEEP SIX

Title	Format	Label	Cat No	Year			Notes
Counting	7"	Liberty	LIB55882	1966	£1.50	£4	
Deep Six	LP	Liberty	LRP3475/LST7475	1966	£5	£12	US

DEERFIELD

Title	Format	Label	Cat No	Year			Notes
Nil Desperandum	LP	Flat Rock			£37.50	£75	US

DEES, SAM

Title	Format	Label	Cat No	Year			Notes
Handle With Care	7"	Atlantic	K10676	1975	£2.50	£6	
It's All Wrong	7"	Major Minor	MM655	1969	£1.50	£4	
Show Must Go On	LP	Atlantic	K50142	1975	£6	£15	
Storybook Children	7"	Atlantic	K10719	1976	£2	£5	with Bettye Swann

DEF LEPPARD

It would be nice to think that the rise to megastardom of Def Leppard had at least something to do with the public's appreciation of the way the group stood by their drummer, Rick Allen, when he lost an arm in an accident. In any event, as with other rock stars of the eighties, Def Leppard have released a multitude of picture discs and special packages geared directly at the collector. There is also a genuine rarity (i.e. one not expressly created by the record company) in the first single, "Getcha Rocks Off", which was a private pressing running to three separate issues.

Title	Format	Label	Cat No	Year			Notes
Animal	CD-s	Phonogram	LEPCD1	1987	£6	£15	
Animal	12"	Vertigo	LEPC1	1987	£5	£12	red vinyl
Armageddon It	CD-s	Phonogram	LEPCD4	1988	£6	£15	
Armageddon It	12"	Phonogram	LEPXB4	1988	£3	£8	boxed, poster, badge, 5 cards
Bringin' On The Heartbreak	7"	Vertigo	LEPP3	1982	£6	£12	
Bringin' On The Heartbreak	12"	Vertigo	LEPP312	1982	£5	£12	
First Strike	LP	Flash	843007	1984	£40	£80	Belgian
Getcha Rocks Off	7"	Bludgeon Riffola	MSB001	1979	£5	£10	yellow label, no PS
Getcha Rocks Off	7"	Bludgeon Riffola	SRTS78CUS232	1979	£50	£100	lyric insert, red label

Getcha Rocks Off	7"	Bludgeon Riffola	SRTS78CUS232	1979	£15	£30	without PS
Getcha Rocks Off	7"	Phonogram	6059240	1979	£7.50	£15	mispress with 2 B sides
Getcha Rocks Off	7"	Vertigo	6059240	1979	£2	£5	no PS
Hello America	7"	Vertigo	LEPP1	1980	£2.50	£6	
Hysteria	LP	Phonogram	HYSPD1	1987	£6	£15	pic disc
Hysteria	CD-s	Phonogram	LEPCD3	1988	£3	£8	
Hysteria	12"	Phonogram	LEPX313	1987	£2.50	£6	envelope sleeve, poster
Let It Go	7"	Vertigo	LEPP2	1981	£2.50	£6	
Let It Go	7"	Vertigo	LEPP2	1981	£6	£12	with patch
Let's Get Rocked	CD-s	Phonogram	DEFCD7	1992	£3	£8	boxed pic disc
Let's Get Rocked	12"	Phonogram	DEFPD7	1992	£3	£8	pic disc
Love Bites	CD-s	Phonogram	LEPCD5	1988	£3	£8	
Love Bites	12"	Phonogram	LEPXB5	1988	£3	£8	boxed, 4 cards
Photograph	7"	Vertigo	VER5	1983	£2.50	£6	
Photograph	7"	Vertigo	VER9	1984	£2	£5	wallet PS
Photograph	7"	Vertigo	VERG9	1984	£7.50	£15	gatefold wallet PS
Photograph	7"	Vertigo	VERP5	1983	£10	£20	3-D sleeve
Photograph	7"	Vertigo	VERQ5	1983	£6	£12	3-D sleeve
Photograph	12"	Vertigo	VERX5	1983	£5	£12	
Photograph	12"	Vertigo	VERX9	1984	£5	£12	same sleeve as VERX5
Pour Some Sugar On Me	7"	Phonogram	LEPS2	1987	£4	£8	shaped pic disc
Release Me (Stumpus Maximus)	12"	Phonogram	LEPDK6	1989	£3	£8	promo
Rock Of Ages	CD	Polygram	0800342	1989	£8	£20	CD Video
Rock Of Ages	7"	Vertigo	VERP6	1983	£4	£8	shaped pic disc
Rock Of Ages	7"	Vertigo	VERQ6	1983	£7.50	£15	cube sleeve
Rock Of Ages	12"	Vertigo	VERX6	1983	£4	£10	
Rocket	CD	Polygram	0809902	1989	£5	£12	CD Video
Rocket	7"	Phonogram	LEPXP6	1989	£2.50	£6	numbered pic disc
Rocket	12"	Phonogram	LEPXP6	1989	£5	£12	pic disc
Too Late For Love	7"	Vertigo	VER8	1983	£2.50	£6	
Too Late For Love	7"	Vertigo	VER8	1983	£15	£30	soccer strip PS
Too Late For Love	12"	Vertigo	VERX8	1983	£4	£10	
Wasted	7"	Vertigo	6059247	1979	£2.50	£6	PS

DEFENDERS

Drag Beat	LP	Del-Fi	DFLP1242	1964	£15	£30	US

DEFENDERS (2)

Set Them Free	7"	Doctor Bird	DB1104	1967	£5	£10	

DEFUNKT

Defunkt	LP	Hannibal	HNBL1301	1981	£4	£10	
Thermonuclear Sweat	LP	Hannibal	HNBL1311	1984	£4	£10	

DEKKER, DESMOND

007	7"	Pyramid	PYR6004	1967	£2.50	£6	chart single, Roland Alphonso B side
007 Shanty Town	LP	Doctor Bird	DLM5007	1967	£30	£60	
Beautiful And Dangerous	7"	Pyramid	PYR6031	1968	£4	£8	
Bongo Gal	7"	Pyramid	PYR6035	1968	£2.50	£6	
Christmas Day	7"	Pyramid	PYR6059	1969	£4	£8	
Double Dekker	LP	Trojan	TRLD401	1973	£6	£15	double
Dracula	7"	Black Swan	WI455	1965	£5	£10	Don Drummond B side
Get Up Edna	7"	Island	WI181	1965	£5	£10	
Hey Grandma	7"	Pyramid	PYR6047	1968	£4	£8	
Honour Your Mother And Father	7"	Island	WI054	1963	£5	£10	
Israelites	LP	Doctor Bird	DLM5013	1969	£20	£40	
Israelites	7"	Cactus	CT57	1975	£1.50	£4	chart single
Israelites	7"	Pyramid	PYR6058	1969	£2	£5	chart single, Beverley's Allstars B side
It Mek	7"	Pyramid	PYR6054	1968	£4	£8	
It Mek	7"	Pyramid	PYR6068	1969	£2	£5	chart single
It Pays	7"	Pyramid	PYR6026	1968	£4	£8	
Jeserene	7"	Island	WI158	1964	£5	£10	
Mother Pepper	7"	Pyramid	PYR6044	1968	£4	£8	
Mother's Young Gal	7"	Pyramid	PYR6012	1967	£4	£8	Soul Brothers B side
Music Like Dirt	7"	Pyramid	PYR6051	1968	£4	£8	
Parents	7"	Island	WI111	1963	£5	£10	
Pickney Girl	7"	Pyramid	PYR6078	1970	£2	£5	chart single
Sabotage	7"	Pyramid	PYR6020	1967	£4	£8	
This Is Desmond Dekker	LP	Trojan	TTL4	1969	£6	£15	chart LP
This Woman	7"	Island	WI202	1965	£5	£10	Lee Perry B side
To Sir With Love	7"	Pyramid	PYR6037	1968	£4	£8	
Unity	7"	Pyramid	PYR6017	1967	£4	£8	
You Can Get It If You Really Want	LP	Trojan	TBL146	1970	£6	£15	
You Can Get It If You Really Want	7"	Trojan	TR7777	1970	£1.50	£4	chart single

DEL AMITRI

Sense Sickness	7"	No Strings	NOSP1	1983	£7.50	£15	
Waking Hours	LP	A&M	AMA9006	1989	£4	£10	band on cover

DEL FUEGO, TERESA

Don't Hang Up	7"	Satril	HH155	1981	£2	£5	

DEL SATINS
Out To Lunch	LP	B.T.Puppy	BTPS1019	1972	£8	£20	US

DEL VIKINGS
Angel Up In Heaven	7"	HMV	POP1145	1963	£4	£8	
Come Go With Me	7"	Dot	DLP3695	1966	£37.50	£75	US
Come Go With Me	7"	London	HLD8405	1957	£35	£70	
Come Go With The Del Vikings	LP	Luniverse	LP1000	1957	£100	£200	US
Confession Of Love	7"	HMV	POP1072	1962	£4	£8	
Del Vikings And The Sonnets	LP	Crown	CLP5368	1963	£8	£20	US
Flat Tyre	7"	Mercury	AMT1027	1959	£15	£30	
Swinging, Singing Record Session	LP	Mercury	MG20353	1958	£60	£120	
They Sing They Swing	LP	Mercury	MG20314	1957	£60	£120	US
Voodoo Man	7"	Mercury	7MT199	1958	£20	£40	
Whispering Bells	7"	London	HLD8464	1957	£12.50	£25	

DELACARDOS
Mister Dillon	7"	HMV	POP890	1961	£7.50	£15	

DELANEY & BONNIE
The sense of well-being and fun that spills over from Delaney and Bonnie's records attracted some famous names to their cause - George Harrison, Dave Mason, and Eric Clapton were all perfectly content to play as sidemen within the band for a while. The LP "Accept No Substitute" was to have appeared on the Apple label, but was eventually released on Elektra. Apple test pressings exist, but no cover has ever been found. Meanwhile, Eric Clapton's thrilling contributions to the Delaney and Bonnie sound can be sampled on the LP "On Tour".

Accept No Substitute (The Original Delaney & Bonnie)	LP	Apple	SAPCOR7	1969	£470	£700	test pressing, no sleeve
Accept No Substitute (The Original Delaney & Bonnie)	LP	Elektra	EKS74039	1969	£5	£12	
Accept No Substitute (The Original Delaney & Bonnie)	LP	Elektra	K42024	1972	£4	£10	
Comin' Home	7"	Atlantic	584308	1969	£1.50	£4	chart single
Get Ourselves Together	7"	Elektra	EKSN45072	1969	£2	£5	
On Tour	LP	Atlantic	2400013	1970	£6	£15	chart LP
Someday	7"	Elektra	EKSN45078	1969	£1.50	£4	

DELANEY, ERIC
Bass Drum Boogie	7"	Parlophone	R4646	1960	£1.50	£4	

DELFONICS
Didn't I (Blow Your Mind This Time)	7"	Bell	BLL1099	1970	£1.50	£4	chart single
La La Means I Love You	LP	Bell	SBLL106	1968	£5	£12	
La-La Means I Love You	7"	Bell	BLL1005	1968	£1.50	£4	
La-La Means I Love You	7"	Bell	BLL1165	1971	£1.50	£4	chart single
Ready or Not (Here I Come)	7"	Bell	BLL1042	1968	£1.50	£4	
Sound Of Sexy Soul	LP	Bell	SBLL121	1969	£5	£12	

DELICATES
Ronnie Is My Lover	7"	London	HLT8953	1959	£30	£60	
Too Young To Date	7"	London	HLT9176	1960	£12.50	£25	

DELICATESSEN
Red Baron's Revenge	7"	Vocalion	VN9286	1967	£1.50	£4	

D'ELL, DENNIS
It Breaks My Heart In Two	7"	CBS	202605	1967	£75	£150	
It Breaks My Heart In Two	7"	CBS	202605	1967	£30	£60	demo
Woman Called Sorrow	7"	Decca	F12647	1967	£1.50	£4	

DELLO, PETE
Into Your Ears	LP	Nepentha	6437001	1971	£25	£50	

DELLS
Always Together	7"	Chess	CRS8084	1969	£1.50	£4	
Bossa Nova Bird	7"	Pye	7N25178	1963	£2.50	£6	
Dock Of The Bay	7"	Chess	CRS8105	1970	£1.50	£4	
Greatest Hits	LP	Chess	CRLS4554	1968	£4	£10	
It's All Up To You	7"	Chess	6145008	1972	£4	£8	
It's Not Unusual	LP	Vee Jay	LP(S)1141	1965	£5	£12	US
It's Not Unusual	7"	President	PT223	1968	£1.50	£4	
Like It Is	LP	Cadet	837	1969	£4	£10	US
Love Is Blue - I Can Sing A Rainbow	LP	Chess	CRLS4555	1969	£4	£10	
Mighty Mighty Dells	LP	Chess	9109100	1975	£4	£10	
Musical Menu	LP	Cadet	822	1968	£4	£10	US
Oh What A Day	7"	Chess	CRS8107	1970	£1.50	£4	
Oh What A Night	LP	Joy	JOYS186	1971	£5	£12	
Oh What A Night	7"	Chess	CRS8102	1970	£1.50	£4	
Oh What A Night	7"	President	PT270	1969	£1.50	£4	
Oh What A Nite	LP	Vee Jay	VJLP1010	1959	£50	£100	US
Oo I Love You	7"	Chess	CRS8066	1967	£4	£6	
Sing A Rainbow/Love Is Blue	7"	Chess	CRS8099	1969	£2	£5	chart single
Stay In My Corner	7"	Chess	CRS8079	1968	£2.50	£6	
There Is	LP	Cadet	804	1968	£4	£10	US
Wear It On Our Face	7"	Chess	CRS8071	1968	£5	£10	
Your Song	12"	20th Century	TC2478	1979	£2.50	£6	

DELMORE BROTHERS
Country And Western	7" EP	Parlophone	GEP8728	1958	£10	£20	
In Memory	LP	King	910	1964	£6	£15	US
In Memory Vol.2	LP	King	920	1964	£6	£15	US
Songs By The Delmore Brothers	LP	King	589	1958	£15	£30	US
Thirtieth Anniversary Album	LP	King	785	1962	£10	£25	US

| Twenty-Four Great Country Songs | LP | King | (S)983 | 1966 | £6 | £15 | US |

DELTA CATS

| I Can't Re-Live | 7" | Bamboo | BAM3 | 1969 | £2.50 | £6 | |
| Unworthy Baby | 7" | Blue Cat | BS128 | 1968 | £4 | £8 | Thrillers B side |

DELTA KINGS

| At Sundown | 7" EP | London | RER1318 | 1961 | £2.50 | £6 | |
| Down The River | LP | London | LTZR15180 | 1960 | £4 | £10 | |

DELTA RHYTHM BOYS

| Mood Indigo | 7" | Brunswick | 05353 | 1954 | £2 | £5 | |
| Sixteen Tons | 7" EP | Felsted | ESD3064 | 1958 | £2 | £5 | |

DELTA SKIFFLE GROUP

| Delta Skiffle Group | 7" EP | Esquire | EP162 | 1958 | £6 | £12 | |

DELTAS

| Georgia | 7" | Blue Beat | BB265 | 1964 | £5 | £10 | |
| Visitor | 7" | Blue Beat | BB275 | 1964 | £5 | £10 | Skatalites B side |

DELTONES

| Rocking Blues | 7" | Top Rank | JAR171 | 1959 | £15 | £30 | |

DELUSION

| Pessimists Paradise | 7" | Wizzo | WIZZO2 | 198- | £2 | £5 | |

DEL-VIKINGS

| Cool Shake | 78 | Mercury | MT169 | 1957 | £5 | £10 | |

DEMENSIONS

| Count Your Blessings Instead Of Sheep | 7" | Coral | Q72437 | 1961 | £1.50 | £4 | |
| Over The Rainbow | 7" | Top Rank | JAR505 | 1960 | £5 | £10 | |

DEMIAN (BUBBLE PUPPY)

| Demian | LP | ABC | S718 | 1971 | £6 | £15 | |

DEMON FUZZ

| Afreaka | LP | Dawn | DNLS3013 | 1971 | £6 | £15 | |

DEMON PACT

| Eaten Alive | 7" | Slime | PACT1 | 1981 | £5 | £10 | |
| Escape | 7" | Slime | PACT2 | 1981 | £7.50 | £15 | test pressing only |

DEMON PREACHER

| Little Miss Perfect | 7" | Small Wonder | SMALL10 | 1978 | £2.50 | £6 | |
| Royal Northern | 7" | Illegal | SRTS78110 | 1978 | £4 | £8 | |

DEMON THOR

| Anno 1972 | LP | United Artists | UAS29393 | 1972 | £10 | £25 | |
| Written In The Sky | LP | United Artists | UAS29496 | 1974 | £10 | £25 | |

DEMONS

| Action By Example | 7" | Crypt Music | DEM1 | 1980 | £2 | £5 | |
| Bless You | 7" | Big Shot | BI523 | 1969 | £2.50 | £6 | |

DEMPSEY, TOMMY & JOHN SWIFT

| Green Grow The Laurel | LP | Trailer | LER2096 | 1976 | £5 | £12 | |

DENE BOYS

| Bye Bye Love | 7" | HMV | POP374 | 1957 | £2.50 | £6 | |
| I Walk Down The Street | 7" | HMV | POP455 | 1958 | £1.50 | £4 | |

DENE FOUR

| Hush-a-Bye | 7" | HMV | POP666 | 1959 | £2 | £5 | |

DENE, TERRY

Bimbombey	7"	Decca	F11100	1959	£2.50	£6	
Come And Get It	7"	Decca	F10938	1957	£5	£10	
Come In And Be Loved	7"	Decca	F10977	1958	£5	£10	
Feminine Look	7"	Aral	PS107	1963	£1.50	£4	
Feminine Look	7"	Aral	PS107	1963	£4	£8	PS
Geraldine	7"	Oriole	CB1562	1960	£4	£8	
Golden Disc	7" EP	Decca	DFE6459	1958	£10	£20	
I've Come Of Age	7"	Decca	F11136	1959	£2.50	£6	
Like A Baby	7"	Oriole	CB1594	1961	£5	£10	
Lucky Lucky Bobby	7"	Decca	F10964	1957	£6	£12	
Pretty Little Pearly	7"	Decca	F11076	1958	£4	£8	
Seven Steps To Love	7"	Decca	F11037	1958	£4	£8	
Stairway Of Love	7"	Decca	F11016	1958	£2.50	£6	chart single
Start Moving	7"	Decca	F10914	1957	£7.50	£15	chart single
Terry Dene No.1	7" EP	Decca	DFE6507	1958	£10	£20	
Terry Dene Now	7" EP	Herald	ELR107	1966	£2.50	£6	
Thank You Pretty Baby	7"	Decca	F11154	1959	£4	£8	
White Sports Coat	7"	Decca	F10895	1957	£10	£20	chart single

DENIMS

| I'm Your Man | 7" | CBS | 201807 | 1965 | £10 | £20 | |

DENISON, ROGER

| I'm On An Island | 7" | Parlophone | R5545 | 1966 | £5 | £10 | |

| She Wanders Through My Mind | 7" | Parlophone | R5566 | 1967 | £4 | £8 | |

DENIZ, HERMANOS

| Mambo Hoo | 7" | Melodisc | CAL13 | 1964 | £2.50 | £6 | |

DENNIS, CATHY

| Irresistable | 12" | Polydor | CATHX7 | 1992 | £8 | £20 | |
| Just Another Dream | 12" | Polydor | CATHR1 | 1989 | £3 | £8 | |

DENNIS, DENZIL

Donkey Train	7"	Trojan	TR614	1968	£4	£8	
Hush Don't You Cry	7"	Trojan	TR615	1968	£4	£8	
Oh Carol	7"	Jolly	JY011	1968	£4	£8	
Seven Nights In Rome	7"	Blue Beat	BB181	1963	£5	£10	

DENNIS, JACKIE

Gingerbread	7"	Decca	F11090	1958	£2	£5	
Jackie Dennis No.1	7" EP.	Decca	DFE6513	1958	£6	£12	
La Dee Dah	7"	Decca	F10992	1958	£4	£8	chart single
Miss Valerie	7"	Decca	F11011	1958	£2.50	£6	
More Than Ever	7"	Decca	F11060	1958	£1.50	£4	
Purple People Eater	7"	Decca	F11033	1958	£4	£8	chart single

DENNISONS

Be My Girl	7"	Decca	F11691	1963	£4	£8	chart single
Nobody Like My Babe	7"	Decca	F11990	1964	£4	£8	
Walking The Dog	7"	Decca	F11880	1964	£4	£8	chart single

DENNY, MARTIN

Afrodesia	LP	London	SAHU6048	1959	£5	£12	stereo
Enchanted Sea	LP	London	SAHG6098	1960	£4	£10	
Exotic Percussion	LP	London	SAHG6187	1961	£4	£10	
Exotic Sounds	7" EP.	London	REU1241	1960	£4	£8	
Exotica	10" LP	London	HBU1079	1957	£6	£15	
Exotica Vol.2	LP	London	SAHG6076	1960	£4	£10	
Exotica Vol.3	LP	London	SAHW6089	1960	£4	£10	
Forbidden Island	LP	London	SAHU6004	1958	£5	£12	
Quiet Village	LP	London	SAHU6055	1960	£4	£10	
Quiet Village	7"	London	SLW4004	1959	£7.50	£15	stereo
Romantica	LP	London	SAHG6215	1962	£4	£10	
Silver Screen	LP	London	SAHG6122	1961	£4	£10	

DENNY, SANDY

Sandy Denny was something of a limited singer: hopeless on uptempo rock material, she nevertheless sounded gorgeous on a slow ballad - as her recording of "The Sea" with Fotheringay proves at a stroke. The small number of early, pre-Fairport Convention tracks are spread somewhat thinly over various LPs. The album with Johnny Silvo, for example, is not a collaboration, but merely includes songs recorded by each separately. The Strawbs LP, however, is a true joint effort.

Like An Old Fashioned Waltz	LP	Island	ILPS9258	1973	£8	£20	
Listen Listen	7"	Island	WIP6142	1972	£1.50	£4	
Make Me A Pallet On Your Floor	7"	Mooncrest	MOON54	1976	£1.50	£4	chart LP
Northstar Grass Man & The Ravens	LP	Island	ILPS9165	1971	£8	£20	
Pass Of Arms EP	7"	Island	WIP6141	1972	£20	£40	PS
Rendezvous	LP	Island	ILPS9433	1977	£6	£15	
Sandy	LP	Island	ILPS9207	1972	£8	£20	
Sandy Denny	LP	Mooncrest	CREST28	1978	£20	£40	1 extra track
Sandy Denny	LP	Saga	EROS8153	1970	£20	£40	
Whispering Grass	7"	Island	WIP6176	1973	£2.50	£6	PS

DENNY, SANDY & JOHNNY SILVO

| Sandy And Johnny | LP | Saga | EROS8041 | 1967 | £20 | £40 | |

DENNY, SANDY & STRAWBS

| All Our Own Work | LP | Pickwick | SHM813 | 1973 | £5 | £12 | |

DENSON, LEE

| New Shoes | 7" | Vik | 0281 | 1956 | £17.50 | £35 | US |

DENTON, MICKEY

| Steady Kind | 7" | London | HLX9398 | 1961 | £1.50 | £4 | |

DENVER, KARL

At The Yew Tree	LP	Decca	LK4540	1963	£6	£15	
Blue Weekend	7"	Decca	F11505	1962	£1.50	£4	chart single
By A Sleepy Lagoon	7" EP.	Decca	DFE8501	1962	£2.50	£6	
Can You Forgive Me	7"	Decca	F11608	1963	£1.50	£4	chart single
Cry A Little Sometime	7"	Mercury	MF878	1965	£1.50	£4	
Dry Tears	7"	Decca	F11553	1962	£1.50	£4	
Indian Love Call	7"	Decca	F11674	1963	£1.50	£4	chart single
Karl Denver	LP	Ace Of Clubs	ACL1131	1962	£4	£10	
Karl Denver Hits	7" EP.	Decca	DFE8504	1962	£2.50	£6	
Little Love, A Little Kiss	7"	Decca	F11470	1962	£1.50	£4	chart single
Love Me With All Your Heart	7"	Decca	F11905	1964	£1.50	£4	chart single
Marcheta	7"	Decca	F11360	1961	£1.50	£4	chart single
Marta	7"	Mercury	MF904	1965	£1.50	£4	
Mexicali Rose	7"	Decca	F11395	1961	£1.50	£4	chart single
My World Of Blue	7"	Decca	F11828	1964	£1.50	£4	chart single
Never Goodbye	7"	Decca	F11431	1962	£1.50	£4	chart single
Sally	7"	Decca	F12025	1964	£1.50	£4	chart single
Still	7"	Decca	F11720	1963	£1.50	£4	chart single
Tip Of My Fingers	7"	Mercury	MF926	1965	£1.50	£4	
Wimoweh	LP	Decca	ACL1098	1961	£6	£15	chart LP

Wimoweh	7"	Decca	F11420	1962	£1.50	£4	chart single

DENVER, NIGEL

Borderline	LP	Decca	LK5014	1969	£5	£12	
Folk, Old And New	LP	Decca	SKL4943	1968	£6	£15	
Rebellion	LP	Decca	SKL4844	1967	£6	£15	
Scottish Nationalist Songs	LP	Major Minor	MMLP1	1967	£6	£15	

DENVERS

Do You Love Me	7" EP	Polydor	27114	1964	£7.50	£15	French

DENZIL & PAT

Dream	7"	Downtown	DT403	1969	£1.50	£4	

DEPECHE MODE

Behind The Wheel (Beatmasters Mix)	12"	Mute	L12BONG15	1988	£2.50	£6	
Behind The Wheel (Shep Pettibone Mix)	12"	Mute	DBONG15	1987	£2.50	£6	promo
Enjoy The Silence	12"	Mute	P12BONG18	1990	£2.50	£6	promo
Enjoy The Silence (The Quad)	CD-s	Mute	XLCDBONG18	1990	£2.50	£6	
Everything Counts (Absolute Mix)	10"	Mute	10BONG16	1989	£2.50	£6	
Everything Counts (edit)	7"	Mute	7BONG16R	1989	£2	£5	promo
Everything Counts (Simenon & Saunders Mix)	CD-s	Mute	LCDBONG16	1989	£6	£15	
Everything Counts (Simenon & Saunders Mix)	12"	Mute	P12BONG16	1989	£3	£8	promo
Master And Servant	12"	Mute	L12BONG6	1984	£3	£8	
Music For The Masses	LP	Mute	STUMM47	1987	£4	£10	clear or blue vinyl
Music For The Masses	LP	Mute	STUMM47	1987	£4	£10	HMV Ltd.ed. with promo 12' (HMV1)
Never Let Me Down Again	CD-s	Mute	CDBONG14	1987	£2.50	£6	
Never Let Me Down Again	12"	Mute	P12BONG14	1987	£3	£8	promo
People Are People (On U Sound Mix)	12"	Mute	L12BONG5	1984	£2.50	£6	
Personal Jesus	cass-s	Mute	PCBONG17	1989	£2.50	£6	4 track promo
Personal Jesus	12"	Mute	P12BONG17	1989	£3	£8	promo
Policy Of Truth (Capitol Mix)	12"	Mute	P12BONG19	1990	£2.50	£6	promo
Policy Of Truth (Trancentral Mix)	CD-s	Mute	LCDBONG19	1990	£2.50	£6	
Sometimes I Wish I Was Dead	7"	Lyntone	LYN10209	1981	£2.50	£6	Flexipop flexi
Strangelove (Blind Mix)	12"	Mute	L12BONG13	1987	£2.50	£6	
Strangelove (Fresh Ground Mix)	12"	Mute	DANCEBONG13	1987	£15	£30	promo
Strangelove (Hijack MIx)	12"	Mute	PP12BONG16	1989	£4	£10	promo
Strangelove (Maxi-Mix)	12"	Mute	S12BONG13	1987	£3	£8	promo
Stripped	12"	Mute	12BONG10	1986	£3	£8	promo
Violator	12"	Mute	PSTUMM64	1990	£4	£10	promo sampler
World In My Eyes (Dub In My Eyes)	CD-s	Mute	LCDBONG20	1990	£3	£8	
World In My Eyes (Mayhem Mode)	12"	Mute	P12BONG20	1990	£2.50	£6	promo

DEPUTIES

Given Half A Chance	7"	Strike	JH305	1966	£2	£5	

DEREK & CLIVE

Live	LP	Island	ILPS9434	1976	£4	£10	

DEREK & THE DOMINOES

Layla And Other Assorted Love Songs	LP	Polydor	2625005	1971	£5	£12	double
Tell The Truth	7"	Polydor	2058057	1970	£12.50	£25	

DEREK & THE FRESHMEN

Gone Away	7"	Oriole	CB305	1965	£2.50	£6	

DERRICK & THE SOUNDS

Morning Papers	7"	Pye	7N17801	1969	£2	£5	
My Guitar	7"	Hit	HIT10		£1.50	£4	
My Sly Sadie	7"	Pye	7N17709	1969	£2	£5	
Power Of Love	7"	Pye	7N17601	1968	£2	£5	

DERRY, GLEN

Blue Sax	7"	Oriole	CB1609	1961	£1.50	£4	

DESANTO, SUGAR PIE

I Don't Wanna Fuss	7"	Pye	7N25267	1964	£5	£10	
Soulful Dress	7"	Chess	CRS8093	1969	£2.50	£6	
Soulful Dress	7"	Pye	7N25249	1964	£7.50	£15	
Sugar Pie	LP	Checker	LP2979	1961	£10	£25	US
There's Gonna Be Trouble	7"	Chess	CRS8034	1966	£4	£8	

DESCENDANTS

Garden Of Eden	7"	CBS	202545	1967	£12.50	£25	

DESHANNON, JACKIE

Are You Ready For This?	LP	Liberty	(S)BLY3085	1966	£5	£12	
Breakin' It Up On The Beatles Tour	LP	Liberty	LRP3390/LST7390	1964	£8	£20	US
C'Mon Let's Live A Little	LP	Liberty	LRP3430/LST7430	1966	£5	£12	US
Come On Down	7"	Liberty	LIB66224	1966	£5	£10	
Dancing Silhouettes	7"	Liberty	LIB10165	1964	£1.50	£4	
Don't Turn Your Back On Me	LP	Liberty	LBY1245	1965	£6	£15	
Don't Turn Your Back On Me	7"	Liberty	LIB10175	1964	£1.50	£4	
Great Performances	LP	Liberty	LBS83117	1968	£4	£10	
In The Wind	LP	Imperial	LP9296/12296	1965	£5	£12	US
Jackie	7" EP	Liberty	LEP2233	1965	£4	£8	

214

Jackie DeShannon	LP	Liberty	LRP3320/LST7320	1963	£6	£15 ....US
Needles And Pins	7"	Liberty	LIB55563	1963	£2	£5
She Don't Understand Him Like I Do	7"	Liberty	LIB10192	1965	£1.50	£4
This Is Jackie DeShannon	LP	Liberty	LBY1182	1965	£5	£12
What The World Needs Now	7"	Liberty	LIB10202	1965	£1.50	£4
When You Walk In The Room	7"	Liberty	LIB55645	1964	£2	£5
You Won't Forget Me	LP	Imperial	LP9294/12294	1965	£5	£12 ....US
You Won't Forget Me	7"	Liberty	LIB55497	1962	£1.50	£4

DESIGN
Day Of The Fox	LP	Regal Zonophone	SLRZ1037	1973	£6	£15
Design	LP	Epic	64322	1970	£8	£20
Tomorrow Is So Far Away	LP	Epic	64653	1971	£8	£20

DESMOND, ANDY
Living On A Shoe String	LP	Konk	KONK103	1975	£6	£15

DESMOND, JOHNNY
Bushel And A Peck	7"	MGM	SP1042	1953	£1.50	£4 ....B side by Art Lund
Don't	7"	Vogue Coral	Q72055	1955	£1.50	£4 ...with Alan Dale and Buddy Greco
Eighteenth Century Music Box	7"	Vogue Coral	Q72235	1957	£1.50	£4
High And The Mighty	7"	Vogue Coral	Q2019	1954	£1.50	£4
Sixteen Tons	7"	Vogue Coral	Q72115	1956	£1.50	£4
White Sports Coat	7"	Vogue Coral	Q72261	1957	£1.50	£4
Yellow Rose Of Texas	7"	Vogue Coral	Q72099	1955	£1.50	£4

DESMOND, LORRAE
Ding Dong Rock-a-Billy	7"	Parlophone	R4361	1957	£5	£10
Get Your Daddy's Car Tonight	7"	Parlophone	R4670	1960	£1.50	£4
Heartbroken	7"	Decca	F10533	1955	£2	£5
Hold My Hand	7"	Decca	F10375	1954	£2.50	£6
House With Love In It	7"	Parlophone	R4239	1956	£1.50	£4
I Can't Tell A Waltz From A Tango	7"	Decca	F10404	1954	£2.50	£6
Kansas City Special	7"	Parlophone	R4320	1957	£2	£5
No One But You	7"	Decca	F10398	1954	£2.50	£6
Secret Of Happiness	7"	Parlophone	R4430	1958	£1.50	£4
Soda Pop Hop	7"	Parlophone	R4463	1958	£1.50	£4
Tall Paul	7"	Parlophone	R4534	1959	£1.50	£4
Two Ships	7"	Parlophone	R4400	1958	£1.50	£4
Wake The Town And Tell The People	7"	Decca	F10612	1955	£2.50	£6
Where Will The Dimple Be?	7"	Decca	F10510	1955	£2.50	£6
Why Oh Why?	7"	Decca	F10461	1955	£2.50	£6
You Won't Be Around	7"	Parlophone	R4287	1957	£1.50	£4

DESMOND, PAUL
Paul Desmond And Friends	LP	Warner Bros	WM4020/WS8020	1961	£6	£15
Two Of A Mind	LP	RCA	RD7525	1962	£6	£15 ...with Gerry Mulligan

DESPERATE BICYCLES
Remorse Code	LP	Refill	RR6	1980	£6	£15

DESTROYERS
Niney Special	7"	Amalgamated	AMG856	1969	£4	£8

DETERGENTS
I Don't Know	7"	Columbia	DB7591	1965	£2.50	£6
Leader Of The Laundromat	7"	Columbia	DB7513	1965	£4	£8
Many Faces Of The Detergents	LP	Roulette	(S)R25308	1965	£6	£15 ....US

DETOURS
Run To Me Baby	7"	CBS	3213	1968	£7.50	£15
Whole Lotta Lovin'	7"	CBS	3401	1968	£12.50	£25

DETROIT
Detroit	LP	Paramount	SPFL277	1971	£5	£12

DETROIT SPINNERS
Detroit Spinners	LP	Tamla Motown	(S)TML11060	1968	£10	£25
For All We Know	7"	Tamla Motown	TMG627	1967	£4	£8
I'll Always Love You	7"	Tamla Motown	TMG523	1965	£15	£30
Sweet Thing	7"	Tamla Motown	TMG514	1965	£15	£30

DEUCE COUP
Clown In Town	7"	Mercury	MF1013	1967	£1.50	£4

DEUCE OF HEARTS
Closer Together	7"	CBS	202345	1966	£1.50	£4

DEUCHAR, JIMMY
Jimmy Deuchar Ensemble	10" LP	Tempo	LAP2	1955	£10	£25
Jimmy Deuchar Quartet	10" LP	Esquire	20059	1956	£8	£20
Pal Jimmy	LP	Tempo	TAP20	1958	£6	£15
Showcase	10" LP	Vogue	LDE023	1953	£10	£25

DEUTER, HARI
Aum	LP	Kuckuck	2375017	1972	£4	£10 ......German
Celebration	LP	Kuckuck	2375040	1976	£4	£10 ......German
Deuter	LP	Kuckuck	2375009	1971	£4	£10 ......German

DEUTSCHER, DRAFI
Drafi .... LP ...... Decca .... SLK16380 .... 1966 ... £15 ....£30 .... German

DEVIANTS
The Deviants, masterminded (if the word is appropriate to such a chaotic organisation) by Mick Farren, were more about social revolution than about music. Pieces like "Let's Loot The Supermarket" describe the group's stance, although they were too disorganised and too full of drugs and alcohol to have ever achieved even this much of a blow against society. Amazingly, many of the original group members managed to continue with some kind of career in rock music - Farren with new versions of the Deviants (and he also became a successful writer) and Duncan Sanderson, Russ Hunter, and Paul Rudolph with the Pink Fairies.

Deviants	LP	Transatlantic ...	TRA204	1969	£15	£30	
Deviants	LP	Transatlantic ...	TRA204	1969	£20	£40	with booklet
Disposable	LP	Stable	SLP7001	1968	£25	£50	
Ptooff	LP	Decca	LKR/SKLR4993	1969	£15	£30	
Ptooff	LP	Underground Impressarios ...	IMP1	1967	£30	£60	
Ptooff!	LP	Psycho	PSYCHO16	1983	£6	£15	
You've Got To Hold On	7"	Stable	STA5601	1968	£10	£20	

DEVLIN, JOHNNY
Hung On You	7"	CBS	202085	1966	£1.50	£4	
Hurtin'	7"	CBS	2751	1967	£1.50	£4	
My Strength: Heart And Soul	7"	CBS	202339	1966	£1.50	£4	
Sometimes	7"	Pye	7N15598	1964	£1.50	£4	
Tender Lovin' Care	7"	CBS	202452	1967	£1.50	£4	

DEVON
Making Love	7"	Nu Beat	NB021	1968	£4	£8	
What A Sin Thing	7"	Blue Cat	BS158	1969	£4	£8	

DEVONNES
I'm Gonna Pick Up My Toys	7"	UK	USA5	1975	£2	£5	

DEVONS
Wine, Wine, Wine	7"	Pic One	111	1966	£15	£30	US

DEVOTED
I Love George Best	7"	Page One	POF076	1968	£1.50	£4	

DEVOTIONS
For Sentimental Reasons	7"	Columbia	DB7256	1964	£6	£12	

DEW DROPS
Somebody Is Knocking	7"	Blue Beat	BB381	1965	£5	£10	

DEXTER, DANNY
Sweet Mama	7"	London	HLU9690	1963	£1.50	£4	

DEXTER, EDDIE
Verse Of Stardust	7"	Capitol	CL14371	1955	£1.50	£4	

DEXTER, RAY & THE LAYABOUTS
Coalman's Lament	7"	Decca	F11538	1962	£5	£10	

DEXY'S MIDNIGHT RUNNERS
It seems incredible that a group with the inspiration and brilliance that Dexy's Midnight Runners had at the beginning of the eighties could so rapidly and so completely fall from favour in the aftermath of a number one hit. The group is now represented by a solitary collectors' item, whose rarity is considerably greater than might be suggested by the low value. On the eve of the group's second album being released, Kevin Rowland had still not come up with his Celtic Soul identity, although the actual music was in place. Accordingly, test pressings of the album that was actually issued as "Too Rye Aye" have a different title and completely different artwork.

Hey Where Are You Going With That Suitcase	LP	Mercury	MERS5	1982	£8	£20	promo of 2nd LP

DEY, TRACY
Go Away	7"	Stateside	SS287	1964	£6	£12	

DHARMA BLUES
The music of the Dharma Blues is a reasonably faithful copy of the country blues - piano and harmonica to the fore - but suffers badly from the perennial problem of white blues records; the vocals are totally unconvincing. The sleeve notes go on at length about how exciting the music is and how relevant it is to the present age, but in truth these versions of some well-known traditional songs are a bit boring. That anyone should be willing to pay a substantial collectors' price for the record, when for a fraction of the price they could buy a good compilation of music by the likes of Memphis Slim or Sonny Terry & Brownie McGhee, is one of the mysteries of record collecting.

Dharma Blues	LP	Major Minor	SMCP5017	1969	£30	£60	

DIALOGUE
Dialogue	LP	Cold Studio		1968	£65	£130	
Dialogue	LP	Cold Studio		1974	£45	£90	

DIALS
Love Is A Treasure	7"	Duke	DU49	1969	£2.50	£6	

DIAMOND BOYS
Hey Little Girl	7"	RCA	RCA1351	1963	£2	£5	

DIAMOND, BRIAN & THE CUTTERS
Big Bad Wolf	7"	Pye	7N15779	1965	£4	£8	
Bone Idol	7"	Pye	7N15952	1965	£2.50	£6	
Jealousy Will Get You Nowhere	7"	Decca	F11724	1963	£4	£8	
Shake Shout And Go	7"	Fontana	TF452	1964	£4	£8	

DIAMOND HEAD
Canterbury	LP	MCA	DH1002	1983	£4	£10	
Diamond Lights	12"	Windsong	DHM005	1981	£3	£8	

Title	Format	Label	Cat No	Year	Low	High	Notes
Kingmaker	7"	MCA	DHMP104	1983	£1.50	£4	pic disc
Lightning To The Nations	LP	Happy Face	MMDHLP105	1981	£10	£25	plain white sleeve
Living On Borrowed Time	LP	MCA	DH1001	1981	£6	£15	with poster
Out Of Phase	12"	MCA	DHMT104	1983	£2.50	£6	
Shoot Out the Lights	7"	Happy Face	MMDH120	1980	£2.50	£6	
Sweet And Innocent	7"	Media	SCREEN1	1980	£2	£5	
Waited Too Long	7"	DHM	DHM004	1981	£1.50	£4	

DIAMOND, JERRY

Title	Format	Label	Cat No	Year	Low	High	Notes
Sunburned Lips	7"	London	HLE8496	1957	£7.50	£15	

DIAMOND, LEE

Title	Format	Label	Cat No	Year	Low	High	Notes
I'll Step Down	7"	Fontana	H310	1961	£2	£5	
Stop Your Crying	7"	Fontana	H345	1961	£2	£5	

DIAMOND, NEIL

Title	Format	Label	Cat No	Year	Low	High	Notes
Beautiful Noise	LP	CBS	Q86004	1976	£4	£10	quad
Brother Love's Travelling Salvation Show	LP	MCA	MUPS382	1969	£4	£10	
Cherry Cherry	7"	London	HLZ10072	1966	£1.50	£4	
Clown Town	7"	Columbia	42809	1963	£60	£120	US
Feel Of Neil Diamond	LP	London	HAZ8307	1966	£5	£12	
Girl You'll Be A Woman Soon	7"	London	HLZ10126	1967	£1.50	£4	
Greatest Hits	LP	Bang	BLPS219	1968	£5	£12	US
Heartlight	12"	Columbia	AS991586	1982	£4	£10	US 1 sided promo pic disc
Hot August Night	LP	Mobile Fidelity	MFSL2024	1978	£6	£15	US audiophile
I Got The Feelin'	7"	London	HLZ10092	1966	£1.50	£4	
Jazz Singer	LP	Mobile Fidelity	MFSL2071	1982	£4	£10	US audiophile
Jonathan Livingstone Seagull	LP	Columbia	HC42550	1981	£4	£10	US audiophile
Just For You	LP	Bang	BLP(S)217	1967	£5	£12	US
Kentucky Woman	7"	London	HLZ10161	1967	£1.50	£4	
New Orleans	7"	London	HLZ10177	1968	£1.50	£4	
Open Ended Interview	7"	Uni	LP1913	1968	£8	£20	US promo
Red Red Wine	7"	London	HLZ10187	1968	£1.50	£4	
Serenade	LP	CBS	Q69067	1974	£4	£10	quad
Solitary Man	7"	London	HLZ10049	1966	£1.50	£4	
Thank The Lord For The Night Time	7"	London	HLZ10151	1967	£1.50	£4	
Touching Me Touching You	LP	Uni	UNLS110	1970	£4	£10	
Velvet Gloves And Spit	LP	MCA	MUPS365	1968	£4	£10	
You Don't Bring Me Flowers	LP	Columbia	HC45625	1980	£4	£10	US audiophile
You Got To Me	7"	London	HLZ10111	1967	£1.50	£4	

DIAMOND RED

Title	Format	Label	Cat No	Year	Low	High	Notes
Diamond Red	LP	Big Tree	89507	1975	£6	£15	US

DIAMONDS

Title	Format	Label	Cat No	Year	Low	High	Notes
Black Denim Trousers & Motorcycle Boots	7"	Vogue Coral	Q72109	1955	£12.50	£25	
Collection Of Golden Hits	LP	Mercury	MG20213	1956	£20	£40	US
Diamonds	LP	Mercury	MG20309	1958	£15	£30	US
Diamonds	LP	Wing	MGW12114	1958	£10	£25	US
Diamonds Are Trumps	10" LP	Mercury	MPT7526	1957	£37.50	£75	
Diamonds Are Trumps	7" EP	Mercury	ZEP10026	1959	£10	£20	
Diamonds Meet Pete Rugulo	LP	Mercury	MG20368/SR60076	1958	£10	£25	US
Diamonds Meet Pete Rugulo	7" EP	Mercury	ZEP10020	1959	£7.50	£15	
Diamonds Vol.1	7" EP	Mercury	MEP9523	1957	£10	£20	
Diamonds Vol.2	7" EP	Mercury	MEP9527	1958	£10	£20	
Diamonds Vol.3	7" EP	Mercury	MEP9530	1958	£10	£20	
Dig The Diamonds	7" EP	Mercury	ZEP10003	1959	£10	£20	
Don't Say Goodbye	78	Mercury	MT167	1957	£2	£5	
Eternal Lovers	7"	Mercury	AMT1004	1958	£5	£10	
High Sign	7"	Mercury	7MT207	1958	£7.50	£15	
Kathy O	7"	Mercury	7MT233	1958	£4	£8	
Love Love Love	78	Mercury	MT121	1956	£2.50	£6	
Oh How I Wish	78	Mercury	MT179	1957	£2.50	£6	
One Summer Night	7"	Mercury	AMT1156	1961	£4	£8	
Pete Rugolo Leads The Diamonds	7" EP	Mercury	SEZ19012	1961	£10	£20	stereo
Pete Rugolo Leads The Diamonds	7" EP	Mercury	ZEP10097	1961	£7.50	£15	
Pop Hits By The Diamonds	LP	Wing	MGW12178	1959	£8	£20	US
Presenting The Diamonds	7" EP	Mercury	MEP9515	1957	£10	£20	
She Say Oom Dooby Oom	7"	Mercury	AMT1024	1959	£5	£10	
Silhouettes	7"	Mercury	7MT187	1958	£7.50	£15	
Songs From The Old West	LP	Mercury	MMC14039	1960	£6	£15	
Star Studded Diamonds	7" EP	Mercury	ZEP10053	1960	£7.50	£15	
Straight Skirts	7"	Mercury	7MT208	1958	£10	£20	
Stroll	7"	Mercury	7MT195	1958	£7.50	£15	
Surprise Package	7" EP	Mercury	ZEP10088	1960	£10	£20	with Ben Hewitt
Tell The Truth	7"	Mercury	AMT1086	1960	£5	£10	

DIAMONDS (2)

Title	Format	Label	Cat No	Year	Low	High	Notes
Lost City	7"	Philips	BF1264	1963	£1.50	£4	

DIANE & THE JAVELINS

Title	Format	Label	Cat No	Year	Low	High	Notes
Heart And Soul	7"	Columbia	DB7819	1966	£7.50	£15	

DI'ANNO, PAUL

Title	Format	Label	Cat No	Year	Low	High	Notes
Di'Anno	LP	FM	WKFMLP1	1984	£4	£10	blue vinyl
Di'Anno	LP	FM	WKFMPD1	1984	£5	£12	pic disc

DIATONES
Ruby Has Gone .... 7" ...... Starlite .... ST45057 .... 1961 ... £4 ....£8 ....

DIBANGO, MANU
Soul Makossa .... LP ..... Atlantic .... SD7267 .... 1972 ... £4 ....£10 .... US

DICE THE BOSS
Brixton Cat .... LP ..... Trojan .... TBL106 .... 1969 ... £6 ....£15 ....
Brixton Cat .... 7" ...... Joe .... DU50 .... 1969 ... £4 ....£8 ....
But Officer .... 7" ...... Joe .... DU52 .... 1969 ... £4 ....£8 ....
Gun The Man Down .... 7" ...... Duke .... DU51 .... 1969 ... £2.50 ....£6 ....
Your Boss DJ .... 7" ...... Joe .... DU57 .... 1969 ... £4 ....£8 ....

DICK & DEE DEE
All My Trials .... 7" ...... Warner Bros .... WB126 .... 1964 ... £1.50 ....£4 ....
Be My Baby .... 7" ...... Warner Bros .... WB156 .... 1965 ... £1.50 ....£4 ....
Goodbye To Love .... 7" ...... London .... HLG9483 .... 1962 ... £2.50 ....£4 ....
Guess Our Love Must Show ... 7" ...... Warner Bros .... WB111 .... 1963 ... £1.50 ....£4 ....
Mountain's High .... LP ..... London .... HLG9408 .... 1961 ... £4 ....£8 ...... chart single
Remember When .... 7" ...... Warner Bros .... WB138 .... 1964 ... £1.50 ....£4 ....
Songs We've Sung On Shindig ... LP ..... Warner Bros .... W(S)1623 .... 1965 ... £5 ....£12 ...... US
Tell Me .... LP ..... Liberty .... LRP3236/LST7236 .... 1962 ... £6 ....£15 ...... US
Tell Me .... 7" ...... Liberty .... LIB55412 .... 1962 ... £1.50 ....£4 ....
Thou Shalt Not Steal .... LP ..... Warner Bros .... W(S)1586 .... 1965 ... £5 ....£12 ...... US
Thou Shalt Not Steal .... 7" ...... Warner Bros .... WB145 .... 1964 ... £1.50 ....£4 ....
Turn Around .... LP ..... Warner Bros .... WM/WS8150 .... 1963 ... £6 ....£15 ....
Turn Around .... 7" ...... Warner Bros .... WB119 .... 1963 ... £1.50 ....£4 ....
Use What You've Got .... 7" ...... Warner Bros .... WB5671 .... 1965 ... £1.50 ....£4 ....
Young And In Love .... LP ..... Warner Bros .... WM/WS8132 .... 1963 ... £6 ....£15 ....
Young And In Love .... 7" ...... Warner Bros .... WB96 .... 1963 ... £1.50 ....£4 ....

DICKEN, DOLES
Piakukaungcung .... 7" ...... London .... HLD8639 .... 1958 ... £2.50 ....£6 ....

DICKENS
Standing Out .... LP ..... Hawkmoon ...... ROCK101P .... 1985 ... £8 ....£20 ....

DICKENS, CHARLES
I Stand Alone .... 7" ...... Pye .... 7N15938 .... 1965 ... £2 ....£5 ....
So Much In Love .... 7" ...... Immediate .... IM025 .... 1966 ... £4 ....£8 ....
That's The Way Love Goes .... 7" ...... Pye .... 7N15887 .... 1965 ... £2 ....£5 ...... chart single

DICKENS, LITTLE JIMMY
May The Bird Of Paradise Fly Up Your 7" .... CBS .... 201969 .... 1965 ... £1.50 ....£4 ....
Nose ....

DICKENSON, VIC
Mainstream .... LP ..... London .... LTZK15182/ .... 1960 ... £6 ....£15 ...... with Joe Thomas
                                              SAHK6066............
Vic Dickenson Septet .... 10" LP Vanguard........ PPT12000 .... 1955 ... £8 ....£20 ....
Vic Dickenson Septet .... 10" LP Vanguard........ PPT12005 .... 1956 ... £8 ....£20 ....
Vic Dickenson Septet .... 10" LP Vanguard........ PPT12015 .... 1957 ... £8 ....£20 ....
Vol.4 .... 10" LP Vanguard........ PPT12019 .... 1958 ... £8 ....£20 ....

DICKIES
The Dickies are an American group, famous for their plethora of coloured vinyl releases and famous too for their irreverent cover versions. Their supercharged interpretations of "Paranoid", "Eve Of Destruction", "Sound Of Silence", and "Silent Night" are great fun, but best of all is the headlong reading of "Nights In White Satin", where the guitar solo is actually (more or less) the same as the flute solo on the original, but played several times faster!
Dawn Of The Dickies .... LP ..... A&M .... AMLH68510 .... 1979 ... £4 ....£10 ... blue or yellow vinyl
Incredible Shrinking Dickies .... LP ..... A&M .... AMLH64742 .... 1979 ... £4 ....£10 .... blue, yellow,
                                                                                                               or orange vinyl
Paranoid .... 10" ..... A&M .... 12008 .... 1978 ... £2.50 ....£6 ..... promo, white vinyl

DICKSON, BARBARA
Do Right Woman .... LP ..... Decca .... SKL5058 .... 1970 ... £25 ....£50 ....
From The Beggar's Mantle .... LP ..... Celtic .... CM029 .... £6 ....£15 ....
From The Beggar's Mantle .... LP ..... Decca .... SKL5116 .... 1972 ... £25 ....£50 ....
John,Paul,George,Ringo,& Bert .... LP ..... RSO............... 2394167 .... 1975 ... £5 ....£12 ....

DICKSON, BARBARA & ARCHIE FISHER
Through The Recent Years .... LP ..... Decca .... SKL5041 .... 1970 ... £15 ....£30 ....

DICTATORS
So Long Little Girl .... 7" ...... Oriole .... CB1934 .... 1963 ... £1.50 ....£4 ....

DIDDLEY, BO
16 All Time Hits .... LP ..... Pye .... NPL28049............... 1964 ... £6 ....£15 ....
500 Per Cent More Man .... 7" ...... Chess .... CRS8026 .... 1966 ... £2 ....£5 ....
Another Dimension .... LP ..... Chess .... 6310107............... 1971 ... £4 ....£10 ....
Another Sugar Daddy .... 7" ...... Chess .... CRS8078 .... 1968 ... £2 ....£5 ....
Beach Party .... LP ..... Checker .... LP(S)2988............... 1963 ... £15 ....£30 ...... US
Beach Party .... LP ..... Pye .... NPL28032............... 1963 ... £6 ....£15 ......chart LP
Big Bad Bo .... LP ..... Chess .... CH50047............... 1974 ... £5 ....£12 ...... US
Black Gladiator .... LP ..... Checker .... LP(S)3013............... 1969 ... £6 ....£15 ...... US
Bo Diddley .... LP ..... Chess .... LP2984 .... 1962 ... £8 ....£20 ...... US
Bo Diddley .... LP ..... Chess .... LP1431 .... 1957 ... £20 ....£40 ...... US
Bo Diddley .... LP ..... Pye .... NPL28026............... 1963 ... £6 ....£15 ......chart LP
Bo Diddley .... 7" ...... Pye .... 7N25210............... 1963 ... £4 ....£8 ....
Bo Diddley 1969 .... 7" ...... Chess .... CRS8088 .... 1969 ... £2 ....£5 ....
Bo Diddley And Company .... LP ..... Checker .... LP2985 .... 1963 ... £17.50 ....£35 ...... US

Title	Format	Label	Catalogue	Year	Price	Price	Notes
Bo Diddley Is A Gunslinger	LP	Checker	LP2977	1961	£20	£40	US
Bo Diddley Is A Gunslinger	LP	Pye	NJL33	1963	£10	£25	chart LP
Bo Diddley Is A Lover	LP	Checker	LP2980	1961	£15	£30	US
Bo Diddley Is A Lover	7"	Pye	7N25227	1963	£2.50	£6	
Bo Diddley Is A Twister	LP	Checker	LP2982	1962	£8	£20	
Bo Diddley Rides Again	LP	Pye	NPL28029	1963	£6	£15	chart LP
Bo's A Lumberjack	7" EP	Pye	NEP44031	1964	£6	£12	
Boss Man	LP	Checker	LP(S)3007	1967	£17.50	£35	US
Diddling	7" EP	Pye	NEP44036	1964	£5	£10	
Five Hundred Per Cent More Man	LP	Checker	LP(S)2996	1964	£6	£15	US
Go Bo Diddley	LP	London	HAM2230	1959	£50	£100	
Great Grandfather	7"	London	HLM8913	1959	£25	£50	
Have Guitar, Will Travel	LP	Checker	LP2974	1959	£10	£25	US
Hey Bo Diddley	LP	Pye	NPL28025	1963	£6	£15	
Hey Bo Diddley	7" EP	Pye	NEP44014	1963	£5	£10	
Hey Good Looking	LP	Chess	CRL4002	1964	£6	£15	
Hey Good Looking	7"	Chess	CRS8000	1965	£4	£8	chart single
I'm A Man	LP	MF	2002	1977	£25	£50	US
I'm A Man	7" EP	Chess	CRE6008	1965	£5	£10	
In The Spotlight	LP	Checker	LP2976	1960	£8	£20	US
In The Spotlight	LP	Pye	NPL28034	1964	£6	£15	
Let Me Pass	LP	Chess	CRL4507	1965	£6	£15	
Let The Kids Dance	7"	Chess	CRS8021	1965	£2	£5	
London Sessions	LP	Checker	6499476	1972	£5	£12	
Mama Keep Your Big Mouth Shut	7"	Pye	7N25258	1964	£2.50	£6	
Memphis	7"	Pye	7N25235	1964	£2.50	£6	
Mona	7"	Pye	7N25243	1964	£4	£8	
Ooh Baby	7"	Chess	CRS8053	1967	£2	£5	
Originator	LP	Chess	CRL4526	1967	£6	£15	
Rhythm And Blues With Bo Diddley	7" EP	London	REU1054	1956	£30	£60	
Road Runner	LP	Checker	LP2982	1962	£15	£30	US
Road Runner	7"	London	HLM9112	1960	£20	£40	
Road Runner	7"	Pye	7N25217	1963	£4	£8	chart single
Rooster Stew	7" EP	Chess	CRE6023	1966	£5	£10	
Say Man	7"	London	HLM8975	1959	£15	£30	
Say Man Back Again	7"	London	HLM9035	1960	£15	£30	
Somebody Beat Me	7"	Chess	CRS8014	1965	£2	£5	
Story Of Bo Diddley	7" EP	Pye	NEP44019	1964	£5	£10	
Surfin' With Bo Diddley	LP	Checker	LP(S)2987	1963	£8	£20	US
Surfin' With Bo Diddley	LP	Marble Arch	MAL751	1968	£4	£10	
We're Gonna Get Married	7"	Chess	CRS8036	1966	£2	£5	
Where It All Began	LP	Chess	CH50016	1972	£8	£20	US
Who Do You Love	7"	Pye	7N25193	1963	£4	£8	
Wrecking My Love Life	7"	Chess	CRS8057	1967	£2	£5	
You Can't Judge A Book By Its Cover	7"	Pye	7N25165	1962	£5	£10	
You Can't Judge A Book By The Cover	7"	Pye	7N25216	1963	£2.50	£6	

DIETRICH, MARLENE

Title	Format	Label	Catalogue	Year	Price	Price
At The Cafe De Paris	10" LP	Philips	BBR8006	1954	£5	£12
Lili Marlene	7"	HMV	POP1196	1963	£1.50	£4
Marlene Dietrich	7" EP	HMV	7EG8257	1957	£2	£5
Marlene Dietrich	7" EP	London	RED1146	1958	£2	£5
Marlene Returns To Germany	7" EP	HMV	7EG8844	1964	£2	£5
Near You	7"	HMV	HLD8492	1957	£2	£5
Souvenir Album	10" LP	Brunswick	LA8591	1953	£5	£12
Where Have All The Flowers Gone	7"	HMV	POP1379	1965	£1.50	£4
Where Have All The Flowers Gone	7"	HMV	POP1563	1966	£1.50	£4

DIF JUZ

Title	Format	Label	Catalogue	Year	Price	Price
Huremics	12"	4AD	BAD109	1981	£4	£10
Vibrating Air	12"	4AD	BAD116	1981	£4	£10

DILLARD & CLARK

Title	Format	Label	Catalogue	Year	Price	Price	Notes
Fantastic Expedition Of Dillard And Clark	LP	A&M	AMLS939	1969	£6	£15	
Gene Clark & Doug Dillard	LP	Ariola	86027	1975	£4	£10	Dutch
Kansas City Southern	LP	Ariola	86436	1975	£6	£15	Dutch
Radio Song	7"	A&M	AMS764	1969	£2	£5	
Through The Morning	LP	A&M	AMLS966	1969	£6	£15	

DILLARD, DOUG

Title	Format	Label	Catalogue	Year	Price	Price	Notes
Banjo Album	LP	Together	STT1003	1970	£6	£15	US
Douglas Flint Dillard	LP	20th Century	T426	1974	£4	£10	US
Duelling Banjos	LP	20th Century	T409	1973	£4	£10	US

DILLARD, MOSES & JOSHUA

Title	Format	Label	Catalogue	Year	Price	Price
My Elusive Dreams	7"	Stateside	SS2059	1967	£4	£8

DILLARDS

Title	Format	Label	Catalogue	Year	Price	Price	Notes
Back Porch Blue Grass	LP	Elektra	EKL/EKS7232	1963	£6	£15	US
Copperfields	LP	Elektra	EKS74054	1970	£5	£12	
Live Almost	LP	Elektra	EKL/EKS7265	1964	£6	£15	US
Nobody Knows	7"	Capitol	CL15420	1965	£1.50	£4	
Pickin' And Fiddlin'	LP	Elektra	EKL/EKS7285	1965	£6	£15	US
Rain Maker	7"	Elektra	EKSN45081	1970	£2	£5	
Reason To Believe	7"	Elektra	EKSN45048	1968	£2	£5	
Roots And Branches	LP	United Artists	UAS29366	1972	£4	£10	
She Sang Hymns Out Of Tune	7"	Elektra	EKSN45062	1969	£1.50	£4	
Tribute To The American Duck	LP	United Artists	UAS29516	1973	£4	£10	
Wheatsheaf Suite	LP	Elektra	EKS74035	1968	£5	£12	

DILLON, PHYLLIS

Don't Stay Away	7"	Doctor Bird	DB1061	1966	£5	£10	Tommy McCook B side
Get On The Right Track	7"	Trojan	TR671	1969	£2.50	£6	Tommy McCook B side
I Wear This Ring	7"	Treasure Isle	TI7041	1968	£5	£10	
It's Rocking Time	7"	Treasure Isle	TI7015	1967	£5	£10	
Lipstick On Your Collar	7"	Trojan	TR686	1969	£2.50	£6	Tommy McCook B side
Love Is All I Had	7"	Trojan	TR651	1969	£2.50	£6	
Midnight Confession	7"	Treasure Isle	TI7070	1971	£2	£5	Tommy McCook B side
One Life To Live	LP	Trojan	TRL41	1972	£8	£20	
One Life To Live One Love To Give	7"	Treasure Isle	TI7058	1970	£2.50	£6	Tommy McCook B side
Things Of The Past	7"	Treasure Isle	TI7003	1967	£5	£10	
This Is A Lovely Way	7"	Trojan	TR006	1967	£4	£8	
This Is Me	7"	Duke Reid	DR2508	1970	£2.50	£6	

DILS

198 Seconds Of The Dils	7"	Dangerhouse	SLA268	1977	£10	£20	

DIMENSIONS

Tears On My Pillow	7"	Parlophone	R5294	1965	£4	£8	

DIMPLES

Love Of A Lifetime	7"	Decca	F12537	1966	£7.50	£15	

DINGER

Air Of Mystery	7"	Face Value	FVRA221	1985	£20	£40	
Air Of Mystery	7"	SRT	SRT394	1985	£20	£40	

DINGLE BROTHERS

Tank De Lard	7"	Doctor Bird	DB1026	1966	£5	£10	

DINGLE SPIKE

Dingle Spike	LP	SRTX	78CUS185	1978	£6	£15	

DINNING, MARK

Mark Dinning is responsible for what is undoubtedly the worst record ever released. Forget all the other candidates for the accolade - "Teen Angel" is the one! The song has one of those lyrics that deal with death - on this occasion, the singer's girlfriend has apparently rushed back into a burning building in order to save a ring that the singer had bought her. The symbol of the romance was more important than the romance itself! Meanwhile, the singer laments: "I'll never kiss your lips again, they buried you today". The epitome of bad taste - and all delivered in a thin, quavery voice so as to pile the pathos on really thick. Needless to say, the record was an American number one!

All Of This For Sally	7"	MGM	MGM1155	1962	£1.50	£4	
Dial A114883		Hickory	451293	1965	£1.50	£4	
Lovin' Touch	7"	MGM	MGM1101	1960	£1.50	£4	
Lovin' Touch	7"	MGM	MGM1101	1960	£1.50	£4	
Teen Angel	LP	MGM	(S)E3828	1960	£15	£30	US
Teen Angel	7"	MGM	MGM1053	1960	£2	£5	chart single
Top Forty	7"	MGM	MGM1125	1961	£1.50	£4	
Wanderin'	LP	MGM	(S)E3855	1960	£8	£20	US
You Win Again	7"	MGM	MGM1069	1960	£1.50	£4	

DINNING SISTERS

Drifting And Dreaming	7"	London	HLF8179	1955	£10	£20	
Hold Me Tight	7"	London	HLF8218	1956	£10	£20	

DINO & DEL

Hey Little Girl Hey Little Boy	7"	Carnival	CV7026	1965	£4	£8	

DINO, DESI & BILLY

I'm A Fool	7" EP	Reprise	RVEP60072	1965	£4	£8	French

DINO, KENNY

Your Ma Said You Cried In Your Sleep Last Night	7"	HMV	POP960	1961	£1.50	£4	

DINOSAUR

Kiss Me Again	7"	Sire	SRE1034	1979	£2	£5	
Kiss Me Again	12"	Sire	SRE1034	1979	£3	£8	

DIO, RONNIE & THE PROPHETS

Love Pains	7"	Atlantic	2145	1962	£7.50	£15	US

DION

Alone With Dion	LP	Laurie	LLP2004	1960	£10	£25	US
Be Careful Of The Stones That You Throw	7"	CBS	AAG161	1963	£2	£5	
Berimbau	7"	HMV	POP1565	1966	£1.50	£4	
By Special Request	LP	Laurie	LLP2016	1963	£10	£25	US
Chosen Few	7"	Jubilee	5294	1957	£12.50	£25	US
Chosen Few	7"	Mohawk	105	1957	£20	£40	US
Come Go With Me	7"	Stateside	SS209	1963	£2	£5	
Dion	LP	London	HAP/SHP8390	1969	£5	£12	
Dion Sings The Fifteen Million Sellers	LP	Laurie	LLP2019	1963	£8	£20	US
Dion Sings To Sandy & All Other Girls	LP	Laurie	LLP2017	1963	£8	£20	US
Dion's Hits	7" EP	Stateside	SE1006	1963	£20	£40	
Donna La Prima Donna	7"	CBS	121053	1963	£4	£8	sung in Italian
Donna The Prima Donna	LP	CBS	(S)BPG62203	1964	£6	£20	
Donna The Prima Donna	7"	CBS	AAG169	1963	£2	£5	

Title	Format	Label	Cat No	Year			Notes
Don't Pity Me	7"	London	HL8799	1959	£7.50	£15	
Drip Drop	7"	CBS	AAG177	1963	£2	£5	
Greatest Hits	LP	Laurie	LLP2013	1962	£8	£20	US
Having Fun	7"	Top Rank	JAR545	1961	£2	£5	
I Can't Go On	7"	London	HL8718	1958	£7.50	£15	
I Wonder Why	7"	London	HLH8646	1958	£15	£30	
I'm Your Hoochie Coochie Man	7"	CBS	AAG188	1964	£2	£5	
In The Still Of The Night	7"	Top Rank	JAR503	1960	£2.50	£6	
Johnny B.Goode	7"	CBS	AAG224	1964	£1.50	£4	
Little Diane	7"	Stateside	SS115	1962	£2	£5	
Lonely Teenager	7"	Top Rank	JAR521	1960	£2	£5	chart single
Love Came To Me	LP	Laurie	LLP2015	1963	£8	£20	US
Love Came To Me	7"	Stateside	SS139	1962	£2	£5	
Lover's Prayer	7"	Pye	7N25038	1959	£5	£10	
Lovers Who Wander	LP	Stateside	SL10034	1962	£10	£25	
Lovers Who Wander	7"	HMV	POP1020	1962	£2	£5	
More Greatest Hits	LP	Laurie	LLP2022	1963	£6	£15	US
Movin' Man	7"	HMV	POP1586	1967	£1.50	£4	
Presenting Dion And The Belmonts	LP	Laurie	LLP2002	1959	£25	£50	US
Presenting Dion And The Belmonts	LP	London	HAU2194	1959	£60	£120	
Reunion	LP	Warner Bros	K46208	1973	£4	£10	
Ruby Baby	LP	CBS	(B)PG62137	1963	£6	£15	
Ruby Baby	7"	CBS	AAG133	1963	£2	£5	
Runaround Sue	LP	HMV	CLP1539	1961	£20	£40	
Runaround Sue	LP	Laurie	LLP2009	1961	£25	£50	US, blue vinyl
Runaround Sue	7"	Top Rank	JAR586	1961	£2	£5	chart single
Sandy	7"	Stateside	SS161	1963	£2	£5	
Spoonful	7"	CBS	201780	1965	£1.50	£4	
Sweet Sweet Baby	7"	CBS	201728	1965	£2	£5	
Swing Along With Dion	7" EP	HMV	7EG8745	1962	£10	£20	
Teenage Clementine	7"	Mohawk	106	1957	£15	£30	US
Teenager In Love	7"	London	HLU8874	1959	£7.50	£15	chart single
This Little Girl	7"	CBS	AAG145	1963	£2	£5	
Together Again	LP	B&C	CAS1002	1969	£4	£10	
Together Again	LP	HMV	CLP/CSD3618	1967	£8	£20	
Toppermost Vol.1	LP	Top Rank	25027	1960	£10	£25	
Wanderer	7"	HMV	POP971	1962	£2	£5	chart single
When You Wish Upon A Star	7"	Top Rank	JAR368	1960	£2.50	£6	
Where Or When	7"	London	HLU9030	1960	£6	£12	
Wish Upon A Star	LP	Laurie	LLP2006	1960	£10	£25	US
Wonder Where I'm Bound	LP	Columbia	CS9773	1969	£4	£10	US

DIPLOMATS

Title	Format	Label	Cat No	Year		
I Can Give You Love	7"	Direction	583899	1968	£4	£8

DIRE STRAITS

Title	Format	Label	Cat No	Year			Notes
Brothers In Arms	7"	Vertigo	DSPIC11	1985	£5	£10	shaped pic disc
Brothers In Arms Special Edition	CD	Vertigo	8842852	1985	£15	£30	promo
Dire Straits	LP	Vertigo	HS9102021	1982	£4	£10	audiophile
Dire Straits Live	LP	Warner Bros	WBMS109	1980	£10	£25	US promo
Making Movies	LP	Vertigo	HS6350034	1982	£4	£10	audiophile
Money For Nothing	7"	Vertigo	DSPIC10	1985	£5	£10	shaped pic disc
Telegraph Road	12"	Vertigo		1982	£4	£10	promo

DIRECT HITS

Title	Format	Label	Cat No	Year		
Blow Up	LP	Whaam	BIG7	1984	£10	£25
Christopher Cooper	7"	Direct	POP001	1985	£1.50	£4
Modesty Blaise	7"	Whaam	WHAAM7	1982	£2.50	£6

DIRECTIONS

Title	Format	Label	Cat No	Year		
Three Bands Tonite	7"	Torch	TOR004	1979	£15	£30

DIRTY BLUES BAND

Title	Format	Label	Cat No	Year		
Dirty Blues Band	LP	Stateside	(S)SL10234	1967	£6	£15
Stone Dirt	LP	Stateside	(S)SL10268	1969	£6	£15

DISCO 2000

Title	Format	Label	Cat No	Year			Notes
Gotta CD	7"	KLF	D2001	1987	£5	£10	white label
Gotta CD	12"	KLF	D2000	1987	£4	£10	
One Love Nation	12"	KLF	D2002	1988	£3	£8	
Uptight	12"	KLF	D2003T	1989	£2.50	£6	

DISCO ZOMBIES

Title	Format	Label	Cat No	Year		
Drums Over London	7"	South Circular	SGS106	1979	£4	£8
Here Come The Buts	7"	Dining Out	TUX2	1981	£2	£5
Invisible EP	7"	Wizzo	WIZZO1	1979	£2.50	£6

DISCS

Title	Format	Label	Cat No	Year		
Not Meant To Be	7"	Columbia	DB7477	1965	£2.50	£6

DISGUISE IN LOVE

Title	Format	Label	Cat No	Year			Notes
Ross Was My Best Friend	7"	Purple Snow	FLAKE1	1982	£2	£5	purple vinyl

DIVINE

Title	Format	Label	Cat No	Year			Notes
Walk Like A Man	7"	Proto	ENAP125	1985	£1.50	£4	shaped pic disc

DIXIE BELLES

Title	Format	Label	Cat No	Year		
Dixie Belles	7" EP	London	REU1434	1964	£4	£8
Down At Papa Joe's	LP	London	HAU/SHU8152	1964	£5	£12
Down At Poppa Joe's	7"	London	HLU9797	1963	£1.50	£4
Southtown USA	7"	London	HLU9842	1964	£1.50	£4

DIXIE CUPS

Title	Format	Label	Catalogue	Year	Price	Price	Notes
Chapel Of Love	LP	Red Bird	RB(S)20100	1965	£8	£20	US
Chapel Of Love	7"	Pye	7N25245	1964	£2.50	£6	chart single
Gee The Moon Is Shining Bright	7"	Red Bird	RB10032	1965	£6	£12	
Iko Iko	LP	Red Bird	RB(S)20103	1965	£8	£20	US
Iko Iko	7"	Red Bird	RB10024	1965	£2	£5	chart single
Little Bell	7"	Red Bird	RB10017	1964	£2.50	£6	
Love Ain't So Bad	7"	HMV	POP1557	1966	£2	£5	
People Say	7"	Red Bird	RB10006	1964	£2.50	£6	
Riding High	LP	HMV	CLP1916	1966	£6	£15	
Two Way Poc-A-Way	7"	HMV	POP1453	1965	£2	£5	
What Kind Of Fool	7"	HMV	POP1524	1966	£4	£8	
You Should Have Seen The Way He Looked At Me	7"	Red Bird	RB10012	1964	£2.50	£6	

DIXIE DRIFTER

Title	Format	Label	Catalogue	Year	Price	Price
Soul Heaven	7"	Columbia	DB7710	1965	£4	£8

DIXIE FOUR

Title	Format	Label	Catalogue	Year	Price	Price
Dixie Four	7" EP	Rarities	RA3	196-	£7.50	£15

DIXIE HUMMINGBIRDS

Title	Format	Label	Catalogue	Year	Price	Price
Dixie Hummingbirds	7" EP	Vocalion	EPVP1277	1964	£5	£10
Final Edition	7" EP	Vocalion	EPVP1281	1964	£5	£10
Have A Talk With Jesus	7"	Vogue	V2422	1964	£2.50	£6

DIXIELAND ALL STARS

Title	Format	Label	Catalogue	Year	Price	Price
Dixiecats	LP	Columbia	33SX1080	1958	£5	£12

DIXIELAND JUG BLOWERS

Title	Format	Label	Catalogue	Year	Price	Price
Boodle-am-Shake	7"	HMV	7M223	1954	£2.50	£6
Hen Party Blues	7"	HMV	7M233	1954	£2.50	£6

DIXIELANDERS

Title	Format	Label	Catalogue	Year	Price	Price
Cyclone	7"	Vocalion	V9209	1963	£1.50	£4

DIXON, BILLY & THE TOPICS

This was one of a number of names tried out by the group that eventually settled on the Four Seasons.

Title	Format	Label	Catalogue	Year	Price	Price	Notes
I Am All Alone	7"	Topix	6002	1960	£30	£60	US
Lost Lullabye	7"	Topix	6008	1960	£30	£60	US

DIXON, ERROL

Title	Format	Label	Catalogue	Year	Price	Price	Notes
Back To The Chicken Shack	7"	Decca	F12826	1968	£6	£12	
Bad Bad Woman	7"	Blue Beat	BB86	1961	£5	£10	
Blues In The Pot	LP	Decca	LK/SKL4962	1968	£25	£50	with Chicken Shack
Errol Sings Fats	7" EP	Decca	DFE8626	1965	£10	£20	
Gloria	7"	Blue Beat	BB337	1965	£5	£10	
Hoop	7"	Direct	DS5002	1967	£4	£8	
I Love You	7"	Island	WI069	1963	£5	£10	
I Need Someone To Love Me	7"	Rainbow	RAI104	1966	£4	£8	
I Want	7"	Fab	FAB1	1966	£2	£5	
Mama Shut Your Door	7"	Blue Beat	BB46	1961	£5	£10	
Mean And Evil Woman	7"	Carnival	CV7004	1963	£4	£8	
Midnight Party	7"	Ska Beat	JB271	1967	£5	£10	
Midnight Train	7"	Blue Beat	BB27	1961	£5	£10	
Morning Train	7"	Island	WI017	1962	£5	£10	
Oo Wee Baby	7"	Carnival	CV7001	1963	£4	£8	
Rocks In My Pillow	7"	Oriole	CB1914	1964	£7.50	£15	
Six Questions	7"	Decca	F12613	1967	£5	£10	
That's How You Got Killed	LP	Transatlantic	TRA225	1970	£15	£30	
True Love Never Runs Smooth	7"	Decca	F12717	1967	£5	£10	
Why Hurt Yourself	7"	Doctor Bird	DB1197	1969	£5	£10	
You're No Good	7"	Blue Beat	BB344	1965	£5	£10	

DIXON, JEFF

Title	Format	Label	Catalogue	Year	Price	Price
Rock	7"	Coxsone	CS7015	1967	£5	£10
Tickle Me	7"	Studio One	SO2051	1968	£6	£12

DIXON, WILLIE

Title	Format	Label	Catalogue	Year	Price	Price	Notes
I Am The Blues	LP	Columbia	CS9987	1970	£6	£15	US
Walking The Blues	7"	London	HLU8297	1956	£400	£600	
Walking The Blues	7"	Pye	7N25270	1964	£6	£12	

DIXON, WILLIE & MEMPHIS SLIM

Title	Format	Label	Catalogue	Year	Price	Price	Notes
Blues Every Which Way	LP	Verve	V(6)3007	1961	£6	£15	US
In Paris	LP	Battle	BV(S)6122	1963	£6	£15	US
Willie's Blues	LP	Bluesville	BV1003	1960	£8	£20	US

DIXXY SISTERS

Title	Format	Label	Catalogue	Year	Price	Price
Game Of Broken Hearts	7"	Columbia	SCM5105	1954	£1.50	£4

DIZZY, JOHNNY

Title	Format	Label	Catalogue	Year	Price	Price	Notes
Sudden Destruction	7"	Ska Beat	JB204	1965	£5	£10	Soulettes B side

DMOCHOWSKI, JED

Title	Format	Label	Catalogue	Year	Price	Price
Sha La La	7"	Whaam!	WHAAM9	1983	£2.50	£6
Stallions Of My Heart	LP	Whaam!	BIG4	1982	£4	£10

DNV

Title	Format	Label	Catalogue	Year	Price	Price	Notes
Mafia	7"	New Pleasures	Z2	1979	£15	£30	fold-out P£

D.O.A.

Disco Sucks	7"	Quintessence ..	QEP002	1979	£10	£20	
Disco Sucks	7"	Sudden Death .	3097	1978	£12.50	£25	
Hardcore '81	LP	Friends	FR010	1981	£30	£60	
Positively D.O.A.	7"	Alternative Tentacles	VIRUS7	1981	£2	£5	
Something Better Change	LP	Friends	FR003	1980	£20	£40	
Triumph Of The Ignoroids	12"	Friends	198-	£20	£40		
War On 45	12"	Alternative Tentacles	VIRUS24	1984	£2.50	£6	

DOBKINS, CARL

Exclusively Yours	7"	Brunswick	05832	1960	£1.50	£4	
If You Don't Want My Lovin'	7"	Brunswick	05811	1959	£7.50	£15	
Luvky Devil	7"	Brunswick	05817	1960	£2.50	£6	chart single
My Heart Is An Open Book	LP	Brunswick	LAT8329	1959	£15	£30	
My Heart Is An Open Book	7"	Brunswick	05804	1959	£2.50	£6	

DOBSON, DOBBY

Cry A Little Cry	7"	King	KG1008	1965	£4	£8	
Loving Pauper	7"	Trojan	TR011	1967	£5	£10	Tommy McCook B side
Seems To Me I'm Losing You	7"	Coxsone	CS7058	1968	£5	£10	Gaylads B side
Strange	LP	Pama	SECO33	1969	£8	£20	
Strange	7"	Blue Cat	BS171	1969	£4	£8	
Tell Me	7"	Blue Beat	BB246	1963	£5	£10	
That Wonderful Sound	LP	Trojan	TBL145	1970	£6	£15	
Walking In The Footsteps	7"	Studio One	SO2068	1968	£6	£12	Soul Vendors B side

DOBSON, LYN

Jam Sandwich	LP	Fresh Air	6370501	1974	£4	£10	

DOCKER, ROY

I'm An Outcast	7"	Pama	PM756	1968	£2.50	£6	
Mellow Moonlight	7"	Domain	D3	1968	£2.50	£6	Music Through Six B side
When	7"	Pama	PM750	1968	£2.50	£6	

DOCTOR & THE MEDICS

Druids Are Here	7"	Whaam!	WHAAM6	1982	£4	£8	

DOCTOR CLAYTON

Pearl Harbour Blues	LP	RCA	INTS1176	1970	£5	£12	
RCA Victor Race Series Vol.6	7" EP	RCA	RCX7177	1965	£6	£12	

DODD ALL STARS

Hip Shuffle	7"	Coxsone	CS7076	1968	£5	£10	
Mother Aitken	7"	Coxsone	CS7096	1969	£5	£10	

DODD, PAT

Stag Party	7"	Pye	7N25030	1959	£1.50	£4	

DODDS, JOHNNY

Johnny Dodds And Kid Ory	LP	Philips	BBL7136	1957	£6	£15	
Johnny Dodds Vol.1	10" LP	London	AL3505	1953	£8	£20	
Johnny Dodds Vol.1	10" LP	Vogue Coral	LRA10025	1955	£8	£20	
Johnny Dodds Vol.2	10" LP	London	AL3513	1954	£8	£20	
Johnny Dodds Vol.3	10" LP	London	AL3555	1956	£8	£20	
Johnny Dodds Vol.4	10" LP	London	AL3560	1957	£8	£20	
Johnny Dodds Washboard Band	10" LP	HMV	DLP1073	1955	£8	£20	

DODDS, NELLA

Come See About Me	7"	Pye	7N25281	1965	£7.50	£15	
Finders Keepers Losers Weepers	7"	Pye	7N25291	1965	£7.50	£15	

DODGERS

Let's Make A Whole Lot Of Love	7"	Downbeat	CHA2	1960	£6	£12	

DODOS

Made Up My Mind	7"	Polydor	56153	1967	£5	£10	

DOE, ERNIE K

Certain Girl	7"	London	HLP9487	1962	£5	£10	
Dancing Man	7"	Action	ACT4502	1968	£2.50	£6	
Gotta Pack My Bags	7"	Action	ACT4512	1968	£2	£5	
Mother In Law	LP	Minit	LP0002	1961	£20	£40	US
Mother In Law	7"	London	HLU9330	1961	£5	£10	chart single
My Mother In Law	7"	Vocalion	VP9233	1965	£2.50	£6	
Te Ta Te Ta Ta	7"	London	HLU9390	1961	£4	£8	

DOG THAT BIT PEOPLE

Dog That Bit People	LP	Parlophone	PCS7125	1971	£120	£220	
Lovely Lady	7"	Parlophone	R5880	1971	£12.50	£25	

DOGFEET

Dogfeet	LP	Reflection	REFL8	1970	£180	£300	
Sad Story	7"	Reflection	RS7	1970	£12.50	£25	

DOGGEREL BANK

The two little known LPs by Doggerel Bank continue the experiments in mixing poetry, wit, and music caried out by the Barrow Poets, with many of the same personnel.

Mister Skillicorn Dances	LP	Charisma	CAS1102	1975	£5	£12
Silver Faces	LP	Charisma	CAS1079	1973	£5	£12

DOGGETT, BILL

3046 People Danced Till 4 a.m.	LP	Warner Bros	WM4042	1961	£4	£10	
As You Desire Me	LP	King	523	1955	£15	£30	US
Back Again With More	LP	King	723	1960	£6	£15	US
Back With More Bill Doggett	LP	Parlophone	PMC1165	1962	£4	£10	
Band With The Beat	LP	Warner Bros	WM4056/WS8056	1962	£4	£10	
Best Of Bill Doggett	LP	King	908	1964	£5	£12	US
Big City Dance Party	LP	King	641	1959	£8	£20	US
Bill Doggett	7" EP	Parlophone	GEP8711	1958	£4	£8	
Bonanza Of 24 Hit Songs	LP	King	959	1966	£4	£10	US
Candle Glow	LP	King	563	1958	£8	£20	US
Christmas	LP	King	600	1959	£8	£20	US
Dame Dreaming	LP	King	532	1956	£15	£30	US
Dame Dreaming	10" LP	Parlophone	PMD1067	1958	£8	£20	
Dance Awhile	LP	King	585	1958	£8	£20	US
Dance Awhile	10" LP	Parlophone	PMD1073	1959	£8	£20	
Doggett Beat	LP	King	557	1958	£15	£30	US
Doggett's Big City Dance Party	LP	Parlophone	PMC1118	1960	£5	£12	
Everybody Dance The Honky Tonk	LP	King	531	1956	£15	£30	US
Fingertips	LP	Columbia	2082	1963	£4	£10	US
Flute Cocktail	7" EP	Parlophone	GEP8694	1958	£2	£5	
For Reminiscent Lovers	LP	King	706	1960	£8	£20	US
High And Wide	LP	King	633	1959	£8	£20	US
Hold It	LP	King	609	1959	£8	£20	US
Honky Tonk	7"		R4231	1956	£12.50	£25	
Honky Tonk	7" EP	Parlophone	GEP8644	1957	£5	£10	
Honky Tonk A La Mod	LP	Roulette	25330	1966	£4	£10	US
Hot Doggett	LP	King	514	1954	£15	£30	US
Hot Ginger	7"	Parlophone	R4379	1957	£6	£12	
Hully Gully Twist	7"	Warner Bros	WB32	1961	£1.50	£4	
Impressions	LP	King	868	1963	£4	£10	US
Jolly Christmas	7" EP	Parlophone	GEP8771	1958	£2.50	£6	
Leaps And Bounds	7"	Parlophone	R4413	1958	£4	£8	
Many Moods	LP	King	778	1961	£6	£15	US
Moondust	LP	King	502	1954	£15	£30	US
On Tour	LP	Parlophone	PMC1124	1960	£8	£20	
Plays American Songs	LP	King	830	1963	£4	£10	US
Plays Duke Ellington	7" EP	Parlophone	GEP8674	1957	£2.50	£6	
Prelude To The Blues	LP	Columbia	1942	1962	£5	£12	US
Rainbow Riot	7" EP	Parlophone	GEP8727	1958	£2.50	£6	
Ram Bunk Shush	7"	Parlophone	R4306	1957	£6	£12	
Salute To Ellington	LP	King	533	1956	£15	£30	US
Slow Walk	7"	Parlophone	R4265	1957	£6	£12	
Smoke	7"	Parlophone	R4629	1960	£2.50	£6	
Swingin' Easy	LP	King	582	1958	£8	£20	US
Swings	LP	Warner Bros	1452	1963	£5	£12	US
Wow	LP	HMV	CLP1884	1965	£5	£12	
You Can't Sit Down	7"	Warner Bros	WB46	1961	£2	£5	

DOGS D'AMOUR

How Come It Never Rains	7"	Supertrack	DOGS1	1987	£4	£8	
How Do You Fall In Love	7"	Kumibeat	JOM3	1984	£25	£50	Finnish
State We're In	7"	Kumibeat		1984	£25	£50	Finnish
(Un)authorised Bootleg	LP	China	WOL7	1988	£10	£25	

DOLBY, THOMAS

Urges	7"	Armageddon	AS7	1981	£2.50	£6	
Urges	7"	Statik	TAK4	1982	£1.50	£4	

DOLDINGER, KLAUS

Blues Happening	LP	World Pacific	20167	1968	£5	£12	German
Doldinger's Motherhood	LP	Liberty	LBS83426	1970	£6	£15	German
In Sudamerika	LP	Philips	843728	1965	£5	£12	German
Made In Germany	LP	Philips	48024	1963	£5	£12	German

DOLENZ, JONES, BOYCE & HART

Dolenz, Jones, Boyce & Hart	LP	Capitol	ST11513	1976	£6	£15	US

DOLENZ, MICKEY

Don't Do It	7"	London	HLH10117	1967	£5	£10	B side b
							Finders Keepers
Huff Puff	7"	London	HLH10152	1967	£5	£10	Obvious B side

DOLL, ANDY

On Stage	LP	Starlite	STLP11	1963	£6	£15	
Wild Desire	7"	Starlite	ST45068	1962	£2.50	£6	

DOLL, LINDA & THE SUNDOWNERS

He Don't Want Your Love Any More	7"	Piccadilly	7N35166	1964	£1.50	£4	

DOLPHIN

Goodbye	LP	Private Stock	PVLP1055	1977	£5	£12	
Molecules	LP	Gale	LP02	1980	£8	£20	

DOLPHINS

Hey Da Da Dow	7"	Stateside	SS375	1965	£1.50	£4	

DOLPHY, ERIC

Title	Format	Label	Catalogue	Year			Notes
Eric Dolphy And Booker Little Memorial Album	LP	Stateside	SL10160	1966	£6	£15	
Out To Lunch	LP	Blue Note	BLP/BST84163	1964	£10	£25	
Outward Bound	LP	Transatlantic	PR7311	1969	£6	£15	

DOLTON, BILLY

Title	Format	Label	Catalogue	Year			Notes
Winkie Doll	7"	Parlophone	R4733	1961	£1.50	£4	

DOM

Title	Format	Label	Catalogue	Year			Notes
Edge Of Time	LP	Melocord	STLP001	1971	£100	£200	German

DOME

Title	Format	Label	Catalogue	Year			Notes
3R4	12"	4AD	CAD16	1980	£2.50	£6	

DOMINO, FATS

Title	Format	Label	Catalogue	Year			Notes
Ain't That A Shame	7"	London	HLU8173	1955	£25	£50	chart single, gold label
Ain't That Just Like A Woman	7"	London	HLP9301	1961	£4	£8	
Be My Guest	7"	London	HLP9005	1959	£4	£8	chart single
Be My Guest	7"	London	HLP9005	1959	£12.50	£25	tri-centre
Big Beat	7" EP	London	REP1261	1960	£6	£12	
Big Beat	7"	London	HL7054	1958	£4	£8	export
Big Beat	7"	London	HLP8575	1958	£6	£12	chart single
Blue Monday	7"	London	HLP8377	1957	£20	£40	chart single, gold label
Blueberry Hill	7"	London	HLU8330	1956	£25	£50	chart single, gold label
Blues For Love Vol.1	7" EP	London	REP1022	1955	£12.50	£25	gold label
Blues For Love Vol.2	7" EP	London	REP1062	1956	£10	£20	gold label
Blues For Love Vol.3	7" EP	London	REP1117	1958	£7.50	£15	
Blues For Love Vol.4	7" EP	London	REP1121	1958	£7.50	£15	
Bo Weevil	7"	London	HLU8256	1956	£30	£60	gold label
Carry On Rocking	LP	London	HAU2041	1956	£20	£40	
Carry On Rocking part 1	7" EP	London	REP1115	1958	£7.50	£15	
Carry On Rocking part 2	7" EP	London	REP1116	1958	£7.50	£15	
Country Boy	7"	London	HLP9073	1960	£4	£8	chart single
Domino '65	LP	Mercury	(S)MCL20070	1965	£4	£10	
Don't Leave Me This Way	78	London	HL8096	1954	£10	£20	
Everybody's Got Something To Hide...	7"	Reprise	RS20810	1969	£1.50	£4	
Fabulous Mr.D	LP	London	HAP2135	1958	£10	£25	
Fantastic Fats	LP	Stateside	(S)SL10240	1968	£5	£12	
Fats	LP	Reprise	RS6439	1971	£180	£300	US
Fats	7" EP	London	REP1073	1957	£30	£60	gold label
Fats Domino	LP	Imperial	LP9009	1956	£30	£60	US
Fats Domino Swings	LP	Imperial	LP9062	1959	£10	£25	US
Fats Is Back	LP	Reprise	RS6304	1968	£4	£10	US
Fats On Fire	LP	HMV	CLP1740/CSD1543	1963	£6	£15	
Getaway With Fats	LP	HMV	CLP1821/CSD1580	1966	£6	£15	
Here Comes Fats	LP	HMV	CLP1690/CSD1520	1963	£6	£15	
Here Comes Fats Vol.1	7" EP	London	REP1079	1957	£7.50	£15	
Here Comes Fats Vol.2	7" EP	London	REP1080	1957	£7.50	£15	
Here Comes Fats Vol.3	7" EP	London	REP1138	1958	£7.50	£15	
Here He Comes Again	LP	Imperial	LP9248	1963	£6	£15	US
Here Stands Fats Domino	LP	Imperial	LP9038	1957	£30	£60	US
Here Stands Fats Domino	LP	London	HAU2052	1957	£15	£30	
Honest Mamas Love Their Papas	7"	Reprise	R20696	1968	£4	£8	
Honey Chile	7"	London	HLU8356	1957	£20	£40	gold label, chart single
I Don't Want To Set The World On Fire	7"	HMV	POP1281	1964	£1.50	£4	
I Know	7"	London	HL8133	1955	£50	£100	gold label
I Left My Heart In San Francisco	7"	Mercury	MF869	1965	£2.50	£6	
I Miss You So	LP	London	HAP2364	1961	£15	£30	
I Want To Walk You Home	7"	London	HLP8942	1959	£6	£12	chart single
I'm Livin' Right	7"	HMV	POP1582	1967	£2.50	£6	
I'm Ready	7"	Liberty	LIB15274	1969	£5	£10	
I'm Walking	7"	London	HLP8407	1957	£10	£20	chart single
It Keeps Raining	7"	Liberty	LIB12055	1967	£2.50	£6	
It Keeps Raining	7"	London	HLP9374	1961	£7.50	£15	chart single
Jambalaya	7"	London	HLP9520	1962	£2.50	£6	chart single
Just A Lonely Man	7"	HMV	POP1265	1963	£2	£5	
Just Domino	LP	London	HAP8039	1963	£15	£30	
Kansas City	7"	HMV	POP1370	1964	£2	£5	
Lady Madonna	7"	Reprise	RS20763	1968	£1.50	£4	
Let The Four Winds Blow	LP	London	HAP2420	1961	£15	£30	
Let The Four Winds Blow	7"	London	HLP9415	1961	£4	£8	
Let's Dance With Domino	LP	Imperial	LP9239	1963	£8	£20	US
Let's Play Fats Domino	LP	London	HAP2223	1959	£10	£25	
Little Mary	7"	London	HLP8663	1958	£7.50	£15	
Lot Of Domino's	LP	London	HAP2312	1960	£10	£25	
Love Me	7"	London	HL8124	1955	£60	£120	gold label
Margie	7"	London	HLP8865	1959	£6	£12	chart single
Mary Oh Mary	7"	HMV	POP1324	1964	£1.50	£4	
Million Record Hits	LP	Imperial	LP9103/12103	1960	£10	£25	US
Million Sellers Vol.1	LP	Liberty	LBY3033	1965	£5	£12	
Million Sellers Vol.2	LP	Liberty	LBY3046	1965	£4	£10	
Million Sellers Vol.3	LP	Liberty	LBL83101	1968	£4	£10	
My Blue Heaven	7"	London	HLU8280	1956	£25	£50	gold label, chart single
My Blue Heaven	7" EP	Liberty	LEP4026	1965	£5	£10	

Title	Format	Label	Cat No	Year			Note
My Girl Josephine	7"	London	HLP9244	1960	£2.50	£6	chart single
My Real Name	7"	London	HLP9557	1962	£5	£10	
Nothing New	7"	London	HLP9590	1962	£5	£10	
Red Sails In The Sunset	7"	HMV	POP1219	1963	£1.50	£4	chart single
Red Sails In The Sunset	7" EP	HMV	7EG8862	1964	£5	£10	
Rock And Rollin'	LP	Imperial	LP9004	1956	£25	£50	US
Rock And Rollin'	LP	London	HAU2028	1956	£20	£40	
Rocking Mister D Vol.1	7" EP	London	REP1206	1959	£7.50	£15	
Rocking Mister D Vol.2	7" EP	London	REP1207	1959	£7.50	£15	
Rocking Mister D Vol.3	7" EP	London	REP1265	1960	£7.50	£15	
Rolling	7" EP	Liberty	LEP4045	1966	£5	£10	
Shurah	7"	London	HLP9327	1961	£5	£10	
Sick And Tired	7"	London	HL7040	1958	£4	£8	export
Sick And Tired	7"	London	HLP8628	1958	£7.50	£15	chart single
Something You Got Baby	7"	HMV	POP1303	1964	£2.50	£6	
Southland USA	LP	Mercury	MG21065	1966	£4	£10	US
Stop The Clock	7"	London	HLP9616	1962	£5	£10	
Tell Me That You Love Me	7"	London	HLP9133	1960	£6	£12	
There Goes My Heart Again	7"	HMV	POP1164	1963	£4	£8	
This Is Fats	LP	Imperial	LP9040	1957	£25	£50	US
This Is Fats	LP	London	HAP2087	1958	£15	£30	
This Is Fats Domino	LP	Imperial	LP9028	1957	£25	£50	US
This Is Fats Domino	LP	London	HAP2073	1956	£15	£30	
Three Nights A Week	7"	London	HLP9198	1960	£4	£8	chart single
Twistin' The Stomp	LP	London	HAP2447	1962	£15	£30	
Valley Of Tears	7"	London	HLP8449	1957	£7.50	£15	chart single
Wait And See	7"	London	HL7028	1957	£4	£8	export
Wait And See	7"	London	HLP8519	1957	£10	£20	
Walking To New Orleans	LP	London	HAP8084	1963	£15	£30	
Walking To New Orleans	7"	Liberty	LIB15098	1968	£1.50	£4	
Walking To New Orleans	7"	London	HLP9163	1960	£4	£8	chart single
What A Party	LP	London	HAP2426	1961	£15	£30	
What A Party	7"	London	HLP9456	1961	£4	£8	chart single
What A Party	7" EP	London	REP1340	1962	£7.50	£15	
What's That You Got	7"	Mercury	MF1104	1969	£2.50	£6	
What's That You Got	7"	Mercury	MF873	1965	£2.50	£6	
When I See You	7"	London	HLP8471	1957	£10	£20	
When I'm Walking	7"	HMV	POP1197	1963	£2.50	£6	
When My Dreamboat Comes Along	7"	London	HLU8309	1956	£25	£50	gold label
When The Saints Go Marching In	7"	London	HLP8822	1959	£6	£12	
Whole Lotta Loving	7"	London	HLP8759	1958	£7.50	£15	
Why Don't You Do Right	7"	HMV	POP1421	1965	£2	£5	
You Always Hurt The One You Love	7"	London	HLP9738	1963	£4	£8	
You Done Me Wrong	78	London	HL8063	1954	£12.50	£25	
You Said You Loved Me	78	London	HL8007	1954	£12.50	£25	
Young School Girl	7"	London	HLP8727	1958	£7.50	£15	

DOMINOES & SWALLOWS

Title	Format	Label	Cat No	Year			Note
Rhythm And Blues	7" EP	Vogue	EPV1113	1956	£50	£100	

DOMINOES (2)

Title	Format	Label	Cat No	Year			Note
Tribute	7"	Melody	MRC002	1968	£4	£8	

DON & DEWEY

Title	Format	Label	Cat No	Year			Note
Get Your Hat	7"	London	HL9897	1964	£4	£8	
Soul Motion	7"	Cameo Parkway	CP750	1966	£6	£12	
Soul Motion	7"	Sue	WI4032	1967	£5	£10	

DON & JUAN

Title	Format	Label	Cat No	Year			Note
What's Your Name	7"	London	HLX9529	1962	£7.50	£15	

DON & THE GOODTIMES

Title	Format	Label	Cat No	Year			Note
Greatest Hits	LP	Burdette	300	1966	£8	£20	US
Happy To Me	7"	Columbia	DB8266	1967	£1.50	£4	
I Could Be So Good	7"	Columbia	DB8199	1967	£1.50	£4	
Where The Action Is	LP	Wand	WDS679	1969	£5	£12	US

DON, DICK & JIMMY

Title	Format	Label	Cat No	Year			Note
Angela Mia	7"	Columbia	SCM5110	1954	£5	£10	
Don, Dick & Jimmy	7" EP	London	REU1043	1955	£7.50	£15	
Make Yourself Comfortable	7"	London	HL8144	1955	£7.50	£15	
Spring Fever	LP	Modern	LMP1205	1956	£10	£25	US
That's The Way I Feel	7"	HMV	POP280	1956	£2.50	£6	
You Can't Have Your Cake & Eat It Too	7"	London	HL8117	1955	£7.50	£15	

DONAHUE, JERRY

Title	Format	Label	Cat No	Year			Note
Theme From Catlow	7"	Philips	6006219	1972	£2	£5	

DONAHUE, SAM

Title	Format	Label	Cat No	Year			Note
Sam Donahue Orchestra	10" LP	Capitol	LCT6019	1955	£6	£15	
Saxaboogie	7"	Capitol	CL14349	1955	£4	£8	

DONALD, MIKE

Title	Format	Label	Cat No	Year			Note
Yorkshire Songs Of The Broad Acres	LP	Folk Heritage	FHR021	1971	£5	£12	

DONALDSON, BOBBY

Title	Format	Label	Cat No	Year			Note
Dixieland - New York!	LP	London	SAHC6007	1959	£5	£12	

DONALDSON, ERIC

Cherry Oh Baby	7"	Dynamic	DYN420	1971	£1.50	£4	Lloyd Charmers B side
Eric Donaldson	LP	Trojan	TRL42	1972	£6	£15	

DONALDSON, LOU

Alligator Boogaloo	LP	Blue Note	BLP/BST84263	1967	£8	£20	
Blues Walk	LP	Blue Note	BLP/BST81593	196-	£10	£25	
Cosmos	LP	Blue Note	BST84370	1970	£5	£12	
Everything I Play Is Funky	LP	Blue Note	BST84337	1969	£6	£15	
Good Gracious	LP	Blue Note	BLP/BST84125	1963	£15	£30	
Gravy Train	LP	Blue Note	BLP/BST84079	196-	£10	£25	
Here 'Tis	LP	Blue Note	BLP/BST84066	196-	£10	£25	
Hot Dog	LP	Blue Note	BST84318	1969	£6	£15	
Light Foot	LP	Blue Note	BLP/BST84053	196-	£15	£30	
Midnight Creeper	LP	Blue Note	BST84280	1968	£6	£15	
Mr.Shing-A-Ling	LP	Blue Note	BLP/BST84271	1967	£8	£20	
Natural Soul	LP	Blue Note	BLP/BST84108	1962	£10	£25	
Pretty Things	LP	Blue Note	BST84359	1970	£5	£12	
Say It Loud	LP	Blue Note	BST84299	1968	£6	£15	
Sunny Side Up	LP	Blue Note	BLP/BST84036	196-	£15	£30	
Sweet Slumber	LP	Blue Note	BLP/BST84254	1967	£8	£20	
Time Is Right	LP	Blue Note	BLP/BST84025	196-	£15	£30	

DONAYS

Devil In His Heart	7"	Oriole	CB1770	1962	£40	£80	

DONEGAN, DOROTHY

Dorothy Donegan Trio	7" EP	MGM	MGMEP532	1956	£2	£5	

DONEGAN, LONNIE

Auntie Maggie's Remedy	7"	Pye	7N17232	1967	£1.50	£4	
Backstairs Session	7" EP	Polygon	JTE107	1956	£7.50	£15	
Backstairs Session	7" EP	Pye	NJE1014	1956	£4	£8	
Battle Of New Orleans	7"	Pye	7N15206	1959	£1.50	£4	chart single
Beans In My Ears	7"	Pye	7N15669	1964	£1.50	£4	
Burning Bridges	7"	Pye	7N45009	1970	£1.50	£4	
Comancheros	7"	Pye	7N15410	1962	£1.50	£4	chart single
Digging My Potatoes	7"	Decca	FJ10695	1956	£5	£10	
Does Your Chewing Gum Lose Its Flavour	7"	Pye	7N15181	1959	£1.50	£4	chart single
Five Hundred Miles Away From Home	7"	Pye	7N15579	1963	£1.50	£4	
Folk Album	LP	Pye	NPL18126	1965	£6	£15	
Fort Worth Jail	7"	Pye	7N15198	1959	£1.50	£4	chart single
Get Out Of My Life	7"	Pye	7N15803	1965	£1.50	£4	
Golden Age Of Donegan	LP	Golden Guinea	GGL0135	1962	£4	£10	chart LP
Golden Age Of Donegan Vol.2	LP	Golden Guinea	GGL0170	1962	£4	£10	chart LP
Grand Coulee Dam	7"	Pye	7N15129	1958	£1.50	£4	chart single
Have A Drink On Me	7"	Pye	7N15354	1961	£1.50	£4	chart single
I Wanna Go Home	7"	Pye	7N15267	1960	£1.50	£4	chart single
I Wanna Go Home	7"	Pye	7N17109	1966	£1.50	£4	
I'll Never Fall In Love Again	7"	Pye	7N15446	1962	£1.50	£4	
Jack O'Diamonds	7"	Pye	7N15116	1957	£1.50	£4	chart single
Kevin Barry	7"	Pye	7N15219	1959	£5	£10	
Lemon Tree	7"	Pye	7N15564	1963	£1.50	£4	
Lively	7"	Pye	7N15312	1960	£1.50	£4	chart single
Lonesome Traveller	7"	Pye	7N15158	1958	£1.50	£4	chart single
Lonnie	10" LP	Pye	NPT19027	1957	£6	£15	
Lonnie Donegan Hit Parade	7" EP	Pye	NEP24031	1957	£4	£8	
Lonnie Donegan Hit Parade Vol.2	7" EP	Pye	NEP24040	1957	£4	£8	
Lonnie Donegan Hit Parade Vol.3	7" EP	Pye	NEP24067	1958	£4	£8	
Lonnie Donegan Hit Parade Vol.4	7" EP	Pye	NEP24081	1958	£2.50	£6	
Lonnie Donegan Hit Parade Vol.5	7" EP	Pye	NEP24104	1959	£2.50	£6	
Lonnie Donegan Hit Parade Vol.6	7" EP	Pye	NEP24114	1959	£2.50	£6	
Lonnie Donegan Hit Parade Vol.7	7" EP	Pye	NEP24134	1961	£2.50	£6	
Lonnie Donegan Hit Parade Vol.8	7" EP	Pye	NEP24149	1961	£2.50	£6	
Lonnie Donegan On Stage	7" EP	Pye	NEP24075	1958	£4	£8	
Lonnie Donegan Skiffle Group	7" EP	Decca	DFE6345	1956	£5	£10	
Lonnie Pops	LP	Decca	SKL5068	1970	£4	£10	
Lonnie's Skiffle Party	7"	Pye	7N15165	1958	£1.50	£4	chart single
Lorelei	7"	Pye	7N15275	1960	£1.50	£4	chart single
Losing By A Hair	7"	Pye	7N15514	1963	£1.50	£4	
Louisiana Man	7"	Pye	7N15893	1965	£1.50	£4	
Market Song	7"	Pye	7N15493	1962	£1.50	£4	with Max Miller
Michael Row The Boat	7"	Pye	7N15371	1961	£1.50	£4	chart single
Midnight Special	7"	Pye	7NJ2006	1958	£2.50	£6	
More Tops With Lonnie	LP	Pye	NPL18063	1961	£5	£12	
My Lovely Juanita	7"	Decca	F12983	1969	£1.50	£4	
My Old Man's A Dustman	7"	Pye	7N15256	1960	£1.50	£4	chart single
Party's Over	7"	Pye	7N15424	1962	£1.50	£4	chart single
Passing Stranger	7"	Oriole	CB1329	1956	£4	£8	B side by Tommy Reilly
Pick A Bale Of Cotton	7"	Pye	7N15455	1962	£1.50	£4	chart single
Pick A Bale Of Cotton	7"	Pye	7N15455	1962	£5	£10	PS
Relax With Lonnie	7" EP	Pye	NEP24107	1959	£2.50	£6	
Rides Again	LP	Pye	NPL18043	1959	£5	£12	
Rise Up	7"	Pye	7N15530	1963	£1.50	£4	
Rock Island Line	7"	Decca	FJ10647	1955	£5	£10	chart single
Sally Don't You Grieve	7"	Pye	7N15148	1958	£1.50	£4	chart single
Sal's Got A Sugar Lip	7"	Pye	7N15223	1959	£1.50	£4	chart single

Title	Format	Label	Cat. No.	Year			Notes
San Miguel	7"	Pye	7N15237	1959	£1.50	£4	chart single
Showcase	10" LP	Pye	NPT19012	1956	£6	£15	
Sing Hallelujah	LP	Pye	NPL18073	1962	£5	£12	
Skiffle Session	7" EP	Pye	NJE1017	1956	£2.50	£6	chart single
Speak To The Sky	7"	Pye	7N45184	1970	£1.50	£4	
Take My Hand	7"	Columbia	DB3850	1956	£5	£10	
There's A Big House	7"	Pye	7N15679	1964	£1.50	£4	
Tom Dooley	7"	Pye	7N15172	1958	£1.50	£4	chart single
Tops With Lonnie	LP	Pye	NPL18034	1958	£5	£12	
Toys	7"	Columbia	DB8371	1968	£1.50	£4	
Virgin Mary	7"	Pye	7N15315	1960	£1.50	£4	chart single
World Cup Willie	7"	Pye	7N15993	1965	£1.50	£4	
Yankee Doodle Donegan	7" EP	Pye	NEP24127	1960	£2.50	£6	

DONLEY, JIMMY

Title	Format	Label	Cat. No.	Year			Notes
Shape You Left Me In	7"	Brunswick	05807	1959	£30	£60	
South Of The Border	7"	Brunswick	05715	1957	£4	£8	

DONNER, RAL

Title	Format	Label	Cat. No.	Year			Notes
Bells Of Love	7"	Stateside	SS109	1962	£5	£10	
I Don't Need You	7"	Parlophone	R4889	1962	£4	£8	
I Got Burned	7"	Reprise	R20141	1963	£6	£12	
Please Don't Go	7"	Parlophone	R4859	1961	£2.50	£6	US
Takin' Care Of Business	LP	Gone	LP5012	1961	£37.50	£75	US
You Don't Know What You Got	7"	Parlophone	R4820	1961	£2	£5	chart single

DONNIE & THE DREAMERS

Title	Format	Label	Cat. No.	Year			Notes
Count Every Star	7"	Top Rank	JAR571	1961	£2.50	£6	

DONOVAN

Donovan is often viewed as a bit of a joke these days, seeming to epitomise all the more pretentious, self-conscious aspects of hippy culture. His achievement in moving onwards from being a pale shadow of Bob Dylan into creating music of genuine invention and charm is considerable, however. The UK album, "Sunshine Superman", which combines the best tracks of two albums issued in America, is like a folk version of "Sgt.Pepper", while the double "Gift From A Flower To A Garden", despite being inevitably too long, is almost as good. This latter album, which was issued as a boxed set, is becoming increasingly scarce, especially with its numerous poetic inserts intact.

Title	Format	Label	Cat. No.	Year			Notes
Atlantis	7"	Pye	7N17660	1968	£1.50	£4	chart single
Barabajagal	LP	Epic	BN26481	1968	£5	£12	US
Brother Sun, Sister Moon	LP	HMV	3C06493393	1970	£10	£25	German
Catch The Wind	7"	Pye	7N15801	1965	£1.50	£4	chart single
Catch The Wind	7" EP	Pye	NEP24287	1968	£2.50	£6	
Catch The Wind	7" EP	Pye	PNV24138	1965	£5	£10	French
Celia Of The Sands	7"	Dawn	DNS1007	1970	£2	£5	with Danny Thompson
Colours	7"	Pye	7N15866	1965	£1.50	£4	chart single
Colours	7" EP	Pye	NEP24229	1965	£2.50	£6	
Colours	7" EP	Pye	PNV24153	1965	£5	£10	French
Donovan	LP	World Records	ST951	1965	£4	£10	
Donovan Vol.1	7" EP	Pye	NEP24239	1966	£2.50	£6	
Epistle To Dippy	7" EP	Epic	9064	1967	£5	£10	French
Fairytale	LP	Pye	NPL18128	1965	£5	£12	chart single
For Little Ones	LP	Epic	LN24/BN26350	1967	£5	£12	US
Gift From A Flower To A Garden	LP	Pye	NPL20000	1968	£20	£40	2 LPs, boxed, mono
Gift From A Flower To A Garden	LP	Pye	NSPL20000	1968	£15	£30	double, boxed, chart LP
Greatest Hits	LP	Pye	N(S)PL18283	1969	£5	£12	
HMS Donovan	LP	Dawn	DNLD4001	1971	£30	£60	double
Hurdy Gurdy Donovan	7" EP	Pye	NEP24299	1968	£4	£8	
Hurdy Gurdy Man	LP	Epic	BN26420	1968	£5	£12	US
Hurdy Gurdy Man	7"	Pye	7N17537	1968	£1.50	£4	chart single
In Concert	LP	Pye	N(S)PL18237	1968	£5	£12	
Jennifer Juniper	LP	Epic		1967	£5	£10	sung in Italian
Jennifer Juniper	7"	Pye	7N17457	1968	£1.50	£4	chart single
Josie	7"	Pye	7N17067	1966	£1.50	£4	
Live In Japan, Spring Tour 1973	LP	Epic	ECPM25	1973	£8	£20	Japanese
Mellow Yellow	LP	Epic	LN24/BN26239	1967	£6	£15	US
Mellow Yellow	7"	Pye	7N17267	1967	£1.50	£4	chart single
Open Road	LP	Dawn	DNLS3009	1970	£6	£15	chart LP
Remember The Alamo	7"	Pye	7N17088	1966	£5	£10	
Riki Tiki Tavi	7"	Dawn	DNS1006	1970	£2	£5	with The Open Road
Summer Day Reflection Song	7" EP	Pye	PNV24170	1966	£5	£10	French
Sunshine Superman	LP	Epic	LN24/BN26217	1966	£6	£15	US, different tracks
Sunshine Superman	LP	Pye	NPL18181	1967	£6	£15	chart LP
Sunshine Superman	7"	Pye	7N17241	1966	£1.50	£4	chart single
There Is A Mountain	7"	Pye	7N17403	1967	£1.50	£4	chart single
To Susan On The West Coast Waiting	7"	Pye	7N17660	1968	£6	£12	
Turquoise	7"	Pye	7N15894	1965	£1.50	£4	chart single
Turquoise	7" EP	Pye	PNV24158	1965	£5	£10	French
Universal Soldier	7" EP	Pye	NEP24219	1965	£2.50	£6	
Universal Soldier	7" EP	Pye	PNV24149	1965	£4	£8	French
Wear Your Love Like Heaven	LP	Epic	LN24/BN26349	1967	£5	£12	US
What's Bin Did And What's Bin Hid	LP	Pye	NPL18117	1965	£5	£12	chart LP

DONOVAN & JEFF BECK GROUP

Title	Format	Label	Cat. No.	Year			Notes
Goo Goo Barabajagal	7"	Pye	7N17778	1969	£2.50	£6	'Bed With Me' B side
Goo Goo Barabajagal	7"	Pye	7N17778	1969	£2	£5	chart single

DONTELLS

Title	Format	Label	Cat. No.	Year			Notes
In Your Heart	7"	Fontana	TF566	1965	£12.50	£25	

DOO, DICKIE & THE DONTS

Title	Format	Label	Cat. No.	Year			Notes
Click Clack	7"	London	HLU8589	1958	£12.50	£25	

Title	Format	Label	Cat No	Year	Price	Price	Notes
Leave Me Alone	7"	London	HLU8754	1958	£12.50	£25	
Madison	LP	United Artists	UAL3094/ UAS6094	1960	£8	£20	US
Teen Scene	LP	United Artists	UAL3097/ UAS6097	1960	£8	£20	US
Wabash Cannonball	7"	Top Rank	JAR318	1960	£1.50	£4	

DOOLEY SISTERS

Title	Format	Label	Cat No	Year	Price	Price	Notes
Ko Ko Mo	7"	London	HL8128	1955	£10	£20	

DOONAN, JOHN

Title	Format	Label	Cat No	Year	Price	Price	Notes
At The Feis	LP	Topic	12TS368	1978	£10	£25	
Flute For The Feis	LP	Leader	LEA2043	1972	£6	£15	

DOORS

Title	Format	Label	Cat No	Year	Price	Price	Notes
13	LP	Elektra	K42062	1971	£4	£10	
Absolutely Live	LP	Elektra	2665002	1970	£6	£15	double, chart LP
Alabama Song	7"	Elektra	EKSN45012	1967	£2.50	£6	
American Prayer	LP	Elektra	K52111	1978	£4	£10	with booklet
Best Of The Doors	LP	Elektra	K242143	1974	£6	£15	quad
Break On Through	7"	Elektra	EKSN45009	1967	£2.50	£6	
Break On Through	7" EP	Vogue	INT18129	1967	£40	£80	French
Doors	LP	Elektra	EKL4007	1967	£10	£25	mono
Doors	LP	Elektra	EKS74007	1967	£8	£20	stereo
Doors	LP	Elektra	EKS74007	1970	£4	£10	red label
Doors	LP	Mobile Fidelity	MFSL1051	1980	£6	£15	US audiophile
End	12"	Elektra	K12400	1980	£2.50	£6	
Hello I Love You	7"	Elektra	EKSN45037	1968	£2	£5	chart single
LA Woman	LP	Elektra	K42090	1971	£6	£15	clear window sleeve, chart LP
Light My Fire	7"	Elektra	EKSN45014	1967	£2.50	£6	chart single
Light My Fire	7" EP	Vogue	INT18145	1967	£25	£50	French
Live At The Hollywood Bowl	LP	Elektra	EKT40F	1987	£8	£20	promo with interview LP
Love Her Madly	7"	Elektra	EK45726	1971	£1.50	£4	
Love Me Two Times	7"	Elektra	EKSN45022	1967	£2.50	£6	
Love Me Two Times	7"	Elektra	K12215	1979	£4	£8	double
Morrison Hotel	LP	Elektra	EKS75007	1970	£6	£15	chart LP
People Are Strange	7"	Elektra	EKSN45017	1967	£2.50	£6	
Roadhouse Blues	7"	Elektra	2101008	1970	£2	£5	
Soft Parade	LP	Elektra	EKS75005	1969	£6	£15	
Strange Days	LP	Elektra	EKL4014	1968	£10	£25	mono
Strange Days	LP	Elektra	EKS74014	1968	£8	£20	stereo
Tell All The People	7"	Elektra	EKSN45065	1969	£2.50	£6	
Touch Me	7"	Elektra	EKSN45050	1969	£2.50	£6	
Unknown Soldier	7"	Elektra	EKSN45030	1968	£2.50	£6	
Waiting For The Sun	LP	Elektra	EKL4024	1968	£8	£20	mono, chart LP
Waiting For The Sun	LP	Elektra	EKS74024	1968	£6	£15	stereo, chart LP
Wishful Sinful	7"	Elektra	EKSN45059	1969	£2.50	£6	
You Make Me Real	7"	Elektra	2101004	1970	£2.50	£6	

DORAN, FELIX

Title	Format	Label	Cat No	Year	Price	Price	Notes
Last Of The Travelling Pipers	LP	Topic	12TS288	1976	£5	£12	

DOREEN

Title	Format	Label	Cat No	Year	Price	Price	Notes
Rude Girls	7"	Rainbow	RAI114	1967	£4	£8	

DOREEN & JACKIE

Title	Format	Label	Cat No	Year	Price	Price	Notes
Welcome Home	7"	Ska Beat	JB208	1965	£5	£10	

DORHAM, KENNY

Title	Format	Label	Cat No	Year	Price	Price	Notes
Jazz Contrasts	LP	London	LTZU15133	1958	£8	£20	
Kenny Dorham Anmd The Jazz Prophets	10" LP	HMV	DLP1184	1958	£8	£20	
Trompeta Toccata	LP	Blue Note	BLP/BST84181	1964	£10	£25	
Unas Mas	LP	Blue Note	BLP/BST84127	1963	£8	£20	
Whistle Stop	LP	Blue Note	BLP/BST84063	1961	£10	£25	

DORMAN, HAROLD

Title	Format	Label	Cat No	Year	Price	Price	Notes
Mountain Of Love	7"	Top Rank	JAR357	1960	£5	£10	
There They Go	7"	London	HLS9386	1961	£4	£8	

DOROTHY

Title	Format	Label	Cat No	Year	Price	Price	Notes
Confess	7"	Industrial	IR0014	1980	£2.50	£6	

DORPER, RALPH

Title	Format	Label	Cat No	Year	Price	Price	Notes
Eraserhead	12"	Operation Twilight	OPT18	1983	£2.50	£6	

DORS, DIANA

Title	Format	Label	Cat No	Year	Price	Price	Notes
Point Of No Return	7"	Pye	7N15242	1960	£1.50	£4	
Swingin' Dors	LP	Pye	NPL18044	1960	£10	£25	

DORSETS

Title	Format	Label	Cat No	Year	Price	Price	Notes
Pork Chops	7"	Sue	WI391	1965	£5	£10	

DORSEY, GERRY

Title	Format	Label	Cat No	Year	Price	Price	Notes
Baby I Do	7"	Pye	7N15622	1964	£1.50	£4	
Baby Turn Around	7"	Hickory	451337	1965	£2.50	£6	
Big Wheel	7"	Parlophone	R4739	1961	£1.50	£4	
Crazy Bells	7"	Decca	F11108	1959	£1.50	£4	

I'll Never Fall In Love Again	7"	Parlophone	R4595	1959	£1.50	£4

DORSEY, JACK ORCHESTRA

Dance Of The Daleks	7"	Polydor	56020	1965	£4	£8

DORSEY, JIMMY

Dixie By Dorsey	10" LP	Columbia	33S1026	1954	£6	£15
Jay Dee's Boogie Woogie	7"	HMV	POP383	1957	£4	£8
So Rare	7"	HMV	POP324	1957	£1.50	£4

DORSEY, LEE

Best Of Lee Dorsey	LP	Sue	ILP924	1965	£15	£30	
Can You Hear Me	7"	Bell	BLL1006	1968	£1.50	£4	
Confusion	7"	Stateside	SS506	1966	£2	£5	chart single
Do Re Mi	7"	Top Rank	JAR606	1962	£4	£8	
Everything I Do Gonna Be Funky	7"	Bell	BLL1074	1969	£1.50	£4	
Get Out Of My Life Woman	7"	Stateside	SS485	1966	£2	£5	chart single
Go Go Girl	7"	Stateside	SS2055	1967	£1.50	£4	
Holy Cow	7"	Stateside	SS552	1966	£2	£5	chart single
I'm Gonna Sit Right Down	7"	Bell	BLL1051	1969	£1.50	£4	
Lee Dorsey	LP	Stateside	(S)SL10177	1966	£6	£15	
Messed Around	7"	Sue	WI399	1966	£5	£10	
My Old Car	7"	Stateside	SS2017	1967	£1.50	£4	
New Lee Dorsey	LP	Stateside	(S)SL10192	1966	£6	£15	chart LP
Rain Rain Go Away	7"	Stateside	SS593	1967	£1.50	£4	
Ride Your Pony	7"	Bell	BLL1060	1969	£1.50	£4	
Ride Your Pony	7"	Stateside	SS441	1965	£2	£5	
Ride Your Pony	7" EP	Stateside	SE1038	1966	£7.50	£15	
Work Work Work	7"	Stateside	SS465	1965	£2	£5	
Working In A Coalmine	7"	Stateside	SS528	1966	£2	£5	chart single
Ya Ya	LP	Fury	1002	1962	£10	£25	US
Ya Ya	7"	President	PT226	1968	£1.50	£4	
Ya Ya	7"	Sue	WI367	1965	£5	£10	
You're Breaking Me Up	7" EP	Stateside	SE1043	1966	£7.50	£15	

DORSEY, TOMMY

And His Orchestra Vol.1	7" EP	Brunswick	OE9012	1954	£2.50	£6
Best Of Tommy Dorsey	7" EP	Ember	EMBEP4513	1961	£2	£5
Dixieland Jazz Vol.1	10" LP	Brunswick	LA8524	1951	£6	£15
Ecstasy	10" LP	Brunswick	LA8669	1954	£4	£10
Tenderly	10" LP	Brunswick	LA8640	1954	£4	£10
Tommy Dorsey	10" LP	Brunswick	LA8610	1953	£4	£10
Tommy Dorsey And His Orchestra	7" EP	HMV	7EG8004	1954	£4	£8
Tommy Dorsey And His Orchestra	7" EP	HMV	7EG8011	1954	£2	£5
Tommy Dorsey No.1	7" EP	RCA	RCX1002	1958	£4	£8
Tommy Dorsey No.3	7" EP	RCA	RCX1023	1959	£2	£5

DOT, JOHNNY & THE DASHERS

I Love An Angel	7"	Salvo	SLO1805	1962	£1.50	£4

DOTTIE & BONNIE

Bunch Of Roses	7"	Island	WI161	1964	£5	£10	Dor Drummond B side
Dearest	7"	Island	WI148	1964	£5	£10	
I'll Know	7"	Ska Beat	JB274	1967	£5	£10	
I'm So Glad	7"	Rio	R43	1964	£5	£10	Douglas Brothers B side
Sun Rises	7"	Island	WI149	1964	£5	£10	Dor Drummond B side
Your Kisses	7"	Island	WI143	1964	£5	£10	

DOUBLE FEATURE

Baby Get Your Head Screwed On	7"	Deram	DM115	1967	£7.50	£15
Handbags And Gladrags	7"	Deram	DM165	1967	£4	£8

DOUBLES

Hey Girl	7"	HMV	POP613	1959	£20	£40

DOUGHNUT RING

Dance Around Julie	7"	Deram	DM215	1968	£7.50	£15

DOUGLAS BROTHERS

Down And Out	7"	Rio	R63	1965	£5	£10	Ronald Wilson B sid
Valley Of Tears	7"	Rio	R57	1965	£5	£10	Charmers B sid

DOUGLAS, CARL

Crazy Feeling	7"	Go	AJ11401	1966	£4	£8	Peter Perry B sid
Let The Birds Sing	7"	Go	AJ11408	1967	£4	£8	
Nobody Cries	7"	United Artists	UP1206	1967	£20	£40	
Sell My Soul To The Devil	7"	United Artists	UP2227	1968	£2.50	£6	

DOUGLAS, CHIC

I'm Not Afraid Anymore	7"	Fontana	H121	1958	£1.50	£4

DOUGLAS, CRAIG

Across The Street	7"	Fontana	TF525	1965	£1.50	£4
Are You Really Mine	7"	Decca	F11075	1958	£1.50	£4
Around The Corner	7"	Fontana	TF580	1965	£1.50	£4
Bandwagon Ball	LP	Top Rank	35103	1961	£6	£15
Change Of Heart	7"	Top Rank	JAR603	1962	£1.50	£4
Come Closer	7"	Fontana	TF475	1964	£1.50	£4

Title	Format	Label	Cat. No.	Year	Price	Price	Notes
Come Softly To Me	7"	Top Rank	JAR110	1959	£1.50	£4	
Counting Up The Kisses	7"	Decca	F11763	1963	£1.50	£4	
Craig	7" EP	Decca	DFE6633	1960	£4	£8	
Craig Douglas	LP	Top Rank	BUY049	1960	£8	£20	chart LP
Craig Sings For Roxy	7" EP	Top Rank	JKR8033	1959	£4	£8	
Craig's Movie Songs	7" EP	Columbia	SEG8219	1963	£4	£8	
Cuddle Up With Craig	7" EP	Decca	DFE8509	1962	£2.50	£6	
Girl Next Door	7"	Top Rank	JAR543	1961	£1.50	£4	
Heart Of A Teenage Girl	7"	Top Rank	JAR340	1960	£1.50	£4	chart single
Hundred Pounds Of Clay	7"	Top Rank	JAR555	1961	£1.50	£4	chart single
Hundred Pounds Of Clay	7"	Top Rank	JAR556	1961	£5	£10	PS
Hundred Pounds Of Clay (censored version)	7"	Top Rank	JAR556	1961	£1.50	£4	
I'm On The Outside Looking In	7"	Fontana	TF690	1966	£1.50	£4	
I'm So Glad I Found Her	7"	Decca	F11722	1963	£1.50	£4	
No Greater Love	7"	Decca	F11523	1962	£1.50	£4	
Oh Lonesome Me	7"	Top Rank	JAR589	1961	£1.50	£4	
Oh What A Day	7"	Top Rank	JAR406	1960	£1.50	£4	chart single
Only Sixteen	7"	Top Rank	JAR159	1959	£1.50	£4	chart single
Our Favourite Melodies	LP	Columbia	33SX1468	1962	£25	£50	
Our Favourite Melodies	7"	Columbia	DB4854	1962	£1.50	£4	chart single
Pretty Blue Eyes	7"	Top Rank	JAR268	1960	£1.50	£4	chart single
Riddle Of Love	7"	Top Rank	JAR204	1959	£1.50	£4	
Silly Boy	7"	Fontana	TF458	1964	£1.50	£4	
Sitting In A Tree House	7"	Decca	F11055	1958	£2	£5	
Teenage Mona Lisa	7"	Decca	F11665	1963	£1.50	£4	
Teenager In Love	7"	Top Rank	JAR133	1959	£1.50	£4	chart single
Time	7"	Top Rank	JAR569	1961	£1.50	£4	chart single
Town Crier	7"	Decca	F11575	1963	£1.50	£4	
When My Little Girl Is Smiling	7"	Top Rank	JAR610	1962	£1.50	£4	chart single
Where's The Girl	7"	Top Rank	JAR515	1960	£1.50	£4	

DOUGLAS, LEW

Title	Format	Label	Cat. No.	Year	Price	Price
Caesar's Boogie	7"	MGM	SP1093	1954	£1.50	£4

DOUGLAS, MARK

Title	Format	Label	Cat. No.	Year	Price	Price
It Matters Not	7"	Ember	EMBS166	1962	£10	£20

DOUGLAS, NORMA

Title	Format	Label	Cat. No.	Year	Price	Price
Be It Resolved	7"	London	HLZ8475	1957	£4	£8

DOUGLAS, ROBB & DEAN

Title	Format	Label	Cat. No.	Year	Price	Price
I Can Make It With You	7"	Deram	DM132	1967	£1.50	£4
Rose Growing In The Ruins	7"	Deram	DM148	1967	£1.50	£4

DOVELLS

Title	Format	Label	Cat. No.	Year	Price	Price	Notes
All The Hits Of The Teen Groups	LP	Parkway	P7010	1962	£8	£20	US
Betty In Bermudas	7"	Cameo Parkway	P882	1963	£1.50	£4	
Biggest Hits	LP	Wyncote	(SW)9114	1965	£5	£12	US
Bristol Stomp	LP	Parkway	P7006	1961	£10	£25	US
Bristol Stomp	7"	Columbia	DB4718	1961	£2.50	£6	
Bristol Twistin' Annie	7"	Columbia	DB4877	1962	£2	£5	
Discotheque	LP	Wyncote	(S)W9052	1965	£5	£12	US
Doin' The New Continental	7"	Columbia	DB4810	1962	£2	£5	
Don't Knock The Twist	LP	Parkway	P7011	1962	£8	£20	US
Dragster On The Prowl	7"	Cameo Parkway	P901	1963	£2	£5	
For Your Hully Gully Party	LP	Parkway	P7021	1963	£8	£20	US
Hully Gully Baby	7"	Cameo Parkway	P845	1962	£2	£5	
You Can't Run Away From Yourself	7"	Cameo Parkway	P861	1963	£2	£5	
You Can't Sit Down	7"	Cameo Parkway	P867	1963	£2	£5	

DOW, NICK

Title	Format	Label	Cat. No.	Year	Price	Price
Burd Margaret	LP	Dingle	DIN306	1978	£5	£12

DOWLANDS

Title	Format	Label	Cat. No.	Year	Price	Price	Notes
All My Loving	7"	Oriole	CB1897	1964	£6	£12	chart single
Breakups	7"	Oriole	CB1815	1963	£12.50	£25	
Don't Ever Change	7"	Oriole	CB1781	1962	£40	£80	
Don't Make Me Over	7"	Columbia	DB7547	1965	£6	£12	
Walk The Line	7"	Oriole	CB1926	1964	£10	£20	
Julie	7"	Oriole	CB1748	1962	£12.50	£25	
Lucky Johnny	7"	Oriole	CB1892	1963	£100	£200	
Wishing And Hoping	7"	Oriole	CB1947	1964	£10	£20	

DOWNBEATS

Title	Format	Label	Cat. No.	Year	Price	Price
Thinking Of You	7"	Starlite	ST45051	1961	£6	£12

DOWNBEATS (2)

Title	Format	Label	Cat. No.	Year	Price	Price	Notes
Chantent En Francais	7" EP	Philips	434932	196-	£4	£8	French
Dans La Rue	7" EP	Philips	434990	196-	£4	£8	French

DOWNES, BOB

Bob Downes was an averagely talented flautist who attempted to haul himself into the first division by surrounding himself with the best British jazz musicians of the time and adopting a suitably "progressive" image. So far, so good, but he also frequently insisted on opening his mouth to sing. Bob Downes has a terrible voice!

Title	Format	Label	Cat. No.	Year	Price	Price
Diversions	LP	Ophenian	BDOM001	1973	£8	£20

Title	Format	Label	Catalogue	Year			Notes
Electric City	LP	Vertigo	6360005	1970	£10	£25	spiral label
Episodes At 4am	LP	Ophenian	BDOM002	1974	£8	£20	
Hell's Angels	LP	Ophenian	BDOM003	1975	£8	£20	
No Time Like The Present	7"	Vertigo	6059011	1970	£1.50	£4	
Open Music - Dream Journey	LP	Philips	SBL7922	1970	£30	£60	

DOWNING, AL
Yes I'm Loving You	7"	Sue	WI341	1964	£6	£12	

DOWNLINERS SECT
All Night Worker	7"	Columbia	DB7817	1966	£6	£12	
Baby What's Wrong	7"	Columbia	DB7300	1964	£6	£12	
Bad Storm Coming	7"	Columbia	DB7712	1965	£6	£12	
Cost Of Living	7"	Columbia	DB8008	1966	£6	£12	
Country Sect	LP	Columbia	33SX1745	1965	£30	£60	
Find Out What's Happening	7"	Columbia	DB7415	1964	£6	£12	
Glendora	7"	Columbia	DB7939	1966	£10	£20	
I Got Mine	7"	Columbia	DB7597	1965	£6	£12	
Little Egypt	7"	Columbia	DB7347	1964	£6	£12	
Nite In Great Newport Street	7" EP	Contrast	RBCSP001	1964	£60	£120	sleeve pictured in Guide
Rock Sects In	LP	Columbia	SX/SCX6028	1966	£30	£60	
Sect	LP	Columbia	33SX1658	1964	£35	£70	
Sect Sing Sick Songs	7" EP	Columbia	SEG8438	1965	£25	£50	
Wreck Of The Old '97	7"	Columbia	DB7509	1965	£6	£12	

DOWNTOWN ALL STARS
Downtown Jump	7"	Downtown	DT426	1969	£1.50	£4	

DOYLE, DANNY
Highwaymen	LP	Granvaile	GRLP001	1981	£5	£12	Irish

DRAFI
Marble Breaks And Iron Bends	7"	Decca	F22353	1966	£2	£5	

DRAG SET
Day And Night	7"	Go	AJ11405	1966	£40	£80	

DRAGON
Dragon	LP	Acorn	CF268	1976	£20	£40	

DRAGONFLY
Almost Abandoned	LP	Retreat	6002	1974	£5	£12	

DRAGONFLY (2)
Dragonfly	LP	Megaphone	MS1202	1968	£15	£30	US

DRAKE, CHARLIE
Hello My Darlings	7" EP	Parlophone	GEP8720	1958	£2	£5	
Hits From The Man In The Moon	7" EP	Parlophone	GEP8903	1964	£2	£5	
Mr.Custer	7"	Parlophone	R4701	1960	£1.50	£4	chart single
My Boomerang Won't Come Back	7"	Parlophone	R4824	1961	£1.50	£4	chart single
Naughty	7"	Parlophone	R4675	1960	£1.50	£4	
Naughty	7" EP	Parlophone	GEP8812	1960	£2	£5	
Sea Cruise	7"	Parlophone	R4552	1959	£1.50	£4	
Splish Splash	7"	Parlophone	R4461	1958	£1.50	£4	chart single
Tom Thumb's Tune	7"	Parlophone	R4496	1958	£1.50	£4	
Volare	7"	Parlophone	R4478	1958	£1.50	£4	chart single
You Never Know	7"	Charisma	CB270	1975	£4	£8	with Peter Gabriel

DRAKE, NICK
Bryter Layter	LP	Island	ILPS9134	1970	£6	£15	
Five Leaves Left	LP	Island	ILPS9105	1969	£6	£15	
Fruit Tree	LP	Island	NDSP100	1979	£10	£25	triple, boxed
Island LP Sampler	LP	Island	RSS7	1979	£8	£20	promo
Pink Moon	LP	Island	ILPS9184	1972	£8	£20	

DRAKE, PETE
Sleepwalk	7"	Philips	BF1332	1964	£1.50	£4	

DRAMATICS
Whatcha See Is Whatcha Get	LP	Stax	2362025	1972	£5	£12	

DRANSFIELD, BARRY
Barry Dransfield	LP	Polydor	2383160	1972	£100	£200	
Bowin' And Scrapin'	LP	Topic	12TS386	1978	£10	£25	

DRANSFIELD, ROBIN
Tidewave	LP	Topic	12TS414	1980	£5	£12	

DRANSFIELD, ROBIN & BARRY
Lord Of All I Behold	LP	Trailer	LER2026	1971	£20	£40	
Popular To Contrary Belief	LP	Free Reed	FRR018	1977	£6	£15	

DRANSFIELDS
Fiddler's Dream	LP	Transatlantic	TRA322	1976	£10	£25	
Rout Of The Blues	LP	Trailer	LER2011	1970	£20	£40	

DRAPER, RUSTY
Chicken Picking Hawk	7"	Mercury	7MT229	1958	£4	£8	
Folsom Prison Blues	7"	London	HLU9989	1965	£2	£5	
Gambling Gal	7"	Mercury	7MT211	1958	£4	£8	

Hits That Sold A Million	LP	Mercury	MMC14040	1960	£5	£12	
Jealous Heart	7"	Mercury	AMT1127	1961	£1.50	£4	
Luck Of The Irish	7"	Mercury	AMT1110	1960	£1.50	£4	
Mule Skinner Blues	7"	Mercury	AMT1101	1960	£2.50	£6	chart single
Mule Skinner Blues	7" EP	Mercury	ZEP10095	1960	£4	£8	
Presenting Rusty Draper	7" EP	Mercury	MEP9506	1956	£7.50	£15	
Rock And Roll Ruby	78	Mercury	MT113	1956	£2.50	£6	
Rusty Draper	7" EP	Mercury	ZEP10016	1959	£4	£8	
Rusty Draper No.1	7" EP	London	REU1431	1964	£5	£10	
Rusty Draper No.2	7" EP	London	REU1432	1964	£5	£10	
Rusty In Gambling Mood	7" EP	Mercury	ZEP10059	1960	£4	£8	
Shopping Around	7"	Mercury	AMT1019	1959	£6	£12	
Sun Will Always Shine	7"	Mercury	AMT1033	1959	£2	£5	
That's Why I Love You Like I Do	7"	London	HLU9786	1963	£1.50	£4	

DREAM

	LP	CBS			£70	£140	Norway
	LP	Polydor			£35	£70	

DREAM POLICE

I've Got No Choice	7"	Decca	F13105	1970	£2	£5	
Living Is Easy	7"	Decca	F12998	1970	£4	£8	
Our Song	7"	Decca	F13078	1970	£2	£5	

DREAMERS

Maybe Song	7"	Columbia	DB8340	1968	£1.50	£4

DREAMERS (2)

Dear Love	7"	Downtown	DT408	1969	£1.50	£4
Sweet Chariot	7"	Downtown	DT407	1969	£1.50	£4

DREAMIES

Auralgraphic Entertainment	LP	Stone Theatre		1968	£50	£100	US

DREAMLETS

Really Now	7"	Ska Beat	JB182	1965	£5	£10	Skatalites B side

DREAMLOVERS

Bird	LP	Columbia	CL2020/CS8820	1963	£8	£20	US
When We Get Married	7"	Columbia	DB4711	1961	£25	£50	

DREAMS

Best Of Dreams	LP	Dolphin	DOLB7002	1969	£8	£20	Irish

DREAMTIMERS

Dancin' Lady	7"	London	HLU9368	1961	£1.50	£4

DREAMWEAVERS

It's Almost Tomorrow	7"	Brunswick	05515	1956	£12.50	£25	chart single
Little Love Can Go A Long Long Way	7"	Brunswick	05568	1956	£10	£20	
You're Mine	7"	Brunswick	05607	1956	£6	£12	

DREGS

Dregs	7"	Disturbing	DRO1	1979	£2	£5

DREVAR, JOHN EXPRESSION

Closer She Gets	7"	MGM	MGM1367	1967	£20	£40
What Greater Love	7"	Polydor	56390	1970	£1.50	£4

DREW, PATTI

Hard To Handle	7"	Capitol	CL15575	1968	£1.50	£4
Workin' On A Groovy Thing	7"	Capitol	CL15557	1968	£2	£5

DR.FEELGOOD & THE INTERNS

Blang Dong	7"	Columbia	DB7228	1964	£5	£10	
Doctor Feelgood	LP	OKeh	M12/S14101	1962	£10	£25	US
Don't Tell Me No Dirty	7"	CBS	202099	1966	£6	£12	
Dr.Feelgood	7"	Columbia	DB4838	1962	£5	£10	
Dr.Feelgood & The Interns	7" EP	Columbia	SEG8310	1964	£10	£20	
Sugar Bee	7"	Capitol	CL15569	1968	£7.50	£15	

DR.HOOK

Cover Of Radio Times	7"	CBS	1037	1973	£5	£10	1 sided promo

DRIFTERS

At The Club	7"	Atlantic	AT4019	1965	£2	£5	chart single
Baby What I Mean	7"	Atlantic	584065	1967	£2	£5	
Clyde McPhatter & The Drifters	LP	Atlantic	8003	1956	£50	£100	US
Come On Over To My Place	7"	Atlantic	AT4023	1965	£2	£5	chart single
Dance With Me	7"	London	HLE8988	1959	£6	£12	chart single
Drifters	LP	Clarion	(SD)608	1964	£6	£15	US
Drifters	7" EP	London	REK1355	1963	£6	£12	
Drifting	7" EP	London	REK1385	1963	£6	£12	
Drifting Vol.2	7" EP	Atlantic	AET6003	1964	£5	£10	
Follow Me	7"	Atlantic	AT4034	1965	£5	£10	
Good Gravy	LP	Atlantic	587144	1968	£6	£15	
Good Life	LP	Atlantic	ATL5023	1965	£6	£15	
Greatest Hits	LP	London	HAK2318	1960	£10	£25	
I Count The Tears	7"	London	HLK9287	1961	£2.50	£6	chart single
I'll Take You Home	7"	London	HLK9785	1963	£2	£5	chart single

Title	Format	Label	Cat No	Year	Price	Price	Notes
I'll Take You Where The Music's Playing	LP	Atlantic	587061	1967	£4	£10	
I'll Take You Where The Music's Playing	LP	Atlantic	ATL/STL5039	1966	£6	£15	
I'll Take You Where The Music's Playing	7"	Atlantic	584152	1968	£1.50	£4	
I'll Take You Where The Music's Playing	7"	Atlantic	AT4040	1965	£2	£5	
In The Land Of Make Believe	7"	London	HLK9848	1964	£2	£5	
I've Got Sand In My Shoes	7"	Atlantic	AT4008	1964	£2	£5	
Lonely Winds	7"	London	HLK9145	1960	£6	£12	
Memories Are Made Of This	7"	Atlantic	AT4084	1966	£4	£8	
Moonlight Bay	7"	London	HLE8686	1958	£37.50	£75	
On Broadway	7"	London	HLK9699	1963	£2	£5	
One Way Love	7"	London	HLK9886	1964	£2	£5	
Our Biggest Hits	LP	Atlantic	587038	1966	£4	£10	
Our Biggest Hits	LP	Atlantic	ATL5015	1965	£5	£12	
Please Stay	7"	London	HLK9382	1961	£2	£5	
Rat Race	7"	London	HLK9750	1963	£2	£5	
Rockin' And Driftin'	LP	Atlantic	587123	1968	£5	£12	
Rockin' And Driftin'	LP	Atlantic	8022	1958	£50	£100	US
Room Full Of Tears	7"	London	HLK9500	1962	£2.50	£6	
Rose By Any Other Name	7"	Atlantic	2091064	1971	£1.50	£4	
Saturday Night At The Movies	7"	Atlantic	584264	1969	£1.50	£4	
Saturday Night At The Movies	7"	Atlantic	AT4012	1964	£2.50	£6	
Save The Last Dance For Me	LP	Atlantic	587063	1967	£4	£10	
Save The Last Dance For Me	LP	Atlantic	HAK2450	1962	£8	£20	
Save The Last Dance For Me	7"	Atlantic	2091110	1971	£1.50	£4	
Save The Last Dance For Me	7"	London	HLK9201	1960	£2	£5	chart single
Save The Last Dance For Me	7" EP	London	REK1282	1961	£6	£12	
Soldier Of Fortune	7"	London	HLE8344	1956	£100	£200	
Some Kind Of Wonderful	7"	London	HLK9326	1961	£2.50	£6	
Souvenirs	LP	Atlantic	590010	1966	£4	£10	
Still Burning In My Heart	7"	Atlantic	584195	1968	£2	£5	
Stranger On The Shore	7"	London	HLK9554	1962	£2	£5	
Sweets For My Sweet	7"	London	HLK9427	1961	£2	£5	
There Goes My Baby	7"	London	HLE8892	1959	£10	£20	
This Magic Moment	7"	London	HLE9081	1960	£6	£12	
Tonight	7" EP	Atlantic	AET6012	1965	£5	£10	
Under The Boardwalk	LP	Atlantic	(SD)8099	1964	£10	£25	US
Under The Boardwalk	7"	Atlantic	AT4001	1964	£2.50	£6	chart single
Up In The Streets Of Harlem	7"	Atlantic	584020	1966	£1.50	£4	
Up On The Roof	LP	Atlantic	(SD)8073	1963	£10	£25	US
Up On The Roof	LP	Atlantic	587/588160	1969	£4	£10	
Up On The Roof	7"	Atlantic	HLK9626	1962	£2.50	£6	
We Gotta Sing	7"	Atlantic	AT4062	1966	£2	£5	
When My Little Girl Is Smiling	7"	Atlantic	2091101	1971	£1.50	£4	
When My Little Girl Is Smiling	7"	London	HLK9522	1962	£2	£5	chart single

DRIFTERS (UK)

Cliff Richard's backing group was originally called the Drifters, and they released two singles under that name in their own right, before changing names to the Shadows, in order to avoid confusion with the more famous American Drifters. In America, a change was made for them for the single "Jet Black" (the B side of the UK "Drifting" single), as this was credited to the Four Jets.

Title	Format	Label	Cat No	Year	Price	Price
Drifting	7"	Columbia	DB4325	1959	£12.50	£25
Feeling Fine	7"	Columbia	DB4263	1959	£20	£40

DRIFTING SLIM

Title	Format	Label	Cat No	Year	Price	Price
Good Morning Baby	7"	Blue Horizon	451005	1966	£12.50	£25

DRIFTWOOD

Title	Format	Label	Cat No	Year	Price	Price
Driftwood	LP	Decca	SKL5069	1970	£6	£15

DRIFTWOOD, JIMMY

Title	Format	Label	Cat No	Year	Price	Price
Country Guitar Vol.13	7" EP	RCA	RCX191	1960	£4	£8
Tall Tales In Song Vol.1	7" EP	RCA	RCX193	1960	£2	£5
Tall Tales In Song Vol.2	7" EP	RCA	RCX195	1960	£2	£5
Tall Tales In Song Vol.3	7" EP	RCA	RCX198	1960	£2	£5

DRISCOLL, JULIE

As far as the general public is concerned, Julie Driscoll is something of a one-hit wonder, having topped the charts with a superb version of Bob Dylan's "This Wheel's On Fire" and then having apparently dropped from sight. In fact, she married jazz pianist Keith Tippett, and as Julie Tippett has appeared on a number of jazz records by her husband and by others. "This Wheel's On Fire" was the most visible product of a profitable association with the Brian Auger Trinity, documented by the various Marmalade recordings credited to one or both of them, and going back, through their membership of Steampacket, to the single "Don't Do It No More".

Title	Format	Label	Cat No	Year	Price	Price
Don't Do It No More	7"	Parlophone	R5296	1965	£5	£10
I Didn't Want To Have To Do It	7"	Parlophone	R5444	1966	£2.50	£6
I Know You Love Me Not	7"	Parlophone	R5588	1967	£2.50	£6
Julie Driscoll	LP	Polydor	2480074	1971	£8	£20
Sunset Glow	LP	Utopia	UTS601	1976	£6	£15
Take Me By The Hand	7"	Columbia	DB7118	1963	£4	£8

DRISCOLL, JULIE & BRIAN AUGER

Title	Format	Label	Cat No	Year	Price	Price	Notes
Julie Driscoll And Brian Auger	LP	MFP	MFP1265	1968	£4	£10	
Open	LP	Marmalade	607/608002	1967	£8	£20	chart LP
Road To Cairo	7"	Marmalade	598011	1969	£2	£5	
Save Me	7"	Marmalade	598004	1967	£2.50	£6	
Streetnoise	LP	Marmalade	608005/6	1968	£15	£30	double
Take Me To The Water	7"	Marmalade	598018	1969	£2	£5	
This Wheel's On Fire	7"	Marmalade	598006	1968	£2	£5	chart single

DRIVE

No Girls	7"	First Strike	FST007	1990	£4	£8

DR.JOHN

Mac Rebennack achieved early notoriety as the only white musician to break into the tough New Orleans R&B session world. With the advent of flower power, he reinvented himself as the voodoo magician, Dr.John, and recorded the weirdly mystical "Gris Gris" album. Three other LPs followed in similar style, before Rebennack reverted back to R&B, while still retaining the Dr.John pseudonym. He continues to be a prolific maker of records, both his own and other people's, for which he is an in-demand session pianist.

Babylon	LP	Atlantic	228018	1969	£6	£15
Desitively Bonaroo	LP	Atlantic	K50035	1974	£4	£10
Gris Gris	LP	Atlantic	587147	1968	£8	£20
Gris Gris	LP	Atlantic	K40168	1972	£6	£15
Gumbo	LP	Atlantic	K40384	1972	£6	£15
Hollywood Know Thy Name	LP	United Artists	UAG29902	1975	£4	£10
In The Right Place	LP	Atlantic	K50017	1973	£5	£12
Mardi Gras	LP	Atlantic	K40554	1975	£4	£10
Remedies	LP	Atlantic	2400015	1970	£6	£15
Sun, Moon, & Herbs	LP	Atlantic	2400161	1971	£6	£15
Sun, Moon, & Herbs	LP	Atlantic	K40250	1971	£5	£12
Wash Mama Wash	7"	Atlantic	2091019	1970	£2	£5

DR.K'S BLUES BAND

Dr.K's Blues Band	LP	Spark	UK101	1968	£10	£25

DR.MARIGOLD'S PRESCRIPTION

Hello Girl	LP	Pye	PNL501	1973	£5	£12
My Old Man Is A Groovy Old Man	7"	Pye	7N17493	1968	£2	£5
Pictures Of Life	LP	Marble Arch	MALS1222	1969	£6	£15
You've Got To Build Your Love	7"	Pye	7N17832	1969	£2	£5

DRONES

Be My Baby	12"	Valer	VRSP1	1977	£8	£20	test pressing
Bone Idol	7"	Valer	VRS1	1977	£2	£5	
Can't See	7"	Fabulous	JC4	1980	£1.50	£4	
Further Temptations	LP	Valer	VRLP1	1977	£6	£15	
Temptations Of A White Collar Worker	7"	Ohms	GOODMIX1	1977	£1.50	£4	PS in plastic bag

DROSSELBART

Drosselbart	LP	Polydor	2371126	1970	£8	£20	German

DR.STRANGELY STRANGE

Dr.Strangely Strange attempted to play the same kind of eccentrically pitched folk music as the Incredible String Band, but found that the market was only big enough for one. "Kip Of The Serenes" is one of the rarest rock releases on the Island label, although one track is well known to the many people who bought the "Nice Enough To Eat" sampler LP.

Heavy Petting	LP	Vertigo	6360009	1970	£30	£60	spiral label
Kip Of The Serenes	LP	Island	ILPS9106	1969	£40	£80	

DR.TECHNICAL & THE MACHINES

Zones	7"	Hawkfan	HWFB1	1983	£4	£8	1 sided

DRUID

Fluid Druid	LP	EMI	EMC3128	1976	£5	£12
Towards The Sun	LP	EMI	EMC3081	1975	£5	£12

DRUID CHASE

Take Me In Your Garden	7"	CBS	3053	1967	£6	£12

DRUIDS

It's Just A Little Bit Too Late	7"	Parlophone	R5134	1964	£4	£8
Long Tall Texan	7"	Parlophone	R5097	1964	£4	£8

DRUIDS (2)

Burnt Offering	LP	Argo	ZFB22	1970	£40	£80
Pastime With Good Company	LP	Argo	ZFB39	1972	£40	£80

DRUIDS OF STONEHENGE

Creation	LP	Uni	(7)3004	1967	£5	£12	US

DRUMBAGO

Dulcimania	7"	Trojan	TR638	1968	£4	£8	Clancy Eccles B side
I Am Drunk	7"	Island	WI085	1963	£5	£10	
I'm Not Worthy	7"	Blue Beat	BB51	1961	£5	£10	Magic Notes B side
Reggae Jeggae	7"	Blue Cat	BS145	1968	£4	£8	Tyrone Taylor B side

DRUMMOND, DON

Allepon	7"	Ska Beat	JB187	1965	£5	£10	Justin Hinds B side
Best Of Don Drummond	LP	Studio One	SOL9008	1968	£50	£100	
Cool Smoke	7"	Island	WI231	1965	£5	£10	Techniques B side
Coolie Boy	7"	Island	WI204	1965	£5	£10	Lord Antics B side
Doctor Dekker	7"	Ska Beat	JB189	1965	£5	£10	Owen & Leon B side
Don De Lion	7"	Ska Beat	JB191	1965	£5	£10	Movers B side
Far East	7"	Blue Beat	BB179	1963	£5	£10	
Heavenless	7"	Studio One	SO2078	1969	£6	£12	Glen Brown B side
Looking Through The Window	7"	Island	WI294	1966	£5	£10	Soul Brothers B side
Man In The Street	7"	Island	WI208	1965	£5	£10	Rita & Bunny B side
Memorial Album	LP	Trojan	TTL23	1969	£10	£25	
Memory Of Don	7"	Trojan	TR678	1969	£2.50	£6	John Holt B side
Musical Storeroom	7"	Island	WI153	1964	£5	£10	Stranger Cole B side
Scandal	7"	Island	WI094	1963	£5	£10	W.Sparks B side
Schooling The Duke	7"	Island	WI021	1962	£5	£10	Basil Gabbidon B side
Scrap Iron	7"	Black Swan	WI406	1963	£5	£10	

Shock	7"	R&B	JB105	1963	£5	£10	Tonettes B side
Ska Town	7"	Blue Beat	BB298	1964	£5	£10	Eric Morris B side
Stampede	7"	Island	WI192	1965	£5	£10	Justin Hinds B side
Treasure Island	7"	Island	WI195	1965	£5	£10	Riots B side
University Goes Ska	7"	Island	WI242	1965	£5	£10	Derrick Morgan B side

DRUSKY, ROY
Just About That Time	7"	Brunswick	05785	1959	£2	£5

DR.WEST'S MEDICINE SHOW & JUNK BAND
Bullets La Verne	7"	Page One	POF23061	1968	£7.50	£15	
Eggplant That Ate Chicago	LP	Page One	POLS17	1968	£10	£25	
Eggplant That Ate Chicago	7"	CBS	202492	1967	£1.50	£4	
Gondoliers, Shakespeares, Overseers	7"	CBS	202658	1967	£1.50	£4	

DRY ICE
Running To The Convent	7"	B&C	CB115	1970	£4	£8

DRY RIB
Dry Season	7"	Clockwork	COR001	1979	£7.50	£15

DR.Z
Lady Ladybird	7"	Fontana	6007023	1970	£12.50	£25	
Three Parts To My Soul	LP	Vertigo	6360048	1971	£85	£170	spiral label

DSCHINN
Dschinn	LP	Bacillus	BLPS19120	1972	£5	£12	German

D'SILVA, AMANCIO
Integration	LP	Columbia	SX/SCX6322	1969	£15	£30
Reflections	LP	Columbia	SCX6465	1970	£10	£25

DUALS
Stick Shift	LP	Sue	LP2002	1961	£25	£50	US
Stick Shift	7"	London	HL9450	1961	£7.50	£15	

DUB SEX
Then And Now	12"	Skysaw	SKY7	1987	£2.50	£6

DUBLINERS
At Home With The Dubliners	LP	Columbia	SCX6380	1969	£8	£20	
At It Again	LP	Major Minor	SMLP34	1968	£5	£12	
Dirty Old Town	7"	Major Minor	MM552	1968	£1.50	£4	
Drop Of The Dubliners	LP	Major Minor	(S)MCP5024	1969	£5	£12	
Drop Of The Hard Stuff	LP	Major Minor	MMLP3	1967	£6	£15	
Dubliners	LP	Major Minor	GOL200	1968	£5	£12	
Dubliners Now	LP	Polydor	2383329	1975	£5	£12	
Fifteen Years On	LP	Polydor	2683070	1977	£6	£15	double
Finnegan Wakes	LP	Hallmark	CHM695	1966	£5	£12	
Finnegan Wakes	LP	Transatlantic	TRA139	1966	£8	£20	
In Concert	LP	Transatlantic	TRA124	1965	£6	£15	
Live At The Albert Hall London	LP	Major Minor	SMLP44	1969	£5	£12	
More Of The Hard Stuff	LP	Major Minor	MMLP/SMLP5	1967	£6	£15	
Plain And Simple	LP	Polydor	2383235	1973	£5	£12	
Revolution	LP	Columbia	SCX6423	1970	£8	£20	

DUBS
Could This Be Magic	7"	London	HLU8526	1957	£60	£120	
Dubs Meet The Shells	LP	Josie	JM/JSS4001	195-	£20	£40	US
Gonna Make A Change	7"	London	HL8684	1958	£100	£200	

DUCKS DELUXE
Ducks Deluxe was one of the better "pub rock" bands to emerge during the seventies. The group included Martin Belmont, Sean Tyla, and Andy McMaster, all of whom found a little success in subsequent years.
Ducks Deluxe	LP	RCA	PL5008	1974	£6	£15	
Last Night Of A Pub Rock Band	LP	Blue Moon	BMLP001	1982	£5	£12	double
Taxi To The Terminal Zone	LP	RCA	SF8402	1974	£6	£15	

DUDLEY
El Pizza	7"	Vogue	V9171	1960	£4	£8

DUDLEY, DAVE
Six Days On The Road	7"	United Artists	UP1029	1963	£1.50	£4

DUFFAS, SHENLEY
Big Mouth	7"	R&B	JB146	1964	£5	£10	Frankie Anderson B side
Christopher Columbus	7"	R&B	JB152	1964	£5	£10	Carl Bryan B side
Digging A Ditch	7"	Black Swan	WI440	1964	£5	£10	
Easy Squeal	7"	Island	WI125	1963	£5	£10	
Fret Man Fret	7"	Island	WI063	1963	£5	£10	
Gather Them In	7"	Black Swan	WI443	1964	£5	£10	
Give To Get	7"	Island	WI036	1962	£5	£10	
I Will Be Glad	7"	Rio	R41	1964	£5	£10	
Know The Lord	7"	Island	WI115	1963	£5	£10	Tommy McCook B side
La La La La	7"	Island	WI182	1965	£5	£10	Upcoming Willows B side
Mother-In-Law	7"	R&B	JB154	1964	£5	£10	Don Drummond B side
No More Wedding Bells	7"	R&B	JB134	1963	£5	£10	

Rukembine	7"	Island	WI186	1965	£5	£10	
What A Disaster	7"	Island	WI093	1963	£5	£10	
You Are Mine	7"	Island	WI184	1965	£5	£10	Upcoming Willows B side

DUFFY

Joker	7"	Chapter One	CH184	1973	£4	£8	
Just In Case You're Interested	LP	Ariola	85846	1975	£8	£20	
Scruffy Duffy	LP	Chapter One	CHSR814	1970	£35	£70	

DUFFY TAYLOR BLUES

I'll Be There	7"	Page One	POF130	1969	£1.50	£4	

DUFFY'S NUCLEUS

Hound Dog	7"	Decca	F22547	1967	£5	£10	
Hound Dog	7" EP	Decca	457142	1967	£15	£30	French

DUKE & DUCHESS

Get Ready For Love	7"	London	HLU8206	1955	£7.50	£15	

DUKE ALL STARS

Letter To Mummy And Daddy	7"	Blue Cat	BS111	1968	£4	£8	

DUKE, BILLY

Sugar 'n' Spice	7"	London	HLU9960	1965	£1.50	£4	

DUKE, DENVER & JEFFREY NULL BLUEGRASS BOYS

Denver Duke & Jeffrey Null Bluegrass Boys	7" EP	Starlite	STEP33	1963	£5	£10	

DUKE, DORIS

I'm A Loser	LP	Mojo	2916001	1971	£5	£12	
Woman	LP	Contempo	CLP519	1975	£5	£12	

DUKE, GEORGE

Aura Will Prevail	LP	BASF	BAP5064	1974	£4	£10	German
Feel	LP	MPS	23124	1974	£4	£10	German
I Love The Blues, She Heard My Cry	LP	BASF	BAP5071	1975	£4	£10	German
Live In Los Angeles	LP	Sunset	SLS50232	1971	£4	£10	US

DUKES, AGGIE

John John	7"	Vogue	V9090	1957	£40	£80	

DUKE'S NOBLEMEN

City Of Windows	7"	Philips	BF1691	1968	£2	£5	

DUKES OF STRATOSPHEAR

As is well known, the Dukes are actually XTC, using the alias to produce one and a half albums worth of material that would be hailed as true masterpieces of sixties psychedelia, if only they had actually been recorded in the sixties!

Psonic Psunspot	LP	Virgin	VP2440	1987	£4	£10	multi-coloured vinyl
You're A Good Man Albert Brown	7"	Virgin	VSY982	1987	£1.50	£4	multi-coloured vinyl

DULCIMER

And I Turned As I Had Turned As A Boy	LP	Nepentha	6437003	1971	£25	£50	
Land Fit For Heroes	LP	private		1980	£5	£12	

DUMB ANGELS

Love And Mercy	7"	Fierce	FRIGHT033	1988	£2.50	£6	

DUMBELLS (ROXY MUSIC)

Giddy Up	7"	EG	EGO3	1976	£4	£8	
Giddy Up	7"	Polydor	POSP209	1981	£2	£5	

DUMMER, JOHN

Blue	LP	Vertigo	6360055	1972	£30	£60	spiral label
Cabal	LP	Mercury	SMCL20136	1969	£25	£50	
Famous Music Band	LP	Fontana	6309008	1970	£30	£60	
John Dummer's Blues Band	LP	Mercury	SMCL20167	1969	£40	£80	
Medicine Weasel	7"	Philips	6006176	1971	£2.50	£6	
Nine By Nine	7"	Fontana	6007027	1970	£5	£10	
Oobleedooblee Jubilee	LP	Vertigo	6360083	1973	£15	£30	spiral label, Sleeve pictured in Guide
Oobleedooblee Jubilee	7"	Vertigo	6059074	1972	£2.50	£6	
This Is John Dummer	LP	Philips	6382039	1972	£20	£40	
Travelling Man	7"	Mercury	MF1040	1968	£5	£10	
Try Me One More Time	LP	Philips	6382040	1973	£20	£40	
Try Me One More Time	7"	Mercury	MF1119	1969	£5	£10	

DUMMIES

Desperate for some more chart success, Slade tried the strategem of issuing singles under the name of the Dummies. They hoped that radio programmers who responded with disinterest to the name of Slade would hear the music of the Dummies with unprejudiced ears. They may have done just that, but unfortunately they still did not appear to like what they heard.

Maybe Tonite	7"	Cheapskate	CHEAP14	1981	£4	£8	

DUMPY'S RUSTY NUTS

Boxhill Or Bust	7"	Cool King	CNK008	1982	£2	£5	with patch
Just For Kicks	7"	Cool King	CNK006	1981	£2.50	£6	

DUNBAR, AYNSLEY

Frank Zappa once described Aynsley Dunbar as the only drummer capable of playing the complicated rhythms some of his pieces contained. A graduate of the John Mayall blues school, Dunbar tried for a couple of years to make his own group a success, before accepting that he could do very well playing drums for other people (Zappa, Jefferson Starship, and Journey). The Aynsley Dunbar Retaliation was a fairly routine blues group, but Blue Whale was a more ambitious affair, being a big band with an open, improvisational approach.

Aynsley Dunbar Retaliation	LP	Liberty	LBL/LBS83154	1968	£8	£20	
Blue Whale	LP	Warner Bros	K46062	1970	£6	£15	
Doctor Dunbar's Prescription	LP	Liberty	LBL/LBS83177	1968	£10	£25	
Remains To Be Heard	LP	Liberty	LBS83316	1970	£8	£20	
To Mum From Aynsley & The Boys	LP	Liberty	LBS83223	1969	£8	£20	
Warning	7"	Blue Horizon	453109	1967	£7.50	£15	
Warning	7"	Blue Horizon	453109	1967	£15	£30	PS
Watch 'n' Chain	7"	Liberty	LBF15132	1968	£4	£8	

DUNBAR, SCOTT

From Lake Mary	LP	Ahura Mazda	AMSSDS1	1971	£8	£20	

DUNCAN, JOHNNY

All Of The Monkeys Ain't In The Zoo	7"	Columbia	DB4167	1958	£2	£5	
Anytime	7"	Columbia	DB4415	1960	£1.50	£4	
Ballad Of Jed Clampett	7"	Columbia	DB7164	1963	£1.50	£4	
Beyond The Sunset	LP	Columbia	33SX1328	1961	£6	£15	
Blue Blue Heartaches	7"	Columbia	DB3996	1957	£2.50	£6	chart single
Dang Me	7"	Columbia	DB7334	1964	£1.50	£4	
Footprints In The Snow	7"	Columbia	DB4029	1957	£2.50	£6	chart single
Footprints In The Snow	7" EP	Columbia	SEG7753	1958	£4	£8	
Goodnight Irene	7"	Columbia	DB4074	1958	£5	£10	
Itching For My Baby	7"	Columbia	DB4118	1958	£2.50	£6	
Johnny Duncan & His Blue Grass Boys	7" EP	Columbia	SEG7708	1957	£6	£12	
Johnny Duncan & His Blue Grass Boys No.2	7" EP	Columbia	SEG7733	1957	£6	£12	
Kansas City	7"	Columbia	DB4311	1959	£1.50	£4	
Kawliga	7"	Columbia	DB3925	1957	£4	£8	
Last Train To San Fernando	7"	Columbia	DB3959	1957	£5	£10	chart single
Legend Of Gunga Din	7"	Pye	7N15380	1961	£1.50	£4	
Long Time Gone	7"	Pye	7N15420	1962	£1.50	£4	
My Little Baby	7"	Columbia	DB7833	1966	£1.50	£4	
My Lucky Love	7"	Columbia	DB4179	1958	£1.50	£4	
Rosalie	7"	Columbia	DB4282	1959	£1.50	£4	
Salute To Hank Williams	LP	Encore	ENC190	1959	£6	£15	
Salutes Hank Williams	10" LP	Columbia	33S1129	1958	£10	£25	
Tennessee Sing Song	7" EP	Columbia	SEG7850	1958	£4	£8	
Tennessee Song Bag	10" LP	Columbia	33S1122	1957	£10	£25	
Tobacco Road	7"	Pye	7N15358	1961	£1.50	£4	

DUNCAN, LESLEY

Despite making several fine records in the late sixties and early seventies, Ms.Duncan's most collectable recording, a charity re-make of her "Sing Children Sing", is sought after primarily because Kate Bush is one of the singers participating in the ensemble - despite the fact that her voice cannot actually be distinguished!

Earth Mother	LP	CBS	64807	1972	£4	£10	
Everything Changes	LP	GM	GML1007	1974	£4	£10	
Exactly Who You Are	7"	CBS	4585	1969	£1.50	£4	
Hey Boy	7"	Mercury	MF939	1965	£1.50	£4	
I Want A Steady Guy	7"	Parlophone	R5034	1963	£2	£5	
Just For The Boy	7"	Mercury	MF847	1965	£2	£5	
Lullaby	7"	RCA	RCA1746	1968	£1.50	£4	
Maybe It's Lost	LP	GM	GML1019	1977	£4	£10	
Moonbathing	LP	GM	GML1017	1975	£4	£10	
Road To Nowhere	7"	RCA	RCA1783	1969	£1.50	£4	
Run To Love	7"	Mercury	MF876	1965	£1.50	£4	
Sing Children Sing	LP	CBS	64202	1971	£4	£10	
Sing Children Sing	7"	CBS	8061	1979	£2	£5	
Sing Children Sing	7"	CBS	8061	1979	£10	£20	PS
Tell Him	7"	Parlophone	R5106	1964	£2	£5	
When My Baby Cries	7"	Mercury	MF830	1964	£2	£5	

DUNCAN, TOMMY

Dance Dance Dance	7"	Sue	WI4002	1966	£6	£12	

DUNKLEY, ERROL

Having A Party	7"	Jackpot	JP702	1969	£4	£8	
I Am Not Your Man	7"	Amalgamated	AMG805	1968	£4	£8	
I Am Not Your Man	7"	Island	WI3150	1968	£5	£10	
I Spy	7"	Amalgamated	AMG820	1968	£4	£8	
Love Me Forever	7"	Rio	R109	1966	£4	£8	Vietnam Allstars B side
Please Stop Your Lying	7"	Amalgamated	AMG800	1968	£4	£8	
Scorcher	7"	Amalgamated	AMG807	1968	£4	£8	
You're Gonna Need Me	7"	Rio	R131	1967	£4	£8	

DUNKLEY, ERROLL

I'll Take You In My Arms	7"	Fab	FAB117	1969	£2.50	£6	King Cannon B side

DUNN, BLIND WILLIE

Jet Black Blues	7"	Columbia	SCM5100	1954	£5	£10	

DUNN, GEORGE

George Dunn	LP	Leader	LEE4042	1973	£10	£25	

DUNNE, PECKER

Introducing The Pecker	LP	Emerald	GES1152	1976	£5	£12	

DUPREE, CHAMPION JACK

Ba' La Fouche	7"	Blue Horizon	573152	1969	£5	£10	
Barrelhouse Woman	7"	Decca	F12611	1967	£5	£10	
Blues Anthology Vol.1	7" EP	Storyville	SEP381	1961	£6	£12	
Blues From The Gutter	LP	London	LTZK15171	1959	£15	£30	
Cabbage Greens	LP	XTRA	XTRA1028	1965	£5	£12	
Champion Jack Dupree	LP	Storyville	670194	1967	£5	£12	
Champion Jack Dupree	LP	Storyville	SLP107	1964	£5	£12	
Champion Jack Dupree	7" EP	XX	MIN716	196-	£4	£8	
Champion Jack Dupree And His Blues Band	LP	Decca	SKL4871	1967	£20	£40	
Champion Of The Blues	LP	Atlantic	(SD)8056	1961	£8	£20	US
Fisherman's Blues	78	Jazz Parade	B16	1951	£3	£8	
From New Orleans To Chicago	LP	Decca	LK/SKL4747	1966	£20	£40	
Heavy Blues	LP	Sire	97010	1969	£4	£10	US
I Haven't Done No One No Harm	7"	Blue Horizon	573140	1968	£5	£10	
I Want To Be A Hippy	7"	Blue Horizon	573158	1968	£5	£10	
Jack Dupree	7" EP	Ember	EMBEP4564	1965	£6	£12	
London Special	7" EP	Decca	DFE8586	1964	£10	£20	
Natural And Soulful Blues	LP	London	LTZK15217/ SAHK6151	1961	£15	£30	
Portraits In Blues	LP	Storyville	SLP161	1964	£5	£12	
Rhythm And Blues Vol.1	7" EP	RCA	RCX7137	1964	£5	£10	
Scooby Dooby Doo	7"	Blue Horizon	763214	1969	£25	£50	
Sings The Blues	LP	King	735	1961	£15	£30	US
Trouble Trouble	LP	Storyville	SLP145	1964	£5	£12	
When You Feel The Feeling You Was Feeling	LP	Blue Horizon	763206	1968	£30	£60	
Whiskey Head Woman	7"	Storyville	A45051	1962	£6	£12	
Women Blues	LP	Folkways	FS3825	1961	£8	£20	US

DUPREE, CHAMPION JACK & JIMMY RUSHING

Two Shades Of Blue	LP	Ember	CJS800	1962	£5	£12	

DUPREE, CHAMPION JACK & TONY MCPHEE

Get Your Head Happy	7"	Blue Horizon	451007	1966	£30	£60	

DUPREE, SIMON & THE BIG SOUND

Broken Hearted Pirates	7"	Parlophone	R5757	1969	£2.50	£6	
Day Time, Night Time	7"	Parlophone	R5594	1967	£2.50	£6	
Eagle Flies Tonight	7"	Parlophone	R5816	1969	£4	£8	
For Whom The Bell Tolls	7"	Parlophone	R5670	1968	£2	£5	chart single
I See The Light	7"	Parlophone	R5542	1966	£4	£8	
Kites	7"	Parlophone	R5646	1967	£2.50	£6	chart single
Part Of My Past	7"	Parlophone	R5697	1968	£2.50	£6	
Reservations	7"	Parlophone	R5574	1967	£4	£8	
Thinking About My Life	7"	Parlophone	R5727	1968	£4	£8	
Thinking About My Life	7" EP	Odeon	FO135	1968	£7.50	£15	French
Without Reservations	LP	Parlophone	PCS7029	1969	£5	£12	black & white label
Without Reservations	LP	Parlophone	PMC/PCS7029	1967	£8	£20	chart LP

DUPREES

Around The Corner	7"	CBS	201803	1965	£2	£5	
Check Yourself	7"	Polydor	2058077	1970	£1.50	£4	
Gone With The Wind	7"	London	HLU9709	1963	£2	£5	
Have You Heard	LP	Coed	LPC906	1963	£15	£30	US
Have You Heard	7"	London	HLU9813	1963	£2	£5	
Have You Heard	7" EP	London	RE10157	1964	£6	£12	French
I'd Rather Be Here In Your Arms	7"	London	HLU9678	1963	£2	£5	
It's No Sin	7"	London	HLU9843	1964	£2	£5	
My Own True Love	7"	Stateside	SS143	1962	£2	£5	
My Special Angel	7"	MGM	MGM1460	1968	£1.50	£4	
She Waits For Him	7"	CBS	202028	1966	£2	£5	
Why Don't You Believe Me	7"	London	HLU9774	1963	£2	£5	
You Belong To Me	LP	Coed	LPC905	1962	£15	£30	US
You Belong To Me	7"	HMV	POP1073	1962	£5	£10	

DURAN DURAN

All She Wants Is	CD-s	EMI	CDDD11	1988	£4	£10	
Big Thing	7"	EMI		1988	£5	£10	promo
Burning The Ground	CD-s	EMI	CDDD13	1989	£8	£20	
Careless Memories	12"	EMI	12EMI5168	1981	£2.50	£6	
Do You Believe In Shame?	CD-s	Parlophone	CDDD12	1989	£4	£10	
Do You Believe In Shame?	7"	Parlophone	DDA/B/C12	1989	£4	£8	triple
Girls On Film	12"	EMI	12EMI5206	1981	£2.50	£6	
I Don't Want Your Love	CD-s	EMI	CDYOUR1	1988	£2.50	£6	
Master Mixes	LP	EMI		198-	£8	£20	double
My Own Way (3 versions)	12"	EMI		1982	£4	£10	promo
Notorious (Latin Rascals mix)	12"	EMI	12DDN45	1986	£3	£8	
Ordinary World	CD-s	Parlophone	CDDDS16	1992	£5	£12	
Planet Earth	12"	EMI	12EMI5137	1981	£2.50	£6	
Reflex	7"	EMI	DURANP2	1984	£1.50	£4	poster sleeve
Reflex	12"	EMI	12DURANP2	1984	£3	£8	pic disc
Serious	CD-s	EMI	CDDD15	1990	£4	£10	
Skin Trade	7"	Parlophone	TRADE1	1987	£4	£8	bum PS
Sound Of Thunder	12"	EMI	PSLP344	1981	£10	£25	promo sampler
Staying Together	CD-s	Atlantic	A9020CD	1988	£3	£8	

DURANTE, JIMMY

In Person	10" LP	MGM	MGMD102	1952	£5	£12		
It's Bigger Than Both Of Us	7"	Brunswick	05445	1955	£1.50	£4		
Jimmy Durante	7" EP.	MGM	MGMEP508	1954	£2	£5		
Jimmy Durante Sings	10" LP	Brunswick	LA8582	1953	£5	£12		
Pupalina	7"	Brunswick	05395	1955	£2	£5		
Schnozzles	7" EP.	MGM	MGMEP597	1957	£2.50	£6		
Swingin' With Rhythm And Blues	7"	Brunswick	05495	1955	£2	£5		

DURHAM, JUDITH

Again And Again	7"	Columbia	DB8290	1967	£4	£8		
For Christmas With Love	LP	Columbia	SCX6374	1969	£5	£12		

DURHAM, TERRY

Crystal Telephone	LP	Deram	DML/SML1042	1969	£6	£15		

DURUTTI COLUMN

Enigma	7"	Sordide Sentimentale	SS45005	1981	£10	£20	French
For Patti	7"	Factory Benelux	FBN100	1982	£12.50	£25	
Live At The Venue London	LP	VU	VINI1	1983	£5	£12	
Return Of The Durutti Column	LP	Factory	FACT14	1980	£6	£15	sandpaper sleeve, with flexi (FACT14C)

DURY, IAN

New Boots And Panties	LP	Stiff	SEEZG4	1977	£4	£10	gold vinyl
Sex & Drugs & Rock'n'Roll	7"	Stiff	FREEBIE1	1978	£1.50	£4	flexi

DUST

Dust	LP	Kama Sutra	2319014	1971	£8	£20	
Hard Attack	LP	Kama Sutra	KSBS2059	1972	£6	£15	US

DUSTY, SLIM

Pub With No Beer	7"	Columbia	DB4212	1958	£1.50	£4	chart single
Slim Dusty And His Country Rockers	7" EP.	Columbia	SEG8009	1960	£5	£10	

DUTCH

What Is Soul	7"	Philips	BF1673	1968	£1.50	£4	

DUTCH SWING COLLEGE

Dutch Swing College	LP	Philips	BBL7099	1956	£4	£10	
Dutch Swing College	10" LP	Philips	BBR8021	1954	£6	£15	
Gems Of Jazz Vol.1	10" LP	Philips	BBR8018	1954	£6	£15	

DUVAL, JOSE

Message Of Love	7"	London	HLR8458	1957	£4	£8	

DUVEEN, BOEING

The psychedelic single by Boeing Duveen, which sets two Lewis Carroll poems to music, is actually the work of Dr.Sam Hutt. Hutt, who specialised in helping people overcome drug addictions (notably at many of the rock festivals, starting at the Isle of Wight in 1969) was one of the many lesser names with a significant role in the sixties and early seventies counter-culture. During the last ten years or so, while continuing to work as a doctor, Hutt has also worked extensively as a country singer - music that he is inclined to tackle for its comic potential - using the name Hank Wangford.

DUVEEN, BOEING & THE BEAUTIFUL SOUP

Jabberwock	7"	Parlophone	R5696	1968	£15	£30		
Jabberwock	7"	Parlophone	R5696	1968	£50	£100	PS

DWYER, FINBARR

Irish Traditional Accordionist	LP	Outlet	OLP1004	1970	£5	£12	Irish

DYKE & THE BLAZERS

Funky Broadway	LP	Original Sound	LP(S)8876	1967	£10	£25	US
Funky Broadway	7"	Pye	7N25413	1967	£6	£12	
Greatest Hits	LP	Original Sound	LPS8877	1969	£8	£20	US

DYLAN, BOB

Bob Dylan has recorded so prolifically over the years that collecting him consists to a large extent of trying to obtain some of the large number of bootleg LPs that have been issued. Apart from documenting some crucially important live performances (such as the famous Albert Hall concert with the Band, albums of which probably have total sales to rival those of Dylan's CBS recordings), these also allow Dylan's many studio out-takes to be heard. Many of these are arguably better than the tracks that were released. A few out-takes are also officially available on scarce promotional releases and on the very first American issue of "Freewheelin'", which included four songs that are not on any of the subsequent releases of the record. These are "Rocks And Gravel" (called 'Solid Gravel' on some pressings), "Let Me Die In My Footsteps", "Gamblin' Willie's Dead Man's Hand", and "Talkin' John Birch Society Blues". It should be stressed that only copies playing these tracks, which are not actually listed on the sleeve, are worth the large sums of money quoted below.

All I Really Want To Do	7" EP.	CBS	5923	1964	£15	£30	French
Another Side Of Bob Dylan	LP	CBS	(S)BPG62429	1964	£4	£10	chart LP
Blonde On Blonde	LP	CBS	66012	1966	£8	£20	double, mono, chart LP
Blonde On Blonde	LP	CBS	66012	1966	£5	£12	double, stereo, chart LP
Blood On The Tracks	LP	Columbia	PC33235	1974	£1750	£2500	test pressing with different versions of 5 tracks
Blowin' In The Wind	7"	Columbia	42856	1963	£75	£150	US
Blowin' In The Wind	7" EP.	CBS	5688	1964	£15	£30	French
Blowing In The Wind	7" EP.	Fontana	TFE18010	1965	£20	£40	with other artists
Bob Dylan	LP	CBS	(S)BPG62022	1962	£5	£12	chart LP
Bob Dylan	LP	Columbia	CL1779	1962	£37.50	£75	US mono, 6 eye logos on label

Title	Format	Label	Cat No	Year	Price Low	Price High	Notes
Bob Dylan	LP	Columbia	CS8579	1962	£50	£100	US stereo, 6 eye logos on label
Bob Dylan	7" EP	CBS	EP6051	1965	£7.50	£15	
Bob Dylan In Concerto	12"	Gong	5A/6B	1976	£25	£50	Italian
Bringing It All Back Home	LP	CBS	(S)BPG62515	1965	£4	£10	chart LP
Can You Please Crawl Out Your Window	7"	CBS	201900	1965	£4	£8	chart single
Can You Please Crawl Out Your Window	7" EP	CBS	6265	1965	£15	£30	French
Desire	LP	CBS	Q86003	1976	£6	£15	quad
Fool Such As I	7"	CBS	2006	1974	£1.50	£4	
Four Songs From Renaldo And Clara	12"	Columbia	AS422	1978	£20	£40	US promo
Freewheelin'	LP	CBS	(S)BPG62193	1963	£4	£10	chart LP
Freewheelin'	LP	Columbia	CL1986	1963	£3500	£5000	US mono, 4 different tracks
Freewheelin'	LP	Columbia	CS8786	1963	£10000	£12000	US stereo, 4 different tracks
George Jackson	7"	CBS	7688	1971	£2.50	£6	
Highway 61 Revisited	LP	CBS	BPG62572	1965	£5	£12	mono, chart LP
Highway 61 Revisited	LP	CBS	SBPG62572	1965	£4	£10	stereo, chart LP
Highway 61 Revisited	LP	Columbia	CS9189	1965	£37.50	£75	US, alternate take of 'From A Buick 6'
Hurricane	7"	CBS	3878	1976	£1.50	£4	
Hurricane	7"	CBS	3878	1976	£2.50	£6	PS
I Threw It All Away	7"	CBS	4219	1969	£1.50	£4	chart single
I Want You	7"	CBS	202258	1966	£4	£8	chart single
I Want You	7" EP	CBS	5769	1966	£12.50	£25	French
If Not For You	7"	CBS	7092	1971	£1.50	£4	
John Wesley Harding	LP	CBS	63252	1968	£4	£10	mono, chart LP
Just Like A Woman	7"	CBS	1158	1973	£1.50	£4	PS
Just Like Tom Thumb's Blues	7" EP	CBS	6270	1966	£15	£30	French
Leopard-Skin Pill-Box Hat	7" EP	CBS	6345	1967	£15	£30	French
Leopardskin Pillbox Hat	7"	CBS	202700	1967	£2.50	£6	
Leopardskin Pillbox Hat	7"	CBS	202700	1967	£12.50	£25	PS
Like A Rolling Stone	7"	CBS	201811	1965	£2	£5	chart single
Like A Rolling Stone	7" EP	CBS	6107	1965	£10	£20	French
Maggie's Farm	7"	CBS	201781	1965	£2	£5	chart single
Million Dollar Bash	7"	CBS	3665	1975	£1.50	£4	
Mixed Up Confusion	7"	CBS	2476	196-	£12.50	£25	French
Mixed Up Confusion	7"	Columbia	442656	1963	£100	£200	US
Mr.Tambourine Man	7" EP	CBS	EP6078	1966	£7.50	£15	
Nashville Skyline	LP	CBS	63601	1969	£5	£12	mono, chart LP
Nashville Skyline	LP	CBS	CQ32872	1974	£8	£20	US quad
Nashville Skyline	LP	Columbia	HC49825	1981	£8	£20	US audiophile
Nine Song Publisher's Sampler	LP	Warner Bros	XTD221567	1963	£400	£600	US promo
On A Night Like This	7"	Island	WIP6168	1974	£1.50	£4	
One Of Us Must Know	7"	CBS	202053	1966	£2.50	£6	chart single
One Too Many Mornings	7" EP	CBS	EP6070	1966	£10	£20	
Planet Waves	LP	Ashes And Sands	7E501	1973	£30	£60	US own label
Planet Waves	LP	Asylum	EQ1003	1974	£10	£25	US quad
Positively Fourth Street	7"	CBS	201824	1965	£2	£5	chart single
Positively Fourth Street	7"	Columbia	43389	1965	£50	£100	US mispress, plays alternate 'Crawl Out Your Window'
Positively Fourth Street	7" EP	CBS	6210	1965	£15	£30	French
Rainy Day Women	7" EP	CBS	202307	1966	£2	£5	chart single
Rainy Day Women No.12 & 35	7" EP	CBS	5660	1966	£15	£30	French
Rita May	7"	CBS	4859	1977	£2.50	£6	PS
Subterranean Homesick Blues	7"	CBS	201753	1965	£2	£5	chart single
Subterranean Homesick Blues	7" EP	CBS	6096	1965	£15	£30	French
Tangled Up In Blue	7"	CBS	3160	1975	£1.50	£4	
Times They Are A-Changin'	LP	CBS	(S)BPG62251	1964	£4	£10	chart LP
Times They Are A-Changin'	LP	Mobile Fidelity	MFSL1114	1984	£6	£15	US audiophile
Times They Are A-Changin'	7"	CBS	201751	1965	£2	£5	chart single
Tonight I'll Be Staying Here With You	7"	CBS	4611	1969	£1.50	£4	
Vs.A.J.Weberman	LP	Folkways	FB5322	1971	£50	£100	US
Watching The River Flow	7"	CBS	7329	1971	£2.50	£6	chart single
Wigwam	7"	CBS	5122	1970	£2	£5	
With God On Our Side	7" EP	CBS	6266	1965	£15	£30	French
With God On Our Side	7" EP	Fontana	TFE18009	1965	£20	£40	with other artists
Ye Playboys And Playgirls	7" EP	Fontana	TFE18011	1965	£20	£40	with other artists

DYLAN, BOB & OTHERS

Title	Format	Label	Cat No	Year	Price Low	Price High	Notes
World Of Folk Music	LP	Warner Bros	XGPB508	1964	£100	£200	US promo

DYMON, FRANKIE

Title	Format	Label	Cat No	Year	Price Low	Price High	Notes
Let It Out	LP	BASF	20212416	1971	£6	£15	German

DYNAMICS

Title	Format	Label	Cat No	Year	Price Low	Price High	Notes
Ice Cream Song	7"	Atlantic	584270	1969	£2	£5	
Misery	7"	London	HLX9809	1963	£6	£12	
So In Love With Me	7"	King	KG1007	1964	£5	£10	

DYNAMICS (2)

Title	Format	Label	Cat No	Year	Price Low	Price High	Notes
Dynamics With Jimmy Hannah	LP	Bolo	BLP8001	1962	£8	£20	US

DYNAMICS (3)

Title	Format	Label	Cat No	Year	Price Low	Price High	Notes
My Friends	7"	Blue Cat	BS104	1968	£4	£8	Neville Irons B side

DYNAMITES

Fire Corner	LP	Trojan	TTL21	1969	£6	£15	
John Public	7"	Duke	DU30	1969	£2.50	£6	
Mr.Midnight	7"	Clandisc	CLA200	1969	£2.50	£6	King Stitt B side
Rahtid	7"	Trojan	TR647	1969	£2.50	£6	Clancy Eccles B side

DYNAMITES (2)

Someone Like Me	7" EP.	Columbia	ESRF1729	1965	£6	£12	French

DYNATONES

Fife Piper	7"	Pye	7N25389	1966	£15	£30	
Steel Guitar Rag	7"	Top Rank	JAR149	1959	£2.50	£6	

DYSON, ALAN

Still Small Voice Of Alan Dyson	LP	Pye	NPL18212	1968	£8	£20	

DYSON, RONNIE

Point Of No Return	7"	CBS	1659	1975	£1.50	£4	
We Can Make It Last Forever	7"	CBS	2430	1974	£2.50	£6	

DZYAN

Dzyan	LP	Aronda	10006	1972	£5	£12	German
Electric Silence	LP	Bacillus	19202	1975	£4	£10	German
Time Machine	LP	Bacillus	19161	1973	£6	£15	German

E

EAGER, VINCE

Title	Format	Label	Catalogue	Year	Price1	Price2	Notes
Any Time Is The Right Time	7"	Piccadilly	7N35110	1963	£1.50	£4	
Five Days Five Days	7"	Parlophone	R4482	1958	£6	£12	
Lonely Blue Boy	7"	Top Rank	JAR307	1960	£2.50	£6	
Love My Life Away	7"	Top Rank	JAR539	1961	£1.50	£4	
Making Love	7"	Top Rank	JAR191	1959	£1.50	£4	
No Other Arms, No Other Lips	7"	Parlophone	R4550	1959	£4	£8	
Tread Softly Stranger	7"	Decca	F11023	1958	£15	£30	2 x 1 sided demos only
Vince Eager & The Vagabonds No.1	7" EP	Decca	DFE6504	1958	£12.50	£25	
When's Your Birthday Baby	7"	Parlophone	R4531	1959	£4	£8	
Why	7"	Top Rank	JAR275	1960	£1.50	£4	
World's Loneliest Man	7"	Top Rank	JAR593	1961	£1.50	£4	

EAGLE

Title	Format	Label	Catalogue	Year	Price1	Price2	Notes
Come Under Nancy's Tent	LP	Pye	NSPL28138	1969	£5	£12	
Kickin' It Back To You	7"	Pye	7N25530	1970	£2	£5	

EAGLES

Title	Format	Label	Catalogue	Year	Price1	Price2	Notes
Desperado	LP	Asylum	K53003	1982	£4	£10	audiophile
Hotel California	LP	Mobile Fidelity	MFSL1126	1981	£5	£12	US audiophile
On The Border	LP	Asylum	EQ1004	1975	£4	£10	US quad
One Of These Nights	LP	Asylum	EQ1039	1975	£4	£10	US quad

EAGLES (2)

Title	Format	Label	Catalogue	Year	Price1	Price2
Andorra	7"	Pye	7N15613	1964	£1.50	£4
Bristol Express	7"	Pye	7N15451	1962	£1.50	£4
Come On Baby	7"	Pye	7N15550	1963	£1.50	£4
Desperadoes	7"	Pye	7N15503	1962	£1.50	£4
Eagles Nest	7"	Pye	7N15571	1963	£1.50	£4
Exodus	7"	Pye	7N15473	1962	£1.50	£4
New Sound TV Themes	7" EP	Pye	NEP24166	1962	£5	£10
Smash Hits	LP	Pye	NPL18084	1963	£10	£25
Wishing And Hoping	7"	Pye	7N15650	1964	£2.50	£6

EAGLIN, SNOOKS

Title	Format	Label	Catalogue	Year	Price1	Price2
Blues Anthology Vol.6	7" EP	Storyville	SEP386	1963	£5	£10
Country Boy	7"	Storyville	A45056	196-	£4	£8
Message From New Orleans	LP	Heritage	HLP1002	1961	£8	£20
New Orleans Street Singer	LP	Storyville	SLP119	1964	£5	£12
Portraits In Blues Vol.1	LP	Storyville	670146	1967	£5	£12
Snooks Eaglin	LP	Folkways	FA2476	1961	£8	£20
That's All Right	LP	Xtra	XTRA5051	1968	£5	£12
Vol.2 - Blues From New Orleans	LP	Storyville	SLP140	1964	£5	£12

EANES, JIM

Title	Format	Label	Catalogue	Year	Price1	Price2
Christmas Doll	7"	Melodisc	1530	1959	£5	£10

EARDLEY, JOHN

Title	Format	Label	Catalogue	Year	Price1	Price2
Down East	LP	Esquire	32040	1958	£15	£30

EARL & DEAN

Title	Format	Label	Catalogue	Year	Price1	Price2
Slowly Going Out Of My Head	7"	Strike	JH323	1966	£1.50	£4

EARLS

Title	Format	Label	Catalogue	Year	Price1	Price2	Notes
Never	7"	London	HL9702	1963	£10	£20	
Remember Me Baby	LP	Old Town	LP104	1963	£30	£60	US
Remember Then	7"	Stateside	SS153	1963	£7.50	£15	

EARTH

Title	Format	Label	Catalogue	Year	Price1	Price2
Resurrection City	7"	CBS	4671	1969	£10	£20
Stranger Of Fortune	7"	Decca	F22908	1969	£5	£10

EARTH & FIRE

Title	Format	Label	Catalogue	Year	Price1	Price2	Notes
Atlantis	LP	Polydor	2925013	1973	£5	£12	Dutch
Best Of Earth And Fire	LP	Polydor	2491004	1975	£4	£10	Dutch
Earth And Fire	LP	Nepentha	6437004	1971	£80	£160	sleeve pictured in Guide
Earth And Fire	LP	Polydor	2441011	1971	£25	£50	Dutch
Song Of Marching Children	LP	Polydor	2925003	1971	£6	£15	Dutch
To The World A Future	LP	Polydor	2925033	1975	£4	£10	Dutch

EARTH BOYS

Title	Format	Label	Catalogue	Year	Price1	Price2
Space Girl	7"	Capitol	CL14979	1959	£2	£5

EARTH OPERA

Title	Format	Label	Catalogue	Year	Price1	Price2
Alfie Finney	7"	Elektra	EKSN45061	1969	£1.50	£4
American Eagle Tragedy	7"	Elektra	EKSN45049	1968	£1.50	£4
Close Your Eyes And Shut The Door	7"	Elektra	EKSN45035	1968	£2	£5
Earth Opera	LP	Elektra	EKS74016	1968	£6	£15
Great American Eagle Tragedy	LP	Elektra	EKS74038	1969	£4	£10

EARTH, WIND & FIRE

Title	Format	Label	Cat No	Year	Price	Price	Notes
Head To The Sky	LP	Columbia	CQ32194	1974	£4	£10	US quad
Last Days And Time	LP	CBS	65208	1973	£5	£12	
Open Our Eyes	LP	Columbia	CQ32712	1974	£4	£10	US quad

EARTHLINGS

Title	Format	Label	Cat No	Year	Price	Price	Notes
Landing Of The Daleks	7"	Parlophone	R5242	1965	£6	£12	

EARTHQUAKE

Title	Format	Label	Cat No	Year	Price	Price	Notes
Live	LP	United Artists	UAS29853	1975	£4	£10	

EARTHQUAKERS

Title	Format	Label	Cat No	Year	Price	Price	Notes
Whistling In The Sunshine	7"	Stateside	SS2050	1967	£2.50	£6	

EARTHQUAKES

Title	Format	Label	Cat No	Year	Price	Price	Notes
Brother Moses	7"	Duke	DU55	1969	£2.50	£6	
Earth Quake	7"	Duke	DU56	1969	£2.50	£6	
I Can't Stop Loving You	7"	Duke	DU54	1969	£2.50	£6	

EASLEY, TIM

Title	Format	Label	Cat No	Year	Price	Price	Notes
Susie Q	7"	Bell	BLL1036	1968	£1.50	£4	

EAST MAIN ST.EXPLOSION

Title	Format	Label	Cat No	Year	Price	Price	Notes
Hop, Skip and Jump	7"	Fontana	TF1039	1969	£1.50	£4	

EAST OF EDEN

East Of Eden were virtually two separate groups, with only violinist Dave Arbus being a member of both. The Harvest recordings, made after the group gained a chart hit with the atypical "Jig A Jig", are routine seventies rock. The Deram LPs, on the other hand, contain fiercely experimental music in which Don Drummond rubs shoulders with Charles Mingus and saxophones, flutes, and violins jostle with each other for supremacy.

Title	Format	Label	Cat No	Year	Price	Price	Notes
East Of Eden	LP	Harvest	SHVL792	1971	£6	£15	
Jig A Jig	7"	Deram	DM297	1970	£1.50	£4	chart single
King Of Siam	7"	Atlantic	584182	1968	£5	£10	
Mercator Projected	LP	Deram	DML/SML1038	1969	£6	£15	
New Leaf	LP	Harvest	SHVL796	1971	£5	£12	
Northern Hemisphere	7"	Deram	DM242	1969	£5	£10	
Ramadhan	7"	Deram	DM338	1971	£4	£8	
Snafu	LP	Deram	SML1050	1970	£6	£15	chart LP

EASTERHOUSE

Title	Format	Label	Cat No	Year	Price	Price	Notes
In Our Own Hands	12"	Easterhouse	EIREX1	1985	£2.50	£6	hand stencilled PS

EASTWOOD, CLINT

Title	Format	Label	Cat No	Year	Price	Price	Notes
Cowboy Favorites	LP	Cameo	C(S)1056	1963	£8	£20	US
I Talk To The Trees	7"	Paramount	PARA3004	1970	£1.50	£4	chart single

EASYBEATS

Title	Format	Label	Cat No	Year	Price	Price	Notes
Come And See Her	7"	United Artists	UP1144	1966	£2.50	£6	
Falling Off The Edge Of The World	LP	United Artists	UAS6667	1968	£10	£25	US
Friday On My Mind	LP	United Artists	UAL3/UAS6588	1967	£15	£30	US
Friday On My Mind	7"	United Artists	UP1157	1966	£2	£5	chart single
Friday On My Mind	7" EP	United Artists	36106	1966	£10	£20	French
Friends	LP	Polydor	2482010	1970	£15	£30	
Friends	7"	Polydor	2001028	1970	£4	£8	
Good Friday	LP	United Artists	(S)ULP1167	1967	£30	£60	
Good Times	7"	United Artists	UP2243	1969	£2	£5	
Heaven & Hell	7" EP	United Artists	36117	1967	£12.50	£25	French
Heaven And Hell	7"	United Artists	UP1183	1967	£2.50	£6	
Hello How Are You	7"	United Artists	UP2209	1968	£2	£5	chart single
I Love Marie	7"	Polydor	56357	1969	£2	£5	
Land Of Make Believe	7"	United Artists	UP2219	1968	£2	£5	
Music Goes Round My Head	7"	United Artists	UP1201	1967	£4	£8	
St.Louis	7"	Polydor	56335	1969	£2.50	£6	
Vigil	LP	United Artists	(S)ULP1193	1968	£15	£30	
Who'll Be The One	7"	United Artists	UP1175	1966	£2	£5	
Who'll Be The One	7" EP	United Artists	36112	1966	£12.50	£25	French

EATER

Title	Format	Label	Cat No	Year	Price	Price	Notes
Album	LP	The Label	TLRLP001	1978	£8	£20	
Lock It Up	12"	The Label	TLR004	1977	£2.50	£6	

EBONIES

Title	Format	Label	Cat No	Year	Price	Price	Notes
Never Gonna Break Your Heart Again	7"	Philips	BF1648	1968	£2	£5	

ECCENTRICS

Title	Format	Label	Cat No	Year	Price	Price	Notes
What You Got	7"	Pye	7N15850	1965	£7.50	£15	

ECCLES, CLANCY

Title	Format	Label	Cat No	Year	Price	Price	Notes
Auntie Lulu	7"	Duke	DU9	1969	£2.50	£6	Slickers B side
Beat Dance	7"	Clandisc	CLA206	1969	£2.50	£6	King Stitt B side
C.N.Express	7"	Pama	PM722	1968	£4	£8	
Constantinople	7"	Trojan	TR648	1969	£2.50	£6	
Fattie Fattie	7"	Trojan	TR658	1969	£2.50	£6	Silverstars B side
Feel The Rhythm	7"	Doctor Bird	DB1156	1968	£5	£10	
Festival '68	7"	Nu Beat	NB006	1968	£4	£8	
Fight	7"	Pama	PM712	1968	£4	£8	
Freedom	LP	Trojan	TTL22	1969	£6	£15	
Freedom	7"	Blue Beat	BB67	1961	£5	£10	
Glory Hallelujah	7"	Island	WI098	1963	£5	£10	
Judgement	7"	Island	WI044	1963	£5	£10	
Miss Ida	7"	Ska Beat	JB198	1965	£5	£10	King Rocky B side

Mother's Advice	7"	Pama	PM703	1967	£4	£8
Open Up	7"	Clandisc	CLA209	1969	£2.50	£6 ... Higgs & Wilson B side
River Jordan	7"	Blue Beat	BB34	1961	£5	£10
Sammy No Dead	7"	Ska Beat	JB194	1965	£5	£10
Shu Be Do	7"	Duke	DU31	1969	£2.50	£6
Sweet Africa	7"	Trojan	TR639	1968	£4	£8
What Will Your Mama Say	7"	Pama	PM701	1967	£4	£8
World Needs Loving	7"	Clandisc	CLA201	1969	£2.50	£6

ECHO & THE BUNNYMEN

Bring On The Dancing Horses	7"	Korova	KOW43	1988	£2	£5 ....shaped pic disc
Crocodiles	7"	Korova	ECHO1	1981	£2	£5 .... promo
Cutter	12"	Korova	KOW26T	1983	£2.50	£6 .... with cassette and poster
Pictures On My Wall	7"	Zoo	CAGE004	1979	£2.50	£6
Puppet	7"	Korova	KOW11	1980	£2.50	£6
Rescue	12"	Korova	KOW1T	1980	£2.50	£6

ECHOES

Baby Blue	7"	Top Rank	JAR553	1961	£4	£8
Born To Be With You	7"	Top Rank	JAR399	1960	£4	£8

ECHOES (2)

Cloak And Dagger	7"	Fontana	267254TF	1962	£1.50	£4
Don't You Believe Them	7"	Philips	BF1370	1964	£1.50	£4
Got To Run	7"	Philips	BF1480	1966	£1.50	£4
Happy Whistler	7"	Fontana	TF392	1962	£1.50	£4
Marching Thru	7"	Fontana	TF415	1963	£1.50	£4
My Little Girl	7"	Fontana	TF439	1964	£1.50	£4
Searchin' For You Baby	7"	Philips	BF1683	1968	£2.50	£6

ECHOES (3)

Are You Mine	7"	Blue Beat	BB89	1961	£5	£10

ECKSTINE, BILLY

At Basin Street East	LP	Mercury	MMC14100/ CMS18066	1962	£4	£10
Basie-Eckstine Incorporated	7" EP	Columbia	SEG8043/ ESG7827	1960	£2	£5
Best Of Mister B No.1	7" EP	Mercury	ZEP10005	1959	£2	£5
Best Of Mister B No.2	7" EP	Emarcy	YEP9509	1959	£2	£5
Billy Eckstine	7" EP	MGM	MGMEP511	1954	£2	£5
Billy Eckstine's Imagination	LP	Mercury	MMB12002	1959	£4	£10
Billy's Best	LP	Mercury	MMC14043	1960	£4	£10
Cashmere Voice	7" EP	MGM	MGMEP523	1955	£2	£5
Cont Basie And Billy Eckstine	LP	Columbia	33SX1202/ SCX3290	1960	£4	£10 ...with Count Basie
Date With Rhythm	7" EP	Parlophone	GEP8672	1957	£2	£5
Enchantment No.1	7" EP	MGM	MGMEP545	1956	£2	£5
Four Great Standards	7" EP	MGM	MGMEP598	1957	£2	£5
Gentle On My Mind	LP	Tamla Motown	(S)TML11101	1969	£8	£20
Golden Saxophones	LP	London	HAD2241/ SAHD6070	1960	£4	£10
Good Jelly Blues	7"	Ember	JBS703	1962	£1.50	£4
Had You Been Around	7"	Tamla Motown	TMG533	1965	£20	£40
Kiss Of Fire	7"	MGM	SP1011	1953	£2.50	£6
Love Me Or Leave Me	7"	MGM	SP1136	1955	£1.50	£4
My Way	LP	Tamla Motown	(S)TML11046	1967	£15	£30
No Cover, No Minimum	LP	Columbia	33SX1327/ SCX3381	1961	£4	£10
No One But You	7"	MGM	SP1101	1954	£2	£5 ....chart single
Once More With Feeling	LP	Columbia	33SX1249/ SCX3322	1960	£4	£10
Prime Of My Life	LP	Tamla Motown	TML11025	1966	£20	£40
Tenderly	10" LP	MGM	MGMD126	1954	£5	£12
That Old Feeling	10" LP	MGM	MGMD138	1956	£5	£12
Weaver Of Dreams	10" LP	MGM	MGMD151	1958	£5	£12

ECKSTINE, BILLY & SARAH VAUGHAN

Best Of Berlin	7" EP	Mercury	SEZ19016	1961	£2	£5 .... stereo
Best Of Irving Berlin	LP	Mercury	MPL6530	1958	£4	£10
Billy Eckstine And Sarah Vaughan	7" EP	MGM	MGMEP690	1959	£2	£5
More Of Irving Berlin	7" EP	Mercury	SEZ19023	1962	£2	£5 .... stereo
Passing Strangers	7"	Mercury	AMT1071	1959	£1.50	£4
Passing Strangers	7"	Mercury	MF1082	1969	£1.50	£4 ... PS, chart single
Passing Strangers	7" EP	Mercury	10025MCE	1965	£2	£5

ECLECTION

Eclection had a very similar sound to the early Fairport Convention and two of its members - Trevor Lucas and Gerry Conway - both played with the more famous group in later years. When singer Kerilee Male left in October 1968, the group took the unusual step of re-recording their current single with Male's replacement, Doris Henderson. Despite this, however, neither version sold particularly well.

Another Time Another Place	7"	Elektra	EKSN45040	1968	£2.50	£6
Eclection	LP	Elektra	EKL4023	1968	£25	£50 ....Mono
Eclection	LP	Elektra	EKS74023	1968	£20	£40
Nevertheless	7"	Elektra	EKSN45033	1968	£4	£8
Nevertheless	7"	Elektra	K12196	1976	£1.50	£4
Please	7"	Elektra	EKSN45042	1968	£2.50	£6
Please	7"	Elektra	EKSN45046	1968	£2.50	£6

EDDIE AND THE HOT RODS

Writing On The Wall	12"	Island	WIP6270	1976	£4	£10 .... PS

EDDIE, JASON

Heart And Soul	7"	Tangerine	DP0010	1969	£2.50	£6	
Singing The Blues	7"	Parlophone	R5473	1966	£30	£60	
Whatcha Gonna Do Baby	7"	Parlophone	R5388	1965	£25	£50	

EDDIE'S CROWD

Baby Don't Look Down	7"	CBS	202078	1966	£10	£20	

EDDY & TEDDY

Bye Bye Butterfly	7"	London	HLU9367	1961	£2	£5	

EDDY, DUANE

1,000,000 Dollars Of Twang	LP	London	HAW2325	1961	£5	£12	chart LP
1,000,000 Dollars Of Twang Vol.2	LP	London	HAW2435	1964	£5	£12	chart LP
Avenger	7"	London	HLW9477	1961	£1.50	£4	
Ballad Of Paladin	7"	RCA	RCA1300	1962	£1.50	£4	chart single
Because They're Young	7"	London	HL7096	1960	£1.50	£4	export
Because They're Young	7"	London	HLW9162	1960	£1.50	£4	chart single
Because They're Young	7" EP	London	REW1252	1960	£4	£8	
Biggest Twang Of All	LP	Reprise	RLP6218	1966	£4	£10	
Biggest Twang Of All	LP	Reprise	RSLP6218	1967	£5	£12	stereo
Bonnie Came Back	7"	London	HLW9050	1960	£2.50	£6	chart single
Bonnie Come Back	7"	London	HL7090	1960	£7.50	£15	export
Boss Guitar	7"	RCA	RCA1329	1963	£1.50	£4	chart single
Break My Mind	7"	CBS	3962	1969	£4	£8	
Cannonball	7"	London	HL8764	1958	£2.50	£6	chart single
Caravan	7"	Parlophone	R4826	1961	£1.50	£4	chart single
Cottonmouth	7" EP	Colpix	PXE304	1965	£10	£20	
Country Twang	7" EP	RCA	RCX7115	1963	£5	£10	
Dance With The Guitar Man	LP	RCA	RD7545	1963	£5	£12	chart LP
Dance With The Guitar Man	LP	RCA	SF7545	1963	£6	£15	stereo
Dance With The Guitar Man	7"	RCA	RCA1316	1962	£1.50	£4	chart single
Daydream	7"	Reprise	RS20504	1966	£2.50	£6	
Deep In The Heart Of Texas	7"	RCA	RCA1288	1962	£1.50	£4	chart single
Drivin' Home	7"	London	HLW9406	1961	£1.50	£4	chart single
Duane A Go Go	LP	Colpix	PXL490	1965	£5	£12	
Duane Does Dylan	LP	Colpix	PXL494	1965	£6	£15	
Duane Does Dylan	LP	Golden Guinea	GGL10337	1968	£4	£10	
Duane Does Dylan	LP	Golden Guinea	GGSL10337	1968	£6	£15	stereo
Especially For You	LP	London	HAW2191	1959	£5	£12	chart LP
Especially For You	LP	London	SAHW6045	1959	£6	£15	stereo
Forty Miles Of Bad Road	7"	London	HL7080	1959	£1.50	£4	export
Forty Miles Of Bad Road	7"	London	HLW8929	1959	£2.50	£6	chart single
Girls Girls Girls	LP	London	HAW2373	1961	£5	£12	
Girls Girls Girls	LP	London	SAHW6173	1961	£6	£15	stereo
Guitar Star	7"	RCA	RCA1425	1964	£1.50	£4	
Guitared And Feathered	7"	RCA	RCA1369	1963	£1.50	£4	
Have Twangy Guitar Will Travel	LP	London	HAW2160	1958	£8	£20	chart LP
House Of The Rising Sun	7"	Colpix	PX788	1964	£1.50	£4	
Kommotion	7"	London	HLW9225	1960	£1.50	£4	chart single
Lonely Boy Lonely Guitar	7"	RCA	RCA1344	1963	£1.50	£4	chart single
Lonely Guitar	LP	RCA	RD7621	1964	£6	£15	
Lonely Guitar	LP	RCA	SF7621	1964	£8	£20	stereo
Lonely One	7"	London	HL7072	1959	£1.50	£4	export
Lonely One	7"	London	HLW8821	1959	£2.50	£6	
Lonely One	7" EP	London	REW1216	1959	£4	£8	
Love Confusion	7"	Target	101	1975	£2.50	£6	
Mister Twang	7" EP	RCA	RCX7129	1963	£5	£10	
Monsoon	7"	Reprise	RS20557	1967	£2.50	£6	
Movie Themes	7" EP	London	REW1303	1961	£4	£8	
Niki Hoeky	7"	Reprise	RS20690	1968	£2.50	£6	
Pepe	7"	London	HLW9257	1961	£1.50	£4	chart single
Pepe	7" EP	London	REW1287	1961	£4	£8	
Peter Gunn	7"	London	HLW8879	1959	£2.50	£6	chart single
Peter Gunn	7"	London	SLW4001	1959	£20	£40	stereo
Ramrod	7"	Ford	500	1957	£60	£120	US
Ramrod	7"	London	HL7057	1958	£1.50	£4	export
Ramrod	7"	London	HL8723	1958	£2.50	£6	
Rebel Rouser	7"	London	HL8669	1958	£4	£8	chart single
Rebel Rouser	7" EP	London	RE1175	1958	£5	£10	
Ring Of Fire	7"	London	HLW9370	1961	£1.50	£4	chart single
Roarin' Twangies	LP	Reprise	R(S)LP6240	1967	£8	£20	
Shazam!	7"	London	HLW9104	1960	£1.50	£4	chart single
Some Kinda Earthquake	7"	London	HLW9007	1959	£1.50	£4	chart single
Son Of Rebel Rouser	7"	RCA	RCA1389	1964	£1.50	£4	
Songs Of Our Heritage	LP	London	HAW2285	1960	£5	£12	chart LP
Songs Of Our Heritage	LP	London	SAHW6119	1960	£6	£15	stereo
Theme From Dixie	7"	London	HLW9324	1961	£1.50	£4	chart single
Trash	7"	Colpix	PX779	1964	£1.50	£4	
Twangin' Golden Hits	LP	RCA	RD7689	1964	£5	£12	
Twangin' Golden Hits	LP	RCA	SF7689	1965	£6	£15	stereo
Twangin' Up A Small Storm	7" EP	RCA	RCX7146	1964	£7.50	£15	
Twangin' Up A Storm	LP	RCA	RD7568	1963	£5	£12	
Twangin' Up A Storm	LP	RCA	SF7568	1963	£6	£15	stereo
Twangs A Country Song	LP	RCA	RD7560	1963	£5	£12	
Twangs A Country Song	LP	RCA	SF7560	1963	£6	£15	stereo
Twang's The Thang	LP	London	HAW2236	1960	£5	£12	chart LP
Twang's The Thang	LP	London	SAHW6068	1960	£6	£15	stereo
Twangsville	LP	RCA	RD7754	1965	£6	£15	
Twangsville	LP	RCA	SF7754	1965	£8	£20	stereo

Twangy	7" EP.	London	REW1257	1960	£4	£8	
Twangy Guitar Silky Strings	LP	RCA	RD7510	1962	£4	£10	chart LP
Twangy Guitar Silky Strings	LP	RCA	SF7510	1962	£6	£15	stereo
Twangy No.2	7" EP.	London	REW1341	1961	£4	£8	
Twistin' And Twangin'	LP	RCA	RD27264	1962	£5	£12	chart LP
Twistin' And Twangin'	LP	RCA	SF5134	1962	£6	£15	stereo
Water Skiing	LP	RCA	RD7656	1964	£6	£15	
Water Skiing	LP	RCA	SF7656	1964	£8	£20	stereo
Yep	7" EP.	London	REW1217	1959	£4	£8	
Yep!	7"	London	HL7076	1959	£7.50	£15	export
Your Baby's Gone Surfin'	7"	RCA	RCA1357	1963	£1.50	£4	chart single

EDDY, PEARL

That's What A Heart Is For	7"	HMV	7M262	1954	£2	£5

EDE, DAVID & THE RABIN ROCK

Easy Go	7"	Pye	7N15280	1960	£1.50	£4

EDEN ROSE

On The Way To Eden	LP	Metema		1971	£100	£200

EDEN, TONI

Grown Up Dreams	7"	Columbia	DB4458	1960	£1.50	£4
Send Me	7"	Decca	F11342	1961	£1.50	£4
Teen Street	7"	Columbia	DB4409	1960	£2.50	£6
Will I Ever	7"	Columbia	DB4527	1960	£1.50	£4

EDEN'S CHILDREN

Eden's Children	LP	Stateside	(S)SL10235	1968	£8	£20	
Sure Looks Real	LP	ABC	S652	1969	£8	£20	US

EDGE

Edge	LP	Nose	NRS48003	1970	£8	£20	US

EDISON, HARRY

Gee Baby Ain't I Good To You	LP	HMV	CLP1350	1960	£8	£20
Harry Edison Quartet	10" LP	Vogue	LDE118	1955	£20	£40
Sweets	LP	Columbia	33CX10087	1957	£8	£20
Swinger	LP	HMV	CLP1277	1959	£8	£20
Swings Buck Clayton	LP	HMV	CLP1321	1960	£8	£20

EDMUND JR., LADA

Larue	7"	MCA	MCA172	1975	£1.50	£4

EDMUNDS, DAVE

Blue Monday	7"	Regal Zonophone	RZ3037	1971	£1.50	£4
College Radio Network Presents Dave Edmunds	LP	Swansong	PR320	1978	£8	£20	US promo
Down Down Down	7"	Regal Zonophone	RZ3059	1972	£1.50	£4
I'm Coming Home	7"	Regal Zonophone	RZ3032	1971	£1.50	£4
Information	12"	Columbia	AS991725	1983	£8	£20	US promo pic disc
Rockpile	LP	Regal Zonophone	SLRZ1026	1971	£10	£25
Rockpile Collection	LP	Regal Zonophone	SRZA8503	1971	£25	£50

EDSELS

Rama Lama Ding Dong	7"	Pye	7N25086	1961	£15	£30

EDWARD BEAR

Bearings	LP	Capitol	ST426	1969	£4	£10

EDWARD H.DAFIS

Ffordd Newydd Eingl-Americanaidd	LP	Sain	1034M	1975	£10	£25
Gret O Fyw						
Hen Ffordd Gymreig O Fyw	LP	Sain	1016M	1974	£17.50	£35
Plant Y Fflam	LP	Sain	1196M	1980	£5	£12
Sneb Yn Becso Dam	LP	Sain	1053M	1976	£8	£20
Yn Erbyn Y Ffactore	LP	Sain	1144M	1979	£5	£12

EDWARDS, BOBBY

You're The Reason	7"	Top Rank	JAR584	1961	£2	£5

EDWARDS, BRENT

Pride	7"	Pye	7N25197	1963	£2	£5

EDWARDS, CHUCK

Downtown Soulville	7"	Soul City	SC104	1968	£4	£8

EDWARDS, GARY

Africa	7"	Oriole	CB1733	1962	£2.50	£6
Hopscotch	7"	Oriole	CB1759	1962	£2.50	£6
Twist Or Bust	7"	Oriole	CB1700	1962	£1.50	£4
Wistful Thinking	7"	Oriole	CB1717	1962	£1.50	£4

EDWARD'S GROUP

Dear Hearts	7"	Island	WI040	1963	£5	£10	Osbourne Graham B side

He Gave You To Me	7"	Island	WI082	1963	£5	£10	
Hey Girl	7"	Island	WI087	1963	£5	£10	
Russian Roulette	7"	Island	WI047	1963	£5	£10	

EDWARDS HAND

Edwards Hand	LP	GRT	10005	1969	£6	£15	US
Rainshine	LP	Regal Zonophone	SRZA8513	1973	£25	£50	
Stranded	LP	RCA	SF8154	1971	£6	£15	

EDWARDS, JACKIE

All My Days	7"	Island	WI008	1962	£5	£10	
Best Of Jackie Edwards	LP	Island	ILP936	1966	£30	£60	
By Demand	LP	Island	ILP940	1966	£30	£60	
By Demand	LP	Trojan	TTL46	1970	£6	£15	
Come Back Girl	7"	Island	WIP6008	1967	£4	£8	
Come On Home	LP	Island	ILP931	1966	£30	£60	
Come On Home	LP	Trojan	TTL45	1970	£6	£15	
Heaven Just Knows	7"	Starlite	ST45046	1961	£6	£12	
He'll Have To Go	7"	Aladdin	WI601	1965	£4	£8	
Hush	7"	Aladdin	WI605	1965	£4	£8	
Hush	7" EP	Island	IEP708	1966	£10	£20	
I Do Love You	LP	Trojan	TRL47	1972	£4	£10	
I Feel So Bad	7"	Island	WI3006	1966	£15	£30	
Julie On My Mind	7"	Island	WIP6026	1968	£4	£8	
Let It Be Me	LP	Direction	863977	1969	£4	£10	
Lonely Game	7"	Decca	F11547	1962	£2.50	£6	
L-O-V-E	7"	Island	WI274	1966	£5	£10	
More Than Words Can Say	7"	Starlite	ST45062	1961	£5	£10	
Most Of Wilfred Jackie Edwards	LP	Island	ILP906	1964	£30	£60	
Most Of Wilfred Jackie Edwards	LP	Trojan	TTL40	1970	£6	£15	
Oh Manio	7"	Direction	584630	1969	£2	£5	
One More Week	7"	Island	WI019	1962	£5	£10	
Only A Fool Breaks His Own Heart	7"	Island	WI3030	1967	£5	£10	
Premature Golden Sands	LP	Island	ILP960/ILPS9060	1967	£30	£60	
Premature Golden Sands	LP	Trojan	TBL156	1970	£5	£12	
Premature Golden Sands	LP	Trojan	TTL57	1970	£6	£15	
Put Your Tears Away	LP	Island	IWPS4	1969	£10	£25	
Royal Telephone	7"	Island	WI3018	1966	£5	£10	
Sacred Songs Vol.1	7" EP	Island	IEP701	1966	£5	£10	no PS
Sacred Songs Vol.2	7" EP	Island	IEP702	1966	£5	£10	no PS
Same One	7"	Aladdin	WI611	1965	£4	£8	
Sea Cruise	7"	Fontana	TF465	1964	£5	£10	
Sometimes	7"	Island	WI270	1966	£5	£10	
Stagger Lee	7"	Sue	WI329	1964	£6	£12	
Stand Up For Jesus	LP	Island	ILP912	1964	£20	£40	
Tell Me Why You Say Goodbye	7"	CBS	5147	1970	£2	£5	
Things You Do	7"	Black Swan	WI416	1964	£5	£10	
Think Twice	7"	Island	WI287	1966	£5	£10	
Too Experienced	7"	Direction	584402	1969	£2	£5	
White Christmas	7"	Island	WI255	1965	£5	£10	
Why Make Believe	7"	Black Swan	WI404	1963	£5	£10	
Why Must I Be Alone	7"	Direction	584096	1969	£2	£5	
You're My Girl	7"	Island	WI3157	1968	£5	£10	
You're My Girl	7"	Island	WIP6042	1968	£4	£8	

EDWARDS, JACKIE & JIMMY CLIFF

Set Me Free	7"	Island	WIP6036	1968	£2.50	£6	

EDWARDS, JACKIE & MILLIE

Best Of Jackie & Millie	LP	Island	ILP963	1968	£30	£60	
Jackie And Millie	LP	Trojan	TBL155	1970	£6	£15	
Pledging My Love	LP	Island	ILP941	1966	£30	£60	

EDWARDS, JIMMY

Love Bug Crawl	7"	Mercury	7MT193	1958	£75	£150	

EDWARDS, NOKIE

Again	LP	Cream	ISP80546	1972	£8	£20	Japanese
King Of Guitars	LP	Stateside	80859	1973	£8	£20	Japanese
Nokie	LP	Cream	CR9006	1971	£4	£10	US
Nokie Edwards	LP	Stateside	97019	1974	£8	£20	Japanese

EDWARDS, RUPIE

Guilty Convict	7"	Blue Beat	BB90	1961	£5	£10	
I Can't Forget	7"	Doctor Bird	DB1163	1968	£5	£10	
Long Lost Love	7"	Crab	CRAB35	1969	£2.50	£6	

EDWARDS, SAMUEL

Israel	7"	Blue Cat	BS159	1969	£4	£8	

EDWARDS, TOM

What Is A Teenage Girl?	7"	Vogue Coral	Q72236	1957	£1.50	£4	

EDWARDS, TOMMY

Baby Let Me Take You Dreaming	7"	MGM	SP1168	1956	£2	£5	
Fool Such As I	7"	MGM	SP1030	1953	£2.50	£6	
For Young Lovers	LP	MGM	C791	1959	£5	£12	
It's All In The Game	LP	MGM	C734	1959	£5	£12	
It's All In The Game	7"	MGM	MGM989	1958	£2	£5	chart singl
I've Been There	7" EP	MGM	MGMEP707	1959	£5	£10	

My Melancholy Baby	7"	MGM	MGM1020	1959	£1.50	£4	chart single
Tommy Edwards	LP	Lion	70120	195-	£6	£15	US
Tommy Edwards Sings	LP	Regent	MG6096	195-	£6	£15	US
Ways Of Love	7" EP.	MGM	MGMEP712	1960	£5	£10	
You Started Me Dreaming	LP	MGM	C824	1960	£6	£15	

EDWARDS, VINCE

Aquarius	7"	United Artists	UP2236	1968	£1.50	£4	
County Durham Dream	7"	United Artists	UP2230	1968	£2	£5	
I Can't Turn Back Time	7"	United Artists	UP1179	1967	£2	£5	
I Like It	7"	United Artists	UP1169	1966	£1.50	£4	
No Not Much	7"	Colpix	PX771	1964	£1.50	£4	
Widget	7"	Capitol	CL14825	1958	£1.50	£4	

EDWARDS, WILFRED & THE CARIBS

Little Bitty Girl	7"	Starlite	ST45076	1962	£5	£10	
Tell Me Darling	7"	Starlite	ST45026	1960	£6	£12	
We're Gonna Love	7"	Starlite	ST45016	1960	£6	£12	

EELA CRAIG

Hats Of Glass	LP	Vertigo	6360638	1977	£10	£25	German
Missa Universalis	LP	Vertigo	6360639	1978	£10	£25	German
One Nighter	LP	Vertigo	6360635	1976	£10	£25	German

E.F. BAND

Night Angel	7"	Aerco	EF1	1980	£2.50	£6	
Self Made Suicide	7"	Redball	RR026	1980	£1.50	£4	

EFENDI'S GARDEN

Efendi's Garden	LP	Babylon	80004	1979	£10	£25	German

EFFIGIES

Haunted Town	12"	Autumn	AU3	1981	£6	£15	

EGANS, WILLIE

Rocks, Boogies And Rolls	LP	Flyright	LP6000	197-	£4	£10	
Willie Egans	7" EP	XX	MIN714	196-	£4	£8	

EGG

The records made by Egg contain the most impressive music of any made by those groups whose dominant voice is that of the keyboards. Organist Dave Stewart has been making records ever since, with Hatfield and the North and other related groups (he's even been in the charts a few times, but not as a member of the Eurythmics!), but he has arguably never bettered the youthful enthusiasm of his work with Egg. The group's music is difficult in places, but only in the same way that Soft Machine's music is. It utilises awkward time signatures and convoluted melody lines, but never forgets its essential function of communicating with an audience.

Civil Surface	LP	Caroline	C1510	1974	£5	£12	
Egg	LP	Nova	SDN14	1970	£6	£15	
Polite Force	LP	Deram	SML1074	1970	£6	£15	
Seven Is A Jolly Good Time	7"	Deram	DM269	1969	£4	£8	

EGGY

You're Still Mine	7"	Spark	SRL1024	1970	£5	£10	

EIGHT-EYED SPY

Diddy Wah Diddy	7"	Fetish	FE19	1982	£2	£5	
Eight-Eyed Spy	LP	Fetish	FR2003	1981	£4	£10	

EIGHTH DAY

Eeny Meeny Miny Mo	7"	Invictus	INV521	1972	£1.50	£4	

EIGHTH WONDER

Baby Baby	12"	CBS	BABEQT1	1988	£6	£15	
I'm Not Scared	CD-s	CBS	SCAREC1	1988	£3	£8	
I'm Not Scared	10"	CBS	SCAREY1	1988	£4	£10	
Stay With Me	12"	CBS	QTX6594	1985	£6	£15	poster PS

EIGHTIES LADIES

Turned On To You	12"	Music Of Life	MOLIF6	1986	£4	£10	

808 STATE

Let Yourself Go	12"	Creed	STATE003	1988	£3	£8	
Newbuild	LP	Creed	STATE002	1988	£6	£15	
Pacific 909	12"	ZTT	ZANG1TX	1989	£2.50	£6	

EILIFF

Eiliff	LP	Philips	6305103	1971	£5	£12	German
Glrlrls	LP	Philips	6305145	1972	£5	£12	German

EIRE APPARENT

Follow Me	7"	Track	604019	1967	£5	£10	
Rock'n'Roll Band	7"	Buddah	201039	1969	£5	£10	
Sunrise	LP	Buddah	203021	1969	£20	£40	

EKSEPTION

3	LP	Philips	6423005	1971	£5	£12	Dutch
4	LP	Philips	6423019	1972	£5	£12	Dutch
5	LP	Philips	6423042	1972	£5	£12	Dutch
Beggar Julia's Time Trip	LP	Philips	6314001	1969	£6	£15	
Ekseption	LP	Philips	6314005	1970	£6	£15	
Trinity	LP	Philips	6423056	1973	£4	£10	Dutch

ELASTIC BAND

Do Unto Others	7"	Decca	F12815	1968	£10	£20	

Expansions On Life	LP	Nova	DN/SND6	1969	£15	£30	
Thinking Of You Baby	7"	Decca	F12763	1968	£10	£20	

ELASTICK BAND
Spazz	7"	Stateside	SS2056	1967	£15	£30	demo

ELBERT, DONNIE
Get Ready	7"	CBS	2807	1967	£2	£5	
In Between The Heartaches	7"	Polydor	56234	1968	£1.50	£4	
Let's Do The Stroll	7"	Parlophone	R4403	1958	£15	£30	
Little Piece Of Leather	7"	Sue	WI377	1965	£6	£12	
Sensational Donnie Elbert Sings	LP	King	629	1959	£30	£60	US
This Old Heart Of Mine	7"	Polydor	56265	1968	£1.50	£4	
Without You	7"	Deram	DM235	1969	£1.50	£4	
You Can Push It Or Pull It	7"	Sue	WI396	1965	£6	£12	

ELCORT
Tammy	7"	Parlophone	R5447	1966	£4	£8	

ELDORADOS
Crazy Little Mama	LP	Vee Jay	VJLP1001	1959	£75	£150	US

ELDORADOS (2)
Eldorados	7" EP	Decca	DFE8543	1963	£7.50	£15	

ELDRIDGE, ROY
Roy And Diz No.2	LP	Columbia	33CX10084	1957	£15	£30	with Dizzy Gillespie
Roy Eldridge	10" LP	Columbia	33C9031	1957	£15	£30	
Roy Eldridge And Dizzy Gillespie	LP	Columbia	33CX10025	1956	£20	£40	
Roy Eldridge Quintet	10" LP	Columbia	33C9005	1955	£20	£40	

ELECAMPANE
Further Adventures Of Mr.Punch	LP	Dame Jane	ODJ2	1978	£10	£25	
When God's On The Water	LP	Dame Jane	ODJ1	1975	£30	£60	

ELECTRIC BANANA
Electric Banana	LP	De Wolfe	DWSLP3040	1967	£8	£20	
Even More Electric Banana	LP	De Wolfe	DWSLP3282	1969	£5	£12	
Hot Licks	LP	De Wolfe	DWSLP3284	1973	£6	£15	
More Electric Banana	LP	De Wolfe	DWSLP3069	1968	£8	£20	
Return Of The Electric Banana	LP	De Wolfe	DWSLP3381	1979	£6	£15	

ELECTRIC CRAYON SET
Hip Shake Junkie	7"	Emergency	MIV3	1989	£4	£8	

ELECTRIC FLAG
At its best, Mike Bloomfield's big band sound marvellous - the driving "Killing Floor" or the long, crafted "Another Country" (both on "A Long Time Comin") - but the Electric Flag's music was extremely uneven. Calling itself An American Music Band, the Electric Flag really wanted to play everything. It would probably have been better, however, if it had not tried to cast its net so wide. As it is, the band seems to lack focus. "Electric Flag" was recorded after many of the original members, including Bloomfield, had left. "The Trip" is a film soundtrack and contains a large number of very short tracks - frustrating.

Electric Flag	LP	CBS	63462	1969	£5	£12	
Groovin' Is Easy	7"	CBS	3584	1968	£4	£8	
Long Time Comin'	LP	CBS	63294	1968	£6	£15	
Sunny	7"	CBS	4066	1969	£4	£8	
Trip	LP	Sidewalk	(S)T5908	1967	£8	£20	US

ELECTRIC JOHNNY
Black Eyes Rock	7"	London	HLU9384	1961	£7.50	£15	

ELECTRIC LIGHT ORCHESTRA
All Over The World	10"	Jet	JET10195	1980	£2.50	£6	blue vinyl
Can't Get It Out Of My Head	7"	Jet	ELO1JB	1977	£4	£8	juke box issue
Discovery	LP	Jet	HZ45769	1981	£5	£12	US audiophile
Eldorado	LP	Jet		1981	£5	£12	US audiophile
Eldorado	LP	Jet	JETLP203	1978	£5	£12	yellow vinyl
Electric Light Orchestra	LP	Harvest	Q4SHVL797	1974	£5	£12	quad
Face The Music	LP	Jet	JETLP201	1978	£6	£15	green vinyl
Four Little Diamonds	12"	Jet	TA3869	1983	£2.50	£6	
Getting To The Point	12"	Epic	QTA7317	1986	£2.50	£6	
Greatest Hits	LP	Jet	HZ46310	1981	£5	£12	US audiophile
Livin' Thing	7"	United Artists	UP36184	1976	£2	£5	blue vinyl
Mr.Blue Sky	7"	Jet	UP36342	1978	£1.50	£4	blue vinyl
New World Record	LP	Jet	JETLP200	1978	£5	£12	red vinyl
Night The Light Went Out In Long Beach	LP	Warner Bros	WBK56058	1974	£5	£12	German
Ole Elo	LP	Jet/United Artists	SP123	1976	£6	£15	US promo, gold vinyl
On The Third Day	LP	Jet	LP202	1978	£5	£12	clear vinyl
Out Of The Blue	LP	Jet	JETDP400	1978	£5	£12	blue vinyl
Roll Over Beethoven	12"	Harvest	PSLP213	1977	£2.50	£6	promo
Roll Over Beethoven/Manhattan Rumble	7"	Harvest	HAR5063	1973	£2	£5	
Secret Messages	LP	Jet	HZ48490	1983	£5	£12	US audiophile
Secret Messages	7"	Jet	PA3720	1983	£1.50	£4	pic disc
Strange Magic	7"	Jet	ELO2JB	1977	£4	£8	juke box issue
Sweet Talking Woman	12"	Jet	SJET12121	1978	£2.50	£6	mauve vinyl
Ticket To The Moon	12"	Jet	JET127018	1981	£2.50	£6	pic disc
Time	LP	Jet	HZ47371	1981	£5	£12	US audiophile
Wild West Hero	12"	Jet	SJET12109	1978	£2.50	£6	yellow vinyl, Jet label
Xanadu	10"	MCA	2315	1980	£75	£150	US promo pic disc

ELECTRIC PRUNES

The Electric Prunes were two groups, both in style and in personnel, for sometime during the recording of "Mass In F Minor" there was a complete change in membership. The 1966-7 releases contain many prime examples of psychedelia, most notably the quartet of singles. "Mass In F Minor", on the other hand, is exactly what it says it is - a rock mass. The album is an interesting and reasonably successful experiment, but it is very short on playing time.

Everybody Knows	7"	Reprise	RS20652	1968	£6	£12	
Get Me To The World On Time	7"	Reprise	RS20564	1967	£5	£10	chart single
Great Banana Hoax	7"	Reprise	RS20607	1967	£6	£12	
I Had Too Much To Dream	LP	Reprise	R(S)6248	1967	£8	£20	US
I Had Too Much To Dream	7"	Reprise	RS20532	1966	£5	£10	chart single
I Had Too Much To Dream	7" EP	Reprise	RVEP60098	1966	£12.50	£25	French
Just Good Old Rock'n'Roll	LP	Reprise	RS6342	1969	£8	£20	US
Long Day's Flight	7"	Reprise	RS23212	1967	£5	£10	
Long Day's Flight	7" EP	Reprise	RVEP60110	1967	£12.50	£25	French
Mass In F Minor	LP	Reprise	R(S)LP6275	1968	£6	£15	
Release Of An Oath	LP	Reprise	R(S)LP6316	1968	£6	£15	
Underground	LP	Reprise	R(S)6262	1967	£15	£30	US

ELECTRIC SANDWICH

Electric Sandwich	LP	Brain	0001018	1972	£25	£50	German

ELECTRIC TOILET

In The Hands Of Karma	LP	Nasco	9004	1970	£35	£70	US
In The Hands Of Karma	LP	Psycho	PSYCHO8	1983	£5	£12	

ELEGANTS

Little Star	7"	HMV	POP520	1958	£7.50	£15	chart single
Please Believe Me	7"	HMV	POP551	1958	£10	£20	

ELEPHANT BAND

Stone Penguin	7"	Mojo	2092036	1972	£2	£5

ELEPHANT'S MEMORY

Elephant's Memory	LP	Apple	SAPCOR22	1972	£6	£15
Power Boogie	7"	Apple	45	1972	£2.50	£6

ELF

Carolina Country Ball	LP	Purple	TPSA3506	1974	£8	£20	
Elf	LP	Epic	KE31789	1972	£8	£20	
Trying To Burn The Sun	LP	MGM	M3G4994	1975	£6	£15	US

ELFENBIEN

Made In Rock	LP	MDM	011246	1977	£6	£15	German

ELGINS

Darling Baby	LP	Tamla Motown	(S)TML11081	1968	£8	£20	
Heaven Must Have Sent You	7"	Tamla Motown	TMG583	1966	£10	£20	
Heaven Must Have Sent You	7"	Tamla Motown	TMG771	1971	£1.50	£4	chart single
It's Been A Long Time	7"	Tamla Motown	TMG615	1967	£7.50	£15	
Put Yourself In My Place	7"	Tamla Motown	TMG551	1966	£12.50	£25	
Put Yourself In My Place	7"	Tamla Motown	TMG642	1968	£2.50	£6	
Put Yourself In My Place	7"	Tamla Motown	TMG787	1971	£1.50	£4	chart single

ELIAS & HIS ZIG ZAG JIVE FLUTES

Tom Hark	7"	Columbia	DB4109	1958	£2	£5	chart single
Zeph Boogie	7"	Columbia	DB4146	1958	£1.50	£4	

ELIAS HULK

Unchained	LP	Youngblood	SSYB8	1970	£75	£150	sleeve pictured in Guide

ELIGIBLES

Faker, Faker	7"	Capitol	CL15067	1959	£1.50	£4
My First Christmas With You	7"	Capitol	CL15098	1959	£1.50	£4

ELIZABETH

Elizabeth	LP	Vanguard	SVRL19010	1968	£6	£15

ELLEDGE, JIMMY

Funny How Time Slips Away	7" EP	RCA	RCX7132	1964	£5	£10
Pink Dally Rue	7"	Hickory	451363	1965	£1.50	£4
Swanee River Rocket	7"	RCA	RCA1274	1962	£2.50	£6

ELLINGTON, DUKE

Anatomy Of A Murder	LP	Philips	BBL7338	1959	£6	£15	
Anatomy Of A Murder	LP	Philips	SBBL514	1960	£6	£15	
At His Very Best	LP	RCA	RD27133	1959	£6	£15	
At Newport	LP	Philips	BBL7133	1957	£6	£15	
At The Bal Masque	LP	Philips	BBL7315/SBBL543	1960	£5	£12	
Back To Back	LP	HMV	CLP1316	1959	£6	£15	with Johnny Hodges
Black, Brown And Beige	LP	Philips	BBL7251/SBBL506	1958	£4	£10	
Blues In Orbit	LP	Philips	BBL7381/SBBL567	1960	£5	£12	
Blues Serenade	10" LP	HMV	DLP1172	1958	£6	£15	
Caravan	7" EP	RCA	RCX1022	1959	£2	£5	
Cosmic Scene	LP	Philips	BBL7287	1959	£8	£20	
Dance To The Duke	7" EP	Capitol	EAP1004	1957	£2	£5	
Dance To The Duke	7" EP	Capitol	EAP1637	1956	£2	£5	
Dance To The Duke No.2	7" EP	Capitol	EAP2637	1956	£2	£5	
Dance To The Duke No.3	7" EP	Capitol	EAP3637	1956	£2	£5	
Drum Is A Woman	LP	Philips	BBL7179	1957	£6	£15	
Duke - 1926	10" LP	London	AL3551	1956	£8	£20	

Title	Format	Label	Catalogue	Year			Notes
Duke Ellington	7" EP	RCA	RCX1006	1958	£2	£5	
Duke Ellington	10" LP	Philips	BBR8060	1955	£10	£25	
Duke Ellington - Betty Roche	7" EP	Philips	BBE12002	1955	£2	£5	
Duke Ellington - Billy Strayhorn	7" EP	Vogue	EPV1051	1955	£2	£5	
Duke Ellington And Al Hibbler	7" EP	HMV	7EG8158	1955	£2	£5	
Duke Ellington And His Orchestra	7" EP	HMV	7EG8033	1954	£2	£5	
Duke Ellington And His Orchestra Vol.1	10" LP	Vogue Coral	LRA10027	1955	£8	£20	
Duke Ellington And His Orchestra Vol.2	10" LP	Vogue Coral	LRA10028	1955	£8	£20	
Duke Ellington And Jimmy Blanton	7" EP	HMV	7EG8189	1956	£2	£5	
Duke Ellington And The Coronets	7" EP	Vogue	EPV1060	1955	£2	£5	
Duke Ellington And The Coronets	10" LP	Vogue	LDE035	1953	£8	£20	
Duke Ellington Orchestra	10" LP	Philips	BBR8086	1956	£10	£25	
Duke Ellington Presents	LP	London	LTZN15078	1957	£6	£15	
Duke Ellington Presents	LP	Parlophone	PMC1136	1961	£5	£12	
Duke Ellington Presents Ivie Anderson	7" EP	HMV	7EG8209	1957	£2	£5	
Duke In London	7" EP	Decca	DFE6376	1957	£2	£5	
Duke Plays Ellington	7" EP	Capitol	EAP1477	1954	£2	£5	
Duke Plays Ellington	10" LP	Capitol	LC6670	1954	£8	£20	
Duke Plays Ellington Part 2	7" EP	Capitol	EAP2477	1954	£2	£5	
Ellington '55	LP	Capitol	LCT6008	1955	£6	£15	
Ellington '55 Part 1	7" EP	Capitol	EAP1521	1955	£2	£5	
Ellington '55 Part 2	7" EP	Capitol	EAP2521	1955	£2	£5	
Ellington '55 Part 3	7" EP	Capitol	EAP3521	1955	£2	£5	
Ellington Highlights, 1940	10" LP	HMV	DLP1034	1954	£8	£20	
Ellington Jazz Party	LP	Philips	BBL7324/SBBL516	1959	£4	£10	
Ellington Showcase	LP	Capitol	T679	1956	£6	£15	
Ellington Sidemen	LP	Philips	BBL7163	1957	£6	£15	
Ellington Uptown	LP	Philips	BBL7003	1954	£6	£15	
Ellington Uptown	LP	Philips	BBL7443	1961	£5	£12	
Ellington's Greatest	10" LP	HMV	DLP1007	1953	£8	£20	
Festival Session	LP	Philips	BBL7355/SBBL556	1960	£5	£12	
Great Ellington Soloists	10" LP	HMV	DLP1025	1954	£8	£20	
Harlem Twist	7" EP	Fontana	TFE17117	1959	£2	£5	
Historically Speaking	LP	Parlophone	PMC1116	1960	£4	£10	
Historically Speaking - The Duke	LP	London	LTZN15029	1957	£6	£15	
In A Mellotone	LP	RCA	RD27134	1959	£6	£15	
Jazz Cocktail	10" LP	Columbia	33S1044	1954	£8	£20	
Masterpieces By Ellington	LP	Columbia	33SX1022	1954	£10	£25	
Mood Ellington	10" LP	Philips	BBR8044	1955	£8	£20	
Newport 1958	LP	Philips	BBL7279	1959	£4	£10	
Newport Jazz Festival	LP	Philips	BBL7152	1957	£6	£15	Side 2 by Buck Clayton
Nutcracker Suite	LP	Philips	BBL7418/SBBL594	1961	£6	£15	
Perfume Suite/Black Brown And Beige	10" LP	HMV	DLP1070	1955	£8	£20	
Piano In THe Background	LP	Philips	BBL7460	1961	£5	£12	
Premiered By Ellington	10" LP	Capitol	LC6616	1953	£8	£20	
Saturday Night Function	10" LP	HMV	DLP1094	1955	£8	£20	
Side By Side	LP	HMV	CLP1374	1961	£6	£15	...with Johnny Hodges
Solitude	LP	Philips	BBL7229	1958	£6	£15	
Such Sweet Thunder	LP	Philips	BBL7203	1958	£6	£15	
Such Sweet Thunder	LP	Realm	RM52421	1967	£5	£12	
Ultra Deluxe	7" EP	Capitol	EAP120114	1961	£2	£5	

ELLINGTON, MARC

Title	Format	Label	Catalogue	Year			
Did You Give The World Some Love	7"	Philips	BF1742	1969	£1.50	£4	
Four In The Morning	7"	Philips	BF1779	1969	£1.50	£4	
I Shall Be Released	7"	Philips	BF1665	1968	£2	£5	
Marc Ellington	LP	Philips	SBL7883	1969	£10	£25	
Marc Time	LP	Xtra	XTRA1154	1972	£6	£15	
Question Of Roads	LP	Philips	6308120	1972	£8	£20	
Rains/Reins Of Change	LP	B&C	CAS193	1971	£8	£20	
Restoration	LP	Philips	6308143	1972	£8	£20	

ELLINGTON, RAY

Title	Format	Label	Catalogue	Year			Notes
ABC Boogie	7"	Columbia	SCM5147	1954	£4	£8	
All's Going Well	7"	Columbia	SCM5088	1954	£1.50	£4	
Charlie Brown	7"	Pye	7N15189	1959	£1.50	£4	
Cloudburst	7"	Columbia	SCM5199	1955	£1.50	£4	
Giddy-Up A Ding Dong	7"	Columbia	DB3838	1956	£4	£8	
Keep That Coffee Hot	7"	Columbia	SCM5274	1956	£1.50	£4	
Ko Ko Mo	7"	Columbia	SCM5177	1955	£4	£8	
Little Red Monkey	7"	Columbia	SCM5050	1953	£1.50	£4	
Long Black Nylons	7"	Columbia	DB4057	1958	£4	£8	
Madison	7"	Ember	EMBS102	1960	£1.50	£4	chart single
Owl Song	7"	Columbia	SCM5104	1954	£1.50	£4	
Play It Boy Play	7"	Columbia	SCM5187	1955	£1.50	£4	
Stranded In The Jungle	7"	Columbia	DB3821	1956	£4	£8	
Swaller-Tail Coat	7"	Columbia	DB4013	1957	£1.50	£4	
That Rock'n'Rollin' Man	7"	Columbia	DB3905	1957	£4	£8	
Who's Got The Money?	7"	Columbia	SCM5250	1956	£1.50	£4	

ELLIOT, DEREK & DOROTHY

Title	Format	Label	Catalogue	Year			
Derek And Dorothy Elliot	LP	Trailer	LER2023	1972	£5	£12	
Yorkshire Relish	LP	Tradition	TSR025	1976	£5	£12	

ELLIOT, JACK

Title	Format	Label	Catalogue	Year			
Jack Elliot Of Birtley	LP	Leader	LER4001	1969	£5	£12	

ELLIOTS OF BIRTLEY

Title	Format	Label	Cat No	Year			Notes
Elliots Of Birtley	LP	Folkways	FG3565	1961	£10	£25	US
Musical Portrait Of A Durham Mining Family	LP	XTRA	XTRA1091	1969	£6	£15	

ELLIOTT, BERN

Title	Format	Label	Cat No	Year			Notes
Guess Who	7"	Decca	F12051	1965	£2.50	£6	
Voodoo Woman	7"	Decca	F12171	1965	£2	£5	

ELLIOTT, BERN & THE CLAN

Title	Format	Label	Cat No	Year			Notes
Good Times	7"	Decca	F11970	1964	£2.50	£6	

ELLIOTT, BERN & THE FENMEN

Title	Format	Label	Cat No	Year			Notes
Bern Elliott & The Fenmen Play	7" EP	Decca	DFE8561	1964	£10	£20	
Money	7"	Decca	F11770	1963	£2	£5	chart single
New Orleans	7"	Decca	F11852	1964	£2	£5	chart single

ELLIOTT, BILL & ELASTIC OZ BAND

Title	Format	Label	Cat No	Year			Notes
God Save Us	7"	Apple	36	1971	£2.50	£6	
God Save Us	7"	Apple	36	1971	£7.50	£15	PS

ELLIOTT, DON

Title	Format	Label	Cat No	Year			Notes
Don Elliott	10" LP	London	LZN14037	1957	£4	£10	
Don Elliott And His Choir	LP	Brunswick	LAT8263	1958	£4	£10	
Musical Offering	LP	HMV	CLP1186	1958	£4	£10	
Six Valves	10" LP	London	LZU14034	1956	£15	£30	with Rusty Dedrick

ELLIOTT, MARI

Title	Format	Label	Cat No	Year			Notes
Silly Billy	7"	GTO	GT58	1976	£5	£10	

ELLIOTT, PETER

Title	Format	Label	Cat No	Year			Notes
Devotion	7"	Parlophone	R4457	1958	£1.50	£4	
To The Aisle	7"	Parlophone	R4355	1957	£1.50	£4	

ELLIOTT, RAMBLING JACK

Title	Format	Label	Cat No	Year			Notes
Blues And Country	7" EP	Collector	JEA6	1964	£4	£8	
Bull Durham Sacks And Railroad Tracks	LP	Reprise	RSLP6387	1970	£5	£12	
Country Style	LP	Stateside	SL10143	1965	£5	£12	
In London	LP	Columbia	33SX1166	1959	£10	£25	
In London	LP	Encore	ENC194	196-	£8	£20	
Jack Elliott	LP	Fontana	TFL6044	1965	£5	£12	
Jack Takes The Floor	10" LP	Topic	10T15	1958	£10	£25	
Kids Stuff	7" EP	Columbia	SEG8046	1960	£2	£5	
More Pretty Girls	7"	Fontana	TF575	1965	£1.50	£4	
Rambling Jack Elliott	LP	Vanguard		1964	£5	£12	US
Rambling Jack Elliott	7" EP	Collector	JEA5	1963	£4	£8	
Rusty Jigs And Sandy Sam	7"	Columbia	DB7593	1965	£1.50	£4	
Sings	LP	Columbia	33SX1291	1961	£8	£20	
Sings The Songs Of Woody Guthrie	LP	Stateside	SL10167	1966	£5	£12	
Talking Woody Guthrie	LP	Topic	12T93	1963	£6	£15	
Woody Guthrie's Blues	8" LP	Topic	T5	195-	£10	£25	

ELLIOTT, RON

Title	Format	Label	Cat No	Year			Notes
Candlestick Maker	LP	Warner Bros	WS1833	1969	£6	£15	US

ELLIOTT, SHAWN

Title	Format	Label	Cat No	Year			Notes
My Girl	7"	Columbia	DB7418	1964	£1.50	£4	

ELLIS, ALTON

Title	Format	Label	Cat No	Year			Notes
Ain't That Loving You	7"	Treasure Isle	TI7016	1967	£5	£10	Tommy McCook B side
Ain't That Loving You	7"	Trojan	TR004	1967	£5	£10	Tommy McCook B side
Better Example	7"	Bamboo	BAM2	1969	£2.50	£6	Duke Morgan B side
Blessings Of Love	7"	Doctor Bird	DB1044	1966	£5	£10	
Breaking Up	7"	Trojan	TR642	1968	£4	£8	
Bye Bye Love	7"	Nu Beat	NB013	1968	£4	£8	Monty Morris B side
Change Of Plans	7"	Studio One	SO2084	1969	£6	£12	Cables B side
Cry Tough	7"	Island	WI3046	1967	£5	£10	Tommy McCook B side
Dance Crasher	7"	Island	WI239	1965	£5	£10	Baba Brooks B side
Diana	7"	Duke	DU14	1969	£2.50	£6	
Diana	7"	Gas	GAS105	1969	£2.50	£6	
Don't Gamble With Love	7"	Island	WI230	1965	£5	£10	
Duke Of Earl	7"	Treasure Isle	TI7010	1967	£5	£10	
Easy Squeeze	7"	Studio One	SO2003	1967	£6	£12	Mr.Foundation B side
Fool	7"	Coxsone	CS7071	1968	£5	£10	Soul Vendors B side
Girl I've Got A Date	7"	Doctor Bird	DB1059	1966	£5	£10	Lyn Taitt & Tommy McCook B side
Greatest Hits	LP	Count Shelly	SSLO02	1973	£8	£20	
I Am Just A Guy	7"	Studio One	SO2028	1967	£6	£12	Soul Vendors B side
I Am Still In Love	7"	Studio One	SO2020	1967	£6	£12	Roy Richards B side
I Can't Stand It	7"	Nu Beat	NB010	1968	£4	£8	
I Can't Stand It	7"	Trojan	TR630	1968	£4	£8	
Laba Laba Reggae	7"	Trojan	TR634	1968	£4	£8	
La-La Means I Love You	7"	Nu Beat	NB014	1968	£4	£8	
Live And Learn	7"	Studio One	SO2037	1968	£6	£12	Heptones B side
Message	7"	Pama	PM707	1968	£4	£8	
Mr.Soul Of Jamaica	LP	Treasure Isle	013	196-	£40	£80	

My Time Is The Right Time	7"	Pama	PM717	1968	£4	£8	Johnny Moore B side
Oowee Baby	7"	Treasure Isle	TI7030	1968	£5	£10	
Preacher	7"	Doctor Bird	DB1049	1966	£5	£10	Lyn Taitt B side
Rock Steady	7"	Treasure Isle	TI7004	1967	£5	£10	Tommy McCook B side
Shake It	7"	Doctor Bird	DB1055	1966	£5	£10	Silvertones B side
Sings Rock And Soul	LP	Coxsone	CSL8008	1967	£50	£100	
Sunday Coming	LP	Bamboo	BDLPS214	1971	£10	£25	
What Does It Take	7"	Duke Reid	DR2501	1970	£2.50	£6	Tommy McCook B side
Willow Tree	7"	Treasure Isle	TI7044	1968	£5	£10	Tommy
Wise Birds Follow Spring	7"	Trojan	TR009	1967	£5	£10	McCook B side
You Made Me So Very Happy	7"	Duke Reid	DR2512	1970	£2.50	£6	Tommy McCook B side

ELLIS, BOBBY

Dollar A Head	7"	Island	WI3136	1968	£5	£10	Rudy Mills B side
Emperor	7"	Island	WI3089	1967	£5	£10	Derrick Harriott B side
Feeling Peckish	7"	Island	WI3091	1967	£5	£10	Keith & Tex B side
Now We Know	7"	Island	WI3092	1967	£5	£10	Rudy Mills B side
Shuntin'	7"	Island	WI3135	1968	£5	£10	Derrick Harriott B side

ELLIS, DON

Don Ellis' updating of the big band sound won many fans from the progressive rock genre, who could readily appreciate Ellis' musical games with unusual time signatures as well the electronics he introduced via his specially built four-valve amplified trumpet. "Autumn" was produced by Al Kooper, who must have realised that his own big band experiments with Blood, Sweat And Tears were made to sound a little ordinary by comparison. Drummer Ralph Humphrey went from Don Ellis to the only other band that could possibly provide him with the same rhythmic challenge - that of Frank Zappa.

Autumn	LP	CBS	63503	1968	£5	£12	
Don Ellis Orchestra Live	LP	Liberty	LBL/LBS83060	1968	£6	£15	
Electric Bath	LP	CBS	63230	1968	£5	£12	
Goes Underground	LP	CBS	63680	1969	£4	£10	
Live At Monterey	LP	Fontana	(S)TL5426	1967	£6	£15	
Live At The Fillmore	LP	CBS	66261	1969	£6	£15	double
Shock Treatment	LP	CBS	63356	1968	£5	£12	

ELLIS, HERB

Herb Ellis	LP	Columbia	33CX10066	1957	£6	£15
Meets Jimmy Giuffre	LP	HMV	CLP1337	1960	£5	£12
Nothing But The Blues	LP	Columbia	33CX10139	1959	£6	£15

ELLIS, HORTENSE

Groovy Kind Of Love	7"	Coxsone	CS7033	1968	£5	£10	Three Tops B side
I'll Come Softly	7"	R&B	JB101	1963	£5	£10	
I've Been A Fool	7"	Blue Beat	BB295	1964	£5	£10	
Midnight Train	7"	Blue Beat	BB119	1962	£5	£10	Duke Reid B side

ELLIS, JIMMY

Ellis Sings Elvis By Request	LP	Boblo	78829		£8	£20	US

ELLIS, LARRY

Nothing You Can Do	7"	Felsted	AF110	1958	£2.50	£6

ELLIS, MATTHEW

Am I	LP	Regal Zonophone	SRZA8505	1971	£8	£20
Matthew Ellis	LP	Regal Zonophone	SRZA8501	1971	£5	£12

ELLIS, SHIRLEY

Clapping Song	7"	London	HLR9961	1965	£2	£5	chart single
Ever See A Diver Kiss His Wife	7"	London	HLR10021	1966	£1.50	£4	
In Action	LP	Congress	CGL/CGS3002	1964	£6	£15	US
Name Game	LP	Congress	CGL/CGS3003	1965	£6	£15	US
Name Game	7"	London	HLR9946	1965	£1.50	£4	
Nitty Gritty	7"	London	HLR9824	1963	£2	£5	
Puzzle Song	7"	London	HLR9973	1965	£1.50	£4	
Soul Time	LP	CBS	(S)BPG63044	1967	£6	£15	
Soul Time	7"	CBS	202606	1967	£5	£10	
Sugar Let's Shing A Ling	7"	CBS	2817	1967	£4	£8	
Sugar, Let's Shing A Ling	LP	Columbia	CL2679/CS9479	1967	£6	£15	US

ELLISON, ANDY

Been A Long Time	7"	Track	604018	1967	£15	£30	John's Children B side
Fool From Upper Eden	7"	CBS	3357	1968	£20	£40	
You Can't Do That	7"	SNB	553308	1968	£20	£40	

ELLISON, LORRAINE

Call Me Any Time You Need Some Lovin'	7"	Mercury	6052073	1971	£4	£8
Stay With Me	LP	Warner Bros	WB1821	1970	£6	£15
Stay With Me	7"	Warner Bros	WB5850	1966	£2	£6
Try A Little Bit Harder	7"	Warner Bros	WB2094	1968	£2.50	£6
You've Really Got A Hold On Me	7"	Warner Bros	WB7394	1970	£1.50	£4

ELMER GANTRY'S VELVET OPERA

Elmer Gantry's Velvet Opera	LP	Direction	863300	1968	£20	£40
Flames	7"	Direction	583083	1967	£2.50	£6
Mary Jane	7"	Direction	583481	1968	£2.50	£6

Volcano	7"	Direction	583924	1969	£2.50	£6	

ELOY
Eloy	LP	Philips		1971	£60	£120	bin cover
Inside	LP	Electrola	1C06429479	1973	£4	£10	German
Planets	LP	Heavy Metal	HMIPD1	1982	£4	£10	pic disc

ELROY, JEFF & THE BLUE BOYS
Honey Machine	7"	Philips	BF1533	1966	£6	£12	

ELVES
Amber Velvet	7"	MCA	MU1114	1970	£4	£8	

ELVIN, LEE & JAY
So The Story Goes	7"	Fontana	H191	1959	£1.50	£4	

EMANON
Raging Pain	7"	Clubland	SJP777	1977	£2	£5	

EMBERS
Chelsea Boots	7"	Decca	F11625	1963	£2	£5	

EMBERS (2)
Rock And Roll Eleven	LP	JCP Recording	2006		£37.50	£75	US

EMBRYO
Apo Calypso	LP	April	0010	1977	£4	£10	German
Bad Heads And Bad Cats	LP	April	005	1976	£4	£10	German
Embryo's Rache	LP	United Artists	UAS29239	1971	£15	£30	German
Father, Son And Holy Ghost	LP	United Artists	UAS29344	1972	£6	£15	German
Live	LP	April	003	1976	£4	£10	German
Opal	LP	Ohr	OMM56003	1970	£20	£40	German
Rock Session	LP	Brain	0001036	1973	£6	£15	German
Steig Aus	LP	Brain	0001023	1973	£6	£15	German
Surfin'	LP	BASF	223853	1975	£4	£10	German
We Keep On	LP	BASF	218651	1974	£4	£10	German

EMERALDS
Don't Listen To Your Friends	7"	Decca	F12096	1965	£1.50	£4	
King Lonely The Blue	7"	Decca	F12304	1965	£10	£20	

EMERALDS (2)
Sitting Bull	7"	London	HL9839	1964	£1.50	£4	

EMERGENCY
Emergency	LP	CBS	64381	1971	£5	£12	German
Entrance	LP	CBS	64928	1972	£4	£10	German
Get To The Country	LP	Brain	0001037	1973	£4	£10	German
Gold Rock	LP	Brain	201104	1973	£4	£10	German
No Compromise	LP	Brain	0001052	1974	£4	£10	German

EMERSON, LAKE & PALMER
Fanfare For The Common Man	12"	Atlantic	K10946T	1977	£4	£10	
Pictures At An Exhibition	LP	Mobile Fidelity	MFSL1031	1979	£6	£15	US audiophile
Works Volume One	LP	Atlantic		1976	£5	£12	promo

EMILY
Old Stone Bridge	7"	Big Fun	001	1987	£1.50	£4	flexi
Old Stone Bridge	7"	Sha La La	007	198-	£1.50	£4	flexi, B side
							by Remember Fun

EMLYN, ENDAF
Hiraeth	LP	Wren	WRL537	1972	£20	£40	
Salem	LP	Sain	1012M	1974	£8	£20	
Syrffio (Mewn Cariad)	LP	Sain	1051M	1976	£6	£15	

EMMET SPICELAND
Emmet Spiceland	LP	Page One	POLS011	1968	£30	£60	
Emmet Spiceland Album	LP	Hawk	HALP166	1977	£25	£50	Irish
Lowlands	7"	Page One	POF089	1968	£1.50	£4	
So Long Marianne	7"	Page One	POF143	1969	£4	£8	

EMMETT
Baby Ain't No Lie	7"	Columbia	DB7582	1965	£2	£5	
Nancy	7"	Columbia	DB7695	1965	£2	£5	

EMOTIONS
Come Dance Baby	7"	London	HLR9640	1962	£4	£8	
Love	7"	London	HLR9701	1963	£4	£8	
So I Can Love You	7"	Stax	STAX123	1969	£1.50	£4	
Somebody New	7"	Deep Soul	DS9104	1970	£2.50	£6	
Story Untold	7"	Stateside	SS237	1963	£2.50	£6	

EMOTIONS (2)
Careless Hands	7"	Caltone	TONE120	1968	£4	£8	
Rainbow	7"	Caltone	TONE100	1967	£4	£8	
Rudeboy Confession	7"	Ska Beat	JB263	1966	£5	£10	
Rumbay	7"	High Note	HS026	1969	£2.50	£6	
Soulful Music	7"	Caltone	TONE118	1968	£4	£8	
Storm	7"	High Note	HS018	1969	£2.50	£6	

EMPERORS

Karate	7"	Pama	PM786	1969 ...	£1.50	£4	
Karate	7"	Stateside	SS565	1966 ...	£4	£8	

EMTIDI

Emtidi	LP	Thorofon	ATH109	1970 ...	£50	£100	German
Saat	LP	Pilz	2029077	1972 ...	£25	£50	German

ENCHANTED FOREST

You're Never Gonna Get My Lovin'	7"	Stateside	SS2080	1968 ...	£1.50	£4

ENCHANTERS

We Got Love	7"	Warner Bros	WB2054	1967 ...	£2.50	£6

END

The End were managed and produced by Bill Wyman, but his patronage brought them little success. A change of name to Tucky Buzzard brought more recordings in the seventies, but only a small increase in sales.

I Can't Get Any Joy	7"	Philips	BF1444	1965 ...	£4	£8
Introspection	LP	Decca	LK/SKL5015	1969 ...	£25	£50
Shades Of Orange	7"	Decca	F12750	1968 ...	£6	£12

ENDEVERS

Remember When We Were Young	7"	Decca	F12817	1968 ...	£1.50	£4
She's My Girl	7"	Decca	F12859	1968 ...	£1.50	£4
Sunny And Me	7"	Decca	F12939	1969 ...	£1.50	£4

ENDLE ST.CLOUD

Thank You All Very Much	LP	International Artists	IALP12	1970 ...	£10	£25

ENDSLEY, MELVIN

I Got A Feeling	7"	RCA	RCA1051	1958 ...	£7.50	£15
I Like Your Kind Of Love	7"	RCA	RCA1004	1957 ...	£10	£20

ENEVOLDSEN, BOB

Bob Enevoldsen Quintet	10" LP	London	LZU14035	1956 ...	£20	£40

ENFORCERS

Musical Fever	7"	Blue Cat	BS120	1968 ...	£4	£8	Ed Nangle B side

ENGEL, SCOTT

Charlie Bop	7"	Vogue	V9150	1959 ...	£30	£60
Living End	7"	Vogue	V9145	1959 ...	£40	£80
Paper Doll	7"	Vogue	V9125	1958 ...	£30	£60
Scott Engel	7" EP	Liberty	LEP2261	1966 ...	£7.50	£15

ENGEL, SCOTT & JOHN STEWART

I Only Came To Dance With You	LP	Tower	ST5026	1965 ...	£10	£25	US
I Only Came To Dance With You	7"	Capitol	CL15440	1966 ...	£2.50	£6	

ENGLAND

England	LP	Deroy	DER1356	1976 ...	£150	£250
Garden Shed	LP	Arista	ARTY153	1977 ...	£15	£30

ENGLAND SISTERS

Heartbeat	7"	HMV	POP710	1960 ...	£7.50	£15	chart single

ENGLAND'S GLORY

England's Glory	LP	private		1973 ...	£60	£120

ENGLEBERG, FRED

Songs Of Fred Engleberg	LP	Elektra	EKL247	1964 ...	£6	£15	US

ENGLISH, JOE

Lay Lady Lay	7"	Fontana	TF1034	1969 ...	£1.50	£4

ENID

And Then There Were None	12"	EMI	12EMI5505	1984 ...	£2.50	£6	
Dambusters March	7"	Pye	7P106	1979 ...	£5	£10	
Fand	LP	Enid	ENID9	1985 ...	£4	£10	
Fool	7"	Pye	7P187	1980 ...	£4	£8	
Golden Earrings	7"	EMI	EMI5109	1980 ...	£4	£8	
Golden Earrings	7"	EMI	INTS540	1977 ...	£5	£10	
Heigh Ho	7"	Bronze	BRO134	1981 ...	£4	£8	
In The Region Of The Summer Stars	LP	Buk	BULP2014	1977 ...	£4	£10	Decca distribution
Itchycoo Park	7"	Sedition	EDIT3314	1986 ...	£2.50	£6	
Itchycoo Park	12"	Sedition	EDITL3314	1986 ...	£2.50	£6	
Jubilee	7"	EMI	INT534	1977 ...	£5	£10	
Live At Hammersmith Vol.1	LP	Enid	ENID1	1984 ...	£4	£10	
Live At Hammersmith Vol.2	LP	Enid	ENID2	1984 ...	£4	£10	
Liverpool Album	LP	The Stand	LE1	198- ...	£4	£10	
Lovers	7"	Buk	BUK3002	1976 ...	£5	£10	
Salome	LP	Enid	ENID4	1986 ...	£4	£10	
Six Pieces	LP	Enid	ENID10	1984 ...	£4	£10	
Six Pieces	LP	Pye	NH116	1979 ...	£4	£10	
Spell	LP	Enid	ENID8	1984 ...	£4	£10	2 x 45rpm discs
The Stand	LP	The Stand	THESTAND1	1983 ...	£10	£25	
The Stand 2	LP	The Stand	STAND2	1985 ...	£10	£25	
Then There Were None	7"	Rak	RAK349	1982 ...	£4	£8	
Touch Me	LP	Enid	ENID5	1984 ...	£4	£10	
When You Wish Upon A Star	7"	Bronze	BRO127	1981 ...	£4	£8	

ENJAYS
All My Love All My Life .... 7" ...... Top Rank .... JAR145................. 1959 ... £2.50 ....£6 ....

ENNIS, RAY & THE BLUE JEANS
What Have They Done To Hazel .... 7" ...... Columbia .... DB8431................. 1968 ... £7.50 ....£15 ....

ENNIS, SEAMUS
Bonnie Bunch Of Roses	.... LP ..... Tradition........ TLP1013 .... 1959 ... £10 ....£25 ....
Bonnie Bunch Of Roses .... LP ..... Tradition........ TLP1013 .... 1959 ... £10 ....£25 ....
Feidlim Tonn Ri's Castle .... LP ..... Claddagh........ CC19 .... 1977 ... £6 ....£15 .... Irish
Forty Years Of Irish Piping .... LP ..... Free Reed .... FR001/2 .... 1976 ... £15 ....£30 .... Double
Fox Chase .... LP ..... Tara................ 1009 .... 1977 ... £6 ....£15 .... Irish
Irish Pipe And Tin Whistle Songs .... LP ..... Olympic......... ALTLAS6129 .... 1976 ... £6 ....£15 .... US
Masters Of Irish Music .... LP ..... Leader............. LEA2003 .... 1969 ... £8 ....£20 ....
Pure Drop .... LP ..... Tara................ 1002 .... 1973 ... £6 ....£15 .... Irish
Wandering Minstrel .... LP ..... Topic.............. 12TS250 .... 1974 ... £6 ....£15 ....

ENO, BRIAN
When his task was to make some sense of the controls of a distinctly non-user-friendly synthesizer, as a member of Roxy Music, Brian Eno always used to describe himself as a non-musician. If this was in any way an accurate description, then the lack of preconceptions has clearly been an advantage for Eno, for his solo career has been distinguished by some very interesting ideas. The novelty of his approach is typified by his experiments with creative musak - what he calls "ambient" music - where the listener is not intended to listen at all closely. Eno's career has thrown up one ultra-rarity: an early, alternative version of his "Music For Films" LP, which was limited to around a hundred copies.
Before And After Science .... LP ..... Polydor .... 2302071 .... 1977 ... £4 ....£10 ....with 4 prints
Discreet Music .... LP ..... Obscure .... OBS3 .... 1975 ... £4 ....£10 ....
Music For Films .... LP ..... Editions EG.... EGM1 .... 1976 ... £100 ....£200 .... different tracks
to '78 issue, sleeve
pictured in Guide

ENOS & SHEILA
La La Bamba .... 7" .... Blue Cat .... BS135 .... 1968 ... £4 ....£8 ....
Tonight You're Mine .... 7" .... Blue Cat .... BS138 .... 1968 ... £4 ....£8 ....

ENTICERS
Calling For Your Love .... 7" .... Atlantic .... 2091136.............. 1971 ... £2.50 ....£6 ....

ENTWISTLE, JOHN
Backtrack 14 (The Ox) .... LP ..... Track .... 2407014.............. 1971 ... £6 ....£15 ....
Rigor Mortis Sets In .... LP ..... Track .... 2406106.............. 1973 ... £5 ....£12 ....
Too Late The Hero .... 7" .... WEA .... K79249P .... 1981 ... £2 ....£5 . autographed pic disc

ENYA
I Want Tomorrow .... CD-s .. BBC .... CDRSL201 .... 1987 ... £6 ....£15 ....

EPICS
Henry Long .... 7" .... CBS .... 3564 .... 1968 ... £2.50 ....£6 ....
How Wrong Can You Be .... 7" .... Pye .... 7N17053.............. 1966 ... £2 ....£5 ....
There's No Pleasing You .... 7" .... Pye .... 7N15829.............. 1965 ... £2 ....£5 ....

EPIDERMIS
Genius Of Original Force .... LP ..... Kerston .... FK65063 .... 1977 ... £8 ....£20 ....German

EPILEPTICS
1970s Have Been Made In Hong Kong . 7" .... Stortbeat .... BEAT8 .... 1979 ... £1.50 ....£4 ....

EPISODE SIX
Episode Six's pleasant but undistinguished harmony music would be very much less collectable were it not for the fact that the group's vocalist was Ian Gillan (and the bass player was Roger Glover), although the likes of "Here There And Everywhere" are light years away from the dynamism of Deep Purple's "Sweet Child In Time" and "Speed King".
.... 7" EP. .... 196- ... £120 ....£220 .... Portuguese
Here There And Everywhere .... 7" EP.. Pye .... PNV24175 .... 1966 ... £120 ....£220 ....French
Here, There, And Everywhere .... 7" .... Pye .... 7N17147.............. 1966 ... £5 ....£10 ....
I Can See Through You .... 7" .... Pye .... 7N17376.............. 1967 ... £5 ....£10 ....
I Hear Trumpets Blow .... 7" .... Pye .... 7N17110.............. 1966 ... £5 ....£10 ....
I Will Warm Your Heart .... 7" .... Pye .... 7N17194.............. 1966 ... £10 ....£20 .... with Sheila Carter
Little One .... 7" .... MGM .... MGM1409 .... 1968 ... £10 ....£20 ....
Love, Hate, Revenge .... 7" .... Pye .... 7N17244.............. 1967 ... £7.50 ....£15 ....
Lucky Sunday .... 7" .... Chapter One ... CH103 .... 1968 ... £6 ....£12 ....
Morning Dew .... 7" .... Pye .... 7N17330.............. 1967 ... £6 ....£10 ....
Mozart Versus The Rest .... 7" .... Chapter One ... CH104 .... 1969 ... £6 ....£12 ....
Put Yourself In My Place .... 7" .... Pye .... 7N17018.............. 1966 ... £6 ....£12 ....

EPITAPH
Epitaph .... LP ..... Polydor .... 2371225 .... 1971 ... £6 ....£15 ....German
Outside The Law .... LP ..... Brain .... 221311................ 1974 ... £6 ....£15 ....German
Stop, Look And Listen .... LP ..... Polydor .... 2371274.............. 1972 ... £6 ....£15 ....German

EPPERSON, MINNIE
Grab Your Clothes .... 7" .... Action .... ACT4503 .... 1968 ... £2.50 ....£6 ....

EPPS, PRESTON
Bongo Bongo Bongo .... LP ..... Original Sound (S)8851 .... 1960 ... £6 ....£15 .... US
Bongo Bongo Bongo .... 7" .... Top Rank .... JAR413................ 1960 ... £1.50 ....£4 ....
Bongo Boogie .... 7" .... Top Rank .... JAR345................ 1960 ... £1.50 ....£4 ....
Bongo In Pastel .... 7" .... Top Rank .... JAR180................ 1959 ... £1.50 ....£4 ....
Bongo Rock .... 7" .... Top Rank .... JAR140................ 1959 ... £4 ....£8 ....
Bongola .... 7" .... Top Rank .... JAR522................ 1960 ... £1.50 ....£4 ....
Surfin' Bongos .... LP ..... Original Sound (S)8872 .... 1963 ... £5 ....£12 .... US

EPPS, PRESTON & SANDY NELSON
Rushing For Percussion .... 7" EP.. Top Rank .... JKP2060 .... 1960 ... £6 ....£12 ....

EPSILON

Epsilon	LP	Bacillus	BLPS19070	1971	£5	£12	German
Move On	LP	Bacillus	BLPS19078	1972	£5	£12	German
Off	LP	Philips	6305216	1974	£4	£10	German

EQUALS

Baby Come Back	7"	President	PT135	1968	£1.50	£4	chart single
Baby Come Back	7" EP	President	PTE1	1968	£2.50	£6	
Black Skin Blue Eyed Boys	7"	President	PT325	1970	£1.50	£4	chart single
Equals	7" EP	President	PTE2	1969	£2	£5	
I Can See But You Don't Know	7"	President	PT303	1970	£4	£8	
Unequalled	LP	President	PTL1006	1967	£4	£10	chart LP
Viva Bobby Joe	7"	President	PT260	1969	£1.50	£4	chart single

EQUATIONS

Waiting On The Shores Of Nowhere	7"	Fontana	TF1035	1969	£1.50	£4

EQUINOX

Hard Rock	LP	Boulevard	4118	1973	£6	£15

EQUIPPE 84

Auschwitz	7"	Major Minor	MM517	1967	£7.50	£15

ERASURE

Abbaesque (Club Mixes)	12"	Mute	ERAS4	1992	£6	£15	promo
Blue Savannah (Der Deutsche Mixes)	12"	Mute	XL12MUTE109	1990	£4	£10	promo
Blue Savannah (Deutsch Mix Part 1)	12"	Mute	P12MUTE109	1990	£2.50	£6	promo
Chains Of Love (Marx Brothers & Foghorn Mixes)	12"	Mute	D12MUTE83	1988	£2.50	£6	promo
Circus (Live In Hamburg)	LP	Mute	LIVE1	1987	£5	£12	promo
Circus (Two Ring Edition)	12"	Mute	LSTUMM35	1987	£6	£15	double promo sampler with card & gift label, 6'x3' sleeve
Crackers International Part II: Stop (Remix)	CD-s	Mute	LCDMUTE93	1988	£4	£10	
Drama (Act 2)	12"	Mute	P12MUTE89	1989	£2.50	£6	promo
Heavenly Action	12"	Mute	D12MUTE42	1985	£20	£40	double
Heavenly Action (Yellow Brick Mix)	12"	Mute	L12MUTE42	1985	£30	£60	
It Doesn't Have To Be This Way	CD-s	Mute	CDMUTE56	1987	£5	£8	
Little Respect	CD-s	Mute	LCDMUTE85	1988	£2.50	£6	
Little Respect (Big Train Mix)	12"	Mute	L12MUTE85	1988	£2.50	£6	
Oh L'Amour	7"	Mute	MUTE45	1986	£2.50	£6	Thomas The Tank Engine PS
Oh L'Amour	12"	Mute	12MUTE45	1986	£8	£20	blue vinyl promo
Oh L'Amour (Funky Sisters Mix)	12"	Mute	L12MUTE45	1986	£6	£15	
Oh L'Amour (remix)	12"	Mute	12MUTE45	1986	£8	£20	Thomas The Tank Engine PS
Push Me Shove Me (Moonbeam Mix)	12"	Mute	ERAS1	1990	£8	£20	promo
Ship Of Fools (Orbital Mix)	12"	Mute	ERAS2	1990	£8	£20	promo
Ship Of Fools (Stephen Hague Remix)	12"	Mute	D12MUTE74	1988	£2.50	£6	promo
Sometimes (Danny Rampling Mix)	12"	Mute	ERAS3	1990	£8	£20	promo
Sometimes (Shiver Mix)	12"	Mute	L12MUTE51	1986	£2.50	£6	
Star (Mark Saunders Mix)	12"	Mute	P12MUTE111	1990	£2.50	£6	promo
Stop	7"	Mute	DJMUTE93	1988	£2.50	£6	promo
Stop	12"	Mute	P12MUTE93	1988	£2.50	£6	promo
Supernature (Daniel Miller & Phil Legg Mix)	12"	Mute	XL12MUTE99	1990	£4	£10	with outer envelope
Who Needs Love Like That (Mexican Mix)	12"	Mute	L12MUTE40	1985	£17.50	£35	
You Surround Me	CD-s	Mute	LCDMUTE99	1989	£2.50	£6	
You Surround Me (Remix)	12"	Mute	P12MUTE99	1989	£2.50	£6	promo
You Surround Me (Syrinx Mix)	12"	Mute	S12MUTE99	1989	£2.50	£6	promo

ERICKSON, ROKY

Beauty And The Beast	LP	One Big Guitar	OBG9003	1987	£8	£20	test pressing only

ERICSON, ROLF

Transatlantic Wail	LP	Nixa	NJL5	1957	£6	£15

EROC

Eroc	LP	Brain	0001069	1975	£4	£10	German
Zwei	LP	Brain	0060007	1976	£4	£10	German

ERROL & HIS GROUP

Gypsy	7"	Blue Beat	BB284	1964	£5	£10

ERVIN, BOOKER

In Between	LP	Blue Note	BST84283	1969	£10	£25

ERWIN, BLUEGRASS

I Won't Cry Alone	7"	Top Rank	JAR252	1959	£1.50	£4

ERWIN, PEE WEE

Oh Play That Thing!	LP	London	LTZT15153/ SAH6011	1959	£4	£10

ESCORTS

C'mon Home Baby	7"	Fontana	TF570	1965	£5	£10	
Dizzie Miss Lizzie	7"	Fontana	TF453	1964	£4	£8	
From Head To Toe	7"	Columbia	DB8061	1966	£10	£20	
I Can Tell	7"	Lyntone	LYN509	1964	£6	£12	flexi, Lance Harvey B side

Title	Format	Label	Cat No	Year	Low	High	Notes
I Don't Want To Go On Without You	7"	Fontana	TF516	1964	£4	£8	
Let It Be Me	7"	Fontana	TF651	1966	£5	£10	
One To Cry	7"	Fontana	TF474	1964	£2.50	£6	chart single

ESCORTS (2)
Title	Format	Label	Cat No	Year	Low	High	Notes
Submarine Race Watching	7"	Coral	Q72458	1963	£1.50	£4	

ESPRIT DE CORPS
Title	Format	Label	Cat No	Year	Low	High	Notes
If (Would It Turn Out Wrong)	7"	Jam	JAM24	1973	£5	£10	
Lonely	7"	Jam	JAM32	1973	£2.50	£6	

ESQUEIXADA SNIFF
Title	Format	Label	Cat No	Year	Low	High	Notes
En Concert	LP	Edigsa	UM2055	1979	£4	£10	Spanish
Ocells	LP	Edigsa	CM456	1979	£4	£10	Spanish

ESQUERITA
Title	Format	Label	Cat No	Year	Low	High	Notes
Esquerita	LP	Capitol	T1186	1959	£100	£200	US
Rocking The Joint	7"	Capitol	CL14938	1958	£30	£60	
Wildcat Shakeout	LP	Ember	SPE6603	196-	£6	£15	

ESQUIRES
Title	Format	Label	Cat No	Year	Low	High	Notes
And Get Away	7"	Stateside	SS2077	1968	£2.50	£6	
Get On Up	7"	Stateside	SS2048	1967	£4	£8	
My Sweet Baby	7"	Action	ACT4618	1973	£1.50	£4	

ESSEX
Title	Format	Label	Cat No	Year	Low	High	Notes
Easier Said Than Done	LP	Columbia	33SX1593	1963	£6	£15	
Easier Said Than Done	7"	Columbia	DB7077	1963	£2.50	£6	chart single
She's Got Everything	7"	Columbia	DB7178	1963	£2.50	£6	
Walkin' Miracle	LP	Columbia	33SX1613	1964	£5	£12	
Walkin' Miracle	7"	Columbia	DB7122	1963	£2.50	£6	
Young And Lively	LP	Roulette	(S)R25246	1964	£5	£12	US

ESSEX, DAVID
Title	Format	Label	Cat No	Year	Low	High	Notes
And The Tears Came Tumbling Down	7"	Fontana	TF559	1965	£10	£20	
Can't Nobody Love You	7"	Fontana	TF620	1965	£10	£20	
Day The Earth Stood Still	7"	Decca	F12967	1969	£7.50	£15	
Just For Tonight	7"	Pye	7N17621	1968	£4	£8	
Love Story	7"	Uni	UN502	1968	£5	£10	
That Takes Me Back	7"	Decca	F12935	1969	£7.50	£15	
Thigh High	7"	Fontana	TF733	1966	£7.50	£15	
This Little Girl Of Mine	7"	Fontana	TF680	1966	£10	£20	

ESTEFAN, GLORIA
Title	Format	Label	Cat No	Year	Low	High	Notes
1-2-3	7"	Epic	6529580	1988	£1.50	£4	poster sleeve
Anything For You	12"	Epic	6516739	1988	£2.50	£6	
Betcha Say That	7"	Epic	6511257	1987	£1.50	£4	
Betcha Say That	12"	Epic	65112589	1987	£2.50	£6	7 tracks
Betcha Say That	12"	Epic	6511258	1987	£2.50	£6	3 tracks
Can't Stay Away From You	CD-s	Epic	6514442	1988	£2.50	£6	3' CD
Can't Stay Away From You	7"	Epic	6514440	1988	£1.50	£4	poster sleeve
Can't Stay Away From You	7"	Epic	6531957	1989	£2.50	£6	shaped pic disc
Can't Stay Away From You	12"	Epic	6514449	1988	£2.50	£6	
Let It Loose	LP	Epic	4509101	1987	£4	£10	
Let It Loose	CD	Epic	4509102	1987	£6	£15	
Oye Mi Canto	CD-s	Epic	6552875	1989	£3	£8	pic disc
Rhythm Is Gonna Get You	7"	Epic	6508057	1988	£1.50	£4	
Rhythm Is Gonna Get You	7"	Epic	6545140	1988	£1.50	£4	calendar PS
Rhythm Is Gonna Get You	7"	Epic	6545147	1988	£2	£5	with badge
Rhythm Is Gonna Get You	7"	Epic	6545149	1988	£2	£5	poster PS
Rhythm Is Gonna Get You	12"	Epic	6508058	1988	£2.50	£6	

ESTES, SLEEPY JOHN
Title	Format	Label	Cat No	Year	Low	High	Notes
1929-1940	LP	Folkways	RF8	1967	£5	£12	
Broke And Hungry	LP	Delmark	DL608	1964	£6	£15	
Brownsville Blues	LP	Delmark	DL613	1965	£6	£15	
Electric Sleep	LP	Delmark	DL619	1966	£5	£12	
In Europe	LP	Delmark	DL611	1965	£5	£12	
Legend	LP	Delmark	DL603	1961	£6	£15	
Legend Of Sleepy John Estes	LP	Esquire	32195	1963	£10	£25	
Portraits In Blues Vol.10	LP	Storyville	SLP172	1965	£5	£12	
Sleepy John's Got The Blues	7" EP	Delmark	DJB3	1966	£4	£8	
Tennessee Jug Busters	LP	77	LA1227	1964	£6	£15	

ESTICK, JACKIE
Title	Format	Label	Cat No	Year	Low	High	Notes
Boss Girl	7"	Blue Beat	BB64	1961	£5	£10	Count Ossie B side
Since You've Been Gone	7"	Island	WI042	1963	£5	£10	
Ska	7"	Ska Beat	JB256	1966	£5	£10	

ETCETERAS
Title	Format	Label	Cat No	Year	Low	High	Notes
Little Lady	7"	Oriole	CB1973	1964	£5	£10	

ETERNAL TRIANGLE
Title	Format	Label	Cat No	Year	Low	High	Notes
I Guess The Lord Must Be In New York	7"	Decca	F12979	1969	£1.50	£4	
Windows	7"	Decca	F12954	1969	£1.50	£4	

ETERNALS
Title	Format	Label	Cat No	Year	Low	High	Notes
Rocking In The Jungle	7"	London	HL8995	1959	£20	£40	tri-centre

ETERNALS (2)
Title	Format	Label	Cat No	Year	Low	High	Notes
Queen Of The Minstrels	7"	Coxsone	CS7091	1969	£5	£10	

ETERNITY'S CHILDREN
Eternity's Children	LP	Tower	ST5123	1968	£5	£12	US
Mrs.Bluebird	7"	Capitol	CL15558	1968	£1.50	£4	
Timeless	LP	Tower	ST5144	1968	£5	£12	US

ETHEL THE FROG
Ethel The Frog	LP	EMI	EMC3329	1980	£6	£15	

ETHERIDGE, CHRIS
L.A. Getaway	LP	Atlantic	K40310	1971	£4	£10	

ETHIOPIANS
Buss Your Mouth	7"	Nu Beat	NB038	1969	£2.50	£6	... Reggae Boys B side
Come On Now	7"	Doctor Bird	DB1141	1968	£5	£10	
Do It Sweet	7"	Doctor Bird	DB1092	1967	£5	£10	
Engine 54	7"	Doctor Bird	DB1147	1968	£5	£10	
Everyday Talking	7"	Doctor Bird	DB1199	1969	£5	£10	
Everything Crash	7"	Doctor Bird	DB1169	1968	£5	£10	
Fire A Muss Muss Tail	7"	Crab	CRAB2	1968	£4	£8	
For You	7"	Island	WI3036	1967	£5	£10	..Soul Brothers B side
Go Rock Steady	LP	Doctor Bird	DLM5011	1968	£50	£100	
Hong Kong Flu	7"	Doctor Bird	DB1185	1969	£5	£10	
I Am Free	7"	Island	WI3015	1966	£5	£10	..Soul Brothers B side
I'm A King	7"	Crab	CRAB7	1969	£4	£8	
I'm Gonna Take Over Now	7"	Rio	R114	1967	£4	£8	..Jackie Mittoo B side
Leave Me Business Alone	7"	Studio One	SO2035	1967	£6	£12	.. Soul Vendors B side
Let's Get Together	7"	Coxsone	CS7022	1967	£5	£10	.. Hamlins B side
Live Good	7"	Ska Beat	JB260	1966	£5	£10	..Soul Brothers B side
Monkey Money	7"	Fab	FAB180	1971	£1.50	£4	
Mother's Tender Care	7"	Duke Reid	DR2507	1970	£2	£5	.... Tommy McCook B side
Mr.Tom	7"	Randys	RAN512	1969	£2.50	£6	
My Testimony	7"	Nu Beat	NB031	1969	£2.50	£6	..J.J.Allstars B side
Not Me	7"	Doctor Bird	DB1172	1969	£5	£10	
Owe Me No Pay Me	7"	Rio	R110	1966	£4	£8	
Pirate	7"	Treasure Isle	TI7067	1971	£2	£5	.... Tommy McCook B side
Reggae Hit The Town	7"	Crab	CRAB4	1968	£4	£8	
Reggae Power	LP	Trojan	TTL10	1969	£8	£20	
Stay In My Lonely Arms	7"	Rio	R126	1967	£4	£8	
Train To Glory	7"	Doctor Bird	DB1148	1968	£5	£10	
Train To Skaville	7"	Rio	R130	1967	£4	£8	...chart single
True Man	7"	Randys	RAN510	1969	£2.50	£6	...........Randy's Allstars B side
Walkie Talkie	7"	Bamboo	BAM26	1970	£2	£5	.... Sound Dimension B side
Well Red	7"	Trojan	TR697	1969	£2.50	£6	..J.J.Allstars B side
What A Fire	7"	Doctor Bird	DB1186	1969	£5	£10	
What To Do	7"	Rio	R123	1967	£4	£8	..Jackie Mittoo B side
Whip	7"	Doctor Bird	DB1096	1967	£5	£10	
Woman Capture Man	LP	Trojan	TBL112	1970	£6	£15	
Woman Capture Man	7"	Trojan	TR666	1969	£2.50	£6	
World Goes Ska	7"	Doctor Bird	DB1103	1967	£5	£10	
You'll Want To Come Back	7"	Bamboo	BAM38	1970	£2	£5	...Jackie Mittoo B side

ETTA & HARVEY
If I Can't Have You	7"	London	HLM9180	1960	£7.50	£15	

EUBANKS, JACK
Searchin'	7"	London	HLU9501	1962	£1.50	£4	
What'd I Say	7"	London	HLU9312	1961	£1.50	£4	

EULENSPYGEL
2	LP	Spiegelei	2876070	1971	£8	£20	German
Auschuss	LP	Spiegelei	2878070	1972	£8	£20	German

EUPHORIA
Euphoria	LP	Heritage	HTS35005	1969	£10	£25	US

EUPHORIA (2)
Gift From Euphoria	LP	Capitol	SKAO363	1969	£20	£40	US

EUREKA BRASS BAND
Jazz At Preservation Hall Vol.1	LP	London	HAK/SHK8162	1964	£5	£12	
New Orleans Parade	LP	Melodisc	MLP12101	1955	£5	£12	

EURYTHMICS
Angel (Remix)	12"	RCA	DAT25	1990	£2.50	£6	
Beethoven	7"	RCA	DA11P	1987	£2.50	£6	poster sleeve
Belinda	7"	RCA	RCA115	1981	£7.50	£15	
I'm Never Gonna Cry Again	7"	RCA	RCA68	1981	£2	£5	chart single
I'm Never Gonna Cry Again	12"	RCA	RCAT68	1981	£8	£20	
It's Alright	7"	RCA	PB40375	1985	£1.50	£4	double
It's Alright	12"	RCA	PB40376	1985	£2.50	£6	double
Julia	7"	Virgin	VSY734	1985	£1.50	£4	pic disc
Julia	12"	Virgin	VS73412	1985	£2.50	£6	pic disc
Love Is A Stranger	7"	RCA	DAP1	1982	£1.50	£4	pic disc
Miracle Of Love	7"	RCA	DA9P	1986	£1.50	£4	pic disc
Right By Your Side	7"	RCA	DA4	1983	£12.50	£25	.. with 4 track cassette
Right By Your Side	7"	RCA	DAP4	1983	£1.50	£4	pic disc

Rough And Tough	CD	RCA	CP353016	1987	£25	£50	US live promo
Sweet Dreams	LP	RCA	RCALP6063	1983	£5	£12	pic disc
Sweet Dreams	7"	RCA	DAP2	1983	£2	£5	pic disc
This Is The House	7"	RCA	RCA199	1982	£6	£12	
This Is The House	12"	RCA	RCAT199	1982	£15	£30	
Touch	LP	RCA	PL70109	1983	£4	£10	pic disc
Walk	7"	RCA	RCA230	1982	£6	£12	
Walk	12"	RCA	RCAT230	1982	£17.50	£35	
Who's That Girl	7"	RCA	DAP3	1983	£1.50	£4	pic disc
You Have Placed A Chill In My Heart	CD-s	RCA	DA16CD	1988	£2.50	£6	black metal tin

EVANS, BILL

Conversations With Myself	LP	Verve	VLP9054	1963	£4	£10
Dig It	LP	Fontana	FJL104	1964	£4	£10
Everybody Digs Bill Evans	LP	Riverside	RLP12291	1958	£6	£15
Explorations	LP	Riverside	RLP351	1961	£6	£15
Portrait In Jazz	LP	Riverside	RLP12315	1959	£6	£15
Waltz For Debby	LP	Riverside	RLP(9)399	1961	£6	£15

EVANS, CHRISTINE

Somewhere There's Love	7"	Philips	BF1496	1966	£4	£8

EVANS, DAVE

Elephantasia	LP	Village Thing	VTS14	1972	£5	£12
Words In Between	LP	Village Thing	VTS6	1971	£5	£12

EVANS, GIL

Although technically an arranger, Gil Evans produced jazz that was so individual that it effectively amounted to re-composition. At his best when creating music around a star soloist ("New Bottle Old Wine" featured Canonball Adderley; "Miles Ahead", "Porgy And Bess", and "Sketches Of Spain" featured Miles Davis and are listed under his name), Evans was ready to record an album with Jimi Hendrix, when the guitarist's untimely end aborted the project. Evans went on to record many of Hendrix's tunes anyway, but although these work very well as modern jazz pieces, they offer no more than a tantalising glimpse of what might have been.

Gil Evans And Ten	LP	Esquire	32070	1959	£8	£20
Great Jazz Standards	LP	Fontana	688000ZL	1965	£4	£10
Great Jazz Standards	LP	Vogue	LAE12234	1960	£6	£15
Great Jazz Standards	7" EP	Vogue	EPV1266	1960	£2	£5
New Bottle, Old Wine	LP	Vogue	LAE12173	1959	£6	£15
Out Of The Cool	LP	HMV	CLP1456	1961	£5	£12
Roots (New Bottle, Old Wine)	LP	Fontana	688003ZL	1965	£4	£10

EVANS, LARRY

Crazy About My Baby	7"	London	HLU8269	1956	£50	£100

EVANS, MAUREEN

All The Angels Sang	7"	CBS	201773	1965	£1.50	£4	
As Long As He Needs Me	7"	Oriole	CB1578	1961	£1.50	£4	
Big Hurt	7"	Oriole	CB1533	1960	£1.50	£4	chart single
Don't Want The Moonlight	7"	Oriole	CB1517	1959	£1.50	£4	
Get Away	7"	Oriole	CB1969	1964	£1.50	£4	
He Knows I Love Him Too Much	7"	Oriole	CB1939	1964	£1.50	£4	
I Love How You Love Me	7"	Oriole	CB1906	1964	£1.50	£4	chart single
Like I Do	LP	Oriole	PS40046	1963	£15	£30	
Like I Do	7"	Oriole	CB1763	1962	£1.50	£4	chart single
Like You Used To Do	7"	Oriole	CB1875	1963	£1.50	£4	
Love,Kisses,& Heartaches	7"	Oriole	CB1540	1960	£1.50	£4	
Mama Wouldn't Like It	7"	Oriole	CB1563	1961	£1.50	£4	
Melancholy Me	7" EP	Oriole	EP7076	1963	£7.50	£15	
My Foolish Heart	7"	Oriole	CB1613	1961	£1.50	£4	
Never In A Million Years	7"	Oriole	CB1743	1962	£1.50	£4	
Never Let Him Go	7"	CBS	201752	1965	£1.50	£4	
Paper Roses	7"	Oriole	CB1550	1960	£1.50	£4	chart single
Pick The Petals	7"	Oriole	CB1804	1963	£1.50	£4	
Somewhere There's Love	7"	CBS	202621	1967	£2	£5	
Till	7"	Oriole	CB1581	1961	£1.50	£4	
Tomorrow Is Another Day	7"	Oriole	CB1806	1963	£1.50	£4	
What A Difference A Day Made	7"	Oriole	CB1851	1963	£1.50	£4	

EVANS, MAUREEN & DAVID KOSSOFF

Oliver	7" EP	Oriole	EP7039	1961	£2	£5

EVANS, PAUL

21 Years In A Tennessee Jail	LP	Kapp	KL1346/KS3346	1964	£6	£15	US
Another Town, Another Jail	LP	Kapp	KL1475/KS3475	1966	£5	£12	US
Brigade Of Broken Hearts	7"	London	HLL9183	1960	£2	£5	
Folk Songs Of Many Lands	LP	Carlton	(STLP)130	1961	£6	£15	US
Happy Go Lucky Me	7"	London	HLL9129	1960	£2	£5	
Hear Paul Evans In Your Home Tonight	LP	Carlton	(STLP)129	1961	£6	£15	US
Hushabye Little Guitar	7"	London	HLL9239	1960	£2	£5	
Midnight Special	7"	London	HLL9045	1960	£4	£8	chart single
Paul Evans	7" EP	London	RER1349	1962	£10	£20	
Seven Little Girls Sitting In The Back Seat	7"	London	HLL8968	1959	£2.50	£6	chart single
Sings The Fabulous Teens	LP	London	HAL2248	1960	£20	£40	

EVANS, RUSSELL & THE NITEHAWKS

Send Me Some Cornbread	7"	Atlantic	584010	1966	£2	£5

EVEN DOZEN JUG BAND

The Even Dozen Jug Band, while in itself having little to distinguish it from the many other folk groups playing in America during the early sixties, was nevertheless a remarkably effective training school for some later well-known musicians. Playing in the group were John Sebastian (soon to form the Lovin' Spoonful), Maria D'Amato (famous later under her married name, Maria Muldaur), Steve Katz (guitarist with the Blues Project and Blood,Sweat,and Tears), guitarist Stefan Grossman, and Joshua Rifkin (later responsible for bringing the works of Scott Joplin to public notice).

Even Dozen Jug Band	LP	Bounty	BY6023	1966	£6	£15	
Even Dozen Jug Band	LP	Elektra	EKS7246	1964	£8	£20	US
Jug Band Songs Of The Southern Mountains	LP	Legacy	LEG119	1965	£6	£15	US

EVERETT, BETTY

Getting Mighty Crowded	7"	Fontana	TF520	1964	£2.50	£6	chart single
I Can't Hear You	7"	Stateside	SS321	1964	£4	£8	
I Can't Say No To You	7"	MCA	BAG3	1969	£1.50	£4	
I Got To Tell Somebody	7"	Liberty	LBF15428	1970	£1.50	£4	
It's In His Kiss	LP	Fontana	TL5136	1965	£10	£25	
It's In His Kiss	LP	Joy	JOY106	1968	£6	£15	
It's In His Kiss	7"	President	PT215	1968	£1.50	£4	chart single
It's In His Kiss	7"	Stateside	SS280	1964	£4	£8	
I've Got A Claim On You	7"	Sue	WI352	1965	£5	£10	
Sugar	7"	Uni	UN517	1970	£1.50	£4	
There'll Come A Time	7"	MCA	MU1055	1969	£1.50	£4	
Very Best Of Betty Everett	LP	Vee Jay	VJLP/VJS1122	1965	£5	£12	US
Your Loving Arms	7"	King	KG1002	1964	£2	£5	
You're No Good	7"	President	PT251	1969	£1.50	£4	
You're No Good	7"	Stateside	SS259	1964	£4	£8	

EVERETT, BETTY & JERRY BUTLER

Delicious Together	LP	Fontana	TL5237	1965	£5	£12	
Let It Be Me	7"	President	PT214	1968	£1.50	£4	
Let It Be Me	7"	Stateside	SS339	1964	£2.50	£6	
Our Day Will Come	7"	President	PT252	1969	£1.50	£4	
Smile	7"	Fontana	TF528	1965	£2	£5	

EVERETT, KENNY

It's Been So Long	7"	MGM	MGM1421	1968	£1.50	£4	
Nice Time	7"	Deram	DM245	1969	£1.50	£4	

EVERETT, VINCE

Endlessly	7"	Fontana	TF818	1967	£1.50	£4	
Every Now And Then	7"	Fontana	TF915	1968	£7.50	£15	
Till I Lost You	7"	Fontana	TF606	1965	£1.50	£4	

EVERGREEN BLUES BAND

Laura	7"	Mercury	MF1025	1968	£2.50	£6	
Midnight Confessions	7"	Mercury	MF1012	1967	£2.50	£6	
Seven Do Eleven	LP	Mercury	SMCL20122	1968	£4	£10	

EVERGREEN BLUESHOES

Ballad Of Evergreen Blueshoes	LP	London	HAU/SHU8399	1969	£5	£12	

EVERLY BROTHERS

Ain't That Lovin' You Baby	7"	Warner Bros	WB129	1964	£1.50	£4	
All I Have To Do Is Dream	7"	London	HLA8618	1958	£4	£8	chart single
Beat 'N' Soul	LP	Warner Bros	W(S)1605	1965	£6	£15	
Bird Dog	7"	London	HLA8685	1958	£4	£8	chart single
Both Sides Of An Evening	LP	Warner Bros	WS8052	1961	£10	£25	stereo
Both Sides Of An Evening	LP	Warner Bros	WM4052	1961	£8	£20	
Both Sides Of An Evening Vol.1	7" EP	Warner Bros	WEP6115	1963	£7.50	£15	
Both Sides Of An Evening Vol.1	7" EP	Warner Bros	WSE6115	1963	£20	£40	stereo
Both Sides Of An Evening Vol.2	7" EP	Warner Bros	WEP6117	1964	£7.50	£15	
Both Sides Of An Evening Vol.2	7" EP	Warner Bros	WSE6117	1964	£20	£40	stereo
Both Sides Of An Evening Vol.3	7" EP	Warner Bros	WEP6138	1965	£7.50	£15	
Bowling Green	7"	Warner Bros	WB7020	1967	£1.50	£4	
Bye Bye Love	7"	London	HLA8440	1957	£7.50	£15	chart single
Cathy's Clown	7"	Warner Bros	WB1	1960	£1.50	£4	chart single
Christmas With The Everly Brothers	LP	Warner Bros	WS8116	1962	£10	£25	stereo
Christmas With The Everly Brothers	LP	Warner Bros	WM8116	1962	£8	£20	
Crying In The Rain	7"	Warner Bros	WB56	1962	£1.50	£4	chart single
Date With The Everly Brothers	LP	Warner Bros	WS8028	1960	£10	£25	stereo
Date With The Everly Brothers	LP	Warner Bros	WM4028	1960	£8	£20	chart LP
Date With The Everly Brothers Vol.1	7" EP	Warner Bros	WEP6107	1963	£7.50	£15	
Date With The Everly Brothers Vol.1	7" EP	Warner Bros	WSE6107	1963	£20	£40	stereo
Date With The Everly Brothers Vol.2	7" EP	Warner Bros	WEP6109	1963	£7.50	£15	
Date With The Everly Brothers Vol.2	7" EP	Warner Bros	WSE6109	1963	£20	£40	stereo
End Of An Era	LP	CBS	66259	1970	£5	£12	double
Especially For You	7" EP	Warner Bros	WEP6034	1961	£7.50	£15	
Especially For You	7" EP	Warner Bros	WSEP2034	1961	£20	£40	stereo
Everly Brothers	LP	Cadence	CLP3003	1958	£15	£30	US
Everly Brothers	LP	London	HAA2081	1958	£15	£30	
Everly Brothers	7" EP	London	REA1113	1958	£6	£12	
Everly Brothers' Best	LP	Cadence	CLP3025	1959	£15	£30	US
Everly Brothers No.2	7" EP	London	REA1148	1958	£6	£12	
Everly Brothers No.3	7" EP	London	REA1149	1958	£6	£12	
Everly Brothers No.4	7" EP	London	REA1174	1959	£6	£12	
Everly Brothers No.5	7" EP	London	REA1229	1960	£7.50	£15	
Everly Brothers No.6	7" EP	London	REA1311	1961	£7.50	£15	
Everly Brothers Show	LP	Warner Bros	WS1858	1970	£6	£12	
Everly Brothers Sing	LP	Warner Bros	W(S)1708	1967	£6	£15	

Title	Format	Label	Cat. No.	Year	Price	Price	Notes
Everly Brothers Single Set	7"	Lightning	SET1	1980	£12.50	£25	15 x 7', boxed & book
Fabulous Style Of The Everly Brothers	LP	Cadence	CLP3040/25040	1960	£15	£30	US
Fabulous Style Of The Everly Brothers	LP	London	HAA2266	1960	£10	£25	chart LP
Ferris Wheel	7"	Warner Bros	WB135	1964	£1.50	£4	chart single
Fifteen Everly Hits Fifteen	LP	Cadence	CLP3062/25062	1963	£10	£25	US
Folk Songs Of The Everly Brothers	LP	Cadence	CLP3059/25059	1962	£15	£30	US
Foreverly Yours	7" EP	Warner Bros	WEP6049	1962	£7.50	£15	
Foreverly Yours	7" EP	Warner Bros	WSEP2049	1962	£20	£40	stereo
Girl Sang The Blues	7"	Warner Bros	WB109	1963	£1.50	£4	chart single
Golden Hits	LP	Warner Bros	WM/WS8108	1962	£5	£12	
Gone Gone Gone	LP	Valiant	VS109	1970	£4	£10	
Gone Gone Gone	LP	Warner Bros	WS8169	1965	£8	£20	stereo
Gone Gone Gone	LP	Warner Bros	WM8169	1965	£6	£15	
Gone Gone Gone	7"	Warner Bros	WB146	1964	£1.50	£4	chart single
Hit Sound Of The Everly Brothers	LP	Warner Bros	WS1676	1967	£8	£20	stereo
Hit Sound Of The Everly Brothers	LP	Warner Bros	W1676	1967	£5	£12	
How Can I Meet Her	7"	Warner Bros	WB67	1962	£1.50	£4	chart single
I'll Never Get Over You	7"	Warner Bros	WB5639	1965	£1.50	£4	chart single
In Our Image	LP	Warner Bros	W1620	1965	£6	£15	mono
In Our Image	LP	Warner Bros	WS1620	1965	£8	£20	stereo
Instant Party	LP	Warner Bros	WS8061	1962	£8	£20	stereo
Instant Party	LP	Warner Bros	WM4061	1962	£6	£15	chart LP
Instant Party	7" EP	Warner Bros	WEP6111	1963	£7.50	£15	
Instant Party	7" EP	Warner Bros	WSE6111	1963	£20	£40	stereo
Instant Party Vol.2	7" EP	Warner Bros	WEP6113	1963	£7.50	£15	
Instant Party Vol.2	7" EP	Warner Bros	WSE6113	1963	£20	£40	stereo
It's Been Nice	7"	Warner Bros	WB99	1963	£1.50	£4	chart single
It's Everly Time	LP	Warner Bros	WS8012	1960	£10	£25	stereo
It's Everly Time	LP	Warner Bros	WM4012	1960	£8	£20	chart LP
It's Everly Time	7" EP	Warner Bros	WEP6056	1962	£7.50	£15	
It's Everly Time	7" EP	Warner Bros	WSEP2056	1962	£20	£40	stereo
It's My Time	7"	Warner Bros	WB7192	1968	£1.50	£4	chart single
I've Been Wrong Before	7"	Warner Bros	WB5754	1966	£1.50	£4	
Leave My Girl Alone	7" EP	Warner Bros	WEP622	1967	£5	£10	
Let It Be Me	7"	London	HLA9039	1960	£1.50	£4	chart single
Lightning Express	7"	London		1962	£30	£60	test pressing
Like Strangers	7"	London	HLA9250	1960	£2.50	£6	chart single
Love Is Strange	7"	Warner Bros	WB5649	1965	£1.50	£4	chart single
Love Is Strange	7" EP	Warner Bros	WEP610	1966	£5	£10	
Love Of The Common People	7"	Warner Bros	WB7088	1967	£1.50	£4	
Mary Jane	7"	Warner Bros	WB7062	1967	£1.50	£4	
Milk Train	7"	Warner Bros	WB7226	1968	£1.50	£4	
Muskrat	7"	Warner Bros	WB50	1961	£1.50	£4	chart single
No One Can Make My Sunshine Smile	7"	Warner Bros	WB79	1962	£1.50	£4	chart single
Not Fade Away	7"	RCA	RCA2286	1972	£1.50	£4	
Oh Boy	7"	Warner Bros	WB6074	1967	£1.50	£4	
Original Greatest Hits	LP	CBS	66255	1970	£5	£12	double
Pass The Chicken And Listen	LP	RCA	SF8332	1973	£5	£12	
People Get Ready	7" EP	Warner Bros	WEP612	1966	£5	£10	
Poor Jenny	7"	London	HLA8863	1959	£4	£8	chart single
Power Of Love	7"	Warner Bros	WB5743	1966	£1.50	£4	
Price Of Love	7"	Warner Bros	WB161	1965	£1.50	£4	chart single
Price Of Love	7"	Warner Bros	WB5628	1965	£1.50	£4	
Price Of Love	7" EP	Warner Bros	WEP604	1965	£5	£10	
Problems	7"	London	HLA8781	1958	£4	£8	chart single
Ridin' High	7"	RCA	RCA2232	1972	£1.50	£4	
Rock 'N' Soul	7" EP	Warner Bros	WEP608	1965	£5	£10	
Rock 'N' Soul Vol.2	7" EP	Warner Bros	WEP609	1965	£5	£10	
Rock'n'Soul	LP	Warner Bros	W(S)1578	1965	£6	£15	
Rock'n'Soul	LP	Warner Bros	WM/WS8171	1965	£6	£15	
Roots	LP	Warner Bros	K46128	1971	£5	£12	
Roots	LP	Warner Bros	W(S)1752	1968	£8	£20	
See See Rider	7" EP	Warner Bros	WEP618	1966	£5	£10	
Sing Great Country Hits	LP	Warner Bros	WM/WS8138	1963	£8	£20	
Sing Great Country Hits Vol.1	7" EP	Warner Bros	WEP6128	1964	£7.50	£15	
Sing Great Country Hits Vol.2	7" EP	Warner Bros	WEP6131	1964	£7.50	£15	
Sing Great Country Hits Vol.3	7" EP	Warner Bros	WEP6132	1964	£7.50	£15	
So It Will Always Be	7"	Warner Bros	WB94	1963	£1.50	£4	chart single
So Sad	7"	Warner Bros	WB19	1960	£1.50	£4	chart single
Somebody Help Me	7" EP	Warner Bros	WEP623	1967	£5	£10	
Songs Our Daddy Taught Us	LP	London	HAA2150	1958	£15	£30	
Songs Our Daddy Taught Us Part 1	7" EP	London	REA1195	1959	£7.50	£15	
Songs Our Daddy Taught Us Part 2	7" EP	London	REA1196	1959	£7.50	£15	
Songs Our Daddy Taught Us Part 3	7" EP	London	REA1197	1959	£7.50	£15	
Stories We Could Tell	LP	RCA	SF8270	1972	£4	£10	
Sun Keeps Shining	7"	Columbia	21496	1956	£100	£200	US
Temptation	7"	Warner Bros	WB42	1961	£1.50	£4	chart single
That'll Be The Day	7"	Warner Bros	WB158	1965	£1.50	£4	chart single
This Little Girl Of Mine	7"	London	HLA8554	1958	£7.50	£15	
Till I Kissed You	7"	London	HLA8934	1959	£4	£8	chart single
Two Yanks In England	LP	Warner Bros	WS1646	1965	£8	£20	stereo
Two Yanks In England	LP	Warner Bros	W1646	1965	£6	£15	with the Hollies
Very Best Of The Everly Brothers	LP	Warner Bros	WM/WS8163	1965	£4	£10	
Wake Up Little Susie	7" EP	Warner Bros	K16407	1974	£2	£5	
Wake Up Little Suzie	7"	London	HLA8498	1957	£5	£10	chart single
Walk Right Back	7"	Warner Bros	WB33	1961	£1.50	£4	chart single
When Will I Be Loved	7"	London	HLA9157	1960	£2.50	£6	chart single
You're My Girl	7"	Warner Bros	WB154	1965	£1.50	£4	
You're The One I Love	7"	Warner Bros	WB143	1964	£1.50	£4	
Yves	7"	Warner Bros	WB7425	1970	£1.50	£4	

EVERLY, DON

Brother Juke Box	LP	DJM	20501	1977	£4	£10	
Don Everly	LP	A&M	AMLH2007	1971	£8	£20	
Sunset Towers	LP	Ode	77023	1974	£6	£15	US

EVERLY, PHIL

Ich Bin Dein	7"	Elektra	ELK12381	1977	£2	£5	sung in German
Mystic Line	LP	Pye	NSPL18473	1975	£6	£15	
Nothing's Too Good For My Baby	LP	Pye	NSPL18448	1974	£6	£15	
Star Spangled Springer	LP	RCA	SF8370	1973	£6	£15	

EVERPRESENT FULLNESS

Everpresent Fullness	LP	White Whale	7132	1970	£6	£15	US

EVERY MOTHER'S SON

Come And Take A Ride In My Boat	7"	MGM	MGM1341	1967	£2.50	£6	
Every Mother's Son	LP	MGM	C(S)8044	1967	£4	£10	US
Pony With The Golden Mane	7"	MGM	MGM1372	1967	£2.50	£6	
Put Your Mind At Ease	7"	MGM	MGM1350	1967	£2.50	£6	

EVERYBODY

Shape Of Things To Come	7"	Page One	POF23163	1970	£1.50	£4	

EVERYONE

Everyone	LP	B&C	CAS1028	1971	£5	£12	

EVERYONE INVOLVED

Circus Keeps On Turning	7"	Arcturus	ARC3	1972	£10	£20	
Either Or	LP	Arcturus	ARC4	1972	£150	£250	

EWAN & DENVER

I Want You So Bad	7"	Giant	GN17	1967	£4	£8	

EWAN & GERRY

Oh Babe	7"	Blue Beat	BB385	1965	£5	£10	
Right Track	7"	Giant	GN4	1967	£4	£8	
Rock Steady Train	7"	Giant	GN9	1967	£4	£8	
Tennessee Waltz	7"	Giant	GN14	1967	£4	£8	

EWELL, DON

Piano Solos Of King Oliver Tunes	LP	Tempo	TAP7	1957	£5	£12	

EXCALIBUR

First Album	LP	Reprise	REP44163	1972	£10	£25	German

EXCELS

California On My Mind	7"	Atlantic	584133	1967	£1.50	£4	

EXCELSIOR SPRING

Happy Miranda	7"	Instant	IN002	1968	£4	£8	

EXCEPTIONS

Eagle Flies On Sunday	7"	CBS	202632	1967	£7.50	£15	
Exceptional Exceptions	LP	President	PTLS1026	1969	£6	£15	
Gaberdine Saturday Night	7"	CBS	2830	1967	£10	£20	
Helicopter	7"	President	PT205	1968	£1.50	£4	
Jack Rabbit	7"	President	PT236	1969	£2	£5	
Pendulum	7"	President	PT271	1969	£1.50	£4	
Rub It Down	7"	President	PT181	1968	£1.50	£4	
Tailor Made Babe	7"	President	PT218	1968	£2	£5	
What More Do You Want	7"	Decca	F12100	1965	£4	£8	

EXCHECKERS

All The World Is Mine	7"	Decca	F11871	1964	£4	£8	

EXCITERS

Do Wah Diddy	7"	United Artists	UP2274	1969	£2.50	£6	
Doo Wah Diddy Diddy	7"	United Artists	UP1041	1964	£5	£10	
Doo Wah Diddy Diddy	7" EP	United Artists	UEP1005	1965	£15	£30	
Exciters	LP	Roulette	(S)R25326	1966	£8	£20	US
Exciters	LP	United Artists	ULP1032	1964	£25	£50	
He's Got The Power	7"	United Artists	UP1017	1963	£2.50	£6	
I Want You To Be My Boy	7"	Columbia	DB7479	1965	£2	£5	
It's So Exciting	7"	United Artists	UP1026	1963	£2.50	£6	
Just Not Ready	7"	Columbia	DB7544	1965	£4	£8	
Little Bit Of Soap	7"	London	HLZ10018	1966	£2.50	£6	
Run Mascara	7"	Columbia	DB7606	1965	£6	£12	
Tell Him	LP	United Artists	UAL3264/ UAS6264	1963	£15	£30	US
Tell Him	7"	United Artists	UP1011	1963	£2.50	£6	chart single
Weddings Make Me Cry	7"	London	HLZ10038	1966	£7.50	£15	

EXCURSION

Night Train	LP	Gemini	GMX5029	1970	£8	£20	

EXECUTIVES

Gaza Strip	7"	CBS	3067	1967	£4	£8	
I Ain't Got Nobody	7"	CBS	4013	1969	£4	£8	
It's Been So Long	7"	Columbia	DB7573	1965	£2.50	£6	
Lock Your Door	7"	Columbia	DB7919	1966	£2.50	£6	
March Of The Mods	7"	Columbia	DB7323	1964	£4	£8	

Return Of The Mods	7"	Columbia	DB7770	1965	£4	£8	
Smokey Atmosphere	7"	CBS	202652	1967	£4	£8	
Strictly For The Beat	7"	Columbia	DB7393	1964	£2.50	£6	
Tracy Took A Trip	7"	CBS	3431	1968	£5	£10	
Tracy Took A Trip	7"	CBS	3431	1968	£10	£20	demo, PS

EXILE

Don't Tax Me	7"	Boring	BO1	1977	£2.50	£6	

EXILES

Freedom, Come All Ye	LP	Topic	12T143	1966	£10	£25	

EXITS

Yodelling	7" EP	Way Out	WOO1		£10	£20	

EXITS (2)

Fashion Plague	7"	Lightning	GIL519	1978	£2	£5	

EXMAGMA

Exmagma	LP	Neusi	B204	1973	£8	£20	German
Goldball	LP	Disjuncta	0009	1973	£6	£15	French

EXOTICS

Cross My Heart	7"	Decca	F11850	1964	£1.50	£4	

EXOTICS (2)

Don't Lead Me On	7"	Columbia	DB8418	1968	£1.50	£4	

EXPERIMENTS WITH ICE

Experiments With Ice	LP	United Dairies	EX001	1981	£6	£15	

EXPLOSIVE

Cities Make The Country Colder	7"	President	PT244	1969	£2	£5	
Crying All Night	7"	President	PT221	1968	£1.50	£4	
Who Planted Thorns In Alice's Garden	7"	President	PT262	1969	£2	£5	

EXPORT

Export	LP	His Master's Vice	VICE1	1980	£5	£12	
Wheeler Dealer	7"	His Master's Vice	VICE2	1981	£1.50	£4	

EXTREEM

On The Beach	7"	Strike	JH326	1966	£2	£5	

EXUMA

Exuma	LP	Mercury	6338018	1970	£6	£15	
Exuma II	LP	Mercury	SR61314	1971	£4	£10	US
Snake	LP	Kama Sutra	KSBS2052	1972	£4	£10	US

EYE FULL TOWER

How About Me	7"	Polydor	56734	1967	£2.50	£6	

EYELESS IN GAZA

Kodak Ghosts Run Amok	7"	Ambivalent Scale	ASR002	1980	£5	£10	

EYES

Arrival Of The Eyes	7" EP	Mercury	MCE10035	1966	£75	£150	sleeve pictured in Guide
Good Day Sunshine	7"	Mercury	MF934	1965	£15	£30	
Man With Money	7"	Mercury	MF910	1966	£30	£60	
My Immediate Pleasure	7"	Mercury	MF897	1966	£20	£40	
When The Night Falls	7"	Mercury	MF881	1965	£25	£50	

EYES OF BLUE

Crossroads Of Time	LP	Mercury	SMCL20134	1968	£15	£30	
In Fields Of Ardath	LP	Mercury	SMCL20164	1969	£15	£30	
Largo	7"	Mercury	MF1049	1968	£4	£8	
Supermarket Full Of Cans	7"	Deram	DM114	1967	£7.50	£15	
Up And Down	7"	Deram	DM106	1966	£7.50	£15	

EZELL, WILL

Chicago Piano	LP	Gannet	12002	1973	£5	£12	
Gin Mill Jazz	10" LP	London	AL3539	1955	£8	£20	

F

FABARES, SHELLEY

Title	Format	Label	Catalogue	Year			Notes
Big Star	7"	Pye	7N25184	1963	£1.50	£4	
I Left A Note To Say Goodbye	7"	Pye	7N25207	1963	£1.50	£4	
Johnny Angel	7"	Pye	7N25132	1962	£2	£5	chart single
Johnny Loves Me	7"	Pye	7N25151	1962	£1.50	£4	
My Prayer	7"	Fontana	TF592	1965	£1.50	£4	
Shelley	LP	Colpix	CLP/CST426	1962	£8	£20	US
Things We Did Last Summer	LP	Colpix	CLP/CST431	1962	£8	£20	US
Things We Did Last Summer	7"	Pye	7N25166	1962	£1.50	£4	

FABIAN

Title	Format	Label	Catalogue	Year			Notes
Fabulous Fabian	LP	HMV	CLP1345	1960	£15	£30	
Good Old Summertime	LP	Chancellor	CHL(S)5012	1960	£10	£25	US
Got The Feeling	7"	HMV	POP659	1959	£5	£10	
Grapevine	7"	HMV	POP869	1961	£1.50	£4	
High Time	LP	RCA	LPM/LSP2314	1960	£8	£20	US
Hold That Tiger	LP	HMV	CLP1301	1959	£15	£30	
Hound Dog Man	7"	HMV	POP695	1960	£5	£10	chart single
I'm A Man	7"	HMV	POP587	1959	£10	£20	
I'm Gonna Sit Right Down And Write Myself A Letter	7"	HMV	POP778	1960	£1.50	£4	
Kissin' And Twistin'	7"	HMV	POP810	1960	£1.50	£4	
Rockin' Hot	LP	Chancellor	CHL5019	1961	£15	£30	US
Sixteen Fabulous Hits	LP	Chancellor	CHL5024	1962	£10	£25	US
String Along	7"	HMV	POP724	1960	£1.50	£4	
Tiger	7"	HMV	POP643	1959	£6	£12	
Tomorrow	7"	HMV	POP800	1960	£1.50	£4	
Turn Me Loose	7"	HMV	POP612	1959	£7.50	£15	
You Know You Belong To Somebody Else	7"	HMV	POP829	1961	£1.50	£4	
Young And Wonderful	LP	HMV	CLP1433	1961	£10	£25	
Young And Wonderful	LP	HMV	CSD1352	1961	£15	£30	stereo
You're Only Young Once	7"	HMV	POP934	1961	£1.50	£4	

FABIAN & FRANKIE AVALON

Title	Format	Label	Catalogue	Year			Notes
Hit Makers	LP	Chancellor	CHL5009	1960	£10	£25	US

FABULOUS DIALS

Title	Format	Label	Catalogue	Year		
Bossa Nova Stomp	7"	Pye	7N25200	1963	£5	£10

FABULOUS FLAMES

Title	Format	Label	Catalogue	Year			Notes
Holy Holy	7"	Clandisc	CLA204	1969	£2.50	£6	Lord Creator B side

FACELLS

Title	Format	Label	Catalogue	Year		
So Fine	7"	Kalypso	AB116	196-	£2.50	£6

FACES

Title	Format	Label	Catalogue	Year			Notes
Borstal Boys	7"	Warner Bros	K16281	1973	£5	£10	
First Step	LP	Warner Bros	K46053	1970	£4	£10	
First Step	LP	Warner Bros	WS3000	1970	£5	£12	chart LP
Long Player	LP	Warner Bros	K46064	1971	£4	£10	
Long Player	LP	Warner Bros	W3011	1971	£5	£12	chart LP
Nod Is As Good As A Wink	LP	Warner Bros	K56006	1971	£4	£10	
Nod Is As Good As A Wink	LP	Warner Bros	K56006	1971	£5	£12	with poster
Ooh La La	LP	Warner Bros	K56011	1973	£4	£10	chart LP

FACTORY

Title	Format	Label	Catalogue	Year		
Path Through the Forest	7"	MGM	MGM1444	1968	£50	£100
Time Machine	7"	Oak	RGJ718	1970	£50	£100
Try A Little Sunshine	7"	CBS	4540	1969	£50	£100

FACTOTUMS

Title	Format	Label	Catalogue	Year		
Cloudy	7"	Pye	7N17402	1967	£2.50	£6
Here Today	7"	Piccadilly	7N35333	1966	£2	£5
I Can't Give You Anything	7"	Piccadilly	7N35355	1966	£2	£5
In My Lonely Room	7"	Immediate	IM009	1965	£5	£10
Mr.And Mrs.Regards	7"	CBS	4140	1969	£2.50	£6
You're So Good To Be	7"	Immediate	IM022	1965	£5	£10

FADING COLOURS

Title	Format	Label	Catalogue	Year		
Just Like Romeo And Juliet	7"	Ember	EMBS229	1966	£2.50	£6

FAGEN, DONALD

Title	Format	Label	Catalogue	Year			Notes
Nightfly	LP	Mobile Fidelity	MFSL1120	1984	£4	£10	US audiophile

FAHEY, BRIAN ORCHESTRA

"At The Sign Of The Swinging Cymbal" is the theme tune of radio's "Pick Of The Pops", although it inevitably sounds incomplete without Alan Freeman's perfectly timed interjections.

Title	Format	Label	Catalogue	Year		
At The Sign Of The Swinging Cymbal	7"	Parlophone	R4686	1960	£2	£5
At The Sign Of The Swinging Cymbal	7"	Parlophone	R4909	1962	£1.50	£4
Twang	7"	United Artists	UP1115	1965	£1.50	£4

FAHEY, JOHN

America	LP	Sonet	SNTF628	1972	£4	£10	
Dance Of Death	LP	Takoma	1004	1965	£6	£15	US
Days Have Gone By	LP	Takoma	1014	1967	£6	£15	US
Death Chants & Breakdowns	LP	Sonet	SNTF608	1969	£6	£15	
Essential John Fahey	LP	Vanguard	VSD55/56	1974	£6	£15	double
Great San Bernadino Birthday Party	LP	Takoma	1008	1966	£6	£15	US
New Possibility	LP	Takoma	1020	1968	£6	£15	US
Requia	LP	Vanguard	SVRL19055	1968	£6	£15	
Transfiguration Of Blind Joe Death	LP	Sonet	SNTF607	1969	£6	£15	
Transfiguration Of Blind Joe Death	LP	Transatlantic	TRA173	1967	£6	£15	
Transfiguration Of Blind Joe Death	LP	Transatlantic	TRA173	1967	£8	£20	with booklet
Voice Of The Turtle	LP	Takoma	1019	1968	£6	£15	US
Yellow Princess	LP	Vanguard	SVRL19033	1968	£6	£15	

FAINE JADE

Introspection: A Faine Jade Recital	LP	R.S.V.P.	8002	1968	£30	£60	US

FAIR, JAD

Zombies Of Mora-Tau	7"	Armageddon	AEP003	1980	£5	£10

FAIR SET

Honey And Wine	7"	Decca	F12168	1965	£2	£5

FAIR, YVONNE

Bitch Is Black	LP	Tamla Motown	STML12008	1975	£5	£12

FAIRBURN, WERLY

All The Time	7"	London	HLC8349	1956	£180	£300

FAIRE, JOHNNY

Bertha Lou	7"	London	HLU8569	1958	£60	£120

FAIRFIELD PARLOUR

"From Home To Home" is the third LP by the English Kaleidoscope. The change of name to Fairfield Parlour brought no more than a marginal improvement to the group's fortunes, however, and the record today is almost as scarce as the first two.

Bordeaux Rose	7"	Prism	PRI1	1976	£4	£8	
Bordeaux Rose	7"	Vertigo	6059003	1970	£4	£8	
From Home To Home	LP	Vertigo	6360001	1970	£35	£70	spiral label
Just Another Day	7"	Vertigo	6059008	1970	£7.50	£15	

FAIRIES

Don't Mind	7"	HMV	POP1445	1965	£35	£70	
Don't Think Twice It's Alright	7"	Decca	F11943	1964	£30	£60	
Get Yourself Home	7"	HMV	POP1404	1965	£50	£100	

FAIRPORT CONVENTION

On their first LP Fairport Convention sound like an English Jefferson Airplane. The folk music influence begins to be felt on "What We Did On Our Holidays" and takes over altogether on "Liege and Lief". Thus over the course of four LPs, recorded in a period of not much more than a year, it is possible to hear the genesis of a new kind of rock music. The personnel changes in the group became rather complicated after this, but the various editions of Fairport Convention - and indeed the many groups derived from it - were able to explore the possibilities of the folk-rock fusion in many fruitful ways. The success of Fairport Convention's annual "reunion" at Copredy testifies to the tremendous loyalty of their considerable number of both fans and past members! Virtually all of the group's records are now collectable to a greater or lesser extent. It should be noted that, unlike many late sixties albums, the mono version of the Polydor LP does not appear to contain any different mixes to the stereo version, but it does somehow manage to deliver a crisper, more dynamic sound, which justifies its higher value.

Airing Cupboard Tapes	cass	Woodworm		1981	£6	£15	
Angel Delight	LP	Island	ILPS9162	1971	£6	£15	chart LP
AT2	LP	Woodworm	WR1	1984	£6	£15	
Babbacombe Lee	LP	Island	ILPS9176	1971	£6	£15	
Bonny Bunch Of Roses	LP	Vertigo	9102015	1977	£6	£15	
Expletive Delighted	LP	Woodworm	WR009	1986	£6	£15	
Fairport Convention	LP	Polydor	582035	1968	£20	£40	mono
Fairport Convention	LP	Polydor	583035	1968	£15	£30	
Farewell Farewell	LP	Simons	GAMA1	1979	£6	£15	chart LP
Full House	LP	Island	ILPS9130	1970	£6	£15	
Full House	LP	Island	ILPS9130	1970	£150	£250	test pressing with 'Poor Will & The Jolly Hangman'
Gottle O'Geer	LP	Island	ILPS9389	1976	£6	£15	
History Of Fairport Convention	LP	Island	ICD4	1972	£8	£20	blue ribbon on seal
History Of Fairport Convention	LP	Island	ICD4	1972	£6	£15	double
If I Had A Ribbon Bow	7"	Track	604020	1968	£6	£12	
If(Stomp)	7"	Polydor	2058014	1970	£4	£8	
In Real Time	LP	Island	ILPS9883	1987	£6	£15	
John Lee	7"	Island	WIP6128	1971	£1.50	£4	
John Lee	7"	Island	WIP6128	1971	£4	£8	PS
Liege And Lief	LP	Island	ILPS9115	1969	£8	£20	chart LP
Live A Movable Feast	LP	Island	ILPS9285	1974	£6	£15	
Live At Broughton Castle	LP	Stony Plain	SP51052	1985	£6	£15	
Live At L.A. Troubadour	LP	Island	HELP28	1976	£15	£30	
Meet On The Ledge	7"	Island	WIP6047	1968	£4	£8	
Moat On The Ledge	LP	Woodworm	WR001	1982	£6	£15	
Nine	LP	Island	ILPS9246	1973	£2	£5	
Now Be Thankful	7"	Island	WIP6089	1970	£6	£15	
Rising For The Moon	LP	Island	ILPS9313	1975	£6	£15	chart LP
Rosie	LP	Island	ILPS9208	1973	£6	£15	
Rosie	7"	Island	WIP6155	1973	£1.50	£4	
Rubber Band	7"	Simons	PMW1	1979	£1.50	£4	
Si Tu Dois Partir	7"	Island	WIP6064	1969	£1.50	£4	chart single
Tippler's Tales	LP	Vertigo	9102022	1978	£6	£15	
Tour Sampler	LP	Island	ISS2	1975	£40	£80	

Unhalfbricking	LP	Island	ILPS9102	1969	£8	£20	chart LP
What We Did On Our Holidays	LP	Island	ILPS9092	1968	£6	£15	
White Dress	7"	Island	WIP6241	1975	£1.50	£4	

FAIRWAYS

Yoko Ono	7"	Mercury	MF1116	1969	£2.50	£6	

FAIRWEATHER

Named after lead singer Andy Fairweather-Low, Fairweather were essentially a slimmed down version of Amen Corner. Seeing the way that rock music was going, the group attempted to put their pop past behind it by signing to RCA's new progressive label, Neon. They blew it, however, by gaining a hit single!

Beginning From An End	LP	Neon	NE1	1971	£5	£12	
Lay It On Me	7"	Neon	NE1000	1971	£2	£5	
Natural Sinner	7"	RCA	RCA1977	1970	£1.50	£4	chart single
Road To Freedom	7"	RCA	RCA2040	1971	£1.50	£4	

FAIRWEATHER, AL

Al And Sandy	LP	Columbia	33SX1159	1959	£6	£15	with Sandy Brown
Al's Pals	LP	Columbia	33SX1221	1960	£6	£15	
Fairweather Friends	10" LP	Nixa	NJT511	1958	£5	£12	

FAIRY'S MOKE

Fairy's Moke	LP	Deroy		1975	£15	£30	

FAIRYTALE

Guess I Was Dreaming	7"	Decca	F12644	1967	£20	£40	
Lovely People	7"	Decca	F12665	1967	£20	£40	

FAITH, ADAM

Adam	LP	Parlophone	PCS3010	1960	£6	£15	stereo, chart LP
Adam	LP	Parlophone	PMC1128	1960	£5	£12	mono, chart LP
Adam	LP	Regal	(S)REG1033	1960	£5	£12	export
Adam	7" EP	Parlophone	GEP8824	1960	£2.50	£6	
Adam	7" EP	Parlophone	SGE2014	1960	£5	£10	stereo
Adam Faith	LP	Amy	8005	1965	£8	£20	US
Adam Faith	LP	Parlophone	PCS3025	1961	£6	£15	stereo, chart LP
Adam Faith	LP	Parlophone	PMC1162	1961	£5	£12	mono, chart LP
Adam No.2	7" EP	Parlophone	GEP8826	1960	£2.50	£6	
Adam No.2	7" EP	Parlophone	SGE2015	1960	£5	£10	stereo
Adam No.3	7" EP	Parlophone	GEP8831	1960	£2.50	£6	
Adam No.3	7" EP	Parlophone	SGE2018	1960	£5	£10	stereo
Adam's Hit Parade	7" EP	Parlophone	GEP8811	1960	£2.50	£6	
Adam's Hit Parade Vol.2	7" EP	Parlophone	GEP8841	1961	£2.50	£6	
Adam's Hit Parade Vol.3	7" EP	Parlophone	GEP8862	1962	£4	£8	
Adam's Latest Hits	7" EP	Parlophone	GEP8877	1963	£4	£8	
All These Things	7" EP	Parlophone	GEP8852	1961	£2.50	£6	
As You Like It	7"	Parlophone	R4896	1962	£1.50	£4	chart single
Baby Take A Bow	7"	Parlophone	R4964	1962	£1.50	£4	chart single
Cheryl's Going Home	7"	Parlophone	R5516	1966	£1.50	£4	chart single
Daddy What'll Happen To Me	7"	Parlophone	R5635	1967	£1.50	£4	
Don't That Beat All	7"	Parlophone	R4930	1962	£1.50	£4	chart single
Don't You Know It	7"	Parlophone	R4807	1961	£1.50	£4	chart single
Easy Going Me	7"	Parlophone	R4766	1961	£1.50	£4	chart single
England's Top Singer	LP	MGM	(S)E3591	1961	£8	£20	US
Faith Alive	LP	Parlophone	PMC1249	1965	£15	£30	chart LP
First Time	7"	Parlophone	R5061	1963	£1.50	£4	chart single
For You	LP	Parlophone	PMC1213	1963	£5	£12	
For You - Adam	7" EP	Parlophone	GEP8904	1964	£4	£8	
From Adam With Love	LP	Parlophone	PCS3038	1962	£6	£15	stereo
From Adam With Love	LP	Parlophone	PMC1192	1962	£5	£12	mono
Hand Me Down Things	7"	Parlophone	R5260	1965	£1.50	£4	
Heartsick Feeling	7"	HMV	POP438	1958	£25	£50	
Hey Little Lovin' Girl	7"	Parlophone	R5673	1968	£1.50	£4	
High School Confidential	7"	HMV	POP557	1958	£15	£30	
How About That	7"	Parlophone	R4689	1960	£1.50	£4	chart single
I Don't Need That Kind Of Love	7"	Parlophone	R5349	1965	£1.50	£4	
I Just Don't Know	7"	Parlophone	R5174	1964	£1.50	£4	
I Love Being In Love With You	7"	Parlophone	R5138	1964	£1.50	£4	chart single
Idle Gossip	7"	Parlophone	R5398	1966	£1.50	£4	
If He Tells You	7"	Parlophone	R5109	1964	£1.50	£4	chart single
Lonely Pup	7"	Parlophone	R4708	1960	£1.50	£4	chart single
Lonesome	7"	Parlophone	R4864	1962	£1.50	£4	chart single
Message To Martha	7"	Parlophone	R5201	1964	£1.50	£4	chart single
Message To Martha - From Adam	7" EP	Parlophone	GEP8929	1965	£4	£8	
On The Move	LP	Parlophone	PMC1228	1964	£8	£20	
Poor Me	78	Parlophone	R4623	1960	£7.50	£15	
Poor Me	7"	Parlophone	R4623	1960	£1.50	£4	chart single
Runk Bunk	78	Top Rank	JAR126	1959	£10	£20	
Runk Bunk	7"	Top Rank	JAR126	1959	£6	£12	
Someone Else's Baby	7"	Parlophone	R4643	1960	£1.50	£4	chart single
Someone's Taken Maria Away	7"	Parlophone	R5289	1965	£1.50	£4	chart single
Songs And Things	7" EP	Parlophone	GEP8939	1965	£5	£10	
Stop Feeling Sorry For Yourself	7"	Parlophone	R5235	1965	£1.50	£4	
Sure Know A Lot About Love	7" EP	Parlophone	GEP8854	1961	£2.50	£6	
This Is It	7"	Parlophone	R4735	1961	£1.50	£4	chart single
Time Has Come	7"	Parlophone	R4837	1961	£1.50	£4	chart single
Time Has Come	7" EP	Parlophone	GEP8851	1961	£2.50	£6	
To Hell With Love	7"	Parlophone	R5649	1967	£1.50	£4	
To Make A Big Man Cry	7"	Parlophone	R5412	1966	£1.50	£4	
Top Of The Pops	7" EP	Parlophone	GEP8893	1964	£5	£10	
Walkin' Tall	7"	Parlophone	R5039	1963	£1.50	£4	chart single

We Are In Love	7"	Parlophone	R5091	1963	£1.50	£4	chart single
What Do You Want	7"	Parlophone	R4591	1959	£1.50	£4	chart single
What Do You Want?	78	Parlophone	R4591	1959	£7.50	£15	
What More Can Anyone Do	7"	Parlophone	R5556	1967	£1.50	£4	
What Now	7"	Parlophone	R4990	1963	£1.50	£4	chart single
When Johnny Comes Marching Home	7"	Parlophone	R4665	1960	£1.50	£4	chart single

FAITH, ADAM & JOHN BARRY

Beat Girl	LP	Columbia	33SX1225	1960	£10	£25	chart LP
Beat Girl	7" EP	Columbia	SEG8138	1962	£12.50	£25	

FAITH, HOPE & CHARITY

So Much Love	7"	Crewe	CRW3	1970	£1.50	£4	

FAITH, HORACE

Black Pearl	7"	Trojan	TR7790	1970	£1.50	£4	chart single
Daddy's Home	7"	Downtown	DT446	1969	£2	£5	
Spinning Wheel	7"	B&C	CB104	1969	£2	£5	

FAITH NO MORE

Anne's Song	7"	Slash	LASHP18	1988	£5	£10	pic disc
Anne's Song	12"	Slash	LASHX18	1988	£3	£8	
Epic	7"	Slash	LASPD21	1990	£2.50	£6	shaped pic disc
Real Thing	LP	Slash	8282171	1989	£4	£10	pic disc
We Care A Lot	12"	Slash	LASHX17	1988	£3	£8	

FAITHFUL, AUSTIN

Ain't That Peculiar	7"	Pyramid	PYR6042	1968	£4	£8	
Eternal Love	7"	Pyramid	PYR6028	1968	£4	£8	Roland Alphonso B side
Uncle Joe	7"	Blue Cat	BS140	1968	£4	£8	

FAITHFUL BREATH

Fading Beauty	LP	Cade	10002	1973	£8	£20	German

FAITHFULL, MARIANNE

A Bientot Nous Deux	7" EP	Decca	457094	1965	£7.50	£15	French
As Tears Go By	7"	Decca	F11923	1964	£1.50	£4	chart single
Blowing In The Wind	7"	Decca	F12007	1964	£2.50	£6	
Come And Stay With Me	7"	Decca	F12075	1965	£1.50	£4	chart single
Come And Stay With Me	7" EP	Decca	457068	1965	£6	£12	French
Come My Way	LP	Decca	LK4688	1965	£8	£20	chart LP
Coquillages	7" EP	Decca	457119	1966	£7.50	£15	French
Counting	7"	Decca	F12443	1966	£1.50	£4	
Counting	7" EP	Decca	457125	1966	£6	£12	French
Dreamin' My Dreams	LP	Nems	NEL6007	1976	£4	£10	
Faithful Forever	LP	London	LL3/PS482	1966	£8	£20	US
Faithless	LP	Nems	NEL6012	1978	£4	£10	
Go Away From My World	LP	London	LL3/PS452	1965	£8	£20	US
Greensleeves	7" EP	Decca	457049	1964	£10	£20	French
Hier Ou Demain	7" EP	Decca	457139	1967	£7.50	£15	French
Is This What I Get For Loving You	7"	Decca	F12524	1966	£1.50	£4	chart single
Love In A Mist	LP	Decca	LK/SKL4854	1967	£10	£25	
Marianne Faithfull	LP	Decca	LK4689	1965	£8	£20	chart LP
Marianne Faithfull	7" EP	Decca	DFE8624	1965	£2.50	£6	
North Country Maid	LP	Decca	LK4778	1966	£8	£20	
Sister Morphine	7"	Decca	F12889	1969	£10	£20	
Summer Nights	7"	Decca	F12193	1965	£1.50	£4	chart single
Summer Nights	7" EP	Decca	457085	1965	£6	£12	French
This Little Bird	7"	Decca	F12162	1965	£1.50	£4	chart single
Tomorrow's Calling	7"	Decca	F12408	1966	£1.50	£4	
World Of Marianne Faithfull	LP	Decca	SPA17	1969	£4	£10	
Yesterday	7"	Decca	F12268	1965	£1.50	£4	chart single
Yesterday	7" EP	Decca	457097	1965	£6	£12	French

FALCONS

Billy The Kid	7"	London	HLU10146	1967	£2	£5	
I Found A Love	7"	London	HLK9565	1962	£12.50	£25	
You're So Fine	7"	London	HLT8876	1959	£20	£40	

FALCONS (2)

Stampede	7"	Philips	BF1297	1964	£2.50	£6	

FALL

Bingo Masters Breakout	7"	Step Forward	SF7	1978	£2	£5	
Dragnet	LP	Step Forward	SFLP4	1979	£4	£10	
Fall In A Hole	LP	Flying Nun	MARK1/2	1983	£15	£30	New Zealand, with 12'
Fiery Jack	7"	Step Forward	SF13	1980	£2	£5	2 PS's
Grotesque	LP	Rough Trade	ROUGH18	1980	£4	£10	
It's The New Thing	7"	Step Forward	SF9	1978	£1.50	£4	
Kicker Conspiracy	7"	Rough Trade	RT143	1983	£2.50	£6	double PS
Live At The Witch Trials	LP	Step Forward	SFLP1	1979	£4	£10	
Marquis Cha Cha	7"	Kamera	ERA014	1982	£7.50	£15	
Rowche Rumble	7"	Step Forward	SF11	1979	£1.50	£4	
Slates	10"	Rough Trade	RT071	1981	£3	£8	
Totale's Turns	LP	Rough Trade	ROUGH10	1980	£4	£10	

FALLEN ANGELS

Fallen Angels	LP	London	HAZ/SHZ8359	1968	£4	£10	
I Don't Want To Fall	7"	London	HL10166	1967	£1.50	£4	
It's A Long Way Down	LP	Roulette	SR42011	1968	£6	£15	US

FALLIN, JOHNNY

Party Kiss	7"	Capitol	CL15043	1959	£6	£12	
Wild Streak	7"	Capitol	CL15091	1959	£7.50	£15	

FALLING LEAVES

Beggar's Parade	7"	Decca	F12420	1966	£6	£12	
She Loves To Be Loved	7"	Parlophone	R5233	1965	£12.50	£25	

FALLOUT

Butchery	LP	I	FLP2	1984	£8	£20	

FALTSKOG, AGNETHA

Agnetha	LP	Cupol	CLP64	1968	£10	£25	Swedish
Agnetha	LP	Cupol	CLPL1002	197-	£5	£12	Swedish
Agnetha	LP	Embassy	EMB31094	1968	£20	£40	Swedish
Agnetha Faltskog	LP	Cupol		1972	£5	£12	Swedish
Agnetha Vol.2	LP	Cupol	CLP80	1969	£8	£20	Swedish
Agnetha Vol.2	LP	Cupol	CLPL1003	197-	£5	£12	Swedish
Basta	LP	Cupol	CLPL1023	1973	£15	£30	Swedish
Can't Shake Loose	7"	Epic	EPCA3812	1983	£1.50	£4	poster PS
Elva Kvinnor I Ett Hus	LP	Cupol	CLPS351	1975	£5	£12	Swedish
Nar En Vacker Tanke Blir En Sang	LP	Cupol	CLPN348	1971	£15	£30	Swedish
Som Jag Ar	LP	Cupol	CLPL1016	197-	£5	£12	Swedish
Som Jag Ar	LP	Cupol	CLPN345	1970	£10	£25	Swedish
Tio Ar Med	LP	Cupol	CLPS352	1979	£5	£12	Swedish

FAME, GEORGIE

Georgie Fame's lengthy and still flourishing career (his earliest recordings are as a member of Billy Fury's backing group) has produced few real collectors' items. Of his series of distinctive, jazz-inflected albums, only the first is in the same price league as his contemporaries - the others sold well when new, but are clearly considered by modern collectors to be too polished and too far removed from how British R&B should sound. Two scarce early singles were credited to the Blue Flames, with no mention of Georgie Fame's name. they are listed in this Guide under the Blue Flames.

Ballad Of Bonnie And Clyde	7"	CBS	3124	1967	£1.50	£4	chart single
Because I Love You	7"	CBS	202587	1967	£1.50	£4	chart single
Because I Love You	7"	CBS	202587	1967	£2	£5	PS
Bend A Little	7"	Columbia	DB7328	1964	£2	£5	
By The Time I Get To Phoenix	7"	CBS	3526	1968	£1.50	£4	
Do Re Mi	7"	Columbia	DB7255	1964	£2.50	£6	
Do The Dog	7" EP	Columbia	ESRF1516	1964	£10	£20	French
Does His Own Thing With Strings	LP	CBS	63650	1970	£4	£10	
Fame At Last	LP	Columbia	33SX1638	1964	£6	£15	chart LP
Fame At Last	7" EP	Columbia	SEG8393	1964	£4	£8	
Fats For Fame	7" EP	Columbia	SEG8406	1965	£5	£10	
Get Away	LP	Imperial	LP9331/12331	1966	£5	£12	US
Get Away	7"	208 Luxembourg		1964	£4	£8	1 sided promo
Get Away	7"	Columbia	DB7946	1966	£1.50	£4	chart single
Get Away	7" EP	Columbia	ESRF1796	1966	£6	£12	French
Get Away	7" EP	Columbia	SEG8518	1966	£4	£8	
Hall Of Fame	LP	Columbia	SX6120	1967	£5	£12	chart LP
In The Meantime	7"	Columbia	DB7494	1965	£1.50	£4	chart single
In The Meantime	7" EP	Columbia	ESRF1645	1964	£6	£12	French
Knock On Wood	7" EP	CBS	EP6363	1967	£2.50	£6	
Like We Used To Be	7"	Columbia	DB7633	1965	£1.50	£4	chart single
Like We Used To Be	7" EP	Columbia	ESRF1706	1965	£6	£12	French
Move It On Over	7" EP	Columbia	SEG8454	1965	£5	£10	
Peaceful	7"	CBS	4295	1969	£1.50	£4	chart single
R&B At The Flamingo	LP	Columbia	SX1599	1964	£10	£25	
R&B At The Flamingo	7" EP	Columbia	SEG8382	1964	£5	£10	
Rhythm And Blue Beat	7" EP	Columbia	SEG8334	1964	£7.50	£15	
Seventh Son	LP	CBS	63786	1969	£4	£10	
Seventh Son	7"	CBS	4659	1969	£1.50	£4	chart single
Shop Around	7"	Columbia	DB7193	1964	£4	£8	
Sitting In The Park	7"	Columbia	DB8096	1966	£1.50	£4	chart single
Sitting In The Park	7" EP	Columbia	ESRF1848	1967	£6	£12	French
Something	7"	Columbia	DB7727	1965	£1.50	£4	chart single
Something	7" EP	Columbia	ESRF1751	1966	£6	£12	French
Sound Venture	LP	Columbia	SX6076	1966	£5	£12	chart LP
Sunny	7"	Columbia	DB8015	1966	£1.50	£4	chart single
Sweet Things	LP	Columbia	SX6043	1966	£5	£12	chart LP
Third Face Of Fame	LP	CBS	63293	1968	£4	£10	
Try My World	7"	CBS	2945	1967	£1.50	£4	chart single
Two Faces Of Fame	LP	CBS	63018	1967	£4	£10	chart LP
Yeah Yeah	7"	Columbia	DB7428	1964	£1.50	£4	chart single
Yeh Yeh	LP	Imperial	LP9282/12282	1965	£5	£12	US
Yeh Yeh	7" EP	Columbia	ESRF1618	1964	£6	£12	French

FAME, GEORGIE & ALAN PRICE

Fame And Price	LP	CBS	64392	1971	£4	£10	

FAMILY

Family's first single, "Scene Thru The Eye Of A Lens", is something of a psychedelic classic, and has not been reissued. "Music In A Doll's House" was to some extent taken over by Dave Mason, who produced the record and played on it. It is a wonderful LP, however, and proof that the real sixties gems have already been discovered, and do not cost a fortune. Subsequent Family records are increasingly ordinary, although each undoubtedly has its moments, and they are all highlighted by the extraordinary Roger Chapman voice.

Family Entertainment	LP	Reprise	RLP6340	1969	£8	£20	with poster, mono, chart LP
Family Entertainment	LP	Reprise	RSLP6340	1969	£6	£15	with poster, stereo, chart LP
In My Own Time	7"	Reprise	K14090	1971	£1.50	£4	chart single, PS

Larf And Sing	7"	Reprise	SAM1	1971	£4	£8	promo
Me My Friend	7"	Reprise	RS23270	1968	£2.50	£6	
Music In A Doll's House	LP	Reprise	RLP6312	1968	£8	£20	with poster, mono, chart LP
Music In A Doll's House	LP	Reprise	RSLP6312	1968	£6	£15	with poster, stereo, chart LP
No Mule's Fool	7"	Reprise	RS27001	1969	£4	£8	PS
Scene Thru The Eye Of A Lens	7"	Liberty	LBF15031	1967	£30	£60	
Second Generation Woman	7"	Reprise	RS23315	1968	£2.50	£6	
Song For Me	LP	Reprise	RSLP9001	1970	£5	£12	chart LP
Strange Band	7"	Reprise	RS27009	1970	£2	£5	PS
Today	7"	Reprise	RS27005	1970	£4	£8	PS

FAMILY AFFAIR
Family Affair	LP	Saga	FID2124	1968	£4	£10	

FAMILY DOGG
Arizona	7"	Bell	BLL1077	1969	£1.50	£4	
Brown Eyed Girl	7"	Fontana	TF968	1968	£2	£5	
Family Dogg	7"	MGM	MGM1360	1967	£4	£8	
I Wear A Silly Grin	7"	Fontana	TF921	1968	£1.50	£4	
Way Of Life	LP	Bell	SP22122	1969	£5	£12	
Way Of Life	7"	Bell	BLL1055	1969	£1.50	£4	chart single

FAMILY OF APOSTOLIC
Family Of Apostolic	LP	Vanguard	SDVL1	1969	£8	£20	double

FAMILY PLANN
Sexy Summer	7"	President	PT441	1975	£1.50	£4	

FAMOUS JUG BAND
Chameleon	LP	Liberty	LBS83355	1970	£6	£15	
Only Friend I Own	7"	Liberty	LBF15224	1969	£4	£8	
Sunshine Possibilities	LP	Liberty	LBS83263	1969	£10	£25	

FAMOUS WARD SINGERS
Famous Ward Singers Vol.1	7" EP	London	EZC19024	1958	£4	£8	
Famous Ward Singers Vol.2	7" EP	London	EZC19033	1958	£4	£8	
Famous Ward Singers Vol.3	7" EP	London	EZC19034	1958	£2.50	£6	
I Knew It Was The Lord	78	London	HL8065	1954	£10	£20	

FAN CLUB
Avenue	7"	M&S	SJP791	1978	£4	£8	

FANKHAUSER, MERRELL
Merrell Fankhauser	LP	Maui	101	1976	£8	£20	US
Merrell Fankhauser & His HMS Bounty	LP	Shamley	SS701	1968	£8	£20	US

FANTASTIC BAGGYS
Summer Means Fun	7"	United Artists	UP36142	1976	£2	£5	Jan And Dean B side
Tell 'Em I'm Surfin'	LP	Imperial	LP9270/12270	1964	£25	£50	US

FANTASTIC FOUR
Fantastic Four	LP	Tamla Motown	(S)TML11105	1969	£8	£20	
I Love You Madly	7"	Tamla Motown	TMG678	1968	£5	£10	

FANTASTIC PUZZLES
Come Back	7"	Inferno	HEAT14	1980	£1.50	£4	

FANTASTICS
Baby Make Your Own Sweet Music	7"	MGM	MGM1434	1968	£2	£5	
Face To Face With Heartache	7"	Deram	DM264	1969	£1.50	£4	

FANTASY
Paint A Picture	LP	Polydor	2383246	1973	£100	£200	
Politely Insane	7"	Polydor	2058405	1973	£10	£20	

FANTONI, BARRY
Little Man In A Little Box	7"	Fontana	TF707	1966	£5	£10	
Nothing Today	7"	Columbia	DB8238	1967	£2	£5	

FAPARDOKLY
Fapardokly	LP	Psycho	PSYCHO5	1983	£5	£12	
Fapardokly	LP	V.I.P.	250	1966	£150	£250	US

FAR CRY
Far Cry	LP	Vanguard	SVRL19041	1969	£5	£12	

FAR EAST FAMILY BAND
Cave Down To Earth	LP	Muland	CD7139M	1975	£8	£20	Japanese
Far Out	LP	Denon		1975	£8	£20	Japanese
Nepporjin	LP	Vertigo	6370850	1975	£6	£15	
Parallel World	LP	Muland	LQ7002M	1976	£8	£20	Japanese
Tenkeyin	LP	All Ears	114797	1977	£6	£15	US
Torn Hatano	LP	Muland		1977	£8	£20	Japanese

FAR OUT
Far Out	LP	Denon		1972	£100	£200	Japanese

FARAWAY FOLK
Introducing The Faraway Folk	7" EP	RA	EP7001	197-	£7.50	£15	

Live At Bolton	LP	RA	LP6006ST	1970	£35	£70	
On The Radio	LP	RA	LP6019	197-	£15	£30	
Only Authorised Employees To Break Bottles	LP	RA	LP6022	197-	£10	£25	
Seasonal Man	LP	RA	RALP6029	1975	£50	£100	
Shadow Of A Pie	7"	Tabitha	TAB3	197-	£2	£5	
Time And Tide	LP	RA	LP6012ST	197-	£35	£70	

FARDON, DON

Good Lovin'	7"	Pye	7N25486	1969	£1.50	£4	
Indian Reservation	7"	Pye	7N25437	1967	£2	£5	
Indian Reservation	7"	Pye	7N25475	1968	£1.50	£4	
Indian Reservation	7"	Young Blood	YB1015	1970	£1.50	£4	chart single
Lament Of The Cherokee Indian Reservation	LP	GNP	2044	1968	£4	£10	US
Letter	7" EP	Vogue	EPL8583	1967	£10	£20	French
We Can Make It Together	7"	Pye	7N25483	1969	£1.50	£4	

FARINA, RICHARD & MIMI

Richard and Mimi Farina were a folk duo typical of the many folk acts that were a dominant strain within the American music of the early sixties. Most managed to come up with a significant song or two - the Farinas' included "Pack Up All Your Sorrows" and "Hard Lovin' Loser", which were recorded by Judy Collins. Richard Farina was killed in a motorcycle accident in 1966, but his wife Mimi, who is Joan Baez' sister, has managed to follow a reasonably successful career since as a musician and actress.

Best Of Richard And Mimi Farina	LP	Vanguard	VSD21/22	1973	£6	£15	double
Celebrations For A Grey Day	LP	Fontana	(S)TFL6060	1965	£6	£15	
Memories	LP	Vanguard	VSD79263	1968	£6	£15	US
Refelctions In A Crystal Wind	LP	Fontana	(S)TFL6075	1965	£6	£15	
Richard & Mimi Farina	LP	Vanguard	VSD79174	1965	£6	£15	US
Richard Farina	LP	Vanguard	VSD79281	1968	£6	£15	US

FARINAS

The Farinas were a blues and soul group from Leicester, but as soon as they began to write their own material, they changed their name - to Family.

I Like It Like That	7"	Fontana	TF493	1964	£15	£30	

FARLOW, TAL

Interpretations	LP	Columbia	33CX10029	1956	£15	£30	
Swinging Guitar	LP	Columbia	33CX10132	1959	£6	£15	
Tal Farlow	10" LP	Columbia	33C9041	1957	£10	£25	

FARLOWE, CHRIS

14 Things To Think About	LP	Immediate	IMLP005	1966	£10	£25	chart LP
Air Travel	7"	Decca	F11536	1962	£10	£20	
Art Of Chris Farlowe	LP	Immediate	IMLP006	1966	£10	£25	chart LP
Best Of Chris Farlowe	LP	Immediate	IMLP010	1968	£6	£15	
Black Sheep Of The Family	7"	Polydor	2066017	1971	£2	£5	
Buzz With The Fuzz	7"	Columbia	DB7614	1965	£30	£60	
Chris Farlowe	LP	Regal	REG2025	1968	£4	£10	export
Chris Farlowe	7" EP	Decca	DFE8665	1965	£20	£40	
Chris Farlowe And The Thunderbirds	LP	Columbia	SX/SCX6034	1966	£15	£30	
Dawn	7"	Immediate	IM074	1969	£4	£8	
Fool	7"	Immediate	IM016	1965	£4	£8	
From Here To Mama Rosa	LP	Polydor	2425029	1970	£5	£12	
Girl Trouble	7"	Columbia	DB7237	1964	£5	£10	
Handbags And Gladrags	7"	Immediate	IM065	1967	£1.50	£4	chart single
Hits	7" EP	Immediate	IMEP004	1966	£7.50	£15	
Hound Dog	7"	Columbia	DB7379	1964	£4	£8	
I Remember	7"	Columbia	DB7120	1963	£4	£8	
In The Midnight Hour	7" EP	Immediate	IMEP001	1965	£7.50	£15	
Just A Dream	7"	Columbia	DB7311	1964	£4	£8	
Just A Dream	7"	Columbia	DB7983	1966	£4	£8	
Last Goodbye	LP	Immediate	IMLP021	1969	£15	£30	
Moanin'	7"	Immediate	IM056	1967	£2	£5	chart single
My Way Of Giving	7"	Immediate	IM041	1967	£2	£8	chart single
Out Of Time	7"	Immediate	IM035	1966	£2	£5	
Out Of Time	7"	Immediate	IM078	1969	£1.50	£4	chart single
Out Of Time	7" EP	Columbia	ESRF1806	1966	£7.50	£15	French
Paint It Black	7"	Immediate	IM071	1968	£2.50	£6	
Paperman Fly In The Sky	7"	Immediate	IM066	1968	£5	£10	
Put Out The Light	7"	Polydor	2066046	1971	£2	£5	
Ride On Baby	7"	Immediate	IM038	1966	£2	£5	chart single
Ride On Baby	7" EP	Columbia	ESRF1837	1966	£7.50	£15	French
Stormy Monday	7"	MFP	MFP1186	1967	£4	£10	
Stormy Monday	7" EP	Island	IEP709	1966	£25	£50	
Think	7"	Immediate	IM023	1966	£2	£5	chart single
We Can Work It Out	7"	Polydor	2058650	1975	£1.50	£4	
Yesterday's Paper	7" EP	Columbia	ESRF1875	1967	£7.50	£15	French
Yesterday's Papers	7"	Immediate	IM049	1967	£2	£5	

FARLOWE, TAL

Tal Farlowe	10" LP	Columbia	33C9052	1957	£6	£15	

FARM

Hearts And Minds	12"	Skysaw	END1	1984	£2.50	£6	
Steps Of Emotion	7"	Admiralty	PRA1	1985	£2.50	£6	

FARM BAND

Farm Band	LP	Mantra	777	197-	£8	£20	US

FARMER, ART

Art Farmer	7" EP	Vogue	EPV1045	1955	£2	£5	

Art Farmer Quintet	10" LP	Esquire	20087	1957	£20	£40	
Art Farmerr Quintet	10" LP	Esquire	20057	1956	£25	£50	
Aztec Suite	LP	London	LTZT15198	1960	£8	£20	
Brass Shout	LP	London	LTZT15184	1960	£8	£20	
Charts	LP	Esquire	32042	1958	£8	£20	
Early Art	LP	Esquire	32120	1961	£8	£20	
Interaction	LP	London	HAK/SHK8135	1964	£6	£15	
Modern Art	LP	London	LTZT15167/	1959	£8	£20	
			SAHT6028				
Music For That Wild Party	LP	Esquire	32037	1958	£10	£25	
Portrait	LP	Contemporary	LAC12197	1959	£5	£12	
Work Of Art	10" LP	Esquire	20033	1954	£20	£40	

FARMER, JULES
Love Me Now	7"	London	HLP8967	1959	£2	£5	

FARMLIFE
Big Country	7"	Whaam!	WHAAM13	1983	£15	£30	test pressing

FARNABY, GILES DREAM BAND
Giles Farnaby's Dream Band	LP	Argo	ZDA158	1973	£50	£100	

FARNER, MARK & DON BREWER
Monumental Funk	LP	Quadico	Q7401	1974	£5	£12	US
Monumental Funk	LP	Quadico	Q7401	1974	£8	£20	US pic disc

FARO, WAYNE SCHMALTZ BAND
There's Still Time	7"	Deram	DM222	1969	£4	£8	

FARON'S FLAMINGOES
See If She Cares	7"	Oriole	CB1834	1963	£5	£10	
Shake Sherry	7"	Oriole	CB1867	1963	£5	£10	

FARR, GARY
Addressed To The Censors Of Love	LP	Atco	SD7034	1973	£5	£12	US
Everyday	7"	Marmalade	598007	1968	£2.50	£6	with Kevin Westlake
Hey Daddy	7"	Marmalade	598017	1969	£5	£10	
Revolution Of The Season	7"	CBS	5430	1971	£2	£5	
Strange Fruit	LP	CBS	64138	1971	£10	£25	
Take Something With You	LP	Marmalade	608013	1969	£20	£40	

FARR, GARY & THE T-BONES
Dem Bones Dem Bones Dem T-Bones	7" EP	Columbia	SEG8414	1965	£30	£60	
Give All She's Got	7"	Columbia	DB7608	1965	£10	£20	

FARRELL, DO & DENA
Young Magic	7"	HMV	POP427	1957	£2.50	£6	

FARRELL, JOE
Joe Farrell Quartet	LP	Philips	6308046	1970	£4	£10	

FARREN, MICK
Carnivorous Circus (Mona)	LP	Transatlantic	TRA212	1970	£20	£40	
Vampires Stole My Lunch Money	LP	Logo	LOGO2010	1978	£4	£10	

FARRIERS & KEMPION
Brummagem Ballads	LP	Broadside	BRO119	1976	£6	£15	

FASCINATIONS
Girls Are Out To Get You	7"	Mojo	2092004	1971	£1.50	£4	chart single
Girls Are Out To Get You	7"	Stateside	SS594	1967	£15	£30	
Girls Are Out To Get You	7"	Sue	WI4049	1968	£7.50	£15	
I'm So Lucky	7"	Mojo	2092018	1971	£2	£5	

FASCINATORS
Chapel Bells	7"	Capitol	CL14942	1958	£17.50	£35	
Oh Rose Marie	7"	Capitol	CL15062	1959	£12.50	£25	

FASHIONS
I.O.U.	7"	Evolution	E2444	1969	£2.50	£6	
I.O.U.	7"	Stateside	SS2115	1968	£2.50	£6	

FAST BREEDER & THE RADIO ACTORS
Nuclear Waste	7"	Virgin	NONUKE235	1978	£2.50	£6	
Nuclear Waste	7"	Virgin	NONUKE235	1978	£7.50	£15	PS

FAST SET
Junction One	7"	Axis	AXIS1	1980	£5	£10	

FAT
Fat	LP	RCA	LPS4368	1970	£6	£15	

FAT LADY SINGS
Be Still	7"	Harbour Sound	HSS1	1988	£2	£5	
Fear And Favour	7"	Good Vibrations	FLS1	1986	£4	£8	

FAT MATTRESS
Even while still a member of the Jimi Hendrix Experience, bassist Noel Redding began playing with his own group in order to switch back to the guitar he had always really preferred. Fat Mattress inevitably attracted attention simply because of Redding's presence, but the sad fact was that the most interesting aspect of the group was the cover of the first LP, which opens out into a two-foot square sheet of card.

Fat Mattress	LP	Polydor	583056	1969	£6	£15	
Fat Mattress 2	LP	Polydor	2383025	1970	£4	£10	
Highway	7"	Polydor	2058053	1970	£2.50	£6	
Magic Forest	7"	Polydor	56367	1969	£4	£8	
Naturally	7"	Polydor	56352	1969	£4	£8	

FATHER YOD

All Or Nothing At All	LP	Higher Key	3304	1974	£30	£60	US
Kahoutek	LP	Higher Key	3301	1973	£30	£60	US

FATHERS ANGELS

Bok To Bach	7"	MGM	MGM1459	1968	£40	£80	

FATS & THE CHESSMEN

Big Ben Twist	7"	Pye	7N25122	1962	£1.50	£4	

FAUN

Faun	LP	Gregar	GG70000	1969	£8	£20	US

FAUST

Faust	LP	Polydor	2310142	1971	£6	£15	
Faust	LP	Polydor	2310142	1971	£8	£20	clear vinyl
Faust 4	LP	Virgin	V2004	1973	£5	£12	
Faust One	LP	Recommended	RRA1	1979	£4	£10	
Faust So Far	LP	Recommended	RR2	1979	£4	£10	with 10 prints
So Far	LP	Polydor	2310196	1972	£5	£12	

FAVOURITE SONS

That Driving Beat	7"	Mercury	MF911	1965	£20	£40	

FAWKES, WALLY

Fawkes On Holiday	10" LP	Decca	LF1312	1958	£6	£15	

FAWKES, WALLY & BRUCE TURNER

Fawkes-Turner Sextet	10" LP	Decca	LF1214	1956	£10	£25	

FAY, BILL

Bill Fay	LP	Nova	SDN12	1970	£10	£25	
Some Good Advice	7"	Deram	DM143	1967	£25	£50	
Time Of Last Persecution	LP	Deram	SML1079	1971	£25	£50	

FAYE, FRANCIS

Frenesi	7"	HMV	POP898	1961	£1.50	£4	
I Wish I Could Shimmy Like My Sister Kate	7"	Vogue	V9186	1961	£4	£8	

FEAR OF FALLING

Like A Lion	7"	Excellent	XL7	1983	£7.50	£15	

FEARNS BRASS FOUNDRY

Don't Change It	7"	Decca	F12721	1968	£4	£8	
Love, Sink And Drown	7"	Decca	F12835	1968	£2.50	£6	

FEATHER, LEONARD

Hi Fi Suite	LP	MGM	C762	1957	£4	£10	with Dick Hyman
One World Jazz	LP	Philips	BBL7361	1960	£4	£10	
Winter Sequence	10" LP	MGM	D135	1955	£20	£40	

FEATHERS, CHARLIE & MAC CURTIS

Rockabilly Kings	LP	Polydor	2310293	1974	£5	£12	

FEDERAL DUCK

Federal Duck	LP	Musicor	MS3162	1968	£6	£15	US

FEDERALS

Boot Hill	7"	Parlophone	R5013	1963	£1.50	£4	
Brazil	7"	Parlophone	R4988	1963	£1.50	£4	
Bucket Full Of Love	7"	Parlophone	R5320	1965	£2	£5	
Climb	7"	Parlophone	R5100	1964	£1.50	£4	
Marlena	7"	Parlophone	R5139	1964	£1.50	£4	
Twilight Time	7"	Parlophone	R5193	1964	£1.50	£4	

FEDERALS (2)

In This World	7"	Camel	CA40	1970	£2	£5	
I've Passed This Way Before	7"	Island	WI3126	1967	£5	£10	
Shocking Love	7"	Island	WI3152	1968	£5	£10	
Wailing Festival	7"	High Note	HS024	1969	£2.50	£6	

FEDERATION

Two Minutes To Love	7"	Twentieth Century	1023	1976	£1.50	£4	

FELDER'S ORIOLES

Backstreet	7"	Piccadilly	7N35332	1966	£5	£10	
Down Home Girl	7"	Piccadilly	7N35247	1965	£6	£12	
Know You Don't Love Me No More	7"	Piccadilly	7N35311	1966	£6	£12	
Sweet Tasting Wine	7"	Piccadilly	7N35269	1965	£6	£12	

FELDMAN, MARTY

Funny He Never Married	7"	Pye	7N17643	1968	£1.50	£4	
Feel A Song Going Off	LP	Decca	LK/SKL4983	1969	£4	£10	
Joyous Time Of Year	7"	Decca	F12857	1968	£1.50	£4	

Marty	LP	Pye	NPL18258	1968	£4	£10	

FELDMAN, MARTY, JOHN CLEESE & OTHERS

At Last The 1948 Show	LP	Pye	NPL18198	1967	£4	£10	

FELDMAN, VICTOR

Arrival Of Victor Feldman	LP	Contemporary	LAC12172	1959	£5	£12	
In London Vol.1	LP	Tempo	TAP8	1957	£5	£12	
In London Vol.2	LP	Tempo	TAP12	1957	£5	£12	
Multi-Recording Session	10" LP	Esquire	20046	1955	£10	£25	
Transatlantic Alliance	LP	Tempo	TAP19	1958	£5	£12	
Vibes To The Power Of Three	LP	Top Rank	30007	1960	£5	£12	with Terry Gibbs & Larry Bunker
Victor Feldman Modern Jazz Quartet	10" LP	Tempo	LAP6	1956	£6	£15	
Victor Feldman's Sextet	10" LP	Tempo	LAP5	1955	£6	£15	
With Kenny Graham	10" LP	Esquire	20064	1956	£8	£20	

FELICE, DEE TRIO

In The Heat	LP	Bethlehem	B1000	1969	£8	£20	US

FELIUS ANDROMEDA

Meditations	7"	Decca	F12694	1967	£15	£30	

FELIX & HIS GUITAR

Chili Beans	7"	London	HLU8875	1959	£2	£5	

FELIX, JULIE

Changes	LP	Fontana	(S)TL5368	1966	£4	£10	chart LP
Flowers	LP	Fontana	(S)TL5437	1967	£4	£10	
Julie Felix	LP	Decca	LK4626	1964	£4	£10	
Julie Felix In Concert	LP	World Record Club	ST842	1968	£4	£10	
Second Album	LP	Decca	LK4724	1965	£4	£10	
Sings Dylan & Guthrie	LP	Decca	LK4683?	1965	£4	£10	
Third Album	LP	Decca	LK4820	1966	£4	£10	
This World Goes Round And Round	LP	Fontana	(S)TL5473	1968	£4	£10	

FELIX, LENNIE

Cat Meets Mice	LP	Columbia	33SX1298	1961	£4	£10	
Cat On A Hot Tin Piano	10" LP	Columbia	33S1144	1959	£4	£10	
Let's Put Out The Cat	LP	Top Rank	35034	1960	£4	£10	
That Cat Felix	10" LP	Nixa	NJT514	1958	£6	£15	

FELIX, MIKE

Blueberry Hill	7"	Decca	F12701	1967	£1.50	£4	
You Belong To Me	7"	Pye	7N17058	1966	£1.50	£4	

FELT

Index	7"	Shanghai	CUS321	1979	£15	£30	
My Face Is On Fire	7"	Cherry Red	CHERRY45	1982	£2	£5	
Something Sends Me To Sleep	7"	Cherry Red	CHERRY26	1981	£2.50	£6	

FELT (2)

Felt	LP	Nasco	9006	1971	£10	£25	US

FEMININE TOUCH

You Make Me Come Alive	7"	Paladin	PAL11	1976	£1.50	£4	

FENCE

The lone single release by the Fence is collected by fans of the Levellers, due to the fact that the latter's drummer Charlie Heather and bass player Jeremy Cunningham made their recording debut here.

Frozen Water	7"	Hag	HAG1	1987	£12.50	£25	

FENDA, JAYMES & THE VULCANS

Mistletoe Love	7"	Parlophone	R5210	1964	£2.50	£6	

FENDER, JAN & BUSTER

Sweet Pea	7"	Fab	FAB164	1971	£2.50	£6	

FENDERMEN

Don't You Just Know It	7"	Top Rank	JAR513	1960	£4	£8	
Mule Skinner Blues	LP	Soma	MG1240	1960	£250	£400	US
Mule Skinner Blues	7"	Top Rank	JAR395	1960	£2.50	£6	chart single

FENMEN

Be My Girl	7"	Decca	F11955	1964	£4	£8	
California Dreamin'	7"	CBS	202075	1966	£4	£8	
I've Got Everything You Need	7"	Decca	F12269	1965	£4	£8	
Rejected	7"	CBS	202236	1966	£7.50	£15	

FENTON, PETER

I Was Lord Kitchener's Valet	7"	Fontana	TF789	1967	£1.50	£4	
Marble Breaks Iron Bends	7"	Fontana	TF748	1966	£1.50	£4	chart single

FENTON, SHANE & THE FENTONES

Bernard Jewry has had two separate singing careers. Best known as Alvin Stardust in the seventies, he was also Shane Fenton in the early sixties, achieving a few minor successes in a style which owed everything to Cliff Richard and Billy Fury.

Eastern Seaboard	7"	Fury	FY305	1972	£4	£8	
Don't Do That	7"	Parlophone	R5047	1963	£2	£5	
Fool's Paradise	7"	Parlophone	R5020	1963	£2	£5	
Good Rocking Tonight	LP	Contour	2870409	1974	£5	£12	
Hey Lulu	7"	Parlophone	R5131	1964	£2	£5	

I Ain't Got Nobody	7"	Parlophone	R4982	1963	£2.50	£6	
I'm A Moody Guy	7"	Parlophone	R4827	1961	£2.50	£6	chart single
It's All Over Now	7"	Parlophone	R4883	1962	£2	£5	chart single
It's Gonna Take Magic	7"	Parlophone	R4921	1962	£2.50	£6	chart single
Too Young For Sad Memories	7"	Parlophone	R4951	1962	£2	£5	
Walk Away	7"	Parlophone	R4866	1962	£2	£5	chart single

FENTONES

Breeze And I	7"	Parlophone	R4937	1962	£2	£5	chart single
Mexican	7"	Parlophone	R4899	1962	£2.50	£6	chart single

FENWAYS

Walk	7"	Liberty	LIB66082	1965	£4	£8

FENWICK, RAY

Keep America Beautiful	LP	Decca	SKL5090	1971	£6	£15

FERGUSON, H-BOMB

Feel Like I Do	78	Esquire	10372	1954	£7.50	£15

FERGUSON, HELENA

Where Is The Party	7"	London	HLZ10164	1967	£7.50	£15

FERGUSON, JESSIE LEE & THE OUTER LIMITS

New Shoes	7"	Pye	7N25492	1969	£2.50	£6

FERGUSON, JOHNNY

Angela Jones	7"	MGM	MGM1059	1960	£1.50	£4

FERGUSON, MAYNARD

Around The Horn	LP	Emarcy	EJL1275	1958	£6	£15	
Boy With Lots Of Brass	LP	Mercury	MMC14050/ CMS18034	1960	£5	£12	
Boy With Lots Of Brass	LP	Mercury	MMC14050	1960	£5	£12	
Dimensions	LP	Emarcy	EJL1287	1958	£8	£20	
Jam Session	LP	Emarcy	EJL1270	1958	£6	£15	
Jazz For Dancing	LP	Columbia	33SX1270/ SCX3338	1960	£5	£12	
Message From Birdland	LP	Columbia	33SX1210/ SCX3245	1960	£5	£12	
Message From Newport	LP	Columbia	33SX1146	1959	£6	£15	
Newport Suite	LP	Columbia	33SX1301/ SCX3363	1961	£5	£12	
Newport Suite	LP	Columbia	33SX1301/ SCX3368	1961	£5	£12	
Swingin' My Way Through College	LP	Columbia	33SX1173	1959	£5	£12	

FERKO STRING BAND

Alabama Jubilee	7"	London	HL8140	1955	£7.50	£15	chart single
Ferko String Band Vol.1	10" LP	London	HBC1064	1956	£4	£10	
Happy Days Are Here Again	7"	London	HL7052	1958	£1.50	£4	export
Happy Days Are Here Again	7"	London	HLF8215	1955	£7.50	£15	
Ma She's Making Eyes At Me	7"	London	HLF8183	1955	£7.50	£15	
Philadelphia Mummers Parade Vol.1	7" EP	London	REF1041	1956	£4	£8	
Philadelphia Mummers Parade Vol.2	7" EP	London	REF1052	1956	£4	£8	

FERLINGHETTI, LAWRENCE

Impeachment Of President Eisenhower	LP	Fantasy	7004	1958	£15	£30	US, red vinyl
Poetry Readings In The Cellar	LP	Fantasy	7002	1957	£15	£30	US, red vinyl

FERNANDO, PHIL

Make Ready For Love	7"	Pye	7N15142	1958	£2	£5

FERNBACH, ANDY

If You Miss Your Connection	LP	Liberty	LBS83233	1969	£30	£60

FERRER, JOE DEVILS BOYS

Rocking Crickets	7"	Oriole	CB1629	1961	£2.50	£6

FERRIS, EUGENE

There Was A Smile In Your Eyes	7"	Planet	PLF112	1966	£5	£10

FERRIS WHEEL

Can't Break The Habit	LP	Pye	NPL18203	1967	£6	£15
Can't Stop Now	7"	Polydor	56366	1969	£2	£5
Let It Be Me	7"	Pye	7N17538	1968	£2	£5
Na Na Song	7"	Pye	7N17631	1968	£2.50	£6
Number One Guy	7"	Pye	7N17387	1967	£6	£12

FERRY, BRYAN

Bride Stripped Bare	LP	Polydor	POLD5003	1978	£50	£100	test pressing with 2 different tracks
Bride Stripped Bare	LP	Polydor	POLD5003	1978	£100	£200	test pressing with 2 different tracks, proof sleeve
Don't Stop The Dance	12"	EG	FERPX2	1985	£2.50	£6	pic disc
Hold On I'm Coming	12"	Polydor	PPSP10	1978	£4	£10	promo

FERRY, CATHERINE

One Two Three	7"	Barclay	BAR42	1976	£4	£8

FEVER TREE

Fever Tree were one of the many San Francisco groups who got to make a few records, but never managed to consolidate them into a long-term career. The group was responsible for a terrific single, "San Francisco Girls", which was something of a Haight-Asbury response to the Beach Boys, with gritty vocals and a keening guitar reclaiming the California girls as their own. In general, however, Fever Tree did not feature the guitar playing enough, preferring a pseudo-classical approach which squandered the group's real strengths without replacing them with anything that was not done better by others.

Another Time Another Place	LP	MCA	MUPS374	1968	£6	£15	
Creation	LP	Uni	73067	1969	£8	£20	US
Fever Tree	LP	UNI	UNL102	1968	£8	£20	mono
Fever Tree	LP	Uni	UNLS102	1968	£6	£15	
For Sale	LP	Ampex	A10113	1970	£6	£15	US
San Francisco Girls	7"	MCA	MU1043	1968	£4	£8	

FICKLE FINGER

Fickle Lizzie Anne	7"	Page One	POF150	1969	£1.50	£4

FICKLE PICKLE

American Pie	7"	B&C	CB177	1972	£2.50	£6
California Calling	7"	B&C	CB178	1972	£2.50	£6
Millionaire	7"	Fontana	TF1069	1970	£4	£8
Sinful Skinful	LP	Explosion		1970	£30	£60

FIDDLER'S DRAM

Fiddler's Dram	LP	Dingles	DID711	1980	£5	£12
To See The Play	LP	Dingles	DIN304	1978	£6	£15

FI-DELS

Try A Little Harder	7"	Jay Boy	BOY69	1973	£1.50	£4

FIELD, KEITH

Day That War Broke Out	7"	Polydor	56278	1968	£4	£8

FIELD MICE

I Can See Myself	7"	Caff	CAFF2	1990	£7.50	£15

FIELDING, ALAN

How Many Nights, How Many Days	7"	Decca	F11404	1962	£1.50	£4
Too Late To Worry, Too Blue To Cry	7"	Decca	F11518	1962	£1.50	£4

FIELDING, JERRY

Dance Date Vol.1	7" EP	London	REP1026	1955	£2.50	£6
When I Grow Too Old To Dream	7"	London	HL8017	1954	£7.50	£15

FIELDING, JERRY ORCHESTRA

Faintly Reminiscent	7"	London	HL7001	1955	£1.50	£4	export
Faintly Reminiscent	10" LP	London	HAPB1022	1954	£4	£10	
Gypsy In My Soul	7"	Brunswick	05399	1955	£1.50	£4	
I'm In Love	7"	London	HL7004	1955	£1.50	£4	
Peanut Vendor	7"	London	HL7002	1955	£1.50	£4	
Plays A Dance Concert	10" LP	London	HAPB1027	1954	£4	£10	
Tea For Two	7"	London	HL7003	1955	£1.50	£4	

FIELDS

Fields	LP	CBS	69009	1971	£10	£25	with poster
Friends Of Mine	7"	CBS	7555	1971	£1.50	£4	

FIELDS (2)

Fields	LP	Uni	UNLS104	1969	£5	£12

FIELDS, ERNIE

Chattanooga Choo Choo	7"	London	HL9100	1960	£2	£5	
In The Mood	LP	London	HA2263	1960	£6	£15	
In The Mood	7"	London	HL8985	1959	£2	£5	chart single
Raunchy	7"	London	HL9227	1960	£2	£5	
Saxy	7" EP	London	RE1260	1960	£10	£20	

FIELDS, KANSAS & MILTON SEALEY

Kansas Fields & Milton Sealey	7" EP	Ducretet	DEP95017	1956	£4	£8

FIELDS OF THE NEPHILIM

Blue Water	7"	Situation 2	SIT48	1987	£4	£8	
Blue Water	12"	Situation 2	SIT48T	1987	£4	£10	with poster
Burning The Fields	12"	Tower	N1	1984	£20	£40	red sleeve
Burning The Fields	12"	Tower	N1	1985	£3	£8	coloured vinyl
Burning The Fields	12"	Tower	N1	1985	£6	£15	green sleeve label with band photos
Chord Of Souls	12"	Situation 2		1988	£5	£12	promo
Preacher Man	7"	Situation 2	SIT46	1987	£7.50	£15	
Psychonaut	7"	Situation 2	SIT57	1989	£2.50	£6	green vinyl

FIESTAS

So Fine	7"	Atlantic	2091121	1971	£1.50	£4
So Fine	7"	London	HL8870	1959	£7.50	£15

FIFTEENTH

Andelain	12"	Tanz	TANZ3	1986	£2.50	£6

FIFTH AVENUE

Bells Of Rhymney	7"	Immediate	IM002	1965	£7.50	£15

FIFTH COLUMN
Benjamin Day	7"	Columbia	DB8068	1966	£2.50	£6	

FIFTH DIMENSION
Go Where You Wanna Go	7"	Liberty	LIB12051	1967	£5	£10	
I'll Be Loving You For Ever	7"	Liberty	LBF15356	1970	£4	£8	
Wedding Bell Blues	7"	Liberty	LBF15288	1970	£1.50	£4	
Working On A Groovy Thing	7"	Liberty	LBF15243	1969	£1.50	£4	

FIFTH ESTATE
Coney Island Sally	7"	Stateside	SS2125	1969	£1.50	£4	
Ding Dong The Witch Is Dead	LP	Jubilee	JGM/JGS8005	1967	£6	£15	US
Ding Dong The Witch Is Dead	7"	Stateside	SS2034	1967	£2	£5	
Do Drop In	7"	Stateside	SS2105	1968	£1.50	£4	
Heigh Ho	7"	Stateside	SS2068	1967	£2	£5	

FIFTY FANTASTICS
God's Got Religion	7"	Dining Out	TUX5	1980	£2	£5	
God's Got Religion	7"	South Circular	SGS108	1979	£2.50	£6	B side by Steppes

FIFTY FOOT HOSE
Cauldron	LP	Limelight	86062	1969	£15	£30	US
I've Paid My Dues	LP	Decca	DL75225	1970	£8	£20	US

FINCHLEY BOYS
Everlasting Tribute	LP	Golden Throat	20019	1968	£35	£70	US

FINDERS KEEPERS
Light	7"	CBS	202249	1966	£4	£8	
Light/Power Of Love	7"	CBS	202249	1966	£20	£40	demo only
On The Beach	7"	Fontana	TF892	1967	£7.50	£15	
Sadie The Cleaning Lady	7"	Fontana	TF938	1968	£4	£8	

FINE WINE
Fine Wine	LP	Polydor	2310438	1976	£5	£12	German

FINGERS
All Kinds Of People	7"	Columbia	DB8112	1967	£6	£12	
I'll Take You Where The Music's Playing	7"	Columbia	DB8026	1966	£2	£5	

FINN, LEE & THE RHYTHM MEN
High Class Feeling	7"	Starlite	ST45103	1963	£60	£120	

FINN MACCUILL
Sink Ye - Swim Ye	LP	private	REL460	1978	£40	£80	

FINN, MICKEY
Garden Of My Mind	7"	Direction	583086	1967	£15	£30	
If I Had You Baby	7"	Polydor	56719	1966	£15	£30	
Sporting Life	7"	Columbia	DB7510	1965	£17.50	£35	

FINN, MICKEY & THE BLUE MEN
Pills	7"	Oriole	CB1927	1964	£10	£20	
Reeling And Rocking	7"	Oriole	CB1940	1964	£12.50	£25	
Tom Hark	7"	Blue Beat	BB203	1963	£10	£20	

FINN, SIMON
Pass The Distance	LP	Mushroom	100MR2	1970	£30	£60	

FINNEGAN, LARRY
Dear One	7"	HMV	POP1022	1962	£4	£8	
It's Walking Talking Time	7"	London	HLU9613	1962	£2.50	£6	
Other Ringo	7"	Ember	EMBS207	1965	£2.50	£6	

FINNEGAN, MIKE
Just One Minute More	7"	CBS	6656	1978	£2	£5	

FIRE
Father's Name Is Dad	7"	Decca	F12753	1968	£30	£60	
Magic Shoemaker	LP	Pye	NSPL18343	1970	£150	£250	sleeve pictured in Guide
Round The Gum Tree	7"	Decca	F12856	1968	£10	£20	

FIRE ESCAPE
Love Special Delivery	7" EP	Vogue	INT18117	1966	£25	£50	French
Psychotic Reaction	LP	GNP Crescendo	2034	1966	£10	£25	US

FIREBALLS
Baby What's Wrong	7"	Stateside	SS417	1965	£1.50	£4	
Bottle Of Wine	LP	Stateside	(S)SL10237	1968	£6	£15	
Bottle Of Wine	7"	Stateside	SS2095	1967	£1.50	£4	
Bulldog	7"	Top Rank	JAR276	1960	£2	£5	
Carioca	7"	Stateside	SS151	1963	£1.50	£4	
Come On, React	7"	Stateside	SS2134	1969	£1.50	£4	
Fireballs	LP	Top Rank	RM324	1960	£15	£30	US
Foot Patter	7"	Top Rank	JAR354	1960	£1.50	£4	
Goin' Away	7"	Stateside	SS2106	1968	£1.50	£4	
Here Are The Fireballs	LP	Warwick	W2042	1961	£10	£25	US
Long Green	7"	London	HLZ10260	1969	£1.50	£4	

Quite A Party	7"	Pye	7N25092	1961	£1.50	£4	chart single
Rik-A-Tik	7"	Stateside	SS106	1962	£1.50	£4	
Torquay	7"	Top Rank	JAR218	1959	£2	£4	
Vaquero	LP	Top Rank	25105	1961	£6	£15	
Vaquero	7"	Top Rank	JAR507	1960	£1.50	£4	

FIRECLOWN

Fireclown	7"	Fireclown		1983	£30	£60	

FIREFLIES

I Can't Say Goodbye	7"	London	HLU9057	1960	£5	£10	
You Were Mine	LP	Taurus	(S)1002	1961	£25	£50	US
You Were Mine	7"	Top Rank	JAR198	1959	£5	£10	

FIREHOUSE FIVE PLUS TWO

Crashes A Party	LP	Good Time Jazz	LAG12236/ SGA5012	1960	£4	£10	
Firehouse Five Plus Two	LP	Good Time Jazz	LAG12079	1958	£4	£10	
Firehouse Five Plus Two	10" LP	Vogue	LDE183	1956	£4	£10	
Firehouse Five Plus Two Vol.2	LP	Good Time Jazz	LAG12089	1958	£4	£10	
Firehouse Five Story Vol.3	LP	Good Time Jazz	LAG12099	1958	£4	£10	
For Lovers	LP	Good Time Jazz	LAG12074	1958	£4	£10	
Goes South	LP	Good Time Jazz	LAG12087	1958	£4	£10	
Goes South Vol.1	10" LP	Good Time Jazz	LDG036	1954	£5	£12	
Goes South Vol.2	10" LP	Good Time Jazz	LDG079	1954	£5	£12	
Goes South Vol.3	10" LP	Good Time Jazz	LDG094	1954	£5	£12	
Goes South Vol.4	10" LP	Good Time Jazz	LDG169	1955	£5	£12	
Goes To Sea	LP	Good Time Jazz	LAG12150/ SGA5003	1958	£4	£10	

FIREMAN

One of the more surprising album releases of 1993 was one whose origin would be guessed by few casual listeners. For the ambient work credited to the Fireman is actually the work of none other than Paul McCartney, working in collaboration with Youth, the producer who has, of course, worked with the Orb. The LP version of "Strawberries.." was issued on clear vinyl only for a very limited period. By the time that most McCartney collectors had realised the involvement of their hero, the record had already been deleted!

Strawberries,Oceans,Ships,Forest	LP	Parlophone	PMCD1452	1993	£15	£30	clear vinyl double

FIRESIGN THEATRE

Dear Friends	LP	CBS	31099	1972	£6	£15	US, double
Don't Crush That Dwarf	LP	CBS	30102	1970	£6	£15	US
Everything You Know Is Wrong	LP	CBS	33141	1974	£5	£12	US
How To Be In Two Places At Once	LP	CBS	65130	1968	£8	£20	US
I Think We're All Bozos On This Bus	LP	CBS	30737	1971	£6	£15	US
In The Next World	LP	CBS	31383	1972	£5	£12	US
Not Insane Or Anything You Want	LP	CBS	31585	1972	£5	£12	US
Tale Of The Giant Rat	LP	CBS	32370	1974	£5	£12	US
TV Or Not TV	LP	CBS	32199	1973	£5	£12	US
Waiting For The Electrician Or Someone Like Him	LP	CBS	65129	1968	£8	£20	

FIRING SQUAD

Little Bit More	7"	Parlophone	R5152	1964	£7.50	£15	

FIRST AID

Nostradamus	LP	Decca	TXS117	1977	£6	£15	

FIRST CHOICE

This Is The House Where Love Died	7"	Pye	7N25613	1973	£50	£100	demo only

FIRST EDITION

Just Dropped In	7"	Reprise	RS20655	1968	£1.50	£4	

FIRST GEAR

Certain Girl	7"	Pye	7N15703	1964	£40	£80	
In Crowd	7"	Pye	7N15763	1965	£7.50	£15	

FIRST MODERN PIANO QUARTET

Gallery Of Gershwin	LP	Coral	LVA9110/SVL3002	1959	£5	£12	

FIRST STEPS

Anywhere Else But Here	7"	English Rose	ER3	1981	£2	£5	
Beat Is Back	7"	English Rose	ER1	1980	£1.50	£4	

FISCHER & EPSTEIN

It's A Beatle World	LP	Swan	514	1964	£6	£15	US

FISCHER, WILD MAN

Evening With Wild Man Fischer	LP	Reprise	RSLP6332	1970	£17.50	£35	

FISHER, ARCHIE

Archie Fisher	LP	XTRA	XTRA1070	1968	£10	£25	
Man With A Rhyme	LP	Folk Legacy	FSS61	1976	£10	£25	U

Orfeo	LP	Decca	SKL5057	1970	£15	£30	

FISHER, ARCHIE, BARBARA DICKSON, JOHN MACKINNON

Fate O' Charlie	LP	Trailer	LER3002	1969	£15	£30	

FISHER, CHIP

At The Sugar Bowl	7" EP	RCA	RCX143	1959	£10	£20	
Poor Me	7"	Parlophone	R4604	1959	£1.50	£4	

FISHER, CILLA & ARTIE TREZISE

Balcanquhal	LP	Trailer	LER2100	1976	£10	£25	
For Foul Day And Fair	LP	Kettle	KAC1	1979	£5	£12	

FISHER, EDDIE

Bundle Of Joy	7" EP	HMV	7EG8207	1957	£2	£5	
Cindy Oh Cindy	7"	HMV	POP273	1956	£6	£12	chart single
Count Your Blessings Instead Of Sheep	7"	HMV	7M266	1954	£2.50	£6	
Downhearted	7"	HMV	7M126	1953	£4	£8	chart single
Dungaree Doll	7"	HMV	7M374	1956	£5	£10	
Even Now	7"	HMV	7M125	1953	£5	£10	
Everything I Have Is Yours	7"	HMV	7M115	1953	£5	£10	chart single
Girl, A Girl	7"	HMV	7M212	1954	£4	£8	
Green Years	7"	HMV	7M257	1954	£2.50	£6	
How Deep Is The Ocean	7"	HMV	7M185	1954	£4	£8	
How Do You Speak To An Angel?	7"	HMV	7M242	1954	£2.50	£6	
I Need You Now	7"	HMV	7M251	1954	£4	£8	chart single
I'm Walking Behind You	7"	HMV	7M133	1953	£4	£8	chart single
I'm Yours	7"	HMV	7M101	1953	£6	£12	
Just Another Polka	7"	HMV	7M146	1953	£5	£10	
Just To Be With You	7"	HMV	7M201	1954	£4	£8	
Kari Waits For Me	7"	RCA	RCA1061	1958	£1.50	£4	
Last Mile Home	7"	RCA	RCA1147	1959	£1.50	£4	
Magic Fingers	7"	HMV	7M353	1956	£2.50	£6	
Many Times	7"	HMV	7M168	1953	£4	£8	
My Friend	7"	HMV	7M235	1954	£4	£8	
My Serenade Is You	10" LP	HMV	DLP1074	1955	£8	£20	
Night And Day	7" EP	HMV	7EG8026	1954	£2.50	£6	
No Other One	7"	HMV	7M402	1956	£2.50	£6	
Oh My Papa	7"	HMV	7M172	1953	£4	£8	chart single
Outside Of Heaven	7"	HMV	7M117	1953	£5	£10	chart single
Sayonara	7"	RCA	RCA1030	1958	£1.50	£4	
Second Chance	7"	RCA	RCA1009	1957	£1.50	£4	
Sings Academy Award Winning Songs	LP	HMV	CLP1095	1956	£5	£12	
Some Day Soon	7"	HMV	POP296	1957	£1.50	£4	
Sweet Heartaches	7"	HMV	7M421	1956	£2.50	£6	
Time For Romance	10" LP	HMV	DLP1040	1954	£8	£20	
Tonight	7"	London	HL9469	1961	£1.50	£4	
Tonight My Heart She Is Crying	7"	HMV	POP342	1957	£2.50	£6	
Trust In Me	7"	HMV	7M116	1953	£6	£12	
Wedding Bells	7"	HMV	7M294	1955	£4	£8	chart single
Wish You Were Here	7"	HMV	7M159	1953	£4	£8	chart single

FISHER FAMILY

Fisher Family	LP	Topic	12T137	1965	£15	£30	

FISHER, RAY

Bonny Birdy	LP	Trailer	LER2038	1972	£10	£25	

FISHER, RAY & ARCHIE

Far Over The Forth	7" EP	Topic	TOP67	1961	£15	£30	

FISHER, TONI

Big Hurt	7"	Top Rank	JAR261	1960	£1.50	£4	chart single

FISK JUBILEE SINGERS

Fisk Jubilee Singers	LP	Topic	12T39	1959	£6	£15	

FIST

Forever Amber	7"	MCA	MCA640	1980	£1.50	£4	
Name, Rank And Serial Number	7"	MCA	MCA615	1980	£2.50	£6	

FITS

Bored Of Education	7"	Stagefright		1979	£1.50	£4	

FITZ & COOZERS

Cover Me	7"	Nu Beat	NB003	1968	£4	£8	

FITZGERALD, ELLA

At Newport	LP	Columbia	33CX10100	1958	£6	£15	Side 2 by Billie Holiday
At The Opera House	LP	Columbia	33CX10126	1958	£8	£20	with Oscar Peterson
But Not For Me	7"	HMV	POP657	1959	£1.50	£4	chart single
Can't Buy Me Love	7"	Verve	VS519	1964	£1.50	£4	chart single
Cole Porter Songbook Vol.1	LP	HMV	CLP1083	1956	£8	£20	
Cole Porter Songbook Vol.2	LP	HMV	CLP1084	1956	£8	£20	
Desafinado	7"	Verve	VS502	1962	£1.50	£4	chart single
Duke Ellington Songbook Vol.1	LP	HMV	CLP1213/4	1958	£15	£30	double
Duke Ellington Songbook Vol.2	LP	HMV	CLP1227/8	1958	£15	£30	double
Ella And Her Fellas	LP	Brunswick	LAT8223	1957	£6	£15	

Ella And Louis	LP	HMV	CLP1098	1956	£6	£15	with Louis Armstrong
Ella And Louis Again No.1	LP	HMV	CLP1146	1957	£6	£15	with Louis Armstrong
Ella And Louis Again No.2	LP	HMV	CLP1147	1957	£6	£15	with Louis Armstrong
Ella At Juan-Les Pins	LP	Verve	VLP9083	1965	£4	£10	
Ella Sings Gershwin	10" LP	Brunswick	LA8648	1954	£15	£30	
Ella Swings Lightly	LP	HMV	CLP1267	1959	£8	£20	
Ella Wishes You A Swinging Christmas	LP	HMV	CLP1397	1960	£8	£20	
Ella's Contribution To The Blues	7"	Brunswick	05539	1956	£1.50	£4	
First Lady Of Song	LP	Brunswick	LAT8264	1958	£6	£15	
Get Ready	7"	Reprise	R20850	1969	£4	£8	
Hello Love	LP	HMV	CLP1383/CSD1315	1960	£8	£20	
How High The Moon	7"	HMV	POP782	1960	£1.50	£4	chart single
Irving Berlin Songbook Vol.1	LP	HMV	CLP1183	1958	£8	£20	
Irving Berlin Songbook Vol.2	LP	HMV	CLP1184	1958	£8	£20	
Lady Is A Tramp	7"	HMV	POP849	1961	£1.50	£4	
Let No Man Write My Epitaph	LP	HMV	CLP1396	1960	£8	£20	
Like Someone In Love	LP	HMV	CLP1166	1958	£8	£20	
Lover, Come Back To Me	7"	Brunswick	05468	1955	£1.50	£4	
Lullabies Of Birdland	LP	Brunswick	LAT8115	1956	£8	£20	
Lullaby Of Birdland	7"	Brunswick	05392	1955	£1.50	£4	
Mack The Knife	LP	HMV	CLP1391	1960	£8	£20	
Mack The Knife	7"	HMV	POP736	1960	£1.50	£4	chart single
Moanin' Low	7"	Brunswick	05427	1955	£1.50	£4	
My One And Only Love	7"	Brunswick	05514	1956	£1.50	£4	
Pete Kelly's Blues	7"	Brunswick	05473	1955	£1.50	£4	
Porgy And Bess Vol.1	LP	HMV	CLP1245	1959	£6	£15	with Louis Armstrong
Porgy And Bess Vol.2	LP	HMV	CLP1246	1959	£6	£15	with Louis Armstrong
Rhythm Is My Business	LP	Verve	VLP9020	1963	£5	£12	
Rodgers And Hart Songbook Vol.1	LP	HMV	CLP1116	1957	£8	£20	
Rodgers And Hart Songbook Vol.2	LP	HMV	CLP1117	1957	£8	£20	
Sings Gershwin Vol.1	LP	HMV	CLP1338/CSD1292	1959	£8	£20	
Sings Gershwin Vol.2	LP	HMV	CLP1339/CSD1293	1959	£8	£20	
Sings Gershwin Vol.3	LP	HMV	CLP1347/CSD1299	1960	£8	£20	
Sings Gershwin Vol.4	LP	HMV	CLP1348/CSD1300	1960	£8	£20	
Sings Gershwin Vol.5	LP	HMV	CLP1353/CSD1304	1960	£8	£20	
Soldier Boy	7"	Brunswick	05477	1955	£1.50	£4	
Songs In A Mellow Mood	LP	Brunswick	LAT8056	1955	£8	£20	
Souvenir Album	10" LP	Brunswick	LA8581	1953	£15	£30	
Souvenir Album	10" LP	Brunswick	LA8665	1954	£8	£20	
Sweet And Hot	LP	Brunswick	LAT8091	1956	£8	£20	
Sweet Songs For Swingers	LP	HMV	CLP1322/CSD1287	1960	£8	£20	
Swingin' Shepherd Blues	7"	HMV	POP486	1958	£1.50	£4	chart single
Who's Afraid	7"	Brunswick	05324	1954	£1.50	£4	
You'll Never Know	7"	Brunswick	05584	1956	£1.50	£4	

FITZGERALD, G.F.
Mouseproof	LP	Uni	UNLS115	1970	£20	£40	

FIVE & A PENNY
You Don't Know Where Your Interest Lies	7"	Polydor	56282	1968	£10	£20	

FIVE A.M. EVENT
Hungry	7"	Pye	7N17154	1966	£30	£60	

FIVE AMERICANS
7.30 Guided Tour	7"	Stateside	SS2097	1968	£2	£5	
Evil, Not Love	7"	Pye	7N25373	1966	£7.50	£15	
I See The Light	LP	Hanna Barbera	LP8503/ST9503	1966	£6	£15	US
I See The Light	7"	Pye	7N25354	1966	£5	£10	
I See The Light	7" EP	Vogue	INT18087	1966	£10	£20	French
Now And Then	LP	Abnak	ABST2071	1968	£5	£12	US
Progressions	LP	Abnak	AB(ST)2069	1967	£5	£12	US
Sound Of Love	7"	Stateside	SS2036	1967	£2	£5	
Sound Of Love	7" EP	Stateside	FSE1007	1967	£10	£20	French
Western Union	LP	Abnak	AB(ST)2067	1967	£5	£12	US
Western Union	7"	Stateside	SS2012	1967	£2	£5	
Western Union	7" EP	Stateside	FSE102	1967	£7.50	£15	French

FIVE BLIND BOYS
Five Blind Boys	7" EP	Vocalion	EPVP1282	1964	£5	£10	

FIVE BLOBS
Blob	7"	Philips	PB881	1958	£1.50	£4	

FIVE BY FIVE
Fire	7"	Pye	7N25477	1968	£7.50	£15	
Next Exit	LP	Paula	LPS2202	1968	£8	£20	US

FIVE CHESTERNUTS
Jean Dorothy	7"	Columbia	DB4165	1958	£30	£60	

FIVE COUNTS
Watermelon Walk	7"	Oriole	CBA1769	1962	£1.50	£4	

FIVE DALLAS BOYS
All The Way	7"	Columbia	DB4041	1957	£1.50	£4	
Big Man	7"	Columbia	DB4154	1958	£1.50	£4	
Boston Tea Party	7"	Columbia	DB4445	1960	£1.50	£4	
Fatty Patty	7"	Columbia	DB4231	1958	£2	£5	

Title	Format	Label	Catalogue	Year	Price	Price	Notes
Five Dallas Boys	7" EP.	Columbia	SEG8035	1960	£2.50	£6	
Gigi	7"	Columbia	DB4244	1959	£1.50	£4	
Morning Papers	7"	Columbia	DB4313	1959	£1.50	£4	
Nightingale Sang In Berkeley Square	7"	Columbia	DB4380	1959	£1.50	£4	
One Finger Oner Thumb Keep Movin'	7"	Columbia	DB4599	1961	£1.50	£4	
Shangri-La	7"	Columbia	DB4005	1957	£1.50	£4	
Twenty-six Miles	7"	Columbia	DB4102	1958	£1.50	£4	

FIVE DAY WEEK STRAW PEOPLE

Title	Format	Label	Catalogue	Year	Price	Price	Notes
Five Day Week Straw People	LP	Saga	FID2123	1968	£30	£60	

FIVE DU-TONES

Title	Format	Label	Catalogue	Year	Price	Price	Notes
Shake A Tail Feather	7"	President	PT134	1968	£1.50	£4	
Shake A Tail Feather	7"	Stateside	SS206	1963	£4	£8	

FIVE EMPREES

Title	Format	Label	Catalogue	Year	Price	Price	Notes
Five Emprees	LP	Freeport	FR3001/FRS4001	1965	£15	£30	US
Little Miss Sad	LP	Freeport	FR3002/FRS4002	1965	£6	£15	US
Little Miss Sad	7"	Stateside	SS470	1965	£1.50	£4	

FIVE FLEETS

Title	Format	Label	Catalogue	Year	Price	Price	Notes
Oh What A Feeling	7"	Felsted	AF103	1958	£60	£120	

FIVE HAND REEL

Title	Format	Label	Catalogue	Year	Price	Price	Notes
Five Hand Reel	LP	Rubber	RUB019	1976	£5	£12	

FIVE KEYS

Title	Format	Label	Catalogue	Year	Price	Price	Notes
Best Of The Five Keys	LP	Aladdin	806	1956	£180	£300	US
Blues Don't Care	7"	Capitol	CL14756	1957	£17.50	£35	
Cos You're My Love	7"	Capitol	CL14545	1956	£30	£60	
Doggone It	7"	Capitol	CL14325	1955	£150	£250	
Fantastic Five Keys	LP	Capitol	T1769	1962	£50	£100	US
Five Keys	LP	King	688	1960	£75	£150	US
Five Keys On Stage	LP	Capitol	T828	1957	£50	£100	US
Five Keys On The Town	LP	Score	LP4003	1957	£150	£250	US
Four Walls	7"	Capitol	CL14736	1957	£15	£30	
From Me To You	7"	Capitol	CL14829	1958	£20	£40	
Ling Ting Tong	78	Capitol	CL14184	1954	£6	£12	
Really O Truly Oh	7"	Capitol	CL14967	1958	£20	£40	
Rhythm And Blues Hits Past And Present	LP	King	692	1960	£75	£150	US
She's The Most	7"	Capitol	CL14582	1956	£30	£60	
That's Right	7"	Capitol	CL14639	1956	£30	£60	
Verdict	7"	Capitol	CL14313	1955	£180	£300	
Wisdom Of A Fool	7"	Capitol	CL14686	1957	£30	£60	

FIVE MAN ELECTRICAL BAND

Title	Format	Label	Catalogue	Year	Price	Price	Notes
Five Man Electrical Band	LP	Capitol	ST165	1969	£6	£15	US

FIVE OF DIAMONDS

Title	Format	Label	Catalogue	Year	Price	Price	Notes
Five Of Diamonds	7" EP.	Oak	RGJ150FD	1965	£100	£200	

FIVE ROYALES

Title	Format	Label	Catalogue	Year	Price	Price	Notes
Dedicated To The One I Love	7"	Ember	EMBS124	1960	£30	£60	
Dedicated To You	LP	King	580	1957	£60	£120	US
Five Royales	LP	King	678	1960	£50	£100	US
Five Royales Sing For You	LP	King	616	1959	£50	£100	US
Rockin' Five Royales	LP	Apollo	LP488	1956	£150	£250	US
Twenty-Four All Time Hits	LP	King	955	1966	£8	£20	US

FIVE SATINS

Title	Format	Label	Catalogue	Year	Price	Price	Notes
Encore	LP	Ember	ELP401	1960	£15	£30	US
Five Satins Sing	LP	Ember	ELP100	1957	£50	£100	US
Five Satins Sing	LP	Ember	ELP100	1957	£250	£400	US, blue vinyl
Five Satins Sing	LP	Mount Vernon	108	196-	£8	£20	US
Shadows	7"	Top Rank	JAR239	1959	£6	£12	
To The Aisle	7"	London	HL8501	1957	£100	£200	
Wonderful Girl	7"	Top Rank	JAR199	1959	£7.50	£15	
Your Memory	7"	MGM	MGM1087	1960	£12.50	£25	

FIVE SMITH BROTHERS

Title	Format	Label	Catalogue	Year	Price	Price	Notes
ABC Boogie	7"	Decca	F10403	1954	£5	£10	
I'm In Favour Of Friendship	7"	Decca	F10527	1955	£4	£8	chart single
You Took My Heart	7"	Decca	F10698	1956	£1.50	£4	
You're As Sweet Today	7"	Decca	F10507	1955	£1.50	£4	

FIVE STAIRSTEPS & CUBIE

Title	Format	Label	Catalogue	Year	Price	Price	Notes
Dear Prudence	7"	Buddah	201083	1969	£1.50	£4	
Five Stairsteps	LP	Windy	C(S)6000	1967	£4	£10	US
Million To One	7"	Pye	7N25448	1968	£2.50	£6	
Stay Close To Me	7"	Buddah	201026	1968	£2	£5	
Stay Close To Me	7"	Buddah	2011092	1971	£1.50	£4	
We Must Be In Love	7"	Buddah	201070	1969	£2	£5	

FIVE THIRTY

Title	Format	Label	Catalogue	Year	Price	Price	Notes
Catcher In The Rye	12"	Other	12OTH2	1985	£8	£20	

FIVE TOWNS

Title	Format	Label	Catalogue	Year	Price	Price	Notes
It Isn't What You've Got	7"	Direction	583115	1967	£1.50	£4	

FIVE'S COMPANY

Ballad Of Fred The Pixie	LP	Saga	FID2151	1969	£5	£12
Session Man	7"	Pye	7N17199	1966	£4	£8
Some Girls	7"	Pye	7N17162	1966	£2.50	£6
Sunday For Seven Days	7"	Pye	7N17118	1966	£4	£8

FIZZBOMBS

Sign On The Line	7"	Narodnik	NRK003	1987	£2	£5

FLACK, ROBERTA

Chapter Two	LP	Atlantic	K40097	1971	£4	£10
Compared To What	7"	Atlantic	584294	1969	£1.50	£4
First Take	LP	Atlantic	588204	1969	£5	£12
Quiet Fire	LP	Atlantic	K40297	1971	£4	£10

FLACK, ROBERTA & DONNY HATHAWAY

Roberta Flack And Donny Hathaway	LP	Atlantic	K40380	1972	£5	£12

FLAIRS

Flairs	LP	Crown	CLP5356	1963	£15	£30	US
Swing Pretty Mama	7"	Oriole	CB1392	1957	£75	£150	

FLAKY PASTRY

Ingredients	LP	Flaky Pastry	FALP001	1976	£8	£20

FLAME

Flame	LP	Stateside	SSL10312	1971	£6	£15
See The Light	7"	Stateside	SS2183	1970	£1.50	£4

FLAMES

Broadway Jungle	7"	Island	WI139	1964	£5	£10	
Helena Darling	7"	Blue Beat	BB205	1963	£5	£10	
He's The Greatest	7"	Island	WI130	1964	£5	£10	
It Takes Time	7"	Blue Beat	BB300	1964	£5	£10	Liges B side
Little Flea	7"	Island	WI136	1964	£5	£10	
When I Get Home	7"	Island	WI138	1964	£5	£10	
You've Lost Your Date	7"	Nu Beat	NB028	1969	£4	£8	

FLAMIN' GROOVIES

Feel A Whole Lot Better	7"	Sire	6078619	1978	£1.50	£4	PS
Flamin' Groovies	LP	Kama Sutra	2683003	1971	£5	£12	double
Flamingo	LP	Kama Sutra	KSBS2021	1971	£5	£12	US
Married Woman	7"	United Artists	UP35464	1972	£2.50	£6	
Shake Some Action	LP	Sire	9103251	1977	£5	£12	
Slow Death	7"	United Artists	REM406	1976	£2	£5	
Slow Death	7"	United Artists	UP35392	1972	£1.50	£4	
Sneekers	10" LP	Snazz	R2371	1969	£8	£20	US
Supersnazz	LP	Epic	BN26487	1969	£6	£15	US
Teenage Head	LP	Kama Sutra	KSBS2031	1971	£5	£12	US
Teenage Head	7"	Kama Sutra	2013031	1971	£1.50	£4	

FLAMING EMBER

Westbound No.9	7"	Hot Wax	HWX101	1969	£1.50	£4

FLAMING YOUTH

Flaming Youth's "Ark II" was a Melody Maker album of the month, but its remarkable lack of commercial success probably goes to show that the music press is very much less influential than it would like to believe. The group's drummer, however, has done very well subsequently - he is Phil Collins, albeit almost unrecogniseable from the picture on the LP cover!

Ark 2	LP	Fontana	STL5533	1969	£8	£20	
From Now On	LP	Fontana	6001003	1970	£5	£10	
Guide Me Orion	7"	Fontana	TF1057	1969	£7.50	£15	PS
Man, Woman And Child	7"	Fontana	6001002	1970	£5	£10	

FLAMINGO, JOHNNY

My Teenage Girl	7"	Vogue	V9089	1957	£20	£40
So Long	7"	Vogue	V9100	1958	£17.50	£35

FLAMINGOS

At Night	7"	Top Rank	JAR519	1960	£7.50	£15	
Boogaloo Party	7"	Philips	BF1483	1966	£7.50	£15	
Boogaloo Party	7"	Philips	BF1786	1969	£1.50	£4	chart single
Buffalo Soldier	7"	Polydor	2066007	1971	£1.50	£4	
Favorites	LP	End	LP(S)307	1960	£20	£40	US
Flamingos	LP	Checker	LP1433/LPS3005	1959	£50	£100	US
Flamingos	LP	Constellation	CS3	1964	£8	£20	US
Flamingos Meet The Moonglows	LP	Vee Jay	LP1052	1962	£15	£30	US
I Only Have Eyes For You	7"	Top Rank	JAR263	1960	£30	£60	
Just For A Kick	7"	London	HLN8373	1957	£150	£250	
Ladder Of Love	7"	Brunswick	05696	1957	£180	£300	
Love Walked In	7"	Top Rank	JAR213	1959	£7.50	£15	
Nobody Loves Me Like You	7"	Top Rank	JAR367	1960	£7.50	£15	
Requestfully Yours	LP	End	LP(S)308	1960	£20	£40	US
Serenade	LP	End	LP(S)304	1959	£20	£40	US
Sound Of The Flamingos	LP	End	LP(S)316	1962	£20	£40	US
Their Hits - Then And Now	LP	Philips	2/PHS600206	1966	£6	£15	US

FLAMMA - SHERMAN

Move Me	7"	SNB	554142	1969	£7.50	£15

FLANAGAN BROTHERS

Salton City	7"	Coral	Q72342	1958	£4	£8

FLANAGAN BROTHERS (2)

Irish Delight	LP	Topic	12T365	1979	£5	£12	

FLANAGAN, TOMMY

Jazz...It's Magic!	LP	Pye	NPL28009	1960	£8	£20	

FLANDERS, MICHAEL & DONALD SWANN

At The Drop Of A Hat	LP	Parlophone	PMC1033/ PCS3001	1957	£4	£10	chart LP
At The Drop Of Another Hat	LP	Parlophone	PMC1216	1964	£4	£10	chart LP
Bestiary Of Flanders And Swann	LP	Parlophone	PMC1164	1961	£4	£10	
Gnu	7"	Parlophone	R4354	1957	£1.50	£4	

FLANDERS, TOMMY

Moonstone	LP	Verve	SVLP6020	1969	£6	£15	

FLARES

Foot Stompin' Hits	LP	London	HAU8034	1963	£10	£25	
Foot Stomping	7"	London	HLU9441	1961	£6	£12	

FLASH

Flash	LP	Sovereign	SVNA7251	1972	£4	£10	
Flash In The Can	LP	Sovereign	SVNA7255	1972	£4	£10	
Out Of Our Hands	LP	Sovereign	SVNA7260	1973	£4	£10	

FLASH & THE BOARD OF DIRECTORS

Busy Signal	7"	Bell	BLL1007	1968	£2	£5	

FLAT EARTH SOCIETY

Waleeco	LP	Fleetwood	3027	1968	£50	£100	US
Waleeco	LP	Psycho	PSYCHO17	1983	£5	£12	

FLATT & SCRUGGS

Ballad Of Jed Clampett	7"	CBS	201793	1965	£1.50	£4	
Country & Western Aces	7" EP	Mercury	10010MCE	1964	£2	£5	
Country & Western Trailblazers No.4	7" EP	Mercury	ZEP10106	1961	£2	£5	
Folk Songs Of Our Land	LP	CBS	BPG62095	1963	£4	£10	

FLAVOUR

Sally Had A Party	7"	Direction	583597	1968	£2	£5	

FLAX

One	LP	Vertigo		1976	£75	£150	

FLEE REKKERS

Blue Tango	7"	Pye	7N15326	1960	£2	£5	
Fabulous Flee Rekkers	7" EP	Pye	NEP24141	1961	£10	£20	
Fireball	7"	Piccadilly	7N35109	1963	£2.50	£6	
Green Jeans	7"	Top Rank	JAR431	1960	£7.50	£15	
Green Jeans	7"	Triumph	RGM1008	1960	£12.50	£25	chart single
Lone Rider	7"	Piccadilly	7N35006	1961	£4	£8	
Stage To Cimmaron	7"	Piccadilly	7N35048	1962	£4	£8	
Sunburst	7"	Piccadilly	7N35081	1962	£2.50	£6	
Sunday Date	7"	Pye	7N15288	1960	£2.50	£6	

FLEETWOOD MAC

Most of the collectable Fleetwood Mac records come from the first part of the group's career, when its sound was very different to the commercial pop style that later became its forte. The Blue Horizon recordings - and especially the eponymous first LP - are probably the most authentic blues recordings to have been made by white, English musicians. Remarkably, that first LP climbed to number four in the album charts, although mint copies of the record have become surprisingly scarce these days.

Albatross	7"	Blue Horizon	573145	1968	£1.50	£4	chart single
Bare Trees	LP	Reprise	K44181	1972	£4	£10	
Black Magic Woman	7"	Blue Horizon	573138	1968	£2	£5	chart single
Blues Jam At Chess	LP	Blue Horizon	766227	1969	£20	£40	double, with other artists
Dragonfly	7"	Reprise	RS27010	1971	£1.50	£4	
Fleetwood Mac	LP	Blue Horizon	763200	1968	£8	£20	chart LP
Fleetwood Mac	LP	Mobile Fidelity	MFSL1012	1978	£6	£15	US audiophile
Fleetwood Mac	LP	Reprise	K54043	1975	£4	£10	white vinyl
Future Games	LP	Reprise	K44153	1971	£4	£10	
Green Manalishi	7"	Reprise	RS27007	1970	£1.50	£4	chart single
Green Manalishi	7"	Reprise	RS27007	1970	£4	£8	PS
Heroes Are Hard To Find	LP	Reprise	K54026	1974	£4	£10	
I Believe My Time Ain't Long	7"	Blue Horizon	3051	1967	£5	£10	
I Believe My Time Ain't Long	7"	Blue Horizon	3051	1967	£10	£20	PS
Kiln House	LP	Reprise	RSLP9004	1970	£5	£12	chart LP
Little Lies	12"	Warner Bros	W8291TP	1987	£2.50	£6	pic disc
Man Of The World	7"	Immediate	IM080	1969	£1.50	£4	chart single
Mirage	LP	Mobile Fidelity	MFSL1119	1984	£4	£10	US audiophile
Mr.Wonderful	LP	Blue Horizon	763205	1968	£10	£25	chart LP
Mystery To Me	LP	Reprise	K44248	1973	£4	£10	
Need Your Love So Bad	7"	Blue Horizon	573139	1968	£2.50	£6	chart single
Need Your Love So Bad	7"	Blue Horizon	573157	1969	£2	£5	chart single
Oh Diane	7"	Warner Bros	FLEET1P	1982	£1.50	£4	pic disc
Oh Well	7"	Reprise	RS27000	1969	£1.50	£4	chart single
Original Fleetwood Mac	LP	Blue Horizon	763875	1971	£3	£12	
Penguin	LP	Reprise	K44235	1973	£4	£10	
Pious Bird Of Good Omen	LP	Blue Horizon	763215	1969	£6	£15	chart LP
Rumours	LP	Nautilus	NR 8	1981	£6	£15	US audiophile
Then Play On	LP	Reprise	RSLP9000	1969	£5	£12	chart LP
Tusk	LP	Warner Bros	PROA866	1979	£5	£12	US promo sampler

285

FLEETWOODS

Almost There	7"	Liberty	LIB10191	1965	£2	£5	
Before And After	LP	Dolton	BLP2/BST8030	1965	£6	£15	US
Best Of The Oldies	LP	Dolton	BLP2/BST8011	1962	£8	£20	US
Come Softly To Me	7"	London	HLU8841	1959	£6	£12	chart single
Come Softly To Me	7"	London	SLU4003	1959	£12.50	£25	stereo
Deep In A Dream	LP	London	HAG2419	1961	£8	£20	
Fleetwoods	LP	Dolton	BLP2/BST8002	1960	£10	£25	US
Fleetwoods Sing For Lovers By Night	LP	Dolton	BLP2/BST8020	1963	£8	£20	US
Folk Rock	LP	Dolton	BLP2/BST8039	1965	£6	£15	US
Goodnight My Love	LP	Dolton	BLP2/BST8025	1963	£8	£20	US
Goodnight My Love	7"	Liberty	LIB75	1964	£1.50	£4	
Graduation's Here	7"	London	HLU8895	1959	£5	£10	
Greatest Hits	LP	Dolton	BLP2/BST8018	1962	£8	£20	US
He's The Great Imposter	7"	London	HLG9426	1961	£4	£8	
Mr.Blue	LP	Top Rank	BUY028	1960	£8	£20	
Mr.Blue	7"	Top Rank	JAR202	1959	£4	£8	
Outside My Window	7"	Top Rank	JAR294	1960	£2	£5	
Outside My Window	7"	Top Rank	JAR294	1960	£5	£10	PS
Ruby Red Baby Blue	7"	Liberty	LIB93	1964	£1.50	£4	
Runaround	7"	Top Rank	JAR383	1960	£2.50	£6	
Softly	LP	London	HAG2388	1961	£15	£30	
Softly	LP	London	SAHG6188	1961	£20	£40	stereo
They Tell Me It's Summer	7"	Liberty	LIB62	1964	£1.50	£4	
Tragedy	7"	London	HLG9341	1961	£4	£8	

FLEMING, HELEN

Eve's Ten Commandments	7"	Blue Beat	BB341	1965	£5	£10	

FLEMONS, WADE

Easy Loving	7"	Top Rank	JAR371	1960	£1.50	£4	
Slow Motion	7"	Top Rank	JAR206	1959	£1.50	£4	
Wade Flemons	LP	Vee Jay	LP1011	1959	£15	£30	US
What's Happening	7"	Top Rank	JAR327	1960	£1.50	£4	

FLESH FOR LULU

Subterraneans	7"	Polydor	FFLD1	1984	£2	£5	double

FLETCHER, DARROW

Pain Gets A Little Deeper	7"	London	HLU10024	1966	£15	£30	

FLETCHER, DON

Two Wrongs Don't Make A Right	7"	Vocalion	VP9271	1966	£4	£8	

FLEUR DE LYS

A legendary psychedelic group, the Fleur De Lys recorded both under their own name and as backing group to singer Sharon Tandy. They produced a number of striking singles, but with little commercial impact. Bryn Haworth, however, began a solo career during the seventies, while Pete Sears ended up as a member of Jefferson Starship.

Circles	7"	Immediate	IM032	1966	£40	£80	
Dong With A Luminous Nose	7"	Polydor	56251	1968	£20	£40	
I Can See A Light	7"	Polydor	56200	1967	£20	£40	
Moondreams	7"	Immediate	IM020	1965	£40	£80	
Mud In Your Eye	7"	Polydor	56124	1966	£40	£80	
Stop Crossing The Bridge	7"	Atlantic	584193	1968	£20	£40	
You're Just A Liar	7"	Atlantic	584243	1969	£20	£40	

FLICK, VIC SOUND

Hang On	7"	Chapter One	CH136	1970	£2	£5	

FLIED EGG

Dr.Siegel's Fried Egg Shooting Machine	LP	Philips		1971	£50	£100	Japanese
Goodbye	LP	Philips	55504	1972	£75	£150	Japanese

FLIES

House Of Love	7"	Decca	F12594	1967	£12.50	£25	
I'm Not Your Stepping Stone	7"	Decca	F12533	1966	£15	£30	
Magic Train	7"	RCA	RCA1757	1968	£7.50	£15	

FLINT, SHELBY

Angel On My Shoulder	7"	Warner Bros	WB30	1961	£1.50	£4	

FLINTLOCK

Hot From The Lock	LP	Pinnacle	PLP8309	1976	£6	£15	
On The Way	LP	Pinnacle	PLP8307	1975	£6	£15	
Stand Alone	LP	Pinnacle	PLP8312	1979	£5	£12	
Tears'n'Cheers	LP	Pinnacle	PLP8310	1977	£6	£15	

FLINTLOCKS

What Goes On	7"	Decca	F12412	1966	£1.50	£4	

FLINTSTONES

Workout	7"	HMV	POP1266	1964	£5	£10	

FLIP & THE DATELINERS

My Johnny Doesn't Come Around Anymore	7"	HMV	POP1359	1964	£12.50	£25	

FLIPS

Rockin' Twist	7"	London	HLU9490	1962	£2	£5	

FLIRTATIONS

Can't Stop Loving You	7"	Deram	DM295	1970	£1.50	£4	
Give Me Love	7"	Deram	DM329	1971	£1.50	£4	
Keep On Searchin'	7"	Deram	DM281	1970	£1.50	£4	
Need Your Loving	7"	Deram	DM351	1972	£1.50	£4	
Nothing But A Heartache	7"	Deram	DM216	1968	£1.50	£4	
Someone Out There	7"	Deram	DM195	1968	£1.50	£4	
Sounds Like The Flirtations	LP	Deram	DML/SML1046	1969	£4	£10	
Take Me In Your Arms And Love Me	7"	Polydor	2058167	1971	£2	£5	
What's Good About Goodbye My Love?	7"	Deram	DM252	1969	£1.50	£4	

FLO & EDDIE

Flo & Eddie	LP	Reprise	K44234	1973	£4	£10	
Flo And Eddie Interview Barry Mann	LP	RCA	DJL11162	1973	£5	£12	US promo
Immoral,Illegal & Fattening	LP	CBS	33554	1974	£4	£10	US
Phlorescent Leech & Eddie	LP	Reprise	K44201	1972	£4	£10	

FLOATING BRIDGE

Floating Bridge	LP	Liberty	LBS83271	1969	£6	£15

FLOCK

The Flock were one of the crop of rock big bands to emerge at the end of the sixties. They were made distinctive by the presence of a violin as a lead instrument; its wielder, Jerry Goodman, later finding a context in which he could shine even brighter, as a member of John McLaughlin's Mahavishnu Orchestra.

Flock	LP	CBS	63733	1969	£6	£15	chart LP
Tired Of Waiting For You	7"	CBS	4932	1970	£2	£5	

FLOH DE COLOGNE

Fliessbandbabys Beat Show	LP	Ohr	OMM556000	1970	£6	£15	German
Geler Symphonie	LP	Ohr	OMM556033	1973	£5	£12	German
Lucky Streik	LP	Ohr	OMM556029	1973	£5	£12	German
Munien	LP	Plane	99201	1974	£4	£10	German
Rockoper Profitgier Live	LP	Ohr	OMM556010	1971	£6	£15	German
Rotkappchen	LP	Plane	20905	1977	£4	£10	German
Tilt	LP	Plane	99202	1975	£4	£10	German
Vietnam	LP	Plane	33101	1968	£6	£15	German

FLOOD, DICK

Three Bells	7"	Felsted	AF125	1959	£1.50	£4

FLOWER TRAVELLING BAND

Anywhere	LP	Philips	8507	1970	£75	£150	Japanese
Made In Japan	LP	Atlantic	S8187	1972	£50	£100	Japanese
Make Up	LP	Atlantic	5073/4	1973	£75	£150	Japanese double
Satori	LP	Atlantic	S8056	1971	£50	£100	Japanese
Satori	7"	Atlantic	2091128	1971	£1.50	£4	

FLOWERPOT MEN

In A Moment Of Madness	7"	Deram	DM248	1969	£1.50	£4	
Let's Go To San Francisco	7"	Deram	DM142	1967	£1.50	£4	chart single
Man Without A Woman	7"	Deram	DM183	1968	£1.50	£4	
Walk In The Sky	7"	Deram	DM160	1967	£2.50	£6	

FLOWERS

Challenge	LP	CBS	10063	1969	£50	£100	Japanese

FLOWERS AND FROLICS

Bees On Horseback	LP	Free Reed	FRR016	1977	£6	£15

FLOWERS, LLOYD

Lovers Town	7"	Blue Beat	BB88	1961	£5	£10

FLOWERS, PHIL

Like A Rolling Stone	7"	A&M	AMS766	1969	£1.50	£4

FLOYD, EDDIE

Big Bird	7"	Stax	601035	1968	£1.50	£4	
Bring It On Home To Me	7"	Stax	STAX108	1968	£1.50	£4	
Bye Bye Baby	7"	Speciality	SPE1001	1967	£4	£8	
California Girl	LP	Stax	SXATS1036	1970	£4	£10	
I've Never Found A Girl	LP	Stax	SXATS1003	1968	£5	£12	
I've Never Found A Girl	7"	Stax	STAX104	1968	£1.50	£4	
Knock On Wood	LP	Atco	228014	1967	£5	£12	
Knock On Wood	LP	Stax	589006	1967	£6	£15	chart LP
Knock On Wood	7"	Atlantic	2091109	1971	£1.50	£4	
Knock On Wood	7"	Atlantic	584041	1966	£2.50	£6	chart single
On A Saturday Night	7"	Stax	601024	1967	£1.50	£4	
Raise Your Hand	7"	Stax	601001	1967	£2	£5	chart single
Rare Stamps	LP	Stax	STS2011	1969	£4	£10	US
Set My Soul On Fire	7"	London	HL10129	1967	£2	£5	
Things Get Better	7"	Stax	601016	1967	£2.50	£6	chart single
You've Got To Have Eddie	LP	Stax	2363010	1971	£4	£10	

FLOYD, KING

Baby Let Me Kiss You	7"	Atlantic	2091079	1971	£1.50	£4	
Got To Have Your Lovin'	7"	Atlantic	2091163	1971	£1.50	£4	
Groove Me	7"	Atlantic	2091051	1971	£1.50	£4	

FLUTE & VOICE

Imaginations Of Light	LP	Pilz	20210882	1971	£10	£25	German

FLYING BURRITO BROTHERS

Burrito Deluxe	LP	A&M	AMLS983	1970	£5	£12
Flying Burrito Brothers	LP	A&M	AMLS64295	1971	£4	£10
Gilded Palace Of Sin	LP	A&M	AMLS931	1969	£5	£12
Last Of The Red Hot Burritos	LP	A&M	AMLS64343	1971	£4	£10
Live In Amsterdam	LP	Bumble	GEXD301	1973	£6	£15 ....double
Older Guys	7"	A&M	AMS794	1970	£1.50	£4
Train Song	7"	A&M	AMS756	1969	£2	£5
Tried So Hard	7"	A&M	AMS816	1970	£1.50	£4

FLYING CIRCUS

Prepared In Peace	LP	Harvest	SHSP4010	1970	£6	£15

FLYING MACHINE

Devil Has Possession Of Your Mind	7"	Pye	7N45001	1970	£1.50	£4
Down To Earth	LP	Pye	NSPL18328	1970	£6	£15
Hanging On THe Edge Of Sadness	7"	Pye	7N17914	1970	£1.50	£4
Send My Baby Home Again	7"	Pye	7N17811	1969	£2	£5
Smile A Little Smile For Me	7"	Pye	7N17722	1969	£2	£5
Yes I Understand	7"	Pye	7N45093	1970	£1.50	£4

FLYNN, STEVE

Mr.Rainbow	7"	Parlophone	R5625	1967	£5	£10
Your Life And My Life	7"	Parlophone	R5689	1968	£2.50	£6

FLYS

Bunch Of Five	7"	Zama	ZA10	1977	£2	£5

FOCAL POINT

Love You Forever	7"	Deram	DM186	1968	£12.50	£25

FOCUS

Hocus Pocus	7"	Blue Horizon	2096004	1971	£1.50	£4
Moving Waves	LP	Blue Horizon	2931002	1971	£4	£10 ....with poster
Tommy	7"	Blue Horizon	2096008	1972	£2.50	£6

FOCUS & P.J.PROBY

Focus Con Proby	LP	EMI	5C06425713	1977	£6	£15 ....European

FOCUS THREE

Ten Thousand Years Behind My Mind	7"	Columbia	DB8279	1967	£12.50	£25

FOETUS

The aggressively avant-garde rock songs made by Jim Thirlwell (or Clint Ruin, as he sometimes likes to be known) are credited to a bewildering variety of names, of which the common denominator is the "Foetus" ingredient. For the sake of imposing some kind of order on the chaos that Thirlwell loves, records originally issued under such diverse descriptions as Foetus Corruptus, Foetus Over Frisco, Foetus Under Glass, Philip & His Foetus Vibrations, and You've Got Foetus On Your Breath are all listed here. Other records have been released using still further variations of the Foetus idea.

Ache	LP	Self Immolation	WOMBOYBL2	1982	£30	£60
Custom Built For Capitalism	12"	Self Immolation	WOMBWSUSC125	1982	£10	£25
Deaf	LP	Self Immolation	WOMBOYBL1	1981	£30	£60
Finely Honed Machine	12"	Self Immolation	OMBUNC712	1985	£15	£30
OKFM	7"	Self Immolation	WOMBS201	1981	£12.50	£25
Rife	LP	Rifle	RIFLE1	198-	£8	£20 ....double
Tell Me, What Is The Bane Of Your Life	7"	Self Immolation	WOMBKX07	1982	£10	£20
Wash It All Off	7"	Self Immolation	WOMBALL007	1981	£10	£20

FOGCUTTERS

Cry Cry Cry	7"	Liberty	LIB55793	1964	£4	£8

FOGERTY, TOM & THE BLUE VELVETS

Come On, Baby	7"	Orchestra	617	1961	£20	£40 ...US
Have You Ever Been Lonely?	7"	Orchestra	1010	1961	£20	£40 ...US
Yes You Did	7"	Orchestra		1962	£20	£40 ...US

FOGGY

How Come The Sun	7"	York	SYK534	1972	£1.50	£4
Kitty Starr	7"	York	SYK542	1972	£2	£5
Patchwork Album	LP	Canon	CNN5957	1976	£10	£25
Simple Gifts	LP	York	FYK411	1972	£20	£40

FOGGY DEW-O

Born To Take The Highway	LP	Decca	SKL5035	1969	£6	£15
Foggy Dew-O	LP	Decca	LK/SKL4940	1968	£8	£20
Reflections	7"	Decca	F12776	1968	£1.50	£4

FOLEY, RED

Beyond The Sunset	LP	Decca	DL8296	1958	£6	£15 ...US
Company's Comin'	LP	Decca	DL(7)4140	1961	£5	£12 ...US
Country Double Date	7" EP	Brunswick	OE9148	1955	£5	£10 ...with Ernest Tub
Dear Hearts And Gentle People	LP	Decca	DL(7)4290	1962	£5	£12 ...US
Golden Favorites	LP	Decca	DL4107	1961	£5	£12 ...US
He Walks With Thee	LP	Decca	DL8767	1958	£6	£15 ...US
Hearts Of Stone	7"	Brunswick	05363	1955	£5	£10

Magic Carpet £120

McGough And McGear £200

Mellow Candle: Swaddling Songs £300

Merseybeats £60

Modern Jazz Quartet Space £35

Stevie R. Moore: Phonography US LP £200

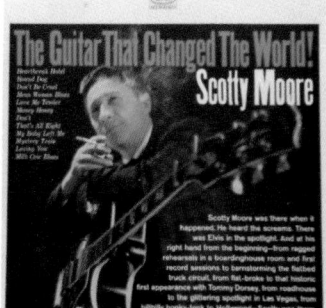

Scotty Moore: The Guitar That Changed The
World (US version with UK cover) £40

Neptune's Empire £80

Open Mind £250

Ora £200

Orange Bicycle £60

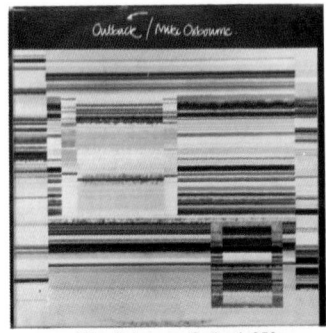

Mike Osbourne: Outback £50

Out Of Darkness £200

Outlaws: Dream Of The West £100

Patto: Hold Your Fire £80

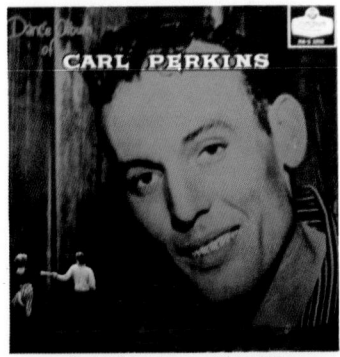

Carl Perkins: Dance Album £60

Elvis Presley: Best Of Elvis 10" LP £200

Elvis Presley: Rock 'N' Roll £200

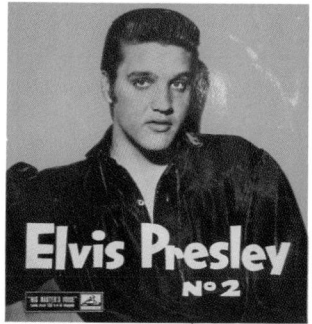

Elvis Presley: Rock 'N' Roll No. 2 £200

Prince Buster: The Outlaw £100

P.J. Proby (As Jet Powers): California License
£80

Queen: Breakthru Uncut Shaped Pic Disc £45

Queen: Hammer To Fall 12" £80

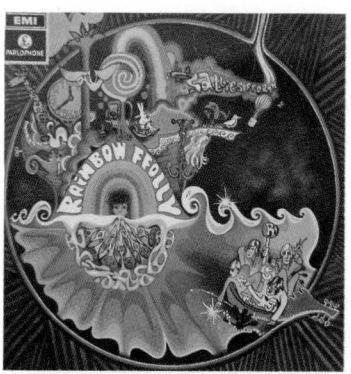

Rainbow Ffolly: Sallies Fforth £110

Rare Amber £80

Raw Material: Time Is £170

Max Roach And Clifford Brown: In Concert Vol 2
10" LP £40

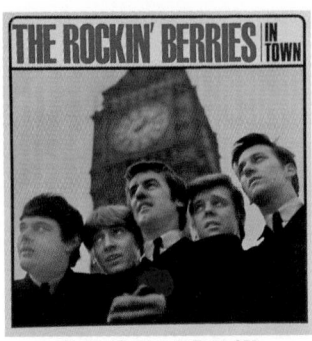

Rockin' Berries: In Town £50

Rolling Stones: Flowers Export LP £80

Rolling Stones: Get Off My Cloud 7" Demo £250

Ronettes £50

Samson: Are You Samson £30

Sandrose £130

Robin Scott: Woman From The Warm Grass £100

Seastone: Mirrored Dreams £100

Second Hand: Death May Be Your Santa Claus £100

Silver Birch £250

Alan Skidmore: Once Upon A Time £40

Skip Bifferty £75

Bob B. Sox And The Blue Jeans: Zip-A-Dee Doo

Spacemen 3: Transparent Radiation 12" £60

Spirogyra: St. Radigunds £80

Bruce Springsteen: Darkness On The Edge Of Town US Promo Pic Disc £120

Ringo Starr: Scouse The Mouse £80

Still Life £80

Sundown Playboys: Saturday Night Special Promo 78 £200

Tea And Symphony: An Asylum For The Musically Insane £60

Teddy Bears: Sing £150

Top Topham: Ascension Heights £60

Twistin' Kings: Twistin' The World Around US LP £100

Tyrannosaurus Rex: My People Were Fair.... £30

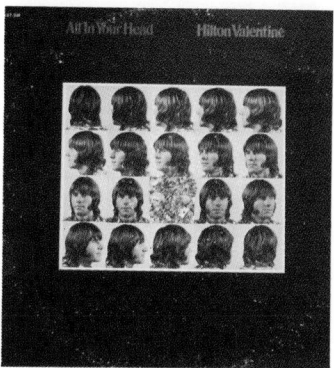

Hilton Valentine: All In Your Head £50

Various: The Sounds Of The R & B Hits £50

Gene Vincent: Cazy Times Mono £40 / Stereo £50

Vipers Skiffle Group: Coffee Bar Session 10" LP £30

Waiting For The Sun £100

Way We Live: A Candle For Judith £100

Houston Wells: Western Style £50

Mike Westbrook: Release £50

Westwood One US Radio Transcription Disc

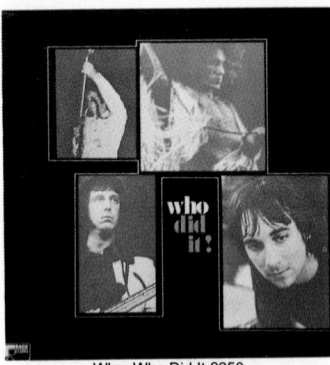

Who: Who Did It £250

Wooden O: A Handful Of Pleasant Delites £60

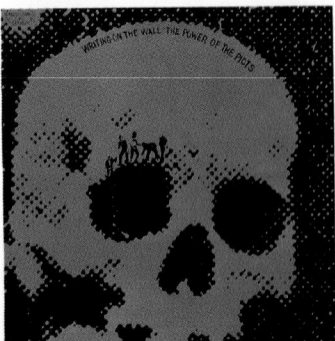

Writing On The Wall: The Power Of The Picts
£130

Zombies: Odessey And Oracle £30

Let's All Sing To Him	LP	Decca	DL(7)8903	1959	£5	£12	US
Let's All Sing With Red Foley	LP	Decca	DL(7)8847	1959	£6	£15	US
Lift Up Your Voice	10" LP	Decca	DL5338	1954	£15	£30	US
My Keepsake Album	LP	Decca	DL8806	1958	£6	£15	US
Night Watch	7"	Brunswick	05508	1955	£2	£5	
Red And Ernie	LP	Brunswick	LAT8206	1957	£8	£20	with Ernest Tubb
Sing Along	LP	Brunswick	LAT8343/STA3034	1960	£5	£12	
Skinnie Minnie Fishtail	7"	Brunswick	05321	1954	£2	£5	
Songs Of Devotion	LP	Decca	DL(7)4198	1961	£5	£12	US
Souvenir Album	LP	Decca	DL8294	1958	£8	£20	US
Souvenir Album	10" LP	Decca	DL5303	1951	£15	£30	US

FOLK BLUES INC.

Don't Hide	7"	Eyemark	EMS1006	1966	£2	£5	
F.B.I.	LP	Good Earth	GDS802	1977	£20	£40	

FOLKES, CALVIN

Hello Everybody	7"	Port-O-Jam	PJ4118	1964	£5	£10	Irving Six B side
My Bonnie	7"	Port-O-Jam	PJ4117	1964	£5	£10	
Someone	7"	Rio	R5	1963	£5	£10	
You'll Never Know	7"	Rio	R8	1963	£5	£10	

FOLKLANDERS

Two Little Fishes	7" EP	Urban	PB001	196-	£5	£10	

FOLKS BROTHERS

Carolina	7"	Blue Beat	BB30	1961	£5	£10	Eric Morris B side

FOLKWAYS

No Other Name	LP	Folk Heritage		1972	£5	£12	

FONTAINE, EDDIE

Cool It Baby	7"	Brunswick	05624	1956	£30	£60	
Nothing Shaking	7"	London	HLM8711	1958	£12.50	£25	
Rock Love	7"	HMV	7M304	1955	£50	£100	

FONTANA, ARLENE

I'm In Love	7"	Pye	7N25010	1959	£2	£5	

FONTANA, WAYNE

24 Sycamore	7"	Fontana	TF827	1967	£1.50	£4	
Charlie Cass/Linda	7"	Fontana	TF1054	1969	£4	£8	
Come On Home	7"	Fontana	TF684	1966	£1.50	£4	chart single
Come On Home	7" EP	Fontana	465307	1966	£7.50	£15	French
Dayton Ohio 1903	7"	Fontana	TF1008	1969	£1.50	£4	
Gina	7"	Fontana	TF889	1967	£1.50	£4	
Give Me Just A Little More Time	7"	Philips	6006035	1970	£15	£30	
Goodbye Bluebird	7"	Fontana	TF737	1966	£1.50	£4	chart single
Impossible Years	7"	Fontana	TF866	1967	£1.50	£4	
It Was Easier To Hurt Her	7"	Fontana	TF642	1965	£1.50	£4	
Never An Everyday Thing	7"	Fontana	TF976	1968	£1.50	£4	chart single
Pamela Pamela	7"	Fontana	TF770	1966	£1.50	£4	
Storybook Children	7"	Fontana	TF911	1968	£1.50	£4	
Wayne One	LP	Fontana	(S)TL5351	1966	£5	£12	
We're Building A Love/Charlie Cass	7"	Fontana	TF1054	1969	£1.50	£4	
Words Of Bartholomew	7"	Fontana	TF933	1968	£1.50	£4	

FONTANA, WAYNE & THE MINDBENDERS

Eric,Rick,Wayne,& Bob	LP	Fontana	TL5257	1966	£17.50	£35	
For You For You	7"	Fontana	TF418	1963	£2.50	£6	
Game Of Love	7"	Fontana	TF535	1965	£1.50	£4	chart single
Game Of Love	7" EP	Fontana	465272	1965	£7.50	£15	French
Game Of Love	7" EP	Fontana	TE17449	1965	£4	£8	
Hello Josephine	7"	Fontana	TF404	1963	£2.50	£6	chart single
Just A Little Bit Too Late	7"	Fontana	TF579	1965	£1.50	£4	chart single
Little Darling	7"	Fontana	TF436	1964	£2.50	£6	
Road Runner	7" EP	Fontana	TE17421	1964	£10	£20	
She Needs Love	7"	Fontana	TF611	1965	£1.50	£4	chart single
She Needs Love	7" EP	Fontana	465295	1965	£7.50	£15	French
Stop Look And Listen	7"	Fontana	TF451	1964	£2.50	£6	chart single
Um Um Um Um Um	7"	Fontana	TF497	1964	£1.50	£4	chart single
Um Um Um Um Um	7" EP	Fontana	TE17435	1964	£5	£10	
Walking On Air	7" EP	Fontana	TE17453	1965	£10	£20	
Wayne Fontana & The Mindbenders	LP	Fontana	SFL13106	1969	£4	£10	chart LP
Wayne Fontana & The Mindbenders	LP	Fontana	TL5230	1965	£10	£25	
Wayne Fontana & The Mindbenders	LP	Wing	WL1166	1967	£6	£15	

FONTANE SISTERS

Adorable	7"	London	HLD8225	1956	£7.50	£15	
Banana Boat Song	7"	London	HLD8378	1957	£7.50	£15	
Billy Boy	7"	London	HLD8861	1959	£4	£8	
Chanson D'Amour	7"	London	HLD8621	1958	£4	£8	
Eddie My Love	7"	London	HL7009	1956	£4	£8	
Eddie My Love	7"	London	HLD8265	1956	£12.50	£25	export
Fontane Sisters	LP	Dot	DLP3004	1956	£15	£30	US
Fontane Sisters No.1	7" EP	London	RED1029	1955	£10	£20	
Fontane Sisters No.2	7" EP	London	RED1037	1955	£10	£20	
Fontanes Sing	LP	London	HAD2053	1957	£15	£30	
Fool Around	7"	London	HLD8488	1957	£5	£10	
Happy Days And Lonely Nights	7"	London	HL8099	1954	£10	£20	
Hearts Of Stone	7"	London	HL8113	1955	£30	£60	

I'm In Love Again	7"	London	HLD8289	1956	£10	£20	
Listen To Your Heart	7"	London	HLD9037	1960	£2	£5	
Please Don't Leave Me	7"	London	HLD8415	1957	£7.50	£15	
Rock Love	7"	London	HL8126	1955	£25	£50	
Rolling Stone	7"	London	HLD8211	1955	£15	£30	
Seventeen	7"	London	HLD8177	1955	£25	£50	
Silver Bells	7"	London	HLD8343	1956	£7.50	£15	
Theme From A Summer Place	7"	London	HLD9078	1960	£1.50	£4	
Tips Of My Fingers	LP	Dot	DLP3531/25531	1963	£6	£15	US
Voices	7"	London	HLD8318	1956	£7.50	£15	with Pat Boone

FOOD
Forever Is A Dream	LP	Capitol	ST304	1969	£8	£20	US

FOOD BRAIN
Social Gathering	LP	Polydor		1970	£40	£80	Japanese

FOOL
Simon and Marijke of the Fool were a design team (the Beatles' shop mural; Eric Clapton's guitar; the Incredible String Band's second LP cover), rather than musicians, but they nevertheless recorded two interesting and eclectic LPs (the second was credited to 'Simon and Marijke"), the first being produced by the Hollies' Graham Nash.

Fool	LP	Mercury	SMCL20138	1969	£15	£30	

FOOLS DANCE
Fools Dance	LP	Lambs To The Slaughter	LTS18	1986	£4	£10	
Fools Dance	LP	Top Hat	TH22	1986	£5	£12	
Fools Dance	LP	Top Hole Turn.	TURN19	1985	£6	£15	
They'll Never Know	7"	Lambs To The Slaughter	LTS22	1987	£4	£8	
They'll Never Know	12"	Lambs To The Slaughter	LTS22T	1987	£5	£12	

FOOTE, CHUCK
You're Running Out Of Kisses	7"	London	HLU9495	1962	£1.50	£4	

FORBES
Beatles	7"	Power Exchange	PX253	1977	£1.50	£4	

FORBES, BILL
My Cherie	7"	Columbia	DB4232	1958	£1.50	£4	
Once More	7"	Columbia	DB4269	1959	£2	£5	
Too Young	7"	Columbia	DB4386	1959	£1.50	£4	chart single
You're Sixteen	7"	Columbia	DB4566	1961	£1.50	£4	

FORCE FIVE
Baby Don't Care	7"	United Artists	UP1102	1965	£10	£20	
Don't Know Which Way To Turn	7"	United Artists	UP1141	1966	£10	£20	
Don't Make My Baby Blue	7"	United Artists	UP1051	1964	£7.50	£15	
I Want You Babe	7"	United Artists	UP1118	1965	£7.50	£15	
Yeah I'm Waiting	7"	United Artists	UP1089	1965	£7.50	£15	

FORCE, ROBERT & ALBERT D'OSSCHE
Cross Over	LP	Sonet	SNKF168	1980	£5	£12	

FORCE WEST
All The Children Sleep	7"	Columbia	DB8174	1967	£4	£8	
Gotta Find Another Baby	7"	Columbia	DB7908	1966	£5	£10	
I Can't Give What I Haven't Got	7"	Decca	F12223	1965	£4	£8	
I'll Be Moving On	7"	CBS	3798	1968	£2.50	£6	
I'll Walk In The Rain	7"	CBS	3632	1968	£2.50	£6	
Sherry	7"	CBS	4385	1969	£4	£8	
When the Sun Comes Out	7"	Columbia	DB7963	1966	£5	£10	

FORD, CLINTON
Dandy	7" EP	Piccadilly	NEP34057	1966	£2	£5	
Old Shep	7"	Oriole	CB1500	1959	£1.50	£4	chart single

FORD, DEAN & THE GAYLORDS
Mr. Heartbreak's Here Instead	7"	Columbia	DB7402	1964	£5	£10	
Name Game	7"	Columbia	DB7610	1965	£5	£10	
Twenty Miles	7"	Columbia	DB7264	1964	£5	£10	

FORD, DEE DEE
Good Morning Blues	7"	London	HLU9245	1960	£12.50	£25	

FORD, EMILE
Emile	LP	Piccadilly	NPL38001	1961	£6	£15	
Emile	7" EP	Pye	NEP24119	1959	£4	£8	
Emile Ford Hit Parade	7" EP	Pye	NEP24124	1960	£4	£8	
Emile Ford Hit Parade Vol.2	7" EP	Pye	NEP24133	1960	£4	£8	
New Tracks With Emile	LP	Pye	NPL18049	1959	£5	£12	
What Do You Want To Make Those Eyes At Me For	7"	Pye	7N15225	1959	£1.50	£4	chart single

FORD, FRANKIE
Alimony	7"	Top Rank	JAR186	1959	£4	£8	Huey Piano
Cheating Woman	7"	Top Rank	JAR282	1960	£7.50	£15	Smith B side
Let's Take A Sea Cruise	LP	Ace	LP1005	1959	£50	£100	US

Sea Cruise	7"	London	HL8850	1959	£15	£30	
Sea Cruise	7"	Sue	WI366	1965	£7.50	£15	
Time After Time	7"	Top Rank	JAR299	1960	£4	£8	
What's Going On	7"	Sue	WI369	1965	£7.50	£15	
You Talk Too Much	7"	London	HLP9222	1960	£7.50	£15	

FORD, JON

Two's Company, Three's A Crowd	7"	Philips	BF1690	1968	£1.50	£4	
You Got Me Where You Want Me	7"	Philips	6006030	1970	£25	£50	

FORD, NEAL & THE FANATICS

Neal Ford And The Fanatics	LP	Hickory	LPS141	1967	£6	£15	US

FORD, PERRY

Bye Bye Baby Goodbye	7"	Parlophone	R4573	1959	£1.50	£4	
Crazy Over You	7"	Parlophone	R4633	1960	£1.50	£4	
Little Grown Up	7"	Parlophone	R4683	1960	£1.50	£4	
Prince Of Fools	7"	Decca	F11497	1962	£1.50	£4	

FORD, ROCKY

New Singing Star	LP	Audio Lab	AL1561	1960	£10	£25	US

FORD, TENNESSEE ERNIE

Anticipation Blues	7" EP	Capitol	EAP120067	1961	£10	£20	
Ballad Of Davy Crockett	7"	Capitol	CL14506	1956	£4	£8	chart single
Blackeyed Susie	7"	Capitol	CL15010	1959	£1.50	£4	
Capitol Presents	10" LP	Capitol	LC6573	1952	£15	£30	
Catfish Boogie	7"	Capitol	CL14006	1953	£10	£20	
Come To The Fair	LP	Capitol	(S)T1473	1961	£4	£10	
First Born	7"	Capitol	CL14657	1956	£1.50	£4	
Gather Round	7" EP	Capitol	EAP11227	1960	£4	£8	
Give Me Your Word	7"	Capitol	CL14005	1953	£5	£10	chart single
His Hands	7"	Capitol	CL14261	1955	£2.50	£6	
In The Middle Of An Island	7"	Capitol	CL14759	1957	£1.50	£4	
Little Red Rocking Hood	7"	Capitol	CL15210	1961	£2.50	£6	
Lonely Man	7"	Capitol	CL14734	1957	£1.50	£4	
Ol' Rockin' Ern	LP	Capitol	T888	1958	£10	£25	
Sixteen Tons	LP	Capitol	T1380	1960	£8	£20	
Sixteen Tons	7"	Capitol	CL14500	1956	£4	£8	chart single
Sixteen Tons	7"	Capitol	CL15403	1965	£1.50	£4	
Sixteen Tons	7" EP	Capitol	EAP1014	1956	£7.50	£15	
Star Carol	7" EP	Capitol	SEP11071	1961	£2	£5	stereo
Sunday Barbecue	7"	Capitol	CL14896	1958	£1.50	£4	
Tennessee Ernie Ford	7" EP	Capitol	EAP1639	1956	£4	£8	
That's All	7"	Capitol	CL14557	1956	£2	£5	
There Is Beauty In Everything	7"	Capitol	CL14273	1955	£2.50	£6	
This Lusty Land	10" LP	Capitol	LC6825	1956	£6	£15	
This Must Be The Place	7"	Capitol	CL14133	1954	£4	£8	with Betty Hutton
Watermelon Song	7"	Capitol	CL14691	1957	£1.50	£4	
Who Will Shoe Your Pretty Little Foot	7"	Capitol	CL14616	1956	£1.50	£4	

FOREHAND, EDDIE BUSTER

Young Boy Blues	7"	Action	ACT4519	1969	£4	£8	

FOREIGNER

Double Vision	LP	Mobile Fidelity	MFSL1052	1982	£5	£12	US audiophile
I Want To Know What Love Is	7"	Atlantic	A9596	1984	£1.50	£4	F shaped disc

FORERUNNERS

Bony Moronie	7"	Solar	SRP100	1964	£1.50	£4	

FOREST

Forest	LP	Harvest	SHVL760	1969	£30	£60	
Forest	LP	Zap	ZAP2	1987	£5	£12	
Full Circle	LP	Harvest	SHVL784	1970	£35	£70	
Full Circle	LP	Zap	ZAP3	1988	£5	£12	
Searching For Shadows	7"	Harvest	HAR5007	1969	£6	£12	

FORESTERS

Broken Hearted Clown	7"	Polydor	56038	1965	£4	£8	
Comin' Home In The Evening	7"	Columbia	DB8176	1967	£2	£5	
Early Morning Hours	7"	Polydor	56104	1966	£4	£8	
How Can I Tell Her	7"	Polydor	56057	1965	£4	£8	
Mr.Smith	7"	Columbia	DB8086	1966	£2	£5	
Sometimes When You're Lonely	7"	Columbia	DB8040	1966	£2.50	£6	

FOREVER AMBER

Love Cycle	LP	Advance		1969	£530	£800	

FOREVER MORE

Words On Black Plastic	LP	RCA	3015	1971	£5	£12	
Yours Forever More	LP	RCA	SF8016	1969	£5	£12	

FORK IN THE ROAD

Can't Turn Around	7"	Ember	EMBS131	1961	£60	£120	

FORMAT

Maxwell's Silver Hammer	7"	CBS	4600	1969	£1.50	£4	

FORMATIONS

At The Top Of The Stairs	7"	MGM	MGM1399	1968	£25	£50	

At The Top Of The Stairs .... 7" ...... Mojo .... 2027001................ 1971 ... £2 ....£5 .... chart single

FORMERLY FAT HARRY
Formerly Fat Harry .... LP ..... Harvest .... SHSP4016 .... 1971 ... £6 ....£15

FORMULA
Close To Me .... 7" ...... HMV .... POP1438 .... 1965 ... £1.50 ....£4

FORMULA ONE
I Just Can't Go To Sleep .... 7" ...... Warner Bros .... WB155 .... 1965 ... £6 ....£12

FORRAY, ANDY
Dream With Me .... 7" ...... Decca .... F12733 .... 1968 ... £10 ....£20
Let The Sunshine In .... 7" ...... Fontana .... TF999 .... 1969 ... £2 ....£5
Proud One .... 7" ...... Parlophone...... R5729 .... 1968 ... £2.50 ....£6
Sarah Jane .... 7" ...... Parlophone...... R5715 .... 1968 ... £2.50 ....£6

FORTES MENTUM
Gotta Go .... 7" ...... Parlophone...... R5768 .... 1969 ... £2.50 ....£6
I Can't Go On .... 7" ...... Parlophone...... R5726 .... 1968 ... £2.50 ....£6
Saga Of A Wrinkled Man .... 7" ...... Parlophone...... R5684 .... 1968 ... £7.50 ....£15

FORTUNA
From The Edinburgh Festival Fringe .... LP ..... Sweet Folk .... SFA058 .... 1976 ... £4 ....£10
1976 .... And Country....

FORTUNE, JOHNNY
Soul Surfer .... LP ..... Park Avenue .... 401 .... 1963 ... £10 ....£25 .... US

FORTUNE, LANCE
Be Mine .... 7" ...... Pye .... 7N15240 .... 1960 ... £2 ....£5 .... chart single
This Love I Have For You .... 7" ...... Pye .... 7N15260 .... 1960 ... £1.50 ....£4 .... chart single

FORTUNES
Caroline .... 7" ...... Decca .... F11809 .... 1964 ... £6 ....£12
Fortunes .... LP ..... Decca .... LK4736 .... 1965 ... £8 ....£20
Freedom .... LP ..... Capitol .... ST647 .... 1971 ... £5 ....£12 .... US
Here Comes That Rainy Day Feeling .... LP ..... Capitol .... ST809 .... 1971 ... £5 ....£12 .... US
Again ....
Here It Comes Again .... 7" ...... Decca .... F12243 .... 1965 ... £1.50 ....£4 .... chart single
I Like The Look Of You .... 7" ...... Decca .... F11912 .... 1964 ... £1.50 ....£4
Idol .... 7" ...... United Artists .. UP1188 .... 1967 ... £1.50 ....£4
Idol .... 7" EP.. United Artists .. 36119 .... 1967 ... £7.50 ....£15 .... French
Is It Really Worth Your While .... 7" ...... Decca .... F12485 .... 1966 ... £1.50 ....£4
Look Homeward Angel .... 7" ...... Decca .... F11985 .... 1964 ... £1.50 ....£4
Our Love Has Gone .... 7" ...... Decca .... F12612 .... 1967 ... £1.50 ....£4
Our Love Has Gone .... 7" ...... Decca .... F12874 .... 1969 ... £1.50 ....£4
Silent Street .... 7" ...... Decca .... F12429 .... 1966 ... £1.50 ....£4
Summertime Summertime .... 7" ...... Decca .... F11718 .... 1963 ... £5 ....£10
Summertime Summertime .... 7" ...... Decca .... F11718 .... 1963 ... £7.50 ....£15 .... PS
That Same Old Feeling .... LP ..... World Pacific ... WPS21904 .... 1970 ... £5 ....£12 .... US
This Golden Ring .... 7" ...... Decca .... F12321 .... 1966 ... £1.50 ....£4 .... chart single
This Golden Ring .... 7" EP.. Decca .... 457105 .... 1966 ... £7.50 ....£15 .... French
You've Got Your Troubles .... 7" ...... Decca .... F12173 .... 1965 ... £1.50 ....£4 .... chart single
You've Got Your Troubles .... 7" EP.. Decca .... 457089 .... 1965 ... £7.50 ....£15 .... French

FORTY-FIVES
Couldn't Believe A Word .... 7" ...... Chopper .... CHEAP5 .... 1979 ... £1.50 ....£4

FORTY-NINE AMERICANS
14 Track Single .... 7" ...... NB .... NB4 .... 1980 ... £1.50 ....£4
E Pluribus Unum .... LP ..... Choo Choo .... CHUG1 .... 1980 ... £4 ....£10
                                                        Train ....

FORTY-NINTH PARALLEL
Forty-Ninth Parallel .... LP ..... Maverick .... MAS7001 .... 1969 ... £25 ....£50 .... US

FORUM
River Is Wide .... 7" ...... London .... HLM10120 .... 1967 ... £1.50 ....£4

FORWOOD, SHIRLEY
Two Hearts .... 7" ...... London .... HLD8402 .... 1957 ... £6 ....£12

FOSTER, FRANK
Frank Foster Quartet .... 10" LP Vogue .... LDE112 .... 1955 ... £50 ....£100
Frank Foster With Elmo Hope .... LP ..... Esquire .... 32033 .... 1957 ... £20 ....£40
Manhattan Fever .... LP ..... Blue Note........ BST84278 .... 1968 ... £10 ....£25

FOSTER, JOHN
John Foster Sings .... LP ..... Island .... ILP939 .... 1966 ... £30 ....£60

FOSTER, LES
Do It Nice .... 7" ...... Big Shot .... BI529 .... 1969 ... £2.50 ....£6
Muriel .... 7" ...... Jolly .... JY022 .... 1968 ... £4 ....£8

FOTHERINGAY
Fotheringay .... LP ..... Island .... ILPS9125 .... 1970 ... £8 ....£20 .... chart LP
Peace In The End .... 7" ...... Island .... WIP6085 .... 1970 ... £1.50 ....£4

FOUNDATIONS
Any Old Time .... 7" ...... Pye .... 7N17503 .... 1968 ... £1.50 ....£4 .... chart single
Baby Now That I've Found You .... 7" ...... Pye .... 7N17366 .... 1967 ... £1.50 ....£4 .... chart single

Title	Format	Label	Cat. No.	Year			Notes
Baby Now That I've Found You	7" EP	Pye	PNV24199	1967	£6	£12	French
Back On My Feet Again	7"	Pye	7N17417	1968	£1.50	£4	chart single
Born To Live And Born To Die	7"	Pye	7N17809	1969	£1.50	£4	chart single
Build Me Up Buttercup	7"	Pye	7N17638	1968	£1.50	£4	chart single
Digging The Foundations	LP	Pye	NPL18290	1969	£4	£10	
From The Foundations	LP	Pye	NPL18206	1967	£4	£10	
In The Bad Bad Old Days	7"	Pye	7N17702	1969	£1.50	£4	chart single
It's All Right	7" EP	Pye	NEP24297	1968	£2.50	£6	
Rocking The Foundations	LP	Pye	NPL18227	1968	£4	£10	
Stoney Ground	7"	MCA	MK5075	1971	£2	£5	
Stoney Ground	7"	MCA	MU5075	1971	£2.50	£6	

FOUNTAIN, JAMES

Title	Format	Label	Cat. No.	Year			
Seven Day Lover	7"	Cream	CRM5002	1976	£1.50	£4	

FOUNTAIN, PETE

Title	Format	Label	Cat. No.	Year			
Salutes The Great Clarinettists	LP	Coral	LVA9132	1960	£4	£10	

FOUR

Title	Format	Label	Cat. No.	Year			
It's Alright	7"	Decca	F11999	1964	£2	£5	

FOUR ACES

Title	Format	Label	Cat. No.	Year			Notes
Bahama Mama	7"	Brunswick	05663	1957	£1.50	£4	
Beyond The Blue Horizon	LP	Decca	DL(7)8944	1959	£5	£12	US
Dreamer	7"	Brunswick	05601	1956	£1.50	£4	
Four Aces	7" EP	Brunswick	OE9458	1959	£2.50	£6	
Four Aces	10" LP	Decca	DL5429	195-	£8	£20	US
Friendly Persuasion	7"	Brunswick	05623	1956	£2.50	£6	chart single
Gal With The Yaller Shoes	7"	Brunswick	05566	1956	£1.50	£4	
Gang That Sang	7"	Brunswick	05256	1954	£2	£5	
Golden Hits	LP	Decca	DL(7)4013	1960	£5	£12	US
Half Of My Heart	7"	Brunswick	05712	1957	£1.50	£4	
Hanging Up A Horseshoe	7"	Brunswick	05758	1958	£1.50	£4	
Heart	7"	Brunswick	05651	1957	£1.50	£4	
Heart And Soul	LP	Decca	DL8228	1956	£6	£15	US
Hits From Broadway	LP	Decca	DL(7)8855	1959	£5	£12	US
Hits From Hollywood	LP	Decca	DL8693	1958	£6	£15	US
If You Can Dream	7"	Brunswick	05573	1956	£1.50	£4	
I'm Yours	7"	Decca	A73010	195-	£4	£8	export
It Shall Come To Pass	7"	Brunswick	05322	1954	£1.50	£4	
It's A Woman's World	7"	Brunswick	05348	1954	£2	£5	
Jingle Bells	7"	Brunswick	05504	1955	£1.50	£4	
Just Squeeze Me	10" LP	Brunswick	LA8614	1953	£8	£20	
Love Is A Many Splendoured Thing	7"	Brunswick	05480	1955	£4	£8	chart single
Melody Of Love	7"	Brunswick	05379	1955	£2	£5	
Mood For Love	LP	Decca	DL8122	1956	£6	£15	US
Mood For Love Vol.1	7" EP	Brunswick	OE9157	1955	£2.50	£6	
Mood For Love Vol.2	7" EP	Brunswick	OE9192	1955	£2.50	£6	
Mr.Sandman	7"	Brunswick	05355	1954	£4	£8	chart single
Presenting	7" EP	Brunswick	OE9090	1955	£5	£10	
Rock and Roll Rhapsody	7"	Brunswick	05743	1958	£1.50	£4	
Sentimental Souvenirs	LP	Decca	DL8191	1956	£6	£15	US
She Sees All The Hollywood Hits	LP	Decca	DL8312	1957	£6	£15	US
Shuffling Along	LP	Decca	DL8567	1958	£6	£15	US
Sing Film Titles	7" EP	Brunswick	OE9324	1957	£4	£8	
Slewfoot	7"	Brunswick	05429	1955	£1.50	£4	
Stranger In Paradise	7"	Brunswick	05418	1955	£4	£8	chart single
Swingin' Aces	LP	Decca	DL(7)8766	1958	£5	£12	US
There Goes My Heart	7"	Brunswick	05401	1955	£1.50	£4	
Three Coins In The Fountain	7"	Brunswick	05308	1954	£5	£10	chart single
Three Sheets To The Wind	7"	Brunswick	05695	1957	£1.50	£4	
To Love Again	7"	Brunswick	05562	1956	£1.50	£4	
Woman In Love	7"	Brunswick	05589	1956	£2.50	£6	chart single
World Outside	7"	Brunswick	05767	1958	£1.50	£4	chart single
World Outside	7"	Brunswick	05773	1959	£1.50	£4	chart single
Written On The Wind	LP	Decca	DL8424	1957	£8	£20	US
You Can't Run Away From It	7"	Brunswick	05613	1956	£1.50	£4	

FOUR ACES (2)

Title	Format	Label	Cat. No.	Year			
River Bank Coberley Again	7"	Island	WI178	1965	£5	£10	
Sweet Chariot	7"	Island	WI179	1965	£5	£10	

FOUR COINS

Title	Format	Label	Cat. No.	Year			
World Outside	7"	Fontana	H168	1958	£2	£5	

FOUR ESCORTS

Title	Format	Label	Cat. No.	Year			
Love Me	7"	HMV	7M277	1954	£1.50	£4	

FOUR ESQUIRES

Title	Format	Label	Cat. No.	Year			Notes
Act Your Age	7"	Pye	7N25027	1959	£1.50	£4	
Adorable	7"	London	HLA8224	1956	£10	£20	
Always And Forever	7"	London	HL8579	1958	£4	£8	
Hideaway	7"	London	HL8746	1958	£2.50	£6	
Look Homeward Angel	7"	London	HL8376	1957	£15	£30	demo
Love Me Forever	7"	London	HLO8533	1958	£6	£12	chart single
Non E Cosi	7"	Pye	7N25012	1959	£1.50	£4	
Sphinx Won't Tell	7"	London	HL8152	1955	£12.50	£25	
Wouldn't It Be Wonderful	7"	Pye	7N25049	1960	£1.50	£4	

FOUR FRESHMEN

Title	Format	Label	Cat. No.	Year			
Day By Day	7"	Capitol	CL14338	1955	£1.50	£4	

Four Freshmen And Five Guitars	7" EP	Capitol	SEP11255	1961	£2	£5		stereo
Four Freshmen And Five Guitars Pt.2	7" EP	Capitol	SEP21255	1961	£2	£5		stereo
Four Freshmen And Five Guitars Pt.3	7" EP	Capitol	SEP31255	1961	£2	£5		stereo
Four Freshmen And Five Saxes	LP	Capitol	T844	1957	£5	£12		
Four Freshmen And Five Trombones	LP	Capitol	LC6812	1956	£5	£12		
Four Freshmen And Five Trumpets	LP	Capitol	T763	1957	£5	£12		
Freshmen Favorites	LP	Capitol	T743	1956	£5	£12		US
Graduation Day	7"	Capitol	CL14610	1956	£1.50	£4		
Love Is Just Around The Corner	7"	Capitol	CL14580	1956	£1.50	£4		
Love Turns Winter To Spring	7"	Capitol	CL14196	1954	£1.50	£4		
Voices In Latin	LP	Capitol	T992	1958	£5	£12		US
Voices In Modern	LP	Capitol	T522	1955	£5	£12		US
Voices In Modern	10" LP	Capitol	LC6685	1954	£5	£12		
You're So Far Above Me	7"	Capitol	CL14633	1956	£1.50	£4		

FOUR GEES
Ethiopia	7"	President	PT160	1967	£2.50	£6	

FOUR GIBSON GIRLS
June, July And August	7"	Oriole	CB1447	1958	£2	£5	
Safety Sue	7"	Oriole	CB1453	1958	£1.50	£4	

FOUR GUYS
Mine	7"	Vogue Coral	Q72054	1955	£2.50	£6	

FOUR HUNDRED BLOWS
Beat The Devil	7"	Concrete Productions	CPROD2	1982	£1.50	£4	

FOUR JACKS
Hey Baby	7"	Decca	F10984	1958	£2	£5	
Hey Baby	7" EP	Decca	DFE6460	1958	£6	£12	

FOUR JONES BOYS
Certain Smile	7"	Columbia	DB4170	1958	£1.50	£4	
Day The Rains Came	7"	Columbia	DB4217	1958	£1.50	£4	
Happiness Street	7"	Decca	F10789	1956	£1.50	£4	
Moments To Remember	7"	Decca	F10671	1955	£1.50	£4	
Priscilla	7"	Decca	F10829	1956	£1.50	£4	
Real Romance	7"	Decca	F10568	1955	£1.50	£4	
Rock-a-Hula Baby	7"	Columbia	DB4046	1957	£2	£5	
Tutti Frutti	7"	Decca	F10717	1956	£2.50	£6	

FOUR JUST MEN
That's My Baby	7"	Parlophone	R5186	1964	£20	£40	

FOUR KENTS
Moving Finger Writes	7"	RCA	RCA1705	1968	£2	£5	

FOUR KESTRELS
Sound Off	7"	Decca	F11333	1961	£1.50	£4	

FOUR KINSMEN
It Looks Like The Daybreak	7"	Decca	F22671	1967	£2.50	£6	

FOUR KNIGHTS
Foolish Tears	7"	Coral	Q72355	1959	£2	£5	
Foolishly Yours	7"	Capitol	CL14290	1955	£2	£5	
Four Knights	LP	Coral	CRL52221	195-	£8	£20	US
Four Knights	7" EP	Capitol	EAP1506	1955	£6	£12	
Honey Bunch	7"	Capitol	CL14244	1955	£10	£20	
In The Chapel In The Moonlight	7"	Capitol	CL14154	1954	£5	£10	
Million Dollar Baby	LP	Coral	CRL(7)57309	1960	£6	£15	US
Saw Your Eyes	7"	Capitol	CL14204	1954	£4	£8	
Spotlight Songs	LP	Capitol	T345	1953	£15	£30	US
Spotlight Songs	10" LP	Capitol	H345	1953	£37.50	£75	US
Spotlight Songs	10" LP	Capitol	LC6604	1953	£8	£20	
Till Then	7"	Capitol	CL14076	1954	£6	£12	chart single
You	7"	Capitol	CL14516	1956	£2	£5	

FOUR LADS
Four Hits	7" EP	London	RER1289	1961	£2.50	£6	
Four Lads	LP	Philips	BBL7256	1958	£5	£12	
Golly	7"	Philips	JK1021	1957	£2	£5	
Moments To Remember	7" EP	Philips	BBE12044	1956	£4	£8	
Standing On The Corner	7"	Philips	PB1000	1960	£1.50	£4	chart single

FOUR LEAVED CLOVER
Why	7"	Oak	RGJ207	1965	£75	£150	

FOUR LOVERS
The earliest recordings made by the group that later became the Four Seasons were these.

Honey Love	7"	RCA	476519	1956	£6	£12	US
Jambalaya	7"	RCA	476646	1956	£7.50	£15	US
Joyride	LP	RCA	LPM1317	1956	£180	£300	US
My Life For Your Love	7"	Epic	9255	1957	£180	£300	US
Never Never	7"	RCA	476768	1957	£7.50	£15	US
Shake A Hand	7"	RCA	476812	1957	£10	£20	US
You're The Apple Of My Eye	7"	RCA	476518	1956	£7.50	£15	US

FOUR MATADORS

Title	Format	Label	Cat No	Year			Notes
Man's Gotta Stand Tall	7"	Columbia	DB7806	1966	£15	£30	

FOUR PALMS

Title	Format	Label	Cat No	Year			Notes
Jeannie,Joanie,Shirley & Tony	7"	Vogue	V9116	1958	£60	£120	

FOUR PENNIES

Title	Format	Label	Cat No	Year			Notes
Black Girl	7"	Philips	BF1366	1964	£1.50	£4	chart single
Do You Want Me To	7"	Philips	BF1296	1964	£2.50	£6	chart single
Four Pennies	7" EP.	Philips	BE12561	1964	£2.50	£6	
I Found Out the Hard Way	7"	Philips	BF1349	1964	£1.50	£4	chart single
Juliet	LP	Wing	WL1146	1967	£6	£15	
Juliet	7"	Philips	BF1322	1964	£1.50	£4	chart single
Keep The Freeway Open	7"	Philips	BF1491	1966	£2.50	£6	
Mixed Bag	LP	Philips	BL7734	1966	£30	£60	sleeve pictured in Guide
No Sad Songs For Me	7"	Philips	BF1519	1966	£2.50	£6	
Smooth Side Of The Four Pennies	7" EP.	Philips	BE12571	1964	£2.50	£6	
Spin With The Four Pennies	7" EP.	Philips	BE12562	1964	£4	£8	
Swinging Side Of The Four Pennies	7" EP.	Philips	BE12570	1964	£5	£10	
Trouble Is My Middle Name	7"	Philips	BF1469	1966	£2	£5	chart single
Two Sides Of The Four Pennies	LP	Philips	BL7642	1964	£8	£20	chart LP
Until It's Time For You To Go	7"	Philips	BF1435	1965	£1.50	£4	chart single
Way Of Love	7"	Philips	BF1398	1965	£2	£5	

FOUR PENNIES (2)

Title	Format	Label	Cat No	Year			Notes
My Block	7"	Stateside	SS198	1963	£5	£10	
When The Boys Are Happy	7"	Stateside	SS244	1963	£4	£8	

FOUR PERFECTIONS

Title	Format	Label	Cat No	Year			Notes
I'm Not Strong Enough	7"	Cream	CRM5006	1976	£2.50	£6	

FOUR PLUS ONE

The group that issued its first single under the name Four Plus One, issued its second as The In Crowd, and eventually, after a few changes in personnel, got round to making an LP - as Tomorrow.

Title	Format	Label	Cat No	Year			Notes
Time Is On My Side	7"	Parlophone	R5221	1965	£20	£40	

FOUR PREPS

Title	Format	Label	Cat No	Year			Notes
Big Man	7"	Capitol	CL14873	1958	£1.50	£4	chart single
Big Man	7" EP.	Capitol	EAP11064	1959	£2.50	£6	
Campus Encores	7" EP.	Capitol	EAP11647	1961	£2	£5	
Dreamy Eyes	7" EP.	Capitol	EAP1862	1957	£2.50	£6	
Four Preps	LP	Capitol	T994	1958	£5	£12	
Got A Girl	7"	Capitol	CL15128	1960	£1.50	£4	US
Lazy Summer Nights	7" EP.	Capitol	EAP11139	1959	£2	£5	chart single
More Money For You And Me	7"	Capitol	CL15217	1961	£1.50	£4	chart single
Things We Did Last Summer	LP	Capitol	T1090	1958	£5	£12	
Twenty Six Miles	7"	Capitol	CL14815	1957	£1.50	£4	
Twenty Six Miles	7" EP.	Capitol	EAP11015	1958	£2.50	£6	

FOUR SAXOPHONES

Title	Format	Label	Cat No	Year			Notes
Four Saxophones In Twelve Tones	10" LP	Vogue	LDE170	1956	£5	£12	

FOUR SEASONS

Title	Format	Label	Cat No	Year			Notes
Ain't That A Shame	LP	Stateside	SL10042	1963	£6	£15	
Ain't That A Shame	7"	Stateside	SS194	1963	£1.50	£4	chart single
All The Song Hits	LP	Philips	2/600150	1964	£4	£10	US
Alone	7"	Stateside	SS315	1964	£2	£5	
Beggin'	7"	Philips	BF1556	1967	£1.50	£4	
Bermuda	7"	Gone	5122	1961	£15	£30	US
Big Girls Don't Cry	LP	Vee Jay	LP/SR1056	1963	£6	£15	US
Big Girls Don't Cry	7"	Stateside	SS145	1963	£1.50	£4	
Big Man In Town	7"	Philips	BF1372	1965	£1.50	£4	chart single
Born To Wander	LP	Philips	BL7611	1964	£6	£15	
Bye Bye Baby	7"	Philips	BF1395	1965	£1.50	£4	
Candy Girl	7"	Stateside	SS216	1963	£2	£5	
Christmas Album	LP	Philips	(S)BL7753	1966	£5	£12	
C'mon Marianne	7"	Philips	BF1584	1967	£1.50	£4	
Dawn	LP	Philips	BL7621	1964	£5	£12	
Dawn	7"	Philips	BF1317	1964	£1.50	£4	
Don't Think Twice	7" EP.	Philips	452049	1965	£7.50	£15	French
Edizione D'Oro	LP	Philips	(S)DBL003	1969	£5	£12	double
Electric Stories	7"	Philips	BF1743	1969	£1.50	£4	
Entertain You	LP	Philips	BL7663	1965	£5	£12	
Four Seasons Sing	7" EP.	Stateside	SE1011	1964	£7.50	£15	
Girl Come Running	7"	Philips	BF1420	1965	£1.50	£4	
Gold Vault Of Hits	LP	Philips	(S)BL7719	1966	£4	£10	
Golden Hits	LP	Vee Jay	LP/SR1065	1963	£5	£12	US
Greetings	LP	Stateside	SL10051	1963	£6	£15	
Hits Of The Four Seasons	cass-s	Philips	MCP1000	1968	£2.50	£6	
I've Got You Under My Skin	7"	Philips	BF1511	1966	£1.50	£4	chart single
I've Got You Under My Skin	7" EP.	Philips	452060	1966	£7.50	£15	French
Let's Hang On	7"	Philips	BF1439	1965	£1.50	£4	chart single
Looking Back	LP	Philips	(S)BL7752	1966	£5	£12	
More Golden Hits	LP	Vee Jay	LP/SR1088	1964	£5	£12	US
More Great Hits Of 1964	LP	Vee Jay	LP/SR1136	1965	£5	£12	US
Opus 17	7"	Philips	BF1493	1966	£1.50	£4	chart single
Peanuts	7"	Stateside	SS262	1964	£2	£5	
Rag Doll	LP	Philips	BL7643	1964	£5	£12	
Rag Doll	7"	Philips	BF1347	1964	£1.50	£4	chart single

Rag Doll	7"	Philips	BF1763	1969	£1.50	£4	PS
Rag Doll	7" EP	Philips	452030	1964	£7.50	£15	French
Recorded Live On Stage	LP	Vee Jay	LP/SR1154	1965	£5	£12	US
Ronnie	7"	Philips	BF1334	1964	£1.50	£4	
Santa Claus Is Coming To Town	7"	Stateside	SS241	1963	£2	£5	
Saturday's Father	7"	Philips	BF1685	1968	£1.50	£4	
Save It For Me	7"	Philips	BF1364	1965	£1.50	£4	
Seasoned Hits	LP	Fontana	SFJL952	1968	£4	£10	
Second Vault Of Golden Hits	LP	Philips	(S)BL7751	1967	£4	£10	
Sherry	LP	Stateside	SL10033	1963	£6	£15	chart LP
Sherry	7"	Stateside	SS122	1962	£1.50	£4	chart single
Sherry	7" EP	Pathe	EMF332	1962	£7.50	£15	French
Since I Don't Have You	7"	Stateside	SS343	1964	£2	£5	
Sing Big Hits	LP	Philips	(S)BL7687	1965	£4	£10	
Stay	LP	Vee Jay	LP/SR1082	1964	£5	£12	US
Tell It To The Rain	7"	Philips	BF1538	1967	£1.50	£4	chart single
Toy Soldier	7"	Philips	BF1411	1965	£1.50	£4	
Walk Like a Man	7"	Stateside	SS169	1963	£1.50	£4	chart single
Watch The Flowers Grow	7"	Philips	BF1621	1967	£1.50	£4	
We Love Girls	LP	Vee Jay	LP/SR1121	1965	£5	£12	US
Whatever You Say	7"	Warner Bros	K16107	1971	£5	£10	
Will You Love Me Tomorrow	7"	Philips	BF1651	1968	£1.50	£4	
Working My Way Back To You	LP	Philips	BL7699	1965	£4	£10	
Working My Way Back To You	7"	Philips	BF1474	1966	£1.50	£4	chart single

FOUR SIGHTS

But I Can Tell	7"	Columbia	DB7227	1964	£1.50	£4	

FOUR SKINS

One Law For Them	7"	Clockwork Fun	CF101	1981	£1.50	£4	

FOUR SPICES

Fire Engine Boogie	7"	MGM	MGM944	1957	£10	£20	

FOUR SQUARES

Four Squares	7" EP	Hollick & Taylor	HT1009	196-	£5	£10	

FOUR TONES

Voom Ba Voom	7"	Decca	F11074	1958	£2	£5	

FOUR TOPHATTERS

Go Baby Go	7"	London	HLA8163	1955	£50	£100	
Wild Rosie	7"	London	HLA8198	1955	£50	£100	

FOUR TOPS

7 Rooms Of Gloom	7"	Tamla Motown	TMG612	1967	£4	£8	chart single
Ask The Lonely	7"	Tamla Motown	TMG507	1965	£12.50	£25	
Baby I Need Your Loving	7"	Stateside	SS336	1964	£10	£20	
Bernadette	7"	Tamla Motown	TMG601	1967	£1.50	£4	chart single
Do What You Gotta Do	7"	Tamla Motown	TMG710	1969	£1.50	£4	chart single
Four Tops	LP	Tamla Motown	TML11010	1965	£15	£30	
Four Tops	7" EP	Tamla Motown	TME2012	1966	£5	£10	
Four Tops Hits	7" EP	Tamla Motown	TME2018	1967	£5	£10	
I Can't Help Myself	7"	Tamla Motown	TMG515	1965	£4	£8	chart single
I Can't Help Myself	7"	Tamla Motown	TMG732	1970	£1.50	£4	chart single
If I Were A Carpenter	7"	Tamla Motown	TMG647	1968	£1.50	£4	chart single
I'm In A Different World	7"	Tamla Motown	TMG675	1968	£1.50	£4	chart single
It's All In The Game	7"	Tamla Motown	TMG736	1970	£1.50	£4	chart single
It's The Same Old Song	7"	Tamla Motown	TMG528	1965	£5	£10	chart single
Jazz Impressions	LP	Workshop	217	1962	£180	£300	US
Keeper Of The Castle	LP	Probe	SPB1064	1972	£4	£10	
Live	LP	Tamla Motown	(S)TML11041	1967	£4	£10	chart LP
Loving You Is Sweeter Than Ever	7"	Tamla Motown	TMG568	1966	£2.50	£6	chart single
On Broadway	LP	Motown	(MS)657	1967	£5	£12	US
On Top	LP	Tamla Motown	(S)TML11037	1966	£5	£12	chart LP
Reach Out	LP	Tamla Motown	(S)TML11056	1967	£4	£10	chart LP
Reach Out & I'll Be There	7"	Tamla Motown	TMG579	1966	£2	£5	chart single
Second Album	LP	Tamla Motown	TML11021	1966	£15	£30	
Shaft In Africa	LP	Probe	SPB1077	1973	£5	£12	
Shake Me Wake Me	7"	Tamla Motown	TMG553	1966	£7.50	£15	
Something About You	7"	Tamla Motown	TMG542	1965	£6	£12	
Standing In The Shadows Of Love	7"	Tamla Motown	TMG589	1967	£2.50	£6	chart single
Walk Away Renee	7"	Tamla Motown	TMG634	1967	£2	£5	chart single
What Is A Man	7"	Tamla Motown	TMG698	1969	£1.50	£4	chart single
Without The One You Love	7"	Stateside	SS371	1965	£12.50	£25	
Yesterday's Dreams	7"	Tamla Motown	TMG665	1968	£1.50	£4	chart single
You Keep Running Away	7"	Tamla Motown	TMG623	1967	£2.50	£6	chart single

FOUR TUNES

12 X 4	LP	Jubilee	LP1039	195-	£25	£50	US
I Gambled With Love	78	London	L1231	1954	£10	£20	
I Sold My Heart To The Junkman	7"	London	HL8151	1955	£25	£50	
Tired Of Waiting	7"	London	HLJ8164	1955	£12.50	£25	

FOUR WINDS

Short Shorts	7"	London	HLU8556	1958	£10	£20	

FOURMOST

Apples,Peaches,Pumpkin Pie	7"	CBS	3814	1968	£6	£12	
Auntie Maggie's Remedy	7"	Parlophone	R5528	1966	£5	£10	

Baby I Need Your Lovin'	7"	Parlophone	R5194	1964	£2	£5	chart single
Easy Squeezy	7"	CBS	4461	1969	£7.50	£15	
Everything In The Garden	7"	Parlophone	R5304	1965	£2.50	£6	
First And Fourmost	LP	Parlophone	PMC1259	1965	£35	£70	sleeve pictured in Guide
Fourmost Sound	7" EP	Parlophone	GEP8892	1964	£20	£40	
Girls Girls Girls	7"	Parlophone	R5379	1965	£2	£5	chart single
Hello Little Girl	7"	Parlophone	R5056	1963	£1.50	£4	chart single
Hello Little Girl	7" EP	Odeon	SOE3748	1963	£20	£40	French
Here There And Everywhere	7"	Parlophone	R5491	1966	£4	£8	
How Can I Tell Her	7"	Parlophone	R5157	1964	£2	£5	chart single
How Can I Tell Her	7" EP	Parlophone	GEP8917	1964	£20	£40	
I'm In Love	7"	Parlophone	R5078	1963	£1.50	£4	chart single
Little Lovin'	7"	Parlophone	R5128	1964	£1.50	£4	chart single
Rosetta	7"	CBS	4041	1969	£6	£12	

FOURMYULA

Honey Chile	7"	Columbia	DB8549	1969	£2.50	£6	

FOURTEEN

Easy To Fool	7"	Olga	S051	1968	£2.50	£6	
Through My Door	7"	Olga	OLE002	1968	£2.50	£6	
Umbrella	7"	Olga	OLE006	1968	£2.50	£6	

FOURTEEN ICED BEARS

Balloon Song	7"	Penetration		1987	£2.50	£6	flexi
Come Get Me	7"	Sarah	SARAH5	1988	£4	£8	
Falling Backwards	7"	Thunderball Surfacer	002	198-	£2	£5	B side by Crocodile Ride
Inside	12"	Frank	COPPOLA1	1986	£4	£10	
Like A Dolphin	12"	Frank	CAPRA202	1987	£2.50	£6	
Mother Sleep	7"	Thunderball	7TBL2	1989	£10	£20	test pressing

FOURTH WAY

Fourth Way	LP	Capitol	ST317	1970	£5	£12	US
Sun And Moon Have Come Together	LP	Harvest	SKAO423	1970	£5	£12	US
Werewolf	LP	Harvest	ST666	1971	£4	£10	US

FOWLEY, KIM

Born To Be Wild	LP	Imperial	LP12413	1968	£8	£20	US
Good Clean Fun	LP	Imperial	LP12443	1969	£8	£20	US
I'm Bad	LP	Capitol	ST11075	1972	£6	£15	US
International Heroes	LP	Capitol	ST11159	1973	£6	£15	US
Lights	7"	Parlophone	R5521	1966	£6	£12	
Lights The Blind Can See	7"	CBS	202338	1966	£4	£8	
Love Is Alive And Well	LP	Tower	(S)T5080	1967	£8	£20	US
Outrageous	LP	Imperial	LP12423	1969	£8	£20	US
They're Coming To Take Me Away	7"	CBS	202243	1966	£4	£8	
Trip	7"	Island	WI278	1966	£5	£10	
Trip	7" EP	Vogue	INT18086	1966	£25	£50	French

FOX

Mr.Carpenter	7"	CBS	3381	1968	£10	£20	

FOX (2)

For Fox Sake	LP	Fontana	6309007	1970	£30	£60	sleeve pictured in Guide
Second Hand Love	7"	Fontana	6007016	1970	£7.50	£15	

FOX, DON

Be My Girl	7"	Decca	F10927	1957	£1.50	£4	
Party Time	7"	Decca	F10955	1957	£1.50	£4	
Pretend You Don't See Her	7"	Decca	F10983	1958	£1.50	£4	
She Was Only Seventeen	7"	Decca	F11057	1958	£2	£5	
T'Ain't What You Do	7"	Triumph	RGM1022	1960	£5	£10	
You Belong To My Heart	7"	B&C	CB110	1969	£1.50	£4	

FOXX, INEZ

You Hurt Me For The Last Time	7"	Stax	2025151	1973	£2	£5	

FOXX, INEZ & CHARLIE

Baby Give It To Me	7"	Direction	584042	1969	£1.50	£4	
Come By Here	LP	Direction	863085	1968	£5	£12	
Come On In	7"	Direction	583816	1968	£2	£5	
Count The Days	7"	Direction	583192	1967	£1.50	£4	
Greatest Hits	LP	Direction	863281	1968	£4	£10	
Here We Go Round	7"	Sue	WI307	1964	£5	£10	
Hi Diddle Diddle	7"	Sue	WI314	1964	£5	£10	
Hummingbird	7"	London	HLC10009	1965	£2	£5	
Hurt By Love	7"	Sue	WI323	1964	£5	£10	chart single
I Ain't Going For That	7"	Direction	582712	1967	£1.50	£4	
Inez & Charles Foxx	LP	London	SHA8241	1965	£5	£12	
Jaybirds	7"	Sue	WI304	1964	£7.50	£15	
La De Da I Love You	7"	United Artists	UP35013	1970	£1.50	£4	
La De Dah I Love You	7"	Sue	WI356	1964	£5	£10	
Mockingbird	LP	Sue	ILP911	1964	£15	£30	
Mockingbird	7"	Sue	WI301	1963	£6	£12	
Mockingbird	7"	United Artists	UP2269	1969	£1.50	£4	chart single
My Momma Told Me	7"	London	HLC9971	1965	£2.50	£6	
No Stranger To Love	7"	Stateside	SS556	1966	£2.50	£6	
Tightrope	7"	Pye	7N25561	1971	£2	£5	

Tightrope	7"	Stateside	SS586	1967	£6	£12	

FOXX, JOHN

No-one Driving	7"	Virgin	VS338	1980	£5	£10	double

FRABJOY & THE RUNCIBLE SPOON

The tracks credited to Graham Gouldman and Kevin Godley on the Marmalade label sampler LP were actually by Frabjoy and the Runcible Spoon. The group also included Lol Creme in its line-up and can be viewed, therefore, as a first dry-run for Ten cc. An album was apparently recorded, but was lost when the Marmalade label folded.

I'm Beside Myself	7"	Marmalade	598019	1969	£5	£10	

FRACTION

	LP	Angelias		197-	£330	£500	

FRAME

Doctor Doctor	7"	RCA	RCA1571	1967	£15	£30	
My Feet Don't Fit His Shoes	7"	RCA	RCA1556	1966	£7.50	£15	

FRAMPTON, PETER

Frampton Comes Alive (edited)	LP	A&M	PR3703	1978	£5	£12	US pic disc

FRANC, PETER

En Route	LP	Dawn	DNLS3051	1973	£5	£12	
Profile	LP	Dawn	DNLS3043	1972	£5	£12	

FRANCIS & THE SWINGERS

Warn The People	7"	Blue Beat	BB379	1965	£5	£10	

FRANCIS, BOBBY

Chain Gang	7"	Doctor Bird	DB1153	1968	£5	£10	
Judy Drowned	7"	Ska Beat	JB193	1965	£5	£10	

FRANCIS, CONNIE

All Time International Hits	LP	MGM	C1012	1965	£5	£12	
All Time International Hits	LP	MGM	CS6083	1965	£6	£15	stereo
Among My Souvenirs	7"	MGM	MGM1046	1959	£1.50	£4	chart single
Another Page	7"	MGM	MGM1334	1967	£1.50	£4	
At The Copa	LP	MGM	C861	1961	£5	£12	
At The Copa	LP	MGM	CS6035	1961	£6	£15	stereo
Award-Winning Motion Picture Hits	LP	MGM	C940	1963	£5	£12	
Award-Winning Motion Picture Hits	LP	MGM	CS6070	1963	£6	£15	stereo
Baby's First Christmas	7"	MGM	MGM1145	1961	£1.50	£4	chart single
Be Anything	7"	MGM	MGM1236	1963	£1.50	£4	
Best Of Connie Francis	LP	MGM	C8041	1967	£5	£12	
Best Of Connie Francis	LP	Readers Digest	GBCFA106	1981	£10	£25	4 LP set
Blue Winter	7"	MGM	MGM1224	1963	£1.50	£4	chart single
Breakin' In A Brand New Broken Heart	7"	MGM	MGM1136	1961	£1.50	£4	
Christmas With Connie	LP	MGM	C797	1959	£10	£25	
Connie And Clyde	LP	MGM	C(S)8086	1968	£6	£15	
Connie Francis	7" EP	MGM	MGMEP686	1958	£7.50	£15	
Connie Francis	7" EP	MGM	MGMEP792	1965	£7.50	£15	
Connie Francis Favourites	7" EP	MGM	MGMEP759	1961	£7.50	£15	
Connie Sings For Mama	7" EP	MGM	MGMEP789	1964	£7.50	£15	
Connie's American hits	7" EP	MGM	MGMEP769	1963	£7.50	£15	
Connie's Greatest Hits	LP	MGM	C831	1960	£5	£12	chart LP
Country And Western Golden Hits	LP	MGM	C812	1960	£10	£25	
Country Music Connie Style	LP	MGM	C916	1962	£6	£15	
Country Music Connie Style	LP	MGM	CS6062	1962	£8	£20	stereo
Do The Twist	LP	MGM	C879	1961	£10	£25	
Don't Break The Heart That Loves You	7"	MGM	MGM1157	1962	£1.50	£4	chart single
Don't Ever Leave Me	7"	MGM	MGM1253	1964	£1.50	£4	
Drowning My Sorrows	7"	MGM	MGM1207	1963	£1.50	£4	
Everybody's Somebody's Fool	7"	MGM	MGM1086	1960	£1.50	£4	chart single
Exciting Connie Francis	LP	MGM	C786	1959	£6	£15	
Faded Orchid	7"	MGM	MGM962	1957	£10	£20	
First Lady Of Record	7" EP	MGM	MGMEP742	1960	£6	£12	
Folk Song Favourites	LP	MGM	C883	1962	£5	£12	
Folk Song Favourites	LP	MGM	CS6054	1962	£6	£15	stereo
Follow The Boys	LP	MGM	C931	1963	£5	£12	
Follow The Boys	LP	MGM	CS6068	1963	£6	£15	stereo
Follow The Boys	7"	MGM	MGM1193	1962	£1.50	£4	
For Mama	LP	MGM	C1006/CS6082	1965	£6	£15	
Forget Domani	7"	MGM	MGM1265	1965	£1.50	£4	
From Italy With Love	7" EP	MGM	MGMEP783	1963	£7.50	£15	
Fun Songs For Children	7"	MGM	C819	1960	£25	£50	
Girl In Love	7" EP	MGM	MGMEP658	1956	£7.50	£15	
Great American Waltzes	LP	MGM	C958	1964	£5	£12	
Great American Waltzes	LP	MGM	CS6075	1964	£6	£15	stereo
Great Country Hits	LP	MGM	ACB00143	1974	£4	£10	
Great Country Hits Vol.2	LP	MGM	ACB00167	1975	£5	£12	
Hawaii Connie	LP	MGM	C(S)8110	1969	£10	£25	
Heartaches	7" EP	MGM	MGMEP677	1958	£6	£12	
Hey Ring A Ding	7" EP	MGM	MGMEP773	1963	£7.50	£15	
I Never Had A Sweetheart	7"	MGM	MGM945	1957	£12.50	£25	
I Was Such A Fool	7"	MGM	MGM1171	1962	£2	£5	
If I Didn't Care	7" EP	MGM	MGMEP697	1959	£7.50	£15	
If My Pillow Could Talk	7"	MGM	MGM1202	1963	£1.50	£4	
I'll Get By	7"	MGM	MGM993	1958	£1.50	£4	chart single
I'm Gonna Be Warm This Winter	7"	MGM	MGM1185	1962	£1.50	£4	chart single
I'm Sorry I Made You Cry	7"	MGM	MGM982	1958	£1.50	£4	chart single
Irish Favourites	LP	MGM	C898	1962	£8	£20	

Title	Format	Label	Catalogue	Year			Notes
Irish Favourites	LP	MGM	CS6056	1962	£10	£25	stereo
Italian Favourites	LP	MGM	C821/CS6002	1960	£6	£15	
Italian Favourites	7" EP	MGM	MGMEP760	1961	£7.50	£15	
Jealous Heart	LP	MGM	C(S)8009	1966	£6	£15	
Jealous Heart	7"	MGM	MGM1293	1966	£1.50	£4	chart single
Jewish Favourites	LP	MGM	C845	1961	£5	£12	
Jewish Favourites	LP	MGM	CS6021	1961	£6	£15	stereo
Lipstick On Your Collar	7"	MGM	MGM1018	1959	£1.50	£4	chart single
Live At Sahara In Las Vegas	LP	MGM	C(S)8036	1967	£6	£15	
Looking For Love	LP	MGM	C983/CS6079	1965	£6	£15	
Love Is Me, Love Is You	7"	MGM	MGM1305	1966	£1.50	£4	
Love Italian Style	LP	MGM	C(S)8050	1968	£5	£12	
Majesty Of Love	7"	MGM	MGM969	1957	£10	£20	with Marvin Rainwater
Mala Femmena	7" EP	MGM	MGMEP780	1963	£7.50	£15	
Mama	7"	MGM	MGM1070	1960	£15	£30	
Mama	7"	MGM	MGM1076	1959	£1.50	£4	chart single
Many Tears Ago	7"	MGM	MGM1111	1960	£1.50	£4	chart single
More Italian Favourites	LP	MGM	C854	1961	£5	£12	
More Italian Favourites	LP	MGM	CS6029	1961	£6	£15	stereo
More Italian Hits	LP	MGM	C930	1963	£5	£12	
More Italian Hits	LP	MGM	CS6067	1963	£6	£15	stereo
Movie Greats Of The Sixties	LP	MGM	C(S)8027	1966	£6	£15	
Mr.Love	7"	MGM	MGM1493	1969	£1.50	£4	
Mr.Twister	7"	MGM	MGM1151	1962	£1.50	£4	
My Child	7"	MGM	MGM1271	1965	£1.50	£4	chart single
My First Real Love	7"	MGM	SP1169	1956	£30	£60	
My Happiness	7"	MGM	MGM1001	1959	£1.50	£4	chart single
My Heart Cries For You	LP	MGM	C(S)8054	1968	£5	£12	
My Heart Cries For You	7"	MGM	MGM1347	1967	£1.50	£4	
My Heart Has A Mind Of Its Own	7"	MGM	MGM1100	1960	£1.50	£4	chart single
My Sailor Boy	7"	MGM	MGM932	1956	£15	£30	
My Thanks To You	LP	MGM	C782	1959	£8	£20	
My Thanks To You	LP	World Record Club	TP618	1966	£4	£10	
My World Is Slipping Away	7"	MGM	MGM1381	1968	£1.50	£4	
Never On Sunday	LP	MGM	C875	1961	£5	£12	
Never On Sunday	LP	MGM	CS6047	1961	£6	£15	stereo
New Kind Of Connie	LP	MGM	C998/CS6080	1965	£5	£12	
Phoenix Love Theme	7"	MGM	MGM1295	1966	£1.50	£4	
Plenty Good Lovin'	7"	MGM	MGM1036	1959	£1.50	£4	chart single
Rock and Roll Million Sellers	LP	MGM	C804	1960	£10	£25	chart LP
Rock And Roll Million Sellers	7" EP	MGM	MGMEP717	1960	£7.50	£15	
Rock And Roll Million Sellers No.2	7" EP	MGM	MGMEP720	1960	£7.50	£15	
Rock And Roll Million Sellers No.3	7" EP	MGM	MGMEP731	1960	£7.50	£15	
Roundabout	7"	MGM	MGM1282	1965	£1.50	£4	
Sings Great Country Favourites	LP	MGM	C1003/CS6081	1965	£6	£15	with Hank Williams Jr
Sixteen Of Connie's Greatest Hits	LP	MGM	C970	1964	£5	£12	
Somebody Else Is Takin' My Place	7"	MGM	MGM1446	1968	£1.50	£4	
Somewhere My Love	7"	MGM	MGM1320	1966	£1.50	£4	
Songs Of Les Reed	LP	MGM	CS8117	1969	£6	£15	
Songs To A Swinging Band	LP	MGM	C870	1961	£5	£12	
Songs To A Swinging Band	LP	MGM	CS6044	1961	£6	£15	stereo
Spanish And Latin American Favourites	LP	MGM	C836	1960	£5	£12	
Spanish And Latin American Favourites	LP	MGM	CS6012	1960	£6	£15	stereo
Spanish Nights And You	7"	MGM	MGM1327	1966	£1.50	£4	
Special Magic Of Connie Francis	LP	MGM	ACB00195	1976	£4	£10	
Stupid Cupid	7"	MGM	MGM985	1958	£1.50	£4	chart single
Summer Of His Years	7"	MGM	MGM1220	1963	£1.50	£4	
Time Alone Will Tell	7"	MGM	MGM1336	1967	£1.50	£4	
Together	7"	MGM	MGM1138	1961	£1.50	£4	chart single
Toward The End Of The Day	7"	MGM	MGM1012	1959	£1.50	£4	
Vacation	7"	MGM	MGM1165	1962	£1.50	£4	chart single
Valentino	7"	MGM	MGM1060	1960	£1.50	£4	chart single
Wedding Cake	7"	MGM	MGM1471	1969	£1.50	£4	
What Kind Of Fool Am I	7" EP	MGM	MGMEP775	1963	£7.50	£15	
Whatever Happened To Rosemary	7"	MGM	MGM1212	1963	£1.50	£4	
When The Boys Meet The Girls	LP	MGM	C(S)8006	1966	£5	£12	
Where The Boys Are	7"	MGM	MGM1121	1961	£1.50	£4	chart single
Where The Boys Are	7" EP	MGM	MGMEP756	1961	£7.50	£15	
Who's Happy Now?	LP	United Artists	ULP30182	1978	£4	£10	
Who's Happy Now?	LP	United Artists	ULP30182	1978	£50	£100	withdrawn sleeve
Who's Sorry Now	7"	MGM	MGM975	1958	£1.50	£4	chart single
Who's Sorry Now	10" LP	MGM	MGMD153	1958	£22.50	£45	
Why Say Goodbye	7"	MGM	MGM1407	1968	£1.50	£4	
You Always Hurt The One You Love	7"	MGM	MGM998	1958	£1.50	£4	chart single
You're My Everything	7" EP	MGM	MGMEP711	1960	£7.50	£15	

FRANCIS, JOE 'KING'

Title	Format	Label	Catalogue	Year			
Have Me Baby	7"	Rio	R90	1966	£4	£8	
I Don't Want You No More	7"	Ska Beat	JB184	1965	£5	£10	
I Got A Ska	7"	Ska Beat	JB262	1966	£5	£10	
Pull It Out	7"	Rainbow	RAI114	1967	£4	£8	
Wicked Woman	7"	Blue Beat	BB323	1964	£5	£10	

FRANCIS, LITTLE WILLIE

Title	Format	Label	Catalogue	Year			
I'm Ashamed	7"	Blue Beat	BB151	1963	£5	£10	

FRANCIS, NAT
Just To Keep You	7"	Blue Beat	BB361	1965	£5	£10	
Mama Kiss Him Goodnight	7"	Blue Beat	BB346	1965	£5	£10	
Three Nights Of Love	7"	Blue Beat	BB376	1965	£5	£10	

FRANCIS, RITCHIE
Songbird	LP	Pegasus	PEG11	1971	£6	£15	

FRANCIS, STEVE
Watch Your Step	7"	King	KG1012	1965	£2	£5	

FRANCIS, WILBERT
Memories Of You	7"	Ska Beat	JB267	1966	£5	£10	

FRANCIS, WINSTON
California Dreaming	LP	Bamboo	BDLPS216	1971	£10	£25	
Games People Play	7"	Studio One	SO2086	1969	£6	£12	Albert Griffiths B side
If Your Heart Be Lonely	7"	Coxsone	CS7087	1969	£5	£10	
Mr.Fix It	LP	Bamboo	BDLP207	1970	£15	£30	
Reggae And Cry	7"	Coxsone	CS7089	1969	£5	£10	Freedom Singers B side
Same Old Song	7"	Bamboo	BAM10	1969	£2.50	£6	Sound Dimension B side
Too Experienced	7"	Punch	PH5	1969	£2.50	£6	Jackie Mittoo B side
Turn Back The Hands Of Time	7"	Bamboo	BAM46	1970	£2	£5	

FRANCISCO
Cosmic Beam Experience	LP	Cosmic Beam	001	1976	£15	£30	US

FRANK, JACKSON C.
The album made by the otherwise obscure Mr.Frank is collectable as a rare outside production by Paul Simon. One track also features the young Al Stewart.
Again	LP	B&C	BCLP4	1978	£40	£80	
Blues Run The Game	7"	Columbia	DB7795	1965	£10	£20	
Jackson C.Frank	LP	Columbia	33SX1788	1965	£75	£150	

FRANKIE & JOHNNY
Climb Every Mountain	7"	Parlophone	R5518	1966	£4	£8	
I'll Hold You	7"	Decca	F22376	1966	£37.50	£75	
I'll Hold You	7"	Inferno	HEAT8	1979	£1.50	£4	

FRANKIE & THE CLASSICALS
I Only Have Eyes For You	7"	Philips	BF1586	1967	£37.50	£75	

FRANKIE GOES TO HOLLYWOOD
As record companies became aware of the collectors' market during the eighties, they realised that it was possible to create instant collectors' items by issuing various limited edition versions of each potential hit record. Arguably the most thorough exploration of the possibilities of this tactic was carried out by ZTT records and Frankie Goes To Hollywood. Each single by the group comes in a bewildering variety of alternative mixes, and different shaped picture discs, with a correspondingly wide range of values. In fact, due to Trevor Horn's skill as a producer, the different mixes make sense on musical grounds, but this is very much a happy accident!
Pleasurefix/Starfix	12"	ZTT	FGTH1	1985	£4	£10	pink label promo
Power Of Love	12"	ZTT	12XZTAS5	1984	£2.50	£6	gatefold sleeve, 5 photos
Rage Hard	CD-s	ZTT	ZCID22	1986	£5	£12	
Relax	cass-s	ZTT	CTIS102	1984	£2.50	£6	
Relax	7"	ZTT	PZTAS1	1983	£2	£5	pic disc
Relax (live version)	cass	Ocean	no number	1985	£6	£15	with FGTH computer game
Relax (Original Mix)	12"	ZTT	12ZTAS1 (1A1U)	1983	£10	£25	33rpm
Relax (Original Mix)	12"	ZTT	12ZTAS1 (1A5)	1984	£6	£15	
Relax (Sex Mix)	12"	ZTT	12PZTAS1	1983	£2.50	£6	pic disc
Relax (Sex Mix)	12"	ZTT	12ZTAS1 (1A2U)	1983	£6	£15	
Relax (The Last Seven Inches)	7"	ZTT	ZTAS1DJ	1983	£2	£5	promo
Relax (The Last Seven Inches)	7"	ZTT	ZTAS1DJ	1983	£2.50	£6	promo, mispressed B side plays 'Ferry(Go)'
Relax (US Mix)/Two Tribes (Carnage)	12"	ZTT	XZTAS3DJ	1984	£4	£10	promo, grey ZTT sleeve
Relax (Warp Mix)	7"	ZTT	ZTAS1	1983	£4	£8	white label promo
Two Tribes	cass-s	ZTT	CTIS103	1984	£2.50	£6	
Two Tribes	7"	ZTT	PZTAS3	1984	£2	£5	pic disc
Two Tribes (Carnage)/War (Hidden)	12"	ZTT	WARTZ3	1984	£2.50	£6	
Two Tribes (Hibakusha)	12"	ZTT	XZIP1	1984	£6	£15	ZTT sleeve
Warriors	CD-s	ZTT	ZCID25	1986	£4	£10	
Warriors (Attack Mix)	12"	ZTT	12ZTAK25	1986	£3	£8	white label promo
Watching The Wildlife (Die Letzen...Mix)	12"	ZTT	ZTE26	1987	£2.50	£6	
Welcome To The Pleasure Dome	LP	ZTT	NEAT1	1984	£6	£15	double pic disc
Welcome To The Pleasure Dome	CD	ZTT	CID101	1984	£10	£25	with San Jose, not Happy Hi
Welcome To The Pleasure Dome	7"	ZTT	PZTAS7	1985	£2	£5	shaped pic disc
Welcome To The Pleasure Dome	7"	ZTT	ZTAS7 (7A7U)	1985	£4	£8	blue label
Welcome To The Pleasure Dome (Tribal/Urban Mix)	12"	ZTT	12ZTAJ7	1985	£6	£15	promo

FRANKLIN, ARETHA
Few of Aretha Franklin's earliest recordings are particularly valuable, despite the fact that they seldom appear on the market. There is a staggering lack of direction on the CBS recordings, as for six years neither Miss Franklin herself nor the record company seemed to have any idea as to the most effective setting for that extraordinary voice. Signing with Atlantic at the end of 1966, Aretha Franklin immediately struck gold with the powerful Southern soul sound of "I Never Loved A Man"; a sound that seemed to have been waiting for Aretha Franklin as much as she had been waiting for the sound!

Title	Format	Label	Cat No	Year	Low	High	Notes
Amazing Grace	LP	Atlantic	K60023	1972	£6	£15	double
Aretha	LP	Fontana	TFL5173	1961	£6	£15	
Aretha Arrives	LP	Atlantic	587/588085	1967	£6	£15	
Aretha Arrives	LP	Atlantic	K40157	1972	£4	£10	
Aretha Gold	LP	Atlantic	588192	1969	£4	£10	
Aretha Now	LP	Atlantic	587/588114	1968	£5	£12	chart LP
Baby I Love You	7"	Atlantic	584127	1967	£2	£5	chart single
Best Of Aretha Franklin	LP	Atlantic	QD8295	1971	£5	£12	US quad
Brand New Me	7"	Atlantic	2091127	1971	£1.50	£4	
Bridge Over Troubled Water	7"	Atlantic	2091090	1971	£1.50	£4	
Call Me	7"	Atlantic	584322	1970	£1.50	£4	
Can't You See Me	7"	CBS	201732	1965	£2	£5	
Cry Like A Baby	7"	CBS	202468	1967	£2	£5	
Don't Play That Song	LP	Atlantic	2400021	1970	£5	£12	
Don't Play That Song	7"	Atlantic	2091027	1970	£1.50	£4	chart single
Eleanor Rigby	7"	Atlantic	584306	1969	£1.50	£4	
Electrifying Aretha Franklin	LP	Columbia	CL1761/CS8561	1962	£5	£12	US
Freeway Of Love	7"	Arista	ARIST22624	1986	£2	£5	pink vinyl
House That Jack Built	7"	Atlantic	584239	1969	£1.50	£4	
I Never Loved A Man	LP	Atlantic	587/588066	1967	£6	£15	chart LP
I Never Loved A Man	7"	Atlantic	584084	1967	£2	£5	
I Say A Little Prayer	LP	Atlantic	2464007	1970	£5	£12	
I Say A Little Prayer	7"	Atlantic	2091111	1971	£1.50	£4	
I Say A Little Prayer	7"	Atlantic	584206	1968	£1.50	£4	chart single
Lady Soul	LP	Atlantic	587/588099	1968	£5	£12	chart LP
Laughing On The Outside	LP	Columbia	CL2079/CS8879	1963	£5	£12	US
Lee Cross	LP	CBS	63160	1967	£5	£12	
Lee Cross	7"	CBS	3059	1967	£2	£5	
Let It Be Me	7"	Atlantic	2091008	1970	£1.50	£4	
Live At Paris Olympia	LP	Atlantic	587/588149	1968	£6	£15	
Live At The Fillmore West	LP	Atlantic	2400136	1971	£5	£12	
Live At The Fillmore West	LP	Atlantic	QD7205	1971	£5	£12	US quad
Love Is The Only Thing	7"	Fontana	H271	1961	£5	£10	
Natural Woman	7"	Atlantic	584141	1967	£2	£5	
Oh No Not My Baby	7"	Atlantic	2091044	1971	£1.50	£4	
Operation Heartbreak	7"	Fontana	H343	1961	£4	£8	
Respect	7"	Atlantic	584115	1967	£2	£5	chart single
Rock Steady	7"	Atlantic	2091168	1971	£1.50	£4	
Runnin' Out Of Fools	LP	Columbia	CL2281/CS9081	1964	£5	£12	US
Satisfaction/Chain Of Fools	7"	Atlantic	584157	1967	£2	£5	chart single
Satisfaction/Night Life	7"	Atlantic	584157	1967	£2.50	£6	
Share Your Love With Me	7"	Atlantic	584285	1969	£1.50	£4	
Since You've Been Gone	7"	Atlantic	584172	1968	£1.50	£4	chart single
Songs Of Faith	LP	Chess	CRL(S)54550	1967	£4	£10	
Soul '69	LP	Atlantic	588163	1969	£5	£12	
Soul Sister	LP	CBS	(S)BPG62744	1966	£5	£12	
Spanish Harlem	7"	Atlantic	2091138	1971	£1.50	£4	chart single
Take A Look	LP	CBS	63269	1967	£4	£10	
Take It Like You Give It	LP	CBS	(S)BPG62969	1967	£5	£12	
Tender...Swinging Aretha Franklin	LP	Columbia	CL1876/CS8676	1962	£5	£12	US
Think	7"	Atlantic	584186	1968	£1.50	£4	chart single
This Girl's In Love With You	LP	Atlantic	2400004	1969	£4	£10	
Today I Sing The Blues	7" EP	Fontana	TE467217	1962	£5	£10	
Unforgettable	LP	Columbia	CL2163/CS8963	1964	£5	£12	US
Until You Come Back To Me	7"	Atlantic	K10399	1974	£1.50	£4	chart single
Weight	7"	Atlantic	584252	1969	£1.50	£4	
Yeah/In Person	LP	CBS	(S)BPG62556	1965	£5	£12	
Young, Gifted And Black	LP	Atlantic	2400188	1971	£4	£10	
You're All I Need To Get By	7"	Atlantic	2091063	1971	£1.50	£4	

FRANKLIN, ERMA

Title	Format	Label	Cat No	Year	Low	High	Notes
Gotta Find Me A Lover	7"	MCA	MU1073	1969	£1.50	£4	
Her Name Is Erma	LP	Epic	LN3824/BN619	1962	£6	£15	US
Open Up Your Soul	7"	London	HLZ10201	1968	£2.50	£6	
Piece Of My Heart	7"	London	HLZ10170	1967	£5	£10	
Right To Cry	7"	London	HLZ10220	1968	£2.50	£6	
Soul Sister	LP	MCA	MUPS394	1970	£6	£15	
Time After Time	7"	Soul City	SC118	1969	£4	£8	

FRANKLIN, MARIE

Title	Format	Label	Cat No	Year	Low	High	Notes
You Ain't Changed	7"	MGM	MGM1455	1968	£1.50	£4	

FRANKS, JOHNNY

Title	Format	Label	Cat No	Year	Low	High	Notes
Good Old Country Music	7"	Melodisc	1459	1958	£1.50	£4	
Tweedle Dee	78	Melodisc	P230	1955	£3	£8	

FRANKSON, BONNIE

Title	Format	Label	Cat No	Year	Low	High	Notes
Dearest	7"	Columbia	DB114	1969	£4	£8	
Dearest	7"	Jolly	JY021	1968	£4	£8	

FRANTIC ELEVATORS

Mick Hucknall was the leader of the Frantic Elevators, who began as a punk group, but who had anticipated the smooth soul sound of Hucknall's Simply Red by the end of their career. The song "Holding Back The Years" was, in fact, recorded by both groups.

Title	Format	Label	Cat No	Year	Low	High	Notes
Holding Back The Years	7"	No Waiting	WAIT1	1982	£7.50	£15	
Hunchback Of Notre Dame	7"	TJM	TJM6	1980	£20	£40	demo
Searching For The Only One	7"	Crackin'	CRAK1	1980	£4	£8	
Voice In The Dark	7"	TJM	TJM5	1980	£5	£10	
You Know What You Told Me	7"	Erics	006	1980	£5	£10	

FRANZ K
Rock In Deutsch	LP	Zebra	2949014	1973	£5	£12	German
Sensemann	LP	Ruhr	007	1972	£20	£40	German

FRASER, JOHN
Presenting	7" EP.	Pye	NEP24068	1958	£2.50	£6	

FRASER, NORMA
Everybody Loves A Lover	7"	Ska Beat	JB223	1965	£5	£10	
First Cut Is The Deepest	7"	Coxsone	CS7017	1967	£5	£10	Bumps Oakley B side
Heartaches	7"	Coxsone	CS7049	1968	£5	£10	Righteous Flames B side
Heartaches	7"	Doctor Bird	DB1032	1966	£5	£10	Tommy McCook B side
Respect	7"	Coxsone	CS7060	1968	£5	£10	
Telling Me Lies	7"	Studio One	SO2025	1967	£6	£12	Viceroys B side

FRATERNITY OF MAN
Don't Bogart Me	7"	Stateside	SS2166	1970	£1.50	£4	US
Fraternity Of Man	LP	ABC	S647	1968	£4	£10	US
Get It On	LP	Dot	DLP25955	1969	£4	£10	US

FRAYS
For Your Precious Love	7"	Decca	F12229	1965	£15	£30	
Walk On	7"	Decca	F12153	1965	£30	£60	

FRAZIER CHORUS
Sloppy Heart	7"	4AD	AD708	1987	£2	£5	promo

FREAK SCENE
Psychedelic Soul	LP	Columbia	CL2556/CS9356	1967	£6	£15	US

FREAKS OF NATURE
The rare Island single credited to the Freaks Of Nature actually features members of Them (after Van Morrison had left the group), backed by the Soft Machine, at a time when Daevid Allen contributions on guitar made the band into a four-piece. Production was by the maverick Kim Fowley.
People Let's Freak Out	7"	Island	WI3017	1966	£12.50	£25	

FREBERG, STAN
Any Requests	7" EP.	Capitol	EAP1496	1955	£2.50	£6	
Banana Boat Song	7"	Capitol	CL14712	1957	£2.50	£6	
Best Of Stan Freberg	LP	Capitol	T2020	1964	£6	£15	
Best Of The Stan Freberg Show	LP	Capitol	WBO1035	1958	£6	£15	US
Child's Garden Of Freberg	LP	Capitol	T777	1957	£8	£20	US
Comedy Caravan	LP	Capitol	T732	1956	£8	£20	US
Face The Funnies	LP	Capitol	T1694	1962	£6	£15	US
Freberg Again	7" EP.	Capitol	EAP120115	1961	£2.50	£6	
Great Pretender	7"	Capitol	CL14571	1956	£5	£10	
Great Pretender	7" EP.	Capitol	EAP120050	1961	£5	£10	
Green Christmas	7"	Capitol	CL14966	1958	£2.50	£6	
Heartbreak Hotel	7"	Capitol	CL14608	1956	£6	£12	chart single
Lone Psychiatrist	7"	Capitol	CL14316	1955	£5	£10	
Madison Avenue Werewolf	LP	Capitol	T1816	1962	£6	£15	US
Mickey Mouse's Birthday Party	LP	Capitol	J3264	1963	£6	£15	US
Old Payola Roll Blues	7"	Capitol	CL15122	1960	£5	£10	chart single
Omaha	7" EP.	Capitol	EAP11101	1959	£2	£5	
Real Saint George	7" EP.	Capitol	EAP1628	1956	£4	£8	
Sh'boom	7"	Capitol	CL14187	1954	£7.50	£15	chart single
Stan Freberg	LP	Capitol	LCT6170/1	1959	£8	£20	double
Stan Freberg With The Original Cast	LP	Capitol	T1242	1959	£6	£15	US
Underground Show Number One	LP	Capitol	(S)T2551	1966	£5	£12	US
United States Of America	LP	Capitol	(S)W1573	1961	£6	£15	US
Yellow Rose Of Texas	7"	Capitol	CL14509	1956	£5	£10	

FRED, JOHN & HIS PLAYBOY BAND
34:40 Of John Fred	LP	Paula	LP(S)2193	1967	£6	£15	US
Agnes English	LP	Pye	NPL28111	1967	£5	£12	
Agnes English	7"	Pye	7N25433	1967	£1.50	£4	
Hey Hey Bunny	7"	Pye	7N25453	1968	£1.50	£4	
John Fred & His Playboys	LP	Paula	LP(S)2191	1966	£6	£15	US
Judy In Disguise	LP	Paula	LPS2197	1968	£6	£15	US
Judy In Disguise	7"	Pye	7N25442	1967	£1.50	£4	chart single
Little Dum Dum	7"	Pye	7N25470	1968	£1.50	£4	
Permanently Stated	LP	Paula	LPS2201	1968	£5	£12	US
Shirley	7"	CBS	3475	1968	£2.50	£6	
Silly Sarah Carter	7"	MCA	MU1088	1969	£1.50	£4	
We Played Games	7"	Pye	7N25462	1968	£1.50	£4	

FREDDIE & THE DREAMERS
Brown And Porters	7"	Columbia	DB8200	1967	£1.50	£4	
Do The Freddie	LP	Mercury	MG2/SR61026	1965	£5	£12	US
Frantic Freddie	LP	Mercury	MG2/SR61053	1965	£5	£12	US
Freddie And The Dreamers	LP	Columbia	33SX1577	1963	£5	£12	chart LP
Freddie And The Dreamers	LP	Mercury	MG2/SR61017	1965	£5	£12	US
Freddie And The Dreamers	7" EP.	Columbia	SEG8323	1964	£2.50	£6	
Freddie And The Dreamers	7" EP.	Columbia	SEG8457	1965	£5	£10	
Freddie Sings Just For You	7" EP.	Columbia	SEG8349	1964	£2.50	£6	
Fun Lovin' Freddie	LP	Mercury	MG2/SR61061	1966	£5	£12	US
Gabardine Mac	7"	Columbia	DB8517	1968	£1.50	£4	
Get Around Downtown Girl	7"	Columbia	DB8606	1969	£1.50	£4	
Hello Hello	7"	Columbia	DB8137	1967	£1.50	£4	

Title	Format	Label	Cat No	Year	Price	Price	Notes
I Love You Baby	7″	Columbia	DB7286	1964	£1.50	£4	chart single
I Understand	7″	Columbia	DB7381	1964	£1.50	£4	chart single
If You Gotta Make A Fool Of Somebody	7″	Columbia	DB7032	1963	£1.50	£4	chart single
If You Gotta Make A Fool Of Somebody	7″ EP	Columbia	SEG8275	1963	£2.50	£6	
If You've Gotta Minute Baby	7″	Columbia	DB7857	1966	£1.50	£4	
I'm Tellin' You Now	7″ EP	Columbia	ESRF1654	1964	£7.50	£15	French
I'm Telling You Now	LP	Tower	(D)T5003	1965	£5	£12	US
I'm Telling You Now	7″	Columbia	DB7086	1963	£1.50	£4	chart single
In Disneyland	LP	Columbia	SX/SCX6069	1966	£5	£12	
Just For You	7″	Columbia	DB7322	1964	£1.50	£4	chart single
King Freddie & Dreaming Knights	LP	Columbia	SX6177	1967	£5	£12	
Little Big Time	7″	Columbia	DB8496	1968	£1.50	£4	
Little You	7″	Columbia	DB7526	1965	£1.50	£4	
Over You	7″	Columbia	DB7214	1964	£1.50	£4	chart single
Playboy	7″	Columbia	DB7929	1966	£1.50	£4	
Ready Freddie Go	7″ EP	Columbia	SEG8403	1965	£5	£10	
Seaside Swingers	LP	Mercury	MG2/SR61031	1965	£5	£12	US
Sing Along Party	LP	Columbia	SX1785	1965	£4	£10	
Some Other Guy	7″ EP	Columbia	ESRF1486	1963	£7.50	£15	French
Songs From What A Crazy World	7″ EP	Columbia	SEG8287	1963	£4	£8	
Thou Shalt Not Steal	7″	Columbia	DB7720	1965	£1.50	£4	chart single
Turn Around	7″	Columbia	DB8033	1966	£1.50	£4	
You Were Mad For Me	LP	Columbia	33SX1663	1964	£5	£12	
You Were Made For Me	7″	Columbia	DB7147	1963	£1.50	£4	chart single
You Were Made For Me	7″ EP	Columbia	SEG8302	1964	£2.50	£6	

FREDDIE & THE DREAMERS & PETER & GORDON

Title	Format	Label	Cat No	Year	Price	Price
Just For You	7″ EP	Columbia	SEG8337	1964	£2.50	£6

FREDDIE & THE RUDIES

Title	Format	Label	Cat No	Year	Price	Price
I Don't Want To Lose That Girl	7″	Downtown	DT427	1969	£1.50	£4

FREDDY & FITZY

Title	Format	Label	Cat No	Year	Price	Price
Do Good	7″	Doctor Bird	DB1033	1966	£5	£10

FREDERICKS, BILL

Title	Format	Label	Cat No	Year	Price	Price
Almost	7″	Polydor	2059035	1978	£2.50	£6

FREDERICKS, DOLORES

Title	Format	Label	Cat No	Year	Price	Price
Cha Cha Joe	7″	Brunswick	05540	1956	£7.50	£15

FREDERICKS, DOTTY

Title	Format	Label	Cat No	Year	Price	Price
Just Wait	7″	Top Rank	JAR106	1959	£2.50	£6

FREDERICKS, MARC

Title	Format	Label	Cat No	Year	Price	Price
Mystic Midnight	7″	London	HLD8281	1956	£6	£12

FREDERICKS, TOMMY

Title	Format	Label	Cat No	Year	Price	Price
Prince Of Players	7″	London	HLU8555	1958	£17.50	£35

FREDRIC

Title	Format	Label	Cat No	Year	Price	Price	Notes
Phases And Faces	LP	Forte	301	1968	£250	£400	US

FREE

With an average age of around eighteen, the members of the newly-formed Free had amazingly still managed to acquire some professional experience - most notably in the case of Andy Fraser, who had played bass (albeit briefly) with John Mayall. They could have been enormous (and the classic "All Right Now" - included in extended form on "Fire And Water" - was indeed a considerable hit), but dissipated their momentum in a welter of petty disputes, leading to members leaving and returning in a quite bewildering manner. The most collectable record remaining from all this is "Kossoff,Kirke,Tetsu And Rabbit", which is prevented from being a Free LP only by the absence of singer Paul Rodgers.

Title	Format	Label	Cat No	Year	Price	Price	Notes
All Right Now	7″	Island	WIP6082	1970	£2	£5	chart single
All Right Now	12″	Island	12PIEP6	1982	£2.50	£6	pic disc
Broad Daylight	7″	Island	WIP6054	1969	£12.50	£25	
Fire And Water	LP	Island	ILPS9120	1970	£6	£15	chart LP
Free	LP	Island	ILPS9104	1969	£8	£20	
Free At Last	LP	Island	ILPS9192	1972	£4	£10	
Free Story	LP	Island	ISLD4	1973	£6	£15	double, chart LP
Heartbreaker	LP	Island	ILPS9217	1972	£4	£10	
Highway	LP	Island	ILPS9138	1970	£5	£12	chart LP
I'll Be Creeping	7″	Island	WIP6062	1969	£10	£20	
I'll Be Creeping	7″	Island	WIP6062	1969	£15	£30	PS
Live	LP	Island	ILPS9160	1971	£5	£12	chart LP
Stealer	7″	Island	WIP6093	1970	£2	£5	
Tons Of Sobs	LP	Island	ILPS9089	1969	£8	£20	
Travellin' In Style	7″	Island	WIP6160	1973	£2	£5	

FREE (2)

Title	Format	Label	Cat No	Year	Price	Price
Keep In Touch	7″	Philips	BF1754	1969	£10	£20
Soul Party	7″	Philips	BF1738	1968	£1.50	£4

FREE AGENTS

Title	Format	Label	Cat No	Year	Price	Price
Free Agents	LP	Groovy	STP1	1980	£6	£15

FREE FERRY

Title	Format	Label	Cat No	Year	Price	Price
Mary What Have You Become	7″	CBS	4456	1969	£4	£8

FREE SOULS

Title	Format	Label	Cat No	Year	Price	Price
I Want To Be Free	7″	Blue Beat	BB264	1964	£5	£10

FREE SPIRITS
Out Of Sight And Sound .... LP ...... ABC .... (S)593 .... 1967 ... £5 ....£12 .... US

FREEBORNE
Peak Impressions .... LP ...... Monitor............ MPS607................ 1967 ... £20 ....£40 .... US

FREED, ALAN
Presents The King's Henchmen .... LP ... Coral CRL57216	£25 ....£50	US
Right Now Right Now .... 7" .... Vogue Coral .... Q72219 .... 1957 ... £25 ....£50		
Rock Around The Block .... LP ... Coral CRL57213	£25 ....£50	US
Rock 'n' Roll Boogie .... 7" .... Vogue Coral .... Q72230 .... 1957 ... £25 ....£50		
Rock'n'Roll Dance Party .... LP ... Vogue Coral .... LVA9033............... 1957 ... £25 ....£50		
Rock'n'Roll Dance Party Vol.2 .... LP ... Vogue Coral .... LVA9066............... 1957 ... £25 ....£50		
Rock'n'Roll Show .... LP ... Brunswick........ BL54043 .... 1958 ... £25 ....£50		US
TV Record Hop .... LP ... Coral CRL57177	£25 ....£50	US

FREEDOM
At Last .... LP ...... Metronome ... MLP15371 .... 1970 ... £10 ....£25
Escape While You Can .... 7" ...... Plexium .... PXM3 .... 1968 ... £2.50 ....£6
Freedom .... LP ...... Probe .... SPBA6252 .... 1970 ... £8 ....£20
Is More Than A Word .... LP ...... Vertigo .... 6360072................. 1972 ... £35 ....£70 .... spiral label
Through The Years .... LP ...... Vertigo .... 6360049................. 1971 ... £20 ....£40 .... spiral label
Where Will You Be Tonight .... 7" ...... Mercury .... MF1033 .... 1968 ... £4 ....£8

FREEDOM SINGERS
I Want Money .... 7" ...... Coxsone .... CS7016 .... 1967 ... £5 ....£10 ..... Slim Smith B side
Work Crazy .... 7" ...... Studio One ...... SO2011 .... 1967 ... £6 ....£12

FREEMAN, ART
Slipping Around .... 7" ...... Atlantic .... 584053................... 1966 ... £20 ....£40

FREEMAN, BOBBY
Betty Lou Got A New Pair Of Shoes ..... 7"..... London .... HLJ8721 .... 1958 ... £12.50 ....£25	
C'Mon And Swim .... LP ..... Autumn .... LP102 .... 1964 ... £8 ....£20	US
C'mon And Swim .... 7" ..... Pye .... 7N25260 .... 1964 ... £5 ....£10	
Do You Wanna Dance .... LP ..... Jubilee .... (SD)JLP1086 .... 1959 ... £15 ....£30	US
Do You Wanna Dance .... 7" ..... London .... HLJ8644 .... 1958 ... £10 ....£20	
Duck .... 7" ..... Pye .... 7N25347 .... 1966 ... £5 ....£10	2 B sides
Ebb Tide .... 7" ..... London .... HLJ9031 .... 1960 ... £2.50 ......£6	
Get In The Swim .... LP ..... Josie .... JM/JGS4007 .... 1965 ... £8 ....£20	US
Lovable Style Of Bobby Freeman .... LP ..... King .... 930 .... 1965 ... £10 ....£25	US
Mary Ann Thomas .... 7" ..... London .... HLJ8898 .... 1959 ... £7.50 ......£15	
Need Your Love .... 7" ..... London .... HLJ8782 .... 1959 ... £10 ....£20	
Shimmy Shimmy .... 7" ..... Parlophone...... R4684 .... 1960 ... £2.50 ......£6	
Swim .... 7" ..... Pye .... 7N25280 .... 1964 ... £6 ....£12	
Twist With Bobby Freeman .... LP ..... Jubilee .... JGM5010 .... 1962 ... £10 ....£25	US

FREEMAN, BUD
Bud Freeman .... LP ..... London .... LTZN15030 .... 1957 ... £6 ....£15
Chicago Style .... 7" EP.. Fontana .... TFE17082 .... 1958 ... £2 ....£5
Classics In Jazz .... 10" LP Capitol .... LC6706 .... 1955 ... £8 ....£20
Comes Jazz .... 10" LP Columbia .... 33S1016 .... 1954 ... £10 ....£25
Jazz For Sale .... 7" EP.. Top Rank .... JKR8021 .... 1959 ... £2 ....£5
Jazz Scene .... 7" EP.. Parlophone...... GEP8783 .... 1959 ... £2 ....£5
Midnight At Eddie Condon's .... LP ..... Emarcy .... EJL1257 .... 1957 ... £6 ....£15
Wolverine Jazz .... 10" LP Brunswick........ LA8526 .... 1951 ... £8 ....£20

FREEMAN, CAROL
Rolling Sea .... 7" ...... CBS .... 202579.................. 1967 ... £4 ....£8

FREEMAN, ERNIE
Big River .... 7"....... London .... HLP9041 .... 1960 ... £2 ....£5
Dumplings .... 7"....... London .... HLP8558 .... 1958 ... £4 ....£8
Dumplin's .... 7"....... London .... HL7029 .... 1957 ... £1.50 ....£4 ....export
Ernie Freeman & His Rhythm Guitar .... 7" EP.. London .... REU1059 .... 1956 ... £10 ....£20
Ernie Freeman Vol.2 .... 7" EP.. London .... REP1210 .... 1959 ... £7.50 ....£15
Indian Love Call .... 7"....... London .... HLP8660 .... 1958 ... £2 ....£5
Raunchy .... 7"....... London .... HLP8523 .... 1957 ... £6 ....£12
Raunchy '65 .... LP ...... London .... HLA9944 .... 1965 ... £2.50 ....£6

FREEMAN, EVELYN
I Heard The Voice .... 7" ...... London .... HLU10287 .... 1969 ... £2 ....£5

FREEMAN, MARGARET
Mister Ting-a-ling .... 7" ...... Starlite .... ST45040 .... 1961 ... £2.50 ....£6

FREEMAN, RUSS & CHET BAKER
Freeman/Baker Quartet .... LP ...... Vogue .... LAE12119 .... 1959 ... £8 ....£20

FREEMAN, STAN
Piano Moods .... 10" LP Columbia........ 33S1056 .... 1955 ... £5 ....£12

FREEWHEELERS
Why Do You Treat Me Like A Fool .... 7" ...... HMV .... POP1406 .... 1965 ... £4 ....£8

FRENCH, DON
Goldilocks .... 7"....... London .... HLW8884 .... 1959 ... £30 ....£60
Little Blonde Girl .... 7"....... London .... HLW8989 .... 1959 ... £27.50 ......£55

FRENCH IMPRESSIONISTS
Santa Baby	7"	Operation Twilight	OPT20	1982	£1.50	£4	

FRENCH, RAY
Since I Lost My Baby	7"	Pye	7N17215	1966	£2.50	£6	

FRENCH REVOLUTION
Nine Till Five	7"	Decca	F22898	1969	£15	£30	

FRENZY
This Is The Last Time	7"	Frenzy	FRENZY1	1981	£2	£5	

FRESH AIR
Running Wild	7"	Pye	7N17736	1969	£40	£80	

FRESH MAGGOTS
Fresh Maggots	LP	RCA	SF8205	1971	£60	£120	

FRESH WINDOWS
Fashion Conscious	7"	Fontana	TF839	1967	£25	£50	

FRESHIES
Baiser	7"	Razz	RAZZXEP1	1978	£5	£10	Chris Sievey B side
I'm In Love With The Girl...	7"	Razz	RAZZ12	1980	£2.50	£6	promo
Men From Banana Island...	7"	Razz	RAZZ3	1979	£1.50	£4	
Straight In At No.2	7"	Razz	RAZZEP2	1979	£2.50	£6	

FRESHMEN
Go Granny Go	7"	Pye	7N17592	1968	£1.50	£4	
Just To See You Smile	7"	Pye	7N17689	1969	£1.50	£4	
Movin' On	LP	Pye		1968	£20	£40	
Papa Oom Mow Mow	7"	Pye	7N17432	1967	£1.50	£4	
Peace On Earth	LP	CBS	64099	1970	£15	£30	
She Sang Hymns Out Of Tune	7"	Pye	7N17757	1969	£1.50	£4	

FRIDAY, CAROL
Everybody I Know	7"	Parlophone	R5369	1965	£7.50	£15	

FRIEDMAN, DEAN
Well, Well, Said The Rocking Chair	LP	Lifesong	LSLP6019	1978	£4	£10	chart LP

FRIEDMAN, PERRY
Vive La Canadienne	7" EP	Topic	TOP56	1961	£2	£5	

FRIEND & LOVER
Reach Out Of The Darkness	7"	Verve	VS1515	1968	£1.50	£4	

FRIENDS
Piccolo Man	7"	Deram	DM198	1968	£7.50	£15	

FRIJID PINK
Defrosted	LP	Deram	SML1077	1970	£6	£15	
Frijid Pink	LP	Deram	SML1062	1970	£6	£15	
Heartbreak Hotel	7"	Deram	DM321	1970	£1.50	£4	
House Of The Rising Sun	7"	Deram	DM288	1970	£2	£5	chart single
Lost Son	7"	Deram	DM347	1971	£1.50	£4	
Music For The People	7"	Deram	DM332	1971	£1.50	£4	
Sing A Song Of Freedom	7"	Deram	DM309	1970	£1.50	£4	
We're Gonna Be There	7"	Deram	DM336	1971	£1.50	£4	

FRISCO, JACKIE
Sugar Baby	7"	Decca	F11566	1963	£1.50	£4	
When You Ask About Love	7"	Decca	F11692	1963	£1.50	£4	

FRITCHIE, VONNIE
Sugar Booger Avenue	7"	London	HLU8178	1955	£12.50	£25	

FRITH, FRED
Guitar Solos	LP	Caroline	C1508	1974	£4	£10	
Guitar Solos 2	LP	Caroline	C1518	1976	£4	£10	

FRIZZELL, LEFTY
Greatest Hits	LP	Columbia	CL2488/CS9288	1966	£6	£15	US
Listen To Lefty	10" LP	Columbia	HL9021	1952	£15	£30	US
One And Only	LP	Columbia	CL1342	1959	£10	£25	US
Puttin' On	LP	Columbia	CL2772/CS9572	1967	£6	£15	US
Sad Side Of Love	LP	Columbia	CL2386/CS9186	1965	£6	£15	US
Saginaw, Michigan	LP	Columbia	CL2169/CS8969	1964	£6	£15	US
Songs Of Jimmie Rodgers	10" LP	Columbia	HL9019	1951	£15	£30	US

FRIZZLE, REV. DWIGHT
Beyond The Black Crack	LP				£20	£40	US

FROEBA, FRANK
Back Room Piano	10" LP	Brunswick	LA8547	1952	£5	£12	
Moonlight Playing Time	10" LP	Brunswick	LA8611	1953	£5	£12	
Parlor Piano	10" LP	Brunswick	LA8555	1953	£5	£12	

FROG, WYNDER K.
Green Door	7"	Island	WIP6006	1967	£4	£8	
Green Door	7" EP	Fontana	460221	1967	£7.50	£15	French

I Am A Man	7"	Island	WIP6014	1967	£4	£8	
Into The Fire	LP	United Artists	6740	1970	£6	£15	US
Jumping Jack Flash	7"	Island	WIP6044	1968	£2.50	£6	
Out Of The Frying Pan	LP	Island	ILP982/ILPS9082	1968	£6	£15	
Sunshine Super Frog	LP	Island	ILP944/ILPS9044	1967	£8	£20	
Sunshine Superman	7"	Island	WI3011	1966	£5	£10	
Turn On Your Lovelight	7"	Island	WI280	1966	£4	£8	

FROGGATT, RAYMOND

Bleach	LP	Bell	BELLS207	1972	£6	£15	
Callow La Vita	7"	Polydor	56249	1968	£1.50	£4	
Lazy Jack	7"	Polydor	56358	1969	£1.50	£4	
Little Bit Of Love	7"	Polydor	56274	1968	£1.50	£4	
Movin' Down South	7"	Polydor	56334	1969	£1.50	£4	
Red Balloon	7"	Polydor	56284	1968	£1.50	£4	
Ring Ting A Ling	7"	Polydor	56314	1969	£1.50	£4	
Rogues And Thieves	LP	Reprise	K44257	1974	£4	£10	
Rosalind	7"	Polydor	56294	1968	£1.50	£4	
Time Goes By	7"	Polydor	56294	1968	£1.50	£4	
Voice And Writing Of Raymond Froggatt	LP	Polydor	583044	1969	£6	£15	

FROGGIE BEAVER

From The Pond	LP	Froggie Beaver	7301	1973	£8	£20	US

FROGMEN

Underwater	7"	Oriole	CB1617	1961	£5	£10

FROGMORTON

At Last	LP	Philips	6308261	1976	£6	£15

FROMAN, JANE

Finger Of Suspicion Points At You	7"	Capitol	CL14209	1954	£4	£8	
I Wonder	7"	Capitol	CL14254	1955	£4	£8	chart single
Jane Froman	7" EP	Capitol	EAP1600	1956	£2.50	£6	
Song From Desiree	7"	Capitol	CL14208	1954	£2	£5	
Songs At Sunset Pt.1	7" EP	Capitol	EAP1889	1957	£2	£5	
Songs At Sunset Pt.2	7" EP	Capitol	EAP2889	1957	£2	£5	
Songs At Sunset Pt.3	7" EP	Capitol	EAP3889	1957	£2	£5	
Summertime In Venice	7"	Capitol	CL14340	1956	£1.50	£4	

FRONT LINE

Got Love	7"	Atlantic	AT4057	1965	£12.50	£25

FRONTIERE, DOM

Jet Rink Ballad	7"	London	HLU8385	1957	£7.50	£15

FROST

Frost Music	LP	Vanguard	VSD6520	1969	£6	£15	US
Rock and Roll Music	LP	Vanguard	SVRL19056	1969	£6	£15	US
Through The Eyes Of Love	LP	Vanguard	VSD6556	1970	£6	£15	US

FROST, DAVID

Deck Of Cards	7"	Parlophone	R5441	1966	£1.50	£4
Frost Report On Britain	LP	Parlophone	PMC7005	1966	£4	£10
Frost Report On Everything	LP	Pye	NPL18199	1967	£4	£10

FROST, DAVID & OTHERS

That Was The Week That Was	LP	Parlophone	PMC1197/ PCS3040	1963	£4	£10	chart L

FROST, FRANK & THE NIGHTHAWKS

Hey Boss Man!	LP	Philips	1975	1961	£250	£400	U

FROST, MAX & THE TROOPERS

Shape Of Things To Come	LP	Tower	ST5147	1968	£10	£25	U
Shape Of Things To Come	7"	Capitol	CL15565	1968	£5	£10	

FROSTY LANE

Frosty Lane	LP	Cutty Wren		1971	£30	£60

FRUGAL SOUND

Abilene	7"	RCA	RCA1595	1967	£1.50	£4
All Strung Out	7"	RCA	RCA1659	1968	£1.50	£4
Backstreet Girl	7"	RCA	RCA1566	1967	£2	£5
Just Outside The Door	7"	Pye	7N17129	1966	£1.50	£4
Norwegian Wood	7"	Pye	7N17062	1966	£2	£5

FRUIT MACHINE

Follow Me	7"	Spark	SRL1003	1969	£15	£30
I'm Alone Today	7"	Spark	SRL1027	1970	£35	£70

FRUMMOX

Here To There	LP	Probe	SPB1007	1969	£6	£15

FRUMPY

All Will Be Changed	LP	Philips	6305067	1971	£6	£15	
By The Way	LP	Vertigo	6360604	1972	£4	£10	
Frumpy 2	LP	Philips	6305098	1972	£8	£20	blue & black vin
Live	LP	Vertigo	6623022	1972	£4	£10	

FRUSCELLA, TONY
Tony Fruscella .... LP .... London .... LTZK15044 .... 1957 ... £10 ....£25 ....

FRUUPP
Future Legends .... LP ..... Dawn .... DNLS3053 .... 1973 ... £10 ....£25 ....
Modern Masquerades .... LP ..... Dawn .... DNLS3070 .... 1975 ... £10 ....£25 ....
Prince Of Heaven .... 7" ..... Dawn .... DNS1087 .... 1974 ... £4 ....£8 ....
Prince Of Heaven's Eyes .... LP ..... Dawn .... DNLH2 .... 1974 ... £10 ....£25 ....
Seven Secrets .... LP ..... Dawn .... DNLS3058 .... 1974 ... £10 ....£25 ....

FUCHS, PAUL & LIMMPE
Anima Sounds .... LP ..... Ohr .... OMM56011 .... 1971 ... £6 ....£15 ....German

FUCHSIA
Fuchsia .... LP ..... Pegasus .... PEG8 .... 1971 ... £30 ....£60 ....

FUGI
Red Moon .... 7" .... Blue Horizon.... 2096005 .... 1971 ... £4 ....£8 ....

FUGITIVES
Fugitive .... 7" .... Vogue .... V9176 .... 1961 ... £6 ....£12 ....

FUGITIVES (2)
Musical Pressure .... 7" .... Doctor Bird ..... DB1082 .... 1967 ... £5 ....£10 ....
Real Gone Loser .... 7" .... Doctor Bird ..... DB1116 .... 1967 ... £5 ....£10 ....

FUGITIVES (3)
Friday At The Cafe A GoGo (Long Hot LP ...... Westchester .... 1005 .... 1969 ... £20 ....£40 .US, with other artists
Summer) ....
Fugitives At Dave's Hideout .... LP ..... Hideout .... 1001 .... 1968 ... £100 .£200 .... US

FUGS
Ballads Of Contemporary Protest .... LP ..... Broadside .... 304 .... 1966 ... £20 ....£40 .... US
Belle Of Avenue A .... LP ..... Reprise .... RS6359 .... 1969 ... £6 ....£15 .... US
Crystal Liaison .... 7" ..... Transatlantic ... BIG115 .... 1968 ... £5 ....£10 ....
First Album .... LP ..... Fontana .... (S)TL5513 .... 1965 ... £8 ....£20 ....
Fugs 4 Rounders Score .... LP ..... ESP .... 2018 .... 1967 ... £8 ....£20 .... US
Fugs II .... LP ..... Fontana .... (S)TL5524 .... 1966 ... £8 ....£20 ....
Golden Filth .... LP ..... Reprise .... RS6396 .... 1970 ... £6 ....£15 .... US
It Crawled Into My Hand Honest ...... LP ..... Transatlantic ... TRA181 .... 1968 ... £6 ....£15 ....
Tenderness Junction .... LP ..... Transatlantic ... TRA180 .... 1968 ... £6 ....£15 ....
Virgin Fugs .... LP ..... Fontana .... (S)TL5501 .... 1967 ... £8 ....£20 ....

FULHAM FURIES
These Boots Are Made For Walking ..... 7" .... GM .... GMS9050 .... 1978 ... £4 ....£8 ....

FULLER, BLIND BOY
1935-40 .... LP ..... Philips .... BBL7510 .... 1957 ... £15 ....£30 ....
Carolina Blues .... LP ..... Flyright .... LP105 .... 196- ... £4 ....£10 ....
On Down Vol.1 .... LP ..... Saydisc .... SDR143 .... 1968 ... £5 ....£12 ....
On Down Vol.2 .... LP ..... Saydisc .... SDR168 .... 1969 ... £5' ....£12 ....

FULLER, BOBBY
Fought The Law .... LP ..... Mustang .... M(S)901 .... 1966 ... £15 ....£30 .... US
Fought The Law .... 7" ..... London .... HLU10030 .... 1966 ... £6 ....£12 ....chart single
KRLA King Of The Wheels .... LP ..... Mustang .... M(S)900 .... 1966 ... £20 ....£40 .... US
Love's Made A Fool Of You .... 7" ..... London .... HLU10041 .... 1966 ... £4 ....£8 ....
Love's Made A Fool Of You .... 7" EP.. London .... RE10179 .... 1966 ... £25 ....£50 .... French
Memorial Album .... LP ..... President .... PTL1003 .... 1967 ... £6 ....£15 ....

FULLER, GIL
Man From Monterey .... LP ..... Fontana .... 688147ZL .... 1966 ... £5 ....£12 ....with Dizzy Gillespie

FULLER, JERRY
Guilty Of Loving You .... 7" ..... London .... HLN9439 .... 1961 ... £1.50 .....£4 ....
Mother Goose At The Bandstand .... 7" ..... Salvo .... SLO1802 .... 1962 ... £2 ....£5 ....
Teenage Love .... LP ..... Lin .... LP100 .... 1960 ... £6 ....£15 .... US
Tennessee Waltz .... 7" ..... London .... HLH8982 .... 1959 ... £2.50 .....£6 ....

FULLER, JESSE
Favourites .... LP ..... Stateside .... SL10154 .... 1965 ... £4 ....£10 ....
Frisco Bound .... LP ..... Cavalier .... 6009 .... 195- ... £15 ....£30 .... US
Frisco Bound .... 10" LP Cavalier .... 5006 .... 195- ... £20 ....£40 .... US
Going Back To My Old Used To Be ...... 7" ..... Fontana .... TF821 .... 1967 ... £5 ....£10 ....
Jesse Fuller .... LP ..... Good Time ...... LAG12159 .... 1958 ... £6 ....£15 ....
 .... Jazz ....
Lone Cat .... LP ..... Good Time ...... LAG12279 .... 1960 ... £6 ....£15 ....
 .... Jazz ....
Move On Down The Line .... LP ..... Topic .... 12T134 .... 1965 ... £8 ....£20 ....
Runnin' Wild .... 7" ..... Good Time ...... GV2427 .... 1967 ... £1.50 .....£4 ....
 .... Jazz ....
San Francisco Bay Blues .... LP ..... Good Time ...... LAG574 .... 1963 ... £6 ....£15 ....
 .... Jazz ....
San Francisco Bay Blues .... LP ..... Stateside .... SL10166 .... 1966 ... £4 ....£10 ....
San Francisco Bay Blues .... LP ..... Vocalion .... VRLP574 .... 196- ... £5 ....£12 ....
San Francisco Bay Blues .... 7" ..... Good Time ...... GV2426 .... 1965 ... £2 ....£5 ....
 .... Jazz ....
Session .... LP ..... Fontana .... TL5313 .... 1966 ... £5 ....£12 ....
Working On The Railroad .... 10" LP Topic .... 10T59 .... 1960 ... £8 ....£20 ....

FULLER, RANDY

It's Love Come What May	7"	President	PTL111	1967	£4	£8	

FULSON, LOWELL

Black Nights	7"	Polydor	56515	1970	£5	£10	
Do You Love	7"	Jet	770	1976	£1.50	£4	
Hung Down Head	LP	Chess	408	196-	£8	£20	US
I Love My Baby	78	London	L1199	1953	£7.50	£15	
In A Heavy Bag	LP	Polydor	2384038	197-	£4	£10	
Lowell Fulson	LP	Kent	KLP5016	1965	£8	£20	US
Lowell Fulson Now	LP	Kent	KST531	1969	£6	£15	US
San Francisco Blues	LP	Fontana	SFJL920	1969	£6	£15	
Stop And Think	7"	Outasite	45502	1966	£12.50	£25	with Leon Blue
Talking Woman	7"	Sue	WI4023	1966	£10	£20	
Too Many Drivers	7"	Sue	WI375	1965	£6	£12	
Tramp	LP	Kent	KLP/KST520	1967	£8	£20	US
Tramp	7"	Fontana	TF795	1967	£7.50	£15	

FUMBLE

Fumble	LP	Sovereign	SVNA7254	1972	£5	£12	
Poetry In Lotion	LP	RCA	SF8403	1974	£5	£12	

FUN FOUR

Singing In The Showers	7"	NMC	NMC010	1980	£1.50	£4	

FUNHOUSE

Out Of Control	7"	Ensign	ENY22	1982	£6	£12	
Out Of Control	12"	Ensign	ENY22	1982	£6	£15	

FUNKADELIC

America Eats Its Young	LP	Westbound	2WB2020	1972	£15	£30	US
Can You Get To That	7"	Janus	6146001	1974	£2	£5	US
Cosmic Slop	LP	Westbound	WB2022	1973	£8	£20	
Electric Spanking Of War Babies	LP	Warner Bros	K56874	1981	£5	£12	
Free Your Mind & Your Ass Will Follow	LP	Pye	NSPL28144	1971	£10	£25	
Funkadelic	LP	Pye	NSPL28137	1970	£10	£25	
Greatest Hits	LP	Westbound	1004	1975	£6	£15	US
Hardcore Jollies	LP	Warner Bros	K56299	1978	£6	£15	
I Got A Thing, You Got A Thing...	7"	Pye	7N25519	1970	£4	£8	
Let's Take It To The Stage	LP	20th Century	W215	1975	£6	£15	
Maggot Brain	LP	Westbound	6310201	1971	£8	£20	
One Nation Under A Groove	LP	Warner Bros	K56359	1978	£4	£10	with 12
Standing On The Verge Of Getting It On	LP	Westbound	1001	1974	£10	£25	US
Tales Of Kidd Funkadelic	LP	Westbound	227	1976	£8	£20	US
Uncle Jam Wants You	LP	Warner Bros	K56712	1979	£6	£15	
You And Your Folks, Me And Mine	7"	Pye	7N25548	1971	£4	£8	

FUNKY JUNCTION

Records like that of Funky Junction's "Tribute To Deep Purple" are essentially exploitative in nature. At least on this occasion the group name is written clearly enough, although the record company was no doubt still rather hoping that potential customers would think the musi really was by Deep Purple. According to rumour, members of Thin Lizzy are actually involved, although if they were, it was not one of the better days. The vocalist is definitely not Phil Lynott.

Tribute To Deep Purple	LP	Gold Award	MER373	1973	£4	£10	

FUREY, FINBAR

Prince Of Pipers	LP	Polydor	2908023	1974	£8	£20	Iris
Traditional Irish Pipe Music	LP	XTRA	XTRA1077	1969	£10	£25	

FUREY, FINBAR & BOB STEWART

Tomorrow We Part	LP	Broadside	BRO133	1979	£5	£12	

FUREY, FINBAR & EDDIE

Dawning Of The Day	LP	Dawn	DNLS3037	1972	£10	£25	
Dream In My Hand	LP	Interchord	264291U	1974	£6	£15	Germa
Finbar And Eddie Furey	LP	Transatlantic	TRA168	1968	£8	£20	
Four Green Fields	LP	Plane	S12F200	1972	£6	£15	Germa
Lonesome Boatman	LP	Transatlantic	TRA191	1969	£8	£20	
Town Is Not Their Own	LP	Harp	HPE613	1969	£6	£15	Iris

FUREY, TED

Traditional Fiddle	LP	Outlet	OLP1020	1973	£10	£25	Iris

FURNITURE

Shaking Story	7"	Guy From Paraguay	PARA1	1980	£2.50	£6	

FURTADO, TOMMY

Sun Tan Sam	7"	London	HLA8418	1957	£6	£12	

FURY, BILLY

Billy Fury is held in high regard as one of the most convincing British rock'n'rollers and yet the proportion of rock to ballads in his output is f too small for the reputation to be sustained by deep enquiry. "The Sound Of Fury" is certainly a competent slice of rockabilly, and Fury wro much of the material himself, but to release an album in this style in 1960 was to indulge in a piece of historical re-creation rather than to part of the development of something new. Cliff Richard's exploration of the Buddy Holly style was much more to the point, and it significant that he survived the onslaught of the Beatles, whereas Billy Fury did not.

All The Way To The USA	7"	Parlophone	R5819	1969	£7.50	£15	
Am I Blue	7" EP	Decca	DFE8558	1963	£10	£20	
Angel Face	78	Decca	F11158	1959	£15	£30	
Angel Face	7"	Decca	F11158	1959	£12.50	£25	tri cent

Title	Format	Label	Cat No	Year	Price	Price	Notes
Because Of Love	7"	Decca	F11508	1962	£1.50	£4	chart single
Best Of Billy Fury	LP	Ace Of Clubs	ACL1229	1967	£6	£15	
Beyond The Shadow Of A Doubt	7"	Parlophone	R5658	1967	£5	£10	
Billy	LP	Decca	LK4533	1963	£10	£25	chart LP
Billy Fury	LP	Ace Of Clubs	ACL1047	1960	£8	£20	
Billy Fury	7" EP	Decca	DFE6694	1961	£12.50	£25	
Billy Fury And The Gamblers	7" EP	Decca	DFE8641	1965	£20	£40	
Billy Fury And The Tornadoes	7" EP	Decca	DFE8525	1963	£10	£20	
Billy Fury Hits	7" EP	Decca	DFE8505	1962	£6	£12	
Billy Fury No.2	7" EP	Decca	DFE6699	1962	£12.50	£20	
Colette	7"	Decca	F11200	1960	£10	£20	chart single, tri centre
Do You Really Love Me Too	7"	Decca	F11792	1963	£1.50	£4	chart single
Don't Let A Little Pride	7"	Decca	F12409	1966	£2.50	£6	
Don't Worry	7"	Decca	F11334	1961	£2.50	£6	chart single
Give Me Your Word	7"	Decca	F12459	1966	£2	£5	chart single
Halfway To Paradise	LP	Ace Of Clubs	ACL1083	1961	£8	£20	chart LP
Halfway To Paradise	7"	Decca	F11349	1961	£1.50	£4	chart single
Halfway To Paradise	7"	NEMS	NES018	1976	£1.50	£4	
Hippy Hippy Shake	7"	Decca	F40719	1964	£10	£20	export
Hippy Hippy Shake	7"	Decca	F40719	1964	£20	£40	export, PS
Hurtin' Is Lovin'	7"	Parlophone	R5560	1967	£6	£12	
I Call For My Rose	7"	Parlophone	R5788	1969	£6	£12	
I Will	7"	Decca	F11888	1964	£2.50	£6	chart single
I'd Never Find Another You	7"	Decca	F11409	1961	£1.50	£4	chart single
I'll Be Your Sweetheart	7"	Warner Bros	K16402	1974	£2.50	£6	
I'll Never Quite Get Over You	7"	Decca	F12325	1966	£2	£5	chart single
I'm Lost Without You	7"	Decca	F12048	1965	£1.50	£4	chart single
In Summer	7"	Decca	F11701	1963	£1.50	£4	chart single
In Thoughts Of You	7"	Decca	F12178	1965	£1.50	£4	chart single
Interview With Stuart Colman	10" LP	Polydor		1982	£6	£15	promo
It's Only Make Believe	7"	Decca	F11939	1964	£1.50	£4	chart single
I've Got A Horse	LP	Decca	LK4677	1965	£15	£30	
Jealousy	7"	Decca	F11384	1961	£1.50	£4	chart single
Lady	7"	Parlophone	R5747	1968	£6	£12	
Last Night Was Made For Love	7"	Decca	F11458	1962	£1.50	£4	chart single
Letter Full Of Tears	7"	Decca	F11437	1962	£2	£5	chart single
Like I've Never Been Gone	7"	Decca	F11582	1963	£1.50	£4	chart single
Long Live Rock	7" EP	Ronco	MREP001	1973	£7.50	£15	with other artists
Loving You	7"	Parlophone	R5605	1967	£5	£10	
Margo	78	Decca	F11128	1959	£10	£20	
Margo	78	Decca	F11128	1959	£6	£12	chart single, tri centre
Maybe Tomorrow	78	Decca	F11102	1959	£10	£20	
Maybe Tomorrow	7"	Decca	F11102	1959	£6	£12	tri-centre, chart single
Maybe Tomorrow	7" EP	Decca	DFE6597	1959	£20	£40	tri centre
My Christmas Prayer	78	Decca	F11189	1959	£17.50	£35	tri centre
My Christmas Prayer	7"	Decca	F11189	1959	£20	£40	tri centre
My Christmas Prayer	7" EP	Decca	DFE8686	1983	£2	£5	
Once Upon A Dream	7"	Decca	F11485	1962	£1.50	£4	chart single
Paradise Alley	7"	Parlophone	R5874	1970	£10	£20	
Phone Box	7"	Parlophone	R5723	1968	£7.50	£15	
Play It Cool	7" EP	Decca	DFE6708	1962	£5	£10	
Run To My Lovin' Arms	7"	Decca	F12230	1965	£2	£5	chart single
Silly Boy Blue	7"	Parlophone	R5681	1968	£10	£20	
Somebody Else's Girl	7"	Decca	F11744	1963	£1.50	£4	chart single
Sound Of Fury	10" LP	Decca	LF1329	1960	£20	£40	chart LP
Suzanne In The Mirror	7"	Parlophone	R5634	1967	£5	£10	
That's Love	7"	Decca	F11237	1960	£2.50	£6	chart single
Thousand Stars	7"	Decca	F11311	1960	£2.50	£6	chart single
We Want Billy	LP	Decca	LK4548	1963	£10	£25	chart LP
We Want Billy	LP	Decca	SKL4548	1963	£15	£30	stereo, chart LP
When Will You Say I Love You	7"	Decca	F11655	1963	£1.50	£4	chart single
Why Are You Leaving	7"	Parlophone	R5845	1970	£7.50	£15	
Will The Real Man Stand Up	7"	Fury	FY301	1972	£5	£10	
Wondrous Place	7"	Decca	F11267	1960	£2.50	£6	chart single

FURYS

Title	Format	Label	Cat No	Year	Price	Price	Notes
I'm Satisfied With You	7"	Jayboy	BOY68	1973	£1.50	£4	
Never More	7" EP	Columbia	ESDF1488	1963	£5	£10	French
Sing Went The Strings Of My Heart	7"	Stateside	SS182	1963	£2	£5	

FUSE

Title	Format	Label	Cat No	Year	Price	Price	Notes
Fuse	LP	Epic	26502	1968	£6	£15	US

FUSION

Title	Format	Label	Cat No	Year	Price	Price	Notes
All I Hear from You	LP	Telephone	TEL101	1980	£6	£15	blue vinyl

FUSION ORCHESTRA

Title	Format	Label	Cat No	Year	Price	Price	Notes
Skeleton In Armour	LP	EMI	EMA758	1973	£20	£40	
When My Mama's Not At Home	7"	EMI	EMI2056	1973	£1.50	£4	

FUT

Desperate to believe in the existence of rare Beatles out-takes, collectors seized on "Have You Heard The Word" as being one such. Unless, of course, it was really the Bee Gees - or, again, perhaps it was actually the Bee Gees and the Beatles singing together? Actually, it was the Fut (whoever they were), just as the label said.

Title	Format	Label	Cat No	Year	Price	Price	Notes
Have You Heard The Word	7"	Beacon	BEA160	1971	£7.50	£15	

FUTURES

Title	Format	Label	Cat No	Year	Price	Price	Notes
You Better Be Certain	7"	Buddah	BDS430	1975	£2.50	£6	

FUZZ FACE

Title	Format	Label	Cat No	Year	Price	Price	Notes
Mighty Quinn	7"	Page One	POF065	1968	£1.50	£4	

FUZZY DUCK

Big Brass Band	7"	Mam	MAM51	1971	£5	£10	
Double Time Woman	7"	Mam	MAM37	1971	£5	£10	
Fuzzy Duck	LP	MAM	MAM1005	1971	£75	£150	
Fuzzy Duck	LP	Reflection	MM05	1990	£6	£15	with 7

FYNN MCCOOL

Fynn McCool	LP	RCA	SF8112	1970	£20	£40	
US Thumbstyle	7"	RCA	RCA1956	1970	£4	£8	

G, TOMMY & THE CHARMS
I Know What I Want	7"	London	HLB10107	1967	£1.50	£4	

G, WINSTON
Cloud Nine	7"	Decca	F12444	1966	£5	£10	
Mother Ferguson's Love Dust	7"	Decca	F12559	1967	£6	£12	
Riding With The Milkman	7"	Decca	F12623	1967	£5	£10	

G, WINSTON & THE WICKED
Like A Baby	7"	Parlophone	R5266	1965	£6	£12	
Until You Were Gone	7"	Parlophone	R5330	1966	£4	£8	

GABBIDON, BASIL
Ena Mena	7"	Blue Beat	BB155	1962	£5	£10	
I Bet You Don't Know	7"	Island	WI076	1963	£5	£10	
I Found My Baby	7"	Island	WI033	1962	£5	£10	
I Was Wrong	7"	Blue Beat	BB69	1961	£5	£10	
I'll Find Love	7"	Blue Beat	BB161	1962	£5	£10	Mellow Larks B side
Independence Blues	7"	Blue Beat	BB124	1962	£5	£10	
Iverene	7"	Blue Beat	BB111	1962	£5	£10	
No More Wedding	7"	Blue Beat	BB38	1961	£5	£10	
Our Melody	7"	Blue Beat	BB129	1962	£5	£10	
St.Louis Woman	7"	Island	WI089	1963	£5	£10	
Tic Toc	7"	Blue Beat	BB288	1964	£5	£10	

GABERLUNZIE
Freedom's Sword	LP	Revival	RVS1010	1974	£6	£15	

GABRIEL & THE ANGELS
Don't Wanna Twist No More	7"	Stateside	SS150	1963	£2	£5	

GABRIEL, PETER
Big Time	CDV	Virgin	VVD241	1988	£3	£8	
Biko	7"	Charisma	CB370	1980	£1.50	£4	chart single
Deutsches Album	LP	Charisma	6302221	1982	£4	£10	4th LP in German
D.I.Y.	7"	Charisma	CB311	1978	£2	£5	
D.I.Y. (remix)	7"	Charisma	CB319	1978	£15	£30	
Ein Deutsches Album	LP	Charisma	6302035	1980	£4	£10	3rd LP in German
Games Without Frontiers (live)	12"	Virgin	GAB122	1983	£2.50	£6	double
Modern Love	7"	Charisma	CB302	1977	£15	£30	pic label
Peter Gabriel 4	LP	Charisma		1982	£6	£15	audiophile
Peter Gabriel Plays Live	LP	Charisma		1983	£25	£50	double, test pressing, original mixes
Schock Den Affen	7"	Charisma	60000876	1982	£5	£10	German
Shock The Monkey	7"	Charisma	SHOCK122	1982	£2	£5	pic disc
Shock The Monkey/instrumental	7"	Charisma	SHOCK1	1982	£2.50	£6	
Solsbury Hill	7"	Charisma	CB301	1977	£2.50	£6	PS
Solsbury Hill	7"	Sound For Industry	SFI381	1978	£1.50	£4	flexi
Spiel Ohne Grenzen	7"	Charisma	6000448	1980	£5	£10	German

GABRIELLI BRASS
Canterbury Tales Theme	7"	Polydor	56252	1968	£2	£5	
Ride Your Pony	7"	Polydor	56047	1965	£4	£8	

GADGETS
The Gadgets performed improvised industrial music which was released on three limited edition albums. One of the trio was Matt Johnson, subsequently the central pillar of The The.

Blue Album	LP	Glass	GLALP006	1983	£4	£10	
Gadgetree	LP	Final Solution	FSLP001	1979	£6	£15	blue or brown cover design/insert
Love,Curiosity,Freckles,& Doubt	LP	Final Solution	FSLP002	1980	£6	£15	

GADSON, MEL
Comin' Down With Love	7"	London	HLX9105	1960	£2	£5	

GAGALACTYCA
Gagalactyca	LP	Holyground	HG1135	1990	£6	£15	

GAILLARD, SLIM
Central Avenue Boogie	78	Vogue	V2044	1951	£1.50	£4	
Jam Man	78	Parlophone	R3291	1950	£1.50	£4	
Musical Aggregations	7" EP	Columbia	SEB10046	1957	£10	£20	
Slim Gaillard No.1	7" EP	Parlophone	GEP8595	1957	£7.50	£15	
Slim Gaillard Rides Again	7" EP	London	RED1251	1960	£10	£20	
Soot Boogie	78	Vogue	V2029	1951	£1.50	£4	

GAINORS
Secret	7"	London	HLU8734	1958	£60	£120	

GALACTIC FEDERATION
March Of The Sky People .... 7" ...... Polydor .... 56093 .... 1966 ... £7.50 ....£15 ....

GALACTIC SUPERMARKET
Galactic Supermarket .... LP ..... Komische .... KM58010 .... 1974 ... £10 ....£25 ....Germar

GALAHADS
Galahads .... LP ..... Liberty .... LRP3371/LST7371 1964 ... £5 ....£12 ....US

GALAXIE 500
Blue Thunder .... 7" ...... Rough Trade ... G5SFI .... 1990 ... £2 ....£5 .... promo
Rain .... 7" ...... Caff .... CAFF9 .... 1988 ... £7.50 ....£15 ....

GALBRAITH, BARRY
Guitar And The Wind .... LP ..... Brunswick........ LAT8273 .... 1959 ... £6 ....£15 ....

GALE, EDDIE
Black Rhythm Happening .... LP ..... Blue Note........ BST84320 .... 1969 ... £6 ....£15 ....
Ghetto Music .... LP ..... Blue Note........ BST84294 .... 1968 ... £6 ....£15 ....

GALE, SUNNY
Certain Smile .... 7" ...... Brunswick........ 05753 .... 1958 ... £1.50 ....£4
C'Est La Vie .... 7" ...... HMV .... 7M344 .... 1955 ... £2 ....£5
Come Go With Me .... 7" ...... Brunswick........ 05661 .... 1957 ... £2 ....£5
Goodnight, Well It's Time To Go .... 7" ...... HMV .... 7M243 .... 1954 ... £2.50 ....£6
Please Love Me Forever .... 7" ...... London .... HLU9322 .... 1961 ... £1.50 ....£4
Send My Baby Back To Me .... 7" ...... HMV .... 7M147 .... 1953 ... £2.50 ....£6
Sunny And Blue .... LP ..... RCA .... LPM1277 .... 1956 ... £6 ....£15 ....US
Two Hearts .... 7" ...... Brunswick........ 05659 .... 1957 ... £2 ....£5

GALLAGHER & LYLE
Trees .... 7" ...... Polydor .... 56170 .... 1967 ... £4 ....£8

GALLAGHER, RORY
Rory Gallagher's brand of tough blues-rock continues to have a significant following despite the fairly low profile that the man himself adopt these days. His earliest recordings with Taste scrape into the collectors' price bracket, but his seventies albums sold too well to be rare. The remain steady sellers, however, at around the eight pound price level.
In The Beginning .... LP ..... Emerald .... GES1110 .... 1974 ... £5 ....£12 ....Iris

GALLAHADS
Ooh-Ah .... 7" ...... Capitol .... CL14282 .... 1955 ... £1.50 ....£4

GALLANTS
Happy Beat .... 7" ...... Capitol .... CL15366 .... 1964 ... £1.50 ....£4
Man From UNCLE Theme .... 7" ...... Capitol .... CL15408 .... 1965 ... £4 ....£8

GALLIARD
I Wrapped Her In Ribbons .... 7" ...... Deram .... DM306 .... 1970 ... £4 ....£8
New Dawn .... LP ..... Deram .... SML1075 .... 1970 ... £30 ....£60
Strange Pleasure .... LP ..... Nova .... SDN4 .... 1969 ... £8 ....£20

GALLION, BOB
Froggy Went A Courtin' .... 7" ...... MGM................ MGM1057 .... 1960 ... £2 ....£5
You Take The Table .... 7" ...... MGM................ MGM1028 .... 1959 ... £1.50 ....£4

GALLION, BOB & RAMSEY KEARNEY
Two Country Greats .... 7" EP.. Hickory .... LPE1508 .... 1965 ... £2 ....£5

GALT, JAMES
Comes The Dawn .... 7" ...... Pye .... 7N15936 .... 1965 ... £2.50 ....£6
With My Baby .... 7" ...... Pye .... 7N17021 .... 1965 ... £10 ....£20

GAMBLERS
Cry Me A River .... 7" ...... Parlophone....... R5557 .... 1967 ... £6 ....£12
Dr.Goldfoot .... 7" ...... Decca .... F12399 .... 1966 ... £5 ....£10
Nobody But Me .... 7" ...... Decca .... F11872 .... 1964 ... £5 ....£10
Now I'm All Alone .... 7" ...... Decca .... F12060 .... 1965 ... £5 ....£10
You've Really Got A Hold On Me .... 7" ...... Decca .... F11780 .... 1963 ... £5 ....£10

GAMBRELL, FREDDIE
Freddie Gambrell .... LP ..... Vogue .... LAE12205 .... 1960 ... £5 ....£12

GAME
Addicted Man .... 7" ...... Parlophone....... R5553 .... 1967 ... £60 ....£120
But I Do .... 7" ...... Pye .... 7N15889 .... 1965 ... £50 ....£100
Gonna Get Me Someone .... 7" ...... Decca .... F12469 .... 1966 ... £50 ....£100
It's Shocking What They Call Me .... 7" ...... Parlophone....... R5569 .... 1967 ... £50 ....£100

GAMMA GOOCHEE
Gamma Goochee .... 7" EP.. Colpix .... 8007 .... 1966 ... £6 ....£12 ....French, B sid
by Nooney Ricke

GAMMER & HIS FAMILIARS
Rocket Ticket .... LP ..... Gammer .... EJ9851 .... 1981 ... £5 ....£12
Will The New Baby .... 12" .... Gammer .... GAMMER5............ 1984 ... £2.50 ....£6
Won't Look Out .... LP ..... Gammer .... EJ9699 .... 1981 ... £5 ....£12

GANDALF
Gandalf .... LP ..... Capitol .... ST121 .... 1969 ... £25 ....£50 L

GANDALF THE GREY
Grey Wizard Am I .... LP ..... G.W.R. .... 7 .... 196- .... £37.50 ....£75 L

GANDERTON, RON WARREN

Guitar Star	LP	Celestial Sound	LPRWG1	1973	£6	£15	
Precious As England	LP	Celestial Sound	LPRWG3	1981	£6	£15	
Sound Ceremony	LP	Celestial Sound	LPRWG2	1974	£6	£15	

GANIM'S ASIA MINORS

Daddy Lolo	7"	London	HLE8637	1958	£2	£5	

GANT, CECIL

Cecil Gant	LP	King	671	1960	£20	£40	US
Cecil's Boogie	LP	Flyright	LP4714	1975	£5	£12	
Incomparable Cecil Gant	LP	Sound	601	1957	£20	£40	US
Rock Little Baby	LP	Flyright	LP4710	1974	£5	£12	

GANT, CLENTT

I'm Just A Lucky So And So	7"	Starlite	ST45023	1960	£1.50	£4	

GANT, DON

Early In The Morning	7"	Hickory	451297	1965	£4	£8	

GANTS

Gants Again	LP	Liberty	LRP3473/LSP7473	1966	£6	£15	US
Gants Galore	LP	Liberty	LRP3455/LST7455	1966	£6	£15	US
Greener Days	7"	Liberty	LIB55940	1967	£2	£5	
Road Runner	LP	Liberty	LRP3432/LST7432	1965	£8	£20	US
Road Runner	7"	Liberty	LIB55829	1965	£6	£12	

GARBUTT, VIN

Valley Of Tees	LP	Trailer	LER2078	1972	£6	£15	
Young Tin Whistle Pest	LP	Trailer	LER2081	1975	£5	£12	

GARCIA, JERRY

Garcia	LP	Warner Bros	K46139	1972	£4	£10	
Hooteroll	LP	CBS	69013	1972	£4	£10	
Live At The Keystone	LP	Fantasy	F79002	1973	£4	£10	

GARDEN ODYSSEY ENTERPRISE

Sad And Lonely	7"	Deram	DM267	1969	£4	£8	

GARDINER, PAUL

The collectability of Paul Gardiner's promotional issue of "Stormtrooper In Drag" derives from the identity of the lead singer on the track, who is Gardiner's friend, Gary Numan.

Stormtrooper In Drag	12"	Beggars Banquet	BEG61T	1981	£75	£150	promo

GARDNER, BORIS

Elizabethan Reggae	7"	Doctor Bird	DB1205	1969	£5	£10	
Hooked On A Feeling	7"	Treasure Isle	TI7056	1969	£4	£8	
Lucky Is The Boy	7"	High Note	HS010	1968	£4	£8	
Never My Love	7"	Duke	DU21	1969	£2.50	£6	
Reggae Happening	LP	Trojan	TBL121	1970	£5	£12	

GARDNER, DAVE

All By Myself	7"	Brunswick	05740	1958	£10	£20	

GARDNER, DON & DEE DEE FORD

Don't You Worry	7"	Soul City	SC101	1968	£4	£8	
Don't You Worry	7"	Stateside	SS130	1962	£4	£8	
I Need Your Loving	7"	Stateside	SS114	1962	£2.50	£6	
In Sweden	LP	Sue	LP1044	1965	£10	£25	US
Need Your Lovin'	LP	Fire	LP105	1962	£25	£50	US

GARFIELD

Out There Tonight	LP	Capricorn	CPO193	1977	£5	£12	US
Strange Streets	LP	Mercury	SRM11082	1976	£5	£12	US

GARFIELD, JOHNNY

Stranger In Paradise	7"	Pye	7N15758	1965	£5	£10	

GARLAND, JUDY

Alone	LP	Capitol	LCT6136	1957	£4	£10	
At The Grove	LP	Capitol	ST1118	1959	£4	£10	stereo
Born In A Trunk	7" EP	Philips	BBE12012	1955	£2.50	£6	
Born To Sing	10" LP	MGM	MGMD1334	1955	£5	£12	
Couple Of Swells	7"	MGM	SP1001	1953	£1.50	£4	with Fred Astaire
Garland For Judy	7" EP	Capitol	EAP120051	1961	£2.50	£6	
Judy	LP	Capitol	LCT6121	1957	£4	£10	
Judy At Carnegie Hall Pt.1	7" EP	Capitol	EAP71569	1961	£2	£5	
Judy At Carnegie Hall Pt.2	7" EP	Capitol	EAP81569	1961	£2	£5	
Judy At The Palace	10" LP	Brunswick	LA8725	1955	£6	£15	
Judy In Love	LP	Capitol	ST1036	1959	£4	£10	stereo
Judy In Love Pt.1	7" EP	Capitol	EAP11036	1959	£2.50	£6	
Judy In Love Pt.2	7" EP	Capitol	EAP21036	1959	£2.50	£6	
Judy In Love Pt.3	7" EP	Capitol	EAP31036	1959	£2.50	£6	
Letter	LP	Capitol	ST1188	1959	£4	£10	stereo
Look For The Silver Lining	7"	MGM	SP1157	1956	£1.50	£4	
Miss Show Business	LP	Capitol	LCT6103	1956	£4	£10	
Star Is Born	LP	Philips	BBL7007	1955	£5	£12	

313

GARLAND, RED

All Morning Long	LP	Esquire	32099	1960	£8	£20	with John Coltrane & Donald Byrd
Manteca	LP	Esquire	32096	1960	£6	£15	with Ray Barreto
Red In Bluesville	LP	Esquire	32116	1961	£6	£15	

GARNER, ERROLL

Afternoon Of An Elf	LP	Mercury	MPL6539	1958	£6	£15	
At The Piano	LP	Mercury	MPL6507	1957	£6	£15	
At The Piano	LP	Philips	BBL7078	1956	£6	£15	
Concert By The Sea	LP	Philips	BBL7106	1957	£5	£12	
Errol	LP	Mercury	MMB12010	1959	£5	£12	
Errol Garner Trio	LP	Vogue	LAE12209	1960	£5	£12	
Errol Garner Trio Vol.1	10" LP	Vogue	LDE034	1953	£8	£20	
Erroll Garner	LP	London	LTZC15126	1958	£5	£12	
Erroll Garner	10" LP	Felsted	L87002	195-	£8	£20	
Garner Touch	LP	Philips	BBL7193	1957	£5	£12	
Giant Jazz Gallery	LP	Philips	BBL7448	1961	£4	£10	
Gone Garner Gonest	LP	Philips	BBL7034	1955	£5	£12	
Gone With Garner	10" LP	Oriole	MG26042	1955	£8	£20	
Mambo Moves Garner	LP	Mercury	MPL6501	1956	£8	£20	
Margie	10" LP	Felsted	EDL87002	1954	£8	£20	
Most Happy Piano	LP	Philips	BBL7282	1958	£5	£12	
Music Maestro Please	LP	Philips	BBL7426	1961	£4	£10	
Other Voices	LP	Philips	BBL7204	1958	£5	£12	
Paris Impressions Vol.1	LP	Philips	BBL7313	1959	£4	£10	
Paris Impressions Vol.2	LP	Philips	BBL7314	1959	£4	£10	
Passport To Fame	10" LP	Felsted	EDL87015	1955	£8	£20	
Penthouse Serenade	LP	London	LTZC15125	1958	£5	£12	
Piano Gems	10" LP	Columbia	33S1059	1955	£8	£20	
Piano Moods	10" LP	Columbia	33S1050	1955	£8	£20	
Piano Wizardry	7" EP.	London	REU1066	1956	£2.50	£6	
Plays For Dancing	10" LP	Philips	BBR8002	1954	£8	£20	
Soliloquy	LP	Philips	BBL7226	1958	£5	£12	
Solo Flight	10" LP	Philips	BBR8045	1955	£8	£20	
Undecided	7" EP.	CBS	REP4006	196-	£2	£5	

GARNETT, COL

With A Girl Like You	7"	Page One	POF002	1966	£2.50	£6	

GARNETT, GALE

I'll Cry Alone	7"	RCA	RCA1451	1965	£1.50	£4	

GARNETT, RAY

Pony Time	7"	RCA	RCA1228	1961	£1.50	£4	

GARON, JESSE & DESPERADOS

Splashing Along	7"	Narodnik	NRK001	1986	£1.50	£4	

GARR, ARTIE

This was the name first used by Art Garfunkel.

Dream Alone	7"	Warwick	515	1959	£12.50	£25	US
Private World	7"	Octavia	8002	1960	£10	£20	US

GARRETT, VERNON

If I Could Turn Back The Hands Of Time	7"	Stateside	SS2006	1967	£7.50	£15	
Shine It On	7"	Action	ACT4508	1968	£2.50	£6	
Shine It On	7"	Stateside	SS2026	1967	£5	£10	

GARRICK, DAVID

A Boy Called David	LP	Piccadilly	NPL38024	1967	£5	£12	
David	7" EP.	Piccadilly	NEP34056	1966	£15	£30	
Dear Mrs.Applebee	7"	Pye	7N35335	1966	£1.50	£4	chart single
Dear Mrs.Applebee	7" EP.	Pye	PNV24182	1966	£6	£12	French
Don't Go Out Into The Rain Sugar	LP	Piccadilly	N(S)PL38035	1968	£4	£10	
I've Found A Love	7" EP.	Pye	PNV24187	1967	£6	£12	French
Lady Jane	7"	Piccadilly	7N35317	1966	£2	£5	chart single

GARRICK, MICHAEL

Anthem	LP	Argo	EAF/ZFA92	1965	£20	£40	
Before Night/Day	LP	Argo	EAF115	1966	£20	£40	
Black Marigolds	LP	Argo	(Z)DA88	1968	£20	£40	
Case Of Jazz	LP	Airborne		1963	£25	£50	
Cold Mountain	LP	Argo	ZDA153	1972	£20	£40	
Epiphany	7"	Argo	AFW105	1971	£4	£8	
Heart Is A Lotus	LP	Argo	ZDA135	1970	£20	£40	with Norma Winstone
Home Stretch Blues	LP	Argo	ZDA154	1972	£20	£40	
Illumination	LP	Impulse	AS49	197-	£8	£20	
Jazz Praises At St.Pauls	LP	Airborne	NBP0021	1968	£20	£40	
Michael Garrick Quartet	7" EP.	Argo	EAF92	196-	£7.50	£15	
Moonscape	LP	Airborne		1964	£25	£50	
Mr.Smith's Apocalypse	LP	Argo	ZAGF1	1971	£20	£40	
October Woman	LP	Argo	(Z)DA33	1964	£20	£40	
Poetry And Jazz In Concert	LP	Argo	(Z)DA26/27	1964	£30	£60	double, with Adrian Mitchell
Poetry And Jazz In Concert 250	LP	Argo	ZPR264/5	1969	£25	£50	double
Promises	LP	Argo	(Z)DA36	1965	£20	£40	
Troppo	LP	Argo	ZDA163	1974	£10	£25	

GARRIE, NICK
Nightmare Of J.B.Stanislas .... LP ..... A-Z .... STECLP107 .... 1970 ... £8 ....£20 ....French

GARRITY, FREDDIE
Little Red Donkey .... 7" ..... Columbia .... DB8348................ 1968 ... £1.50 .....£4
Oliver In The Overworld .... LP ..... Starline .... SRS5019 .... 1970 ... £5 ....£12

GARVIN, REX
I Gotta Go Now .... 7" ..... Atlantic .... 584097................ 1967 ... £4 ....£8
Sock It To Them JB .... 7" ..... Atlantic .... 584028................ 1966 ... £2.50 .....£6

GARY & STU
Harlan Fare .... LP ..... Carnaby .... 6302012............. 1971 ... £20 ....£40

GARY & THE ARIELS
Say You Love Me .... 7" ..... Fontana .... TF476 .... 1964 ... £4 ....£8

GARY, BARRY
Fireball XL5 .... 7" ..... Melodisc .... 1591 .... 1964 ... £10 ....£20 ....PS

GARYBALDI
Astrolabia .... LP ..... Fonit .... 1973 ... £60 ....£120
Nuda .... LP ..... CGD .... 1972 ... £37.50 .....£75

GAS WORKS
Gas Works .... LP ..... Regal   SLRZ1036 .... 1973 ... £6 ....£15
                                                    Zonophone......

GASH
Young Man's Gash .... LP ..... Brain .... 0001014 .... 1972 ... £15 ....£30 ....German

GASKIN
End Of The World .... LP ..... Rondelet .... ABOUT4............. 1981 ... £6 ....£15
I'm No Fool .... 7" ..... Rondelet .... ROUND7.............. 1981 ... £2.50 .....£6
Mony Mony .... 7" ..... Rondelet .... ROUND21............ 1982 ... £2.50 .....£6

GASS
Dream Baby .... 7" ..... CBS .... 202647............... 1967 ... £2 ....£5
Gass .... LP ..... Polydor .... 2383022............. 1970 ... £6 ....£15
New Breed .... 7" ..... Parlophone ..... R5456 .... 1966 ... £7.50 .....£15
One Of These Days .... 7" ..... Parlophone ..... R5344 .... 1965 ... £4 ....£8

GASS COMPANY
Everybody Needs Love .... 7" ..... President .... PT170 .... 1968 ... £5 ....£10

GATES, DAVID
Happiest Man Alive .... 7" ..... Top Rank .... JAR504 .... 1960 ... £5 ....£10

GATES OF EDEN
In Your Love .... 7" ..... Pye .... 7N17252............. 1967 ... £5 ....£10
Mini Shirts .... 7" EP.. Pye .... PNV24181........... 1966 ... £12.50 .....£25 ....French
One To Seven .... 7" ..... Pye .... 7N17278............. 1967 ... £6 ....£12
Too Much On My Mind .... 7" ..... Pye .... 7N17195............. 1966 ... £5 ....£10

GATOR CREEK
Gator Creek .... LP ..... Mercury .... 6338035............. 1970 ... £4 ....£10

GAUCHOS
Gauchos Featuring Jim Doval .... LP ..... ABC .... (S)506 .... 1965 ... £6 ....£15 ....US

GAUGERS
Beware Of The Aberdonian .... LP ..... Topic .... 12TS284 .... 1976 ... £8 ....£20

GAUGHAN, DICK
Coppers And Brass .... LP ..... Topic .... 12TS315 .... 1977 ... £5 ....£12
Gaughan .... LP ..... Topic .... 12TS384 .... 1978 ... £5 ....£12
Kist O'Gold .... LP ..... Trailer .... LER2103 .... 1977 ... £5 ....£12
No More Forever .... LP ..... Trailer .... LER2072 .... 1972 ... £6 ....£15

GAUGHAN, DICK & ANDY IRVINE
Parallel Lines .... LP ..... Folk Freak ...... FF4007.............. 1982 ... £5 ....£12 ....German

GAVIN, FRANKIE & ALEC FINN
Frankie Gavin And Alec Finn .... LP ..... Shanachie ...... 29008.............. 1977 ... £5 ....£12 ....US

GAVIN, JIMMY
I Sit In My Window .... 7" ..... London .... HLU8478............ 1957 ... £20 ....£40

GAYDEN, MAC
McGavock Gayden .... LP ..... EMI............. EMA760 .... 1973 ... £8 ....£20

GAYE, MARVIN
Abraham, Martin And John .... 7" ..... Tamla Motown TMG734 .... 1970 ... £1.50 .....£4 ....chart single
Ain't That Peculiar .... 7" ..... Tamla Motown TMG539 .... 1965 ... £6 ....£12
Can I Get A Witness .... 7" ..... Stateside .... SS243 .... 1963 ... £12.50 .....£25
Chained .... 7" ..... Tamla Motown TMG676 .... 1968 ... £5 ....£10
Greatest Hits .... LP ..... Tamla Motown (S)TML11065 ..... 1968 ... £4 ....£10 ....chart LP
Hello Broadway .... LP ..... Tamla Motown TML11015 ..... 1965 ... £25 ....£50
How Sweet It Is .... LP ..... Tamla Motown TML11004 ..... 1965 ... £15 ....£30
How Sweet It Is .... 7" ..... Stateside .... SS360 .... 1964 ... £10 ....£20 ....chart single
I Heard It Through The Grapevine ...... 7" ..... Tamla Motown TMG686 .... 1969 ... £1.50 .....£4 ....chart single
I'll Be Doggone .... 7" ..... Tamla Motown TMG510 .... 1965 ... £15 ....£30

In The Groove	LP	Tamla Motown	(S)TML11091	1969	£6	£15	
Inner City Blues	7"	Tamla Motown	TMG817	1972	£1.50	£4	
Let's Get It On	7"	Tamla Motown	TMG868	1973	£7.50	£15	demo, PS
Little Darling	7"	Tamla Motown	TMG574	1966	£6	£12	chart single
Marvin Gaye	LP	Stateside	SL10100	1964	£25	£50	
Marvin Gaye	7" EP	Tamla Motown	TME2016	1966	£10	£20	
Marvin Gaye & His Girls	LP	Tamla Motown	(S)TML11123	1969	£5	£12	
Moods Of Marvin Gaye	LP	Tamla Motown	(S)TML11033	1966	£6	£15	
MPG	LP	Tamla Motown	(S)TML11119	1969	£6	£15	
On Stage Recorded Live	LP	Tamla	242	1963	£25	£50	US
One More Heartache	7"	Tamla Motown	TMG552	1966	£6	£12	
Originals From Marvin Gaye	7" EP	Tamla Motown	TME2019	1967	£10	£20	
Pretty Little Baby	7"	Tamla Motown	TMG524	1965	£6	£12	
Pride And Joy	7"	Oriole	CBA1846	1963	£25	£50	
Soulful Moods Of Marvin Gaye	LP	Tamla	221	1961	£50	£100	US
Stubborn Kind Of Fellow	7"	Oriole	CBA1803	1963	£25	£50	
Take This Heart Of Mine	7"	Tamla Motown	TMG563	1966	£6	£12	
That Stubborn Kind Of Fella	LP	Tamla	239	1963	£40	£80	US
That's The Way Love Is	LP	Tamla Motown	(S)TML11136	1970	£6	£15	
That's The Way Love Is	7"	Tamla Motown	TMG718	1969	£1.50	£4	
Too Busy Thinking About My Baby	7"	Tamla Motown	TMG705	1969	£1.50	£4	chart single
Tribute To The Great Nat King Cole	LP	Tamla Motown	STML11022	1966	£25	£50	stereo
Tribute To The Great Nat King Cole	LP	Tamla Motown	TML11022	1966	£15	£30	mono
Trouble Man	LP	Tamla Motown	STML11225	1973	£4	£10	
Trouble Man	7"	Tamla Motown	TMG846	1973	£1.50	£4	
Try It Baby	7"	Stateside	SS326	1964	£10	£20	
What's Going On	LP	Tamla Motown	STML11190	1971	£4	£10	
What's Going On	7"	Tamla Motown	TMG775	1971	£1.50	£4	
When I'm Alone I Cry	LP	Tamla	251	1964	£20	£40	US
You	7"	Tamla Motown	TMG640	1968	£2	£5	
Your Unchanged Love	7"	Tamla Motown	TMG618	1967	£4	£8	
You're A Wonderful One	7"	Stateside	SS284	1964	£10	£20	

GAYE, MARVIN & KIM WESTON

It Takes Two	7"	Tamla Motown	TMG590	1967	£4	£8	chart single
Take Two	LP	Tamla Motown	(S)TML11049	1967	£6	£15	
What Good Am I Without You	7"	Stateside	SS363	1964	£10	£20	

GAYE, MARVIN & MARY WELLS

Once Upon A Time	7"	Stateside	SS316	1964	£10	£20	chart single
Together	LP	Stateside	SL10097	1964	£25	£50	

GAYE, MARVIN & TAMMI TERRELL

Ain't No Mountain High Enough	7"	Tamla Motown	TMG611	1967	£2	£5	
Ain't Nothing Like The Real Thing	7"	Tamla Motown	TMG655	1968	£2	£5	chart single
Easy	LP	Tamla Motown	(S)TML11132	1970	£4	£10	
Good Lovin' Ain't Easy To Come By	7"	Tamla Motown	TMG697	1969	£1.50	£4	chart single
Greatest Hits	LP	Tamla Motown	(S)TML11153	1970	£4	£10	chart LP
If I Could Build My Whole World Around You	7"	Tamla Motown	TMG635	1967	£2	£5	chart single
Onion Song	7"	Tamla Motown	TMG715	1969	£1.50	£4	chart single
United	LP	Tamla Motown	(S)TML11062	1968	£6	£15	
You Ain't Livin' Till You're Lovin'	7"	Tamla Motown	TMG681	1969	£1.50	£4	chart single
Your Precious Love	7"	Tamla Motown	TMG625	1967	£2	£5	
You're All I Need To Get By	LP	Tamla Motown	(S)TML11084	1968	£5	£12	
You're All I Need To Get By	7"	Tamla Motown	TMG668	1968	£1.50	£4	chart single

GAYLADS

Go Away	7"	Blue Cat	BS110	1968	£4	£8	Soul Vendors B side
Goodbye Daddy	7"	Island	WI281	1966	£5	£10	
I'm Free	7"	Studio One	SO2038	1968	£6	£12	Soul Vendors B side
It's Hard To Confess	7"	Doctor Bird	DB1124	1968	£5	£10	
Lady With The Red Dress On	7"	Doctor Bird	DB1014	1966	£5	£10	
Looking For A Girl	7"	Fab	FAB62	1968	£4	£8	
Love Me With All Your Heart	7"	Studio One	SO2017	1967	£6	£12	
No Good Girl	7"	Island	WI3025	1967	£5	£10	
Put On Your Style	7"	Rio	R125	1967	£4	£8	Soul Brothers B side
Rock Steady	LP	Coxsone	CSL8005	1967	£50	£100	
Same Things	7"	Upsetter	US323	1969	£2.50	£6	
She Want It	7"	Doctor Bird	DB1145	1968	£5	£10	
Stop Making Love	7"	Island	WI3002	1966	£5	£10	
Sunshine Golden 18	LP	Coxsone	CSL8006	1967	£50	£100	
Tears From My Eyes	7"	Studio One	SO2002	1967	£6	£12	
There'll Come A Day	7"	R&B	JB159	1964	£5	£10	Billy Cooke B side
Whap Whap	7"	R&B	JB165	1964	£5	£10	
You Had Your Chance	7"	Trojan	TR688	1969	£2.50	£6	
You Should Never Do That	7"	Doctor Bird	DB1031	1966	£5	£10	Winston Stewart B side
You'll Never Leave Him	7"	Island	WI291	1966	£5	£10	

GAYLETTS

I Like Your World	7"	Island	WI3141	1968	£5	£10	
If You Can't Be Good	7"	Big Shot	BI502	1968	£4	£8	
Silent River Runs Deep	7"	Island	WI3129	1968	£5	£10	
Son Of A Preacher Man	7"	Big Shot	BI516	1969	£2.50	£6	
Son Of A Preacher Man	7"	London	HLJ10302	1970	£1.50	£4	

GAYLORDS

He's A Good Face	7"	Columbia	DB7805	1966	£10	£20	

GAYLORDS (2)
Chipmunk Ska	7"	Island	WI269	1966	£5	£10	

GAYNAIR, WILTON
Blue Bogey	LP	Tempo	TAP25	1960	£5	£12	

GAYNOR, ROSEMARY
Ain't That A Shame	7"	Columbia	SCM5196	1955	£1.50	£4	

GAYTEN, PAUL
Hunch	7"	London	HLM8998	1959	£40	£80	

G-CLEFS
Girl Has To Know	7"	London	HLU9530	1962	£5	£10	
I Understand	7"	London	HLU9433	1961	£2.50	£6	chart single
Ka Ding Dong	7"	Columbia	DB3851	1956	£60	£120	
Make Up Your Mind	7"	London	HLU9563	1962	£5	£10	

GEDDES AXE
Return Of The Gods	7"	ACS	ACS1	1981	£4	£8	
Sharpen Your Wits	7"	Steel City	AXE1	1982	£1.50	£4	

GEE, MATTHEW
Jazz By Gee	LP	London	LTZU15075	1957	£10	£25	

GEESIN, RON
As He Stands	LP	Ron	RON28	1973	£6	£15	
Electrosound	LP	KPM	1102	1972	£4	£10	
Electrosound Vol.2	LP	KPM	KPM1154	1975	£4	£10	
Mr.Mayor Stamp Your Foot	7" EP.	private	RRG319/320	1965	£25	£50	
Patrons	LP	Ron	RON31	1975	£6	£15	
Raise Of The Eyebrows	LP	Transatlantic	TRA161	1967	£8	£20	
Right Through	LP	Ron	RON323	1979	£6	£15	

GEESIN, RON & ROGER WATERS
Body	LP	Harvest	SHSP4008	1970	£4	£10	

GELLER, HERB
Herb Geller	LP	Emarcy	EJL1268	1958	£8	£20	

GEMINI
Space Walk	7"	Columbia	DB7638	1965	£7.50	£15	

GENE & DEBBE
Go With Me	7"	London	HLE10165	1967	£1.50	£4	
Lovin' Season	7"	London	HLE10203	1968	£1.50	£4	
Playboy	7"	London	HLE10179	1968	£2.50	£6	

GENE & EUNICE
Bom Bom Lulu	7"	Vogue	V9136	1959	£12.50	£25	
Doodle Doodle Do	7"	Vogue	V9083	1957	£15	£30	
I Gotta Go Home	7"	Vogue	V9062	1956	£25	£50	
I Mean Love	7"	Vogue	V9106	1958	£15	£30	
Let's Get Together	7"	Vogue	V9071	1957	£15	£30	
Poco Loco	7"	London	HL8956	1959	£10	£20	
This Is My Story	7"	Vogue	V9066	1957	£30	£60	
Vow	7"	Vogue	V9126	1958	£10	£20	

GENE LOVES JEZEBEL
Bruises	7"	Situation 2	SIT24	1983	£1.50	£4	
Bruises	12"	Situation 2	SIT24T	1983		£8	
Cow	12"	Situation 2	SIT36T	1985	£2.50	£6	with poster
Discover	LP	Beggars Banquet	BEG73	1986	£5	£12	with Glad To Be Alive LP
Screaming	7"	Situation 2	SIT20	1982	£1.50	£4	
Screaming	12"	Situation 2	SIT20T	1982		£8	
Shaving My Neck	12"	Situation 2	SIT18T	1982	£8	£20	
Sweetest Thing	7"	Beggars Banquet	BEG156	1986	£2	£5	with cassette (161F)

GENERAL HUMBERT
General Humbert	LP	Dolphin	DOLM50115	1976	£10	£25	Irish
General Humbert II	LP	Gael Linn	CEF095	1982	£5	£12	Irish

GENERATION X
Wild Youth	7"	Chrysalis	CHS2189	1977	£6	£12	mispressed B-side, plays 'No No No'

GENESIS

Genesis' first LP was produced by Jonathan King - an unlikely choice f, or a determinedly progressive group, except that King and Genesis were all ex-pupils of Charterhouse. The record has been reissued several times - the first being as early as 1973 - but the original "From Genesis To Revelation" is quite scarce. Even more so are the early singles, of which "Happy The Man", "I Know What I Like", and "The Carpet Crawlers" all have non-album B sides. The albums "Trespass" and "Nursery Cryme" are still available, of course, but their inclusion here refers to the original pressings with their deep pink Charisma labels.

3 X 3	7" EP.	Charisma	GEN1	1982	£2	£5	pic disc
Carpet Crawlers	7"	Charisma	CB251	1975	£7.50	£15	
Counting Out Time	7"	Charisma	CB238	1974	£7.50	£15	
Firth Of Fifth	7"	Genesis Information	GI01	1983	£2	£5	flexi
Foxtrot/Selling England By The Pound	LP	Charisma	CGS103	1975	£37.50	£75	boxed, poster
From Genesis To Revelation	LP	Decca	LK4990	1969	£40	£80	mono

317

Title	Format	Label	Catalog	Year			Notes
From Genesis To Revelation	LP	Decca	SKL4990	1969	£15	£30	stereo
Happy The Man	7"	Charisma	CB181	1972	£25	£50	
Happy The Man	7"	Charisma	CB181	1972	£80	£160	PS
I Know What I Like	7"	Charisma	CB224	1974	£2	£5	chart single
Illegal Alien	7"	Charisma	ALS1	1984	£2	£5	shaped pic disc
In The Beginning	LP	Decca	SKL4990	1974	£8	£20	
Knife	7"	Charisma	CB152	1971	£25	£50	
Knife	7"	Charisma	CB152	1971	£100	£200	PS
Looking For Someone	7"	Charisma	GS1	1970	£150	£250	
Man On The Corner	7"	Charisma	CB393	1982	£2.50	£6	PS
Nursery Cryme	LP	Charisma	CAS1052	1971	£6	£15	dark pink label
Nursery Cryme	LP	Charisma	CAS1052	1972	£15	£30	with tour label
Paperlate	7"	Charisma	JBGEN1	1982	£1.50	£4	juke box issue
Silent Sun	7"	Decca	F12735	1968	£50	£100	
That's All	7"	Charisma/ Virgin	TATA1	1983	£2	£5	pic disc
Tonight Tonight Tonight	CD-s	Virgin	CDEP1	1987	£15	£30	with Invisible Touch
Trespass	LP	Charisma	CAS1020	1970	£6	£15	dark pink label
Trespass/Nursery Cryme	LP	Charisma	CGS102	1975	£37.50	£75	boxed, poster
Trick Of The Tail	LP	Mobile Fidelity	MFSL1062	1981	£8	£20	US audiophile
Trick Of The Tail	7"	Charisma	CB277	1976	£1.50	£4	juke box issue, purple label
Twilight Alehouse	7"	Charisma	no number	1975	£10	£20	flexi
When The Sour Turns To Sweet	LP	Metal Masters	MACHMP4	1986	£4	£10	pic disc
Where The Sour Turns To Sweet	7"	Decca	F12949	1969	£50	£100	
Winter's Tale	7"	Decca	F12775	1968	£50	£100	

GENESIS (2)
The recordings of this not especially collectable group are included here mainly to make it clear that they have no connection with those of the much better known Genesis.

In The Beginning	LP	Mercury	SR61175	1968	£4	£10	US

GENGHIS KHAN

Love You	7"	Wabbit	WAB61/63	1983	£2.50	£6	double

GENTILES

Goodbye Baby	7"	Pye	7N17530	1968	£4	£8	

GENTLE GIANT
Gentle Giant's intricately constructed and faultlessly performed music seems to epitomise what the Vertigo label was all about. The album "Octopus", in particular, stands as something of a landmark within the progressive rock genre. One can hear the band, on successive albums, learning how to create music that requires a high degree of skill for its execution and an even higher degree of inventiveness for its original creation. At the same time, the music is perfectly accessible, if a little hard to dance to! Gentle Giant's ancestor, by the way, was Simon Dupree and the Big Sound, both groups revolving around the Shulman brothers, although they have little in common musically.

Acquiring The Taste	LP	Vertigo	6360041	1971	£8	£20	spiral label
Gentle Giant	LP	Vertigo	6360020	1970	£8	£20	spiral label
In A Glass House	LP	WWA	WWA002	1973	£8	£20	
Octopus	LP	Vertigo	6360080	1972	£6	£15	spiral label
Power And The Glory	LP	WWA	WWA010	1974	£6	£15	
Three Friends	LP	Vertigo	6360070	1972	£8	£20	spiral label

GENTLE INFLUENCE

Always Be A Part Of My Living	7"	Pye	7N17743	1969	£2.50	£6	
Never Trust In Tomorrow	7"	Pye	7N17666	1969	£2.50	£6	

GENTLE, JOHNNY

After My Laughter Came Tears	7"	Philips	PB1069	1960	£1.50	£4	
Gentle Touch	7" EP	Philips	BBE12345	1959	£7.50	£15	
Milk From The Coconut	7"	Philips	PB945	1959	£1.50	£4	
This Friendly World	7"	Philips	PB988	1960	£1.50	£4	
Wendy	7"	Philips	PB908	1959	£1.50	£4	

GENTLE PEOPLE

It's Too Late	7"	Columbia	DB8276	1967	£2	£5	

GENTLE, TIM & THE GENTLEMEN

Without You	7"	Oriole	CB1988	1965	£4	£8	

GENTLEMEN & THEIR LADIES

Like Her	7"	Pye	7N25731	1976	£1.50	£4	

GENTRY, BOBBIE

Ode To Billy Joe	7"	Capitol	CL15511	1967	£1.50	£4	chart single

GENTRYS

Brown Paper Sack	7"	MGM	MGM1296	1966	£5	£10	
Everyday I Have To Cry	7"	MGM	MGM1312	1966	£2	£5	
Gentrys	LP	MGM	GAS127	1966	£8	£20	US
Gentrys	LP	Sun	117	1970	£6	£15	US
Keep On Dancing	LP	MGM	(S)E4336	1965	£8	£20	US
Keep On Dancing	7"	MGM	MGM1284	1965	£2	£5	
Keep On Dancing	7" EP	MGM	63628	1965	£7.50	£15	French
Time	LP	MGM	(S)E4346	1966	£8	£20	US

GENTS

Faker	7"	Posh	POSH001	1981	£1.50	£4	

GEORDIE

Don't Be Fooled By The Name	LP	EMI	EMA764	1974	£5	£12	
Hope You Like It	LP	EMI	EMC3001	1973	£4	£10	
Save The World	LP	EMI	EMC3134	1976	£6	£15	

GEORGE & BEN

Title	Format	Label	Cat. No.	Year			Notes
Boa Constrictions Natural Vine	LP	Vanguard		1968	£6	£15	

GEORGE, BARBARA

Title	Format	Label	Cat. No.	Year			Notes
I Know	7"	London	HL9513	1962	£4	£8	
I Know You Don't Love Me Anymore	LP	A.F.O.	5001	1962	£30	£60	US
Send For Me	7"	Sue	WI316	1964	£7.50	£15	

GEORGE, LLOYD

Title	Format	Label	Cat. No.	Year			Notes
Sing Real Loud	7"	London	HLP9562	1962	£10	£20	

GEORGETTES

Title	Format	Label	Cat. No.	Year			Notes
Down By The River	7"	Pye	7N25058	1960	£2.50	£6	
Love Like A Fool	7"	London	HL8548	1958	£10	£20	

GEORGIA TOM

Title	Format	Label	Cat. No.	Year			Notes
Georgia Tom And Friends	LP	Riverside	RLP8803	196-	£6	£15	

GEORGIE & THE MONARCHS

The rare single by Georgie and The Monarchs features the recording debut of Van Morrison, who played saxophone for the band.

Title	Format	Label	Cat. No.	Year			Notes
Boo-Zooh	7"	CBS	1307	1963	£15	£30	.PS, German or Dutch

GERMS

Title	Format	Label	Cat. No.	Year			Notes
Forming	7"	What	WHAT01	1977	£5	£10	
Germicide - Live At The Whiskey	LP	Bomp	SCALP001A	1977	£5	£12	
Germicide - Live At The Whiskey	LP	Mohawk	SCALP001A	1981	£4	£10	
GI	LP	Slash	SR103	1981	£5	£12	
Lexicon Devil	7"	Slash	SLA002	1978	£25	£50	various different sleeves
What We Do Is Secret	12"	Slash	SREP108	1981	£5	£12	

GERONIMO BLACK

Title	Format	Label	Cat. No.	Year			Notes
Geronimo Black	LP	MCA	MCF2683	1974	£5	£12	

GERRARD, DENNY

Title	Format	Label	Cat. No.	Year			Notes
Gerrard	LP	Nova	SDN10	1970	£15	£30	with High Tide

GERRY & THE HOLOGRAMS

Here is a record to file next to the Stiff album "The Wit And Wisdom Of Ronald Reagan". The LP is completely silent. It is impossible to tell what, if anything, is recorded on the single by Gerry & The Holograms. For the record is painted and glued into its sleeve, rendering it completely unplayable. As concepts go, this one has a kind of anarchic brilliance about it!

Title	Format	Label	Cat. No.	Year			Notes
Emperor's New Music	7"	Absurd	A5	1979	£4	£8	unplayable record

GERRY & THE PACEMAKERS

Title	Format	Label	Cat. No.	Year			Notes
Don't Let The Sun Catch You Crying	LP	Laurie	LLP/SLP2024	1964	£8	£20	US
Don't Let The Sun Catch You Crying	7"	Columbia	DB7268	1964	£1.50	£4	chart single
Don't Let The Sun Catch You Crying	7" EP	Columbia	ESRF1549	1964	£7.50	£15	French
Don't Let The Sun Catch You Crying	7" EP	Columbia	SEG8346	1964	£5	£10	
Ferry Cross The Mersey	7"	Columbia	33SX1693/SCX3544	1965	£8	£20	chart LP
Ferry Cross The Mersey	7"	Columbia	DB7437	1964	£1.50	£4	chart single
Ferry Cross The Mersey	7" EP	Columbia	ESRF1637	1964	£7.50	£15	French
Gerry In California	7" EP	Columbia	SEG8388	1965	£6	£12	
Girl On A Swing	LP	Laurie	LLP/SLP2037	1965	£8	£20	US
Girl On The Swing	7"	Columbia	DB8044	1966	£2	£5	
Greatest Hits	LP	Laurie	LLP/SLP2031	1965	£6	£15	US
Hits From Ferry Cross The Mersey	7" EP	Columbia	SEG8397	1965	£6	£12	
How Do You Do It	7"	Columbia	DB4987	1963	£1.50	£4	chart single
How Do You Do It	7" EP	Columbia	ESDF1490	1963	£6	£12	French
How Do You Do It	7" EP	Columbia	SEG8257	1963	£5	£10	
How Do You Like It	LP	Columbia	33SX1546	1963	£8	£20	chart LP, mono
How Do You Like It	LP	Columbia	SCX3492	1963	£10	£25	stereo
I Like It	7"	Columbia	DB7041	1963	£1.50	£4	chart single
I'll Be There	LP	Laurie	LLP/SLP2030	1964	£8	£20	US
I'll Be There	7"	Columbia	DB7504	1965	£1.50	£4	chart single
I'm The One	7"	Columbia	DB7189	1964	£1.50	£4	chart single
I'm The One	7" EP	Columbia	SEG8311	1964	£5	£10	
It's Gonna Be Alright	7"	Columbia	DB7353	1964	£1.50	£4	chart single
It's Gonna Be Alright	7" EP	Columbia	SEG8367	1964	£6	£12	
La La La	7"	Columbia	DB7835	1966	£2	£5	
Remember	7"	DJM	DJS298	1974	£2	£5	
Rip It Up	7" EP	Columbia	SEG8426	1965	£7.50	£15	
Second Album	LP	Laurie	LLP/SLP2027	1964	£8	£20	US
Walk Hand In Hand	7"	Columbia	DB7738	1965	£1.50	£4	chart single
You'll Never Walk Alone	LP	MFP	MFP1153	1967	£4	£10	
You'll Never Walk Alone	LP	Regal		196-	£6	£15	export
You'll Never Walk Alone	7"	Columbia	DB7126	1963	£1.50	£4	chart single
You'll Never Walk Alone	7" EP	Columbia	ESRF1446	1963	£7.50	£15	French
You'll Never Walk Alone	7" EP	Columbia	SEG8295	1963	£6	£12	

GERVASE

Title	Format	Label	Cat. No.	Year			Notes
Pepper Grinder	7"	Decca	F12822	1968	£4	£8	

GESTURES

Title	Format	Label	Cat. No.	Year			Notes
Run Run Run	7"	Stateside	SS379	1965	£6	£12	

GETZ, STAN

Title	Format	Label	Cat. No.	Year			Notes
At Storyville	10" LP	Vogue	LDE089	1954	£20	£40	
At Storyville Vol.1	LP	Vogue	LAE12158	1959	£8	£20	
At Storyville Vol.2	LP	Vogue	LAE12199	1959	£8	£20	
At The Opera House	LP	Columbia	33CX10127	1958	£8	£20	with J.J.Johnson

Title		Label	Cat No	Year			
At The Shrine No.1	LP	Columbia	33CX10000	1955	£15	£30	
At The Shrine No.2	LP	Columbia	33CX10001	1955	£15	£30	
Big Band Bossa Nova	LP	Verve	VLP9024	1963	£4	£10	. with Gary McFarland
Focus	LP	HMV	CLP1577	1962	£4	£10	
Getz Au Go Go	LP	Verve	VLP9081	1964	£4	£10	
Girl From Ipanema	7"	Verve	VS520	1964	£1.50	£4	with Astrud
							& Joao Gilberto
Greatest Hits	LP	Stateside	SL10161	1966	£4	£10	
Imported From Europe	LP	HMV	CLP1351	1960	£6	£15	
Interpretations	LP	Columbia	33CX10057	1956	£20	£40	
Jazz Samba	LP	Verve	(S)VLP9013	1962	£4	£10	with Charlie Byrd
Jazz Samba Encore	LP	Verve	(S)VLP9038	1963	£4	£10	with Luiz Bonfa
Soft Swing	LP	HMV	CLP1320	1960	£6	£15	
Stan Getz	LP	Columbia	33CX10082	1957	£8	£20	
Stan Getz Plays	10" LP	Esquire	20007	1953	£20	£40	
Stan Getz Quartet	LP	Esquire	32011	1956	£15	£30	
Stan Getz Quartet	10" LP	Vogue	LDE147	1955	£15	£30	
Stan Meets Chet	LP	HMV	CLP1292	1959	£10	£25	with Chet Baker
Steamer	LP	HMV	CLP1276	1959	£8	£20	

GHERKIN, AMOS QUARTET
Theme From An Unmade Silent Movie	7"	Parlophone	R5872	1970	£1.50	£4	

GHEZZI, WESS & DORI
Fallin'	7"	Bradleys	BRAD7515	1975	£2	£5	

GHOST
I've Got To Get To Know You	7"	Gemini	GMS014	1970	£7.50	£15	
When You're Dead	7"	Gemini	GMS007	1969	£10	£20	
When You're Dead - One Second	LP	Gemini	GME1004	1970	£50	£100	sleeve
							pictured in Guide

GHOST DANCE
Gathering Dust	LP	Karbon	KARXL303	1986	£4	£10	
Grip Of Love	7"	Karbon	KAR604	1986	£2	£5	
Grip Of Love	12"	Karbon	KAR604T	1986	£2.50	£6	
Heart Full Of Soul	7"	Karbon	KAR606	1986	£2.50	£6	promo
Heart Full Of Soul	12"	Karbon	KAR606T	1986	£2.50	£6	
River Of No Return	12"	Karbon	KAR602T	1986	£2.50	£6	
When I Call	7"	Karbon	KAR608	1987	£2.50	£6	promo

GHOULS
Dracula's Deuce	LP	Capitol	(S)T2215	1965	£5	£12	US

GIANT CRAB
Cool It Helios	LP	Uni	73057	1969	£6	£15	
Giant Crab Comes Forth	LP	Uni	73037	1968	£6	£15	US
Hot Line Conversation	7"	Uni	UN509	1968	£1.50	£4	

GIANT SUNFLOWER
Big Apple	7"	CBS	2805	1967	£5	£10	
Mark Twain	7"	CBS	3033	1967	£5	£10	

GIANTS
Live	LP	Polydor	237626	1964	£15	£30	German

GIBB, BARRY
I'll Kiss Your Memory	7"	Polydor	2058030	1970	£1.50	£4	

GIBB, MAURICE
Railroad	7"	Polydor	2058013	1970	£1.50	£4	
Sing A Rude Song	LP	Polydor		1970	£8	£20	

GIBB, ROBIN
August October	7"	Polydor	56371	1970	£1.50	£4	chart single
One Million Years	7"	Polydor	56368	1969	£1.50	£4	
Robin's Reign	LP	Polydor	583085	1970	£4	£10	
Saved By The Bell	7"	Polydor	56337	1969	£1.50	£4	chart single
Saved By The Bell/Alexandria Good	7"	Polydor	BM56337	1969	£6	£12	
Time							

GIBBONS, STEVE
Short Stories	LP	Wizard	SWZA5501	1971	£15	£30	

GIBBS, GEORGIA
Arrivederci Roma	7"	Mercury	7MT210	1958	£2	£5	
Balling The Jack	7"	Vogue Coral	Q72088	1955	£5	£10	
Great Balls Of Fire	7"	RCA	RCA1029	1958	£6	£12	
Happiness Street	7" EP	Mercury	MEP9505	1956	£2.50	£6	
Her Nibbs Miss Gibbs	10" LP	Mercury	MPT7511	1957	£10	£25	
Hucklebuck	7"	Columbia	DB4259	1959	£2	£5	
Hula Hoop Song	7"	Columbia	DB4201	1958	£1.50	£4	
I'll Be Seeing You	7" EP	Mercury	EP13265	1955	£2	£5	
I'll Know	7"	Vogue Coral	Q72182	1956	£2.50	£6	
Silent Lips	7" EP	Mercury	MEP9516	1957	£6	£12	
Sings The Oldies	10" LP	Mercury	MPT7500	1956	£10	£25	
Stroll That Stole My Heart	7"	London	HLP9098	1960	£2	£5	
Sugar Candy	7"	RCA	RCA1011	1957	£1.50	£4	
Swinging With Her Nibbs	LP	Mercury	MPL6508	1957	£6	£15	

GIBBS, MICHAEL

Just Ahead	LP	Polydor	2683011	1972	£15	£30	double
Michael Gibbs	LP	Deram	SML1063	1970	£25	£50	
Nairam	7"	Bronze	BRO21	1975	£1.50	£4	
Tanglewood '63	LP	Deram	SML1087	1971	£15	£30	

GIBBS, SIR

People Grudgeful	7"	Amalgamated	AMG822	1968	£4	£8	

GIBBS, TERRY

Launching A New Sound In Music	LP	Mercury	MMC14018	1959	£5	£12	
Swing Is Here	LP	HMV	CLP1394/CSD1324	1960	£5	£12	
Swingin' With Terry Gibbs	LP	Emarcy	EJL1263	1957	£6	£15	
Terry Gibbs	LP	Emarcy	EJL1269	1958	£6	£15	
Terry Gibbs	LP	Emarcy	EJT752	1957	£6	£15	
Terry Gibbs	LP	Vogue Coral	LVA9013	1956	£6	£15	
Terry Gibbs	10" LP	Vogue Coral	LRA10035	1955	£15	£30	

GIBSON, DEBBIE

Electric Youth	LP	WEA	WX231Y	1988	£6	£15	yellow vinyl, poster
Electric Youth	12"	WEA	A8919TP	1989	£2.50	£6	pic disc
Foolish Beat	12"	WEA	A9059TP	1988	£2.50	£6	pic disc
Lost In Your Eyes	12"	WEA	A8970TP	1989	£2.50	£6	pic disc
Only In My Dreams	7"	WEA	A9322P	1988	£1.50	£4	pic disc
Only In My Dreams	7"	WEA	A9322W	1988	£1.50	£4	poster PS
Only In My Dreams	12"	Atlantic	A9322TP	1987	£8	£20	pic disc
Only In My Dreams	12"	WEA	A9322T	1987	£15	£30	
Out Of The Blue	CD-s	Atlantic	A9091CD	1988	£3	£8	
Out Of The Blue	12"	WEA	A9091T	1988	£4	£10	with poster
Shake Your Love	12"	WEA	A9187T	1987	£2.50	£6	with poster
Shake Your Love	12"	WEA	A9187TP	1987	£6	£15	pic disc
We Could Be Together	7"	WEA	A8896P	1989	£1.50	£4	pic disc

GIBSON, DON

Big Hearted Me	7"	RCA	RCA1158	1959	£1.50	£4	
Blue And Lonesome	7" EP	RCA	RCX1050	1960	£5	£10	
Blue Blue Day	7"	RCA	RCA1073	1958	£1.50	£4	
Don't Tell Me Your Trouble	7"	RCA	RCA1150	1959	£1.50	£4	
Give Myself A Party	7"	RCA	RCA1098	1958	£1.50	£4	
God Walks These Hills	LP	RCA	RD7641	1964	£5	£12	
I Wrote A Song	LP	RCA	RD/SF7576	1963	£5	£12	
Lonesome Number One	7"	RCA	RCA1272	1962	£1.50	£4	chart single
Look Who's Blue	LP	RCA	LPM/LSP2184	1960	£6	£15	US
Look Who's Blue	7" EP	RCA	RCX213	1962	£5	£10	
May You Never Be Alone	7" EP	RCA	RCX7122	1963	£5	£10	
No One Stands Alone	LP	RCA	LPM/LSP1918	1959	£6	£15	US
Oh Lonesome Me	LP	RCA	LPM1743	1958	£8	£20	US
Oh Lonesome Me	7"	RCA	RCA1056	1958	£1.50	£4	
Sea Of Heartbreak	7"	RCA	RCA1243	1961	£1.50	£4	chart single
Some Favourites Of Mine	LP	RCA	RD/SF7506	1962	£5	£12	
Songs By Don Gibson	LP	Lion	70069	1958	£15	£30	US
Stranger To Me	7"	RCA	RCA1110	1959	£1.50	£4	
Sweet Dreams	LP	RCA	LPM/LSP2269	1960	£6	£15	US
Sweet Dreams	7"	MGM	SP1177	1956	£40	£80	
That Gibson Boy	LP	RCA	RD27158	1960	£5	£12	
That Gibson Boy	7" EP	RCA	RCX214	1962	£5	£10	

GIBSON, HENRY

Grass Menagerie	LP	Epic	15120	1969	£5	£12	US

GIBSON, JODY & THE MULESKINNERS

Kissin' Time	7"	Parlophone	R4579	1959	£1.50	£4	
So You Think You've Got Troubles	7"	Parlophone	R4645	1960	£1.50	£4	

GIBSON, STEVE & THE RED CAPS

Silhouettes	7"	HMV	POP417	1957	£20	£40	
Steve Gibson & The Red Caps	10" LP	Mercury	MG25116	195-	£60	£120	US

GIBSON, WAYNE

Come On Let's Go	7"	Decca	F11800	1964	£5	£10	
Ding Dong The Witch Is Dead	7"	Parlophone	R5357	1965	£7.50	£15	
For No One	7"	Columbia	DB7998	1966	£2.50	£6	
Kelly	7"	Pye	7N15680	1964	£2.50	£6	chart single
Linda Lu	7"	Decca	F11713	1963	£5	£10	
One Little Smile	7"	Columbia	DB7683	1965	£10	£20	
Portland Town	7"	Pye	7N15798	1965	£4	£8	
Under My Thumb	7"	Columbia	DB7911	1966	£6	£12	

GIBSONS

Any Time	7"	CBS	202015	1965	£1.50	£4	
Come Summertime	7"	CBS	202063	1966	£1.50	£4	
Magic Book	7"	Deram	DM119	1967	£1.50	£4	
Ode To A Doll's House	7"	Major Minor	MM547	1968	£2	£5	
Two Kinds Of Lovers	7"	Deram	DM103	1966	£1.50	£4	

GIDIAN

Feeling	7"	Columbia	DB8041	1966	£4	£8	
Fight For Your Love	7"	Columbia	DB7916	1966	£2.50	£6	
Try Me Out	7"	Columbia	DB7826	1966	£7.50	£15	

GIFT
Blue Apple	LP	Nova	8002	1974	£5	£12	German
Gift	LP	Telefunken	SLE14680	1972	£8	£20	German

GIFTED CHILDREN
Painting By Numbers	7"	Whaam!	WHAAM001	1981	£10	£20

GIGUERE, RUSS
Hexagram II	LP	Warner Bros	WS1910	1971	£6	£15	US

GIGYMEN
Gigymen	LP	Spaceward	3S3/EDENLP76	1975	£8	£20

GILA
Bury My Heart At Wounded Knee	LP	Warner Bros	46234	1973	£5	£12	German
Gila	LP	BASF	20211096	1971	£15	£30	German

GILBERT
Disappear	7"	CBS	3089	1967	£4	£8
Mister Moody's Garden	7"	Major Minor	MM613	1969	£4	£8
What Can I Do	7"	CBS	3399	1968	£4	£8

GILBERT & LEWIS
Ends With The Sea	7"	4AD	AD106	1981	£1.50	£4

GILBERTO, ASTRUD
Astrud Gilberto Album	LP	Verve	SVLP9087	1969	£4	£10
Beach Samba	LP	Verve	SVLP9187	1968	£4	£10
I Haven't Got Anything Better To Do	LP	Verve	SVLP9242	1969	£4	£10
Shadow Of Your Smile	LP	Verve	SVLP9107	1970	£4	£10
Windy	LP	Verve	SVLP9233	1969	£4	£10

GILES, GILES & FRIPP
Although this is the group that evolved into King Crimson, little of the music on "Cheerful Insanity" sounds much like that produced by any King Crimson line-up. Instead, much of it is of the novelty-song variety, with flat "English" vocals conveying lyrics that aim to be whimsical, but which mostly sound embarassing. The record is certainly distinctive, however, and in places Robert Fripp does reveal himself to be a highly talented guitarist, even if conveying no hint that he would ever become a major influence within seventies rock.

Cheerful Insanity Of Giles, Giles And Fripp	LP	Deram	DML/SML1022	1968	£20	£40
Cheerful Insanity Of Giles, Giles And Fripp	LP	Deram	SPA423	1970	£15	£30
One In A Million	7"	Deram	DM188	1968	£17.50	£35
Thursday Morning	7"	Deram	DM210	1968	£17.50	£35

GILFELLON, TOM
In The Middle Of The Tune	LP	Topic	12TS282	1976	£8	£20
Loving Mad Tom	LP	Trailer	LER2079	1972	£6	£15

GILGAMESH
Gilgamesh	LP	Caroline	CA2007	1975	£5	£12

GILKYSON, TERRY & THE EASYRIDERS
Golden Minutes Of Folk Music	10" LP	Brunswick	LA8618	1953	£6	£15
Lonesome Rider	7" EP	Fontana	TFE17327	1960	£2.50	£6
Marianne	7"	Philips	JK1007	1958	£4	£8
Remember The Alamo	LP	London	HAR2323	1961	£5	£12
Rolling	LP	London	HAR2301/SAHR6111	1961	£5	£12
Rolling	7" EP	London	RER1333	1961	£4	£8
Strolling Blues	7" EP	Fontana	TFE17326	1960	£2.50	£6

GILLAN
Child In Time	LP	Oyster	2490136	1976	£4	£10	
Child In Time	LP	Polydor	ACBR261	1976	£4	£10	
Glory Road	LP	Virgin	V2171	1980	£4	£10	with LP For Gillan Fans Only
Living For The City	7"	Virgin	VSY519	1982	£2	£5	pic disc
Mad Elaine	7"	Island	WIP6423	1978	£1.50	£4	
Magic	LP	Virgin	VP2238	1982	£4	£10	pic disc

GILLES ZEITSCHIFF
Gilles Zeitschiff	LP	Kosmische	KM58012	1974	£6	£15	German

GILLESPIE, DANA
Andy Warhol	7"	RCA	RCA2446	1974	£2	£5
Box Of Surprises	LP	Decca	SKL5012	1969	£6	£15
Donna Donna	7"	Pye	7N15872	1965	£2.50	£6
Pay You Back With Interest	7"	Pye	7N17280	1967	£2.50	£6
Thank You Boy	7"	Pye	7N15962	1965	£2.50	£6
You Gotta Know My Mind	7"	Decca	F12847	1968	£2	£5

GILLESPIE, DARLENE
Darlene Of The Teens	LP	Disneyland	WDL3010		£10	£25	US

GILLESPIE, DIZZY
Always	7" EP	Verve	VRE5022	1966	£2	£5	
Be Bop	7" EP	Philips	BE12552	1964	£2	£5	
Birks Works	7" EP	Columbia	SEB10096	1957	£2	£5	
Champ	7" EP	Vogue	EPV1094	1956	£2	£5	
Diz And Don	7" EP	MGM	MGMEP579	1957	£2	£5	..2 tracks by Don Byas
Diz 'n' Bird In Concert	7" EP	Vogue	LAE12252	1961	£4	£10	with Charlie Parker

Dizzy Atmosphere	LP	London	LTZU15121	1958	£8	£20	
Dizzy Gillespie	LP	RCA	RD7827	1965	£4	£10	
Dizzy Gillespie	7" EP	Vogue	EPV1022	1955	£2	£5	
Dizzy Gillespie	7" EP	Vogue	EPV1078	1956	£2	£5	
Dizzy Gillespie	10" LP	Columbia	33C9030	1957	£20	£40	
Dizzy Gillespie And His Orchestra	LP	Columbia	33CX10002	1955	£15	£30	
Dizzy Gillespie And His Orchestra	7" EP	Vogue	EPV1157	1956	£2	£5	
Dizzy Gillespie And His Orchestra	7" EP	Vogue	EPV1158	1956	£2	£5	
Dizzy Gillespie And His Orchestra	10" LP	HMV	DLP1047	1954	£20	£40	
Dizzy Gillespie And His Orchestra	10" LP	Vogue	LDE076	1954	£20	£40	
Dizzy Gillespie And His Orchestra	10" LP	Vogue	LDE135	1955	£20	£40	
Dizzy Gillespie And Stuff Smith	LP	HMV	CLP1291	1959	£8	£20	
Dizzy Gillespie Plays	10" LP	Vogue	LDE017	1953	£20	£40	
Dizzy Gillespie Plays - Johnny Richards Conducts	10" LP	Vogue	LDE033	1953	£20	£40	
Dizzy Gillespie With Strings	7" EP	Vogue	EPV1049	1955	£2	£5	
Dizzy Gillespie-Stan Getz Sextet	10" LP	Columbia	33C9027	1956	£40	£80	
Dizzy Gillespie/Stan Getz Sextet	7" EP	HMV	7EG8596	1960	£2	£5	
Dizzy Gillespie/Stan Getz Sextet	10" LP	Columbia	33C9009	1955	£20	£40	
Dizzy In Greece	LP	Columbia	33CX10144	1959	£8	£20	
Dizzy With Strings	7" EP	Esquire	EP193	1958	£2	£5	
Duets	LP	Columbia	33CX10121	1958	£15	£30	with Sonny Rollins & Sonny Stitt
Film Themes	7" EP	Philips	BE12583	1965	£2	£5	
For Musicians Only	LP	Columbia	33CX10095	1958	£8	£20	with Stan Getz and Sonny Stitt
Gillespiana	LP	HMV	CLP1484/CSD1392	1962	£8	£20	
Greatest	LP	RCA	RD27242	1961	£4	£10	
Greatest Trumpet Of Them All	LP	HMV	CLP1381	1960	£8	£20	
Have Trumpet, Will Excite	LP	HMV	CLP1318	1959	£8	£20	
Mellow Sounds	7" EP	HMV	7EG8577	1960	£2	£5	
More Mellow Sounds	7" EP	HMV	7EG8646	1961	£2	£5	
New Sound In Jazz	7" EP	Philips	430793BE	1963	£2	£5	
Newport Jazz Festival 1957	LP	Columbia	33CX10111	1958	£6	£15	Side 2 by Count Basie
One More Time	7" EP	Columbia	SEB10087	1957	£2	£5	with Charlie Parker
Operatic Strings	LP	Fontana	TL5343	1967	£4	£10	
Operatic Strings	10" LP	Esquire	20003	1953	£20	£40	
Operatic Strings - Jealousy	10" LP	Felsted	EDL87006	1954	£20	£40	
Paris Concert	10" LP	Vogue	LDE039	1954	£20	£40	
Pile Driver	7" EP	Columbia	SEB10075	1957	£2	£5	
Portrait Of Duke Ellington	LP	HMV	CLP1431	1961	£8	£20	
Two By Two	7" EP	MGM	MGMEP681	1958	£2	£5	2 tracks by Kai Winding

GILLEY, MICKEY

Lonely Wine	LP	Astro	101	1964	£100	£200	US

GILLUM, JAZZ

1938-47	LP	RCA	RD7816	1968	£6	£15	
Jazz Gillum	LP	Folkways	FS3826	1961	£8	£20	
Jazz Gillum	LP	XTRA	XTRA1111	1971	£4	£10	
You Got To Reap What You Sow	LP	RCA	INTS1177	1970	£4	£10	

GILMER, JIMMY

Ain't Gonna Tell Nobody	7"	London	HLD9872	1964	£2	£5	
Buddy's Buddy	LP	Dot	DLP3577	1964	£8	£20	
Campusology	LP	Dot	DLP3709/25709	1966	£6	£15	US
Daisy Petal Picking	7"	London	HLD9827	1964	£2	£5	
Firewater	LP	Dot	DLP25856	1968	£5	£12	US
Folkbeat	LP	Dot	DLP3668/25668	1965	£6	£15	US
I'm Gonna Go Walkin'	7"	London	HLD9632	1962	£2	£5	
Look At Me	7"	London	HLD9898	1964	£2	£5	
Lucky 'Leven	LP	Dot	DLP3643/25643	1965	£6	£15	US
She Belongs To Me	7"	Stateside	SS472	1965	£1.50	£4	
Sugar Shack	LP	London	HAD/SHD8150	1964	£10	£25	
Sugar Shack	7"	London	HLD9789	1963	£2	£5	chart single
Sugar Shack	7" EP	London	RE10154	1964	£7.50	£15	French, B side by the Surfaris
Thunder 'N' Lightnin'	7"	Stateside	SS418	1965	£1.50	£4	
Torquay	LP	Dot	DLP3512/25512	1963	£8	£20	US

GILMOUR, DAVE

Blue Light	12"	Harvest	12HAR5226	1984	£2.50	£6	

GILMOUR, DAVID

Love On The Air	7"	Harvest	HARP5229	1984	£1.50	£4	shaped pic disc

GILREATH, JAMES

Little Band Of Gold	7"	Pye	7N25190	1963	£1.50	£4	chart single
Lollipops, Lace And Lipstick	7"	Pye	7N25213	1963	£1.50	£4	

GILTRAP, GORDON

Giltrap	LP	Philips	6308175	1973	£10	£25	
Gordon Giltrap	LP	Transatlantic	TRA175	1968	£8	£20	
Portrait	LP	Transatlantic	TRA202	1969	£6	£15	
Testament Of Time	LP	MCA	MKPS2020	1971	£15	£30	

GIN BOTTLE SEVEN

Gin Bottle Jazz	LP	London	LTZU15115	1958	£6	£15	

GINGER & THE SNAPS
This is an alternative name used by the Honeys and, like those records, these are keenly sought by Beach Boys completists.

Love Me The Way That I Love You	7"	Tore	1008	1961	£15	£30		US
Seven Days In September	7"	MGM	13413	1965	£30	£60		US

GINGER JUG BAND

Ginger Jug Band	LP	private	GJB001	197-	£10	£25	

GINHOUSE

Ginhouse	LP	B&C	CAS1031	1971	£20	£40	

GINNY & GALLIONS

Two Sides	LP	Downey	DS1003	1964	£6	£15	US

GINO & GINA

Pretty Baby	7"	Mercury	7MT230	1958	£12.50	£25	

GINSBERG, ALLEN

Allen Ginsberg Reads Kaddish	LP	Atlantic	4001	1966	£8	£20	US
At The ICA	LP	Saga		1967	£8	£20	
G Thing	LP	Douglas		1968	£8	£20	US
Howl And Other Poems	LP	Fantasy	7006	1959	£15	£30	US, red vinyl
September On Jessore Road	7"	Evatone		1972	£7.50	£15	US
Songs Of Innocence And Experience	LP	Forecast	FVS3083	1969	£8	£20	US

GIORDANO, LOU
This very rare single was co-produced by Buddy Holly and Phil Everly, who can also be heard on both sides of the record.

Stay Close To Me	7"	Brunswick	955115	1959	£210	£350	US

GIORGIO

Baby I Need You	7"	Electratone	EP1003	196-	£5	£10	
Bla Bla Diddley	7"	Page One	POF028	1967	£1.50	£4	
Bla Bla Diddly	7" EP.	DiscAZ	1093	1967	£6	£12	French
Full Stop	7"	Page One	POF003	1966	£1.50	£4	
Girl Without A Heart	7"	Polydor	56101	1966	£1.50	£4	

GIRARD, GEORGE

Stompin' At The Famous Door	LP	HMV	CLP1123	1957	£6	£15	

GIRL SATCHMO

Blue Beat Chariot	7"	Blue Beat	BB227	1963	£5	£10	
Don't Be Sad	7"	Blue Beat	BB156	1962	£5	£10	
Mash Potato	7"	Blue Beat	BB45	1961	£5	£10	
Take You For A Ride	7"	Fab	FAB111	1969	£2.50	£6	
Twist Around The Town	7"	Blue Beat	BB79	1961	£5	£10	

GIRL WONDER

Mommy Out Of The Light	7"	Doctor Bird	DB1015	1966	£5	£10	

GIRLFRIENDS

Jimmy Boy	7"	Colpix	PX712	1963	£4	£8	

GIRLIE

African Meeting	7"	Duke	DU42	1969	£2.50	£6	
Boss Cocky	7"	Treasure Isle	TI7053	1969	£4	£8	... Love Shocks B side
Madame Straggae	7"	Bullet	BU400	1969	£2.50	£6	... Laurel Aitken B side

GIRLS TOGETHER OUTRAGEOUSLY

Permanent Damage	LP	Straight	STS1059	1969	£20	£40	

GIUFFRE, JIMMY

Easy Way	LP	HMV	CLP1344	1960	£6	£15	
Jimmy Giuffre	10" LP	Capitol	LC6699	1955	£15	£30	
Jimmy Giuffre Clarinet	LP	London	LTZK15059	1957	£6	£15	
Jimmy Giuffre Three	LP	London	LTZK15130	1958	£6	£15	
Music Man	LP	London	LTZK15216	1961	£6	£15	
Trav'lin' Light	LP	London	LTZK15137	1958	£6	£15	

GIZMO

Just Like Master Bates	LP	Ace	ACE001	1979	£15	£30	white vinyl
Just Like Master Bates/Victims	LP	Gizmo		198-	£25	£50	.. autographed double
Psychedelic Rock And Roll	7"	MCM	4	197-	£2.50	£6	
Victims	LP	Sleep'N'Eat		1979	£15	£30	

GLACIERS

From Sea To Ski	LP	Mercury	MG2/SR60895	1964	£5	£12	US

GLACKIN, PADDY & PADDY KEENAN

Doublin	LP	Tara	2007	1979	£5	£12	Irish

GLACKIN, PADDY, MICK GAVIN, MICHAEL O'BRIEN

Flags Of Dublin	LP	Topic	12TS383	1978	£5	£12	

GLADIATORS

Bleak House	7"	HMV	POP1134	1963	£6	£12	

GLADIATORS (2)

As Long As I Live	7"	Direction	584507	1969	£1.50	£4	
Girl Don't Make Me Wait	7"	Direction	583854	1968	£1.50	£4	
Twelfth Of Never	7"	Direction	584660	1969	£1.50	£4	
Waiting On The Shores Of Nowhere	7"	Direction	584308	1969	£1.50	£4	

GLADIATORS (3)
Train Is Coming .... 7" ...... Doctor Bird ...... DB1114 .... 1967 ... **£5** .... **£10** ....

GLADIOLAS
Little Darling .... 7" ...... London .... HLO8435 .... 1957 ... **£50** ...... **£100** ....

GLASEL, JOHNNY
Jazz Session .... 10" LP HMV .... DLP1198 .... 1958 ... **£8** .... **£20** ....

GLASER, TOMPALL
Land - Folk Songs .... LP ..... Decca .... DL(7)4041 .... 1960 ... **£6** .... **£15** .... US

GLASS FAMILY
Electric Band .... LP ..... Warner Bros .... WS1776 .... 1968 ... **£8** .... **£20** .... US

GLASS MENAGERIE
Do My Thing Myself .... 7" ...... Polydor .... 56341 .... 1969 ... **£2.50** .... **£6** ....
Frederick Jordan .... 7" ...... Pye .... 7N17615 .... 1968 ... **£10** .... **£20** ....
Have You Forgotten Who You Are ...... 7" ...... Polydor .... 56318 .... 1969 ... **£2.50** .... **£6** ....
She's A Rainbow .... 7" ...... Pye .... 7N17518 .... 1968 ... **£2.50** .... **£6** ....
You Didn't Have To Be So Nice ...... 7" ...... Pye .... 7N17568 .... 1968 ... **£2.50** .... **£6** ....

GLASS OPENING
Silver Bells And Cockle Shells .... 7" ...... Plexium .... P1236 .... 1968 ... **£30** .... **£60** ....

GLASS, PHILIP
Music In Fifths/Music In Similar ...... LP ..... Chatham .... LP1003 .... 197- ... **£8** .... **£20** .... US
Motion .... Square ....
Music With Changing Parts .... LP ..... Chatham .... LP1001/2 .... 197- ... **£15** .... **£30** ....US double
.... Square ....
Two Pages .... LP ..... Folkways .... FTS33902 .... 197- .... **£4** .... **£10** .... US

GLEASON, JACKIE
Autumn Leaves .... 7" ...... Capitol .... CL14363 .... 1955 ... **£1.50** .... **£4** ....
In The Good Old Summertime .... 7" ...... Capitol .... CL14323 .... 1955 ... **£1.50** .... **£4** ....
Rain .... 7" ...... Capitol .... CL14289 .... 1955 ... **£1.50** .... **£4** ....
What Is A Boy? .... 7" ...... Brunswick ...... 04775 .... 1960 ... **£2** .... **£5** ....

GLEN & LLOYD
Feel Good Now .... 7" ...... Doctor Bird ...... DB1099 .... 1967 ... **£5** .... **£10** ....
Live And Let Others Live .... 7" ...... Ska Beat ...... JB250 .... 1966 ... **£5** .... **£10** ....

GLENCOE
Glencoe .... LP ..... Epic .... 65207 .... 1972 ... **£4** .... **£10** ....
Spirit Of Glencoe .... LP ..... Epic .... 65717 .... 1973 ... **£4** .... **£10** ....

GLENN, LLOYD
Chica Boo .... LP ..... Aladdin .... 808 .... 1956 ... **£15** .... **£30** .... US
Chica Boo .... LP ..... Aladdin .... 808 .... 1956 ... **£50** .... **£100** .... US, red vinyl

GLENN, TYREE
At The Embers .... LP ..... Esquire .... 32061 .... 1958 ... **£5** .... **£12** ....

GLITTER, GARY
Records by the man who was christened Paul Gadd can also be found listed in the Guide under the names Paul Raven, Paul Monday, and Rubber Bucket.
When I'm On I'm On .... 7" ...... Eagle .... ERS009 .... 1981 ... **£2** .... **£5** ....

GLITTERHOUSE
Barbarella .... 7" ...... Stateside .... SS2129 .... 1968 ... **£1.50** .... **£4** ...... 2 different B sides

GLOBAL VILLAGE TRUCKING CO.
Global Village Trucking Co. .... LP ..... Caroline .... C1516 .... 1976 ... **£4** .... **£10** ....

GLOBE SHOW
Yes Or No .... 7" ...... Page One .... POF128 .... 1969 ... **£2** .... **£5** ....

GLOOMYS
Daybreak .... 7" ...... Columbia .... DB8391 .... 1968 ... **£4** .... **£8** ....

GLORIES
Love You But Give Me My Freedom ... 7" ...... Direction .... 583084 .... 1967 ... **£2** .... **£5** ....
Stand Accused .... 7" ...... CBS .... 2736 .... 1967 ... **£7.50** .... **£15** ....
My Sweet Sweet Baby .... 7" ...... Direction .... 583646 .... 1968 ... **£1.50** .... **£4** ....
Sing Me A Love Song .... 7" ...... Direction .... 583300 .... 1968 ... **£1.50** .... **£4** ....

GLORY
Meat Music Sampler .... LP ..... Texas .... 69 .... 1969 ... **£15** .... **£30** .... US
.... Revolution ......

GLOVE
Like An Animal .... 7" ...... Wonderland .... SHE3 .... 1983 ... **£2.50** .... **£6** ...... chart single
Like An Animal .... 12" ...... Wonderland .... SHEX3 .... 1983 ... **£4** .... **£10** ....
Punish Me With Kisses .... 7" ...... Wonderland .... SHE5 .... 1983 ... **£4** .... **£8** ....

GLOVER, ROGER
Butterfly Ball .... LP ..... Purple .... TPSA7514 .... 1974 ... **£5** .... **£12** ....

GMT
One By One .... 12" ...... Mausoleum ..... BONE1283102 ...... 1991 ... **£2.50** .... **£6** ....

GNIDROLOG

In Spite Of Harry's Toenail	LP	RCA	SF8261	1971	£10	£25	sleeve
Lady Lake	LP	RCA	SF8322	1972	£30	£60	pictured in Guide

GNOMES OF ZURICH

Hang On Baby	7"	CBS	202556	1967	£6	£12
High Hopes	7"	CBS	2694	1967	£6	£12
Please Mr.Sun	7"	Planet	PLF121	1966	£7.50	£15
Second Fiddle	7"	RCA	RCA1606	1967	£7.50	£15

G-NOTES

Ronnie	7"	Oriole	CB1456	1958	£2.50	£6

GOBBLEDEGOOKS

Where Have You Been	7"	Decca	F12023	1964	£5	£10

GO-BETWEENS

I Need Two Heads	7"	Postcard	80-4	1980	£2.50	£6	cream or brown sleeves

GOBLIN

Suspiria	LP	EMI	EMC3222	1977	£8	£20

GODDARD, GEOFF

Girl Bride	7"	HMV	POP938	1961	£6	£12
My Little Girl's Come Home	7"	HMV	POP1068	1962	£7.50	£15
Saturday Dance	7"	HMV	POP1160	1963	£7.50	£15
Sky Man	7"	HMV	POP1213	1963	£15	£30

GODDING, BRIAN

For those of us who waited years for guitarist Brian Godding's solo LP (after admiring his playing in Blossom Toes and the Mike Westbrook band), it is rather distressing to find the record becoming unavailable only months after its release. Reckless Records is not the first collectors shop to try its hand at running its own record label and neither is it the first to find that the problems of distribution and achieving actual sales can be enormous.

Slaughter On Shaftesbury Avenue	LP	Reckless	RECK16	1989	£4	£10

GODFATHERS

Lonely Man	7"	Corporate Image	7GFTR010	1985	£1.50	£4
Lonely Man	12"	Corporate Image	GFTR010	1985	£2.50	£6

GODFREY & STEWART

Joined By The Heart	LP	The Stand	HEARTLP	198-	£6	£15
Seed And The Sower	LP	Enid	ENID11	1986	£5	£12

GODFREY, HUGH

A Dey Pon Dem	7"	Coxsone	CS7001	1967	£5	£10	Soul Brothers B side
Go Tell Him	7"	Studio One	SO2015	1967	£6	£12

GODFREY, ROBERT JOHN

To all intents and purposes, Robert John Godfrey is the Enid. His solo album is effectively the first Enid album, therefore, and the hardest to find of the fully released series as it was not reissued on vinyl.

Fall Of Hyperion	LP	Charisma	CAS1084	1974	£10	£25

GODIEGO

Water Margin	LP	Satril	SATL4009	1978	£5	£12

GODLEY & CREME

Consequences	LP	Mercury	CONS017	1977	£6	£15	triple, boxe
Consequences	LP	Mercury	LKP1001	1977	£6	£15	prom

GODS

Ken Hensley, the leader of Uriah Heep, began his career as a member of The Gods. The original line-up also included guitarist Mick Taylor who can be heard playing on the Polydor single. The 1976 release is a compilation LP - the Gods broke up in 1969.

Baby's Rich	7"	Columbia	DB8486	1968	£6	£12
Come On Down To My Boat Baby	7"	Polydor	56168	1967	£20	£40
Genesis	LP	Columbia	SX/SCX6286	1968	£35	£70
Gods	LP	Harvest	SHSM2011	1976	£5	£12
Hey Bulldog	7"	Columbia	DB8544	1969	£6	£12
Maria	7"	Columbia	DB8572	1969	£6	£12
To Samuel A Son	LP	Columbia	SCX6372	1970	£35	£70

GOD'S GIFT

These Days	7"	Newmarket		1979	£2.50	£6

GODZ

Contact High	LP	Fontana	STL5500	1967	£6	£15	
Godz 2	LP	Fontana	STL5512	1969	£6	£15	
Godzundheit	LP	ESP	2017	1970	£6	£15	U
Third Testament	LP	ESP	1077	1969	£6	£15	U

GOGMAGOG

I Will Be There	12"	Food For Thought	YUMT109	1985	£4	£10

GO-GO'S

Automatic	7"	Initial	IRS101	1981	£1.50	£4	pic dis
Our Lips Are Sealed	7"	IRS	PFP1007	1981	£2.50	£6	pink vin
We Got The Beat	7"	Stiff	BUY78	1980	£2	£5	

GO-GO'S (2)

I'm Gonna Spend My Christmas With A Dalek	7"	Oriole	CB1982	1964	£12.50	£25
Swim	LP	RCA	LPM/LSP2930	1964	£8	£20 .... US

GOINS, HERBIE & NIGHT-TIMERS

Incredible Miss Brown	7"	Parlophone	R5533	1966	£6	£12
Incredible Miss Brown	7" EP	Odeon	MEO133	1966	£12.50	£25 .... French
Number One In Your Heart	LP	Parlophone	PMC7026	1967	£20	£40
Number One in Your Heart	7"	Parlophone	R5478	1966	£15	£30

GOLDBERG, BARRY

Another Day	7"	Pye	7N25465	1968	£1.50	£4
Blowing My Mind	LP	Epic	LN24/BN26199	1966	£6	£15 .... US
Reunion	LP	Pye	NSPL28116	1968	£6	£15
Two Jews Blues	LP	Buddah	203020	1969	£5	£12

GOLDEN APPLES OF THE SUN

Monkey Time	7"	Decca	F12194	1965	£15	£30 .... demo
Monkey Time	7"	Immediate	IM010	1965	£10	£20

GOLDEN CRUSADERS

Hey Good Looking	7"	Columbia	DB7357	1964	£5	£10
I Don't Care	7"	Columbia	DB7485	1965	£5	£10
I'm In Love With You	7"	Columbia	DB7232	1964	£5	£10

GOLDEN DAWN

Power Plant	LP	International Artists	IA4	1967	£17.50	£35 .... US

GOLDEN DAWN (2)

My Secret World	7"	Sarah	009	1988	£1.50	£4 .... with poster

GOLDEN EARRING

Another Forty-Five Miles	7"	Major Minor	MM679	1970	£2	£5
Back Home	7"	Polydor	2001073	1970	£1.50	£4
Eight Miles High	LP	Major Minor	SMLP65	1969	£8	£20
Eight Miles High	LP	Polydor	656019	1969	£6	£15
Hearing Earring	LP	Track	2406109	1973	£5	£12
It's Alright But It Could Be Better	7"	Major Minor	MM633	1969	£2	£5
Just A Little Bit Of Peace	7"	Major Minor	MM601	1969	£2	£5
Just Earring	LP	Polydor	736007	1964	£10	£25 .... Dutch
Miracle Mirror	LP	Polydor	1236283		£8	£20 .... Dutch
On The Double	LP	Polydor	2653001		£17.50	£35 .... Dutch double
Seven Tears	LP	Polydor	2310135	1971	£6	£15
That Day	7"	Polydor	56514	1970	£5	£10
Together	LP	Polydor	2310210	1972	£6	£15
Winter Harvest	LP	Polydor	736068	196-	£10	£25 .... Dutch

GOLDEN FLEECE

Athens 6 a.m.	7"	Decca	F12669	1967	£1.50	£4

GOLDEN GATE QUARTET

Get On Board	LP	Columbia	33SX1370	1961	£4	£10
Golden Gate Quartet	LP	Regal	SREG2071	1969	£5	£12
Moses Smote The Waters	7"	Columbia	SCM5054	1953	£2	£5
Shout For Joy!	LP	Columbia	33SX1172	1959	£5	£12
Sings Great Spirituals	7" EP	Columbia	SEG7700	1957	£2	£5
That Golden Chariot	10" LP	Fontana	TFR6009	1958	£5	£12

GOLDEN GATE STRINGS

Mr.Tambourine Man	7"	Columbia	DB7634	1965	£1.50	£4

GOLDENROD

Goldenrod	LP	Chartmaker	CSG1101	1968	£35	£70 .... US

GOLDIE

Going Back	7"	Immediate	IM026	1966	£7.50	£15
Do	7"	Fontana	TF693	1966	£4	£8

GOLDIE & THE GINGERBREADS

Can't You Hear My Heartbeat	7"	Decca	F12070	1965	£2.50	£6 .... chart single
Can't You Hear My Heartbeat	7" EP	Decca	457072	1965	£10	£20 .... French
Sailor Boy	7"	Decca	F12199	1965	£1.50	£4
That's Why I Love You	7"	Decca	F12126	1965	£2.50	£6

GOLDING, JOHN

Discarded Verse	LP	Cottage	101S	1974	£5	£12

GOLDSBORO, BOBBY

Autumn Of My Life	7"	United Artists	UP2223	1968	£4	£8
Bobby Goldsboro Album	LP	United Artists	UAL3/UAS6358	1964	£6	£15 .... US
Broomstick Cowboy	7"	United Artists	UP1120	1966	£1.50	£4
Hold On	7"	United Artists	UP1166	1966	£2.50	£6
H-O-N-E-Y	7"	United Artists	UP2215	1968	£1.50	£4
Honey	LP	United Artists	(S)ULP1195	1968	£5	£12
I Can't Stop Loving You	LP	United Artists	UAL3/UAS6381	1964	£6	£15 .... US
I Know You Better Than That	7"	United Artists	UP1135	1966	£1.50	£4
If You Wait For Love	7"	United Artists	UP1104	1965	£1.50	£4
It Hurts Me	7"	United Artists	UP1156	1967	£1.50	£4
It's Too Late	LP	United Artists	(S)ULP1135	1966	£5	£12

It's Too Late	7"	United Artists	UP1128	1966	£7.50	£15	
Little Things	LP	United Artists	UAL3/UAS6425	1965	£6	£15	US
Little Things	7"	United Artists	UP1079	1965	£2.50	£6	
Little Things	7" EP	United Artists	UEP1006	1965	£6	£12	
Love Arrester	7"	United Artists	UP2264	1968	£1.50	£4	
Runaround	7"	Stateside	SS193	1963	£4	£8	
Solid Goldsboro	LP	United Artists	(S)ULP1163	1967	£5	£12	
Take Your Love	7"	United Artists	UP1146	1966	£5	£10	
Talented Bobby Goldsboro	7" EP	United Artists	UEP1016	1966	£6	£12	
Too Many People	7"	United Artists	UP1177	1967	£10	£20	
Voodoo Woman	7"	United Artists	UP1091	1965	£1.50	£4	

GOLDSMITH
Life Is Killing Me	7"	Bedlam	BLM001	1983	£5	£10	

GOLDTONES
Goldtones Featuring Randy Seol	LP	LaBrea	L8011		£6	£15	US

GOLIATH
Goliath	LP	CBS	64229	1970	£8	£20	
Port And Lemon Lady	7"	CBS	5312	1971	£2.50	£6	

GOLLIWOGS
The Golliwogs were the same group that later found considerable success as Creedence Clearwater Revival.
Brown-Eyed Girl	7"	Vocalion	VF9266	1966	£10	£20	
Don't Tell Me No Lies	7"	Fantasy	590	1964	£10	£20	US
Fight Fire	7"	Vocalion	VF9283	1967	£10	£20	
Golliwogs	LP	Fantasy	FAN5996	1975	£4	£10	
Walking On The Water	7"	Scorpio	408	1966	£10	£20	US
You Came Walking	7"	Fantasy	597	1965	£10	£20	US
You Got Nothin' On Me	7"	Fantasy	599	1965	£10	£20	US

GOLOWIN, SERGIUS
Lord Krishna Von Goloka	LP	Kosmische	KM58002	1973	£6	£15	German

GOLSON, BENNY
Benny Golson And The Philadelphians	LP	London	LTZK15176/ SAHT6061	1960	£8	£20	
Groovin' With Golson	LP	Esquire	32105	1960	£8	£20	
Stockholm Sojourn	LP	Stateside	SL10150	1965	£4	£10	with Art Farme

GOMORRHA
Gomorrha	LP	Cornet	15038	1970	£8	£20	German
I Turned To See Whose Voice It Was	LP	Brain	0001003	1971	£10	£25	German
Trauma	LP	BASF	20204138	1972	£6	£15	German

GONDOLIERS
God's Green Acres	7"	Starlite	ST45001	1958	£2	£5	

GONELLA, NAT
Salute To Satchmo	10" LP	Columbia	33S1146	1959	£5	£12	

GONG
Angel's Egg	LP	Virgin	V2007	1973	£15	£30	with boo
Camembert Electrique	LP	Byg	529353	1971	£8	£20	French, with inse
Continental Circus	LP	Philips	6332033	1971	£8	£20	
Flying Teapot	LP	Virgin	V2002	1973	£4	£10	
Magick Brother	LP	Byg	529029	1970	£15	£30	Frenc
Magick Brother	LP	Byg	5293305	1970	£10	£25	Frenc

GONKS
That's All Right Mama	7"	Decca	F11984	1964	£4	£8	

GONSALVES, PAUL
Hummingbird	LP	Deram	SML1064	1970	£4	£10	

GONZALES
Gonzales	LP	EMI	EMC3046	1974	£10	£25	

GONZALEZ, BELLE
Belle	LP	Columbia	SCX6484	1971	£30	£60	

GOOD EARTH
It's Hard Rock & All That	LP	Saga	FID2112	1968	£5	£12	

GOOD, JACK FAT NOISE
Fat Noise	7"	Decca	F11233	1960	£2.50	£6	

GOOD RATS
Hobo	7"	London	HLR10237	1969	£1.50	£4	

GOOD SHIP LOLLIPOP
Maxwell's Silver Hammer	7"	Ember	EMBS276	1970	£2.50	£6	

GOOD TIME LOSERS
Trafalgar Square	7"	Fontana	TF791	1967	£2	£5	

GOODBYE MR MACKENZIE
Face To Face	12"	Claude	MAC1	1986	£3	£8	
Rattler	7"	Precious	JEWEL2	1986	£2	£5	
Rattler	12"	Precious	JEWEL2T	1986	£3	£8	

GOODEES
Condition Red	7"	Stax	STAX113	1969	£5	£10	

GOODHAND-TAIT, PHILIP
I Think I'll Write A Song	LP	DJM	DJLPS416	1971	£4	£10	
I'm Gonna Put Some Hurt On You	7"	Parlophone	R5448	1966	£4	£8	
Love Has Got A Hold On Me	7"	Decca	F12868	1969	£2.50	£6	
No Problem	7"	Parlophone	R5498	1966	£4	£8	
Rehearsal	LP	DJM	DJLPS411	1971	£4	£10	
Songfall	LP	DJM	DJLPS425	1972	£4	£10	
You Can't Take Love	7"	Parlophone	R5547	1966	£4	£8	

GOODISON, JOHNNY
Little Understanding	7"	Deram	DM319	1970	£1.50	£4	

GOODMAN, BENNY
1937-1938 Jazz Concert No.2 Vol.1	LP	Philips	BBL7009	1955	£8	£20	
1937-1938 Jazz Concert No.2 Vol.2	LP	Philips	BBL7010	1955	£8	£20	
After Hours	10" LP	Capitol	LC6565	1952	£8	£20	
Benny Goodman Band	10" LP	Capitol	LC6831	1956	£6	£15	
Benny Goodman Orchestra	LP	Capitol	LCT6012	1955	£8	£20	
Benny Goodman Orchestra	10" LP	HMV	DLP1112	1956	£8	£20	
Benny Goodman Orchestra	10" LP	HMV	DLP1116	1956	£6	£15	
Benny Goodman Orchestra And Quartet	LP	Capitol	LCT6104	1956	£6	£15	
Benny Goodman Quartet	10" LP	HMV	DLPC6	1955	£8	£20	
Benny Goodman Sextet	LP	Philips	BBL7021	1955	£5	£12	
Benny Goodman Sextet	10" LP	Fontana	TFR6006	1958	£6	£15	
Benny Goodman Small Groups	10" LP	Capitol	LC6810	1956	£6	£15	
Benny Goodman Story Vol.1	LP	Brunswick	LAT8102	1956	£6	£15	
Benny Goodman Story Vol.2	LP	Brunswick	LAT8103	1956	£6	£15	
Benny Goodman Trio	10" LP	Fontana	TFR6022	1959	£5	£12	
Benny Goodman Trio	10" LP	HMV	DLPC11	1956	£6	£15	
Benny In Brussels	LP	Philips	BBL7299	1959	£4	£10	
Benny In Brussels	LP	Philips	BBL7300	1959	£4	£10	
Benny Rides Again	LP	Columbia	33SX1038	1955	£6	£15	
Carnegie Hall Jazz Concert Vol.1	LP	Philips	BBL7000	1954	£8	£20	
Carnegie Hall Jazz Concert Vol.2	LP	Philips	BBL7001	1954	£8	£20	
Classics In Jazz	10" LP	Capitol	LC6680	1954	£8	£20	
Dizzy Fingers	10" LP	Capitol	LC6601	1953	£8	£20	
Easy Does It	10" LP	Capitol	LC6557	1952	£8	£20	
Goodman Touch	10" LP	Capitol	LC6620	1953	£8	£20	
Happy Session	LP	Philips	BBL7318	1959	£4	£10	
Let's Hear The Melody	10" LP	Philips	BBR8064	1955	£6	£15	
Makes History	LP	Philips	BBL7073	1956	£6	£15	
Plays For Fletcher Henderson Fund	LP	Columbia	33SX1020	1954	£8	£20	
Presents Eddie Sauter Arrangements	LP	Philips	BBL7043	1955	£6	£15	
Session For Sextet	10" LP	Columbia	33S1048	1954	£8	£20	
Session For Sextet No.2	LP	Columbia	33SX1035	1955	£6	£15	
Session For Six	10" LP	Capitol	LC6526	1951	£8	£20	

GOODMAN, DAVE
Justifiable Homicide	7"	The Label	TLR008	1978	£15	£30	Steve Jones & Paul Jones named on sleeve

GOODTIMERS
It's Twistin' Time	7"	Fontana	H360	1962	£2	£5	

GOODWIN, RON
Limelight	7"	Parlophone	MSP6035	1953	£2	£5	chart single

GOOFERS
Dipsy Doodle	7"	Vogue Coral	Q72289	1957	£7.50	£15	
Flip Flop And Fly	7"	Vogue Coral	Q72074	1955	£17.50	£35	
Goofie Dry Bones	7"	Vogue Coral	Q72094	1955	£7.50	£15	
Hearts Of Stone	7"	Vogue Coral	Q72051	1955	£17.50	£35	
Push Push Push Cart	7"	Vogue Coral	Q72267	1957	£7.50	£15	
Sick Sick Sick	7"	Vogue Coral	Q72124	1956	£7.50	£15	
Tennessee Rock And Roll	7"	Vogue Coral	Q72171	1956	£12.50	£25	

GOONS
Best Of The Goon Shows	LP	Parlophone	PMC1108	1959	£4	£10	chart LP
Best Of The Goon Shows No.2	LP	Parlophone	PMC1129	1960	£4	£10	chart LP
Eeh Ah Oh Oooh	7"	Decca	F10885	1957	£2	£5	
Goons	7" EP.	Decca	DFE6396	1956	£5	£10	
I'm Walking Backwards For Christmas	7"	Decca	F10756	1956	£2.50	£6	chart single
My September Love	7"	Parlophone	R4251	1956	£2.50	£6	
Russian Love Song	7"	Decca	F10945	1957	£2	£5	
Unchained Melodies	10" LP	Decca	LF1332	1964	£6	£15	
Ying Tong Song	7"	Decca	F10780	1956	£2.50	£6	chart single

GOPAL, SAM
Sam Gopal is a percussionist whose work can be found on several albums by the likes of Daevid Allen, G.F.Fitzgerald, and Isaac Guillory. The demand for his solo album, however, derives primarily from the fact that it is Lemmy, of future Motorhead fame, who plays guitar on the album.

Escalator	LP	Stable	SLE8001	1969	£30	£60	sleeve pictured in Guide
Escalator	7"	Stable	SLE8001	1969	£10	£20	promo sampler
Horse	7"	Stable	STA5602	1969	£7.50	£15	

GORDON, BARRY
Nuttin' For Christmas	7"	MGM	MGM935	1956	£1.50	£4	

GORDON, DEXTER
Daddy Plays The Horn	LP	London	LTZN15098	1957	£20	£40	
Dexter Calling	LP	Blue Note	BLP/BST84083	1961	£10	£25	
Doin' Alright	LP	Blue Note	BLP/BST84077	1961	£15	£30	
Gettin' Around	LP	Blue Note	BLP/BST84204	1965	£10	£25	
Go!	LP	Blue Note	BLP/BST84112	1962	£10	£25	
One Flight Up	LP	Blue Note	BLP/BST84176	1964	£10	£25	
Our Man In Paris	LP	Blue Note	BLP/BST84146	1963	£10	£25	
Swingin' Affair	LP	Blue Note	BLP/BST84133	1963	£10	£25	

GORDON, JOE FOLK FOUR
Gay Gordons	LP	HMV	CLP1379/CSD1314	1960	£5	£12	
Johnnie Lad	7" EP	HMV	7EG8454	1960	£2	£5	

GORDON, PHIL
Down The Road Apiece	7"	Brunswick	05545	1956	£2	£5	

GORDON, RABBI JOSEPH
Competition	7"	Bam Caruso	NRIC030	1985	£4	£8	no PS

GORDON, RONNIE
Coming Home	7"	R&B	JB127	1963	£5	£10	

GORDON, ROSCOE
Just A Little Bit	7"	Stateside	SS204	1963	£7.50	£15	
Just A Little Bit	7"	Top Rank	JAR332	1960	£10	£20	
Keep On Doggin'	7"	Vocalion	VP9245	1965	£7.50	£15	
No More Doggin'	7"	Island	WI272	1966	£7.50	£15	
Surely I Love You	7"	Island	WI256	1965	£6	£12	

GORDON, VINCENT
Everybody Bawlin'	7"	Duke	DU37	1969	£2.50	£6	Silvertones B side
Soul Trombone	7"	Coxsone	CS7085	1969	£5	£10	Larry & Alvin B side

GORE, LESLEY
All About Love	LP	Mercury	20076MCL	1965	£5	£12	
Boys Boys Boys	LP	Mercury	20020MCL	1964	£5	£12	
California Nights	LP	Mercury	MG2/SR61120	1967	£5	£12	US
California Nights	LP	Mercury	MF963	1966	£1.50	£4	
Girl Talk	LP	Mercury	20033MCL	1964	£5	£12	
Girl Talk	LP	Wing	WL1183	1967	£4	£10	
Golden Hits	LP	Mercury	MG2/SR61024	1965	£5	£12	US
Golden Hits Vol.2	LP	Mercury	SR61185	1968	£5	£12	US
I Don't Wanna Be A Loser	7"	Mercury	MF821	1964	£1.50	£4	
I Won't Love You Any More	7"	Mercury	MF889	1965	£2	£5	
I'll Cry If I Want To	LP	Mercury	MMC14127	1963	£6	£15	
I'm Fallin' Down	7"	Mercury	MF984	1966	£2.50	£6	
It's My Party	7"	Mercury	AMT1205	1963	£1.50	£4	chart single
Judy's Turn To Cry	7"	Mercury	AMT1210	1963	£1.50	£4	
Lesley Gore	7" EP	Mercury	10017MCE	1964	£5	£10	
Look Of Love	7"	Mercury	MF846	1965	£1.50	£4	
Magic Colours	7"	Mercury	MF1017	1968	£1.50	£4	
Maybe I Know	7"	Mercury	MF829	1964	£1.50	£4	chart single
My Town, My Guy And Me	LP	Mercury	20071MCL	1965	£5	£12	
My Town, My Guy, And Me	7"	Mercury	MF872	1965	£1.50	£10	
She's A Fool	7"	Mercury	AMT1213	1963	£1.50	£4	
Sings Of Mixed-Up Hearts	LP	Mercury	20001MCL	1964	£5	£12	
Sometimes I Wish I Were A Boy	7"	Mercury	MF837	1964	£1.50	£4	
Sunshine, Lollipops And Rainbows	7"	Mercury	MF862	1965	£1.50	£4	
That's The Way Boys Are	7"	Mercury	MF810	1964	£1.50	£4	
You Don't Own Me	7"	Mercury	MF803	1964	£1.50	£4	
Young Love	7"	Mercury	MF902	1966	£1.50	£4	

GORME, EYDIE
Blame It On The Bossa Nova	7"	CBS	AAG131	1963	£1.50	£4	chart single
Climb Up The Wall	7"	Vogue Coral	Q2014	1954	£2	£5	
Everybody Go Home	7"	CBS	202470	1967	£1.50	£4	
Everybody Go Home	7"	CBS	AAG170	1963	£1.50	£4	
Eydie Gorme	LP	HMV	CLP1156	1958	£4	£10	
Eydie Gorme's Delight	LP	Coral	LVA9086	1958	£4	£10	
Eydie In Love	LP	HMV	CLP1250	1959	£4	£10	
Eydie Swings The Blues	LP	HMV	CLP1170	1958	£4	£10	
Give A Fool A Chance	7"	Vogue Coral	Q72092	1955	£1.50	£4	
Gorme Sings Showstoppers	LP	HMV	CLP1257	1959	£4	£10	
I'll Remember April	7" EP	HMV	GES5795	1959	£2	£5	stereo
Kiss In Your Eyes	7"	HMV	POP400	1957	£1.50	£4	
Love Is A Season	LP	HMV	CLP1290	1959	£4	£10	
Love Is A Season	7" EP	HMV	GES5789	1959	£2	£5	stereo
Love Me Forever	7"	HMV	POP432	1958	£2	£5	chart single
Make Yourself Comfortable	7"	Vogue Coral	Q72044	1955	£1.50	£4	
Sincerely Yours	7"	London	HL8227	1956	£6	£12	
Soldier Boy	7"	Vogue Coral	Q72103	1955	£1.50	£4	
Sure	7"	Vogue Coral	Q2027	1954	£1.50	£4	
Take A Deep Breath	7"	Vogue Coral	Q72085	1955	£1.50	£4	
Vamps The Roaring Twenties	LP	HMV	CLP1201	1958	£4	£10	
Yes My Darling Daughter	7"	CBS	AAG105	1962	£1.50	£4	chart single

GORME, EYDIE & STEVE LAWRENCE

Cozy	LP	HMV	CLP1463	1962	£4	£10
Golden Hits	LP	HMV	CLP1404/CSD1329	1961	£4	£10
I Want To Stay Here	7"	CBS	AAG163	1963	£1.50	£4 .... chart single
Steve And Eydie	7" EP	CBS	AGG20035	1963	£2	£5
Steve Lawrence And Eydie Gorme	7" EP	Coral	FEP2017	1959	£2	£5
We Got Us	LP	HMV	CLP1372/CSD1310	1960	£4	£10

GORSHIN, FRANK

Riddler	7"	Pye	7N25402	1966	£2.50	£6
Riddler	7"	Pye	7N25402	1966	£5	£10 ...... PS

GOSPEL CLASSICS

More Love That's What We Need	7"	Chess	CRS8080	1968	£10	£20

GOSPEL GARDEN

Finders Keepers	7"	Camp	602006	1968	£4	£8

GOSPEL JUBILEERS

Wake Up Jonah	7"	Top Rank	JAR322	1960	£1.50	£4

GOSPEL OAK

Gospel Oak	LP	Uni	UNLS113	1970	£6	£15

GOTHENBURG, FREDA

Like A Dream	7"	GHM	GHM1	1979	£1.50	£4 plays from centre out!

GOTHIC HORIZON

If You Can Smile	7"	Argo	AFW107	1973	£4	£8
Jason Lodge Poetry Book	LP	Argo	ZFB26	1970	£40	£80
Tomorrow Is Another Day	LP	Argo	ZDA150	1972	£40	£80

GOULDER, DAVE

Requiem For Steam	LP	Big Ben	BB004	1973	£5	£12

GOULDER, DAVE & LIZ DYER

January Man	LP	Argo	ZFB10	1970	£6	£15
Raven And The Crow	LP	Argo	ZFB30	1971	£6	£15

GOULDMAN, GRAHAM

Graham Gouldman Thing	LP	RCA	LPM/LSP3954	1968	£10	£25 ...... US
Nowhere To Go	7"	CBS	7739	1972	£2.50	£6
Stop Stop Stop	7"	Decca	F12334	1966	£10	£20
Upstairs Downstairs	7"	RCA	RCA1667	1968	£6	£12
Windmills Of Your Mind	7"	Spark	SRL1026	1969	£4	£8

GOVE

Dead Letter Blues	7"	London	HLE10295	1969	£4	£8

GOWEN, ALAN

Before A Word Is Said	LP	Europa	JF2007	1981	£4	£10 ...... French
Two Rainbows Daily	LP	Red	ROUGE1	1980	£4	£10

GRAAS, JOHN

Jazz Studio 2	LP	Brunswick	LAT8046	1954	£8	£20 ...... with Herb Geller
Jazz Studio 3	LP	Brunswick	LAT8069	1955	£8	£20 ...with Gerry Mulligan

GRABHAM, MICK

Mick The Lad	LP	United Artists	UAS29341	1972	£6	£15

GRACIE, CHARLIE

Angel Of Love	7"	Coral	Q72373	1959	£6	£12
Butterfly	7"	Parlophone	R4290	1957	£15	£30 ...... chart single, gold label
Cool Baby	7"	London	HLU8521	1957	£10	£20 ......chart single
Crazy Girl	7"	London	HLU8596	1958	£12.50	£25
Doodlebug	7"	Coral	Q72362	1959	£6	£12
Fabulous	7"	Parlophone	R4313	1957	£12.50	£25 ...... chart single, gold label
Fabulous Charlie Gracie	7" EP	Parlophone	GEP8630	1957	£12.50	£25
He'll Never Love You Like I Do	7"	Stateside	SS402	1965	£25	£50
Night And Day USA	7"	London	HLU9603	1962	£6	£12
Oh Well-a	7"	Coral	Q72381	1959	£6	£12
Race	7"	Columbia	DB4477	1960	£6	£12
Wandering Eyes	7"	London	HL8467	1957	£10	£20 ......chart single

GRACIOUS

Beautiful	7"	Polydor	56333	1968	£12.50	£25
Gracious	LP	Vertigo	6360002	1970	£25	£50 ...... spiral label
This Is Gracious	LP	Philips	6382004	1972	£30	£60

GRADED GRAINS

Animal Magic	7"				£55	£110

GRADUATE

Rock musicians whose respected careers start from shakey beginnings have difficulty forgetting the fact when they are unwise enough to commit them to vinyl. Two of the grinning mod revivalists on the cover of the Graduate LP are Roland Orzabel and Curt Smith, later of Tears For Fears. The extraordinary perfectionism applied to the recording of the 'Seeds Of Love' album shows how these two like to be taken seriously. With Graduate's forgettable music in their past, however, life is hard.

Ambition	7"	Precision	PAR111	1980	£2	£5
Elvis Should Play Ska	7"	Precision	PAR100	1980	£1.50	£4 ......no PS

Ever Met A Day	7"	Precision	PAR104	1980	£2	£5	
Made One	7"	Blue Hat	5BHR	198-	£4	£8	
Shut Up	7"	Precision	PAR117	1981	£1.50	£4	no PS

GRAHAM, BILLY & THE ESCALATORS

Ooh-Poo-Pah-Doo	7"	Atlantic	584073	1967	£1.50	£4

GRAHAM, BOBBY

Interest in the two singles released by drummer Bobby Graham is due primarily to the fact that they were co-recordings with guitarist Jimmy Page.

Skin Deep	7"	Fontana	TF521	1965	£7.50	£15
Teensville	7"	Fontana	TF667	1966	£7.50	£15

GRAHAM, CHICK & THE COASTERS

Dance Baby Dance	7"	Decca	F11932	1964	£4	£8
Education	7"	Decca	F11859	1964	£4	£8

GRAHAM, DAVEY

All That Moody	LP	Eron	007	1976	£60	£120	
Both Sides Now	7"	Decca	F12841	1968	£2.50	£6	
Complete Guitarist	LP	Kicking Mule	SNKF138	1978	£4	£10	
Dance For Two People	LP	Kicking Mule	SNKF158	1979	£4	£10	
Folk Blues & Beyond	LP	Decca	LK4649	1964	£20	£40	
From A London Hootenanny	7" EP	Decca	DFE8538	1963	£7.50	£15	2 tracks by The Thamesiders
Godington Boundary	LP	President	PTLS1039	1970	£8	£20	
Guitar Player	LP	Golden Guinea	GGL0224	1962	£10	£25	
Hat	LP	Decca	SKL5011	1969	£25	£50	
Holly Kaleidoscope	LP	Decca	SKL5056	1970	£25	£50	
Large As Life & Twice As Natural	LP	Decca	SKL4969	1968	£20	£40	
Midnight Man	LP	Decca	LK4780	1966	£25	£50	

GRAHAM, DAVEY & ALEXIS KORNER

3/4 AD	7" EP	Topic	TOP70	1962	£25	£50

GRAHAM, DAVEY & SHIRLEY COLLINS

Folk Roots New Routes	LP	Decca	LK4652	1964	£50	£100
Folk Routes New Routes	LP	Righteous	GDC001	1980	£8	£20

GRAHAM, ERNIE

Ernie Graham	LP	Liberty	LBS83485	1971	£10	£25

GRAHAM, KENNY

Afro-Cubists	10" LP	Esquire	20012	1953	£8	£20
Afro-Cubists	10" LP	Esquire	20023	1953	£8	£20
Kenny Graham And His Satellites	LP	MGM	C764	1958	£6	£15
Kenny Graham's Afro Cubists	LP	Nixa	NJL12	1957	£6	£15

GRAHAM, LEN

Wind And Water	LP	Topic	12TS334	1977	£5	£12

GRAHAM, LOU

Wee Willie Brown	7"	Coral	Q72322	1958	£60	£120

GRAINER, RON ORCHESTRA

Maigret Theme	7"	Warner Bros	WB24	1960	£1.50	£4
Man In A Suitcase	7"	Pye	7N17383	1967	£2	£5
Prisoner	7"	RCA	RCA1635	1967	£15	£30
Prisoner Arrival	7" EP	Six Of One	6OF1	1979	£5	£10
That Was The Week That Was	7"	Decca	F11597	1963	£1.50	£4
Theme Music From Inspector Maigret	7" EP	Warner Bros	WEP6012	1960	£4	£8

GRAMMER, BILLY

Billy Grammer Hits	7" EP	Felsted	GEP1005	1959	£15	£30	
Gotta Travel On	7"	London	HLU8752	1958	£4	£8	
Kissing Tree	7"	Felsted	AF121	1959	£4	£8	
Rainbow Round My Shoulder	7"	Brunswick	05851	1961	£2.50	£6	
Travellin' On	LP	Monument	MLP/SLP14000	1961	£8	£20	US
Willy, Quit Your Playing	7"	Felsted	AF128	1959	£4	£8	

GRANAHAN, GERRY

It Hurts	7"	Top Rank	JAR262	1960	£5	£10	B side Richie Robin
No Chemise Please	7"	London	HL8668	1958	£7.50	£15	

GRAND FUNK RAILROAD

Following in the footsteps of such American groups as Iron Butterfly and Blue Cheer, Grand Funk Railroad presented a form of heavy metal in which loud excess took precedence over everything - certainly over genuine instrumental skill. The group's approach must have appealed to Frank Zappa's sense of kitsch, however, for he produced an album for them, calling it "Good Singing, Good Playing" - and he played guitar on the record as well.

Caught In The Act	LP	Capitol	ESTSP15	1975	£5	£12	double
Closer To Home	LP	Capitol	EST471	1970	£4	£10	
E Pluribus Funk	LP	Capitol	EAS853	1972	£4	£10	
Good Singing, Good Playing	LP	EMI	INA1503	1976	£4	£10	
Grand Funk	LP	Capitol	EST406	1970	£4	£10	
Live	LP	Capitol	EST633	1971	£5	£12	double
Mark,Don,& Mel 1969-71	LP	Capitol	ESTSP10	1972	£5	£12	double
On Time	LP	Capitol	EST307	1969	£5	£12	
Phoenix	LP	Capitol	11099	1973	£4	£10	
Shinin' On	LP	Capitol	11278	1974	£4	£10	
Survival	LP	Capitol	ESW764	1971	£4	£10	
We're An American Band	LP	Capitol	SMAS11207	1973	£4	£10	

332

We're An American Band	LP	Capitol	SMAS11207	1973	£5	£12	US, yellow vinyl

GRANDFATHER
Dear Mr.Time	LP	Square	SQA101	1970	£30	£60

GRANDISONS
All Right	7"	RCA	RCA1339	1963	£1.50	£4

GRANDMA'S ROCKERS
Homemade Apple Pie	LP	Fredlo	6727	1967	£150	£250	US

GRANGER, GERRI
Just Tell Him Jane Said Hello	7"	London	HLX9759	1963	£1.50	£4

GRANNIE
Grannie	LP	SRT	SRT71138	1971	£180	£300

GRANNY'S INTENTIONS
Hilda The Builder	7"	Deram	DM214	1968	£5	£10
Honest Injun	LP	Deram	SML1060	1970	£15	£30
Julie Don't Love Me Anymore	7"	Deram	DM184	1968	£5	£10
Story Of David	7"	Deram	DM158	1967	£6	£12
Take Me Back	7"	Deram	DM293	1970	£4	£8

GRANT, EARL
Earl Grant	7" EP	Brunswick	OE9460	1960	£5	£10
End	LP	Brunswick	LAT8297	1959	£4	£10
End	7"	Brunswick	05762	1958	£2	£5
House Of Bamboo	7"	Brunswick	05824	1960	£6	£12
Nothin' But The Blues	LP	Brunswick	LAT8332	1960	£4	£10
Stand By Me	7"	Brunswick	05945	1965	£2	£5
Swinging Gently	7" EP	Brunswick	OE9493	1963	£2	£5

GRANT, ERKEY & THE EARWIGS
I'm A Hog For You	7"	Pye	7N15521	1963	£7.50	£15

GRANT, GOGI
Both Ends Of The Candle	LP	RCA	RD27054	1958	£4	£10	
Goin' Home	7"	London	HLG9185	1960	£1.50	£4	
Golden Ladder	7"	London	HLB8550	1958	£4	£8	
If You Want To Get To Heaven - Shout!	LP	London	HAG2242/SAHG6072	1960	£6	£15	
Kiss Me, Honey Honey, Kiss Me	7"	RCA	RCA1105	1959	£1.50	£4	
Suddenly There's A Valley	7"	London	HLB8192	1955	£7.50	£15	
Suddenly There's Gogi Grant	LP	London	HAB2032	1957	£8	£20	
Wayward Wind	7"	London	HLB8282	1956	£7.50	£15	chart single
We Believe In Love	7"	London	HLB8257	1956	£7.50	£15	
You're In Love	7"	London	HLB8364	1957	£6	£12	

GRANT, GOGI & TONY MARTIN
Gigi	LP	RCA	RD27097	1959	£4	£10

GRANT, JULIE
Baby Baby	7"	Pye	7N15756	1965	£1.50	£4	
Come To Me	7"	Pye	7N15684	1964	£1.50	£4	chart single
Count On Me	7"	Pye	7N15508	1963	£1.50	£4	chart single
This Is Julie Grant	7" EP	Pye	NEP24171	1962	£2.50	£6	
Up On The Roof	7"	Pye	7N15483	1962	£1.50	£4	chart single

GRANT, LEE & THE CAPITOLS
Breaking Point	7"	Parlophone	R5531	1966	£6	£12

GRANT, NORMAN ORCHESTRA
Jive Medley	7"	Starlite	ST45060	1961	£1.50	£4

GRANT, TOP
Money Money Money	7"	Island	WI074	1963	£5	£10
Riverbank Cobberley	7"	Island	WI072	1963	£5	£10
Searching	7"	Island	WI034	1962	£5	£10
Suzie	7"	Island	WI052	1962	£5	£10
War In Africa	7"	Island	WI077	1963	£5	£10

GRAPEFRUIT
Around Grapefruit	LP	Stateside	(S)SL5008	1969	£6	£15	
C'mon Marianne	7"	RCA	RCA1716	1968	£1.50	£4	chart single
Dear Delilah	7"	RCA	RCA1656	1968	£1.50	£4	chart single
Deep Water	LP	RCA	SF8030	1969	£6	£15	
Deep Water	7"	RCA	RCA1855	1969	£2.50	£6	
Elevator	7"	RCA	RCA1677	1968	£2	£5	
Lady Godiva	7"	RCA	RCA1907	1969	£2	£5	
Round Going Round	7"	Stateside	SS8011	1969	£2.50	£6	
Sha Sha	7"	Deram	DM343	1971	£1.50	£4	
Someday Soon	7"	Stateside	SS8005	1968	£2.50	£6	

GRAPPELLY, STEPHANE
Stephane Grappelly	10" LP	Felsted	SDL86048	1956	£8	£20
Stephane Grappelly And His Quintet	LP	Felsted	PDL85027	1957	£8	£20

GRASS ROOTS
All Good Things Come To An End	7"	Stateside	SS8012	1969	£1.50	£4
Bella Linda	7"	Stateside	SS8006	1969	£2	£5

Golden Grass	LP	Dunhill	(S)SL5005	1969	£4	£10	
Heaven Knows	7"	Stateside	SS8033	1969	£1.50	£4	
I'd Wait A Million Years	7"	Stateside	SS8029	1969	£1.50	£4	
Leaving It Behind	LP	Stateside	SSL5012	1969	£4	£10	
Let's Live For Today	LP	Dunhill	D(S)50020	1967	£5	£12	US
Let's Live For Today	7"	Pye	7N25422	1967	£2.50	£6	
Melody For You	7"	RCA	RCA1682	1968	£1.50	£4	
Midnight Confessions	7"	RCA	RCA1737	1968	£4	£8	
River Is Wide	7"	Stateside	SS8018	1969	£1.50	£4	
Their Sixteen Greatest Hits	LP	ABC	QD40013	1974	£4	£10	US quad
Things I Should Have Said	7"	Pye	7N25431	1967	£2.50	£6	
Where Were You When I Needed You	LP	Dunhill	D(S)50011	1966	£5	£12	US
Where Were You When I Needed You	7"	RCA	RCA1532	1966	£2	£5	
Where Were You When I Needed You	7" EP	RCA	86906	1966	£10	£20	French
Who Will You Be Tomorrow	7"	Stateside	SS8023	1969	£1.50	£4	

GRATEFUL DEAD

American Beauty	LP	Mobile Fidelity	MFSL1014	1978	£6	£15	US audiophile
American Beauty	LP	Warner Bros	WS1893	1971	£5	£12	
Anthem Of The Sun	LP	Warner Bros	WS1749	1968	£5	£12	
Aoxomoxoa	LP	Warner Bros	WS1790	1969	£5	£12	
Blues For Allah	LP	United Artists	UAS29895	1975	£4	£10	
Born Cross-Eyed	7"	Warner Bros	WB7186	1967	£7.50	£15	
Dark Star	7"	Warner Bros	SAM79	1977	£2.50	£6	
Dead Zone	CD			198-	£50	£100	6 discs, booklet, poster
Europe '72	LP	Warner Bros	K66019	1972	£8	£20	triple
From The Mars Hotel	LP	Grateful Dead	K59302	1974	£5	£12	
From The Mars Hotel	LP	Mobile Fidelity	MFSL1172	1980	£8	£20	US audiophile
From The Mars Hotel	LP	United Artists	UAS29904	1976	£4	£10	
Grateful Dead	LP	Warner Bros	W(S)1689	1967	£6	£15	
Grateful Dead Live	LP	Warner Bros	K66009	1971	£6	£15	double
Historic Dead	LP	Polydor	2310171	1972	£6	£15	
Historic Dead	LP	Sunflower	SNF5004	1971	£8	£20	US
History Of The Grateful Dead (Bear's Choice)	LP	Warner Bros	K46246	1973	£5	£12	
Let Me Sing Your Blues Away	7"	Warner Bros	K19301	1973	£2	£5	
Live Dead	LP	Warner Bros	K66002	1971	£6	£12	green label, double
Live Dead	LP	Warner Bros	WS1830	1970	£6	£15	double
One More Saturday Night	7"	Warner Bros	K16167	1972	£2.50	£6	
Skeletons From The Closet	LP	Warner Bros	K56024	1974	£4	£10	
Steal Your Face	LP	United Artists	UAD60131/2	1976	£8	£20	double & bonus LP
Stealin'	7"	Scorpio	201	1966	£50	£100	US
Terrapin Station	LP	Direct Disk	SD16619	1979	£15	£30	US audiophile
Uncle John's Band	7"	Warner Bros	WB7410	1970	£4	£8	
U.S.Blues	7"	United Artists	UP36030	1974	£2	£5	
Vintage Dead	LP	Polydor	2310172	1972	£6	£15	
Vintage Dead	LP	Sunflower	SNF5001	1970	£8	£20	US
Wake Of The Flood	LP	Grateful Dead	K49301	1973	£5	£12	
Wake Of The Flood	LP	United Artists	UAS29903	1976	£4	£10	
Workingman's Dead	LP	Warner Bros	WS1869	1970	£5	£12	chart LP

GRAVENITES, NICK

My Labours	LP	CBS	63818	1969	£6	£15	
Steelyard Blues	LP	Liberty	352662	1973	£5	£12	US

GRAVES, CONLEY

Genius At Work	LP	Brunswick	LAT8116	1956	£5	£12	

GRAVY TRAIN

Ballad Of A Peaceful Man	LP	Vertigo	6360051	1971	£75	£150	spiral label
Climb Aboard The Gravy Train	7"	Dawn	DNS1115	1975	£1.50	£4	
Gravy Train	LP	Vertigo	6360023	1970	£15	£30	spiral label
Second Birth	LP	Dawn	DNLS3046	1973	£15	£30	
Staircase To The Day	LP	Dawn	DNLH1	1974	£15	£30	
Starbright Starlight	7"	Dawn	DNS1058	1974	£2	£5	
Strength Of A Dream	7"	Dawn	DNS1036	1973	£2	£5	

GRAY, BARRY

Adventures Of Twizzle	7" EP	HMV	7EG8339	1957	£5	£10	
Captain Scarlet	7"	Pye	7N17391	1967	£6	£12	
Fireball XL5	7"	Melodisc	1591	1964	£5	£10	
Joe 90	7"	Pye	7N17625	1969	£2	£5	
Robot Man	7"	Philips	326587BF	1963	£6	£12	PS, with Mary Jane
Robot Man	7"	Philips	326587BF	1963	£2.50	£6	with Mary Jane
Supercar Club	7"	National	LYN250	1962	£7.50	£15	
Supercar: Flight Of Fancy	LP	Golden Guinea	GGL0106	1961	£15	£30	
Thunderbirds Are Go!	LP	United Artists	SULP1159	1967	£35	£70	stereo
Thunderbirds Are Go!	LP	United Artists	ULP1159	1966	£30	£60	mono
Thunderbirds Theme	7"	Pye	7N17016	1965	£5	£10	
Thunderbirds Theme	7"	Pye	7N17016	1965	£10	£20	PS
Twizzle: Stories And Songs	7" EP	HMV	7EG8417	1957	£5	£10	

GRAY BROTHERS

Always	7"	Blue Cat	BS124	1968	£4	£8	

GRAY, CLAUDE

Country And Western Aces	7" EP	Mercury	10012MCE	1964	£4	£8	

GRAY, DOBIE

Dobie Gray Sings For In Crowders	LP	Charger	CHRM/CHRS2002	1965	£6	£15	US

In Crowd	7"	London	HL10268	1969	£1.50	£4	
In Crowd	7"	London	HL9953	1965	£4	£8	chart single
Out On The Floor	7"	Black Magic	BM107	1975	£1.50	£4	chart single
See You At The Go-Go	7"	Pye	7N25307	1965	£10	£20	

GRAY, DOLORES

After You Get What You Want	7"	Brunswick	05382	1955	£1.50	£4	
Rock Love	7"	Brunswick	05407	1955	£5	£10	
There'll Be Some Changes Made	7"	Capitol	CL14732	1957	£1.50	£4	

GRAY, GLENN

Glenn Gray And The Casa Loma Orchestra	LP	Capitol	LCT6128	1957	£4	£10	

GRAY, HERBIE

We're Staying Here	7"	Giant	GN38	1968	£4	£8	

GRAY, JERRY

Jerry Gray And His Orchestra	LP	Brunswick	LAT8164	1957	£5	£12	

GRAY, JOHNNIE

Apache	7"	Fontana	H134	1958	£5	£10	
Tequila	7"	Fontana	H123	1958	£5	£10	

GRAY, OWEN

Am Satisfy	7"	Collins Downbeat	CR007	1968	£4	£8	Sir Collins B side
Ay Ay Ay	7"	Fab	FAB96	1969	£2.50	£6	
Best Twist	7"	Blue Beat	BB113	1962	£5	£10	
Big Mabel	7"	Blue Beat	BB147	1962	£5	£10	
Call Me My Pet	7"	Blue Beat	BB188	1963	£5	£10	
Collins Greetings	7"	Collins Downbeat	CR003	1967	£4	£8	
Come On Baby	7"	Chek	TD101	1962	£4	£8	
Cupid	LP	Melodisc	MLP12153	196-	£6	£15	
Cutest Little Woman	7"	Blue Beat	BB8	1961	£5	£10	
Days I'm Living	7"	Blue Beat	BB365	1965	£5	£10	
Do You Want To Jump	7"	Blue Beat	BB108	1962	£5	£10	
Dolly Baby	7"	Island	WI020	1962	£5	£10	
Don't Take Your Love Away	7"	Camel	CA34	1969	£1.50	£4	
Draw Me Nearer	7"	Blue Beat	BB217	1963	£5	£10	
Every Beat Of My Heart	7"	Camel	CA37	1969	£1.50	£4	
Experienced	7"	Trojan	TR670	1969	£2	£5	
Get Drunk	7"	Blue Beat	BB43	1961	£5	£10	
Girl What You Doing To Me	7"	Camel	CA25	1969	£1.50	£4	
Give It To Me	7"	Coxsone	CS7053	1968	£5	£10	
Give Me A Little Sign	7"	Coxsone	CS7047	1968	£5	£10	
Groovin'	7"	Downtown	DT423	1969	£1.50	£4	Herbie Gray B side
Help Me	7"	Island	WIP6000	1967	£5	£10	
I Can't Stop Loving You	7"	Blue Cat	BS156	1969	£4	£8	
I Can't Stop Loving You	7"	Trojan	TR650	1969	£2	£5	
I Feel Good	7"	Starlite	ST45078	1962	£4	£8	
I'm Gonna Take You Back	7"	Collins Downbeat	CR010	1968	£4	£8	Glen Adams B side
I'm So Lonely	7"	Collins Downbeat	CR004	1967	£4	£8	Sir Collins B side
I'm Still Waiting	7"	Island	WI048	1962	£5	£10	
In My Dreams	7"	Starlite	ST45088	1962	£4	£8	
It's Gonna Work Out Fine	7"	Aladdin	WI603	1965	£4	£8	
Jenny Lee	7"	Starlite	ST45019	1960	£2.50	£6	
Linda Lu	7"	Island	WI607	1965	£4	£8	
Lovey Dovey	7"	Downtown	DT428	1969	£1.50	£4	Herbie Gray B side
Lovey Dovey	7"	Trojan	TR632	1968	£2.50	£6	
Mash It	7"	Starlite	ST45032	1961	£4	£8	
Midnight Track	7"	Island	WI030	1962	£5	£10	
No Good Woman	7"	Blue Beat	BB103	1962	£5	£10	
On The Beach	7"	Dice	CC3	1962	£5	£10	
Paradise	7"	Island	WI267	1966	£5	£10	
Please Let Me Go	7"	Starlite	ST45015	1960	£2	£5	
Pretty Girl	7"	Blue Beat	BB127	1962	£5	£10	
Reggae Dance	7"	Duke	DU12	1969	£2.50	£6	
Reggae With Soul	LP	Trojan	TTL24	1969	£5	£12	
Rocking In My Feet	7"	Blue Beat	BB75	1961	£5	£10	
Seven Lonely Days	7"	Duke	DU33	1969	£2.50	£6	
She's Gone To Napoli	7"	Blue Beat	BB114	1963	£5	£10	with Laurel Aitken
Shook Shimmy And Shake	7"	Island	WI252	1965	£5	£10	
Sings	LP	Starlite	STLP5	1961	£50	£100	
Snow Falling	7"	Blue Beat	BB201	1963	£5	£10	
Sugar Dumpling	7"	Pama	PM810	1970	£2	£5	
Swing Low	7"	Fab	FAB126	1969	£2.50	£6	
These Foolish Things	7"	Blue Cat	BS123	1968	£4	£8	
They Got To Move	7"	Blue Beat	BB136	1962	£5	£10	
Three Coins In The Fountain	7"	Fab	FAB90	1969	£2.50	£6	
Tree In The Meadow	7"	Blue Beat	BB139	1962	£5	£10	
Twist Baby	7"	Island	WI002	1962	£5	£10	
Understand My Love	7"	Fab	FAB120	1969	£2.50	£6	
You Don't Know Like I Know	7"	Island	WI258	1965	£5	£10	

GRAY, WARDELL

Memorial Album Vol.1	LP	Stateside	SL10144	1965	£4	£10	
Memorial Album Vol.2	LP	Stateside	SL10145	1965	£4	£10	

Memorial Vol.1	LP	Esquire	32016	1956	£15	£30
Memorial Vol.2	LP	Esquire	32023	1957	£15	£30

GRAY, WARDELL & DEXTER GORDON

Chase And Steeplechase	10" LP	Brunswick	LA8646	1954	£30	£60

GRAYZELL, RUDY

Looking At The Moon	7"	London	HL8094	1954	£25	£50

GRAZINA

Be My Baby	7"	HMV	POP1212	1963	£2	£5
Don't Be Shy	7"	HMV	POP1149	1963	£2	£5
Lover Please Believe Me	7"	HMV	POP1094	1962	£2.50	£6

GREAT AWAKENING

The instrumental version of "Amazing Grace" credited to The Great Awakening starts with a single electric guitar, then rapidly adds further guitars until a whole choir of them are wailing away at the traditional theme. Then the guitars are stripped away until the solo guitar is left to finish the piece. It is extraordinarily effective - and the only clue to the artist responsible is in the "Cohen" arranging credit. This is, in fact, David Cohen, guitarist with Country Joe And The Fish, who, by means of extensive over-dubbing, makes up the Great Awakening on his own.

Amazing Grace	7"	London	HLU10284	1969	£4	£8

GREAT, JOHNNY B

School Is In	7"	Decca	F11740	1963	£1.50	£4
You'll Never Leave Me	7"	Decca	F11804	1964	£1.50	£4

GREAT LEAP FORWARD

Controlling The Edges Of Tone	7"	Ron Johnson	ZRON20	1987	£1.50	£4

GREAT SATURDAY NIGHT SWINDLE

Great Saturday Night Swindle	LP	CBS		1977	£15	£30	Irish

GREAT SOCIETY

Conspicuous Only In Its Absence	LP	CBS	63476	1968	£6	£15	
How It Was	LP	CBS	CS9702	1968	£8	£20	US
Someone To Love	7"	North Beach	1001	1966	£25	£50	US

GREATEST SHOW ON EARTH

Going's Easy	LP	Harvest	SHVL783	1970	£10	£25	
Greatest Show On Earth	LP	Harvest	SHSM2004	1975	£8	£20	double
Horizons	LP	Harvest	SHVL769	1970	£10	£25	

GREAVES, R.B.

Fire And Rain	7"	Atlantic	2091013	1970	£1.50	£4
Paperback Writer	7"	Atlantic	2091170	1971	£1.50	£4
Take A Letter Maria	7"	Atco	226007	1969	£1.50	£4

GRECO, BUDDY

At Mister Kelly's	LP	Vogue Coral	LVA9021	1956	£5	£12
I've Grown Accustomed To Her Face	7"	London	HLR8613	1958	£1.50	£4
My Buddy	LP	Fontana	TFL5098	1960	£4	£10
Songs Fro Swinging Losers	LP	Fontana	TFL5125/STFL552.	1961	£4	£10
With All My Heart	7"	London	HLR8452	1957	£5	£10

GRECO, JULIETTE

Juliette Greco Sings	10" LP	Philips	BBR8023	1954	£5	£12

GREEK FOUNTAIN RIVER FRONT BAND

Takes Requests	LP	Montel	LLP110	1965	£25	£50	US

GREEN, AL

Back Up Train	LP	Action	ACLP6008	1969	£6	£15	
Back Up Train	7"	Bell	BLL1188	1971	£2.50	£6	
Back Up Train	7"	Stateside	SS2079	1968	£5	£10	
Don't Hurt Me No More	7"	Action	ACT4540	1969	£2.50	£6	
Full Of Fire (extended)	7"	London	HLU10511	1975	£2	£5	promo only

GREEN ANGELS

Exile's Dream	7"	Parlophone	R5512	1966	£2	£5
Let It Happen	7"	Parlophone	R5390	1965	£4	£8

GREEN BEAN

Garden's Lovely	7"	Regal Zonophone	RZ3017	1969	£2	£5

GREEN BULLFROG

Green Bullfrog	LP	MCA	MKPS2021	1972	£8	£20

GREEN, GARLAND

Jealous Kind Of Fellow	7"	MCA	BAG9	1969	£1.50	£4

GREEN, GRANT

Alive	LP	Blue Note	BST84360	1970	£5	£12
Am I Blue	LP	Blue Note	BLP/BST84139	1965	£15	£30
Carryin' On	LP	Blue Note	BST84327	1969	£6	£15
Feelin' The Spirit	LP	Blue Note	BLP/BST84132	1963	£15	£30
Goin' West	LP	Blue Note	BST84310	1969	£6	£15
Grant's First Stand	LP	Blue Note	BLP/BST84064	1961	£20	£40
Grantstand	LP	Blue Note	BLP/BST84086	196-	£15	£30
Green Is Beautiful	LP	Blue Note	BST84342	1970	£5	£12
Green Street	LP	Blue Note	BLP/BST84071	1962	£15	£30
I Want To Hold Your Hand	LP	Blue Note	BLP/BST84202	1966	£15	£30
Idle Moments	LP	Blue Note	BLP/BST84154	1964	£15	£30

Latin Bit	LP	Blue Note	BLP/BST84111	1963	£15	£30	
Shades Of Green	LP	Blue Note	BST84413	1970	£5	£12	
Street Of Dreams	LP	Blue Note	BLP/BST84253	1968	£8	£20	
Sunday Mornin'	LP	Blue Note	BLP/BST84099	1962	£20	£40	
Talkin' About!	LP	Blue Note	BLP/BST84183	1964	£20	£40	
Visions	LP	Blue Note	BST84373	1970	£5	£12	

GREEN, HUGHIE & MONICA ROSE

Cuddle Up	7"	Columbia	DB8085	1966	£1.50	£4	

GREEN, IAN

Last Pink Rose	7"	Polydor	56194	1967	£4	£8	
Revelation	LP	CBS	63840	1970	£6	£15	
Revelation	7"	CBS	4623	1969	£2	£5	
When You Love A Man	7"	CBS	3997	1969	£2	£5	

GREEN, KATHE

If I Thought You'd Ever Change Your Mind	7"	Deram	DM279	1969	£1.50	£4	
Run The Length Of Your Wildness	LP	Deram	SML1039	1969	£15	£30	

GREEN ON RED

Two Bibles	LP	private		1981	£8	£20	US

GREEN, PETER

Like B.B.King before him, Peter Green discovered the knack of playing a single note on the guitar with real soul. Performances like "The Supernatural", with John Mayall, or "I Loved Another Woman" and "Love That Burns" with Fleetwood Mac are testimony and tribute to an outstanding blues guitar voice. "The End Of The Game" is a different kind of guitar playing. In place of soul and beauty, there is anger and anguish, burning out of every twisted note of these largely improvised instrumentals. It is no wonder that Green's next act was to quit the music business, give away all his money, and embark on a life of withdrawn paranoia from which he has never really recovered, despite the occasional foray back into the recording studio.

Apostle	7"	PVK	PV16	1978	£1.50	£4	
Beast Of Burden	7"	Reprise	K14141	1972	£2	£5	
Blue Guitar	LP	Creole	CRX5	1981	£5	£12	blue or black vinyl
Case Of The Blues	LP	Nightflite	NTFL2001	1987	£4	£10	
Clown	7"	Headline	LIN2	1982	£1.50	£4	
Come On Down	LP	Homestead	MHS031	1986	£4	£10	
End Of The Game	LP	Reprise	RSLP9006	1970	£5	£12	
Give Me Back My Freedom	7"	PVK	PV103	1981	£1.50	£4	
Heavy Heart	7"	Reprise	K14092	1971	£1.50	£4	
Heavy Heart	7"	Reprise	RS27012	1971	£2	£5	
In The Skies	LP	PVK	PVLS101	1979	£5	£12	green or black vinyl
In The Skies	7"	PVK	PV24	1980	£1.50	£4	
Kolors	LP	Headline	HED2	1983	£5	£12	
Little Dreamer	LP	PVK	PVLS102	1980	£5	£12	
Loser Two Times	7"	PVK	PV41	1980	£1.50	£4	
Promised Land	7"	PVK	PV112	1981	£1.50	£4	
Walkin' The Road	7"	PVK	PV36	1980	£1.50	£4	
Whatcha Gonna Do?	LP	PVK	PET1	1981	£5	£12	
White Sky	LP	Headline	HED1	1982	£5	£12	

GREEN RIVER BOYS

Big Bluegrass Special	LP	Capitol	(S)T1810	1962	£10	£25	US

GREEN, URBIE

All About Urbie Green	LP	HMV	CLP1158	1958	£6	£15	
Urbie Green Orchestra	LP	London	LTZN15002	1956	£8	£20	

GREENBAUM, NORMAN

Spirit In The Sky	LP	Reprise	RS6365	1969	£5	£12	US
Spirit In The Sky	7"	Reprise	RS20885	1970	£1.50	£4	

GREENBEATS

If This World Were Mine	7"	Pye	7N15718	1964	£1.50	£4	
Please Don't Tell	7"	Pye	7N15648	1964	£1.50	£4	
Pretty Woman	7"	Spin	SP2007	1967	£1.50	£4	
So Sad	7"	Pye	7N15843	1965	£1.50	£4	
You Win Again	7"	Pye	7N17463	1968	£1.50	£4	

GREENE, BERNIE & HIS STEREO MAD-MEN

Musically Mad	LP	RCA	LPM/LSP1929	1958	£8	£20	US

GREENE, CLAUDE 'FATS'

Fats Shake 'Em Up	7"	Island	WI290	1966	£5	£10	

GREENE, DODO

My Hour Of Need	LP	Blue Note	BLP/BST9001	1962	£20	£40	

GREENE, LORNE

Ringo	7"	RCA	RCA1428	1964	£1.50	£4	chart single

GREENSLADE

Bedside Manners Are Extra	LP	Warner Bros	K46259	1973	£5	£12	
Greenslade	LP	Warner Bros	K46207	1973	£5	£12	
Spyglass Guest	LP	Warner Bros	K56055	1974	£5	£12	
Time And Tide	LP	Warner Bros	K56126	1975	£5	£12	

GREENSLADE, ARTHUR

Rockin' Susannah	7"	Decca	F11363	1961	£1.50	£4	

GREENSLADE, DAVE
"The Pentateuch" is not so much a double LP that includes a book, as a book that just happens to have a couple of records tucked into pockets in its cover. The illustrations, packed with a wealth of often disturbing detail, are the essence of "The Pentateuch" - Dave Greenslade's rather simple keyboard music just cannot match their impact. Now if only Patrick Woodruffe, or some other talented illustrator, would get together with Vangelis, or, better still, Tomita...

Cactus Choir	LP	Warner Bros....	K56306	1976	£5	£12		
Pentateuch	LP	EMI	EMC3321/2	1979	£6	£15	double with book

GREENWICH, ELLIE
Composes, Produces And Sings	LP	United Artists..	UAS6648	1968	£6	£15	US
I Want You To Be My Baby	7"	United Artists..	UP1180	1967	£2	£5	
Sunshine After The Rain	7"	United Artists..	UP2214	1968	£2	£5	

GREENWOOD, NICK
Although when Vincent Crane was perfectly capable of supplying a bass line with his organ pedals, Arthur Brown's management insisted on adding a bass player to the Crazy World. This was Nick Greenwood - later a member of Khan. Kingdom records issued his solo LP in 1972, which is now extremely scarce.

Cold Cuts	LP	Kingdom	KVLP9002	1972	£180	£300

GREGG, BOBBY & FRIENDS
Jam	7"	Columbia	DB4825	1962	£2	£5

GREGORY, IAN
Can't You Hear The Beat	7"	Pye	7N15397	1961	£5	£10	chart single
How Many Times	7"	Columbia	DB7085	1963	£2.50	£5	
Mr.Lovebug	7"	Pye	7N15435	1962	£4	£8	
Time Will Tell	7"	Pye	7N15295	1960	£4	£8	

GREGORY, JOHNNY
Bonanza	7" EP	Fontana	TFE17331	1960	£4	£8
Maverick	7" EP	Fontana	TFE17325	1960	£4	£8
Route Sixty-Six	7" EP	Fontana	TFE17382	1962	£2.50	£6
TV Thrillers	7" EP	Fontana	TFE17389	1962	£4	£8

GREGORY, JOHNNY ORCHESTRA
Bonanza	7"	Fontana	H286	1960	£2.50	£6
Route 66	7"	Fontana	H341	1961	£2.50	£6
TV Western Themes	LP	Fontana	TFL5110/ STFL5338	1961	£4	£10
Wagon Train	7"	Fontana	H288	1961	£2.50	£6

GREGORY, TONY
Baby Come On Home	7"	Doctor Bird	DB1007	1966	£5	£10	
Get Out Of My Life	7"	Island	WI3029	1967	£5	£10	Soul Brothers B side
Give Me One More Chance	7"	Doctor Bird	DB1016	1966	£5	£10	
Only A Fool	7"	Coxsone	CS7013	1967	£5	£10	
Sings	LP	Coxsone	CSL8011	1967	£50	£100	

GREMLINS
Coming Generation	7"	Mercury	MF981	1966	£5	£10
You Gotta Believe It	7"	Mercury	MF1004	1967	£5	£10

GREY, RONNIE & THE JETS
Run Manny Run	7"	Capitol	CL14329	1955	£10	£20

GREYHOUND
Black And White	LP	Trojan	TRLS27	1971	£5	£12

GRIER, ROOSEVELT
C'mon Cupid	7"	Pama	PM784	1969	£2	£5
People Make The World	7"	Action	ACT4515	1968	£2	£5
Who's Got The Ball Y'All	7"	Pama	PM774	1969	£2	£5

GRIFFIN
I Am The Noise In Your Head	7"	Bell	BLL1075	1969	£10	£20
In The Darkness	7"	MGM	2006088	1972	£2	£5

GRIFFIN, JAMES
Summer Holiday	LP	Reprise	R(9)6091	1963	£5	£12	US

GRIFFIN, JOHNNY
Big Soul-Band	LP	Riverside	RLP12331	1960	£6	£15	
Change Of Pace	LP	Riverside	RLP368	1961	£6	£15	
Lookin' At Monk	LP	Jazzland	JLP39	1961	£8	£20	with Eddie 'Lockjaw' Davis
Tough Tenors	LP	Jazzland	JLP31	1960	£8	£20	with Eddie 'Lockjaw' Davis

GRIFFITH, ANDY
Andy Griffith	7" EP	Capitol	EAP1630	1956	£4	£8
Ko Ko Mo	7"	Capitol	CL14263	1955	£2.50	£6
Mama Guitar	7"	Capitol	CL14766	1957	£2	£5
Midnight Special	7"	Capitol	CL14936	1958	£1.50	£4
No Time For Sergeants	7"	Capitol	CL14619	1956	£1.50	£4

GRIFFITHS, MARCIA
Don't Let Me Down	7"	Escort	ES808	1969	£2.50	£6	Reggaeites B side
Feel Like Jumping	7"	Coxsone	CS7055	1968	£5	£10	Horace Taylor B side
Funny	7"	Island	WI285	1966	£5	£10	King Sparrow B side
Hound Dog	7"	Studio One	SO2008	1967	£6	£12	Hugh Godfrey B side
Mojo Girl	7"	Coxsone	CS7035	1968	£5	£10	Hamlins B side

Mr.Everything	7"	Rio	R121	1966	£4	£8	Soul Brothers B side
Put A Little Love In Your Heart	7"	Trojan	TR693	1969	£2.50	£6	J Boys B side
Talk	7"	High Note	HS029	1969	£4	£8	
Tell Me Now	7"	Gas	GAS111	1969	£4	£8	Stan Hope B side
Truly	7"	Studio One	SO2059	1968	£6	£12	Simms & Robinson B side
Words	7"	Studio One	SO2047	1968	£6	£12	Sharks B side
You Keep Me On The Move	7"	Studio One	SO2069	1968	£6	£12	Mr.Foundation B side

GRIGNARD, FERRE

Hash Bamboo Shuffle	7" EP	Philips	434337	196-	£5	£10	French
La Si Do 25	7" EP	Barclay	71199	1968	£6	£12	French
Ring Ring I've Got To Sing	7" EP	Philips	434330	196-	£5	£10	French

GRIMES, CAROL

Fools Meeting (with Delivery)	LP	B&C	CAS1023	1970	£15	£30	
Warm Blood	LP	Caroline	CA2001	1974	£5	£12	

GRIMES, TINY

Callin' The Blues	LP	Esquire	32092	1960	£6	£15	

GRIMMS

Grimms	LP	Island	HELP11	1973	£4	£10	
Rocking Duck	LP	Island	ILPS9248	1973	£4	£10	
Sleepers	LP	DJM	DJLPS470	1976	£4	£10	

GRIN

Grin	LP	Epic	64272	1971	£4	£10	
One Plus One	LP	Epic	64652	1972	£4	£10	

GRINGO

Gringo	LP	MCA	MKPS2017	1971	£5	£12	

GRINNE, JOE

Mr.Editor	7"	Coxsone	CS7098	1969	£5	£10	

GRISBY DYKE

Adventures Of Miss Rosemary La Page	7"	Deram	DM232	1969	£2.50	£6	

GROBSCHNITT

Ballermann	LP	Brain	20001050	1974	£5	£12	German double
Grobschnitt	LP	Brain	0001008	1972	£10	£25	German
Jumbo (English Lyrics)	LP	Brain	0001076	1975	£4	£10	German
Jumbo (German Lyrics)	LP	Brain	0001081	1975	£4	£10	German

GRODECK WHIPPERJENNY

Grodeck Whipperjenny	LP	People	3000	196-	£8	£20	US

GROOM, DEWEY

Butane Blues	7"	Starlite	ST45085	1962	£4	£8	
Heartaches For Sale	7"	Starlite	ST45105	1963	£2	£5	
Walking Papers	7"	Starlite	ST45095	1963	£2.50	£6	

GROOP

Lovin' Tree	7"	CBS	3351	1968	£2	£5	

GROOVE

Wind	7"	Parlophone	R5783	1969	£4	£8	

GROOVE FARM

Baby Blue Marine	7"	Lyntone	LYN18632	1988	£4	£8	flexi, B side by Sea Urchins, no PS
Baby Blue Marine	7"	Lyntone	LYN18632	1988	£6	£12	flexi, B side by Sea Urchins, PS
Driving In Your New Car	7"	Subway Organisation	SUBWAY22N	1988	£6	£12	promo
Only The Most Ignorant...	7"	Raving Pop Blast	RPBGF2	1989	£2	£5	
Sore Heads And Happy Hearts	7"	Raving Pop Blast	RPBGF1	1987	£2.50	£6	

GROOVERS

You've Got To Cry	7"	Island	WI3080	1967	£5	£10	Alva Lewis B side

GROOVEY, WINSTON

Free The People	LP	Pama	PMP2011	1969	£5	£12	
Funky Chicken	7"	Jackpot	JP708	1969	£2	£5	Cimarrons B side
Funny	7"	Jackpot	JP709	1969	£2	£5	Cimarrons B side
Island In The Sun	7"	Nu Beat	NB041	1969	£2	£5	
Josephine	7"	Nu Beat	NB042	1969	£2	£5	
You Can't Turn Your Back On Me	7"	Attack	ATT8019	1969	£2	£5	Pama Dice B side

GROOV-U

On Campus	LP	Gateway	GLP3010		£6	£15	US

GROSSETT, G.G.

Greater Sounds	7"	Crab	CRAB33	1969	£2.50	£6	
Run Girl Run	7"	Crab	CRAB10	1969	£2.50	£6	Dennis Walks B side

GROSSMAN, STEFAN

Aunt Molly Murray's Farm	LP	Sonet	SNTF640	1973	£5	£12	

Bottleneck Serenade	LP	Transatlantic ...	TRA293	1975	£5	£12	
Country Blues Guitar	LP	Kicking Mule	SNKF129	1979	£5	£12	
Finger Picking Guitar Techniques	LP	XTRA	XTRA1138	1974	£5	£12	with booklet
Gramercy Park Sheik	LP	Fontana	STLS485	1969	£8	£20	
Gramercy Park Sheik	LP	Sonet	SNTF627	1972	£5	£12	
Guitar Instrumentals	LP	Transatlantic ...	TRA274	1973	£5	£12	
Hot Dogs	LP	Transatlantic ...	TRA257	1972	£5	£12	
How To Play Ragtime Guitar	LP	XTRA	XTRA1151	1975	£5	£12	with booklet
Live	LP	Transatlantic ...	TRA264	1973	£6	£15	double
Ragtime Cowboy Jew	LP	Transatlantic ...	TRA223	1970	£8	£20	double
Those Pleasant Days	LP	Transatlantic ...	TRA246	1971	£5	£12	
Yazoo Basin Boogie	LP	Kicking Mule	SNKF134	1977	£5	£12	
Yazoo Basin Boogie	LP	Transatlantic ...	TRA217	1970	£5	£12	

GROSVENOR, LUTHER

Under Open Skies	LP	Island	ILPS9168	1971	£4	£10	

GROUNDHOGS

Tony McPhee is a guitarist with a particularly good understanding of the blues, as his numerous session appearances on records by people like John Lee Hooker and Champion Jack Dupree testify. He was also one of the first musicians involved in the British blues boom of the late sixties to realise that it would not be possible to keep recycling the same twelve bar repertoire indefinitely without the public losing interest. "Blues Obituary" announced the end of an era with music that while obviously inspired by a love of the blues, nevertheless ranged very much more widely. Subsequently, McPhee became a little too convinced that he could play like Jimi Hendrix, but each Groundhogs LP still has its moments, with "Split" being something of a minor classic.

BDD	7"	Liberty	LBF15263	1969	£4	£8	
Best Of 1969-72	LP	United Artists	600063/4	1974	£5	£12	double
Black Diamond	LP	United Artists ..	UAG29994	1976	£4	£10	
Blues Obituary	LP	Liberty	LBS83253	1969	£15	£30	
Crosscut Saw	LP	United Artists ..	UAG29917	1976	£4	£10	
Eccentric Man	7"	Liberty	LBF15346	1970	£4	£8	
Hoggin' The Stage	LP	Psycho	PSYCHO24	1984	£8	£20	double with EP
Hogwash	LP	United Artists ..	UAG29419	1972	£4	£10	
I'll Never Fall In Love Again	7"	Planet	PLF104	1966	£15	£30	credited to John Lee's Groundhogs
Scratching The Surface	LP	Liberty	LBL/LBS83199	1968	£20	£40	
Solid	LP	WWA	WWA004	1974	£4	£10	
Split	LP	Liberty	LBS83401	1971	£4	£10	chart LP
Thank Christ For The Bomb	LP	Liberty	LBS83295	1970	£5	£12	chart LP
Who Will Save The World	LP	United Artists ..	UAG29237	1972	£4	£10	chart LP
You Don't Love Me	7"	Liberty	LBF15174	1968	£5	£10	

GROUP 1850

Agemo's Trip To Mother Earth	LP	Philips	SBL7884	1968	£35	£70	
Live	LP	Orange		1975	£6	£15	
Live 2	LP	Rubber		1974	£15	£30	
Live On Tour	LP	Rubber		1973	£15	£30	
Paradise Now	LP	Discotoon		1969	£35	£70	
Polyandri	LP	Rubber		1974	£15	£30	

GROUP B

I Know Your Name Girl	7"	Vocalion	VF9284	1967	£1.50	£4	

GROUP IMAGE

Mouth In The Clouds	LP	Stable	SLE8005	1969	£8	£20	

GROUP ONE

Chanson D'Amour	7"	HMV	POP492	1958	£1.50	£4	
She's Neat	7"	HMV	POP463	1958	£2	£5	

GROUP SIX

Rock A Boogie	7"	Oriole	CB1488	1959	£5	£10	

GROUP TWO

It's Raining Outside	7"	Columbia	DB8374	1968	£1.50	£4	

GROUP X

Roti Calliope	7"	Fontana	TF417	1963	£2	£5	
There Are 8 Million Cossack Melodies	7"	Fontana	267274TF	1963	£2	£5	
There Are 8 Million Cossack Melodies	7"	Fontana	267274TF	1963	£5	£10	PS

GROVE, BOBBY

It Was For You	LP	King	831	1963	£5	£12	US

GROWING CONCERN

Growing Concern	LP	Mainstream	S6108	1968	£8	£20	US

GROWL

Growl	LP	Discreet	DS2209	1974	£5	£12	US

GRUNBLATT, GEORGES

K-Priss	LP	Polydor	2473911	1980	£8	£20	French

GRUNSKY, JACK

Toronto	LP	Kuckuck	2375002	1970	£4	£10	German

GRUNT FUTTOCK

Rock'n'Roll Christian	7"	Regal Zonophone	RZ3042	1972	£7.50	£15	

GRYCE, GIGI

Gigi Gryce Octet	10" LP	Vogue	LDE113	1955	£20	£40	
Gigi Gryce Orchestra	10" LP	Vogue	LDE070	1954	£20	£40	

Jazz Time Paris Vol.2	10" LP	Vogue	LDE048	1954	£20	£40	....with Clifford Brown

GRYPHON

The growing influence of folk music during the early seventies led a few groups to try the integration of medieval instruments into a folk-rock setting. The most successful of these was Gryphon, whose "Midnight Mushrumps" in particular is something of a landmark. Later albums found the group retreating to a more ordinary rock sound, but Richard Harvey subsequently made much use of his love for medieval music in his solo career.

Gryphon	LP	Transatlantic	TRA262	1973	£6	£15	
Midnight Mushrumps	LP	Transatlantic	TRA282	1974	£5	£12	
Raindance	LP	Transatlantic	TRA302	1975	£4	£10	
Red Queen To Gryphon Three	LP	Transatlantic	TRA287	1974	£4	£10	
Treason	LP	Harvest	SHSP4063	1977	£4	£10	

G.T.O.'S

She Rides With Me	7"	Polydor	56721	1967	£4	£8	

GUARNIERI, JOHNNY

Songs Of Will Hudson And Eddie De Lange	LP	Vogue Coral	LVA9049	1957	£6	£15	

GUESS WHO

American Woman	7"	RCA	RCA1943	1970	£1.50	£4	chart single
Hey Ho What You Do To Me	7" EP.	Vogue	INT18038	1965	£10	£20	French
His Girl	7"	King	KG1044	1966	£5	£10	chart single
Laughing	7"	RCA	RCA1870	1969	£1.50	£4	
Miss Felicity Grey	7"	Fontana	TF861	1967	£4	£8	
Shakin' All Over	7"	Pye	7N25305	1965	£4	£8	
These Eyes	7"	RCA	RCA1832	1969	£1.50	£4	
This Time Long Ago	7"	Fontana	TF831	1967	£2.50	£6	

GUEST, EARL

Foxy	7"	Columbia	DB7212	1964	£4	£8	
Twisting John	7"	Columbia	DB4926	1962	£2	£5	
Winkle Picker Stomp	7"	Columbia	DB4707	1962	£2.50	£6	

GUEST, REG SYNDICATE

Underworld	LP	Mercury	20089MCL	1966	£6	£15	
Underworld	7"	Mercury	MF927	1965	£25	£50	

GUILLOTEENS

I Don't Believe	7"	Pye	7N25324	1965	£12.50	£25	

GUITAR, BONNIE

Dark Moon	LP	Dot	DLP3335/25335	1962	£4	£10	US
Moonlight And Shadows	LP	London	HAD2122	1958	£6	£15	
Very Precious Love	7"	London	HLD8591	1958	£2.50	£6	
Whispering Hope	LP	Dot	DLP3151/ DLP25151	1959	£5	£12	US

GUITAR CRUSHER WITH JIMMY SPRUILL

Since My Baby Hit The Numbers	7"	Blue Horizon	573149	1969	£7.50	£15	

GUITAR JUNIOR

Pick Me Up On Your Way Down	LP	Goldband	1085	1960	£5	£12	US

GUITAR NUBBIT

Georgia Chain Gang	7"	Bootleg	501	1964	£10	£20	

GUITAR RED

Just You And I	7"	Pye	7N25219	1963	£4	£8	

GUITAR SHORTY

Carolina Slide Guitar	LP	Flyright	LP500	1972	£5	£12	

GUITAR SLIM

Things That I Used To Do	LP	Speciality	2120	1964	£6	£15	US

GULDA, FRIEDRICH

At Birdland	LP	Decca	LK4188	1958	£8	£20	
Man Of Letters	LP	Decca	LK4189	1958	£8	£20	

GULLIN, LARS

Holiday For Piano	10" LP	Esquire	20015	1953	£25	£50	
Lars Gullin Compositions	10" LP	Esquire	20019	1953	£25	£50	
New Sounds From Europe Vol.3	10" LP	Vogue	LDE052	1954	£25	£50	

GULLIVER

Gulliver	LP	Elektra	2410006	1970	£4	£10	

GULLIVER'S PEOPLE

Hi Fo Fum	7"	Parlophone	R5464	1966	£1.50	£4	
On A Day Like This	7"	Parlophone	R5709	1968	£1.50	£4	
Somehow Somewhere	7"	Columbia	DB8588	1969	£1.50	£4	
Splendour in The Grass	7"	Parlophone	R5435	1966	£2	£5	

GUN

The Gun were a guitar trio fronted by Adrian Gurvitz, who has popped up periodically ever since. "Race With The Devil" was the Gun's calling card, a classic piece of hard rock, powered by one of those simple guitar riffs that seems to have been waiting around for ever for someone to just come along and play it. Not much of the rest of the Gun's material is in the same class, unfortunately.

Drives You Mad	7"	CBS	4052	1969	£1.50	£4	
Gun	LP	CBS	63552	1968	£6	£15	
Gunsight	LP	CBS	63683	1969	£10	£25	

Hobo	7"	CBS	4443	1969	£2	£5	2 different B sides
Race With The Devil	7"	CBS	3764	1968	£2	£5	chart single, 2 different B sides
Running Wild	7"	CBS	4952	1970	£2	£5	

GUNGO, KID
Hold The Pussy	7"	Escort	ES801	1969	£2	£5

GUNN, JON
If You Wish It	7"	Deram	DM166	1967	£2	£5
I've Just Made My Mind Up	7"	Deram	DM133	1967	£4	£8

GUNNER, JIM
Desperado	7"	Fontana	H313	1961	£4	£8
Hoolee Jump	7"	Decca	F11276	1960	£2.50	£6

GUNS 'N' ROSES
With a raunchy image and music to match, Guns 'n' Roses have slipped effortlessly into the niche left vacant by the semi-retired Rolling Stones. The fact that the group is too young to have a particularly extensive back-catalogue is no problem for colletors. The record company is only too willing to provide instant collectors' items in the form of limited edition releases of one sort or another. (The US promotional door mat - definitely an item for the collector who must have everything - has been selling for £60!)

Civil War	12"	WEA	SAM694	1991	£6	£15	promo
Don't Cry	CD-s	Geffen	GFSTD9	1991	£3	£8	
It's So Easy	7"	Geffen	GEF22	1987	£4	£8	
It's So Easy	12"	Geffen	GEF22T	1987	£4	£10	
It's So Easy	12"	Geffen	GEF22TP	1987	£20	£40	pic disc
Live ?!*@ Like A Suicide	LP	Uzi Suicide	USR001	1986	£40	£80	US, Sleeve pictured in Guide
Live And Let Die	CD-s	Geffen	GFSTD17	1991	£2.50	£6	
Night Train	CD-s	Geffen	GEF60CD	1989	£2.50	£6	
Nightrain	7"	Geffen	GEF60P	1989	£2.50	£6	shaped pic disc
November Rain	CD-s	Geffen	GFSTD18	1992	£3	£8	pic disc
Paradise City	CD-s	Geffen	GEF50CD	1989	£3	£8	
Paradise City	7"	Geffen	GEF50P	1989	£4	£8	shaped pic disc, clear background
Paradise City	7"	Geffen	GEF50P	1989	£7.50	£15	shaped pic disc, white background
Paradise City	7"	Geffen	GEF50X	1989	£4	£8	holster pack
Patience	CD-s	Geffen	GEF56CD	1989	£3	£8	
Sweet Child O' Mine	CD-s	Geffen	GEF55CD	1989	£3	£8	
Sweet Child Of Mine	7"	Geffen	GEF55P	1989	£7.50	£15	shaped pic disc
Sweet Child Of Mine	12"	Geffen	GEF43TV	1988	£6	£15	metallic sleeve
Sweet Child Of Mine	10"	Geffen	GEF43TE	1988	£8	£20	revolving sleeve
Welcome To The Jungle	CD-s	Geffen	GEF47CD	1988	£5	£12	
Welcome To The Jungle	7"	Geffen	GEF30	1987	£6	£12	
Welcome To The Jungle	12"	Geffen	GEF30T	1987	£15	£30	
Welcome To The Jungle	12"	Geffen	GEF30TP	1987	£15	£30	pic disc
Welcome To The Jungle	12"	Geffen	GEF30TW	1987	£6	£15	poster sleeve
Welcome To The Jungle	12"	Geffen	GEF47T	1988	£4	£10	with patch
Welcome To The Jungle	12"	Geffen	GEF47TP	1988	£6	£15	pic disc
Welcome To The Jungle	12"	Geffen	GEF47TW	1988	£2.50	£6	poster sleeve

GUNTER, ARTHUR
Black And Blues	LP	Excello	8017	1970	£37.50	£75	US
Blues After Hours	LP	Blue Horizon	2431012	1971	£17.50	£35	

GUNTHER, HARDROCK
Mountain Music	7" EP	Brunswick	OE9167	1955	£7.50	£15

GURU GURU
Dance Of The Flames	LP	Atlantic	K50044	1974	£4	£10	
Der Elektrolurch	LP	Brain	20001057	1974	£6	£15	German doubl
Don't Call Us We'll Call You	LP	Atlantic	K50022	1973	£4	£10	
Guru Guru	LP	Brain	0001025	1973	£5	£12	Germa
Hinten	LP	Ohr	556027	1971	£6	£15	Germa
Kan Guru	LP	Brain	0001007	1972	£5	£12	Germa
This Is Guru Guru	LP	Brain	200145	1973	£4	£10	Germa
UFO	LP	Ohr	556005	1970	£6	£15	Germa

GURUS
Blue Snow Night	7"	United Artists	UP1160	1966	£5	£10

GUSTAFSON, JOHNNY
Just To Be With You	7"	Polydor	56022	1965	£4	£8
Take Me For A Little While	7"	Polydor	56043	1965	£5	£10

GUTHRIE, ARLO
Alice's Restaurant	LP	Reprise	RLP6267	1967	£5	£12	chart L
Alice's Restaurant Soundtrack	LP	United Artists	UAS29061	1969	£5	£12	
Alice's Rock'n'Roll Restaurant	7"	Reprise	RS20877	1970	£2	£5	
Arlo	LP	Reprise	RSLP6299	1968	£5	£12	
Hobo's Lullabye	LP	Reprise	K44169	1972	£4	£10	
Last Of The Brooklyn Cowboys	LP	Reprise	K44236	1973	£4	£10	
Motorcycle Song	7"	Reprise	RS20644	1967	£2	£5	
Running Down The Road	LP	Reprise	RSLP6346	1969	£4	£10	
Valley Of Pray	7"	Reprise	RS20951	1970	£1.50	£4	dem
Washington County	LP	Reprise	RSLP6411	1970	£4	£10	

GUTHRIE, WOODY

Bound For Glory	LP	Topic	12T21	1958	£10	£25	
Dust Bowl Ballads	LP	RCA	RD7642	1964	£8	£20	
Greatest Songs	LP	Vanguard	VSD35/36	1972	£6	£15	US double
Guthrie's Story	LP	Topic	12T31	1958	£10	£25	
Hard It Ain't Hard	7" EP.	Melodisc	EPM784	1958	£5	£10	
Hey Lolly Lolly	7" EP.	Melodisc	EPM791	1959	£5	£10	
More Songs By Guthrie	LP	Melodisc	MLP12106	1955	£10	£25	
Poor Boy	LP	XTRA	XTRA1065	1968	£5	£12	
Songs To Grow On Vol.1	LP	XTRA	XTRA1067	1968	£5	£12	
Woody Guthrie	LP	Ember	CW129	1968	£5	£12	
Woody Guthrie	LP	XTRA	XTRA1012	1965	£5	£12	
Worried Man Blues	7" EP.	Melodisc	EPM785	1958	£5	£10	

GUY, BOB

"Dear Jeepers" is an early Frank Zappa composition.

Dear Jeepers	7"	Donna	1380	1963	£30	£60	US

GUY, BUDDY

Blues Today	LP	Vanguard	SVRL19004	1968	£5	£12	
Buddy And The Juniors	LP	Harvest	SHSP4006	1970	£6	£15	
Buddy Guy & Junior Wells Play The Blues	LP	Atlantic	K40240	1972	£5	£12	
Coming At You	LP	Vanguard	SVRL19001	1968	£5	£12	
Crazy Music	7" EP.	Chess	CRE6004	1965	£5	£10	
First Time I Met The Blues	LP	Python	KM2	1969	£8	£20	
Hold That Plane	LP	Vanguard	VSD79323	1972	£4	£10	
Honey Dripper	7"	Atlantic	K10195	1972	£1.50	£4	
Hot And Cool	LP	Vanguard	SVRL79290	1969	£4	£10	
I Was Walking Through The Woods	LP	Chess	LP409	196-	£8	£20	US
Left My Blues In San Francisco	LP	Chess	LPS1527	1969	£6	£15	US
Let Me Love You Baby	7"	Chess	CRS8004	1965	£4	£8	
Man And His Blues	LP	Vanguard	SVRL19002	1968	£8	£20	
Mary Had A Little Lamb	7"	Fontana	TF951	1968	£4	£8	
This Is Buddy Guy	LP	Vanguard	SVRL19008	1969	£8	£20	

GUYS

You Go Your Way	7"	Tepee	TPRSP1001	1969	£2.50	£6

GYGAFO

Legend Of The Kingfisher	LP	Holyground	HG1155	1989	£25	£50	1973 LP with 1989 cover

GYPSIES

Jerk it	7"	CBS	2785	1967	£10	£20

GYPSY

Brenda And The Rattlesnake	LP	United Artists	UAS29420	1972	£4	£10
Gypsy	LP	United Artists	UAS29155	1971	£4	£10

H

HABIBIYYA
If Man But Knew .... LP ...... Island .... HELP7 .... 1972 ... £5 .... £12

HABITS
Elbow Baby .... 7" ...... Decca .... F12348 .... 1966 ... £6 .... £12

HACKENSACK
Moving On .... 7" ...... Island .... WIP6149 .... 1972 ... £5 .... £10
Up The Hardway .... LP ...... Polydor .... 2383263 .... 1974 ... £30 .... £60

HACKETT, BOBBY
At The Embers .... LP ...... Capitol .... T1077 .... 1959 ... £4 .... £10
Bobby Hackett Jazz Band .... 10" LP Capitol .... LC6824 .... 1956 ... £5 .... £12
Gotham Jazz Scene .... LP ...... Capitol .... T857 .... 1958 ... £4 .... £10
Jazz Session .... 10" LP Columbia .... 33S1053 .... 1955 ... £6 .... £15
Rendezvous .... LP ...... Capitol .... T719 .... 1956 ... £4 .... £10
Trumpet Solos .... 10" LP Brunswick .... LA8587 .... 1953 ... £6 .... £15

HACKETT, STEVE
Cell 151 .... 12" .... Charisma .... CELL12/13 .... 1983 ... £4 .... £10 ....
Clocks - The Angel Of Mons .... 12" .... Charisma .... CB34112 .... 1979 ... £2.50 .... £6 ....double

HADEN, CHARLIE
Liberation Music Orchestra .... LP ...... Probe .... SPB1037 .... 1969 ... £5 .... £12

HAFFY'S WHISKEY SOUR
Shot In The Head .... 7" ...... Deram .... DM345 .... 1971 ... £2 .... £5

HAFLER TRIO
Bang! - An Open Letter .... LP ...... Doublevision ... DVR4 .... 1984 ... £4 .... £10
Three Ways Of Saying Two .... LP ...... Charrm .... 3 .... 1986 ... £5 .... £12

HAGAR, SAMMY
Sammy Hagar .... LP ...... Capitol .... EST11599 .... 1977 ... £4 .... £10 ....red vinyl

HAGER, JOAN
Happy Is A Girl Named Me .... 7" ...... Brunswick .... 05650 .... 1957 ... £4 .... £8

HAGGARD, MERLE
I'm A Lonesome Fugitive .... LP ...... Capitol .... (S)T2702 .... 1967 ... £4 .... £10
Legend Of Bonnie And Clyde .... LP ...... Capitol .... (S)T2912 .... 1968 ... £4 .... £10
Mama Tried .... LP ...... Capitol .... (S)T2972 .... 1968 ... £4 .... £10

HAHN, JERRY BROTHERHOOD
Jerry Hahn Brotherhood .... LP ...... Columbia .... CS1044 .... 1970 ... £5 .... £12 ....US

HAHN, JOYCE
Gonna Find Me A Bluebird .... 7" ...... London .... HLA8453 .... 1957 ... £4 .... £8

HAIG, AL
Al Haig Trio .... 10" LP Vogue .... LDE092 .... 1954 ... £20 .... £40
Jazz Will O' The Wisp .... LP ...... XTRA .... XTRA1125 .... 1971 ... £4 .... £10

HAINES, NORMAN
Daffodil .... 7" ...... Parlophone ...... R5871 .... 1970 ... £10 .... £20
Den Of Iniquity .... LP ...... Parlophone ...... PCS7130 .... 1971 ... £250 ...... £400
Give To You Girl .... 7" ...... Parlophone ...... R5960 .... 1972 ... £10 .... £20

HAIR
Hair Piece .... LP ...... Columbia .... SCX6452 .... 1970 ... £50 .... £100 ....sleeve
pictured in Guide

HAIRBAND
Band On The Wagon .... LP ...... Bell .... SBLL69 .... 1969 ... £10 .... £25
Big Louis .... 7" ...... Bell .... BLL1076 .... 1969 ... £5 .... £10

HAIRCUT 100
Blue Hat For A Blue Day .... LP ...... Arista .... HCC101 .... 1982 ... £4 .... £10 ....test pressing only
Whistle Down The Wind .... 7" ...... Arista .... CLIP5 .... 1983 ... £1.50 ...... £4

HAIRY CHAPTER
Can't Get Through .... LP ...... Bacillus .... 6494002 .... 1971 ... £5 .... £12 ....German
Can't Get Through .... LP ...... Bacillus .... BLPS19074 .... 1971 ... £5 .... £12 ....German
Eyes .... LP ...... Opp .... 521 .... 1970 ... £5 .... £12 ....German

HAIRY ONES
Get Off My Cloud .... 7" EP.. Barclay .... 70898 .... 1965 ... £6 .... £12 ....French

HAL HOPPERS
Baby I've Had It .... 7" ...... London .... HL8129 .... 1955 ... £7.50 ...... £15
Do Nothing Blues .... 7" ...... London .... HL8107 .... 1954 ... £10 .... £20

HALE & THE HUSHABYES

The group name disguises the combined forces of Jackie DeShannon, Sonny and Cher, the Blossoms, and Brian Wilson.

Yes Sir, That's My Baby	7"	Apogee	104	1964	£45	£90	US
Yes Sir, That's My Baby	7"	Reprise	0299	1964	£20	£40	US

HALEY, BILL

Bill Haley & His Comets	7" EP	Brunswick	OE9459	1959	£15	£30	tri centre
Bill Haley And His Comets	7" EP	Warner Bros	WEP6001	1960	£7.50	£15	
Bill Haley And The Comets	LP	Valiant	VS103	1970	£5	£12	
Bill Haley And The Comets	LP	Warner Bros	W(S)1738	1960	£8	£20	US
Bill Haley And The Comets	LP	XTRA	XTRA1027	1965	£6	£15	
Bill Haley Vol.1	7" EP	Warner Bros	WEP6133	1964	£7.50	£15	
Bill Haley Vol.2	7" EP	Warner Bros	WEP6136	1964	£7.50	£15	
Bill Haley's Chicks	LP	Ace Of Hearts	AH66	1964	£5	£12	
Bill Haley's Chicks	LP	Brunswick	LAT8295	1959	£15	£30	
Bill Haley's Chicks	LP	Brunswick	STA3011	1959	£20	£40	stereo
Bill Haley's Chicks	LP	Decca	DL(7)8821	1959	£20	£40	US
Bill Haley's Juke Box	LP	Warner Bros	W1391	1960	£10	£25	
Bill Haley's Juke Box	7" EP	Warner Bros	WEP6025	1961	£7.50	£15	
Bill Haley's Juke Box	7" EP	Warner Bros	WSEP2025	1961	£10	£20	stereo
Billy Goat	7"	Brunswick	05688	1957	£6	£12	
Birth Of The Boogie	7"	Brunswick	05910	1964	£5	£10	
Caldonia	7"	Brunswick	05805	1959	£7.50	£15	
Candy Kisses	7"	Warner Bros	WB6	1960	£2.50	£6	
Crazy Man Crazy	78	London	L1190	1953	£10	£20	
Crazy Man, Crazy	7"	Pye	7N25455	1968	£5	£10	
Dim Dim The Lights	7"	Brunswick	05373	1955	£20	£40	gold label
Dim Dim The Lights	7" EP	Brunswick	OE9129	1955	£10	£20	gold label
Dipsy Doodle	7"	Brunswick	05719	1957	£10	£20	
Don't Knock The Rock	7"	Brunswick	05640	1957	£7.50	£15	chart single
Farewell So Long Goodbye	7"	London	HLF8161	1955	£50	£100	gold label
Forty Cups Of Coffee	7"	Brunswick	05658	1957	£7.50	£15	
Goofing Around	7"	Brunswick	05641	1957	£7.50	£15	
Green Door	7"	Brunswick	05917	1964	£5	£10	
Greentree Boogie	7"	London	HL8142	1955	£50	£100	gold label
He Digs Rock And Roll	LP	Decca	DL8315	1956	£37.50	£75	US
I Got A Woman	7"	Brunswick	05788	1959	£6	£12	
I'm Gonna Dry Every Little Tear	78	Melodisc	1376	1956	£7.50	£15	
King Of Rock	LP	Ember	EMB3396	1968	£4	£10	
Lean Jean	7"	Brunswick	05752	1958	£6	£12	
Live It Up	10" LP	London	HAPB1042	1955	£40	£80	gold label
Live It Up Pt.1	7" EP	London	REF1049	1956	£12.50	£25	
Live It Up Pt.2	7" EP	London	REF1050	1956	£12.50	£25	
Live It Up Pt.3	7" EP	London	REF1058	1956	£12.50	£25	
Mambo Rock	7"	Brunswick	05405	1955	£20	£40	gold label, chart single
Mary Mary Lou	7"	Brunswick	05735	1958	£6	£12	
Mister Rock'n'Roll	LP	Ember	EMB3401	1969	£4	£10	
Ooh Looka There Ain't She Pretty	7"	Brunswick	05810	1959	£5	£10	
Pat-A-Cake	78	London	L1216	1953	£10	£20	
Razzle Dazzle	7"	Brunswick	05453	1955	£15	£30	gold label, chart single
Real Live Rock'n'Roll	LP	Ember	EMB3386	1967	£4	£10	
Rip It Up	7"	Brunswick	05615	1956	£7.50	£15	chart single
Rip It Up!	LP	MCA	MUP318	1968	£4	£10	
Rock Around The Clock	LP	Ace Of Hearts	AH13	1961	£6	£15	chart LP
Rock Around The Clock	LP	Brunswick	LAT8117	1956	£15	£30	
Rock Around The Clock	LP	Decca	DL8225	1955	£50	£100	US
Rock Around The Clock	7"	Brunswick	05317	1954	£25	£50	gold label, chart single
Rock Around The Clock	7"	Decca	AD1010	1968	£2	£5	export
Rock Around The Clock	7"	Warner Bros	WB133	1964	£4	£10	
Rock Around The Clock	7" EP	Brunswick	OE9250	1956	£7.50	£15	2 covers
Rock 'n' Roll	7" EP	Brunswick	OE9214	1956	£7.50	£15	
Rock 'n' Roll	7" EP	London	REF1031	1955	£20	£40	
Rock 'n' Roll Stage Show	LP	Brunswick	LAT8139	1956	£15	£30	
Rock 'n' Roll Stage Show	LP	Decca	DL8345	1956	£37.50	£75	US
Rock 'n' Roll Stage Show Pt.1	7" EP	Brunswick	OE9278	1956	£7.50	£15	
Rock 'n' Roll Stage Show Pt.2	7" EP	Brunswick	OE9279	1956	£7.50	£15	
Rock 'n' Roll Stage Show Pt.3	7" EP	Brunswick	OE9280	1956	£7.50	£15	
Rock The Joint	LP	Golden Guinea	GGL0282	1963	£5	£12	
Rock The Joint	LP	London	HAF2037	1957	£25	£50	
Rock The Joint	LP	London	HLF8371	1957	£50	£100	gold label, chart single
Rock With Bill Haley & The Comets	LP	Essex	LP202	1956	£50	£100	US
Rock With Bill Haley & The Comets	LP	Somerset	P4600	1956	£10	£25	US
Rock With Bill Haley And The Comets	LP	Trans World	202	1956	£20	£40	US
Rock-A-Beatin' Boogie	7"	Brunswick	05509	1955	£15	£30	gold label, chart single
Rockin' Around The World	LP	Decca	DL8692	1957	£20	£40	US
Rockin' Around The World	7" EP	Brunswick	DL9446	1959	£15	£30	
Rockin' Chair On The Moon	7"	London	HLF8194	1955	£50	£100	gold label
Rockin' The Joint	LP	Brunswick	LAT8268	1957	£15	£30	
Rockin' The Joint	LP	Decca	DL8775	1958	£20	£40	US
Rockin' The Oldies	LP	Ace Of Hearts	AH35	1962	£5	£12	
Rockin' The Oldies	LP	Brunswick	LAT8219	1957	£15	£30	
Rockin' The Oldies	LP	Decca	DL8569	1957	£20	£40	US
Rockin' The Oldies Pt.1	7" EP	Brunswick	OE9349	1958	£10	£20	
Rockin' The Oldies Pt.2	7" EP	Brunswick	OE9350	1958	£10	£20	
Rockin' The Oldies Pt.3	7" EP	Brunswick	OE9351	1958	£10	£20	

Rockin' Through The Rye	7"	Brunswick	05582	1956	£7.50	£15 ....chart single
Rudy's Rock	7"	Brunswick	05616	1956	£7.50	£15 ....chart single
Saints Rock 'n' Roll	7"	Brunswick	05565	1956	£7.50	£15 ....chart single
See You Later Alligator	7"	Brunswick	05530	1956	£15	£30 ....gold label, chart single
Shake, Rattle And Roll	7"	Brunswick	05338	1954	£20	£40 ....gold label, chart single
Shake, Rattle And Roll	10" LP	Decca	DL5560	1954	£180	£300 ....US
Skinnie Minnie	7"	Brunswick	05742	1958	£7.50	£15
Skokiaan	7"	Brunswick	05818	1960	£4	£8
Spanish Twist	7"	London	HLU9471	1961	£5	£10
Strictly Instrumental	LP	Brunswick	LAT8326	1960	£15	£30
Strictly Instrumental	LP	Decca	DL(7)8964	1959	£17.50	£35 ....US
Tenor Man	7"	Stateside	SS196	1963	£2	£5
Twisting Knights At The Round Table	LP	Columbia	33SX1460	1962	£8	£20
Whoa Mabel	7"	Brunswick	05766	1958	£7.50	£15

HALEY, BILL & FOUR ACES

They Sold A Million No.15	7" EP	Brunswick	OE9431	1959	£7.50	£15

HALF NELSON

Half Nelson was the name originally used by Sparks. The one LP made under this name was reissued as "Sparks" a year later.

Half Nelson	LP	Bearsville	BV2048	1972	£6	£15 ....US

HALL, BOB & ALEXIS KORNER

Pinetop's Boogie Woogie	7"	Logo	GO331	1978	£2	£5

HALL, CONNIE & JAMES O'GWYNN

Country And Western Trailblazers No.3	7" EP	Mercury	ZEP10080	1960	£2	£5

HALL, DEREK & MIKE COOPER

Out Of The Shades	7" EP	Kennet	KRS766	196-	£4	£8

HALL, DICKSON

Fabulous Country Hits No.1	7" EP	London	RER1158	1958	£4	£8
Fabulous Country Hits No.2	7" EP	London	RER1159	1958	£4	£8
Fabulous Country Hits No.3	7" EP	London	RER1160	1958	£4	£8
Fabulous Country Hits Way Out West	LP	Kapp	KL1067	1957	£5	£12 ....US
Outlaws Of The Old West	LP	MGM	E3263	1956	£5	£12 ....US
Outlaws Of The Old West	7" EP	MGM	MGMEP626	1957	£5	£10
Outlaws Of The Old West	10" LP	MGM	E329	1954	£6	£15 ....US
Twenty-Five All-Time Country & Western Hits	LP	Epic	LN3427	1958	£5	£12 ....US

HALL, EDMOND

Celestial Express	LP	Blue Note	B6505	1969	£5	£12
Petite Fleur	LP	London	LTZT15166	1959	£4	£10
Rumpus On Rampart Street	LP	Top Rank	35050	1960	£4	£10

HALL, EDMUND

Edmund Hall All Stars	10" LP	London	LZC14005	1955	£6	£15

HALL, GERRI

Who Can I Run To	7"	Sue	WI4026	1966	£25	£50 ....demo

HALL, JIM

Jazz Guitar	LP	Vogue	LAE12072	1958	£8	£20

HALL, JIMMY GRAY

Be That Way	7"	Epic	EPC2312	1974	£4	£8

HALL, JUANITA

Sings The Blues	LP	Storyville	SLP113	1964	£6	£15
Storyville Blues Anthology Vol.2	7" EP	Storyville	SEP382	1962	£4	£8

HALL, LARRY

Ladder Of Love	7"	Salvo	SLO1811	1962	£2	£5

HALL, RENE

Twitchy	7"	London	HLU8581	1958	£10	£20

HALL, ROBIN

Last Leaves Of Traditional Ballads	10" LP	Collector	JFS4002	1961	£6	£15

HALL, ROBIN & JIMMIE MACGREGOR

Football Crazy	7"	Collector	JDS3	1960	£1.50	£4
Football Crazy	7"	Decca	F11266	1960	£1.50	£4

HALL, RONNIE

I'll Stand Aside	7"	Fontana	TF569	1965	£4	£8

HALL, ROY

Blue Suede Shoes	7"	Brunswick	05555	1956	£100	£200
See You Later Alligator	7"	Brunswick	05531	1956	£250	£400
Three Alley Cats	7"	Brunswick	05627	1956	£120	£220

HALL, TERRY

Lenny The Lion	7" EP	Decca	DFE/STO8554	1963	£2	£5

HALL, TONY

Fieldvole Music	LP	Free Reed	FRR012	1977	£10	£25

HALLADAY, CHANCE

John Henry	7"	Vogue	V9203	1962	£2	£5	

HALLBERG, BENGT

New Sounds From Sweden	10" LP	Esquire	20014	1953	£25	£50	

HALLELUJAH

Hallelujah Babe	LP	Metronome	LMLP15805	1971	£30	£60	German

HALLELUJAH SKIFFLE GROUP

I Saw The Light	7"	Oriole	CB1429	1958	£1.50	£4	

HALLIARD

The Halliard were a folk trio led by Nic Jones, whose later solo work consists of particularly fine traditional interpretations. Tragically, Jones' career was cut short by a serious car accident, which left him unable to play the guitar.

Halliard And Jon Raven	LP	Broadside	BRO106	1968	£40	£80	
It's The Irish In Me	LP	Saga	SOC1058	1968	£25	£50	

HALLYDAY, JOHNNY

America's Rockin' Hits	LP	Philips	BBL7556	1961	£40	£80	
Hey Little Girl	7"	Philips	373012BF	1963	£2.50	£6	
Johnny Hallyday	7" EP	Vogue	VRE5013	1966	£40	£80	
Olympia '64	LP	Philips		1964	£8	£20	French
Pour Moi Tu Es La Seule	7"	Philips	BF1449	1965	£4	£8	
Rocking	7" EP	Philips	432813BE	1962	£40	£80	
Shake The Hand Of A Fool	7"	Philips	PB1238	1962	£2.50	£6	
Twistin' The Rock	LP	Vogue		1962	£8	£20	French

HALOS

Halos	LP	Warwick	W2046	1962	£30	£60	US
Nag	7"	London	HLU9424	1961	£7.50	£15	

HAMBLEN, STUART

Go On By	7"	HMV	7MC30	1955	£4	£8	export
Hell Train	7"	HMV	7M394	1956	£2.50	£6	
This Ole House	7"	HMV	7MC20	1954	£5	£10	export

HAMBRO, LENNY

Lenny Hambro And Eddie Bert	10" LP	London	LZC14025	1956	£8	£20	
Message From Hambro	LP	Philips	BBL7161	1957	£6	£15	

HAMEL, PETER MICHAEL

Buddhist Meditation East West	LP	Harmonia Mundi	29222926	1975	£5	£12	German double
Hamel	LP	Vertigo	67641055	1972	£6	£15	German double
Voice Of Silence	LP	Vertigo	6360613	1973	£5	£12	German

HAMFATS, HARLEM

Harlem Hamfats	LP	Ace Of Hearts	AH27	1962	£5	£12	

HAMILL, CLAIRE

Abracadabra	LP	Konk	KONK104	1975	£4	£10	
October	LP	Island	ILPS9225	1973	£4	£10	
One House Left Standing	LP	Island	ILPS9182	1971	£4	£10	
Stage Door Johnnies	LP	Konk	KONK101	1974	£4	£10	

HAMILTON & THE MOVEMENT

I'm Not the Marrying Kind	7"	CBS	202573	1967	£7.50	£15	
Really Saying Something	7"	Polydor	BM56026	1965	£10	£20	

HAMILTON, CHICO

Chico Hamilton Quintet	LP	Vogue	LAE12039	1957	£8	£20	
Chico Hamilton Quintet	LP	Vogue	LAE12045	1957	£8	£20	
Chico Hamilton Trio	LP	Vogue	LAE12077	1958	£8	£20	
Chico Hamnilton Quintet	LP	Vogue	LAE12085	1958	£6	£15	
Ellington Suite	LP	Vogue	LAE12210	1960	£6	£15	
Introducing Freddie Gambrell	LP	Vogue	LAE12160	1959	£6	£15	
Original	LP	Vogue	LAE12239	1961	£5	£12	

HAMILTON, GAVIN

It Won't Be The Same	7"	King	KG1067	1967	£7.50	£15	

HAMILTON, GUY

Lifetime Of Loneliness	7"	HMV	POP1418	1965	£2.50	£6	

HAMILTON IV, GEORGE

Before This Day Ends	7"	HMV	POP813	1960	£1.50	£4	
I Know Where I'm Going	7"	HMV	POP505	1958	£1.50	£4	chart single
On Campus	LP	HMV	CLP1202	1958	£5	£12	
Rose And A Candy Bar	7"	London	HL8361	1957	£40	£80	gold label
Sing Me A Sad Song	LP	HMV	CLP1263	1959	£5	£12	
Why Don't They Understand	7"	HMV	POP429	1957	£4	£8	chart single
Your Cheatin' Heart	7"	HMV	POP534	1958	£2	£5	

HAMILTON, M.

Something Gotta Ring	7"	Ska Beat	JB265	1967	£5	£10	

HAMILTON, ROY

Come Out Swinging	7" EP	Fontana	TFE17170	1959	£5	£10	
Crazy Feeling	7"	Fontana	H143	1958	£5	£10	
Dark End Of The Street	7"	Deep Soul	DS9106	1970	£5	£10	

Don't Let Go	7"	Fontana	H113	1958	£7.50	£15	
I Need Your Loving	7"	Fontana	H193	1959	£5	£10	
Mood Moves	7" EP	Fontana	TFE17163	1959	£4	£8	
Pledging My Love	7"	Fontana	H180	1959	£5	£10	
Theme From The VIPs	7"	MGM	MGM1210	1963	£1.50	£4	
There She Is	7"	MGM	MGM1251	1964	£50	£100	
Thousand Years Ago	7"	MGM	MGM1268	1965	£2.50	£6	
Tore Up Over You	7"	RCA	RCA1500	1966	£2.50	£6	
Why Fight The Feeling	7" EP	Fontana	TFE17160	1959	£5	£10	
You Can Have Her	7"	Fontana	H298	1961	£4	£8	
You're Gonna Need Magic	7"	Fontana	H320	1961	£4	£8	

HAMILTON, RUSS

Drifting And Dreaming	7"	Oriole	CB1451	1958	£1.50	£4	
Gonna Find Me A Bluebird	7"	MGM	MGM1096	1960	£1.50	£4	
I Don't Know Why	7"	Oriole	CB1406	1958	£1.50	£4	
I Wonder Who's Kissing Her Now	7"	Oriole	CB1459	1958	£1.50	£4	
It's A Sin To Tell A Lie	7"	Oriole	CB1531	1960	£1.50	£4	
Little One	7"	Oriole	CB1404	1958	£1.50	£4	
My Unbreakable Heart	7"	Oriole	CB1506	1959	£1.50	£4	
Rainbow	LP	Kapp	KL1076	1957	£15	£30	US
Reprieve Of Tom Dooley	7"	Oriole	CB1492	1959	£1.50	£4	
Russ Hamilton	7" EP	Oriole	EP7005	1958	£5	£10	
Smile Smile Smile	7"	Oriole	CB1508	1959	£1.50	£4	
Things I Didn't Say	7"	Oriole	CB1465	1959	£1.50	£4	
Things No Money Can Buy	7"	Oriole	CB1527	1960	£1.50	£4	
We Will Make Love	LP	Oriole	MG20031	1958	£15	£30	
We Will Make Love	7"	Oriole	CB1359	1957	£1.50	£4	chart single
Wedding Ring	7"	Oriole	CB1388	1957	£1.50	£4	chart single

HAMILTON, SCOTT

Good Day Sunshine	7"	Parlophone	R5492	1966	£1.50	£4	

HAMLINS

Everyone Got To Be There	7"	Studio One	SO2036	1967	£6	£12	Minstrels B side
Sentimental Reasons	7"	Coxsone	CS7048	1968	£5	£10	Soul Vendors B side
Sugar And Spice	7"	Blue Cat	BS115	1968	£4	£8	Soul Vendors B side

HAMMER, JACK

Crazy Twist	7"	Oriole	CB1728	1962	£1.50	£4	
Kissing Twist	7"	Oriole	CB1645	1961	£1.50	£4	
Number 2539	7"	Oriole	CB1753	1962	£1.50	£4	
Thanks	7"	Polydor	56091	1966	£2	£5	
What Greater Love	7"	United Artists	UP35029	1969	£10	£20	
Young Only Once	7"	Oriole	CB1634	1961	£1.50	£4	

HAMMER, JAN

First Seven Days	LP	Atlantic	K50184	1975	£4	£10	
Like Children	LP	Atlantic	K50092	1974	£4	£10	

HAMMERS

Baby And Me	7"	President	PT247	1969	£2	£5	
Sugar Baby	7"	President	PT276	1969	£2	£5	

HAMMERSMITH

Hammersmith	LP	Mercury	SRM11040	1975	£5	£12	US
It's For You	LP	Mercury	SRM11102	1976	£5	£12	US

HAMMERSMITH GORILLAS

You Really Got Me	7"	Penny Farthing	PEN849	1974	£2.50	£6	

HAMMILL, PETER

Chameleon In The Shadow Of The Night	LP	Charisma	CAS1067	1973	£4	£10	
Fool's Mate	LP	Charisma	CAS1037	1971	£6	£15	
Future Now	LP	Charisma	CAS1137	1978	£4	£10	
In Camera	LP	Charisma	CAS1089	1974	£4	£10	
Nadir's Last Chance	LP	Charisma	CAS1099	1975	£4	£10	
Over	LP	Charisma	CAS1125	1977	£4	£10	
PH7	LP	Charisma	CAS1146	1979	£4	£10	
Polaroid	7"	Charisma	CB339	1979	£2.50	£6	credited to Rikki Nadir
Silent Corner And The Empty Stage	LP	Charisma	CAS1083	1974	£4	£10	
Vision	LP	GIR	92111016	1978	£4	£10	US compilation

HAMMOND, JOHN

Best Of (Southern Fried)	LP	Vanguard	VSD11/12	1974	£6	£15	double
Big City Blues	LP	Fontana	TFL6046	1964	£8	£20	
Brown Eyed Handsome Man	7"	Atlantic	584190	1968	£4	£8	
Country Blues	LP	Vanguard	VRS/VSD79198	1965	£8	£20	US
I Can Tell	LP	Atlantic	SD8152	1968	£8	£20	US
I Live The Life I Love	7"	Fontana	TF560	1965	£7.50	£15	
I'm Satisfied	LP	CBS	65051	1972	£6	£15	
John Hammond	LP	Vanguard	VRS9132	1963	£8	£20	US
Little Big Man	LP	CBS	30545	1971	£6	£15	US
Mirrors	LP	Vanguard	VRS/VSD79245	1968	£8	£20	US
So Many Roads	LP	Fontana	TFL6059	1965	£8	£20	
Sooner Or Later	LP	Atlantic	SD8206	1968	£8	£20	US
Source Point	LP	CBS	64365	1971	£6	£15	
Southern Fried	LP	Atlantic	SD8251	1970	£6	£15	US
When I Need	LP	CBS	30549	1971	£6	£15	US

HAMNER, CURLEY

Twistin' And Turnin'	7"	Felsted	SD80061	1959	£1.50	£4

HAMPSHIRE, SUSAN

When Love Is True	7"	Decca	F12185	1965	£1.50	£4

HAMPTON, LIONEL

All American Award Concert	LP	Brunswick	LAT8086	1956	£6	£15	
Apollo Hall Concert 1954	LP	Philips	BBL7015	1955	£6	£15	
At The Pasadena Auditorium	LP	Vogue	LAE12014	1956	£6	£15	
At The Pasadena Auditorium	7" EP.	Vogue	EPV1161	1957	£2	£5	
Hamp 1956	LP	Oriole	MG20012	1956	£6	£15	
Hamp's Big Band	LP	Audio Fidelity..	AFLP1913/	1960	£5	£12	
			AFSD5913				
Hamp's Boogie Woogie	7"	Vogue	V2406	1957	£6	£12	
Hamp's Boogie Woogie	7" EP.	Columbia	SEB10108	1959	£2	£5	
Hamp's Boogie Woogie	10" LP	Brunswick	LA8527	1951	£10	£25	
Hampton And The Old World	LP	Philips	BBL7119	1957	£6	£15	
High And The Mighty	LP	Columbia	33CX10146	1959	£6	£15	
Hot Mallets	LP	HMV	CLP1023	1955	£6	£15	
In Paris Vol.1	10" LP	Felsted	EDL87007	1954	£10	£25	
In Paris Vol.2	10" LP	Felsted	EDL87008	1954	£10	£25	
Jazz Flamenco	LP	RCA	RD27006	1957	£6	£15	
Jazz Time Paris Vol.1	10" LP	Vogue	LDE043	1954	£10	£25	
Jivin' The Vibes	LP	Camden	CDN129	1959	£4	£10	
Lionel Hampton	LP	Felsted	PDL85006	1956	£8	£20	
Lionel Hampton And His All Stars	LP	Columbia	33CX10086	1957	£8	£20	
Lionel Hampton And His Orchestra	7" EP.	MGM	MGMEP552	1956	£2	£5	
Lionel Hampton And Stan Getz	LP	Columbia	33CX10041	1956	£15	£30	
Lionel Hampton Group	LP	Vogue	LAE12034	1957	£6	£15	
Lionel Hampton Orchestra	7" EP.	Oriole	EP7046	1962	£2	£5	
Lionel Hampton Plays Love Songs	LP	HMV	CLP1136	1957	£6	£15	
Lionel Hampton Quartet	LP	Columbia	33CX10006	1955	£10	£25	
Lionel Hampton Quartet	10" LP	Columbia	33C9011	1955	£10	£25	
Lionel Hampton Vol.3	10" LP	Vogue	LDE063	1954	£10	£25	
Lionel Hampton-Art Tatum-Buddy Rich	LP	Columbia	33CX10045	1956	£8	£20	
Trio							
Many Splendored Vibes	LP	Columbia	33SX1500	1962	£4	£10	
Moonglow	10" LP	Brunswick	LA8551	1952	£10	£25	
New French Sound Vol.1	LP	Felsted	PDL85002	1955	£6	£15	
New Sounds From Europe Vol.2	10" LP	Vogue	LDE051	1954	£10	£25	
One And Only Lionel Hampton	LP	Fontana	Z4053	1961	£4	£10	
Open House	LP	Camden	CDN138	1960	£4	£10	
Perdido	7"	Vogue	V2405	1957	£5	£10	

HAMPTON, SLIDE

Jazz With A Twist	LP	London	HAK/SHK8008	1962	£5	£12

HANCOCK, HERBIE

Jazz pianist Herbie Hancock has tried his hand at a particularly wide range of styles over the years, from straightforward "modern" jazz to hiphop. The trilogy of early seventies recordings, "Mwandishi", "Crossings", and "Sextant" find him entering the composed electric jazz world defined by Weather Report. Typically, they are amongst the most impressive jazz recordings of the period, and arguably they are Hancock's personal best. "Crossings" is especially fine. "Treasure Chest" is an anthology of music taken from these electric jazz recordings and from Hancock's sixties work. It also includes a short track whose music is taken from "Crossings", but in a remixed form not otherwise available.

Blind Man, Blind Man	7"	Blue Note	451887	1963	£1.50	£4	
Crossings	LP	Warner Bros	K46164	1972	£5	£12	
Direct Step	LP	CBS Sony	30AP1032	1979	£6	£15	Japanese
Empyrean Isles	LP	Blue Note	BLP/BST84175	1965	£10	£25	
Fat Albert Rotunda	LP	Warner Bros	K46039	1974	£6	£15	
Fat Albert Rotunda	LP	Warner Bros	WS1834	1971	£8	£20	
Fat Mama	7"	Warner Bros	WB7358	1970	£1.50	£4	
Inventions And Dimensions	LP	Blue Note	BLP/BST84147	1964	£10	£25	
Live In Japan	LP	CBS Sony	98/99	1975	£10	£25	Japanese double
Live Under The Sky	LP	CBS Sony	1037875	1976	£6	£15	Japanese
Maiden Voyage	LP	Blue Note	BLP/BST84195	1966	£10	£25	
Mwandishi	LP	Warner Bros	K46077	1971	£5	£12	
My Point Of View	LP	Blue Note	BLP/BST84126	1964	£10	£25	
Prisoner	LP	Blue Note	BST84321	1969	£6	£15	
Sextant	LP	CBS	65582	1972	£5	£12	
Speak Like A Child	LP	Blue Note	BST84279	1968	£6	£15	
Takin' Off	LP	Blue Note	BLP/BST84109	1964	£15	£30	
Treasure Chest	LP	Warner Bros	2WS2807	1974	£6	£15	US double

HANCOCK, TONY

Blood Donor	7" EP.	Pye	NEP24175	1963	£2	£5	
Blood Donor & Radio Ham	LP	Pye	NPL18068	1961	£4	£10	chart LP
Hancock's Half Hour	7" EP.	Pye	NEP24170	1963	£2	£5	
It's Hancock	LP	Decca	LK4740	1965	£4	£10	
Little Pieces Of Hancock	7" EP.	Pye	NEP24146	1961	£2	£5	
Little Pieces Of Hancock Vol.2	7" EP.	Pye	NEP24161	1962	£2	£5	
Pieces Of Hancock	LP	Pye	NPL18054	1960	£5	£12	chart LP
This Is Hancock	LP	Pye	NPL18045	1960	£5	£12	chart LP
Wing Commander Hancock	7"	Pye	7N15575	1963	£1.50	£4	

HAND, OWEN

Something New	LP	Transatlantic	TRA127	1966	£25	£50

HANDLE, JOHNNY

Collier Lad	LP	Topic	12TS270	1975	£5	£12

HANDSOME BEASTS
All Riot Now	7"	Heavy Metal	HEAVY1	1981	£1.50	£4	
Breaker	7"	Heavy Metal	HEAVY2	1981	£1.50	£4	
Sweeties	7"	Heavy Metal	HEAVY11	1982	£1.50	£4	

HANDY, WAYNE
Say Yeah	7"	London	HL8547	1958	£75	£150

HANFORD, PAUL
Minute You're Gone	7"	Oriole	CB1866	1963	£2	£5

HANK & THE MELLOWMEN
Santa Anno	7"	Lyntone	LYN153/4	196-	£1.50	£4	flexi
So In Love With You	7"	Lyntone	LYN201	196-	£1.50	£4	flexi

HANLY, MICHAEL
As I Went Over Blackwater	LP	Mulligan	LUN040	1980	£5	£12	Irish
Kiss In The Morning Early	LP	Mulligan	LUN005	1976	£5	£12	Irish

HANLY, MICHAEL & MICHAEL O'DONNEL
Celtic Folkweave	LP	Polydor	2908013	1974	£20	£40	Irish

HANNA BARBERA
Flintstones - Goldilocks & The Bearosauruses	7" EP	Hanna Barbera	HBE3	1966	£5	£10
Flintstones - Hansel And Gretel	7" EP	Hanna Barbera	HBE1	1966	£5	£10
Flintstones - Mary Poppins	7" EP	Hanna Barbera	HBE6	1966	£5	£10
Flintstones - Three Little Pigs	7" EP	Hanna Barbera	HBE9	1966	£5	£10
Snagglepuss Tales - Wizard Of Oz	7" EP	Hanna Barbera	HBE4	1966	£2.50	£6
Top Cat - Robin Hood	7" EP	Hanna Barbera	HBE7	1966	£2	£5
Uncle Remus - Brer Rabbit & The Tar Baby	7" EP	Hanna Barbera	HBE2	1966	£2	£5
Yogi Bear & Boo Boo - Jack & The Beanstalk	7" EP	Hanna Barbera	HBE5	1966	£2.50	£6
Yogi Bear & Boo Boo - Little Red Riding Hood	7" EP	Hanna Barbera	HBE8	1966	£2.50	£6

HANNA, BOBBY
Blame It On Me	7"	Decca	F12695	1967	£2.50	£6
Thanks To You	7"	Decca	F12604	1967	£1.50	£4
To Wait For Love	7"	Decca	F12833	1968	£1.50	£4
Too Much Love	7"	Decca	F12738	1968	£1.50	£4
Winter Love	7"	Decca	F22917	1969	£1.50	£4
Written On The Wind	7"	Decca	F12783	1968	£2.50	£6

HANNA, GEORGE & SARAH ANNE O'NEILL
On The Shores Of Lough Neagh	LP	Topic	12TS372	1978	£6	£15

HANNA, JOSH
Shut Your Mouth	7"	Decca	F12532	1966	£5	£10

HANNA, KEN
Ken Hanna Orchestra	10" LP	London	HAPB1031	1954	£4	£10

HANNIBAL
Hannibal's only album is definitely a neglected gem from the progressive era. Occasionally let down a little by the lyrics, the music is nevertheless sparkling and inventive, these qualities being enhanced by fluent jazz-rock playing from all concerned. The keyboard player turned up on a few Roy Wood records, but remarkably none of the members of Hannibal were able to sustain a career in music.
Hannibal	LP	B&C	CAS1022	1970	£10	£25
Winds Of Change	7"	B&C	HB1	1974	£4	£8

HANNIBAL, LANCE
Read The News	7"	Blue Cat	BS148	1968	£4	£8	Rico B side

HANOI ROCKS
Back To Mystery City	LP	Lick	LICLP1	1985	£4	£10	white vinyl
Don't You Ever Leave Me	12"	CBS	TA4885	1984	£3	£8	
Don't You Ever Leave Me	12"	CBS	WA4885	1984	£4	£10	pic disc
Malibu Beach	7"	Lick	LIXPD1	1983	£5	£10	pic disc
Self Destruction Blues	LP	Lick	LICLPPD4	1985	£4	£10	pic disc
Underwater World	12"	CBS	TA4732	1984	£2.50	£6	
Underwater World	12"	CBS	WA4732	1984	£4	£10	pic disc
Up Around The Bend	7"	CBS	DA4513	1984	£5	£10	double
Up Around The Bend	12"	CBS	TA4513	1984	£2.50	£6	with transfer

HANSSON & KARLSSON
Man At The Moon	LP	Polydor	46265	1968	£6	£15	Swedish
Monument	LP	Polydor	46260	1969	£6	£15	
Rex	LP	Polydor	46264	1968	£6	£15	Swedish
Swedish Underground	LP	Polydor	184196	1967	£8	£20	

HANUMAN
Hanuman	LP	Kuckuck	2375012	1972	£6	£15	German

HA'PENNYS
Love Is Not The Same	LP	Fersch	1110	1968	£75	£150	US

HAPPENINGS
Breaking Up Is Hard To Do	7"	B.T.Puppy	BTS45543	1968	£1.50	£4
Crazy Rhythm	7"	B.T.Puppy	BTS45545	1969	£1.50	£4
Go Away Little Girl	7"	Fontana	TF766	1966	£1.50	£4

Title	Format	Label	Catalogue	Year			Notes
Go Away Little Girl	7" EP	Vogue	INT18100	1966	£4	£8	French
Golden Hits	LP	B.T.Puppy	BTLPS1004	1968	£6	£15	US
Goodnight My Love	7"	Stateside	SS587	1967	£1.50	£4	
Greatest Hits	LP	Jubilee	JGS8030	1969	£5	£12	US
Happenings	LP	B.T.Puppy	(S)1001	1966	£6	£15	US
I Got Rhythm	7"	Stateside	SS2013	1967	£1.50	£4	chart single
I Got Rhythm	7" EP	B.T.Puppy	701	1967	£4	£8	French
Music Music Music	7"	B.T.Puppy	BTS45538	1968	£1.50	£4	
My Mammy	7"	B.T.Puppy	BTS45530	1967	£1.50	£4	chart single
My Mammy	7"	Pye	7N25501	1967	£1.50	£4	chart single
New Day Comin'	7"	B.T.Puppy	BTS45546	1969	£1.50	£4	
Piece Of Mind	LP	Jubilee	JGS8028	1969	£5	£12	US
Psycle	LP	B.T.Puppy	(S)1003	1967	£6	£15	US
Randy	7"	B.T.Puppy	BTS45540	1968	£1.50	£4	
See You In September	LP	Fontana	TL5383	1967	£5	£12	
See You In September	7"	Fontana	TF735	1966	£1.50	£4	
See You In September	7" EP	Vogue	INT18090	1966	£4	£8	French, B side by Jimmy Mays & Soul Breed
Why Do Fools Fall In Love	7"	B.T.Puppy	BTS45532	1967	£1.50	£4	

HAPPENINGS & TOKENS
Back To Back	LP	B.T.Puppy	(S)1002	1967	£5	£12	US

HAPPY CONFUSION
Yes Sir	7"	Penny Farthing	PEN706	1970	£1.50	£4	

HAPPY FAMILY
Puritans	7"	4AD	AD204	1982	£2	£5	

HAPPY MAGAZINE
Satisfied Street	7"	Polydor	56233	1968	£2.50	£6	
Who Belongs To You	7"	Polydor	56307	1968	£2	£5	

HAPPY MONDAYS
Squirrel And G Man	LP	Factory	FACT170	1987	£5	£12	plastic sleeve with 'Desmond'
Step On (Melon Mix)	12"	Factory	FAC272	1990	£4	£10	1 sided promo

HAPSHASH & THE COLOURED COAT
Colinda	7"	Liberty	LBF15188	1969	£6	£12	
Human Host And Heavy Metal Kids	LP	Liberty	MLL/MLS40001E	1967	£15	£30	red vinyl
Human Host And The Heavy Metal Kids	LP	Liberty	MLS40001E	1967	£8	£20	
Western Flyer	LP	Liberty	LBL/LBS83212	1969	£8	£20	

HARBOUR LITES
Come Back Silly Girl	7"	HMV	POP1426	1965	£1.50	£4	
I Would Give All	7"	HMV	POP1465	1965	£2	£5	
Run For Your Life	7"	Fontana	TF682	1966	£2	£5	

HARD CORPS
Dirty	7"	Survival	SUR026	1984	£4	£8	
Dirty	12"	Hard Corps	1	1984	£15	£30	
Dirty	12"	Survival	SUR12026	1984	£3	£8	
Je Suis Passee	12"	Immaculate	12IMMAC2	1985	£4	£10	
Je Suis Passee	12"	Polydor	HARDA1	1985	£8	£20	plastic sleeve, poster
Je Suis Passee	12"	Polydor	HARDX1	1985	£2.50	£6	
To Breathe	7"	Polydor	HARD2	1985	£12.50	£25	
To Breathe	12"	Polydor	HARDX2	1985	£15	£30	

HARD MEAT
Hard Meat	LP	Warner Bros	WS1852	1970	£4	£10	
Rain	7"	Island	WIP6066	1969	£5	£10	
Through A Window	LP	Warner Bros	WS1879	1970	£4	£10	

HARD ROAD
No Problem	LP	Goodstuff	LP1002	1979	£8	£20	

HARD STUFF
Bolex Dementia	LP	Purple	TPSA7507	1973	£6	£15	
Bullet Proof	LP	Purple	TPSA7505	1972	£6	£15	

HARD TRAVELLIN'
Hard Travellin'	LP	Flams Ltd	PR1065	1971	£50	£100	

HARDCAKE SPECIAL
Hardcake Special	LP	Brain	0001060	1974	£4	£10	German

HARDEN, WILBUR
Mainstream 1958	LP	London	LTZC15159	1959	£8	£20	with John Coltrane

HARDIN & YORK
For The World	LP	Decca	SKL5095	1971	£4	£10	
Tomorrow Today	LP	Bell	SBLL125	1969	£4	£10	
World's Smallest Big Band	LP	Bell	SBLL136	1970	£4	£10	

HARDIN, EDDIE
Driving	7"	Decca	F13252	1971	£1.50	£4	
Home Is Where You Find It	LP	Decca	TXS106	1972	£4	£10	
Why Does Everybody Put Me Down	7"	Decca	F13307	1972	£1.50	£4	

HARDIN, TIM

Tim Hardin's fragile voice made his own interpretations of his best material the most moving versions of all - and he wrote some classic songs; "Hang On To A Dream", "If I Were A Carpenter", and "Reason To Believe" among them. Particularly moving is his "Suite For Susan Moore and Damian", which is a kind of stream-of-consciousness tribute to his wife and child. It was a real tragedy when this precious talent succumbed to heroin addiction in 1980.

Archetypes	LP	MGM	4952	1973	£5	£12	US
Best Of Tim Hardin	LP	Verve	2317003	1970	£4	£10	
Bird On A Wire	LP	CBS	64335	1970	£4	£10	
Don't Make Promises	7"	Verve	VS1516	1968	£2	£5	
Hang On To a Dream	7"	Verve	VS1504	1966	£1.50	£4	chart single
Lady Came From Baltimore	7"	Verve	VS1511	1967	£2	£5	
Live In Concert	LP	Verve	(S)VLP6010	1968	£6	£15	
Nine	LP	GM	1004	1974	£4	£10	
Painted Head	LP	CBS	65209	1973	£4	£10	
Simple Song Of Freedom	7"	CBS	4441	1969	£1.50	£4	
Suite For Susan Moore & Damian	LP	CBS	63571	1970	£6	£15	
This Is Tim Hardin	LP	Atco	587/588082	1967	£6	£15	
Tim Hardin 1	LP	Verve	(S)VLP5018	1966	£6	£15	
Tim Hardin 1/Tim Hardin 2	LP	Verve	2683048	1974	£6	£15	double
Tim Hardin 2	LP	Verve	(S)VLP6002	1967	£6	£15	
Tim Hardin 4	LP	Verve	(S)VLP6016	1969	£6	£15	

HARDING, RICHARD

Jezebel	7"	HMV	POP887	1961	£2	£5

HARDMAN, ROSEMARY

Eagle Over Blue Mountain	LP	Plant Life	PLR014	1978	£6	£15	
Firebird	LP	Trailer	LER2075	1972	£8	£20	
Jerseyburger	LP	Alida Star Cottage	ASC7754	1975	£75	£150	
Queen Of Hearts	LP	Folk Heritage	FHR002M	1969	£15	£30	
Second Season Came	LP	Trailer	LER3018	1971	£8	£20	with Bob Axford
Stopped In My Tracks	LP	Plant Life	PLR023	1980	£6	£15	
Weakness Of Eve	LP	Plant Life	PLR053	1983	£6	£15	

HARDY, DAVE

Leaving The Dales	LP	Red Rag	RRR008	1976	£5	£12

HARDY, FRANCOISE

As one of France's top sixties pop music stars, Francoise Hardy also gained a considerable following in Britain. The EPs "C'Est Fab" and "C'Est Francoise" in particular sold well enough to enter the lower reaches of the charts - a rare feat for records sung in a language other than English.

All Because Of You	7"	United Artists	UP35070	1969	£1.50	£4	
All Over The World	7"	Pye	7N15802	1965	£2	£5	chart single
Autumn Rendezvous	7"	Vogue	VRS7014	1966	£1.50	£4	
Autumn Rendezvous	7" EP	Vogue	VRE5018	1967	£2	£5	
Catch A Falling Star	7"	Pye	7N15612	1964	£1.50	£4	
C'Est Fab	7" EP	Pye	NEP24188	1964	£2.50	£6	
C'Est Francoise	7" EP	Pye	NEP24193	1964	£2	£5	
Chante En Allemand	7" EP	Vogue	VRE5012	1966	£2	£5	
Comment Te Dire Adieu	7"	United Artists	UP35011	1969	£1.50	£4	chart single
Dis Lui Non	7" EP	Vogue	VRE5003	1965	£2	£5	
Et Meme	7"	Pye	7N15740	1964	£1.50	£4	
Francoise	LP	Vogue	VRL3028	1967	£4	£10	
Francoise	7" EP	Vogue	VRE5000	1965	£2	£5	
Francoise Hardy	LP	Pye	NPL18094	1964	£5	£12	
Francoise Hardy	LP	Vogue	VRL3000	1965	£5	£12	
Francoise Hardy	LP	Vogue	VRL3021	1966	£5	£12	
Francoise Hardy	7" EP	Vogue	VRE5001	1965	£2	£5	
Francoise Hardy Sings In English	LP	Vogue	VRL3025	1966	£5	£12	
Francoise Sings In English	7" EP	Pye	NEP24192	1964	£2	£5	
In Vogue	LP	Pye	NPL18099	1964	£5	£12	
Just Call And I'll Be There	7"	Vogue	VRS7001	1966	£1.50	£4	
La Maison Ou J'Ai Grandi	7"	Vogue	VRS7011	1966	£1.50	£4	
L'Amitie	7" EP	Vogue	VRE5015	1966	£2	£5	
Le Meilleur De Francoise Hardy	LP	Vogue	VRL3023	1966	£4	£10	
Le Temps Des Souvenirs	7" EP	Vogue	VRE5008	1965	£2	£5	
Mon Amie La Rose	7" EP	Vogue	VRE5017	1967	£2	£5	
Now You Want To Be Loved	7"	United Artists	UP1208	1968	£1.50	£4	
On Se Quitte Toujours	7"	Vogue	VRS7026	1967	£1.50	£4	
Pourtant Tu M'Aimes	7"	Pye	7N15696	1964	£1.50	£4	
Si C'Est Ca	7"	Vogue	VRS7020	1966	£1.50	£4	
So Many Friends	7"	Vogue	VRS7004	1966	£1.50	£4	
Soon Is Slipping Away	7"	United Artists	UP35105	1970	£1.50	£4	
This Little Heart	7"	Vogue	VRS7010	1966	£1.50	£4	
Tous Les Garcons Et Les Filles	7"	Pye	7N15653	1964	£1.50	£4	chart single
Voila	7"	Vogue	VRS7025	1966	£1.50	£4	
Voila!	LP	Vogue	VRL3031	1967	£4	£10	
Will You Love Me Tomorrow	7"	United Artists	UP2253	1968	£1.50	£4	

HARDY, LAVELL

Don't Lose Your Groove	7"	Direction	583261	1968	£1.50	£4

HARE, COLIN

Didn't I Tell You	7"	Warner Bros	K16203	1972	£1.50	£4
March Hare	LP	Penny Farthing	PELS516	1971	£15	£30

HARGRAVE, RON

Latch On	7"	MGM	MGM956	1957	£530	£800	pictured in Guide

HARLEY, STEVE
Big Big Deal .... 7" ..... EMI .... EMI2233 .... 1974 ... £7.50 .... £15 ....

HARMONIA
De Luxe .... LP ..... Brain .... 0001073 .... 1975 ... £4 .... £10 .... German
Harmonia .... LP ..... Brain .... 0001044 .... 1974 ... £4 .... £10 .... German

HARMONICA FATS
Tore Up .... 7" ...... Action .... ACT4507 .... 1968 ... £5 .... £10
Tore Up .... 7" ...... Stateside .... SS184 .... 1963 ... £6 .... £12

HARMONICA FRANK
In the pages of "Mystery Train", the acclaimed sociological study of American themes as revealed in the work of various rock musicians, Greil Marcus chooses the almost forgotten figure of white bluesman Frank Floyd to illustrate his thesis. As it happens, the single that Harmonica Frank recorded for Sun is one of the rarest releases on a particularly collectable label - anyone in possession of a copy can virtually name their own price!
Rockin' Chair Daddy .... 7" ...... Sun .... 205 .... 1954 ... £1050 ..£1500 .... US

HARMONISERS
Mother Hen .... 7" ...... Duke .... DU32 .... 1969 ... £2.50 .... £6 .... Winston
                                                                                                                                                    Sinclair B side

HARMONY FLAMES
USA Hit Parade No.1 .... 7" EP.. Fontana .... TFE17152 .... 1959 ... £2 .... £5

HARMONY GRASS
Cecilia .... 7" ...... RCA .... RCA1932 .... 1970 ... £1.50 .... £4
First Time Loving .... 7" ...... RCA .... RCA1828 .... 1969 ... £1.50 .... £4
I Remember .... 7" ...... RCA .... RCA1885 .... 1969 ... £1.50 .... £4
Move In A Little Bit Closer Baby .... 7" ...... RCA .... RCA1772 .... 1968 ... £1.50 .... £4 .... chart single
This Is Us .... LP ..... RCA .... SF8034 .... 1969 ... £4 .... £10

HARNER, BILLY
What About The Music .... 7" ...... Kama Sutra ..... 2013029 .... 1971 ... £2 .... £5
What About The Music .... 7" ...... Kama Sutra .... 2013029 .... 1971 ... £150 .... £250 .... with
                                                                                                                                                    instrumental version

HARPER, BUD
Mr.Soul .... 7" ...... Vocalion .... VP9252 .... 1965 ... £7.50 .... £15

HARPER, DON
Dr.Who Theme .... 7" ...... EMI .... EMI923 .... 1973 ... £1.50 .... £4

HARPER, HERBIE
Herbie Harper Octet .... 10" LP London .... LZN14031 .... 1956 ... £10 .... £25

HARPER, JOE 'HARMONICA'
Lazy Train .... 7" ...... MGM .... MGM983 .... 1958 ... £1.50 .... £4

HARPER, LEE POPCORN
Love Is Coming .... 7" ...... Page One .... POF053 .... 1968 ... £1.50 .... £4

HARPER, MIKE
You've Got Too Much Going For You .. 7" ...... Concord .... CON026 .... 197- ... £5 .... £10

HARPER, ROY
Bank Of The Dead .... 7" ...... Harvest .... HAR5059 .... 1972 ... £1.50 .... £4
Born In Captivity .... LP ..... Hardup .... PUB5002 .... 198- ... £5 .... £12
Bullinamingvase .... LP ..... Harvest .... SHSP4060 .... 1977 ... £6 .... £15 .... with 'Watford
                                                                                                                                                    Gap', chart LP
Bullinamingvase .... LP ..... Harvest .... SHSP4060 .... 1977 ... £8 .... £20 .... with 7' (PSR407)
Come Out Fighting Ghengis Smith ...... LP ..... CBS .... (S)BPG63184 .... 1967 ... £8 .... £20
Commercial Break .... LP ..... Harvest .... SHSP4077 .... 1977 ... £100 .... £200 .... test pressing
Flashes From The Archives Of Oblivion LP ..... Harvest .... SHDW405 .... 1974 ... £8 .... £20 .... double
Flat Baroque And Beserk .... LP ..... Harvest .... SHVL776 .... 1970 ... £5 .... £12
Folkjokeopus .... LP ..... Liberty .... LBS83231 .... 1969 ... £6 .... £15
Forever .... 7" ...... Harvest .... HAR5080 .... 1974 ... £1.50 .... £4
Grown-Ups Are Just Silly Children .... 7" ...... Harvest .... HAR5102 .... 1975 ... £1.50 .... £4
Home .... 7" ...... Harvest .... HAR5089 .... 1974 ... £1.50 .... £4
Introducing Roy Harper .... LP ..... Chrysalis .... PRO620 .... 1977 ... £15 .... £30 .... US promo
Life Goes By .... 7" ...... CBS .... 3371 .... 1968 ... £7.50 .... £15
Life Mask .... LP ..... Harvest .... SHVL808 .... 1973 ... £5 .... £12
Midspring Dithering .... 7" ...... CBS .... 203001 .... 1967 ... £10 .... £20
Mrs.Space .... 7" ...... Harvest .... PSR408 .... 1977 ... £2.50 .... £6 .... promo
One Of Those Days In England .... 7" ...... Harvest .... HAR5120 .... 1977 ... £2 .... £5
Playing Games .... 7" ...... Harvest .... HAR5203 .... 1980 ... £1.50 .... £4
Sail Away .... 7" ...... Harvest .... HAR5140 .... 1977 ... £1.50 .... £4
Sophisticated Beggar .... LP ..... Birth .... RAB3 .... 1972 ... £8 .... £20
Sophisticated Beggar .... LP ..... Strike .... JHL105 .... 1967 ... £20 .... £40
Sophisticated Beggar .... LP ..... Youngblood ..... SYB7 .... 1970 ... £8 .... £20
Stormcock .... LP ..... Harvest .... SHVL789 .... 1971 ... £5 .... £12
Take Me In Your Eyes .... 7" ...... Strike .... JH304 .... 1966 ... £10 .... £20 .... PS
Valentine .... LP ..... Harvest .... SHSP4027 .... 1974 ... £5 .... £12 .... chart LP
When An Old Cricketer Leaves The   7" ...... Harvest .... HAR5096 .... 1975 ... £2 .... £5
Crease
When An Old Cricketer Leaves The   7" ...... Harvest .... HAR5160 .... 1978 ... £2 .... £5 .... PS
Crease
Work Of Heart .... LP ..... Awareness ...... AWL1002 .... 1988 ... £4 .... £10 .... with 2 singles

HARPERS BIZARRE

59th Street Bridge Song	7"	Warner Bros	WB5890	1967	£2	£5	chart single
59th Street Bridge Song	7" EP.	Warner Bros	WEP1454	1967	£10	£20	French
Anything Goes	LP	Warner Bros	WS1716	1967	£6	£15	US
Anything Goes	7"	Warner Bros	WB7063	1967	£2	£5	chart single
Anything Goes	7"	Warner Bros	WB7388	1970	£1.50	£4	
As Time Goes By	LP	Forest Bay Co.	7545	1976	£4	£10	US
Battle Of New Orleans	7"	Warner Bros	WB7223	1968	£1.50	£4	
Best Of Harpers Bizarre	LP	Warner Bros	K56044	1974	£5	£12	
Come To The Sunshine	7"	Warner Bros	WB7528	1967	£1.50	£4	
Cotton Candy Sandman	7"	Warner Bros	WB7172	1968	£1.50	£4	
Feelin' Groovy	LP	Warner Bros	WS1693	1967	£6	£15	US
Harpers Bizarre 4	LP	Warner Bros	WS1716	1969	£6	£15	US
I Love You Alice B.Toklas	7"	Warner Bros	WB7238	1969	£1.50	£4	
Secret Life Of Harpers Bizarre	LP	Warner Bros	W(S)1739	1968	£6	£15	

HARPO, SLIM

Baby Scratch My Back	LP	Excello	LP8005	1966	£10	£25	US
Baby Scratch My Back	7"	Stateside	SS491	1966	£5	£10	
Best Of Slim Harpo	LP	Excello	LP8010	1969	£6	£15	US
Folsom Prison Blues	7"	Blue Horizon	573175	1970	£6	£12	
He Knew The Blues	LP	Blue Horizon	763854	1970	£17.50	£35	
I'm A King Bee	7"	Stateside	SS557	1966	£7.50	£15	
I'm Goona Keep What I've Got	7"	President	PT164	1968	£1.50	£4	
I'm Your Breadmaker Baby	7"	Stateside	SS581	1967	£6	£12	
Long Drink Of The Blues	LP	Stateside	SL10135	1965	£10	£25	with Lightnin' Slim
Raining In My Heart	LP	Excello	LP8003	1961	£20	£40	US
Raining In My Heart	7"	Pye	7N25098	1961	£4	£8	
Raining In My Heart	7"	Pye	7N25220	1963	£4	£8	
Shake Your Hips	7"	Stateside	SS527	1966	£7.50	£15	
Slim Harpo Knew The Blues	LP	Excello	LP8013	1970	£6	£15	US
Something Inside Me	7"	Liberty	LBF15176	1968	£5	£10	Papa Lightfoot B side
Tip On In	LP	President	PTL1017	1968	£6	£15	
Tip On In	7"	President	PT187	1968	£1.50	£4	
Trigger Finger	LP	Blue Horizon	2431013	1971	£17.50	£35	

HARRIOTT, DERRICK

Another Lonely Night	7"	Big Shot	BI511	1969	£2.50	£6	
Be True	7"	Blue Beat	BB178	1963	£5	£10	
Best Of Derrick Harriott	LP	Island	ILP928	1965	£30	£60	
Best Of Derrick Harriott	LP	Trojan	TTL43	1970	£6	£15	
Best Of Derrick Harriott Vol.2	LP	Island	ILP983	1968	£30	£60	
Born To Love You	7"	Island	WI3147	1968	£5	£10	Ike & Crystalites B side
Derrick	7"	Ska Beat	JB199	1965	£5	£10	
Happy Times	7"	Island	WI3064	1967	£5	£10	
Have Faith In Me	7"	Blue Beat	BB131	1962	£5	£10	
I'm Only Human	7"	Island	WI170	1965	£5	£10	
John Tom	7"	Doctor Bird	DB1002	1966	£5	£10	Audrey Williams B side
Loser	7"	Island	WI3063	1967	£5	£10	
Message From A Black Man	7"	Song Bird	SB1028	1970	£2.50	£6	
My Three Loves	7"	Island	WI237	1965	£5	£10	
Psychedelic Train	LP	Trojan	TBL141	1970	£6	£15	
Reggae Hits	LP	Trojan	TBL116	1970	£6	£15	
Riding For A Fall	7"	Songbird	SB1013	1969	£2.50	£6	
Rock Steady Party	LP	Island	ILP955	1967	£30	£60	
Rocksteady Party	LP	Trojan	TTL54	1970	£15	£30	
Sings Jamaica Reggae	LP	Pama	SECO13	1969	£15	£30	
Sitting On Top	7"	Songbird	SB1014	1969	£2.50	£6	
Standing In	7"	Big Shot	BI505	1968	£4	£8	
Together	7"	Island	WI245	1965	£5	£10	
Undertaker	LP	Trojan	TBL114	1970	£6	£15	
Walk The Streets	7"	Island	WI3077	1967	£5	£10	Bobby Ellis B side
What Can I Do	7"	Island	WI157	1964	£5	£10	

HARRIOTT, JOE

Abstract	LP	Columbia	33SX1477	1962	£25	£50	
Blue Harriott	7" EP.	Columbia	SEG7939	1959	£10	£20	
Cool Jazz With Joe	7" EP.	Melodisc	EPM7117	195-	£10	£20	
Free Form	LP	Jazzland	JLP49	1961	£25	£50	
Guy Called Joe	7" EP.	Columbia	SEG8070	1961	£10	£20	
High Spirits	LP	Columbia	33SX1692	1964	£25	£50	
Hum-Dono	LP	Columbia	SCX6354	1969	£20	£40	
Indo-Jazz Suite	LP	Columbia	SX/SCX6025	1966	£25	£50	
Joe Harriott	7" EP.	Polygon	JTE106	195-	£10	£20	
Joe Harriott Quartet	7" EP.	Columbia	SEG7665	1957	£10	£20	
Memorial	LP	One Up	OU2011	1973	£20	£40	
Movement	LP	Columbia	33SX1627	1963	£25	£50	
No Strings	7" EP.	Pye	NJE1003	195-	£10	£20	
Personal Portrait	LP	Columbia	SX/SCX6249	1968	£20	£40	
Southern Horizons	LP	Jazzland	JLP37	1961	£25	£50	
Swings High	LP	Melodisc	SLP12150	1967	£25	£50	
Tony Kinsey Trio And Joe Harriott	7" EP.	Esquire	EP36	195-	£10	£20	
Tony Kinsey Trio And Joe Harriott	7" EP.	Esquire	EP52	195-	£10	£20	
Tony Kinsey Trio And Joe Harriott	7" EP.	Esquire	EP82	195-	£10	£20	

HARRIS, ANITA

Something Must Be Done	7"	Pye	7N17069	1966	£1.50	£4	
Willingly	7"	Decca	F12082	1965	£1.50	£4	

HARRIS, BARRY

Preminado	LP	Riverside	RLP354	1961	£6	£15

HARRIS, BETTY

Cry To Me	7"	London	HL9796	1963	£4	£8
Nearer To You	7"	Stateside	SS2045	1967	£6	£12
Ride Your Pony	7"	Action	ACT4535	1969	£4	£8
Soul Perfection	LP	Action	ACLP6007	1969	£6	£15
What A Sad Feeling	7"	Stateside	SS475	1965	£5	£10

HARRIS, BILL

Bill Harris	LP	Emarcy	EJL1267	1958	£5	£12

HARRIS, BRENDA JO

I Can Remember	7"	Roulette	RO503	1968	£1.50	£4

HARRIS, DON 'SUGARCANE'

Cupful Of Dreams	LP	BASF	MPS68030	1973	£4	£10	
Don 'Sugarcane' Harris	LP	Epic	26286	1970	£4	£10	US
Fiddler On The Rock	LP	BASF	MPS68028	1970	£4	£10	
Got The Blues	LP	BASF	MPS68029	1972	£4	£10	
Keep On Driving	LP	BASF	MPS68027	1970	£4	£10	
Sugarcane	LP	Epic	30027	1971	£4	£10	

HARRIS, EDDIE

Breakfast At Tiffany's	LP	Stateside	SL10009	1962	£5	£12
Electrifying Eddie Harris	LP	Atlantic	781985	1968	£5	£12
Goes To The Movies	LP	Stateside	SL10049	1963	£5	£12
Listen Here	7"	Atlantic	584218	1969	£1.50	£4
Mighty Like A Rose	LP	Stateside	SL10018	1963	£5	£12
Silver Cycles	LP	Atlantic	588177	1969	£4	£10

HARRIS, EMMYLOU

Gliding Bird	LP	Jubilee	JGS8031	1969	£25	£50	US, colour cover
Quarter Moon In A Ten Cent Town	LP	Mobile Fidelity	MFSL1015	1978	£4	£10	US audiophile

HARRIS, JET

Besame Mucho	7"	Decca	F11466	1962	£1.50	£4	chart single
Big Bad Bass	7"	Decca	F11841	1964	£2	£5	
Jet Harris	7" EP	Decca	DFE8502	1962	£5	£10	
Main Title Theme	7"	Decca	F11488	1962	£1.50	£4	chart single
My Lady	7"	Fontana	TF849	1967	£5	£10	
Theme For A Fallen Idol	7"	SRT	SRTS75355	1975	£1.50	£4	

HARRIS, JET & TONY MEEHAN

Applejack	7"	Decca	F11710	1963	£1.50	£4	chart single
Diamonds	7"	Decca	F11563	1963	£1.50	£4	chart single
Diamonds	7" EP	Decca	DFE7099	1963	£6	£12	export
Jet And Tony	7" EP	Decca	DFE8528	1963	£5	£10	
Scarlet O'Hara	7"	Decca	F11644	1963	£1.50	£4	chart single

HARRIS, JOHNNY

Movements	LP	Warner Bros	K46054	1972	£8	£20

HARRIS, JUNE

Over And Over Again	7"	CBS	201774	1965	£4	£8

HARRIS, MAJOR

Just The Thing That I Do	7"	Atlantic	K10690	1975	£1.50	£4

HARRIS, PAT

Hippy Hippy Shake	7"	Pye	7N15567	1963	£4	£8

HARRIS, PEPPERMINT

Peppermint Harris	LP	Time	5	1962	£5	£12	US

HARRIS, PHIL

I Guess I'll Have To Change My Plan	7"	HMV	7M231	1954	£1.50	£4
I Wouldn't Touch You With A Ten Foot Pole	7"	HMV	7M289	1955	£1.50	£4
Take Your Girlie To The Movies	7"	HMV	7M199	1954	£1.50	£4

HARRIS, RICHARD

MacArthur Park	7"	RCA	RCA1699	1968	£1.50	£4
Tramp Shining	7"	RCA	RD/SF7947	1968	£4	£10
Tramp Shining	LP	Stateside	SSL5019	1969	£4	£10
Yard Went On Forever	LP	Stateside	SSL5001	1968	£4	£10
Yard Went On Forever	7"	Stateside	SS8001	1968	£1.50	£4

HARRIS, ROLF

Favourites	7" EP	Columbia	SEG8531	1967	£2	£5	
Jake The Peg	7" EP	Columbia	SEG8516	1966	£2	£5	
Ringo For President	7"	Columbia	DB7349	1964	£1.50	£4	
Sun Arise	7"	Columbia	DB4888	1962	£1.50	£4	chart single
Tie Me Kangaroo Down Sport	7"	Columbia	DB4483	1960	£1.50	£4	chart single

HARRIS, RONNIE

Cabaret	7"	Columbia	SCM5206	1955	£1.50	£4
Cry Upon My Shoulder	7"	Columbia	DB3814	1956	£1.50	£4
Don't Go To Strangers	7"	Columbia	SCM5159	1955	£1.50	£4
Hello Mrs.Jones	7"	Columbia	SCM5178	1955	£1.50	£4

Title	Format	Label	Catalogue	Year			Notes
Hold My Hand	7"	Columbia	SCM5138	1954	£1.50	£4	
I Love Paris	7"	Columbia	SCM5139	1954	£1.50	£4	
I've Changed My Mind A Thousand Times	7"	Columbia	SCM5242	1956	£1.50	£4	
On The Way To Your Heart	7"	Columbia	SCM5189	1955	£1.50	£4	
Stranger In Paradise	7"	Columbia	SCM5176	1955	£1.50	£4	
That's Right	7"	Columbia	DB3836	1956	£1.50	£4	
What Is The Reason?	7"	Columbia	SCM5266	1956	£1.50	£4	

HARRIS, ROY

Title	Format	Label	Catalogue	Year			Notes
Bitter And The Sweet	LP	Topic	12TS217	1972	£5	£12	
Champions Of Folly	LP	Topic	12TS256	1975	£5	£12	

HARRIS, SHAKEY JAKE

Title	Format	Label	Catalogue	Year			Notes
Devil's Harmonica	LP	Polydor	2391015	1972	£6	£15	
Further On Up The Road	LP	Liberty	83217	1969	£6	£15	

HARRIS SISTERS

Title	Format	Label	Catalogue	Year			Notes
Kissing Bug	7"	Capitol	CL14232	1955	£4	£8	

HARRIS, SUE

Title	Format	Label	Catalogue	Year			Notes
Hammers And Tongues	LP	Free Reed	FRR020	1978	£6	£15	

HARRIS, THURSTON

Title	Format	Label	Catalogue	Year			Notes
Be Baba Leba	7"	Vogue	V9108	1958	£50	£100	
Do What You Did	7"	Vogue	V9098	1958	£50	£100	
Hey Little Girl	7"	Vogue	V9146	1959	£30	£60	
In The Bottom Of My Heart	7"	Vogue	V9144	1959	£30	£60	
Little Bitty Pretty One	7"	Sue	WI4016	1966	£7.50	£15	
Little Bitty Pretty One	7"	Vogue	V9092	1957	£35	£70	
Purple Stew	7"	Vogue	V9139	1959	£30	£60	
Runk Bunk	7"	Vogue	V9149	1959	£30	£60	
Slip Slop	7"	Vogue	V9151	1959	£30	£60	
Smokey Joes	7"	Vogue	V9122	1958	£30	£60	
Tears From My Heart	7"	Vogue	V9127	1958	£30	£60	

HARRIS, WEE WILLIE

Title	Format	Label	Catalogue	Year			Notes
Listen To The River Roll Along	7"	Polydor	56140	1966	£1.50	£4	
Love Bug Crawl	7"	Decca	F10980	1958	£12.50	£25	
No Chemise Please	7"	Decca	F11044	1958	£10	£20	
Rocking At The Two I's	7"	Decca	F10970	1957	£12.50	£25	
Rocking With Wee Willie	7" EP	Decca	DFE6465	1958	£25	£50	
Someone's In The Kitchen With Diana	7"	Parlophone	R5504	1966	£1.50	£4	
Wild One	7"	Decca	F11217	1960	£5	£10	
You Must Be Joking	7"	HMV	POP1198	1963	£2	£5	

HARRIS, WYNONIE

Title	Format	Label	Catalogue	Year			Notes
Adam Come And Get Your Rib	78	Vogue	V2166	1953	£5	£10	
Battle Of The Blues	7" EP	Bluebeat	BBEP301	1961	£25	£50	
Bloodshot Eyes	78	Vogue	V2127	1952	£5	£10	
Bloodshot Eyes	7"	Vogue	V2127	1956	£30	£60	tri centre
Do It Again Please	78	Vogue	V2133	1952	£5	£10	
Drinkin' Wine Spo Dee O Dee	78	Vogue	V2006	1951	£5	£10	
Good Morning Judge	78	Vogue	V2128	1952	£5	£10	
Good Rockin' Blues	LP	King	KS1086	1970	£5	£12	US
Lovin' Machine	78	Vogue	V2111	1952	£5	£10	
Put It Back	78	Vogue	V2134	1952	£5	£10	
Teardrops From My Eyes	78	Vogue	V2144	1952	£5	£10	
Wynonie Mister Blues Harris	7" EP	Vogue	EPV1103	1956	£75	£150	

HARRIS, WYNONIE & EDDIE 'CLEANHEAD' VINSON

Title	Format	Label	Catalogue	Year			Notes
Jump Blues	LP	Polydor	2343048	1972	£4	£10	

HARRIS, WYNONIE, AMOS MILBURN & PRINCE WATERFORD

Title	Format	Label	Catalogue	Year			Notes
Party After Hours	10" LP	Aladdin	703	1956	£75	£150	US
Party After Hours	10" LP	Aladdin	703	1956	£150	£250	US, red vinyl

HARRISON, DANNY

Title	Format	Label	Catalogue	Year			Notes
I'm A Rolling Stone	7"	Coral	Q72479	1965	£7.50	£15	
Introducing Danny Harrison	7" EP	Starlite	STEP23	1962	£4	£8	

HARRISON, EARL

Title	Format	Label	Catalogue	Year			Notes
Humphrey Stomp	7"	London	HL10121	1967	£12.50	£25	

HARRISON, GEORGE

"Songs By George Harrison" consists of three out-takes from "Somewhere In England" together with a live version of "For You Blue". It is available as either a CD or a vinyl single, but in either case only as a bonus within a deluxe, partly hand-made, edition of a book of George Harrison's lyrics. £250 was the new selling price of the last sets to be available in 1992 and they were produced as a limited edition of 2,500 copies. (A few promotional copies extra to the main edition were also made available). The value of the set may well not rise any further, since it is likely that all collectors interested in the set will already have acquired one during the lengthy period of time it took for the edition to sell out.

Title	Format	Label	Catalogue	Year			Notes
All Things Must Pass	LP	Apple	STCH639	1971	£6	£15	3 LP box, poster, chart LP
Bangla Desh	7"	Apple	R5912	1971	£25	£50	PS
Dark Horse	7"	Apple	R6001	1975	£2.50	£6	PS
Dark Horse Radio Special	LP	Dark Horse	SP22002	1974	£100	£200	US promo
Electronic Sound	LP	Apple	ZAPPLE2	1969	£25	£50	
Faster	7"	Dark Horse	K17423	1979	£2.50	£6	
Faster	7"	Dark Horse	K17423P	1979	£6	£12	pic disc
Gone Troppo	LP	Dark Horse	9237341	1982	£8	£20	US audiophile promo
Got My Mind Set On You	7"	Dark Horse	W8178	1987	£5	£10	green label

Title	Format	Label	Catalogue	Year	Price	Price	Notes
Got My Mind Set On You	7"	Dark Horse	W8178	1987	£1.50	£4	red label
Got My Mind Set On You	7"	Dark Horse	W8178B	1987	£2	£5	boxed set
Got My Mind Set On You	12"	Dark Horse	W8178TP	1987	£3	£8	pic disc
My Sweet Lord	7"	Apple	R5884	1971	£5	£10	PS - colour head shot of George
Somewhere In England	LP	Dark Horse	DHK3472	1980	£15	£30	US original issue with 4 different tracks
Songs By George Harrison	CD	Genesis publications	SGHCD777	1988	£150	£250	issued with ltd. ed. book
Songs By George Harrison	7"	Genesis publications	SGH777	1988	£150	£250	issued with ltd. ed. book
Thirty-Three And A Third Dialogue Album	LP	Dark Horse	PRO649	1976	£15	£30	US promo
This Guitar	7"	Apple	R6012	1976	£4	£8	
Wonderwall	LP	Apple	APCOR1	1968	£25	£50	mono
Wonderwall	LP	Apple	SAPCOR1	1968	£10	£25	stereo
You	7"	Apple	R6007	1975	£2.50	£6	PS

HARRISON, GEORGE & OTHERS

Title	Format	Label	Catalogue	Year	Price	Price	Notes
Concert For Bangla Desh	LP	Apple	STCX3385	1972	£8	£20	3 LPs, booklet, boxed, chart LP

HARRISON, GEORGE & VICKI BROWN

Title	Format	Label	Catalogue	Year	Price	Price	Notes
Shanghai Surprise	7"		SHANGHAI1	1986	£250	£400	promo only

HARRISON, NOEL

Title	Format	Label	Catalogue	Year	Price	Price	Notes
At The Blue Angel	LP	Philips	BBL7399	1960	£4	£10	
Great Electric Experiment Is Over	LP	Reprise	RSLP6321	1969	£5	£12	
It's All Over Now Baby Blue	7"	Decca	F12345	1966	£1.50	£4	
Love Minus Zero/No Limit	7"	Decca	F12918	1969	£1.50	£4	
Noel Harrison	7" EP	Decca	DFE8616	1965	£2.50	£6	
Noel Harrison	7" EP	HMV	7EG8383	1957	£2.50	£6	
To Ramona	7" EP	Decca	DFE8639	1965	£2.50	£6	
Trees	7"	Decca	F12201	1965	£1.50	£4	
Windmills Of Your Mind	7"	Reprise	RS20758	1969	£1.50	£4	chart single
Young Girl Of Sixteen	7"	Decca	F12314	1966	£1.50	£4	

HARRISON, WILBERT

Title	Format	Label	Catalogue	Year	Price	Price	Notes
Get It While You Can	7"	Action	ACT4613	1973	£2	£5	
I'm Broke	7"	Island	WI031	1962	£5	£10	
Kansas City	LP	Sphere Sound	(S)SR7000	1964	£10	£25	US
Kansas City	7"	Top Rank	JAR132	1959	£5	£10	
Let's Stick Together	7"	Sue	WI363	1965	£5	£10	
Let's Work Together	LP	London	HA/SH8415	1969	£6	£15	
Let's Work Together	7"	London	HL10307	1970	£2	£5	
Wilbert Harrison	LP	Buddah	BDS5092	1972	£5	£12	US

HARRISON, WILBERT & BABY WASHINGTON

Title	Format	Label	Catalogue	Year	Price	Price	Notes
Battle Of The Giants	LP	Joy	JOYS191	1971	£5	£12	

HARRISON, YVONNE

Title	Format	Label	Catalogue	Year	Price	Price	Notes
Chase	7"	Caltone	TONE102	1967	£4	£8	

HARSH REALITY

Title	Format	Label	Catalogue	Year	Price	Price	Notes
Heaven And Hell	LP	Philips	SBL7891	1969	£30	£60	
Heaven And Hell	7"	Philips	BF1769	1969	£5	£10	
Tobacco Ash Sunday	7"	Philips	BF1710	1968	£5	£10	

HART, BOB, PERCY WEBB, ERNEST AUSTIN

Title	Format	Label	Catalogue	Year	Price	Price	Notes
Flash Company	LP	Topic	12TS243	1974	£5	£12	

HART, CAJUN

Title	Format	Label	Catalogue	Year	Price	Price	Notes
Got To Find A Way	7"	Warner Bros	WB7258	1969	£60	£120	

HART, DERRY & THE HARTBEATS

Title	Format	Label	Catalogue	Year	Price	Price	Notes
Come On Baby	7"	Decca	F11138	1959	£5	£10	

HART, MICKEY

Title	Format	Label	Catalogue	Year	Price	Price	Notes
Rolling Thunder	LP	Warner Bros	K46182	1972	£6	£15	

HART, MIKE

Title	Format	Label	Catalogue	Year	Price	Price	Notes
Basher,Chalky,Pongo,& Me	LP	Polydor	2310211	1972	£6	£15	
Mike Hart Bleeds	LP	Dandelion	63756	1970	£6	£15	
Yawney Morning Song	7"	Dandelion	4781	1970	£1.50	£4	

HART, TIM

Title	Format	Label	Catalogue	Year	Price	Price	Notes
Drunken Sailor And Other Kids Songs	LP	MFP	4156351	1983	£4	£10	
Tim Hart	LP	Chrysalis	CHR1218	1979	£6	£15	

HART, TIM & MADDY PRIOR

Title	Format	Label	Catalogue	Year	Price	Price	Notes
Folk Songs Of Olde England 1	LP	Tepee	ARPS3	1968	£10	£25	
Folk Songs Of Olde England 2	LP	Tepee	ARPS4	1969	£10	£25	
Summer Solstice	LP	B&C	CAS1035	1971	£6	£15	

HARTE, FRANK

Title	Format	Label	Catalogue	Year	Price	Price	Notes
Daybreak And A Candle-End	LP	Spin	995	1987	£5	£12	Irish
Through Dublin City	LP	Topic	12T218	1973	£5	£12	

HARTFORD, JOHN

Title	Format	Label	Catalogue	Year	Price	Price	Notes
Earthwords And Music	LP	RCA	LSP3796	1967	£4	£10	US

Gentle On My Mind	LP	RCA	LSP4068	1968	£4	£10		US
Housing Project	LP	RCA	LSP3998	1968	£4	£10		US
Iron Mountain Depot	LP	RCA	LSP4337	1970	£4	£10		US
John Hartford	LP	RCA	LSP4156	1969	£4	£10		US
Looks At Life	LP	RCA	LSP3687	1967	£4	£10		US
Love Album	LP	RCA	LSP3884	1968	£4	£10		US

HARTLEY, KEEF

The Keef Hartley Band was one of the many groups to emerge from the John Mayall school of blues, and one of the best. They favoured a tough, riff-based approach to blues-rock, and by gradually adding brass instruments the group became a key element within the growth of jazz-rock. The first two albums are the best - after that Miller Anderson, who was both the lead singer and the lead guitarist, became a little too fond of writing sensitive, reflective material, which did not really suit the band. "Little Big Band", however, which presents the group's most exciting music re-arranged for a much bigger unit, is a splendid return to form.

Battle Of North West Six	LP	Deram	SML1054	1969	£6	£15	
Best Of The Keef Hartley Band	LP	Deram	DPA3011/2	1974	£6	£15	double
Dance To The Music	7"	Deram	DM380	1973	£1.50	£4	
Halfbreed	LP	Deram	SML1037	1969	£6	£15	
Lancashire Hustler	LP	Deram	SDL13	1973	£5	£12	
Leave It Till The Morning	7"	Deram	DM250	1969	£2.50	£6	
Little Big Band	LP	Deram	SDL4	1971	£8	£20	
Overdog	LP	Deram	SDL2	1971	£6	£15	
Roundabout	7"	Deram	DM316	1970	£2	£5	
Seventy Second Brave	LP	Deram	SDL9	1972	£5	£12	
Time Is Near	LP	Deram	SML1071	1970	£6	£15	chart LP
Waiting Around	7"	Deram	DM273	1969	£2	£5	

HARVEY & DOC WITH THE DWELLERS

Oh Baby	7"	Annette	1002	1964	£7.50	£15	US

HARVEY & THE MOONGLOWS

Ten Commandments Of Love	7"	London	HLM8730	1958	£50	£100

HARVEY, ALEX

Agent OO Soul	7"	Fontana	TF610	1965	£10	£20	
Ain't That Just Too Bad	7"	Polydor	56017	1965	£15	£30	
Alex Harvey And His Soul Band	LP	Polydor	LPHM46424	1964	£30	£60	
Blues	LP	Polydor	LPHM46441	1964	£30	£60	sleeve pictured in Guide
Framed	LP	Vertigo	6360081	1972	£20	£40	spiral label
Got My Mojo Working	7"	Polydor	NH52907	1964	£12.50	£25	
I Just Wanna Make Love To You	7"	Polydor	NH52264	1964	£10	£20	
Mafia Stole My Guitar	LP	RCA	PL25257	1979	£4	£10	
Maybe Someday	7"	Decca	F12660	1967	£12.50	£25	
Midnight Moses	7"	Fontana	TF1063	1969	£10	£20	
Next	LP	Vertigo	6360103	1974	£5	£12	
Penthouse Tapes	LP	Vertigo	9102007	1975	£4	£10	chart LP
Presents The Loch Ness Monster	LP	K-Tel	NE984	1977	£15	£30	
Roman Wall Blues	LP	Fontana	(S)TL5534	1969	£40	£80	
Sunday Song	7"	Decca	F12640	1967	£12.50	£25	
Work Song	7"	Fontana	TF764	1966	£10	£20	

HARVEY BOYS

Nothing Is Too Good For You	7"	London	HLA8397	1957	£7.50	£15

HARVEY, JANCIS

Distance Of Doors	LP	Pilgrim King	KLP5	1973	£10	£25
Portrait Of Jancis Harvey	LP	Westwood		1976	£10	£25
Time Was Now	LP	Westwood	WR5054	1975	£20	£40

HARVEY, PETER

Rainin' In My Heart	7"	Columbia	DB4873	1962	£1.50	£4

HARVEY, PHIL

The name of Phil Harvey (also appearing as Harvey and Doc) covers the identity of Phil Spector.

Bumbershoot	7"	Imperial	5583	1959	£25	£50	US

HARVEY, P.J.

Dry	LP	Too Pure	PURED10	1992	£10	£25	with demos LP
Dry	CD	Too Pure	PURECDD10	1992	£15	£30	with demos CD

HARVEY, RICHARD

Richard Harvey was the dominant influence within Gryphon and his interest, knowledge, and skill with medieval instruments has kept him busy as a session musician and soundtrack composer ever since. "A New Way Of Seeing" was produced specially for a new equipment launch by the computer company ICL and has never been issued commercially, although the considerable number of copies that have found their way on to the collectors' market since attention was drawn to the record in the first edition of the Music Master Price Guide have had the effect of depressing the record's value.

Divisions On A Ground	LP	Transatlantic	TRA292	1975	£25	£50
New Way Of Seeing	LP	ICL	ICL001	1979	£10	£25

HARWOOD, CHRIS

Nice To Meet Miss Christine	LP	Birth	RAB1	1970	£15	£30

HASKELL, GORDON

It Is And It Isn't	LP	Atlantic	K40311	1972	£8	£20
Sail In My Boat	LP	CBS	63741	1969	£40	£80

HASKELL, JACK

Around The World	7"	London	HL8426	1957	£5	£10

HASLAM, MICHAEL

There Goes The Forgotten Man	7"	Parlophone	R5267	1965	£2.50	£6

HASSLES

The first recordings by Billy Joel (apart from a little unspecified session work) were with the Hassles, whose only claim to fame this is.

Hassles	LP	United Artists	UAS6631	1968	£8	£20	US
Hour Of The Wolf	LP	United Artists	UAS6699	1969	£8	£20	US
You Got Me Humming	7"	United Artists	UP1199	1967	£4	£8	

HAT & TIE

Bread To Spend	7"	President	PT122	1967	£10	£20
Chance For Romance	7"	President	PT105	1966	£4	£8

HATCH, TONY ORCHESTRA

Crossroads	7"	Pye	7N15754	1965	£2.50	£6	PS
Crossroads	7"	Pye	7N17169	1966	£1.50	£4	
Out Of This World Theme	7"	Pye	7N15460	1962	£1.50	£4	

HATE

Hate Kills	LP	Famous	SFMA5752	1970	£20	£40

HATFIELD & THE NORTH

Afters	LP	Virgin	VR5	1980	£8	£20	
Hatfield & The North	LP	Virgin	V2008	1974	£4	£10	
Rotters Club	LP	Virgin	V2030	1975	£4	£10	chart LP

HATFIELD, BOBBY

Oowee Baby, I Love You	7"	Warner Bros	K16163	1972	£1.50	£4

HATHAWAY, DONNY

Donny Hathaway	LP	Atlantic	K40241	1970	£4	£10
Everything Is Everything	LP	Atlantic	K40063	1970	£5	£12
Extension Of A Man	LP	Atlantic	K40487	1973	£4	£10
Ghetto	7"	Atco	226010	1970	£2	£5
Live	LP	Atlantic	K40369	1972	£5	£12

HAVEN, ALAN

Images	7"	Fontana	TF542	1965	£2.50	£6

HAVEN ST.

	LP	Rissole			£25	£50

HAVENS, RICHIE

1983	LP	Verve	2620001	1969	£6	£15	double
Alarm Clock	LP	Polydor	2310080	1971	£4	£10	
Electric Havens	LP	Transatlantic	TRA187	1966	£5	£12	
Great Blind Degree	LP	Polydor	2480049	1972	£4	£10	
Handsome Johnny	7"	Verve	VS1524	1969	£1.50	£4	
Lady Madonna	7"	Verve	VS1519	1969	£1.50	£4	
Live On Stage	LP	Polydor	2659015	1972	£5	£12	double
Mixed Bag	LP	Verve	(S)VLP6008	1967	£5	£12	
Mixed Bag 2	LP	Polydor	2310356	1974	£4	£10	
Oxford Town	7"	Transatlantic	BIG119	1969	£1.50	£4	
Portfolio	LP	Polydor	2480166	1973	£4	£10	
Richie Havens' Record	LP	Transatlantic	TRA199	1965	£5	£12	
Rocky Raccoon	7"	Verve	VS1521	1969	£1.50	£4	
Something Else Again	LP	Verve	(S)VLP6005	1968	£5	£12	
State Of Mind	LP	Verve	2304050	1971	£4	£10	
Stonehenge	LP	Verve	(S)VLP6021	1968	£4	£10	
There's A Hole In The Future	7"	Verve	VS1523	1969	£1.50	£4	
Three Day Eternity	7"	Verve	VS1512	1968	£1.50	£4	

HAWES, HAMPTON

All Night Session Vol.1	LP	Contemporary	LAC12161	1959	£6	£15
All Night Session Vol.2	LP	Contemporary	LAC12162	1959	£6	£15
All Night Session Vol.3	LP	Contemporary	LAC12163	1959	£6	£15
Everybody Likes Hampton Hawes	LP	Contemporary	LAC12091	1958	£6	£15
Hampton Hawes Quartet	10" LP	Esquire	20079	1956	£10	£25
This Is Hampton Hawes	LP	Contemporary	LAC12081	1958	£8	£20
Trio Vol.1	LP	Vogue	LAE12059	1957	£8	£20
Vol.1 - The Trio	LP	Contemporary	LAC12056	1957	£8	£20

HAWKE, TOMMY

Good Gravy	7"	Top Rank	JAR348	1960	£2	£5

HAWKES, CHIP

Nashville Album	LP	RCA	PL25044	1977	£10	£25

HAWKINS, BUDDY BOY & WILLIAM MOORE

Buddy Boy Hawkins/William Moore	7" EP	Heritage	RE102	195-	£6	£12

HAWKINS, COLEMAN

Alive At The Village Gate	LP	Verve	VLP9044	1963	£5	£12	
Back In Bean's Bag	LP	CBS	BPG62157	1964	£4	£10	
Bean And The Boys	7" EP	Esquire	EP192	1958	£2	£5	
Blue Saxophones	LP	Columbia	33CX10143	1959	£8	£20	with Ben Webster
Capitol Presents Coleman Hawkins & Sonny Greer	10" LP	Capitol	LC6650	1954	£20	£40	
Cattin'	LP	Fontana	SJL131	1966	£4	£10	
Classics In Jazz	10" LP	Capitol	LC6580	1953	£20	£40	
Coleman Hawkins	LP	Moodsville	MV7	1961	£6	£15	
Coleman Hawkins	7" EP	Vogue	EPV1021	1955	£2	£5	
Coleman Hawkins All Stars	LP	Swingsville	SV2005	1962	£6	£15	
Coleman Hawkins Group	LP	London	LTZC15048	1957	£8	£20	

Title	Format	Label	Catalogue	Year	Price	Price	Notes
Coleman Hawkins Group	7" EP	Mercury	EP16029	195-	£2	£5	
Coleman Hawkins Sextet	7" EP	Esquire	EP235	1961	£2	£5	
Desafinado	LP	HMV	CLP1630/CSD1484	1963	£5	£12	
Genius Of Coleman Hawkins	LP	HMV	CLP1293	1959	£8	£20	
Gilded Hawk	LP	Capitol	T819	1957	£8	£20	
Hawk Eyes	LP	Esquire	32102	1960	£8	£20	
Hawk Flies High	LP	London	LTZU15117	1958	£8	£20	
Hawk Returns	7" EP	London	EZC19020	1958	£2.50	£6	
Hawk Talks	LP	Brunswick	LAT8242	1958	£10	£25	
Hawk Talks	7" EP	Brunswick	OE9166	1955	£2	£5	
High And Mighty Hawk	LP	Felsted	FAJ7005/SJA2005	1959	£15	£30	
Lucky Duck	7"	Brunswick	05459	1955	£2.50	£6	
Meditations	LP	Fontana	TL5273	1965	£4	£10	
Newport Jazz Festival 1957	LP	Columbia	33CX10103	1958	£6	£15	with Roy Eldridge
Soul	LP	Esquire	32095	1960	£8	£20	
Stasch	LP	Swingsville	SVLP2013	1962	£6	£15	
Swing!	LP	Fontana	FJL102	1964	£4	£10	
Ten Coleman Hawkins Specials	10" LP	HMV	DLP1055	1954	£20	£40	
Today And Now	LP	HMV	CLP1689	1964	£5	£12	
With The Red Garland Trio	LP	Swingsville	SV2001	1962	£6	£15	

HAWKINS, DALE

Title	Format	Label	Catalogue	Year	Price	Price	Notes
Hot Dog	7"	London	HLM9060	1960	£10	£20	
La Do Da Da	7"	London	HLM8728	1958	£12.50	£25	
LA, Memphis & Tyler, Texas	LP	Bell	SBLL127	1970	£6	£15	
Let's All Twist	LP	Roulette	(S)R25175	1962	£20	£40	US
Liza Jane	7"	London	HLM9016	1959	£10	£20	
Oh Susie Q	LP	Checker	6467301	1973	£4	£10	
Susie Q	7"	Janus	no number	1971	£10	£20	promo, & 3 tracks by other artists
Susie Q	7"	London	HL8482	1957	£100	£200	
Suzie-Q	LP	Chess	1429	1958	£100	£200	US
Yea Yea Classcutter	7"	London	HLM8842	1959	£12.50	£25	

HAWKINS, HAWKSHAW

Title	Format	Label	Catalogue	Year	Price	Price	Notes
All New Hawkshaw Hawkins	LP	London	HA8181	1964	£5	£12	
Country And Western	7" EP	Parlophone	GEP8742	1958	£10	£20	
Grand Ole Opry Favorites	LP	King	592	1958	£8	£20	US
Hawkshaw Hawkins	LP	King	587	1958	£8	£20	US
Hawkshaw Hawkins	LP	King	599	1959	£8	£20	US
Hawkshaw Hawkins - Country And Western	7" EP	Vogue	VE170117	1958	£15	£30	
Lonesome 7-7203	7"	London	HL9737	1963	£2.50	£6	
Taken From Our Vaults Vol.1	LP	King	(S)858	1963	£5	£12	US
Taken From Our Vaults Vol.2	LP	King	(S)870	1963	£5	£12	US
Taken From Our Vaults Vol.3	LP	King	(S)873	1963	£5	£12	US

HAWKINS, RONNIE

Title	Format	Label	Catalogue	Year	Price	Price	Notes
Arkansas Rockpile	LP	Roulette	RCP1003	1970	£4	£10	
Best Of Ronnie Hawkins & His Band	LP	Roulette	SR42045	1970	£6	£15	US
Bitter Green	7"	Atlantic	2091007	1970	£2	£5	
Clara	7"	Columbia	DB4442	1960	£7.50	£15	
Down In The Alley	7"	Atlantic	584320	1970	£2	£5	
Folk Ballads	LP	Columbia	33SX1295	1960	£10	£25	mono
Folk Ballads	LP	Columbia	SCX3358	1960	£20	£40	stereo
Forty Days	7"	Columbia	DB4319	1959	£15	£30	
Hawk	LP	Cotillion	SD9039	1971	£4	£10	US
Hey, Bo Diddley	7"	Quality	6128	1959	£50	£100	Canadian
Mary Lou	7"	Columbia	DB4345	1959	£10	£20	
Mojo Man	LP	Roulette	R25390	1964	£8	£20	US
Mr.Dynamo	LP	Columbia	33SX1238	1960	£20	£40	mono
Mr.Dynamo	LP	Columbia	SCX3315	1960	£40	£80	stereo
Mr.Dynamo	LP	Roulette	SR25102	1960	£75	£150	US, red vinyl
Rocking With Ronnie	7" EP	Columbia	ESG7792	1960	£30	£60	stereo
Rocking With Ronnie	7" EP	Columbia	SEG7983	1960	£20	£40	
Rocking With Ronnie No.2	7" EP	Columbia	ESG7795	1960	£30	£60	stereo
Rocking With Ronnie No.2	7" EP	Columbia	SEG7988	1960	£20	£40	
Rock'n'Roll Resurrection	LP	Monument	MNT65122	1972	£4	£10	
Ronnie Hawkins	LP	Atlantic	2400009	1970	£5	£12	
Ronnie Hawkins	LP	Roulette	(S)R25078	1959	£25	£50	US
Ronnie Hawkins	LP	Roulette	SR25078	1959	£75	£150	US, red vinyl
Ronnie Hawkins	LP	Yorkville	YVS33002	1968	£5	£12	Canadian
Rrrracket Time	LP	WLW	WLW101	1965	£6	£15	Canadian
Songs Of Hank Williams	LP	Roulette	(S)R25137	1960	£10	£25	US
Southern Love	7"	Columbia	DB4412	1960	£6	£12	
Who Do You Love	7"	Columbia	DB7036	1963	£7.50	£15	
Who Do You Love	7"	Roulette	RO512	1969	£1.50	£4	

HAWKINS, SCREAMING JAY

Title	Format	Label	Catalogue	Year	Price	Price	Notes
At Home	LP	Epic	LN3448	1956	£100	£200	US
I Hear Voices	7"	Sue	WI379	1965	£7.50	£15	
I Put A Spell On You	LP	Direction	863481	1969	£8	£20	
I Put A Spell On You	LP	Epic	LN3457	1957	£60	£120	US
I Put A Spell On You	78	Fontana	H107	1958	£30	£60	
I Put A Spell On You	7"	Direction	584097	1969	£4	£8	
Night And Day	LP	Planet	PLL1001	1966	£30	£60	
Night At Forbidden City	LP	Sounds Of Hawaii	5015	196-	£10	£25	US
Screaming Jay Hawkins	LP	Philips	PHS600336	1970	£6	£15	US
Whammy	7"	Columbia	DB7460	1965	£6	£12	

Title	Format	Label	Catalog #	Year			Notes
What That Is	LP	Mercury	SMCL20178	1969	£6	£15	

HAWKS
Title	Format	Label	Catalog #	Year			Notes
Grissle	7"	Stateside	SS2147	1968	£2.50	£6	...B side by the Sheep

HAWKS (2)
Title	Format	Label	Catalog #	Year			Notes
Words Of Hope	7"	Five Believers	FB001	198-	£2.50	£6	

HAWKSWORTH, JOHNNY ORCHESTRA
Title	Format	Label	Catalog #	Year			Notes
Lunar Walk	7"	Pye	7N15969	1965	£2.50	£6	

HAWKWIND
By overlaying simple riff music with electronic noise Hawkwind succeeded in creating the perfect backdrop for Michael Moorcock's science fiction and sword and sorcery novels. The link was cemented by Moorcock himself contributing to many of the group's records; by Hawkwind returning the favour in supplying the music for Moorcock's own "New World's Fair" LP; and by Moorcock inspiring the creation of a science fiction novel in which the members of Hawkwind were the main characters. Here is the origin of the close inter-relation between fantasy and heavy metal music. The perfect artefact to summarise all this is the Hawkwind LP "Warrior On The Edge Of Time", whose cover showing a mounted hero waiting on the edge of a precipice opens out into a cardboard shield.

Title	Format	Label	Catalog #	Year			Notes
Approved History Of Hawkwind	LP	Samurai	SAMR046	1986	£10	£25	set of 3 pic discs
Choose Your Masques	LP	RCA	RCALP6055	1982	£5	£12	
Chronicle Of The Black Sword	LP	Flicknife	SHARP033	1985	£4	£10	
Church Of Hawkwind	LP	RCA	RCALP9004	1982	£6	£15	with booklet
Doremi Fasolatido	LP	United Artists	UAG29364	1972	£5	£12	..with poster, chart LP
Hall Of The Mountain Grill	LP	United Artists	UAG29672	1974	£4	£10	chart LP
Hawkfan 12	LP	Hawkfan	HWFB2	1986	£6	£15	with poster,insert,bag
Hawkwind	LP	Liberty	LBS83348	1970	£6	£15	
Hurry On Hawkwind	7" EP	United Artists	USEP1	1973	£25	£50	
Hurry On Sundown	7"	Liberty	LBF15382	1970	£25	£50	
Hurry On Sundown	12"	Flicknife	FLEP100	1982	£2.50	£6	pic disc
In Search Of Space	LP	United Artists	UAG29202	1971	£5	£12	chart LP, with booklet
Kings Of Speed	7"	United Artists	UP35808	1975	£12.50	£25	PS
Levitation	LP	Bronze	BRON530	1980	£4	£10	blue vinyl
Official Picture Log Book	LP	Flicknife	HWBOX01	1987	£10	£25	3 pic discs, interview LP, boxed
PXR5	LP	Charisma	CDS4016	1979	£4	£10	with poster
Roadhawks	LP	United Artists	UAK29919	1976	£4	£10	with poster
Silver Machine	7"	RCA	RCAP267	1982	£2.50	£8	pic disc
Silver Machine	7"	Samurai	HW001	1986	£2.50	£6	shaped pic disc
Silver Machine	7"	United Artists	UP35381	1972	£4	£8	silver & blue PS
Silver Machine	7"	United Artists	UPP35381	1983	£2.50	£6	pic disc
Sonic Attack	LP	RCA	RCALP6004	1981	£4	£10	with insert
Sonic Attack	7"	United Artists	WD3637	1973	£50	£100	1 sided promo, cloth sleeve
Space Ritual	LP	United Artists	UAD60037/8	1973	£6	£15	double, chart LP
Stonehenge: This Is Hawkwind Do Not Panic	LP	Flicknife	SHARP022	1984	£4	£10	with 12'
Urban Guerilla	7"	United Artists	UP35566	1973	£2.50	£6	chart single
Warrior On The Edge Of Time	LP	United Artists	UAG29766	1975	£5	£12	shield cover, chart LP
Who's Gonna Win The War	7"	Bronze	BRO109	1980	£2.50	£6	cream label

HAWKWIND/BEATLES
Title	Format	Label	Catalog #	Year			Notes
Silver Machine	7"	United Artists	UPP35381	1982	£10	£20	mispress - B side plays 'Ask Me Why'

HAYDOCK'S ROCKHOUSE
Title	Format	Label	Catalog #	Year			Notes
Cupid	7"	Columbia	DB8050	1966	£7.50	£15	
Lovin' You	7"	Columbia	DB8135	1967	£7.50	£15	

HAYES, BILL
Title	Format	Label	Catalog #	Year			Notes
Ballad Of Davy Crockett	7"	London	HLA8220	1956	£7.50	£15	chart single
Berry Tree	7"	London	HL8149	1955	£10	£20	
Das Ist Musik	7"	London	HL8300	1956	£6	£12	
Donkey Song	7"	MGM	SP1036	1953	£7.50	£15	
Great Pioneers Of The West	7" EP	London	REA1051	1956	£7.50	£15	
Kwela Kwela	7"	London	HLA8239	1956	£7.50	£15	
Legend Of Wyatt Earp	7"	London	HLA8325	1956	£6	£12	
Sings The Best Of Disney	7" EP	HMV	7EG8355	1957	£2	£5	
Wimoweh	7"	London	HLR8833	1959	£4	£8	
Wringle Wrangle	7"	London	HL8430	1957	£6	£12	

HAYES, ISAAC
Title	Format	Label	Catalog #	Year			Notes
Black Moses	LP	Stax	2628004	1972	£5	£12	double
Blue Hayes	LP	Stax	2465016	1971	£5	£12	
Hot Buttered Soul	LP	Stax	SXATS1028	1969	£5	£12	
I Stand Accused	7"	Stax	STAX154	1970	£1.50	£4	
Isaac Hayes Movement	LP	Stax	2325014	1970	£5	£12	
Isaac Hayes Movement	LP	Stax	SXATS1032	1970	£5	£12	
Presenting Isaac Hayes	LP	Stax		1967	£6	£15	
Shaft	LP	Stax	2659007	1971	£6	£15	double
To Be Continued	LP	Stax	2325016	1971	£5	£12	
Walk On By	7"	Stax	STAX133	1969	£1.50	£4	

HAYES, LINDA & THE PLATTERS
Title	Format	Label	Catalog #	Year			Notes
Please Have Mercy	7"	Parlophone	MSP6174	1955	£75	£150	

HAYES, TUBBY
Title	Format	Label	Catalog #	Year			Notes
100% Proof	LP	Fontana	(S)TL5410	1966	£15	£30	
Change Of Setting	LP	World Record Club	T631	196-	£6	£15	..with Paul Gonsalves
Down In The Village	LP	Fontana	680998TL/ 886163TY	1963	£75	£150	

Title	Format	Label	Cat No	Year	Price	Price	Notes
Eighth Wonder	7" EP	Tempo	EXA82	1958	£10	£20	
Evening With Mr.Percussion	LP	Ember	EMB3337	1961	£15	£30	with Tony Kinsey
Jazz Couriers	LP	Tempo	TAP15	1957	£25	£50	
Just Friends	LP	Columbia	SX6003	196-	£8	£20	with Paul Gonsalves
Late Spot At Scott's	LP	Fontana	TL5200	1964	£25	£50	
Mexican Green	LP	Fontana	SFJL911	1969	£20	£40	
Modern Jazz Scene	7" EP	Tempo	EXA36	1956	£10	£20	
Ode To Ernie	7"	Tempo	A148	1957	£2	£5	
Palladium Jazz Date	LP	Fontana	(S)TFL570	196-	£6	£15	with Cleo Laine
Return Visit	LP	Fontana	(S)TL5195	1964	£20	£40	
Sally	7"	Fontana	H397	1962	£1.50	£4	
This Is Jazz	LP	Philips	6382041	1970	£5	£12	
Tubbs	LP	Fontana	TFL5142/STFL562	1961	£15	£30	
Tubbs In New York	LP	Fontana	TFL5183/STFL595	1961	£40	£80	
Tubbs In New York	LP	Wing	WL1162	1967	£8	£20	
Tubby Hayes And His Orchestra	7" EP	Tempo	EXA14	1955	£10	£20	
Tubby Hayes And His Orchestra	7" EP	Tempo	EXA17	1955	£10	£20	
Tubby Hayes Orchestra	LP	Fontana	6309002	1970	£8	£20	
Tubby Hayes Quartet	7" EP	Tempo	EXA27	1956	£10	£20	
Tubby Hayes Quartet	7" EP	Tempo	EXA28	1956	£10	£20	
Tubby Hayes Quintet	LP	Tempo	TAP6	1956	£25	£50	
Tubby Hayes Quintet	7" EP	Tempo	EXA55	1957	£10	£20	
Tubby Tours	LP	Fontana	(S)TL5221	1966	£15	£30	
Tubby's Groove	LP	Tempo	TAP29	1961	£25	£50	

HAYES, TUBBY & JACK COSTANZO

Equation In Rhythm	LP	Fontana	TFL5190/STFL598	1962	£20	£40	

HAYMARKET SQUARE

Magic Lantern	LP	Chaparral	201	1968	£75	£150	US

HAYNES, ROY

Roy Haynes Band	10" LP	Vogue	LDE130	1955	£20	£40	
We Three	LP	Esquire	32103	1960	£15	£30	with Phineas Newborn & Paul Chambers

HAYWARD, JUSTIN

I Can't Face The World Without You	7"	Parlophone	R5496	1966	£20	£40	
London Is Behind Me	7"	Pye	7N17014	1965	£20	£40	

HAYWARD, RICK

Rick Hayward	LP	Blue Horizon	2431006	1971	£20	£40	

HAYWARD, SUSAN

I'll Cry Tomorrow	7" EP	MGM	MGMEP555	1956	£2.50	£6	

HAYWOOD, JOE

Warm And Tender Love	7"	Island	WI218	1965	£5	£10	

HAYWOOD, LEON

Ain't No Use	7"	Vocalion	VP9280	1966	£5	£10	
Ever Since You Were Sweet Sixteen	7"	Vocalion	VP9288	1967	£6	£12	
I Was Sent To You	7"	Capitol	CL15634	1970	£2	£5	
It's Got To Be Mellow	LP	MCA	MUPS369	1969	£4	£10	
Soul Cargo	LP	Vocalion	VAL8064	1967	£6	£15	

HAZE

Hazecolor Dia	LP	Bacillus	BLPS19075	1971	£4	£10	German

HAZEL & THE JOLLY BOYS

Stop Them	7"	Doctor Bird	DB1063	1966	£5	£10	

HAZELWOOD, LEE

Words Mean Nothing	7"	London	HLW9223	1960	£5	£10	

HAZLEWOOD, LEE

Love And Other Crimes	LP	Reprise	RSLP6297	1968	£6	£15	
My Baby Cried All Night Long	7"	MGM	MGM1348	1967	£2.50	£6	
Ode To Billie Joe	7"	Reprise	RS20613	1967	£1.50	£4	
Poet, Fool Or Bum	LP	Stateside	SSL10315	1974	£6	£15	
Rainbow Woman	7"	Reprise	RS20667	1968	£2	£5	
Sand	7"	MGM	MGM1310	1966	£1.50	£4	
Trouble Is A Lonesome Town	LP	London	HAN/SHN8398	1970	£6	£15	

HAZZARD, TONY

Sound Of The Candyman's Trumpet	7"	CBS	3452	1968	£2	£5	
Tony Hazzard Sings	LP	CBS	63608	1969	£5	£12	
You'll Never Put Shackles On Me	7"	Columbia	DB7927	1966	£2	£5	

HEAD MACHINE

Orgasm	LP	Major Minor	SMLP79	1970	£60	£120	sleeve pictured in Guide

HEAD, MURRAY

Alberta	7"	Columbia	DB7635	1965	£1.50	£4	
Bells Of Rhymney	7"	Columbia	DB7771	1965	£1.50	£4	
Nigel Lived	LP	CBS	65503	1973	£4	£10	
Say It Ain't So	LP	Island	ILPS9347	1975	£4	£10	
Say It Ain't So Joe	7"	Island	WIP6252	1975	£1.50	£4	
She Was Perfection	7"	Immediate	IM053	1967	£7.50	£15	

Someday Soon	7"	Columbia	DB8102	1967	£1.50	£4	
Superstar	7"	MCA	MK5019	1969	£1.50	£4	

HEAD, ROY

Apple Of My Eye	7"	Vocalion	VP9254	1966	£2	£5	
Just A Little Bit	7"	Pye	7N25340	1965	£2.50	£6	
Just A Little Bit Of Roy Head	7" EP.	Pye	NEP44053	1966	£6	£12	
Most Wanted Woman In Town	7"	London	HLD10487	1975	£2.50	£6	
My Babe	7"	Vocalion	VP9269	1966	£2	£5	
Roy Head And The Traits	LP	TNT	101	1965	£25	£50	US
Some People	LP	Stateside	SSL5033	1970	£4	£10	
To Make A Big Man Cry	7"	London	HLZ10097	1966	£2	£5	
Treat Her Right	7"	Vocalion	VP9248	1965	£2	£5	chart single
Treat Me Right	LP	Scepter	(S)S532	1965	£6	£15	US
Wigglin' And Gigglin'	7"	Vocalion	VP9274	1966	£1.50	£4	

HEAD SHOP

Head Shop	LP	Epic	BN26476	1969	£8	£20	US

HEADHUNTERS

Straight From The Gate	LP	Arista	SPART1046	1977	£5	£12	
Survival Of The Fittest	LP	Arista	ARTY116	1975	£8	£20	

HEADLINERS

That's The Way I Must Go	7"	Decca	F12209	1965	£1.50	£4	
What Became Of Love	7"	Decca	F12279	1965	£1.50	£4	

HEADS, HANDS & FEET

Heads, Hands & Feet	LP	Island	ILPS9149	1971	£6	£15	
Old Soldiers Never Die	LP	Atlantic	K40465	1973	£4	£10	
Tracks	LP	Island	ILPS9185	1972	£6	£15	

HEALY, PAT

Just Before Dawn	LP	Vogue	VA160131	1959	£6	£15	

HEANEY, JOE

As I Roved Out	7" EP.	Collector	JEI7	1961	£2.50	£6	
Irish Traditional Songs In Gaelic And English	LP	Topic	12T91	1963	£6	£15	
Morrissey And The Russian Sailor	7" EP.	Collector	JEI5	1960	£2.50	£6	
O Mo Dhuchas	LP	Gael-Linn	CEF051	1976	£5	£12	Irish

HEART

Dreamboat Annie	LP	Mushroom	MRS5005	1976	£10	£25	US pic disc
Dreamboat Annie	LP	Nautilus	NR 3	1979	£6	£15	US audiophile
Heart Box Set	LP	Capitol	HGIFT1	1990	£8	£20	3 LPs boxed with booklet
Little Queen	LP	Portrait	HR44799	1981	£6	£15	US audiophile
Magazine	LP	Arista	SPART1024	1977	£8	£20	1st version, without 1978 recordings
Magazine	LP	Mushroom	MRS1SP	1978	£8	£20	US, pic disc
Nothin' At All	7"	Capitol	CL406	1986	£1.50	£4	heart shaped pic disc
With Love From Heart	LP	Capitol	LOVE2	1988	£6	£15	2 LPs boxed with inserts

HEARTBEATS

Thousand Miles Away	LP	Roulette	(S)R25107	1960	£25	£50	US

HEARTBREAKERS

It's Not Enough	7"	Track	2094142	1977	£30	£60	
One Track Mind	7"	Track	2094137	1977	£1.50	£4	

HEARTBREAKERS (2)

Frank Zappa plays guitar on "Every Time I See You".

Every Time I See You	7"	Donna	1381	1964	£30	£60	US

HEARTS

Dear Abby	7"	Stateside	SS268	1964	£2	£5	

HEARTS (2)

Young Woman	7"	Parlophone	R5147	1964	£10	£20	

HEARTS & FLOWERS

Now Is The Time	LP	Capitol	(S)T2762	1967	£20	£40	US
Of Horses, Kids, & Forgotten Women	LP	Capitol	ST2868	1968	£20	£40	US
Rock'n'Roll Gypsies	7"	Capitol	CL15492	1967	£4	£8	
She Sang Hymns Out Of Tune	7"	Capitol	CL15549	1968	£4	£8	

HEARTS OF SOUL

Waterman	7"	Columbia	DB8670	1970	£5	£10	

HEATH, JIMMY

Really Big	LP	Riverside	RLP333	1960	£6	£15	
Triple Threat	LP	Riverside	RLP400	1962	£6	£15	

HEATH, TED

Al Jolson Classics No.1	7" EP.	Decca	DFE6510	1958	£2	£5	
At Carnegie Hall	LP	Decca	LK4165	1957	£4	£10	
At The London Palladium	LP	Decca	LK4062	1953	£5	£12	
At The London Palladium Vol.3	LP	Decca	LK4097	1955	£5	£12	
At The London Palladium Vol.4	LP	Decca	LK4134	1956	£4	£10	

Australian Suite	7" EP..	Decca	DFE6300	1956	£5	£10	
Beaulieu Festival Suite	7" EP..	Decca	DFE6625	1960	£4	£8	
Beaulieu Festival Suite	7" EP..	Decca	STO135	1960	£5	£10	stereo
Bell Bell Boogie	7"..	Decca	F10540	1955	£1.50	£4	
Creep	7"..	Decca	F10222	1954	£1.50	£4	
Dig Deep	7"..	Decca	F10425	1955	£1.50	£4	
Faithful Hussar	7"..	Decca	F10746	1956	£1.50	£4	
Fats Waller Album	LP	Decca	LK4074	1954	£5	£12	
Fats Waller Album	7" EP..	Decca	DFE6159	1955	£5	£10	
Fats Waller Album No.2	7" EP..	Decca	DFE6160	1955	£2.50	£6	
First American Tour	LP	Decca	LK4167	1957	£4	£10	
Four Classics	7" EP..	Decca	DFE6323	1956	£2.50	£6	
Four Hits FRom The All Time Top Twelve	7" EP..	Decca	DFE6579	1959	£2	£5	
Four Hits From The All Time Top Twelve	7" EP..	Decca	STO122	1959	£4	£8	stereo
Gershwin For Moderns	LP	Decca	LK4098	1955	£4	£10	
Gershwin For Moderns No.1	7" EP..	Decca	DFE6290	1956	£2.50	£6	
Gershwin For Moderns No.2	7" EP..	Decca	DFE6354	1956	£2.50	£6	
Great Film Hits	7" EP..	Decca	STO155	1961	£2	£5	stereo
Haitian Ritual	7"..	Decca	F10477	1955	£1.50	£4	
Hits I Missed	LP	Decca	LK4275	1958	£4	£10	
Hits I Missed	LP	Decca	SKL4003	1958	£5	£12	stereo
Hits I Missed	7" EP..	Decca	STO103	1958	£2.50	£6	stereo
Hits I Missed No.1	7" EP..	Decca	DFE6509	1958	£2	£5	
Hundredth London Palladium Sunday Concert	LP	Decca	LK4075	1954	£5	£12	
Hundredth London Palladium Sunday Concert Vol.1	7" EP..	Decca	DFE6189	1955	£2.50	£6	
Hundredth London Palladium Sunday Concert Vol.2	7" EP..	Decca	DFE6190	1955	£2.50	£6	
Hundredth London Palladium Sunday Concert Vol.3	7" EP..	Decca	DFE6191	1955	£2.50	£6	
Kern For Moderns	LP	Decca	LK4121	1956	£4	£10	
Kern For Moderns No.1	7" EP..	Decca	DFE6304	1956	£2.50	£6	
Kern For Moderns No.2	7" EP..	Decca	DFE6305	1956	£2.50	£6	
Kern For Moderns No.3	7" EP..	Decca	DFE6306	1956	£2.50	£6	
Listen To My Music	10" LP	Decca	LF1060	1952	£5	£12	
London Palladium Highlights	7" EP..	Decca	DFE6120	1955	£2.50	£6	
London Palladium Highlights No.2	7" EP..	Decca	DFE6317	1956	£2.50	£6	
London Palladium Highlights No.3	7" EP..	Decca	DFE6346	1956	£2.50	£6	
London Palladium Highlights No.4	7" EP..	Decca	DFE6373	1956	£2.50	£6	
Lush Slide	7"..	Decca	F10273	1954	£1.50	£4	
Moments At Montreux	7" EP..	Decca	STO8532	1963	£2	£5	stereo
My Very Good Friends The Bandleaders	7" EP..	Decca	DFE6642	1960	£2.50	£6	
Old English No.1	7" EP..	Decca	DFE6511	1958	£2.50	£6	
Olde Englyshe	LP	Decca	LK4363	1958	£4	£10	
Our Kind Of Jazz	7" EP..	Decca	DFE6500	1958	£2	£5	
Peg O' My Heart	7"..	Decca	F10447	1955	£1.50	£4	
Recalls The Fabulous Dorseys No.1	7" EP..	Decca	DFE6451	1957	£2	£5	
Rodgers For Moderns	LP	Decca	LK4148	1956	£4	£10	
Selection	10" LP	Decca	LF1064	1952	£5	£12	
Seven Eleven	7"..	Decca	F10200	1954	£1.50	£4	
Skin Deep	7"..	Decca	F10246	1954	£1.50	£4	chart single
Spotlight On Sidemen	LP	Decca	LK4204	1957	£4	£10	
Strike Up The Band	LP	Decca	LK4064	1953	£5	£12	
Swing Session	LP	Decca	SKL4030	1959	£5	£10	stereo
Swing Session	7" EP..	Decca	STO109	1959	£5	£10	stereo
Swings In Hi Stereo	7" EP..	Decca	STO113	1959	£2.50	£6	stereo
Swings In Hi-Stereo	LP	Decca	SKL4023	1958	£4	£10	
Ted Heath And His Music	7" EP..	Decca	DFE6025	1955	£5	£10	
Ted Heath And His Music No.2	7" EP..	Decca	DFE6027	1955	£5	£10	
Ted Heath And His Music No.3	7" EP..	Decca	DFE6403	1957	£2.50	£6	
Ted Heath And His Music No.4	7" EP..	Decca	DFE6432	1957	£2.50	£6	
Ted Heath And His Music No.5	7" EP..	Decca	DFE6487	1958	£2	£5	
Tempo For Dancers	10" LP	Decca	LF1037	1951	£6	£15	
Viva Verrell	7"..	Decca	F10272	1954	£1.50	£4	

HEATHER BLACK

Heather Black	LP	American Playboy	1001	196-	£25	£50	US

HEAVEN

Brass Rock	LP	CBS	66293	1971	£6	£15	double

HEAVEN 17

Height Of The Fighting	7"..	Virgin	VS483	1982	£5	£10	

HEAVY JELLY

A joke review of an imaginary band called "Heavy Jelly" in one of the rock weeklies, led to the formation of two separate bands, adopting the name in an attempt to make the joke real. The first of these became familiar to many people through a track included on the Island sampler album "Nice Enough To Eat". Also released as a single, "I Keep Singing The Same Old Song" was actually the work of the group Skip Bifferty, who never seriously intended to use the new name for subsequent work (although a whole album was actually recorded, without being given a full release). As it happens, the single is rather good. A second Heavy Jelly, in which John Mayall's departing bass player Steve Thompson joined singer Jackie Lomax and members of Aynsley Dunbar's Retaliation, did actually gig for a short while, and issued the single "Chewn In" on the Head label.

I Keep Singing The Same Old Song	7"..	Island	WIP6049	1968	£5	£10	
Take Me Down	LP	Island		1969	£50	£100	demo

HEAVY JELLY (2)
Chewn In	7"	Head	HDS4001	1969	£7.50	£15

HEBB, BOBBY
Everything Is Coming Up Roses	7"	Philips	BF1610	1967	£1.50	£4
I Love Everything About You	7"	Philips	BF1570	1967	£1.50	£4
Love Me	7"	Philips	BF1541	1967	£2	£5
Satisfied Mind	7"	Philips	BF1522	1966	£4	£8
Sunny	LP	Philips	2/PHS600212	1966	£6	£15	US
Sunny	7"	Philips	BF1503	1966	£1.50	£4	chart single
Sunny	7" EP.	Philips	452056	1966	£5	£10	French
You Want To Change Me	7"	Philips	BF1702	1968	£10	£20

HEBBERT, MICHAEL
Rampin Cat	LP	Free Reed	FRR009	1977	£5	£12

HECKSTALL-SMITH, DICK
Colosseum broke apart during the extensive rehearsals of the difficult "Pirate's Dream", but the piece was rescued for Dick Heckstall-Smith's solo LP. This is close enough to the sound of Colosseum to make it the legitimate follow-up to "Colosseum Live" and is something of an odd record for a saxophonist to have made, as Heckstall-Smith's own contributions do not exactly dominate the centre stage. The record is, however, a fine addition to the small body of adventurous song-writing otherwise largely occupied by the works of Jack Bruce. Meanwhile the very scarce Heckstall-Smith EP provides a kind of glimpse of an alternative world; the start of the career of a straight-ahead jazz saxophonist, that actually proceded on rather different lines.

Jazz Gumbo Vol.2	LP	Nixa	NJT510	1958	£15	£30	Side 2 by Wally Fawkes & Bruce Turner
Story Ended	LP	Bronze	ILPS9196	1972	£8	£20
Very Special Old Jazz	7" EP.	Pye	NJE1037	1957	£15	£30

HEDAYAT, DASHIELL (DAEVID ALLEN)
Melmoth La Devanture	LP	Arion	30T079	1969	£15	£30	French
Obsolete	LP	CBS	SR83512	1971	£8	£20

HEDGEHOG PIE
Green Lady	LP	Rubber	RUB014	1975	£15	£30
Hedgehog Pie	LP	Rubber	RUB009	1975	£6	£15
His Round	LP	Rubber	RUB002	1972	£6	£15
Just Act Normal	LP	Rubber	RUB024	1978	£8	£20
Lambton Worm	7" EP.	Rubber	TUB12	1976	£15	£30

HEDGEHOPPERS ANONYMOUS
Baby	7"	Decca	F12400	1966	£1.50	£4
Daytime	7"	Decca	F12479	1966	£1.50	£4
Don't Push Me	7"	Decca	F12298	1965	£1.50	£4
It's Good News Week	7"	Decca	F12241	1965	£1.50	£4	chart single
Stop Press	7"	Decca	F12530	1966	£1.50	£4

HEFTI, NEAL
Batman Theme	7"	RCA	RCA1521	1966	£5	£10

HEIGHT, DONALD
365 Days	7"	London	HLZ10116	1967	£7.50	£15
Rags To Riches	7"	Avco	6105005	1971	£4	£8
Talk Of The Grapevine	7"	London	HLZ10062	1966	£12.50	£25

HEINZ
Country Boy	7"	Decca	F11768	1963	£1.50	£4	chart single
Diggin' My Potatoes	7"	Columbia	DB7482	1965	£5	£10	chart single
Don't Think Twice It's Alright	7"	Columbia	DB7559	1965	£4	£8
Dreams Do Come True	7"	Decca	F11652	1963	£5	£10
End Of The World	7"	Columbia	DB7656	1965	£6	£12
Heart Full Of Sorrow	7"	Columbia	DB7779	1965	£6	£12
Heinz	7" EP.	Decca	DFE8545	1963	£10	£20
Just Like Eddie	7"	Decca	F11693	1963	£1.50	£4	chart single
Live It Up	7" EP.	Decca	DFE8559	1963	£10	£20
Movin' In	7"	Columbia	DB7942	1966	£6	£12
Please Little Girl	7"	Decca	F11920	1964	£4	£8
Questions I Can't Answer	7"	Columbia	DB7374	1964	£4	£8	chart single
Tribute To Eddie	LP	Decca	LK4599	1964	£15	£30
You Were There	7"	Decca	F11831	1964	£2.50	£6	chart single

HELDEN
Holding On	7"	Zica	ZICA01	1983	£2	£5
Holding On	12"	Zica	12ZICA01	1983	£4	£10

HELDON
Agneta Nilsson	LP	Urus	000011	1976	£5	£12	French
Allez Teia	LP	Disjuncta	000002	1975	£6	£15	French
Guerilla Electronique	LP	Disjuncta	000001	1974	£6	£15	French
Interface	LP	Cobra	37013	1976	£4	£10	French
It's Always Rock And Roll	LP	Disjuncta	000006/7	1975	£6	£15	French double
Stand By	LP	Egg	900578	1979	£4	£10	German
Un Reve Sans Consequence Speciale	LP	Cobra	37002	1976	£4	£10	French

HELL PREACHERS INC.
Supreme Psychedelic Underground	LP	Marble Arch	MALS1169	1969	£15	£30

HELL, RICHARD
It was the American Richard Hell who invented the punk style. The ripped clothing comes from him, as does the nihilist attitude - Richard Hell's theme song is "Blank Generation". He was originally the bass player for Television, which is presumably why that group tend to be classed as punk/new wave, despite a fascination with long guitar solos.

Blank Generation	LP	Sire	SR6037	1977	£5	£12	with inner sleeve
Blank Generation	7"	Ork	81976	1976	£6	£12	US
Blank Generation	7"	Sire	6078608	1977	£2.50	£6	
I Could Live With You In Another World	7"	Stiff	BUY7	1976	£2	£5	

HELLING, DAVE

Christine	7"	Planet	PLF101	1966	£5	£10
It Ain't Me Babe	7"	Stateside	SS409	1965	£2	£5

HELLIONS

Three singles, but all of them unsuccessful, for a group that included two future members of Traffic (Dave Mason and Jim Capaldi) and one future member of Spooky Tooth and Mott The Hoople (Luther Grosvenor/Ariel Bender).

Daydreaming Of You	7"	Piccadilly	7N35213	1965	£10	£20
Little Lovin'	7"	Piccadilly	7N35265	1965	£10	£20
Tomorrow Never Comes	7"	Piccadilly	7N35232	1965	£10	£20

HELLMET

Hellmet	LP	Deram			£10	£25

HELLO

Another School Day	7"	Bell	BLL1333	1973	£5	£10
You Move Me	7"	Bell	BLL1238	1972	£5	£10

HELMS, BOBBY

Best Of Bobby Helms	LP	Columbia	CL2060/CS8860	1963	£6	£15	US
Bobby Helms	7" EP	Brunswick	OE9461	1960	£10	£20	
Fraulein	7"	Brunswick	05711	1957	£1.50	£4	
I Guess I'll Miss The Prom	7"	Brunswick	05801	1959	£1.50	£4	
Jacqueline	7"	Brunswick	05748	1958	£2	£5	
Jingle Bell Rock	7"	Brunswick	05765	1958	£5	£10	chart single
Love My Lady	7"	Brunswick	05741	1958	£2	£5	
My Lucky Day	7"	Brunswick	05813	1959	£1.50	£4	
My Special Agent	7"	Brunswick	05721	1957	£4	£8	chart single
New River Train	7"	Brunswick	05786	1959	£1.50	£4	
No Other Baby	7"	Brunswick	05730	1958	£2.50	£6	chart single
Sad Eyed Baby	7"	Brunswick	05852	1961	£1.50	£4	
Schoolboy Crush	7"	Brunswick	05754	1958	£4	£8	
To My Special Angel	LP	Brunswick	LAT8250	1957	£20	£40	

HELMS, JIMMY

Magnificent Sanctuary Band	7"	Capitol	CL15762	1973	£1.50	£4

HELP YOURSELF

Beware Of The Shadow	LP	United Artists	UAS29413	1972	£4	£10	
Help Yourself	LP	Liberty	LBS83484	1971	£15	£30	
Return Of Ken Whaley/Happy Days	LP	United Artists	UDG4001	1973	£10	£25	double
Running Down Deep	7"	Liberty	LBF15459	1971	£2	£5	
Strange Affair	LP	United Artists	UAS29287	1972	£4	£10	

HEMLOCK

Hemlock	LP	Deram	SML1102	1973	£15	£30
Mr.Horizontal	7"	Deram	DM379	1973	£1.50	£4

HENDERSON, BERTHA & ROSA HENDERSON

Female Blues Vol.2	7" EP	Collector	JEL14	1961	£5	£10

HENDERSON, BILL

Bill Henderson	LP	Stateside	SL10019	1963	£4	£10
Sweet Pumpkin	7"	Top Rank	JAR412	1960	£5	£10

HENDERSON, BOBBY

Handful Of Keys	LP	Vanguard	PPL11007	1957	£6	£15

HENDERSON, DORIS

Doris Henderson was the second female lead singer to be employed by folk-rock pioneers, The Eclection. She had earlier made two very scarce folk LPs on which she is backed by John Renbourn and Danny Thompson.

Hangman	7"	Columbia	DB7567	1965	£5	£10
Message To Pretty	7"	Fontana	TF811	1967	£5	£10
There You Go	LP	Columbia	SX6001	1965	£75	£150
Watch The Stars	LP	Fontana	(S)TL5385	1967	£75	£150

HENDERSON, FLETCHER

At Connie's Inn	10" LP	HMV	DLP1066	1955	£10	£25	
Big Band Story Vol.1	7" EP	Collector	JE115	1959	£2	£5	
Birth Of Big Band Jazz	10" LP	London	AL3547	1955	£10	£25	
Fletcher Henderson	10" LP	Audubon	AAF-AAK	195-	£50	£100	6 LP set
Fletcher Henderson Jazz Group	7" EP	Collector	JE111	1959	£2	£5	

HENDERSON, JOE

Big Love	7"	London	HLU9615	1962	£1.50	£4
In 'n Out	LP	Blue Note	BLP/BST84166	1964	£8	£20
Inner Urge	LP	Blue Note	BLP/BST84189	1965	£8	£20
Joe Henderson	7" EP	London	REU1376	1963	£5	£10
Mode For Joe	LP	Blue Note	BLP/BST84227	1966	£8	£20
Our Thing	LP	Blue Note	BLP/BST84152	1963	£10	£25
Page One	LP	Blue Note	BLP/BST84140	1963	£8	£20
Snap Your Fingers	7"	London	HLU9553	1962	£1.50	£4

HENDRICKS, BOBBY

I'm Coming Home	7"	Mercury	AMT1163	1961	£2	£5

Itchy Twitchy Feeling	7"	London	HL8714	1958	£15	£30	
Itchy Twitchy Feeling	7"	Sue	WI315	1964	£6	£12	
Little John Green	7"	Top Rank	JAR193	1959	£2.50	£6	

HENDRICKS, JON

Good Git-Together	LP	Vogue	LAE12231	1960	£4	£10	

HENDRIX, JIMI

Collecting Jimi Hendrix begins with a copy of "Electric Ladyland", which is as good a demonstration of the power and potential of rock music as one is likely to find anywhere. There are any number of examples of Hendrix' genius as a guitarist to be found amongst the double album's tracks, while for those who still believe that Hendrix was all about noise and bombast, there is "1983..A Merman I Should Turn To Be", an extended composition in which the resources of the recording studio are tested to the limit, yet to a largely gentle and subtle effect. With regard to actual collectors' items, there is the original "puppet" cover for "Band Of Gypsies"; the scarce red vinyl edition of "The Cry Of Love"; and the even scarcer record club compilation "Electric Hendrix". None, however, can give the excitement and emotional impact of an hour and a half spent in "Electric Ladyland".

6 Singles Pack	7"	Polydor	2608001	1980	£7.50	£15	6 x 7'
All Along The Watchtower	7"	Track	604025	1968	£2	£5	chart single
All I Want	7" EP	Visadisc	348	1967	£5	£10	French
And A Happy New Year	7"	Reprise	PRO595	196-	£25	£50	US promo
Angel	7"	Track	2094007	1971	£1.50	£4	
Are You Experienced	LP	Track	612001	1967	£8	£20	mono, chart LP
Are You Experienced	LP	Track	613001	1967	£6	£15	stereo, chart LP
Axis: Bold As Love	LP	Reprise	R6281	1968	£75	£150	US mono
Axis: Bold As Love	LP	Track	612003	1967	£8	£20	mono, chart LP
Axis: Bold As Love	LP	Track	612003	1967	£15	£30	with lyric sheet
Axis: Bold As Love	LP	Track	613003	1967	£6	£15	stereo, chart LP
Band Of Gypsys	LP	Track	2406002	1970	£5	£12	kaftan g-fold, chart LP
Band Of Gypsys	LP	Track	2406002	1970	£8	£20	puppet cover, chart LP
Burning Of The Midnight Lamp	7"	Track	604007	1967	£2.50	£6	chart single
Crosstown Traffic	7"	Track	604029	1969	£2.50	£6	chart single
Cry Of Love	LP	Track	2408101	1971	£4	£10	chart LP
Cry Of Love	LP	Track	2408101	1971	£400	£600	red vinyl
Electric Hendrix	LP	Track	2856002	1968	£330	£500	
Electric Ladyland	LP	Track	613008/9	1968	£8	£20	double, chart LP
Electric Ladyland Part 1	LP	Track	613010	1968	£5	£12	
Electric Ladyland Part 2	LP	Track	613017	1968	£5	£12	
Fire	7"	Track	604033	1969	£2.50	£6	
Gloria	7"	Polydor	JIMI1	1978	£2	£5	1 sided
Gypsy Eyes	7"	Track	2094010	1971	£4	£8	PS, chart single
Hear My Train A-Comin'	7"	Reprise	K14286	1973	£2	£5	
Hey Joe	7"	Polydor	56139	1966	£2.50	£6	chart single
Hey Joe	7" EP	Barclay	071111	1967	£10	£20	French
Jimi Hendrix	LP	St.Michael		1978	£25	£50	
Johnny B Goode	7"	Polydor	2001277	1972	£2	£5	chart single
Little Drummer Boy	12"	Reprise	PROA840	1979	£20	£40	US promo
Live And Unreleased - The Radio Show	LP	Castle	HBCD100	1989	£20	£40	3 CD set
Live And Unreleased - The Radio Show	LP	Castle	HBLP100	1989	£20	£40	5 LP set, sleeve pictured in Guide
Purple Haze	7"	Track	604001	1967	£2.50	£6	chart single
Purple Haze	7"	Track	604001	1967	£4	£8	white Track label
Smash Hits	LP	Polydor	ACB00219	1973	£5	£12	US
Smash Hits	LP	Reprise	MS2025	1969	£20	£40	US, with poster
Smash Hits	LP	Track	612/613004	1968	£5	£12	chart LP
Voodoo Chile	7"	Track	2095001	1970	£2.50	£6	chart single, PS
Wind Cries Mary	7"	Track	604004	1967	£2.50	£6	chart single
Wind Cries Mary	7" EP	Barclay	071157	1967	£10	£20	French

HENDRIX, JIMI & CURTIS KNIGHT

Ballad Of Jimi	7"	London	HL10321	1970	£4	£8	
Get That Feeling	LP	London	HAU/SHU8349	1968	£5	£12	chart LP
How Would You Feel	7"	Track	604009	1967	£2.50	£6	
Hush Now	7"	London	HL10160	1967	£4	£8	
No Such Animal	7"	RCA	RCA2033	1970	£2	£5	
No Such Animal	7"	RCA	RCA2033	1970	£5	£10	PS
Strange Things	LP	London	HAU/SHU8369	1968	£5	£12	

HENDRIX, MARGIE

I Call You Lover...	7"	Mercury	MF976	1966	£2	£5	
Restless	7"	Mercury	MF1001	1967	£5	£10	

HENKE, MEL

Mel Henke	LP	Contemporary	LAC12112	1958	£8	£20	

HENLEY, LARRY

My Reasons For Living	7"	Hickory	451272	1964	£7.50	£15	

HENNIG, SONNY

Tranengas	LP	Kuckuck	2375008	1971	£8	£20	German

HENRI, ADRIAN

Adrian Henri	LP	Charivari		196-	£15	£30	
Adrian Henri And Hugo Williams	LP	Argo	PLP1194	196-	£15	£30	

HENRY, BOB

I Need Someone	7"	Philips	BF1450	1965	£4	£8	

HENRY, CLARENCE 'FROGMAN'

Ain't Got No Home	7"	London	HLN8389	1957	£60	£120	
Ain't Got No Home	7"	London	HLU10025	1966	£2	£5	

Alive And Well And Living In New Orleans	LP	Roulette	SR42039	1969	£5 £12	US
But I Do	7"	Pye	7N25078	1961	£2 £5	chart single
Clarence Henry Hit Parade	7" EP	Pye	NEP44007	1961	£12.50 £25	
Dream Myself A Sweetheart	7"	Pye	7N25141	1962	£1.50 £4	
Jealous Kind	7"	Pye	7N25169	1962	£1.50 £4	
Little Green Frog	7"	London	HLU9936	1964	£4 £8	
Little Too Much	7"	Pye	7N25123	1962	£1.50 £4	
Lonely Street	7"	Pye	7N25108	1961	£1.50 £4	chart single
Standing In The Need Of Love	7"	Pye	7N25115	1961	£2 £5	
You Always Hurt The One You Love	LP	Pye	NPL28017	1961	£20 £40	
You Always Hurt The One You Love	7"	Pye	7N25089	1961	£2 £5	chart single

HENRY COW

Leg End	LP	Virgin	V2005	1973	£4 £10
Unrest	LP	Virgin	V2011	1974	£4 £10

HENRY, HOUND HEAD & FRANKIE JAXON

Male Blues Vol.6	7" EP	Collector	JEL10	1960	£7.50 £15

HENRY III

I'll Reach The End	7"	Island	WI3081	1967	£5 £10	Don Tony Lee B side
So Much Love	7"	RCA	RCA1568	1967	£4 £8	
Thank You Girl	7"	Island	WI3078	1967	£5 £10	

HENRY, PIERRE

Messe De Liverpool	LP	Philips	6510001		£5 £12	French
Messe Pour Le Temps Present	LP	Philips	836893	1965	£5 £12	French

HENRY, RICHARD

Oh Girl	7"	Regal Zonophone	RZ3014	1968	£2 £5

HENRY, ROBERT

Walk Away Like A Winner	7"	Philips	BF1476	1966	£12.50 £25

HENSKE, JUDY

Death Defying	LP	Reprise	RS6203	1965	£6 £15	
High Flying Bird	LP	Elektra	EKL/EKS7241	1964	£6 £15	US
Judy Henske	LP	Elektra	EKL/EKS7231	1963	£6 £15	US
Little Bit Of Sunshine	LP	Mercury	MG2/SR61010	1965	£6 £15	US

HENSKE, JUDY & JERRY YESTER

Farewell Aldebaran	LP	Straight	STS1052	1969	£8 £20	
Road To Nowhere	7"	Reprise	RS20485	1966	£2.50 £6	
Rosebud	LP	Reprise	RS6426	1971	£8 £20	US

HENSLEY, ROBERT HENRY

You're Gonna See Me Cry	7"	Polydor	56295	1968	£2.50 £6

HENSON, NICKY

Till I See You Cry	7"	Parlophone	R4976	1963	£1.50 £4

HEP STARS

This Swedish group had future Abba star, Benny Andersson, as keyboard player and songwriter.

Hep Stars	LP	Olga	LP004	1966	£10 £25	Swedish
It's Been A Long Long Time	LP	Cupol	CLPNS342	196-	£6 £15	Swedish
Jul Med..	LP	Olga	LP006	1966	£6 £15	Swedish
Let It Be Me	7"	Olga	OLE13	1968	£20 £40	
Malaika	7"	Olga	OLE14	1968	£6 £12	
Malaika	7"	Olga	OLE14	1968	£10 £20	PS
Pa Svenska	7"	Olga	LP011	196-	£8 £20	Swedish
Songs We Sang	LP	Olga	LP007	196-	£8 £20	Swedish
Sunny Girl	7"	Decca	F22446	1966	£10 £20	
Wedding	7"	Olga	OLE001	1967	£6 £12	

HEPBURN & THE CARRIBEAN BAND

Gene And Dinah	7"	Kalypso	XX13	1960	£1.50 £4

HEPTONES

Change Is Gonna Come	7"	Studio One	SO2005	1967	£6 £12	
Cool Rasta	LP	Trojan	TRLS128	1976	£4 £10	
Cry Baby Cry	7"	Studio One	SO2049	1968	£6 £12	
Dock Of The Bay	7"	Studio One	SO2052	1968	£6 £12	King Rocky B side
Equal Rights	7"	Coxsone	CS7068	1968	£5 £10	
Fat Girl	7"	Studio One	SO2014	1967	£6 £12	Delroy Wilson B side
Gunmen Coming To Town	7"	Rio	R104	1966	£4 £8	Tommy McCook B side
Heptones	LP	Studio One	SOL9002	1967	£50 £100	
Heptones And Friends	LP	Trojan	TBL183	1972	£6 £15	
Hurry Up	7"	Upsetter	US339	1970	£2 £5	
Shall Be Released	7"	Bamboo	BAM11	1969	£2.50 £6	
Shall Be Released	7"	Studio One	SO2083	1969	£6 £12	
If I Knew	7"	Studio One	SO2021	1967	£6 £12	
Love Won't Come Easy	7"	Coxsone	CS7052	1968	£5 £10	
Nightfood	LP	Island	ILPS9381	1976	£4 £10	
On Top	LP	Studio One	SOL9010	1968	£50 £100	
Only Sixteen	7"	Studio One	SO2033	1967	£6 £12	
Party Time	7"	Studio One	SO2055	1968	£6 £12	
Schoolgirls	7"	Caltone	TONE105	1967	£4 £8	
Soul Power	7"	Coxsone	CS7082	1968	£5 £10	

We've Got Love	7"	Ska Beat	JB266	1967	£5	£10		
Why Did You Leave	7"	Studio One	SO2026	1967	£6	£12	Gaylads B side
Why Must I	7"	Studio One	SO2027	1967	£6	£12	Slim Smith B side

HERB & KAY

This Ole House	7"	Parlophone	MSP6127	1954	£5	£10	

HERBAL MIXTURE

Love That's Died	7"	Columbia	DB8021	1966	£25	£50	
Machines	7"	Columbia	DB8083	1966	£25	£50	

HERBIE & THE ROYALISTS

Soul Of The Matter	LP	Saga	FID2121	1968	£6	£15	

HERBIE'S PEOPLE

One Little Smile	7"	CBS	202058	1966	£4	£8	
Residential Area	7"	CBS	202584	1967	£4	£8	
Sweet And Tender Romance	7"	CBS	202005	1965	£7.50	£15	

HERD

From The Underworld	7"	Fontana	TF856	1967	£1.50	£4	chart single
Game	7"	Fontana	TF1011	1969	£2.50	£6	
Goodbye Baby Goodbye	7"	Parlophone	R5284	1965	£6	£12	
I Can Fly	7"	Fontana	TF819	1967	£2.50	£6	
I Don't Want Our Loving To Die	7"	Fontana	TF925	1968	£1.50	£4	chart single
Lookin' Thru You	LP	Fontana	SRF67579	1968	£8	£20	US
Nostalgia	LP	Bumble	GEMP5001	1972	£6	£15	US
Paradise Lost	LP	Fontana	(S)TL5458	1968	£8	£20	chart LP
Paradise Lost	7"	Fontana	TF887	1967	£1.50	£4	chart single
She Was Really Saying Something	7"	Parlophone	R5353	1965	£7.50	£15	
So Much In Love	7"	Parlophone	R5413	1966	£10	£20	
Sunshine Cottage	7"	Fontana	TF975	1968	£2.50	£6	

HERDSMEN

Blow In Paris	10" LP	Vogue	LDE058	1954	£5	£12	
Blow In Paris Vol.2	10" LP	Vogue	LDE091	1954	£5	£12	

HERETICS

Evening With The Heretics	LP	Heritage	101	1975	£10	£25	

HERITAGE

Remorse Code	LP	Rondelet		1982	£5	£12	
Strange Place To Be	7"	Rondelet	ROUND8	1981	£2.50	£6	

HERMAN, BONGO

True Grit	7"	Song Bird	SB1018	1970	£2.50	£6	

HERMAN, WOODY

At Carnegie Hall Vol.1	10" LP	MGM	D108	1952	£8	£20	
At Carnegie Hall Vol.2	10" LP	MGM	D110	1953	£8	£20	
At The Monterey Jazz Festival	LP	London	LTZK15200/ SAHK6100	1960	£5	£12	
Blues Groove	LP	Capitol	T784	1957	£6	£15	
Classics In Jazz	LP	Capitol	T20809	1965	£4	£10	
Classics In Jazz	10" LP	Capitol	LC6560	1952	£8	£20	
Fancy Woman	7"	London	HL8031	1954	£7.50	£15	
Fourth Herd	LP	Jazzland	JLP17	1960	£5	£12	
Girl Upstairs	7"	Capitol	CL14333	1955	£1.50	£4	
Herd From Mars Vol.1	7" EP	London	REP1001	1954	£2	£5	
Herd From Mars Vol.2	7" EP	London	REP1002	1955	£2	£5	
Herd Rides Again	LP	Top Rank	35038	1959	£5	£12	
Here's Herman	10" LP	Columbia	33S1060	1955	£8	£20	
Hush	7"	Chess	CRS8095	1969	£1.50	£4	
Jackpot!	LP	Capitol	T748	1956	£6	£15	
Jazz - The Utmost!	LP	Columbia	33CX10129	1959	£8	£20	
Men From Mars	10" LP	London	HAPB1018	1954	£8	£20	
Mexican Hat Trick	7"	Capitol	CL14231	1955	£1.50	£4	
Moody Woody	LP	Top Rank	BUY009	1960	£5	£12	
Music For Tired Lovers	LP	Philips	BBL7056	1955	£6	£15	with Erroll Garner
Muskrat Ramble	7"	Capitol	CL14183	1954	£2.50	£6	
Sequence In Jazz	10" LP	Columbia	33S1068	1955	£8	£20	
Sorry 'Bout The Whole Darned Thing	7"	London	HL8122	1955	£7.50	£15	
Stomping At The Savoy	10" LP	London	HAPB1014	1953	£8	£20	
Summer Sequence	10" LP	Fontana	TFR6015	1958	£6	£15	
Three Herds	LP	Philips	BBL7123	1958	£6	£15	
Thundering Herds Vol.1	LP	CBS	BPG62158	1964	£4	£10	
Thundering Herds Vol.2	LP	CBS	BPG62159	1964	£4	£10	
Thundering Herds Vol.3	LP	CBS	BPG62160	1964	£4	£10	
Twelve Shades Of Blue	LP	Philips	BBL7124	1957	£6	£15	
Woodchopper's Ball	LP	Brunswick	LAT8092	1956	£6	£15	
Woody Herman	LP	HMV	CLP1130	1957	£6	£15	
Woody Herman Band	10" LP	Capitol	LCT6014	1955	£8	£20	
Wooftie	7"	London	HL8013	1954	£7.50	£15	

HERMAN'S HERMITS

Best Of Herman's Hermits	LP	Columbia	SCXC27	196-	£6	£15	export
Best Of Herman's Hermits Vol.2	LP	Columbia	SCXC32	196-	£6	£15	export
Bet Yer Life I Do	7"	RAK	RAK102	1970	£1.50	£4	chart single
Blaze	LP	Columbia	SCXC35	196-	£8	£20	export
Both Sides Of Herman's Hermits	LP	Columbia	SX6084	1966	£5	£12	
Dandy	7" EP	Columbia	SEG8520	1967	£5	£10	

370

East West	7"	Columbia	DB8076	1966	£1.50	£4	chart single
Here Comes The Star	7"	Columbia	DB8626	1969	£1.50	£4	chart single
Hermania	7" EP	Columbia	SEG8380	1965	£5	£10	
Herman's Hermits	LP	Columbia	33SX1727	1965	£5	£12	chart LP
Herman's Hermits	LP	Regal	SREG1117	196-	£4	£10	export
Herman's Hermits' Hits	7" EP	Columbia	SEG8442	1965	£4	£8	
Hold On - Soundtrack Songs	7" EP	Columbia	SEG8503	1966	£5	£10	
I Can Take Or Leave Your Loving	7"	Columbia	DB8327	1968	£1.50	£4	chart single
I'm Henry VIII, I Am	7" EP	Columbia	ESRF1707	1965	£5	£10	French
I'm Into Something Good	7"	Columbia	DB7338	1964	£1.50	£4	chart single
I'm Into Something Good	7" EP	Columbia	ESRF1615	1964	£5	£10	French
Je Suis Anglais	7" EP	Columbia	ESRF1750	1966	£7.50	£15	French
Just A Little Bit Better	7"	Columbia	DB7670	1965	£1.50	£4	chart single
Lady Barbara	7"	RAK	RAK106	1970	£1.50	£4	chart single
London Look	7" EP	Yardley	SLE15	1967	£7.50	£15	French, promo
Mrs.Brown You've Got A Lovely Daughter	LP	Columbia	SCX6303	1968	£5	£12	
Mrs.Brown You've Got A Lovely Daughter	7"	Columbia	ESRF1663	1965	£5	£10	French
Mrs.Brown You've Got A Lovely Daughter	7" EP	Columbia	SEG8440	1965	£4	£8	
Museum	7" EP	Columbia	ESRF1865	1967	£5	£10	French
Must To Avoid	7"	Columbia	DB7791	1965	£1.50	£4	chart single
Must To Avoid	7" EP	Columbia	SEG8477	1966	£4	£8	
My Sentimental Friend	7"	Columbia	DB8563	1969	£1.50	£4	chart single
No Milk Today	7"	Columbia	DB8012	1966	£1.50	£4	chart single
Show Me Girl	7"	Columbia	DB7408	1964	£1.50	£4	chart single
Silhouettes	7"	Columbia	DB7475	1965	£1.50	£4	chart single
Sleepy Joe	7"	Columbia	DB8404	1968	£1.50	£4	chart single
Something's Happening	7"	Columbia	DB8504	1968	£1.50	£4	chart single
Sunshine Girl	7"	Columbia	DB8446	1968	£1.50	£4	chart single
There's A Kind Of Hush	LP	Columbia	SCXC34	196-	£8	£20	export
There's A Kind Of Hush	LP	Columbia	SX/SCX6174	1967	£5	£12	
There's A Kind Of Hush	7"	Columbia	DB8123	1967	£1.50	£4	chart single
There's A Kind Of Hush	7" EP	Columbia	ESRF1846	1967	£5	£10	French
This Door Swings Both Ways	7"	Columbia	DB7947	1966	£1.50	£4	chart single
Train	7"	Buddah	BDS700	1974	£10	£20	
Wonderful World	7"	Columbia	DB7546	1965	£1.50	£4	chart single
Years May Come, Years May Go	7"	Columbia	DB8656	1970	£1.50	£4	chart single
You Won't Be Leaving	7"	Columbia	DB7861	1966	£1.50	£4	chart single

HERON

Bye And Bye	7"	Dawn	DNX2509	1971	£4	£8	PS
Heron	LP	Dawn	DNLS3010	1970	£20	£40	
Take Me Back Home	7"	Dawn	DNS1015	1970	£2.50	£6	
Twice As Nice	LP	Dawn	DNLS3025	1972	£20	£40	double

HERON, MIKE

Mike Heron's Reputation	LP	Neighborhood	NBH80637	1975	£4	£10	
Smiling Men With Bad Reputations	LP	Island	ILPS9146	1971	£5	£12	

HERSANG, JIMMY JAMES

Bewildered And Blue	7"	Dice	CC4	1962	£5	£10	

HERVEY, PAT & ART SNIDER

Can't Get You Out Of My Mind	7"	President	PT110	1967	£2.50	£6	

HESITATIONS

Born Free	7"	London	HLR10180	1968	£4	£8	
Impossible Dream	7"	London	HLR10198	1968	£2.50	£6	
New Born Free	LP	London	HAR/SHR8360	1968	£4	£10	

HESTER, CAROLYN

Ain't That Rain	7"	Dot	DS16750	1965	£2	£5	
At Town Hall	LP	Dot	DLP3649	1966	£5	£12	
Carolyn Hester	LP	CBS	(S)BPG62033	1966	£5	£12	
Carolyn Hester	LP	Columbia	CL1796/CS8596	1962	£5	£12	US
Carolyn Hester Coalition	LP	Pye	NSPL28121	1969	£4	£10	
Come On Back	7"	Dot	DS26750	1965	£1.50	£4	
Playboys And Playgirls	7"	Dot	DS16751	1965	£1.50	£4	
Reason To Believe	7"	CBS	202409	1966	£2	£5	
That's My Song	LP	Dot	DLP3604/25604	1964	£5	£12	US
This Is My Living	LP	Columbia	CL2031/CS8831	1963	£5	£12	US
This LIfe I'm Living	LP	Realm	RM2338	1967	£4	£10	
What Does It Get You	7"	Dot	DS26751	1965	£1.50	£4	

HEWETT SISTERS

Baby-O	7"	HMV	POP567	1959	£4	£8	

HEWITT, BEN

Break It Up	7" EP	Mercury	ZEP10035	1959	£25	£50	
For Quite A While	7"	Mercury	AMT1055	1959	£6	£12	
I Want A Girl	7"	Mercury	AMT1084	1960	£10	£20	
You Break Me Up	7"	Mercury	AMT1041	1959	£12.50	£25	

HEWITT, GARTH

Lion And The Lamb	LP	Myrrh	MYR1001	1973	£6	£15	

HEYWOOD, ANNE

I'd Rather Have Roses	7"	Top Rank	JAR130	1959	£1.50	£4	

HEYWOOD, EDDIE

Soft Summer Breeze	7"	Mercury	7MT131	1957	£2	£5

HI FI FOUR

Davy You Upset My Life	7"	Parlophone	MSP6210	1956	£25	£50

HI FI'S

Baby's In Black	7"	Pye	7N15788	1965	£4	£8
I Keep Forgettin'	7"	Pye	7N15710	1964	£7.50	£15
It's Gonna Be Morning	7"	Alp	595010	1966	£12.50	£25
Take Me Or Leave Me	7"	Piccadilly	7N35130	1963	£4	£8
Will Ya Won't Ya	7"	Pye	7N15635	1964	£4	£8

HI LITERS

Dance Me To Death	7"	Mercury	AMT1011	1958	£20	£40

HIATT, JOHN

Hanging Round The Observatory	LP	Epic		1974	£5	£12	US
Overcoats	LP	Epic	33190	1975	£4	£10	US

HIBBLER, AL

After The Lights Go Down Low	7"	Brunswick	05552	1956	£1.50	£4	
Around The Corner From The Blues	7"	Brunswick	05703	1957	£1.50	£4	
Danny Boy	7"	London	HL7086	1959	£1.50	£4	export
Eleventh Hour Melody	7"	Brunswick	05523	1956	£2	£5	
He	7"	Brunswick	05492	1955	£2	£5	
Now I Lay Me Down To Dream	7"	London	HL8184	1955	£7.50	£15	
They Say You're Laughing At Me	7"	Brunswick	05454	1955	£5	£10	
Unchained Melody	7"	Brunswick	05420	1955	£6	£12	chart single

HICKEY, EDDIE

Another Sleepless Night	7"	Decca	F11241	1960	£1.50	£4

HICKEY, ERSEL

Don't Be Afraid Of Love	7"	Fontana	H198	1959	£12.50	£25

HICKMAN, DWAYNE

I'm A Lover Not A Fighter	7"	Capitol	CL15164	1960	£2.50	£6

HICKORY

Green Light	7"	CBS	3963	1969	£10	£20

HICKORY STIX

Hello My Darling	7"	Oak	RGJ149	1964	£37.50	£75

HICKS, COLIN & THE CABIN BOYS

La Dee Dah	7"	Pye	7N15125	1958	£2.50	£6
Little Boy Blue	7"	Pye	7N15163	1958	£4	£8
Wild Eyes And Tender Lips	7"	Pye	7N15114	1957	£6	£12

HICKS, MARVA

Looking Over My Shoulder	7"	Infinity	INFT102	1979	£2.50	£6

HIDEAWAYS

Hideout	7"	Action	ACT4544	1969	£1.50	£4

HIGGINS, CHUCK

Pachuko Hop	LP	Combo	LP300	1960	£20	£40	US, Higgins cove
Pachuko Hop	LP	Combo	LP300	1960	£50	£100	US, nude cove

HIGGINS, LIZZIE

Up And Awa Wi The Laverock	LP	Topic	12TS260	1975	£5	£12

HIGGS & WILSON

Come On Home	7"	Starlite	ST45042	1961	£5	£10	
How Can I Be Sure	7"	Blue Beat	BB95	1962	£5	£10	
If You Want Pardon	7"	Blue Beat	BB190	1963	£5	£10	Baba Brooks B sid
It Is The Day	7"	Starlite	ST45036	1961	£5	£10	
Lazy Saturday Night	7"	Island	WI081	1963	£5	£10	Prince Buster B sid
Let Me Know	7"	R&B	JB109	1963	£5	£10	
Love Is Not For Me	7"	Rio	R29	1964	£5	£10	
Pretty Baby	7"	Starlite	ST45035	1961	£5	£10	
Sha Ba Ba	7"	Starlite	ST45053	1961	£5	£10	
When You Tell Me	7"	Blue Beat	BB3	1960	£5	£10	

HIGGS, JOE

I Am The Song	7"	Island	WI3026	1967	£5	£10	
Neighbour Neighbour	7"	Coxsone	CS7004	1967	£5	£10	Melodians B sid
You Hurt My Soul	7"	Island	WI3131	1968	£5	£10	Lyn Tait B sid

HIGH

Long Live The High	7"	CBS	4164	1969	£4	£8

HIGH & MIGHTY

Tryin' To Stop Cryin'	7"	HMV	POP1548	1966	£10	£20

HIGH BROOM

Dancing In The Moonlight	7"	Island	WIP6088	1970	£2.50	£6

HIGH KEYS

Que Sera Sera	7"	London	HLK9768	1963	£5	£10

HIGH LEVEL RANTERS

Bonny Pit Laddie	LP	Topic	212TS271/2	1975	£6	£15	Double
Four In A Bar	LP	Topic	12TS388	1979	£5	£12	
High Level	LP	Trailer	LER2030	1971	£5	£12	
Keep Your Feet Still Geordie Hinnie	LP	Trailer	LER2020	1970	£5	£12	
Lads Of Northumbria	LP	Trailer	LER2007	1969	£5	£12	
Mile To Ride	LP	Trailer	LER2037	1972	£5	£12	
Northumberland For Ever	LP	Topic	12TS186	1968	£6	£15	
Northumberland For Ever	LP	Topic	12TS186	197-	£5	£12	reissue with different cover

HIGH LEVEL RANTERS & MARTIN WYNDHAM-READ

English Sporting Ballads	LP	Broadside	BRO128	1977	£10	£25

HIGH NUMBERS

"I'm The Face" is one of the most celebrated single rarities. The High Numbers was, of course, the original name of the Who. The group also recorded a version of "The Kids Are Alright" before the name change, but this was not given a full release.

I'm The Face	7"	Back Door	DOOR4	1980	£4	£8	PS, chart single
I'm The Face	7"	Fontana	TF480	1964	£100	£200	
Kids Are Alright	7"	Fontana		1964	£250	£400	demo

HIGH SOCIETY

People Passing By	7"	Fontana	TF771	1966	£5	£10

HIGH TIDE

High Tide were a heavy group from the time when the heavy metal style was not so rigidly set as to preclude a more experimental approach like this. A heavily distorted guitar is here partnered by an electric violin (courtesy of Simon House, who was later to join Hawkwind) and the two instruments manage to create an extraordinary maelstrom of sound. The singer, meanwhile, is a Jim Morrison sound-alike, the slightly doom-laden voice sounding very effective in this context.

High Tide	LP	Liberty	LBS83294	1970	£15	£30	sleeve pictured in guide
High Tide	LP	Psycho	PSYCHO27	1984	£4	£10	
Sea Shanties	LP	Liberty	LBS83264	1969	£15	£30	
Sea Shanties	LP	Psycho	PSYCHO26	1984	£4	£10	

HIGH TIDE (2)

Baby Dancing	7"	Sunday Morning		1981	£2.50	£6	no PS

HIGHTOWER, DEAN

Twangy - With A Beat	LP	HMV	CLP1360	1960	£6	£15

HIGHTOWER, DONNA

Take One	LP	Capitol	T1133	1959	£5	£12

HIGHTOWER, ROSETTA

Go Pray For Tomorrow	7"	CBS	7668	1971	£1.50	£4
Hightower	LP	CBS	64201	1971	£4	£10
Can't Give Back The Love	7"	Toast	TT509	1968	£1.50	£4
Pretty Red Balloons	7"	Toast	TT506	1968	£1.50	£4

HIGHWAY

Highway	LP	EMI	EMA3019	1974	£5	£12
Smoking At The Edge	LP	EMI	EMA770	1975	£5	£12

HIGHWAYMEN

Gypsy Rover	7"	HMV	POP948	1961	£1.50	£4	chart single
Highwaymen	LP	HMV	CLP1510	1961	£6	£15	
Michael	7"	HMV	POP910	1961	£1.50	£4	chart single

HILARY HILARY

How Come You're So Dumb	7"	Modern	STP2	1980	£12.50	£25

HILDEBRAND, DIANE

Early Morning Blues And Greens	LP	Elektra	EKS74031	1969	£4	£10

HI-LITES

For Your Precious Love	LP	Dandee	DLP206	195-	£6	£15	US

HILL, ANDREW

Andrew!!!	LP	Blue Note	BLP/BST84203	1965	£10	£25
Black Fire	LP	Blue Note	BLP/BST84151	1963	£10	£25
Compulsion	LP	Blue Note	BLP/BST84217	1965	£8	£20
Grass Roots	LP	Blue Note	BST84303	1968	£5	£12
Judgement	LP	Blue Note	BLP/BST84159	1964	£8	£20
Lift Every Voice	LP	Blue Note	BST84330	1969	£5	£12
Point Of Departure	LP	Blue Note	BLP/BST84167	1964	£10	£25
Smoke Stack	LP	Blue Note	BLP/BST84160	1964	£10	£25

HILL, BENNY

Can't Tell A Waltz From A Tango	7"	Decca	F10442	1955	£2	£5
Who Done It	7"	Columbia	SCM5238	1956	£1.50	£4

HILL, BUNKER

Hide And Go Seek	7"	Stateside	SS135	1962	£4	£8

HILL, DAVID

All Shook Up	7"	Vogue	V9076	1957	£40	£80
That's Love	7"	RCA	RCA1041	1958	£60	£120

373

HILL, JESSE

Ooh Poo Pah Doo	7"	London	HLU9117	1960	£6	£12

HILL, Z.Z.

Brand New Z.Z.Hill	LP	Mojo	2916013	1972	£4	£10
Gimme Gimme	7" EP	Sue	IEP711	1966	£25	£50
I Keep On Loving You	7"	United Artists	UP35727	1975	£1.50	£4
Make Me Yours	7"	Action	ACT4532	1969	£6	£12
Someone To Love	7"	R&B	MRB5005	1965	£7.50	£15
Whole Lot Of Soul	LP	Action	ACLP6004	1969	£8	£20

HILLAGE, STEVE

Green	LP	Virgin	V2098	1978	£4	£10	green vinyl
Rainbow Dome Musick	LP	Virgin	VR1	1979	£5	£12	clear vinyl

HILLERY, JANE

You've Got A Hold On Me	7"	Columbia	DB7918	1966	£5	£10

HILLMEN

Hillmen	LP	Together	STT1012	1970	£8	£20	US

HILLOW HAMMET

Hammer	LP	House Of Fox	2	1968	£8	£20	US

HILLTOPPERS

Alone	7"	London	HLD9038	1960	£2	£5	
Do The Bop	7"	London	HLD8278	1956	£17.50	£35	
Fallen Star	7"	London	HLD8455	1957	£6	£12	
From The Vine Came The Grape	7"	London	HL8026	1954	£12.50	£25	
Hilltoppers	LP	Dot	DLP3073	1958	£8	£20	US
Hilltoppers Vol.2	7" EP	London	RED1030	1955	£7.50	£15	
Hilltoppers Vol.3	7" EP	London	RED1099	1957	£7.50	£15	
If I Didn't Care	7"	London	HL8092	1954	£10	£20	
I'm Serious	7"	London	HLD8441	1957	£6	£12	
Joker	7"	London	HLD8528	1957	£7.50	£15	
Kentuckian Song	7"	London	HLD8168	1957	£7.50	£15	
Marianne	7"	London	HLD8381	1957	£7.50	£15	chart single
My Treasure	7"	London	HLD8255	1956	£7.50	£15	
Only You	7"	London	HLD8221	1956	£7.50	£15	chart single
Poor Butterfly	7"	London	HL8070	1954	£10	£20	
Presenting The Hilltoppers	7" EP	London	RED1012	1955	£7.50	£15	
Searching	7"	London	HLD8208	1955	£7.50	£15	
So Tired	7"	London	HLD8333	1956	£7.50	£15	
Tops In Pops	LP	London	HAD2071	1957	£8	£20	
Towering Hilltoppers	LP	London	HAD2029	1957	£8	£20	
Tryin'	7"	London	HLD8298	1956	£7.50	£15	chart single
Will You Remember	7"	London	HL8081	1954	£10	£20	
You Sure Look Good To Me	7"	London	HLD8603	1958	£4	£8	
You Try Somebody Else	7"	London	HL8116	1955	£7.50	£15	

HI-LO'S

All Over The Place	LP	Philips	SBBL589	1960	£4	£10	stereo
All That Jazz	LP	Columbia	CL1259/CS8077	1959	£4	£10	US
Broadway Playbill	LP	Columbia	CL1416/CS8213	1959	£4	£10	US
Hi-Lo's	LP	Kapp	KL1027	195-	£4	£10	US
Hi-Lo's, I Presume	LP	Starlite	7007	195-	£5	£12	US
In Stereo	LP	Omega	11	195-	£4	£10	US
Listen To The Hi-Lo's	LP	Starlite	7006	195-	£5	£12	US
Love Nest	LP	Philips	BBL7235	1958	£5	£12	
Now Hear This	LP	Philips	BBL7177	1957	£5	£12	
On Hand	LP	Kapp	KL1194	195-	£4	£10	US
On Hand	LP	Starlite	7008	195-	£5	£12	US
Suddenly It's The Hi-Lo's	LP	Philips	BBL7154	1957	£5	£12	
They Didn't Believe Me	7" EP	London	REU1110	1958	£2.50	£6	
Under Glass	LP	London	HAU2026	1957	£6	£15	
Under Glass	7" EP	London	REU1077	1957	£2.50	£6	

HILTON, RONNIE

Always	7" EP	HMV	7EG8121	1955	£2.50	£6	
Around The World	7"	HMV	POP338	1957	£1.50	£4	chart single
Blossom Fell	7"	HMV	7M285	1955	£4	£8	chart single
By The Fireside	10" LP	HMV	DLP1109	1955	£6	£15	
For Those In Love	7" EP	HMV	7EG8198	1957	£2.50	£6	
For Those In Love No.2	7" EP	HMV	7EG8202	1957	£2.50	£6	
For Those In Love No.3	7" EP	HMV	7EG8270	1957	£2	£5	
He	7"	HMV	7M336	1955	£2.50	£6	
Here Comes My Love	7"	HMV	7M382	1956	£2	£5	
Hey There	7" EP	HMV	7EG8149	1955	£2.50	£6	
Hit Parade	7" EP	HMV	7EG8446	1957	£2	£5	
I May Never Pass This Way Again	7"	HMV	POP468	1958	£1.50	£4	chart single
I'm Beginning To See The Light	LP	HMV	CLP1295	1959	£4	£10	
Magic Moments	7"	HMV	POP446	1958	£1.50	£4	chart single
My Loving Hands	7"	HMV	7M303	1955	£2.50	£6	
No Other Love	7"	HMV	7M390	1956	£10	£20	chart single
Song For You	7" EP	HMV	7EG8375	1957	£2	£5	
Two Different Worlds	7"	HMV	POP274	1956	£4	£8	chart single
Who Are We	7"	HMV	7M413	1956	£4	£8	chart single
Wisdom Of A Fool	7"	HMV	POP291	1957	£2	£5	
Woman In Love	7"	HMV	POP248	1956	£4	£8	chart single
Wonderful Wonderful	7"	HMV	POP364	1957	£1.50	£4	chart single

| Young And Foolish | 7" | HMV | 7M358 | 1956 | £4 | £8 | chart single |

HILTONAIRES
| Best Of The Hiltonaires | LP | Coxsone | CSL8004 | 1967 | £50 | £100 | |

HIM & OTHERS
| I Mean It | 7" | Parlophone | R5510 | 1966 | £70 | £140 | |

HINDS, JUSTIN
Botheration	7"	Island	WI171	1965	£5	£10	
Botheration	7"	Treasure Isle	TI7063	1971	£2	£5	Vincent Hinds B side
Carry Go Bring Come	7"	Treasure Isle	TI7005	1967	£5	£10	
Drink Milk	7"	Duke	DU67	1970	£2.50	£6	
Here I Stand	7"	Treasure Isle	TI7002	1967	£5	£10	
Higher The Monkey Climbs	7"	Doctor Bird	DB1048	1966	£5	£10	
Jordan River	7"	Ska Beat	JB176	1964	£5	£10	
Jump Out Of Frying Pan	7"	Island	WI174	1965	£5	£10	
Mighty Redeemer	7"	Treasure Isle	TI7068	1971	£2	£5	
Never Too Young	7"	Island	WI244	1965	£5	£10	Skatalites B side
On A Saturday Night	7"	Island	WI3048	1967	£5	£10	
On A Saturday Night	7"	Treasure Isle	TI7014	1967	£5	£10	
Once A Man	7"	Treasure Isle	TI7017	1967	£5	£10	Tommy McCook B side
Peace And Love	7"	Island	WI236	1965	£5	£10	Skatalites B side
Rub Up, Push Up	7"	Island	WI194	1965	£5	£10	
Say Me Say	7"	Duke Reid	DR2511	1970	£2.50	£6	
Turn Them Back	7"	Island	WI232	1965	£5	£10	Tommy McCook B side
You Should've Known Better	7"	Trojan	TR652	1969	£2.50	£6	Tommy McCook B side

HINDS, NEVILLE
| Black Man's Time | 7" | Upsetter | US384 | 1971 | £1.50 | £4 | Upsetters B side |
| Sunday Gravy | 7" | Duke Reid | DR2503 | 1970 | £2.50 | £6 | John Holt B side |

HINES, EARL
Blues In Thirds	LP	Fontana	SFJL902	1967	£4	£10	
Earl Hines	LP	Philips	BBL7185	1957	£8	£20	
Earl Hines And His All Stars	10" LP	Mercury	MG25018	1954	£25	£50	
Earl Hines And His Orchestra	7" EP.	HMV	7EG8114	1955	£2	£5	
Earl's Backroom And Cozy's Caravan	LP	Felsted	FAJ7002	1958	£6	£15	with Cozy Cole
Earl's Pearls	LP	MGM	C833	1960	£5	£12	
Fatha Plays Fats	LP	Vogue	LAE12067	1957	£5	£12	
Fats Waller Songs	10" LP	Vogue Coral	LRA10031	1955	£20	£40	
Grand Terrace Swing	10" LP	HMV	DLP1132	1957	£15	£30	
Jazz Means Hines	LP	Fontana	TL5378	1967	£4	£10	
Midnight In New Orleans	7" EP.	MGM	MGMEP573	1956	£2	£5	
Paris One Night Stand	LP	Philips	BBL7222	1958	£6	£15	
Piano Moods	10" LP	Columbia	33S1063	1955	£20	£40	
Spontaneous Explorations	LP	Stateside	SL10116	1965	£5	£12	

HINES, FRAZER
| Who Is Dr.Who | 7" | Major Minor | MM579 | 1968 | £1.50 | £4 | |

HINES, SONNY
| Anytime, Anyday, Anywhere | 7" | King | KG1009 | 1965 | £2 | £5 | |

HINES, WINSTON
| Cool Down | 7" | Camel | CA20 | 1969 | £2 | £5 | Eric Fratter B side |

HINGE
| Village Postman | 7" | RCA | RCA1721 | 1968 | £7.50 | £15 | |

HINTON, EDDIE
| Very Extremely Dangerous | LP | Capricorn | CPN0204 | 1978 | £5 | £12 | US |

HINTON, JOE
Funny How Time Slips Away	LP	Backbeat	B60	1965	£6	£15	US
Funny How Time Slips Away	7"	Vocalion	VP9224	1964	£5	£10	
Just A Kid Named Joe	7"	Vocalion	VP9258	1966	£2.50	£6	

HINTON, MILT
| Milt Hinton Band | LP | London | LTZN15001 | 1956 | £8 | £20 | |

HI-NUMBERS
| Heart Of Stone | 7" | Decca | F12233 | 1965 | £12.50 | £25 | |

HIPPY BOYS
Cat Nip	7"	Camel	CA29	1969	£2.50	£6	
Doctor No Go	7"	High Note	HS021	1969	£2	£5	
Dog In A Me Minte	7"	Bullet	BU412	1969	£2	£5	
Love	7"	Trojan	TR668	1969	£2	£5	
Michael Row The Boat Ashore	7"	Trojan	TR669	1969	£2	£5	
Reggae Pressure	7"	High Note	HS035	1969	£2	£5	
Reggae With The Hippy Boys	LP	Big Shot	BSLP5005	1969	£10	£25	
That's Your Excuse	7"	Bullet	BU413	1969	£2	£5	

HIPSTER IMAGE
| Can't Let You Go | 7" | Decca | F12137 | 1965 | £12.50 | £25 | |

HIRT, AL
SWingin' Dixie .... LP ...... Audio Fidelity .. AFLP1877/ .... 1960 ... £6 ....£15 ....
AFSD5877 ....

HIS NAME IS ALIVE
How Ghosts Affect Relationships .... 7" .... 4AD .... HNIA1 .... 1990 ... £2 ....£5 ....promo

HI-SPOTS
Lend Me Your Comb .... 7" ...... Melodisc .... 1457 .... 1958 ... £6 ....£12
Secretly .... 7" ...... Melodisc .... 1473 .... 1958 ... £4 ....£8

HIT PACK
Never Say No To Your Baby .... 7" ...... Tamla Motown TMG513 .... 1965 ... £17.50 ....£35

HIT PARADE
Forever .... 7" ...... JSH .... JSH1 .... 1984 ... £2 ....£5
My Favourite Girl .... 7" ...... JSH .... JSH2 .... 1984 ... £1.50 ......£4

HIT SQUAD
Wax On The Melt .... 12" ..... Eastern Bloc .... EASTERN01 .... 1988 ... £25 ....£50 ....promo

HITCHCOCK, ALFRED
Music To Be Murdered By .... LP ...... London .... HAP2130 .... 1958 ... £10 ....£25
Music To Be Murdered By .... LP ...... London .... SHP6012 .... 1959 ... £15 ....£30 ....stereo

HITCHCOCK, ROBYN
Man Who Invented Himself .... 7" ...... Armageddon ... AS008 .... 1981 ... £1.50 ......£4
Man Who Invented Himself .... 7" ...... Armageddon ... AS008 .... 1981 ... £4 ....£8 ..with flexi (4SPURT1)

HI-TENSION
Hi-Tension .... 12" ..... Island .... IPR2007 .... 1977 ... £2.50 ......£6
There's A Reason .... 12" ..... Island .... 12WIP6493 .... 1979 ... £3 ....£8

HI-TONES
Ten Virgins .... 7" ...... Island .... WI086 .... 1963 ... £5 ....£10
You Hold The Key .... 7" ...... R&B .... JB123 .... 1963 ... £5 ....£10 ....Dor
Drummond B side

HITTERS (BRINSLEY SCHWARZ)
Hypocrite .... 7" .... United Artists .. UP35530 .... 1973 ... £2.50 ......£6

HOBBITS
Daffodil Days .... 7" ...... MCA .... MU1002 .... 1968 ... £1.50 ......£4
Down To Middle Earth .... LP ...... MCA .... MUP301 .... 1967 ... £8 ....£20
Men And Doors .... LP ...... Decca .... DL75009 .... 1968 ... £6 ....£15 ....US

HOBBS, CHRISTOPHER, JOHN ADAMS & GAVIN BRYARS
Ensemble Pieces .... LP ...... Obscure .... OBS2 .... 1975 ... £4 ....£10

HOBBY SHOP
Why Must It Be This Way .... 7" ...... Columbia .... DB8395 .... 1968 ... £2 ....£5

HOBOKEN
Hoboken .... LP ...... Oak .... 1973 ... £330 ......£500

HOCKRIDGE, EDMUND
By The Fountains Of Rome .... 7" EP .. Pye .... NEP24026 .... 1957 ... £2.50 ......£6
Edmund Hockridge .... 7" EP .. Pye .... NEP24019 .... 1956 ... £2.50 ......£6

HODES, ART
Funky Piano .... LP ...... Blue Note .... B6502 .... 1969 ... £4 ....£10
Sittin' In Vol.1 .... LP ...... Blue Note .... B6508 .... 1969 ... £4 ....£10

HODGE, CHRIS
We're On Our Way .... 7" ...... Apple .... 43 .... 1972 ... £6 ....£12 ....PS

HODGE, MARVA
Ghetto .... 7" ...... Polydor .... 56792 .... 1970 ... £1.50 ......£4

HODGES, CHARLES
Try A Little Love .... 7" ...... Major Minor .... MM654 .... 1969 ... £6 ....£12

HODGES, EDDIE
Bandit Of My Dreams .... 7" ...... London .... HLA9305 .... 1962 ... £4 ....£8
Eddie Hodges .... 7" EP .. London .... REA1353 .... 1963 ... £12.50 ....£25
I'm Gonna Knock On Your Door .... 7" ...... London .... HLA9369 .... 1961 ... £2 ....£5 ....chart singl
Just A Kid In Love .... 7" ...... MGM .... MGM1232 .... 1963 ... £1.50 ......£4
Love Minus Zero: No Limit .... 7" ...... Stateside .... SS469 .... 1965 ... £1.50 ......£4
Made To Love .... 7" ...... London .... HLA9576 .... 1962 ... £1.50 ......£4 ....chart singl
New Orleans .... 7" ...... Stateside .... SS442 .... 1965 ... £1.50 ......£4

HODGES, JOHNNY
Big Sound .... LP ...... Columbia .... 33CX10136 .... 1959 ... £8 ....£20
Blues-A-Plenty .... LP ...... HMV .... CLP1430 .... 1961 ... £6 ....£15
Ellingtonia '56 .... LP ...... Columbia .... 33CX10055 .... 1956 ... £8 ....£20
In A Tender Mood .... LP ...... Columbia .... 33C9051 .... 1957 ... £15 ....£30
Johnny Hodges With The Ellington All LP ...... Columbia .... 33CX10098 .... 1958 ... £6 ....£15
Stars
Memories Of Ellington .... LP ...... Columbia .... 33CX10013 .... 1955 ... £20 ....£40
Wings And Things .... LP ...... Verve .... (S)VLP9117 .... 1965 ... £4 ....£10 ....with Wild Bill Dav
With The Ellingtonians .... 10" LP .. Vogue .... LDE011 .... 1952 ... £20 ....£40

HOELDERLIN

Clown And Clouds	LP	Spiegelei	160607	1976	£6	£15	German
Hoelderlin	LP	Spiegelei	160601	1975	£6	£15	German
Hoelderlin Traum	LP	Pilz	20213145	1972	£8	£20	German
Live Traumstadt	LP	Spiegelei	180602	1978	£5	£12	German double
Rare Birds	LP	Spiegelei	160608	1977	£4	£10	German

HOGAN, ANNIE

Plays Kickabye	12"	Doublevision	DVR9	1985	£2.50	£6	

HOGAN, SILAS

Trouble At Home	LP	Blue Horizon	2431008	1971	£20	£40	

HOGARTH

Suzie's Getting Married	7"	Liberty	LBF15156	1968	£2	£5	

HOGG, SMOKEY

I'm So Lonely	LP	Realm	RM197	1964	£6	£15	
Sings The Blues	LP	Ember	EMB3405	1971	£5	£12	
Smokey Hogg	LP	Time	6	1962	£8	£20	US

HOGS

"Blues Theme" is collectable on two counts - the B side is a Frank Zappa production, while the Hogs afterwards changed their name to the Chocolate Watch Band.

Blues Theme	7"	HBR	511	1966	£30	£60	US

HOGSNORT RUPERT'S ORIGINAL FLAGON BAND

Pretty Girl	7"	Columbia	DB8711	1970	£1.50	£4	

HOKUS POKE

Earth Harmony	LP	Vertigo	6360064	1972	£25	£50	spiral label

HOLDE FEE

Malaga	LP	private	1383001	1975	£4	£10	German

HOLDEN, RANDY

Population II	LP	Hobbit	5002	1968	£25	£50	US

HOLDEN, RON

I Love You So	LP	Donna	DLP(S)2111	1960	£15	£30	US
Love You So	7"	London	HLU9116	1960	£12.50	£25	

HOLDER, RAM BROTHERS

Ram Blues	7"	Parlophone	R5471	1966	£4	£8	

HOLDER, RAM JOHN

Black London Blues	LP	Beacon	BEAS2	1974	£10	£25	
Bootleg Blues	LP	Beacon	BEAS17	1974	£6	£15	
I Just Came To Get My Baby	7"	Beacon	BEA108	1968	£1.50	£4	
I Need Somebody	7"	Columbia	DB8157	1967	£1.50	£4	
It Won't Be Long Before I Love You	7"	Columbia	DB8262	1967	£1.50	£4	
You Simply Are	LP	Fresh Air	9299470	1975	£5	£12	

HOLDSWORTH, ALLAN

Velvet Darkness	LP	CTI	6068	1977	£6	£15	

HOLIDAY, BILLIE

An Evening With Billie Holiday	7" EP	Columbia	SEB10035	1956	£2	£5	
At Jazz At The Philharmonic	10" LP	Columbia	33C9023	1956	£25	£50	
Billie Holiday	LP	Fontana	TL5287	1966	£5	£12	
Billie Holiday	LP	MGM	C792	1959	£6	£15	
Billie Holiday	LP	Stateside	SL10007	1962	£6	£15	
Billie Holiday	7" EP	Columbia	SEB10009	1955	£2	£5	
Billie Holiday	7" EP	Vogue	EPV1128	1956	£2.50	£6	
Billie Holiday	10" LP	Columbia	33S1034	1954	£25	£50	
Billie Holiday Memorial	LP	Fontana	TFL5106	1960	£6	£15	
Billie Holiday Sings	7" EP	Columbia	SEB10048	1956	£2	£5	
Blue	7" EP	Fontana	TFE17026	1960	£2	£5	
Detour Ahead	7"	Vogue	V2408	1956	£1.50	£4	
Don't Worry 'Bout Me	7"	MGM	MGM1033	1959	£1.50	£4	
Embraceable You	7" EP	Melodisc	EPM7125	195-	£2.50	£6	
Favourites	10" LP	Philips	BBR8032	1955	£20	£40	
Lady Day	7" EP	Fontana	TFE17010	1959	£2	£5	
Lady Day Vol.1	7" EP	Brunswick	OE9172	1955	£2	£5	
Lady Day Vol.2	7" EP	Brunswick	OE9199	1956	£2	£5	
Lady Day Vol.3	7" EP	Brunswick	OE9251	1956	£2	£5	
Lady In Satin	LP	Fontana	TFL5032	1959	£8	£20	
Lady Sings The Blues	LP	Columbia	33CX10092	1957	£15	£30	
Last Live Recording	LP	Island	ILP929	1966	£6	£15	
Lover Man	10" LP	Brunswick	LA8676	1954	£20	£40	
Music For Torching	LP	Columbia	33CX10019	1956	£20	£40	
Once Upon A Time	LP	Fontana	TL5262	1965	£5	£12	
Solitude	LP	Columbia	33CX10076	1957	£15	£30	
Songs For Distingue Lovers	LP	Columbia	33CX10145	1959	£8	£20	
Unforgettable Lady Day	LP	HMV	CLP1414	1960	£6	£15	
Velvet Moods	LP	Columbia	33CX10064	1957	£15	£30	

HOLIDAY, CHICO

Chico Holiday	7" EP	RCA	RCX171	1959	£10	£20	
God, Country And My Baby	7"	Coral	Q72443	1961	£1.50	£4	
Young Ideas	7"	RCA	RCA1117	1959	£2.50	£6	

377

HOLIDAY, JIMMY

Baby I Love You	7"	Liberty	LIB12040	1966	£5	£10
Everybody Needs Help	7"	Liberty	LIB12053	1967	£4	£8
Give Me Your Love	7"	Liberty	LIB12048	1967	£4	£8
Give Me Your Love	7"	Minit	MLF11008	1968	£4	£8
How Can I Forget	7"	Vocalion	V9206	1963	£7.50	£15
I Lied	7"	London	HLY9868	1964	£2	£5

HOLIDAY, JIMMY & CLYDIE KING

Oh Darling How I Miss You	7"	Polydor	56035	1965	£4	£8
One Man In My Life	7"	Polydor	56166	1967	£4	£8
Ready Willing And Able	7"	Liberty	LIB12058	1967	£7.50	£15

HOLIDAY, JOE

Joe Holiday Rhythm	10" LP	Esquire	20027	1954	£20	£40

HOLIDAY, JOHNNY

Holiday For Romance	7" EP..	London	RED1227	1959	£2	£5
Sentimental Holiday	7" EP..	London	RED1226	1959	£2	£5

HOLIDAYS

I'll Love You Forever	7"	Polydor	56720	1966	£30	£60

HOLLAND & DOZIER

Why Can't We Be Lovers	7"	Invictus	INV525	1972	£2	£5

HOLLAND, EDDIE

Eddie Holland	LP	Motown	604	1963	£25	£50	US
If It's Love	7"	Oriole	CBA1808	1963	£150	£250	
Jamie	7"	Fontana	H387	1962	£100	£200	

HOLLAND, TONY

Sidewalk	7"	HMV	POP1135	1963	£5	£10

HOLLIDAY, BRENDA

Hurt A Little Everyday	7"	Tamla Motown	TMG581	1966	£40	£80	demo only

HOLLIDAY, MICHAEL

All Of You	7"	Columbia	DB3973	1957	£2.50	£6	
All Time Favourites	7" EP..	Columbia	SEG7761	1958	£2.50	£6	
Best Of Michael Holliday	LP	Columbia	33SX1586	1964	£4	£10	
Four Feather Falls	7" EP..	Columbia	SEG7986/ ESG7793	1960	£7.50	£15	chart single
Gal With The Yaller Shoes	7"	Columbia	SCM5273	1956	£4	£8	
Happy Holliday	LP	Columbia	33SX1354	1961	£5	£12	
Happy Holliday	7" EP..	Columbia	SEG8161	1962	£2	£5	
Hi!	10" LP	Columbia	33S1114	1958	£8	£20	
Holliday Mixture	LP	Columbia	33SX1262/ SCX3331	1960	£5	£12	
I'll Always Be In Love With You	7"	Columbia	DB4155	1958	£1.50	£4	chart single
In A Sentimental Mood	7" EP..	Columbia	ESG7864	1961	£4	£8	stereo
In A Sentimental Mood	7" EP..	Columbia	SEG8115	1961	£2.50	£6	
In Love	7"	Columbia	DB4087	1958	£1.50	£4	chart single
Melody Mike	7" EP..	Columbia	SEG7818	1958	£4	£8	
Memories Of Mike	7" EP..	Columbia	SEG8373	1964	£2	£5	
Mike	LP	Columbia	33SX1170	1959	£5	£12	
Mike And The Other Fella	7" EP..	Columbia	SEG7892	1959	£2.50	£6	
Mike No.1	7" EP..	Columbia	ESG7784	1960	£4	£8	stereo
Mike No.1	7" EP..	Columbia	SEG7972	1960	£2.50	£6	
Mike No.2	7" EP..	Columbia	ESG7803	1960	£4	£8	stereo
Mike No.2	7" EP..	Columbia	SEG7996	1960	£2.50	£6	
Mike No.3	7" EP..	Columbia	ESG7842	1961	£4	£8	stereo
Mike No.3	7" EP..	Columbia	SEG8074	1961	£2.50	£6	
Mike Sings Country And Western Style	7" EP..	Columbia	SEG8242	1963	£2	£5	
Mike Sings Ragtime	7" EP..	Columbia	ESG7856	1961	£4	£8	stereo
Mike Sings Ragtime	7" EP..	Columbia	SEG8101	1961	£2.50	£6	
More Happy Holliday	7" EP..	Columbia	SEG8186	1962	£2	£5	
Music With Mike	7" EP..	Columbia	SEG7683	1957	£4	£8	
My Guitar And Me	7" EP..	Columbia	SEG7638	1956	£2.50	£6	
My House Is Your House	7"	Columbia	DB3919	1957	£2.50	£6	chart single
Nothin' To Do	7"	Columbia	SCM5252	1956	£4	£8	
Old Cape Cod	7"	Columbia	DB3992	1957	£1.50	£4	
Relax With Mike	7" EP..	Columbia	SEG7752	1958	£2.50	£6	
Sentimental Journey	7" EP..	Columbia	SEG7836	1958	£2.50	£6	
Sixteen Tons	7"	Columbia	SCM5221	1956	£5	£10	
Stairway Of Love	7"	Columbia	DB4121	1958	£1.50	£4	chart single
Starry Eyed	7"	Columbia	DB4378	1959	£1.50	£4	chart single
Story Of My Life	7"	Columbia	DB4058	1958	£1.50	£4	chart single
Ten Thousand Miles	7"	Columbia	DB3813	1956	£5	£10	chart single
To Bing From Mike	LP	Columbia	33SX1425/ SCX3441	1962	£5	£12	
Wringle Wrangle	7"	Columbia	DB3948	1957	£2	£5	
Yaller Yaller Gold	7"	Columbia	DB3871	1957	£2	£5	

HOLLIDAY, SUSAN

Any Day Now	7"	Columbia	DB7403	1964	£2.50	£6
I Wanna Say Hello	LP	Columbia	SX6067	1966	£20	£40
Sometimes	7"	Columbia	DB7616	1965	£4	£8

HOLLIER, TIM

Title	Format	Label	Cat. No.	Year			Notes
Message To A Harlequin	LP	United Artists	(S)ULP1211	1968	£6	£15	
Sky Sail	LP	Philips	6308044	1971	£6	£15	

HOLLIES

The Hollies were easily one of the most successful of the first wave of British beat groups to emerge in the sixties and yet they seldom seem to receive much credit for the fact. Inevitably they tended to labour in the shadow of the Beatles and their records show a similar pattern of development. "Butterfly" is a kind of Lance Corporal Pepper - it uses the same kind of inventive arranging and is one of the more interesting albums of the period. Dare one say that it is actually much more of a psychedelic classic than celebrated rarities like those of Kaleidoscope?

Title	Format	Label	Cat. No.	Year			Notes
After The Fox	7"	United Artists	UP1152	1966	£10	£20	with Peter Sellers
Ain't That Just Like Me	7"	Parlophone	R5030	1963	£2.50	£6	chart single
Baby	7"	Polydor	2058199	1972	£1.50	£4	chart single
Boulder To Birmingham	7"	Polydor	2058694	1976	£1.50	£4	
Bus Stop	LP	Imperial	LP9330/12330	1966	£8	£20	US
Bus Stop	7"	Parlophone	R5469	1966	£1.50	£4	chart single
Bus Stop	7" EP	Odeon	MEO125	1966	£40	£80	French, sleeve with group picture
Bus Stop	7" EP	Odeon	MEO125	1966	£10	£20	French, sleeve with titles only
Butterfly	LP	Parlophone	PMC/PCS7039	1967	£8	£20	
Butterfly	LP	Parlophone	PMC7039	1987	£10	£25	mono
Carrie Anne	7" EP	Fontana	460211	1967	£10	£20	French
Carrie-Anne	7"	Parlophone	R5602	1967	£1.50	£4	chart single
Confessions Of The Mind	LP	Parlophone	PCS7116	1970	£5	£12	chart LP
Day That Curly Billy Shot Down Crazy Sam McGhee	7"	Polydor	2058403	1973	£1.50	£4	chart single
Distant Light	LP	Parlophone	PAS10005	1971	£4	£10	
Everything You Wanted To Hear	LP	Epic	AS138	1972	£10	£25	US promo
Evolution	LP	Parlophone	PMC/PCS7022	1967	£8	£20	chart LP
For Certain Because	LP	Parlophone	PMC/PCS7011	1966	£10	£25	chart LP
Gasoline Alley Bred	7"	Parlophone	R5862	1970	£1.50	£4	chart single
He Ain't Heavy He's My Brother	7"	Parlophone	R5806	1969	£1.50	£4	chart single
Hear! Here!	LP	Imperial	LP9299/12299	1965	£15	£30	US
Here I Go Again	LP	Imperial	LP9265/12265	1964	£20	£40	US
Here I Go Again	7"	Parlophone	R5137	1964	£1.50	£4	chart single
Here I Go Again	7" EP	Parlophone	GEP8915	1964	£12.50	£25	
Hey Willy	7"	Parlophone	R5905	1971	£1.50	£4	chart single
Hollies	LP	Parlophone	PMC1261	1965	£15	£30	chart LP
Hollies	LP	Regal	SREG2024	1967	£10	£25	export
Hollies	7" EP	Parlophone	GEP8909	1964	£10	£20	
Hollies - Beat Group	LP	Imperial	LP9312/12312	1966	£8	£20	US
Hollies Greatest	LP	Parlophone	PMC/PCS7057	1968	£4	£10	chart LP
I Can't Let Go	7"	Parlophone	R5409	1966	£1.50	£4	chart single
I Can't Let Go	7" EP	Parlophone	GEP8951	1966	£15	£30	
I Can't Tell The Bottom From The Top	7"	Parlophone	R5837	1970	£1.50	£4	chart single
If I Needed Someone	7"	Parlophone	R5392	1965	£1.50	£4	chart single
If I Needed Someone	7" EP	Odeon	MEO101	1965	£15	£30	French
I'm Alive	7"	Parlophone	R5287	1965	£1.50	£4	chart single
I'm Alive	7" EP	Odeon	SOE3770	1965	£15	£30	French
I'm Alive	7" EP	Parlophone	GEP8942	1965	£15	£30	
I'm Down	7"	Polydor	2058533	1974	£1.50	£4	
In The Hollies Style	LP	Parlophone	PMC1235	1965	£20	£40	
In The Hollies Style	7" EP	Parlophone	GEP8934	1965	£12.50	£25	
Jennifer Eccles	7"	Parlophone	R5680	1968	£1.50	£4	chart single
Jesus Was A Crossmaker	7"	Epic	510989	1973	£4	£8	US
Just One Look	7"	Parlophone	R5104	1964	£1.50	£4	chart single
Just One Look	7" EP	Parlophone	GEP8911	1964	£10	£20	
Kill Me Quick	7"	Parlophone	QMSP16410	1967	£15	£30	Italian
King Midas In Reverse	7"	Parlophone	R5637	1967	£1.50	£4	chart single
Like Every Time Before	7"	Hansa	14093	1968	£5	£10	German
Listen To Me	7"	Parlophone	R5733	1968	£1.50	£4	chart single
Long Cool Woman In A Black Dress	7"	Parlophone	R5939	1972	£1.50	£4	chart single
Look Through Any Window	7"	Parlophone	R5322	1965	£1.50	£4	chart single
Look Through Any Window	7" EP	Odeon	SOE3773	1965	£15	£30	French
Magic Woman Touch	7"	Polydor	2058289	1972	£1.50	£4	
Maker - Would You Believe	7" EP	Fontana	460249	1968	£12.50	£25	French
Music For 5am	7"	Mercury	YARD002	196-	£5	£10	with other artists
Non Prego Per Me	7"	Parlophon	QMSP16402	1967	£15	£30	Italian
On A Carousel	7"	Parlophone	R5562	1967	£1.50	£4	chart single
On A Carousel	7" EP	Fontana	460201	1967	£12.50	£25	French
Out On The Road	LP	Hansa	87119	1973	£8	£20	German
Romany	LP	Polydor	2383144	1972	£4	£10	
Sandy	7"	Polydor	2058595	1975	£1.50	£4	
Searchin'	7"	Parlophone	R5052	1963	£1.50	£4	chart single
Sing Dylan	LP	Parlophone	PMC/PCS7078	1969	£6	£15	chart LP
Sing Hollies	LP	Parlophone	PCS7092	1969	£4	£10	
Son Of A Rotten Gambler	7"	Polydor	2058476	1974	£1.50	£4	
Sorry Suzanne	7"	Parlophone	R5765	1969	£1.50	£4	chart single
Star	7"	Polydor	2058719	1976	£1.50	£4	
Stay	7"	Parlophone	R5077	1963	£1.50	£4	chart single
Stay	7" EP	Odeon	SOE3749	1963	£15	£30	French
Stay With The Hollies	LP	Parlophone	PCS3054	1964	£20	£40	stereo
Stay With The Hollies	LP	Parlophone	PMC1220	1964	£10	£25	chart LP
Stay With The Hollies	LP	World Records	ST1035	1968	£6	£15	
Stop Stop Stop	LP	Imperial	LP9339/12339	1967	£8	£20	US
Stop Stop Stop	7"	Parlophone	R5508	1966	£1.50	£4	chart single
Tell Me To My Face	7" EP	Odeon	MEO144	1967	£15	£30	French
Up Front	LP	St.Michael	21020101	1978	£8	£20	
Vintage Hollies	LP	World Records	ST979	1967	£6	£15	
We're Through	7"	Parlophone	R5178	1964	£1.50	£4	chart single

Title	Format	Label	Catalogue	Year	Price	Price	Notes
We're Through	7" EP	Parlophone	GEP8927	1964	£12.50	£25	
Would You Believe	LP	Parlophone	PCS7008	1966	£17.50	£35	stereo
Would You Believe	LP	Parlophone	PMC7008	1966	£10	£25	
Yes I Will	7"	Parlophone	R5232	1965	£1.50	£4	chart single

HOLLOW MEN

Title	Format	Label	Catalogue	Year	Price	Price	Notes
Drowning Man	12"	Blind Eye	BE007	1989	£2.50	£6	fully autographed
Gold And Ivory	12"	Evensong	EVE212	1987	£2.50	£6	with postcard
Late Flowering Lust	7"	Evensong	EVE107	1985	£4	£8	
White Train	7"	Gigantic	GI101	1988	£2.50	£6	promo

HOLLOWAY, BRENDA

Title	Format	Label	Catalogue	Year	Price	Price	Notes
Artistry Of Brenda Holloway	LP	Tamla Motown	(S)TML11083	1968	£30	£60	
Every Little Bit Hurts	LP	Tamla	257	1965	£25	£50	US
Every Little Bit Hurts	7"	Stateside	SS307	1964	£15	£30	
Hurt A Little Everyday	7"	Tamla Motown	TMG581	1966	£12.50	£25	
Just Look What I've Done	7"	Tamla Motown	TMG608	1967	£7.50	£15	
Just Look What You've Done	7"	Tamla Motown	TMG700	1969	£4	£8	
Operator	7"	Tamla Motown	TMG519	1965	£20	£40	
Together Till The End Of Time	7"	Tamla Motown	TMG556	1966	£17.50	£35	
When I'm Gone	7"	Tamla Motown	TMG508	1965	£35	£70	
You've Made Me So Very Happy	7"	Tamla Motown	TMG622	1967	£7.50	£15	

HOLLOWAY, PATRICE

Title	Format	Label	Catalogue	Year	Price	Price	Notes
Love And Desire	7"	Capitol	CL15484	1966	£30	£60	

HOLLOWAY, STANLEY

Title	Format	Label	Catalogue	Year	Price	Price	Notes
'Ere's 'Olloway	LP	Philips	BBL7237	1958	£4	£10	
Famous Adventures With Old Sam And The Ramsbottoms	10" LP	Columbia	33S1093	1956	£5	£12	

HOLLY

Title	Format	Label	Catalogue	Year	Price	Price	Notes
Hobo Joe	7"	Erics	ERICS007	1979	£4	£8	
Yankee Rose	7"	Erics	ERICS003	1979	£2.50	£6	

HOLLY, BUDDY

There is a strong case for viewing Buddy Holly as the true father of the music we call rock. It was Buddy Holly and the Crickets who set the pattern for the line-up that is still considered as the classic one for a rock group - lead and rhythm guitars, bass guitar and drums. His songs too, based on blues chord progressions but with bright, major tonalities, defined a style that has been revisited by song-writers from Lennon and McCartney to Costello and all points in between. It should be noted, incidentally, that while most of Holly's records were credited to him by name, a few were credited merely to the Crickets. All, however, are listed here.

Title	Format	Label	Catalogue	Year	Price	Price	Notes
Baby I Don't Care	7"	Coral	Q72432	1961	£2	£5	chart single
Best Of Buddy Holly	LP	Coral	CX(S)B8	1966	£8	£20	US
Blue Days Black Nights	7"	Brunswick	05581	1956	£150	£250	
Bo Diddley	7"	Coral	Q72463	1963	£2	£5	chart single
Brown Eyed Handsome Man	7"	Coral	Q72459	1963	£2	£5	chart single
Brown-Eyed Handsome Man	LP	MCA	MUP(S)314	1968	£4	£10	yellow label
Buddy By Request	7" EP	Coral	FEP2065	1964	£10	£20	
Buddy Holly	LP	Coral	CRL57210	1958	£75	£150	US
Buddy Holly	LP	Coral	LVA9085	1958	£8	£20	
Buddy Holly	LP	Vogue Coral	LVA9085	1958	£20	£40	
Buddy Holly	7" EP	Coral	FEP2002	1958	£12.50	£25	
Buddy Holly	7" EP	Coral	FEP2002	1958	£75	£150	no glasses cover
Buddy Holly And The Crickets	LP	Coral	CRL(7)57405	1962	£17.50	£35	US
Buddy Holly No.1	7" EP	Brunswick	OE9456	1959	£20	£40	tri-centre
Buddy Holly No.2	7" EP	Brunswick	OE9457	1959	£20	£40	tri-centre
Buddy Holly Sings	7" EP	Coral	FEP2070	1965	£15	£30	
Buddy Holly Story	LP	Coral	CRL57279	1959	£30	£60	US
Buddy Holly Story	LP	Coral	LVA9105	1959	£6	£15	chart LP
Buddy Holly Story	LP	World Records	SM301-5	1975	£10	£25	5 LPs, boxed
Buddy Holly Story	7" EP	Coral	FEP2032	1959	£10	£20	tri-centre
Buddy Holly Story 2	LP	Coral	LVA9127	1960	£6	£15	chart LP
Buddy Holly Story Vol.2	LP	Coral	CRL57326	1959	£25	£50	US
Chirping Crickets	LP	Brunswick	BL54038	1957	£100	£200	US
Chirping Crickets	LP	Coral	LVA9081	1958	£15	£30	
Chirping Crickets	LP	Vogue Coral	LVA9081	1958	£20	£40	
Complete Buddy Holly	LP	MCA	CDMSP807	1978	£20	£40	6 LPs, book, boxed
Early In The Morning	78	Coral	Q72333	1958	£5	£10	
Early In The Morning	7"	Coral	Q72333	1958	£5	£10	chart single
Four More	7" EP	Coral	FEP2060	1960	£10	£20	
Giant	LP	MCA	MUPS371	1969	£4	£10	yellow label
Good Rockin'	LP	Vocalion	VL73923	1971	£25	£50	US
Great Buddy Holly	LP	Vocalion	VL(7)3811	1967	£8	£20	US
Greatest Hits	LP	Ace Of Hearts	AH148	1967	£4	£10	
Greatest Hits	LP	Coral	CRL(7)57492	1967	£8	£20	US
Heartbeat	LP	Marks & Spencer	IMP114	1978	£15	£30	
Heartbeat	78	Coral	Q72346	1958	£7.50	£15	
Heartbeat	78	Coral	Q72392	1960	£10	£20	
Heartbeat	7"	Coral	Q72346	1958	£5	£10	chart single
Heartbeat	7" EP	Coral	FEP2015	1959	£10	£20	
He's The One	LP	MCA	MUP(S)315	1968	£4	£10	yellow label
Holly In The Hills	LP	Coral	CRL(7)57463	1965	£17.50	£35	US
Holly In The Hills	LP	Coral	LVA9227	1965	£15	£30	with 'Reminiscing', chart LP
Holly In The Hills	LP	Coral	LVA9227	1965	£10	£25	with 'Wishing'
It Doesn't Matter Anymore	78	Coral	Q72360	1959	£7.50	£15	
It Doesn't Matter Anymore	7"	Coral	Q72360	1959	£2.50	£6	chart single
It's So Easy	78	Coral	Q72343	1958	£6	£12	
It's So Easy	7"	Coral	Q72343	1958	£4	£8	

Title	Format	Label	Cat No	Year	Price	Price	Notes
It's So Easy	7" EP	Coral	FEP2014	1959	£10	£20	
Late Great Buddy Holly	7" EP	Coral	FEP2044	1960	£7.50	£15	
Learning The Game	78	Coral	Q72411	1960	£37.50	£75	
Learning The Game	7"	Coral	Q72411	1960	£2.50	£6	chart single
Listen To Me	LP	MCA	MUP(S)312	1968	£4	£10	yellow label
Listen To Me	78	Coral	Q72288	1958	£5	£10	
Listen To Me	7"	Coral	Q72288	1958	£6	£12	chart single
Listen To Me	7"	Coral	Q72449	1962	£2	£5	chart single
Look At Me	7"	Coral	Q72445	1961	£2	£5	
Love's Made A Fool Of You	7"	Coral	Q72475	1964	£2.50	£6	chart single
Maybe Baby	78	Coral	Q72307	1958	£2.50	£6	
Maybe Baby	7"	Coral	Q72307	1958	£5	£10	chart single
Maybe Baby	7"	Coral	Q72483	1966	£5	£10	
Midnight Shift	78	Brunswick	05800	1959	£12.50	£25	
Midnight Shift	7"	Brunswick	05800	1959	£12.50	£25	
Oh Boy	78	Coral	Q72298	1957	£2.50	£6	
Oh Boy	7"	Coral	Q72298	1957	£5	£10	chart single
Oh Boy	7"	Decca	AD1012	1968	£5	£10	export
Peggy Sue	78	Vogue Coral	Q72293	1957	£3	£8	
Peggy Sue	7"	Coral	Q72293	1958	£5	£10	chart single
Peggy Sue	7"	Vogue Coral	Q72293	1957	£7.50	£15	
Peggy Sue Got Married	78	Coral	Q72376	1959	£20	£40	
Peggy Sue Got Married	7"	Coral	Q72376	1959	£4	£8	chart single
Rave On	LP	MCA	MUP(S)313	1968	£4	£10	yellow label
Rave On	78	Coral	Q72325	1958	£5	£10	
Rave On	7"	Coral	Q72325	1958	£5	£10	chart single
Rave On	7"	Decca	AD1009	1968	£5	£10	export
Rave On	7" EP	Coral	FEP2005	1958	£10	£20	
Reminiscing	LP	Coral	LVA9212	1963	£8	£20	chart LP
Reminiscing	7"	Coral	Q72455	1962	£2	£5	chart single
Rock & Roll Collection	LP	Decca	DXSE7207	1972	£4	£10	US
Showcase	LP	Coral	LVA9222	1964	£8	£20	chart LP
Showcase Vol.1	7" EP	Coral	FEP2068	1964	£25	£50	
Showcase Vol.2	7" EP	Coral	FEP2069	1964	£25	£50	
Sound Of The Crickets	7" EP	Coral	FEP2003	1958	£10	£20	
That Tex Mex Sound	7" EP	Coral	FEP2066	1964	£25	£50	
That'll Be The Day	LP	Ace Of Hearts	AH3	1961	£6	£15	chart LP
That'll Be The Day	LP	Decca	DL8707	1958	£180	£300	US
That'll Be The Day	78	Vogue Coral	Q72279	1957	£3	£8	
That'll Be The Day	7"	Coral	Q72279	1957	£5	£10	chart single
That'll Be The Day	7"	Vogue Coral	Q72279	1957	£6	£12	
That'll Be The Day	7" EP	Coral	FEP2062	1960	£10	£20	
Think It Over	78	Coral	Q72329	1958	£5	£10	
Think It Over	7"	Coral	Q72329	1958	£5	£10	chart single
True Love Ways	LP	MCA	MUP(S)319	1968	£4	£10	yellow label
True Love Ways	78	Coral	Q72397	1960	£20	£40	
True Love Ways	7"	Coral	Q72397	1960	£2	£5	chart single
What To Do	7"	Coral	Q72419	1961	£2	£5	chart single
What To Do	7"	Coral	Q72469	1963	£2	£5	chart single
Wishing	LP	MCA	MUP(S)320	1968	£4	£10	yellow label
Wishing	7"	Coral	Q72466	1963	£2	£5	chart single
Wishing	7" EP	Coral	FEP2067	1964	£12.50	£25	
You've Got Love	7"	Coral	Q72472	1964	£2	£5	

HOLLY, STEVE
| Strange World | 7" | Planet | PLF107 | 1966 | £5 | £10 | |

HOLLYWOOD ARGYLES
Alley Oop	LP	Lute	L9001	1960	£75	£150	US
Alley Oop	7"	London	HLU9146	1960	£6	£12	chart single
Gun Totin' Critter Called Jack	7"	Top Rank	JAR530	1960	£2.50	£6	

HOLLYWOOD FLAMES
Buzz Buzz Buzz	7"	London	HL7030	1957	£7.50	£15	export
Buzz Buzz Buzz	7"	London	HL8545	1958	£12.50	£25	
If I Thought You Needed Me	7"	London	HLE9071	1960	£10	£20	
Much Too Much	7"	London	HLW8955	1959	£10	£20	

HOLLYWOOD HURRICANES
| Beavershot | 7" | Prima | PR1009 | 1964 | £1.50 | £4 | |

HOLLYWOOD, KENNY
| Magic Star | 7" | Decca | F11546 | 1962 | £7.50 | £15 | |

HOLLYWOOD PERSUADERS
The B side of "Tijuana" was written by Frank Zappa, who also played guitar on the song.
| Tijuana | 7" | Original Sound | 39 | 1963 | £12.50 | £25 | US |

HOLLYWOOD VINES
| When Johnny Comes Sliding Home | 7" | Capitol | CL15191 | 1961 | £2 | £5 | |

HOLM, MIKE
| Mendocino | 7" | Major Minor | MM659 | 1969 | £2 | £5 | |

HOLMAN, BILL
Bill Holman Octet	10" LP	Capitol	KPL101	1954	£15	£30	
Cousin Jack	7"	Capitol	KC65000	1954	£1.50	£4	
Fabulous Bill Holman	LP	Coral	LVA9088	1958	£10	£25	
In A Jazz Orbit	LP	HMV	CLP1289	1959	£6	£15	

HOLMAN, EDDIE

Hey There Lonely Girl	7"	Probe	PRO551	1971	£1.50	£4	
Hey There Lonely Girl	7"	Stateside	SS2159	1970	£5	£10	
I Surrender	7"	Action	ACT4547	1969	£12.50	£25	
Since I Don't Have You	7"	Stateside	SS2170	1970	£4	£8	
This Can't Be True	7"	Cameo Parkway	P960	1965	£12.50	£25	
This Could Be A Night To Remember	7"	Salsoul	SZ2026	1977	£1.50	£4	

HOLMES, ELDRIDGE

Beverley	7"	Pama	PM746	1968	£2	£5	

HOLMES, JAKE

Above Ground Sound	LP	Tower	ST5079	1967	£6	£15	US
Jake Holmes	LP	Polydor	583578	1969	£4	£10	
Saturday Night	7"	Ember	EMBS269	1969	£1.50	£4	

HOLMES, JOE & LEN GRAHAM

After Dawning	LP	Topic	12TS401	1979	£5	£12	
Chaste Muses, Bards And Sages	LP	Free Reed	FRR007	1976	£6	£15	

HOLMES, RICHARD 'GROOVE'

Comin' On Home	LP	Blue Note	BST84372	1970	£4	£10	
Richard 'Groove' Holmes	LP	Transatlantic	PR7493	1968	£5	£12	

HOLOCAUST

Comin' Through	12"	Phoenix	12PSP4	1982	£2.50	£6	
Heavy Metal Mania	7"	Phoenix	PSP1	1980	£1.50	£4	
Heavy Metal Mania	12"	Phoenix	12PSP1	1980	£3	£8	
Lovin' Feelin' Danger	7"	Phoenix	PSP3	1981	£2.50	£6	
Nightcomers	LP	Phoenix	PSLP1	1981	£5	£12	
Smokin' Valves	12"	Phoenix	12PSP2	1980	£3	£8	

HOLT, JOHN

Ali Baba	7"	Trojan	TR661	1969	£2.50	£6	
Come Out Of My Bed	7"	Duke Reid	DR2506	1970	£2	£5	Winston Wright B side
Greatest Hits	LP	Melodisc	MLP12170	197-	£5	£12	
Have Sympathy	7"	Trojan	TR694	1969	£2.50	£6	Harry J B side
Holt	LP	Trojan	TRL(S)43	1972	£4	£10	
I Cried A Tear	7"	Island	WI041	1963	£5	£10	
John Holt And Friends	LP	Melodisc	MLP12191	197-	£5	£12	
Let's Build Our Dreams	7"	Treasure Isle	TI7061	1971	£2	£5	Tommy McCook B side
Love I Can Feel	LP	Bamboo	BDLPS210	1970	£10	£25	
OK Fred	LP	Melodisc	MLP12180	197-	£5	£12	
Paragons Medley	7"	Treasure Isle	TI7066	1971	£2	£5	Tommy McCook B side
Sea Cruise	7"	Unity	UN549	1970	£2.50	£6	
Sister Big Stuff	7"	Treasure Isle	TI7065	1971	£2	£5	Tommy McCook B side
Still In Chains	LP	Trojan	TRL(S)37	1972	£4	£10	
Tonight	7"	Trojan	TR643	1968	£4	£8	
What You Gonna Do Now	7"	Trojan	TR674	1969	£2.50	£6	
Wooden Heart	7"	Trojan	TR7702	1969	£2.50	£6	

HOLTS, ROOSEVELT

Presenting The Country Blues	LP	Blue Horizon	763201	1968	£17.50	£35	

HOLY MACKEREL

Holy Mackerel	LP	CBS	65297	1972	£6	£15	

HOLY MODAL ROUNDERS

Alleged In Their Own Time	LP	Rounder	3004	1972	£6	£15	US
Good Taste Is Timeless	LP	Metromedia	MD1039	1967	£6	£15	US
Holy Modal Rounders	LP	Prestige	PR7410	1965	£6	£15	US
Holy Modal Rounders	LP	Transatlantic	TRA7451	1970	£6	£15	
Holy Modal Rounders 2	LP	Prestige	PRS7451	1967	£6	£15	US
Indian War Whoop	LP	ESP	1068	1969	£6	£15	US
Moray Eels Eat The Holy Modal Rounders	LP	Elektra	EKL4026	1968	£6	£15	
Stampfel And Weber	LP	Fantasy	F24711	1972	£8	£20	US double

HOMBRES

Let It All Hang Out	7"	Verve	VS1510	1967	£6	£12	
Let It Out	LP	Verve	FT(S)3036	1967	£6	£15	US

HOME

Alchemist	LP	CBS	65550	1973	£4	£10	
Home	LP	CBS	64752	1972	£5	£12	
Pause For A Hoarse Horse	LP	Epic	64365	1971	£8	£20	
unreleased album	LP	CBS		197-	£50	£100	test pressing

HOME SERVICE

Alright Jack	LP	Making Waves	SPIN119	1986	£5	£12	
Mysteries	LP	Coda	NAT001	1984	£6	£15	

HOMER & JETHRO

Barefoot Ballads	LP	RCA	LPM1412	1957	£6	£15	US
Battle Of Kookamonga	7"	RCA	RCA1148	1959	£1.50	£4	

Title	Format	Label	Cat#	Year			Notes
Homer & Jethro Fracture Frank	10" LP	RCA	LPM3112	1953	£10	£25	US
Loesser							
Life Can Be Miserable	LP	RCA	LPM/LSP1880	1958	£5	£12	US
Musical Madness	LP	Audio Lab	AL1513	1958	£10	£25	US
Swappin' Partners	7"	HMV	7M211	1954	£2	£5	US
They Sure Are Corny	LP	KIng	639	1959	£6	£15	US
Wanted For Murder Of The Standards	7" EP.	Parlophone	GEP8791	1959	£2	£5	
Worst Of Homer And Jethro	LP	RCA	LPM1560	1957	£6	£15	US

HONDELLS

Title	Format	Label	Cat#	Year			Notes
Cheryl's Going Home	7"	Mercury	MF967	1967	£4	£8	
Go Little Honda	LP	Mercury	MG2/SR60940	1964	£8	£20	US
Hondells	LP	Mercury	MG2/SR60982	1965	£8	£20	MG
Little Honda	7"	Mercury	MF834	1964	£4	£8	
Younger Girl	7"	Mercury	MF925	1965	£2.50	£6	

HONEST MEN

Title	Format	Label	Cat#	Year			Notes
Cherie	7"	Tamla Motown	TMG706	1969	£7.50	£15	

HONEY CONE

Title	Format	Label	Cat#	Year			Notes
Honey Cone	LP	Hot Wax	SHW5002	1969	£5	£12	

HONEY DREAMERS

Title	Format	Label	Cat#	Year			Notes
Sing Gershwin	7" EP.	Vogue	VE170124	1958	£2	£5	

HONEYBUS

Title	Format	Label	Cat#	Year			Notes
Delighted To See You	7"	Deram	DM131	1967	£2	£5	
Do I Still Figure In Your Life	7"	Deram	DM152	1967	£2.50	£6	
For You Baby	7"	Warner Bros	K16250	1973	£1.50	£4	
Girl Of Independent Means	7"	Deram	DM207	1968	£2	£5	
I Can't Let Maggie Go	7"	Deram	DM182	1968	£1.50	£4	chart single
Recital	LP	Warner Bros	K46248	1973	£75	£150	
She Is The Female To My Soul	7"	Bell	BLL1205	1972	£1.50	£4	
She Sold Blackpool Rock	7"	Deram	DM254	1969	£2.50	£6	
Story	LP	Deram	SML1056	1970	£20	£40	
Story	7"	Deram	DM289	1970	£2.50	£6	

HONEYCOMBS

Title	Format	Label	Cat#	Year			Notes
All Systems Go	LP	Pye	NPL18132	1965	£35	£70	
Colour Slide	7" EP.	Pye	PNV24126	1964	£12.50	£25	French
Don't Love You No More	7"	Pye	7N15781	1965	£10	£20	
Eyes	7"	Pye	7N15736	1964	£2	£5	
Have I The Right	7"	Pye	7N15664	1964	£1.50	£4	chart single
Have I The Right	7" EP.	Pye	PNV24122	1964	£12.50	£25	French, B side by the Kinks
Honeycombs	LP	Golden Guinea	GGL0350	1965	£8	£20	
Honeycombs	LP	Pye	NPL18097	1964	£20	£40	
Is It Because	7"	Pye	7N15705	1964	£1.50	£4	chart single
It's So Hard	7"	Pye	7N17138	1966	£4	£8	
Something Better Beginning	7"	Pye	7N15827	1965	£2	£5	chart single
That Loving Feeling	7"	Pye	7N17173	1966	£4	£8	
That's The Way	7"	Pye	7N15890	1965	£1.50	£4	chart single
That's The Way	7" EP.	Pye	NEP24230	1965	£7.50	£15	
This Year Next Year	7"	Pye	7N15979	1965	£2	£5	
Who Is Sylvia	7"	Pye	7N17059	1966	£2.50	£6	

HONEYDEW

Title	Format	Label	Cat#	Year			Notes
Honeydew	LP	Argo	ZFB15	1971	£5	£12	

HONEYS

The Honeys consisted of Brian Wilson's wife Marilyn, her sister Diane Rovell, and their cousin Ginger Blake. Their records were produced by Brian Wilson, who applied the same imagination and innovation as he did on his own records with the Beach Boys.

Title	Format	Label	Cat#	Year			Notes
He's A Doll	7"	Warner Bros	5430	1964	£75	£150	US
One You Can't Have	7"	Capitol	5093	1963	£37.50	£75	US
Pray For Surf	7"	Capitol	5034	1963	£37.50	£75	US
Shoot The Curl	7"	Capitol	4952	1963	£25	£50	US
Surfing Down The Swanee River	7"	Capitol	CL15299	1963	£12.50	£25	
Tonight You Belong To Me	7"	Capitol	2454	1969	£15	£30	US

HONEYTONES

Title	Format	Label	Cat#	Year			Notes
Don't Look Now But	7"	London	HLX8671	1958	£12.50	£25	

HOOK

Title	Format	Label	Cat#	Year			Notes
Show You The Way	7"	Uni	UN507	1969	£2.50	£6	

HOOKER, EARL

Title	Format	Label	Cat#	Year			Notes
Boogie Don't Blot	7"	Blue Horizon	573166	1969	£6	£12	
Don't Have To Worry	LP	Stateside	SSL10298	1969	£8	£20	
Sweet Black Angel	LP	Blue Horizon	763850	1970	£20	£40	

HOOKER, JOHN LEE

Title	Format	Label	Cat#	Year			Notes
Alone	LP	Speciality	SNTF5005	1974	£4	£10	
Best Of John Lee Hooker	LP	Joy	JOYS156	1969	£5	£12	
Big Maceo Merriweather & John Lee Hooker	LP	Fortune	3002	196-	£8	£20	US
Big Soul	LP	Joy	JOYS147	1969	£6	£15	
Blue!	LP	Fontana	FJL119	1965	£6	£15	
Blues Of John Lee Hooker	7" EP.	Stateside	SE1019	1964	£7.50	£15	
Boom Boom	7"	Stateside	SS203	1963	£4	£8	
Burnin'	LP	Joy	JOY(S)124	1969	£6	£15	
Burning Hell	LP	Riverside	RLP008	1965	£6	£15	

Title	Format	Label	Cat. No.	Year	Price	Price	Notes
Coast To Coast Blues Band	LP	United Artists	UAS29235	1971	£5	£12	
Concert At Newport	LP	Joy	JOYS142	1969	£6	£15	
Democrat Man	7" EP	Riverside	REP3207	1960	£5	£10	
Detroit Special	LP	Atlantic	K40405	1972	£4	£10	
Dimples	LP	DJM	DJD28026	1977	£5	£12	double
Dimples	7"	President	PT295	1970	£1.50	£4	
Dimples	7"	Stateside	SS297	1964	£4	£8	chart single
Don't Turn Me From Your Door	LP	Atlantic	K40507	1974	£4	£10	
Don't Turn Me From Your Door	LP	London	HAK8097	1963	£10	£25	
Down At The Landing	7" EP	Chess	CRE6000	1965	£7.50	£15	
Driftin' Blues	LP	Atlantic	590003	1967	£6	£15	
Driftin' Through The Blues	LP	Ember	(ST)EMB3371	1966	£5	£12	
Endless Boogie	LP	Probe	SPB1034	1971	£5	£12	
Folk Blues	LP	Fontana	688700ZL	1964	£6	£15	
Folk Blues	LP	Riverside	RLP1238	1962	£6	£15	
Folklore Of John Lee Hooker	LP	Joy	JOYS133	1969	£6	£15	
Folklore Of John Lee Hooker	LP	Stateside	SL10014	1962	£10	£25	
Free Beer And Chicken	LP	ABC	ABCL5059	1974	£4	£10	
High Priced Woman	7"	Pye	7N25255	1964	£4	£8	
Hooker Hopkins Hogg	LP	Sonet	SNTF5013	1973	£4	£10	with Lightnin' Hopkins & Smokey Hogg
House Of The Blues	LP	Marble Arch	MAL663	1965	£6	£15	
House Of The Blues	LP	Pye	NPL28042	1964	£8	£20	
I Love You Honey	7"	Stateside	SS341	1964	£4	£8	
I Want To Shout The Blues	LP	Stateside	SL10074	1964	£8	£20	
I'm In The Mood	7"	Sue	WI361	1965	£7.50	£15	
I'm John Lee Hooker	LP	Joy	JOY(S)101	1968	£6	£15	
I'm John Lee Hooker	LP	Vee Jay	LP1007	1959	£15	£30	US
I'm John Lee Hooker	7" EP	Stateside	SE1023	1964	£7.50	£15	
In Person	LP	Joy	JOYS152	1969	£6	£15	
It Serves You Right To Suffer	LP	HMV	CLP5032/CSD3542	1966	£8	£20	
John Lee Hooker	LP	New World	NW6003	1975	£4	£10	
John Lee Hooker	LP	XTRA	XTRA114	1971	£6	£15	
John Lee Hooker	7" EP	Atlantic	AET6010	1965	£5	£10	
John Lee Hooker Sings The Blues	LP	King	727	1961	£17.50	£35	US
Johnny Lee	LP	Green Bottle	GN4002	1973	£5	£12	
Journey	7" EP	Chess	CRE6014	1966	£7.50	£15	
Let's Go Out Tonight	7"	Chess	CRS8039	1966	£4	£8	
Life At Cafe Au Go-Go	LP	HMV	CLP/CSD3612	1966	£8	£20	
Live At Soledad Prison	LP	ABC	716	1972	£5	£12	
Love Blues	7" EP	Pye	NEP44034	1964	£7.50	£15	
Mad Man Blues	LP	Checker	6467305	1973	£4	£10	
Mai Lee	7"	Planet	PLF114	1966	£6	£12	
Need Somebody	78	London	HL8037	1954	£10	£20	
Never Get Out Of These Blues Alive	LP	Probe	SPB1057	1972	£4	£10	
On Campus	LP	Vee Jay	LP/SR1066	1963	£6	£15	US
Plays And Sings The Blues	LP	Chess	CRL4500	1965	£6	£15	
Preachin' The Blues	LP	Stateside	SL10053	1964	£10	£25	
Real Folk Blues	LP	Chess	CRL4527	1966	£5	£12	
Real Folk Blues Vol.3	7" EP	Chess	CRE6021	1966	£7.50	£15	
Serves You Right To Suffer	7" EP	Impulse	9103	1973	£2.50	£6	
Shake It Baby	7"	Polydor	NH52930	1964	£4	£8	
Simply The Truth	LP	Stateside	(S)SL10280	1969	£6	£15	
Sings The Blues	LP	Ember	EMB3356	1965	£5	£12	
Slim's Stomp	LP	Polydor	2310256	1973	£4	£10	
That's Where It's At	LP	Polydor	2362017	1971	£4	£10	
That's Where It's At	LP	Stax	SXATS1025	1970	£6	£15	
Thinking Blues	7" EP	Ember	EMBEP4561	1964	£7.50	£15	
Travellin'	LP	Joy	JOYS129	1969	£6	£15	
Tupelo Blues	LP	Storyville	673020	1970	£6	£15	
Urban Blues	LP	Stateside	(S)SL10246	1968	£6	£15	
Walking The Boogie	7" EP	Chess	CRE6007	1966	£7.50	£15	
Wednesday Evening	7" EP	Riverside	REP3202	1960	£5	£10	
Whistlin' And Moanin' Blues	78	Vogue	V2102	1952	£10	£20	
You're Leavin' Me Baby	LP	Storyville	673005	1970	£6	£15	

HOOKER, JOHN LEE & CANNED HEAT

Title	Format	Label	Cat. No.	Year	Price	Price	Notes
Hooker And Heat	LP	Liberty	LPS103/4	1971	£8	£20	double

HOOKER, JOHN LEE & EARL

Title	Format	Label	Cat. No.	Year	Price	Price
If You Miss 'Im ... I Got 'Im	LP	Probe	SPB1016	1971	£6	£15

HOOKER, JOHN LEE & JIMMY REED

Title	Format	Label	Cat. No.	Year	Price	Price
Rhythm And Blues	7" EP	Stateside	SE1008	1962	£7.50	£15

HOOKFOOT

Title	Format	Label	Cat. No.	Year	Price	Price
Hookfoot	LP	DJM	DJLPS413	1971	£4	£10

HOOKS, MARSHALL & CO.

Title	Format	Label	Cat. No.	Year	Price	Price
I Want The Same Thing Tomorrow	7"	Blue Horizon	2096002	1971	£2.50	£6
Marshall Hooks & Co.	LP	Blue Horizon	2431003	1971	£15	£30

HOOTENANNY SINGERS

This Swedish group had the future Abba star, Bjorn Ulvaeus, as singer and songwriter.

Title	Format	Label	Cat. No.	Year	Price	Price	Notes
Basta	LP	Polar	POLL101	196-	£6	£15	Swedish
Bellman Pa Vart Satt	LP	Polar	POLS214	196-	£6	£15	Swedish
Civila	LP	Polar	POLS211	196-	£6	£15	Swedish
Dan Andersson Pa Vart Satt	LP	Polar	POLS249	197-	£6	£15	Swedish
De Basta Med...& Bjorn Ulvaeus	LP	Polar	POLL103	196-	£6	£15	Swedish

Evert Taube	LP	Polar	POLS204	196-	£6	£15	Swedish
Evert Taube Pa Vart Satt	LP	Polar	POLS260	197-	£6	£15	Swedish
Frogg	7" EP	Pathe	EGF794	1964	£5	£10	French
Gabriella	7"	United Artists	UP1082	1965	£7.50	£15	
Hootenanny Singers	LP	Polar	POLS201	196-	£6	£15	Swedish
International	LP	Polar	POLP206	196-	£6	£15	Swedish
Manga Ansikten	LP	Polar	POLP209	196-	£6	£15	Swedish
No Time	7" EP	Pathe	EGF880	1965	£5	£10	French
Skillingtryck	LP	Polar	POLS225	1970	£6	£15	Swedish
Vara Backraste Visor	LP	Polar	POLS229	197-	£6	£15	Swedish
Vara Backraste Visor 2	LP	Polar	POLS236	197-	£6	£15	Swedish

HOPE, BOB

Paris Holiday	7"	London	HLU8593	1958	£2	£5	with Bing Crosby

HOPE, ELMO

Informal Jazz	LP	Esquire	32039	1958	£20	£40	
With Frank Butler And James Bond	LP	Vocalion	LAEH590	1966	£5	£12	

HOPE, LYNN

Blue Moon	7"	Vogue	V9081	1957	£7.50	£15	
Eleven Till Two	7"	Vogue	V9082	1957	£7.50	£15	
Lynn Hope	LP	Aladdin	820	195-	£30	£60	US
Lynn Hope & His Tenor Sax	7" EP	Vogue	VE170103	1957	£15	£30	
Lynn Hope & His Tenor Sax	7" EP	Vogue	VE170146	1960	£15	£30	
Lynn Hope And His Tenor Sax	10" LP	Aladdin	707	195-	£45	£90	US
Shocking	7"	Blue Beat	BB21	1961	£5	£10	
Temptation	7"	Vogue	V9115	1958	£6	£12	
Tenderly	LP	Score	LP4015	1957	£20	£40	US

HOPETOWN & GLENMORE

Skinny Leg Girl	7"	Fab	FAB43	1968	£4	£8	

HOPKIN, MARY

Earth Song/Ocean Song	LP	Apple	SAPCOR21	1971	£6	£15	
Knock Knock Who's There	7"	Apple	26	1970	£2	£5	PS
Let My Name Be Sorrow	7"	Apple	34	1971	£5	£10	PS
Llais Swynol Mary Hopkin	7" EP	Cambrian	CEP414	1968	£2.50	£6	
Lontana Dagli Occhi	7"	Apple	7	1969	£4	£8	European
Mary Ac Edward	7" EP	Cambrian	CEP420	1969	£2.50	£6	
Postcard	LP	Apple	APCOR5	1969	£6	£15	mono
Postcard	LP	Apple	SAPCOR5	1969	£4	£10	chart LP
Prince En Avignon	7"	Apple	9	1969	£4	£8	European
Que Sera Sera	7"	Apple	27	1970	£4	£8	European
Temma Harbour	7"	Apple	22	1970	£2.50	£6	PS
Think About Your Children	7"	Apple	30	1970	£4	£8	PS
Those Were The Days	LP	Apple	SAPCOR23	1972	£30	£60	
Water, Paper And Clay	7"	Apple	39	1971	£1.50	£4	
Water, Paper And Clay	7"	Apple	39	1971	£2	£15	PS

HOPKINS, LIGHTNIN'

Autobiography In Blues	LP	Tradition	TLP1040	1960	£10	£25	US
Blue Bird Blues	LP	Fontana	688803ZL	1966	£5	£12	
Blues	LP	Ace Of Hearts	(Z)AH183	1970	£4	£10	
Blues From East Texas	LP	Heritage	H1000	1960	£15	£30	with Joel Hopkins
Blues In The Bottle	LP	XTRA	XTRA5036	1968	£6	£15	
Blues/Folk	LP	Time	1	1962	£6	£15	US
Blues/Folk Vol.2	LP	Time	3	1962	£6	£15	US
Burnin' In L.A.	LP	Fontana	688801ZL	1965	£5	£12	
California Mudslide And Earthquake	LP	Liberty	LBS83293	1970	£5	£12	
Country Blues	LP	Tradition	TLP1035	1960	£10	£25	US
Dirty Blues	LP	Mainstream	MSL1001	1973	£4	£10	
Dirty House Blues	LP	Realm	RM171	1964	£5	£12	
Down Home Blues	LP	Stateside	SL10155	1965	£8	£20	
Earth Blues	LP	Minit	MLL/MLS40006	1968	£6	£15	
Fast Life Woman	LP	Verve	V8453	1962	£8	£20	US
Free Form Patterns	LP	International Artists	6	1968	£37.50	£75	US
Goin' Away	LP	Bluesville	BV1073	1964	£6	£15	US
Got To Move Your Baby	LP	XTRA	XTRA5044	1968	£6	£15	
His Greatest Hits	LP	Bluesville	BV1084	1964	£6	£15	US
Hootin' The Blues	LP	Stateside	SL10110	1965	£8	£20	
King Of Dowling Street	LP	Liberty	LBL83254	1969	£6	£15	
Last Night Blues	LP	Bluesville	BV1029	1961	£8	£20	US
Last Night Blues	LP	Fontana	688301ZL	1964	£5	£12	
Last Of The Great Blues Singers	LP	Time	70004	1960	£8	£20	US
Let's Work Awhile	LP	Blue Horizon	2431005	1971	£20	£40	
Lightnin'	LP	Bluesville	BV1019	1961	£8	£20	US
Lightnin'	LP	Poppy	60002	1969	£4	£10	US
Lightnin' And The Blues	LP	Herald	1012	1960	£75	£150	US
Lightnin' Hopkins	LP	77	LA121	1960	£8	£20	
Lightnin' Hopkins	LP	Folkways	FS3822	1961	£8	£20	US
Lightnin' Hopkins	LP	Fontana	688807ZL	1966	£5	£12	
Lightnin' Hopkins	LP	Vee Jay	LP1044	1962	£10	£25	US
Lightnin' Hopkins And The Blues	LP	Imperial	LP9211/12211	1962	£8	£20	US
Lightnin' Hopkins On Stage	LP	Imperial	LP9180	1962	£8	£20	US
Lightnin' Hopkins Strums The Blues	LP	Score	4022	1960	£37.50	£75	US
Lightnin' Strikes	LP	A&M	AMLB40001/2	1971	£5	£12	double
Lightnin' Strikes	LP	Joy	JOY(S)115	1969	£4	£10	US
Lightnin' Strikes	LP	Stateside	SL10031	1963	£8	£20	

Lightnin' Strikes	LP	Verve	(S)VLP5014	1966	£5	£12	
Lonesome Lightnin'	LP	Polydor	2941005	1972	£5	£12	
Low Down Dirty Blues	LP	Mainstream	MSL1031	1975	£4	£10	
Mojo Hand	LP	Fire	104	1962	£25	£50	US
My Life In The Blues	LP	Prestige	PR7370	1965	£6	£15	US
Nothin' But The Blues	LP	Mount Vernon	104	196-	£6	£15	US
Roots Of Hopkins	LP	Verve	(S)VLP5003	1966	£5	£12	
Roots Of Lightnin' Hopkins	LP	XTRA	XTRA1127	1971	£6	£15	
Sings The Blues	LP	Realm	RM128	1963	£5	£12	
Smokes Like Lightnin'	LP	Bluesville	BV1070	1963	£6	£15	US
Something Blue	LP	Verve	FV(S)3013	1967	£6	£15	US
Soul Blues	LP	Prestige	PR(S)7377	1966	£6	£15	US
There's Good Rockin' Tonight	LP	Storyville	616001	1970	£6	£15	
Time For Blues	LP	Ember	EMB3389	1967	£5	£12	
Walkin' This Road By Myself	LP	Bluesville	BV1057	1961	£8	£20	US

HOPKINS, LIGHTNIN' & JOHN LEE HOOKER

Lightnin' Hopkins And John Lee Hooker	LP	Storyville	SLP174	1965	£6	£15	

HOPKINS, LIGHTNIN', SONNY TERRY & BROWNIE MCGHEE

Blues Hoot	LP	Stateside	SL10076	1964	£6	£15	

HOPKINS, LINDA

I Diddle Dum Dum	7"	Coral	Q72423	1961	£7.50	£15	
Mama's Doing The Twist	7"	Coral	Q72448	1962	£6	£12	

HOPKINS, NICKY

High On A Hill	7"	Fontana	TF906	1968	£4	£8	
Mr.Big	7"	CBS	202055	1966	£5	£10	
Mr.Pleasant	7"	Polydor	56175	1967	£6	£12	
Revolutionary Piano	LP	CBS	62679	1966	£8	£20	
Tin Man Was A Dreamer	LP	CBS	65416	1973	£4	£10	

HOPPER, HUGH

1984	LP	CBS	65466	1973	£4	£10	
Cruel But Fair	LP	Compendium	FIDARDO4	1976	£5	£12	
Hopper Tunity Box	LP	Compendium	FIDARDO7	1977	£5	£12	

HOPSCOTCH

Look At The Lights Go Up	7"	United Artists	UP2231	1969	£4	£8	

HOPSON, WASH SINGERS

He's Gotta Blessing	7"	Action	ACT4546	1969	£1.50	£4	

HORACE & THE IMPERIALS

Young Love	7"	Nu Beat	NB012	1968	£4	£8	

HORDE CATALYTIQUE POUR LA FIN

Gestation Sonore	LP	Futura	SON003	1971	£6	£15	French

HORDEN RAIKES

Horden Raikes	LP	Folk Heritage	FHR026	1972	£6	£15	
King Cotton	LP	Folk Heritage	FHR042	1972	£6	£15	

HORIZON

She's A Rainbow	7"	Parlophone	R5947	1972	£1.50	£4	

HORIZON (2)

Stage Struck	7"	SRT	SRTS81432	1981	£2.50	£6	

HORN, PAUL

In Kashmir	LP	Liberty	LBL83084	1968	£4	£10	
Inside	LP	Epic	EPC65201	1969	£4	£10	
Inside Two	LP	Epic	31600	1973	£4	£10	US
Special Edition	LP	Island	ISLD6	1974	£5	£12	double
Visions	LP	Epic	32837	1974	£4	£10	US

HORNE, KENNETH & OTHERS

Beyond Our Ken	LP	Parlophone	PMC1238	1964	£4	£10	

HORNE, LENA

It's All Right With Me	7"	HMV	7M319	1955	£1.50	£4	
It's Love	LP	RCA	LPM1148	1955	£8	£20	US
Lena Horne	7" EP	MGM	MGMEP503	1954	£2	£5	
Let's Put Out The Lights	7" EP	RCA	SRC7012	1959	£2	£5	stereo
Love Me Or Leave Me	7"	HMV	7M309	1955	£1.50	£4	
Stormy Weather	LP	RCA	LPM1375	1956	£8	£20	US

HORNSEY AT WAR

Dead Beat Revival	7"	War	WAR001	197-	£2	£5	

HORRORCOMIC

Jesus Christ	7"	B&C	BCS18	1979	£2.50	£6	

HORSE

Horse	LP	RCA	SF8109	1970	£60	£120	sleeve pictured in Guide

HORSLIPS

Horslips were employing traditional musical elements from their native Ireland long before the Pogues and the Waterboys made it fashionable. Their first LP, "Happy To Meet", comes within an intricate package that is designed to look like a concertina and which is not often found in mint condition.

Drive The Cold Winter Away	LP	Oats	MOO9	1976	£4 .... £10	
Happy To Meet Sorry To Part	LP	Oats	MOO3	1972	£8 .... £20	.... octagonal cover
Live	LP	Oats	MOO10	1976	£8 .... £20	.... Irish double
Loneliness	7"	DJM	DJT15001	1979	£1.50 ...... £4	..... shamrock-shaped disc, green vinyl
Tain	LP	Oats	MOO5	1973	£5 .... £12	

HORTON, JOHNNY

All Grown Up	7"	CBS	AAG132	1963	£1.50 ...... £4	
Battle Of New Orleans	7"	Philips	PB932	1959	£2 .... £5	.... chart single
Country And Western Aces	7" EP	Mercury	10008MCE	1964	£10 .... £20	
Done Rovin'	LP	Briar	104	195-	£30 .... £60	.... US
Done Rovin'	LP	London	HAU8096	1963	£15 .... £30	.... US
Fantastic	LP	Mercury	MG20478	1959	£15 .... £30	.... US
Fantastic Johnny Horton	7" EP	Mercury	ZEP10074	1960	£10 .... £20	
Free And Easy Songs	LP	SESAC	1201	1959	£37.50 ...... £75	.... US
Greatest Hits	LP	Columbia	CL1596/CS8396	1961	£6 .... £15	.... US
Honky Tonk Man	LP	Philips	BBL7536	1961	£8 .... £20	
I Can't Forget You	LP	Columbia	CL2299/CS9099	1965	£5 .... £12	.... US
Johnny Horton	LP	Dot	DLP3221	1962	£8 .... £20	.... US
Johnny Horton Makes History	LP	Columbia	CL1478/CS8269	1960	£6 .... £15	.... US
Johnny Reb	7"	Philips	PB951	1959	£2.50 ...... £6	
Mr.Moonlight	7"	Philips	PB1130	1961	£1.50 ...... £4	
North to Alaska	7"	Philips	PB1062	1960	£1.50 ...... £4	.... chart single
Ole Slew Foot	7"	Philips	PB1170	1961	£1.50 ...... £4	
Sink The Bismarck	7"	Philips	PB995	1960	£2 .... £5	
Sleepy Eyed John	7"	Philips	PB1132	1961	£1.50 ...... £4	
Spectacular Johnny Horton	LP	Philips	BBL7464	1960	£8 .... £20	
Take Me Like I Am	7"	Philips	PB976	1959	£1.50 ...... £4	
Voice Of Johnny Horton	LP	Fontana	FJL306	1965	£4 .... £10	
Words	7"	Philips	PB1226	1962	£2 .... £5	

HORTON, WALTER 'SHAKEY'

Soul Of Blues Harmonica	LP	Argo	4037	1964	£20 .... £40	.... US
With Hot Cottage	LP	XTRA	XTRA1135	1974	£4 .... £10	

HOT CHOCOLATE BAND

Give Peace A Chance	7"	Apple	18	1969	£10 .... £20	

HOT DOGGERS

Surfin' USA	LP	Epic	LN24/BN26054	1963	£15 .... £30	.... US

HOT POOP

Does Their Stuff	LP	Hot Poop	3072	1975	£10 .... £25	.... US

HOT POTATO

Hot Potato	LP	private	PMTB1	1973	£37.50 ...... £75	

HOT ROD ALLSTARS

Lick A Pop	7"	Duke	DU59	1969	£2.50 ...... £6	

HOT SPRINGS

It's All Right	7"	Columbia	DB7821	1966	£2.50 ...... £6	

HOT TODDYS

Shakin' And Stompin'	7"	Pye	7N25020	1959	£6 .... £12	

HOT TUNA

America's Choice	LP	Grunt	BFD10820	1975	£5 .... £12	.... US quad
Yellow Fever	LP	Grunt	BFD11238	1975	£5 .... £12	.... US quad

HOT VULTURES

Carrion On	LP	Red Rag	RRR005	1976	£6 .... £15	
East Street Shakes	LP	Red Rag	RRR015	1978	£5 .... £12	

HOTLEGS

Hotlegs were not the one-hit wonders they might appear to be. The group who scored with a novelty recording, "Neanderthal Man", were only waiting for successful song-writer Graham Gouldman to join them before starting to make records as Ten cc.

Lady Sadie	7"	Philips	6006140	1971	£1.50 ...... £4	
Neanderthal Man	7"	Fontana	6007019	1970	£1.50 ...... £4	.... chart single
Songs	LP	Philips	6308080	1971	£5 .... £12	
Thinks School Stinks	LP	Philips	6308057	1971	£4 .... £10	

HOTRODS

I Don't Love You No More	7"	Columbia	DB7693	1965	£12.50 ...... £25	

HOTZENPLOTZ

Songs Aus Der Schau	LP	Ho	1001	1972	£6 .... £15	.... German

HOUNDS

My World Fell Down	7" EP	Pathe	EGF983	1966	£6 .... £12	.... French

HOURGLASS

Hourglass	LP	Liberty	LBL/LBS83219	1968	£6 .... £15	
Hourglass	LP	United Artists	USD303/4	1973	£5 .... £12	.... double
Power Of Love	LP	Liberty	LST7555	1968	£6 .... £15	.... US

HOUSE OF LORDS
In The Land Of Dreams .... 7" ..... B&C .... CB112 .... 1969 ... £4 ....£8 ....

HOUSE OF LOVE
Christine	7"	Creation	CRE053	1988 ...	£2.50	.....£6	....
Christine	12"	Creation	CRE053T	1988 ...	£5	.£12	....
Destroy The Heart	7"	Creation	CRE057	1988 ...	£2	...£5	....
House Of Love	LP	Creation	CRELP034	1988 ...	£5	.£12 ...	with 7' (CREFRE01)
Real Animal	12"	Creation	CRE044T	1987 ...	£8	.£20	....
Shine On	7"	Creation	CREFRE5	1988 ...	£2.50	.....£6	.... flexi
Shine On	12"	Creation	CRE043T	1987 ...	£8	.£20	....

HOUSE, SON
Father Of The Folk Blues	LP	CBS	(S)BPG62604	1966 ...	£5	.£12	....
John The Revelator	LP	Liberty	LBS83391	1970 ...	£6	.£15	....
Vocal Intensity	LP	Saydisc	SL504	196- ...	£5	.£12	....

HOUSE, SON & J.D.SHORT
Son House And J.D.Short .... LP ..... XTRA .... XTRA1080 .... 1969 ... £6 ....£15 ....

HOUSEHOLD
Guess I'll Learn How To Fly	7"	United Artists..	UP1190	1967 ...	£1.50	...£4	....
Twenty-First Summer	7"	United Artists..	UP2210	1968 ...	£1.50	...£4	....

HOUSTON, CISCO
Cisco Special .... LP ..... Top Rank .... 30028 .... 1960 ... £25 ....£50 ....

HOUSTON, CISSY
Cissy Houston	LP	Janus	6310205	1971 ...	£4	.£10	....
I Just Don't Know What To Do With Myself	7"	Pye	7N25537	1970 ...	£5	.£10	....
Presenting Cissy Houston	LP	Major Minor ...	SMLP80	1970 ...	£5	.£12	....

HOUSTON, DAVID
Almost Persuaded	7"	Columbia........	DB7997	1966 ...	£1.50	...£4	....
Blue Prelude	7"	London	HL8147	1955 ...	£7.50	.£15	....
Mountain Of Love	7"	Columbia........	DB7159	1963 ...	£1.50	...£4	....
My Elusive Dreams (with Tammy Wynette)	7"	Columbia........	DB8246	1967 ...	£1.50	...£4	....

HOUSTON, JOE
Joe Houston Blows All Night Long	LP	Modern	LMP1206	1956 ...	£8	.£20	.... US
Rockin' At The Drive-In	LP	Combo	LP400	1960 ...	£25 ..	.£50	.... US
Where Is Joe?	LP	Combo	LP100	1960 ...	£25 ..	.£50	.... US

HOUSTON, SAM
My Mother's Eyes .... 7" ...... Island .... WI172 .... 1965 ... £5 ... £10 ....

HOUSTON, THELMA
Black California	7"	Mowest............	MW3004.	1973 ...	£5	.£10	.... demo only
I Want To Go Back There Again	7"	Tamla Motown	TMG799	1972 ...	£1.50	...£4	....
I've Got The Music In Me	LP	Sheffield Lab...	2.	1974 ...	£5	.£12 ...	US audiophile
Jumpin' Jack Flash	7"	Stateside	SS8026	1969 ...	£1.50	...£4	....
Save The Country	7"	Stateside	SS8036	1970 ...	£1.50	...£4	....
Sunshower	LP	Stateside	SSL5010	1969 ...	£4	.£10	....

HOUSTON, WHITNEY
Didn't We Almost Have It All	CD-s ..	Arista	RISCD31	1987 ...	£2.50	.....£6	....
I Wanna Dance With Somebody	CD-s ..	Arista	RISCD1	1987 ...	£2.50	.....£6	....
Love Will Save The Day	CD-s ..	Arista	661516	1988 ...	£3	...£8	.... pic disc
Love Will Save The Day	7"	Arista	111516P	1988 ...	£1.50	...£4	.... pic disc
Whitney Houston	LP	Arista	WHIT1	1986 ...	£4	.£10	.... with cards,book,calendar, boxed

HOWARD, BRIAN & THE SILHOUETTES
Back In The USA	7"	Fontana	TF464	1964 ...	£6	.£12	....
Somebody Help Me	7"	Columbia........	DB4914.	1962 ...	£7.50	.£15	....
Worrying Kind	7"	Columbia........	DB7067	1963 ...	£6	.£12	....

HOWARD, HARLAN
All-Time Favorite Country Songwriter .	LP	Monument	MLP/SLP18038	1965 ...	£5	.£12	.... US
Harlan Howard Sings Harlan Howard ..	LP	Capitol	(S)T1631	1961 ...	£5	.£12	.... US

HOWARD, JAN
One You Slip Around With .... 7" ...... London .... HL7088 .... 1960 ... £2 ...... £5 ....export

HOWARD, JOHNNY
Mind Reader	7"	Decca	F11423	1962 ...	£1.50	...£4	....
Orbit	7"	Decca	F11298	1960 ...	£1.50	...£4	....
Rinky Dink	7"	Decca	F11925	1964 ...	£1.50	...£4	....

HOWE, CATHERINE
What A Beautiful Place .... LP ..... Reflection .... 1971 ... £20 ....£40 ....

HOWELL, EDDIE
Man From Manhattan .... 7" ...... Warner Bros .. K16701 .... 1976 ... £12.50 .....£25 .... with Queen

HOWERD, FRANKIE
At The Establishment	LP	Decca	LK4556	1963 ...	£5	.£12	....
It's All Right With Me	7"	Columbia........	DB4230.	1958 ...	£2	...£5	....

Kiddy Geddin	7"	Decca	F10420	1954	£2.50	£6	
Something Funny Happened On The Way To The Forum	LP	Pye		196-	£4	£10	

HOWLAND, CHRIS

Ma He's Making Eyes At Me	7"	Columbia	DB4114	1958	£1.50	£4	
Susie Darlin'	7"	Columbia	DB4194	1959	£1.50	£4	

HOWLIN' WOLF

AKA Chester Burnett	LP	Chess	60016	1972	£5	£12	US
Back Door Wolf	LP	Chess	CH50045	1974	£5	£12	US
Big City Blues	LP	Ember	EMB3370	1966	£6	£15	
Down In The Bottom	7"	Pye	7N25101	1961	£5	£10	
Evil	LP	Chess	LP1540	1969	£6	£15	US
Evil	7"	Chess	CRS8097	1969	£2.50	£6	
Howlin' Wolf	LP	Chess	LP1469	1962	£20	£40	US
Howlin' Wolf	LP	Python	PLP13	1971	£8	£20	
Howlin' Wolf Album	LP	Chess	CRLS4543	1969	£5	£12	
Just Like I Treat You	7"	Pye	7N25192	1963	£4	£8	
Killing Floor	7"	Chess	CRS8010	1965	£4	£8	
Little Girl	7"	Pye	7N25269	1964	£4	£8	
Live And Cookin'	LP	Chess	CH50015	1972	£4	£10	US
London Sessions	LP	Rolling Stones.	COC49101	1971	£4	£10	
Love Me Darling	7"	Pye	7N25283	1964	£4	£8	
Message To The Young	LP	Chess	6310108	1971	£4	£10	
Moanin' In The Moonlight	LP	Chess	LP1434	1958	£25	£50	US
Moaning In The Moonlight	LP	Chess	CRL4006	1964	£8	£20	
Moaning In The Moonlight	LP	Marble Arch	MAL665	1967	£4	£10	
More Real Folk Blues	LP	Chess	LP1512	1966	£8	£20	US
Ooh Baby	7"	Chess	CRS8016	1965	£4	£8	
Poor Boy	LP	Chess	CRL4508	1965	£8	£20	
Real Folk Blues	LP	Chess	LP1502	1966	£8	£20	US
Real Folk Blues Vol.1	7" EP.	Chess	CRE6017	1966	£7.50	£15	
Rhythm & Blues With Howlin' Wolf	7" EP.	London	REU1072	1956	£20	£40	
Smokestack Lightning	7"	Pye	7N25244	1964	£4	£8	chart single
Smokestack Lightning	7" EP.	Pye	NEP44015	1963	£6	£12	
Tell Me	7" EP.	Pye	NEP44032	1964	£6	£12	
This Is Howlin' Wolf's New Album	LP	Cadet	319	1969	£6	£15	US

HOWLIN' WOLF, JUNIOR PARKER, & BOBBY BLAND

Blues For Mr.Crump	LP	Polydor	2383257	1974	£5	£12	

HOYLE, LINDA

Linda Hoyle was the singer with Affinity and her jazz-inflected tones on that group's album suggested that she could make a good jazz record. Her solo LP, recorded with members of Nucleus, is exactly that.

Pieces Of Me	LP	Vertigo	6360060	1971	£60	£120	spiral label

H.P.LOVECRAFT

H.P.Lovecraft 2	LP	Philips	SBL7872		2		
Wayfarin' Stranger	7"	Philips	BF1620	1967	£4	£8	
White Ship	7"	Philips	BF1639	1968	£4	£8	
White Ship (This Is H.P.Lovecraft)	LP	Philips	6336210	1970	£8	£20	

HUBBARD, FREDDIE

Blue Spirits	LP	Blue Note	BLP/BST84196	1965	£8	£20	
Breaking Point	LP	Blue Note	BLP/BST84172	1964	£8	£20	
Goin' Up	LP	Blue Note	BLP/BST84056	196-	£10	£25	
Hub Cap	LP	Blue Note	BLP/BST84073	1961	£15	£30	
Hub-Tones	LP	Blue Note	BLP/BST84115	1962	£8	£20	
Night Of The Cookers Vol.1	LP	Blue Note	BLP/BST84207	1965	£8	£20	
Night Of The Cookers Vol.2	LP	Blue Note	BLP/BST84208	1965	£8	£20	
Open Sesame	LP	Blue Note	BLP/BST84040	196-	£15	£30	
Ready For Freddie	LP	Blue Note	BLP/BST84085	196-	£8	£20	

HUCKNALL, MICK

Early Years	mini LP	TJM	TJM101	1987	£6	£15	

HUDSON, JOHNNY

Makin' Up Is Hard To Do	7"	Decca	F11679	1963	£1.50	£4	

HUDSON, KEITH

Tambourine Man	7"	Big Shot	BI528	1969	£2.50	£6	

HUDSON PEOPLE

Trip To Your Mind	12"	Hithouse	HIT1	197-	£8	£20	

HUDSON, ROCK

Rock Gently	LP	Stanyan	10014	1971	£5	£12	US

HUE & CRY

Here Come Everybody	12"	Stampede	STAMP2	1986	£5	£12	

HUEYS

Coo Coo Over You	7"	London	HLU10264	1969	£2.50	£6	

HUGHES, DANNY

Hi Ho Silver Lining	7"	Pye	7N17750	1969	£2.50	£6	

HUGHES, FRED

Baby Boy	7"	Brunswick	BR37	1976	£1.50	£4	

| Oo Wee Baby I Love You | 7" | Fontana | TF583 | 1965 | £7.50 | £15 | |
| Send My Baby Back | LP | Wand | WD(S)664 | 1965 | £6 | £15 | US |

HUGHES, JIMMY

Chains Of Love	7"	Stax	STAX126	1969	£1.50	£4	
Goodbye My Love	7"	Sue	WI4006	1966	£6	£12	
Hi Heel Sneakers	7"	Atlantic	584135	1967	£2.50	£6	
I'm Qualified	7"	London	HL9680	1963	£6	£12	
Neighbour Neighbour	7"	Atlantic	584017	1966	£2.50	£6	
Steal Away	LP	Vee Jay	(SR)1102	1965	£6	£15	US
Steal Away	7"	Pye	7N25254	1964	£4	£8	
Sweet Things You Do	7"	Stax	STAX117	1969	£1.50	£4	
Why Not Tonight	LP	Atco	(SD)33209	1967	£6	£15	US

HUGO & LUIGI

La Plume De Ma Tante	7"	RCA	RCA1127	1959	£1.50	£4	chart single
Shenandoah Rose	7"	Columbia	DB3978	1957	£2.50	£6	
Twilight In Tennessee	7"	Columbia	DB4156	1958	£1.50	£4	

HULL, ALAN

| We Can Sing Together | 7" | Transatlantic | BIG129 | 1970 | £4 | £8 | |

HULLABALOOS

Did You Ever	7" EP	Roulette	VREX65033	1965	£12.50	£25	French
Don't Stop	7"	Columbia	DB7626	1965	£2	£5	
England's Newest Singing Sensations	LP	Roulette	(S)R25297	1965	£6	£15	US
Hullabaloos On Hullabaloo	LP	Roulette	(S)R25310	1965	£6	£15	US
I'll Show You How To Love	7"	Columbia	DB7558	1965	£2	£5	
I'm Gonna Love You Too	7"	Columbia	DB7392	1964	£2.50	£6	
I'm Gonna Love You Too	7" EP	Roulette	VREX65024	1964	£12.50	£25	French

HULTGREEN, GEORG

| Say Hello | 7" | Warner Bros | WB8017 | 1970 | £4 | £8 | |

HUMAN BEANS

| Morning Dew | 7" | Columbia | DB8230 | 1967 | £25 | £50 | |

HUMAN BEAST

| Human Beast Vol.1 | LP | Decca | SKL5053 | 1970 | £60 | £120 | sleeve pictured in Guide |

HUMAN BEINZ

Evolutions	LP	Capitol	ST2926	1968	£8	£20	US
Nobody But Me	LP	Capitol	ST2906	1968	£8	£20	US
Nobody But Me	LP	Gateway	GLP3012	1968	£10	£25	US
Nobody But Me	7"	Capitol	CL15529	1968	£7.50	£15	
Turn On Your Lovelight	7"	Capitol	CL15542	1968	£7.50	£15	

HUMAN INSTINCT

Burning Up Years	LP			1969	£180	£300	New Zealand
Can't Stop Loving You	7"	Mercury	MF951	1965	£10	£20	
Day In My Mind's Mind	7"	Deram	DM167	1967	£12.50	£25	
Go Go	7"	Mercury	MF990	1966	£10	£20	
Pins In It	LP	Pye		1971	£180	£300	New Zealand
Renaissance Fair	7"	Deram	DM177	1968	£10	£20	
Rich Man	7"	Mercury	MF927	1966	£12.50	£25	
Stoned Guitars	LP	Allied	ARBS107	1970	£210	£350	New Zealand

HUMAN LEAGUE

Empire State Human	7"	Virgin	VS351	1980	£2	£5	double
Holiday '80	7"	Virgin	SV105	1980	£2.50	£6	double, purple & blue label
Holiday '80	7"	Virgin	VS105	1980	£1.50	£4	double, green & red label
Holiday '80	12"	Virgin	SV105	1980	£4	£10	

HUMAN ZOO

| Human Zoo | LP | Accent | 5055 | 1969 | £8 | £20 | US |

HUMBLE PIE

As Safe As Yesterday Is	LP	Immediate	IMSP025	1969	£5	£12	chart LP
Natural Born Bugie	7"	Immediate	IM082	1969	£1.50	£4	
Town And Country	LP	Immediate	IMSP027	1969	£5	£12	

HUMBLEBUMS

"He's humble..," Billy Connolly used to quip when explaining the origin of his group's name. Originally a folk duo featuring Connolly and fellow Glaswegian Tam Harvey, the Humblebums broadened their appeal a litle when Harvey was replaced by singer-songwriter Gerry Rafferty. Some of Rafferty's songs with the group are amongst the best that Paul McCartney never wrote, although both Rafferty and Connolly have become rather more famous since.

Complete	LP	Transatlantic	TRAT288	1974	£10	£25	3 LP set
First Collection	LP	Transatlantic	TRA186	1969	£4	£10	
Humblebums	LP	Transatlantic	TRA201	1969	£4	£10	
Open Up The Door	LP	Transatlantic	TRA218	1970	£4	£10	
Saturday Roundabout Sunday	7"	Transatlantic	BIG122	1969	£1.50	£4	
Shoeshine Boy	7"	Transatlantic	BIG130	1970	£1.50	£4	

HUMES, HELEN

Helen Humes And The Benny Carter All Stars	LP	Contemporary	LAC12245	1961	£5	£12	
If I Could Be With You	7"	Vogue	V2048	1956	£1.50	£4	
When The Saints Come Marching In	7"	Contemporary	CV2415	1959	£1.50	£4	

HUMES, HELEN & JIMMY WITHERSPOON
Rhythm & Blues Concert .... 7" EP.. Vogue .... EPV1198 .... 1958 ... £10 ....£20 ....

HUMPHREY, BOBBI
Flute-In .... LP ..... Blue Note........ BST84379............ 1970 ... £4 ....£10

HUMPHREY, DELLA
Don't Make The Good Girls So Bad ...... 7" ..... Action .... ACT4525 .... 1969 ... £2 ....£5

HUMPY BONG
Don't You Be Too Long .... 7" .... Parlophone...... R5859 .... 1970 ... £2 ....£5

HUNGER
Strickly From Hunger .... LP ..... Public .... 1006 .... 1969 ... £25 ....£50 .... US
Strictly From Hunger .... LP ..... Psycho .... PSYCHO14 .... 1984 ... £5 ....£12

HUNGRY WOLF
Hungry Wolf .... LP ..... Philips .... 6308009............. 1970 ... £30 ....£60

HUNT & TURNER
Magic Landscape .... LP ..... Village Thing .... VTS11................... 1972 ... £6 ....£15

HUNT, GERALDINE
Never Never Leave Me .... 7" .... Roulette .... RO515 .... 1969 ... £2 ....£5

HUNT, MARSHA
Desdemona .... 7" .... Track .... 604034............. 1969 ... £6 ....£12
Keep The Customer Satisfied .... 7" .... Track .... 604037............. 1970 ... £2 ....£5 ....chart single
Walk On Gilded Splinters .... 7" .... Track .... 604030............. 1969 ... £2.50 .....£6 ....chart single
Woman Child .... LP ..... Track .... 2410101............ 1971 ... £8 ....£20

HUNT, PEE WEE
Dixieland Detour .... 10" LP Capitol .... LC6608 .... 1953 ... £8 ....£20
It's Never Too Late To Fall In Love .... 7" .... Capitol .... CL14225 .... 1955 ... £1.50 .....£4
Save Your Love For Me .... 7" .... Capitol .... CL14286 .... 1955 ... £1.50 .....£4
Swingin' Around .... 10" LP Capitol .... LC6671 .... 1954 ... £8 ....£20

HUNT, TOMMY
Greatest Hits .... LP ..... Dynamo .... 8001 .... 1967 ... £6 ....£15 .... US
I Just Don't Know What To Do With ...... LP ..... Scepter .... (S)S506 .... 1962 ... £6 ....£15 .... US
Myself
I Need A Woman Of My Own .... 7" .... Direction .... 583216............... 1968 ... £1.50 .....£4
I'm Wondering .... 7" .... Top Rank .... JAR605............... 1962 ... £4 ....£8

HUNT, WILLIE AMOS
Would You Believe .... 7" .... Camp .... 602003............... 1967 ... £17.50 ...£35

HUNTER, DANNY
Lost Weekend .... 7" .... Fontana .... H300 .... 1961 ... £1.50 .....£4
Make It Up .... 7" .... HMV .... POP722 .... 1960 ... £4 ....£8
Who's Gonna Walk Ya Home? .... 7" .... HMV .... POP775 .... 1960 ... £2.50 .....£6

HUNTER, DAVE
Don't Throw Your Love To The Wind ... 7" .... RCA................ RCA1841 .... 1969 ... £1.50 .....£4
She's A Heartbreaker .... 7" .... RCA................ RCA1766 .... 1968 ... £4 ....£8

HUNTER, GREG
Five O'Clock World .... 7" .... Parlophone...... R5483 .... 1966 ... £2.50 .....£6

HUNTER, IVORY JOE
Fabulous Ivory Joe Hunter .... LP ..... Goldisc .... 403 .... 1961 ... £10 ....£25 .... US
Golden Hits .... LP ..... Smash .... MGS2/SRS67037.. 1963 ... £6 ....£15 .... US
Almost Lost My Mind .... 78 .... MGM .... MGM271 .... 1950 ... £6 ....£12
Get That Lonesome Feeling .... LP ..... MGM .... E3488 .... 1957 ... £30 ....£60 .... US
I'm Hooked .... 7" .... Capitol .... CL15220 .... 1961 ... £4 ....£8
Ivory Joe Hunter .... LP ..... Atlantic .... 8008 .... 1958 ... £30 ....£60 .... US
Ivory Joe Hunter .... LP ..... Sage .... 603 .... 1959 ... £20 ....£40 .... US
Ivory Joe Hunter .... LP ..... Sound .... 603 .... 1957 ... £30 ....£60 .... US
Love's A Hurting Game .... 7" .... London .... HLE8486 .... 1957 ... £37.50 ...£75
May The Best Man Win .... 7" .... Capitol .... CL15226 .... 1961 ... £4 ....£8
Since I Met You Baby .... 7" .... Columbia .... DB3872 .... 1957 ... £45 ....£90
Sings The Old And The New .... LP ..... Atlantic .... 8015 .... 1958 ... £30 ....£60 .... US
Sixteen Of His Greatest Hits .... LP ..... King .... 605 .... 1958 ... £45 ....£90 .... US
Tear Fell .... 7" .... London .... HLE8261 .... 1956 ... £60 ....£120 .... US
This Is Ivory Joe Hunter .... LP ..... Dot .... DLP3569/25569 .. 1964 ... £6 ....£15 .... US

HUNTER MUSKETT
Every Time You Move .... LP ..... Nova .... SDN20 .... 1970 ... £50 ....£100 .... US
Hunter Muskett .... LP ..... Bradley .... BRADL1003.......... 1969 ... £8 ....£20 .... US
John Blair .... 7" .... Bradley .... BRAD303............. 1973 ... £1.50 .....£4 .... PS

HUNTER, ROBERT
Alligator Moon .... LP .... 1978 ... £5 ....£12 .... US
Amagamalin Street .... LP ..... Relix .... RRLP2003............ 1984 ... £6 ....£15 ....US double
Jack O'Roses .... LP ..... Dark Star .... DSLP8001 .... 1979 ... £5 ....£12 .... US
Tales Of Great Rum Runners .... LP ..... Round .... RX101 .... 1974 ... £6 ....£15 .... US
Tiger Rose .... LP ..... Round .... RX105 .... 1975 ... £5 ....£12 .... US

HUNTER, TAB
Don't Let It Get Around .... 7" .... London .... HLD8535 .... 1958 ... £6 ....£12
Can't Stop Loving You .... 7" .... London .... HLD9559 .... 1962 ... £2.50 .....£6

My Only Love	7"	Warner Bros	WB8	1960	£1.50	£4	
Ninety-Nine Ways	7"	London	HLD8410	1957	£5	£10	chart single
R.F.D. Tab Hunter	LP	Warner Bros	W(S)1367	1960	£8	£20	US
Tab Hunter	LP	Warner Bros	WM4008	1960	£8	£20	mono
Tab Hunter	LP	Warner Bros	WS8008	1960	£10	£25	stereo
Tab Hunter	7" EP	Warner Bros	WSEP2023	1961	£7.50	£15	
Tab Hunter	7" EP	Warner Bros	WEP6023	1961	£6	£12	
Waitin' For The Fall	7"	Warner Bros	WB20	1960	£1.50	£4	
When I Fall In Love	LP	Warner Bros	W(S)1292	1959	£8	£20	US
Wild Side Of Life	7"	London	HLD9381	1961	£4	£8	
Young Love	LP	London	HAD2401	1961	£10	£25	
Young Love	LP	London	SAHG6201	1961	£15	£30	stereo
Young Love	7"	London	HLD8380	1957	£10	£20	chart single
Young Love	7" EP	London	RED1134	1958	£7.50	£15	

HUNTERS

Golden Earrings	7"	Fontana	H303	1961	£2	£5	
Hits From The Hunters	LP	Fontana	TFL5175/STFL572	1962	£15	£30	
Storm	7"	Fontana	H323	1961	£2	£5	
Teen Scene	LP	Fontana	TFL5140/STFL561	1961	£15	£30	
Teen Scene	7"	Fontana	H276	1960	£2.50	£6	
Teen Scene	7"	Fontana	TF514	1964	£1.50	£4	

HUNTERS (2)

Russian Spy And I	7"	RCA	RCA1541	1966	£5	£10

HURDY GURDY

Hurdy Gurdy	LP	CBS	64781	1971	£75	£150

HURLEY, RED VINCENT

When	7"	Pye	7N45583	1976	£1.50	£4

HURT, MISSISSIPPI JOHN

Immortal	LP	Vanguard	SVRL19005	197-	£4	£10	
Immortal	LP	Vanguard	VRS/VSD79248	1967	£6	£15	US
Last Sessions	LP	Vanguard	VSD79327	1972	£4	£10	
Mississippi John Hurt	LP	Fontana	TFL6079	1967	£6	£15	
Mississippi John Hurt	LP	Vanguard	VSD19/20	1973	£6	£15	double
Original 1928 Recordings	LP	Spookane	SPL1001	1971	£15	£30	
Today	LP	Vanguard	VRS/VSD79220	1966	£6	£15	US

HUSH

Grey	7"	Fontana	TF944	1968	£30	£60

HUSKER DU

Amusement	7"	Reflex	38285	1980	£20	£40	US
Could You Be The One	12"	Warner Bros	W8456T	1987	£2.50	£6	
Don't Want To Know If You're Lonely	12"	Warner Bros	W8746T	1986	£2.50	£6	
Everything Falls Apart	LP	Reflex	REFLEXD	1982	£10	£25	US
Ice Cold Ice	12"	Warner Bros	W8276T	1987	£2.50	£6	
In A Free Land	7"	New Alliance	NAR010	1982	£20	£40	US
Sorry Somehow	7"	WEA	W8612F	1986	£2.50	£6	double
Sorry Somehow	12"	Warner Bros	W8612T	1986	£2.50	£6	

HUSKY, FERLIN

Black Sheep	7"	Capitol	CL15094	1959	£1.50	£4	
Born To Lose	LP	Capitol	T1204	1959	£6	£15	US
Boulevard Of Broken Dreams	LP	Capitol	T880	1957	£6	£15	US
Country Music Holiday	7" EP	Capitol	EAP1921	1957	£4	£8	
Country Round Up	7" EP	Parlophone	GEP8795	1959	£10	£20	
Country Tunes Sung From The Heart	7"	King	647	1959	£6	£15	US
Draggin' The River	7"	Capitol	CL15027	1959	£1.50	£4	
Easy Livin'	LP	King	728	1960	£6	£15	US
Fallen Star	7"	Capitol	CL14753	1957	£7.50	£15	
Ferlin Husky Hits	7" EP	Capitol	EAP1837	1957	£4	£8	
Ferlin's Favorites	LP	Capitol	T1280	1960	£6	£15	US
Ferlin's Favourites Part 1	7" EP	Capitol	EAP11280	1960	£4	£8	
Ferlin's Favourites Part 2	7" EP	Capitol	EAP21280	1960	£4	£8	
Ferlin's Favourites Part 3	7" EP	Capitol	EAP31280	1960	£4	£8	
Gone	LP	Capitol	T1383	1960	£6	£15	US
Gone	7"	Capitol	CL14702	1957	£5	£10	
I Feel That Old Heartache Again	7"	Capitol	CL14916	1958	£2.50	£6	
I Will	7"	Capitol	CL14954	1958	£1.50	£4	
Kingdom Of Love	7"	Capitol	CL14922	1958	£2	£5	
Make Me Live Again	7"	Capitol	CL14745	1957	£2	£5	
My Reason For Living	7"	Capitol	CL14995	1959	£1.50	£4	
Sittin' On A Rainbow	LP	Capitol	T976	1959	£6	£15	US
Slow Down Brother	7"	Capitol	CL14883	1958	£5	£10	
Songs Of The Home And Heart	LP	Capitol	T718	1956	£8	£20	US
Songs Of The Home And Heart	7" EP	Capitol	EAP1718	1957	£5	£10	
Wang Dang Do	7"	Capitol	CL14824	1958	£5	£10	
Wings Of A Dove	7"	Capitol	CL15160	1960	£1.50	£4	

HUSTLER

High Street	LP	A&M	AMLS68276	1974	£5	£12
Play Loud	LP	A&M	AMLH33001	1975	£5	£12

HUSTLERS

Gimme What I Want	7"	Philips	BF1275	1963	£2.50	£6
Sick Of Giving	7"	Mercury	MF817	1964	£6	£12
You Can't Sit Down	7"	Mercury	MF807	1964	£5	£10

HUTCHERSON, BOBBY

Components	LP	Blue Note	BLP/BST84213	1965	£6	£15
Dialogue	LP	Blue Note	BLP/BST84198	1965	£6	£15
Happenings	LP	Blue Note	BLP/BST84231	1966	£5	£12
Head On	LP	Blue Note	BST84376	1970	£4	£10
Now	LP	Blue Note	BST84333	1969	£4	£10
San Francisco	LP	Blue Note	BST84362	1970	£4	£10
Stick-Up	LP	Blue Note	BLP/BST84244	1966	£5	£12
Total Eclipse	LP	Blue Note	BST84291	1968	£4	£10

HUTCHINGS, ASHLEY

Compleat Dancing Master	LP	Island	HELP17	1974	£5	£12
Hour With Cecil Sharp And Ashley Hutchings	LP	Dambusters	DAM014	1986	£10	£25
Kickin' Up The Sawdust	LP	Harvest	SHSP4073	1977	£20	£40
Rattlebone & Ploughjack	LP	Island	HELP24	1976	£5	£12
Son Of Morris On	LP	Harvest	SHSM2012	1976	£5	£12

HUTCHINS, SAM

Dang Me	7"	Bell	BLL1044	1969	£1.50	£4

HUTSON, LEROY

All Because Of You	7"	Warner Bros	K16536	1975	£2	£5
Leroy Hutson	LP	Warner Bros	K56139	1975	£20	£40
Man	LP	Buddah	BDLP4013	1974	£5	£12

HUTTO, J.B.

Hawk Squat	LP	Delmark	DS617	1970	£6	£15

HUTTON, BETTY

Capitol Presents	10" LP	Capitol	LC6639	1954	£4	£10
Somebody Loves Me	7"	HMV	7M103	1953	£2	£5

HUTTON, DANNY

Funny How Love Can Be	7"	MGM	MGM1314	1966	£1.50	£4

HUTTON SISTERS

Ko Ko Mo	7"	Capitol	CL14250	1955	£6	£12

HYATT, CHARLIE

Kiss Me Neck	LP	Island	ILP932	1966	£30	£60

HYATT, CHARLIE & BAM

Rass!	7" EP	Island	IEP707	1966	£5	£10

HYGRADES

She Cared	7"	Columbia	DB7734	1965	£1.50	£4

HYLAND, BRIAN

Bashful Blonde	LP	London	HAR2289	1961	£20	£40	
Country Meets Folk	LP	HMV	CLP1759	1963	£10	£25	
Four Little Heels	7"	London	HLR9203	1960	£1.50	£4	chart single
Get The Message	7"	Philips	BF1601	1967	£1.50	£4	
Ginny Come Lately	7"	HMV	POP1013	1962	£1.50	£4	chart single
Here's To Our Love	LP	Philips	PHM2/PHS600136	1964	£8	£20	US
Hung Up In Your Eyes	7"	Philips	BF1555	1967	£1.50	£4	
I Gotta Go	7"	London	HLR9262	1961	£1.50	£4	
I May Not Live To See Tomorrow	7"	HMV	POP1113	1963	£1.50	£4	
If Mary's There	7"	HMV	POP1143	1963	£1.50	£4	
I'm Afraid To Go Home	7"	HMV	POP1188	1963	£1.50	£4	
Itsy Bitsy Teeny Weeny...	7"	London	HLR9161	1960	£2	£5	chart single
Joker Went Wild	LP	Philips	BL7762	1966	£6	£15	
Joker Went Wild	7"	Philips	BF1508	1966	£4	£8	
Let Me Belong To You	LP	HMV	CLP1553	1962	£20	£40	
Let Me Belong To You	7"	HMV	POP915	1961	£1.50	£4	
Let Us Make Our Own Mistakes	7"	HMV	POP1237	1963	£1.50	£4	
Night I Cried	7"	HMV	POP955	1961	£1.50	£4	
Rockin' Folk	LP	Philips	PHM2/PHS600158	1965	£6	£15	US
Rosemary	7"	London	HLR9113	1960	£4	£8	
Run, Run, Look And See	7"	Philips	BF1528	1966	£1.50	£4	
Sealed With A Kiss	LP	ABC-Paramount	(S)431	1962	£10	£25	US
Sealed With A Kiss	7"	HMV	POP1051	1962	£1.50	£4	chart single
Sealed With A Kiss	7" EP	HMV	7EG8780	1962	£7.50	£15	
Somewhere In The Night	7"	HMV	POP1169	1963	£1.50	£4	
Stay Away From Her	7"	Philips	BF1429	1965	£1.50	£4	
Three Thousand Miles	7"	Philips	BF1486	1965	£1.50	£4	
Warmed Over Kisses	7"	HMV	POP1079	1962	£1.50	£4	chart single

HYMAN, C.

Ska Is Movin' On	7"	Ska Beat	JB200	1965	£5	£10

HYMAN, DICK

Electrics	LP	Command		1968	£25	£50	US
Swings	7" EP	MGM	MGMEP646	1958	£2.50	£6	
Threepenny Opera Theme	7"	MGM	SP1164	1956	£1.50	£4	chart single

I D COMPANY
I D Company	LP	Horzu	SHZE801BL	1970	£8	£20	German

I JAH MAN
Haile I Hymn	LP	Island	ILPS9521	1978	£4	£10	

I LIFE
Kiss You Gave	7"	R&B	JB140	1964	£5	£10	

I LUV WIGHT
Let The World Wash In	7"	Philips	6006043	1970	£10	£20	
Let The World Wash In	7"	Philips	6006043	1970	£30	£60	PS

IAN & SYLVIA
Best Of Ian And Sylvia	LP	Vanguard	SVRL19004	1968	£4	£10	
Early Morning Rain	LP	Fontana	TF6053	1965	£4	£10	
Four Strong Winds	LP	Vanguard	VSD2149	1964	£4	£10	US
Four Strong Winds	7"	Fontana	TF426	1963	£1.50	£4	
Ian And Sylvia	LP	Vanguard	VSD2113	1962	£4	£10	US
Northern Journey	LP	Vanguard	VSD79154	1964	£4	£10	US
Play One More	LP	Vanguard	VSD79215	1966	£4	£10	US

IAN & THE ZODIACS
Beechwood 45789	7"	Oriole	CB1849	1963	£10	£20	
Gear Again - 12 Hits	LP	Wing	WL1074	1965	£15	£30	
Just The Little Things I Like	7"	Fontana	TF548	1965	£6	£12	
No Money, No Honey	7"	Fontana	TF708	1966	£6	£12	
Wade In The Water	7"	Fontana	TF753	1966	£12.50	£25	

IAN, JANIS
For All The Seasons Of Your Mind	LP	Verve	(S)VLP6003	1968	£5	£12	
Janis Ian	LP	Verve	(S)VLP6001	1967	£5	£12	
Secret Life Of Eddie Fink	LP	Verve	FTS3048	1968	£5	£12	US
Society's Child	7"	Verve	VS1503	1967	£2	£5	
Society's Child	7"	Verve	VS1506	1967	£2	£5	
Sunflakes Fall, Snowrays Call	7"	Verve	VS1513	1968	£2.50	£6	
Who Really Cares	LP	Verve	FTS3063	1969	£4	£10	US

ICARUS
Devil Rides Out	7"	Spark	SRL1012	1969	£6	£12	
Marvel World	LP	Pye	NSPL28161	1971	£50	£100	

ICE
Anniversary Of Love	7"	Decca	F12680	1967	£15	£30	
Ice Man	7"	Decca	F12749	1968	£15	£30	

ICE (2)
Saga Of The Ice King	LP	Storm	SR3307	1979	£50	£100	with blue booklet, sleeve pictured in Guide

ICICLE WORKS
Ascending	cass	private		198-	£6	£15	
Little Girl Lost	CD-s	Beggars Banquet	BEG215	1988	£4	£10	pic disc
Love Is A Wonderful Colour	7"	Beggars Banquet	BEG99	1983	£1.50	£4	double
Love Is A Wonderful Colour	7"	Beggars Banquet	BEG99P	1983	£2.50	£6	pic disc
Love Is A Wonderful Colour	12"	Beggars Banquet	BEG99PT	1983	£2.50	£6	pic disc
Nirvana	7"	Troll Kitchen	WORKS1	1983	£4	£8	

ID
Inner Sounds Of The Id	LP	RCA	LPM/LSP3805	1967	£5	£12	US

ID (2)
Where Are We Going?	LP	Aura	1000	1976	£6	£15	US

IDEALS
Knee Socks	7"	Pye	7N25103	1961	£5	£10	

IDES OF MARCH
Hole In My Soul	7"	London	HLU10183	1968	£1.50	£4	
Melody	7"	Warner Bros	WB7426	1970	£1.50	£4	
Superman	7"	Warner Bros	WB7403	1970	£1.50	£4	
Vehicle	7"	Warner Bros	WB7378	1970	£1.50	£4	chart single
You Wouldn't Listen	7"	London	HLU10058	1966	£1.50	£4	

IDLE FLOWERS
All I Want Is You	7"	Miles Ahead	AHEAD1	1984	£5	£10	

IDLE RACE

The Idle Race produced intelligent pop music with occasional touches of psychedelia (most notably in the single "Imposters Of Life's Magazine"). The group's records displayed a degree of production skill and craftsmanship unusual in a little-known pop act of the time, but then the group's leader was Jeff Lynne.

Birthday Party	LP	Liberty	LBL/LBS83132	1968	£15	£30
Birthday Party	LP	Sunset	SLS50381	1976	£5	£12
Come With Me	7"	Liberty	LBF15242	1969	£5	£10
Dancing Flower	7"	Regal Zonophone	RZ3036	1971	£2.50	£6
Days Of Broken Arrows	7"	Liberty	LBF15218	1969	£5	£10
End Of The Road	7"	Liberty	LBF15101	1968	£5	£10
I Like My Toys	7"	Liberty	LBF15129	1968	£12.50	£25 ... demo
Idle Race	LP	Liberty	LBS83211	1969	£15	£30
Imposters Of Life's Magazine	7"	Liberty	LBF15026	1967	£7.50	£15
On With The Show	LP	Sunset	SLS50354	1973	£5	£12
Skeleton And The Roundabout	7"	Liberty	LBF15054	1968	£5	£10
Skeleton And The Roundabout	7"	United Artists	UP36060	1976	£1.50	£4
Time Is	LP	Regal Zonophone	SLRZ1017	1971	£35	£70 ... sleeve pictured in Guide

IDOL, BILLY

Hot In The City	7"	Chrysalis	CHS2625	1982	£1.50	£4 ... pic disc
Rebel Yell	7"	Chrysalis	IDOLP2	1984	£1.50	£4 ... square pic disc

IDOLS

Don't Walk Away	7"	Mercury	MF840	1965	£1.50	£4

IF

If was a jazz-rock group formed by the previously mainstream jazz players Dick Morrissey and Terry Smith (saxophone and guitar respectively). It was interesting as a group formed from the jazz side of the jazz-rock divide, but was ultimately less convincing than the likes of Colosseum or Manfred Mann Chapter Three. Morrissey reappeared later as co-leader of the successful fusion group, Morrissey-Mullen.

If	LP	Island	ILPS9129	1970	£8	£20
If 2	LP	Island	ILPS9137	1970	£8	£20
If 3	LP	United Artists	UAG29158	1971	£6	£15
If 4	LP	United Artists	UAG29315	1972	£6	£15
Raise The Level Of Your Conscious	7"	Island	WIP6083	1970	£1.50	£4

IFE, KRIS

Haven't We Had A Good Time	7"	Parlophone	R5770	1969	£1.50	£4
Hush	7"	MGM	MGM1369	1967	£1.50	£4
Imagination	7"	Parlophone	R5741	1968	£2	£5
Sands Of Time	7"	Music Factory	CUB3	1968	£2.50	£6
This Woman's Love	7"	MGM	MGM1390	1968	£1.50	£4

IFIELD, FRANK

Babes In The Wood	LP	Columbia	SX/SCX6009	1966	£4	£10

IGGINBOTTOM

The LP by Igginbottom marks the recording debut of the guitarists' guitarist, Allan Holdsworth, in a surprisingly understated context.

Igginbottom's Wrench	LP	Deram	SML1051	1969	£40	£80

IGUANA

Iguana	LP	Polydor	2383108	1972	£6	£15

IGUANAS

This Is What I Was Made For	7"	RCA	RCA1484	1965	£2.50	£6

IHRE KINDER

2375004	LP	Kuckuck	2375004	1970	£6	£15 ... German
Anfang Ohne Ende	LP	Kuckuck	2375016	1972	£5	£12 ... German
Ihre Kinder	LP	Philips	844393	1969	£8	£20 ... German
Leere Hande	LP	Kuckuck	2375001	1970	£8	£20 ... German
Werdohl	LP	Kuckuck	2375013	1971	£6	£15 ... German

IKARUS

Ikarus	LP	Plus	4	1971	£8	£20 ... German

IKETTES

Fine Fine Fine	7"	Stateside	SS434	1965	£4	£8
Fine Fine Fine	7" EP	Stateside	SE1033	1965	£12.50	£25
I'm Blue	7"	London	HLK9508	1962	£4	£8
I'm So Thankful	7"	Polydor	56506	1970	£2	£5
I'm So Thankful	7"	Polydor	56533	1970	£1.50	£4
Never More Lonely For You	7"	Polydor	56516	1970	£1.50	£4
Peaches 'n' Cream	7"	Stateside	SS407	1965	£5	£10
Prisoner Of Love	7"	Sue	WI389	1965	£7.50	£15
Soul Hits	LP	Modern	M(ST)102	1965	£10	£25 ... US
Whatcha Gonna Do	7"	London	HLU10081	1966	£4	£8

ILANIT

I'm No One	7"	Pye	7N25739	1977	£2.50	£6

ILL WIND

Flashes	LP	ABC	S641	1968	£8	£20 ... US

ILLINOIS SPEED PRESS

Duet	LP	CBS	9976	1970	£8	£20 ... US
Illinois Speed Press	LP	CBS	63691	1969	£8	£20

ILLUSION

Did You See Her Eyes	7"	Dot	122	1969	£4	£8

If It's So	LP	Paramount	SPFL264	1970	£6	£15	
Illusion	LP	Steed	(S)LPD531	1969	£6	£15	
Together	LP	Dot	SLPD537	1970	£6	£15	

ILLUSIVE DREAM
Electric Garden	7"	RCA	RCA1791	1969	£4	£8	

ILMO SMOKEHOUSE
Ilmo Smokehouse	LP	Beautiful Sound	3002	1971	£8	£20	US

ILORI, SOLOMON
African High Life	LP	Blue Note	BLP/BST84136	1963	£15	£30	

IMAGE
Come To The Party	7"	Parlophone	R5281	1965	£17.50	£35	
Home Is Anywhere	7"	Parlophone	R5352	1965	£12.50	£25	
I Can't Stop Myself	7"	Parlophone	R5442	1966	£10	£20	

IMAGES
I Only Have Myself To Blame	7"	Polydor	BM56011	1965	£6	£12	

IMAN CALIFATO INDEPENDIENTE
Camuno Del Aguila	LP	CBS	84277	1978	£10	£25	Spanish

IMLACH, HAMISH
Before And After	LP	XTRA	XTRA1059	1967	£5	£12	
Fine Old English Tory Times	LP	XTRA	XTRA1128	1972	£5	£12	
Murdered Ballads	LP	XTRA	XTRA1131	1973	£5	£12	
Old Rarity	LP	XTRA	XTRA1121	1971	£5	£12	
Two Sides Of Hamish Imlach	LP	XTRA	XTRA1069	1968	£5	£12	

IMMORTALS
No Turning Back	7"	MCA	MCA1057	1986	£12.50	£25	
No Turning Back	12"	MCA	MCAT1057	1986	£15	£30	

IMORTALS
Ultimate Warlord	7"	Excaliber	EXC517	1982	£10	£20	
Ultimate Warlord	12"	Excaliber	EXC517	1982	£10	£25	

IMPAC
Too Far Out	7"	CBS	202402	1966	£15	£30	

IMPACS
Impact!	LP	King	(KS)886	1964	£8	£20	US
Weekend With The Impacs	LP	King	(KS)916	1964	£8	£20	US

IMP-ACTS
Dum Dum Song	7" EP	Pye	PNV24152	1965	£7.50	£15	French, B side by Kenny Bernard

IMPACTS
Wipe Out	LP	Del-Fi	DFLP/DFS1234	1963	£6	£15	US

IMPALAS
Oh What A Fool	7"	MGM	MGM1031	1959	£5	£10	
Peggy Darling	7"	MGM	MGM1068	1960	£2	£5	
Sorry	7"	MGM	MGM1015	1959	£6	£12	chart single
Sorry	7" EP	MGM	MGMEP696	1959	£25	£50	
Sorry I Ran All The Way Home	LP	Cub	(S)8003	1959	£50	£100	US

IMPERSONATORS
Make It Easy On Yourself	7"	Big Shot	BI524	1969	£2.50	£6	

IMPOSSIBLE DREAMERS
Books Books Books	7"	Merciful Release	MR1	1980	£4	£8	
Life On Earth	12"	One Hundred Things	MR5	1982	£2.50	£6	

IMPOSSIBLE YEARS
Scenes We'd Like To See	12"	Dreamworld	DREAM1	1985	£2.50	£6	

IMPOSTERS
Apache '69	7"	Mercury	MF1080	1969	£5	£10	

IMPRESSIONS
Ain't Got Time	7"	Buddah	2011068	1971	£1.50	£4	
Amen	LP	Buddah	2359009	1970	£5	£12	
Amen	7"	HMV	POP1492	1965	£2.50	£6	
Big 16	LP	HMV	CLP1935/CSD1642	1965	£8	£20	
Big 16 Vol.2	LP	Stateside	(S)SL10279	1969	£5	£12	
Can't Satisfy	7"	HMV	POP1545	1966	£5	£10	
Can't Satisfy	7"	Stateside	SS2139	1969	£2	£5	
Check Out Your Mind	LP	Buddah	2318017	1971	£5	£12	
Check Out Your Mind	7"	Buddah	2011030	1970	£1.50	£4	
Fabulous Impressions	LP	HMV	CLP/CSD3631	1967	£6	£15	
Fool For You	7"	Buddah	201021	1968	£2	£5	
For Your Precious Love	LP	Joy	JOY(S)104	1968	£5	£12	
Gypsy Woman	7"	HMV	POP961	1961	£7.50	£15	
I Need You	7"	HMV	POP1472	1965	£2.50	£6	
I'm So Proud	7"	HMV	POP1295	1964	£4	£8	

Title	Format	Label	Cat No	Year	Low	High	Notes
I'm The One Who Loves You	7"	HMV	POP1129	1963	£4	£8	
Impressions	LP	ABC	(S)450	1963	£10	£25	US
Inner City Blues	7"	Buddah	2011099	1971	£1.50	£4	
It's All Right	7"	HMV	POP1226	1963	£4	£8	
It's All Right	7" EP.	HMV	7EG8896	1965	£7.50	£15	
Keep On Pushing	LP	ABC	(S)493	1964	£8	£20	US
Keep On Pushing	7"	HMV	POP1317	1964	£4	£8	
Love Me	7"	Buddah	2011087	1971	£1.50	£4	
Meeting Over Yonder	7"	HMV	POP1446	1965	£2.50	£6	
Mighty Mighty Spade And Whitey	7"	Buddah	201062	1969	£2	£5	
Never Ending Impressions	LP	HMV	CLP1743	1964	£8	£20	
One By One	LP	ABC	(S)523	1965	£8	£20	US
People Get Ready	LP	ABC	(S)505	1965	£8	£20	US
People Get Ready	7"	HMV	POP1408	1965	£4	£8	
Ridin' High	LP	HMV	CLP/CSD3548	1966	£6	£15	
Since I Lost The One I Love	7"	HMV	POP1516	1966	£4	£8	
Soulfully	7" EP.	HMV	7EG8954	1966	£7.50	£15	
Talking About My Baby	7"	HMV	POP1262	1964	£4	£8	
This Is My Country	LP	Buddah	203012	1969	£5	£12	
Too Slow	7"	HMV	POP1526	1966	£2.50	£6	
Turn On To Me	7"	Buddah	2011045	1970	£1.50	£4	
We're A Winner	LP	Stateside	(S)SL10239	1968	£5	£12	
We're A Winner	7"	Stateside	SS2083	1968	£2	£5	
Woman's Got Soul	7"	HMV	POP1429	1965	£4	£8	
You Always Hurt Me	7"	HMV	POP1581	1967	£4	£8	
You Must Believe Me	7"	HMV	POP1343	1964	£4	£8	
Young Mod's Forgotten Story	LP	Buddah	2359003	1970	£5	£12	
You've Been Cheating	7"	HMV	POP1498	1966	£5	£10	

IMPROVED SOUND LIMITED

Title	Format	Label	Cat No	Year	Low	High	Notes
Improved Sound Kimited	LP	Liberty	LBS83505/6	1971	£6	£15	German double

IMPS

Title	Format	Label	Cat No	Year	Low	High	Notes
Dim Dumb Blonde	7"	Parlophone	R4398	1958	£2.50	£6	

IN BETWEENS

Title	Format	Label	Cat No	Year	Low	High	Notes
Take A Heart	7" EP.	Barclay	2017	1966	£100	£200	French
Take A Heart	7" EP.	Barclay	70907	1965	£50	£100	French
You Better Run	7"	Columbia	DB8080	1966	£65	£130	

IN CAMERA

Title	Format	Label	Cat No	Year	Low	High	Notes
Die Laughing	7"	4AD	AD8	1980	£1.50	£4	
Fin	12"	4AD	BAD205	1982	£2.50	£6	
IV Songs	12"	4AD	BAD19	1980	£2.50	£6	

IN CROWD

The soul singles of the In Crowd gave no indication that the group would ever evolve into that cornerstone of psychedelia, Tomorrow. "That's How Strong My Love Is" was recorded before Steve Howe joined the group, but the other singles all feature his guitar playing, in behind Keith West's singing.

Title	Format	Label	Cat No	Year	Low	High	Notes
Stop! Wait A Minute	7"	Parlophone	R5328	1965	£15	£30	
That's How Strong My Love Is	7"	Parlophone	R5276	1965	£30	£60	chart single
Why Must They Criticise	7"	Parlophone	R5364	1965	£12.50	£25	

IN CROWD (2)

Title	Format	Label	Cat No	Year	Low	High	Notes
Where In The World	7"	Deram	DM272	1969	£7.50	£15	

IN THE NURSERY

Title	Format	Label	Cat No	Year	Low	High	Notes
Sonority - A Strength	12"	New European	BADVC55	1985	£3	£8	
Temper	12"	Sweatbox	SOX008	1985	£2.50	£6	
When Cherished Dreams Come True	LP	Paragon	VIRTUE2	1983	£6	£15	
Witness To A Scream	7"	Paragon	VIRTUE5	1984	£6	£12	

IN TWO A CIRCLE

Title	Format	Label	Cat No	Year	Low	High	Notes
Rise	12"	Arcadia	ARC001	1986	£3	£8	

INADEQUATES

Title	Format	Label	Cat No	Year	Low	High	Notes
Audie	7"	Capitol	CL15051	1959	£2	£5	

INCAS

Title	Format	Label	Cat No	Year	Low	High	Notes
I'll Keep Holding On	7"	Parlophone	R5551	1966	£10	£20	
Keele Rag Record	7" EP.	Lyntone	LYN765/6	196-	£15	£30	with other artists

INCOGNITO

Title	Format	Label	Cat No	Year	Low	High	Notes
Parisienne Girl	12"	Ensign	ENY4412	1980	£2.50	£6	

INCREDIBLE BONGO BAND

Title	Format	Label	Cat No	Year	Low	High	Notes
Bongo Rock	LP	DJM	20452	1976	£8	£20	
Bongo Rock	7"	MGM	2006161	1973	£1.50	£4	

INCREDIBLE HOG

Title	Format	Label	Cat No	Year	Low	High	Notes
Volume One	LP	Dart	65372	1973	£50	£100	

INCREDIBLE STRING BAND

Title	Format	Label	Cat No	Year	Low	High	Notes
5000 Spirits Or The Layers Of The Onion	LP	Elektra	EUK/EUKS7257	1967	£6	£15	chart LP
At The Lighthouse Dance	7"	Island	WIP6158	1973	£1.50	£4	
Be Glad For The Song Has No Ending	LP	Island	ILPS9140	1970	£5	£12	
Big Huge	LP	Elektra	EKL/EKS74037	1968	£6	£15	
Big Ted	7"	Elektra	EKSN45074	1969	£2.50	£6	
Black Jack Diamond	7"	Island	WIP6145	1972	£1.50	£4	
Changing Horses	LP	Elektra	EKS74057	1969	£6	£15	chart LP

Earth Span	LP	Island	ILPS9211	1972	£5	£12	
Hangman's Beautiful Daughter	LP	Elektra	EKL/EKS74021	1968	£6	£15	chart LP
Hangman's Beautiful Daughter	LP	Elektra	EUK/EUKS7258	1968	£6	£15	
Hard Rope & Silken Twine	LP	Island	ILPS9270	1974	£5	£12	
I Looked Up	LP	Elektra	EKS74061	1970	£6	£15	chart LP
Incredible String Band	LP	Elektra	EKL322	1966	£20	£40	
Incredible String Band	LP	Elektra	EUK254	1966	£20	£40	chart LP
Incredible String Band	LP	Elektra	EUK254	1966	£25	£50	white Elektra label
Liquid Acrobat As Regards The Air	LP	Island	ILPS9172	1971	£5	£12	chart LP
No Ruinous Feud	LP	Island	ILPS9229	1973	£5	£12	
Painting Box	7"	Elektra	EKSN45028	1968	£2.50	£6	
Seasons They Change	LP	Island	ISLD9	1976	£6	£15	double
This Moment	7"	Elektra	2101003	1970	£1.50	£4	
U	LP	Elektra	2665001	1970	£6	£15	double, chart LP
Wee Tam	LP	Elektra	EKL/EKS74036	1968	£6	£15	
Wee Tam/The Big Huge	LP	Elektra	EKL/EKS74036/7	1968	£10	£25	double

INCREDIBLES
There's Nothing Else To Say	7"	Stateside	SS2053	1967	£25	£50	

INDEX
Index	LP			1969	£100	£200	US

INDIAN SUMMER
Indian Summer	LP	Neon	NE3	1971	£15	£30	

INFANTS JUBILATE
Exploding Galaxy	7"	Music Factory	CUB5	1968	£12.50	£25	

INFESTED
Flies	7"	Dead City		197-	£50	£100	existence doubtful
No But I've Got A Dark Brown Overcoat	7"	Great Disaster		197-	£50	£100	existence doubtful

INFLUENCE
I Want To Live	7"	Orange	OAS201	1969	£1.50	£4	

INFORMATION
Face To The Sun	7"	Evolution	E24615	1970	£4	£8	
Orphan	7"	Beacon	BEA3121	1968	£2.50	£6	

INGLE, RED
Cigareets, Whuskey, & Wild Wild Women	7" EP	Capitol	EAP20052	1959	£7.50	£15	

INGMANN, JORGEN
Africa	7"	Fontana	267237	1962	£1.50	£4	
Apache	LP	Atco	(SD)33130	1961	£8	£20	US
Cherokee	7"	Fontana	H311	1961	£1.50	£4	
Drina	7" EP	Columbia	SEG8340	1964	£4	£8	
Many Guitars Of Jorgen Ingmann	LP	Atco	(SD)33139	1962	£6	£15	US
Milord	7"	Fontana	H333	1961	£1.50	£4	
Swinging Guitar	LP	Mercury	MG20200	1956	£8	£20	US
Violetta	7"	Fontana	267184	1962	£1.50	£4	
Violetta	7"	Fontana	H353	1961	£1.50	£4	

INGOES
Dansez Le Monkiss	7" EP	Riviera	231141	1966	£20	£40	French

INGRAM, LUTHER
Home Don't Seem Like A Home	7"	Stax	STAX148	1970	£1.50	£4	
My Honey And Me	7"	Stax	STAX142	1970	£1.50	£4	

INITIALS
School Days	7"	London	HLR9860	1964	£4	£8	

INJAROC
Halen Y Ddaer!	LP	Sain	1094M	1977	£8	£20	

INKSPOTS
Charlie Fuqua's Inkspots	7" EP	HMV	7EG8410	1957	£5	£10	
Ebb Tide	7"	Parlophone	MSP6074	1954	£6	£12	
Here In My Lonely Room	7"	Parlophone	MSP6063	1954	£6	£12	
Inkspots	10" LP	Britone	LP1003	195-	£6	£15	
Melody Of Love	7"	Parlophone	MSP6152	1955	£6	£12	chart single
Souvenir	10" LP	Brunswick	LA8590	1953	£8	£20	
Street Of Dreams	10" LP	Brunswick	LA8710	1955	£6	£15	
Swing High Swing Low Vol.1	7" EP	Brunswick	OE9158	1955	£4	£8	
Yesterdays	7"	Parlophone	MSP6126	1954	£6	£12	
Yesterdays	7" EP	Parlophone	GEP8673	1957	£5	£10	

INNER CITY UNIT
Maximum Effect	LP	Avatar	AALP5004	1981	£4	£10	
Pass Out	LP	Riddle	RID002	1980	£4	£10	

INNES, NEIL
How Sweet To Be An Idiot	LP	United Artists	UAG29492	1973	£6	£15	
Lie Down And Be Counted	7"	United Artists	UP35745	1975	£1.50	£4	
Momma B	7"	United Artists	UP35639	1974	£1.50	£4	
Recycled Vinyl Blues	7"	United Artists	UP35676	1974	£1.50	£4	
Rutland Times	LP	BBC	REB233	1976	£4	£10	

What Noise Annoys A Noisy Oyster ..... 7" .... United Artists .. UP35772 .... 1975 ... £1.50 ....£4 ....

INNOCENCE
Lifetime Loving You .... 7" .... Kama Sutra ..... KAS206 .... 1967 ... £1.50 ....£4 ....
Mairzy Doats .... 7" EP.. Kama Sutra ..... 617107 .... 1967 ... £5 ....£10 ....French
There's Got To Be A Word .... 7" .... Kama Sutra ..... KAS203 .... 1966 ... £1.50 ....£4 ....

INNOCENTS
Gee Whiz .... 7" .... Top Rank .... JAR541 .... 1961 ... £4 ....£8 ....
Honest I Do .... 7" .... Top Rank .... JAR508 .... 1960 ... £5 ....£10 ....

INNOCENTS (2)
Fine Fine Bird .... 7" .... Columbia .... DB7173 .... 1963 ... £2.50 ....£6 ....
Stepping Stones .... 7" .... Columbia .... DB7098 .... 1963 ... £4 ....£8 ....
Stick With Me Baby .... 7" .... Columbia .... DB7314 .... 1964 ... £2.50 ....£6 ....

INNOCENTS (2) & LEROYS
Medley .... 7" .... Regal .... RZ502 .... 1964 ... £2 ....£5 ....
Zonophone......

INNOCENTS (3)
One Way Love .... 7" .... Kingdom........... KV8010 .... 1980 ... £2.50 ....£6 ....

INSECT TRUST
At a time when rock was blossoming with new approaches and unusual instruments, the Insect Trust still managed to sound unique. They are like a folk group, with a strong female lead singer, into which a couple of avant garde jazz saxophonists have unaccountably wandered. The combination still sounds fresh today.
Hoboken Saturday Night .... LP ..... Atco .... SD33313 .... 1970 ... £8 ....£20 .... US
Insect Trust .... LP ..... Capitol .... EST109 .... 1968 ... £8 ....£20 ....

INSPIRAL CARPETS
Butterfly .... 7" .... Playtime .... AMUSE4 .... 1988 ... £2 ....£5 ....promo only
Cow .... cass.. private .... 198- ... £5 ....£12 ....
Find Out Why .... 12" .... Cow.................. DUNG5T .... 1989 ... £4 ....£10 ....signed,
with newsletter
Garage Full Of Flowers .... 7" .... Debris .... DEB06 .... 1987 ... £2 ....£5 ....flexi
Keep The Circle Around .... cass-s Cow.................. DUNG4 .... 1989 ... £4 ....£10 ....demo
Keep The Circle Around .... 7" .... Playtime .... AMUSE2 .... 1988 ... £10 ....£20 ....
Keep The Circle Around .... 12" .... Cow.................. MOO1 .... 1989 ... £4 ....£10 ....test pressing
Keep The Circle Around .... 12" .... Playtime .... AMUSE2T .... 1988 ... £10 ....£25 ....
Move .... 7" .... Cow.................. DUNG6X .... 1989 ... £1.50 ....£4 ....with badge
Songs Of Shallow Intensity .... cass.. private .... 198- ... £5 ....£12 ....
Train Surfing .... 12" .... Cow.................. MOO2 .... 1989 ... £2.50 ....£6 ....
Train Surfing .... 12" .... Playtime .... AMUSE4T .... 1988 ... £10 ....£25 ....promo
Waiting For Ours .... cass.. private .... 198- ... £5 ....£12 ....

INSPIRATIONS
Touch Me,Hold Me,Kiss Me .... 7" .... Polydor .... 56730 .... 1967 ... £30 ....£60 ....

INSPIRATIONS (2)
Reggae Fever .... LP ..... Trojan .... TTL27 .... 1970 ... £6 ....£15 ....

INSTANT SUNSHINE
Here We Go Again .... 7" .... Page One .... POF085 .... 1968 ... £1.50 ....£4 ....
Live At Tiddy Dols .... LP ..... Page One .... POL007 .... 1968 ... £25 ....£50 ....

INTERCONTINENTAL EXPRESS
London .... LP ..... Compendium .. FIDARDO8............. 1976 ... £5 ....£12 ....

INTERNATIONAL SUBMARINE BAND
The International Submarine Band, led by Gram Parsons, is often credited with making the first country-rock LP, for "Safe At Home" pre-dates the Byrds' "Sweetheart Of The Rodeo", in which Parsons was also involved.
Luxury Liner .... 7" .... LHI .... 1205 .... 1967 ... £5 ....£10 .... US
Miller's Cave .... 7" .... LHI .... 1217 .... 1967 ... £5 ....£10 .... US
Russians Are Coming .... 7" .... Ascot .... 2218 .... 1966 ... £6 ....£12 .... US
Safe At Home .... LP ..... LHI .... LHI12001 .... 1968 ... £30 ....£60 ..... US, coloured label
Safe At Home .... LP ..... Shiloh .... RI4088 .... 1979 ... £5 ....£12 .... US
Sum Up Broke .... 7" .... Columbia .... 43935 .... 1966 ... £5 ....£10 .... US

INTERNS
Cry To Me .... 7" .... Philips .... BF1345 .... 1964 ... £5 ....£10 ....
Don't You Dare .... 7" .... Philips .... BF1320 .... 1964 ... £4 ....£8 ....
Is It Really What You Want .... 7" .... Parlophone....... R5479 .... 1966 ... £10 ....£20 ....
Please Say Something Nice .... 7" .... Parlophone....... R5586 .... 1967 ... £2.50 ....£6 ....

INTRA VEIN
Speed Of The City .... 7" .... Bum .... FP001 .... 1979 ... £2.50 ....£6 ....PVC sleeve

INTRIGUES
In A Moment .... LP ..... Yew.................. YS777 .... 1970 ... £6 ....£15 .... US
In A Moment .... 7" .... London .... HL10293 .... 1969 ... £2.50 ....£6 ....

INTRUDERS
Cowboys To Girls .... LP ..... Gamble .... KZ5004 .... 1968 ... £6 ....£15 .... US
Cowboys To Girls .... 7" .... Ember .... EMBS254 .... 1969 ... £2.50 ....£6 ....
Cowboys To Girls .... 7" .... Ember .... EMBS325 .... 1972 ... £1.50 ....£4 ....
Intruders Are Together .... LP ..... Gamble .... (KZ)5001 .... 1967 ... £6 ....£15 .... US
Slow Drag .... 7" .... Action .... ACT4523 .... 1969 ... £4 ....£8 ....
United .... 7" .... London .... HL10069 .... 1966 ... £10 ....£20 ....

INVADERS
Limbo Girl .... 7" .... Blue Beat .... BB105 .... 1962 ... £5 ....£10 ....

Limbo Girl	7"	Columbia	DB105	1967	£4	£8	
Soulful Music	7"	Studio One	SO2044	1968	£6	£12	Soul Vendors B side
Stop Teasing	7"	Blue Beat	BB109	1962	£5	£10	
Stop Teasing	7"	Columbia	DB109	1968	£4	£8	

INVADERS (2)

On The Right Track	LP	Justice	JLP125	1967	£75	£150	US

INVICTAS

A Go-Go	LP	Sahara	101	1965	£15	£30	US
Green Bow Tie	7"	United Artists	UP1013	1964	£1.50	£4	

INVITATIONS

Hallelujah	7"	Stateside	SS453	1965	£5	£10	
Let's Love	7"	Polydor	2066366	1973	£1.50	£4	
What's Wrong With Me Baby	7"	Stateside	SS478	1965	£20	£40	
What's Wrong With My Baby	7"	Mojo	2092055	1972	£1.50	£4	

INXS

Don't Change	7"	Mercury	INXS1	1983	£2.50	£6	
Don't Change	12"	Mercury	INXS121	1983	£5	£12	
Just Keep Walking	7"	RCA	RCA89	1981	£12.50	£25	PS
Kick	LP	Mercury	MERHP114	1987	£4	£10	pic disc
Listen Like Thieves	LP	Mercury	MERH82	1986	£5	£12	with LP The Swing
Listen Like Thieves	7"	Mercury	INXSP6	1986	£2	£5	shaped pic disc
Listen Like Thieves	12"	Mercury	INXS612	1986	£2.50	£6	with poster
Need You Tonight	12"	Mercury	INXS812	1987	£2.50	£6	
One Thing	7"	Mercury	INXS2	1983	£2	£5	
One Thing	12"	Mercury	INXS212	1983	£5	£12	2 tracks
One Thing	12"	Mercury	INXS222	1983	£4	£10	3 tracks
Original Sin	7"	Mercury	INXS3	1984	£4	£8	
Original Sin	12"	Mercury	INXS312	1984	£5	£12	
This Time	7"	Mercury	INXSD4	1986	£2	£5	double
What You Need	12"	Mercury	INXSD512	1986	£3	£8	double

IONA

Cuckoo	LP	Silverscales	KOO13913	1978	£25	£50	
Iona	LP	Celtic Music	CM001	197-	£15	£30	

IPSISSIMUS

Hold On	7"	Parlophone	R5774	1969	£10	£20	

IQ

Awake And Nervous	12"	Jim White	IQPROMO101	1984	£15	£30	
Barbell Is In	7"	Sahara	IQ1002	1984	£2.50	£6	
Barbell Is In	12"	Sahara	IQ121002	1984	£4	£10	
Beef In A Box	7"	Lyntone	LYN12028/9	1982	£2	£5	with other artists
Corners	7"	Sahara	IQ1003	1985	£2.50	£6	
Corners	12"	Sahara	IQ121003	1985	£4	£10	
Different Magic Roundabout	7"	fan club	ONEMOREBOXER1	1988	£5	£10	
Fascination	7"	fan club	ANOTHERBOXER1	1987	£7.50	£15	
Hollow Afternoon	7"	IQ	IQFREEB1	1984	£15	£30	
It All Stops Here	7"	Samurai	IQSD1	1986	£7.50	£15	shaped pic disc
Nine In A Pond Is Here	LP	fan club	BOXER1	1985	£15	£30	double
Nomzamo	7"	fan club	OTHERBOXER1	1986	£7.50	£15	
Promises	12"	Squawk	VERX34	1987	£4	£10	
Sold On You	CD-s	Squawk	VERCD42	1989	£2.50	£6	
Tales From The Lush Attic	LP	COSL	MAJ1001	1984	£5	£12	brown sleeve
Tales From The Lush Attic	LP	MJL	MAJ1001	1983	£6	£15	blue sleeve
Wake	LP	Sahara	SAH136	1985	£5	£12	

IRELAND, TONY

Johny O'Cockley's Well	LP	Peak	3581	1983	£5	£12	German

IRISH COFFEE

Irish Coffee	LP	Triangle		1971	£100	£200	Belgium

IRON BUTTERFLY

Ball	LP	Atlantic	228011	1969	£5	£12	
Heavy	LP	Atco	2465015	1967	£6	£15	
In-A-Gadda-Da-Vida	LP	Atco	588166	1968	£5	£12	
In-A-Gadda-Da-Vida	7"	Atlantic	2091024	1970	£1.50	£4	
Live	LP	Atlantic	2400014	1970	£5	£12	
Metamorphosis	LP	Atlantic	2401003	1970	£4	£10	
Possession	7"	Atlantic	584188	1968	£2	£5	
Soul Experience	7"	Atlantic	584254	1969	£2	£5	

IRON MAIDEN

Iron Maiden's striking death mascot has found particularly effective use as a recurring theme on the group's record covers and picture discs. Many of these are now very collectable, as befits a group that is probably the most successful of the New Wave of British Heavy Metal (though Def Leppard might argue the point).

Aces High	12"	EMI	12EMIP5502	1984	£5	£12	pic disc
Bring Your Daughter To Your Slaughter	7"	EMI	EMPD171	1990	£1.50	£4	pic disc
Can I Play With Madness	7"	EMI	EMP49	1988	£1.50	£4	shaped pic disc
Clairvoyant	7"	EMI	EMP79	1988	£2.50	£6	shaped pic disc
Evil That Men Do	7"	EMI	EMP64	1988	£1.50	£4	shaped pic disc
Fear Of The Dark	7"	EMI	EMPD263	1992	£2.50	£6	shaped pic disc, B side plays Tailgunner
First Ten Years	CD-s	EMI	CDIRN1-10	1990	£30	£60	10 CD's, boxed

Title	Format	Label	Cat No	Year	Price1	Price2	Notes
First Ten Years	12"	EMI	IRN1-10	1990	£25	£50	10 double records, boxed
Flight Of Icarus	cass-s	EMI	TCIM4	1983	£2.50	£6	
Flight Of Icarus	12"	EMI	12EMIP5378	1983	£6	£15	pic disc
Infinite Dreams	7"	EMI	EMPD117	1989	£2.50	£6	shaped pic disc
Maiden Japan	12"	EMI	12EMI5219	1981	£3	£8	
No Prayer For The Dying	LP	EMI	EMDPD1017	1990	£4	£10	pic disc
No Prayer For The Dying	10"	EMI		1990	£20	£40	boxed promo
Number Of The Beast	LP	EMI	EMCP3400	1982	£8	£20	pic disc
Number Of The Beast	7"	EMI	EMI5287	1982	£4	£8	red vinyl
Piece Of Mind	LP	Capitol		1983	£15	£30	US pic disc
Powerslave	LP	EMI	POWERP1	1984	£10	£25	pic disc
Purgatory	7"	EMI	EMI5184	1981	£10	£20	chart single
Run To The Hills	7"	EMI	EMI5263	1982	£2	£5	chart single
Run To The Hills	7"	EMI	EMIP5263	1982	£5	£10	
Run To The Hills	7"	EMI	EMIP5263	1982	£20	£40	pic disc with band photo on both sides
Run To The Hills	12"	EMI	12EMIP5542	1985	£3	£8	pic disc
Run To The Hills (Live)	7"	EMI	EMI5542	1985	£2	£5	with Christmas card
Running Free	7"	EMI	EMI5032	1980	£7.50	£15	chart single
Running Free	7"	EMI	EMI5532	1985	£2	£5	poster sleeve
Running Free	12"	EMI	12EMIP5532	1985	£4	£10	pic disc
Sanctuary	7"	EMI	EMI5065	1980	£5	£10	chart single, censored PS
Sanctuary	7"	EMI	EMI5065	1980	£7.50	£15	uncensored PS
Seventh Son Of A Seventh Son	LP	EMI	EMDP1006	1988	£4	£10	pic disc with banner
Soundhouse Tapes	7" EP	Rock Hard	ROK1	1979	£25	£50	
Stranger In A Strange Land	7"	EMI	EMI5589	1986	£2	£5	poster sleeve
Stranger In A Strange Land	12"	EMI	12EMIP5589	1986	£4	£10	pic disc
Trooper	7"	EMI	EMIP5397	1983	£7.50	£15	shaped pic disc
Twilight Zone	cass-s	EMI	EMI5145	1981	£2	£5	
Twilight Zone	7"	EMI	EMI5145	1981	£50	£100	brown vinyl mispress
Twilight Zone	7"	EMI	EMI5145	1981	£4	£8	chart single
Twilight Zone	7"	EMI	EMI5145	1981	£10	£20	red or clear vinyl
Two Minutes To Midnight	12"	EMI	12EMIP5489	1984	£4	£10	pic disc
Wasted Years	7"	EMI	EMIP5583	1986	£6	£12	shaped pic disc
Women In Uniform	7"	EMI	EMI5105	1980	£4	£8	chart single
Women In Uniform	12"	EMI	12EMI5105	1980	£3	£8	

IRON MAIDEN (2)

Title	Format	Label	Cat No	Year	Price1	Price2	Notes
Falling	7"	Gemini	GMS006	1971	£2.50	£6	

IRVINE, ANDY & PAUL BRADY

Title	Format	Label	Cat No	Year	Price1	Price2	Notes
Andy Irvine And Paul Brady	LP	Mulligan	LUN668	1976	£5	£12	Irish

IRVING, LONNIE

Title	Format	Label	Cat No	Year	Price1	Price2	Notes
Pinball Machine	7"	Melodisc	1546	1960	£5	£10	

IRWIN, BIG DEE

Title	Format	Label	Cat No	Year	Price1	Price2	Notes
Ain't That Lovin' You Baby	7"	Polydor	56715	1966	£1.50	£4	with Suzie
Donkey Walk	7"	Stateside	SS261	1964	£2	£5	
Heigh Ho	7"	Colpix	PX11140	1964	£1.50	£4	
I Can't Stand The Pain	7"	Minit	MLF11013	1969	£1.50	£4	
Personality	7"	Colpix	PX11150	1964	£1.50	£4	
You Satisfy My Needs	7"	Stateside	SS450	1965	£12.50	£25	

IRWIN, BIG DEE & LITTLE EVA

Title	Format	Label	Cat No	Year	Price1	Price2	Notes
I Wish You A Merry Christmas	7"	Colpix	PX11121	1964	£1.50	£4	
Swinging On A Star	LP	Golden Guinea	GSGL10497	1965	£4	£10	
Swinging On A Star	7"	Colpix	PX11010	1963	£1.50	£4	chart single
Swinging On A Star	7" EP	Colpix	PXE301	1963	£7.50	£15	

IRWIN, PEE WEE

Title	Format	Label	Cat No	Year	Price1	Price2	Notes
Dixieland Band	LP	London	HAA2009	1956	£4	£10	

ISAACS, DAVID

Title	Format	Label	Cat No	Year	Price1	Price2	Notes
Good Father	7"	Upsetter	US302	1969	£2	£5	Slim Smith B side
He'll Have To Go	7"	Upsetter	US311	1969	£2	£5	
I Can't Take It Anymore	7"	Punch	PH6	1969	£2	£5	Lloyd Douglas B side
I'd Rather Be Lonely	7"	Island	WI261	1966	£5	£10	
I've Got Memories	7"	Upsetter	US305	1969	£2	£5	
Place In The Sun	7"	Trojan	TR616	1968	£4	£8	Upsetters B side
Who To Tell	7"	Upsetter	US319	1969	£2	£5	Busty Brown B side

ISKRA 1903

Title	Format	Label	Cat No	Year	Price1	Price2	Notes
Free Improvisation	LP	Deutsche Grammophon	2563298/299/300	1974	£25	£50	3 LP set with other artists

ISLAND BOYS

Title	Format	Label	Cat No	Year	Price1	Price2	Notes
Go Calypso No.1	7" EP	London	RER1122	1958	£2	£5	
Go Calypso No.2	7" EP	London	RER1123	1958	£2	£5	
Go Calypso No.3	7" EP	London	RER1124	1958	£2	£5	

ISLE, JIMMY

Title	Format	Label	Cat No	Year	Price1	Price2	Notes
Billy Boy	7"	Top Rank	JAR274	1960	£2	£5	
Diamond Ring	7"	London	HLS8832	1959	£15	£30	

ISLEY BROTHERS

Title	Format	Label	Cat No	Year	Price1	Price2	Notes
Behind A Painted Smile	LP	Tamla Motown	(S)TML11112	1969	£8	£20	
Behind A Painted Smile	7"	Tamla Motown	TMG693	1969	£1.50	£4	chart single
Brothers Isley	LP	Stateside	SSL10300	1970	£5	£12	

Got To Have You Back	7"	Tamla Motown	TMG606	1967	£4	£8	
How Deep Is The Ocean	7"	RCA	RCA1190	1960	£5	£10	
Guess I'll Always Love You	7"	Tamla Motown	TMG572	1966	£6	£12	chart single
Guess I'll Always Love You	7"	Tamla Motown	TMG683	1969	£2	£5	chart single
I Turned You On	7"	Major Minor	MM631	1969	£1.50	£4	
Isley Brothers	7" EP	RCA	RCX7149	1964	£12.50	£25	
It's Our Thing	LP	Major Minor	SMLP59	1969	£5	£12	
It's Your Thing	7"	Major Minor	MM621	1969	£1.50	£4	chart single
Last Lost Girl	7"	Atlantic	AT4010	1964	£5	£10	
Love The One You're With	7"	Stateside	SS2193	1971	£1.50	£4	
Nobody But Me	7"	Stateside	SS218	1963	£4	£8	
Put Yourself In My Place	7"	Tamla Motown	TMG708	1969	£1.50	£4	chart single
Respectable	7"	RCA	RCA1172	1960	£6	£12	
Shake It With Me Baby	7"	United Artists	UP1050	1964	£2.50	£6	
Shout	LP	RCA	RD27165/SF7055	1960	£15	£30	
Shout	7"	RCA	RCA1149	1959	£6	£12	
Soul On The Rocks	LP	Tamla Motown	(S)TML11066	1968	£6	£15	
Take Me In Your Arms	7"	Tamla Motown	TMG652	1968	£5	£10	
Take Some Time Out	LP	Scepter	SC(S)552	1966	£5	£12	US
Take Some Time Out For Love	7"	Tamla Motown	TMG566	1966	£6	£12	
Take Some Time Out For Love	7"	Tamla Motown	TMG719	1969	£1.50	£4	
Tango	7"	United Artists	UP1034	1963	£2.50	£6	
Tell Me It's Just A Rumour Baby	7"	Tamla Motown	TMG877	1973	£1.50	£4	
Tell Me Who	7"	RCA	RCA1213	1960	£5	£10	
This Old Heart Of Mine	LP	Tamla Motown	STML11034	1966	£5	£12	chart LP
This Old Heart Of Mine	7"	Tamla Motown	TMG555	1966	£2	£5	chart single
Twist And Shout	LP	Wand	WD(S)653	1962	£8	£20	US
Twist And Shout	7"	Stateside	SS112	1962	£4	£8	chart single
Twisting And Shouting	LP	United Artists	ULP1064	1964	£6	£15	
Twisting With Linda	7"	Stateside	SS132	1962	£2.50	£6	
Warpath	7"	Stateside	SS2188	1971	£1.50	£4	
Was It Good To You	7"	Stateside	SS2162	1970	£1.50	£4	

IT BITES

All In Red	7"	Virgin	VS839	1986	£1.50	£4	
Calling All The Heroes	7"	Virgin	VSD872	1986	£2.50	£6	double
Calling All The Heroes	7"	Virgin	VSY872	1986	£4	£8	pic disc
Midnight	7"	Virgin	VSS1065	1988	£4	£8	square pic disc
Whole New World	7"	Virgin	VSD896	1986	£2.50	£6	double

ITALS

Don't Throw It Away	7"	Giant	GN12	1967	£4	£8	Caribbeats B side
New Loving	7"	Giant	GN8	1967	£4	£8	Soul Brothers B side

ITHACA

Game For All Who Know	LP	Merlin	HF6	1972	£330	£500	

IT'S A BEAUTIFUL DAY

Choice Quality Stuff	LP	CBS	64314	1971	£4	£10	chart LP
It's A Beautiful Day	LP	CBS	63722	1968	£5	£12	
It's A Beautiful Day	LP	Columbia	CS9768	1969	£20	£40	US, topless girl on cover
It's A Beautiful Day	LP	San Francisco Sound	11790	1985	£6	£15	US audiophile
Live At Carnegie Hall	LP	CBS	64929	1972	£4	£10	
Marrying Maiden	LP	CBS	64065	1970	£5	£12	chart LP
Soapstone Mountain	7"	CBS	4933	1970	£2.50	£6	
White Bird	7"	CBS	4457	1969	£4	£8	

IVAN

Real Wild Child	7"	Coral	Q72341	1958	£150	£250	

IVAN'S MEADS

Sins Of A Family	7"	Parlophone	R5342	1965	£6	£12	
We'll Talk About It Tomorrow	7"	Parlophone	R5503	1966	£6	£12	

IVES, BURL

Australian Folk Songs	10" LP	Brunswick	LA8739	1956	£4	£10	
Ballads And Folk Songs Vol.1	10" LP	Brunswick	LA8583	1953	£4	£10	
Burl Ives	10" LP	Brunswick	LA8552	1953	£4	£10	
Down To The Sea In Ships	LP	Brunswick	LAT8142	1956	£4	£10	
Dying Stockman	7"	Brunswick	05551	1956	£1.50	£4	
Folk Songs - Dramatic And Humorous	10" LP	Brunswick	LA8633	1954	£4	£10	
Goober Peas	7"	Brunswick	05510	1956	£1.50	£4	
Women	10" LP	Brunswick	LA8641	1954	£4	£10	

IVEYS

The Iveys was the original name for the group Badfinger. The album "Maybe Tomorrow" received a limited release in Europe, but the British and American issues were cancelled. (A UK cover for the album, however, was sold at auction in 1988). Counterfeits of the European issue exist, but they do not have the Apple labels of the originals.

Dear Angie	7"	Apple	14	1969	£75	£150	European
Maybe Tomorrow	LP	Apple	SAPCOR8	1969	£150	£250	European
Maybe Tomorrow	7"	Apple	5	1968	£20	£40	

IVORY, JACK

Hi Heeled Sneakers	7"	Atlantic	AT4075	1966	£4	£8	
Soul Discovery	LP	Atco	(SD)33178	1965	£6	£15	US

IVY LEAGUE

Four And Twenty Hours	7"	Piccadilly	7N35365	1967	£1.50	£4	
Funny How Love Can Be	7"	Piccadilly	7N35222	1965	£1.50	£4	chart single

Funny How Love Can Be	7" EP..	Piccadilly	NEP34038	1965	£5	£10	
Holly And The Ivy League	7" EP..	Piccadilly	NEP34046	1965	£5	£10	
My World Fell Down	7"......	Piccadilly	7N35348	1966	£1.50	£4	
Our Love Is Slipping Away	7"......	Piccadilly	7N35267	1965	£1.50	£4	
Our Love Is Slipping Away	7" EP..	Piccadilly	NEP34048	1966	£5	£10	
Running Around In Circles	7"......	Piccadilly	7N35294	1966	£1.50	£4	
Sounds Of The Ivy League	LP......	Marble Arch ...	MAL741	1967	£6	£15	
Suddenly Things	7"......	Piccadilly	7N35397	1967	£1.50	£4	
Thank You For Loving Me	7"......	Pye	7N17386	1967	£1.50	£4	
That's Why I'm Crying	7"......	Piccadilly	7N35228	1965	£1.50	£4	chart single
That's Why I'm Crying	7" EP..	Pye	PNV24143	1965	£7.50	£15	French
This Is The Ivy League	LP......	Piccadilly	NPL38015	1965	£8	£20	
Tomorrow Is Another Day	LP......	Marble Arch ...	MAL821	1968	£4	£10	
Tossing And Turning	7"......	Piccadilly	7N35251	1965	£1.50	£4	chart single
Tossing And Turning	7" EP..	Piccadilly	NEP34042	1965	£5	£10	
What More Do You Want	7"......	Piccadilly	7N35200	1964	£2	£5	
Willow Tree	7"......	Piccadilly	7N35326	1966	£1.50	£4	chart single

IVY THREE

Yogi	7"......	London	HLW9178	1960	£2	£5	

IWAN, DAFYDD

Myn Duw, Mi A Wn Y Daw!	7" EP..	Sain	SAIN2	1969	£4	£8	
Pam Fod Eira Yn Wyn?	7" EP..	Sain	SAIN18	1971	£2.50	£6	

J, DAVID & ALAN MOORE
This Vicious Cabaret .... 12" ..... Glass............... GLASS12032 .... 1984 ... £3 ....£8 ....

J, HARRY ALL STARS
Liquidator .... LP ...... Trojan .... TBL104 .... 1970 ... £4 ....£10 ....
Liquidator .... 7" ...... Trojan .... TR675 .... 1969 ... £1.50 ....£4 ....chart single

JACKAL
Underneath The Arches .... 12" ..... Criminal .... CRI12134.............. 1986 ... £2.50 ....£6 ....
                                                                        Damage ....

JACKIE & BRIDIE
Folk World Of Jackie And Bridie .... LP ...... Concord........... .... 1970 ... £10 ....£25 ....

JACKIE & DOREEN
Adorable You .... 7" ...... Ska Beat........... JB209 .... 1965 ... £5 ....£10 ....

JACKIE & MILLIE
In A Dream .... 7" ...... Island .... WIP6012............ 1967 ... £4 ....£8 ....
My Desire .... 7" ...... Island .... WI265 .... 1966 ... £5 ....£10 ....
This Is My Story .... 7" ...... Island .... WI253 .... 1965 ... £5 ....£10 Sound System B side

JACKIE & ROY
You Smell So Good .... 7" ...... Vogue .... V9101 .... 1958 ... £15 ....£30 ....

JACKPOTS
Jack In The Box .... LP ...... Sonet .... 1968 ... £10 ....£25 ....

JACKS
Jacks .... LP ...... Crown .... CLP5021 .... 1957 ... £8 ....£20 .... US
Jumpin' With The Jacks .... LP ...... RPM .... LRP3006 .... 195- ... £37.50 .....£75 .... US

JACKSON & SMITH
Ain't That Loving You Baby .... 7" ...... Polydor .... BM56051 .... 1965 ... £4 ....£8 ....
Party '66 .... 7" ...... Polydor .... BM56086 .... 1966 ... £2.50 ....£6 ....

JACKSON, ALEXANDER & THE TURNKEYS
Whip .... 7" ...... Sue................... WI386 .... 1965 ... £10 ....£20 ....

JACKSON, BO WEEVIL
Some Scream High Yellow .... 7" ...... Jazz Collector .. JDL81 .... 1959 ... £4 ....£8 ....
Why Do You Moan? .... 7" ...... Collector .... JDL127 .... 1959 ... £1.50 ....£4 ....

JACKSON BROTHERS
Tell Him No .... 7" ...... London .... HLX8845 .... 1959 ... £7.50 ....£15 ....

JACKSON, BULL MOOSE
Bull Moose Jackson .... LP ...... Audio Lab....... AL1524 .... 1959 ... £25 ....£50 .... US
Nosey Joe .... 78 ...... Vogue .... V2129 .... 1952 ... £3 ....£8 ....

JACKSON, CALVIN
Calvin Jackson Quartet .... LP ...... Philips .... BBL7084 .... 1956 ... £4 ....£10 ....
Rave Notice .... LP ...... Philips .... BBL7107 .... 1958 ... £4 ....£10 ....

JACKSON, CHRIS
I'll Never Forget You .... 7" ...... Soul City........... SC112 .... 1969 ... £6 ....£12 ....
Since There's No Doubt .... 7" ...... Soul City........... SC120 .... 1969 ... £25 ....£50 ....test pressing

JACKSON, CHUCK
Any Day Now .... LP ...... Wand .... LP/WDS654........... 1962 ... £8 ....£20 .... US
Any Day Now .... 7" ...... Pye .... 7N25276 .... 1964 ... £4 ....£8 ....
Any Day Now .... 7" ...... Stateside .... SS102 .... 1962 ... £4 ....£8 ....
Beg Me .... 7" ...... Pye .... 7N25247 .... 1964 ... £4 ....£8 ....
Breaking Point .... 7" ...... Top Rank .... JAR607 .... 1962 ... £6 ....£12 ....
Chains Of Love .... 7" ...... Pye .... 7N25384 .... 1966 ... £12.50 .....£25 ....
Chuck Jackson Arrives .... LP ...... Tamla Motown (S)TML11071 .... 1968 ... £8 ....£20 ....
Dedicated To The King .... LP ...... Wand .... LP/WDS680......... 1966 ... £8 ....£20 .... US
Encore .... LP ...... Wand .... LP/WDS655......... 1963 ... £8 ....£20 .... US
Girls Girls Girls .... 7" ...... Tamla Motown TMG651 .... 1968 ... £4 ....£8 ....
Goin' Back To Chuck Jackson .... LP ...... Tamla Motown (S)TML11117 .... 1969 ... £5 ....£12 ....
Greatest Hits .... LP ...... Wand .... LP/WDS683......... 1967 ... £6 ....£15 .... US
Money Come Back .... 7" ...... Tamla Motown TMG729 .... 1970 ... £4 ....£8 ....
Can't Break Away .... 7" ...... Probe .... PRO617 .... 1974 ... £1.50 ....£4 ....
Don't Want To Cry .... LP ...... Wand .... LP/WDS650......... 1961 ... £8 ....£20 .... US
Don't Want To Cry .... 7" ...... Top Rank .... JAR564 .... 1961 ... £7.50 ....£15 ....
Keep Forgettin' .... 7" ...... Stateside .... SS102 .... 1962 ... £4 ....£8 ....
Need You .... 7" ...... Pye .... 7N25301 .... 1965 ... £2.50 ....£6 ....
Only Get The Feeling .... 7" ...... Probe .... PRO595 .... 1973 ... £2 ....£5 ....
If I Didn't Love You .... 7" ...... Pye .... 7N25321 .... 1965 ... £2.50 ....£6 ....
I've Got The Need .... 7" ...... All Platinum..... 6146310............... 1975 ... £1.50 ....£4 ....
Mr.Everything .... LP ...... Wand .... LP/WDS667......... 1965 ... £8 ....£20 .... US
On Tour .... LP ...... Wand .... LP/WDS658......... 1964 ... £8 ....£20 .... US

Shame On Me	7"	Pye	7N25439	1967	£2	£5	
Since I Don't Have You	7"	Pye	7N25287	1965	£12.50	£25	
Tell Him I'm Not Home	7"	Stateside	SS171	1963	£4	£8	
These Chains Of Love	7"	Pye	DDS116	1975	£1.50	£4	
Through All Times	LP	Probe	SPB1084	1972	£5	£12	
Tribute To Rhythm And Blues	LP	Pye	NPL28082	1967	£6	£15	
Tribute To Rhythm And Blues Vol.2	LP	Wand	LP/WDS676	1966	£6	£15	US

JACKSON, CHUCK & MAXINE BROWN

Hold On, We're Coming	LP	Wand	LP/WDS678	1966	£6	£15	US
Saying Something	LP	Pye	NPL28091	1967	£5	£12	
Something You Got	7"	Pye	7N25308	1965	£4	£8	

JACKSON, CHUCK & TAMMI TERRELL

Early Show	LP	Wand	LP/WDS682	1967	£6	£15	US

JACKSON, DEON

Love Makes The World Go Around	7"	Atlantic	AT4070	1966	£7.50	£15	
Love Makes The World Go Round	LP	Atco	(SD)33188	1966	£6	£15	US
Love Makes The World Go Round	7"	Contempo	CS9031	1975	£1.50	£4	
Love Takes A Long Time Growing	7"	Atlantic	584012	1966	£5	£10	
Ooh Baby	7"	Atlantic	584159	1968	£4	£8	

JACKSON FIVE

ABC	7"	Tamla Motown	TMB738	1970	£30	£60	demo, PS
ABC	7"	Tamla Motown	TMG738	1970	£1.50	£4	chart single
Anthology	LP	Tamla Motown	TMSP6004	1977	£5	£12	double
Doctor My Eyes	7"	Tamla Motown	TMG842	1973	£1.50	£4	chart single
Goin' Places	LP	Epic	PAL348351G	1978	£4	£10	US pic disc
Hallelujah Day	7"	Tamla Motown	TMG856	1973	£1.50	£4	chart single
I Want You Back	7"	Tamla Motown	TMG724	1970	£1.50	£4	chart single
I'll Be There	7"	Tamla Motown	TMG758	1970	£1.50	£4	chart single
Jacksons	LP	CBS	AL34229	1977	£4	£10	US pic disc
Little Bitty Pretty One	7"	Tamla Motown	TMG825	1972	£1.50	£4	chart single
Looking Through The Windows	7"	Tamla Motown	TMG833	1972	£1.50	£4	chart single
Looking Through The Windows	7"	Tamla Motown	TMG833	1972	£7.50	£15	demo, PS
Love You Save	7"	Tamla Motown	TMG746	1970	£1.50	£4	chart single
Mama's Pearl	7"	Tamla Motown	TMG769	1971	£1.50	£4	chart single
Moving Violations	LP	Tamla Motown	STML11290	1975	£6	£15	
Never Can Say Goodbye	7"	Tamla Motown	TMG778	1971	£1.50	£4	chart single
Santa Claus Is Coming To Town	7"	Tamla Motown	TMG837	1972	£1.50	£4	chart single
Skywriter	7"	Tamla Motown	TMG865	1973	£1.50	£4	chart single
Skywriter	7"	Tamla Motown	TMG865	1973	£7.50	£15	demo, PS
Sugar Daddy	7"	Tamla Motown	TMG809	1972	£1.50	£4	chart single
Talk And Sing To Valentine Readers	7"	Lyntone	LYN2639	1974	£2	£5	flex
Third Album	LP	Tamla Motown	STML11174	1971	£4	£10	

JACKSON, FRED

Hootin' 'n Tootin'	LP	Blue Note	BLP/BST84094	1962	£20	£40	

JACKSON, GEORGE

Find 'Em, Fool 'Em And Forget 'Em	7"	Capitol	CL15605	1969	£2.50	£6	
Let 'Em Know You Care	7"	London	HLU10413	1973	£2.50	£6	

JACKSON, GORDON

Me And My Zoo	7"	Marmalade	598010	1969	£2	£5	
Song For Freedom	7"	Marmalade	598021	1969	£2	£5	
Thinking Back	LP	Marmalade	608012	1969	£8	£20	

JACKSON, HAROLD & THE TORNADOES

Move It On Down The Line	7"	Vogue	V9105	1958	£20	£40	

JACKSON HEIGHTS

Bump And Grind	LP	Vertigo	6360092	1973	£6	£15	
Doubting Thomas	7"	Charisma	JH1	1970	£1.50	£4	
Fifth Avenue Bus	LP	Vertigo	6360067	1972	£8	£20	spiral label
King Progress	LP	Charisma	CAS1018	1970	£4	£10	
Ragamuffin's Fool	LP	Vertigo	6360077	1973	£8	£20	spiral label

JACKSON, JANET & CLIFF RICAHRD

Two To The Power Of Love	7"	A&M	AM210	1984	£1.50	£4	
Two To The Power Of Love	12"	A&M	AMX210	1984	£2.50	£6	

JACKSON, JERRY

Gypsy Eyes	7"	London	HLR9689	1963	£5	£10	
It's Rough Out There	7"	Cameo Parkway	P100	1962	£37.50	£75	

JACKSON, JIM

RCA Victor Race Series Vol.7	7" EP	RCA	RCX7182	1966	£5	£10	

JACKSON, JIMMY

Country And Blues	7" EP	Columbia	SEG7768	1958	£10	£20	
I Shall Not Be Moved	7"	Columbia	DB3898	1957	£6	£12	
Love A Love A Love A	7"	Columbia	DB4085	1958	£2.50	£6	
River Line	7"	Columbia	DB3957	1957	£5	£10	
Rock 'n' Skiffle	7" EP	Columbia	SEG7750	1958	£10	£20	
Sitting In The Balcony	7"	Columbia	DB3937	1957	£7.50	£15	
This Little Light Of Mine	7"	Columbia	DB4153	1958	£2.50	£6	
White Silver Sands	7"	Columbia	DB3988	1957	£2.50	£6	

JACKSON, J.J.

Although he called his group "The Greatest Little Soul Band", the music that J.J.Jackson played was actually jazz-rock. Indeed, the soul band description was probably a marketing mistake. Fans of Colosseum and Manfred Mann Chapter Three would have loved this, but they looked no further than the cover. More precise is the comparison with the group If, whose leaders Dick Morrissey and Terry Smith both played with Jackson. The sleeve notes to the MCA album end with the words: "go and see the band and you'll realise that if they aren't the biggest thing in the country in six months, there's no justice". Sadly, there was none.

Title	Format	Label	Cat#	Year			Notes
And Proud Of It	LP	Perception	PLP12		£6	£15	US
But It's Alright	LP	Calla	C(S)1101	1967	£6	£15	US
But It's Alright	7"	Warner Bros	WB7276	1969	£1.50	£4	
Come See Me	7"	Strike	JH329	1967	£2.50	£6	
Courage Ain't Strength	7"	Warner Bros	WB6029	1968	£1.50	£4	
Do The Boogaloo	7"	Polydor	56718	1966	£2.50	£6	
Down But Not Out	7"	Warner Bros	WB2090	1968	£1.50	£4	
Great J.J.Jackson	LP	Warner Bros	WS1797	1969	£6	£15	US
Greatest Little Soul Band	LP	MCA	SKA100	1969	£6	£15	
J.J.Jackson's Dilemma	LP	RCA	SF8093	1970	£6	£15	
Sho Nuff	7"	Warner Bros	WB2082	1967	£2	£5	
Something For My People	7"	MCA/Soul Bag.	BAG6	1969	£1.50	£4	
Tenement Halls	7"	MCA/Soul Bag.	BAG4	1969	£1.50	£4	
With The Greatest Little Soul Band	LP	Strike	JHL104	1967	£6	£15	

JACKSON, JOE

Title	Format	Label	Cat#	Year			Notes
I'm The Man	7"	A&M	SP1800	1980	£6	£12	US 5 x 7", poster, boxed

JACKSON, LEVI

Title	Format	Label	Cat#	Year			Notes
This Beautiful Day	7"	Columbia	DB8807	1971	£17.50	£35	

JACKSON, LIL' SON

Title	Format	Label	Cat#	Year			Notes
Rockin' And Rollin'	LP	Imperial	9142	1961	£30	£60	US

JACKSON, MAHALIA

Title	Format	Label	Cat#	Year			Notes
Great Gettin' Up Morning	LP	Philips	BBL7362	1960	£4	£10	
I Believe	LP	Philips	BBL7456/SBBL610	1961	£4	£10	
Just As I Am	LP	Top Rank	30006	1960	£4	£10	
Mahalia Jackson	10" LP	Vogue	LDE005	1952	£5	£12	
Newport 1958	LP	Philips	BBL7289/SBBL547	1959	£5	£12	
Power And The Glory	LP	Philips	BBL7391/SBBL576	1960	£4	£10	

JACKSON, MICHAEL

Michael Jackson has made the two biggest selling albums ever, and has in the process acquired a legion of fans keen to collect anything they can find. Within the collectors' market, Jackson has joined the select few stars for whom there are dealers specialising exclusively in his music. The "Dangerous" picture disc is a distinct oddity, in that it does not actually play Michael Jackson's music at all. Copies were produced for promo and test purposes before it was realised that the vinyl release was going to be a double. A commercial picture disc was never produced in consequence (although double album picture discs, such as Frankie Goes To Hollywood's "Welcome To The Pleasure Dome", have been issued in the past). The Michael Jackson Megamix 12" was withdrawn and half the original thousand copies were destroyed. Counterfeits exist of the remainder, these are identifiable by the fact that they play at 33rpm, whereas the real thing plays at 45rpm despite the label stating that it is actually 33rpm).

Title	Format	Label	Cat#	Year			Notes
Ain't No Sunshine	7"	Tamla Motown	TMG826	1972	£1.50	£4	chart single
Another Part Of Me	CD-s	Epic	6530042	1988	£4	£10	
Another Part Of Me	7"	Epic	6528440	1988	£2.50	£6	poster PS
Another Part Of Me	7"	Epic	6528449	1988	£1.50	£4	with backstage pass
Bad	LP	Epic	4502900	1987	£4	£10	pic disc
Bad	cass	Epic	450290	1987	£6	£15	with note pad, pen, calendar
Bad	7"	Epic	EPCMJ5	1988	£7.50	£15	5 pic discs
Bad	12"	Epic	6511556	1987	£5	£12	red vinyl
Ben	7"	Tamla Motown	TMG834	1972	£1.50	£4	chart single
Billie Jean (Meanjean Mix)	CD-s	Epic		198-	£20	£40	
Dangerous	LP	Epic		1991	£700	£1000	US sample pic disc - plays Richard Clayderman!
Dangerous	CD	Epic	4658029	1992	£6	£15	10'-square pop-up pack
Dirty Diana	CD-s	Epic	6515469	1988	£3	£8	
Dirty Diana	12"	Epic	6528646	1988	£3	£8	poster PS
E.T.	LP	MCA	MCA70000	1982	£40	£80	with book and poster, boxed
E.T.	cass	MCA		1982	£6	£15	with book & poster, boxed
Got To Be There	7"	Tamla Motown	TMG797	1972	£1.50	£4	chart single
Happy	7"	Tamla Motown	TMG986	1983	£5	£10	pic disc
Happy	7"	Tamla Motown	TMG986	1983	£4	£8	poster PS
Just Can't Stop Loving You	7"	Epic	6502020	1987	£2.50	£6	poster PS
Just Can't Stop Loving You	12"	Epic	6502026	1987	£3	£8	with poster
Leave Me Alone	CD-s	Epic	6546722	1989	£3	£8	
Liberian Girl	CD-s	Epic	6549472	1989	£3	£8	
Liberian Girl	7"	Epic	6549479	1989	£2.50	£6	mobile pack
Man In THe Mirror	CD-s	Epic	6513882	1988	£3	£8	
Man In The Mirror	7"	Epic	EPC6513889	1988	£2.50	£6	shaped pic disc
Morning Glow	7"	Tamla Motown	TMG863	1973	£1.50	£4	
Megamix	12"	Epic	XPR1242	198-	£30	£60	
Off The Wall	LP	Epic	EPC83458	1980	£8	£20	with 7' pic disc
Off The Wall	LP	Epic	HE47545	1980	£5	£12	US audiophile
Rockin' Robin	7"	Tamla Motown	TMG816	1972	£1.50	£4	chart single
Singles Pack	7"	Epic	MJ1	1983	£12.50	£25	9 x red vinyl
Smooth Criminal	CD-s	Epic	6530263	1987	£4	£10	
Smooth Criminal	7"	Epic	6530260	1987	£2.50	£6	boxed with postcards
Smooth Criminal	12"	Epic	6530261	1987	£4	£10	with advent calendar

Smooth Criminal (Funkin' Smooth Mix)	12"	Epic		1988	£15 ....£30	
Smooth Criminal (Smokin' Gun Mix) ...	12"	Epic		1988	£20 ....£40	
Smooth Criminal (Vancouver Feetbeat)	12"	Epic		1988	£17.50 .....£35	
Thriller	LP	Epic	EPC1185930	1982	£8 ....£20	pic disc
Thriller	LP	Epic	HE48112	1982	£8 ....£20	US audiophile
Way You Make Me Feel	CD-s ..	Epic	6512759	1987	£3 ....£8	
Way You Make Me Feel	7"	Epic	6512753	1987	£2 ....£5	double groove
You Can't Win	7"	Epic	EPC7135	1979	£4 ....£8	pic disc

JACKSON, MICHAEL & PAUL MCCARTNEY

Girl Is Mine	7"	Epic	EPCA112729	1982	£5 ....£10	pic disc

JACKSON, MILLIE

Caught Up	LP	Polydor	2391147	1975	£4 ....£10	
If Loving You Is Wrong	7"	Polydor	2066536	1975	£1.50 .....£4	
It Hurts So Good	LP	Polydor	2391091	1972	£4 ....£10	
Loving Arms	7"	Polydor	2066612	1975	£2 ....£5	
Millie	LP	Spring	6701	1973	£4 ....£10	US
Millie Jackson	LP	Polydor	2391025	1972	£4 ....£10	
My Man's A Sweet Man	7"	Mojo	2093022	1972	£1.50 .....£4	chart single
Still Caught Up	LP	Polydor	2391183	1975	£4 ....£10	

JACKSON, MILT

At The Museum Of Modern Art	LP	Mercury	LML/SML4016	1965	£4 ....£10	
Bags And Flutes	LP	London	LTZK15177	1960	£5 ....£12	
Bags Meets Wes	LP	Riverside	RLP(9)407	1962	£5 ....£12	with Wes Montgomery
Bags' Opus	LP	London	LTZK15172/ SAHT6049	1959	£5 ....£12	
Ballad Artistry	LP	London	LTZK15220/ SAHK6163	1961	£5 ....£12	
Ballad Artistry	7" EP..	London	REK1315	1962	£2 ....£5	
Ballads And Blues	LP	London	LTZK15064	1957	£8 ....£20	
Bean Bags	LP	London	LTZK15196/ SAHK6095	1960	£5 ....£12	with Coleman Hawkins
Born Free	LP	Mercury	LML/SML4028	1966	£4 ....£10	
In A New Setting	LP	Mercury	LML/SML4008	1965	£4 ....£10	
Jackson Ville	LP	London	LTZK15091	1957	£8 ....£20	
Jackson's Ville	LP	London	LTZC15091	1957	£8 ....£20	
Jazz Skyline	LP	London	LTZC15074	1957	£8 ....£20	
Jazz Skyline	LP	London	LTZK15074	1957	£8 ....£20	
Milt Jackson	LP	Blue Note.	BLP/BST81509	1962	£10 ....£25	with Thelonious Monk
Milt Jackson	LP	Philips	BBL7459	1961	£5 ....£12	
Milt Jackson And His New Group	10" LP	Vogue	LDE044	1954	£25 ....£50	
Milt Jackson Quartet	LP	Esquire	32009	1955	£10 ....£25	
Milt Jackson Quartet	LP	Realm	RM119	1963	£5 ....£12	
Milt Jackson Quartet	10" LP	London	LZC14006	1955	£15 ....£30	
Milt Jackson Quintet	10" LP	Esquire	20042	1955	£20 ....£40	
Milt Jackson Septet	7" EP..	London	EZC19004	195-	£2.50 .....£6	
Modern Jazz Quartet/Quintet	LP	Esquire	32134	1962	£5 ....£12	
Opus De Jazz	LP	London	LTZC15026	1957	£10 ....£25	
Plenty, Plenty Soul	LP	London	LTZK15141	1959	£6 ....£15	
Statements	LP	HMV	CLP1589/CSD1455	1963	£5 ....£12	
Vibrations	LP	Atlantic	ATL/SAL5012	1964	£5 ....£12	
Wizard Of The Vibes	LP	Vogue	LAE12046	1957	£6 ....£15	

JACKSON, PAPA CHARLIE

Long Gone Lost John	78	Tempo	R30	1950	£2.50 .....£6	
Papa Charlie Jackson	7" EP..	Heritage	R100	1960	£7.50 .....£15	

JACKSON, PYTHON LEE

In A Broken Dream	7" EP..	Young Blood ...	YEP89	1985	£2.50 .....£6	prom

JACKSON, RALPH

Cause I Love You	7"	Atlantic	584258	1969	£1.50 .....£4	

JACKSON, ROOT & JENNY

Lean On Me	7"	Beacon	BEA110	1968	£1.50 .....£4	

JACKSON, SHIRLEY

Broken Home	7"	Decca	F11788	1963	£2.50 .....£6	

JACKSON, SHOVELVILLE K.

Be Careful Of Stones That You Throw .	7"	Melodisc	1683	196-	£4 ....£8	

JACKSON, SIMONE

Doing What You Know Is Wrong	7" EP..	Pye	PNV24111	1963	£4 ....£8	Frenc

JACKSON SISTERS

I Believe In Miracles	7"	Mums	MUM1829	1973	£7.50 .....£15	

JACKSON, STONEWALL

Dynamic Stonewall Jackson	LP	Columbia	CL1391/CS8186	1959	£6 ....£15	U
Greatest Hits	LP	CBS	BPG62587	1965	£5 ....£12	
I'm Gonna Find You	7"	Philips	PB1073	1960	£1.50 .....£4	
Sadness In A Song	LP	Columbia	CL1770/CS8570	1962	£6 ....£15	U
Waterloo	7"	Philips	PB941	1959	£2.50 .....£6	chart single

JACKSON, TONY & THE VIBRATIONS

It must have seemed a good idea to Tony Jackson, as the lead singer of the Searchers, to strike out on his own. Unfortunately, it turned out that his personal following was only a fraction of the following enjoyed by the Searchers as a group. None of Tony Jackson's singles got anywhere at all, while the remaining Searchers gained at immediate number one, with "Needles And Pins".

Anything Else You Want	7"	CBS	202408	1966	£10	£20
Bye Bye Baby	7"	Pye	7N15685	1964	£5	£10 .... chart single
Follow Me	7"	CBS	202297	1966	£12.50	£25
Love Potion No.9	7"	Pye	7N15766	1965	£10	£20
Never Leave Your Baby's Side	7"	CBS	202069	1966	£10	£20
Stage Door	7"	Pye	7N15876	1965	£7.50	£15
This Little Girl Of Mine	7"	Pye	7N15745	1964	£7.50	£15
Tony Jackson Group	7" EP	Estudio		1967	£120	£220 .... Portuguese
You're My Number One	7"	CBS	202039	1966	£10	£20
You're My Number One	7" EP	CBS	5726	1966	£50	£100 .... French

JACKSON, WALTER

Any Way That You Want Me	7"	Atlantic	584311	1970	£2	£5
Corner In The Sun	7"	Columbia	DB8054	1966	£4	£8
It's An Uphill Climb To The Bottom	7"	Columbia	DB7949	1966	£6	£12
Speak Her Name	7"	Columbia	DB8154	1967	£4	£8
Welcome Home	7"	Columbia	DB7620	1965	£4	£8

JACKSON, WANDA

Wanda Jackson was one of the best female rock'n'roll singers, although her competition was rather limited. Adopting the same rasping tones as Brenda Lee on her uptempo material, Wanda Jackson's older voice had a greater depth and hence rather more power. In common with most of the American singers of her generation, she took the country route once the initial rock'n'roll years were over.

Blues In My Heart	LP	Capitol	(S)T2306	1964	£4	£10
If I Cried Every Time You Hurt Me	7"	Capitol	CL15249	1962	£4	£8
In The Middle Of A Heartache	7"	Capitol	CL15234	1962	£4	£8
Let's Have A Party	7"	Capitol	CL15147	1960	£6	£12 .... chart single
Let's Have A Party	7" EP	Capitol	EAP11041	1959	£15	£30
Little Bitty Tear	7" EP	Capitol	EAP120353	1962	£7.50	£15
Love Me Forever	LP	Capitol	(S)T1911	1963	£5	£12 .... US
Lovin' Country Style	LP	Decca	DL4224	1962	£8	£20 .... US
Mean Mean Man	7"	Capitol	CL15176	1961	£6	£12 .... chart single
Reaching	7"	Capitol	CL15090	1959	£5	£10
Right Or Wrong	LP	Capitol	T1596	1961	£8	£20
Right Or Wrong	7"	Capitol	CL15223	1961	£2.50	£6
Rockin' With Wanda	LP	Capitol	T1384	1960	£25	£50
There's A Party Goin' On	LP	Capitol	T1511	1961	£25	£50
Two Sides Of Wanda Jackson	LP	Capitol	(S)T2030	1964	£6	£15
Wanda Jackson	LP	Capitol	T1041	1958	£25	£50 .... US
Wonderful Wanda	LP	Capitol	T1776	1962	£6	£15
You're The One For Me	7"	Capitol	CL15033	1959	£5	£10

JACKY

White Horses	7"	Philips	BF1674	1968	£1.50	£4 .... chart single

JACOBITES

Like Now	7"	Pye	7N17852	1969	£2.50	£6

JACOBS, DICK

Big Beat	7"	Vogue Coral	Q72245	1957	£4	£8
Man With The Golden Arm	7"	Vogue Coral	Q72154	1956	£1.50	£4
Rock-a-Billy Gal	7"	Vogue Coral	Q72260	1957	£1.50	£4
Skiffle Sound	LP	Coral	LVA9076	1957	£8	£20

JACOBS, HANK

Monkey Hips And Rice	7"	Sue	WI313	1964	£7.50	£15
So Far Away	LP	Sue	1023	1964	£8	£20 .... US

JACQUES, BRIAN & BRIGANTINE

Gig Wid Brig	LP	Sweet Folk & Country	SFAO11	1974	£5	£12

JACQUET, ILLINOIS

Blow Illinois Blow	7"	Vogue	V2387	1956	£1.50	£4
Groovin' With Jacquet	LP	Columbia	33CX10085	1957	£20	£40
Illinois Jacquet	10" LP	Columbia	33C9018	1956	£20	£40
Illinois Jacquet	10" LP	Vogue	LDE026	1953	£25	£50

JADE

Fly On Strange Wings	LP	DJM		1970	£15	£30

JADE WARRIOR

Jade Warrior were essentially a duo - Tony Duhig and Jon Field - whose music is perfectly decribed by their album covers. Mostly instrumental, with a hint of the orient and an emphasis on a gentle textural beauty, Jade Warrior's music laid down the ground rules for much of what is defined as "new age".

Demon Trucker	7"	Vertigo	6059069	1972	£4	£8
Eclipse	LP	Vertigo			£100	£200 .... promo only
Floating World	LP	Island	ILPS9290	1974	£5	£12
Jade Warrior	LP	Vertigo	6360033	1971	£15	£30 .... spiral label
Kites	LP	Island	ILPS9393	1976	£5	£12
Last Autumn's Dream	LP	Vertigo	6360079	1972	£15	£30 .... spiral label
Released	LP	Vertigo	6360062	1971	£20	£40 .... spiral label
Waves	LP	Island	ILPS9318	1975	£5	£12
Way Of The Sun	LP	Island	ILPS9552	1978	£5	£12

JADES

Both sides of the rare single by the Jades were written by a sixteen-year old Lou Reed, who also played rhythm guitar. This is his recording debut.

Leave Her For Me .... 7" .... Time .... 1002 .... 1957 ... £30 .... £60 .... US

JAGGER, MICK
Memo From Turner	7"	Decca	F13067	1970	£2.50	£6	chart single
Memo From Turner	7"	Decca	F13067	1970	£12.50	£25	export, PS
Mick Jagger Tells All	CD	RCA		198-	£65	£130	US promo
Ned Kelly	LP	United Artists	UAS5213	1970	£8	£20	with other artists
Performance	LP	Warner Bros	WS2554	1970	£5	£12	with other artists

JAGS
Cry Wolf	7"	Decca	F11397	1961	£2.50	£6	

JAGUAR
Axe Crazy	7"	Neat	NEAT16	1982	£4	£8	
Back Street Woman	7"	Heavy Metal	HEAVY10	1981	£2	£5	

JAGUARS
Opus To Spring	7"	Impression	IMP101	196-	£2.50	£6	

JAIM
Prophesy Fulfilled	LP	Ethereal	1001	1970	£8	£20	US

JAKE & THE FAMILY JEWELS
Jake & The Family Jewels	LP	Polydor	2425027	1970	£4	£10	

JAKLIN
Jaklin	LP	Stable	SLE8003	1969	£100	£200	

JAM
Beat Surrender	7"	Polydor	PODJ540	1982	£60	£120	autographed double, handwritten lyrics
Beat Surrender	7"	Polydor	PODJ540	1982	£2.50	£6	promo, censored version
Beat Surrender	12"	Polydor	POSP540X	1982	£8	£20	mispressed B side
Funeral Pyre	7"	Fan Club		1982	£7.50	£15	flexi
Going Underground	7"	Polydor	POSPJ113/ 2816024	1980	£2	£5	double
In The City	7"	Polydor	2058866	1977	£2	£5	chart single
News Of The World	7"	Polydor	2058995	1978	£10	£20	mispress with 2 B sides
Snap!	LP	Polydor	SNAP1	1983	£5	£12	double, with 7' (SNAP45)
Snap! Medley	7"	Polydor	LEE1	1983	£7.50	£15	promo
Tales From The Riverbank	7"	Fan Club	no number	1982	£7.50	£15	flexi
When You're Young	7"	Fan Club	no number	1981	£7.50	£15	flexi
When You're Young	7"	Polydor	POSP69	1979	£10	£20	mispress with 2 B sides

JAMAICA CALYPSONIANS
Dr.Kinsey Report	7"	Dice	RL101	196-	£2.50	£6	

JAMAICAN SHADOWS
Dirty Dozen	7"	Upsetter	US320	1969	£2.50	£6	
Have Mercy	7"	Coxsone	CS7005	1967	£5	£10	

JAMAICANS
Bab Boom	7"	Treasure Isle	TI7012	1967	£5	£10	Tommy McCook B side
Cool Night	7"	Doctor Bird	DB1109	1967	£5	£10	
Dedicated To You	7"	Trojan	TR007	1967	£5	£10	
Early In The Morning	7"	Escort	ES806	1969	£2	£5	
Peace And Love	7"	Treasure Isle	TI7037	1968	£5	£10	
Things You Say You Love	7"	Treasure Isle	TI7007	1967	£5	£10	

JAMAL, AHMAD
Ahmad Jamal	LP	London	LTZM15170	1959	£6	£15	
Alhambra	LP	Pye	NJL38	1962	£5	£12	
But Not For Me	LP	London	LTZM15162	1959	£6	£15	
Cry Young	LP	Chess	CRL4532	1968	£5	£12	
Macanudo	LP	Pye	NJL50	1963	£5	£12	
Standard-Eyes	LP	Chess	CRL4530	1968	£5	£12	

JAMES
Chain Mail	7"	Blanco Y Negro	JIM3	1986	£2	£5	
Chain Mail	12"	Blanco Y Negro	JIM3T	1986	£4	£10	
Come Home	CD-s	Rough Trade	RTT245CD	1989	£2.50	£6	
James II	7"	Factory	FAC119	1985	£2.50	£6	
Jimone	7"	Factory	FAC78	1984	£4	£8	
Sit Down	CD-s	Rough Trade	RTT225CD	1989	£3	£8	
Sit Down	7"	Rough Trade	RT225	1989	£1.50	£4	
Sit Down	12"	Rough Trade	RTT225	1989	£3	£8	
So Many Ways	7"	Blanco Y Negro	JIM4	1986	£2	£5	
So Many Ways	12"	Blanco Y Negro	JIM4T	1986	£4	£10	
What For	12"	Blanco Y Negro	NEG31T	1988	£3	£8	

Yaho	12"	Blanco Y Negro	NEG26T	1988	£3	£8

JAMES BOYS

Mule	7"	Direction	583721	1968	£2	£5

JAMES BROTHERS

Does It Have To Be Me	7"	Page One	POF088	1968	£1.50	£4
I Forgot To Give You Love	7"	Page One	POF077	1968	£1.50	£4

JAMES, CALVIN

Some Things You Never Get Used To	7"	Columbia	DB7516	1965	£4	£8

JAMES, DICK

Garden Of Eden	7"	Parlophone	R4255	1957	£4	£8	chart single
He	7"	Parlophone	MSP6190	1955	£2.50	£6	
I Only Know I Love You	7"	Parlophone	R4220	1956	£1.50	£4	
Joker	7"	Parlophone	MSP6047	1953	£2.50	£6	
Mother Nature And Father Time	7"	Parlophone	MSP6039	1953	£2.50	£6	
Robin Hood	7"	Parlophone	MSP6199	1956	£6	£12	chart single
Sing A Song Of Beatles	7"	Parlophone	R5212	1964	£2	£5	
Skiffling Sing Song	7"	Parlophone	R4375	1957	£1.50	£4	
Unchained Melody	7"	Parlophone	MSP6170	1955	£4	£8	
Westward Ho The Wagons	7"	Parlophone	R4314	1957	£1.50	£4	

JAMES, ELMORE

All Them Blues	LP	DJM	DJLMD8008	1975	£5	£12	double
Anthology Of The Blues Legend	LP	Kent	KLP9001	196-	£6	£15	US
Best Of Elmore James	LP	Sue	ILP918	1965	£20	£40	
Blues After Hours	LP	Crown	CLP5168	1961	£15	£30	US
Calling The Blues	7"	Sue	WI392	1965	£15	£30	
Cotton Patch Hotfoots	LP	Polydor	2383200	1973	£4	£10	
Dust My Blues	7"	Sue	WI335	1964	£7.50	£15	
I Need You	LP	Sphere Sound	7008	1964	£8	£20	US
I Need You	7"	Sue	WI4007	1966	£7.50	£15	
It Hurts Me Too	7"	Sue	WI383	1965	£7.50	£15	
King Of The Slide Guitar	LP	Ace	CH68	1983	£4	£10	yellow vinyl
Late Fantastically Great Elmore James	LP	Ember	EMB3397	1968	£5	£12	
Legend Of Elmore James	LP	United Artists	UAS29109	1970	£6	£15	
Memorial Album	LP	Sue	ILP927	1965	£20	£40	
Original Folk Blues	LP	Kent	KLP5022	1964	£10	£25	US
Resurrection Of Elmore James	LP	Kent	KLP9010	196-	£6	£15	US
Sky Is Crying	LP	Sphere Sound	7002	1964	£8	£20	US
Something Inside Of Me	LP	Bell	MBLL/SBLL104	1968	£8	£20	
To Know A Man	LP	Blue Horizon	766230	1969	£20	£40	double
Whose Muddy Shoes	LP	Chess	1537	1969	£6	£15	US

JAMES, ELMORE & JOHN BRIM

Tough	LP	Blue Horizon	763204	1968	£15	£30

JAMES, ETTA

All I Could Do Was Cry	7"	London	HLM9139	1960	£7.50	£15	
Anything To Say You're Mine	7"	Pye	7N25080	1961	£4	£8	
At Last	LP	Argo	(S)4003	1961	£8	£20	US
At Last	LP	Chess	CRL4524	1967	£5	£12	
At Last	7"	Pye	7N25079	1961	£4	£8	
Etta James	LP	Argo	(S)4013	1962	£6	£15	US
Etta James Sings For Lovers	LP	Argo	(S)4018	1962	£6	£15	US
Fool That I Am	7"	Pye	7N25113	1961	£4	£8	
I Got You Babe	7"	Chess	CRS8076	1968	£2	£5	
I Prefer You	7"	Chess	CRS8052	1967	£4	£8	
Miss Etta James	LP	Kent	3002	196-	£6	£15	US
Miss Etta James	LP	Kent	3002	196-	£8	£20	US, red vinyl
My Dearest Darling	7"	London	HLM9234	1960	£6	£12	
Pushover	7"	Pye	7N25205	1963	£4	£8	
Queen Of Soul	LP	Argo	(S)4040	1965	£5	£12	US
Rock With Me Henry	7"	Sue	WI359	1965	£7.50	£15	
Rocks The House	LP	Chess	CRL4502	1963	£5	£12	
Second Time Around	LP	Argo	(S)4011	1961	£6	£15	US
Security	7"	Chess	CRS8069	1967	£2.50	£6	
Something's Got A Hold Of Me	7"	Pye	7N25131	1962	£5	£10	
Soul Of Etta James	LP	Ember	EMB3390	1968	£5	£12	
Stop The Wedding	7"	Pye	7N25162	1962	£4	£8	
Tell Mama	LP	Chess	CRL4536	1968	£5	£12	
Tell Mama	7"	Chess	CRS8063	1967	£4	£8	
Top Ten	LP	Argo	(S)4025	1963	£6	£15	US
You Got It	7"	Chess	CRS8082	1968	£2.50	£6	

JAMES, ETTA & SUGAR PIE DESANTO

Do I Make Myself Clear	7"	Chess	CRS8025	1965	£5	£10

JAMES GANG

Funk No.48	7"	Stateside	SS2158	1970	£1.50	£4	
Miami	LP	Atco	QD36102	1974	£5	£12	US quad
Stop	7"	Stateside	SS2173	1970	£2	£5	
Yer Album	LP	Stateside	SSL10295	1969	£4	£10	

JAMES, HARRY

Harry James	LP	Capitol	LCT6107	1956	£5	£12
Harry James Orchestra	LP	Philips	BBL7036	1955	£6	£15
Wild About Harry	LP	Capitol	LCT6146	1957	£5	£12

JAMES, HOMESICK
Crossroads	7"	Sue	WI319	1964	£7.50	£15
Set A Date	7"	Sue	WI330	1965	£7.50	£15

JAMES, HOMESICK & SNOOKY PRIOR
Homesick James And Snooky Prior	LP	Caroline	C1502	1974	£4	£10

JAMES, JASON
Miss Pilkington's Maid	7"	CBS	2705	1967	£6	£12

JAMES, JESSE
Lonesome Day Blues	78	Vocalion	V1037	1954	£3	£8

JAMES, JIMMY
Ain't Love Good	7"	Piccadilly	7N35349	1966	£4	£8	
Ain't Love Good Ain't Love Proud	7" EP	Pye	PNV24183	1966	£6	£12	French
Help Yourself	7"	Trojan	TR7806	1970	£5	£10	
Hi Diddley Dee Dum Dum	7"	Piccadilly	7N35320	1966	£2.50	£6	
I Can't Get Back Home To My Baby	7"	Piccadilly	7N35360	1967	£4	£8	
I Feel Alright	7"	Piccadilly	7N35298	1966	£2.50	£6	
Jimmy James & The Vagabonds	7" EP	Piccadilly	NEP34053	1966	£6	£12	
Jump Children	7"	R&B	JB112	1963	£5	£10	
New Religion	LP	Piccadilly	NPL38027	1966	£6	£15	
New Religion	7" EP	Pye	PNV24188	1967	£6	£12	French
No Good To Cry	7"	Piccadilly	7N35374	1967	£2.50	£6	
No Good To Cry	7" EP	Pye	PNV24193	1967	£6	£12	French
Open Up Your Soul	LP	Pye	N(S)PL18231	1968	£6	£15	
Red Red Wine	7"	Pye	7N17579	1968	£1.50	£4	chart single
Shoo Be Doo You're Mine	7"	Columbia	DB7653	1965	£4	£8	
Thinking Of You	7"	Black Swan	WI437	1964	£2.50	£6	
This Heart Of Mine	7"	Piccadilly	7N35331	1966	£4	£8	
This Is Jimmy James	LP	Marble Arch	MAL823	1968	£4	£10	
You Don't Stand A Chance	LP	Pye	NSPL18457	1975	£5	£12	
Your Love	7"	Ska Beat	JB242	1966	£5	£10	

JAMES, JOHN
Acoustica Eclectica	LP	Stoptime	STOP101	1984	£5	£12	
Descriptive Guitar Instrumentals	LP	Kicking Mule	SNKF128	1976	£5	£12	
Head In The Clouds	LP	Transatlantic	TRA305	1975	£6	£15	
John James	LP	Transatlantic	TRA242	1971	£6	£15	
Live In Concert	LP	Kicking Mule	SNKF136	1978	£5	£12	
Morning Brings The Light	LP	Transatlantic	TRA219	1970	£6	£15	
Sky In My Pie	LP	Transatlantic	TRA250	1971	£6	£15	with Pete Berryman

JAMES, JONI
After Hours	LP	MGM	C933	1963	£5	£12	
Almost Always	7"	MGM	SP1041	1953	£5	£10	
Am I In Love	7"	MGM	SP1089	1954	£4	£8	
At Carnegie Hall	LP	MGM	(S)E3800	1959	£5	£12	US
Award Winning Album	LP	MGM	E3346	1956	£6	£15	US
Award Winning Album	10" LP	MGM	E234	195-	£8	£20	US
Country Girl Style	LP	MGM	(S)E4101	1962	£5	£12	US
Give Us This Day	LP	MGM	E3528	1958	£6	£15	US
Give Us This Day	LP	MGM	MGM918	1957	£2	£5	
Have You Heart	7"	MGM	SP1025	1953	£4	£8	
How Important Can It Be	7"	MGM	SP1125	1955	£2.50	£6	
Hundred Strings And Joni In	LP	MGM	C839/CS6015	1961	£5	£12	
Hollywood							
I Feel A Song Comin' On	LP	MGM	(S)E4053	1962	£5	£12	US
I Love You	7" EP	MGM	MGMEP651	1958	£2	£5	
I Need You Now	7"	MGM	SP1081	1954	£2.50	£6	
I'll Never Stand In Your Way	7"	MGM	SP1064	1954	£5	£10	
I'm Your Girl	LP	MGM	(S)E4054	1962	£5	£12	US
In A Garden Of Roses	7"	MGM	SP1100	1954	£2.50	£6	
In The Still Of The Night	LP	MGM	E3328	1956	£6	£15	US
Is This The End Of The Line	7"	MGM	SP1135	1955	£2.50	£6	
Joni James	7" EP	MGM	MGMEP504	1954	£5	£10	
Joni James Sings Sweet	LP	MGM	(S)E3772	1959	£5	£12	US
Joni James Sings To You	7" EP	MGM	MGMEP518	1955	£4	£8	
Let There Be Love	10" LP	MGM	D127	1954	£8	£20	
Little Girl Blue	7" EP	MGM	MGMEP530	1956	£4	£8	
Love Letters	7" EP	MGM	MGMEP558	1956	£2	£5	
Mama Don't Cry At My Wedding	7"	MGM	SP1105	1954	£2.50	£6	
Merry Christmas From Joni	LP	MGM	E3468	1957	£6	£15	US
Mood Is Blue	LP	MGM	(S)E3991	1961	£5	£12	US
Mood Is Romance	LP	MGM	(S)E3990	1961	£5	£12	US
Mood Is Swinging	LP	MGM	(S)E3987	1961	£5	£12	US
One Hundred Strings And Joni	LP	MGM	C777	1959	£5	£12	
Only Trust Your Heart	7"	MGM	MGM954	1957	£1.50	£4	
Sings Irish Favourites	LP	MGM	C823/CS6005	1960	£5	£12	
Songs Of Hank Williams	LP	MGM	C785	1959	£5	£12	
Songs Of Hank Williams	7" EP	MGM	ES3501	1960	£5	£10	stereo
Songs Of Hank Williams	7" EP	MGM	MGMEP728	1960	£4	£8	
Stage Songs	7" EP	MGM	MGMEP595	1957	£2	£5	
Swings Sweet	LP	MGM	C825	1960	£5	£12	
There Must Be A Way	7"	MGM	MGM1002	1959	£1.50	£4	chart single
Ti Voglio Bene	LP	MGM	C809	1960	£5	£12	
Why Don't You Believe Me?	7"	MGM	SP1013	1953	£5	£10	chart single
You Are My Love	7"	MGM	SP1149	1956	£2.50	£6	
Your Cheatin' Heart	7"	MGM	SP1026	1953	£5	£10	

You're My Everything	7"	MGM	SP1094	1954	£2.50	£6	

JAMES, LEONARD
Boppin' And A-Strollin'	LP	Decca	DL8772	1958	£8	£20	US

JAMES, NICKY
Every Home Should Have One	LP	Threshold	THS10	1973	£4	£10	
Stagger Lee	7"	Columbia	DB7747	1965	£6	£12	
Would You Believe	7"	Philips	BF1635	1968	£2.50	£6	

JAMES, RICKY
Knee Deep In The Blues	7"	HMV	POP306	1957	£6	£12	
Party Doll	7"	HMV	POP334	1957	£7.50	£15	

JAMES, ROGER FOUR
Better Than Here	7"	Columbia	DB7813	1966	£2.50	£6	
Better Than Here	7"	Columbia	DB7829	1966	£1.50	£4	

JAMES, RUBY
Getting Mighty Crowded	7"	Fontana	TF1051	1969	£2.50	£6	

JAMES, SKIP
Devil Got My Woman	LP	Vanguard	VSD79273	1968	£6	£15	
Greatest Of The Delta Blues Singers	LP	Storyville	670185	1967	£6	£15	
I'm So Glad	LP	Vanguard	VDP20001	1978	£4	£10	
Original 1930-31 Recordings	LP	Spokane	SPL1003	1970	£15	£30	
Skip James Today	LP	Vanguard	VSD79219	1965	£6	£15	

JAMES, SONNY
Are You Mine	7"	Capitol	CL14879	1958	£1.50	£4	
Cat Came Back	7"	Capitol	CL14635	1956	£6	£12	chart single
Dear Love	7"	Capitol	CL14742	1957	£2.50	£6	
First Date, First Kiss, First Love	7"	Capitol	CL14708	1957	£4	£8	
Honey	LP	Capitol	T988	1958	£8	£20	
I Can See It In Your Eyes	7"	Capitol	CL14915	1958	£1.50	£4	
Jenny Lou	7"	London	HL9132	1960	£2.50	£6	
Kathleen	7"	Capitol	CL14848	1958	£2.50	£6	
Let Me Be The One To Love You	7"	Capitol	CL14952	1958	£1.50	£4	
Mighty Lovable Man	7"	Capitol	CL14788	1957	£6	£12	
Pure Love	7"	Capitol	CL15046	1959	£1.50	£4	
Red Mud	7"	Capitol	CL15079	1959	£1.50	£4	
Sonny	LP	Capitol	T867	1957	£10	£25	
Southern Gentleman	LP	Capitol	T779	1957	£10	£25	
Talk Of The School	7"	Capitol	CL15022	1959	£1.50	£4	
This Is Sonny James	LP	Capitol	T1178	1959	£8	£20	US
Twenty Feet Of Muddy Water	7"	Capitol	CL14664	1956	£5	£10	
Uh Uh Umm	7"	Capitol	CL14814	1957	£6	£12	
Young Love	LP	London	HAD8049	1963	£20	£40	
Young Love	7"	Capitol	CL14683	1957	£5	£10	chart single
Young Love	7" EP	Capitol	EAP1827	1957	£7.50	£15	
You're The Only World I Know	7" EP	Capitol	EAP120654	1964	£5	£10	
Yo-yo	7"	Capitol	CL14991	1959	£4	£8	

JAMES, SULLIVAN BAND
Goodbye Mr.Heartache	7"	Parlophone	R5465	1966	£4	£8	

JAMES, TOMMY & THE SHONDELLS
Tommy James and the Shondells produced a kind of basic guitar pop whose closest British equivalent was perhaps the Troggs. Records like "Hanky Panky", "Mony Mony", and "I Think We're Alone Now" were enormous American hits and have proved to be a considerable influence on the kind of straight-forward teenage rock typified by the likes of the Ramones and the Runaways.

Ball And Chain	7"	Roulette	RO518	1969	£1.50	£4	
Ball Of Fire	7"	Roulette	RO511	1969	£1.50	£4	
Best Of Tommy James And The Shondelles	LP	Roulette	SR42040	1970	£5	£12	US
Cellophane Symphony	LP	Roulette	SR42030	1969	£6	£15	US
Crimson And Clover	LP	Roulette	SR42023	1968	£6	£15	US
Crimson And Clover	7"	Roulette	RO502	1968	£2	£5	
Crystal Blue Persuasion	7"	Roulette	RO507	1969	£2	£5	
Do Something To Me	7"	Roulette	RO500	1967	£2	£5	
Getting Together	LP	Roulette	SR25357	1968	£6	£15	US
Hanky Panky	LP	Roulette	(S)R25336	1966	£6	£15	US
Hanky Panky	7"	Roulette	RK7000	1966	£2.50	£6	chart single
Hanky Panky	7" EP	Roulette	VREX65044	1966	£6	£12	French, B side by Dave Baby Cortez
I Think We're Alone Now	LP	Roulette	(S)R25353	1967	£6	£15	US
I Think We're Alone Now	7"	Major Minor	MM511	1967	£1.50	£4	
I Think We're Alone Now	7" EP	Roulette	VREX65049	1967	£6	£12	French
It's Only Love	LP	Roulette	(S)R25344	1967	£6	£15	US
It's Only Love	7"	Pye	7N25398	1966	£1.50	£4	
It's Only Love	7" EP	Roulette	VREX65048	1966	£6	£12	French
Mirage	7" EP	Roulette	VREX65051	1967	£6	£12	French
Mony Mony	LP	Roulette	SR42012	1968	£6	£15	US
Mony Mony	7"	Major Minor	MM567	1968	£1.50	£4	
Out Of The Blue	7"	Major Minor	MM548	1967	£1.50	£4	
Say I Am	7" EP	Roulette	VREX65045	1966	£6	£12	French
She	7"	Roulette	RO513	1969	£1.50	£4	
Something Special	LP	Roulette	SR25355	1968	£6	£15	US
Sweet Cherry Wine	7"	Roulette	RO506	1969	£1.50	£4	
Wish It Were You	7"	Major Minor	MM558	1968	£1.50	£4	

JAMESON, BOBBY
"Gotta Find My Roogalator" was arranged by Frank Zappa.

All I Want Is My Baby	7"	Decca	F12032	1964	£10	£20
Gotta Find My Roogalator	7"	Penthouse	503	1962	£20	£40 ... US
I Wanna Love You	7"	London	HL9921	1964	£2.50	£6
Rum-Pum	7"	Brit	WI1001	1965	£5	£10

JAMESON RAID

Hypnotist	7"	Blackbird	BRAID001	1980	£2.50	£6
Seven Days Of Splendour	7"	GBH	GRC1	1979	£4	£8

JAMESON, STEPHEN

Stephen Jameson	LP	Dawn	DNLS3044	1973	£5	£12

JAMIE WEDNESDAY
Jim Morrison and Leslie Carter - later to be known as Jim Bob and Fruitbat when trading as Carter The Unstoppable Sex Machine - led the five-piece Jamie Wednesday, before deciding to try and make it as a duo.

Vote For Love	7"	Pink	7PINKY6	1985	£1.50	£4 ... no PS
Vote For Love	12"	Pink	PINKY6	1985	£2.50	£6
We Three Kings Of Orient Aren't	7"	Pink	7PINKY10	1986	£1.50	£4 ... no PS
We Three Kings Of Orient Aren't	12"	Pink	PINKY10	1986	£2.50	£6

JAMIES

Summertime Summertime	7"	Columbia	DB4885	1962	£5	£10
Summertime Summertime	7"	Fontana	H153	1958	£7.50	£15

JAMIE'S AGENT ORANGE

Losing My Way	7"	Emma	EC002	1990	£2	£5

JAMME

Jamme	LP	Stateside	SSL5024	1970	£5	£12

JAMMER, JOE

Bad News	LP	Regal Zonophone	SRZA8515	1973	£6	£15

JAN & ARNIE

Jennie Lee	7"	London	HL8653	1958	£12.50	£25

JAN & DEAN

Baby Talk	7"	London	HLN8936	1959	£7.50	£15
Batman	7"	Liberty	LIB55860	1966	£2.50	£6
Clementine	7"	London	HLU9063	1960	£5	£10
Command Performance	LP	Liberty	LRP3403/LST7403	1965	£6	£15 ... US
Dead Man's Curve	7"	Liberty	LIB55672	1964	£2	£5
Dead Man's Curve/New Girl In School	LP	Liberty	LBY1220	1964	£6	£15
Drag City	LP	Liberty	LRP3339/LST7339	1963	£6	£15 ... US
Drag City	7"	Liberty	LIB55641	1964	£2	£5
Drag City	7" EP	Liberty	LEP2155	1964	£7.50	£15 ... French
Filet Of Soul	LP	Liberty	LBY1339	1966	£6	£15
Folk And Roll	LP	Liberty	LBY1304	1965	£6	£15
From All Over The World	7"	Liberty	LIB55766	1965	£2.50	£6
Golden Hits	LP	Liberty	LBL/LBS83016	1967	£4	£10
Golden Hits	LP	Liberty	LBY1279	1962	£6	£15
Golden Hits Vol.2	LP	Liberty	LRP3417/LST7417	1965	£5	£12 ... US
Golden Hits Vol.3	LP	Liberty	LRP3460/LST7460	1966	£5	£12 ... US
Heart And Soul	7"	London	HLH9395	1961	£5	£10 ... chart single
Honolulu Lulu	7"	Liberty	LIB55613	1963	£2	£5
I Found A Girl	7"	Liberty	LIB55833	1965	£1.50	£4
Jan & Dean	LP	Dore	101	1960	£37.50	£75 ... US with photo
Linda	7"	Liberty	LIB55531	1963	£2	£5
Little Old Lady From Pasadena	LP	Liberty	LRP3377/LST7377	1964	£6	£15 ... US
Little Old Lady From Pasadena	7"	Liberty	LIB55704	1964	£2	£5
Little Old Lady From Pasadena	7" EP	Liberty	LEP2189	1964	£7.50	£15 ... French
Meet Batman	LP	Liberty	LBY1309	1966	£8	£20
Norwegian Wood	7"	Liberty	LIB10225	1966	£2.50	£6
Pop Symphony No.1	LP	Liberty	LRP3414/LST7414	1965	£6	£15 ... US
Popsicle	LP	Liberty	LRP3458/LST7458	1966	£6	£15 ... US
Popsicle	7"	Liberty	LIB10244	1966	£2.50	£6
Ride The Wild Surf	LP	Liberty	LBY1229	1964	£6	£15
Ride The Wild Surf	7"	Liberty	LIB55724	1964	£2	£5
Save For A Rainy Day	LP	J&D	101	1967	£37.50	£75 ... US
Sidewalk Surfin'	7"	Liberty	LIB55727	1965	£2	£5
Sunday Kind Of Love	7"	Liberty	LIB55397	1962	£2	£5
Surf City	LP	Liberty	LBY1163	1963	£6	£15
Surf City	7"	Liberty	LIB55580	1963	£2	£5 ... chart single
Surf City	7" EP	Liberty	LEP2112	1963	£7.50	£15 ... French
Surf 'N' Drag Hits	7" EP	Liberty	LEP2213	1965	£6	£12
Take Linda Surfing	LP	Liberty	LRP3294/LST7294	1963	£8	£20 . US, with Beach Boys
Tennessee	7"	Liberty	LIB10252	1966	£5	£10
There's A Girl	7"	London	HLU8990	1959	£6	£12
Titanic Twosome	7" EP	Liberty	LEP2258	1966	£6	£12
Yellow Balloon	7"	CBS	202630	1967	£4	£8
You Really Know How To Hurt A Guy	7"	Liberty	LIB55792	1964	£2.50	£6

JAN & KELLY

And Then He Kicked Me	7"	Philips	BF1323	1964	£1.50	£4
I Could Have Died	7"	Philips	BF1253	1962	£1.50	£4
Oo He Didn't	7"	Philips	326567BF	1962	£1.50	£4
Oo I Can't	7"	Philips	BF1265	1963	£1.50	£4
There Was A Girl There Was A Boy	7"	Philips	BF1377	1964	£1.50	£4

414

Time For A Laugh	7" EP	Philips	BE12536	1963	£2.50	£6	

JAN DUKES DE GREY

Mice & Rats In The Loft	LP	Transatlantic	TRA234	1971	£15	£30	
Sorcerers	LP	Nova	SDN8	1970	£10	£25	

JANE

Fire, Water, Earth And Air	LP	Brain	0001084	1975	£4	£10	German
Here We Are	LP	Brain	0001032	1973	£4	£10	German
Lady Jane	LP	Brain	0001066	1975	£4	£10	German
Three	LP	Brain	0001048	1974	£4	£10	German
Together	LP	Brain	0001002	1972	£4	£10	German

JANES, PETER

Do You Believe	7"	CBS	3299	1968	£2.50	£6	

JANIE

You Better Not Do That	7"	Capitol	CL15180	1961	£2	£5	

JANIS, CONRAD

Dixieland Jam Session	LP	London	LTZU15095	1957	£5	£12	

JANIS, JOHNNY

Better To Love You	7"	London	HLU8650	1958	£4	£8	
For The First Time	LP	ABC-Paramount	LP140	1957	£10	£25	US

JANSCH, BERT

With Davy Graham maintaining a deliberately low profile, it was left to Bert Jansch to define the sound and style of folk guitar playing in the sixties. His serviceable folk-singer's voice gives added interest to his records, but the guitar is the real focus - beginning with a faultless version of Graham's difficult "Angie" and moving onwards from there.

Avocet	LP	Charisma	CLASS6	1979	£5	£12	
Bert Jansch	LP	Transatlantic	TRA125	1965	£6	£15	
Bert Jansch	7" EP	Transatlantic	TRAEP145	1966	£7.50	£15	
Birthday Blues	LP	Transatlantic	TRA179	1968	£6	£15	
Black Birds Of Brittany	7"	Streetsong	1	1978	£4	£8	PS, with Richard Harvey
From The Outside	LP	Konexion	KOMA788006	1985	£5	£12	
Heartbreak	LP	Logo	LOGO1035	1982	£5	£12	
It Don't Bother Me	LP	Transatlantic	TRA132	1965	£6	£15	
Jack Orion	LP	Transatlantic	TRA143	1966	£6	£15	
L.A. Turnaround	LP	Charisma	CAS1090	1974	£5	£12	
Life Depends On Love	7"	Transatlantic	BIG102	1968	£2.50	£6	
Live At La Foret	LP	Columbia	YX7273AK	1980	£6	£15	Japanese
Lucky Thirteen	LP	Vanguard	VSD79212	1966	£6	£15	US
Moonshine	LP	Reprise	K44225	1973	£6	£15	
Nicola	LP	Transatlantic	TRA157	1967	£6	£15	
Rare Conundrum	LP	Charisma	CAS1127	1977	£6	£15	
Rosemary Lane	LP	Transatlantic	TRA235	1971	£5	£12	
Sampler	LP	Transatlantic	TRASAM10	1969	£4	£10	
Thirteen Down	LP	Sonet	SNKF162	1980	£5	£12	

JANSCH, BERT & JOHN RENBOURN

Bert & John	LP	Transatlantic	TRA144	1966	£6	£15	
Stepping Stones	LP	Vanguard	VSD6506	1969	£5	£12	US (As 'Bert & John' with 2 extra tracks)

JANUS

Gravedigger	LP	Electrola	IC06229433	1974	£20	£40	German

JAPAN

The pretty-boy posing of Japan was an unlikely environment for intelligent, questing music to be produced, and yet with each record release, the group became more and more of a vital force. Peaking with the refreshingly innovative "Ghosts", it was perhaps inevitable that David Sylvian would then wish to continue the quest on his own.

Don't Rain On My Parade	7"	Ariola	AHA510	1978	£5	£10	
Ghosts	7"	Virgin	VSY472	1982	£1.50	£4	pic disc
I Second That Emotion	7"	Ariola	AHA559	1980	£2	£5	red vinyl
Interview Album	LP	Ariola		1979	£6	£15	US promo
Life In Tokyo	12"	Ariola	AHAD540	1979	£2.50	£6	red vinyl
Sometimes I Feel So Low	7"	Ariola	AHA529	1978	£2	£5	
Sometimes I Feel So Low	7"	Ariola	AHA529	1978	£4	£8	blue vinyl
Unconventional	7"	Ariola	AHA525	1978	£6	£12	PS

JARMELS

Little Bit Of Soap	7"	Top Rank	JAR580	1961	£7.50	£15	
She Loves To Dance	7"	Top Rank	JAR560	1961	£5	£10	

JARR, COOK E.

Pledging My Love	7"	RCA	RCA1820	1969	£1.50	£4	

JARRE, JEAN MICHEL

There is no rarer record than Jean Michel Jarre's "Music For Supermarkets" - the LP was issued in a limited edition of just one copy and auctioned (in 1983, when it fetched a sum of the order of £10000. Meanwhile, there are a couple of other rare Jarre albums which the keen collector does stand a reasonable chance of obtaining, although at a considerable price nonetheless, for the early soundtracks have never had a UK issue and are scarce even in their countries of origin.

Calypso	CD-s	Polydor	PZCD84	1990	£3	£8	
Deserted Palace	LP	Polydor	SF1029	1972	£100	£200	US promo
Equinoxe 4 (remix)	12"	Polydor	JM1	1979	£5	£12	promo
Equinoxe 5	7"	Polydor	POSP20	1978	£2	£5	etched autograph
Equinoxe 7 (live)	7"	Polydor	2001968	1980	£4	£8	
La Cage	7"	Pathe	C00611739	1971	£210	£350	French

Les Granges Brulees	LP	Eden	ER6250293	1973	£100	£200	French
London Kid	CD-s	Polydor	PZCD32	1988	£4	£10	
Magnetic Fields 4 (remix)	7"	Polydor	POSP363	1981	£2.50	£6	
Orient Express	7"	Polydor	POSP430	1982	£2.50	£6	
Orient Express	12"	Polydor	POSPX430DJ	1982	£10	£25	promo
Oxygene	LP	Polydor	C8813	1988	£5	£12	HMV box set
Oxygene	CD	Polydor	C8813	1988	£6	£15	HMV box set
Oxygene 4	CD-s	Polydor	PZCD55	1989	£3	£8	
Rendezvous 4 (remix)	12"	Polydor	POSPX788	1986	£8	£20	2 different sleeves
Revolutions	CD-s	Polydor	PZCD25	1988	£6	£15	
Tenth Anniversary	CD	Polydor	8337372	1987	£20	£40	boxed set
Zoolook (remix)	12"	Polydor	POSPX718	1984	£6	£15	
Zoolookologie (remix)	7"	Polydor	POSPG740	1985	£6	£12	double
Zoolookologie (remix)	12"	Polydor	POSPX740	1985	£6	£15	

JARRETT, KEITH
Mourning Of A Star	LP	Atlantic	K40309	1972	£4	£10	

JARVIS, MARIAN
Penny For Your Thoughts	7"	Chelsea	2005038	1975	£2	£5	

JARVIS STREET REVUE
Mr.Oil Man	LP	Columbia			£60	£120	Canadian

JASMINE MINKS
Think	7"	Creation	CRE004	1984	£5	£10	
What's Happening	7"	Creation	CRE018	1985	£2	£5	
Where The Traffic Goes	7"	Creation	CRE008	1984	£4	£8	

JASON CREST
Black Mass	7"	Philips	BF1809	1969	£30	£60	
Juliano The Bull	7"	Philips	BF1650	1968	£7.50	£15	
Lemon Tree	7"	Philips	BF1687	1968	£7.50	£15	
Turquoise Tandem Cycle	7"	Philips	BF1633	1968	£10	£20	
Waterloo Road	7"	Philips	BF1752	1969	£6	£12	

JASON'S GENERATION
It's Up To You	7"	Polydor	56042	1966	£15	£30	

JASPAR, BOBBY
Bobby Jaspar	LP	London	LTZU15128	1958	£10	£25	
Bobby Jaspar And His All Stars	LP	Felsted	PDL85017	1956	£10	£25	
New Jazz Group	10" LP	Vogue	LDE167	1956	£10	£25	
New Jazz Vol.1	10" LP	Vogue	LDE125	1955	£20	£40	
New Sounds From Europe Vol.4	10" LP	Vogue	LDE041	1954	£20	£40	

JASPER
Liberation	LP	Spark	SRLP103	1969	£150	£250	

JASPER WRAITH
Jasper Wraith	LP	Sunflower	SNF5003	1971	£6	£15	US

JAWBONE
Gotta Go	7"	B&C	CB190	1972	£4	£8	
How's Ya Pa	7"	Carnaby	CNS4007	1970	£5	£10	
Jawbone	LP	Carnaby	CNLS6004	1970	£30	£60	sleeve pictured in Guide
Way Way Down	7"	Carnaby	CNS4020	1971	£5	£10	

JAXON, BOB
Ali Baba	7"	London	HL8156	1955	£10	£20	
Beach Party	7"	RCA	RCA1019	1957	£30	£60	

JAXON, FRANKIE
Male Blues Vol.6	7" EP	Collector	JE110	1959	£5	£10	

JAY
I Rise, I Fall	7"	Coral	Q72471	1964	£6	£12	

JAY & JOYA
I'll Be Lonely	7"	Trojan	TR633	1968	£4	£8	Supersonics B side

JAY & THE AMERICANS
At The Cafe Wha	LP	United Artists	UAL3300/ UAS6300	1963	£6	£15	US
Blockbusters	LP	United Artists	UAL3417/ UAS6417	1965	£6	£15	US
Cara Mia	7"	United Artists	UP1094	1965	£1.50	£4	
Come A Little Bit Closer	LP	United Artists	UAL3407/ UAS6407	1964	£6	£15	US
Come A Little Bit Closer	7" EP	United Artists	36054	1964	£7.50	£15	French
Come A Little Bit Closer	7" EP	United Artists	UEP1003	1965	£6	£12	
Come A Little Closer	7"	United Artists	UP1069	1964	£1.50	£4	
Come Dance With Me	7"	United Artists	UP1039	1964	£1.50	£4	
Crying	7"	United Artists	UP1132	1966	£1.50	£4	
En Francais	7" EP	United Artists	36102	1966	£10	£20	French
Got Hung Up Along The Way	7"	United Artists	UP1191	1967	£10	£20	
Greatest Hits	LP	United Artists	UAL3453/ UAS6453	1965	£6	£15	US
Greatest Hits Vol.2	LP	United Artists	UAL3555/ UAS6555	1966	£6	£15	US

Jay And The Americans	LP	United Artists	ULP1117	1966	£5	£12		
Kansas City	7" EP	United Artists	36027	1963	£7.50	£15	French
Let's Lock The Door	7"	United Artists	UP1075	1965	£2	£5	
Livin' Above Your Head	LP	United Artists	UAL3534/	1966	£6	£15	US
			UAS6534				
Living Above Your Head	7"	United Artists	UP1142	1966	£10	£20	
Living With Jay & The Americans	7" EP	United Artists	UEP1017	1966	£6	£12	
Raining In My Sunshine	7"	United Artists	UP1162	1966	£1.50	£4	
She Cried	LP	United Artists	UAL3222/	1962	£6	£15	US
			UAS6222				
She Cried	7"	HMV	POP1009	1962	£4	£8	
Some Enchanted Evening	7"	United Artists	UP1108	1965	£2	£5	
Some Enchanted Evening	7" EP	United Artists	36065	1965	£7.50	£15	French
Strangers Tomorrow	7"	United Artists	UP1018	1963	£1.50	£4	
Sunday And Me	LP	United Artists	UAL3474/	1966	£6	£15	US
			UAS6474				
Sunday And Me	7"	United Artists	UP1119	1966	£2	£5	
Sunday And Me	7" EP	United Artists	36074	1965	£7.50	£15	French
Think Of The Good Times	7"	United Artists	UP1088	1965	£1.50	£4	
This Is It	7"	United Artists	UP1002	1964	£1.50	£4	
This Magic Moment	7"	United Artists	UP2268	1969	£1.50	£4	
Tonight	7" EP	United Artists	36018	1962	£7.50	£15	French
Try Some Of This	LP	United Artists	UAL3562/	1967	£6	£15	US
			UAS6562				
Why Can't You Bring Me Home	7"	United Artists	UP1129	1966	£1.50	£4	

JAY & THE TECHNIQUES

Apples,Peaches,Pumpkin Pie	LP	Philips	(S)BL7834	1967	£4	£10	
Apples,Peaches,Pumpkin Pie	7"	Philips	BF1597	1967	£2.50	£6	
Baby Make Your Own Sweet Music	7"	Mercury	MF1034	1968	£2.50	£6	
Keep The Ball Rolling	7"	Philips	BF1618	1967	£1.50	£4	
Strawberry Shortcake	7"	Philips	BF1644	1968	£1.50	£4	

JAY BEE FOUR

Lucille	7" EP	Barclay	70751	1965	£6	£12	French

JAY BOYS

Splendour Splash	7"	Trojan	TR665	1969	£2	£5	Trevor Shield B side

JAY, DAVID & RENE HALKETT

Nothing	7"	4AD	AD112	1981	£2.50	£6	with lyric sheet

JAY, LAURIE COMBO

Love In My Heart	7"	HMV	POP1300	1964	£1.50	£4
Maybe	7"	HMV	POP1335	1964	£1.50	£4
Shades Of Red	7"	Ember	JBS710	1962	£1.50	£4
Song Called Soul	7"	Decca	F12083	1965	£7.50	£15
Teenage Idol	7"	HMV	POP1234	1963	£1.50	£4

JAY, LONNIE & THE JAYNES

Around And Around We Go	7"	Stateside	SS197	1963	£1.50	£4

JAY, PETER & THE BLUEMEN

Just Too Late	7"	Triumph	RGM1000	1960	£6	£12

JAY, PETER & THE JAYWALKERS

Before The Beginning	7"	Piccadilly	7N35325	1966	£4	£8	
Can Can '62	7"	Decca	F11531	1962	£2	£5	chart single
Parade Of Tin Soldiers	7"	Decca	F11757	1963	£2	£5	
Paradise Garden	7"	Pye	7N15290	1960	£6	£12	
Parchman Farm	7"	Piccadilly	7N35220	1965	£5	£10	
Poet And Peasant	7"	Decca	F11659	1963	£2	£5	
Tonight You're Gonna Fall	7"	Piccadilly	7N35212	1964	£2.50	£6	
Totem Pole	7"	Decca	F11593	1963	£2	£5	
Where Did Our Love Go	7"	Piccadilly	7N35199	1964	£2.50	£6	
You Girl	7"	Decca	F11840	1964	£2	£5	

JAYBIRDS

Although these singles conform to the Embassy label's policy of issuing sound-alike versions of current chart hits, the fact that the Jaybirds later became Ten Years After gives them a modest collectability.

All Day And All Of The Night	7"	Embassy	WB663	1964	£5	£10
Juliet	7"	Embassy	WB635	1964	£2.50	£6
Tell Me When	7"	Embassy	WB624	1964	£4	£8

JAYBIRDS (2)

Somebody Help Me	7"	Sue	WI4013	1966	£6	£12

JAYE, JERRY

My Girl Josephine	7"	London	HLU10128	1967	£6	£12

JAYE SISTERS

Sure Fire Love	7"	London	HLT9011	1959	£10	£20

JAYHAWKS

Stranded In The Jungle	7"	Parlophone	R4228	1956	£60	£120

JAYNETTS

Sally Go Round The Roses	LP	Tuff	LP13	1963	£25	£50	US
Sally Go Round The Roses	7"	Stateside	SS227	1963	£2	£5	

JAYS
Shock A Boom .... 7" ...... Fontana .... TF402 .... 1963 ... £1.50 .... £4 ....

JAYWALKERS
Can't Live Without You .... 7" .... Cream .... 5003 .... 1976 ... £1.50 .... £4

JAZZ AT STORYVILLE
Jazz At Storyville .... LP ...... London .... LTZC15061 .... 1957 ... £6 .... £15

JAZZ AT THE PHILHARMONIC
1955 Vol.1	LP	Columbia	33CX10078	1957	£6	£15
1955 Vol.2	LP	Columbia	33CX10079	1957	£6	£15
Jam Concert No.1	LP	Columbia	33CX10059	1956	£6	£15
Jam Session	LP	Columbia	33CX10030	1956	£6	£15
Jam Session	LP	Emarcy	EJL103	1956	£6	£15
Jam Session Group	LP	Columbia	33CX10043	1956	£6	£15
Jam Session No.2	LP	Columbia	33CX10021	1956	£6	£15
Jam Session No.5	LP	Columbia	33CX10067	1957	£6	£15
Midnight Jazz At Carnegie Hall	LP	Columbia	33CX10020	1956	£8	£20
New Vol.1	LP	Columbia	33CX10032	1956	£6	£15
New Vol.2	LP	Columbia	33CX10033	1956	£6	£15
New Vol.3	LP	Columbia	33CX10034	1956	£6	£15
New Vol.4	LP	Columbia	33CX10035	1956	£6	£15
New Vol.5	LP	Columbia	33CX10036	1956	£6	£15
New Vol.7	LP	Columbia	33CX10037	1956	£6	£15
Volume 1	LP	Columbia	33CX10009	1955	£8	£20
Volume 2	LP	Columbia	33CX10010	1955	£8	£20
Volume 3	LP	Columbia	33CX10011	1955	£8	£20

JAZZ BUTCHER
Christmas freebie .... 7" ...... Glass .... 198- ... £2.50 .... £6

JAZZ CITY WORKSHOP
Jazz City Workshop .... LP ...... London .... LTZN15037 .... 1957 ... £5 .... £12

JAZZ COURIERS
Couriers Of Jazz	LP	London	LTZL15188	1960	£10	£25
In Concert	LP	MFP	MFP1072	1966	£4	£10
In Concert	LP	Tempo	TAP22	1958	£10	£25
Jazz Couriers	7" EP	Tempo	EXA75	1957	£2.50	£6
Jazz Couriers	7" EP	Tempo	EXA87	1958	£2.50	£6
Last Word	LP	Tempo	TAP26	1959	£10	£25

JAZZ CRUSADERS
Thing .... LP ...... Fontana .... 688149ZL .... 1966 ... £5 .... £12

JAZZ GIANTS
Jazz Giants .... 10" LP Emarcy .... EJT751 .... 1957 ... £6 .... £15

JAZZ IN A STABLE GROUP
Jazz In A Stable .... LP ...... Esquire .... 32018 .... 1956 ... £6 .... £15

JAZZ MESSAGE GROUP
Jazz Message .... LP ...... London .... LTZC15028 .... 1957 ... £5 .... £12

JAZZ MODES
Jazz Modes .... LP ...... London .... LTZK15203/ .... 1961 ... £10 .... £25
SAHK6117
Most Happy Fella .... LP ...... London .... LTZK15191 .... 1960 ... £10 .... £25

JAZZ ROCK EXPERIENCE
Jazz Rock Experience .... LP ...... Nova .... SDN19 .... 1970 ... £8 .... £20

JAZZ STUDIO FOUR GROUP
Jazz Studio Four .... LP ...... Brunswick .... LAT8098 .... 1956 ... £5 .... £12

JAZZ TODAY UNIT
Jam Session .... 10" LP Polygon .... JTL1 .... 1955 ... £5 .... £12

JAZZ WAVE LTD.
On Tour .... LP ...... Blue Note .... BST89905 .... 1970 ... £4 .... £10

JB'S
Breakin' Bread	LP	Polydor	2391161	1975	£10	£25
Damn Right I Am Somebody	LP	Polydor	2391125	1974	£15	£30
Doing It To Death	LP	Polydor	2391087	1974	£17.50	£35
Doing It To Death	7"	Polydor	2066322	1973	£1.50	£4
Food For Thought	LP	Polydor	2391034	1972	£15	£30
Gimme Some More	7"	Mojo	2093007	1974	£2	£5
Givin' Up Food For Funk	7"	Mojo	2093021	1974	£2	£5
Giving Up Food For Funk	LP	Polydor	2391204	1976	£15	£30
Grunt	7"	Mojo	2027002	1971	£2.50	£6
Hot Pants Road	7"	Mojo	2093016	1974	£2	£5
Hustle With Speed	LP	Polydor	2391194	1975	£10	£25
JB Shout	7"	Mojo	2093025	1974	£1.50	£4
Pass The Peas	LP	Polydor	2918004	1972	£15	£30
These Are The JB's	7"	Polydor	2001115	1971	£2	£5

JEAN & THE STATESIDERS
Putty In Your Hands .... 7" ...... Columbia .... DB7287 .... 1964 ... £2.50 .... £6
You Won't Forget Me .... 7" ...... Columbia .... DB7439 .... 1965 ... £2 .... £5

JEAN & THE STATESIDES
Mama Didn't Lie .... 7" ...... Columbia .... DB7651 .... 1965 ... £2.50 ....£6 ....

JEAN, CATHY & THE ROOMATES
Please Love Me .... 7" .... Parlophone ...... R4764 .... 1961 ... £7.50 ......£15 ....

JEAN, EARL
I'm Into Something Good .... 7" ...... Colpix .... PX729 .... 1964 ... £7.50 ......£15 ....
Randy .... 7" ...... Colpix .... PX748 .... 1964 ... £5 ....£10 ....

JEAN, LANA
It Hurts To be Sixteen .... 7" ...... Pye .... 7N25214 .... 1963 ... £5 ....£10 ....

JEANNIE
Don't Lie To Me .... 7" ...... Piccadilly .... 7N35147 .... 1963 ... £2.50 ....£6 ....
I Want You .... 7" ...... Piccadilly .... 7N35164 .... 1964 ... £4 ....£8 ....
With Another Girl .... 7" ...... Parlophone ...... R5343 .... 1965 ... £1.50 ....£4 ....

JEANS, AUDREY
Ticky Ticky Tick .... 7" ...... Decca .... F10768 .... 1956 ... £2.50 ....£6 ....

JEEPS
Ain't It A Great Big Laugh .... 7" ...... Strike .... JH315 .... 1966 ... £1.50 ....£4 ....
He Saw Eesaw .... 7" ...... Strike .... JH308 .... 1966 ... £1.50 ....£4 ....

JEFFERSON AIRPLANE
After Bathing At Baxters .... LP ..... RCA .... RD/SF7926 .... 1967 ... £6 ....£15 ....black label
Ballad Of You And Me And Pooneil ...... 7" .... RCA .... RCA1647 .... 1967 ... £4 ....£8 ....
Bark .... LP ..... Grunt .... FTR1001 .... 1971 ... £4 ....£10 ...bag sleeve, chart LP
Bless Its Pointed Little Head .... LP ..... RCA .... RD/SF8019 .... 1969 ... £15 ....£30 .. US interview promo
Bless Its Pointed Little Head .... LP ..... RCA .... RD/SF8019 .... 1969 ... £5 ....£12 ....chart LP
Crown Of Creation .... LP ..... RCA .... RD/SF7976 .... 1968 ... £6 ....£15 ....black label
Greasy Heart .... 7" ...... RCA .... RCA1711 .... 1968 ... £4 ....£8 ....
If You Feel Like China Breaking .... 7" ...... RCA .... RCA1736 .... 1968 ... £4 ....£8 ....
Long John Silver .... LP ..... Grunt .... FTR1007 .... 1972 ... £4 ....£10 .... open-out
cover, chart LP
Long John Silver .... 7" ...... Grunt .... 650506 .... 1972 ... £1.50 ....£4 ....
Mexico .... 7" ...... RCA .... RCA1989 .... 1970 ... £2.50 ....£6 ....
Pretty As You Feel .... 7" ...... Grunt .... 650500 .... 1971 ... £1.50 ....£4 ....
Somebody To Love .... 7" ...... RCA .... RCA1594 .... 1967 ... £2 ....£5 ....
Surrealistic Pillow .... LP ..... RCA .... LPM/LSP3766 ... 1967 ... £6 ....£15 ....US
Surrealistic Pillow .... LP ..... RCA .... RD/SF7889 .... 1967 ... £6 ....£15 ....black label
Surrealistic Pillow .... 7" EP. RCA .... 86560 .... 1967 ... £10 ....£20 ....French
Takes Off .... LP ..... RCA .... INT1476 .... 1974 ... £5 ....£12 ....
Takes Off .... LP ..... RCA .... LPM/LSP3584 ... 1966 ... £8 ....£20 ....US
Takes Off .... LP ..... RCA .... LPM/LSP3584 ... 1966 ... £50 ....£100 .... US with
'Runnin' Round The
World'
Takes Off .... LP ..... RCA .... SF8195 .... 1971 ... £6 ....£15 ....
Trial By Fire .... 7" ...... Grunt .... 65511 .... 1972 ... £1.50 ....£4 ....
Volunteers .... LP ..... RCA .... APDI0320 .... 1973 ... £6 ....£15 ....US quad
Volunteers .... LP ..... RCA .... SF8076 .... 1969 ... £5 ....£12 ....chart LP
Volunteers .... 7" ...... RCA .... RCA1933 .... 1970 ... £2 ....£5 ....
White Rabbit .... 7" ...... RCA .... RCA1631 .... 1967 ... £2.50 ....£6 ....
White Rabbit .... 7" ...... RCA .... RCA1964 .... 1970 ... £1.50 ....£4 ....
Wild Turkey .... 7" ...... Grunt .... 65500 .... 1972 ... £1.50 ....£4 ....

JEFFERSON, BLIND LEMON
Blind Lemon .... LP ..... Riverside .... 126 .... £8 ....£20 ....US
Blind Lemon Jefferson .... LP ..... Milestone .... M47022 .... 1975 ... £5 ....£12 ....double
Blind Lemon Jefferson .... 10" LP Poydras .... 99 .... 195- ... £6 ....£15 ....
Blind Lemon Jefferson & Rambling ...... LP ..... Heritage .... HLP1007 .... 195- ... £20 ....£40 ....
Thomas
Folk Blues .... 10" LP London .... AL3508 .... 1953 ... £10 ....£25 ....
Folk Blues .... 10" LP Riverside .... 1014 .... £10 ....£25 ....US
Folk Blues Classics .... LP ..... Riverside .... 125 .... £8 ....£20 ....US
Immortal .... LP ..... CBS .... 63738 .... 1969 ... £6 ....£15 ....
Penitentiary Blues .... 10" LP London .... AL3546 .... 1955 ... £10 ....£25 ....
Penitentiary Blues .... 10" LP Riverside .... 1053 .... £10 ....£25 ....US
Sings The Blues .... 10" LP London .... AL3564 .... 1957 ... £10 ....£25 ....
Volume 1 .... LP ..... Matchbox .... RL301 .... 197- ... £4 ....£10 ....
Volume 2 .... LP ..... Matchbox .... RL306 .... 197- ... £4 ....£10 ....
Volume 3 .... LP ..... Matchbox .... RL331 .... 197- ... £4 ....£10 ....

JEFFERSON, BLIND LEMON & BUDDY BOY HAWKINS
Male Blues Vol.5 .... 7" EP.. Collector .... JEL8 .... 1960 ... £5 ....£10 ....

JEFFERSON, BLIND LEMON & ED BELL
Male Blues Vol.7 .... 7" EP.. Collector .... JEL13 .... 1961 ... £2.50 ....£6 ....

JEFFERSON, BLIND LEMON & LEADBELLY
Male Blues Vol.8 .... 7" EP.. Collector .... JEL24 .... 1964 ... £5 ....£10 ....

JEFFERSON, EDDIE
Some Other Time .... 7" ...... Stateside .... SS591 .... 1967 ... £4 ....£8 ....

JEFFERSON, GEORGE PAUL
Looking For My Mind .... 7" ...... Fontana .... TF923 .... 1968 ... £5 ....£10 ....

JEFFERSON STARSHIP
Dragonfly .... LP ..... Grunt .... BFD10717 .... 1974 ... £5 ....£12 ....US quad

Gold	LP	Grunt	DJL13363	1978	£6	£15	US promo pic disc
Red Octopus	LP	Grunt	BFD10999	1975	£5	£12	US quad
Spitfire	LP	Grunt	BFD11557	1976	£5	£12	US quad

JEFFREY, JOE
My Pledge Of Love	7"	Pye	7N25494	1969	£1.50	£4

JELLY BEANS
Baby Be Mine	7"	Red Bird	RB10011	1964	£4	£8
I Wanna Love Him So Bad	7"	Pye	7N25252	1964	£4	£8
You Don't Mean Me No Good	7"	Right On	R102	1975	£2.50	£6

JELLYBREAD
Jellybread have the distinction of being perhaps the least collectable of the Blue Horizon roster. Pete Wingfield, pianist and leader of the band, would suggest that the reason for this lies in the records not being very good! In fact, the group's blend of soul and blues has worn remarkably well. The lack of guitar histrionics no doubt makes the group sound unexciting to fans of their British blues contemporaries, but it also helps to give Jellybread a distinctive sound that makes their music much less tied to its era. A scarce privately pressed album (theoretically limited to 99 copies, but actually more in the region of 500) predates the Blue Horizon material and is the most vital music recorded by the group.

65 Parkway	LP	Blue Horizon	2431002	1970	£8	£20
65 Parkway	LP	Blue Horizon	763866	1970	£10	£25
Back To Begin Again	LP	Blue Horizon	2931004	1972	£25	£50
Chairman Mao's Boogaloo	7"	Blue Horizon	573162	1969	£2.50	£6
Comment	7"	Blue Horizon	573169	1970	£2	£5
Creepin' And Crawlin'	7"	Blue Horizon	2096001	1971	£2	£5
Down Along The Cove	7"	Blue Horizon	2096006	1971	£2	£5
First Slice	LP	Blue Horizon	763853	1969	£8	£20
Jellybread	LP	Liphook	IBC/LP/3627	1969	£40	£80
Old Man Hank	7"	Blue Horizon	573180	1970	£2	£5
Rockin' Pneumonia	7"	Blue Horizon	573174	1970	£2	£5

JENKINS, JOHNNY
Ton Ton Macoute	LP	Atlantic	2400033	1970	£5	£12
Voodoo In You	7"	Atco	226009	1969	£1.50	£4

JENKINS, MARTIN
Carry Your Smile	LP	Oblivion	OBL002	1984	£6	£15

JENNINGS, WAYLON
Waylon Jennings is one of the best known of country artists and as a pioneer of the "outlaw" sound, reflecting a deliberate move away from the showbiz concerns of the Grand Ole Opry, he has been enormously influential on the modern breed of rock-inflected country singers. The reason for the inclusion here of the American single, "Jole Blon", however, lies in the identity of the song's producer and guitarist. This is Buddy Holly, in whose group at the time Jennings played bass.

At JD's	LP	Sounds	1001	1964	£37.50	£75	US
Folk Country	LP	RCA	LPM/LSP3523	1966	£5	£12	US
Hangin' On	LP	RCA	LSP3918	1968	£4	£10	US
Jole Blon	7"	Brunswick	955130	1959	£50	£100	US
Leavin' Town	LP	RCA	LPM/LSP3620	1966	£5	£12	US
Love Of The Common People	LP	RCA	LPM/LSP3825	1967	£4	£10	US
Only The Greatest	LP	RCA	SF8003	1968	£4	£10	
Waylon Sings Ol' Harlan	LP	RCA	LPM/LSP3660	1967	£5	£12	US

JENSEN, KRIS
Claudette	7"	Fontana	267267TF	1963	£4	£8	
Come Back To Me	7"	Hickory	451256	1964	£1.50	£4	
Donna Donna	7"	Hickory	451224	1964	£2.50	£6	
Looking For Love	7"	Hickory	451243	1964	£1.50	£4	
Somebody's Smiling	7"	Hickory	451285	1965	£2.50	£6	
That's A Whole Lotta Love	7"	Hickory	451311	1965	£2.50	£6	
Torture	LP	Hickory	MH110	1962	£8	£20	US
Torture	7"	Fontana	267241TF	1962	£2.50	£6	

JENSEN, KRIS & SUE THOMPSON
Introducing Kris Jensen And Sue Thompson	7" EP	Hickory	LPE1507	1965	£5	£10

JENSENS
Deep Thinking	7"	Philips	BF1686	1968	£4	£8

JEREMY & THE SATYRS
Jeremy and The Satyrs, led by flautist Jeremy Steig, were one of the first American groups to bring jazz skills and sounds to rock. This was fledgling jazz-rock, with the two halves meeting on equal terms (unlike Blood, Sweat and Tears, for example, where the jazz content was no more than superficial). The Satyrs' experiment only lasted for one album, but each member has been a familiar session name ever since - Eddie Gomez, Donald McDonald, Warren Bernhardt, and Adrian Guillory.

Jeremy & The Satyrs	LP	Reprise	RS6282	1968	£6	£15	US

JERICHO
Jericho	LP	A&M	AMLS68079	1972	£30	£60
Mama's Gonna Take You Home	7"	A&M	AMS7037	1972	£10	£20

JERICHO JONES
Junkies,Monkeys,& Donkeys	LP	A&M	AMLH68050	1971	£35	£70

JERMZ
Power Cut	7"	One Way	EFP1	1985	£2	£5

JERONIMO
Cosmic Blues	LP	Bellaphon	BI1530	1970	£8	£20	German
Time Ride	LP	Bellaphon	BLPS19095	1972	£8	£20	German

JERRYO
Karate Boogaloo	7"	London	HLZ10162	1967	£1.50	£4

JERUSALEM

Jerusalem	LP	Deram	SDL6	1972	£30	£60	
Kamakazi Moth	7"	Deram	DMS358	1972	£4	£8	

JESS & JAMES

Move	7"	MGM	MGM1389	1968	£2.50	£6	
Something For Nothing	7"	MGM	MGM1420	1968	£2	£5	

JESTERS

Casa Pedro	7"	R&L	RL15/16	196-	£2	£5	

JESUS & MARY CHAIN

Blues From A Gun	10"	Blanco Y Negro	NEGTE41	1989	£5	£12	
Happy When It Rains	7"	Blanco Y Negro	NEGB025	1987	£2	£5	boxed, cards
Head On	7"	Blanco Y Negro	NEG42	1989	£10	£20	4 x 7' boxed set
Just Like Honey	7"	Blanco Y Negro	NEGF017	1985	£2.50	£6	double
Never Understand	7"	Blanco Y Negro	NEG008	1985	£1.50	£4	
Never Understand	12"	Blanco Y Negro	NEG8T	1985	£3	£8	
Some Candy Talking	7"	Blanco Y Negro	NEGF019	1986	£1.50	£4	double
Some Candy Talking	12"	Blanco Y Negro	NEG19T	1986	£2.50	£6	with poster
Upside Down	7"	Creation	CRE012	1984	£6	£12	black, red & white PS
Upside Down	7"	Creation	CRE012	1984	£2.50	£6	pink, blue, or yellow PS
Upside Down	12"	Creation	CRE012T	1984	£25	£50	demo only
You Trip Me Up	12"	Blanco Y Negro	NEG13T	1985	£2.50	£6	

JESUS JONES

A prediction - Jesus Jones' "Liquidiser" album will, in years to come, be seen as one of the major rock music milestones. Its sophisticated blend of high energy guitar rock with modern sampling technology works so well and so seamlessly that it is easy to pass over what has been achieved here. But when, in addition, the songs themselves are so well crafted and memorable, the result is so obviously a masterpiece that it becomes astonishing that the group is not more highly rated that it seems to be!

Bring It On Down (Liquidiser Mix)	12"	Food	12FOODDJ22	1989	£2.50	£6	promo
Info Freako	CD-s	Food	CDFOOD18	1989	£2.50	£6	
Info Freako (Dance Extravaganza)	12"	Food	12FOODX18	1989	£3	£8	

JESUS LOVES YOU

After The Love	12"	More Protein	PRTX12	1989	£4	£10	
One On One	12"	More Protein	PROT712	1990	£6	£15	black 'spunk' PS

JET SET

VC10	7"	Delta	DW5001	1962	£2	£5	
VC10	7"	Delta	DW5001	1962	£4	£8	PS
You Got Me Hooked	7"	Parlophone	R5199	1964	£2.50	£6	

JETHRO TULL

The first record made by Jethro Tull, the MGM single "Sunshine Day", was mistakenly credited to "Jethro Toe". Both sides of the record - less bluesy than the music on "This Was", but easily recogniseable as the same group - were subsequently made available on the Polydor compilation "Rare Tracks", but the single itself hardly sold at all and is extremely scarce. Copies that correct the spelling of the group's name on the label are counterfeits, this being emphasized by their having American-style large centre holes on what is supposed to be a UK release.

1982 Tour Sampler	LP	Chrysalis	47PDJ	1982	£6	£15	US promo
Aqualung	LP	Chrysalis	CH41044	1973	£10	£25	US quad
Aqualung	LP	Island	ILPS9145	1971	£4	£10	chart LP
Aqualung	LP	Mobile Fidelity	MFSL1061	1980	£15	£30	US audiophile
Benefit	LP	Chrysalis	ILPS9123	1970	£4	£10	chart LP
Benefit	LP	Island	6339009	1970	£6	£15	German, gatefold sleeve, poster
Benefit	LP	Island	ILPS9123	1970	£10	£25	pink label
Broadsword	7"	Chrysalis	CHSP2619	1982	£2.50	£6	pic disc
Broadsword & The Beast	LP	Mobile Fidelity	MFSL1092	1982	£6	£15	US audiophile
Coronach	12"	Chrysalis	TULLX2	1986	£6	£15	
Home	7"	Chrysalis	CHS2394	1979	£4	£8	
Inside	7"	Chrysalis	CHS2012	1973	£2.50	£6	
Jethro Tull Radio Show	LP	Chrysalis	PRO622	1976	£8	£20	US promo
Living In The Past	LP	Chrysalis	CJT1	1972	£100	£200	double, leather cover
Living In The Past	LP	Chrysalis	CJT1	1972	£5	£12	hard cover double, chart LP
Living In The Past	7"	Island	WIP6056	1969	£2	£5	chart single
Love Story	7"	Island	WIP6048	1968	£5	£10	'Henderson' song-writing credit
Love Story	7"	Island	WIP6048	1968	£2	£5	chart single
Moths/Beltane	7"	Chrysalis	CHS2214	1978	£10	£20	
North Sea Oil	7"	Chrysalis	CHS2378	1979	£2	£5	
Passion Play	7"	Chrysalis	CHS2012	1973	£25	£50	
Ring Out Solstice Bells	7"	Chrysalis	CHS2443	1976	£1.50	£4	
Ring Out Solstice Bells	7"	Chrysalis	CXP2275	1976	£1.50	£4	PS
Song For Jeffrey	7"	Island	WIP6043	1968	£10	£20	
Stand Up	LP	Island	ILPS9103	1969	£6	£15	chart LP
Stitch In Time	7"	Chrysalis	CHS2260	1978	£2	£5	
Sunshine Day	7"	MGM	MGM1384	1968	£50	£100	credited to Jethro Toe
Sweet Dream	7"	Chrysalis	WIP6070	1969	£1.50	£4	chart single

Thick As A Brick	LP	Chrysalis	CHR1003	1972	£6	£15	newspaper sleeve
This Was	LP	Island	ILP985	1968	£15	£30	mono
This Was	LP	Island	ILPS9085	1968	£8	£20	chart LP
Under Wraps	LP	Chrysalis	CDLP1461	1984	£4	£10	pic disc
War Child	LP	Chrysalis	CH41067	1974	£8	£20	US quad
Whistler	7"	Chrysalis	CHS2135	1977	£1.50	£4	

JETSTREAMS
Bongo Rock	7"	Decca	F11149	1959	£5	£10	

JEWELS
But I Do	7"	Colpix	PX11048	1965	£6	£12	
Opportunity	7"	Colpix	PX11034	1964	£6	£12	

JIGSAW
Aurora Borealis	LP	Philips	6308072	1971	£20	£40	
Broken Hearted	LP	BASF	BAG22291065	1973	£8	£20	
I've Seen The Film	LP	BASF	BAP5051	1974	£8	£20	
I've Seen The Film	7"	BASF	BA1002	1974	£2.50	£6	
Jesu Joy Of Man's Desiring	7"	Philips	6006131	1971	£2.50	£6	
Keeping My Head Above Water	7"	Philips	6006182	1971	£2.50	£6	
Let Me Go Home	7"	Music Factory	CUB6	1968	£20	£40	
Letherslade Farm	LP	Philips	6309033	1970	£25	£50	
Lollipop And Goody Man	7"	Fontana	6007017	1970	£5	£10	
Mister Job	7"	Music Factory	CUB4	1968	£1.50	£4	
One Way Street	7"	MGM	MGM1410	1968	£1.50	£4	
One Way Street	7"	Philips	6006112	1970	£5	£10	
You're Not The Only Girl	7"	BASF	BA1010	1974	£2.50	£6	

JILL & THE BOULEVARDS
Eugene	7"	Columbia	DB4823	1962	£2.50	£6	

JILL & THE Y'VERNS
My Soulful Dress	7"	Oak	RGJ503	196-	£10	£20	

JIM & JEAN
Changes	7" EP	Verve	519901	1967	£6	£12	French

JIM & JOE
Fireball Mail	7"	London	HL9831	1964	£5	£10	

JIM & MONICA
Slippin' And Slidin'	7"	Stateside	SS266	1964	£5	£10	

JIMMIE & THE NIGHT HOPPERS
Night Hop	7"	London	HLP8830	1959	£7.50	£15	

JIV-A-TONES
Flirty Gertie	7"	Felsted	AF101	1958	£60	£120	

JIVE FIVE
I'm A Happy Man	7"	United Artists	UP1106	1965	£4	£8	
Jive Five	LP	United Artists	UAL3455/ UAS6455	1965	£10	£25	U
My True Story	7"	Parlophone	R4822	1961	£50	£100	
What Time Is It	7"	Stateside	SS133	1962	£10	£20	

JIVERS
Little Mama	7"	Vogue	V9060	1956	£100	£200	
Ray Pearl	7"	Vogue	V9068	1957	£100	£200	

JIVERS (2)
Wear My Crown	7"	Trojan	TR604	1968	£2.50	£6	

JIVING JUNIORS
Don't Leave Me	7"	Island	WI027	1962	£5	£10	
Lollipop Girl	7"	Blue Beat	BB4	1960	£5	£10	
My Heart's Desire	7"	Blue Beat	BB5	1960	£5	£10	
Over The River	7"	Blue Beat	BB36	1961	£5	£10	
Slop And Mash	7"	Starlite	ST45049	1961	£4	£8	
Sugar Dandy	7"	Island	WI003	1962	£5	£10	
Sugar Dandy	7"	Island	WI129	1963	£5	£10	
Tu Woo Up Tu Woo	7"	Starlite	ST45028	1960	£5	£10	

J.J.ALLSTARS
Memphis Underground	7"	Trojan	TR691	1969	£2	£5	

JO, DAMITA
I'd Do It Again	7"	HMV	JO390	1954	£2.50	£6	expo
I'll Save The Last Dance For You	7" EP	Mercury	ZEP10118	1961	£5	£10	

JO JO GUNNE
Beggin' You Baby	7"	Decca	F12906	1969	£1.50	£4	
Every Story Has An End	7"	Decca	F12807	1968	£1.50	£4	

JOBRIATH
Creatures Of The Street	LP	Elektra	K42163	1974	£4	£10	
Jobriath	LP	Elektra	EKS75070	1973	£4	£10	

JODIMARS
Cloud Ninety-nine	7"	Capitol	CL14700	1957	£12.50	£25	
Dance To The Bop	7"	Capitol	CL14642	1956	£12.50	£25	

Lotsa Love	7"	Capitol	CL14627	1956	£12.50	£25	
Midnight	7"	Capitol	CL14663	1956	£12.50	£25	
Rattle Shaking Daddy	7"	Capitol	CL14641	1956	£12.50	£25	
Well Now Dig This	LP	Ember	SPE6608	196-	£5	£12	
Well Now Dig This	7"	Capitol	CL14518	1956	£15	£30	

JODOROWSKY, ALEXANDRO
El Topo	LP	Apple	SWAO3388		£5	£12	US

JODY GRIND
Far Canal	LP	Transatlantic	TRA221	1970	£8	£20	
One Step On	LP	Transatlantic	TRA210	1969	£8	£20	

JOE & ANN
Gee Baby	7"	Black Swan	WI468	1965	£5	£10	

JOE & EDDIE
Walkin' Down The Line	7"	Vocalion	VP9250	1965	£2.50	£6	

JOE, AL T.
Fatso	7"	Blue Beat	BB169	1963	£5	£10	
Goodbye Dreamboat	7"	Blue Beat	BB166	1963	£5	£10	
I'm On My Own	7"	Dice	CC9	1962	£5	£10	
Jacqueline	7"	Blue Beat	BB368	1965	£5	£10	
You Cheated On Me	7"	Blue Beat	BB126	1962	£5	£10	

JOE SOAP
Keep It Clean	LP	Polydor	2383233	1973	£6	£15	

JOEL, BILLY
52nd Street	LP	Columbia	HC45609	1981	£4	£10	US audiophile
Ballad Of Billy The Kid	7"	Philips	6078018	1973	£10	£20	
Billy Joel	LP	Columbia	ABS1	1978	£37.50	£75	US promo, 5 LPs, boxed
Cold Spring Harbour	LP	Philips	6369150	1972	£5	£12	recorded too fast
Entertainer	7"	Philips		1973	£12.50	£25	
Honesty	7"	CBS	7150	1979	£7.50	£15	
Interchords	LP	Columbia	AS402	1976	£6	£15	US interview promo
Now Playing	LP	CBS	BJ1	1978	£6	£15	promo
Piano Man	LP	Columbia	CQ32544	1974	£5	£12	US quad
Piano Man	LP	Philips	6369160	1973	£10	£25	
She's Got A Way	7"	Philips	6078001	1972	£4	£8	
Songs From The Attic	LP	Columbia	AS1343	1981	£8	£20	US sampler & interview promo
Souvenir	LP	Columbia	AS326	1974	£8	£20	US 1 sided live promo
Stranger	LP	Columbia	HC34987	1980	£4	£10	US audiophile
Streetlife Serenade	LP	Columbia	PCQ33146	1974	£4	£10	US quad
Turnstiles	LP	Columbia	PCQ33848	1976	£4	£10	US quad

JOE'S ALLSTARS
Battle Cry Of Biafra	7"	Joe	DU28	1969	£1.50	£4	
Hey Jude	7"	Joe	DU24	1969	£1.50	£4	
Tony B's Theme	7"	Joe	JRS9	1970	£2.50	£6	

JOEY & THE CONTINENTALS
She Rides With Me	7"	Polydor	56520	1970	£2.50	£6	

JOEY & THE GENTLEMEN
Like I Love You	7"	Fontana	TF444	1964	£4	£8	

JOHN & PAUL
People Say	7"	London	HLU9997	1965	£4	£8	

JOHN & SANDRA
John And Sandra	LP	Argo	ZFB2	1970	£4	£10	

JOHN, ANDREW
Machine Stops	LP	CBS	64835	1971	£6	£15	

JOHN BULL BREED
I'm A Man	7"	Polydor	56065	1966	£37.50	£75	

JOHN, DAVID & THE MOOD
Bring It To Jerome	7"	Parlophone	R5255	1965	£40	£80	
Diggin' For Gold	7"	Parlophone	R5301	1965	£50	£100	
Pretty Thing	7"	Vocalion	V9220	1964	£60	£120	

JOHN, ELTON
Border Song	7"	DJM	DJS217	1970	£1.50	£4	
Candle In The Wind	LP	St.Michael	20940102	1978	£10	£25	
Captain Fantastic	LP	DJM	DJLPX1	1975	£40	£80	brown vinyl
Captain Fantastic	LP	DJM	DJLPX1	1975	£35	£70	brown vinyl, autographed cover
Captain Fantastic	LP	DJM	DJV2300	1978	£5	£12	pic disc
Elton John	LP	DJM	DJM14512	1978	£20	£40	5 LPs, boxed
Empty Garden	7"	Rocket	XPPIC77	1982	£1.50	£4	pic disc
Empty Sky	LP	DJM	DJLPM403	1969	£5	£12	mono
Empty Sky	LP	DJM	DJLPS403	1969	£4	£10	stereo
Friends	7"	DJM	DJS244	1971	£1.50	£4	
Games	LP	Viking	105	1970	£37.50	£75	US, with other artists
Gli Opera	7"	Rocket		1977	£4	£8	sung in Italian

Title	Format	Label	Catalog	Year			Notes
Goaldigger Song	7"	Rocket	GOALD1	1977	£30	£60	
Goodbye Yellow Brick Road	LP	DJM	DJE29001	1976	£5	£12	yellow vinyl
Goodbye Yellow Brick Road	LP	Nautilus	10003	1980	£10	£25	US audiophile
Goodbye Yellow Brick Road	LP	Superdisk	SD216614	1982	£6	£15	audiophile
Greatest Hits Volume One	LP	Nautilus		1981	£5	£12	US audiophile
I'm Still Standing	7"	Rocket	EJPIC1	1983	£4	£8	shaped pic disc
It's Me That You Need	7"	DJM	DJS205	1969	£7.50	£15	
It's Me That You Need	7"	DJM	DJS205	1969	£25	£50	PS
I've Been Loving You	7"	Philips	BF1643	1968	£40	£80	
Je Veux De La Tendresse	7"	Rocket	6000675	1980	£2.50	£6	sung in French
Lady Samantha	7"	Philips	BF1739	1969	£12.50	£25	
Live In Australia With The Melbourne S.O.	LP	Rocket	EJBXL1	1987	£5	£12	double
Mama Can't Buy You Love	7"	Rocket	XPRES20	1979	£7.50	£15	
Nikita	7"	Rocket	EJSD9	1985	£2	£5	double, pop-up PS
Rock And Roll Madonna	7"	DJM	DJS222	1970	£4	£8	
Rocket Man	7"	DJM	DJX501	1972	£6	£12	gatefold PS
Sad Songs	7"	Rocket	PHPIC7	1984	£4	£8	shaped pic disc
Single Man	LP	MCA	MCAP14591	1979	£4	£10	US pic disc
Singles Collection	7"	DJM	EJBOX12	1978	£20	£40	12 singles, boxed
Superior Sound Of Elton John	CD	DJM	8100622	1983	£8	£20	remix compilation
Wrap Her Up	7"	Rocket	EJPIC10	1985	£4	£8	shaped pic disc, with George Michael
Wrap Her Up	7"	Rocket	EJSC10	1985	£1.50	£4	cube bag sleeve, with George Michael
Wrap Her Up	7"	Rocket	EJSP10	1985	£4	£8	with George Michael, shaped pic disc

JOHN, ELTON & CLIFF RICHARD
Slow Rivers	7"	Rocket	EJSP13	1986	£1.50	£4	pic disc

JOHN, ELTON & FRANCE GALL
Les Areuse	7"			1981	£1.50	£4	sung in French
Les Areuse	12"			1981	£2.50	£6	sung in French

JOHN, ELTON & JOHN LENNON
I Saw Her Standing There	7"	DJM	DJS10965	1981	£1.50	£4	black & red label
I Saw Her Standing There	7"	DJM	DJS10965	1981	£5	£10	black & white label
I Saw Her Standing There	7"	DJM	DJS354	1975	£1.50	£4	PS

JOHN, LITTLE WILLIE
Action	LP	King	691	1960	£20	£40	US
Come On And Join Little Willie John	LP	London	HA8126	1964	£15	£30	
Fever	LP	King	395564	1956	£30	£60	US
Fever	7"	Parlophone	R4209	1956	£12.50	£25	
Free At Last	LP	King	KS1081	1970	£8	£20	US
Heartbreak	7"	Parlophone	R4674	1960	£7.50	£15	
Leave My Kitten Alone	7"	Parlophone	R4571	1959	£7.50	£15	
Let's Rock While The Rocking's Good	7"	Parlophone	R4472	1958	£10	£20	
Little Willie Sings All Originals	LP	King	K(S)949	1966	£10	£25	US
Mr.Little Willie John	LP	King	603	1958	£25	£50	US
Sleep	7"	Parlophone	R4699	1960	£6	£12	
Sure Things	LP	King	739	1961	£15	£30	US
Sweet, The Hot, The Teenage Beat	LP	King	767	1961	£15	£30	US
Talk To Me	LP	King	395596	1958	£25	£50	US
Talk To Me	7"	Parlophone	R4432	1958	£7.50	£15	
These Are My Favorite Songs	LP	King	895	1964	£15	£30	US
Uh Uh Baby	7"	Parlophone	R4396	1958	£7.50	£15	

JOHN, MABLE
Able Mable	7"	Stax	601034	1968	£2	£5	
It's Catching	7"	Atlantic	584022	1966	£2.50	£6	
Same Time Same Place	7"	Stax	601010	1967	£2.50	£6	

JOHN, ROBERT
Don't Leave Me	7"	CBS	3730	1968	£1.50	£4	
If You Don't Want My Love	7"	CBS	3436	1968	£2	£5	

JOHN, SAMMIE
Little John	7"	Stateside	SS585	1967	£2	£5	

JOHN THE POSTMAN
Psychedelic Rock'n'Roll 5 Skinners	12"	Bent	BIGBENT4	197-	£3	£8	
Puerile	12"	Bent	BIGBENT2	197-	£3	£8	

JOHN THE REVELATOR
Wild Blues	LP	Decca	6419002	1970	£8	£20	Dutch

JOHNNIE & JOE
Over the Mountain Across The Sea	7"	London	HLM8682	1958	£60	£120	

JOHNNY & CHAS & THE GUNNERS
Bobby	7"	Decca	F11365	1961	£7.50	£15	

JOHNNY & JACK
Hits	LP	RCA	LPM2017	1959	£5	£12	US
Honey I Need You	7"	HMV	7MC21	1954	£1.50	£4	export
Tennessee Mountain Boys	LP	RCA	LPM1587	1957	£5	£12	US

JOHNNY & JOHN
Bumper To Bumper	7"	Polydor	BM56087	1966	£5	£10	

JOHNNY & JUDY
Bother Me Baby .... 7" ...... Vogue .... V9128 .... 1959 ... £60 ......£120 ....

JOHNNY & THE ATTRACTIONS
Young Wings Can Fly .... 7" ...... Doctor Bird ...... DB1118 .... 1967 ... £5 ....£10 ....Dudley
Williamson B side

JOHNNY & THE BLUEBEATS
Shame .... 7" ...... Blue Beat .... BB229 .... 1963 ... £5 ....£10 ....

JOHNNY & THE COPYCATS
I'm A Hog For You Baby .... 7" ...... Narco .... AB102 .... 196- ... £12.50 .....£25 ....

JOHNNY & THE HURRICANES
Beatnik Fly	7"	London	HLI9072	1960	£2	£5	chart single
Big Sound	LP	London	HAX2322	1960	£10	£25	chart LP
Crossfire	7"	London	HL8899	1959	£10	£20	tri-centre
Down Yonder	7"	London	HLX9134	1960	£2	£5	chart single
Greens And Jeans	7"	London	HLX9660	1963	£2	£5	
Hep Canary	7"	London	HL7099	1960	£12.50	£25	export
Ja-Da	7"	London	HLX9289	1961	£1.50	£4	chart single
Johnny & The Hurricanes	LP	Warwick	W(ST)2007	1959	£25	£50	US
Johnny & The Hurricanes	7" EP.	London	REX1347	1962	£7.50	£15	
Johnny & The Hurricanes Vol.2	7" EP.	London	REX1414	1964	£10	£20	
Live At The Star Club	LP	Atila	1030	1962	£20	£40	US
Minnesota Fats	7"	London	HLX9617	1962	£2	£5	
Money Honey	7"	Stateside	SS347	1964	£2.50	£6	
Old Smokey	7"	London	HLX9378	1961	£1.50	£4	chart single
Red River Rock	LP	London	HA2227	196-	£4	£10	black label
Red River Rock	LP	London	HA2227	1960	£15	£30	plum label
Red River Rock	7"	London	HL8948	1959	£4	£8	chart single, tri-centre
Reveille Rock	7"	London	HL9017	1959	£4	£8	chart single, tri-centre
Rocking Goose	7"	London	HLX9190	1960	£2	£5	chart single
Rocking Goose	7" EP.	London	REX1284	1961	£7.50	£15	
Salvation	7"	London	HLX9536	1962	£2	£5	
Stormsville	LP	London	HAI2269	1960	£10	£25	chart LP, Sleeve pictured in guide
Traffic Jam	7"	London	HLX9491	1962	£2	£5	

JOHNNY & THE SELF ABUSERS
It is unlikely that Johnny & The Self Abusers would have become international stars if they had retained that name. Fortunately they decided to change it to Simple Minds...
Saints And Sinners .... 7" ...... Chiswick .... NS22 .... 1977 ... £5 ....£10 ....PS

JOHNNY & THE VIBRATIONS
Bird Stompin' .... 7" ...... Warner Bros .... WB107 .... 1963 ... £1.50 ....£4 ....

JOHNNY'S BOYS
Sleepwalk .... 7" ...... Decca .... F11156 .... 1959 ... £2 ....£5 ....

JOHNNY'S JAZZ
R.J. Boogie .... 7" ...... Decca .... FJ10663 .... 1956 ... £1.50 ....£4 ....

JOHN'S CHILDREN
The collectability of John's Children derives mainly from the fact that Marc Bolan played with the group for a short time. "Desdemona" is a Bolan song, as is the withdrawn and extremely scarce "Midsummer Night's Scene". (Other unreleased Marc Bolan contributions were included on his LP "Beginning Of Doves"). Many of the other John's Children recordings were actually made by session musicians (including Jeff Beck on the B side of "Just What You Want"), as the group were too incompetent to do the job themselves.
Come And Play With Me In The Garden	7"	Track	604005	1967	£10	£20	
Come And Play With Me In The Garden	7"	Track	604005	1967	£30	£60	PS
Desdemona	7"	Track	604003	1967	£10	£20	
Desdemona	7"	Track	604003	1967	£25	£50	PS, sleeve pictured in Guide
Go Go Girl	7"	Track	604010	1967	£15	£30	
Just What You Want	7"	Columbia	DB8124	1967	£25	£50	
Love I Thought I'd Found	7"	Columbia	DB8030	1966	£25	£50	
Love I Thought I'd Found	7"	Columbia	DB8030	1966	£75	£150	PS
Midsummer Night's Scene	7"	Track	604005	1967	£700	£1000	test pressing
Orgasm	LP	White Whale	WW7128	1967	£30	£60	US

JOHNS, GLYN
I'll Follow The Sun .... 7" ...... Pye .... 7N15818 .... 1965 ... £2.50 ....£6 ....
January Blues .... 7" ...... Decca .... F11478 .... 1962 ... £1.50 ....£4 ....
Mary Anne .... 7" ...... Immediate .... IM013 .... 1965 ... £5 ....£10 ....
Today You're Gone .... 7" ...... Lyntone .... LYN827/8 .... 196- ... £1.50 ....£4 ....

JOHNS, GLYNIS
I Can't Resist Men .... 7" ...... Columbia .... SCM5149 .... 1954 ... £1.50 ....£4 ....

JOHNSON, BETTY
1492	7"	London	HLU8432	1957	£12.50	£25	
Betty Johnson	LP	Atlantic	8017	1958	£10	£25	US
Does Your Heart Beat For Me	7"	London	HLE8839	1959	£10	£20	
Dream	7"	London	HLE8678	1958	£7.50	£15	
Dream	7" EP.	London	REE1221	1959	£15	£30	
Honky Tonk Rock	7"	London	HLU8326	1956	£40	£80	
Hoopa Hula	7"	London	HLE8725	1958	£12.50	£25	
I Dreamed	7"	London	HLU8365	1957	£15	£30	
I'll Wait	7"	London	HLU8307	1956	£15	£30	

Title	Format	Label	Cat. No.	Year	Price	Price	Notes
Little Blue Man	7"	London	HLE8557	1958	£12.50	£25	
Songs You Heard When You Fell In Love	LP	London	HAE2163	1959	£10	£25	
There's Never Been A Night	7"	London	HLE8701	1958	£15	£30	

JOHNSON, BLIND WILLIE

Title	Format	Label	Cat. No.	Year	Price	Price	Notes
Blind Willie Johnson	LP	Folkways	10	1965	£5	£12	US
Blues	LP	Folkways	3585	1957	£8	£20	US
Treasures Of North American Negro Music No.2	7" EP	Fontana	TFE17052	1958	£5	£10	

JOHNSON, BOBBY & THE ATOMS

Title	Format	Label	Cat. No.	Year	Price	Price	Notes
Do It Again A Little Bit Slower	7"	Ember	EMBS245	1967	£2.50	£6	

JOHNSON, BRYAN

Title	Format	Label	Cat. No.	Year	Price	Price	Notes
Looking High	7" EP	Decca	DFE6664	1961	£2	£5	
Looking High,High,High	7"	Decca	F11213	1960	£1.50	£4	chart single

JOHNSON, BUBBER

Title	Format	Label	Cat. No.	Year	Price	Price	Notes
Come Home	LP	King	395569	1957	£20	£40	US
Confidential	7"	Parlophone	R4259	1957	£7.50	£15	
Sings Sweet Love Songs	LP	King	624	1959	£15	£30	US

JOHNSON, BUDD

Title	Format	Label	Cat. No.	Year	Price	Price	Notes
Blues A La Mode	LP	Felsted	FAJ7007/SJA2007	1959	£10	£25	

JOHNSON, BUDDY & ELLA

Title	Format	Label	Cat. No.	Year	Price	Price	Notes
Buddy Johnson Wails	LP	Mercury	MG20072	1958	£15	£30	US
Buddy Johnson Wails	7" EP	Mercury	ZEP10009	1959	£15	£30	US
Go Ahead And Rock And Roll	LP	Roulette	(S)R25085	1959	£15	£30	US
Rock And Roll	10" LP	Mercury	MPT7515	1957	£20	£40	US
Rock'n'Roll	LP	Mercury	MG20209	1956	£15	£30	US
Rock'n'Roll Stage Show	LP	Wing	MGW12005	1956	£15	£30	US
Swing Me	LP	Mercury	MG20347	1958	£15	£30	US
Walkin'	LP	Mercury	MG20322	1958	£15	£30	US

JOHNSON, BUNK

Title	Format	Label	Cat. No.	Year	Price	Price	Notes
Bunk And Lu	LP	Good Time Jazz	LAG12121	1958	£5	£12	with Lu Watters
Bunk Johnson And His New Orleans Band	LP	Columbia	33SX1015	1954	£6	£15	
Bunk Johnson And His Superior Jazz Band	LP	Goodtime Jazz	LAG545	1963	£5	£12	
Bunk Johnson And The Yerba Buena Jazz Band	10" LP	Goodtime Jazz	LDG110	1955	£8	£20	
Bunk Johnson's Band 1944	LP	Storyville	SLP152	1962	£5	£12	
One You Love	7" EP	Melodisc	EPM752	1955	£2.50	£6	

JOHNSON, DANIEL

Title	Format	Label	Cat. No.	Year	Price	Price	Notes
Come On My People	7"	Island	WI250	1965	£5	£10	

JOHNSON, DICK

Title	Format	Label	Cat. No.	Year	Price	Price	Notes
Dick Johnson Quartet	LP	Emarcy	EJT753	1957	£10	£25	

JOHNSON, GENERAL

Title	Format	Label	Cat. No.	Year	Price	Price	Notes
All In The Family	7"	Arista	ARIST45	1976	£1.50	£4	

JOHNSON, HENRY

Title	Format	Label	Cat. No.	Year	Price	Price	Notes
Till I Found The Lord	7"	Flyright	45002	196-	£1.50	£4	

JOHNSON, JAMES P.

Title	Format	Label	Cat. No.	Year	Price	Price	Notes
Daddy Of The Piano	10" LP	Brunswick	LA8548	1952	£5	£12	
Early Harlem Piano	10" LP	London	AL3511	1954	£8	£20	
Fats Waller Favourites	10" LP	Brunswick	LA8622	1953	£8	£20	
Feeling Blue	7"	Columbia	SCM5127	1954	£2.50	£6	
Harlem Party Piano	10" LP	London	HBU1057	1956	£8	£20	B side by Luckey Roberts
James P.Johnson	7" EP	HMV	7EG8164	1956	£4	£8	
James P.Johnson	7" EP	Tempo	EXA65	1957	£4	£8	
James P.Johnson	10" LP	London	AL3540	1955	£8	£20	
Jimmy Johnson And Joe Sullivan	7" EP	Fontana	TFE17246	1960	£2	£5	
Louisiana Sugar Babies	7" EP	HMV	7EG8215	1957	£7.50	£15	with Fats Waller

JOHNSON, JIMMY

Title	Format	Label	Cat. No.	Year	Price	Price	Notes
Don't Answer The Door	7"	Sue	WI387	1965	£6	£12	

JOHNSON, J.J.

Title	Format	Label	Cat. No.	Year	Price	Price	Notes
Blue Trombone	LP	Fontana	TFL5137	1961	£5	£12	
Boneology	LP	Realm	RM195	1964	£5	£12	
Dial JJ5	LP	Fontana	TFL5021	1958	£5	£12	
First Place	LP	Fontana	TFL5005	1958	£5	£12	
J Is For Jazz	LP	Philips	BBL7143	1957	£8	£20	
Jay & Kai Plus Six	LP	Fontana	TFL5022	1958	£5	£12	with Kai Winding
Jay Jay Johnson Vol.1	LP	Blue Note	BLP/BST81505	196-	£10	£25	
Jay Jay Johnson Vol.2	LP	Blue Note	BLP/BST81506	196-	£10	£25	
J.J. In Person	LP	Fontana	TFL5041/STFL512.	1960	£5	£12	
J.J.Johnson Quintet	10" LP	Vogue	LDE162	1955	£25	£50	
J.J.Johnson Sextet	10" LP	Vogue	LDE124	1955	£25	£50	

JOHNSON, JOHNNY & THE BANDWAGON

Title	Format	Label	Cat. No.	Year	Price	Price	Notes
Baby Make Your Own Sweet Music	7"	Direction	583520	1968	£1.50	£4	

Blame It On The Pony Express	7"	Bell	BLL1128	1970	£1.50	£4	chart single
Breaking Down The Walls Of Heartache	7"	Direction	583670	1968	£1.50	£4	chart single
Johnny Johnson And The Bandwagon	LP	Direction	863500	1968	£5	£12	
Let's Hang On	7"	Direction	584180	1969	£1.50	£4	chart single
Sweet Inspiration	7"	Bell	BLL1111	1970	£1.50	£4	chart single
You	7"	Direction	583923	1969	£1.50	£4	

JOHNSON, JUDI

How Many Times	7"	HMV	POP1399	1965	£2	£5	

JOHNSON, LARRY

Presenting The Country Blues	LP	Blue Horizon	763851	1970	£15	£30	

JOHNSON, LAURIE

Avengers	LP	Marble Arch	MAL695	1967	£5	£12	
Avengers	7"	Pye	7N17015	1965	£2.50	£6	
Avengers	7"	Pye	7N17015	1965	£7.50	£15	PS
Brass Band Swinging	LP	Columbia	33SX1231	1960	£5	£12	
Laurie Johnson & The London Jazz Orchestra	LP	Columbia	SCX6412	1970	£6	£15	
New Avengers Theme	7"	EMI	EMI2526	1976	£2	£5	PS
Professionals Main Title	7"	Unicorn-Kachana	C15	1980	£1.50	£4	PS

JOHNSON, LONNIE

Another Night To Cry	LP	Bluesville	BV1062	1963	£6	£15	US
Blues And Ballads	LP	Bluesville	BV1011	1960	£8	£20	US
Blues By Lonnie Johnson	LP	Bluesville	BV1007	1960	£8	£20	US
Blues For Everybody	78	Melodisc	1186	1951	£3	£8	
Idle Hours	LP	Bluesville	BV1044	1961	£8	£20	US
Jelly Roll Baker	78	Vogue	V2015	1951	£3	£8	
Keep What You Got	78	Melodisc	1221	1952	£3	£8	
Little Rockin' Chair	78	Vogue	V2079	1951	£3	£8	
Lonesome Road	LP	King	395520	195-	£30	£60	US
Lonesome Road	7" EP	Parlophone	GEP8635	1957	£7.50	£15	
Lonnie Johnson	LP	Storyville	616010	1969	£5	£12	
Lonnie Johnson	LP	XTRA	XTRA1037	1966	£6	£15	
Lonnie's Blues	7" EP	Parlophone	GEP8663	1957	£7.50	£15	
Lonnie's Blues No.2	7" EP	Parlophone	GEP8693	1958	£7.50	£15	
Losing Game	LP	Bluesville	BV1024	1961	£8	£20	US
Portraits In Blues Vol.6	LP	Storyville	SLP162	1964	£5	£12	
Sings 24 Twelve Bar Blues	LP	King	K(S)958	1966	£15	£30	US
Solid Blues	78	Melodisc	1138	1951	£3	£8	
Woman Blues	LP	Bluesville	BV1054	1963	£6	£15	US

JOHNSON, LOU

Always Something There To Remind Me	7"	London	HLX10269	1969	£1.50	£4	
Always Something There To Remind Me	7"	London	HLX9917	1964	£6	£15	
Magic Potion	7"	London	HLX9805	1963	£10	£20	
Magic Potion Of Lou Johnson	7" EP	London	REX1438	1964	£12.50	£25	
Message To Martha	7"	London	HLX9929	1964	£4	£8	chart single
Please Stop The Wedding	7"	London	HLX9965	1965	£4	£8	
Unsatisfied	7"	London	HLX9994	1965	£12.50	£25	

JOHNSON, LUTHER

With The Muddy Waters Blues Band	LP	Transatlantic	TRA188	1968	£5	£12	

JOHNSON, MARV

Ain't Gonna Be That Way	7"	London	HLT9165	1960	£5	£10	chart single
Come To Me	7"	London	HLT8856	1959	£25	£50	
Happy Days	7"	London	HLT9265	1961	£5	£10	
I Believe	LP	United Artists	UAL3187/ UAS6187	1962	£15	£30	US
I Love The Way You Love	7"	London	HL7095	1960	£4	£8	export
I Love The Way You Love Me	7"	London	HLT9109	1960	£5	£10	chart single
I Miss You Baby	7"	Tamla Motown	TMG713	1969	£1.50	£4	chart single
I'll Pick A Rose For My Rose	LP	Tamla Motown	(S)TML11111	1969	£6	£15	
I'll Pick A Rose For My Rose	7"	Tamla Motown	TMG680	1969	£2	£5	chart single
Marvellous Marv	LP	London	HAT2271	1960	£25	£50	
Merry-Go-Round	7"	London	HLT9311	1961	£7.50	£15	
More Marv Johnson	LP	United Artists	UAL3118/ UAS6118	1960	£20	£40	US
Move Two Mountains	7"	London	HLT9187	1960	£4	£8	
So Glad You Chose Me	7"	Tamla Motown	TMG737	1970	£2	£5	
Why Do You Want To Let Me Go	7"	Tamla Motown	TMG525	1965	£25	£50	
You Got What It Takes	7"	London	HLT9013	1959	£2.50	£6	chart single

JOHNSON, MATT

Burning Blue Soul	LP	4AD	CAD113	1981	£10	£25	psychedelic eye sleeve

JOHNSON, MIRRIAM

Lonesome Road	7"	London	HLW9337	1961	£2.50	£6	

JOHNSON, NORMAN

Take It Baby	7"	Action	ACT4545	1969	£7.50	£15	
You're Everything	7"	Action	ACT4529	1969	£7.50	£15	
You're Everything	7"	Action	ACT4601	1971	£6	£12	

JOHNSON, PETE

Boogie Woogie Mood	LP	Vogue Coral	LRA10016	1955	£6	£15
J.J.Boogie	7"	Vogue	V2007	1956	£10	£20
Pete Johnson	7" EP.	Vogue	EPV1039	1955	£15	£30
Pete Johnson	10" LP	London	AL3549	1955	£10	£25
Pete's Blues	LP	Savoy	MG14018	195-	£10	£25 ..... US
Roll Em Boy	7" EP.	Top Rank	JKR8009	1959	£7.50	£15
Swanee River Boogie	7"	Vogue	V2008	1956	£10	£20

JOHNSON, PETE & ALBERT AMMONS

Eight To The Bar	10" LP	HMV	DLP1011	1953	£15	£30

JOHNSON, PLAS

Big Twist	7"	Capitol	CL14772	1957	£5	£10
Bop Me Daddy	10" LP	London	HBU1078	1957	£10	£25
Dinah	7"	Capitol	CL14903	1958	£5	£10
Popcorn	7"	Capitol	CL14836	1958	£5	£10
Robbins Nest Cha Cha	7"	Capitol	CL14973	1959	£2.50	£6
You Send Me	7"	Capitol	CL14816	1957	£5	£10

JOHNSON, PROFESSOR GOSPEL SINGERS

Where Shall I Be	7" EP.	Brunswick	OE9352	1958	£4	£8

JOHNSON, RAY

Calypso Blues	7"	Vogue	V9093	1958	£10	£20
If You Don't Want Me Baby	7"	Vogue	V9073	1957	£12.50	£25

JOHNSON, ROBERT

Blues Legend 1936-7	LP	Smokestack	SSLP1	196-	£8	£20
King Of The Delta Blues Singers	LP	CBS	BPG62456	1963	£5	£12
King Of The Delta Blues Singers Vol.2	LP	CBS	64102	1970	£5	£12
Robert Johnson	LP	Kokomo	K1000	1967	£8	£20
Robert Johnson	LP	Philips	BBL7539	1962	£8	£20

JOHNSON, ROY LEE

So Anna Just Love Me	7"	Action	ACT4518	1969	£2	£5

JOHNSON, RUBY

If I Ever Needed Love	7"	Stax	601020	1967	£4	£8

JOHNSON, TEDDY & PEARL CARR

Meet Teddy And Pearl	7" EP.	Pye	NEP24112	1959	£2.50	£6
Sing Little Birdie	7"	Columbia	DB4275	1959	£1.50	£4

JOHNSON, THEO

Masters Of War	7"	Island	WI604	1965	£5	£10

JOHNSTON, ADRIENNE

Adrienne Of The Johnstons	LP	RCA	SF8416	1975	£5	£12

JOHNSTON BROTHERS

Bandit	7"	Decca	F10302	1954	£1.50	£4
Chee Chee-oo Chee	7"	Decca	F10513	1955	£1.50	£4
Creep	7"	Decca	F10234	1954	£2	£5
Dreamboat	7"	Decca	F10526	1955	£1.50	£4
Give Her My Love	7"	Decca	F10828	1956	£2	£5 ..... chart single
Heart	7"	Decca	F10860	1957	£1.50	£4 ..... chart single
Hernando's Hideaway	7"	Decca	F10608	1955	£4	£8 ..... chart single
How Little We Know	7"	Decca	F10747	1956	£1.50	£4
I Get So Lonely	7"	Decca	F10286	1954	£1.50	£4
I Like Music - You Like Music	7"	Decca	F10939	1957	£1.50	£4
In The Middle Of The House	7"	Decca	F10781	1956	£4	£8 ..... chart single
Join In And Sing	7"	Decca	F10414	1954	£1.50	£4
Join In And Sing Again	7"	Decca	F10636	1955	£2	£5 ..... chart single
Join In And Sing No.3	7"	Decca	F10814	1956	£2	£5 ..... chart single
Majorca	7"	Decca	F10451	1955	£1.50	£4
Mambo In THe Moonlight	7"	Decca	F10401	1954	£1.50	£4
No Other Love	7"	Decca	F10721	1956	£2	£5 ..... chart single
Right To Be Wrong	7"	Decca	F10490	1955	£1.50	£4
Sh'boom	7"	Decca	F10364	1954	£4	£8

JOHNSTON, BRUCE

Original Surfer Stomp	7"	London	HL9780	1963	£10	£20 ..... US
Surfer's Pajama Party	LP	Del-Fi	DFLP/DFST1228	1963	£20	£40 ..... US
Surfin' Round The World	LP	Columbia	CL2057/CS8857	1963	£25	£50 ..... US

JOHNSTONS

Alamo	7"	Pye	7N17205	1966	£1.50	£4
Barley Corn	LP	Transatlantic	TRA185	1969	£8	£20
Bitter Green	LP	Transatlantic	TRA211	1970	£8	£20
Both Sides Now	7"	Transatlantic	BIG113	1968	£1.50	£4
Colours Of The Dawn	LP	Transatlantic	TRA231	1971	£6	£15
Curragh Of Kildare	7"	Pye	7N17315	1967	£1.50	£4
Give A Damn	LP	Transatlantic	TRA184	1968	£8	£20
Give A Damn	7"	Transatlantic	BIG116	1968	£1.50	£4
Going Home	7"	Pye	7N17144	1966	£1.50	£4
I Never Will Marry	7"	Pye	7N17430	1967	£1.50	£4
If I Sang My Sang	LP	Transatlantic	TRA251	1972	£6	£15
Johnstons	LP	Transatlantic	TRA169	1968	£10	£25
Johnstons Sampler	LP	Transatlantic	TRASAM16	1970	£5	£12
My House	7"	Transatlantic	BIG121	1969	£1.50	£4

Streets Of London	7"	Transatlantic	BIG132	1970	£1.50	£4	
They'll Never Get Their Man	7"	Transatlantic	TRASP17	1967	£1.50	£4	
Travelling People	LP	Hallmark	HMA237	1967	£10	£25	
Travelling People	LP	Marble Arch	MAL808	1967	£10	£25	

JOINER, ARKANSAS JUNIOR HIGH SCHOOL BAND

National City	7"	London	HLG9147	1960	£2	£5	

JOKERS

Dogfight	7"	Salvo	SLO1806	1962	£6	£12	

JOKERS WILD

The ultra-collectability of the Jokers Wild's privately pressed record derives not so much from the fact that the drummer, Willie Wilson, was later in Quiver, nor from the fact that the bassist, Ricky Wills, was later in Cochise and the re-formed Small Faces, but from the presence of the lead guitarist, who is David Gilmour - subsequently to be found playing within the ranks of Pink Floyd.

Don't Ask Me Why	7"	private		1966	£150	£250	
Jokers Wild	LP	private		1966	£530	£800	1 sided

JOLLIVER ARKANSAW

Home	LP	Bell	SBLL119	1969	£8	£20	US

JOLSON, AL

Al Jolson	7" EP	Fontana	TFE17024	1958	£2	£5	
Jolson Memories	10" LP	Brunswick	LA8512	1951	£4	£10	
Jolson Sings Again	10" LP	Brunswick	LA8502	1950	£4	£10	
Souvenir	10" LP	Brunswick	LA8509	1951	£4	£10	
Souvenirs Vol.3	10" LP	Brunswick	LA8575	1953	£4	£10	
Souvenirs Vol.4	10" LP	Brunswick	LA8570	1953	£4	£10	
Souvenirs Vol.6	10" LP	Brunswick	LA8655	1954	£4	£10	
Stephen Foster Songs	10" LP	Brunswick	LA8554	1953	£4	£10	
They Sold A Million No.2	7" EP	Brunswick	OE9418	1959	£2	£5	
They Sold A Million No.3	7" EP	Brunswick	OE9419	1959	£2	£5	

JON

Is It Love	7"	Columbia	DB8249	1967	£12.50	£25	
So Much For Mary	7"	Parlophone	R5604	1967	£2.50	£6	
So Much For Mary	7"	Parlophone	R5604	1967	£6	£12	PS

JON & ALUN

Relax Your Mind	LP	Decca	LK/SKL4547	1963	£6	£15	

JON & JEANNIE

Lover's Holiday	7"	Beacon	3105	1968	£1.50	£4	

JON & ROBIN & THE IN CROWD

Do It Again A Little Bit Slower	7"	Stateside	SS2027	1967	£2	£5	
Do It Again A Little Bit Slower	7" EP	Barclay	071178	1967	£6	£12	French

JON & VANGELIS

Friends Of Mr.Cairo	12"	Polydor	POSPX258	1981	£2.50	£6	blue metal can

JONES, AL

Mad Mad World	7"	HMV	POP451	1958	£30	£60	

JONES, ALUN

Alun Ashworth Jones	LP	Parlophone	PMC/PCS7081	1969	£8	£20	
Jonesville	LP	Village Thing	VTS19	1972	£6	£15	

JONES, BEVERLY

Boy I Saw With You	7"	HMV	POP1109	1963	£1.50	£4	
Heatwave	7"	Parlophone	R5189	1964	£2	£5	
Wait Until My Bobby Gets Home	7"	HMV	POP1201	1963	£1.50	£4	
Why Do Lovers Break Each Others' Hearts	7"	HMV	POP1140	1963	£1.50	£4	

JONES, BRIAN

The one record credited to Brian Jones comes from the brief period between his leaving the Rolling Stones and his death, but it actually does not feature him at all. His decision to sponsor an ethnic band, however, is entirely symptomatic of his questing, open-minded approach at the time - the same approach as made the Stones' "Their Satanic Majesties Request" into one of the high points of sixties psychedelia, whatever the contrary views of modern critics may say. The Joujouka pipers, incidentally, turn up again in an intriguing meeting with saxophonist Ornette Coleman, on his album, "Dancing In Your Head".

Pipes Of Pan At Joujouka	LP	Rolling Stones	COC49100	1971	£20	£40	

JONES, CAROL

Boys With Eyes Of Blue	7"	Triumph	RGM1012	1960	£12.50	£25	

JONES, CASEY & THE ENGINEERS

One Way Ticket	7"	Columbia	DB7083	1963	£10	£20	

JONES, CASEY & THE GOVERNORS

Don't Ha Ha	7" EP	President	425	1964	£25	£50	French
Don't Ha Ha	7" EP	Riviera	231087	1965	£15	£30	French

JONES, CURTIS

In London	LP	Decca	LK4587	1964	£8	£20	
Now Resident In Europe	LP	Blue Horizon	763207	1968	£15	£30	
RCA Victor Race series Vol.9	7" EP	RCA	RCX7184	1966	£7.50	£15	

JONES, DAVY

The Davy Jones whose records are listed here is the actor who became a member of the Monkees. Just to confuse matters, another Davy Jones also had records issued on the Pye label, but during 1960 to 1962. He has no connection with the Monkees whatsoever. A third Davy Jones made records with the Lower Third and the King Bees on the Vocalion and Parlophone labels. These are rare, but are listed in the Guide under the name used by Jones later on - David Bowie. A David Jones who made one single for Philips in 1965 does not appear to have any connection with either the Monkees or David Bowie.

Title	Format	Label	Cat No	Year	Low	High	Notes
Davy Jones	LP	Bell	6067	1971	£4	£10	US
Davy Jones	LP	Pye	NPL18178	1967	£8	£20	
It Ain't Me Babe	7"	Pye	7N17302	1967	£2	£5	
It Ain't Me Babe	7"	Pye	7N17302	1967	£5	£10	PS
It Ain't Me Babe	7" EP	Pye	PNV24189	1967	£10	£20	French
Rainy Jane	7"	Bell	BLL1163	1971	£1.50	£4	
Theme For A New Love	7"	Pye	7N17380	1967	£2	£5	
Theme For A New Love	7"	Pye	7N17380	1967	£5	£10	PS
Theme For A New Love	7"	Pye	7N25432	1967	£2.50	£6	
What Are We Going To Do	7"	Colpix	PX784	1965	£2	£5	

JONES, DILL

Title	Format	Label	Cat No	Year	Low	High	Notes
Piano Moods Vol.2	7" EP	Polygon	JTE104	1956	£4	£8	
Piano Moods Vol.5	7" EP	Pye	NJE1024	1956	£2	£5	

JONES, ELVIN

Title	Format	Label	Cat No	Year	Low	High	Notes
Coalition	LP	Blue Note	BST84361	1970	£4	£10	
Elvin Jones	LP	Blue Note	BST84414	1970	£4	£10	
Genesis	LP	Blue Note	BST84369	1970	£4	£10	
Poly-Currents	LP	Blue Note	BST84331	1969	£5	£12	
Puttin' It Together	LP	Blue Note	BST84282	1968	£5	£12	
Ultimate	LP	Blue Note	BST84305	1968	£5	£12	

JONES, ETTA

Title	Format	Label	Cat No	Year	Low	High	Notes
Don't Go To Strangers	LP	Prestige	PRLP7186	1960	£5	£12	US
From The Heart	LP	Prestige	PRLP7214	1962	£5	£12	US
Holler	LP	Prestige	PRLP7284	1963	£5	£12	US
Lonely And Blue	LP	Prestige	PRLP7241	1962	£5	£12	US
Love Shout	LP	Prestige	PRLP7272	1963	£5	£12	US
Sings	LP	King	544	1958	£10	£25	US
Sings	LP	King	707	1961	£8	£20	US
So Warm	LP	Prestige	PRLP7204	1961	£5	£12	US
Something Nice	LP	Prestige	PRLP7194	1961	£5	£12	US

JONES, GEORGE

Title	Format	Label	Cat No	Year	Low	High	Notes
Accidentally On Purpose	7"	Mercury	AMT1100	1960	£4	£8	
Ballad Side Of George Jones	LP	Mercury	MG2/SR60836	1963	£5	£12	US
Best Of American Country Music Vol.4	7" EP	Ember	EMBEP4548	1964	£4	£8	
Big Harlen Taylor	7"	Mercury	AMT1078	1959	£4	£8	
Blue And Lonesome	LP	Mercury	MG2/SR60906	1964	£5	£12	US
Blue Grass Hootenanny	LP	United Artists	ULP1077	1965	£4	£10	with Melba Montgomery
Blue Moon Of Kentucky	LP	United Artists	(S)ULP1137	1966	£4	£10	with Melba Montgomery
C & W Aces	7" EP	Mercury	10009MCE	1964	£5	£10	
Candy Hearts	7"	Mercury	AMT1124	1961	£4	£8	US
Country & Western £1 Male Singer	LP	Mercury	MG2/SR60937	1964	£5	£12	US
Country And Western	7" EP	Mercury	ZEP10012	1959	£10	£20	with Jimmie Skinner
Country And Western Hits	LP	Mercury	MG2/SR60624	1961	£5	£12	US
Country And Western Winners	LP	Mercury	SMWL21003	1968	£5	£12	
Country Church Time	LP	Mercury	MG20462	1959	£8	£20	US
Country Heart	LP	Musicor	P2(S)5094	1966	£4	£10	US
Country Song Hits	7" EP	Melodisc	EPM7109	195-	£15	£30	
Crown Prince Of Country Music	LP	Ember	CW101	1963	£4	£10	
Crown Prince Of Country Music	LP	Starday	SLP125	1960	£6	£15	US
Duets Country Style	LP	Mercury	MG2/SR60747	1962	£5	£12	US, with Margie Singleton
Fabulous Country Music Sound	LP	Ember	CW109	1964	£4	£10	
Fabulous Country Music Sound	LP	Starday	SLP151	1962	£6	£15	US
Fourteen Country Favourites	LP	Mercury	MG20306	1958	£8	£20	US
From The Heart	LP	Mercury	MG2/SR60694	1962	£5	£12	US
George Jones	LP	London	HAB8259	1966	£6	£15	
George Jones	7" EP	Mercury	ZEP10036	1959	£20	£40	
George Jones And Gene Pitney	LP	Stateside	SL10147	1965	£4	£10	with Gene Pitney
George Jones Salutes Hank Williams	LP	Mercury	MG20257/ SR60257	1958	£5	£12	
George Jones Song Book	LP	London	HAB8340	1967	£6	£15	
George Jones Story	LP	Starday	SLP366	1966	£6	£15	US
Grand Ole Opry's New Star	LP	Starday	SLP101	1958	£25	£50	US
Great George Jones	LP	United Artists	(S)ULP1136	1966	£4	£10	
Greatest Hits	LP	London	HAB8125	1964	£5	£12	
Greatest Hits	LP	Mercury	SMCL20107	1967	£4	£10	
Heartaches And Tears	LP	Mercury	MG2/SR60990	1965	£5	£12	US
Hits Of His Country Cousins	LP	United Artists	ULP1037	1963	£5	£12	
I Get Lonely In A Hurry	LP	United Artists	ULP1091	1965	£5	£12	
I Saw Me	7"	United Artists	UP1015	1963	£2.50	£6	
I Wish Tonight Would Never End	LP	United Artists	ULP1050	1964	£5	£12	
If My Heart Had Windows	7"	Stateside	SS2145	1969	£1.50	£4	
It's Country Time Again	LP	Stateside	SL10173	1966	£4	£10	with Gene Pitney
Love Bug	LP	Stateside	(S)SL10184	1966	£4	£10	
More New Favourites	LP	United Artists	ULP1074	1964	£5	£12	
Mr.Country And Western Music	LP	Stateside	SL10157	1965	£4	£10	
Musical Loves, Life And Sorrows...	LP	Musicor	MS3159	1968	£4	£10	US
My Favourites Of Hank Williams	LP	United Artists	ULP1014	1963	£5	£12	

Title	Format	Label	Catalog	Year	Low	High	Notes
New Favourites	LP	United Artists	ULP1007	1962	£5	£12	
Novelty Side Of George Jones	LP	Mercury	MG2/SR60793	1963	£6	£15	US
Race Is On	7"	United Artists	UP1080	1965	£2.50	£6	
She Thinks I Still Care	7"	HMV	POP1037	1962	£4	£8	
Singing The Blues	LP	Mercury	MG2/SR61029	1965	£5	£12	US
Sings Like The Dickens	LP	United Artists	ULP1082	1965	£5	£12	
Sings The Songs Of Dallas Frazier	LP	Stateside	(S)SL10236	1968	£4	£10	US
Song Book And Picture Album	LP	Starday	SLP401	1967	£6	£15	US
Treasure Of Love	7"	Mercury	AMT1021	1959	£6	£12	
Trouble In Mind	LP	United Artists	ULP1101	1965	£5	£12	
Variety Is The Spice	LP	Stateside	(S)SL10215	1967	£4	£10	
We Found Heaven Right Here On Earth	LP	Stateside	(S)SL10195	1967	£4	£10	
What's In Our Hearts	LP	United Artists	ULP1070	1964	£4	£10	with Melba Montgomery
White Lightning	7"	Mercury	AMT1036	1959	£12.50	£25	
White Lightning And Other Favorites	LP	Mercury	MG20477	1959	£8	£20	US
Who Shot Sam	7"	Mercury	AMT1058	1959	£7.50	£15	

JONES, GLORIA

Title	Format	Label	Catalog	Year	Low	High	Notes
Finders Keepers	7"	Stateside	SS555	1966	£7.50	£15	
Get It On	7"	EMI	EMI2437	1976	£1.50	£4	
Heartbeat	7"	Capitol	CL15429	1966	£6	£12	
Tin Can People	7"	Tamla Motown	TMG910	1974	£2	£5	

JONES, GRACE

Title	Format	Label	Catalog	Year	Low	High	Notes
La Vie En Rose	12"	Island	IPR2004	1986	£2.50	£6	promo

JONES, GRANDPA

Title	Format	Label	Catalog	Year	Low	High	Notes
Country And Western	7" EP	Parlophone	GEP8766	1958	£12.50	£25	
Country Round Up	7" EP	Parlophone	GEP8781	1959	£10	£20	
Dark As A Dungeon	7"	Brunswick	05676	1957	£10	£20	
Do You Remember?	LP	King	845	1963	£8	£20	US
Evening With Grandpa Jones	LP	Decca	DL4364	1963	£8	£20	US
Grandpa Sings Jimmie Rodgers	7" EP	London	REU1417	1964	£10	£20	
Greatest Hits	LP	King	554	1958	£8	£20	US
Make The Rafters Ring	LP	London	HAU/SHU8010	1962	£8	£20	
Meet Grandpa Jones	7" EP	Parlophone	GEP8666	1957	£10	£20	
Mountain Music Vol.3	7" EP	Brunswick	OE9455	1959	£7.50	£15	
Other Side Of Grandpa Jones	LP	King	888	1964	£8	£20	US
Rollin' Along	LP	King	809	1963	£8	£20	US
Sixteen Sacred Gospel Songs	LP	King	822	1963	£8	£20	US
Strictly Country Tunes	LP	King	625	1959	£8	£20	US
Yodelling Hits	LP	London	HAU/SHU8119	1964	£8	£20	

JONES, HANK

Title	Format	Label	Catalog	Year	Low	High	Notes
Hank Jones Quartet	LP	London	LTZC15118	1958	£8	£20	
Hank Jones Quartet/Quintet	LP	London	LTZC15014	1956	£10	£25	
Have You Met Hank Jones?	LP	London	LTZC15079	1958	£10	£25	

JONES, HEATHER

Title	Format	Label	Catalog	Year	Low	High	Notes
Jiawl!	LP	Sain	1047M	1976	£8	£20	
Mae'r Olwyn Yn Troi	LP	Sain	1008M	1973	£10	£25	

JONES, HUW

Title	Format	Label	Catalog	Year	Low	High	Notes
Dwr	7"	Sain	SAIN1	1969	£5	£10	PS

JONES, JANIE

Title	Format	Label	Catalog	Year	Low	High	Notes
Back On My Feet Again	7"	President	PT309	1970	£1.50	£4	
Charlie Smith	7"	Pye	7N17550	1968	£1.50	£4	
Girl's Song	7"	Major Minor	MM577	1968	£1.50	£4	
Gunning For You	7"	HMV	POP1514	1966	£5	£10	
Tickle Me Tootsie Wootsies	7"	Columbia	DB8173	1967	£1.50	£4	
Witches Brew	7"	HMV	POP1495	1965	£6	£12	chart single

JONES, JERRY

Title	Format	Label	Catalog	Year	Low	High	Notes
Live At The Kingston Hotel, Jamaica	LP	Bamboo	BALPS213	1971	£10	£25	

JONES, JIMMY

Title	Format	Label	Catalog	Year	Low	High	Notes
39-21-46	7"	Stateside	SS2041	1967	£2.50	£6	
Good Timin'	LP	MGM	C832	1960	£15	£30	
Good Timin'	7"	MGM	MGM1078	1960	£1.50	£4	chart single
Good Timin'	7"	MGM	MGM1405	1968	£1.50	£4	
Handy Man	7"	MGM	MGM1051	1960	£2	£5	chart single
I Just Go For You	7"	MGM	MGM1091	1960	£1.50	£4	chart single
I Say Love	7"	MGM	MGM1133	1961	£1.50	£4	
I Told You So	7"	MGM	MGM1123	1961	£1.50	£4	chart single
Jimmy Handyman Jones	7" EP	MGM	MGMEP745	1960	£12.50	£25	
Mister Music Man	7"	MGM	MGM1146	1961	£1.50	£4	
Ready For Love	7"	MGM	MGM1103	1960	£1.50	£4	chart single
Walkin'	7"	Columbia	DB7592	1965	£12.50	£25	
You're Much Too Young	7"	MGM	MGM1168	1962	£1.50	£4	

JONES, JO

Title	Format	Label	Catalog	Year	Low	High	Notes
Jo Jones	LP	Top Rank	25039	1959	£4	£10	
Jo Jones Special	LP	Vanguard	PPL11002	1956	£6	£15	
Jo Jones Trio	LP	Top Rank	35039	1960	£4	£10	

JONES, JOE

Title	Format	Label	Catalog	Year	Low	High	Notes
You Talk Too Much	LP	Roulette	(S)R25143	1961	£8	£20	US
You Talk Too Much	7"	Columbia	DB4533	1960	£4	£8	

JONES, JOHN PAUL

Title	Format	Label	Cat No	Year			Notes
Baja	7"	Pye	7N15637	1964	£25	£50	

JONES, JOHNNY & THE KING CASUALS

Title	Format	Label	Cat No	Year			Notes
Soul Poppin'	7"	MCA	MU1031	1968	£1.50	£4	

JONES, JONAH

Title	Format	Label	Cat No	Year			Notes
I Dig Chicks	LP	Capitol	T1193	1959	£4	£10	
Jonah Jones Sextet	10" LP	London	LZN14003	1955	£8	£20	
Jonah Jones-Alix Combelle Sextet	10" LP	Vogue	LDE145	1955	£8	£20	
Jumpin' With Jonah	LP	Capitol	(S)T1039	1959	£4	£10	
Swinging At The Cinema	LP	Capitol	T1083	1959	£4	£10	

JONES, KEN

Title	Format	Label	Cat No	Year			Notes
Joxsville	7"	Parlophone	R4788	1961	£1.50	£4	
On The Rebound	7"	Parlophone	R4763	1961	£1.50	£4	

JONES, LINDA

Title	Format	Label	Cat No	Year			Notes
For Your Precious Love	7"	London	HLU10368	1972	£2	£5	
Hypnotised	LP	Loma	5907	1967	£10	£25	US
Hypnotised	7"	Warner Bros	WB2070	1967	£12.50	£25	
I Just Can't Live My Life	7"	Warner Bros	K16621	1975	£4	£8	
Your Precious Love	LP	Turbo	7007	1973	£6	£15	US

JONES, MAGGIE

Title	Format	Label	Cat No	Year			Notes
Columbia Recordings In Chronological Order Vol.1	LP	VJM	VLP23	1970	£5	£12	
Columbia Recordings In Chronological Order Vol.2	LP	VJM	VLP25	1970	£5	£12	

JONES, NIC

Title	Format	Label	Cat No	Year			Notes
Ballads And Songs	LP	Trailer	LER2014	1970	£10	£25	
From The Devil To A Stranger	LP	Transatlantic	TRA507	1978	£6	£15	
Nic Jones	LP	Trailer	LER2027	1971	£8	£20	
Noah's Ark Trap	LP	Trailer	LER2091	1977	£10	£25	

JONES, NIGEL MAZLYN

Title	Format	Label	Cat No	Year			Notes
Breaking Cover	LP	Isle Of Light	IOL0230	1982	£8	£20	
Sentinel	LP	Avada	AVA105	1978	£10	£25	
Ship To Shore	LP	Isle Of Light	IOL666/1	1976	£20	£40	

JONES, PALMER

Title	Format	Label	Cat No	Year			Notes
Great Magic Of Love	7"	Direction	583603	1968	£2	£5	

JONES, PAUL

Title	Format	Label	Cat No	Year			Notes
And The Sun Will Shine	7"	Columbia	DB8379	1968	£7.50	£15	
Aquarius	7"	Columbia	DB8514	1969	£1.50	£4	chart single
Come Into My Music Box	LP	Columbia	SCX6347	1969	£10	£25	
Crucifix In A Horseshoe	LP	Vertigo	6360059	1971	£10	£25	spiral label
High Time	7"	HMV	POP1554	1966	£1.50	£4	chart single
High Time	7" EP	Pathe	EGF952	1966	£6	£12	French
It's Getting Better	7"	Columbia	DB8567	1969	£1.50	£4	
I've Been A Bad Bad Boy	7"	HMV	POP1576	1967	£1.50	£4	chart single
I've Been A Bad Bad Boy	7" EP	Pathe	EGF965	1966	£6	£12	French
Love Me Love My Friends	LP	HMV	CLP/CSD3602	1967	£8	£20	
My Way	LP	HMV	CLP/CSD3586	1966	£8	£20	
Privilege	LP	HMV	CLP3523	1966	£8	£20	
Privilege	7" EP	HMV	7EG8974	1966	£5	£10	
Privilege	7" EP	Pathe	EGF982	1966	£6	£12	French
Sheena Is A Punk Rocker	7"	RSO	RSO003	1978	£1.50	£4	
Sons And Lovers	7"	Columbia	DB8303	1967	£1.50	£4	
Thinkin' Ain't For Me	7"	HMV	POP1602	1967	£1.50	£4	chart single
When I Was Six Years Old	7"	Columbia	DB8417	1968	£1.50	£4	

JONES, QUINCY

Title	Format	Label	Cat No	Year			Notes
Around The World	LP	Mercury	MMC14098/CMS18064	1962	£4	£10	
Big Band Bash	7" EP	Mercury	ZEP10047	1960	£2.50	£6	
Birth Of A Band	LP	Mercury	MMC14038/CMS18026	1960	£5	£12	
Birth Of A Band	7" EP	Mercury	ZEP10109/SEZ19017	1961	£2	£5	
Birth Of A Band Part 2	7" EP	Mercury	ZEP10119/SEZ19021	1961	£2	£5	
Double Six Meet Quincy Jones	7" EP	Columbia	SEG8088	1961	£2	£5	
Go West, Man	LP	HMV	CLP1157	1958	£6	£15	
Great Wide World Of Quincy Jones	LP	Mercury	MMC14046/CMS18031	1960	£5	£12	
I Dig Dancers	LP	Mercury	MMC14080/CMS18055	1961	£4	£10	
Quintessence	LP	HMV	CLP1581/CSD1452	1962	£5	£12	
Soul Bossa Nova	7"	Mercury	AMT1195	1962	£2	£5	
This Is How I Feel About Jazz	LP	HMV	CLP1162	1958	£6	£15	

JONES, RICK

Title	Format	Label	Cat No	Year			Notes
Twixt You And Me	LP	Argo	ZFB27	1971	£4	£10	

JONES, RONNIE

Title	Format	Label	Cat No	Year			Notes
Anyone Who Knows What Love Is	7"	Decca	F12146	1965	£4	£8	
I Need Your Loving	7"	Decca	F12012	1964	£4	£8	
I'm So Clean	7"	Parlophone	R5326	1965	£10	£20	

In My Love Mind	7"	Polydor	56222	1967	£2.50	£6	
Little Bitty Pretty One	7"	CBS	2699	1967	£1.50	£4	
Little Bitty Pretty One	7"	CBS	3304	1968	£2	£5	
My Love	7"	Decca	F12066	1965	£5	£10	

JONES, SAMANTHA

And Suddenly	7"	United Artists	UP2258	1968	£7.50	£15	
It's All Because Of You	7"	United Artists	UP1072	1965	£1.50	£4	
Surrounded By A Ray Of Sunshine	7"	United Artists	UP1185	1967	£12.50	£25	

JONES, SANDIE

Music Of Love	7"	Polydor	2058223	1972	£5	£10	

JONES, SPIKE

Deep Purple	7"	HMV	7MC3	1954	£1.50	£4	
Fun In Hi Fi	7" EP	HMV	7EG8286	1957	£4	£8	export
Hot Lips	7"	HMV	7M121	1953	£4	£8	
I Saw Mommy Kissing Santa Claus	7"	HMV	7M160	1953	£2	£5	
I Wanna Go Back To West Virginia	7"	HMV	7MC17	1954	£1.50	£4	export
Omnibust TV Schedule	LP	London	HAG2270/ SHG6090	1960	£5	£12	
Secret Love	7"	HMV	7M324	1955	£2	£5	
Sixty Years Of Music America Hates Best	LP	London	HAG2298/ SHG6109	1961	£5	£12	
Spike Jones In Hi Fi	7" EP	Warner Bros	WEP6044	1961	£2.50	£6	
Spike Jones In Stereo	7" EP	Warner Bros	WSEP2044	1961	£6	£12	
Spike Jones No.1	7" EP	RCA	RCX1030	1959	£4	£8	
Spike Jones No.2	7" EP	RCA	RCX1037	1959	£4	£8	
Spooktacular Sound	LP	Warner Bros	WB4004/WS8004	1960	£5	£12	

JONES, THAD

Leonard Feather Presents Mad Thad	LP	Nixa	NJL13	1957	£20	£40	
Thad Jones	LP	Vogue	LDE172	1956	£20	£40	

JONES, THAD & MEL LEWIS JAZZ ORCHESTRA

Central Park North	LP	United Artists	UAS29058	1969	£4	£10	
Consummation	LP	Blue Note	BST84346	1970	£4	£10	
Live At The Village Vanguard	LP	United Artists	USS7008	1967	£5	£12	
Monday Night	LP	United Artists	UAS29016	1968	£5	£12	
Presenting Thad Jones-Mel Lewis & The Jazz Orchestra	LP	United Artists	SULP1169	1967	£5	£12	

JONES, THELMA

House That Jack Built	7"	Soul City	SC110	1969	£4	£8	
Stranger	7"	Sue	WI4047	1968	£5	£10	

JONES, TOM

Bama Lama Bama Loo	7" EP	Decca	457078	1965	£5	£10	French
Chills And Fever	7"	Decca	F11966	1964	£5	£10	
Detroit City	7"	Decca	F22563	1967	£2.50	£6	export
Detroit City	7" EP	Decca	457141	1967	£4	£8	French
Green Green Grass Of Home	7"	Decca	F12516	1966	£2.50	£6	export
Green Green Grass Of Home	7" EP	Decca	457134	1967	£4	£8	French
It's Not Unusual	7"	Decca	F12062	1965	£1.50	£4	chart single
It's Not Unusual	7" EP	Decca	457065	1965	£4	£8	French
Little Lonely One	7"	Columbia	DB7566	1965	£4	£8	
Little Lonely One	7" EP	Columbia	ESRF1684	1965	£5	£10	French, B side by Beau Brummell
Lonely Joe	7"	Columbia	DB7733	1965	£2.50	£6	
Not Responsible	7" EP	Decca	457118	1966	£4	£8	French
On Stage	7" EP	Decca	DFE8617	1965	£2.50	£6	
Stop Breaking My Heart	7"	Decca	F12349	1966	£2	£5	
Stop Breaking My Heart	7" EP	Decca	457107	1966	£4	£8	French
Thunderball	7"	Decca	F12292	1966	£1.50	£4	chart single
Till	7"	Decca	FR13237	1971	£2	£5	export
To Make A Big Man Cry	7"	Decca	F12315	1966	£2.50	£6	export
Tom Jones	7" EP	Columbia	SEG8464	1965	£6	£12	
What A Party	7" EP	Decca	457127	1966	£4	£8	French
What A Party	7" EP	Decca	DFE8668	1965	£2.50	£6	
What's New Pussycat	7" EP	Decca	457088	1965	£4	£8	French
With These Hands	7" EP	Decca	457082	1965	£4	£8	French

JONES, U.K.

Let Me Tell Ya	7"	Deram	DM231	1969	£2	£5	

JONES, WIZZ

Ballad Of Hollis Brown	7"	Columbia	DB7776	1965	£4	£8	with Pete Stanley
Legendary Me	LP	Village Thing	VTS4	1970	£15	£30	
Magical Flight	LP	Plant Life	PLR009	1977	£5	£12	
Right Now	LP	CBS	64809	1971	£20	£40	
Roll On River	LP	Folk Freak	FF4006	1981	£6	£15	German, with Werner Lammerhirt
Sixteen Tons Of Bluegrass	LP	Columbia	SX6083	1966	£60	£120	with Pete Stanley
Solo Flight	LP	Autogram	FLLP507	1973	£15	£30	with EP, German
When I Leave Berlin	LP	Village Thing	VTS24	1974	£6	£15	
Wizz Jones	LP	United Artists	(S)ULP1209	1969	£60	£120	

JONESY

Alan Bown's R&B band was a significant part of the sixties rock scene in Britain, even if it never managed to break through into the firs division. Part of the problem was no doubt due to the difficulty Bown himself faced in finding a strong image when he was neither a singer no a guitarist, but a trumpet player. Within Jonesy, Bown finally dealt with the problem by relegating himself to the status of band membe rather than leader, but it is his trumpet playing that gives the band's slant on jazz-rock such a distinctive edge. If the electric-period Miles Davi had ever decided to play within a song-based band, it might have sounded something like this.

Growing	LP	Dawn	DNLS3055	1973	£8	£20
Keeping Up	LP	Dawn	DNLS3048	1973	£8	£20
No Alternative	LP	Dawn	DNLS3042	1972	£10	£25

JONNS, HARLEM RESHUFFLE

Everything Under The Sun	7"	Fontana	TF1004	1969	£4	£8
Harlem Jonns Reshuffle	7"	Fontana	STL5509	1969	£4	£10
You Are The One I Love	7"	Fontana	TF970	1968	£4	£8

JONSTON MCPHILBRY

She's Gone	7"	Fontana	TF663	1966	£15	£30

JOOLZ

Hex	LP	Columbia	SCX6711	1987	£4	£10

JOPLIN, JANIS

Cry Baby	7"	CBS	7217	1971	£1.50	£4	
Down On Me	7"	CBS	8241	1972	£1.50	£4	
I Got Dem Ol' Kozmic Blues Again	LP	CBS	63546	1969	£4	£10	
In Concert	LP	CBS	67241	1972	£5	£12	doubl
Janis	LP	CBS	88115	1974	£5	£12	doubl
Me And Bobby McGhee	7"	CBS	7019	1971	£1.50	£4	
Move Over	7"	CBS	9136	1971	£2	£5	
Pearl	LP	CBS	64188	1971	£4	£10	
Pearl	LP	CBS	Q64188	1974	£6	£15	qua
Piece Of My Heart	7"	CBS	3960	1976	£1.50	£4	P

JORDAN BROTHERS

Never Never	7"	London	HLW8908	1959	£7.50	£15
No Wings On My Angel	7"	London	HLW9308	1961	£2	£5
Things I Didn't Say	7"	London	HLW9235	1960	£2.50	£6

JORDAN, CHRISTOPHER

Knack	7" EP	United Artists	36075	1965	£4	£8	Frenc

JORDAN, DICK

Hallelujah I Love Her So	7"	Oriole	CB1534	1960	£1.50	£4	chart singl
Little Christine	7"	Oriole	CB1548	1960	£1.50	£4	chart singl

JORDAN, DUKE

Duke Jordan	10" LP	Vogue	LDE099	1954	£20	£40
Flight To Jordan	LP	Blue Note	BLP/BST84046	196-	£25	£50

JORDAN, FRED

Songs Of A Shropshire Farm Worker	LP	Topic	12T150	1966	£6	£15
When The Frost Is On The Pumpkin	LP	Topic	12TS233	1974	£5	£12

JORDAN, LOUIS

Dad Gum Ya Hide Boy	78	Melodisc	1031	1954	£3	£8	
Go Blow Your Horn	LP	Score	4007	195-	£25	£50	U
Greatest Hits	LP	Decca	DL5035	1967	£5	£12	U
Is You Is Or Is You Ain't My Baby	7"	Melodisc	1616	196-	£4	£8	with Chris Barb
Let The Good Times Roll	LP	Ace Of Hearts	AH85	1965	£6	£15	
Let The Good Times Roll	LP	Coral	CP59	1970	£4	£10	
Let The Good Times Roll	LP	Decca	DL8551	1958	£10	£25	U
Louis Jordan	7" EP	Melodisc	EPM766	1956	£25	£50	
Man, We're Wailin'	LP	Mercury	MPL6541	1958	£10	£25	
Messy Bessy	78	Melodisc	1349	1956	£3	£8	
Ooo Wee	7"	Downbeat	CHA3	1960	£7.50	£15	
Saturday Night Fish Fry	78	Brunswick	04402	1950	£2.50	£6	
Somebody Up There Digs Me	LP	Mercury	MG20242	1957	£15	£30	U
Somebody Up There Digs Me	10" LP	Mercury	MPT7521	1957	£15	£30	

JORDAN, SHEILA

Portrait	LP	Blue Note	BLP/BST89002	1962	£20	£40

JORDANAIRES

Beautiful City	10" LP	RCA	LPM3081	1953	£15	£30	U
Don't Be Cruel	7"	Capitol	CL15281	1963	£5	£10	
Gloryland	LP	Capitol	T1167	1959	£8	£20	U
Heavenly Spirit	LP	Capitol	T1011	1958	£8	£20	
Little Miss Ruby	7"	Capitol	CL14921	1958	£5	£10	
Peace In The Valley	LP	Decca	DL8681	1957	£10	£25	U
Spotlight On The Jordanaires	LP	Capitol	T1742	1962	£8	£20	
Sugaree	7"	Capitol	CL14687	1957	£12.50	£25	
Summer Vacation	7"	Capitol	CL14773	1957	£5	£10	

JOSEF K

Chance Meeting	7"	Absolute	ABS1	1980	£10	£20	
Chance Meeting	7"	Postcard	81-5	1981	£2	£5	with postca
It's Kinda Funny	7"	Postcard	80-5	1980	£1.50	£4	
It's Kinda Funny	7"	Postcard	80-5	1980	£4	£8	colour insert in b
Only Fun In Town	LP	Postcard	81-7	1981	£6	£10	
Radio Drill Time	7"	Postcard	80-3	1980	£2	£5	
Radio Drill Time	7"	Postcard	80-3	1980	£7.50	£15	with post

Sorry For Laughing	LP	Postcard	81-1	1981	£50	£100	test pressing
Sorry For Laughing	LP	Postcard	81-1	1981	£100	£200	test pressing with proof sleeve

JOSEFUS
Dead Man	LP	Hookah	330	1969	£37.50	£75	US
Josefus	LP	Mainstream	6127	1970	£8	£20	US

JOSHUA
Joshua	LP	Key	KL014	1973	£25	£50	

JOSIE, MARVA
Crazy Stockings	7"	Polydor	56711	1966	£2.50	£6	

JOURNEY
Departure	LP	Columbia	HC46339	1981	£5	£12	US audiophile
Dream After Dream	LP	Columbia	HC47998	1982	£5	£12	US audiophile
Escape	LP	Columbia	HC47408	1981	£5	£12	US audiophile
Escape	LP	Mobile Fidelity	MFSL1144	1981	£8	£20	US audiophile
Infinity	LP	Columbia	HC4912	1981	£5	£12	US audiophile

JOURNEYMEN
Introducing The Journeymen	LP	Ember	EMB3382	1967	£6	£15	
Journeymen	LP	Capitol	(S)T1629	1961	£6	£15	US
Live	LP	Capitol		1962	£10	£25	US
New Directions In Folk Music	LP	Capitol	(S)T1951	1963	£6	£15	US

JOY & DAVID
Joe's Been A Gitting There	7"	Parlophone	R4855	1961	£4	£8	
Let's Go See Grandma	7"	Triumph	RGM1002	1960	£5	£10	
My Very Good Friend The Milkman	7"	Decca	F11291	1960	£4	£8	
Rocking Away The Blues	7"	Decca	F11123	1959	£6	£12	
Whoopee	7"	Parlophone	R4477	1958	£4	£8	

JOY, CARL & THE JOYBOYS
Be My Girl	7"	Top Rank	JAR529	1961	£2.50	£6	
Bye Bye Baby Goodbye	7"	Brunswick	05806	1959	£2.50	£6	

JOY DIVISION
Atmosphere	7"	Sordide Sentimentale	SS33002	1980	£20	£40	A4 folder
Earcom 2	12"	Fast Products	FAST9	1979	£5	£12	with other artists
Factory Sample	7" EP	Factory	FAC2	1979	£15	£30	double, 5 stickers, with other artists
Ideal Beginning	7"	Enigma	PSS138	1981	£7.50	£15	
Ideal For Living	7"	Enigma	PSS139	1978	£37.50	£75	PS
Ideal For Living	12"	Anonymous	ANON1	1978	£25	£50	
Still	LP	Factory	FACT40	1981	£6	£15	double, hard cloth cover

JOY, RODDIE
Come Back Baby	7"	Red Bird	RB021	1965	£15	£30	

JOY UNLIMITED
Daytime Night Time	7"	Page One	POF23147	1969	£2	£5	
Minne	LP	BASF	1222331	1975	£5	£12	German
Oh Darlin'	7"	Page One	POF23160	1969	£2	£5	
Overground	LP	Polydor	2371050	1970	£8	£20	German
Reflections	LP	BASF	20216861	1973	£6	£15	German
Schmetterlinge	LP	Pilz	2021090/1	1971	£10	£25	German double
Turbulence	LP	Page One	POLS028	1970	£10	£25	

JOYRIDE
Friend Sound	LP	RCA		1969	£6	£15	

JSD BAND
Country Of The Blind	LP	Regal Zonophone	SLRZ1018	1971	£15	£30	
JSD Band	LP	Fly	HIFLY11	1972	£4	£10	
Story So Far	7"	Regal Zonophone	JSD1	1971	£7.50	£15	promo with release sheet & photo
Travelling Days	LP	Cube	HIFLY14	1973	£4	£10	

JUBALAIRES
King's Highway	7" EP	Brunswick	OE9198	1955	£2	£5	

JUDAS JUMP
Beer Drinking Woman	7"	Parlophone	R5873	1970	£2	£5	
Run For Your Life	7"	Parlophone	R5828	1970	£2	£5	
Scorch	LP	Parlophone	PAS10001	1970	£5	£12	
This Feelin' We Feel	7"	Parlophone	R5838	1970	£2.50	£6	

JUDAS PRIEST
Tyrant	12"	Gull	GULS7612	1983	£3	£8	white vinyl

JUDD
Judd	LP	Penny Farthing	PELS504	1970	£10	£25	

JUDGE HAPPINESS
Hey Judge	7"	Mynah	SCS8501	1985	£10	£20	
Hey Judge	7"	Mynah	SCS8501	1985	£25	£50	PS

JUDGE, TERRY & THE BARRISTERS
Come With Me And Love Me	7"	Fontana	TF599	1965	£4	£8
Hey Look At Her	7"	Oriole	CB1896	1963	£1.50	£4
I Don't Care	7"	Oriole	CB1938	1964	£1.50	£4

JUG TRUST
Cat And Mouse	7"	Parlophone	R5825	1970	£1.50	£4

JUGGERNAUTS
Come Throw Yourself	7"	Supreme	842	1984	£2	£5

JUICE ON THE LOOSE
Juice On The Loose	LP	Juice	JJOS1	1981	£4	£10

JUICY LUCY
Get A Whiff Of This	LP	Bronze	ILPS9157	1971	£4	£10	
Juicy Lucy	LP	Vertigo	VO2	1969	£6	£15	.. spiral label, chart LP
Lie Back & Enjoy It	LP	Vertigo	6360014	1970	£5	£12	.. spiral label, chart LP
Pieces	LP	Polydor	2310160	1972	£4	£10	
Pretty Woman	7"	Vertigo	6059015	1970	£1.50	£4	chart single
Who Do You Love	7"	Vertigo	V1	1970	£1.50	£4	chart single

JULIAN
Sue Saturday	7"	Pye	7N15236	1959	£6	£12

JULIAN, DON
Greatest Oldies	LP	Amazon	1009	1963	£10	£25	US

JULIAN'S TREATMENT
Phantom City	7"	Youngblood	YB1009	1972	£5	£10	
Time Before This	LP	Youngblood	SYB2	1972	£50	£100	double, sleeve pictured in Guide

JULY
The LP by July is a typical piece of psychedelia from 1968 - full of interesting ideas and sounds, but definitely a formative record for the musicians involved. These include Tony Duhig and Jon Field, who went on to form Jade Warrior, and Tom Newman, later a solo artist and also studio engineer for Virgin records.

Dandelion Seeds	LP	Bam Caruso	KIRI097	1987	£6	£15	
Hello Who's There	7"	Major Minor	MM580	1968	£25	£50	
July	LP	Epic	BN26416	1969	£35	£70	US
July	LP	Major Minor	MMLP/SMLP29	1968	£180	£300	
My Clown	7"	Major Minor	MM568	1968	£30	£60	

JUMBLE LANE
Jumble Lane	LP	Holyground	HG115	1971	£250	£400

JUMBO
Jumbo	LP	Philips			£35	£70

JUMPING JACKS
Lady Play Your Mandolin	7"	Capitol	CL14597	1956	£1.50	£4
Tried And Tested	7"	HMV	POP440	1958	£6	£12

JUNCO PARTNERS
As Long As I Have You	7"	Columbia	DB7665	1965	£25	£50
Junco Partners	LP	Philips	6308032	1971	£15	£30

JUNCO PARTNERS (2)
Swinging Sixties Boys	7"	Rigid	JUNK1028	1979	£1.50	£4

JUNCTION 32
Junction 32	LP	Holyground	HG119	1975	£180	£300

JUNE BRIDES
Every Conversation	7"	Pink	PINKY2	1984	£1.50	£4
In The Rain	7"	Pink	PINKY1	1984	£5	£10

JUNE, ROSANNE
Charge Of The Light Brigade	7"	London	HLU8352	1956	£7.50	£15

JUNE, ROSEMARY
I'll Always Be In Love With You	7"	Fontana	H141	1958	£2	£5	
I'll Be With You In Apple Blossom Time	7"	Pye	7N25005	1959	£1.50	£4	chart single

JUNIORS
Both guitarist Mick Taylor and bass-player John Glascock (later with Jethro Tull) were members of the Juniors - an appropriate name indeed for Taylor, as he was barely fifteen when he made his recording debut on the band's single.

There's A Pretty Girl	7"	Columbia	DB7339	1964	£12.50	£25

JUNIOR'S EYES
Battersea Power Station	LP	Regal Zonophone	SLRZ1008	1969	£15	£30
Mr.Golden Trumpet Player	7"	Regal Zonophone	RZ3009	1968	£6	£12
Star Child	7"	Regal Zonophone	RZ3023	1969	£5	£10

Woman Love	7"	Regal Zonophone	RZ3018	1969	£5	£10	
Woman Love/White Light Part 2	7"	Regal Zonophone	RZ3018	1969	£6	£12	

JUNOFF, LENA
Yesterday Has Gone	7"	Olga	008	1968	£7.50	£15	

JUPP, ERIC ORCHESTRA
Eric Jupp & His Orchestra	7" EP..	Columbia	SEG7589	1955	£5	£10	
Perfect Combination	7" EP..	Columbia	SEG7621	1956	£2.50	£6	
Rhythm And Blues	7" EP..	Columbia	SEG7603	1956	£5	£10	

JUST FOUR MEN
Don't Come Any Closer	7"	Parlophone	R5241	1965	£20	£40	
That's My Baby	7"	Parlophone	R5208	1964	£20	£40	

JUST PLAIN JONES
Crazy Crazy	7"	CBS	7480	1971	£1.50	£4	

JUST PLAIN SMITH
February's Child	7"	Sunshine	SUN7702	1969	£50	£100	

JUST US
What Are We Gonna Do	7" EP..	Kapp	KEV13036	1966	£6	£12	French

JUSTE, SAMANTHA
No One Needs My Love Today	7"	Go	AJ11402	1966	£2.50	£6	

JUSTICE, JIMMY
Ain't That Funny	7"	Pye	7N15443	1962	£1.50	£4	chart single
Don't Let The Stars Get In Your Eyes	7"	Pye	7N15528	1963	£1.50	£4	
Don't Say That Again	7"	Pye	7N15601	1964	£1.50	£4	
Understand Just How You Feel	7"	Pye	7N15301	1960	£4	£8	
Wake Up Crying	7"	Pye	7N15502	1963	£1.50	£4	
I'm Past Forgetting	7"	RCA	RCA1681	1968	£10	£20	
Jimmy Justice Hit Parade	7" EP.	Pye	NEP24159	1962	£6	£12	
Little Bit Of Soap	7"	Pye	7N15376	1961	£2	£5	
Little Cracked Bell	7"	Pye	7N15509	1963	£1.50	£4	
Only Heartbreaks For Me	7"	Pye	7N15863	1965	£1.50	£4	
Parade Of Broken Hearts	7"	Pye	7N15469	1962	£1.50	£4	
Smash Hits	LP	Pye	NPL18085	1962	£6	£15	
Spanish Harlem	7"	Pye	7N15457	1962	£1.50	£4	chart single
Two Sides Of Jimmy Justice	LP	Pye	NPL18080	1962	£8	£20	
Teacher	7"	Pye	7N15351	1961	£2.50	£6	
When My Little Girl Is Smiling	7"	Pye	7N15421	1962	£1.50	£4	chart single
You're Gonna Need My Lovin'	7"	Pye	7N15558	1963	£1.50	£4	

JUSTICE, KAY & THE ESCORTS
If You Took Your Love From Me	7"	Columbia	SCM5132	1954	£1.50	£4	

JUSTIFIED ANCIENTS OF MU MU
"1987" is an entirely brilliant example of the art of disc jockey-as-producer, consisting of a kaleidoscope of bits of other people's records welded together into an inspired whole. Unfortunately, some of these other people - Benny Andersson and Bjorn Ulvaeus of Abba to be precise - took exception to their music being used in this way and obtained a court order for the recall of all remaining copies of the record. In a way, the JAMMS were able to have the last laugh, for they later successfully advertised "the last remaining five copies" of the record at £1000 each. Collectors do not have to pay as much as this, however - £60 is enough to acquire on of the copies that appears on the market from time to time.

1987	LP	KLF	JAMSLP1	1987	£30	£60	
1987	cass	KLF	JAMSCLP1	1987	£30	£60	
1987 - The 45 Edits	12"	KLF	JAMS25T	1987	£5	£12	
All You Need Is Love	7"	KLF	JAMS23	1987	£6	£12	
All You Need Is Love	12"	KLF	JAMS23	1987	£15	£30	1 sided promo
All You Need Is Love	12"	KLF	JAMS23T	1987	£8	£20	
Burn The Beat	12"	KLF	JAMS26T	1988	£5	£12	
Down Town	7"	KLF	JAMS27	1987	£1.50	£4	no PS
Down Town	12"	KLF	JAMS27	1987	£5	£12	1 sided promo
Down Town	12"	KLF	JAMS27T	1987	£4	£10	
It's Grim Up North	12"	KLF	JAMS28T	1988	£30	£60	1 sided, grey vinyl
Made In Wales (Who Killed The Jams)	LP	KLF	JAMSLP2	1988	£5	£12	
Whitney Joins The J.A.M.S	12"	KLF	JAMS24T	1987	£6	£15	

JUSTIN, JAY
Sell Summertime	7"	Columbia	DB8439	1968	£1.50	£4	

JUSTINE
Justine	LP	Uni	UNLS111	1970	£5	£12	

JUSTIS, BILL
Cloud Nine	LP	Philips	1950	1959	£50	£100	US
College Man	7"	London	HLS8614	1958	£6	£12	
I'm Gonna Learn To Dance	7"	Mercury	AMT1201	1963	£2	£5	
Raunchy	7"	London	HLS8517	1957	£5	£10	chart single

JUVENILES
Bo Diddley	7"	Pye	7N25349	1966	£30	£60	

JYNX
Bow	7"	Columbia	DB7304	1964	£10	£20	

K

K, MOSES & THE PROPHETS
I Went Out With My Baby Tonight .... 7" .... Decca .... F12244 .... 1965 ... £4 .... £8 ....

K9'S
K9 Hassle .... 7" .... Dog Breath ..... WOOF1 .... 1985 ... £4 .... £8 ....

KAK
Kak .... LP ...... Epic .... BN26429 .... 1969 ... £30 .... £60 .... US

KALA
Kala .... LP ...... Bradleys .... BRADL1002 .... 1973 ... £5 .... £12 ....

KALASANDRO
Chi Chi .... 7" .... Warner Bros .... WB13 .... 1960 ... £1.50 ...... £4 ....

KALB, DANNY & STEFAN GROSSMAN
Crosscurrents .... LP ...... Cotillion .... SD9007 .... 1969 ... £6 .... £15 .... US

KALEIDOSCOPE
The two LPs made by Kaleidoscope were among the first of the more obscure psychedelic records to attract the attention of collectors. Accordingly, they reached the hundred pound mark some time before other similar records, but have stayed there while more recent "discoveries" have leap-frogged ahead. In truth, the records are interesting, but lack the finesse of the established classics of the period (like "Music From A Doll's House" or "Dear Mr.Fantasy"). They have the kudos of rarity, but, as is usually the case, their lack of renown is not without reason.

Balloon	7"	Fontana	TF1048	1969 ...	£25 .... £50 ....
Do It Again For Jeffrey	7"	Fontana	TF1002	1969 ...	£12.50 .... £25 ....
Dream For Julie	7"	Fontana	TF895	1968 ...	£12.50 .... £25 ....
Faintly Blowing	LP	5 Hours Back ..	TOCK006	1987 ...	£6 .... £15 ....
Faintly Blowing	LP	Fontana	STL5491	1969 ...	£50 .... £100 .... sleeve pictured in Guide
Flight From Ashiya	7"	Fontana	TF863	1967 ...	£7.50 ...... £15 ....
Flight From Ashiya	7"	Fontana	TF863	1967 ...	£15 .... £30 .... PS
Jenny Artichoke	7"	Fontana	TF964	1968 ...	£10 .... £20 ....
Tangerine Dream	LP	5 Hours Back ..	TOCK005	1987 ...	£6 .... £15 ....
Tangerine Dream	LP	Fontana	(S)TL5448	1967 ...	£50 .... £100 ....

KALEIDOSCOPE (US)
The American Kaleidoscope had a sound like no other group of the time. Over the course of three LPs (a fourth, "Bernice" is an unfortunate fall from grace; "When Scopes Collide" is a later attempt at a reunion) and culminating with the magnificent "Incredible", which entirely lives up to its name, the group maintained a questing, innovative approach. A key factor was their fascination with Middle Eastern music, which gives some of Kaleidoscope's material a world music flavour very much ahead of its time. Both Chris Darrow and David Lindley have recorded much music since Kaleidoscope's demise, although little of it has been in the same league.

Beacon From Mars	LP	Epic	LN24/BN26333	1968 ...	£20 .... £40 .... US
Bernice	LP	CBS	64005	1970 ...	£5 .... £12 ....
Incredible	LP	Epic	BN26467	1969 ...	£10 .... £25 .... US
Side Trips	LP	Epic	LN24/BN26305	1967 ...	£15 .... £30 .... US, Sleeve pictured in Guide
When Scopes Collide	LP	Island	ILPS9462	1976 ...	£4 .... £10 ....

KALEIDOSKOP
Kaleidoskop .... LP ...... Lava .... TCH0002 .... 1974 ... £10 .... £25 .... German

KALIN TWINS
Chicken Thief	7"	Brunswick	05826	1960 ...	£2 .... £5 ....
Cool	7"	Brunswick	05797	1959 ...	£2 .... £5 ....
Forget Me Not	7"	Brunswick	05759	1958 ...	£1.50 ...... £4 ....
Kalin Twins	LP	Decca	DL8812	1958 ...	£15 .... £30 .... US
Kalin Twins	7" EP ..	Brunswick	OE9449	1959 ...	£7.50 ...... £15 ....
Meaning Of The Blues	7"	Brunswick	05814	1959 ...	£2 .... £5 ....
Momma Poppa	7"	Brunswick	05848	1961 ...	£1.50 ...... £4 ....
Oh My Goodness	7"	Brunswick	05775	1959 ...	£2 .... £8 ....
One More Time	7"	Brunswick	05862	1961 ...	£1.50 ...... £4 ....
Sweet Sugar Lips	7"	Brunswick	05803	1959 ...	£1.50 ...... £4 ....
When	7"	Brunswick	05751	1958 ...	£2 .... £5 .... chart single
When	7" EP ..	Brunswick	OE9383	1958 ...	£7.50 ...... £15 ....
King Went The Strings Of My Heart	7"	Brunswick	05844	1960 ...	£2 .... £5 ....

KALLEN, KITTY
Forgive Me	7"	Brunswick	05447	1955 ...	£2 .... £5 ....
Go On With The Wedding	7"	Brunswick	05536	1956 ...	£2.50 ...... £6 ....
How Lonely Can I Get	7"	Brunswick	05494	1955 ...	£2 .... £5 ....
I'm A Lonely Little Petunia	7"	Brunswick	05402	1955 ...	£2 .... £5 ....
In The Chapel In The Moonlight	7"	Brunswick	05261	1954 ...	£5 .... £10 ....
It's A Lonesome Old Town	LP	Decca	DL8397	1958 ...	£6 .... £15 .... US
Kiddy Geddin	7"	Brunswick	05359	1954 ...	£4 .... £8 ....
Kitty Who?	7"	Brunswick	05431	1955 ...	£2 .... £5 ....
Let's Make The Most Of Tonight ...	7"	Brunswick	05475	1955 ...	£2 .... £5 ....
Little Lie	7"	Brunswick	05394	1955 ...	£2.50 ...... £6 ....
Little Things Mean A Lot	LP	Vocalion	VL3679	1959 ...	£5 .... £12 .... US
Little Things Mean A Lot	7"	Brunswick	05287	1954 ...	£12.50 .... £25 .... chart single
Long Lonely Nights	7"	Brunswick	05705	1957 ...	£1.50 ...... £4 ....

Pretty Kitty Kalen Sings	10" LP	Mercury	MG25206	195-	£8	£20	US
Spirit Of Christmas	7"	Brunswick	05357	1954	£4	£8	
True Love	7"	Brunswick	05612	1956	£1.50	£4	

KANE, AMORY

Him Or Me	7"	CBS	5111	1970	£1.50	£4	
Just To Be There	LP	CBS	63849	1970	£6	£15	
Memories Of Time Unwound	LP	MCA	MUP(S)348	1968	£8	£20	
Reflections Of Your Face	7"	MCA	MU1036	1968	£2	£5	
You Were On My Mind	7"	UNI	UNS518	1970	£1.50	£4	

KANE, EDEN

Boys Cry	7"	Fontana	TF438	1964	£1.50	£4	chart single
Come Back	7"	Fontana	TF413	1963	£1.50	£4	
Eden Kane	LP	Ace Of Clubs	ACL1133	1962	£8	£20	
Eden Kane Hits	7" EP	Decca	DFE8503	1962	£7.50	£15	
Forget Me Not	7"	Decca	F11418	1962	£1.50	£4	chart single
Get Lost	7"	Decca	F11381	1961	£1.50	£4	chart single
Hangin' Around	7"	Fontana	TF508	1964	£1.50	£4	
Hot Chocolate Crazy	7"	Pye	7N15284	1960	£5	£10	
House To Let	7"	Decca	F11504	1962	£1.50	£4	
I Don't Know Why	7"	Decca	F11460	1962	£1.50	£4	chart single
If You Want This Love	7"	Fontana	TF582	1965	£1.50	£4	
It's Eden	LP	Fontana	TL5211	1964	£15	£30	
It's Eden	7" EP	Fontana	TFE17424	1964	£6	£12	
Magic Town	7"	Decca	F12342	1966	£5	£10	
Rain Rain Go Away	7"	Fontana	TF462	1964	£1.50	£4	
Six Great New Swingers	7" EP	Decca	DFE8567	1964	£7.50	£15	
Smoke Gets In Your Eyes	LP	Wing	WL1218	1966	£5	£12	
Sounds Funny To Me	7"	Decca	F11568	1963	£1.50	£4	
Tomorrow Night	7"	Fontana	TF398	1963	£1.50	£4	
Tomorrow Night	7"	Fontana	TF398	1963	£2.50	£6	P
Well I Ask You	7"	Decca	F11353	1961	£1.50	£4	chart singl
Well I Ask You	7" EP	Decca	DFE6696	1962	£7.50	£15	

KANE, LEE

Around And Around	7"	Capitol	CL14328	1955	£1.50	£4	
Every Day	7"	Capitol	CL14297	1955	£1.50	£4	

KANE, PAUL

Paul Kane was one of the names tried by Paul Simon during the early years of his career.

He Was My Brother	7"	Tribute	128	196-	£25	£50	U

KANGAROO

Kangaroo	LP	MGM	SE4586	1968	£6	£15	U

KANSAS

Strange how all the groups called after place names seem to have the same sound! Regardless of the musical content, however, the LP "Poin Of Know Return" by Kansas has a particularly striking cover, showing a galleon in full sail, just about to fall over the edge of the world. Th record is available as a picture disc, which shows off the artwork even more dramatically, but this was unfortunately issued as an America promotional release only and is scarce.

Leftoverture	LP	Kirshner	HZ44224	1981	£6	£15	US audiophil
Point Of Know Return	LP	Kirshner	HZ44929	1981	£6	£15	US audiophil
Point Of Know Return	LP	Kirshner	JZ34929	1977	£15	£30	US promo pic dis
Vinyl Confessions	LP	Kirshner	HZ48002	1982	£6	£15	US audiophil

KANSAS CITY MELROSE & CASINO SIMPSON

Kansas City Melrose And Casino Simpson	LP	Chicago Piano	12001	1972	£5	£12	

KANTNER, PAUL

Blows Against The Empire	LP	RCA	LSP4448	1970	£30	£60	US clear vin
Blows Against The Empire	LP	RCA	SF8163	1970	£4	£10	with bookle
Planet Earth Rock'n'Roll Orchestra	LP	RCA	4320	1983	£5	£12	US clear vin
Sunfighter	LP	Grunt	FTR1002	1971	£4	£10	with bookle

KAPLAN

Do You Believe In Magic	7"	Philips	BF1636	1968	£2	£5	
I Love It	7"	Philips	BF1699	1968	£1.50	£4	

KARAS, ANTON

Harry Lime Theme	7"	Decca	F9235	1960	£2	£5	

KARAT

Karat	LP	Amiga	855573	1977	£4	£10	East Germa

KARLOFF, BORIS

Evening With Karloff And His Friends	LP	Decca	DL(7)4833	1967	£5	£12	U
How The Grinch Stole Christmas	LP	MGM	(S)E901	1966	£5	£12	U
Tales Of The Frightened Vol.1	LP	MGM	MG2/SR60815	1963	£8	£20	L
Tales Of THe Frightened Vol.2	LP	MGM	MG2/SR60816	1963	£8	£20	U

KARMEN, STEVE & JIMMY RADCLIFFE

Breakaway	7"	United Artists	UP35770	1975	£1.50	£4	

KARTHAGO

Karthago	LP	BASF	20211851	1971	£4	£10	Germa

KASENATZ-KATZ SINGING ORCHESTRAL CIRCUS

Kasenatz-Katz Singing Orchestral Circus	LP	Pye	NSPL28119	1968	£4	£10	

Down In Tennessee	7"	Pye	7N25472	1968	£1.50	£4	
Quick Joey Small	7"	Buddah	201022	1968	£1.50	£4	chart single
We Can Work It Out	7"	Pye	7N25480	1969	£1.50	£4	

KATCH 22
100,000 Years	7"	Fontana	TF984	1968	£2	£5
Major Catastrophe	7"	Fontana	TF768	1966	£10	£20
Makin' Up My Mind	7"	Fontana	TF874	1967	£2	£5
Mrs.Jones	7"	CBS	4644	1969	£2	£5
Out Of My Life	7"	Fontana	TF1005	1969	£2	£5
Soft Rock And Allsorts	LP	Saga	EROS8047	1968	£5	£12
World's Getting Smaller	7"	Fontana	TF930	1968	£2	£5

KATE
Hold Me Now	7"	CBS	3815	1968	£6	£12
Shout It	7"	CBS	4123	1969	£6	£12
Strange Girl	7"	CBS	3631	1968	£6	£12

KATTONG
Gitarre Vor'm Bauch	LP	Schwann		1971	£20	£40	German
Stiehl Dem Volk Die Geduld	LP	Schwann	AMS519	1972	£20	£40	German

KATZ, DICK
Kool For Katz	10" LP	Pye	NPT19033	1959	£5	£12

KATZ, MICKEY
David Crockett	7"	Capitol	CL14579	1956	£1.50	£4
Poiple Kishke Eater	7"	Capitol	CL14926	1958	£1.50	£4

KAUFMANN, BOB
Trip Through A Blown Mind	LP	LHI	12002	1967	£8	£20	US

KAY, ARTHUR ORIGINALS
Ska Wars	7"	Red Admiral	NYMPH1	1980	£1.50	£4

KAY, JOHN
Forgotten Songs & Unsung Heroes	LP	Probe	SPB1054	1972	£4	£10	
John Kay And The Sparrows	LP	Columbia	CS9758	1970	£5	£12	US
My Sporting Life	LP	Probe	SPBA6274	1973	£4	£10	

KAY, KATHIE
House With Love In It	7"	HMV	POP265	1956	£2	£5
Jimmy Unknown	7"	HMV	7M363	1956	£2.50	£6
Suddenly There's A Valley	7"	HMV	7M335	1955	£2.50	£6

KAYAK
Kayak	LP	Harvest	SHSP4036	1974	£4	£10	
Phantom Of The Night	LP	Janus	JXS7039	1978	£8	£20	US pic disc
Royal Bed Bouncer	LP	Vertigo	6360530	1975	£4	£10	
See See The Sun	LP	Harvest	SHSP4033	1973	£4	£10	

KAYE, DANNY
At The Palace	10" LP	Brunswick	LA8660	1954	£5	£12
Children's Favourites	7" EP	Brunswick	OE9022	1954	£2	£5
Court Jester	LP	Brunswick	LAT8097	1956	£4	£10
Danny Kaye	10" LP	Brunswick	LA8507	1951	£5	£12
Hans Christian Anderson	10" LP	Brunswick	LA8572	1953	£5	£12
Knock On Wood	10" LP	Brunswick	LA8668	1954	£5	£12
Pure Delight	LP	Fontana	TFR6008	1958	£4	£10

KAYE, DAVE
Fool Such As I	7"	Decca	F11866	1964	£5	£10
In My Way	7"	Decca	F12073	1965	£5	£10
Yesterday When I Was Young	7"	Major Minor	MM641	1969	£2.50	£6

KAYE, LINDA
I Can't Stop Thinking About You	7"	Columbia	DB7915	1966	£6	£12

KAYE, SHIRLEY
Make Me Yours	7"	Trojan	TR015	1968	£5	£10

KAYE SISTERS
Are You Ready Freddy?	7"	Philips	PB806	1958	£2.50	£6	
At The Colony	7" EP	Philips	BBE12256	1959	£5	£10	
Favourites	7" EP	Philips	BBE12392	1960	£2	£5	
Ivory Tower	7"	HMV	7M401	1956	£6	£12	chart single
Kaye Sisters	7" EP	Philips	BBE12166	1957	£4	£8	
Lay Down Your Arms	7"	HMV	POP251	1956	£5	£10	
Paper Roses	7"	Philips	PB1024	1960	£2	£5	
Stroll Me	7"	Philips	PB832	1958	£2	£5	

KAYE, THOMAS JEFFERSON
Thomas Jefferson Kaye	LP	Probe	SPB1074	1973	£4	£10

KAYE, TONY & THE HEARTBEATS
Dream World	7"	Pye	7N25412	1967	£1.50	£4

KEANE, DOLORES
There Was A Maid	LP	Claddagh	CC23	1978	£5	£12	Irish

KEANE, DOLORES & JOHN FAULKNER
Broken Hearted I'll Wander	LP	Mulligan	LUN033	1979	£5	£12	Irish

KEANE, SHAKE
That's The Voice	LP	Ace Of Clubs	ACL1219	1967	£4	£10	
With The Keating Sound	LP	Decca	SKL4720	1965	£5	£12	

KEATING, JOHNNY
Swinging Scots	LP	London	LTZD15122	1958	£6	£15	
Z Cars	7" EP.	Piccadilly	NEP34011	1962	£2	£5	
Z Cars Theme	7"	Piccadilly	7N35032	1962	£1.50	£4	

KEENAN, PADDY
Paddy Keenan	LP	Gael Linn	CEF045	1975	£6	£15	Irish

KEENE, REX
Happy Texas Ranger	7"	Columbia	DB3831	1956	£2	£5	

KEFFORD, ACE STAND
For Your Love	7"	Atlantic	584260	1969	£10	£20	

KEITH
98.6	LP	Mercury	20103MCL	1967	£4	£10	
98.6	7"	Mercury	MF955	1967	£2	£5	chart single
Ain't Gonna Lie	7"	Mercury	MF940	1966	£2	£5	
Daylight Saving Time	7"	Mercury	MF989	1966	£2	£5	
Sugar Man	7"	Mercury	MF1002	1967	£2	£5	
Tell It To My Face	7" EP.	Mercury	126220	1967	£5	£10	French
Tell Me To My Face	7"	Mercury	MF968	1967	£1.50	£4	chart single

KEITH & ENID
Just A Closer Walk	7"	Dice	CC20	1963	£5	£10	
Keith And Enid Sing	LP	Island	ILP901	1963	£30	£60	
Lost My Love	7"	Island	WI429	1964	£5	£10	
Never Leave My Throne	7"	Starlite	ST45047	1961	£5	£10	
Sacred Vow	7"	Dice	CC14	1963	£5	£10	
Send Me	7"	Blue Beat	BB11	1961	£5	£10	Trenton Spence B side
Sing	7"	Trojan	TBL154	1970	£5	£12	
Sing	LP	Trojan	TTL37	1970	£6	£15	
When It's Spring	7"	Blue Beat	BB125	1962	£5	£10	
Worried Over You	7"	Blue Beat	BB6	1960	£5	£10	
You're Gonna Break My Heart	7"	Starlite	ST45067	1961	£5	£10	

KEITH & KEN
You'll Love Jamaica	LP	London	HAR/SHR8229	1965	£8	£20	

KEITH & TEX
Hypnotizing Eyes	7"	Island	WI3137	1968	£5	£10	
Tighten Up Your Gird	7"	Explosion	EX2008	1969	£2.50	£6	
Tonight	7"	Island	WI3085	1967	£5	£10	Lyn Taitt B side

KEITH, BRIAN
When The First Tear Shows	7"	Page One	POF103	1968	£1.50	£4	

KEITH, BRYAN
Mean Mama	7"	London	HLU9707	1963	£4	£8	

KEITH, RON
Party Music	7"	A&M	AMS7217	1976	£10	£20	

KELLER, JERRY
Here Comes Jerry Keller	LP	London	HAR2261/ SAHR6083	1960	£15	£30	
Here Comes Summer	7"	London	HLR8890	1959	£1.50	£4	chart single
If I Had A Girl	7"	London	HLR8980	1959	£1.50	£4	
Now Now Now	7"	London	HLR9106	1960	£1.50	£4	

KELLUM, MURRAY
Long Tall Texan	7"	London	HLU9830	1964	£2	£5	Glen Sutton B side

KELLY BROTHERS
Falling In Love Again	7"	Sue	WI4034	1967	£12.50	£25	
Sweet Soul	LP	President	PTL1019	1968	£10	£25	
That's What You Mean To Me	7"	Blue Horizon	573177	1970	£4	£8	
You Put Your Touch On Me	7"	President	PT143	1968	£1.50	£4	

KELLY, CHARLIE
So Nice Like Rice	7"	Island	WI3155	1968	£5	£10	Stranger Cole B side

KELLY, DAVE
Black Blue Kelly	LP	Mercury	6310001	1971	£40	£80	
Keeps It In The Family	LP	Mercury	SMCL20151	1969	£35	£70	

KELLY, GENE
'S Wonderful	7"	MGM	SP1015	1953	£1.50	£4	
Singin' In The Rain	7"	MGM	SP1012	1953	£4	£8	
Song And Dance Man	10" LP	MGM	D117	1953	£5	£12	
S'Wonderful	10" LP	MGM	D133	1955	£5	£12	

KELLY, JO-ANN
Blues And Gospel	7" EP.	GW	EP1	1961	£50	£100	
Do It	LP	Red Rag	RRR006	1976	£15	£30	with Peter Emery
Jo Ann Kelly	LP	CBS	63841	1969	£40	£80	

With Fahey, Mann, & Miller	LP	Blue Goose	2009	1972	£15	£30		US

KELLY, JO-ANN & TONY MCPHEE
Same Thing On Their Minds	LP	Sunset	SLS50209	1971	£20	£40	

KELLY, JOHN
Fiddle And Concertina Player	LP	Free Reed	FRS504	1975	£5	£12	

KELLY, JONATHAN
Denver	7"	Parlophone	R5805	1969	£2	£5	
Don't You Believe It	7"	Parlophone	R5851	1970	£4	£8	
Jonathan Kelly	LP	Parlophone	PCS7114	1970	£8	£20	
Make A Stranger Your Friend	7"	Parlophone	R5830	1970	£2	£5	

KELLY, KEITH
Cold White And Beautiful	7"	Parlophone	R4797	1961	£1.50	£4	
Listen Little Girl	7"	Parlophone	R4676	1960	£2	£5	chart single
Save Your Love For Me	7"	CBS	201794	1965	£1.50	£4	
Tease Me	7"	Parlophone	R4640	1960	£2	£5	chart single
With You	7"	Parlophone	R4713	1960	£1.50	£4	

KELLY, PAT
Cool Breezing	LP	Pama	PMLP2013	1971	£8	£20	
How Long Will It Take	7"	Gas	GAS115	1969	£4	£8	
Little Boy Blue	7"	Giant	GN37	1968	£4	£8	
Sings	LP	Pama	PMLP12	1969	£8	£20	
Somebody's Song	7"	Island	WI3121	1968	£5	£10	Beverley Simmons B side
Workman Song	7"	Gas	GAS110	1969	£4	£8	

KELLY, PAUL
Chills And Fever	7"	Atlantic	AT4053	1965	£6	£12	
Sweet Sweet Lovin'	7"	Philips	BF1591	1967	£4	£8	

KELLY, PETE SOULUTION
Midnight Confessions	7"	Decca	F12755	1968	£5	£10	

KELLY, STAN
Ballad Of Armagh Jail	7"	Transatlantic	TRASP21	1968	£1.50	£4	
Liverpool Packet	7" EP	Topic	TOP27	1960	£2.50	£6	
Songs For Swinging Landlords	7" EP	Topic	TOP60	1961	£5	£10	

KELLY, WYNTON
Kelly Great	LP	Top Rank	35107	1961	£6	£15	

KELSEY, REV.SAMUEL
Rev.Kelsey	7" EP	Brunswick	OE9256	1956	£6	£12	
Wedding Ceremony Of Sister R.Tharpe	78	Vocalion	V1014	1952	£3	£8	

KEMP, WAYNE
Watch Your Step	7"	Atlantic	584006	1966	£1.50	£4	

KEMPION
Cam Ye O'er Frae France	LP	Sweet Folk & Country		197-	£6	£15	
Kempion	LP	Broadside	BRO123	1977	£5	£12	

KENDALL, JOHNNY & THE HERALDS
St.James Infirmary	7"	RCA	RCA1416	1964	£4	£8	

KENDALL SISTERS
Won't You Be My Baby	7"	London	HLM8622	1958	£12.50	£25	

KENDRICK, GRAHAM
Bright Side Up	LP	Key	KL016	1973	£8	£20	
Footsteps On The Sea	LP	Key	KL101	1973	£8	£20	
Paid On The Nail	LP	Key	KL024	1974	£6	£15	with Peter Roe

KENDRICK, LINDA
Friend Of Mine	7"	Polydor	56146	1966	£1.50	£4	
It's The Little Things	7"	Polydor	56076	1966	£7.50	£15	

KENDRICK, NAT & THE SWANS
Dish Rag	7"	Top Rank	JAR387	1960	£5	£10	
Mashed Potato	7"	Top Rank	JAR351	1960	£5	£10	

KENNEDY, JERRY
Dancing Guitars Rock Elvis' Hits	LP	Smash	MGS2/SRS67004	1962	£5	£12	US

KENNEDY, NORMAN
Norman Kennedy	LP	Folk Legacy	FSS34	1968	£6	£15	US

KENNER, CHRIS
I Like It Like That	7"	London	HLU9410	1961	£5	£10	
Land Of A Thousand Dances	LP	Atlantic	587008	1966	£8	£20	
Land Of A Thousand Dances	7"	Sue	WI351	1965	£7.50	£15	

KENNY & CASH
Knees	7"	Decca	F12283	1965	£4	£8	

KENNY & CORKY
Nuttin' For Christmas .... 7" ...... London .... HLX9002 .... 1959 ... £2 ....£5 ....

KENNY & THE CADETS
The single by Kenny and the Cadets is an early spin-off from the Beach Boys, as the record features both Brian and Carl Wilson (together with their mother!).
Barbie .... 7" ...... Randy .... 422 .... 1962 ... £60 ....£120 .... US

KENNY & THE KASUALS
Garage Kings .... LP ..... Mark .... 7000 .... 1969 ... £10 ....£25 .... US
Impact Sound .... LP ..... Mark .... 5000 .... 1966 ... £150 ......£250 .... US
Teen Dreams .... LP ..... Mark .... 6000 .... 1968 ... £50 ....£100 ....US, red vinyl

KENNY & THE WRANGLERS
Doobie Doo .... 7" ...... Parlophone ..... R5275 .... 1965 ... £4 ....£8 ....
Somebody Help Me .... 7" ...... Parlophone ..... R5224 .... 1964 ... £4 ....£8 ....

KENSINGTON MARKET
Aardvark .... LP ..... Warner Bros ... WS1780 .... 1969 ... £5 ....£12 .... US
Avenue Road .... LP ..... Warner Bros .... WS1754 .... 1968 ... £5 ....£12 .... US

KENT & DIMPLE
Day Is Done .... 7" ...... Island .... WI046 .... 1963 ... £5 ....£10

KENT & JEANIE
Daddy .... 7" ...... Blue Beat .... BB98 .... 1962 ... £5 ....£10

KENT, AL
You Gotta Pay The Price .... 7" ...... Mojo .... 2092015 .... 1971 ... £5 ....£10 .... demo only
You Gotta Pay The Price .... 7" ...... Track .... 604016 .... 1967 ... £15 ....£30

KENT, ENOCH
Sings The Butcher Boy And Other   7" EP.. Topic .... TOP81 .... 1962 ... £5 ....£10
Ballads ....

KENT, PAUL
Paul Kent .... LP ..... B&C .... CAS1044 .... 1971 ... £6 ....£15
P.C.Kent .... LP ..... RCA .... SF8083 .... 1970 ... £6 ....£15

KENT, RICHARD STYLE
Crocodile Tears .... 7" ...... MCA .... MU1032 .... 1968 ... £5 ....£10
Little Bit O' Soul .... 7" ...... Mercury .... MF1090 .... 1969 ... £5 ....£10
Marching Off To War .... 7" ...... Columbia .... DB8182 .... 1967 ... £7.50 .....£15
No Matter What You Do .... 7" ...... Columbia .... DB7964 .... 1966 ... £12.50 ...£25
You Can't Put Me Down .... 7" ...... Columbia .... DB8051 .... 1966 ... £7.50 .....£15

KENT, SHIRLEY
Sings For Charec 67 .... 7" ...... Keele   103 .... 1966 ... £10 ....£20 ....with The
                                                          University ....   Master Singers

KENTIGERN
Kentigern .... LP ..... Topic .... 12TS394 .... 1979 ... £5 ....£12

KENTON, STAN
Artistry In Rhythm .... 10" LP Capitol .... LC6545 .... 1952 ... £10 ....£25
A-Ting-A-Ling .... 7" ...... Capitol .... CL14259 .... 1955 ... £1.50 .....£4
Back To Balboa .... LP ..... Capitol .... T995 .... 1958 ... £6 ....£15
Ballad Style .... LP ..... Capitol .... (S)T1068 .... 1959 ... £5 ....£12
City Of Glass .... 10" LP Capitol .... LC6577 .... 1953 ... £10 ....£25
Classics .... 10" LP Capitol .... LC6676 .... 1954 ... £10 ....£25
Concert In Progressive Jazz .... 10" LP Capitol .... LC6679 .... 1952 ... £10 ....£25
Cuban Fire .... LP ..... Capitol .... LCT6118 .... 1956 ... £8 ....£20
Encores .... 10" LP Capitol .... LC6523 .... 1951 ... £10 ....£25
Formative Years .... LP ..... Brunswick .... LAT8122 .... 1956 ... £6 ....£15
In Hi-Fi .... LP ..... Capitol .... LCT6109 .... 1956 ... £8 ....£20
Innovations In Modern Music .... LP ..... Capitol .... LCT6006 .... 1954 ... £10 ....£25
Kenton Era Vol.1 .... LP ..... Capitol .... LCT6157 .... 1958 ... £6 ....£15
Kenton Era Vol.2 .... LP ..... Capitol .... LCT6158 .... 1958 ... £6 ....£15
Kenton Era Vol.3 .... LP ..... Capitol .... LCT6159 .... 1958 ... £6 ....£15
Kenton Era Vol.4 .... LP ..... Capitol .... LCT6160 .... 1958 ... £6 ....£15
Kenton Showcase .... LP ..... Capitol .... LCT6009 .... 1955 ... £8 ....£20
Kenton Sidemen .... LP ..... Vogue .... LAE12028 .... 1957 ... £6 ....£15
Kenton With Voices .... LP ..... Capitol .... LCT6138 .... 1957 ... £6 ....£15
Lush Interlude .... LP ..... Capitol .... T1130 .... 1959 ... £5 ....£12
Milestones .... 10" LP Capitol .... LC6517 .... 1951 ... £10 ....£25
New Concepts Of Artistry In Rhythm ... 10" LP Capitol .... LC6595 .... 1953 ... £10 ....£25
Portraits On Standards .... 10" LP Capitol .... LC6697 .... 1955 ... £10 ....£25
Presents .... 10" LP Capitol .... LC6548 .... 1952 ... £10 ....£25
Rendezvous With Kenton .... LP ..... Capitol .... (S)T932 .... 1958 ... £6 ....£15
Road Show Vol.1 .... LP ..... Capitol .... (S)T11327 .... 1961 ... £4 ....£10
Road Show Vol.2 .... LP ..... Capitol .... (S)T21327 .... 1961 ... £4 ....£10
Sketches On Standards .... 10" LP Capitol .... LC6602 .... 1953 ... £10 ....£25
Stage Door Swings .... LP ..... Capitol .... (S)T1166 .... 1959 ... £5 ....£12
Standards In Silhouette .... LP ..... Capitol .... (S)T1394 .... 1961 ... £4 ....£10
This Modern World .... 10" LP Capitol .... LC6667 .... 1954 ... £10 ....£25
West Side Story .... LP ..... Capitol .... (S)T1609 .... 1961 ... £4 ....£10

KEN-TONES
Get With It .... 7" ...... Parlophone ..... MSP6229 .... 1956 ... £2 ....£5
I Saw Esau .... 7" ...... Parlophone ..... R4257 .... 1957 ... £1.50 .....£4

KENTUCKY BOYS
Don't Fetch It	7"	HMV	7M312	1955	£2	£5	

KENTUCKY COLONELS
Appalachian Swing	LP	World Pacific	(S)T1821	1964	£8	£20	US
Kentucky Colonels	LP	United Artists	UAS29514	1974	£4	£10	
New Sound Of Bluegrass	LP	Briar	M109	1963	£8	£20	US

KENWRIGHT, BILL
I Want To Go Back There Again	7"	Columbia	DB8239	1967	£1.50	£4	

KERN, WOODY
Awful Disclosures Of Maria Monk	LP	Pye	NSPL18273	1967	£8	£20	
Biography	7"	Pye	7N17672	1969	£2.50	£6	

KEROUAC, JACK
Blues And Haikus	LP	Hanover	HML5006	1959	£25	£50	US
Poetry For The Beat Generation	LP	Dot	DLP3154	1959	£37.50	£75	US
Poetry For The Beat Generation	LP	Hanover	HML5000	1959	£25	£50	US
Readings On The Beat Generation	LP	Verve	MGV15005	1959	£25	£50	US

KERR, ANITA QUARTET
Anita Kerr Quartet	7" EP	RCA	RCX7164	1964	£2	£5	

KERR, PATRICK
Magic Potion	7"	Decca	F12069	1965	£5	£10	

KERR, RICHARD
From Now Until Then	LP	Warner Bros	K46206	1972	£6	£15	
Happy Birthday Blues	7"	Deram	DM138	1967	£1.50	£4	

KERRIES
Coulters Candy	7"	Major Minor	MM541	1967	£1.50	£4	
Kerries	LP	Major Minor	MMLP/SMLP9	1967	£6	£15	

KERRY, CHRIS
Seven Deadly Sins	7"	Mercury	MF957	1965	£5	£10	
Watermelon Man	7"	Mercury	MF985	1966	£2.50	£6	

KESEY, KEN & THE GRATEFUL DEAD
Acid Test	LP	Psycho	PSYCHO4	1983	£10	£25	
Acid Test	LP	Sound City	EX27690	1967	£50	£100	US

KESSEL, BARNEY
Barney Kessel	10" LP	Vogue	LDE085	1954	£15	£30	
Barney Kessel Vol.2	10" LP	Contemporary	LDC153	1955	£15	£30	
Easy Like	LP	Contemporary	LAC12082	1958	£10	£25	
Music To Listen To Barney Kessel By	LP	Contemporary	LAC12068/ SCA5002	1958	£6	£15	
Plays Carmen	LP	Contemporary	LAC12214	1960	£5	£12	
Plays Standards	LP	Contemporary	LAC12098	1959	£5	£12	
Poll Winners	LP	Contemporary	LAC12122	1959	£6	£15	
Poll Winners Ride Again	LP	Vogue	LAC12186	1959	£5	£12	with Ray Brown & Shelly Manne
Poll Winners Three	LP	Contemporary	LAC12237	1960	£4	£10	with Ray Brown & Shelly Manne
Slow Burn	LP	Phil Spector	2307011	1977	£4	£10	
Some Like It Hot	LP	Contemporary	LAC12206	1960	£5	£12	
To Swing Or Not To Swing	LP	Contemporary	LAC12058	1958	£6	£15	

KESTREL
Kestrel	LP	Cube	HIFLY19	1975	£50	£100	

KESTRELS
All These Things	7"	Decca	F11391	1961	£1.50	£4	
Don't Want To Cry	7"	Piccadilly	7N35079	1962	£1.50	£4	
I Can't Say Goodbye	7"	Pye	7N15248	1960	£2	£5	
Kestrels	LP	Donegall	MAU500	1958	£6	£15	
Love Me With All Your Heart	7"	Piccadilly	7N35144	1963	£1.50	£4	
Smash Hits	LP	Piccadilly	NPL38009	1963	£6	£15	
There Comes A Time	7"	Pye	7N15234	1959	£2	£5	
There's A Place	7"	Piccadilly	7N35126	1963	£1.50	£4	
Walk Right In	7"	Piccadilly	7N35104	1963	£1.50	£4	
Wolverton Mountain	7"	Piccadilly	7N35056	1962	£1.50	£4	

KEY LARGO
Key Largo	LP	Blue Horizon	763859	1970	£8	£20	
Voodoo Rhythm	7"	Blue Horizon	573178	1971	£4	£8	

KEYES, EBONY
Sitting In The Ring	7"	Piccadilly	7N35358	1966	£2	£5	

KEYES, KAROL
Can't You Hear The Music	7"	Fontana	TF846	1967	£1.50	£4	
Fool In Love	7"	Columbia	DB7899	1966	£2	£4	
One In A Million	7"	Columbia	DB8001	1966	£12.50	£25	
You Beat Me To The Punch	7"	Fontana	TF517	1964	£7.50	£15	

KEYES, TROY
Love Explosions	7"	Stateside	SS2087	1968	£4	£8	
Love Explosions	7"	Stateside	SS2149	1969	£2	£5	

KEYMEN
Gazackstahagen .... 7" ...... HMV .... POP584 .... 1959 ... £1.50 ....£4 ....

KEYNOTES
Dime And A Dollar .... 7" ...... Decca .... F10302 .... 1954 ... £1.50 ....£4 .....Johnston Brothers
B side

Steam Heat .... 7" ...... Decca .... F10643 .... 1955 ... £4 ....£8 ....

KHAN
Space Shanty .... LP ...... Deram .... SDLR11 .... 1972 ... £8 ....£20 ....

KHAN, ASHISH
Ashish Khan .... LP ...... Liberty .... LBL83083E .... 1968 ... £5 ....£12 ....

KHAN, USTAD ALI AKBAR
Dhun Palas Kafi .... LP ..... Transatlantic ... TRA183 .... 1969 ... £4 ....£10 ....
Music From India No.5 .... LP ..... HMV .... ASD2367 .... 1969 ... £4 ....£10 ....
Peaceful Music .... LP ..... Mushroom ...... 100MR14 .... 1971 ... £20 ....£40 ....

KHAN, USTAD VILAYET
Raga Tilakkamod .... LP ..... Transatlantic ... TRA239 .... 1970 ... £6 ....£15 ....
Ustad Vilayet Khan .... LP ..... Track .... 1971 ... £6 ....£15 ....

KHANDARS
Don't Dig A Hole For Me .... 7" ...... Blue Beat .... BB332 .... 1965 ... £5 ....£10 ....Buster's Allstars
B side

KHANS
New Orleans 2am .... 7" ...... London .... HLU9555 .... 1962 ... £1.50 ....£4 ....

KHARTOMB
Swahili Lullaby .... 7" ...... Whaam!......... WHAAM14 .... 1983 ... £1.50 ....£4 ....

KHAVAS JUTE
.... LP ..... Infinity .... £65 ....£130 ....

KHAZAD-DOOM
Level Six And A Half .... LP ..... LPL .... £30 ....£60 .... US

KICKSTANDS
Black Boots And Bikes .... LP ..... Capitol .... (S)T2078............... 1964 ... £5 ....£12 .... US

KIDD, JOHNNY & THE PIRATES
Always And Ever .... 7" ...... HMV .... POP1269 .... 1964 ... £2 ....£5 .....chart single
Birds And The Bees .... 7" ...... HMV .... POP1397 .... 1965 ... £2.50 ....£6 .....chart single
Hungry For Love .... 7" ...... HMV .... POP1228 .... 1963 ... £2 ....£5 .....chart single
Hurry On Back To Love .... 7" ...... HMV .... POP978 .... 1962 ... £2.50 ....£6 ....
If You Were The Only Girl .... 7" ...... HMV .... POP674 .... 1959 ... £4 ....£8 ....
I'll Never Get Over You .... 7" ...... HMV .... POP1173 .... 1963 ... £2 ....£5 .....chart single
It's Got To Be You .... 7" ...... HMV .... POP1520 .... 1965 ... £4 ....£8 ....
Jealous Girl .... 7" ...... HMV .... POP1309 .... 1964 ... £2 ....£5 ....
Johnny Kidd & The Pirates .... 7" EP. HMV .... 7EG8834 .... 1964 ... £10 ....£20 ....
Linda Lu .... 7" ...... HMV .... POP853 .... 1961 ... £4 ....£8 .....chart single
Please Don't Bring Me Down .... 7" ...... HMV .... POP919 .... 1961 ... £4 ....£8 ....
Please Don't Touch .... 7" ...... HMV .... POP615 .... 1959 ... £4 ....£8 .....chart single
Restless .... 7" ...... HMV .... POP790 .... 1960 ... £2.50 ....£6 .....chart single
Send For That Girl .... 7" ...... HMV .... POP1559 .... 1966 ... £4 ....£8 ....
Shakin' All Over .... LP ..... Starline .... SRS5100 .... 1971 ... £5 ....£12 ....
Shakin' All Over .... 7" EP. HMV .... 7EG8628 .... 1960 ... £10 ....£20 ....
Shakin' All Over .... 7" EP. Pathe .... EGF813 .... 1965 ... £25 ....£50 ....French
Shaking All Over .... 7" ...... HMV .... POP753 .... 1960 ... £2.50 ....£6 .....chart single
Shaking All Over '65 .... 7" ...... HMV .... POP1424 .... 1965 ... £2.50 ....£6 ....
Shot Of Rhythm And Blues .... 7" ...... HMV .... POP1088 .... 1962 ... £2.50 ....£6 ....
Whole Lotta Woman .... 7" ...... HMV .... POP1353 .... 1964 ... £2 ....£6 .....chart single
You've Got What It Takes .... 7" ...... HMV .... POP698 .... 1960 ... £2.50 ....£6 .....chart single

KIDS NEXT DOOR
Inky Dinky Spider .... 7" ...... London .... HLR9993............. 1965 ... £1.50 ....£4 ....

KIDZ NEXT DOOR
What's It All About? .... 7" ...... Warner Bros .... K17492 .... 1979 ... £2 ....£5 ....

KILBURN & THE HIGH ROADS
Handsome .... LP ..... Dawn .... DNLS3065 .... 1975 ... £4 ....£10 ....

KILDAIRE, ROY
What About It .... 7" ...... Blue Beat .... BB226 .... 1963 ... £5 ....£10 ....

KILEEN, JUDY
Just Walking In The Rain .... 7" ...... London .... HLU8328 .... 1956 ... £7.50 ....£15 ....

KILFENORA CEILI BAND
Kilfenora Ceili Band .... LP ..... Transatlantic ... TRS108............. 1974 ... £6 ....£15 ....

KILGORE, MERLE
Dear Mama .... 7" ...... Melodisc .... 1545................. 1960 ... £5 ....£10 ....
Ernie .... 7" ...... London .... HLP8392 .... 1957 ... £40 ....£80 ....
Forty Two In Chicago .... 7" ...... Mercury .... AMT1193 .... 1962 ... £4 ....£8 ....
It Can't Rain All The Time .... 7" ...... London .... HL8103 .... 1954 ... £25 ....£50 ....

KILGORE, THEOLA
I'll Keep Trying .... 7" ..... Sue............ WI4035 .... 1967 ... £5 .... £10 ....

KILLEN, LOU & SALLY
Bright Shining Morning .... LP ..... Front Hall ... FHR06 .... 1975 ... £10 ...... £25 .... US

KILLEN, LOUIS
Ballads And Broadsides .... LP ..... Topic............ 12T126 .... 1965 ... £10 ...... £25
Northumbrian Garland .... 7" EP.. Topic............ TOP75 .... 1962 ... £5 .... £10

KILLEN, LOUIS & JOHNNY HANDLE
Collier's Rant .... 7" EP.. Topic............ TOP74 .... 1962 ... £5 .... £10

KILLEN, LOUIS, JOHNNY HANDLE, COLIN ROSS
Along The Coaly Tyne .... LP ..... Topic............ 12T189 .... 1969 ... £10 ...... £25

KILLEN, LOUIS, TOM GILFELLON, JOHNNY HANDLE, COLIN ROSS
Tommy Armstrong Of Tyneside .... LP ..... Topic............ 12T122 .... 1965 ... £6 .... £15

KILLERMETERS
Twisted Wheel .... 7" ..... Gem............ GEMS22 .... 1980 ... £5 .... £10
Why Should It Happen To Me .... 7" ..... Psycho............ P2620 .... 1979 ... £15 ...... £30 .... PS
Why Should It Happen To Me .... 7" ..... Psycho............ P2620 .... 1979 ... £7.50 ...... £15 .... without PS

KILLIGREW
Killigrew .... LP ..... Penny Farthing PELS513............ 1971 ... £5 .... £12

KILLING FLOOR
Call For The Politicians .... 7" ..... Penny Farthing PEN745 .... 1970 ... £7.50 ...... £15
Killing Floor .... LP ..... Spark .... SRLP102 .... 1970 ... £50 ...... £100
Original Killing Floor .... LP ..... Spark .... SRLM2004 .... 1973 ... £40 ...... £80 .... sleeve
pictured in Guide
Out Of Uranus .... LP ..... Penny Farthing PELS511 .... 1970 ... £40 ...... £80

KILLING JOKE
Kings And Queens .... 12" ..... EG............ EGOY21 .... 1985 ... £2.50 ...... £6
Love Like Blood .... 12" ..... EG............ EGOY20 .... 1985 ... £2.50 ...... £6
Me Or You .... 12" ..... EG............ EGOXD14 .... 1983 ... £4 .... £10 .... double
Nervous System .... 12" ..... Island............ WIP6550 .... 1981 ... £2.50 ...... £6
Nervous System .... 10" ..... Malicious Damage MD410 .... 1979 ... £5 .... £12 .... with 5 inserts
Requiem .... 12" ..... Malicious Damage EGMDX100 .... 1980 ... £2.50 ...... £6
Sanity .... 7" ..... EG............ EGO30 .... 1986 ... £4 .... £8 .... with Wardance cassette
Wardance .... 7" ..... Malicious Damage MD540 .... 1980 ... £1.50 ...... £4 .... with insert

KILOWATTS
Bring It On Home .... 7" ..... Doctor Bird ...... DB1140 .... 1968 ... £5 .... £10

KILTIES
Teach You To Rock .... 7" ..... Beltona .... BL2666 .... 1956 ... £4 .... £8

KIMBER, WILLIAM
Art Of William Kimber .... LP ..... Topic............ 12T249 .... 1974 ... £5 .... £12
William Kimber .... LP ..... EFSDS............ LP1001 .... 197- ... £6 .... £15

KIMBER, WILLIAM E.
Kilburn Towers .... 7" ..... Parlophone...... R5735 .... 1968 ... £1.50 ...... £4

KIMBLE, STEVIE
Some Things Take A Little Time .... 7" ..... Decca .... F12378 .... 1966 ... £6 .... £12

KIMMEL, JOHN J.
Early Recordings Of Irish Traditional Dance Music .... LP ..... Leader............ LEO2060 .... 1977 ... £6 .... £15

KINETIC
Live Your Life .... 7" EP.. Vogue .... EPL8544 .... 1967 ... £6 .... £12 .... French
Suddenly Tomorrow .... 7" EP.. Vogue .... EPL8520 .... 1967 ... £6 .... £12 .... French

KING, AL
Think Twice Before You Speak .... 7" ..... Sue............ WI4045 .... 1968 ... £7.50 ...... £15

KING, ALBERT
Big Blues .... LP ..... King............ 852 .... 1962 ... £20 ...... £40 .... US
Born Under A Bad Sign .... LP ..... Stax............ 723 .... 1967 ... £6 .... £15 .... US
Born Under A Bad Sign .... 7" ..... Stax............ 601015 .... 1967 ... £2 .... £5
Breaking Up Somebody's Home .... 7" ..... Stax............ 2025162 .... 1973 ... £1.50 ...... £4
Cold Feet .... 7" ..... Stax............ 601029 .... 1968 ... £2 .... £5
Crosscut Saw .... 7" ..... Atlantic............ 584099 .... 1967 ... £4 .... £8
Does The King's Things .... LP ..... Stax............ SXATS1017 .... 1968 ... £5 .... £12
King Of The Blues Guitar .... LP ..... Atlantic............ 588173 .... 1969 ... £5 .... £12
Live Wire Blues Power .... LP ..... Stax............ (S)XATS1002 .... 1968 ... £5 .... £12
Lucy .... 7" ..... Stax............ 601042 .... 1968 ... £2 .... £5
Travelling To California .... LP ..... Polydor............ 2343026 .... 1967 ... £6 .... £15
Years Gone By .... LP ..... Stax............ SXATS1022 .... 1970 ... £4 .... £10

KING, ALBERT & OTIS RUSH
Door To Door .... LP ..... Chess .... 1538 .... 1969 ... £5 .... £12 .... US

KING, ANNA

Baby Baby Baby	7"	Philips	BF1402	1965	£2.50	£6	with Bobby Byrd
Back To Soul	LP	Philips	(S)BL7655	1965	£8	£20	
Back To Soul	7" EP	Philips	BE12584	1965	£5	£10	

KING, B.B.

Ain't Nobody Home	7"	Probe	PRO546	1971	£1.50	£4	
Ask Me No Questions	7"	Probe	PRO528	1970	£1.50	£4	
B.B.King	LP	Crown	CLP5359	1963	£6	£15	US
B.B.King Sings Spirituals	LP	Crown	CLP5119/CST152	1960	£6	£15	US
B.B.King Sings Spirituals	LP	Crown	CST152	1960	£8	£20	US, red vinyl
B.B.King Story Vol.1	LP	Blue Horizon	763216	1968	£15	£30	
B.B.King Story Vol.2	LP	Blue Horizon	763226	1969	£15	£30	
B.B.King Wails	LP	Crown	CLP5115/CST147	1960	£6	£15	US
B.B.King Wails	LP	Crown	CST147	1960	£8	£20	US, red vinyl
Best Of B.B.King	LP	Galaxy	202	1963	£6	£15	US
Blues	LP	Crown	CLP5063	1960	£6	£15	US
Blues In My Heart	LP	Crown	CLP5309	1962	£6	£15	US
Blues Is King	LP	HMV	CLP3608	1967	£8	£20	
Blues On Top Of Blues	LP	Stateside	(S)SL10238	1968	£8	£20	
Chains And Things	7"	Probe	PRO516	1970	£1.50	£4	
Completely Well	LP	Stateside	SSL10299	1970	£8	£20	
Confessin' The Blues	LP	HMV	CLP3514	1966	£8	£20	
Don't Answer The Door	7"	HMV	POP1568	1966	£4	£8	
Don't Waste My Time	7"	Stateside	SS2141	1969	£1.50	£4	
Easy Listening Blues	LP	Crown	CLP5286	1962	£6	£15	US
Electric B.B.King	LP	Stateside	SSL10284	1969	£8	£20	
Every Day I Have The Blues	7"	Blue Horizon	573161	1969	£4	£8	
Great B.B.King	LP	Crown	CLP5143	1961	£6	£15	US
Guess Who	LP	Probe	SPB1063	1973	£5	£12	
Hummingbird	7"	Stateside	SS2176	1970	£2	£5	
In London	LP	Probe	SPB1041	1971	£6	£15	
Indianola Mississippi Seed	LP	Probe	SPBA6255	1970	£6	£15	
Jungle	7"	Polydor	56735	1967	£2	£5	
King Of The Blues	LP	Crown	CLP5167/CST195	1961	£6	£15	US
King Of The Blues	LP	Crown	CST195	1961	£8	£20	US, red vinyl
L.A. Midnight	LP	Probe	SPB1051	1972	£5	£12	
Live And Well	LP	Stateside	SSL10297	1970	£8	£20	
Live At Cook County Jail	LP	Probe	SPB1032	1971	£6	£15	
Live At The Regal	LP	HMV	CLP1870	1965	£8	£20	
Lucille	LP	Stateside	(S)SL10272	1969	£8	£20	
Mr.Blues	LP	ABC	(S)456	1963	£6	£15	US
My Kind Of Blues	LP	Crown	CLP5188	1961	£6	£15	US
Night Life	7"	HMV	POP1580	1967	£2.50	£6	
Paying The Cost To Be The Boss	7"	Stateside	SS2112	1968	£2	£5	
R&B And Soul	LP	Ember	EMB3379	1967	£6	£15	
Rock Me Baby	7"	Ember	EMBS196	1964	£5	£10	
So Excited	7"	Stateside	SS2169	1970	£2	£5	
Take A Swing With Me	LP	Blue Horizon	2431004	1970	£17.50	£35	Sleeve pictured in guide
Think It Over	7"	HMV	POP1594	1967	£2.50	£6	
Thrill Is Gone	7"	Stateside	SS2161	1970	£2.50	£6	
To Know You Is To Love You	LP	Probe	SPB1083	1973	£5	£12	
Tomorrow Night	7"	HMV	POP1101	1962	£5	£10	
Twist With B.B.King	LP	Crown	CLP5248	1962	£6	£15	US
Woman I Love	7"	Blue Horizon	573144	1968	£5	£10	
You Never Know	7"	Sue	WI358	1965	£6	£12	

KING, B.B. & BOBBY BLAND

Together For The First Time	LP	ABC	ABCD605	1974	£6	£15	double

KING BEES

On Your Way Down The Drain	7" EP	RCA	86521	1966	£12.50	£25	French

KING, BEN E.

Amor Amor	7"	London	HLK9416	1961	£1.50	£4	chart single
Cry No More	7"	Atlantic	AT4043	1965	£2	£5	
Don't Play That Song	LP	London	HAK8012	1962	£8	£20	
Don't Play That Song	7"	London	HLK9544	1962	£2	£5	
Don't Take Your Love From Me	7"	Atlantic	584184	1968	£5	£10	
Goodbye My Old Gal	7"	Crewe	CRW2	1970	£1.50	£4	
Goodnight My Love, Pleasant Dreams	7"	Atlantic	AT4065	1966	£2.50	£6	
Greatest Hits	LP	Atco	SD33165	1964	£6	£15	US
Grooving	7"	London	HLK9840	1964	£1.50	£4	
Here Comes The Night	7"	London	HLK9457	1961	£2	£5	
How Can I Forget	7"	London	HLK9691	1963	£1.50	£4	
How Can I Forget	7" EP	London	REK1361	1963	£7.50	£15	
I Could Have Danced All Night	7"	London	HLK9819	1963	£1.50	£4	
I Swear By The Stars Above	7"	Atlantic	584046	1966	£1.50	£4	
I (Who Have Nothing)	7"	London	HLK9778	1963	£1.50	£4	
I'm Standing By	7"	London	HLK9631	1962	£2	£5	
I'm Standing By	7" EP	London	REK1386	1963	£7.50	£15	
It's Amazing	7"	Atlantic	2091100	1971	£1.50	£4	
It's Amazing	7"	Atlantic	584205	1968	£1.50	£4	
Let The Water Run Down	7"	Atlantic	AT4007	1964	£2	£5	
Record	7"	Atlantic	AT4025	1965	£4	£8	
Save The Last Dance For Me	7"	Atlantic	584090	1967	£1.50	£4	
Seven Letters	LP	Atlantic	588125	1968	£5	£12	
Seven Letters	7"	Atlantic	584149	1968	£1.50	£4	
Seven Letters	7"	Atlantic	AT4018	1965	£2.50	£6	

So Much Love	7"	Atlantic	584008	1966	£1.50	£4	
Songs For Soulful Lovers	LP	Atlantic	587/588055	1966	£4	£10	
Songs For Soulful Lovers	LP	London	HAK/SHK8026	1963	£8	£20	
Spanish Harlem	LP	Atco	SD33133	1961	£6	£15	US
Spanish Harlem	LP	Atlantic	590011	1967	£4	£10	chart LP
Spanish Harlem	7"	London	HLK9258	1961	£2	£5	chart single
Stand By Me	7"	London	HLK9358	1961	£2	£5	chart single
Tears Tears Tears	7"	Atlantic	584106	1967	£1.50	£4	
Till I Can't Take It Anymore	7"	Atlantic	584238	1969	£1.50	£4	
Too Bad	7"	London	HLK9586	1962	£1.50	£4	
What Is Soul	7"	Atlantic	584069	1967	£2	£5	
What Is Soul?	LP	Atlantic	587072	1967	£6	£15	
What Now My Love	7" EP	Atlantic	AET6004	1964	£6	£12	
Yes	7"	London	HLK9517	1962	£2	£5	

KING, BOB

Hey Honey	7"	Oriole	CB1497	1959	£20	£40	

KING BROTHERS

76 Trombones	7"	Parlophone	R4737	1961	£1.50	£4	chart single
Doll House	7"	Parlophone	R4715	1960	£1.50	£4	chart single
Harmony Kings	7" EP	Parlophone	GEP8638	1957	£4	£8	
Hop, Skip And Jump	7"	Parlophone	R4554	1959	£2.50	£6	
In The Middle Of An Island	7"	Parlophone	R4338	1957	£1.50	£4	chart single
King Brothers	LP	Parlophone	PMC1060	1958	£5	£12	
King Size Hits	7" EP	Parlophone	GEP8838	1961	£2	£5	
Kings Of Song	7" EP	Parlophone	GEP8760	1958	£2	£5	
Leaning On A Lamp Post	7"	Parlophone	R4513	1959	£1.50	£4	
Little By Little	7"	Parlophone	R4288	1957	£2	£5	
Mais Oui	7"	Parlophone	R4672	1960	£1.50	£4	chart single
Making Love	7"	Parlophone	R4577	1959	£1.50	£4	
Put A Light In The Window	7"	Parlophone	R4389	1958	£1.50	£4	chart single
Sitting In A Tree House	7"	Parlophone	R4469	1958	£1.50	£4	
Six Five Jive	7"	Parlophone	R4410	1958	£2	£5	
Standing On The Corner	7"	Parlophone	R4639	1960	£1.50	£4	chart single
Torero	7"	Parlophone	R4438	1958	£1.50	£4	
Wake Up Little Susie	7"	Parlophone	R4367	1957	£1.50	£4	chart single
White Sports Coat	7"	Parlophone	R4310	1957	£1.50	£4	chart single

KING, BUZZY

Schoolboy Blues	7"	Top Rank	JAR278	1960	£2.50	£6	

KING CANNON

Soul Pipe	7"	Duke	DU13	1969	£2.50	£6	
Soul Scorcher	7"	Trojan	TR663	1969	£2.50	£6	
Thunderstorm	7"	Trojan	TR636	1968	£2.50	£6	Burt Walters B side

KING, CARL

Out Of My Depth	7"	CBS	202407	1966	£4	£8	

KING, CAROLE

It Might As Well Rain Until September	7"	London	HLU9591	1962	£2	£5	chart single
Music	LP	Ode	SQ88013	1971	£4	£10	US quad
Road To Nowhere	7"	London	HLU10036	1966	£4	£8	
Tapestry	LP	Epic/Ode	HE44946	1980	£6	£15	US audiophile

KING, CLAUDE

Burning Of Atlanta	7"	CBS	AAG119	1962	£2	£5	
Commancheros	7"	Philips	BF1199	1961	£1.50	£4	
Sweet Loving	7"	Philips	BF1173	1961	£1.50	£4	
Tiger Woman	7" EP	CBS	EP6067	1965	£2.50	£6	
Wolverton Mountain	7"	CBS	AAG108	1962	£2	£5	

KING, CLYDIE

One Part Two Part	7"	Minit	MLF11014	1969	£2.50	£6	

KING CRIMSON

Cat Food	7"	Island	WIP6080	1970	£4	£8	PS
Court Of The Crimson King	7"	Island	WIP6071	1969	£4	£8	
Earthbound	LP	Island	HELP6	1972	£4	£10	
In The Court Of The Crimson King	LP	Island	ILPS9111	1969	£5	£12	chart LP
In The Court Of The Crimson King	LP	Mobile Fidelity	MFSL1075	1980	£10	£25	US audiophile
In The Wake Of Poseidon	LP	Island	ILPS9127	1970	£5	£12	chart LP
Islands	LP	Island	ILPS9175	1971	£4	£10	chart LP
Lizard	LP	Island	ILPS9141	1970	£4	£10	chart LP
Night Watch	7"	Island	WIP6189	1974	£1.50	£4	
Return Of King Crimson	LP	EG		1981	£5	£12	interview promo
Thela Hun Ginjeet	12"	EG	KCX001	1981	£2.50	£6	promo
Twenty-First Century Schizoid Man	7"	Island	WIP6274	1976	£5	£10	PS

KING, DANNY & MAYFAIR SET

Amen	7"	Columbia	DB7792	1965	£6	£12	
Pretty Things	7"	Columbia	DB7456	1965	£12.50	£25	
Tossing And Turning	7"	Columbia	DB7276	1964	£7.50	£15	

KING, DAVE

Birds And The Bees	7"	Decca	F10741	1956	£1.50	£4	
Christmas And You	7"	Decca	F10791	1956	£2	£5	chart single
Memories Are Made Of This	7"	Decca	F10684	1956	£2.50	£6	chart single
No.2	7" EP	Decca	DFE6514	1958	£5	£10	
Selection	7" EP	Decca	DFE6385	1956	£5	£10	

Shake Me I Rattle	7"	Decca	F10947	1957	£1.50	£4	
Story Of My Life	7"	Decca	F10973	1958	£1.50	£4	
You Can't Be True To Two	7"	Decca	F10720	1956	£2	£5	chart single

KING, DEE

Sally Go Round The Roses	7"	Piccadilly	7N35316	1966	£1.50	£4	

KING EARL BOOGIE BAND

Plastic Jesus	7"	Dawn	DNS1024	1972	£1.50	£4	
Starlight	7"	Dawn	DNS1028	1972	£1.50	£4	
Trouble At Mill	LP	Dawn	DNLS3040	1972	£5	£12	

KING FIGHTER

People Will Talk	7"	Jump Up	JU518	1967	£2.50	£6	

KING, FREDDIE

Bonanza Of Instrumentals	LP	King	(S)928	1965	£6	£15	US
Bossa Nova And Blues	LP	King	821	1962	£15	£30	US
Boy-Girl-Boy	LP	King	777	1962	£15	£30	US
Driving Sideways	7"	Sue	WI349	1965	£7.50	£15	
Freddie King Goes Surfin'	LP	King	(S)856	1963	£10	£25	US
Freddie King Is A Blues Master	LP	Atlantic	588186	1969	£8	£20	
Freddie King Sings The Blues	LP	King	762	1961	£17.50	£35	US
Getting Ready	LP	A&M	AMLS65004	1971	£5	£12	
Hide Away	LP	King	KS1059	1969	£6	£15	US
Hideaway	7"	Parlophone	R4777	1961	£7.50	£15	
His Early Years	LP	Polydor	2343047	1971	£4	£10	
King Of R&B Vol.2	LP	Polydor	2343009	1969	£5	£12	
Let's Hide Away And Dance Away	LP	King	773	1961	£17.50	£35	US
Live Performances Volume 1	LP	Black Bear	904	1972	£6	£15	
Live Performances Volume 2	LP	Black Bear	905	1972	£6	£15	
Play It Cool	7"	Atlantic	584235	1969	£2	£5	
Texas Cannonball	LP	A&M	AMLS68113	1972	£4	£10	
Twenty-Four Vocals And Instrumentals	LP	King	964	1966	£6	£15	US
Volume 1	LP	Python	KM5	1969	£8	£20	
Volume 2	LP	Python	KM7	1969	£8	£20	

KING GEORGE

I'm Gonna Be Somebody	7"	RCA	RCA1573	1967	£5	£10	

KING, HANK

Country And Western	7" EP	Starlite	GRK510	1966	£2.50	£6	
Country And Western	7" EP	Starlite	STEP41	1963	£5	£10	

KING, JAY W.

I'm So Afraid	7"	Stateside	SS505	1966	£10	£20	

KING, JONATHAN

Everyone's Gone To The Moon	7"	Decca	F12187	1965	£1.50	£4	chart single
Everyone's Gone To The Moon	7" EP	Decca	457090	1965	£6	£12	French
Or Then Again	LP	Decca	LK/SKL4908	1967	£4	£10	

KING KURT

America	7"	Polydor	KURTP1	1986	£1.50	£4	shaped pic disc
Banana Banana	7"	Stiff	BUY206	1984	£2	£5	shaped pic disc
Destination Zululand	7"	Stiff	BUY189	1983	£2.50	£6	shaped pic disc
Mack The Knife	7"	Stiff	BUY199	1984	£1.50	£4	pic disc
Mack The Knife	7"	Stiff	PBUY199	1984	£2	£5	shaped pic disc
Zulu Beat	7"	Thin Sliced	TSR2	1982	£2.50	£6	60& coloured vinyl sleeve combinations

KING, MARK

Clocks Go Forward	12"	Polydor	MKX2DJ	1984	£4	£10	promo
I Feel Free	7"	Polydor	MK1	1984	£2	£5	
I Feel Free	12"	Polydor	MKX1	1984	£2.50	£6	

KING, MARTIN LUTHER

Great March To Freedom	LP	Tamla Motown	TML11076	1968	£50	£100	
I Have A Dream	7"	Pama	PM732	1968	£4	£8	
In THe Struggle For Freedom	LP	Hallmark	CHM631	1968	£4	£10	

KING, NOSMO

Goodbye	7"	Pye	7N45383	1974	£2	£5	

KING OF MONTEGO BAY

Burn	7"	Blue Beat	BB322	1964	£5	£10	

KING OF THE SLUMS

Spider Psychiatry	7"	SLR	SLR001	1986	£5	£10	

KING, PAUL

Been In The Pen Too Long	LP	Dawn	DNLS3035	1972	£5	£12	

KING, PEE WEE

Bimbo	7"	HMV	7MC14	1954	£2	£5	export

KING PING MEH

Concrete	LP	Nova	628370	1975	£4	£10	Germa
King Ping Meh	LP	Polydor	2371259	1971	£20	£40	Germa
King Ping Meh 2	LP	Zebra	2944005	1972	£8	£20	Germa

King Ping Meh 3	LP	Zebra	2949011	1973	£8	£20	German
King Ping Meh 6	LP	Bacillus	BAC2046	1977	£4	£10	German
Virtues And Sins	LP	Nova	622015	1974	£4	£10	German

KING, RAMONA
It's In His Kiss	7"	Warner Bros	WB125	1964	£1.50	£4	

KING, REG
Reg King	LP	United Artists	UAS29157	1971	£15	£30	

KING ROCKY
King Is Back	7"	Studio One	SO2045	1968	£6	£12	Three Tops B side

KING, SAMMY
Great Balls Of Fire	7"	HMV	POP1285	1964	£4	£8	
Only You	7"	HMV	POP1384	1965	£1.50	£4	
Past Caring	7"	HMV	POP1540	1966	£1.50	£4	
Rag Doll	7"	HMV	POP1330	1964	£2	£5	

KING, SID & THE FIVE STRINGS
Booger Red	78	Philips	PB589	1956	£7.50	£15	

KING, SOLOMON
She Wears My Ring	LP	Columbia	SX/SCX6250	1968	£4	£10	
She Wears My Ring	7"	Columbia	DB8306	1967	£2	£5	
She Wears My Ring	7"	Columbia	DB8325	1967	£1.50	£4	
This Beautiful Day	7"	Columbia	DB8676	1970	£17.50	£35	chart single

KING SPORTY
D.J.Special	7"	Banana	BA323	1970	£2	£5	Richard & Mad B side
Inspiration	7"	Banana	BA321	1970	£2	£5	
Lover's Version	7"	Banana	BA322	1970	£2	£5	Dudley Sibley B side

KING STITT
Back Out Version	7"	Banana	BA332	1971	£2.50	£6	Vegetables B side
Herbsman Shuffle	7"	Clandisc	CLA207	1969	£2.50	£6	Higgs & Wilson B side
King Of Kings	7"	Clandisc	CLA223	1970	£2.50	£6	Dynamites B side
On The Street	7"	Clandisc	CLA203	1969	£2.50	£6	Cynthia Richards B side
Rhyming Time	7"	Banana	BA334	1971	£2.50	£6	
Vigerton Two	7"	Clandisc	CLA202	1969	£2.50	£6	

KING, TEDDI
Miss Teddi King With Ruby Braff	10" LP	Vogue	LDE142	1955	£25	£50	
Now In Vogue	LP	Vogue	VA160109	1957	£20	£40	

KING, TEDDY
Mexican Divorce	7"	Fab	FAB27	1967	£4	£8	Soul Tops B side

KINGDOM
Kingdom	LP	Speciality	2135	1970	£10	£25	US

KINGDOM COME
Galactic Zoo Dossier	LP	Polydor	2310130	1972	£6	£15	
Journey	LP	Polydor	2310254	1973	£6	£15	
Kingdom Come	LP	Polydor	2310178	1973	£6	£15	
Lost Ears	LP	Gull	GUD2003/4	1977	£6	£15	double

KINGDOMS
The record credited to Kingdoms marks the recording debut of Guy Chadwick, who was later to find much more success with his band the House Of Love.
Heartland	7"	Regard	RG114	1984	£2.50	£6	
Heartland	7"	Regard	RGT114	1984	£5	£10	

KINGLY BAND
Bitter And The Sweet	7"	Decca	F12926	1969	£2	£5	

KINGMAKER
Celebrated Working Man	7"	Sacred Heart	NONE1	1991	£5	£10	promo

KINGPINS
It Won't Be This Way Always	LP	King	865	1963	£8	£20	US
Ungaua	7"	London	HLU8658	1958	£6	£12	

KINGPINS (2)
Two Right Feet	7"	Oriole	CB1986	1965	£6	£12	

KING'S GALLIARD
Morning Dew	LP	Dolphin	DOLM5014	1976	£5	£12	Irish

KING'S HENCHMEN
Alan Freed Presents Vol.1	7" EP	Coral	FEP2025	1959	£40	£80	

KINGS IV
Some Like It Hot	7"	London	HLT8914	1959	£2	£5	

KINGSLEY, CHARLES CREATION
Summer Without Sun	7"	Columbia	DB7758	1965	£12.50	£25	

KINGSMEN
15 Great Hits	LP	Wand	WD(S)674	1966	£5	£12	US
Annie Fanny	7"	Pye	7N25322	1965	£2.50	£6	

Title	Format	Label	Catalogue	Year	Price	Price	Notes
Climb	7"	Pye	7N25311	1965	£4	£8	
Climb	7" EP.	Vogue	INT18015	1965	£6	£12	French
Daytime Shadows	7"	Pye	7N25406	1967	£5	£10	
Death Of An Angel	7"	Pye	7N25273	1964	£4	£8	
Fever	7" EP.	Pye	NEP44063	1966	£5	£10	
Gamma Goochee	7" EP.	Vogue	INT18065	1966	£6	£12	French
Greatest Hits	LP	Marble Arch	MAL829	1968	£4	£10	
How To Stuff A Wild Bikini	7" EP.	Vogue	INT18025	1965	£6	£12	French
In Person	LP	Wand	WD(S)657	1964	£6	£15	US
Jolly Green Giant	7"	Pye	7N25292	1965	£4	£8	
Killer Joe	7"	Pye	7N25370	1966	£5	£10	
Kingsmen	7" EP.	Pye	NEP44023	1964	£4	£8	
Little Latin Lupe Lu	7"	Pye	7N25262	1964	£4	£8	
Little Latin Lupe Lu	7" EP.	Vogue	EPL8273	1964	£6	£12	French
Louie Louie	7"	Pye	7N25231	1963	£4	£8	chart single
Louie Louie	7"	Pye	7N25366	1966	£2	£5	
Louie Louie	7" EP.	Vogue	EPL8172	1963	£6	£12	French, B side by Jocko Henderson
Mojo Workout	7" EP.	Pye	NEP44040	1965	£6	£12	
Money	7" EP.	Vogue	EPL8209	1964	£6	£12	French
On Campus	LP	Pye	NPL28068	1965	£5	£12	
Volume II	LP	Pye	NPL28054	1964	£6	£15	
Volume III	LP	Wand	WD(S)662	1965	£5	£12	US

KINGSMEN (2)

Title	Format	Label	Catalogue	Year	Price	Price	Notes
Better Believe It	7"	London	HLE8735	1958	£7.50	£15	
Conga Rock	7"	London	HLE8812	1959	£10	£20	
Weekend	7" EP.	London	REE1211	1959	£17.50	£35	

KINGSTON, JOE

Title	Format	Label	Catalogue	Year	Price	Price
Time Is On My Friends	7"	Blue Beat	BB253	1964	£5	£10

KINGSTON PETE

Title	Format	Label	Catalogue	Year	Price	Price
Little Boy Blue	7"	Blue Beat	BB403	1965	£5	£10

KINGSTON TRIO

The Kingston Trio were enormously popular in America, their harmonised approach to folk music inspiring many future rock stars to begin their careers in music. The line of influence leads from the Kingston Trio to Haight-Asbury, to the music of Jefferson Airplane and the Grateful Dead, and from there to the entire sound of modern AOR. John Stewart was a member of the Kingston Trio on the later releases.

Title	Format	Label	Catalogue	Year	Price	Price	Notes
Aspen Gold	LP	Nautilus	NR2	1979	£6	£15	US audiophile
Encores	LP	Capitol	(S)T1612	1961	£4	£10	
Folk Era	LP	Capitol	(S)T2180	1964	£6	£15	
From The Hungry i	LP	Capitol	T1107	1959	£5	£12	
Goin' Places	LP	Capitol	(S)T1564	1961	£4	£10	
Greenback Dollar	7"	Capitol	CL15287	1963	£1.50	£4	
Greenback Dollar	7" EP.	Capitol	EAP120460	1963	£2	£5	
Here We Go Again Part 1	7" EP.	Capitol	EAP11258	1960	£2	£5	
Here We Go Again Part 2	7" EP.	Capitol	EAP21258	1960	£2	£5	
Here We Go Again Part 3	7" EP.	Capitol	EAP31258	1960	£2	£5	
Kingston Trio	LP	Capitol	T996	1958	£6	£15	
Kingston Trio	7" EP.	Brunswick	OE9511	1965	£4	£8	
Lemon Tree	7" EP.	Capitol	EAP120655	1964	£2	£5	
Make Way!	LP	Capitol	(S)T1474	1961	£4	£10	
M.T.A.	7" EP.	Capitol	EAP11119	1959	£2	£5	
Raspberries Strawberries	7" EP.	Capitol	EAP11182	1959	£2	£5	
Scarlet Ribbons	7"	Capitol	CL14918	1958	£1.50	£4	
Stereo Concert	LP	Capitol	ST1183	1959	£6	£15	
String Along	LP	Capitol	(S)T1397	1960	£4	£10	
Time To Think	7" EP.	Capitol	EAP42011	1962	£2	£5	
Tom Dooley	7"	Capitol	CL14951	1958	£1.50	£4	chart single
Tom Dooley	7" EP.	Capitol	EAP11136	1959	£2	£5	
Where Have All The Flowers Gone	7"	Capitol	CL15242	1962	£1.50	£4	
Worried Man	7" EP.	Capitol	EAP11322	1960	£2	£5	

KINGSTONIANS

Title	Format	Label	Catalogue	Year	Price	Price
Fun Galore	7"	Doctor Bird	DB1126	1968	£5	£10
I Need You	7"	Trojan	TR770	1969	£2	£5
Mix It Up	7"	Trojan	TR627	1968	£2.50	£6
Mother Miserable	7"	Coxsone	CS7066	1968	£5	£10
Mummy And Daddy	7"	Doctor Bird	DB1123	1968	£5	£10
Nice Nice	7"	Big Shot	BI526	1969	£2.50	£6
Put Down Your Fire	7"	Doctor Bird	DB1120	1968	£5	£10
Sufferer	LP	Trojan	TBL113	1970	£5	£12
Sufferer	7"	Big Shot	BI508	1968	£4	£8
Winey Winey	7"	Rio	R140	1967	£4	£8

KINKS

The Kinks' long career is shot through with many collectors' items, although the majority of these come from the early, hit-making years. All the original Pye albums are becoming increasingly scarce, although their value is held down by the Kinks being seemingly irredeemably out of fashion. The original pressing of "Village Green Preservation Society" was withdrawn and replaced with a version containing more tracks, but the shorter album does contain one or two different mixes. The American compilations, "Kink Kronikles" and "The Great Lost Kinks Album", are highly sought after in the UK as they contain many tracks that are not otherwise available. Meanwhile, no Kinks records have sold as few copies as the first two singles, "Long Tall Sally" and "You Still Want Me" - most copies appearing on the market are likely, therefore, to be demos.

Title	Format	Label	Catalogue	Year	Price	Price	Notes
All Day And All Of The Night	7"	Pye	7N15714	1964	£1.50	£4	chart single
All Day And All Of The Night	7" EP.	Pye	PNV24127	1964	£10	£20	French
All The Good Times	LP	Pye	IIPP100	1973	£20	£40	4 LPs, boxed
Apeman	7"	Pye	7N45016	1970	£1.50	£4	chart single
Arthur	LP	Pye	NPL18317	1969	£8	£20	mono
Arthur	LP	Pye	NSPL18317	1969	£6	£15	
Autumn Almanac	7"	Pye	7N17400	1967	£1.50	£4	chart single

Title	Format	Label	Catalogue	Year	Price	Price	Notes
Autumn Almanac/David Watts	7"	Pye	7N17405	1967	£12.50	£25	export
Celluloid Heroes	7"	RCA	RCA2299	1972	£1.50	£4	
Dandy	7" EP	Pye	PNV24177	1966	£7.50	£15	French
Days	7"	Pye	7N17573	1968	£1.50	£4	chart single
Dead End Street	7"	Pye	7N17222	1966	£1.50	£4	chart single
Dead End Street	7" EP	Pye	PNV24184	1966	£7.50	£15	French
Dedicated Follower Of Fashion	7"	Pye	7N17064	1966	£1.50	£4	chart single
Dedicated Follower Of Fashion	7" EP	Pye	PNV24167	1966	£7.50	£15	French
Dedicated Kinks	7" EP	Pye	NEP24258	1966	£20	£40	
Drivin'	7"	Pye	7N17776	1969	£1.50	£4	
Ducks On The Wall	7"	RCA	RCA2546	1975	£1.50	£4	
Everybody's Gonna Be Happy	7"	Pye	7N15813	1965	£1.50	£4	chart single
Everybody's In Showbiz	LP	RCA	DPS2035	1972	£6	£15	double
Face To Face	LP	Pye	NPL18149	1966	£6	£15	chart LP
Face To Face	LP	Pye	NSPL18149	1966	£10	£25	stereo
Give The People What They Want	LP	Arista	AL9567	1981	£4	£10	US, different mixes
Give The People What They Want	LP	Arista	SPART1171	1981	£8	£20	test pressing, US stock
God's Children	7"	Pye	7N8001	1971	£5	£10	export
Got Love If You Want It	7" EP	Pye	PNV24131	1964	£25	£50	French
Great Lost Kinks Album	LP	Reprise	MS2172	1973	£20	£40	US
Greatest Hits	LP	PRT	KINK1	1983	£5	£12	with 10' LP (Dead End Street)
Greatest Hits	LP	Reprise	R(S)6217	1966	£5	£12	US
Holiday Romance	7"	RCA	RCA2478	1974	£1.50	£4	
How Are You	7"	Music Week		1986	£2	£5	promo
Kinda Kinks	LP	Pye	NPL18112	1965	£6	£15	chart LP
Kinda Kinks	LP	Reprise	R(S)6173	1965	£6	£15	US
Kink Kronikles	LP	Reprise	RS6454	1972	£15	£30	US
Kinks	LP	Pye	NPL18096	1964	£6	£15	chart LP
Kinks	LP	Pye	NPL18326	1970	£6	£15	double
Kinks	LP	Pye	NSPL83021	1964	£37.50	£75	stereo
Kinks	7" EP	Pye	AMEP1001	1975	£5	£10	export, red or blue vinyl
Kinks' Kinkdom	LP	Reprise	R(S)6185	1965	£6	£15	US
Kinks Kontroversy	LP	Pye	NPL18131	1966	£6	£15	chart LP
Kinksize	LP	Reprise	R(S)6158	1965	£6	£15	US
Kinksize Hits	7" EP	Pye	NEP24203	1964	£5	£10	
Kinksize Session	7" EP	Pye	NEP24200	1964	£5	£10	
Kwyet Kinks	7" EP	Pye	NEP24221	1965	£6	£12	
Live At Kelvin Hall	LP	Pye	NPL18191	1967	£6	£15	
Live At Kelvin Hall	LP	Pye	NSPL18191	1967	£8	£20	stereo
Lola	7"	Pye	7N17961	1970	£1.50	£4	chart single
Lola vs Powerman	LP	Pye	NSPL18359	1970	£6	£10	
Long Tall Sally	7"	Pye	7N15611	1964	£17.50	£35	
Low Budget Interview	LP	Arista	SP69	1979	£8	£20	US promo
Mirror Of Love	7"	RCA	RCA5015	1974	£1.50	£4	
Mirror Of Love	7"	RCA	RCA5042	1974	£1.50	£4	
Misfits	LP	Mobile Fidelity	MFSL1070	1981	£4	£10	US audiophile
Mister Pleasant	7" EP	Pye	PNV24191	1967	£7.50	£15	French
Mr.Pleasant	7"	Pye	7N17314	1967	£12.50	£25	export
Muswell Hillbillies	LP	RCA	SF8423	1971	£5	£12	
No More Looking Back	7"	RCA	RCM1	1976	£1.50	£4	
Percy	LP	Pye	NSPL18365	1971	£5	£12	
Percy	7"	Pye	7NX8001	1971	£1.50	£4	
Percy	7"	Pye	7NX8001	1971	£2	£5	PS
Plastic Man	7"	Pye	7N17724	1969	£1.50	£4	chart single
Predictable	7"	Arista	ARIPD426	1981	£1.50	£4	pic disc
Preservation Act 1	LP	RCA	SF8392	1973	£4	£10	
Preservation Act 2	LP	RCA	5040	1974	£6	£15	double
See My Friend	7"	Pye	7N15919	1965	£1.50	£4	chart single
Set Me Free	7"	Pye	7N15854	1965	£1.50	£4	chart single
Shangri-La	7"	Pye	7N17812	1969	£1.50	£4	
Shangri-La/Last Of The Steam Powered Trains	7"	Pye	7N17812	1969	£37.50	£75	demo
Sitting In The Midday Sun	7"	RCA	RCA2387	1973	£1.50	£4	
Something Else	LP	Pye	NPL18193	1967	£8	£20	chart LP
Something Else	LP	Pye	NSPL18193	1967	£10	£25	stereo
Something Else	7" EP	Pye	NEP24296	1968	£75	£150	
Sunny Afternoon	7"	Pye	7N17125	1966	£1.50	£4	chart single
Sunny Afternoon	7" EP	Pye	PNV24173	1966	£7.50	£15	French, R.Davies,Quaife facing left on sleeve
Sunny Afternoon	7" EP	Pye	PNV24173	1966	£10	£20	French, R.Davies,Quaife facing right on sleeve
Supersonic Rocket Ship	7"	RCA	RCA2211	1972	£1.50	£4	chart single
Sweet Lady Genevieve	7"	RCA	RCA2418	1973	£1.50	£4	
Then, Now And In Between	LP	Reprise	PRO328	1969	£100	£200	US, boxed with various items of memorabilia
Till The End Of The Day	7"	Pye	7N15981	1965	£1.50	£4	chart single
Till The End Of The Day	7" EP	Pye	PNV24160	1965	£7.50	£15	French
Tired Of Waiting For You	7"	Pye	7N15759	1965	£1.50	£4	chart single
Tired Of Waiting For You	7" EP	Pye	PNV24132	1965	£12.50	£25	French
Victoria	7"	Pye	7N17865	1969	£1.50	£4	chart single
Village Green Preservation Society	LP	Pye	N(S)PL18233	1967	£75	£150	12 tracks
Village Green Preservation Society	LP	Pye	N(S)PL18233	1968	£6	£15	
Vol.5	7" EP	Pye	PNV24140	1965	£10	£20	French
Waterloo Sunset	7"	Pye	7N17321	1967	£1.50	£4	chart single
Waterloo Sunset	7" EP	Pye	PNV24194	1967	£7.50	£15	French

Well Respected Man	7"	Pye	7N17100	1966	£12.50	£25	expo
Well Respected Man	7" EP.	Pye	PNV24151	1965	£7.50	£15	Frenc
Wonderboy	7"	Pye	7N17468	1968	£1.50	£4	chart singl
You Can't Stop The Music	7"	RCA	RCA2567	1975	£1.50	£4	
You Really Got Me	LP	Reprise	R(S)6143	1965	£6	£15	U!
You Really Got Me	7"	PRT	KBD1	1983	£2	£5	pic dis
You Really Got Me	7"	Pye	7N15673	1964	£1.50	£4	chart singl
You Still Want Me	7"	Pye	7N15636	1964	£37.50	£75	

KINSEY, TONY

Foursome	7" EP.	Parlophone	SGE2008	195-	£5	£10	
How To Succeed	LP	Decca	LK4534	1963	£8	£20	
Jazz At The Flamingo Session	LP	Decca	LK4207	1957	£15	£30	
Presenting The Tony Kinsey Quartet No.1	7" EP.	Decca	DFE6282	1956	£5	£10	
Presenting The Tony Kinsey Quartet No.2	7" EP.	Decca	DFE6283	1956	£5	£10	
Red Bird - Jazz And Poetry	7" EP.	Parlophone	SGE2004	195-	£5	£10	
Time Gentlemen Please	LP	Decca	LK4274	1959	£6	£15	
Tony Kinsey Quintet	LP	Decca	LK4186	1957	£10	£25	

KINSMEN

Glasshouse Green Splinter Red	7"	Decca	F22724	1968	£5	£10	
It's Good To See You	7"	Decca	F22777	1968	£4	£8	

KIPPINGTON LODGE

There was a time when Nick Lowe was not a feature of the rock music scene, although it does not seem like it! His career actually begins her as singer and bass player for the group that was later renamed after the guitarist, Brinsley Schwarz.

In My Life	7"	Parlophone	R5776	1969	£10	£20	
Kippington Lodge	7" EP.	EMI	NUT2894	1978	£2	£5	
Rumours	7"	Parlophone	R5677	1968	£7.50	£15	
Shy Boy	7"	Parlophone	R5645	1967	£7.50	£15	
Tell Me A Story	7"	Parlophone	R5717	1968	£7.50	£15	
Tomorrow Today	7"	Parlophone	R5750	1968	£10	£20	

KIRBY

Bottom Line	7"	Hot Wax	WAX1	1978	£2.50	£6	
Composition	LP	Hot Wax	HW2	1978	£30	£60	
Love Letters	7"	Anchor	ANC1031	1976	£4	£8	

KIRBY, KATHY

Best Of Kathy Kirby	LP	Ace Of Clubs	ACL1235	1968	£4	£10	
Big Man	7"	Decca	F11506	1962	£1.50	£4	
Come Back Here With My Heart	7"	Columbia	DB8521	1969	£2	£5	
Dance On	7"	Decca	F11682	1963	£1.50	£4	chart sing
Do You Really Have A Heart	7"	Columbia	DB8910	1972	£2.50	£6	
I Almost Called Your Name	7"	Columbia	DB8400	1968	£2	£5	
I'll Catch The Sun	7"	Columbia	DB8559	1969	£2	£5	
In All The World	7"	Columbia	DB8192	1967	£1.50	£4	
Is That All There Is?	7"	Columbia	DB8634	1969	£2	£5	
Kathy Kirby	7" EP.	Decca	DFE8547	1963	£2	£5	
Kathy Kirby Vol.2	7" EP.	Decca	DFE8596	1965	£2	£5	
Let Me Go Lover	7"	Decca	F11832	1964	£1.50	£4	chart sing
Little Song For You	7"	Columbia	DB8965	1973	£2.50	£6	
Love Can Be	7"	Pye	7N15313	1960	£1.50	£4	
Make Someone Happy	LP	Decca	LK4746	1966	£5	£12	
My Thanks To You	LP	Columbia	SX/SCX6259	1968	£30	£60	
My Way	7"	Columbia	DB8721	1970	£2.50	£6	
No One's Gonna Hurt You Any More	7"	Columbia	DB8139	1967	£1.50	£4	
Secret Love	7"	Decca	F11759	1963	£1.50	£4	chart sing
Singer With The Band	7"	Orange	OAS216	1973	£1.50	£4	
Sings Sixteen Hits From Stars And Garters	LP	Decca	LK4575	1963	£4	£10	
So Here I Go	7"	Columbia	DB8795	1971	£2.50	£6	
Song For Europe	7" EP.	Decca	DFE8611	1965	£2	£5	
Turn Around	7"	Columbia	DB8302	1967	£1.50	£4	
Wheel Of Fortune	7"	Columbia	DB8682	1969	£2	£5	
You're The One	7"	Decca	F11892	1964	£1.50	£4	chart sing

KIRBY, LARRY & THE ENCORES

My Baby Don't Love Me	7"	Top Rank	JAR143	1959	£1.50	£4	

KIRCHIN BAND

Ivor & Basil Kirchin Band	7" EP.	Parlophone	GEP8569	1956	£5	£10	
Kirchin Bandbox	7" EP.	Parlophone	GEP8531	1955	£4	£8	
Mambo Macoco	7"	Parlophone	MSP6144	1954	£1.50	£4	
Mother Goose Jumps	7"	Decca	F10434	1955	£2	£5	
Rock Around The World	7"	Parlophone	R4266	1957	£2	£5	
Rockin' And Rollin'	7"	Parlophone	R4237	1956	£2.50	£6	
Roller	7"	Parlophone	R4222	1956	£1.50	£4	

KIRK, DEE

I'll Cry	7"	Salvo	SLO1809	1962	£5	£10	

KIRK, ROLAND

Domino	LP	Mercury	MCL20045	1965	£5	£12	
Hip!	LP	Fontana	FJL114	1965	£4	£10	
I Talk With The Spirits	LP	Mercury	(S)LML4005	1966	£4	£10	
Kirk In Copenhagen	LP	Mercury	MCL20021	1964	£5	£12	
Kirk's Work	LP	Esquire	32164	1962	£8	£20	with Jack McD
Meets The Benny Golson Orchestra	LP	Mercury	20002MCL	1964	£5	£12	

Meets The Benny Golson Orchestra	7" EP..	Mercury	10015MCE	1964	£2	£5	
Natural Black Inventions: Root Strata	LP	Atlantic	2400164	1971	£4	£10	
Rip, Rig And Panic	LP	Mercury	(S)LML4015	1965	£4	£10	
Roland Speaks	7" EP..	Mercury	10016MCE	1965	£2	£5	
Slightly Latin	LP	Mercury	(S)LML4019	1967	£4	£10	
We Free Kings	LP	Mercury	MCL20037	1965	£4	£10	
We Free Kings	LP	Mercury	MMC14126	1963	£6	£15	

KIRKBYS

It's A Crime	7"	RCA	RCA1542	1966	£15	£30	

KIRKPATRICK, JOHN

Plain Capers	LP	Free Reed	FRR010	1976	£5	£12	

KIRKPATRICK, JOHN & SUE HARRIS

Jump At The Sun	LP	Trailer	LER2033	1972	£8	£20	
Rose Of Britain's Isle	LP	Topic	12TS247	1974	£5	£12	

KIRSCH, JULIAN

Clever Little Man	7"	Columbia	DB8541	1969	£2.50	£6	

KISS

2000 Man	7"	Casablanca	NB1001	1980	£5	£10	
2000 Man	12"	Casablanca	NBL1001	1980	£3	£8	No PS
Alive	LP	Casablanca	CALD5001	1977	£20	£40	red vinyl double
Alive	LP	Casablanca	CBC4011/2	1976	£5	£12	double
Alive Vol.11	LP	Casablanca	CALD5004	1977	£5	£12	double
Alive Vol.11	LP	Casablanca	CALD5004	1977	£8	£20	double, with booklet
Animalize	LP	Phonogram	PIC8224951	1984	£4	£10	pic disc
Asylum	LP	Mercury	PIC8260991	1989	£4	£10	pic disc
Beth	7"	Casablanca	CBX519	1976	£6	£12	
Creatures Of The Night	7"	Casablanca	PIC6302219	1982	£4	£10	pic disc
Creatures Of The Night	7"	Casablanca	KISS4	1983	£1.50	£4	chart single
Creatures Of The Night	12"	Casablanca	KISS412	1982	£4	£10	
Creatures Of The Night	12"	Casablanca	KISSD4	1982	£6	£15	1 sided, double groove, etched autographs
Destroyer	LP	Casablanca	CAL2009	1977	£17.50	£35	red vinyl
Destroyer	LP	Casablanca	PIC6399064	1982	£4	£10	pic disc
Double Platinum	LP	Casablanca	CALD5005	1978	£5	£12	double
Dressed To Kill	LP	Casablanca	CAL2008	1977	£17.50	£35	red vinyl
Dressed To Kill	LP	Casablanca	CBC4004	1975	£5	£12	
Dynasty	LP	Casablanca	CALH2051	1979	£17.50	£35	red vinyl
Dynasty	LP	Casablanca	PIC9128024	1982	£4	£10	pic disc
Elder	LP	Casablanca	PIC6302163	1981	£4	£10	pic disc
Hard Luck Woman	7"	Casablanca	CAN102	1977	£1.50	£4	
Hard Luck Woman	7"	Casablanca	CAN102	1977	£7.50	£15	PS
Hotter Than Hell	LP	Casablanca	CAL2007	1977	£17.50	£35	red vinyl
Hotter Than Hell	LP	Casablanca	PIC6399058	1982	£4	£10	pic disc
I Was Made For Lovin' You	7"	Casablanca	CAN152	1979	£1.50	£4	chart single
I Was Made For Lovin' You	12"	Casablanca	CANL152	1979	£5	£12	
Killer	7"	Casablanca	KISS3	1982	£4	£8	
Killer	12"	Casablanca	KISS312	1982	£5	£12	
Killers	LP	Casablanca	PIC6302193	1982	£4	£10	pic disc
Kiss	LP	Casablanca	CAL2006	1977	£17.50	£35	red vinyl
Kiss	LP	Casablanca	CBC4003	1975	£5	£12	
Kiss	LP	Casablanca	PIC6399057	1982	£4	£10	pic disc
Let's Put The X In Sex	12"	Vertigo	KIZZA2	1988	£2.50	£6	promo
Lick It Up	LP	Mercury	PIC8142971	1989	£4	£10	pic disc
Lick It Up	7"	Vertigo	KISSP5	1983	£2.50	£6	poster sleeve
Lick It Up	7"	Vertigo	KPIC5	1983	£10	£20	shaped sleeve
Love Gun	LP	Casablanca	CALH2017	1977	£17.50	£35	red vinyl
Love Gun	LP	Casablanca	CALH2017	1977	£5	£12	with card gun and inner sleeve
Love Gun	LP	Casablanca	PIC6399063	1982	£4	£10	pic disc
Nothin' To Lose	7"	Casablanca	CBX503	1975	£10	£20	
Originals	LP	Casablanca	NBLP7032	1976	£25	£50	US, 3 LP set with inserts
Rock And Roll All Nite	7"	Casablanca	CAN126	1978	£7.50	£15	PS
Rock And Roll All Nite	7"	Casablanca	CBX510	1975	£7.50	£15	
Rock And Roll Over	LP	Casablanca	CALH2001	1977	£17.50	£35	red vinyl
Rock and Roll Over	LP	Casablanca	PIC6399060	1982	£4	£10	pic disc
Rocket Ride	7"	Casablanca	CAN117	1978	£2	£5	
Rocket Ride	12"	Casablanca	CANL117	1977	£2.50	£6	
Shout It Out Loud	7"	Casablanca	CBX516	1976	£5	£10	
Smashes, Thrashes And Hits	LP	Mercury	8368871	1988	£5	£12	US pic disc, gatefold sleeve
Talk To Me	7"	Mercury	MER19	1980	£2.50	£6	
Then She Kissed Me	7"	Casablanca	CAN110	1977	£4	£8	
Then She Kissed Me	12"	Casablanca	CANL110	1977	£3	£8	
Unmasked	LP	Mercury	PIC6302032	1980	£4	£10	pic disc
What Makes The World Go Round	7"	Mercury	KISS1	1980	£2.50	£6	
World Without Heroes	7"	Casablanca	KISS2	1981	£1.50	£4	
World Without Heroes	7"	Casablanca	KISSP2	1982	£2.50	£6	pic disc

KISS - ACE FREHLEY

Ace Frehley	LP	Casablanca	NBLP7121	1978	£6	£15	US with poster & paper
Ace Frehley	LP	Casablanca	NBPIX7121	1978	£8	£20	pic disc
New York Groove	7"	Casablanca	CAN135	1979	£5	£10	

Title	Format	Label	Cat No	Year			Notes
New York Groove	7"	Casablanca	CAN135	1979	£12.50	£25	with mask, blue vinyl

KISS - GENE SIMMONS

Title	Format	Label	Cat No	Year			Notes
Gene Simmons	LP	Casablanca	NBLP7120	1978	£6	£15	US with poster & paper
Radioactive	7"	Casablanca	CAN134	1979	£4	£8	
Radioactive	7"	Casablanca	CAN134	1979	£7.50	£15	with mask, red vinyl
To Ace, Paul & Peter	LP	Casablanca	NBPIX7120	1978	£8	£20	pic disc

KISS - PAUL STANLEY

Title	Format	Label	Cat No	Year			Notes
Hold Me Touch Me	7"	Casablanca	CAN140	1979	£4	£8	
Hold Me, Touch Me	7"	Casablanca	CAN140	1979	£7.50	£15	with mask, purple vinyl
Paul Stanley	LP	Casablanca	NBLP7123	1978	£6	£15	US with poster & paper
To Ace, Gene & Peter	LP	Casablanca	NBPIX7123	1978	£8	£20	pic disc

KISS - PETER CRISS

Title	Format	Label	Cat No	Year			Notes
Peter Criss	LP	Casablanca	NBLP7122	1978	£6	£15	US with poster & paper
To Ace, Paul & Gene	LP	Casablanca	NBPIX7122	1978	£8	£20	pic disc
You Matter To Me	7"	Casablanca	CAN139	1979	£7.50	£15	with mask, green viny

KIT KATS

Title	Format	Label	Cat No	Year			Notes
Do Their Thing Live	LP	Jamie	LPM/LPS3032	1967	£6	£15	US
It's Just A Matter Of Time	LP	Jamie	LPM/LPS3029	1966	£6	£15	US
That's The Way	7"	London	HLW10075	1966	£1.50	£4	

KITCHEN CINQ

Title	Format	Label	Cat No	Year			Notes
Everything But	LP	LHI	12000	1967	£6	£15	US

KITCHENS OF DISTINCTION

Title	Format	Label	Cat No	Year			Notes
Last Gasp Death Shuffle	7"	Gold Rush	GRR3	1987	£4	£8	

KITT, EARTHA

Title	Format	Label	Cat No	Year			Notes
Bad But Beautiful	LP	MGM	C878	1962	£4	£10	
Bad But Beautiful No.1	7" EP	MGM	MGMEP772	1963	£2	£5	
Bad But Beautiful No.2	7" EP	MGM	MGMEP774	1963	£2	£5	
Bad But Beautiful No.3	7" EP	MGM	MGMEP777	1963	£2	£5	
C'Est Si Bon	7"	HMV	7M288	1955	£2	£5	
Diamonds Are A Girl's Best Friend	7"	MGM	SP1178	1956	£1.50	£4	
Down To Eartha	LP	RCA	RD27084	1958	£4	£10	
Down To Eartha	10" LP	HMV	DLP1087	1955	£5	£12	
Eartha Kitt	7" EP	HMV	7EG8258	1957	£2	£5	
Eartha Kitt Revisited	7" EP	London	RER1266	1960	£2	£5	
Easy Does It	7"	HMV	7M246	1954	£2	£5	
Fabulous	LP	London	HAR2207/ SHR6058	1960	£4	£10	
Honolulu Rock-a-Roll-a	7"	HMV	7M422	1956	£6	£12	
I Want To Be Evil	7"	RCA	RCA1093	1958	£1.50	£4	
Just An Old Fashioned Girl	7"	HMV	POP309	1957	£2	£5	
Just An Old Fashioned Girl	7"	RCA	RCA1087	1958	£1.50	£4	
Let's Do It	7"	HMV	7M234	1954	£2	£5	
Love Is A Gamble	7"	London	HLR8969	1959	£2	£5	
Monotonous	7"	HMV	7M282	1955	£2	£5	
Please Do It	7"	MGM	SP1153	1956	£1.50	£4	
Revisited	LP	London	HAR2296/ SHR6107	1960	£4	£10	
Saint Louis Blues	7" EP	RCA	SRC7009	1959	£2.50	£6	
Somebody Bad Stole De Wedding Bell	7"	HMV	7M198	1954	£2	£5	
St.Louis Blues	LP	RCA	RD27076	1958	£4	£10	
That Bad Eartha	LP	RCA	RD27067	1958	£4	£10	
That Bad Eartha	10" LP	HMV	DLP1067	1955	£5	£12	
That Blue Eartha	7" EP	RCA	SRC7015	1959	£2.50	£6	
That's The Way	7"	London	HL7119	1963	£2	£5	expo
There Is No Cure For L'Amour	7"	HMV	POP346	1957	£1.50	£4	
Thursday's Child	LP	HMV	CLP1104	1957	£5	£12	
Thursday's Child	7"	RCA	RD27099	1959	£4	£10	
Under The Bridges Of Paris	7"	HMV	7M191	1954	£4	£8	chart singl

KLAN

Title	Format	Label	Cat No	Year			Notes
Fify The Fly	7" EP	Palette	22029	1967	£7.50	£15	Frenc
Stop Little Girl	7" EP	Palette	22024	1967	£7.50	£15	Frenc

KLEIN, ALAN

Title	Format	Label	Cat No	Year			Notes
Age Of Corruption	7"	Parlophone	R5370	1965	£2	£5	
Honey Pie	7"	Page One	POF119	1969	£2.50	£6	
It Ain't Worth The Lonely Road	7"	Parlophone	R5292	1965	£2	£5	
Striped Purple Shirt	7"	Oriole	CB1719	1962	£6	£12	
Three Coins In The Sewer	7"	Oriole	CB1737	1962	£6	£12	

KLEINOW, SNEAKY PETE

Title	Format	Label	Cat No	Year			Notes
Sneaky Pete	LP	Shiloh	SLP4086	1970	£5	£12	U

KLF

Title	Format	Label	Cat No	Year			Notes
3 am Eternal	12"	KLF	KLF005R	1991	£2.50	£6	stickered P
3 am Eternal (Live At The S.S.L.)	12"	KLF	KLF005S	1991	£2.50	£6	white lab
3 am Eternal (Xmas Top Of The Pops Version)	12"	KLF	KLF005TOTP	1992	£20	£40	
America	7"	KLF	PUB1	199-	£7.50	£15	prom

Title	Format	Label	Catalogue	Year	Price	Price	Notes
America: What Time Is January	12"	KLF	92PROMO2	1992	£20	£40	1 sided white label
America: What Time Is Love	12"	KLF	92PROMO1	1992	£2.50	£6	white label
Burn The Beat II	7"	KLF	KLF002	1988	£1.50	£4	
Burn The Beat II	12"	KLF	KLF002T	1988	£5	£12	
Chill Out	LP	KLF	JAMSLP5	1989	£6	£15	
Chill Out	CD	KLF	JAMSCD5	1989	£10	£25	
Justified And Ancient	12"	KLF	USA4X	1992	£15	£30	pic disc
Justified And Ancient (All Bound For Mu Mu Land)	12"	KLF	CHOICE1	1991	£4	£10	white label
Justified And Ancient (Anti-Acapella Version)	12"	KLF	CHOICE3	1991	£20	£40	1 sided white label
Justified And Ancient (Stand By The JAMS)	12"	KLF	CHOICE2	1991	£4	£10	white label
Kylie In A Trance	12"	KLF	KLF010RR	1989	£15	£30	
Kylie Said To Jason	CD-s	KLF	KLF010CD	1989	£4	£10	
Kylie Said To Jason	7"	KLF	KLF010	1989	£1.50	£4	
Kylie Said To Jason	12"	KLF	KLF010P	1989	£3	£8	with poster
Kylie Said To Jason	12"	KLF	KLF010T	1989	£2.50	£6	
Kylie Said To Jason (Trance Kylie Express)	12"	KLF	KLF010R	1989	£6	£15	
Last Train To Trancentral (Remixes)	12"	KLF	KLF008R	1989	£8	£20	
Make It Rain	12"	KLF	LPPROMO1	1988	£6	£15	promo
What Time Is Love?	CD-s	KLF	KLF004CD	1990	£2.50	£6	
What Time Is Love ('89 Primal Remix)	12"	KLF	KLF004R	1989	£6	£15	
What Time Is Love (Live At Trancentral)	12"	KLF	KLF004P	1989	£15	£30	promo
What Time Is Love? (Live At Trancentral)	12"	KLF	KLF004X	1990	£6	£15	
What Time Is Love (Moody Boys vs The KLF)	12"	KLF	KLF004Y	1990	£2.50	£6	
What Time Is Love Story	LP	KLF	JAMSLP4	1989	£10	£25	
What Time Is Love Story	CD	KLF	JAMSCD4	1989	£15	£30	
What Time Is Love (Trance Mix)	12"	KLF	KLF004T	1989	£5	£12	
White Room	LP	KLF	JAMSLP6	1989	£4	£10	
White Room	CD	KLF	JAMSCD6	1989	£6	£15	

KLINGER, TONY & MICHAEL LYONS

Title	Format	Label	Catalogue	Year	Price	Price
Extreems	LP	Deram	SML1095	1971	£6	£15

KLINT, PETER

Title	Format	Label	Catalogue	Year	Price	Price
Walkin' Proud	7"	Mercury	MF997	1966	£5	£10

KLOOGER, ANNETTE

Title	Format	Label	Catalogue	Year	Price	Price
Magic Touch	7"	Decca	F10733	1956	£1.50	£4
Mama Teach Me To Dance	7"	Decca	F10776	1956	£1.50	£4
Rock And Roll Waltz	7"	Decca	F10701	1956	£2	£5
Why Do Fools Fall In Love	7"	Decca	F10738	1956	£2	£5
Wisdom Of A Fool	7"	Decca	F10844	1957	£1.50	£4

KNACK

Title	Format	Label	Catalogue	Year	Price	Price	Notes
Did You Ever Have To Make Up Your Mind	7"	Piccadilly	7N35315	1966	£2.50	£6	
I'm Aware	7" EP	Capitol	EAP120923	1966	£7.50	£15	French
It's Love Baby	7"	Decca	F12278	1965	£10	£20	
Marriage Guidance And Advice Bureau	7"	Piccadilly	7N35367	1967	£2.50	£6	
Save All My Love For Joey	7"	Piccadilly	7N35347	1966	£2.50	£6	
Stop!	7"	Piccadilly	7N35322	1966	£2.50	£6	
Who'll Be The Next In Line	7"	Decca	F12234	1965	£10	£20	

KNACKS

Title	Format	Label	Catalogue	Year	Price	Price	Notes
Baby	7" EP	Barclay	70857	1965	£6	£12	French

KNICKERBOCKERS

Title	Format	Label	Catalogue	Year	Price	Price	Notes
Can You Help Me	7"	London	HLH10102	1967	£5	£10	
Fabulous Knickerbockers	LP	London	HA8294	1966	£17.50	£35	
High On Love	7"	London	HLH10061	1966	£6	£12	
Jerk & Twine Time	LP	Challenge	LP621	1965	£15	£30	US
Lies	7"	Elektra	K12102	1973	£2	£5	B side by The Electric Prunes
Lies	7"	London	HLH10013	1966	£6	£12	
Lies	7" EP	London	RE10178	1966	£25	£50	French
Lloyd Thaxton Presents	LP	Challenge	LP12664	1965	£15	£30	US
One Track Mind	7"	London	HLH10035	1966	£5	£10	
Rumours, Gossip, Words Untrue	7"	London	HLH10093	1966	£5	£10	

KNIGHT, BAKER

Title	Format	Label	Catalogue	Year	Price	Price
Would You Believe It	7"	Reprise	RS20465	1966	£2.50	£6

KNIGHT BROTHERS

Title	Format	Label	Catalogue	Year	Price	Price
Temptation 'Bout To Get Me	7"	Chess	CRS8015	1965	£5	£10
That'll Get It	7"	Chess	CRS8046	1966	£5	£10

KNIGHT, CURTIS

Title	Format	Label	Catalogue	Year	Price	Price
Devil Made Me Do It	7"	Dawn	DNS1049	1974	£1.50	£4
Fancy Meeting You Here	7"	RCA	RCA1888	1969	£2.50	£6
Second Coming	LP	Dawn	DNLS3060	1974	£4	£10

KNIGHT, GLADYS

Title	Format	Label	Catalogue	Year	Price	Price
Tastiest Hits	LP	Bell	MBLL103	1968	£5	£12
Why Don't You Leave Me	7"	Contempo	CS2021	1974	£1.50	£4

KNIGHT, GLADYS & THE PIPS

Didn't You Know	7"	Tamla Motown	TMG728	1970	£1.50	£4	
End Of Our Road	7"	Tamla Motown	TMG645	1968	£2.50	£6	
Every Beat Of My Heart	7"	Ember	EMBS326	1972	£1.50	£4	
Everybody Needs Love	LP	Tamla Motown	(S)TML11058	1968	£5	£12	
Everybody Needs Love	7"	Tamla Motown	TMG619	1967	£2.50	£6	
Everybody Needs Love/ Stepping Closer To Your Heart	7"	Tamla Motown	TMG619	1967	£12.50	£25	demo
Feelin' Bluesy	LP	Tamla Motown	(S)TML11080	1968	£5	£12	
Friendship Train	7"	Tamla Motown	TMG756	1970	£1.50	£4	
Giving Up	7"	Stateside	SS318	1964	£6	£12	
Gladys Knight & The Pips	LP	Maxx	3000	1964	£8	£20	US
Gladys Knight & The Pips	LP	Sphere Sound	7006	1964	£8	£20	US
I Heard It Through The Grapevine	7"	Tamla Motown	TMG629	1967	£4	£8	chart single
I Wish It Would Rain	7"	Tamla Motown	TMG674	1968	£2	£5	
If I Were Your Woman	7"	Tamla Motown	TMG765	1971	£1.50	£4	
It Should Have Been Me	7"	Tamla Motown	TMG660	1968	£2	£5	
Just Walk In My Shoes	7"	Tamla Motown	TMG576	1966	£12.50	£25	
Just Walk In My Shoes	7"	Tamla Motown	TMG813	1972	£1.50	£4	chart single
Letter Full Of Tears	LP	Fury	1003	1962	£25	£50	US
Letter Full Of Tears	7"	Sue	WI394	1965	£6	£12	
Lovers Always Forgive	7"	Stateside	SS352	1964	£6	£12	
Make Me The Woman You Go Home To	7"	Tamla Motown	TMG805	1972	£1.50	£4	
Nitty Gritty	LP	Tamla Motown	(S)TML11135	1970	£4	£10	
Nitty Gritty	7"	Tamla Motown	TMG714	1969	£2	£5	
Silk 'n' Soul	LP	Tamla Motown	(S)TML11100	1969	£4	£10	
Take Me In Your Arms And Love Me	7"	Tamla Motown	TMG604	1967	£2	£5	chart single

KNIGHT, JASON

Our Love Is Getting Stronger	7"	Pye	7N17399	1967	£12.50	£25	

KNIGHT, MARIE

Come Tomorrow	7"	Fontana	H354	1962	£5	£10	
Cry Me A River	7"	Stateside	SS419	1965	£4	£8	
That's No Way To Treat A Girl	7"	Kent	TOWN102	1985	£1.50	£4	Jack Montgomery B side

KNIGHT, ROBERT

Blessed Are The Lonely	7"	Monument	MON1016	1968	£1.50	£4	
Everlasting Love	LP	Monument	(S)LMO5015	1968	£4	£10	
Everlasting Love	7"	Monument	MON1008	1968	£1.50	£4	chart single
Isn't It Lonely Together	7"	Bell	BLL1029	1968	£1.50	£4	
Love On A Mountain Top	7"	Monument	MON1017	1968	£2	£5	

KNIGHT, ROBERT (2)

Free Me	7"	London	HLD9496	1962	£1.50	£4	

KNIGHT, SONNY

But Officer	7"	Vogue	V9134	1959	£40	£80	export
Confidential	7"	London	HL7016	1957	£20	£40	
Confidential	7"	London	HLD8362	1957	£60	£120	gold label
If You Want This Love	LP	Aura	AR/AS3001	1964	£5	£12	US

KNIGHT, TERRY & THE PACK

I (Who Have Nothing)	7"	Cameo Parkway	C102	1966	£20	£40	
Reflections	LP	Cameo	C2007	1967	£6	£15	US
Terry Knight & The Pack	LP	Lucky Eleven	(S)8000	1966	£6	£15	US

KNIGHT, TONY

Did You Ever Hear The Sound	7"	Decca	F11989	1964	£7.50	£15	
How Sweet	7"	Decca	F12109	1965	£7.50	£15	

KNIGHTS

Hot Rod High	LP	Capitol	(S)T2189	1964	£10	£25	US

KNIGHTS (2)

Across The Road	LP	Ace	MG200854	1966	£37.50	£75	US
Knights 1967	LP	Ace	MG201303	1967	£32.50	£65	US

KNOCKER JUNGLE

Knocker Jungle	LP	Ember	NR5052	1970	£20	£40	

KNOCKOUTS

Darling Lorraine	7"	Top Rank	JAR279	1960	£7.50	£15	
Go Ape With The Knockouts	LP	Tribute	1202	1964	£10	£25	US

KNOPFLER, DAVID

Soul Kissing	7"	Peach River	BBPR7	1983	£2	£5	

KNOPFLER, MARK

Arguably, the instantly memorable theme that he wrote for the film "Local Hero" is the best piece of music that Mark Knopfler has ever produced.

Comfort And Joy	12"	Vertigo	MARK1	1984	£10	£25	1 sided promo
Going Home	12"	Vertigo	DSTR412	1983	£2.50	£6	
Joy	7"	Vertigo	DSDJ7	1984	£10	£20	promo only
Joy	12"	Vertigo	DSTR712	1984	£10	£25	

KNOX, BUDDY

All Time Loser	7"	Liberty	LIB55694	1964	£2	£5	

Title	Format	Label	Cat. No.	Year	Price	Price	Notes
Buddy Knox	LP	Roulette	R25003	1957	£30	£60	US
Chi-Hua-Hua	7"	Liberty	LIB55411	1962	£2.50	£6	
C'mon Baby	7"	Columbia	DB4180	1958	£7.50	£15	
Devil Woman	7"	Columbia	DB4014	1957	£10	£20	
God Knows I Love You	7"	United Artists	UP35019	1969	£2.50	£6	
Golden Hits	LP	Liberty	LBY1114	1962	£10	£25	
Gypsy Man	LP	United Artists	UAS6689	1969	£5	£12	US
I Think I'm Gonna Kill Myself	7"	Columbia	DB4302	1959	£7.50	£15	
Ling Ting Tong	7"	London	HLG9331	1961	£4	£8	
Lovey Dovey	7"	London	HLG9268	1961	£6	£12	
Party Doll	7"	Columbia	DB3914	1957	£30	£60	chart single, gold label
Rock A Buddy Knox	7" EP	Columbia	SEG7732	1957	£30	£60	
Rock Reflections	LP	Sunset	SLS50206	1971	£4	£10	
Rock Your Little Baby To Sleep	7"	Columbia	DB3952	1957	£15	£30	gold label
Shadaroom	7"	Liberty	LIB55592	1963	£2	£5	
She's Gone	7"	Liberty	LIB55473	1962	£2.50	£6	chart single
Swinging Daddy	7"	Columbia	DB4077	1958	£10	£20	
Three Eyed Man	7"	London	HLG9472	1961	£4	£8	

KNOX, BUDDY & JIMMY BOWEN

Title	Format	Label	Cat. No.	Year	Price	Price	Notes
Buddy Knox And Jimmy Bowen	LP	Roulette	R25048	1957	£45	£90	US

KOCJAN, KRYSIA

Title	Format	Label	Cat. No.	Year	Price	Price	Notes
Krysia	LP	RCA	LPL15052	1974	£4	£10	

KODAKS

Title	Format	Label	Cat. No.	Year	Price	Price	Notes
Kodaks Vs. The Starlites	LP	Sphere Sound	LP7005	1964	£25	£50	US

KODIAKS

Title	Format	Label	Cat. No.	Year	Price	Price	Notes
Tell Me Rhonda	7"	Decca	F12942	1969	£2.50	£6	

KOERNER, RAY & GLOVER

Title	Format	Label	Cat. No.	Year	Price	Price	Notes
Blues, Rags And Hollers	LP	Audiophile	AP78	1963	£8	£20	US
Good Old Koerner, Ray And Glover	LP	Mill City	MCR172	1972	£5	£12	US
Lots More Blues, Rags And Hollers	LP	Elektra	EKL/EKS7267	1964	£8	£20	US
Return Of Koerner, Ray And Glover	LP	Elektra	EKL/EKS7305	1966	£6	£15	US

KOERNER, SPIDER JOHN

Title	Format	Label	Cat. No.	Year	Price	Price	Notes
Spider Blues	LP	Elektra	EKL/EKS7290	1965	£6	£15	US
Won't You Give Me Some Love	7"	Elektra	EKSN45005	1967	£4	£8	

KOERNER, SPIDER JOHN & WILLIE MURPHY

Title	Format	Label	Cat. No.	Year	Price	Price	Notes
Friends And Lovers	7"	Elektra	EKSN45063	1969	£4	£8	
Running Jumping Standing Still	LP	Elektra	EKL/EKS74041	1968	£8	£20	
Running Jumping Standing Still	LP	Elektra	K42026	1971	£6	£15	

KOFFMAN, MOE

Title	Format	Label	Cat. No.	Year	Price	Price	Notes
Cool Ghoul	7"	Palette	PG9036	1962	£1.50	£4	
Little Pixie	7"	London	HLJ8633	1958	£1.50	£4	
Little Pixie	7" EP	London	REJ1163	1958	£5	£10	
Mighty Peculiar	7"	CBS	3544	1968	£1.50	£4	
Shepherd's Cha-Cha	7"	London	HLJ8813	1959	£1.50	£4	
Swingin' Shepherd Blues	7"	London	HLJ8549	1958	£2	£5	chart single

KOKOMO

Title	Format	Label	Cat. No.	Year	Price	Price	Notes
Asia Minor	7"	London	HLU9305	1961	£1.50	£4	chart single
Journey Home	7"	London	HLU9497	1962	£1.50	£4	

KOLETTES

Title	Format	Label	Cat. No.	Year	Price	Price	Notes
Who's That Guy	7"	Pye	7N25278	1964	£5	£10	

KOLLEKTIV

Title	Format	Label	Cat. No.	Year	Price	Price	Notes
Kollektiv	LP	Brain	0001034	1973	£6	£15	German

KOMACK, JIMMIE

Title	Format	Label	Cat. No.	Year	Price	Price	Notes
Cold Summer Blues	7"	Vogue Coral	Q2031	1954	£4	£8	
Rock-A-Bye Your Baby With A Dixie Melody	7"	Vogue Coral	Q72087	1955	£2	£5	
Wabash 47473	7"	Vogue Coral	Q72061	1955	£2.50	£6	

KOMKOL

Title	Format	Label	Cat. No.	Year	Price	Price	Notes
Index	LP	Kanal Leub	25	1972	£6	£15	German

KONGOS, JOHN

Title	Format	Label	Cat. No.	Year	Price	Price	Notes
Confusions About Goldfish	LP	Dawn	DNLS3002	1969	£4	£10	
Flim Flam Pharisee	7"	Dawn	DNS1002	1969	£1.50	£4	
He's Gonna Step On You Again	7"	Fly	BUG8	1971	£1.50	£4	PS
I Love Mary	7"	Piccadilly	7N35341	1966	£1.50	£4	
Tokoloshe Man	7"	Fly	BUG14	1971	£1.50	£4	chart single

KONITZ, LEE

Title	Format	Label	Cat. No.	Year	Price	Price	Notes
Collates	LP	XTRA	XTRA5049	1968	£5	£12	
Inside Hi-Fi	LP	London	LTZK15092	1957	£8	£20	
Konitz In Hi-Fi	LP	Atlantic	590027	1969	£5	£12	
Lee Konitz	10" LP	Vogue	LDE060	1954	£25	£50	
Lee Konitz	10" LP	Vogue	LDE129	1955	£25	£50	
Lee Konitz	10" LP	Vogue	LDE154	1955	£25	£50	
Lee Konitz With The Gerry Mulligan Quartet	LP	Vogue	LAE12181	1959	£8	£20	
Lee Konitz With Warne Marsh	LP	London	LTZK15025	1957	£10	£25	

Real Lee Konitz	LP	London	LTZK15147	1959	£8	£20
Very Cool	LP	Columbia	33CX10119	1958	£8	£20
You And Lee	LP	HMV	CLP1406/CSD1331	1960	£6	£15

KONRADS
Baby It's Too Late Now	7"	CBS	201812	1965	£1.50	£4

KONSTRUKTIVITS
Glenacaul	LP	Sterile	SR10	1986	£6	£15
Psyko Genetika	LP	Third Mind	TM02	198-	£6	£15

KOOBAS
First Cut Is The Deepest	7"	Columbia	DB8419	1968	£12.50	£25	
Gypsy Fred	7"	Columbia	DB8187	1967	£12.50	£25	
Koobas	LP	Columbia	SX/SCX6271	1969	£150	£250	sleeve pictured in Guide
Sally	7"	Columbia	DB8103	1967	£6	£12	
Sweet Music	7"	Columbia	DB7988	1966	£7.50	£15	
Take Me For A Little While	7"	Pye	7N17012	1965	£10	£20	
You'd Better Make Up Your Mind	7"	Pye	7N17087	1966	£6	£12	

KOOL
Look At Me, Look At Me	7"	CBS	203003	1967	£1.50	£4
Lovin'	7"	MCA	MU1085	1969	£1.50	£4
Step Out Of Your Mind	7"	CBS	2865	1967	£2	£5

KOOL & THE GANG
Best Of Kool And The Gang	LP	Polydor	2347002	1974	£20	£40
Funky Man	7"	Mojo	2027005	1971	£1.50	£4
Kool And The Gang	7"	London	HLZ10308	1970	£2	£5
Light Of Worlds	LP	Polydor	2310357	1974	£4	£10
Live At P.J.'s	LP	Polydor	2347001	1974	£15	£30
Live At The Sex Machine	LP	Polydor	2343083	1976	£4	£10
Live At The Sex Machine	LP	Polydor	2347003	1974	£6	£15
Love The Life You Live	7"	Mojo	2027006	1972	£1.50	£4
Music Is The Message	LP	Polydor	2347004	1974	£8	£20
Music Is The Message	7"	Mojo	2027009	1972	£1.50	£4
Spirit Of The Boogie	LP	Polydor	2310416	1975	£4	£10
Wild And Peaceful	LP	Polydor	2310299	1974	£4	£10

KOOPER, AL
Easy Does It	LP	CBS	66252	1970	£5	£12	double
Hey Western Union Man	7"	CBS	4160	1969	£4	£8	
Kooper Session	LP	CBS	63797	1970	£4	£10	with Shuggie Otis
Parchman Farm	7"	Mercury	MF885	1965	£6	£12	
You Never Know Who Your Friends Are	7"	CBS	4011	1969	£2.50	£6	

KOOPER, AL & STEPHEN STILLS
Season Of The Witch	7"	CBS	3770	1968	£2.50	£6

KOOPER, AL, MIKE BLOOMFIELD & STEVE STILLS
Super Session	LP	CBS	63396	1968	£5	£12	
Super Session	LP	CBS	Q63396	1973	£6	£15	quad
Super Session	LP	Mobile Fidelity	MFSL1178	1984	£5	£12	US audiophile

KOPPYCATS (IAN & THE ZODIACS)
Beatles Best	LP	Fontana	SFL13052-3	1968	£15	£30	double

KORBERG, TOMMY
Dear Mrs.Jones	7"	Sonet	SON2005	1969	£2.50	£6

KORDA, PAUL
Go On Home	7"	Columbia	DB7994	1966	£6	£12
Passing Strangers	LP	MAM	MAM1003	1971	£5	£12
Seagull	7"	Parlophone	R5778	1969	£2	£5

KORNER, ALEXIS
Somewhat like John Mayall, Alexis Korner's importance within the development of rock music had more to do with the musicians he managed to discover than with what he actually played himself. "R & B From The Marquee", viewed as being of crucial significance at the time, today sounds rather thin and ineffectual, and an unlikely base from which to begin a rock revolution. In truth, musicians like Charlie Watts, Jack Bruce, and Robert Plant achieved far more after they left Korner than they ever did with him. Nevertheless, Alexis Korner was an important catalyst - a position best demonstrated on the double LP "Bootleg Him", which provides a useful survey of his career via a well chosen selection of out-takes and otherwise unreleased tracks.

Accidentally Born In New Orleans	LP	Transatlantic	TRA269	1973	£10	£25	
Ain't That Peculiar	7"	CBS	3877	1976	£1.50	£4	
Alexis	LP	RAK	SRAK501	1971	£10	£25	
Alexis Korner	LP	Polydor	2374109	1974	£8	£20	German
Alexis Korner Blues Incorporated	7" EP	Tempo	EXA102	1958	£15	£30	
All Stars Blues Inc	LP	Transatlantic	TRASAM7	1969	£6	£15	
At The Cavern	LP	Oriole	PS40058	1964	£50	£100	
Blues At The Roundhouse	LP	77		1957	£100	£200	
Blues From The Roundhouse Vol.1	7" EP	Tempo	EXA76	1957	£15	£30	
Blues Incorporated	LP	Ace Of Clubs	ACL1187	1965	£25	£50	
Blues Incorporated	LP	Polydor	236206	1967	£25	£50	
Bootleg Him	LP	RAK	SRAKSP51	1972	£15	£30	double
Both Sides	LP	Metronome	MLP15364	1969	£15	£30	German
C.C.Rider	7"	King	KG1017	1965	£7.50	£15	
County Jail	7"	Tempo	A166	1957	£10	£20	
Get Off My Cloud	LP	CBS	69155	1975	£6	£15	
Get Off My Cloud	7"	CBS	3520	1975	£1.50	£4	

460

Title	Format	Label	Cat No	Year	Price	Price	Notes
I Need Your Loving	7"	Parlophone	R5206	1963	£7.50	£15	
I Wonder Who	LP	Fontana	STL5381	1967	£50	£100	
Just Easy	LP	Intercord	INT60099	1978	£6	£15	German
Little Baby	7"	Parlophone	R5247	1965	£7.50	£15	
Me	LP	Jeton	1003305	1979	£6	£15	German
Mr.Blues	LP	Mushroom	35434	1974	£8	£20	German
New Church	LP	Metronome		1970	£15	£30	German
New Generation Of Blues	LP	Liberty	LBL/LBS83147	1968	£15	£30	
Party LP	LP	Intercord	170000	1980	£6	£15	German
R&B At The Marquee	LP	Ace Of Clubs	ACL1130	1962	£15	£30	
Red Hot From Alex	LP	Transatlantic	TRA117	1964	£50	£100	
River's Invitation	7"	Fontana	TF706	1966	£7.50	£15	
Rosie	7"	Fontana	TF817	1967	£7.50	£15	
Sky High	LP	Spot	JW551	1965	£150	£250	
Snape Live On Tour	LP	Brain	20001039	1974	£8	£20	German
Up-Town	7"	Lyntone	LYN299	196-	£10	£20	flexi
What's That Sound I Hear	LP	Sunset	SLS50245	1971	£6	£15	

KORNFELD, ARTIE TREE

Title	Format	Label	Cat No	Year	Price	Price	Notes
Time To Remember	LP	Probe	SPB1022	1970	£5	£12	

KOSSOFF, KIRKE, TETSU & RABBIT

Title	Format	Label	Cat No	Year	Price	Price	Notes
Kossoff, Kirke, Tetsu & Rabbit	LP	Island	ILPS9188	1971	£15	£30	

KOSSOFF, PAUL

Title	Format	Label	Cat No	Year	Price	Price	Notes
Back Street Crawler	LP	Island	ILPS9264	1973	£4	£10	
Croydon June 15th 1975	LP	Street Tones	STLP1002	1983	£8	£20	double
Hunter	LP	Street Tones	STLP001	1981	£4	£10	
Leaves In The Wind	LP	Street Tones	STLP002	1982	£4	£10	
Mr.Big/Blue Soul	LP	Street Tones	SDLP0012PD	1983	£6	£15	pic disc

KOTHARI, CHIM

Title	Format	Label	Cat No	Year	Price	Price	Notes
Sitar And Spice	7"	Deram	DM108	1966	£4	£8	
Sound Of Sitar	LP	Deram	DML1002	1966	£15	£30	

KOTTKE, LEO

Title	Format	Label	Cat No	Year	Price	Price	Notes
Circle Around The Sun	LP	Symposium	2001	1970	£6	£15	
Live In Europe	LP	Chrysalis	CHR1284	1980	£6	£15	

KOVAC, ROLAND SET

Title	Format	Label	Cat No	Year	Price	Price	Notes
Roland Kovac Set	LP				£180	£300	

KRAAN

Title	Format	Label	Cat No	Year	Price	Price	Notes
Kraan	LP	Speigelei	28778/9	1973	£8	£20	German
Winthrup	LP	Speigelei	28523/9	1972	£8	£20	German

KRACKER

Title	Format	Label	Cat No	Year	Price	Price	Notes
Kracker Brand	LP	Rolling Stones	COC49102	1973	£6	£15	test pressing only

KRAFTWERK

Title	Format	Label	Cat No	Year	Price	Price	Notes
Comet Melody 2	7"	Vertigo	6147015	1975	£1.50	£4	
Computer Welt	LP	Kling Klang	06446311	1981	£6	£15	sung in German
Das Model	12"	Kling Klang	06245176	1978	£3	£8	sung in German
Die Mensch Maschine	LP	Kling Klang	05832843	1977	£6	£15	sung in German
Kraftwerk	LP	Vertigo	6641077	1973	£25	£50	spiral label double
Kraftwerk 1	LP	Philips	6305058	1971	£25	£50	German
Kraftwerk 2	LP	Philips	6305117	1972	£25	£50	German, sleeve pictured in Guide
Man Machine	LP	Capitol	EST11728	1978	£30	£60	red vinyl
Musique Non Stop	12"	EMI	12EMI5588	1986	£2.50	£6	
Neon Lights	12"	Capitol	CL15998	1978	£2.50	£6	luminous vinyl
Pocket Calculator	cass-s	EMI	TCEMI5175	1981	£4	£10	
Pocket Calculator	7"	EMI		1981	£1.50	£4	promo, English/German versions
Pocket Calculator	12"	EMI	12EMI5175	1981	£2.50	£6	
Radioaktivitat	LP	Kling Klang	06482087	1975	£6	£15	sung in German
Ralf And Florian	LP	Vertigo	6360616	1973	£8	£20	
Ralf And Florian	LP	Vertigo	6360616	1973	£15	£30	with poster
Robots (alternate mix)	7"	Capitol	CL15981	1978	£7.50	£15	PS
Showroom Dummies	12"	Capitol	CL16098	1979	£2.50	£6	
Showroom Dummies	12"	Capitol	CLX104	1977	£2.50	£6	
Technopop	LP	EMI	EMC3407	1983	£25	£50	
Telephone Call	12"	EMI	12EMI5602	1987	£2.50	£6	
Tour De France	cass-s	EMI	TCEMI5413	1983	£3	£8	
Tour De France	12"	EMI	12EMI5413	1984	£4	£10	
Trans Europa Express	LP	Kling Klang	06482306	1977	£6	£15	sung in German

KRAMER, BILLY J.

Title	Format	Label	Cat No	Year	Price	Price	Notes
1941	7"	NEMS	563396	1968	£1.50	£4	
Colour Of My Love	7"	MGM	MGM1474	1969	£1.50	£4	
Town Of Tuxley Toymaker	7"	Reaction	591014	1967	£6	£12	
World Without Love	7"	NEMS	563635	1968	£1.50	£4	

KRAMER, BILLY J. & THE DAKOTAS

Title	Format	Label	Cat No	Year	Price	Price	Notes
Bad To Me	7"	Parlophone	R5049	1963	£1.50	£4	chart single
Bad To Me	7" EP	Odeon	SOE3743	1963	£7.50	£15	French, B side by the Dakotas
Billy J Plays The States	7" EP	Parlophone	GEP8928	1965	£10	£20	
Billy J.Kramer	LP	Regal	REG1057	196-	£5	£12	
Do You Want To Know A Secret	7"	Parlophone	R5023	1963	£1.50	£4	chart single

From A Window	7"	Parlophone	R5156	1964	£1.50	£4	chart single
From A Window	7" EP	Parlophone	GEP8921	1964	£7.50	£15	
I'll Keep You Satisfied	LP	Imperial	LP9273/12273	1964	£6	£15	US
I'll Keep You Satisfied	7"	Parlophone	R5073	1963	£1.50	£4	chart single
I'll Keep You Satisfied	7" EP	Parlophone	GEP8895	1964	£6	£12	
It's Gotta Last Forever	7"	Parlophone	R5234	1965	£1.50	£4	
Kramer Hits	7" EP	Parlophone	GEP8885	1963	£7.50	£15	
Listen	LP	Parlophone	PCS3047	1963	£6	£15	stereo
Listen	LP	Parlophone	PMC1209	1963	£5	£12	chart LP
Little Children	LP	Imperial	LP9267/12267	1964	£8	£20	US
Little Children	7"	Parlophone	R5105	1964	£1.50	£4	chart single
Little Children	7" EP	Odeon	SOE3753	1964	£7.50	£15	French
Little Children	7" EP	Parlophone	GEP8907	1964	£6	£12	
Neon City	7"	Parlophone	R5362	1965	£1.50	£4	
Trains And Boats And Planes	LP	Imperial	LP9291/12291	1965	£6	£15	US
Trains And Boats And Planes	7"	Parlophone	R5285	1965	£1.50	£4	chart single
We're Doing Fine	7"	Parlophone	R5408	1966	£1.50	£4	
You Make Me Feel Like Someone	7"	Parlophone	R5482	1966	£1.50	£4	

KRAUT

Kill For Cash	7"	Cabbage		198-	£10	£20	
Unemployed	7"	Cabbage	K0002	1982	£7.50	£15	

KRAVETZ, JEAN JACQUES

Kravetz	LP	Vertigo	6360605	1972	£10	£25	German

KRAVITZ, LENNY

Live In Amsterdam	LP	Virgin	LENNY1	199-	£15	£30	promo

KRAY CHERUBS

No	7"	Fierce	FRIGHT014	1988	£5	£10	1 sided

KRAZY KATS

Movin' Out	LP	Damon	12478		£8	£20	US

KRENZ, BILL RAGTIMERS

Goofus	7"	London	HLU8258	1956	£6	£12	

KREW

Everything Is Alright	7" EP	Riviera	231214	1966	£6	£12	French

KREW KATS

Samovar	7"	HMV	POP894	1961	£4	£8	
Trambone	7"	HMV	POP840	1961	£2.50	£6	chart single

KRIEGEL, VOLKER

Lift	LP	MPS	21217531	1973	£4	£10	German
Mild Maniac	LP	MPS	21220206	1974	£4	£10	German
Missing Link	LP	MPS	33214311	1972	£6	£15	German double
Spectrum	LP	MPS	2120874	1971	£5	£12	German

KRIMSON KAKE

Feelin' Better	7"	Penny Farthing	PEN707	1970	£2	£5	

KRISTINA, SONJA

Let The Sunshine In	7"	Polydor	56299	1968	£4	£8	
Sonja Kristina	LP	Chopper	CHOPE5	1980	£15	£30	
St.Tropez	7"	Chopper	CHOP101	1980	£1.50	£4	

KRISTOFFERSON, KRIS

Cisco Pike	7" EP	CBS	EP9154	1972	£2	£5	
Kristofferson	LP	Monument	SMO5042	1970	£5	£12	US

KROKODIL

Getting Up For The Morning	LP	Bellaphon	BLPS19117	1972	£5	£12	German
Invisible World Revealed	LP	United Artists	UAS292501	1971	£6	£15	German
Krokodil	LP	Liberty	LBS83306	1969	£6	£15	
Musik	LP	United Artists	UAS293971	1971	£5	£12	German
Swamp	LP	Liberty	LBS83417	1970	£6	£15	
Sweat And Swim	LP	Bellaphon	7502	1973	£5	£12	German double

KRUGER, JEFF

Jazz At The Flamingo	LP	Tempo	TAP5	1956	£10	£25	

KRUPA, GENE

Collates	10" LP	Columbia	33C9000	1955	£8	£20	
Drummin' Man	10" LP	Columbia	33S1051	1955	£8	£20	
Gene Krupa And Buddy Rich	LP	Columbia	33CX10040	1956	£6	£15	
Gene Krupa Orchestra	LP	HMV	CLP1087	1956	£6	£15	
Jazz At The Philharmonic	LP	Columbia	33CX10015	1955	£10	£25	
Krupa Rocks	LP	Columbia	33CX10133	1959	£6	£15	
Plays Gerry Mulligan Arrangements	LP	HMV	CLP1281	1959	£6	£15	
Rhythm Parade	10" LP	Columbia	33S1064	1955	£8	£20	
Rockin' Mr.Krupa	10" LP	Columbia	33C9032	1957	£8	£20	
Selections From The Benny Goodman Story	LP	Columbia	33CX10027	1956	£8	£20	with Lionel Hampton & Teddy Wilson

KUBAN, BOB & THE IN MEN

Cheater	7"	Bell	BLL1027	1968	£2	£5	
Cheater	7"	Stateside	SS488	1966	£15	£30	

Cheater	7" EP.	Columbia	ESRF1761	1966	£7.50	£15	French
Look Out For The Cheater	LP	Musicland	(SLP)3500	1966	£8	£20	US
Teaser	7"	Stateside	SS514	1966	£7.50	£15	

KUBAS

| I Love Her | 7" | Columbia | DB7451 | 1965 | £7.50 | £15 | |

KUFF LINX

| So Tough | 7" | London | HLU8583 | 1958 | £50 | £100 | |

KUHN, ROLF

| Streamline | LP | Vanguard | PPL11009 | 1958 | £4 | £10 | |

KULT

| No Home Today | 7" | CBS | 4276 | 1969 | £30 | £60 | |

KUPFERBERG, TULI

| No Deposit No Return | LP | ESP | 1035 | 1966 | £6 | £15 | US |
| No Deposit No Return | LP | ESP | 1035 | 1966 | £8 | £20 | US, gold vinyl |

KUSTOM KINGS

| Kustom City, USA | LP | Smash | MGS2/SRS67051 | 1964 | £8 | £20 | US |

KUTI, FELA RANSOME

Afrodisiac	LP	Regal Zonophone	SLRZ1034	1973	£8	£20	
Black President	LP	Arista	SPART1167	1981	£4	£10	
Everything Scatter	LP	Creole	CRLP509	1979	£4	£10	
Gentlemen	LP	Creole	CRLP502	1979	£4	£10	
Shakara	LP	Creole	CRLP501	1975	£5	£12	
Yellow Fever	LP	Decca	PFS4412	1978	£4	£10	
Zombie	LP	Creole	CRLP511	1977	£4	£10	

KWESKIN, JIM JUG BAND

American Aviator	LP	Reprise	6353	1969	£5	£12	US
Garden Of Joy	LP	Reprise	R(S)6266	1967	£5	£12	US
Greatest Hits	LP	Vanguard	VSD13/14	1973	£6	£15	double
Jim Kweskin Jug Band	LP	Fontana	TFL6036	1964	£5	£12	
Jug Band Music	LP	Vanguard	VRS/VSD79163	1966	£5	£12	US
Jump For Joy	LP	Vanguard	VSD79243	1967	£5	£12	US
Relax Your Mind	LP	Vanguard	VSD79188	1966	£6	£15	US
See Reverse Side For Title	LP	Fontana	(S)TFL6080	1967	£5	£12	
Unblushing Brassiness	LP	Vanguard	VSD2158	1963	£8	£20	US
Whatever Happened To Those Good Old Days	LP	Vanguard	SVRL19046	1968	£5	£12	

KYDDS

| Sun Is A Laughing Child | 7" | NEMS | 564095 | 1969 | £1.50 | £4 | |

KYTES

| Frosted Panes | 7" | Pye | 7N17179 | 1966 | £6 | £12 | |
| Running In The Water | 7" | Island | WI6027 | 1968 | £12.50 | £25 | |

L

LA DE DA BAND
Come Together .... 7" ...... Parlophone...... R5810 .... 1969 ... £4 ....£8

LA DONNE, PATTIE
Friends An Lovers .... 7" ...... Duke................ DU23 .... 1969 ... £2.50 ....£6 ...Joe's Allstars B side

LA PERVERSITA
La Perversita .... LP ...... Invisible .... 10005................. 1979 ... £4 ....£10 ....French

LA PESTE
Better Off Dead .... 7" ...... Backlash .... CB711 .... 1978 ... £6 ....£12

LA ROCA, PETE
Basra .... LP ...... Blue Note........ BLP/BST84205 ...... 1965 ... £15 ....£30

LA ROSA, JULIUS
Domani	7"	London	HLA8170	1955	£7.50	£15
Green Fields	7"	London	HLR9092	1960	£1.50	£4
Jingle Bells	7"	London	HLA8353	1956	£6	£12
Julius La Rosa Sings	7" EP	London	REP1005	1954	£7.50	£15
Lipstick And Candy And Rubber Sole Shoe	7"	HMV	7M384	1956	£1.50	£4
Mobile	7"	London	HL8154	1955	£7.50	£15
No Other Love	7"	London	HLA8272	1956	£6	£12
Suddenly There's A Valley	7"	London	HLA8193	1955	£7.50	£15
Torero	7"	RCA	RCA1063	1958	£1.50	£4 ....chart single

LABELLE, PATTI & THE BLUEBELLES
All Or Nothing	7"	Atlantic	AT4055	1965	£4	£8
Apollo Presents The Bluebelles	LP	Newtown	631	1963	£10	£25 ...US
Danny Boy	7"	Cameo Parkway	P935	1965	£4	£8
Down The Aisle	7"	Sue	WI324	1964	£5	£10
Dreamer	LP	Atlantic	(SD)8101	1965	£6	£15 ...US
Groovy Kind Of Love	7"	Atlantic	AT4064	1966	£2	£5
I Sold My Heart To The Junkman	7"	HMV	POP1029	1962	£5	£10
On Stage	LP	Parkway	7043	1965	£8	£20 ...US
Over The Rainbow	LP	Atlantic	587001	1966	£6	£15
Patti's Prayer	7"	Atlantic	584007	1966	£1.50	£4
Sleigh Bells, Jingle Bells And Bluebelles	LP	Newtown	632	1963	£8	£20 ...US
Take Me For A Little While	7"	Atlantic	584072	1967	£2	£5

LACE
I'm A Gambler .... 7" ...... Page One....... POF135 .... 1969 ... £2.50 ....£6
People People .... 7" ...... Columbia......... DB8499............... 1968 ... £6 ....£12

LACEY, DAVE & THE CORVETTES
That's What They All Say .... 7" ...... Philips............. BF1419 .... 1965 ... £1.50 ....£4

LACKEY & SWEENEY
Junk Store Songs For Sale .... LP ...... Village Thing ... VTS23................. 1973 ... £6 ....£15

LADDERS
Gotta See Jane .... 7" ...... Statik............... TAK2 .... 1983 ... £1.50 ....£4
Gotta See Jane .... 12" ..... Statik............... TAK212 .... 1983 ... £2.50 ....£6

LADD'S BLACK ACES
Ladd's Black Aces .... 10" LP London .... AL3556 .... 1956 ... £5 ....£12

LADNIER, TOMMY
Blues And Stomps Vol.1 .... 10" LP London .... AL3524 .... 1954 ... £8 ....£20
Plays The Blues With Ma Rainey & Edmonia Henderson .... 10" LP London .... AL3548 .... 1955 ... £8 ....£20

LADY
Lady .... LP ...... Vertigo .... 6360636 .... 1976 ... £5 ....£12 ....German

LADY JUNE
Linguistic Leprosy .... LP ...... Caroline .... C1509 .... 1974 ... £6 ....£15

LADYBIRDS
Wanna Fly .... 7" ...... Columbia .... DB7523............... 1965 ... £1.50 ....£4
Lady Bird .... 7" ...... Columbia .... DB7197............... 1964 ... £1.50 ....£4
Memories .... 7" ...... Columbia .... DB7351............... 1964 ... £1.50 ....£4
White Cliffs Of Dover .... 7" ...... Columbia .... DB7250............... 1964 ... £1.50 ....£4

LAFAYETTES
Nobody But You .... 7" ...... RCA................ RCA1299 .... 1962 ... £1.50 ....£4
Nobody But You .... 7" EP.. RCA................ 75724................ 1962 ... £6 ....£12 ....French

LAIBACH

Krst Pod Triglavom - Baptism	LP	Sub Rosa	SUB3306/7-9	1987	£10	£25	boxed double
Krst Pod Triglavom - Baptism	LP	Sub Rosa	SUB3306/7-9	1987	£8	£20	double
Panorama	12"	East West	12EWS3	1984	£2.50	£6	
Rekapitulacija	LP	Walter Ulbricht		1985	£10	£25	boxed double
Rekapitulacija	LP	Walter Ulbricht		1985	£8	£20	double

LAINE, CLEO

All About Me	LP	Fontana	680992TL	1962	£4	£10	
Cleo Laine	10" LP	Esquire	15007	1955	£6	£15	
Cleo's Choice	10" LP	Pye	NPT19024	1958	£5	£12	
Shakespeare And All That Jazz	LP	Fontana	STL5209	1964	£4	£10	
She's The Tops	LP	MGM	C765	1958	£4	£10	

LAINE, DENNY

The singles released by Denny Laine on the Deram label represented a bold experiment by the former Moody Blue and future Wing. Abandoning the usual rock group line-up, Laine surrounded himself with a small group of amplified violins and cellos - the Electric String Band - and thereby anticipated some of what was later achieved by the Electric Light Orchestra. Sadly, Laine's innovations found little public support and he never again attempted anything similar.

Say You Don't Mind	7"	Deram	DM122	1967	£2.50	£6	
Say You Don't Mind	7"	Deram	DM227	1971	£1.50	£4	
Too Much In Love	7"	Deram	DM171	1968	£5	£10	

LAINE, FRANKIE

All Of Me	7" EP	Mercury	MEP9500	1956	£5	£10	
All Time Hits	7" EP	Mercury	ZEP10062	1960	£5	£10	
Annabel Lee	7"	Philips	PB797	1958	£1.50	£4	
Autumn Leaves	7" EP	Philips	BBE12216	1958	£5	£10	
Balladeer	LP	Philips	BBL7357	1960	£4	£10	
Call Of The Wild	LP	CBS	(S)BPG62082	1962	£5	£12	
Command Performance	LP	Columbia	CL625	1956	£8	£20	US
Concert Date	LP	Mercury	MG20085	1955	£8	£20	US
Cry Of The Wild Goose	10" LP	Mercury	MPT7007	1956	£6	£15	
Deuces Wild	LP	Philips	BBL7535/SBBL663	1962	£4	£10	
Deuces Wild No.1	7" EP	CBS	AGG20003	1962	£2.50	£6	
Deuces Wild No.2	7" EP	CBS	AGG20007	1962	£2.50	£6	
Deuces Wild No.3	7" EP	CBS	AGG20011	1962	£2.50	£6	
Favorites	10" LP	Mercury	MG25007	195-	£10	£25	US
Foreign Affair	LP	Philips	BBL7238	1958	£5	£12	
Frankie And Johnnie	7" EP	Philips	BBE12153	1957	£6	£12	with Johnnie Ray
Frankie Laine	7" EP	Columbia	SEG7505	1954	£5	£12	
Frankie Laine Songs	10" LP	Mercury	MG10002	1952	£15	£30	
Georgia On My Mind	7" EP	Mercury	MEP9000	1956	£5	£10	
Golden Hits	LP	Mercury	MG20587	1960	£5	£12	US
Good Evening Friends	7"	Philips	JK1026	1957	£7.50	£15	chart single with Johnnie Ray
Greater Sin	7"	Philips	JK1032	1957	£5	£10	
Greatest Hits	LP	Columbia	CL1231	1959	£6	£15	US
Guys And Dolls	10" LP	Columbia	CL2567	195-	£10	£25	US
Hell Bent For Leather	LP	Philips	BBL7468/SBBL616	1961	£4	£10	
I Believe	7" EP	Philips	BBE12005	1955	£5	£10	
I'd Give My Life	7"	Columbia	SCM5085	1954	£6	£12	*
I'm Just A Poor Bachelor	7"	Columbia	SCM5031	1953	£7.50	£15	
Jazz Spectacular	LP	Philips	BBL7080	1956	£6	£15	
Jealousy	7"	Columbia	SCM5017	1953	£10	£20	
Juba Juba Jubilee	LP	Philips	BBL7111	1957	£6	£15	
Juba Juba Jubilee	7" EP	Philips	BBE12103	1956	£5	£10	
Love Is A Golden Ring	7"	Philips	JK1009	1957	£5	£10	chart single
Lover's Laine	10" LP	Columbia	CL2504	195-	£10	£25	U
Lovin' Up A Storm	7"	Philips	PB836	1958	£2	£5	
Moby Dick	7" EP	Philips	BBE12087	1956	£5	£10	
Moonlight Gambler	7"	Philips	JK1000	1956	£5	£10	chart single
Moonlight Gambler	7" EP	Philips	BBE12130	1957	£5	£10	
Mr.Rhythm	10" LP	Philips	BBR8068	1955	£8	£20	
Mr.Rhythm Sings	10" LP	Mercury	MG10001	1952	£15	£30	
Mr.Rhythm Sings	10" LP	Mercury	MG25097	1954	£10	£25	
My Gal And A Prayer	7"	Philips	PB821	1958	£1.50	£4	U
One For My Baby	10" LP	Columbia	CL2548	195-	£10	£25	U
Rawhide	7"	Philips	PB965	1959	£1.50	£4	chart single
Reunion In Rhythm	LP	Philips	BBL7294/SBBL541	1959	£5	£12	
Rockin'	LP	Philips	BBL7155	1957	£6	£15	
Ruby And The Pearl	7"	Columbia	SCM5016	1953	£7.50	£15	
Showcase Of Hits	LP	Philips	BBL7263	1958	£6	£15	
Sings	10" LP	Columbia	33S1047	1954	£10	£25	
Sings For Us	LP	Mercury	MG20083	1955	£8	£20	U
Song Of The Open Road	7" EP	CBS	AGG20036	1963	£2.50	£6	
Songs By Frankie Laine	LP	Mercury	MG20069	1955	£8	£20	U
Songs By Frankie Laine	10" LP	Mercury	MG25098	1954	£10	£25	U
Stay As Sweet As You Are	7" EP	Mercury	MEP9520	1957	£5	£10	
Swan Song	7"	Columbia	SCM5073	1953	£6	£12	
That's My Desire	LP	Mercury	MG20080	1955	£8	£20	U
That's My Desire	10" LP	Mercury	MPT7513	1957	£6	£15	
Torching	LP	Philips	BBL7260	1958	£4	£10	
Voice Of Your Choice	10" LP	Philips	BBR8014	1954	£10	£25	
Wanderlust	LP	CBS	(S)BPG62126	1963	£5	£12	
Western Favourites	7" EP	Philips	BBE12447	1960	£6	£12	
With All My Heart	LP	Mercury	MG20105	1955	£8	£20	U
Without Him	7"	Philips	JK1017	1957	£5	£10	

LAINE, LINDA & THE SINNERS

Title	Format	Label	Cat. No.	Year		
Doncha Know	7"	Columbia	DB7204	1964	£4	£8
Don't Say It Baby	7"	Columbia	DB7549	1965	£5	£10
Low Grades And High Fever	7"	Columbia	DB7370	1964	£4	£8

LAKE, BONNIE & HER BEAUX

Title	Format	Label	Cat. No.	Year		
Miracle Of Love	7"	Brunswick	05622	1956	£6	£12

LAMAR, LEE

Title	Format	Label	Cat. No.	Year		
Sophia	7"	London	HLB8508	1957	£12.50	£25

LAMB, CHRIS & THE UNIVERSALS

Title	Format	Label	Cat. No.	Year		
Mysterious Land	7"	Decca	F12176	1965	£2	£5

LAMBE, JEANNIE

Title	Format	Label	Cat. No.	Year		
Miss Disc	7"	CBS	202636	1967	£5	£10

LAMBERT, HENDRICKS & ROSS

Title	Format	Label	Cat. No.	Year		
Hottest New Group In Jazz	LP	Philips	BBL7368/SBBL562	1960	£5	£12
Sing A Song Of Basie	LP	HMV	CLP1203	1958	£8	£20
Swingers	LP	Vogue	LAE12219	1960	£8	£20

LAMEGO, DANNY & HIS JUMPIN' JACKS

Title	Format	Label	Cat. No.	Year			
Big Weekend	LP	Forget-Me-Not	105A	1964	£8	£20	US

LAMP SISTERS

Title	Format	Label	Cat. No.	Year		
Woman With The Blues	7"	Sue	WI4048	1968	£10	£20

LANA SISTERS

The Lana Sisters were not actually related to each other, but did include the young Mary O'Brien, who had yet to assume her better-known stage name of Dusy Springfield.

Title	Format	Label	Cat. No.	Year		
Buzzin'	7"	Fontana	H176	1959	£4	£8
Mister Dee-Jay	7"	Fontana	H190	1959	£4	£8
Ring-a My Phone	7"	Fontana	H148	1958	£6	£12
Sitting In The Back Seat	7"	Fontana	H221	1959	£2.50	£6
Someone Loves You, Joe	7"	Fontana	H252	1960	£1.50	£4
Twosome	7"	Fontana	H283	1960	£1.50	£4
You've Got What It Takes	7"	Fontana	H235	1960	£2.50	£6

LANCASTRIANS

Title	Format	Label	Cat. No.	Year			
Ballad Of The Green Berets	7"	Pye	7N17072	1966	£2	£5	
Let's Lock The Door	7"	Pye	7N15791	1965	£2.50	£6	
Lonely Man	7"	Pye	7N15927	1965	£2.50	£6	
There'll Be No More Goodbyes	7"	Pye	7N15846	1965	£2.50	£6	
This World Keeps Going Round	7"	Pye	7N17043	1966	£6	£12	
We'll Sing In The Sunshine	7"	Pye	7N15732	1964	£2.50	£6	chart single

LANCE, MAJOR

Title	Format	Label	Cat. No.	Year			
Ain't No Soul	7"	Columbia	DB8122	1967	£12.50	£25	
Ain't No Soul	7"	Contempo	C9	1973	£1.50	£4	
Beat	7"	Soul City	SC114	1969	£4	£8	
Best Of Major Lance	LP	Epic	EPC81519	1976	£5	£12	
Come See	7"	Columbia	DB7527	1965	£5	£10	
Everybody Loves A Good Time	7"	Columbia	DB7787	1965	£6	£12	
Follow That Leader	7"	Atlantic	584277	1969	£2.50	£6	
Gimme Little Sign	7"	Contempo	CS2017	1974	£1.50	£4	
Greatest Hits	LP	OKeh	OKM12110/OKS14110	1965	£10	£25	US
Hey Little Girl	7"	Columbia	DB7168	1963	£6	£12	
I Wanna Make Up	7"	Stax	2025124	1973	£1.50	£4	
I'm So Lost	7"	Columbia	DB7463	1965	£5	£10	
Investigate	7"	Columbia	DB7967	1966	£12.50	£25	
Live At The Torch	LP	Contempo	COLP1001	1973	£5	£12	
Matador	7"	Columbia	DB7271	1964	£6	£12	
Monkey Time	LP	OKeh	OKM12105/OKS14105	1963	£20	£40	US
Monkey Time	7"	Columbia	DB7099	1963	£10	£20	
Pride And Joy	7"	Columbia	DB7609	1965	£6	£12	
Rhythm	7"	Columbia	DB7365	1964	£6	£12	
Rhythm Of Major Lance	LP	Columbia	33SX1728	1965	£30	£60	
Right Track	7"	Contempo	C1	1973	£1.50	£4	
Stay Away From Me	7"	Buddah	2011046	1970	£1.50	£4	
Sweeter As The Days Go By	7"	Atlantic	584302	1969	£2	£5	
Too Hot To Hold	7"	Columbia	DB7688	1965	£6	£12	
Um Um Um Um Um Um	LP	OKeh	OKM12106/OKS14106	1964	£25	£50	US
Um Um Um Um Um Um	7"	Columbia	DB7205	1964	£5	£10	chart single
Um Um Um Um Um Um	7" EP	Columbia	SEG8318	1964	£15	£30	
You're Everything I Need	7"	Pye	7N45487	1975	£1.50	£4	

LANCELOT, RICK & THE SEVEN KNIGHTS

Title	Format	Label	Cat. No.	Year		
Say Girl	7"	RCA	RCA1502	1966	£1.50	£4

LANCERS

Title	Format	Label	Cat. No.	Year		
Alphabet Rock	7"	Vogue Coral	Q72128	1956	£7.50	£15
First Travelling Saleslady	7"	Vogue Coral	Q72183	1956	£1.50	£4
Get Out Of The Car	7"	Vogue Coral	Q72081	1955	£5	£10
Jo-Ann	7"	Vogue Coral	Q72100	1955	£4	£8
Man Is As Good As His Word	7"	Vogue Coral	Q72157	1956	£2.50	£6
Mister Sandman	7"	Vogue Coral	Q2038	1954	£6	£12
Never Leave Me	7"	Vogue Coral	Q72220	1957	£1.50	£4

Oh Sweet Mama	10" LP	London	HAPB1029	1954	£15	£30
Presenting The Lancers	7" EP	London	REP1027	1955	£6	£12
So High So Low So Wide	7"	London	HL8079	1954	£12.50	£25
Stop Chasing Me Baby	7"	London	HL8027	1954	£12.50	£25
Stroll	7"	Coral	Q72300	1958	£1.50	£4
Timberjack	7"	Vogue Coral	Q72062	1955	£4	£8

LAND, HAROLD

Fox	LP	Vogue	LAE12269	1961	£8	£20
Harold In The Land Of Jazz	LP	Contemporary	LAC12178	1959	£8	£20

LANDER, BOB & THE SPOTNICKS

Midnight Special	7"	Oriole	CB1784	1962	£4	£8
My Old Kentucky Home	7"	Oriole	CB1756	1962	£7.50	£15

LANDIS, BILL & BRETT

Baby Talk	7"	Parlophone	R4570	1959	£1.50	£4

LANDIS, JERRY

Jerry Landis was one of the many pseudonyms adopted by Paul Simon in the years before he discovered folk music. In America, the "He Was My Brother" single was issued under the name Paul Kane.

Anna Belle	7"	MGM	12822	1959	£10	£20	US
He Was My Brother	7"	Oriole	CB1390	1962	£12.50	£25	
I'm Lonely	7"	Canadian American	130	1961	£10	£20	US
Just A Boy	7"	Warwick	552	1960	£10	£20	US
Just A Boy	7"	Warwick	588	1960	£10	£20	US
Lisa	7"	Amy	875	1962	£12.50	£25	US
Play Me A Sad Song	7"	Warwick	616	1961	£10	£20	US

LANDIS, JOYA

Kansas City	7"	Trojan	TR620	1968	£4	£8
Moonlight Lover	7"	Trojan	TR641	1968	£4	£8

LANDON, NEIL

I Still Love You	7"	Decca	F12451	1966	£1.50	£4

LANDS, HOAGY

I'm Yours	7"	Stateside	SS2085	1968	£2	£5
Next In Line	7"	Stateside	SS2030	1967	£50	£100
Next In Line	7"	UK	USA14	1975	£1.50	£4
Why Didn't You Let Me Know	7"	Action	ACT4605	1972	£1.50	£4

LANE BROTHERS

Mimi	7"	London	HLR9150	1960	£4	£8

LANE, DES

Moonbird	7"	Top Rank	JAR203	1959	£1.50	£4
Penny-Whistle Rock	7"	Decca	F10821	1956	£2	£5
Rock Mister Piper	7"	Decca	F10847	1957	£2	£5

LANE, MICKEY LEE

Hey Sah-lo-ney	7"	Stateside	SS456	1965	£12.50	£25
Shaggy Dog	7"	Stateside	SS354	1964	£2	£5

LANE, PENNY

Loving Or Losing You	7"	Columbia	DB8377	1968	£1.50	£4

LANE, TONY & THE DELTONES

It's Great	7"	Sabre	SA455	1964	£1.50	£4

LANG, DON

Come Go With Me	7"	HMV	POP335	1957	£7.50	£15	
Don Lang	10" LP	HMV	DLP1151	1957	£25	£50	
Don't Open That Door	7"	HMV	POP805	1960	£2	£5	
Four Brothers	7"	HMV	7M354	1956	£7.50	£15	
Hand Jive	10" LP	HMV	DLP1179	1958	£40	£80	
Hey Daddy	7"	HMV	POP510	1958	£2	£5	
Hoot And A Holler	7"	HMV	POP649	1959	£2	£5	
Percy Green	7"	HMV	POP623	1959	£1.50	£4	
Queen Of The Hop	7"	HMV	POP547	1958	£4	£8	
Red Planet Rock	7"	HMV	POP414	1957	£7.50	£15	
Reveille Rock	7"	HMV	POP682	1959	£2.50	£6	
Rock And Roll Blues	7"	HMV	7M416	1956	£7.50	£15	
Rock Around The Islands	7"	HMV	7M381	1956	£7.50	£15	
Rock Mister Piper	7"	HMV	POP289	1957	£7.50	£15	
Rock 'n' Roll	7" EP	HMV	7EG8208	1957	£25	£50	
Sink The Bismarck	7"	HMV	POP714	1960	£4	£8	chart singl
Six Five Hand Jive	7"	HMV	POP434	1958	£6	£12	
Six Five Special	7"	HMV	POP350	1957	£6	£12	chart singl
Sweet Sue	7"	HMV	POP260	1956	£5	£10	
Tequila	7"	HMV	POP465	1958	£5	£10	
Twenty Top Twenty Twists	LP	Ace Of Clubs	ACL1111	1962	£6	£15	
White Silver Sands	7"	HMV	POP382	1957	£4	£8	
Wicked Women	7"	Decca	F11483	1962	£1.50	£4	
Wiggle Wiggle	7"	HMV	POP585	1959	£2.50	£6	
Witch Doctor	7"	HMV	POP488	1958	£2.50	£6	chart singl

LANG, EDDIE & LONNIE JOHNSON

Blue Guitars	LP	Parlophone	PMC7019	1967	£8	£20
Blue Guitars Vol.2	LP	Parlophone	PMC7106	1970	£8	£20

LANG, K.D.

Blue Bayou	CD-s	Virgin	VSCD1193	1989	£2.50	£6	with Roy Orbison
Blue Bayou	12"	Virgin	VST1193	1989	£2.50	£6	with Roy Orbison
Crying	CD-s	Virgin	VSCD1166	1989	£3	£8	with Roy Orbison
Crying	CD-s	Virgin	VSCD1173	1989	£2.50	£6	with Roy Orbison
Crying	12"	Virgin	VST1166	1989	£2.50	£6	with Roy Orbison
Crying	12"	Virgin	VST1173	1989	£2.50	£6	with Roy Orbison
Damned Old Dog	7"	Bumstead		1983	£25	£50	Canadian
Miss Chatelaine	12"	Sire	W0135TW	1992	£2.50	£6	with poster
Our Day Will Come	7"	Sire	W7697	1988	£7.50	£15	
Our Day Will Come	12"	Sire	W7697T	1988	£25	£50	
Ridin' The Rails	7"	Warner Bros	W9535	1990	£5	£10	Darlene Love B side
Sugar Moon	7"	Sire	W7841	1988	£7.50	£15	
Sugar Moon	12"	Sire	W7841T	1988	£20	£40	

LANG, RAY

Last Train	7"	Brunswick	05683	1957	£1.50	£4

LANGE, STEVIE

Remember My Name	7"	Jive	JIVE23	1983	£2	£5	no PS
Remember My Name	7"	RCA	LIM1	1981	£2	£5	
Remember My Name	7"	RCA	RCA152	1981	£4	£8	

LANGHORN, GORDON

Give A Fool A Chance	7"	Decca	F10591	1955	£1.50	£4

LANGLEY, PERPETUAL

So Sad	7"	Planet	PLF110	1966	£5	£10
Surrender	7"	Planet	PLF115	1966	£5	£10

LANGTON, PHIL TRIO

Phil Langton Trio	LP	Holyground		196-	£6	£15

LANSON, SNOOKY

It's Almost Tomorrow	7"	London	HLD8223	1956	£20	£40	
Last Minute Love	7"	London	HLD8236	1956	£50	£100	
Seven Days	7"	London	HL7005	1956	£7.50	£15	
Seven Days	7"	London	HLD8249	1956	£50	£100	export

LANZA, MARIO

Great Caruso	LP	HMV	ALP1071	1953	£4	£10
On Broadway	10" LP	HMV	BLP1091	1957	£4	£10
Operatic Arias	LP	HMV	ALP1202	1954	£4	£10
Songs Of Romance	10" LP	HMV	BLP1071	1955	£4	£10
Touch Of Your Hand	10" LP	HMV	BLP1094	1957	£4	£10

LANZON & HUSBAND

Nostalgia	LP	Bradleys	1006	1976	£8	£20

LARD FREE

I'm Around About Midnight	LP	Vamp	VP59502	1975	£6	£15	French
Lard Free	LP	Cobra	37007	1977	£4	£10	French
Lard Free	LP	Vamp	VP59500	1973	£10	£25	French

LARKINS, ELLIS

Manhattan At Midnight	LP	Brunswick	LAT8189	1957	£6	£15
Melodies Of Harold Arlen	10" LP	Brunswick	LA8694	1955	£8	£20

LARKS

Jerk	LP	Money	LP1102	1965	£15	£30	US
Jerk	7"	Pye	7N25284	1964	£7.50	£15	
Soul Kaleidoscope	LP	Money	LP/MS1107	1966	£8	£20	US
Superslick	LP	Money	MY/MS1110	1967	£8	£20	US

LARNER, SAM

Garland For Sam	LP	Topic	12T244	1974	£4	£10
Now Is The Time For Fishing	LP	Folkways	FG3507	1961	£6	£15

LARO

Jamaican Referendum Calypso	7"	Kalypso	XX21	196-	£2.50	£6

LARRY & ALVIN

Can't You Understand	7"	Studio One	SO2067	1968	£6	£12	
Lonely Room	7"	Studio One	SO2080	1969	£6	£12	
Love Got Me	7"	Coxsone	CS7081	1968	£5	£10	Bob Andy B side

LARRY & JOHNNY

An attempt on the part of Larry Williams and Johnny Guitar Watson to cash in on the success of the Beatles produced considerably less income than did the fact that the Beatles covered some of Williams' songs, 'Slow Down", "Bad Boy", and "Dizzy Miss Lizzy", themselves.

Beatle Time	7"	Outasite	45501	1965	£12.50	£25

LARRY & TOMMY

You've Gotta Bend A Little	7"	Polydor	56741	1968	£2.50	£6

LA'S

Way Out	7"	Go! Discs	GOLAS1	1987	£1.50	£4	
Way Out	12"	Go! Discs	GOLAR112	1987	£4	£10	5 tracks
Way Out	12"	Go! Discs	GOLAS112	1987	£2.50	£6	

LASSIES

Sleepy Head	7"	Brunswick	05571	1956	£1.50	£4

LAST CHANT
Run Of The Dove .... 7" ..... Chicken Jazz.... JAZZ4 .... 1981 ... £2.50 ....£6 ....

LAST EXIT
Last Exit was a rock group formed from within the ranks of the Newcastle Big Band, and like its parent organisation, played in pubs and clubs around Newcastle. The singer/bass player was Gordon Sumner - better known as Sting - and it is he that can be heard on the group's locally produced single. (The Last Exit that recorded in the eighties has nothing to do with Sting, although, as it happens, the group's music is rathe - an exhilarating brand of improvised noise-funk that makes virtually any other music sound tame).
Whispering Voices .... 7" ...... Wudwink .... WUD01 .... 1975 ... £10 ....£20 ....

LAST FLIGHT
Dance To The Music .... 7" ...... Heavy Metal .... HEAVY5 .... 1981 ... £2 ....£5 ....

LAST POETS
The sound of Black Power. The Last Poets deliver their angry, razor-sharp rants over a percussion backing - and if that sounds like description of rap music, then that is exactly what it is. The rhythms are 1971 rhythms (no drum machines), but the style and the stance is the same.
Chastisement .... LP ..... Blue Thumb..... 539 .... 1972 ... £6 ....£15 .... US
Last Poets .... LP ..... Douglas .... Z30811 .... 1971 ... £6 ....£15 .... US
Right On .... LP ..... Juggernaut..... 8802 .... 1971 ... £6 ....£15 .... US
This Is Madness .... LP ..... Douglas .... DGL69012 .... 1971 ... £6 ....£15 ....

LAST RESORT
Having Fun? .... 7" ...... Red Meat .... RMRS01 .... 1978 ... £2 ....£5 ....

LATEEF, YUSEF
Before Dawn .... LP ..... Columbia........ 33CX10124 .... 1958 ... £10 ....£25 ....
Eastern Sounds .... LP ..... Fontana .... 688202ZL .... 1964 ... £5 ....£12 ....
Live At Pep's .... LP ..... HMV .... CLP3547 .... 1964 ... £5 ....£12 ....
Sounds Of Yusef .... LP ..... Esquire .... 32069 .... 1958 ... £10 ....£25 ....

LATTER, GENE
Always .... 7" ...... CBS .... 202655 .... 1967 ... £1.50 ....£4 ....
Catch My Soul .... 7" ...... Parlophone..... R5896 .... 1971 ... £2 ....£5 ....
Help Me Judy, Help Me .... 7" ...... Parlophone..... R5800 .... 1969 ... £1.50 ....£4 ....
Just A Minute Or Two .... 7" ...... Decca .... F12364 .... 1966 ... £1.50 ....£4 ....
Little Piece Of Leather .... 7" ...... CBS .... 2843 .... 1967 ... £7.50 ....£15 ....
Mother's Little Helper .... 7" ...... Decca .... F12397 .... 1966 ... £4 ....£8 ....
My Life Ain't Easy .... 7" ...... Spark .... SRL1015 .... 1970 ... £1.50 ....£4 ....
Old Iron Bell .... 7" ...... Spark .... SRL1031 .... 1971 ... £1.50 ....£4 ....
Sign On The Dotted Line .... 7" ...... Spark .... SRL1022 .... 1970 ... £2.50 ....£6 ....
Something Inside Me Died .... 7" ...... CBS .... 202483 .... 1967 ... £2.50 ....£6 ....
Tiger Bay .... 7" ...... Parlophone..... R5815 .... 1969 ... £1.50 ....£4 ....
Too Busy Thinkin' 'Bout My Baby ...... 7" ...... Parlophone..... R5913 .... 1971 ... £2 ....£4 ....
Tribute To Otis .... 7" ...... Direction .... 583245 .... 1968 ... £1.50 ....£4 ....
With A Child's Heart .... 7" ...... CBS .... 2986 .... 1967 ... £1.50 ....£4 ....

LAUGHING APPLE
Ha-Ha He-He .... 7" ...... Autonomy ...... AUT001 .... 1981 ... £2.50 ....£6 ....
Participate .... 7" ...... Autonomy ...... AUT002 .... 1981 ... £2 ....£5 ....
Precious Feeling .... 7" ...... Essential .... ESS001 .... 1982 ... £2.50 ....£6 ....

LAUGHING GRAVY
This Beach Boys cover was actually co-produced by Brian Wilson and features Dean Torrence of Jan and Dean on vocals.
Vegetables .... 7" ...... White Whale.... 261 .... 1967 ... £30 ....£60 .... U

LAUGHING WIND
Laughing Wind .... LP ..... Tower .... 1967 ... £10 ....£25 .... U

LAUPER, CYNDI
Money Changes Everything .... 12" .... Portrait........... TA6009 .... 1985 ... £3 ....£8 ....
She Bop .... 7" ...... Portrait........... WA4620 .... 1984 ... £2 ....£5 .... pic di
Time After Time .... 7" ...... Portrait........... WA4290 .... 1984 ... £2.50 ....£6 .... pic di
What's Going On .... 7" ...... Portrait........... CYNP1 .... 1987 ... £1.50 ....£4 .... pic di

LAURENCE, ZACK
Beatle Concerto .... 7" EP.. HMV .... 7EG8968 .... 1966 ... £2.50 ....£6 ....
Sleeveshaker .... 7" ...... Parlophone..... R5000 .... 1963 ... £1.50 ....£4 ....

LAURENZ, JOHN
Goodbye Stranger Goodbye .... 7" ...... London .... HL8138 .... 1955 ... £7.50 ....£15 ....

LAURIE
I Love Onions .... 7" ...... Decca .... F12424 .... 1966 ... £1.50 ....£4 ....

LAURIE, CY
Cy Laurie Jazz Band .... LP ..... Esquire .... 32008 .... 1955 ... £4 ....£10 ....
Cy Laurie Jazz Band .... 10" LP Esquire .... 20037 .... 1955 ... £5 ....£12 ....

LAURIE, LINDA
All Winter Long .... 7" ...... Top Rank .... JAR277 .... 1960 ... £1.50 ....£4 ....
Ambrose .... 7" ...... London .... HL8807 .... 1959 ... £2 ....£5 ....

LAVA
Tears Are Going Home .... LP ..... Brain .... 0001031 .... 1973 ... £6 ....£15 .... Germ

LAVERN, ROGER & THE MICRONS
Christmas Stocking .... 7" ...... Decca .... F11791 .... 1963 ... £6 ....£12 ....

LAVETTE, BETTY
Doin' The Best I Can .... 7" ...... Atlantic .... K11198 .... 1978 ... £1.50 ....£4 ....

He Made A Woman Out Of Me	7"	Polydor	56786	1969	£2.50	£6
I Feel Good All Over	7"	Pama	PM748	1968	£4	£8
I Feel Good All Over	7"	Stateside	SS2015	1967	£5	£10
Let Me Down Easy	7"	Mojo	2092030	1972	£1.50	£4
Your Turn To Cry	7"	Atlantic	K10299	1973	£1.50	£4

LAWRENCE, AZIE

Jamaica Blues	7"	Melodisc	1563	1960	£4	£8
No Dice	7"	Starlite	ST45041	1961	£4	£8
Palms Of Victory	7"	Blue Beat	BB71	1961	£5	£10
Pempelem	7"	Blue Beat	BB222	1963	£5	£10
West Indians In England	7"	Starlite	ST45022	1960	£2	£5
You Didn't Want To Know	7"	Melodisc	1572	1960	£4	£8

LAWRENCE, DIANE

I Won't Hang Around Like A Hound Dog	7"	Doctor Bird	DB1075	1967	£5	£10
Treat Me Nice	7"	Jolly	JY005	1968	£4	£8

LAWRENCE, ELLIOT

Gerry Mulligan Arrangements	LP	Vogue	LAE12057	1957	£4	£10
Plays Tiny Kahn & Johnny Mandel Arrangements	LP	Vogue	LAE12101	1958	£4	£10
Swinging At The Steel Pier	LP	Vogue	LAE12071	1958	£4	£10

LAWRENCE, GENE

Meringue Triniana	7"	Jump Up	JU510	1967	£2.50	£6

LAWRENCE, LARRY

Goofin' Off	7"	Pye	7N25042	1959	£1.50	£4
Jug-a-Roo	7"	Ember	EMBS106	1960	£1.50	£4

LAWRENCE, LEE

Beyond The Stars	7"	Columbia	SCM5175	1955	£2	£5	
By You By You By You	7"	Columbia	DB3885	1957	£2	£5	
Chapel Of The Roses	7"	Columbia	DB3922	1957	£1.50	£4	
Don't Tell Me Not To Love You	7"	Columbia	SCM5228	1956	£2	£5	
High Upon A Mountain	7"	Columbia	DB3830	1956	£4	£8	
Lee Lawrence	7" EP	Columbia	SEG7780	1958	£2	£5	
Lights Of Paris	7"	Decca	F10438	1955	£1.50	£4	
Little Mustard Seed	7"	Decca	F10285	1954	£2.50	£6	
Lonely Ballerina	7"	Columbia	DB3981	1957	£1.50	£4	
More Than A Millionaire	7"	Columbia	SCM5190	1955	£1.50	£4	
My Own True Love	7"	Decca	F10422	1955	£2	£5	
My World Stood Still	7"	Columbia	SCM5181	1955	£2	£5	
Presenting Lee Lawrence	10" LP	Decca	LF1132	1953	£4	£10	
Rock 'n' Roll Opera	7"	Columbia	DB3855	1956	£7.50	£15	
Story Of Tina	7"	Decca	F10367	1954	£2.50	£6	
Suddenly There's A Valley	7"	Columbia	SCM5201	1955	£5	£10	chart single
Things I Didn't Do	7"	Decca	F10408	1954	£2	£5	
Valley Valparaiso	7"	Columbia	SCM5283	1956	£2	£5	
We Believe In Love	7"	Columbia	SCM5254	1956	£1.50	£4	
Will You Be Mine Alone?	7"	Decca	F10485	1955	£1.50	£4	

LAWRENCE, STEVE

Banana Boat Song	7"	Vogue Coral	Q72228	1957	£2.50	£6	
Come Waltz With Me	LP	CBS	(S)BPG62088	1963	£4	£10	
Fabulous	7"	Vogue Coral	Q72264	1957	£2.50	£6	
Footsteps	7"	HMV	POP726	1960	£1.50	£4	chart single
Fraulein	7"	Vogue Coral	Q72281	1957	£2.50	£6	
Girls Girls Girls	7"	London	HLT9166	1960	£1.50	£4	chart single
Here's Steve Lawrence No.1	7" EP	Coral	FEP2010	1959	£2	£5	
Here's Steve Lawrence No.2	7" EP	Coral	FEP2012	1959	£2	£5	
Only Have Eyes For You	7"	Coral	Q72353	1959	£1.50	£4	
Lawrence Goes Latin	LP	United Artists	(S)ULP1022	1963	£4	£10	
Never Mind	7"	Vogue Coral	Q72286	1957	£1.50	£4	
Open Up The Gates Of Mercy	7"	Vogue Coral	Q72114	1955	£2.50	£6	
Party Doll	7"	Vogue Coral	Q72243	1957	£2.50	£6	
Portrait Of My Love	LP	HMV	CLP1504/CSD1404	1962	£4	£10	
Pretty Blue Eyes	7"	HMV	POP689	1960	£1.50	£4	
Songs Everybody Knows	LP	Coral	LVA9219	1964	£4	£10	
Speedo	7"	Vogue Coral	Q72133	1956	£5	£10	
Steve Lawrence	LP	Top Rank	BUY033	1960	£4	£10	
Steve Lawrence Sound	LP	HMV	CLP1462/CSD1374	1961	£4	£10	
Swing Softly With Me	LP	HMV	CLP1326	1960	£4	£10	
This Night	7"	Parlophone	MSP6038	1953	£4	£8	
Too Little Time	7"	Parlophone	MSP6080	1954	£4	£8	
Winners	LP	CBS	BPG62124	1963	£4	£10	
You Can't Hold A Memory In Your Arms	7"	Parlophone	MSP6106	1954	£4	£8	

LAWRIE, BILLY

Rock And Roller	7"	RCA	RCA2439	1973	£1.50	£4
Roll Over Beethoven	7"	Polydor	56363	1969	£10	£20

LAWS, RONNIE

Pressure Sensitive	LP	Blue Note	BNLA452	1975	£4	£10

LAWSON, JULIET

Boo	LP	Sovereign	SVNA7257	1972	£10	£25

LAWSON, SHIRLEY
Star	7"	Soul City	SC108	1969	£10	£20

LAWSON-HAGGART JAZZ BAND
Blues On The River	10" LP	Brunswick	LA8580	1953	£5	£12
Jelly Roll's Jazz	10" LP	Brunswick	LA8576	1953	£5	£12
King Oliver's Jazz	10" LP	Brunswick	LA8593	1953	£5	£12
Louis' Hot 5's And 7's	10" LP	Brunswick	LA8698	1955	£5	£12
Ragtime Jamboree	10" LP	Brunswick	LA8635	1954	£5	£12
South Of The Mason-Dixon Line	10" LP	Brunswick	LA8703	1955	£5	£12
Windy City Jazz	10" LP	Brunswick	LA8639	1954	£5	£12

LAWSON-HAGGART ROCKIN' BAND
Boppin' At The Hop	LP	Brunswick	LAT8288/STA3010	1959	£15	£30
Boppin' At The Hop	7" EP	Brunswick	OE9451	1959	£10	£20

LAWTON, LOU
Doin' The Philly Dog	7"	Ember	EMBS232	1967	£10	£20
I'm Just A Fool	7"	Speciality	SPE1005	1967	£7.50	£15

LAY, SAM
In Bluesland	LP	Blue Thumb	BTS8814	1969	£5	£12

LAYNE, OSSIE
Come Back	7"	R&B	MRB5006	1965	£2	£5

LAYTON, EDDIE
Doodles	7"	Mercury	AMT1064	1959	£1.50	£4

LAZARUS, KEN & THE CREW
Monkey Man	7"	London	HLJ10301	1970	£1.50	£4

LAZY LESTER
I'm A Lover Not A Fighter	7"	Stateside	SS277	1964	£4	£8
Made Up My Mind	LP	Blue Horizon	2431007	1971	£30	£60

LAZY SMOKE
Corridor Of Faces	LP	Heyoka		1972	£75	£150

LE CHEILE
Airis	LP	Inchecronin	INC7423	1978	£6	£15
Lord Mayo	LP	Inchecronin	INC7424	1978	£6	£15

LE FORGE, JACK
Our Crazy Affair	7"	Stateside	SS444	1965	£1.50	£4

LE MAT
Waltz Of The Fool	7"	Whaam!	WHAAM8	1982	£1.50	£4

LE ORME
Collage	LP	Philips	6323007	1971	£6	£15	Italian
Contrappunti	LP	Philips	6323035	1974	£6	£15	Italian
Felona And Serona	LP	Charisma	CAS1072	1973	£6	£15	
Florian	LP	Philips	6323086	1979	£4	£10	Italian
In Concert	LP	Philips	6323028	1974	£6	£15	Italia
Piccola Rapsodie Dell Ape	LP	Philips	6323102	1980	£4	£10	Italia
Smogmagica	LP	Philips	6323041	1975	£5	£12	Italia
Storia O Legganda	LP	Philips	6323052	1977	£4	£10	Italia
Uomo Di Pezza	LP	Philips	6323013	1972	£6	£15	Italia
Venerdi	LP	Polydor	2393341	1982	£4	£10	Italia
Verita Nascoste	LP	Philips	6323045	1976	£5	£12	Italia

LE SAGE, BILL
Bill's Recipes	LP	Saga	STM6019	1959	£5	£12

LEA VALLEY SKIFFLE GROUP
Lea Valley Skiffle Group	7" EP	Esquire	EP163	1958	£7.50	£15

LEADBELLY
Alabama Bound	7"	HMV	MH190	1955	£6	£12	with Golden Gate Quarte
Backwater Blues	78	Capitol	CL13282	1950	£3	£8	
Classics In Jazz	10" LP	Capitol	LC6597	1953	£20	£40	
Demon Of A Man	LP	Storyville	SLP124	1964	£5	£12	
From The Last Sessions	LP	Folkways	3019	1967	£5	£12	U
Good Morning Blues	LP	RCA	RD7567	1963	£5	£12	
Goodnight Irene	LP	Storyville	616004	197-	£5	£12	
His Guitar, His Voice, His Piano	LP	Capitol	T1821	1963	£5	£12	
How Long Blues	7" EP	Melodisc	EPM763	1956	£7.50	£15	
Huddie Ledbetter	10" LP	Folkways	2013	1960	£8	£20	U
Keep Your Hands Off Her	LP	Verve	(S)VLP5011	1967	£5	£12	
Last Sessions Vol.1	LP	Melodisc	MLP12113	1959	£6	£15	
Last Sessions Vol.2	LP	Melodisc	MLP12114	1959	£6	£15	
Leadbelly	LP	Ember	CW132	197-	£4	£10	
Leadbelly	LP	Storyville	616003	1969	£5	£12	
Leadbelly	7" EP	Capitol	EAP120111	1961	£5	£10	
Leadbelly	7" EP	Melodisc	EPM777	1958	£7.50	£15	
Leadbelly	7" EP	Storyville	SEP337	196-	£5	£10	
Leadbelly	10" LP	Capitol	H369	195-	£37.50	£75	U
Leadbelly	10" LP	Folkways	14	1960	£5	£12	U
Leadbelly	10" LP	Folkways	24	1960	£5	£12	U

Title	Format	Label	Cat. No.	Year	Low	High	Notes
Leadbelly	10" LP	Folkways	43	1960	£5	£12	US
Leadbelly	10" LP	Folkways	4	1960	£5	£12	US
Leadbelly 2	LP	Storyville	SLP139	1964	£5	£12	
Leadbelly Set	LP	XTRA	XTRAD1017	1965	£10	£25	Double
Leadbelly Vol.1	10" LP	Melodisc	MLP511	1957	£6	£15	
Leadbelly Vol.2	10" LP	Melodisc	MLP512	1957	£6	£15	
Leadbelly Vol.3	10" LP	Melodisc	MLP515	1958	£6	£15	
Ledbetter's Best	7" EP	Capitol	EAP11821	1961	£5	£10	
Ledbetter's Best	7" EP	Capitol	EAP41821	1961	£5	£10	
Legendary Performances Never Before Released	LP	CBS	64103	1970	£4	£10	
Library Of Congress Recordings	LP	Elektra	EKL301/2	1966	£10	£25	US, 3 LPs boxed
Memorial Vol.3	LP	Stinson	SLP48	1962	£6	£15	US, red vinyl
Midnight Special	LP	RCA	LPV505	1964	£6	£12	
Party Plays And Songs	7" EP	Melodisc	EPM787	1959	£5	£10	
Plays Party Songs	10" LP	Melodisc	MLP517	1958	£6	£15	
Rock Island Line	7" EP	RCA	RCX146	1959	£4	£8	
Rock Island Line	10" LP	Folkways	2014	1960	£8	£20	US
Saga Of Leadbelly	LP	Melodisc	MLP12107	1958	£6	£15	
See See Rider	7" EP	Melodisc	EPM782	1958	£7.50	£15	
Shout On	LP	XTRA	XTRA1126	1971	£6	£15	
Sinful Songs	10" LP	Allegro	4027	195-	£15	£30	US
Sings And Plays	LP	Saga	SOC994	1965	£5	£12	
Sings Folk Songs	LP	XTRA	XTRA1046	1966	£6	£15	
Storyville Blues Anthology Vol.7	7" EP	Storyville	SEP387	1963	£5	£10	
Take This Hammer	LP	Verve	(S)VLP5002	1965	£5	£12	

LEADERS
| Night People | 7" | Fontana | TF602 | 1965 | £1.50 | £4 | |

LEADERS (2)
| Tit For Tat | 7" | Amalgamated | AMG804 | 1968 | £4 | £8 | Marvetts B side |

LEADING FIGURES
| Oscillation '67 | LP | Deram | DML/SML1006 | 1967 | £6 | £15 | |
| Sound And Movement | LP | Ace Of Clubs | SCL1225 | 1967 | £6 | £15 | |

LEAFHOUND
Some records gain a reputation within the collectors' market out of all proportion to their musical worth. The Leafhound LP is very much a case in point - the cover and its title imply some kind of psychedelic masterpiece, whereas the music is actually rather ordinary hard rock, with a singer who would love to be Robert Plant, but who sadly is not. The lead guitarist manages the odd nice phrase or two, though...

Growers Of Mushrooms	LP	Decca	SKLR5094	1971	£470	£700	
Growers Of Mushrooms	LP	Discwasher	TP396	1978	£25	£50	US, with poster
Leafhound	LP	Telefunken	14604	197-	£25	£50	German

LEAGUE OF GENTLEMEN
| Each Little Falling Tear | 7" | Columbia | DB7666 | 1965 | £6 | £12 | |
| How Can You Tell | 7" | Planet | PLF109 | 1966 | £10 | £20 | |

LEANDER, MIKE
| Heroes | 7" | Decca | F11849 | 1964 | £1.50 | £4 | |

LEAPER, BOB
| High Wire | 7" | Pye | 7N15700 | 1965 | £1.50 | £4 | |

LEAPERS CREEPERS SLEEPERS
| Ba Boo | 7" | Island | WI275 | 1966 | £5 | £10 | |

LEAR, KEVIN 'KING'
Count Me Out	7"	Polydor	BM56203	1967	£5	£10	
Cry Me A River	7"	Page One	POF109	1968	£5	£10	
Power Of Love	7"	Page One	POF087	1968	£2	£5	
Snake	7"	Page One	POF1332	1969	£4	£8	

LEARY, TIMOTHY
L.S.D.	LP	Pixie	CA1069	1966	£15	£30	US
Turn On, Tune In, Drop Out	LP	ESP	1027	1966	£10	£25	US
Turn On, Tune In, Drop Out	LP	Mercury	MG2/SR61131	1967	£8	£20	US
You Can Be Anyone This Time Around	LP	Douglas	1	196-	£15	£30	US

LEATHER COATED MINDS
| Trip Down Sunset Strip | LP | Fontana | (S)TL5412 | 1967 | £25 | £50 | |

LEATHER NUN
| Slow Death | 7" | Industrial | IR0006 | 1979 | £4 | £8 | |

LEATHERCOATED MINDS
The album by the Leathercoated Minds contains the recording debut of J.J.Cale, although those seeking the roots of his inimitable sleepy guitar and singing style will be disappointed. Instead the music is exactly the kind of fare that bad sixties films included in their soundtracks whenever a party was shown. As is often the case in the record collectors' market, a high price tag is no guarantee of musical quality!

LEAVES
All The Good That's Happening	LP	Capitol	(S)T2638	1967	£15	£30	US
Hey Joe	LP	Mire	(LPS)3005	1966	£15	£30	US
Hey Joe	7"	Fontana	TF713	1966	£7.50	£15	

LEAVILL, OTIS
I Love You	7"	Atlantic	2091015	1970	£1.50	£4	
Love Uprising	7"	Atlantic	2091035	1970	£1.50	£4	
There's Nothing Better	7"	Atlantic	2091160	1971	£1.50	£4	

LED ZEPPELIN

Original pressings of the Led Zeppelin LPs I - IV are easily identified by their purple and red Atlantic labels and pre-Kinney catalogue numbers, but for the very first LP, it is possible to identify which copies were issued during the few weeks following its release. These all have covers on which the title and company name are printed in turquoise, instead of the orange which has been used on every copy since. Similarly, the very first copies of the third LP are identifiable by the message "Do what thou wilt" scratched in the vinyl, although there are many more copies like this than some collectors imagine. The rarest Led Zeppelin records are the early UK singles, which exist in demonstration form only due to the group's constant refusal to allow their full commercial release.

Black Dog	7"	Atlantic	2849	1971	£1.50	£4	US
Communication Breakdown	7"	Atlantic	584269	1969	£75	£150	demo
Dazed And Confused	7" EP	Atlantic	1019	1969	£100	£200	US
D'yer Maker	7"	Atlantic	2986	1973	£1.50	£4	US
D'yer Maker	7"	Atlantic	K10296	1973	£30	£60	demo
Good Times Bad Times	7"	Atlantic	2613	1969	£5	£10	US
Houses Of THe Holy	7" EP	Atlantic	PR213	1973	£30	£60	US promo
Immigrant Song	7"	Atlantic	2777	1970	£4	£8	US
In Through The Out Door	LP	Swansong	SSK59410	1979	£40	£80	set of 6 LPs in different sleeves A-F
Led Zeppelin	LP	Atlantic	588171	1969	£5	£12	chart LP
Led Zeppelin	LP	Atlantic	588171	1969	£10	£25	turquoise lettering on cover
Led Zeppelin	7" EP	Atlantic	171	1970	£30	£60	US
Led Zeppelin 2	LP	Atlantic	588198	1969	£5	£12	chart LP
Led Zeppelin 2	LP	Mobile Fidelity	MFSL1065	1980	£10	£25	US audiophile
Led Zeppelin 3	LP	Atlantic	2401002	1970	£10	£25	'Do what thou wilt' scratched in vinyl
Led Zeppelin 3	LP	Atlantic	2401002	1970	£5	£12	chart LP
Led Zeppelin 3	LP	Atlantic	2401012	1970	£60	£120	test pressing with alternate mixes
Led Zeppelin 3	LP	Atlantic	SD7201	1971	£20	£40	US mono pressing
Led Zeppelin 4	LP	Atlantic	2401012	1971	£4	£10	chart LP
Led Zeppelin 4	LP	Atlantic	K50008/C8814	1988	£6	£15	HMV boxed set
Led Zeppelin 4	LP	Atlantic	K50008	1978	£15	£30	purple vinyl
Led Zeppelin IV	CD	Atlantic	K50008/C8814	1988	£8	£20	HMV boxed set
Over The Hills And Far Away	7"	Atlantic	2970	1973	£1.50	£4	US
Remasters	CD-s	Atlantic	CDLZ1	1990	£10	£25	4 track promo
Remasters	10"	Atlantic	LZ2	1990	£10	£25	4 track promo
Rock And Roll	7"	Atlantic	2865	1972	£1.50	£4	US
Stairway To Heaven	7"	Atlantic	LZ3	1990	£50	£100	promo with letter
Stairway To Heaven	7"	Atlantic	LZ3LC	1990	£6	£12	jukebox issue
Stairway To Heaven	7" EP	Atlantic	PR175	1973	£37.50	£75	US promo, PS
Stairway To Heaven	7" EP	Atlantic	PR269	1973	£12.50	£25	US promo
Trampled Underfoot	7"	Swan Song	DC1	1979	£6	£12	custom sleeve
Whole Lotta Love	7"	Atlantic	2690	1969	£1.50	£4	US
Whole Lotta Love	7"	Atlantic	584309	1969	£180	£300	demo

LED ZEPPELIN & DUSTY SPRINGFIELD

Climb Aboard Led Zeppelin/Dusty In Memphis	LP	Atlantic	TLST135	1969	£20	£40	US promo

LEE, ARTHUR

Ninth Wave	7"	Capitol	4980	1964	£15	£30	US
Vindicator	LP	A&M	AMLS64356	1972	£6	£15	

LEE, BENNY

Love Plays The Strings Of My Banjo	7"	Parlophone	MSP6214	1956	£1.50	£4	
Rock 'n' Rollin' Santa Claus	7"	Parlophone	R4245	1956	£5	£10	
Sweet Heartaches	7"	Parlophone	MSP6252	1956	£1.50	£4	

LEE, BRENDA

Ain't Gonna Cry No More	7"	Brunswick	05963	1966	£1.50	£4	
Ain't That Love	7"	Brunswick	05720	1957	£30	£60	
All Alone Am I	LP	Brunswick	LAT/STA8530	1962	£6	£15	chart LP
All Alone Am I	7"	Brunswick	05882	1963	£1.50	£4	chart single
All Alone Am I	7" EP	Brunswick	OE9492	1963	£6	£12	
All The Way	LP	Brunswick	LAT8383/STA3048	1961	£6	£15	chart LP
Alone With You	7"	Brunswick	05911	1964	£1.50	£4	
As Usual	7"	Brunswick	05899	1964	£1.50	£4	chart single
Bill Bailey	7"	Brunswick	05780	1959	£6	£12	tri-centre
Break It To Me Gently	7"	Brunswick	05864	1962	£1.50	£4	chart single
By Request	LP	Brunswick	LAT/STA8576	1964	£6	£15	
Bye Bye Blues	LP	Brunswick	LAT/STA8649	1966	£5	£12	chart LP
Call Me	LP	MCA	MUP(S)321	1968	£5	£12	
Christmas Will Be Just Another Lonely Day	7"	Brunswick	05921	1964	£1.50	£4	chart single
Coming On Strong	LP	Brunswick	LAT/STA8672	1967	£6	£15	
Coming On Strong	7"	Brunswick	05967	1966	£1.50	£4	chart single
Dum Dum	7"	Brunswick	05854	1961	£1.50	£4	chart single
Emotions	LP	Brunswick	LAT8376/STA3044	1961	£8	£20	
Emotions	7"	Brunswick	05847	1961	£1.50	£4	chart single
Fairyland	7"	Decca	BM31186	1958	£20	£40	export
Fool Number One	7"	Brunswick	05860	1961	£1.50	£4	chart single
For The First Time	LP	MCA	MUP(S)332	1968	£4	£10	with Pete Fountain
Four From Sixty Four	7" EP	Brunswick	OE9510	1965	£7.50	£15	
Good Life	LP	MCA	MUP(S)322	1968	£4	£10	
Grandma What Great Songs	LP	Brunswick	LAT8319	1958	£15	£30	
Here Comes That Feeling	7"	Brunswick	05871	1962	£1.50	£4	chart single
I Want To Be Wanted	7"	Brunswick	05839	1960	£1.50	£4	chart single
I Wonder	7"	Brunswick	05891	1963	£1.50	£4	chart single
I'm Gonna Lassoo Santa Claus	7"	Brunswick	05628	1956	£37.50	£75	
I'm Sorry	7"	Brunswick	05833	1960	£4	£8	chart single

Title	Format	Label	Cat No	Year	Price	Price	Notes
Is It True	7"	Brunswick	05915	1964	£1.50	£4	chart single
It Started All Over Again	7"	Brunswick	05876	1962	£1.50	£4	chart single
Johnny One Time	LP	MCA	MUP(S)396	1970	£4	£10	
Let Me Sing	LP	Brunswick	LAT/STA8548	1963	£6	£15	
Let's Jump The Broomstick	7"	Brunswick	05823	1960	£2	£5	chart single
Losing You	7"	Brunswick	05886	1963	£1.50	£4	chart single
Love You	LP	Ace Of Hearts	AH59	1963	£6	£15	
Love You Till I Die	7"	Brunswick	05685	1957	£30	£60	
Love You Till I Die	7" EP	Brunswick	OE9462	1961	£15	£30	tri-centre
Merry Christmas	LP	MCA	MUP(S)330	1968	£4	£10	
Merry Christmas From Brenda	LP	Brunswick	LAT/STA8590	1964	£8	£20	
Miss Dynamite	LP	Brunswick	LAT8347	1959	£10	£25	
Pretend	7" EP	Brunswick	OE9482	1962	£7.50	£15	
Reflections In Blue	LP	MCA	MUP(S)306	1968	£5	£12	
Ride Ride Ride	7"	Brunswick	05970	1967	£1.50	£4	
Ring A My Phone	7"	Brunswick	05755	1958	£25	£50	
Rockin' Around The Christmas Tree	7"	Brunswick	05880	1962	£1.50	£4	chart single
Rusty Bells	7"	Brunswick	05943	1965	£1.50	£4	
Show For Christmas Seals	LP	Decca	MG(7)9226	1962	£6	£15	US
Sincerely	LP	Brunswick	LAT8396/STA3056	1961	£6	£15	
Speak To Me Pretty	7"	Brunswick	05867	1962	£1.50	£4	chart single
Speak To Me Pretty	7" EP	Brunswick	OE9488	1962	£6	£12	
Sweet Impossible You	7"	Brunswick	05896	1963	£1.50	£4	chart single
Sweet Nothings	7"	Brunswick	05819	1960	£7.50	£15	chart single, tri-centre
Ten Golden Years	LP	Decca	DL(7)4757	1966	£5	£12	US, gatefold
Thanks A Lot	7"	Brunswick	05927	1965	£1.50	£4	chart single
That's All	LP	Brunswick	LAT/STA8516	1962	£6	£15	chart LP
That's All Right	7"	Decca	AD1003	1968	£5	£10	export
Think	7"	Brunswick	05903	1964	£1.50	£4	chart single
This Is Brenda Lee	LP	Brunswick	LAT8360	1960	£8	£20	
Too Little Time	7"	Brunswick	05957	1966	£1.50	£4	
Too Many Rivers	LP	Brunswick	LAT/STA8622	1965	£6	£15	
Too Many Rivers	7"	Brunswick	05936	1965	£1.50	£4	chart single
Top Teen Hits	LP	Brunswick	LAT/STA8603	1965	£6	£15	
Tribute To Al Jolson	7" EP	Brunswick	OE9499	1964	£7.50	£15	
Truly Truly True	7"	Brunswick	05933	1965	£1.50	£4	
Versatile Brenda Lee	LP	Brunswick	LAT8614	1965	£5	£12	
Where's The Melody	7"	Brunswick	05976	1967	£2.50	£6	
You Can Depend On Me	7"	Brunswick	05849	1961	£1.50	£4	

LEE, BUNNY ALL STARS

Title	Format	Label	Cat No	Year	Price	Price	Notes
Leaping With Mr.Lee	LP	Island	ILP986	1968	£30	£60	

LEE, BYRON

Title	Format	Label	Cat No	Year	Price	Price	Notes
Caribbean Jungle	LP	Island	ILP905	1964	£20	£40	
Dumplings	7"	Blue Beat	BB2	1960	£5	£10	Buddy Davidson B side
Every Day Will Be Like A Holiday	7"	Major Minor	MM615	1969	£2	£5	
Jamaica Ska	7"	Parlophone	R5182	1964	£2.50	£6	
Joy Ride	7"	Starlite	ST45045	1961	£2.50	£6	
Mash Mr.Lee	7"	Blue Beat	BB28	1961	£5	£10	Keith Lynn B side
Mr.Walker	7"	Trojan	TR631	1968	£2.50	£6	
My Sweet Lord	7"	Dynamic	DYN409	1971	£1.50	£4	
Night Train From Jamaica	7"	MGM	MGM1256	1964	£2.50	£6	
Reggae	LP	Trojan	TRLS18	1972	£4	£10	
Reggae Blast Off	LP	Trojan	TBL110	1970	£4	£10	
Reggae Hot Cool Easy	LP	Trojan	TRLS40	1972	£4	£10	
Reggae Splash Down	LP	Trojan	TRLS28	1972	£4	£10	
River Bank	7"	Parlophone	R5124	1964	£2.50	£6	
Rocksteady Explosion	LP	Trojan	TTL5	1969	£4	£10	
Say Bye Bye	7"	Parlophone	R5140	1964	£2.50	£6	
Ska Time	7" EP	Atlantic	AET6014	1965	£7.50	£15	
Sloopy	7"	Doctor Bird	DB1003	1966	£5	£10	
Sloopy	7"	Pyramid	PYR6015	1967	£4	£8	
Soul Limbo	7"	Trojan	TR624	1968	£2.50	£6	
Soul Serenade	7"	Duke	DU39	1969	£2.50	£6	
Sound Of Jamaica	LP	Tower Hall	LP006	1970	£10	£25	US
Sour Apples	7"	Parlophone	R5125	1964	£2.50	£6	
Too Late	7"	Parlophone	R5177	1964	£2.50	£6	
Walk Like A Dragon	7"	Island	WI220	1965	£5	£10	Ken Lazarus B side
Way Back Home	7"	Dynamic	DYN414	1971	£1.50	£4	

LEE, CURTIS

Title	Format	Label	Cat No	Year	Price	Price	Notes
Get My Bag	7"	CBS	2717	1967	£7.50	£15	
Night At Daddy Gees	7"	London	HLX9533	1962	£4	£8	
Pledge Of Love	7"	London	HLX9313	1961	£4	£8	
Pretty Little Angel Eyes	7"	London	HLX9397	1961	£4	£8	chart single
Under The Moon Of Love	7"	London	HLX9445	1961	£5	£10	
With All My Heart	7"	Top Rank	JAR317	1960	£10	£20	

LEE, DAVE

Title	Format	Label	Cat No	Year	Price	Price	Notes
Adam Adamant	7"	Fontana	TF723	1966	£2	£5	
Take Four	7"	Decca	F11600	1963	£1.50	£4	

LEE, DEREK

Title	Format	Label	Cat No	Year	Price	Price	Notes
Girl	7"	Parlophone	R5468	1966	£4	£8	

LEE, DICKIE

Title	Format	Label	Cat No	Year	Price	Price	Notes
Don't Want To Think About Paula	7"	Mercury	AMT1200	1962	£1.50	£4	
I Saw Linda Yesterday	7"	Mercury	AMT1196	1962	£2.50	£6	

Laurie	7"	Stateside	SS433	1965	£1.50	£4	
Patches	7"	Mercury	AMT1190	1962	£1.50	£4	
Penny A Kiss, A Penny A Hug	7"	MGM	MGM1013	1959	£10	£20	

LEE, DINAH

I Can't Believe What You Say	7"	Aladdin	WI608	1965	£4	£8	
I'll Forgive You Then Forget You	7"	Aladdin	WI606	1965	£4	£8	

LEE, DON TONY

It's Reggae Time	7"	Big Shot	BI504	1968	£4	£8	Errol Dunkley B side
It's Reggae Time	7"	Island	WI3160	1968	£5	£10	Errol Dunkley B side
Lee's Special	7"	Doctor Bird	DB1106	1967	£5	£10	Lloyd & The Groovers B side

LEE, FREDDIE FINGERS

Bossy Boss	7"	Columbia	DB8002	1966	£2	£5	
Friendly Undertaker	7"	Fontana	TF619	1965	£6	£12	
I'm Gonna Buy Me A Dog	7"	Fontana	TF655	1966	£5	£10	

LEE, JACKIE

Duck	LP	Joy	JOYS192	1971	£4	£10	
Duck	LP	London	HAM8336	1967	£5	£12	
Duck	LP	Mirwood	SW7000	1966	£8	£20	US
Duck	7"	Fontana	TF646	1965	£5	£10	
Duck	7"	London	HLM10233	1968	£1.50	£4	
Oh My Darling	7"	Jayboy	BOY66	1972	£2	£5	
Whether It's Right Or Wrong	7"	B&C	CB105	1969	£2	£5	with Delores Hall
Would You Believe	7"	Jayboy	BOY28	1970	£1.50	£4	

LEE, JACKIE (2)

Rancho	7"	Top Rank	JAR286	1960	£1.50	£4	

LEE, JACKIE (3)

I Know, Know, Know	7"	Columbia	DB7860	1966	£1.50	£4	
Lonely Clown	7"	Columbia	DB7685	1965	£1.50	£4	
Rupert	7"	Pye	7N45003	1970	£1.50	£4	chart single
Town I Live In	7"	Columbia	DB8052	1966	£1.50	£4	

LEE, JAMIE & THE ATLANTICS

In The Night	7"	Decca	F11571	1963	£10	£20	

LEE, JIMMY

All My Life	7"	Starlite	ST45059	1961	£7.50	£15	

LEE, JOHNNIE

Cindy Lou	7"	Fontana	H257	1960	£1.50	£4	
Kiss Tomorrow Goodbye	7"	CBS	202591	1967	£2	£5	
Lonely Joe	7"	Fontana	H306	1961	£1.50	£4	
Poetry In Motion	7"	Fontana	H280	1960	£1.50	£4	

LEE, JULIA

Party Time	LP	Capitol	T228	1955	£15	£30	US
Party Time	10" LP	Capitol	LC6535	1952	£20	£40	

LEE, LADY

When Love Comes Along	7"	Decca	F11961	1964	£1.50	£4	

LEE, LAURA

As Long As I Got You	7"	Chess	CRS8070	1968	£2	£5	
Dirty Man	7"	Chess	CRS8062	1967	£2	£5	
Rip Off	7"	Hot Wax	HWX115	1972	£1.50	£4	
To Win Your Heart	7"	Tamla Motown	TMG831	1972	£1.50	£4	
Two Sides Of Laura Lee	LP	Hot Wax	SHW5009	1972	£5	£12	
Wedlock Is A Padlock	7"	Hot Wax	HWX118	1973	£1.50	£4	
Woman's Love Rights	LP	Hot Wax	SHW5006	1972	£5	£12	
You've Got The Love To Save Me	7"	Hot Wax	HWX119	1973	£1.50	£4	

LEE, LAURA (2)

Brand New Heartbeat	7"	Decca	F11513	1962	£2.50	£6	
Tell Tommy I Miss Him	7"	Triumph	RGM1030	1960	£7.50	£15	

LEE, LEAPY

King Of The Whole Wide World	7"	Decca	F12369	1966	£10	£20	
Little Arrows	7"	MCA	MU1028	1968	£1.50	£4	chart single

LEE, NICKIE

And Black Is Beautiful	7"	Deep Soul	DS9103	1970	£2.50	£6	

LEE, PEGGY

All Aglow Again	LP	Capitol	T1366	1961	£4	£10	
Alright Okay You Win	7" EP	Capitol	EAP11213	1959	£2.50	£6	
Basin Street East Presents	LP	Capitol	(S)T1520	1962	£4	£10	
Baubles, Bangles And Beads	7"	Brunswick	05421	1955	£1.50	£4	
Beauty And The Beat	LP	Capitol	(S)T1219	1960	£4	£10	with George Shearing
Beauty And The Beat Pt.1	7" EP	Capitol	EAP71219	1960	£2	£5	with George Shearing
Beauty And The Beat Pt.2	7" EP	Capitol	EAP81219	1960	£2	£5	with George Shearing
Beauty And The Beat Pt.3	7" EP	Capitol	EAP91219	1960	£2	£5	with George Shearing
Bella Notte	7"	Brunswick	05483	1955	£1.50	£4	
Black Coffee	LP	Ace Of Hearts	AH5	1961	£4	£10	
Black Coffee	LP	Decca	DL8358	1956	£6	£15	US
Black Coffee	10" LP	Brunswick	LA8629	1953	£6	£15	

Title	Format	Label	Cat. No.	Year			Notes
Blues Cross Country	LP	Capitol	(S)T1671	1962	£4	£10	
Capitol Presents Peggy Lee	10" LP	Capitol	LC6584	1953	£6	£15	
Christmas Carousel	LP	Capitol	(S)T1423	1961	£4	£10	
Dream Street	LP	Brunswick	LAT8171	1957	£6	£15	
Favourites	7" EP..	Capitol	EAP120074	1961	£2	£5	
Fever	7"	Capitol	CL14902	1958	£1.50	£4	chart single
Fever	7" EP..	Capitol	EAP11052	1959	£2.50	£6	
He Needs Me	7"	Brunswick	05472	1955	£1.50	£4	
He's A Tramp	7"	Brunswick	05482	1955	£2.50	£6	
I Belong To You	7"	Brunswick	05435	1955	£1.50	£4	
I Go To Sleep	7"	Capitol	CL15413	1965	£1.50	£4	
I Like Men	LP	Capitol	(S)T1131	1959	£4	£10	
If You Go	LP	Capitol	(S)T1630	1962	£4	£10	
I'm A Woman	7" EP..	Capitol	EAP41857	1961	£2.50	£6	
In The Name Of Love	7" EP..	Capitol	EAP42096	1963	£2	£5	
Is That All There Is?	LP	Capitol	T386	1956	£5	£12	US
Johnny Guitar	7"	Brunswick	05286	1954	£2.50	£6	
Jump For Joy	LP	Capitol	(S)T979	1957	£5	£12	
Jump For Joy	7" EP..	Capitol	EAP1979	1958	£2	£5	
Lady And The Tramp	10" LP	Brunswick	LA8731	1956	£6	£15	
Latin A La Lee	LP	Capitol	(S)T1290	1960	£4	£10	
Latin A La Lee Pt.1	7" EP..	Capitol	SEP51290	1961	£2.50	£6	stereo
Latin A La Lee Pt.2	7" EP..	Capitol	SEP61290	1961	£2.50	£6	stereo
Latin A La Lee Pt.3	7" EP..	Capitol	SEP71290	1961	£2.50	£6	stereo
Let Me Go Lover	7"	Brunswick	05360	1955	£2.50	£6	
Man I Love	LP	Capitol	T864	1956	£5	£12	US
Mink Jazz	LP	Capitol	(S)T1850	1964	£4	£10	
Miss Wonderful	LP	Brunswick	LAT8287	1959	£4	£10	
Mr.Wonderful	7"	Brunswick	05671	1957	£1.50	£4	chart single
My Best To You	10" LP	Capitol	H204	1952	£8	£20	US
My Best To You	10" LP	Capitol	LC6817	1956	£6	£15	
Ole A La Lee	LP	Capitol	(S)T1475	1966	£4	£10	
Ole A La Lee Pt.1	7" EP..	Capitol	SEP11475	1961	£2.50	£6	stereo
Ole A La Lee Pt.2	7" EP..	Capitol	SEP21475	1961	£2.50	£6	stereo
Ooh That Kiss	7"	Brunswick	05461	1955	£1.50	£4	
Peggy With Benny	7" EP..	Philips	BBE12172	1958	£2.50	£6	with Benny Goodman
Pete Kelly's Blues	LP	Brunswick	LAT8078	1955	£6	£15	
Pete Kelly's Blues No.1	7" EP..	Brunswick	OE9153	1955	£2	£5	
Pete Kelly's Blues No.2	7" EP..	Brunswick	OE9154	1955	£2	£5	
Presenting Peggy Lee	7" EP..	Brunswick	OE9282	1956	£2	£5	
Pretty Eyes	LP	Capitol	(S)T1401	1960	£4	£10	
Rendezvous	10" LP	Capitol	H155	1952	£8	£20	US
Sea Shells	LP	Brunswick	LAT8266	1958	£5	£12	
Sisters	7"	Brunswick	05345	1954	£2	£5	
Songs In An Intimate Style	10" LP	Brunswick	LA8717	1955	£6	£15	
Songs In Intimate Style	10" LP	Decca	DL5539	1953	£8	£20	US
Straight Ahead	7"	Brunswick	05368	1955	£2	£5	
Sugar	7"	Brunswick	05471	1955	£1.50	£4	
Sugar And Spice	7" EP..	Capitol	EAP11772	1961	£2	£5	
Things Are Swingin'	LP	Capitol	T1049	1959	£4	£10	
Things Are Swingin'	7" EP..	Capitol	EAP11049	1959	£2	£5	
Three Cheers For Mister Magoo	7"	Brunswick	05549	1956	£1.50	£4	

LEE, ROBERTA

Title	Format	Label	Cat. No.	Year			Notes
Ridin' To Tennessee	7"	Brunswick	05388	1955	£1.50	£4	
True Love And Tender Care	7"	HMV	7M261	1954	£1.50	£4	

LEE, ROBIN

Title	Format	Label	Cat. No.	Year			Notes
Gamblin' Man	7"	Reprise	R20068	1962	£4	£8	

LEE, ROY

Title	Format	Label	Cat. No.	Year			Notes
Two Initials	7"	Decca	F11406	1961	£1.50	£4	

LEE, VINNY & THE RIDERS

Title	Format	Label	Cat. No.	Year			Notes
Gamblers Guitar	7"	HMV	POP856	1961	£4	£8	

LEEMAN, MARK FIVE

Title	Format	Label	Cat. No.	Year			Notes
Blow My Blues Away	7"	Columbia	DB7648	1965	£7.50	£15	
Follow Me	7"	Columbia	DB7955	1966	£6	£12	
Forbidden Fruit	7"	Columbia	DB7812	1966	£6	£12	
Portland Town	7"	Columbia	DB7452	1965	£6	£12	

LEER, THOMAS

Title	Format	Label	Cat. No.	Year			Notes
Private Plane	7"	Oblique	ER101	1978	£2.50	£6	

LEES, JOHN

Title	Format	Label	Cat. No.	Year			Notes
Best Of My Love	7"	Polydor	2058513	1974	£1.50	£4	

LEESIDERS

Title	Format	Label	Cat. No.	Year			Notes
Leesiders	LP	Ash	ALP105S	1970	£25	£50	

LEFEVRE, RAYMOND

Title	Format	Label	Cat. No.	Year			Notes
Soul Coaxing	7"	Major Minor	MM559	1968	£1.50	£4	chart single

LEFT BANKE

Title	Format	Label	Cat. No.	Year			Notes
Desiree	7"	Philips	BF1614	1967	£4	£8	
Desiree	7"	Philips	BF1614	1967	£7.50	£15	PS
Ivy Ivy	7"	Philips	BF1575	1967	£2.50	£6	
Pretty Ballerina	7"	Philips	BF1540	1967	£2.50	£6	
Too	LP	Smash	SRS67113	1968	£15	£30	US
Walk Away Renee	LP	Philips	(S)BL7773	1967	£15	£30	

Walk Away Renee	7"	Philips	BF1517	1966	£4	£8	

LEFT END
Spoiled Rotten	LP	Polydor	PD6022	1975	£8	£20	US

LEFT HANDED MARIAGE
On The Right Side Of The Left Handed Marriage	LP	private		1967	£470	£700	

LEGAY
No One	7"	Fontana	TF904	1969	£30	£60	

LEGEND
Don't You Know	7"	Vertigo	6059036	1971	£4	£8	
Georgia George	7"	Bell	BLL1082	1970	£4	£8	
Legend	LP	Bell	MBLL/SBLL115	1969	£25	£50	...sleeve pictured in Guide
Life	7"	Vertigo	6059021	1971	£2.50	£6	
Moonshine	LP	Vertigo	6360063	1972	£25	£50	spiral label
National Gas	7"	Bell	BLL1048	1969	£4	£8	
Red Boot Album	LP	Vertigo	6360019	1971	£25	£50	spiral label

LEGEND (2)
73 In '83	7"	Creation	CRE001	1983	£2.50	£6	
73 In '83	7"	Creation	CRE001	1983	£5	£10	.with flexi (by Pastels/ Laughing Apple)
Destroys The Blues	7"	Creation	CRE010	1984	£2.50	£6	

LEGEND (3)
Death In The Nursey	LP	Workshop	WR3477	1982	£4	£10	
Legend	LP	Workshop		1980	£4	£10	

LEGEND (4)
Legend	LP	Megaphone	101	1970	£8	£20	US

LEGENDS
I've Found Her	7"	Pye	7N15904	1965	£2.50	£6	
Let Loose	LP	Capitol	(S)T1925	1963	£8	£20	US
Let Loose	LP	Ermine	101	1963	£15	£30	US
Tomorrows's Gonna Be Another Day	7"	Parlophone	R5581	1967	£7.50	£15	
Under The Sky	7"	Parlophone	R5613	1967	£5	£10	

LEGRAND, MICHEL
Legrand Jazz	LP	Philips	BBL7328/SBBL510	1959	£5	£12	
Legrand Piano	LP	Philips	BBL7378/SBBL572	1960	£5	£12	
Never Say Never Again	LP	Seven Seas	K28P4122	1983	£25	£50	Japanese

LEGRAND, MICHEL & GIL ASKEY
Love Theme From Lady Sings The Blues	7"	Tamla Motown	TMG848	1973	£1.50	£4	
Love Theme From Lady Sings The Blues	7"	Tamla Motown	TMG848	1973	£7.50	£15	demo, PS

LEGS DIAMOND
Diamond Is A Hard Rock	LP	Mercury	SRM11191	1979	£10	£25	US
Fire Power	LP	Cream	1010	1978	£5	£12	US
Legs Diamond	LP	Mercury	SRM11136	1978	£10	£25	US

LEHRER, TOM
Evening Wasted	LP	Decca	LK4332/SKL4097	1960	£6	£15	chart LP
More Of Tom Lehrer	10" LP	Decca	LF1323	1959	£6	£15	
Poisoning Pigeons In The Park	7"	Decca	F11243	1960	£1.50	£4	
Poisoning Pigeons In The Park	7"	Decca	F11243	1960	£4	£8	PS
Pollution	7"	Reprise	RS23049	1966	£1.50	£4	
Songs By Tom Lehrer	10" LP	Decca	LF1311	1958	£6	£15	chart LP
Tom Lehrer Revisited	LP	Decca	LK4375	1960	£5	£12	

LEIBER, JERRY
Scooby-Doo	LP	Kapp	KL1127	1959	£10	£25	US

LEIBER STOLLER ORCHESTRA
Blue Baion	7"	HMV	POP1050	1962	£4	£8	
Yakety Yak	LP	Atlantic	(SD)847	1960	£8	£20	US

LEIBSTANDARTE SS
Triumph Of The Will	LP	Come Organisation		1981	£30	£60	
Weltanschauung	LP	Come Organisation		198-	£30	£60	

LEIGH, ANDY
Magician	LP	Polydor	2343034	1970	£6	£15	

LEMER, PETE
Local Colour	LP	ESP	1057	1968	£30	£60	US

LEMMINGS
Out Of My Mind	7"	Pye	7N15837	1965	£4	£8	
You Can't Blame Me For Trying	7"	Pye	7N15899	1965	£4	£8	

LEMON KITTENS
Big Dentist	LP	Illuminated	JAMS131	1982	£20	£40	

Title	Format	Label	Catalogue	Year	Price	Price	Notes
Cake Beast	12"	United Dairies	UD07	1981	£8	£20	
Spoonfed And Writhing	7"	Step Forward	SF10	1979	£6	£12	
We Buy A Hammer For Daddy	LP	United Dairies	UD02	1980	£25	£50	

LEMON LINE

Title	Format	Label	Catalogue	Year	Price	Price	Notes
For Your Precious Love	7"	Decca	F12688	1967	£1.50	£4	

LEMON MEN

Title	Format	Label	Catalogue	Year	Price	Price	Notes
I've Seen You Cut Lemons	7"	Polydor	56365	1969	£2	£5	

LEMON PIPERS

Title	Format	Label	Catalogue	Year	Price	Price	Notes
Green Tambourine	LP	Buddah	2349006	1970	£4	£10	
Green Tambourine	LP	Pye	NPL28112	1968	£5	£12	
Green Tambourine	7"	Pye	7N25444	1968	£1.50	£4	chart single
Jelly Jungle	7"	Pye	7N25464	1968	£4	£8	
Jungle Marmalade	LP	Pye	NSPL28118	1969	£4	£10	
Rice Is Nice	7"	Pye	7N25454	1968	£1.50	£4	chart single

LEMON PIPERS & 1910 FRUITGUM COMPANY

Title	Format	Label	Catalogue	Year	Price	Price	Notes
Presenting	7" EP	Pye	NEP44091	1968	£2.50	£6	

LEMON TREE

Title	Format	Label	Catalogue	Year	Price	Price	Notes
It's So Nice To Come Home	7"	Parlophone	R5739	1968	£5	£10	
William Chalker's Time Machine	7"	Parlophone	R5671	1968	£6	£12	

LEMONHEADS

Title	Format	Label	Catalogue	Year	Price	Price	Notes
Different Drum	7"	Roughneck	HYPE3	1990	£1.50	£4	
Gonna Get Along Without Ya Now	7"	Atlantic	A7709	1991	£2	£5	
Gonna Get Along Without Ya Now	12"	Atlantic	TA7709	1991	£3	£8	
Hate Your Friends	LP	Taang!	T15	1987	£8	£20	US, yellow label and sleeve lettering
Hate Your Friends	LP	Taang!	T15	1987	£6	£15	US, yellow label, sleeve lettering, vinyl
It's A Shame About Ray	10"	Atlantic	A7423TE	1992	£2.50	£6	
Laughing All The Way To The Cleaners	7"	Armory Arms	1/2/Huh-Bag1	1986	£37.50	£75	US
Luka	7"	Taang!	TAANG031	1989	£2	£5	

LENNON, FREDDIE

John Lennon's father was one of the many people who tried to divert a little piece of Beatlemania in his own direction, but with no more success than most of the others.

Title	Format	Label	Catalogue	Year	Price	Price	Notes
That's My Life	7"	Piccadilly	7N35290	1966	£15	£30	
That's My Life	7" EP	Pye	PNV24172	1966	£20	£40	French, B side by Brian Diamond & The Cutters

LENNON, JIMMY & THE ATLANTICS

Title	Format	Label	Catalogue	Year	Price	Price	Notes
I Learned To Yodel	7"	Decca	F11825	1964	£6	£12	

LENNON, JOHN

The expensive albums recorded by John Lennon and Yoko Ono together are rare because, at the height of the Beatles influence and popularity, even John Lennon could not sell records of a foetal heartbeat, inconsequential chatter, ambient noises, and the like. Later Lennon-Ono collaborations include some excellent and underrated pieces of rock avant garde, such as the superbly cathartic "Open Your Box", but the early records are strictly for the completist. The American "Roots" album is not a bootleg (although bootleg copies of the Adam VIII original do exist). The owner of the label claimed that Lennon had assigned the album to him and began an intensive TV advertising campaign for it. Lennon disagreed, however, and won a court injunction for the record's withdrawal. "Roots" is of particular interest to collectors because it consists of the original version of the LP that became "Rock'n'Roll" - all the tracks are Phil Spector productions and the selection of songs is slightly different.

Title	Format	Label	Catalogue	Year	Price	Price	Notes
Cold Turkey	7"	Apple	1001	1969	£6	£12	PS
Cold Turkey	7"	Apple	1001	1969	£100	£200	two skulls (on one side) PS
Every Man Has A Woman Who Loves Him	7"	Polydor	POSP712	1984	£1.50	£4	with poster
Give Peace A Chance	7"	Apple	13	1969	£5	£10	PS
Give Peace A Chance	7"	Apple	R5795	1969	£10	£20	
Happy First Birthday Capital Radio	7"	Warner Bros	SAM20	1974	£10	£20	promo
Imagine	LP	Apple	PAS10004	1971	£4	£10	inner, postcard, chart LP
Imagine	LP	Apple	Q4PAS10004	1974	£50	£100	quad
Imagine	LP	Mobile Fidelity	MFSL1153	1984	£6	£15	US audiophile
Imagine	LP	Apple	R6009	1975	£4	£8	PS
Imagine	7"	Parlophone	RP6199	1988	£1.50	£4	pic disc
Instant Karma	7"	Apple	1003	1970	£6	£12	PS
John Lennon Collection	LP	Geffen	LS2023	1982	£6	£15	US audiophile promo
John Lennon On Ronnie Hawkins	7"	Atlantic	PRO104	1970	£22.50	£45	US promo
John Lennon On Ronnie Hawkins	7"	Cotillion	PR105	1970	£15	£30	US promo
Milk And Honey	LP	Polydor	POLHP5	1984	£6	£15	pic disc (thin & dished)
Milk And Honey	LP	Polydor	POLHP5	1984	£10	£25	pic disc, thick
Mind Games	7"	Apple	R5994	1973	£2.50	£6	PS
Number Nine Dream (2 versions)	7"	Apple	R6003DJ	1974	£10	£20	promo
Power To The People	7"	Apple	R5892	1971	£4	£8	PS
Roots	LP	Adam VIII	LP8018	1975	£100	£200	US
Stand By Me	7"	Apple	R6005	1975	£1.50	£4	
Whatever Gets You Thru The Night	7"	EMI	PSR369	1974	£100	£200	interview promo
Woman Is The Nigger Of The World	7"	Apple	R5953	1972	£100	£200	demo only
You Know My Name	7"	Apple	1002	1969	£1050	£1500	test pressing

LENNON, JOHN & YOKO ONO

Title	Format	Label	Catalogue	Year	Price	Price	Notes
Double Fantasy	LP	Nautilus	NR47	1980	£10	£25	US audiophile, poster
Happy Xmas (War Is Over)	7"	Apple	R5970	1972	£6	£12	PS, green vinyl

KYA Peace Talk	LP	Capitol	KYA1969	1969	£15	£30	US promo
Live Peace In Toronto	LP	Apple	CORE2001	1969	£20	£40	with calendar
Unfinished Music No.1: Two Virgins	LP	Apple	APCOR2	1968	£470	£700	mono
Unfinished Music No.1: Two Virgins	LP	Apple	SAPCOR2	1968	£60	£120	stereo
Unfinished Music No.2: Life With The Lions	LP	Apple	ZAPPLE1	1969	£30	£60	
Unfinished Music No.2: Life With The Lions	LP	Apple	ZAPPLE1	1969	£35	£70	with card insert
Wedding Album	LP	Apple	SAPCOR11	1969	£65	£130	boxed, inserts

LENNON, JULIAN

Too Late For Goodbyes	7"	Charisma	JLY1	1984	£2.50	£6	pic disc
Valotte	7"	Charisma	JLS2	1984	£2.50	£6	shaped pic disc

LENNON SISTERS

Graduation Day	7"	Vogue Coral	Q72176	1956	£1.50	£4	
Sad Movies	7"	London	HLD9417	1961	£1.50	£4	
Shake Me I Rattle	7"	Vogue Coral	Q72285	1957	£2.50	£6	
Young And In Love	7"	Vogue Coral	Q72259	1957	£1.50	£4	

LENOIR, J.B.

Alabama Blues	LP	CBS	62593	1966	£8	£20	
Crusade	LP	Polydor	2482014	1970	£4	£10	
I Sing The Way I Feel	7"	Sue	WI339	1965	£6	£12	
J.B.Lenoir	LP	Python	PLP25	1972	£8	£20	
J.B.Lenoir	LP	Rarity	LP2	1975	£6	£15	
Man Watch Your Woman	7"	Bootleg	503	1965	£10	£20	
Mojo Boogie	7"	Blue Horizon	451004	1966	£12.50	£25	
Natural Man	LP	Chess	1410	1963	£8	£20	US

LENT, ROBIN

Scarecrow's Journey	LP	Nepentha	6437002	1971	£8	£20	

LENTILMAS

The Lentilmas flexi-disc was a promotional release given away to journalists as a 1977 Christmas present. The record is supposed to contain Christmas carols sung by the Sex Pistols.

	7"	Virgin		1977	£60	£120	flexi

LENTON, VAL

You Don't Care	7"	Immediate	IM008	1965	£7.50	£15	

LEONARD, DEKE

Nothing Is Happening	7"	United Artists	UP35556	1973	£2	£5	demo

LEONETTI, TOMMY

Dream Lover	7"	RCA	RCA1107	1959	£1.50	£4	
Ever Since You Went Away	7"	Capitol	CL14272	1955	£1.50	£4	
That's What You Made Me	7"	Capitol	CL14199	1954	£1.50	£4	

LEO'S SUNSHIPP

Give Me The Sunshine	12"	Grapevine	REDC3	1979	£4	£10	

LEROY & ROCKY

Love Me Girl	7"	Studio One	SO2042	1968	£6	£12	Wrigglers B side

LEROYS

California GL903	7"	HMV	POP1368	1964	£2	£5	
Chills	7"	HMV	POP1312	1964	£4	£8	
Don't Cry Baby	7"	HMV	POP1274	1964	£2.50	£6	
Money	7"	Lyntone	LYN504	1963	£4	£8	flexi

LES COMPAGNONS DE LA CHANSON

Galley Slave	7"	Columbia	SCM5056	1953	£1.50	£4	
Song Successes In English	7" EP	Columbia	SEG7829	1958	£2	£5	
Three Bells	7"	Columbia	DB4358	1959	£1.50	£4	chart single
Three Bells	7"	Columbia	SCM5005	1953	£2	£5	

LES FLAMBEAUX

Les Flambeaux	LP	Mushroom	100MR13	1971	£15	£30	

LES HOBEAUX

Dynamo	7"	HMV	POP444	1958	£5	£10	
Mama Don't Allow	7"	HMV	POP403	1957	£4	£8	
Oh Mary Don't You Weep	7"	HMV	POP377	1957	£4	£8	
Soho Skiffle	7" EP	HMV	7EG8297	1957	£7.50	£15	

LES MISSILES

Les Missiles De France	7" EP	Columbia	SEG8371	1964	£2	£5	

LES PLAYERS

Les Players	7" EP	Polydor	EPH27129	1965	£2	£5	

LES SAUTERELLES

Heavenly Club	7"	Decca	F22824	1968	£12.50	£25	

LES YPER SOUND

Too Fortiche	7"	Fontana	TF880	1967	£20	£40	

LES ZARJAZ

One Charming Nyte	7"	Creation	CRE013	1985	£2	£5	

LESH, PHIL & NED LAGIN

Seastones	LP	Round	RX106	1975	£8	£20	US

LESLEY, LORNE

So High So Low	7"	Parlophone	R4581	1959	£1.50	£4
We're Gonna Dance	7"	Polydor	NH66956	1960	£2.50	£6

LESLEY, MICHAEL

Make Up Or Break Up	7"	Pye	7N15959	1965	£4	£8

LESLIE, JOHN & CHRIS

Ship Of Time	LP	Cottage	COT901	1976	£8	£20

LESTER, KETTY

But Not For Me	7"	London	HLN9574	1962	£1.50	£4	chart single
Ketty Lester	7" EP	London	REN1348	1962	£7.50	£15	
Looking For A Better World	7"	RCA	RCA1460	1965	£1.50	£4	
Love Letters	LP	Era	EL/ES108	1963	£8	£20	US
Love Letters	7"	London	HLN9527	1962	£2	£5	chart single
Roses Grow With Thorns	7"	RCA	RCA1403	1964	£7.50	£15	
Some Things Are Better Left Unsaid	7"	RCA	RCA1394	1964	£25	£50	
Soul Of Me	LP	RCA	RD7669	1964	£4	£10	
West Coast	7"	Capitol	CL15427	1965	£7.50	£15	
When A Man Loves A Woman	7"	Capitol	CL15447	1966	£1.50	£4	
Where Is Love	LP	RCA	RD7712	1965	£4	£10	
You Can't Lie To A Liar	7"	London	HLN9608	1962	£1.50	£4	

LETTERMEN

Lettermen	7" EP	Capitol	EAP41669	1961	£2.50	£6

LETTS, DON & JAH WOBBLE

Steel Leg: Stratetime And The Wide Man	7"	Virgin	VS239	1979	£2.50	£6

LEVEE BREAKERS

Baby I'm Leaving You	7"	Parlophone	R5291	1965	£7.50	£15

LEVEE CAMP MOAN

Levee Camp Moan	LP	County		1969	£250	£400
Peacock Farm	LP	County		1969	£250	£400

LEVEL 42

Children Say	7"	Polydor	POSPP911	1987	£1.50	£4	pic disc
Chinese Way	12"	Polydor	POSPPX538	1983	£3	£8	double
Chinese Way	12"	Polydor	POSPX538	1983	£6	£15	yellow vinyl
Hot Water	12"	Polydor	POSPA799	1986	£8	£20	
Leaving Me Now	10"	Polydor	POSPT776	1985	£2.50	£6	
Love Meeting Love	12"	Elite	DAZZ5	1980	£20	£40	no PS
Love Meeting Love	12"	Polydor	POSPX170	1980	£2.50	£6	no PS
Micro-Kid	12"	Polydor	POSPX643	1983	£6	£15	double
Micro-Kid	12"	Polydor	POSPX643	1983	£3	£8	with cassette
Out Of Sight Out Of Mind	7"	Polydor	POSPP570	1983	£2	£5	pic disc
Out Of Sight Out Of Mind	12"	Polydor	POSPP570	1984	£8	£20	pic disc
Out Of Sight Out Of Mind	12"	Polydor	POSPX570	1984	£2.50	£6	
Sandstorm	12"	Elite	DAZZ4	1980	£45	£90	promo
Something About You	10"	Polydor	POSPT759	1985	£2.50	£6	
Strategy	LP	Elite	LEVLP1	1981	£250	£400	test pressing only
To Be With You Again	7"	Polydor	POSPP855	1987	£1.50	£4	pic disc
Wings Of Love	7"	Polydor	POSP200	1980	£1.50	£4	no PS
Wings Of Love	12"	Polydor	POSPX200	1980	£4	£10	no PS
Wings Of Love (Remix)	12"	Polydor	POSPX200	1981	£6	£15	no PS
You Can't Blame Louis	12"	Polydor	POSPX500	1982	£20	£40	test pressing, no PS

LEVELLERS

Agreement Of The People	cass	private		1989	£6	£15	
All The Free Commons Of England	cass	private		1988	£6	£15	
Carry Me	12"	Hag	HAG005	1989	£8	£20	Brighton address on sleeve
Live 1992	LP	On The Fiddle	OTFLP2	1992	£5	£12	
Outside Inside	7"	Hag	HAG006	1989	£6	£12	promo only
Outside Inside	12"	Hag	HAG126	1989	£3	£8	Twickenham address on sleeve
Police On My Back	12"	On The Fiddle	OTFEP1	1991	£2.50	£6	

LEVENE, GERRY & THE AVENGERS

Doctor Feelgood	7"	Decca	F11815	1964	£10	£20

LEVEY, STAN

Grand Stan	LP	London	LTZN15100	1957	£6	£15
This Time The Drum's On Me	LP	Parlophone	PMC1086	1959	£6	£15

LEVIATHAN

Flames	7"	Elektra	EKSN45075	1969	£7.50	£15
Remember The Times	7"	Elektra	EKSN45052	1968	£10	£20
War Machine	7"	Elektra	EKSN45057	1969	£10	£20

LEVINE, HANK

Image	7"	HMV	POP1390	1965	£1.50	£4
Image	7"	HMV	POP947	1961	£4	£8

LEVITATION
Need For Not	LP	Rough Trade	R2861	1992	£5	£12	with 7'

(LEV001) and etching

LEVON & THE HAWKS
Go Go, Lisa Jane	7"	Atco	6625	1968	£7.50	£15	US
Stones I Throw	7"	Atlantic	AT4054	1965	£7.50	£15	

LEVY, BEN
Doren	7"	Ska Beat	JB245	1966	£5	£10	
I'll Make You Glad	7"	Ska Beat	JB255	1966	£5	£10	

LEWIE, JONA
On The Other Hand There's A Fist	LP	Stiff	SEEZP8	1978	£4	£10	pic disc

LEWIS, ALVA
Return Home	7"	Caltone	TONE111	1967	£4	£8	King Rock B side

LEWIS, BARBARA
Baby I'm Yours	LP	Atlantic	ATL5042	1966	£8	£20	
Baby I'm Yours	7"	Atlantic	AT4031	1965	£4	£8	
Baby What Do You Want Me To Do	7"	Atlantic	584061	1967	£7.50	£15	
Don't Forget About Me	7"	Atlantic	AT4068	1966	£4	£8	
Hello Stranger	LP	Atlantic	(SD)8086	1963	£10	£25	US
Hello Stranger	7"	Atlantic	584153	1968	£2	£5	
Hello Stranger	7"	London	HLK9724	1963	£5	£10	
It's Magic	LP	Atlantic	587002	1966	£6	£15	
Make Me Belong To You	7"	Atlantic	584037	1966	£2	£5	
Make Me Your Baby	7"	Atlantic	AT4041	1965	£4	£8	
Pushing A Good Thing Too Far	7"	Atlantic	AT4013	1964	£4	£8	
Sho-Nuff	7"	Atlantic	584174	1968	£2.50	£6	
Snap Your Fingers	LP	Atlantic	(SD)8090	1964	£10	£25	US
Snap Your Fingers	7"	London	HLK9832	1964	£5	£10	
Snap Your Fingers	7" EP	Atlantic	AET6015	1965	£10	£20	
Some Day We're Gonna Love Again	7"	Atlantic	2091143	1971	£2.50	£6	
Straighten Up Your Heart	7"	London	HLK9779	1963	£5	£10	
Workin' On A Groovy Thing	LP	Atlantic	SD8173	1968	£6	£15	US

LEWIS, BOBBY
I'm Tossing And Turning Again	7"	Stateside	SS126	1962	£4	£8	
One Track Mind	7"	Parlophone	R4831	1961	£4	£8	
Tossing And Turning	LP	Beltone	4000	1961	£25	£50	US
Tossing And Turning	7"	Parlophone	R4794	1961	£5	£10	

LEWIS, DAVE
Giving Gas	7" EP	Pye	NEP44057	1966	£6	£12	

LEWIS, DAVID
Songs Of David Lewis	LP	private	AX1	1970	£330	£500	

LEWIS, FURRY
Back On My Feet Again	LP	Bluesville	BV(S)1036	1961	£10	£25	US
Early Years 1927-9	LP	Spookane	SPL1004	1971	£10	£25	
Furry Lewis	LP	Folkways	FS3823	1961	£10	£25	
Furry Lewis	LP	Xtra	XTRA116	1971	£5	£12	
In Memphis	LP	Saydisc	SDR190	1970	£4	£10	
Presenting The Country Blues	LP	Blue Horizon	763228	1969	£20	£40	

LEWIS, GARY & THE PLAYBOYS
Count Me In	7"	Liberty	LIB55778	1965	£4	£8	
Count Me In	7" EP	Liberty	LEP2236	1965	£7.50	£15	French
Everybody Loves A Clown	LP	Liberty	LRP3428/LST7428	1965	£6	£15	US
Everybody Loves A Clown	7"	Liberty	LIB55818	1965	£1.50	£4	
Everybody Loves A Clown	7" EP	Liberty	LEP2241	1965	£7.50	£15	French
Girls In Love	7"	Liberty	LIB55971	1967	£1.50	£4	
Golden Greats	LP	Liberty	LRP3468/LST7468	1966	£6	£15	US
Green Grass	7"	Liberty	LIB55880	1966	£1.50	£4	
Hits Again	LP	Liberty	LRP3452/LST7452	1966	£6	£15	US
Jill	7"	Liberty	LBF15025	1967	£2.50	£6	
Just Our Style	LP	Liberty	LBY1322	1967	£5	£12	
Listen	LP	Liberty	LRP3524/LST7524	1967	£5	£12	US
Loser	7"	Liberty	LIB55949	1967	£1.50	£4	
My Heart's Symphony	7"	Liberty	LIB55898	1966	£6	£12	
New Directions	LP	Liberty	LRP3519/LST7519	1967	£5	£12	US
Orangutan	7"	Liberty	LBF15335	1970	£1.50	£4	
Paint Me A Picture	7"	Liberty	LIB55914	1966	£1.50	£4	
Save Your Heart For Me	7"	Liberty	LIB55809	1965	£1.50	£4	
Sealed With A Kiss	7"	Liberty	LBF15131	1968	£1.50	£4	
Session With Gary Lewis	LP	Liberty	LRP3419/LST7419	1965	£6	£15	US
She's Just My Style	LP	Liberty	LRP3435/LST7435	1966	£6	£15	US
She's Just My Style	7"	Liberty	LIB55846	1966	£1.50	£4	
Sure Gonna Miss Her	7"	Liberty	LIB55865	1966	£1.50	£4	
This Diamond Ring	LP	Liberty	LBY1259	1965	£8	£20	
This Diamond Ring	7"	Liberty	LIB10187	1965	£1.50	£4	
This Diamond Ring	7" EP	Liberty	LEP2216	1965	£7.50	£15	French
Where Will The Words Come From	7"	Liberty	LIB55933	1967	£1.50	£4	
Where Will The Words Come From	7" EP	Liberty	LEP2270	1967	£7.50	£15	French
You Don't Have To Paint Me A Picture	LP	Liberty	LRP3487/LST7487	1967	£5	£12	US

LEWIS, GEORGE
Blues From The Bayou	LP	HMV	CLP1371/CSD1309	1960	£6	£15	

Title	Format	Label	Catalog #	Year			Notes
Concert	LP	Blue Note	BLP/BST81208	196-	£8	£20	
Dallas Blues	7" EP	Storyville	SEP504	196-	£2	£5	
Doctor Jazz	LP	HMV	CLP1413/CSD1337	1961	£6	£15	
George Lewis	7" EP	Tempo	EXA101	1959	£2	£5	
George Lewis	7" EP	Tempo	EXA62	1957	£2	£5	
George Lewis	7" EP	Tempo	EXA66	1957	£2	£5	
George Lewis	7" EP	Tempo	EXA97	1958	£2	£5	
George Lewis And His New Orleans Allstars	10" LP	Vogue	LDE012	1952	£8	£20	
George Lewis And His New Orleans Ragtime Band	10" LP	Esquire	20086	1957	£6	£15	
George Lewis And His New Orleans Stompers	LP	Vogue	LAE12005	1955	£8	£20	
George Lewis And His New Orleans Stompers	7" EP	Tempo	EXA15	1956	£2	£5	
George Lewis And His New Orleans Stompers	7" EP	Vogue	EPV1066	1955	£2	£5	
George Lewis And His New Orleans Stompers	7" EP	Vogue	EPV1081	1956	£2	£5	
George Lewis In Hi Fi	7" EP	Vogue	EPV1220	1959	£2	£5	
George Lewis In Hi Fi	7" EP	Vogue	EPV1252	1959	£2	£5	
George Lewis Jam Session	10" LP	Vogue	LDE082	1954	£8	£20	
George Lewis Ragtime Band	LP	Tempo	TAP13	1957	£6	£15	
George Lewis Ragtime Band	10" LP	Esquire	20067	1956	£8	£20	
George Lewis Ragtime Band	10" LP	Esquire	20073	1956	£8	£20	
George Lewis' Ragtime Band	7" EP	Tempo	EXA70	1957	£2	£5	
George Lewis Vol.1	LP	Blue Note	BLP/BST81205	196-	£8	£20	
George Lewis Vol.2	LP	Blue Note	BLP/BST81206	196-	£8	£20	
High Society	7" EP	Storyville	SEP503	196-	£2	£5	
Ice Cream	7" EP	Storyville	SEP315	195-	£2	£5	
Isle Of Capri	7" EP	Storyville	SEP365	1961	£2	£5	
Jazz At Preservation Hall Vol.4	LP	London	HAK/SHK8165	1964	£6	£15	
Jazz At Vespers	LP	London	LTZU15112	1958	£6	£15	
Jazz From New Orleans	7" EP	Storyville	SEP349	1960	£2	£5	
Louisiana	7" EP	Storyville	SEP322	195-	£2	£5	
Muskrat Ramble	7" EP	Storyville	SEP369	1961	£2	£5	
New Orleans Music	7" EP	Good Time Jazz	EPG1182	195-	£2	£5	
New Orleans Ragtime Band Vol.1	7" EP	Esquire	EP125	1957	£2	£5	
New Orleans Ragtime Band Vol.2	7" EP	Esquire	EP135	1957	£2	£5	
New Orleans Ragtime Band Vol.3	7" EP	Esquire	EP155	1957	£2	£5	
New Orleans Ragtime Band Vol.4	7" EP	Esquire	EP175	1958	£2	£5	
New Orleans Ragtime Band Vol.5	7" EP	Esquire	EP209	1959	£2	£5	
New Orleans Ragtime Band Vol.6	7" EP	Esquire	EP211	1959	£2	£5	
New Orleans Ragtime Band Vol.7	7" EP	Esquire	EP215	1959	£2	£5	
New Orleans Ragtime Band Vol.8	7" EP	Esquire	EP219	1959	£2	£5	
New Orleans Ragtime Band Vol.9	7" EP	Esquire	EP225	1960	£2	£5	
Newport Jazz Festival 1957	LP	Columbia	33CX10099	1958	£6	£15	Side 2 by Turk Murphy
Panama	7" EP	Storyville	SEP321	195-	£2	£5	
Perennial George Lewis	LP	Columbia	33CX10131	1959	£6	£15	
Raggin' And Stompin'	10" LP	Columbia	33C9042	1959	£6	£15	
Smile Darn Ya Smile	LP	77	LA1228	1964	£6	£15	
Sounds Of New Orleans	7" EP	HMV	7EG8540	1960	£2	£5	
Till We Meet Again	7" EP	Storyville	SEP361	1961	£2	£5	
Vol.1 Jazz Band	10" LP	London	HAPB1041	1955	£8	£20	
Vol.2 All Stars	10" LP	London	HBU1045	1956	£8	£20	
Willie The Weeper	7" EP	Storyville	SEP325	195-	£2	£5	

LEWIS, HOPETON

Title	Format	Label	Catalog #	Year			Notes
Boom Shacka Lacka	7"	Duke Reid	DR2505	1970	£2.50	£6	Tommy McCook B side
Everybody Rocking	7"	Island	WI3076	1968	£5	£10	
Grooving Out On Life	LP	Trojan	TRL36	1971	£5	£12	
Judgement Day	7"	Treasure Isle	TI7071	1972	£2	£5	Earl Lindo B side
Let Me Come On Home	7"	Island	WI3056	1967	£5	£10	
Let The Little Girl Dance	7"	Island	WI3059	1967	£5	£10	
Rock A Shacka	7"	Island	WI3068	1967	£5	£10	
Rock Steady	7"	Island	WI3054	1967	£5	£10	
Run Down	7"	Island	WI3057	1967	£5	£10	
Take It Easy	LP	Island	ILP957	1967	£30	£60	
Testify	7"	Duke Reid	DR2516	1970	£2.50	£6	Tommy McCook B side
To The Other Man	7"	Treasure Isle	TI7060	1971	£2	£5	Tommy McCook B side

LEWIS, JENNIFER

Title	Format	Label	Catalog #	Year			Notes
Bring It To Me	7"	Columbia	DB7662	1965	£1.50	£4	

LEWIS, JERRY

Title	Format	Label	Catalog #	Year			Notes
Capitol Presents	10" LP	Capitol	LC6591	1953	£4	£10	
Rock-a-bye Your Baby With A Dixie Melody	7"	Brunswick	05636	1957	£1.50	£4	chart single

LEWIS, JERRY LEE

Title	Format	Label	Catalog #	Year			Notes
Another Place, Another Time	7"	Mercury	MF1020	1968	£1.50	£4	
Another Time, Another Place	LP	Mercury	SMWL21011	1969	£4	£10	
Baby Baby Bye Bye	7"	London	HLS9131	1960	£4	£8	chart single
Baby Hold Me Close	7"	Philips	BF1407	1965	£1.50	£4	
Break Up	7"	London	HLS8700	1958	£6	£12	

483

Title	Format	Label	Cat. No.	Year	Price	Price	Notes
Breathless	LP	London	HAS8323	1966	£10	£25	
Breathless	7"	London	HLS8592	1958	£6	£12	chart single
By Request - More Greatest Live Show On Earth	LP	Philips	(S)BL7746	1967	£5	£12	
Carry Me Back To Old Virginia	7"	London	HLS9980	1965	£2.50	£6	
Country Songs For City Folks	LP	Philips	BL7688	1965	£5	£12	
Country Style	7" EP	Philips	BE12599	1966	£5	£10	
Fabulous Jerry Lee Lewis Vol.1	7" EP	Sun	JLLEP001	197-	£5	£10	
Fabulous Jerry Lee Lewis Vol.2	7" EP	Sun	JLLEP002	197-	£5	£10	
Four More From Jerry Lee Lewis	7" EP	London	RES1378	1963	£10	£20	
Golden Hits	LP	Philips	BL7622	1964	£5	£12	
Good Golly Miss Molly	7"	London	HL7120	1963	£5	£10	export
Good Golly Miss Molly	7"	London	HLS9688	1963	£1.50	£4	chart single
Got You On My Mind	LP	Fontana	SFJL964	1968	£4	£10	
Great Balls Of Fire	7"	London	HLS8529	1957	£7.50	£15	chart single
Great Balls Of Fire	7"	Mercury	MF1024	1964	£1.50	£4	
Great Balls Of Fire	7"	Mercury	MF1110	1969	£1.50	£4	
Greatest Live Show On Earth	LP	Philips	(S)BL7650	1964	£5	£12	
Hang Up My Rock & Roll Shoes	7"	London	HLS9202	1960	£4	£8	
Hi Heel Sneakers	7"	Philips	BF1371	1965	£1.50	£4	
High School Confidential	7"	London	HL7050	1958	£7.50	£15	export
High School Confidential	7"	London	HLS8780	1959	£7.50	£15	chart single
Hit The Road Jack	7"	Mercury	AMT1216	1963	£2	£5	
I'll Sail My Ship Alone	7"	London	HLS9083	1960	£4	£8	
I'm On Fire	LP	Mercury	SMCL20156	1969	£4	£10	
I'm On Fire	7"	Philips	BF1324	1964	£2.50	£6	
In The Mood	7"	London	HL7123	1963	£12.50	£25	export
It Won't Happen With Me	7"	London	HLS9414	1961	£2	£5	
It's A Hang Up Baby	7"	Philips	BF1594	1967	£1.50	£4	
Jerry Lee Lewis	LP	London	HAS2138	1959	£15	£30	
Jerry Lee Lewis	LP	Sun	SLP1230	1958	£30	£60	US
Jerry Lee Lewis No.1	7" EP	London	RES1140	1958	£12.50	£25	tri-centre
Jerry Lee Lewis No.2	7" EP	London	RES1186	1959	£12.50	£25	tri-centre
Jerry Lee Lewis No.3	7" EP	London	RES1187	1959	£10	£20	
Jerry Lee Lewis No.4	7" EP	London	RES1296	1961	£10	£20	
Jerry Lee Lewis No.5	7" EP	London	RES1336	1962	£7.50	£15	
Jerry Lee Lewis No.6	7" EP	London	RES1351	1963	£7.50	£15	
Jerry Lee Lewis Vol.2	LP	London	HAS2440	1962	£10	£25	chart LP
Jerry Lee's Greatest	LP	Sun	SLP1265	1961	£37.50	£75	US
Let's Talk About Us	7"	London	HLS8941	1959	£4	£8	tri-centre
Lewis Boogie	7"	London	HLS9867	1964	£4	£8	
Little Queenie	7"	London	HLS8993	1959	£5	£10	tri-centre
Live At The Star Club Hamburg	LP	Philips	BL7646	1965	£5	£12	with The Nashville Teens
Long Tall Sally	7"	Mercury	MF1105	1969	£2	£5	
Loving Up A Storm	7"	London	HLS8840	1959	£5	£10	chart single
Memphis Beat	LP	Philips	(S)BL7706	1967	£5	£12	
Memphis Beat	7"	Philips	BF1521	1966	£1.50	£4	
Rambling Rose	7"	London	HLS9526	1962	£2	£5	
Return Of Rock	LP	Philips	(S)BL7668	1967	£5	£12	
Rocking Pneumonia	7"	Philips	BF1425	1965	£1.50	£4	
Save The Last Dance For Me	7"	London	HL7117	1962	£12.50	£25	export
She Still Comes Around	LP	Mercury	SMCL21047	1969	£4	£10	
Shotgun Man	7"	Philips	BF1615	1967	£1.50	£4	
Soul My Way	LP	Mercury	20117MCL	1968	£5	£12	
Sunstroke	LP	Ember	NR5038	1966	£4	£10	with Carl Perkins
Sweet Little Sixteen	7"	London	HLS9584	1962	£1.50	£4	chart single
Teenage Letter	7"	London	HLS9722	1963	£2.50	£6	
Together	LP	Mercury	SMCL20172	1970	£4	£10	with Linda Gail Lewis
What'd I Say	7"	London	HLS10193	1968	£1.50	£4	
What'd I Say	7"	London	HLS9335	1961	£1.50	£4	chart single
When I Get Paid	7"	London	HLS9446	1961	£2	£5	
Whole Lotta Shaking Goin' On	LP	London	HAS8251	1965	£10	£25	
Whole Lotta Shaking Going On	7"	London	HLS8457	1957	£10	£20	chart single
You Win Again	7"	London	HLS8559	1958	£10	£20	

LEWIS, JIMMY

Title	Format	Label	Cat. No.	Year	Price	Price	Notes
Girl From Texas	7"	Minit	MLF11002	1968	£7.50	£15	

LEWIS, JOHN

Title	Format	Label	Cat. No.	Year	Price	Price	Notes
Afternoon In Paris	LP	Oriole	MG20036	1960	£4	£10	with Sacha Distel
Cool!	LP	Fontana	FJL106	1964	£4	£10	
Golden Striker	LP	London	LTZK15218	1961	£4	£10	
Grand Encounter	LP	Vogue	LAE12065	1958	£10	£25	with Bill Perkins
Improvised Meditations And Excursions	LP	London	LTZK15186	1960	£5	£12	
Odds Against Tomorrow	LP	London	HAT2220	1960	£5	£12	
Wonderful World Of Jazz	LP	London	LTZK15237	1961	£5	£12	

LEWIS, LINDA

Title	Format	Label	Cat. No.	Year	Price	Price	Notes
You Turn My Bitter Into Sweet	7"	Polydor	56173	1967	£20	£40	

LEWIS, MARGARET

Title	Format	Label	Cat. No.	Year	Price	Price	Notes
Something's Wrong Baby	7"	Starlite	ST45081	1962	£5	£10	

LEWIS, MEADE LUX

Title	Format	Label	Cat. No.	Year	Price	Price	Notes
Barrel House Piano	LP	Tops	L1533		£8	£20	US
Blues Piano Artistry	LP	Riverside	9402		£8	£20	US
Boogie Woogie And Blues	7" EP	Melodisc	EPM7107	1956	£15	£30	

Title	Format	Label	Catalogue	Year			Notes
Boogie Woogie Piano And Drums No.1	7" EP..	Columbia	SEB10030	1956	£5	£10	
Boogie Woogie Piano And Drums No.2	7" EP..	Columbia	SEB10052	1957	£5	£10	
House Party	LP	Philips	652014BL	1962	£6	£15	
Jazz At The Philharmonic	10" LP	Columbia	33C9021	1956	£6	£15	with Slim Gaillard
Meade Lux Lewis	7" EP..	Vogue	EPV1065	1955	£15	£30	
Out Of The Roaring Twenties	LP	HMV	DLP1176	1958	£6	£15	
Yancey's Last Ride	LP	Columbia	33CX10094	1957	£8	£20	

LEWIS, MIA

Title	Format	Label	Catalogue	Year			Notes
Nothing Lasts Forever	7"	Parlophone	R5526	1966	£5	£10	

LEWIS, RAMSEY

Title	Format	Label	Catalogue	Year			Notes
1-2-3	7"	Chess	CRS8055	1967	£1.50	£4	
At The Bohemian Caverns	LP	Pye	NJL55	1965	£5	£12	
Back To The Blues	LP	Cadet	732	1964	£4	£10	US
Barefoot Sunday Blues	LP	Cadet	723	1964	£4	£10	US
Choice	LP	Chess	CRL4518	1966	£5	£12	
Cry Baby Cry	7"	Chess	CRS8096	1969	£2	£5	
Dancin' In The Street	LP	Chess	CRL(S)4533	1968	£4	£10	
Down To Earth	LP	Fontana	SFJL962	1968	£4	£10	
Function At The Junction	7"	Chess	CRS8058	1967	£1.50	£4	
Girl Talk	7"	Chess	CRS8061	1967	£1.50	£4	
Goin' Latin	LP	Chess	CRL4528	1967	£5	£12	
Hang On Ramsey	LP	Chess	CRL4517	1966	£6	£15	chart LP
Hang On Sloopy	7"	Chess	CRS8024	1965	£2	£5	
Hard Day's Night	7"	Chess	CRS8029	1966	£1.50	£4	
Hard Day's Night	7" EP..	Chess	CRE6019	1966	£4	£8	
Hi Heel Sneakers	7"	Chess	CRS8031	1966	£1.50	£4	
Hour With	LP	Cadet	645	1959	£6	£15	US
In Crowd	LP	Chess	CRL4511	1965	£6	£15	
In Crowd	7"	Chess	CRS8020	1965	£4	£8	
Julia	7"	Chess	CRS8104	1970	£1.50	£4	
More Music From Soul	LP	Cadet	680	1962	£5	£12	US
More Sounds Of Christmas	LP	Chess	CRL4504	1965	£5	£12	
Movie Album	LP	Chess	CRL4531	1967	£5	£12	
Never On Sunday	LP	Cadet	686	1962	£5	£12	US
Pot Luck	LP	Cadet	715	1964	£4	£10	US
Saturday Night After The Movies	7"	Chess	CRS8060	1967	£1.50	£4	
Soul Man	7"	Chess	CRS8064	1967	£1.50	£4	
Sound Of Christmas	LP	Cadet	693	1964	£4	£10	US
Stretchin' Out	LP	Cadet	665	1962	£5	£12	US
Swingin'	LP	Cadet	771	1966	£5	£12	US
Uptight	7"	Chess	CRS8044	1966	£2	£5	
Wade In The Water	LP	Chess	CRL4522	1966	£6	£15	
Wade In The Water	7"	Chess	CRS8041	1966	£4	£8	

LEWIS, RICHARD

Title	Format	Label	Catalogue	Year			Notes
Hey Little Girl	7"	Downbeat	CHA1	1960	£5	£10	

LEWIS SISTERS

Title	Format	Label	Catalogue	Year			Notes
You Need Me	7"	Tamla Motown	TMG536	1965	£20	£40	

LEWIS, SMILEY

Title	Format	Label	Catalogue	Year			Notes
Big Mamou	78	London	L1189	1953	£20	£40	
Don't Be That Way	7"	London	HLU8337	1956	£180	£300	
Hear You Knocking	LP	Imperial	LP9141	1961	£60	£120	US
Hear You Knocking	7"	Liberty	LBF15337	1970	£1.50	£4	
One Night	7"	London	HLU8312	1956	£180	£300	
Shame Shame Shame	7"	London	HLP8367	1957	£120	£220	
Shame, Shame, Shame	LP	Liberty	LBS83308	1970	£6	£15	

LEWIS, STEVIE

Title	Format	Label	Catalogue	Year			Notes
Take Me For A Little While	7"	Mercury	MF871	1965	£4	£8	

LEWIS, TINY

Title	Format	Label	Catalogue	Year			Notes
Too Much Rocking	7"	Parlophone	R4617	1959	£30	£60	

LEYTON, JOHN

Title	Format	Label	Catalogue	Year			Notes
All I Want Is You	7"	HMV	POP1374	1964	£2.50	£6	with Mike Sarne & Grazina Frame
Always Yours	LP	HMV	CLP1664	1962	£17.50	£35	
Beautiful Dreamer	7"	HMV	POP1230	1963	£2	£5	
Beautiful Dreamer	7" EP..	HMV	7EG8843	1964	£10	£20	
Cupboard Love	7"	HMV	POP1122	1963	£1.50	£4	chart single
Dancing In The Graveyard	7"	York	SYK551	1973	£1.50	£4	
Don't Let Her Go Away	7"	HMV	POP1338	1964	£2.50	£6	
Down The River Nile	7"	HMV	POP1054	1962	£2	£5	
Girl On The Floor Above	7"	HMV	POP798	1960	£25	£50	
I'll Cut Your Tail Off	7"	HMV	POP1175	1963	£2	£5	chart single
John Leyton	LP	York	FYK416	1973	£5	£12	
John Leyton	7" EP..	Top Rank	JKP3016	1962	£12.50	£25	
John Leyton Hit Parade	7" EP..	HMV	7EG8747	1962	£7.50	£15	
Johnny Remember Me	7"	Top Rank	JAR577	1961	£1.50	£4	chart single
Lone Rider	7"	HMV	POP992	1962	£2.50	£6	chart single
Lonely City	7"	HMV	POP1014	1962	£1.50	£4	chart single
Lonely Johnny	7"	HMV	POP1076	1962	£2	£5	
Make Love To Me	7"	HMV	POP1264	1964	£2	£5	
On Lovers' Hill	7"	HMV	POP1204	1963	£2	£5	

Rock 'n' Roll	7"	York	YR210	1974	£1.50	£4	
Son This Is She	7"	HMV	POP956	1961	£1.50	£4	chart single
Tell Laura I Love Her	7"	Top Rank	JAR426	1960	£12.50	£25	
Tell Laura I Love Her	7" EP.	HMV	7EG8854	1964	£12.50	£25	
Two Sides Of John Leyton	LP	HMV	CLP1497	1961	£10	£25	
Wild Wind	7"	Top Rank	JAR585	1961	£1.50	£4	chart single

LIAR
Set The World On Fire	LP	Bearsville	K55524	1978	£4	£10	pic disc

LIBERACE
I Don't Care	7"	Columbia	DB4834	1956	£1.50	£4	chart single

LIBERMAN, JEFFREY
Jeffrey Liberman	LP	Librah	1545	1975	£20	£40	US
Solitude Within	LP	Librah	6969	1975	£20	£40	US

LIED DES TEUFELS
Lied Des Teufels	LP	Kuckuck	2375019	1973	£4	£10	German

LIFE
Hands Of The Clock	7"	Polydor	56778	1969	£2.50	£6	
Life After Death	LP	Polydor	2383295	1974	£20	£40	

LIFE (2)
Cats' Eyes	7"	Philips	6006280	1973	£4	£8	blue paper label

LIFE 'N' SOUL
Here Comes Yesterday Again	7"	Decca	F12851	1968	£4	£8	
Peacefully Asleep	7"	Decca	F12659	1967	£4	£8	

LIFETIME
"Emergency" and "Turn It Over" are densely electric albums like no others. Tony Williams, the group's leader, was the drummer with Miles Davis during the sixties. Lifetime was his idea of a rock group, but filtered through his jazz background, it did not sound very much like anyone else's. Larry Young makes the organ sound like a banshee, pressing adjacent treble keys down all at the same time; John McLaughlin, who has just discovered the delights of high amplification, employs a ferocious fuzz-tone; while Tony Williams plays his customary churning multi-layered rhythms. Unfortunately, the group was plagued by management problems and when Jack Bruce joined during the recording of "Turn It Over" these only became worse. Later Lifetime recordings are much more routine affairs, although "Believe It", with Allan Holdsworth in fine form on guitar, has its moments.

Believe It	LP	CBS	69201	1976	£4	£10	
Emergency	LP	Polydor	583574	1969	£15	£30	double
Million Dollar Legs	LP	CBS	81510	1976	£4	£10	
One Word	7"	Polydor		1970	£2	£5	
Turn It Over	LP	Polydor	2425019	1970	£6	£15	

LIGGINS, JOE & THE HONEYDRIPPERS
I've Got A Right To Cry	78	Parlophone	R3309	1950	£6	£12	

LIGHT FANTASIC
Jeanie	7"	RCA	RCA2331	1973	£6	£12	

LIGHT OF DARKNESS
Light Of Darkness	LP	Philips	6305062	1970	£75	£150	Germa

LIGHTCRUST DOUGHBOYS
Lightcrust Doughboys	LP	Audio Lab	AL1525	1959	£15	£30	US

LIGHTFOOT, GORDON
Back Here On Earth	LP	United Artists	SULP1239	1969	£4	£10	
Bitter Green	7"	United Artists	UP35020	1969	£1.50	£4	
Black Day In July	7"	United Artists	UP2216	1968	£1.50	£4	
Circle Is Small	7"	United Artists	UP2272	1969	£1.50	£4	
Day Before Yesterday	7"	Fontana	TF405	1963	£2.50	£6	
Did She Mention My Name	LP	United Artists	SULP1199	1968	£4	£10	
Early Lightfoot	LP	United Artists	UAS29012	1969	£4	£10	
Early Morning Rain	7"	United Artists	UP35036	1969	£1.50	£4	
If You Could Read My Mind	7"	Reprise	R20974	1970	£1.50	£4	chart single
I'm Not Sayin'	7"	Warner Bros	WB5621	1966	£1.50	£4	
I'm The One	7"	Decca	F11527	1962	£2.50	£6	
Just Like Tom Thumb's Blues	7"	United Artists	UP1109	1965	£2	£5	
Lightfoot	LP	United Artists	UAL3487/ UAS6487	1965	£4	£10	U
Negotiations	7"	Fontana	267275	1963	£2.50	£6	
Sunday Concert	LP	United Artists	UAS29040	1969	£4	£10	
Way I Feel	LP	United Artists	UAL3587/ UAS6587	1967	£4	£10	U

LIGHTFOOT, PAPA GEORGE
Natchez Trace	LP	Liberty	LBS83353	1969	£5	£12	

LIGHTFOOT, TERRY
Alleycat	LP	Columbia	33SX1721	1965	£4	£10	
Jazz Gumbo Vol.1	10" LP	Nixa	NJT503	1956	£5	£12	
Trad Parade	LP	Columbia	33SX1290/ SCX3354	1961	£5	£12	
Tradition In Colour	LP	Columbia	33SX1073	1958	£5	£12	

LIGHTHOUSE
Eight Miles High	7"	RCA	RCA1884	1969	£2	£5	U
Lighthouse	LP	RCA	LSP4173	1969	£6	£15	U
One Fine Morning	LP	Vertigo	6342010	1971	£8	£20	spiral label
One Fine Morning	7"	Vertigo	6073152	1972	£1.50	£4	

Peacing It All Together	LP	RCA	SF8121	1970	£6	£15	
Suite Feeling	LP	RCA	SF8103	1970	£6	£15	
Take It Slow	7"	Vertigo	6073153	1972	£1.50	£4	
Thoughts Of Moving On	LP	Vertigo	6342011	1971	£8	£20	spiral label

LIGHTNIN' ROD

Hustler's Convention	LP	United Artists	UALA156F	1973	£5	£12	US

LIGHTNIN' ROD & JIMI HENDRIX

"Doriella Du Fontane" is one of the more overlooked records involving Jimi Hendrix. Although released in 1984, and featuring Hendrix in the unaccustomed role of providing rhythmic support to a rapper, the record is not the result of an eighties remixing project. Lightnin' Rod was a member of the Last Poets, whose blend of street poetry and percussion anticipates the work of artists like Public Enemy by some years. His collaboration with Jimi Hendrix was recorded during the guitarist's lifetime and represents an important reminder of Hendrix's occasional wish to reaffirm his blackness.

Doriella Du Fontane	12"	Celluloid	CRT332	1984	£3	£8	

LIGHTNIN' SLIM

Bell Ringer	LP	Excello	(S)8004	1965	£8	£20	US
Downhome Blues Part 1	LP	Python	PLP8	1969	£8	£20	
High And Low Down	LP	Excello	8018	1971	£4	£10	US
Just A Little Bit	7"	Blue Horizon	2096013	1972	£6	£12	
London Gumbo	LP	Blue Horizon	2931005	1972	£20	£40	
Rooster Blues	LP	Blue Horizon	763863	1970	£15	£30	
Rooster Blues	LP	Excello	8000	1960	£17.50	£35	US

LIGHTNING RAIDERS

Criminal World	7"	Revenge	REVS200	1981	£4	£8	

LIGHTSHINE

Feeling	LP	Trefiton	HS1049ST	1973	£60	£120	German

LILAC ANGELS

I'm Not Afraid To Say Yes	LP	Dingerland	09490211	1973	£4	£10	German

LILAC TIME

Return To Yesterday	7"	Swordfish	LILAC1	1988	£2	£5	no PS
Return To Yesterday	12"	Swordfish	12LILAC1	1988	£3	£8	

LIMBUS

Cosmic Music Experience	LP	CPM	LPS001	1969	£45	£90	German
Mandalas	LP	Ohr	OMM56001	1970	£6	£15	German

LIMELIGHT

Ashes To Ashes	7"	Future Earth	FER010	1982	£2	£5	
Limelight	LP	Avatar		1981	£10	£25	with 7'
Limelight	LP	Future Earth	FER008	1980	£10	£25	
Metal Man	7"	Future Earth	FER006	1980	£2	£5	

LIMELIGHT (BRINSLEY SCHWARZ)

Should Have Known Better	7"	United Artists	UP35779	1975	£2.50	£6	

LIMELITERS

Four Folk Songs	7" EP	RCA	RCX7151	1964	£2	£5	
Fun And Folk	7" EP	RCA	RCX7126	1963	£2	£5	
Limeliters	LP	Elektra	EKL180	1961	£5	£12	

LIMEYS

Cara Lin	7"	Decca	F12382	1966	£10	£20	
Can't Find My Way Through	7"	Pye	7N15820	1965	£1.50	£4	
Mountain's High	7"	Decca	F12466	1966	£1.50	£4	
Some Tears Fall Dry	7"	Pye	7N15909	1965	£1.50	£4	

LINCOLN, PETER

In The Day Of My Youth	7"	Major Minor	MM520	1967	£2.50	£6	

LINCOLN, PHILAMORE

North Wind Blew South	LP	Epic	BN26497	1967	£6	£15	US
Running By The River	7"	Nems	563711	1968	£2	£5	

LIND, BOB

Don't Be Concerned	LP	Fontana	(S)TL5340	1966	£4	£10	
Elusive Butterfly	7"	Fontana	TF670	1966	£1.50	£4	chart single
Hey Nellie Nellie	7"	Verve	VS1501	1967	£1.50	£4	
Remember The Rain	7"	Fontana	TF702	1966	£1.50	£4	chart single
San Francisco Woman	7"	Fontana	TF750	1966	£1.50	£4	

LINDE, DENNIS

Linde Manor	LP	Intrepid	IT74004	1970	£6	£15	US

LINDEN, KATHY

Billy	7"	Felsted	AF102	1958	£2	£5	
Goodbye Jimmy Goodbye	7"	Felsted	AF122	1959	£1.50	£4	
Kathy In Love Vol.1	7" EP	Felsted	GEP1001	1959	£5	£10	
Kathy In Love Vol.2	7" EP	Felsted	GEP1004	1959	£5	£10	
Kissin' Conversation	7"	Felsted	AF111	1958	£2	£5	
Mary Lou Wilson And Johnny Brown	7"	Felsted	AF130	1960	£2	£5	
Oh Johnny Oh Johnny Oh	7"	Felsted	AF108	1958	£1.50	£4	
That Certain Boy	LP	Felsted	7501	195-	£10	£25	US
You Don't Know Girls	7"	Felsted	AF124	1959	£1.50	£4	
You'd Be Surprised	7"	Felsted	AF105	1958	£2	£5	

LINDENBERG, UDO

Daumen Im Wind	LP	Telefunken	SLE14679	1972	£4	£10	German
Lindenberg	LP	Telefunken	SLE14637	1971	£4	£10	German

LINDH, BJORN J:SON

Cous Cous	LP	Metronome	MLP15450	1972	£4	£10	Swedish
Fran Storsted Till Grodspad	LP	SR	RELP1135	1971	£5	£12	Swedish

LINDISFARNE

Lindisfarne became quite popular in their day, achieving the remarkable feat, for a group marketed as being "progressive", of gaining a pai of top ten single hits. Today, their cheery, sing-along folk-rock is not highly regarded and even the fact that their earliest albums are on the collectable Charisma pink label does not appear to be enough to give them a collectors' value.

Clear White Light	7"	Charisma	CB137	1970	£5	£10	
Lady Eleanor	7"	Charisma	CB153	1971	£1.50	£4	PS

LINDYS

Boy With The Eyes Of Blue	7"	Decca	F11272	1960	£1.50	£4	
Train Of Love	7"	Decca	F11253	1960	£2.50	£6	

LINK, LANCELOT & THE EVOLUTION

Revolution	LP	Probe	SPBA6258	1970	£4	£10	

LINN COUNTY

Fever Shot	LP	Mercury	SMCL20165	1969	£5	£12	
Proud Flesh Soothseer	LP	Mercury	SMCL20142	1968	£5	£12	
Till The Break Of Dawn	LP	Philips	SBL7923	1970	£5	£12	

LINN, ELMO

Sam Houston	7"	Starlite	ST45101	1963	£4	£8	

LIONS OF JUDAH

Our Love's A Growin' Thing	7"	Fontana	TF1016	1969	£4	£8	

LIP MOVES

Guest	7"	Tichonderoga	HP1	1979	£2	£5	

LIPSCOMB, MANCE

Trouble In Mind	LP	Reprise	R(9)2012	1961	£5	£12	U

LIQUID SMOKE

Liquid Smoke	LP	Avco	33005	1969	£17.50	£35	

LISTEN

The lead singer of Listen was Robert Plant and he is, in fact, the only member of the group to appear on the single credited to them.

You Better Run	7"	CBS	202456	1965	£55	£110	

LITTER

$100 Fine	LP	Hexagon	HX681	1969	£75	£150	U
Distortions	LP	Warwick	UR5M1940	1968	£100	£200	U
Emerge	LP	Probe	CLPS4504	1969	£8	£20	

LITTLE ANGELS

'87 EP	12"	Song Management	LAN001	1987	£10	£25	
Big Bad EP	CD-s	Polydor	LTLCD2	1989	£2.50	£6	
Big Bad EP	12"	Polydor	LTLEP2	1989	£2.50	£6	
Ninety Degrees In The Shade	7"	Polydor	LTLD1	1988	£4	£8	poster sleev
Ninety Degrees In The Shade	12"	Polydor	LTLX1	1988	£2.50	£6	
Ninety Degrees In The Shade	12"	Polydor	LTLXP1	1988	£4	£10	shaped pic dis
Too Posh To Mosh	LP	Powerstation	AMP14	1987	£10	£25	

LITTLE ANTHONY & THE IMPERIALS

Bayou Bayou Baby	7"	Top Rank	JAR366	1960	£6	£12	
Best Of Little Anthony And The Imperials	LP	DCP	DC3809/DS6809	1966	£6	£15	U
Better Use Your Head	7"	United Artists	UP1137	1966	£10	£20	
Goin' Out Of My Head	LP	United Artists	ULP1100	1966	£8	£20	
Goin' Out Of My Head	7"	United Artists	UP1073	1964	£4	£8	
Gonna Fix You Good	7"	United Artists	UP1151	1966	£12.50	£25	
Hurt	7"	United Artists	UP1126	1966	£1.50	£4	
Hurt So Bad	7"	United Artists	UP1083	1965	£4	£8	
I Miss You So	7"	United Artists	UP1112	1965	£1.50	£4	
I'm On The Outside Lookin' In	LP	United Artists	ULP1089	1964	£10	£25	
I'm On The Outside Looking In	7"	United Artists	UP1065	1964	£2.50	£6	
Little Anthony And The Imperials	7" EP	United Artists	UEP1004	1965	£12.50	£25	
My Love Is A Rainbow	7"	United Artists	UP1189	1967	£1.50	£4	
Oh Yeah	7"	London	HL8848	1959	£10	£20	
Shades Of The 40s	LP	End	311	1960	£20	£40	U
Shimmy Shimmy Ko Ko Bop	7"	Top Rank	JAR256	1959	£6	£12	
Take Me Back	7"	United Artists	UP1098	1965	£2	£5	
Tears On My Pillow	7"	London	HLH8704	1958	£12.50	£25	
We Are Little Anthony & The Imperials	LP	End	303	1960	£30	£60	U

LITTLE ARCHIE

I Need You	7"	Atlantic	584209	1968	£1.50	£4	

LITTLE BEVERLEY

What A Guy	7"	Pama	PM731	1968	£2.50	£6	

LITTLE, BIG TINY

School Day	7"	Vogue Coral	Q72263	1957	£10	£20	

LITTLE BILL & THE BLUENOTES
I Love An Angel .... 7" ...... Top Rank .... JAR176 .... 1959 ... £2.50 ....£6 ....

LITTLE BOY BLUE
Dark End Of The Street .... 7" ...... Jackpot .... JP701 .... 1969 ... £2.50 ....£6 ....
Since You Are Gone .... 7" ...... Jackpot .... JP705 .... 1969 ... £2.50 ....£6 ....

LITTLE BOY BLUES
In The Woodland Of Weir .... LP ..... Fontana .... MGF2/SRF67578... 1967 ... £8 ....£20 .... US

LITTLE CAESAR & THE ROMANS
Memories Of Those Oldies But .... LP ..... Del-Fi .... DFLP1218 .... 1961 ... £10 ....£25 .... US
Goodies ....

LITTLE DARLINGS
Little Bit Of Soul .... 7" ...... Fontana .... TF539 .... 1965 ... £20 ....£40 ....

LITTLE DIPPERS
Forever .... 7" ...... Pye .... 7N25051 .... 1960 ... £1.50 ....£4 ....
Lonely .... 7" ...... London .... HLG9269 .... 1961 ... £2 ....£5 ....

LITTLE EVA
Keep Your Hands Off My Baby .... 7" ...... London .... HLU9633 .... 1962 ... £1.50 ....£4 ....chart single
Let's Turkey Trot .... 7" ...... London .... HLU9687 .... 1963 ... £1.50 ....£4 ....chart single
Lllllocomotion .... LP ..... London .... HAU8036 .... 1963 ... £10 ....£25 ....
Locomotion .... 7" ...... London .... HL9581 .... 1962 ... £2 ....£5 ....chart single
Please Hurt Me .... 7" ...... Colpix .... PX11119 .... 1963 ... £1.50 ....£4 ....
Run To Her .... 7" ...... Colpix .... PX11035 .... 1964 ... £2 ....£5 ....
Stand By Me .... 7" ...... Stateside .... SS477 .... 1965 ... £4 ....£8 ....
Trouble With Boys .... 7" ...... Colpix .... PX11013 .... 1963 ... £4 ....£8 ....

LITTLE FEAT
Waiting For Columbus .... LP ..... Mobile Fidelity MFSL2013 .... 1978 ... £8 ....£20 US audiophile double

LITTLE FREE ROCK
Little Free Rock .... LP ..... Transatlantic ... TRA608 .... 1969 ... £25 ....£50 ....

LITTLE GEORGE
Mary Anne .... 7" ...... Rio .... R45 .... 1964 ... £5 ....£10 ....Edward's
Allstars B side

LITTLE HANK
Mr.Bang Bang Man .... 7" ...... London .... HLU10090 .... 1966 ... £12.50 ....£25 ....
Mr.Bang Bang Man .... 7" ...... Monument .... MON1045 .... 1970 ... £2.50 ....£6 ....

LITTLE JOE
Peanuts .... 7" ...... Reprise .... R20142 .... 1963 ... £2.50 ....£6 ....
Stay .... 7" ...... Fontana .... H281 .... 1960 ... £5 ....£10 ....

LITTLE JOEY & THE FLIPS
Bongo Stomp .... 7" ...... Pye .... 7N25152 .... 1962 ... £2 ....£5 ....

LITTLE JOHNNY & THE THREE TEENAGERS
Baby Lover .... 7" ...... Decca .... F10990 .... 1958 ... £4 ....£8 ....

LITTLE LUMAN
Hurry Harry .... 7" ...... Rio .... R44 .... 1964 ... £5 ....£10 ....Roland
Alphonso B side

LITTLE LUTHER
Eenie Meenie Minie Mo .... 7" ...... Pye .... 7N25266 .... 1964 ... £12.50 ....£25 ....

LITTLE MAC & THE BOSS SOUNDS
In The Midnight Hour .... 7" ...... Atlantic .... 584031 .... 1966 ... £2 ....£5 ....

LITTLE, MARIE
Factory Girl .... LP ..... Argo .... ZFB19 .... 1971 ... £40 ....£80 ....
Marie Little .... LP ..... Trailer .... LER2084 .... 1973 ... £8 ....£20 ....

LITTLE MILTON
Little Milton is a fine blues singer and an even finer blues guitarist - very much in the manner of B.B.King on both counts - but most of his releases are soul records, where he is rather more ordinary. The "Grits And Groceries" LP provides a reasonable balance between the styles, with the outstanding track being a smouldering version of "I Can't Quit You Baby" (also the B side of the "Grits Ain't Groceries" single).
Behind Closed Doors .... 7" ...... Stax .... STXS2003 .... 1974 ... £1.50 ....£4 ....
Blindman .... 7" ...... Pye .... 7N25289 .... 1965 ... £2.50 ....£6 ....
Early In The Morning .... 7" ...... Sue .... WI4021 .... 1966 ... £7.50 ......£15 ....
Grits Ain't Groceries .... LP ..... Chess .... CRLS4552 .... 1969 ... £5 ....£12 ....
Grits Ain't Groceries .... 7" ...... Chess .... CRS8087 .... 1969 ... £4 ....£8 ....
If Walls Could Talk .... LP ..... Checker .... 3012 .... 1970 ... £4 ....£10 ....US
Let's Get Together .... 7" ...... Chess .... CRS8101 .... 1969 ... £4 ....£8 ....
Little Milton Sings Big Blues .... LP ..... Checker .... 3002 .... 1966 ... £8 ....£20 ....US
We're Gonna Make It .... LP ..... Checker .... 2995 .... 1965 ... £15 ....£30 ....US
We're Gonna Make It .... 7" ...... Chess .... CRS8013 .... 1965 ... £4 ....£8 ....
Who's Cheating Who .... 7" ...... Chess .... CRS8018 .... 1965 ... £5 ....£10 ....

LITTLE MR.LEE & THE CHEROKEES
Young Lover .... 7" ...... Vocalion .... VP9268 .... 1966 ... £7.50 ......£15 ....

LITTLE NORMA
Ten Commandments Of Woman .... 7" ...... Dice .... CC26 .... 1964 ... £5 ....£10 ....

LITTLE RAY

"I Been Trying" is an early example of Arthur Lee's song-writing, although Lee does not appear to be otherwise involved in the record.

Title	Format	Label	Cat. No.	Year	Price	Price	Notes
I Been Trying	7"	Donna	1404	1964	£10	£20	US

LITTLE RICHARD

Title	Format	Label	Cat. No.	Year	Price	Price	Notes
Baby Face	7"	London	HL7056	1958	£2	£5	export
Baby Face	7"	London	HLU8770	1958	£5	£10	chart single
Baby What You Want Me To Do	7"	Action	ACT4528	1969	£2.50	£6	
Bama Lama Bama Loo	7"	London	HL9896	1964	£2.50	£6	chart single
Blueberry Hill	7"	Fontana	TF519	1964	£2.50	£6	
By The Light Of The Silvery Moon	7"	London	HL7079	1959	£4	£8	export
By The Light Of The Silvery Moon	7"	London	HLU8831	1959	£5	£10	chart single
Coming Home	LP	Coral	LVA9220	1964	£6	£15	
Crying In The Chapel	7"	London	HLK9708	1963	£2.50	£6	
Do You Feel It	7" EP	Stateside	SE1042	1966	£6	£12	
Explosive Little Richard	LP	Columbia	SX/SCX6136	1967	£6	£15	
Fabulous Little Richard	LP	London	HAU2193	1959	£10	£25	
Four Dynamic Numbers	7" EP	Summit	LSE2049	1963	£5	£10	with Brock Peters
Get Down And Get With It	7"	Columbia	DB8116	1967	£12.50	£25	
Girl Can't Help It	7"	London	HLO8382	1957	£30	£60	chart single, gold label
Good Golly Miss Molly	7"	London	HLU8560	1958	£7.50	£15	chart single
Great Hits	LP	Fontana	TL5314	1966	£4	£10	
He Got What He Wanted	7"	Mercury	AMT1189	1962	£2	£5	chart single
Here's Little Richard	LP	London	HAO2055	1957	£10	£25	
Here's Little Richard	LP	London	HAO2055	1957	£17.50	£35	glossy red rear sleeve
Here's Little Richard	LP	Speciality	100	1957	£75	£150	US
He's Back	7" EP	London	REK1400	1963	£5	£10	
Holy Mackrel	7"	Stateside	SS508	1966	£4	£8	
I Don't Know What You've Got	7"	Fontana	TF652	1966	£2.50	£6	
I Don't Wanna Discuss It	7"	Columbia	DB8263	1967	£7.50	£15	
I Got It	7"	London	HLU9065	1960	£5	£10	
I Need Love	7"	Columbia	DB8058	1966	£5	£10	
It Ain't What You Do	7"	Sue	WI4015	1966	£6	£12	
It's Real	LP	Mercury	MCL20036	1965	£5	£12	
It's Real	LP	Mercury	MG2/SR60656	1961	£8	£20	US
Jenny Jenny	7"	London	HL7022	1957	£5	£10	export
Jenny Jenny	7"	London	HLO8470	1957	£7.50	£15	chart single
Joy Joy Joy	7"	Mercury	AMT1165	1961	£2.50	£6	
Kansas City	7"	London	HLU8868	1959	£5	£10	chart single
Keep A Knocking	7"	London	HLO8509	1957	£7.50	£15	chart single
King Of The Gospel Singers	LP	Fontana	SFL13010	1968	£4	£10	
Little Bit Of Something	7"	Columbia	DB8240	1967	£12.50	£25	
Little Richard	LP	Camden	CAL420	1956	£25	£50	US
Little Richard	LP	Camden	CDN125	1959	£8	£20	with Buck Ram Orchestra
Little Richard	LP	Mercury	MCL20019	1965	£5	£12	
Little Richard	LP	Speciality	SP2103	1957	£15	£30	US
Little Richard & His Band Vol.1	7" EP	London	REO1071	1957	£7.50	£15	gold label
Little Richard & His Band Vol.2	7" EP	London	REO1074	1957	£7.50	£15	gold label
Little Richard & His Band Vol.3	7" EP	London	REO1103	1957	£7.50	£15	
Little Richard & His Band Vol.4	7" EP	London	REO1106	1957	£7.50	£15	
Little Richard & His Band Vol.5	7" EP	London	REU1208	1959	£7.50	£15	
Little Richard & His Band Vol.6	7" EP	London	REU1234	1960	£7.50	£15	
Little Richard & His Band Vol.7	7" EP	London	REU1235	1960	£7.50	£15	
Little Richard 2	LP	London	HAU2126	1958	£10	£25	
Little Richard Is Back	LP	Fontana	TL5235	1965	£5	£12	
Little Richard Sings Freedom Songs	LP	Egmont	EGM9207	1963	£6	£15	
Little Richard Sings Gospel	LP	Fidelio	ATL4124	1964	£4	£10	
Little Richard/Memphis Slim	7" EP	Vocalion	VEP170155	1964	£15	£30	with Memphis Slim
Long Tall Sally	7"	London	HLO8366	1957	£30	£60	chart single, gold label
Lucille	7"	London	HLO8446	1957	£7.50	£15	chart single
Ooh My Soul	7"	London	HL7049	1958	£2.50	£6	export
Ooh My Soul	7"	London	HLO8647	1958	£6	£12	chart single
Peace In The Valley	7"	Mercury	MF841	1964	£2	£5	
Poor Dog	7"	Columbia	DB7974	1966	£7.50	£15	
Pray Along With Little Richard	LP	Egmont	EGM9270	1963	£5	£12	
Pray Along With Little Richard Vol.1	LP	Top Rank	25025	1960	£15	£30	plain white sleeve
Pray Along With Little Richard Vol.2	LP	Top Rank	25026	1960	£25	£50	plain white sleeve
Really Movin' Gospel	LP	Ember	NR5022	1965	£4	£10	
Rip It Up	7"	London	HLO8336	1956	£37.50	£75	chart single, gold label
She Knows How To Rock	7"	London	HL7074	1959	£5	£10	export
She's Together	7"	Decca	AD1006	1968	£5	£10	export
Sings Gospel	LP	Stateside	SL10054	1964	£6	£15	
Travelling Shoes	7"	London	HLK9756	1963	£2.50	£6	
Whole Lotta Shakin' Goin' On	7"	London	HL7085	1959	£10	£20	export
Whole Lotta Shaking Going On	7"	Stateside	SS340	1964	£2.50	£6	
Without Love	7"	Sue	WI4001	1966	£6	£12	

LITTLE ROYS

Title	Format	Label	Cat. No.	Year	Price	Price	Notes
Bongonyah	7"	Camel	CA36	1969	£2.50	£6	

LITTLE SISTER

Title	Format	Label	Cat. No.	Year	Price	Price	Notes
Somebody's Watching You	7"	Atlantic	2091053	1971	£1.50	£4	
You're The One	7"	Atlantic	2091001	1970	£1.50	£4	

LITTLE TONY & HIS BROTHERS

Title	Format	Label	Cat. No.	Year	Price	Price	Notes
Let Her Go	7"	Durium	DRS54008	1958	£1.50	£4	

Little Tony	LP	Durium		195-	£8	£20	

LITTLE TONY & THE BROTHERS

Four And Twenty Thousand Kisses	7"	Durium	DC16657	1961	£2	£5	
Hippy Hippy Shake	7"	Decca	F11169	1959	£2.50	£6	
I Can't Help It	7"	Decca	F11164	1959	£1.50	£4	
I Love You	7"	Decca	F21218	1960	£1.50	£4	
Long Is The Lonely Night	7"	Durium	DRS54012	1965	£1.50	£4	
Non E Normale	7" EP	Durium	DRE52012	1966	£4	£8	
Presenting Little Tony	7" EP	Durium	U20058	1958	£10	£20	
Princess	7"	Decca	F21223	1960	£2	£5	
Teddy Girl	7"	Decca	F21247	1960	£2.50	£6	
Too Good	7"	Decca	F11190	1959	£1.50	£4	chart single
Who's That Knocking	7"	Durium	DC16639	1959	£5	£10	

LITTLE WALTER

Best Of Little Walter	LP	Chess	LP1428	1958	£15	£30	US
Hate To See You Go	LP	Chess	LPS1535	1969	£4	£10	US
Little Walter	LP	Marble Arch	MAL815	1968	£4	£10	
Little Walter	LP	Pye	NPL28043	1964	£8	£20	
Little Walter & His Jukes	7" EP	London	REU1061	1956	£35	£70	
Little Walter And His Dukes	LP	Python	PLPKM20	1969	£8	£20	
My Babe	7"	London	HLM9175	1960	£10	£20	
My Babe	7"	Pye	7N25263	1964	£4	£8	

LIVELY ONES

Great Surf Hits	LP	Del-Fi	DFLP/DFST1238	1963	£8	£20	US
Surf Drums	LP	London	HA8082	1963	£8	£20	
Surf Rider	LP	London	HA8107	1963	£8	£20	
Surfin' South Of The Border	LP	Del-Fi	DFLP/DFST1240	1964	£8	£20	US
This Is Surf City	LP	Del-Fi	DFLP/DFST1237	1963	£8	£20	US

LIVERPOOL BEATS

New Merseyside Sound	LP	Rondo	2026	1964	£8	£20	US

LIVERPOOL FISHERMEN

Swallow The Anchor	LP	Mushroom	150MR9	1971	£50	£100	

LIVERPOOL FIVE

Arrive	LP	RCA	LPM/LSP3583	1966	£5	£12	US
Heart	7" EP	RCA	86493	1965	£10	£20	French
Out Of Sight	LP	RCA	LPM/LSP3682	1967	£5	£12	US

LIVERPOOL KIDS

Beatle Mash	LP	Palace	777	1964	£8	£20	US

LIVERPOOL SCENE

The first Liverpool Scene consisted of the three poets Roger McGough, Brian Patten, and Adrian Henri, with music supplied by guitarist Andy Roberts. The group that performs on the RCA records is more of a regular rock group, although it is still one that tends to act as an umbrella for the individual talents beneath - Henri and Roberts as before, with poet/saxophonist Mike Evans and singer/guitarist Mike Hart also making telling contributions. Each LP is tremendously varied, encompassing rock, jazz, and folk; poetry, comedy, and drama - a real pot pourri, in fact, but it worked.

Amazing Adventures Of	LP	RCA	SF7995	1968	£6	£15	
Bread On The Night	LP	RCA	SF8057	1969	£5	£12	
Heirloon	LP	RCA	SF8134	1970	£5	£12	
Incredible New Liverpool Scene	LP	CBS	63045	1967	£15	£30	
Recollections	LP	Charisma	CS3	1972	£4	£10	
Son Son	7"	RCA	RCA1762	1968	£1.50	£4	
St.Adrian & Co.	LP	RCA	SF8100	1970	£5	£12	
Woo Woo	7"	RCA	RCA1816	1969	£1.50	£4	

LIVERPOOLS

Beatle-Mania In The USA	LP	Wyncote	9001	1964	£8	£20	US
Hit Sounds From England	LP	Wyncote	9061	1965	£8	£20	US

LIVIN' BLUES

Bamboozle	LP	Philips	6413024	1971	£4	£10	Dutch
Dutch Treat	LP	Dwarf	2003	1971	£6	£15	US
Hell's Session	LP	Philips	6440315	1969	£4	£10	Dutch
Rockin' At The Tweedmill	LP	Philips	6423052	1972	£4	£10	German
Wang Dang Doodle	LP	Philips	6440125	1970	£4	£10	Dutch

LIVING DAYLIGHTS

Always With Him	7"	Philips	BF1613	1967	£10	£20	
Let's Live For Today	7"	Philips	BF1561	1967	£6	£12	
Let's Live For Today	7" EP	Fontana	460234	1967	£10	£20	French

LIVING IN TEXAS

And David Cried	7"	Rhythmic	RMNS2	1983	£2	£5	

LIZA & THE JET SET

How Can I Know?	7"	Parlophone	R5248	1965	£4	£8	

LLAN

Realise	7"	CBS	202405	1966	£7.50	£15	

LLOYD & CECIL

Come Over Here	7"	Blue Beat	BB49	1961	£5	£10	C.Byrd B side

LLOYD & DEVON

Love Is The Key	7"	Punch	PH14	1967	£4	£8	Virtues B side
Out Of The Fire	7"	Blue Cat	BS151	1968	£4	£8	

LLOYD & GLEN

Keep On Pushing	7"	Doctor Bird	DB1071	1967	£5	£10	...Bobby Aitken B side
That Girl	7"	Coxsone	CS7011	1967	£5	£10	

LLOYD & JOHNNY

My Argument	7"	Island	WI3158	1968	£5	£10	George Dekker B side

LLOYD & THE GROOVERS

Do It To Me Baby	7"	Caltone	TONE108	1967	£4	£8	.......Diplomats B side
Listen To The Music	7"	Caltone	TONE112	1968	£4	£8	.......Diplomats B side
My Heart My Soul	7"	Caltone	TONE109	1967	£4	£8	.......Diplomats B side

LLOYD, A.L.

Best Of A.L.Lloyd	LP	XTRA	XTRA5023	1966	£10	£25	
First Person	LP	Topic	12T118	1965	£10	£25	
Leviathan!	LP	Topic	12T174	1967	£10	£25	
Outback Ballads	LP	Topic	12T51	1960	£10	£25	
Selection From The Penguin Book Of English Folk Songs	LP	Collector	JGB5001	1961	£20	£40	

LLOYD, A.L. & EWAN MACCOLL

English And Scottish Folk Ballads	LP	Topic	12T103	1964	£10	£25	

LLOYD, A.L. & TREVOR LUCAS

Great Australian Legend	LP	Topic	12TS203	1971	£40	£80	

LLOYD, A.L., ANNE BRIGGS, FRANKIE ARMSTRONG

Bird In The Bush	LP	Topic	12T135	1965	£30	£60	

LLOYD, CHARLES

Dream Weaver	LP	Atlantic	587025	1966	£5	£12	
Forest Flower	LP	Atlantic	SD1473	1967	£5	£12	US
In Europe	LP	Atlantic	588108	1968	£4	£10	
Journey Within	LP	Atlantic	587/588101	1968	£5	£12	
Love-In	LP	Atlantic	587/588077	1967	£5	£12	
Soundtrack	LP	Atlantic	SD1519	1969	£4	£10	US
Waves	LP	A&M	SP3044	1972	£4	£10	US

LLOYD, JIMMY

Call On Me	7"	Philips	326568BF	1963	£1.50	£4	
Prince Of Players	7"	Philips	PB795	1958	£1.50	£4	
Teenage Sonata	7"	Philips	PB1010	1960	£1.50	£4	
Witch Doctor	7"	Philips	PB827	1958	£2.50	£6	

LLOYD, KATHY

Our Future Has Only Just Begun	7"	Decca	F10464	1955	£1.50	£4	
Teach Me Tonight	7"	Decca	F10418	1954	£1.50	£4	
Tomorrow Night	7"	Decca	F10386	1954	£1.50	£4	

LLOYD, MARK

Everybody Tries	7"	Parlophone	R5332	1965	£1.50	£4	
I Keep Thinking About You	7"	Parlophone	R5277	1965	£2	£5	

LLOYD, PEGGY

Dixieland Honky Tonk	7" EP	London	REP1017	1955	£4	£8	

LLOYDIE & THE LOWBITES

Censored	LP	Lowbite	LOW1	1971	£8	£20	

LLOYD'S ALLSTARS

Love Kiss Blue	7"	Doctor Bird	DB1178	1969	£5	£10	...... Uniques B side

LLOYD-WEBBER, ANDREW

Joseph And The Amazing Technicolour Dreamcoat	LP	Decca		1968	£4	£10	

LLYGOD FFYRNIG

N.C.B.	7"	Pwdwr	PWDWR1	1978	£6	£12	

LOADER, DICKIE

Heatwave	7"	Palette	PG9015	1961	£6	£12	

LOADING ZONE

Loading Zone	LP	RCA	LSP3959	1968	£6	£15	US
One For All	LP	Umbrella	US101	1968	£15	£30	US

LOCHLIN, HANK

Best Of Hank Lochlin	LP	King	672	1961	£6	£15	US
Country Guitar Vol.3	7" EP	RCA	RCX115	1958	£5	£10	
Encores	LP	King	738	1961	£6	£15	US
Encores	7" EP	Parlophone	GEP8875	1963	£7.50	£15	
Foreign Love	LP	RCA	LPM1673	1958	£6	£15	US
Happy Journey	LP	RCA	LPM/LSP2464	1962	£5	£12	US
Irish Songs Country Style	LP	RCA	RD7623	1964	£4	£10	
Irish Songs Country Style	7" EP	RCA	RCX7150	1964	£4	£8	
Please Help Me, I'm Falling	LP	RCA	RD27201	1961	£5	£12	
Please Help Me, I'm Falling	7"	RCA	RCA1188	1960	£1.50	£4	
Seven Days	7" EP	RCA	RCX217	1962	£5	£10	
Tribute To Roy Acuff	LP	RCA	LPM/LSP2597	1962	£5	£12	US
Waltz Of The Wind	7" EP	RCA	RCX7116	1963	£5	£10	
Ways Of Love	LP	RCA	LPM/LSP2680	1963	£5	£12	US

LOCKETS
Doncha Know .... 7" ...... Pye .... 7N25232 .... 1963 ... £4 ....£8

LOCKJAW
Journalist Jive .... 7" ...... Raw .... RAW19 .... 1978 ... £1.50 ....£4
Radio Call Sign .... 7" ...... Raw .... RAW8 .... 1977 ... £1.50 ....£4

LOCKRAN, GERRY
Blues At Sunrise .... LP ..... Saga .... FID2165 .... 1969 ... £4 ....£10
Blues Vendetta .... LP ..... Waverley ...... ZLP2091 .... 1968 ... £6 ....£15
Essential .... LP ..... Spark .... SRLP104 .... 1969 ... £6 ....£15
Hey Jude .... 7" ...... Decca .... F12873 .... 1969 ... £1.50 ....£4
Hold On I'm Coming .... LP ..... Planet .... PLL1002 .... 1967 ... £20 ....£40
Standing On Your Own .... 7" ...... Decca .... F12919 .... 1969 ... £1.50 ....£4

LOCKYER, MALCOLM
Eccentric Dr.Who .... 7" ...... Columbia .... DB7663 .... 1965 ... £4 ....£8

LOCOMOTIVE
Mr.Armageddan .... 7" ...... Parlophone ..... R5758 .... 1969 ... £5 ....£10
Roll Over Mary .... 7" ...... Parlophone ..... R5835 .... 1970 ... £4 ....£8
Rudi's In Love .... 7" ...... Parlophone ..... R5781 .... 1968 ... £2 ....£5
Rudi's In Love .... 7" ...... Parlophone ..... R5915 .... 1971 ... £1.50 ....£4
Rudy A Message To You .... 7" ...... Direction .... 583114 .... 1967 ... £2 ....£5
We Are Everything You See .... LP ..... Parlophone ..... PCS7093 .... 1969 ... £65 ....£130
You Must Be Joking .... 7" ...... Parlophone ..... R5801 .... 1969 ... £5 ....£10

LOFGREN, NILS
Back It Up .... LP ..... A&M .... SP8362 .... 1975 ... £5 ....£12 ....US promo

LOFT
Up The Hill And Down The Slope .... 7" ...... Creation .... CRE015 .... 1985 ... £4 ....£8
Why Does The Rain Fall .... 7" ...... Creation .... CRE009 .... 1984 ... £5 ....£10

LOFTON, CRIPPLE CLARENCE
Blues Pianist .... 10" LP .. Vogue .... LDE122 .... 1955 ... £10 ....£25
Cripple Clarence Lofton .... 7" EP.. Vogue .... EPV1209 .... 1959 ... £7.50 ....£15
Lost Recording Date .... 10" LP .. London .... AL3531 .... 1954 ... £10 ....£25

LOGUE, CHRISTOPHER & TONY KINSEY
Red Bird Jazz And Poetry .... 7" EP.. Parlophone ...... GEP8765 .... 1958 ... £5 ....£10

LOLLIPOP SHOPPE
Lollipop Shoppe .... LP ..... Uni .... 73019 .... 1968 ... £8 ....£20 ....US

LOMAN, LAURIE
Whither Thou Goest .... 7" ...... London .... HL8101 .... 1954 ... £10 ....£20

LOMAX, ALAN
Alan Lomax Sings .... 7" EP.. Pye .... NJE1055 .... 1957 ... £5 ....£10
Blues In The Mississippi Night .... LP ..... Pye .... NJL8 .... 1957 ... £4 ....£10
Dirty Old Town .... 7" ...... Decca .... F10787 .... 1956 ... £2.50 ....£6
Great American Ballads .... LP ..... HMV .... CLP1192 .... 1958 ... £4 ....£10
Oh Lula .... 7" EP.. Decca .... DFE6367 .... 1956 ... £5 ....£10
Presents American Song Train .... LP ..... Pye .... NPL18013 .... 1958 ... £4 ....£10
Songs From Texas .... 7" EP.. Melodisc .... EPM788 .... 1959 ... £5 ....£10
Sounds Of The South .... LP ..... Atlantic .... 590033 .... 1969 ... £5 ....£12

LOMAX ALLIANCE
Try As You May .... 7" ...... CBS .... 2729 .... 1967 ... £4 ....£8

LOMAX, JACKIE
Genuine Imitation Life .... 7" ...... CBS .... 2554 .... 1968 ... £2.50 ....£6
How The Web Was Woven .... 7" ...... Apple .... 23 .... 1970 ... £2 ....£5
How The Web Was Woven .... 7" ...... Apple .... 23 .... 1970 ... £7.50 ....£15 ....PS
Interview With Jackie Lomax .... LP ..... Warner Bros .. PRO520 .... 1972 ... £8 ....£20 ....US promo
Is This What You Want .... LP ..... Apple .... APCOR6 .... 1969 ... £8 ....£20 ....mono
Is This What You Want .... LP ..... Apple .... SAPCOR6 .... 1969 ... £6 ....£15 ....stereo
New Day .... 7" ...... Apple .... 11 .... 1969 ... £5 ....£10
Sour Milk Sea .... 7" ...... Apple .... 3 .... 1968 ... £7.50 ....£15

LOMBARDO, GUY
Cherry Pink And Apple Blossom White 7" ...... Brunswick .... 05443 .... 1955 ... £1.50 ....£4

LOMBARDY, AL
Blues .... 7" ...... London .... HL8076 .... 1954 ... £10 ....£20
In A Little Spanish Town .... 7" ...... London .... HL8127 .... 1955 ... £10 ....£20

LONDON & BRIDGES
It Just Ain't Right .... 7" ...... CBS .... 202056 .... 1966 ... £10 ....£20

LONDON JAZZ FOUR
Elizabethan Songbook .... LP ..... CBS .... 63512 .... 1969 ... £4 ....£10
Norwegian Wood .... 7" ...... Polydor .... BM56092 .... 1966 ... £1.50 ....£4
Take A New Look At The Beatles ...... LP ..... Polydor .... 582005 .... 1967 ... £4 ....£10

LONDON JAZZ QUARTET
London Jazz Quartet .... LP ..... Tempo .... TAP28 .... 1960 ... £10 ....£25

LONDON, JIMMY
Bridge Over Troubled Waters .... LP ..... Trojan .... TRL39 .... 1972 ... £6 ....£15

LONDON, JOE
It Might Have Been	7"	London	HLW9008	1959	£2	£5

LONDON, JULIE
About The Blues	LP	London	HAU2091	1958	£8	£20
All Through The Night	LP	Liberty	(S)LBY1300	1966	£4	£10
All Through The Night	7" EP	Liberty	LEP2260	1966	£4	£8
Around Midnight	LP	London	HAG2299	1961	£6	£15
Baby Baby All The Time	7"	London	HLU8279	1956	£10	£20	gold label
Best Of Julie London	LP	Liberty	LBY1023	1962	£4	£10
Boy On A Dolphin	7"	London	HLU8414	1957	£5	£10
Calendar Girl	LP	London	HAU2038	1957	£8	£20
Charade	7"	Liberty	LIB10205	1965	£1.50	£4
Cry Me A River	7"	London	HLU8240	1956	£12.50	£25	chart single, gold label
Desafinado	7" EP	Liberty	LEP2103	1963	£4	£8
End Of THe World	LP	Liberty	LRP3300/LST7300	1963	£4	£10	US
Feeling Good	LP	Liberty	(S)LBY1281	1966	£4	£10
For The Night People	LP	Liberty	(S)LBY1334	1967	£4	£10
Girl Talk	7"	Liberty	LIB10274	1967	£1.50	£4
Great Performances	LP	Liberty	LBL/LBS83049	1968	£4	£10
I Want To Find Out For Myself	7"	Liberty	LIB55666	1964	£1.50	£4
I'm Coming Back To You	7"	Liberty	LIB55605	1963	£2.50	£6
In Person At The Americana	LP	Liberty	LBY1222	1965	£5	£12
Julie	LP	London	HAU2112	1958	£8	£20
Julie At Home	LP	London	HAG2280/SAHG6097	1960	£6	£15
Julie Is Her Name	LP	Liberty	LST7027	1957	£15	£30	US, blue vinyl
Julie Is Her Name	LP	London	HAU2005	1956	£10	£25
Julie Is Her Name Vol.2	LP	London	HAU2186/SAHU6042	1959	£6	£15
Julie London	LP	Liberty	LRP3342/LST7342	1964	£4	£10	US
Julie Part 1	7" EP	London	REU1180	1959	£5	£10
Julie Part 2	7" EP	London	REU1181	1959	£5	£10
Julie Part 3	7" EP	London	REU1182	1959	£5	£10
Latin In A Satin Mood	LP	Liberty	(S)LBY1136	1963	£4	£10
London By Night	LP	London	HAU2171	1959	£6	£15
London's Girl Friends Vol.1	7" EP	London	REN1092	1957	£10	£20
Lonely Girl	LP	Liberty	LRP3012	1956	£8	£20	US
Love Letters	LP	Liberty	(S)LBY1083	1962	£4	£10
Love On The Rocks	LP	Liberty	(S)LBY1113	1963	£4	£10
Make Love To Me	LP	London	HAU2083	1958	£8	£20
Make Love To Me Part 1	7" EP	London	REU1151	1958	£6	£12
Make Love To Me Part 2	7" EP	London	REU1152	1958	£6	£12
Make Love To Me Part 3	7" EP	London	REU1153	1958	£6	£12
Man Of The West	7"	London	HLU8769	1958	£2.50	£6
Meaning Of The Blues	7"	London	HLU8394	1957	£7.50	£15	gold label
Must Be Catchin'	7"	London	HLU8891	1959	£4	£8
My Strange Affair	7"	London	HLU8657	1958	£2.50	£6
Nice Girls Don't Stay For Breakfast	LP	Liberty	(S)LBY1364	1967	£4	£10
Our Fair Lady	LP	Liberty	(S)LBY1251	1965	£4	£10
Saddle The Wind	7"	London	HLU8602	1958	£4	£8
Sanctuary	7"	London	HLG9360	1961	£2	£5
Send For Me	LP	London	HAG2353/SAHG6154	1961	£6	£15
Send For Me	7"	Liberty	LIB10189	1965	£1.50	£4
Sings Film Songs	7" EP	London	REU1076	1957	£7.50	£15	gold label
Sophisticated Lady	LP	Liberty	LRP3203/LST7203	1962	£4	£10	US
Swing Me An Old Song	LP	London	HAW2225	1960	£6	£15
There'll Be Some Changes Made	7"	Liberty	LIB10078	1963	£1.50	£4
Whatever Julie Wants	LP	London	HAG2405/SAHG6205	1962	£6	£15
Wonderful World Of Julie London	LP	Liberty	(S)LBY1185	1964	£4	£10
Your Number Please	LP	London	HAW2229	1960	£6	£15
Yummy Yummy Yummy	LP	Liberty	LBL/LBS83183	1969	£4	£10

LONDON, LAURIE
Basin Street Blues	7"	Parlophone	R4450	1958	£1.50	£4
Gospel Train	7"	Parlophone	R4408	1958	£1.50	£4
Handed Down	7"	Parlophone	R4388	1958	£1.50	£4
He's Got The Whole World In His Hands	7"	Parlophone	R4359	1957	£1.50	£4	chart single
I Gotta Robe	7"	Parlophone	R4426	1958	£1.50	£4
I'm Afraid	7"	Parlophone	R4635	1960	£1.50	£4
Laurie London	LP	Capitol	T1016	1958	£8	£20	US
Laurie London	7" EP	Parlophone	GEP8664	1957	£6	£12
Little Laurie London No.2	7" EP	Parlophone	GEP8689	1958	£6	£12
My Mother	7"	Parlophone	R4474	1958	£1.50	£4
Old Time Religion	7"	Parlophone	R4601	1959	£1.50	£4
Pretty-Eyed Baby	7"	Parlophone	R4557	1959	£1.50	£4
Up Above My Head	7"	Parlophone	R4499	1958	£1.50	£4

LONDON, MARK
Stranger In The World	7"	Pye	7N15825	1965	£4	£8

LONDON, PETER
Bless You	7"	Pye	7N15957	1965	£7.50	£15

LONDON WAITS
Serenadio	7"	Immediate	IM030	1966	£7.50	£15

LONE RANGER

Adventures Of The Lone Ranger	LP	Decca	DL8578		£10	£25	US
Lone Ranger No.1	7" EP.	Brunswick	OE9394	1959	£2.50	£6	
Lone Ranger No.2	7" EP.	Brunswick	OE9395	1959	£2.50	£6	
Lone Ranger No.3	7" EP.	Brunswick	OE9396	1959	£2.50	£6	

LONESOME, JOHNNY

Marie Marie	7"	HMV	POP837	1961	£1.50	£4	

LONESOME STONE

Lonesome Stone	LP	Reflection	RL306	1973	£10	£25	

LONESOME SUNDOWN

Lonesome Lonely Blues	LP	Blue Horizon	763864	1970	£25	£50	

LONESOME TRAVELLERS

Lonesome Travellers	LP	Tradition	TSR004	1970	£10	£25	
Lost Children	LP	Nebula	NEB100	1971	£8	£20	

LONG & THE SHORT

Choc Ice	7"	Decca	F12043	1964	£4	£8	chart single
Letter	7"	Decca	F11964	1964	£4	£8	chart single

LONG, SHORTY

Chantilly Lace	7"	Tamla Motown	TMG600	1967	£2.50	£6	
Function At The Junction	7"	Tamla Motown	TMG573	1966	£6	£12	
Here Comes The Judge	LP	Tamla Motown	(S)TML11086	1968	£6	£15	
Here Comes The Judge	7"	Tamla Motown	(S)TML663	1968	£2.50	£6	chart single
Night Fo' Last	7"	Tamla Motown	TMG644	1968	£4	£8	
Out To Get You	7"	Tamla Motown	TMG512	1965	£15	£30	
Prime Of Shorty Long	LP	Tamla Motown	(S)TML11144	1970	£6	£15	

LONG TALL SHORTY

By Your Love	7"	Warner Bros	K17491	1979	£10	£20	
If I Was You	7"	Dr.Creation	LYN9904	1981	£1.50	£4	flexi
On The Streets Again	7"	Diamond	DIA002	1985	£2	£5	with poster
Win Or Lose	7"	Ramkup	CAC007	1981	£12.50	£25	

LONGBOATMEN

Take Her Any Time	7"	Polydor	56115	1966	£70	£140	

LONGBRANCH PENNYWHISTLE

Longbranch Pennywhistle was a duo comprising J.D.Souther and Glenn Frey, both of whom have been familiar faces within the American country-rock scene ever since - Frey being a member of the Eagles.

Longbranch Pennywhistle	LP	Amos	AAS7007	1969	£8	£20	US

LONGET, CLAUDINE

Colours	LP	A&M	AMLS929	1968	£5	£12	with Randy Newman

LOOP

Collision	7"	Chapter 22	LCHAP27	1988	£1.50	£4	
Fade Out	LP	Chapter 22	CHAPLLP34	1988	£5	£12	2 45rpm discs, signed
Keep On Movin'	12"	Rock The House	T001	1987	£2.50	£6	
Sixteen Dreams	12"	Head	HEAD5	1987	£5	£12	
Soundhead	7"	Cheree	CHEREE1	1988	£2.50	£6	flexi, B side by The Telescopes
Spinning	7"	Head	HEADL7	1987	£2	£5	no PS
Spinning	12"	Head	HEAD7	1987	£4	£10	

LOOSE ENDS

Send The People Away	7"	Decca	F12437	1966	£6	£12	
Taxman	7"	Decca	F12476	1966	£6	£12	

LOOT

Baby Come Closer	7"	Page One	POF013	1966	£2.50	£6	
Baby Come Closer	7" EP.	Fontana	460206	1967	£10	£20	French
Don't Turn Around	7"	CBS	3231	1968	£4	£8	
I've Just Gotta Love You	7"	Page One	POF026	1967	£5	£10	
She's A Winner	7"	Page One	POF095	1968	£6	£12	2 different B sides
Try To Keep It Secret	7"	Page One	POF115	1969	£6	£12	
Whenever You're Ready	7"	CBS	2938	1967	£4	£8	
Whenever You're Ready	7" EP.	Palette	22021	1967	£10	£20	French

LOPEZ, TRINI

At P.J.'s	LP	Reprise	R6093	1963	£4	£10	
Gonna Get Along Without Ya Now	7"	Reprise	R20547	1967	£1.50	£4	chart single
If I Had A Hammer	7"	Reprise	R20198	1963	£1.50	£4	chart single
I'm Coming Home Cindy	7"	Reprise	R20455	1966	£1.50	£4	chart single
Jean Marie	7"	London	HL9808	1963	£1.50	£4	
Kansas City	7"	Reprise	R20236	1963	£1.50	£4	chart single
La Bamba	7"	Reprise	R20480	1966	£1.50	£4	
Lemon Tree	7"	Reprise	R20336	1964	£1.50	£4	
More Of Trini Lopez	LP	London	HA8160	1964	£5	£12	
Teenage Love Songs	LP	London	HA8132	1964	£6	£15	

LOR, DENISE

If I Give My Heart To You	7"	Parlophone	MSP6120	1954	£1.50	£4	

LORAN, KENNY

Mama's Little Baby	7"	Capitol	CL15081	1959	£10	£20	

495

L'ORANGE MECHANIK
Symphony .... 7" ...... Artpop .... POP44 .... 1985 ... £2 ....£5 ....

LORD BEGINNER
Victory Test Match .... 7" ...... Melodisc .... CAL1 .... 1963 ... £4 ....£8 ....

LORD BLAKEY
Maria .... 7" ...... Jump Up .... JU502 .... 1967 ... £2.50 ....£6 ....

LORD, BRIAN & THE MIDNIGHTERS
The Brian Lord single features both Frank Zappa and his colleague in the Mothers Of Invention, Ray Collins.
Big Surfer .... 7" ...... Capitol .... 4981 .... 1963 ... £15 ....£30 .... US
Big Surfer .... 7" ...... Vigah .... 001 .... 1963 ... £50 ....£100 .... US

LORD BRISCO
Jonah .... 7" ...... Island .... WI187 .... 1965 ... £5 ....£10 ..... Baba Brooks B side
My Love Has Come .... 7" ...... Black Swan ..... WI450 .... 1964 ... £5 ....£10 ..... Baba Brooks B side
Spiritual Mambo .... 7" ...... Black Swan ..... WI447 .... 1964 ... £5 ....£10 ..... Baba Brooks B side
Trojan .... 7" ...... Black Swan ..... WI454 .... 1964 ... £5 ....£10 ....

LORD BRYNNER
Congo War .... 7" ...... Island .... WI266 .... 1966 ... £5 ....£10 ....

LORD BUCKLEY
Bad Rapping The Marquis De Sade ...... LP ..... World Pacific ... WPS21889 .... 1969 ... £6 ....£15 .... US
Best Of Lord Buckley .... LP ..... Crestview .... CRV(7)801 .... 1963 ... £6 ....£15 .... US
Best Of Lord Buckley .... LP ..... Elektra .... EKS74047 .... 1969 ... £5 ....£12 .... US
Blowing His Mind And Yours Too ...... LP ..... World Pacific ... WP1849 .... 1966 ... £6 ....£15 .... US
Buckley's Best .... LP ..... Liberty .... LBS83191 .... 1968 ... £6 ....£15 .... US
Hipsters, Flipsters, & Finger Poppin'   10" LP RCA .... LPM3246 .... 195- ... £25 ....£50 .... US
Daddies
In Concert .... LP ..... World Pacific ... WP1815 .... 1964 ... £6 ....£15 .... US
Lord Buckley .... LP ..... Bizarre .... RS6389 .... 1970 ... £6 ....£15 .... US
Most Immaculately Hip Autocrat .... LP ..... Straight........... STS1054 .... 1970 ... £6 ....£15 .... US
Way Out Humor Of Lord Buckley .... LP ..... World Pacific ... WP1279 .... 1959 ... £8 ....£20 .... US

LORD BURGESS & HIS SUN ISLANDERS
Calypso Au Go-Go .... LP ...... Pye .... NPL28109............ 1968 ... £5 ....£12 ....

LORD CREATOR
Big Bamboo .... 7" ...... Jump Up .... JU524 .... 1967 ... £2.50 ....£6 ....
Drive With Care .... 7" ...... National .... NC2001 .... 1964 ... £4 ....£8 ....
                                                            Calypso...........
Evening News .... 7" ...... Blue Beat ...... BB292 .... 1964 ... £5 ....£10 ....
Independent Jamaica .... 7" ...... Island .... WI001 .... 1962 ... £7.50 ....£15 ....
Jamaica Jump Up .... 7" ...... Jump Up .... JU503 .... 1967 ... £2.50 ....£6 ....
Jamaica's Anniversary .... 7" ...... Port-O-Jam ... PJ4119 .... 1964 ... £5 ....£10 ....
Obeah Wedding .... 7" ...... Doctor Bird ..... DB1029 .... 1966 ... £5 ....£10 ..... Bertram Ennis B side
Peeping Tom .... 7" ...... Kalypso .... XX24 .... 196- ... £4 ....£8 ....
Rhythm Of The Blues .... 7" ...... Port-O-Jam ... PJ4005 .... 1964 ... £5 ....£10 ....
We Will Be Lovers .... 7" ...... Island .... WI105 .... 1963 ... £5 ....£10 ....
Wicked Lady .... 7" ...... Black Swan ..... WI463 .... 1965 ... £5 ....£10 .... Maytals B side

LORD CRISTO
Dumb Boy And The Parrot .... 7" ...... Jump Up .... JU515 .... 1967 ... £2.50 ....£6 ....
Election War Zone .... 7" ...... Jump Up .... JU517 .... 1967 ... £2.50 ....£6 ....

LORD DANIEL
Small Island Gal .... 7" ...... Kalypso .... XX26 .... 196- ... £2.50 ....£6 ....

LORD INVADER
Kings Of Calypso Vol.2 .... 7" EP.. Pye .... NEP24038 .... 1957 ... £2.50 ....£6 ....

LORD IVANHOE
Kings Of Calypso Vol.6 .... 7" EP.. Pye .... NEP24087 .... 1958 ... £2.50 ....£6 ....

LORD, JON
Sarabande .... LP ...... Purple .... TPSA7516 .... 1976 ... £4 ....£10 ....

LORD KITCHENER
Black Pudding .... 7" ...... Melodisc .... 1498 .... 1959 ... £2.50 ....£6 ....
Black Pudding .... 7" ...... Melodisc .... CAL19 .... 1964 ... £2.50 ....£6 ....
Calypsos Too Hot To Handle .... LP ..... Melodisc .... 12129 .... 196- ... £8 ....£20 ....
Calypsos Too Hot To Handle .... LP ..... Melodisc .... 12199 .... 196- ... £6 ....£15 .... extra tracks
Calypsos Too Hot To Handle Vol.2 .... LP ..... Melodisc .... 12130 .... 196- ... £8 ....£20 ....
Calypsos Too Hot To Handle Vol.2 .... LP ..... Melodisc .... 12200 .... 196- ... £6 ....£15 .... extra tracks
Carnival .... 7" ...... Melodisc .... CAL23 .... 1964 ... £2.50 ....£6 ....
Come Back In The Morning .... 7" ...... Melodisc .... CAL21 .... 1964 ... £2.50 ....£6 ....
Drink A Rum .... 7" ...... Melodisc .... CAL5 .... 1963 ... £2.50 ....£6 ....
Dr.Kitch .... 7" ...... Aladdin .... WI612 .... 1965 ... £4 ....£8 ....
Dr.Kitch .... 7" ...... Jump Up .... JU511 .... 1967 ... £2.50 ....£6 ....
Federation .... 7" ...... Melodisc .... CAL14 .... 1964 ... £2.50 ....£6 ....
If You're Brown .... 7" ...... Melodisc .... 1531 .... 1959 ... £2.50 ....£6 ....
Jamaica Turkey .... 7" ...... Melodisc .... 1577 .... 1960 ... £2.50 ....£6 ....
Jamaica Turkey .... 7" ...... Melodisc .... CAL22 .... 1964 ... £2.50 ....£6 ....
Kitch .... 7" ...... Melodisc .... CAL2 .... 1963 ... £2.50 ....£6 ....
KItch - King Of Calypso .... 10" LP Melodisc .... MLP500 .... 1955 ... £8 ....£20 ....
Kitch Mambo Calypso .... 7" ...... Melodisc .... CAL10 .... 1964 ... £2.50 ....£6 ....
Kitch Take It Easy .... 7" ...... Melodisc .... CAL4 .... 1963 ... £2.50 ....£6 ....
Kitch You So Sweet .... 7" ...... Jump Up .... JU530 .... 1967 ... £2.50 ....£6 ....
Life Begins At Forty .... 7" ...... Melodisc .... CAL11 .... 1964 ... £2.50 ....£6 ....

Title	Format	Label	Cat No	Year	Price1	Price2	Notes
Love In The Cemetary	7"	Jump Up	JU504	1967	£2.50	£6	
Muriel And The Bug	7"	Melodisc	CAL3	1963	£2.50	£6	
Road	7"	Jump Up	JU506	1967	£2.50	£6	
Romeo	7"	Melodisc	CAL12	1964	£2.50	£6	
Too Late Kitch	7"	Melodisc	CAL6	1963	£2.50	£6	
Wife And Mother	7"	Melodisc	CAL7	1963	£2.50	£6	

LORD LEBBY
Title	Format	Label	Cat No	Year	Price1	Price2	Notes
Caledonia	7"	Starlite	ST45018	1960	£20	£40	
Sweet Jamaica	7"	Kalypso	XX05	1960	£2	£5	

LORD MELODY
Title	Format	Label	Cat No	Year	Price1	Price2	Notes
Happy Holiday	7"	Melodisc	CAL16	1964	£2	£5	
Rock 'n' Roll Calypso	7"	Kalypso	XX14	1960	£2	£5	

LORD NELSON
Title	Format	Label	Cat No	Year	Price1	Price2	Notes
I Got A Itch	7"	Stateside	SS189	1963	£2.50	£6	
It's Delinquency	7"	Stateside	SS281	1964	£2.50	£6	
Party For Santa Claus	7"	Jump Up	JU527	1967	£2.50	£6	
Proud West Indian	7" EP	Stateside	SE1024	1964	£4	£8	

LORD POWER
Title	Format	Label	Cat No	Year	Price1	Price2	Notes
Temptation	7"	Coxsone	CS7079	1968	£5	£10	Al & Vibrators B side

LORD RIGBY
Title	Format	Label	Cat No	Year	Price1	Price2	Notes
Carnival Jamaica	7"	National Calypso	NC2000	1964	£2.50	£6	
Milkman	7"	Kalypso	XX29	196-	£2	£5	

LORD ROCKINGHAM'S XI
Title	Format	Label	Cat No	Year	Price1	Price2	Notes
Hoots Mon	7"	Decca	F11059	1958	£1.50	£4	chart single
Oh Boy	7" EP	Decca	DFE6555	1958	£10	£20	
Ra Ra Rockingham	7"	Decca	F11139	1959	£2	£5	
Return Of Lord Rockingham's XI	LP	Columbia	SCX6291	1968	£5	£12	
Rockingham Twist	7"	Decca	F11426	1962	£1.50	£4	
Squelch	7"	Decca	F11024	1958	£2.50	£5	
Wee Tom	7"	Decca	F11104	1959	£2	£5	chart single

LORD ROSE & THE BEACHCOMBERS
Title	Format	Label	Cat No	Year	Price1	Price2	Notes
Independent Jamaica	7"	Kalypso	XX25	196-	£2	£5	

LORD SITAR
Title	Format	Label	Cat No	Year	Price1	Price2	Notes
Lord Sitar	LP	Columbia	SCX6256	1968	£5	£12	

LORD TANAMO
Title	Format	Label	Cat No	Year	Price1	Price2	Notes
Come Down	7"	Island	WI108	1963	£5	£10	
I Had A Dream	7"	Rio	R21	1964	£5	£10	Osborne Graham B side
I Love You Truly	7"	Caribou	CRC3	196-	£4	£8	
I'm In The Mood For Ska	7"	Ska Beat	JB224	1965	£5	£10	
Mothers Love	7"	Ska Beat	JB243	1966	£5	£10	
Sweet Dreaming	7"	Kalypso	XX20	1960	£2.50	£6	

LORD, TONY
Title	Format	Label	Cat No	Year	Price1	Price2	Notes
World's Champion	7"	Planet	PLF102	1966	£5	£10	

LORDAN, JERRY
Title	Format	Label	Cat No	Year	Price1	Price2	Notes
All My Own Work	LP	Parlophone	PCS3014	1961	£25	£50	stereo
All My Own Work	LP	Parlophone	PMC1133	1961	£20	£40	mono
I'll Stay Single	7"	Parlophone	R4588	1959	£1.50	£4	chart single
Let's Try Again	7"	Parlophone	R4748	1961	£1.50	£4	
One Good Solid 24 Carat Reason	7"	Parlophone	R4903	1962	£1.50	£4	
Ring, Write, Or Call	7"	Parlophone	R4695	1960	£1.50	£4	
Sing Like An Angel	7"	Parlophone	R4653	1960	£1.50	£4	chart single
Who Could Be Bluer	7"	Parlophone	R4627	1960	£2	£5	chart single

LORDS
Title	Format	Label	Cat No	Year	Price1	Price2	Notes
Best Of The Lords	LP	Columbia	29783	1971	£8	£20	German
Don't Mince Matters	7"	Columbia	DB8121	1967	£15	£30	
Gloryland	7"	Columbia	DB8367	1968	£2.50	£6	
Good Side Of June	LP	Columbia	74244	1968	£10	£25	German
Hey Baby	7" EP	Columbia	ESRF1656	1965	£15	£30	French
In Black And White	LP	Columbia	83859	1965	£15	£30	German
Inside Out	LP	Columbia	28887	1971	£8	£20	German
Lords	LP	Columbia	31972	1974	£5	£12	German
Lords 2	LP	Columbia	84013	1966	£10	£25	German
Shakin' All Over	LP	Columbia	28478	1970	£8	£20	German
Some Folks	LP	Columbia		1967	£10	£25	German
Ulleogamaxbe	LP	Columbia	74343	1969	£10	£25	German

LORDS OF THE NEW CHURCH
Title	Format	Label	Cat No	Year	Price1	Price2	Notes
Dance With Me	12"	Illegal	PFSX1022	1983	£2.50	£6	pic disc
Russian Roulette	7"	Illegal	ILSP0033	1983	£1.50	£4	pic disc

LOREN, SOPHIA
Title	Format	Label	Cat No	Year	Price1	Price2	Notes
Boccaccio '70	LP	RCA	FOC/FSO5	1962	£8	£20	US
In Rome	LP	Columbia	OL6310		£8	£20	US

LORRIE, MYRNA
Title	Format	Label	Cat No	Year	Price1	Price2	Notes
Life's Changing Scene	7"	London	HLU8294	1956	£7.50	£15	
Underway	7"	London	HLU8187	1955	£12.50	£25	

LORY, DICK

Cool It Baby	7"	London	HLD8348	1956	£70	£140
I Got Over You	7"	Liberty	LIB55529	1963	£2	£5
My Last Date	7"	London	HLG9284	1961	£4	£8
Pain Is Here	7"	Liberty	LIB55415	1962	£2	£5

LOS BRAVOS

Black Is Black	LP	Decca	LK4822	1966	£6	£15	
Black Is Black	7"	Decca	F22419	1966	£1.50	£4	chart single
Black Is Black	7" EP.	Barclay	071050	1966	£6	£12	French
Bring A Little Lovin'	7"	Decca	F22765	1968	£1.50	£4	
Going Nowhere	7"	Decca	F22529	1966	£1.50	£4	
Going Nowhere	7" EP.	Barclay	071091	1966	£6	£12	French, 2 different sleeves
I Don't Care	7"	Decca	F22484	1966	£1.50	£4	chart single
I'm All Ears	7"	Decca	F22615	1967	£1.50	£4	
Like Nobody Else	7"	Decca	F22682	1967	£1.50	£4	
Los Bravos	LP	Decca	LK/SKL4905	1968	£6	£15	
Los Bravos	LP	Eclipse	ECJR2026	1970	£4	£10	
Save Me Save Me	7"	Decca	F22853	1968	£1.50	£4	

LOS BRINCOS

Lola	7"	Page One	POF023	1967	£12.50	£25
Nobody Wants You Now	7"	Page One	POF031	1967	£4	£8

LOS CANARIOS

Get On Your Knees	7"	Major Minor	MM532	1967	£5	£10
Three Two One Ah	7"	Major Minor	MM502	1967	£2	£5

LOS CINCOS

Most Exclusive Residence For Sale	7"	Philips	BF1525	1966	£2	£5

LOS LOBOS

Just Another Band From East LA	LP	New Vista	1001	1978	£37.50	£75	US
Si Se Puede!	LP	Pan American	101	1976	£25	£50	US

LOSS, JOE

Thunderbirds	7"	HMV	POP1500	1966	£2.50	£6

LOST & FOUND

Everybody's Here	LP	International Artists	IALP3	1967	£10	£25	US

LOST JOCKEY

Professor Slack	7"	Operation Twilight	OPT11	1982	£2	£5

LOTHAR & THE HAND PEOPLE

Presenting Lothar And The Hand People	LP	Capitol	ST2997	1968	£10	£25	US
Sdrawkcab	7"	Capitol	CL15610	1969	£5	£10	
Space Hymn	LP	Capitol	ST247	1969	£15	£30	US

LOTIS, DENNIS

Bidin' My Time	LP	Columbia	33SX1089	1958	£5	£12
Chain Reaction	7"	Decca	F10471	1955	£1.50	£4
Face Of An Angel, Heart Of A Devil	7"	Decca	F10469	1955	£1.50	£4
Honey Love	7"	Decca	F10392	1954	£2.50	£6
How About You	LP	Pye	NPL18002	1957	£5	£12
Such A Night	7"	Decca	F10287	1954	£4	£8

LOU, BONNIE

Barnyard Hop	7"	Parlophone	MSP6178	1955	£5	£10	
Blue Tennessee Rain	7"	Parlophone	MSP6117	1954	£6	£12	
Bo Weevil	7"	Parlophone	MSP6234	1956	£5	£10	
Dancin' In My Socks	7"	Parlophone	MSP6188	1955	£7.50	£15	
Don't Stop Kissing Me Goodnight	7"	Parlophone	MSP6095	1954	£6	£12	
Drop Me A Line	7"	Parlophone	MSP6173	1955	£5	£10	
Hand-Me-Down Heart	7"	Parlophone	MSP6036	1953	£12.50	£25	
Huckleberry Pie	7"	Parlophone	MSP6108	1954	£6	£12	
I'm Available	7"	Parlophone	DP545	195-	£7.50	£15	export
La Dee Dah	7"	Parlophone	R4409	1958	£20	£40	with Rusty York
Lonesome Lover	7"	Parlophone	MSP6253	1956	£7.50	£15	
Miss The Love	7"	Parlophone	MSP6223	1956	£4	£8	
No Rock'n'Roll Tonight	7"	Parlophone	R4215	1956	£5	£10	
Papaya Mama	7"	Parlophone	MSP6051	1953	£10	£20	
Runnin' Away	7"	Parlophone	R4350	1957	£5	£10	
Seven Lonely Days	7"	Parlophone	MSP6021	1953	£12.50	£25	
Tennessee Mambo	7"	Parlophone	MSP6151	1955	£6	£12	
Tennessee Wig Walk	7"	Parlophone	MSP6048	1953	£12.50	£25	chart single
Texas Polka	7"	Parlophone	MSP6072	1954	£6	£12	
Tweedle Dee	7"	Parlophone	MSP6161	1955	£7.50	£15	
Two Step Side Step	7"	Parlophone	MSP6132	1954	£6	£12	

LOUDERMILK, JOHN D.

Angela Jones	7"	RCA	RCA1323	1962	£2.50	£6	
Country Love Songs	LP	RCA	LSP4040	1968	£4	£10	US
Language Of Love	LP	RCA	RD27248/SF5123	1962	£6	£15	
Language Of Love	7"	RCA	RCA1269	1962	£1.50	£4	chart single
Open Mind Of John D.Loudermilk	LP	RCA	LSP4097	1969	£4	£10	US
Sidewalks	7"	RCA	RCA1761	1968	£1.50	£4	

Sings A Bizarre Collection	LP	RCA	RD/SF7890	1967	£5	£12	
Suburban Attitudes In Country Verse	LP	RCA	LPM/LSP3807	1967	£5	£12	US
Thou Shalt Not Steal	7"	RCA	RCA1287	1962	£1.50	£4	
Twelve Sides Of John D.Loudermilk	LP	RCA	RD/SF7515	1962	£6	£15	

LOUDEST WHISPER

| Children Of Lir | LP | Polydor | | 197- | £330 | £500 | Irish |
| Name Of The Game | 7" | Polydor | 2078113 | 1980 | £10 | £20 | Irish |

LOUIS, JOE HILL

| Blues In The Morning | LP | Polydor | 2383214 | 1974 | £5 | £12 | |
| Heartache Baby | 7" | Bootleg | 502 | 1965 | £10 | £20 | |

LOUISIANA RED

I Done Woke Up	7"	Sue	WI337	1964	£6	£12	
Keep Your Hands Of My Woman	7"	Columbia	DB7270	1964	£4	£8	
Lowdown Back Porch Blues	LP	Columbia	33SX1612	1964	£10	£25	
Seventh Son	LP	Polydor	2941002	1972	£5	£12	
Sings The Blues	LP	Atlantic	K40436	1972	£4	£10	

LOUSSIER, JACQUES

| Air On A G String | 7" | Decca | F22383 | 1966 | £1.50 | £4 | |
| Air On A G String | 7" | Decca | F22876 | 1969 | £1.50 | £4 | |

LOUVIN BROTHERS

Country Christmas	LP	Capitol	(S)T1616	1961	£5	£12	US
Country Love Ballads	LP	Capitol	T1106	1959	£10	£25	US
Country Love Ballads	7" EP	Capitol	EAP11106	1959	£2.50	£6	US
Encore	LP	Capitol	T1547	1961	£5	£12	US
Family Who Prays	LP	Capitol	T1061	1958	£10	£25	US
Ira And Charlie	LP	Capitol	T910	1958	£20	£40	US
Ira And Charlie	7" EP	Capitol	EAP1910	1957	£5	£10	
Keep Your Eyes On Jesus	LP	Capitol	(S)T1834	1963	£5	£12	US
Knoxville Girl	7"	Capitol	CL14989	1959	£2	£5	
Louvin Brothers	LP	MGM	E3426	1956	£50	£100	US
My Baby's Gone	LP	Capitol	T1385	1960	£10	£25	US
Nearer My God To Thee	LP	Capitol	T825	1957	£20	£40	US
Satan Is Real	LP	Capitol	T1277	1960	£10	£25	US
Sing And Play Their Current Hits	LP	Capitol	(S)T2091	1964	£5	£12	US
Tragic Songs Of Life	LP	Capitol	T769	1957	£25	£50	US
Tragic Songs Of Life	7" EP	Capitol	EAP1769	1957	£5	£10	
Tribute To The Delmore Brothers	LP	Capitol	T1449	1960	£8	£20	US
Weapon Of Prayer	LP	Capitol	(S)T1721	1962	£5	£12	US
You're Learning	7"	Capitol	CL15078	1959	£1.50	£4	

LOUVIN, CHARLIE

I Forgot To Cry	LP	Capitol	(S)T2787	1967	£5	£12	US
I'll Remember Always	LP	Capitol	(S)T2689	1967	£5	£12	US
Less And Less	LP	Capitol	(S)T2208	1965	£5	£12	US
Lonesome Is Me	LP	Capitol	(S)T2482	1966	£5	£12	US
Many Moods Of Charlie Louvin	LP	Capitol	(S)T2437	1966	£5	£12	US
Will You Visit Me On Sundays	LP	Capitol	ST2958	1968	£5	£12	US

LOUVIN, IRA

| Unforgettable Ira Louvin | LP | Capitol | (S)T2413 | 1965 | £5 | £12 | US |

LOVABLES

| You're The Cause Of It | 7" | Stateside | SS2108 | 1968 | £5 | £10 | |

LOVE

The personnel of Love varies from album to album, but the group always revolves around the singing and writing talents of Arthur Lee. His is an inconsistent talent, but at his best he is little short of brilliant. All of Love's albums (except perhaps the first, on which the group have barely emerged from their garage punk beginnings) contain moments of pure magic, although none is entirely flawless. The critics' favourite is "Forever Changes", whose largely gentle sound is enhanced by modest orchestration, but the heavier, guitar-centred "Four Sail" actually has songs of greater distinction. It is a very fine, and very underrated record. The first side of "Da Capo" has some excellent songs too, but the album as a whole is let down by the extended jam on side two, which does not really work. "Out Here" and "False Start" are similar in sound to "Four Sail", though overall neither is in the same league. Each contains one masterpiece, however - "The Everlasting First" is a collaboration with Jimi Hendrix, who makes a typically fine contribution to an unusually structured song; while "Love Is More Than Words" is dominated by a long, highly charged guitar solo that turns the track into one of the classic pieces of rock improvisation.

Alone Again Or	7"	Elektra	2101019	1971	£1.50	£4	
Alone Again Or	7"	Elektra	EKSN45024	1968	£2.50	£6	
Andmoreagain	7"	Elektra	EKSN45026	1968	£4	£8	
Da Capo	LP	Elektra	EKL4005/ EKS74005	1967	£8	£20	
Do The Merlin	7"	LSD	1009	1966	£150	£250	US
Everlasting First	7"	Harvest	HAR5030	1970	£5	£10	with Jimi Hendrix
False Start	LP	Harvest	SHVL787	1970	£6	£15	
Forever Changes	LP	Elektra	EKL4013	1967	£8	£20	mono
Forever Changes	LP	Elektra	EKS74013	1967	£6	£15	chart LP
Forever Changes	LP	Elektra	EKS74013	1970	£4	£10	red label
Four Sail	LP	Elektra	EKS74049	1969	£8	£20	
Four Sail	LP	Elektra	K42030	1976	£5	£10	
I'm With You	7"	Elektra	EKSN45086	1970	£2	£5	
Laughing Stock	7"	Elektra	EKSN45038	1968	£5	£10	
Love	LP	Elektra	EKL4001	1966	£10	£25	mono
Love	LP	Elektra	EKS74001	1966	£8	£20	stereo
Love	LP	Elektra	K42068	1972	£4	£10	
Love Masters	LP	Elektra	K32002	1972	£4	£10	
Love Revisited	LP	Elektra	2469001	1970	£5	£12	
My Little Red Book	7"	London	HLZ10053	1966	£6	£12	
My Little Red Book	7" EP	Vogue	INT18072	1966	£25	£50	French

Out Here	LP	Harvest	SHDW3/4	1970	£10	£25	double, chart LP
Reel To Real	LP	RSO	2394145	1974	£5	£12	
Seven And Seven Is	7"	London	HLZ10073	1966	£6	£12	
Seven And Seven Is	7" EP.	Vogue	INT18095	1966	£25	£50	French
She Comes In Colours	7"	Elektra	EKSN45010	1967	£4	£8	
Softly To Me	7"	Elektra	EKSN45016	1967	£2.50	£6	
Stand Out	7"	Harvest	HAR5014	1970	£4	£8	
Time Is Like A River	7"	RSO	2090151	1975	£2	£5	

LOVE & TEARS

Love And Tears	LP	Polydor	2371334	1973	£5	£12	German

LOVE AFFAIR

Bring On Back The Good Times	7"	CBS	4300	1969	£1.50	£4	chart single
Day Without Love	7"	CBS	3674	1968	£1.50	£4	chart single
Everlasting Love	7"	CBS	3125	1967	£1.50	£4	chart single
Everlasting Love Affair	LP	CBS	63416	1969	£5	£12	
New Day	LP	CBS	64109	1970	£5	£12	
One Road	7"	CBS	3994	1969	£1.50	£4	chart single
Rainbow Valley	7"	CBS	3366	1968	£1.50	£4	chart single
Rainbow Valley	7"	CBS	3366	1968	£2.50	£6	PS
She Smiled Sweetly	7"	Decca	F12558	1967	£7.50	£15	

LOVE CHILDREN

Easy Squeezy	7"	Deram	DM268	1969	£1.50	£4	
Paper Chase	7"	Deram	DM303	1970	£2	£5	

LOVE, CHRISTOPHER

Curse Goes On	7"	London	HLU10263	1969	£4	£8

LOVE, DARLENE

Boy I'm Gonna Marry	7"	London	HLU9725	1963	£6	£12	
Fine Fine Boy	7"	London	HLU9815	1963	£6	£12	
Lord If You're A Woman	7"	Phil Spector	2010019	1977	£1.50	£4	
Wait Till My Bobby Gets Home	7"	London	HLU10244	1969	£4	£8	
Wait Till My Bobby Gets Home	7"	London	HLU9765	1963	£6	£12	
Wait Till My Bobby Gets Home	7" EP.	London	REU1411	1964	£50	£100	

LOVE, GARFIELD & JIMMY SPRUILL

Next Time You See Me	7"	Blue Horizon	573150	1969	£6	£12

LOVE GENERATION

She Touched Me	7"	Liberty	LBF15018	1967	£2	£5

LOVE, MARY

Hurt is Just Beginning	7"	Stateside	SS2135	1969	£7.50	£15
Lay This Burden Down	7"	Stateside	SS2009	1967	£12.50	£25
You Turned My Bitter Into Sweet	7"	King	KG1024	1965	£30	£60

LOVE, RONNIE

Chills And Fever	7"	London	HLD9272	1961	£4	£8

LOVE SCULPTURE

Love Sculpture evolved from the Human Beans as a blues group and showcase for the flashy guitar playing of Dave Edmunds. The success of their version of Khachaturian's 'Sabre Dance' led them to try another classical reworking, but due to copyright problems, "Mars" was only made available on the US version of "Forms And Feelings" and has not been reissued since.

Blues Helping	LP	Parlophone	PCS7059	1968	£8	£20	
Blues Helping	LP	Parlophone	PMC7059	1968	£10	£25	mono
Forms And Feelings	LP	Parlophone	PCS7090	1969	£10	£25	
Forms And Feelings	LP	Parrot	PAS71035	1969	£15	£30	US
In The Land Of The Few	7"	Parlophone	R5831	1970	£4	£8	
River To Another Day	7"	Parlophone	R5664	1968	£6	£12	
Sabre Dance	7"	Parlophone	R5744	1968	£1.50	£4	chart single
Seagull	7"	Parlophone	R5807	1969	£4	£8	
Wang Dang Doodle	7"	Parlophone	R5731	1968	£6	£12	

LOVE, WILLIE & WILLIE NIX

Two Willies From Memphis	LP	Highway 51	H700	1966	£20	£40

LOVECRAFT

Valley Of The Moon	LP	Reprise	RS6419	1970	£6	£15	US

LOVED ONES

Loved One	7" EP.	Festival	1528	196-	£6	£12	French

LOVEJOY, JOY

In Orbit	7"	Chess	6145010	1972	£1.50	£4

LOVERS

Let's Elope	7"	Vogue	V9111	1958	£60	£120

LOVICH, LENE

I Saw Mommy Kissing Santa Claus	7"	Polydor	2058812	1976	£5	£10
I Think We're Alone Now (Japanese)	7"	Stiff	BUYJ32	1978	£2.50	£6

LOVIN'

All You've Got	7"	Page One	POF041	1967	£12.50	£25
Keep On Believing	7"	Page One	POF035	1967	£10	£20

LOVIN' SPOONFUL

Almost Grown	7" EP.	Vogue	INT18032	1965	£7.50	£15	French
Darling Be Home Soon	7"	Kama Sutra	KAS207	1967	£1.50	£4	chart single

Title	Format	Label	Cat. No.	Year	Price	Price	Notes
Darling Be Home Soon	7" EP	Kama Sutra	617108	1967	£5	£10	French
Day Blues	7" EP	Kama Sutra	KEP303	1967	£4	£8	
Daydream	LP	Pye	NPL28078	1966	£5	£12	chart LP
Daydream	7"	Pye	7N25361	1966	£1.50	£4	chart single
Daydream	7" EP	Kama Sutra	617102	1966	£5	£10	French
Did You Ever Have To Make Up Your Mind	7" EP	Kama Sutra	KEP300	1966	£4	£8	
Do You Believe In Magic	LP	Pye	NPL28069	1965	£5	£12	
Do You Believe In Magic	7"	Pye	7N25327	1965	£2	£5	
Do You Believe In Magic	7" EP	Kama Sutra	617101	1965	£7.50	£15	French
Do You Believe In Magic	7" EP	Kama Sutra	KEP306	1967	£4	£8	
Everything Playing	LP	Kama Sutra	KLP404	1968	£4	£10	
Hums Of The Lovin' Spoonful	LP	Kama Sutra	KLP401	1967	£4	£10	
Jug Band Music	7" EP	Kama Sutra	KEP301	1966	£4	£8	
Loving You	7" EP	Kama Sutra	KEP305	1967	£4	£8	
Money	7"	Kama Sutra	KAS211	1967	£1.50	£4	
Nashville Cats	7"	Kama Sutra	KAS204	1967	£1.50	£4	chart single
Nashville Cats	7" EP	Kama Sutra	617106	1967	£5	£10	French
Nashville Cats	7" EP	Kama Sutra	KEP304	1967	£4	£8	
Never Going Back	7"	Kama Sutra	KAS213	1967	£1.50	£4	
Rain On The Roof	7"	Kama Sutra	KAS201	1966	£1.50	£4	
Rain On The Roof	7" EP	Kama Sutra	617105	1966	£5	£10	French
Revelation Revolution '69	LP	Kama Sutra	KLP406	1969	£4	£10	
She Is Still A Mystery	7"	Kama Sutra	KAS210	1967	£1.50	£4	
Six O'Clock	7"	Kama Sutra	KAS208	1967	£1.50	£4	
Six O'Clock	7"	Kama Sutra	617110	1967	£5	£10	French
Summer In The City	7"	Kama Sutra	KAS200	1966	£1.50	£4	chart single
Summer In The City	7" EP	Kama Sutra	617103	1966	£5	£10	French
Summer In The City	7" EP	Kama Sutra	KEP302	1966	£4	£8	
You Didn't Have To Be So Nice	7"	Pye	7N25344	1966	£2	£5	
You're A Big Boy Now	LP	Kama Sutra	KLP402	1967	£4	£10	

LOVING AWARENESS

Title	Format	Label	Cat. No.	Year	Price	Price	Notes
Loving Awareness	LP	More Love	ML001	1976	£4	£10	

LOVING KIND

Title	Format	Label	Cat. No.	Year	Price	Price	Notes
Accidental Love	7"	Piccadilly	7N35299	1966	£5	£10	
Ain't That Peculiar	7"	Piccadilly	7N35342	1966	£6	£12	
I Love The Things You Do	7"	Piccadilly	7N35318	1966	£5	£10	

LOW, BRUCE

Title	Format	Label	Cat. No.	Year	Price	Price	Notes
Just Walking In The Rain	7"	HMV	JO464	1956	£2	£5	export

LOWE, JEZ

Title	Format	Label	Cat. No.	Year	Price	Price	Notes
Galloways	LP	Fellside	FE049	1985	£5	£12	
Old Durham Road	LP	Fellside	FE034	1983	£5	£12	

LOWE, JIM

Title	Format	Label	Cat. No.	Year	Price	Price	Notes
Blue Suede Shoes	7"	London	HLD8276	1956	£30	£60	
By You By You By You	7"	London	HLD8368	1957	£10	£20	gold label
Close The Door	7"	London	HLD8171	1955	£15	£30	gold label
Door Of Fame	LP	Mercury	MG20246	1957	£15	£30	US
Four Walls	7"	London	HLD8431	1957	£10	£20	
Green Door	7"	London	HLD8317	1956	£12.50	£25	chart single, gold label
He'll Have To Go	7"	London	HLD9043	1960	£5	£10	
Love Is A $64,000 Question	7"	London	HLD8288	1956	£15	£30	gold label
Rock A Chicka	7"	London	HLD8538	1958	£35	£70	
Songs They Sing Behind The Green Door	LP	London	HAD2108	1958	£25	£50	
Wicked Women	LP	London	HAD2146	1959	£25	£50	

LOWE, MUNDELL

Title	Format	Label	Cat. No.	Year	Price	Price	Notes
Mundell Lowe Quartet	LP	London	LTZU15020	1957	£8	£20	
Mundell Lowe Quintet	10" LP	HMV	DLP1084	1955	£8	£20	

LOWE, NICK

Nick Lowe's response to David Bowie releasing an album called "Low", was to make a record called "Bowi", although this was unfortunately only a four track single, rather than an album. The humour of the concept is enough to make one listen fondly to the music regardless (actually the songs are quite memorable), but not quite enough to make the record into a collectors' item.

Title	Format	Label	Cat. No.	Year	Price	Price	Notes
Bowi	12"	Stiff	LAST1	1977	£4	£10	promo
Live At The El Mocambo	7"	Columbia		1978	£6	£12	Canadian promo

LOWE, PETER

Title	Format	Label	Cat. No.	Year	Price	Price	Notes
Banana Boat Song	7"	Parlophone	R4270	1957	£1.50	£4	
Hear My Song Of Love	7"	Parlophone	R4199	1956	£2	£5	

LOWTHER, HENRY

Henry Lowther is a classically trained violinist who took up the trumpet in order to play jazz and plays both instruments as a session musician on numerous LP releases. He played on the fringes of jazz as a member of Manfred Mann, John Mayall's Bluesbreakers, and the Keef Hartley Band, and he is featured on several of the British jazz albums to be made during the late sixties and early seventies. His own moment came with the LP "Child Song", which is as fresh and sparkling as British jazz gets. The record is also, unfortunately, as rare as British jazz gets, and commands a correspondingly high price.

Title	Format	Label	Cat. No.	Year	Price	Price	Notes
Child Song	LP	Deram	SML1070	1970	£40	£80	

LOYD, MARK

Title	Format	Label	Cat. No.	Year	Price	Price	Notes
When Evening Falls	7"	Parlophone	R5423	1966	£10	£20	

LUCAS

Title	Format	Label	Cat. No.	Year	Price	Price	Notes
Go Now	7"	Polar	1036		£1.50	£4	

LUCAS & THE MIKE COTTON SOUND

Mother In Law	7"	MGM	MGM1427	1968	£4	£8	
Step Out Of Line	7"	Pye	7N17313	1967	£6	£12	
We Got A Thing Going Baby	7"	MGM	MGM1398	1968	£5	£10	

LUCAS, BUDDY

I Want To Know	7"	Pye	7N25045	1960	£1.50	£4	

LUCAS, TREVOR

Overlander	LP	Reality	RY1002	1966	£100	£200	
Waltzing Matilda	7"	Reality	RE505	1966	£10	£20	

LUCIFER

Big Gun	LP	private	LLP1	1972	£30	£60	
Don't Care	7"	private	L001/002	1971	£5	£10	
Exit	LP	private	LLP2	1972	£30	£60	
Fuck You	7"	private	L003/004	1972	£5	£10	
Prick	7"	Lucifer	L005/006	1972	£5	£10	

LUCIFER'S FRIEND

Lucifer's Friend	LP	Philips	6305068	1971	£6	£15	German
Where The Groupies Killed The Blues	LP	Vertigo	6360602	1973	£4	£10	German

LUDLOWS

Wind And The Sea	LP	Pye	NPL18150	1966	£4	£10	

LUDUS

Seduction	12"	New Hormones	ORG16	1981	£3	£8	double

LUKE, ROBIN

Chicka Chicka Honey	7"	London	HLD8771	1958	£6	£12	
Robin Luke	7" EP	London	RED1222	1959	£20	£40	
Susie Darling	7"	London	HLD8676	1958	£4	£8	chart single

LULU

Boat That I Row	7"	Columbia	DB8169	1967	£1.50	£4	chart single
Boom Bang-A-Bang	7" EP	Columbia		1969	£5	£10	French
Boy	7"	Columbia	DB8425	1968	£1.50	£4	chart single
Call Me	7"	Decca	F12326	1966	£1.50	£4	
Can't Hear You No More	7"	Decca	F11965	1964	£1.50	£4	
Chocolate Ice	7" EP	Decca	457099	1966	£5	£10	French
Here Comes The Night	7"	Decca	F12017	1964	£1.50	£4	chart single
I'm A Tiger	7"	Columbia	DB8500	1968	£1.50	£4	chart single
Leave A Little Love	7"	Decca	F12169	1965	£1.50	£4	chart single
Love Loves To Love Love	7"	Columbia	DB8295	1967	£1.50	£4	chart single
Love Loves To Love Lulu	LP	Columbia	SX/SCX6201	1968	£4	£10	
Lulu	LP	Ace Of Clubs	ACL1232	1967	£4	£10	
Lulu	7" EP	Decca	DFE8597	1965	£6	£12	
Lulu's Album	LP	Columbia	SX/SCX6365	1969	£4	£10	
Man With The Golden Gun	7"	Chelsea	2005015	1974	£2	£5	
Me The Peaceful Heart	7"	Columbia	DB8358	1968	£1.50	£4	chart single
Satisfied	7"	Decca	F12128	1965	£1.50	£4	
Satisfied	7" EP	Decca	457084	1965	£5	£10	French
Shout	7"	Decca	F11884	1964	£1.50	£4	chart single
Shout	7" EP	Decca	457045	1964	£6	£12	French
Something To Shout About	LP	Decca	LK4719	1965	£6	£15	
Tell It Like It Is	7"	Decca	F12254	1965	£1.50	£4	
That's Really Some Good	7" EP	Decca	457052	1964	£5	£10	French
To Sir With Love	LP	Fontana	STL5446	1967	£5	£12	with The Mindbenders
To Sir With Love	7"	Columbia	DB8221	1967	£1.50	£4	chart single
Try To Understand	7"	Decca	F12214	1965	£1.50	£4	chart single
What A Wonderful Feelin'	7"	Decca	F12491	1966	£1.50	£4	
What A Wonderful Feeling	7" EP	Decca	457132	1966	£5	£10	French

LUMAN, BOB

Ain't Got Time To Be Unhappy	7"	CBS	3602	1968	£5	£10	
Bad Bad Day	7"	Hickory	451289	1965	£2.50	£6	
Bigger Men Than I	7"	Hickory	451238	1964	£1.50	£4	
Come On And Sing	7"	Hickory	451410	1965	£1.50	£4	
Dreamy Doll	7"	Warner Bros	WB12	1960	£1.50	£4	
Great Snowman	7"	Warner Bros	WB37	1961	£1.50	£4	chart single
Hey Joe	7"	Warner Bros	WB75	1962	£1.50	£4	
I Like Your Kind Of Love	7"	Hickory	451221	1964	£1.50	£4	
Let's Think About Living	LP	Warner Bros	WS8025	1960	£25	£50	stereo
Let's Think About Living	LP	Warner Bros	WM4025	1960	£20	£40	chart LP
Let's Think About Living	7"	Warner Bros	WB18	1960	£2	£5	chart single
Let's Think About Living	7" EP	Warner Bros	WEP6046	1961	£10	£20	
Let's Think About Living	7" EP	Warner Bros	WSEP2046	1961	£15	£30	stereo
Let's Think About Living No.2	7" EP	Warner Bros	WEP6055	1962	£10	£20	
Let's Think About Living No.2	7" EP	Warner Bros	WSEP2055	1962	£15	£30	stereo
Let's Think About Living No.3	7" EP	Warner Bros	WEP6102	1962	£10	£20	
Let's Think About Living No.3	7" EP	Warner Bros	WSE6102	1962	£15	£30	stereo
Livin' Lovin' Sounds	LP	Hickory	LPM124	1964	£6	£15	
Old George Dickie	7"	Hickory	451277	1964	£1.50	£4	
Private Eye	7"	Warner Bros	WB49	1961	£1.50	£4	
Run On Home Baby Brother	7"	Hickory	451266	1964	£1.50	£4	
Why Why Bye Bye	7"	Warner Bros	WB28	1960	£1.50	£4	chart single

LUMAN, BOB & BOBBY LORD

Can't Take The Country From The Boys	LP	Hickory	LPM121	1964	£5	£12	
Hickory Showcase Vol.2	7" EP.	Hickory	LPE1501	1964	£5	£10	
Hickory Showcase Vol.3	7" EP.	Hickory	LPE1504	1964	£5	£10	

LUMLEY, RUFUS

I'm Standing	7"	Stateside	SS516	1966	£30	£60	

LUNAR TWO

Get It, Take It	7"	Spot	JWS551	196-	£1.50	£4	

LUNCEFORD, JIMMIE

For Dancer's Only	10" LP	Brunswick	LA8738	1956	£8	£20	
Jimmie Lunceford Orchestra	LP	Brunswick	LAT8027	1954	£6	£15	
Lunceford Special	LP	Philips	BBL7037	1955	£6	£15	

LUREX, LARRY

Larry Lurex is Freddie Mercury, and his single, issued just before the start of Queen's career is sought after in both its UK and US incarnations. The latter, however, turns up suspiciously often and it is likely that many copies are actually counterfeits.

I Can Hear Music	7"	Anthem	104	1973	£25	£50	US
I Can Hear Music	7"	EMI	EMI2030	1973	£50	£100	

LURKERS

Shadow	7"	Beggars Banquet	BEG1	1978	£2	£5	red, blue, or white vinyl

LUSHER, DON

Rock'n'Roll	7"	Decca	F10560	1955	£1.50	£4	

LUSTMORD

Lustmord	LP	Sterile	SR3	1982	£20	£40	

LUTCHER, NELLIE

Blues In The Night	7"	Brunswick	05352	1954	£4	£8	
It's Been Said	7"	Brunswick	05437	1955	£2	£5	
My Mother's Eyes	7"	Capitol	CL15106	1959	£1.50	£4	
Nellie Lutcher	7" EP.	Philips	BBE12045	1956	£7.50	£15	
Our New Nellie	LP	London	HAU2036	1957	£8	£20	
Real Gone	LP	Capitol	T232	195-	£8	£20	US
Real Gone	LP	MFP	MFP1038	1966	£4	£10	
Real Gone	7" EP.	Capitol	EAP20066	1960	£7.50	£15	
Real Gone	10" LP	Capitol	LC6506	1951	£15	£30	
Whee! Nellie	10" LP	Epic	1108	195-	£10	£25	US
Whose Honey Are You	7"	Brunswick	05497	1955	£2	£5	

LUTHA

	LP				£100	£200	New Zealand

LUTHER

It's Good For The Soul	7"	Atlantic	K10781	1976	£10	£20	

LUTHER & LITTLE EVA

Ain't Got No Home	7"	Parlophone	R4292	1957	£60	£120	

LUTHER, FRANK

While few people will be familiar with the name of Frank Luther, everyone who ever listened to "Children's Favourites" with Uncle Mac will know Luther's classic children's song. Now, after me, "I'm a troll, foll-de-roll!"

Three Billygoats Gruff	7"	Decca	F9051	1954	£2.50	£6	

LUV BUG

You Can Count On Me	7"	Roxy-Ritz	TEASE2	1986	£1.50	£4	

LUV MACHINE

Luv Machine	LP	Polydor	2460102	1971	£50	£100	sleeve pictured in Guide

LUVVERS

House On The Hill	7"	Parlophone	R5459	1966	£10	£20	

L-VOAG

Way Out	LP	Axis	No.9	1979	£4	£10	

LYMON, FRANKIE & THE TEENAGERS

ABC's In Love	7"	Columbia	DB3858	1956	£10	£20	
Frankie Lymon & The Teenagers	7" EP.	Columbia	SEG7734	1957	£12.50	£25	
Goody Goody	7"	Columbia	DB3983	1957	£5	£10	chart single
Promise To Remember	7"	Columbia	DB3819	1956	£10	£20	
I Want You To Be My Girl	7"	Columbia	SCM5285	1956	£12.50	£25	
I'm Not A Juvenile Delinquent	7"	Columbia	DB3878	1957	£10	£20	chart single
I'm Not A Juvenile Delinquent	7" EP.	Columbia	SEG7694	1957	£12.50	£25	
In London	10" LP	Columbia	33S1127	1958	£50	£100	
Jerry Blavatt Presents The Teenagers	LP	Roulette	R25250	1964	£25	£50	US
Little Bitty Pretty One	7"	Columbia	DB4499	1960	£7.50	£15	
Mama Don't Allow It	7"	Columbia	DB4134	1958	£5	£10	
My Girl	7"	Columbia	DB4028	1957	£7.50	£15	
No Matter What You've Done	7"	Columbia	DB4245	1959	£6	£12	
Only Way To Love	7"	Columbia	DB4245	1959	£4	£8	
Out In The Cold Again	7"	Columbia	DB3942	1957	£10	£20	
Rock And Roll	LP	Roulette	R25036	1958	£50	£100	US
Rockin' With Frankie	10" LP	Columbia	33S1134	1957	£150	£250	

Teenage Love	7"	Columbia	DB3910	1957	£10	£20	
Teenage Rock	7" EP	Columbia	SEG7662	1957	£12.50	£25	
Teenagers	LP	Gee	GLP701	1957	£100	£200	US red label
Teenagers	LP	Gee	GLP701	1961	£30	£60	US grey label
Teenagers At The London Palladium	LP	Roulette	R25013	1958	£50	£100	US
Thumb Thumb	7"	Columbia	DB4073	1958	£6	£12	
Why Do Fools Fall In Love	7"	Columbia	SCM5265	1956	£15	£30	chart single
Why Do Fools Fall In Love?	7"	King	KG1043	1966	£2.50	£6	

LYMON, LEWIS

Too Young	7"	Oriole	CB1419	1958	£75	£150	

LYNCH, DERMOTT

Adults Only	7"	Doctor Bird	DB1115	1967	£5	£10	
Hot Shot	7"	Blue Cat	BS101	1968	£4	£8	
I Got Everything	7"	Blue Cat	BS122	1968	£4	£8	
Something Is Worrying Me	7"	Blue Cat	BS129	1968	£4	£8	Trevor B side
You Went Away	7"	Blue Cat	BS130	1968	£4	£8	Trevor B side

LYNCH, KENNY

Along Comes Love	7"	Columbia	DB8498	1968	£1.50	£4	
Drifter	7"	Columbia	DB8599	1969	£4	£8	
Hey Girl	7" EP	HMV	7EG8820	1963	£5	£10	
I'll Stay By You	7"	HMV	POP1430	1965	£1.50	£4	chart single
It's Too Late	7"	HMV	POP1577	1967	£4	£8	
Kenny Lynch	7" EP	HMV	7EG8855	1964	£5	£10	
Loving You Is Sweeter Than Ever	7"	Columbia	DB8703	1970	£2	£5	
Misery	7"	HMV	POP1136	1963	£1.50	£4	chart single
Mountain Of Love	7"	HMV	POP751	1960	£1.50	£4	
Movin' Away	7"	HMV	POP1604	1967	£4	£8	
My Own Two Feet	7"	HMV	POP1367	1964	£5	£10	
Puff	7"	HMV	POP1057	1962	£1.50	£4	chart single
Stand By Me	7"	HMV	POP1280	1964	£1.50	£4	chart single
Up On The Roof	LP	HMV	CLP1635	1963	£10	£25	mono
Up On The Roof	LP	HMV	CSD1489	1963	£20	£40	stereo
Up On The Roof	7"	HMV	POP1090	1962	£1.50	£4	chart single
We Like Kenny	LP	MFP	MFP1022	1966	£4	£10	
What Am I To You	7"	HMV	POP1321	1964	£1.50	£4	chart single
What Am I To You	7" EP	HMV	7EG8881	1965	£5	£10	
You Can Never Stop Me Loving You	7"	HMV	POP1165	1963	£1.50	£4	chart single

LYNCH, LEE & THE BLUE ANGELS

You Won't See Me	7"	Decca	F12375	1966	£1.50	£4	

LYNDELL, LINDA

Bring Your Love Back To Me	7"	Stax	601041	1968	£7.50	£15	

LYNGSTAD, ANNI-FRID

Anni-Frid Lyngstad	LP	Columbia	04851017	197-	£6	£15	Swedish
Frida	LP	Columbia	06234380	1971	£25	£50	Swedish
Frida	LP	Columbia	E05434549	197-	£5	£12	Swedish
Frida Ensam	LP	Polar	POLS265	1976	£5	£12	Swedish

LYNN, BARBARA

Barbara Lynn Story	LP	Sue	ILP949	1967	£20	£40	
Here Is Barbara Lynn	LP	Atlantic	SD8171	1968	£6	£15	US
Letter To Mommy And Daddy	7"	Sue	WI4028	1967	£5	£10	
Oh Baby	7"	London	HLW9918	1964	£4	£8	
Sister Of Soul	LP	Jamie	JLP(S)3026	1964	£8	£20	US
Until Then I Suffer	7"	Atlantic	2091133	1971	£4	£8	
You Can't Buy Me Love	7"	Immediate	IM011	1965	£7.50	£15	
You Left The Water Running	7"	London	HLU10094	1966	£5	£10	
You'll Lose A Good Thing	LP	Jamie	JLP(S70)3023	1962	£8	£20	US
You'll Lose A Good Thing	7"	Sue	WI4038	1967	£6	£12	

LYNN, BOBBY

Earthquake	7"	Bell	BLL1168	1971	£1.50	£4	
Earthquake	7"	Stateside	SS2088	1968	£10	£20	

LYNN, KARI

Lonesome And Sorry	7"	Oriole	CB1644	1961	£1.50	£4	
Yo Yo	7"	Oriole	CB1632	1961	£1.50	£4	

LYNN, LORETTA

Before I'm Over You	LP	Decca	DL(7)4541	1964	£6	£15	US
Blue Kentucky Girl	LP	Decca	DL(7)4665	1965	£6	£15	US
Country Christmas	LP	Decca	DL(7)4817	1966	£5	£12	US
Hymns	LP	Decca	DL(7)4695	1965	£5	£12	US
I Like 'Em Country	LP	Decca	DL(7)4744	1966	£5	£12	US
Loretta Lynn Sings	LP	Decca	DL(7)4457	1963	£8	£20	US
Mr.& Mrs.Used To Be	LP	Decca	DL(7)4639	1965	£5	£12	US, with Ernest Tubb
Songs From My Heart	LP	Decca	DL(7)4620	1965	£6	£15	US
You Ain't Woman Enough	LP	Decca	DL(7)4783	1966	£5	£12	US

LYNN, PATTI

Johnny Angel	7"	Fontana	H391	1962	£1.50	£4	chart single
Patti	7" EP	Fontana	TFE17392	1962	£5	£10	
Tell Me Telstar	7"	Fontana	267247TF	1962	£1.50	£4	

LYNN, TAMMI

I'm Gonna Run Away From You	7"	Atlantic	AT4071	1966	£10	£20	

504

I'm Gonna Run Away From You ...... 7" ...... Mojo .... 2092001 .... 1971 ... £1.50 ....£4 ....chart single

LYNN, VERA
Auf Wiedersehn Sweetheart	7"	Decca	F9927	1959	£1.50	£4	chart single
Faithful Hussar	7"	Decca	F10846	1957	£1.50	£4	chart single
House With Love In It	7"	Decca	F10799	1956	£1.50	£4	chart single
My Son My Son	7"	Decca	F10372	1954	£5	£10	chart single
Travellin' Home	7"	Decca	F10903	1957	£1.50	£4	chart single
Who Are We?	7"	Decca	F10715	1956	£1.50	£4	chart single

LYNNE, GLORIA
I Should Care	7"	London	HLY9888	1964	£1.50	£4	
I Wish You Love	7"	London	HLY9846	1964	£1.50	£4	

LYNNE, SUE
Don't Pity Me	7"	RCA	RCA1822	1969	£30	£60	

LYNOTT, PHIL
Solo In Soho	LP	Vertigo	PHIL1	1980	£4	£10	pic disc

LYNTON, JACKIE
The backing group on the A side of "All Of Me" is called The Jury. The bass player is Pat Donaldson - kept busy on a variety of sessions following his stints with Zoot Money and with Fotheringay - while the guitarist is Albert Lee, here making his first recording.
All Of Me	7"	Piccadilly	7N35064	1962	£5	£10	
I'm Talkin' About You	7"	Piccadilly	7N35156	1963	£1.50	£4	
Laura	7"	Piccadilly	7N35190	1964	£1.50	£4	
Little Child	7"	Piccadilly	7N35177	1964	£1.50	£4	

LYNYRD SKYNYRD
Free Bird	7"	MCA	MCA251	1976	£1.50	£4	PS
Free Bird	7"	MCA	MCA275	1976	£1.50	£4	PS
Freebird	12"	MCA	MCATP251	1982	£2.50	£6	pic disc
Street Survivors	LP	MCA	3029	1977	£4	£10	US, amended sleeve

LYON, BARBARA
Band Of Gold	7"	Columbia	SCM5232	1956	£1.50	£4	
Birds And The Bees	7"	Columbia	SCM5276	1956	£1.50	£4	
It's Better In The Dark	7"	Columbia	DB3826	1956	£1.50	£4	
Letter To A Soldier	7"	Columbia	DB3865	1956	£2.50	£6	chart single
My Four Friends	7" EP	Columbia	SEG7640	1956	£5	£10	
Tell Me	7"	Triumph	RGM1027	1960	£7.50	£15	
Whisper	7"	Columbia	SCM5207	1955	£1.50	£4	
Yes You Are	7"	Columbia	SCM5186	1955	£1.50	£4	

LYONS, JOHN
May Morning Dew	LP	Topic	12TS248	1974	£6	£15	

LYONS, TIM
Easter Snow	LP	Innisfree	SIF1014	1978	£5	£12	US
Green Linnet	LP	Trailer	LER3036	1972	£5	£12	

LYRICS
A Get It	7"	Coxsone	CS7003	1967	£5	£10	Ken Parker B side
Music Like Dirt	7"	Coxsone	CS7067	1968	£5	£10	

LYTELL, JIMMY
Hot Cargo	7"	London	HL8873	1959	£2.50	£6	

LYTLE, JOHNNY
Blue Vibes	LP	Jazzland	JLP22	1960	£4	£10	

LYTTELTON, HUMPHREY
Baby Doll	7"	Parlophone	R4277	1957	£1.50	£4	
Bad Penny Blues	7"	Parlophone	CMSP41	1958	£10	£20	
Blues In The Night	LP	Columbia	33SX1239/ SCX3316	1960	£5	£12	
Buona Sera	7"	Parlophone	R4392	1958	£1.50	£4	
Dixie Theme	7"	Parlophone	R4368	1957	£1.50	£4	
Early Call	7"	Parlophone	R4333	1957	£1.50	£4	
East Coast Trot	7"	Parlophone	MSP6076	1954	£1.50	£4	
Hand Me Down Love	7"	Parlophone	R4428	1958	£1.50	£4	
Here's Humph	10" LP	Parlophone	PMD1049	1957	£6	£15	
Humph At The Conway	LP	Parlophone	PMC1012	1954	£6	£15	
Humph In Perspective	LP	Parlophone	PMC1070	1958	£5	£12	
Humph Swings Out	10" LP	Parlophone	PMD1044	1956	£6	£15	
Humphrey Lyttelton And His Band	LP	Esquire	32007	1955	£5	£12	
Humph's Blues No.2	7" EP	Parlophone	GEP8645	1957	£4	£8	
I Play As I Please	LP	Decca	LK4276	1958	£5	£12	
It's Mardi Gras	7"	Parlophone	R4262	1957	£1.50	£4	
Jazz At The Royal Festival Hall	10" LP	Parlophone	PMD1032	1955	£5	£12	
Jazz Concert	10" LP	Parlophone	PMD1006	1953	£6	£15	
Jazz Session With Humph	10" LP	Parlophone	PMD1035	1956	£6	£15	
Just Once For All Time	7"	Parlophone	MSP6093	1954	£1.50	£4	
Kater Street Rag	7"	Parlophone	MSP6045	1953	£1.50	£4	
Kath Meets Humph	10" LP	Parlophone	PMD1052	1958	£6	£15	with Kathy Stobart
La Paloma	7"	Decca	F11058	1958	£1.50	£4	
Love Love Love	7"	Parlophone	R4212	1956	£1.50	£4	
Mainly Traditional	7"	Parlophone	MSP6097	1954	£1.50	£4	
Martiniquen Song	7"	Parlophone	MSP6061	1953	£1.50	£4	
Maryland My Maryland	7"	Parlophone	MSP6033	1953	£1.50	£4	
Mezzy's Tune	7"	Parlophone	MSP6128	1954	£1.50	£4	

Muskrat Ramble	7"	Parlophone	MSP6023	1953	£1.50	£4
Out Of The Gallion	7"	Parlophone	MSP6001	1953	£1.50	£4
Saturday Jump	7"	Parlophone	R4519	1959	£1.50	£4
Shake It And Break It	7"	Parlophone	MSP6034	1953	£1.50	£4
Summertime	7"	Parlophone	R4578	1959	£1.50	£4
Triple Exposure	LP	Parlophone	PMC1110	1959	£5	£12
When The Saints Go Marching In	7"	Tempo	A10	1956	£1.50	£4

LYTTLE, JOHNNY

Gonna Get That Boat	7"	Minit	MLF11006	1968	£2.50	£6

M

MABLE JOY

Title	Format	Label	Cat	Year			Notes
Mable Joy	LP	Real		1975	£15	£30	

MABON, WILLIE

Title	Format	Label	Cat	Year			Notes
Got To Have Some	7"	Sue	WI320	1964	£6	£12	
I'm The Fixer	7"	Sue	WI382	1965	£6	£12	
Just Got Some	7"	Sue	WI331	1965	£6	£12	
Willie Mabon	LP	Chess	1439	195-	£20	£40	US

MACBETH, DAVID

Title	Format	Label	Cat	Year			Notes
Blue Blue Blue	7"	Pye	7N15291	1960	£1.50	£4	
Have I Told You Lately That I Love You	7"	Piccadilly	7N35072	1962	£1.50	£4	
Just A Twinkle	7"	Decca	F11402	1961	£1.50	£4	
Keep On Walking	7"	Pye	7N15364	1961	£1.50	£4	
Living Dangerously	7"	Pye	7N15250	1960	£1.50	£4	
Mister Blues	7"	Pye	7N15231	1959	£1.50	£4	chart single
Nothing Matters But You	7"	Decca	F11906	1964	£1.50	£4	
Once Upon A Star	7"	Pye	7N15274	1960	£1.50	£4	
Puppet Song	7"	Pye	7N15325	1961	£1.50	£4	
Roses Are Red	7"	Piccadilly	7N35062	1962	£1.50	£4	
Very Good Year For Girls	7"	Piccadilly	7N35092	1962	£1.50	£4	

MACCOLL, EWAN

Title	Format	Label	Cat	Year			Notes
As We Were A-Sailing	LP	Argo	ZDA137	1970	£6	£15	with other artists
Barrack Room Ballads	10" LP	Topic	10T26	1958	£15	£30	
Best Of Ewan MacColl	LP	PRE	13004	1961	£10	£25	
Blow Boys Blow	LP	XTRA	XTRA1052	1967	£5	£12	with A.L.Lloyd
Bundook Ballads	LP	Topic	12T130	1965	£10	£25	
English And Scottish Popular Ballads	LP	Folkways	FG3509	1961	£6	£15	US
English And Scottish Popular Ballads Vol.2	LP	Folkways	FG3510	1961	£6	£15	US
Popular Scottish Songs	LP	Folkways	FW8757	1960	£6	£15	US
Second Shift	10" LP	Topic	10T25	1958	£15	£30	
Shuttle And Cage	10" LP	Topic	10T13	1958	£15	£30	
Solo Flight	LP	Argo	ZFB12	1972	£6	£15	
Songs Of Robert Burns	LP	Folkways	FW8758	1959	£8	£20	US
Still I Love Him	10" LP	Topic	10T50	1960	£20	£40	with Isla Cameron
Streets Of Song	LP	Topic	12T41	1960	£10	£25	with Dominic Behan

MACCOLL, EWAN & PEGGY SEEGER

Title	Format	Label	Cat	Year			Notes
Amorous Muse	LP	Argo	(Z)DA84	1968	£6	£15	
Amorous Muse	LP	Argo	ZFB66	1972	£6	£15	
Angry Muse	LP	Argo	(Z)DA83	1968	£6	£15	
Angry Muse	LP	Argo	ZFB65	1972	£6	£15	
Bothy Ballads Of Scotland	LP	Folkways	FW8759	1961	£6	£15	US
Chorus From The Gallows	LP	Topic	12T16	1960	£15	£30	
Folkways Record Of Contemporary Songs	LP	Folkways	FW8736	1973	£5	£12	US
Jacobite Rebellions	LP	Topic	12T79	1962	£10	£25	
Long Harvest Vol.1	LP	Argo	(Z)DA66	1967	£6	£15	
Long Harvest Vol.10	LP	Argo	(Z)DA75	1967	£6	£15	
Long Harvest Vol.2	LP	Argo	(Z)DA67	1967	£6	£15	
Long Harvest Vol.3	LP	Argo	(Z)DA68	1967	£6	£15	
Long Harvest Vol.4	LP	Argo	(Z)DA69	1967	£6	£15	
Long Harvest Vol.5	LP	Argo	(Z)DA70	1967	£6	£15	
Long Harvest Vol.6	LP	Argo	(Z)DA71	1967	£6	£15	
Long Harvest Vol.7	LP	Argo	(Z)DA72	1967	£6	£15	
Long Harvest Vol.8	LP	Argo	(Z)DA73	1967	£6	£15	
Long Harvest Vol.9	LP	Argo	(Z)DA74	1967	£6	£15	
Manchester Angel	LP	Topic	12T147	1966	£15	£30	
New Briton Gazette	LP	Folkways	FW8734	1973	£6	£15	US
Paper Stage Vol.1	LP	Argo	(Z)DA98	1969	£6	£15	
Paper Stage Vol.2	LP	Argo	(Z)DA99	1969	£6	£15	
Songs Of Two Rebellions	LP	Folkways	FW8756	1960	£6	£15	US
Steam Whistle Ballads	LP	Topic	12T104	1964	£8	£20	
Traditional Songs And Ballads	LP	Folways	FW8760	1964	£6	£15	US
Two Way Trip	LP	Folkways	FW8755	1961	£6	£15	US
Wanton Muse	LP	Argo	(Z)DA85	1968	£6	£15	
Wanton Muse	LP	Argo	ZFB67	1972	£6	£15	
We Are The Engineers	7"	AUEW	AUEW1	196-	£4	£8	
World Of Ewan MacColl And Peggy Seeger	LP	Argo	SPA102	1970	£5	£12	
World Of Ewan MacColl And Peggy Seeger Vol.2	LP	Argo	SPA216	1972	£4	£10	

MACCOLL, EWAN, PEGGY SEEGER & CHARLES PARKER

Title	Format	Label	Cat	Year			Notes
Ballad Of John Axon	LP	Argo	DA139	1971	£10	£25	
Ballad Of John Axon	LP	Argo	RG474	1965	£10	£25	
Big Hewer	LP	Argo	DA140	1971	£8	£20	
Big Hewer	LP	Argo	RG-	1967	£10	£25	
Fight Game	LP	Argo	DA141	1971	£6	£15	

Fight Game	LP	Argo	RG539	1968	£10	£25	
On The Edge	LP	Argo	DA136	1971	£6	£15	
On The Edge	LP	Argo	RG-	196-	£10	£25	
Singing The Fishing	LP	Argo	DA142	1971	£6	£15	
Singing The Fishing	LP	Argo	RG-	196-	£10	£25	
Travelling People	LP	Argo	DA133	1970	£15	£30	

MACCOLL, KIRSTY
The daughter of traditional folk master, Ewan MacColl, is one of our most underrated singer-songwriters. She scored an early success with the witty "There's A Boy Works Down The Guy Shop Swears He's Elvis" , but she is otherwise best known for her cover versions of Billy Bragg's "New England" and Ray Davies' "Days". Despite her relative lack of success, however, she continues to deliver classy collections of her clever and imaginative material. Her recording debut was as a young teenager with the family - Peggy Seeger's "Penelope Isn't Waiting Any More".

| You Caught Me Out | 7" | Stiff | BUY57 | 1979 | £4 | £8 | demo |

MACEO & ALL THE KING'S MEN
It is extraordinary how the same musicians as formed James Brown's band in the late sixties lack a significant percentage of their drive and rhythmic power when Brown is not there. Here is the proof that James Brown is indeed the master of his own music.

Funky Music Machine	LP	Contempo	CRM114	1975	£10	£25	
Funky Music Machine	LP	Mojo	2916017	1972	£25	£50	
Got To Get 'Cha	7"	Pye	7N25571	1972	£2	£5	

MACEO & THE MACKS

Cross The Tracks	12"	Urban	URBX1	1987	£3	£8	
Us	LP	Polydor	2391122	1974	£10	£25	
Us	LP	Urban	URBLP8	1988	£5	£12	

MACERO, TEO

| Teo | LP | Esquire | 32113 | 1961 | £10 | £25 | |

MACHITO

| Kenya | LP | Columbia | 33SX1103 | 1958 | £8 | £20 | |

MACK, JOHNNY

| Reggae All Night Long | 7" | Columbia | DB116 | 1970 | £4 | £8 | |

MACK, LONNIE

For Collectors Only	LP	Elektra	2410007	1970	£6	£15	
Glad I'm In The Band	LP	Elektra	EKL/EKS74040	1969	£6	£15	
Hills Of Indiana	LP	Elektra	K42097	1972	£5	£12	
Lonnie On The Move	7"	Stateside	SS312	1964	£2.50	£6	
Memphis	7"	Elektra	EKSN45044	1969	£2	£5	
Memphis	7"	Stateside	SS207	1963	£4	£8	
Sa-Ba-Hoola	7"	Stateside	SS393	1965	£5	£10	
Save Your Money	7"	Elektra	EKSN45060	1969	£1.50	£4	
Save Your Money	7"	President	PT142	1967	£1.50	£4	
Soul Express	7"	President	PT198	1968	£1.50	£4	
Wham	7"	Stateside	SS226	1963	£4	£8	
Wham Of The Memphis Man	LP	President	PTL1004	1967	£8	£20	
Whatever's Right	7"	Elektra	EKS74050	1969	£6	£15	
Where There's A Will	7"	President	PT127	1967	£1.50	£4	

MACK SISTERS

| Long Range Love | 7" | London | HLU8331 | 1956 | £10 | £20 | |

MACK, WARNER

Country Touch	LP	Brunswick	LAT8658	1966	£6	£15	
Drifting Apart	LP	Brunswick	LAT8684	1967	£5	£12	
Golden Country Hits	LP	London	HAR/SHR8002	1962	£6	£15	
Golden Country Hits Vol.2	LP	London	HAR/SHR8025	1963	£6	£15	
Rock A Chicka	7"	Brunswick	05728	1958	£40	£80	

MACKAY, MAHNA

| Mah Na Mah Na | 7" | Parlophone | R5808 | 1969 | £1.50 | £4 | |

MACKAY, RABBIT

| Bug Cloth | LP | MCS | MUPS351 | 1968 | £4 | £10 | |
| Hard Time Woman | 7" | MCA | MU1041 | 1968 | £1.50 | £4 | |

MACKERAL

| Trying Again | 7" | Columbia | DB8388 | 1968 | £1.50 | £4 | |

MACKINTOSH, KEN

Applejack	7"	HMV	POP300	1957	£4	£8	
Big Guitar	7"	HMV	POP464	1958	£1.50	£4	
Creeping Tom	7"	HMV	7M343	1955	£1.50	£4	
Dizzy Fingers	7"	HMV	7M417	1956	£1.50	£4	
Highway Patrol	7"	HMV	POP270	1956	£1.50	£4	
Keep It Moving	7"	HMV	POP358	1957	£1.50	£4	
Ken Mackintosh	10" LP	HMV	DLP1093	1955	£5	£12	
No Hiding Place	7"	HMV	POP713	1960	£1.50	£4	
One Night Stand	10" LP	HMV	DLP1178	1958	£5	£12	
Raunchy	7"	HMV	POP426	1957	£1.50	£4	
Regimental Rock	7"	HMV	POP287	1957	£2	£4	
Rock Man Rock	7"	HMV	POP327	1957	£4	£8	
Six Five Blues	7"	HMV	POP396	1957	£1.50	£4	
Swinging Shepherd Blues	7"	HMV	POP441	1958	£1.50	£4	
Teenager's Special	7" EP	HMV	7EG8170	1956	£7.50	£15	

MACLAINE, PETE & CLAN

| U.S. Mail | 7" | Decca | F11699 | 1963 | £2 | £5 | |

MACLEAN, DOUGIE
Snaigow	LP	Plant Life	PLR022	1980	£6	£15	

MACLENNAN, DOLINA & ROBIN GRAY
By Mormond Braes	7" EP	Topic	TOP68	1964	£4	£8	

MACLEOD, JOHN FIRST XI
Don't Shoot The Ref	7"	Fontana	TF696	1966	£1.50	£4	

MACLISE, ANGUS
Trance	7"	Fierce	FRIGHT010	1987	£2.50	£6	

MACMAHON, DOLLY
Dolly	LP	Claddagh	CC3	1966	£5	£12	Irish

MACNEE, PATRICK & HONOR BLACKMAN
Kinky Boots	7"	Decca	F11843	1964	£2.50	£6	

MACON, UNCLE DAVE
Uncle Dave Macon No.1	7" EP	RCA	RCX7112	1963	£5	£10	
Uncle Dave Macon No.2	7" EP	RCA	RCX7113	1963	£5	£10	

MACRAE, GORDON
Bella Notte	7"	Capitol	CL14361	1955	£2	£5	
By The Light Of The Silvery Moon	10" LP	Capitol	LC6599	1953	£4	£10	
Capitol Presents	10" LP	Capitol	LC6592	1953	£4	£10	
C'Est Magnifique	7"	Capitol	CL14168	1954	£2	£5	
Count Your Blessings Instead Of Sheep	7"	Capitol	CL14193	1954	£2	£5	
Desert Song	10" LP	Capitol	LC6606	1953	£4	£10	
Here's What I'm Here For	7"	Capitol	CL14222	1955	£2	£5	
Jim Bowie	7"	Capitol	CL14334	1955	£2	£5	
Merry Widow	10" LP	Capitol	LC6564	1952	£4	£10	
Naughty Marietta	10" LP	Capitol	LC6663	1954	£4	£10	
Roberta	10" LP	Capitol	LC6666	1954	£4	£10	
Romantic Ballads	10" LP	Capitol	LC6805	1956	£4	£10	
Stranger In Paradise	7"	Capitol	CL14276	1955	£2	£5	
Student Prince	10" LP	Capitol	LC6613	1953	£4	£10	
You Forgot	7"	Capitol	CL14293	1955	£2	£5	

MACRAE, JOSH
Josh MacRae	LP	Transatlantic	TRA150	1966	£4	£10	
Messing About On The River	7"	Pye	7N15319	1960	£1.50	£4	chart single
Talking Army Blues	7"	Top Rank	JAR290	1960	£1.50	£4	chart single
Walking Talking Singing	7" EP	Pye	NEP24131	1960	£4	£8	
Wild Side Of Life	7"	Pye	7N15308	1960	£1.50	£4	chart single

MAD CATS
Losing You	7"	Coxsone	CS7099	1969	£5	£10	Winston Jarrett

MAD LADS
Don't Have To Shop Around	7"	Atlantic	AT4051	1965	£4	£8	
I Want Someone	7"	Atlantic	AT4083	1966	£4	£8	
Mad Lads In Action	LP	Volt	414	1966	£6	£15	US
Sugar Sugar	7"	Atlantic	584038	1966	£2.50	£6	

MAD MAGAZINE
Fink Along With Mad	LP	Big Top	1206	196-	£6	£15	US
Mad Twists Rock'n'Roll	LP	Big Top	1305	1963	£6	£15	US

MAD RIVER
Mad River	LP	Capitol	ST2985	1968	£8	£20	US
Paradise Bar & Grill	LP	Capitol	ST185	1969	£6	£15	US

MAD ROY
Home Version	7"	Banana	BA326	1971	£2	£5	
Nannie Goat Version	7"	Banana	BA324	1970	£2	£5	
Universal Love	7"	Banana	BA327	1971	£2	£5	Roland Alphonso B side

MADARA, JOHNNY
Be My Girl	7"	HMV	POP389	1957	£1.50	£4	

MADDEN, TOM & FRANK WARREN
Little Thatched Cabin	LP	Inchecronin	INC7727	1977	£8	£20	

MADDOX BROTHERS & ROSE
Collection Of Standard Sacred Songs	LP	King	669	1960	£15	£30	US
I'll Write Your Name In The Sand	LP	King	752	1961	£10	£25	US
Maddox Brothers And Rose	LP	King	677	1961	£10	£25	US

MADDOX, JOHNNY
Crazy Otto Medley	7"	London	HL8134	1955	£7.50	£15	
Dixieland Band	7"	London	HLD8347	1956	£6	£12	
Dixieland Blues	LP	London	HAD2175/ SHD6022	1959	£5	£12	
Do Do Do	7"	London	HLD8203	1955	£7.50	£15	
Hands Off	7"	London	HLD8277	1956	£7.50	£15	
Honky Tonk Jazz	7" EP	London	RED1150	1958	£2.50	£6	
Hurdy Gurdy Song	7"	London	HLD8826	1959	£1.50	£4	
My Old Flames	LP	London	HAD2101	1958	£5	£12	

Old Fashioned Love	7" EP.. London	RED1270	1961	£2	£5	
Plays	10" LP London	HBD1060	1956	£10	£25	
Presenting Johnny Maddox	7" EP.. London	REP1020	1955	£5	£10	
Presenting Johnny Maddox No.2	7" EP.. London	REP1040	1955	£4	£8	
Yellow Dog Blues	7" London	HLD8540	1958	£2.50	£6	

MADDOX, ROSE

Alone With You	LP Capitol	(S)T1993	1963	£5	£12	US
Big Bouquet Of Roses	LP Capitol	(S)T1548	1961	£5	£12	US
Gambler's Love	7" Capitol	CL15023	1959	£1.50	£4	
Glorybound Train	LP Capitol	(S)T1437	1960	£5	£12	US
One Rose	LP Capitol	(S)T1312	1960	£5	£12	US
Precious Memories	LP Columbia	CL1159	1958	£8	£20	US
Rose Maddox Sings Bluegrass	LP Capitol	(S)T1779	1962	£5	£12	US

MADE IN SHEFFIELD

Amelia Jane	7" Fontana	TF871	1967	£6	£12

MADE IN SWEDEN

Live At The Golden Circle	LP Sonet	SLP2506	1970	£5	£12
Mad River	LP Sonet	SNTF621	1971	£5	£12
Made In England	LP Sonet	SLP2512	1970	£5	£12
Made In Sweden	LP Sonet	SLP71	1969	£5	£12
Snakes In A Hole	LP Sonet	SLP2504	1969	£5	£12

MADIGAN, BETTY

I'm Gonna Make You Love Me	7" MGM	MGM1482	1969	£1.50	£4

MADNESS

Carols On 45	7" Lyntone	LYN10719	1982	£1.50	£4	flexi
Keep Moving	LP Stiff	PSEEZ53	1984	£4	£10	pic disc
Madness Pack	7" Stiff	GRAB1	1982	£10	£20	6 x 7 in plastic wallet
Prince	7" 2-Tone	TT3	1979	£2.50	£6	paper labels, no PS
Return Of The Los Palmas 7	7" Stiff	BUYIT108	1981	£5	£10	with comic
Swan Lake	12" Stiff	MAD1	1979	£8	£20	promo
Sweetest Girl	7" Zarjazz	JAZZD8	1986	£1.50	£4	double
Take It Or Leave It	7" Lyntone	LYN10353	1982	£2	£5	flexi
Uno Paso Adalante	7" Stiff	MO1922	1980	£2.50	£6	sung in Spanish
Yesterday's Men	7" Zarjazz	JAZZD5	1985	£2	£5	pic disc double pack

MADONNA

Astute marketing has kept Madonna at the top for far longer than seemed likely when her pictures first started to appear on teenage bedroom walls. Virtually everything she has released is now a collectors' item of some kind, with particular interest being generated by the series of picture disc releases. The value of many of these is much higher than can be explained merely by their rarity, although the early "Crazy For You" is reckoned to be one of the scarcest commercially released picture discs of all. More valuable still, by quite a long way, is the withdrawn picture disc release of "Erotica".

Angel	7" Sire	W8881P	1985	£7.50	£15	shaped pic disc
Angel	7" Sire	W8881P	1985	£10	£20	shaped pic disc, plinth
Borderline	7" Sire	W9260F	1984	£10	£20	double
Borderline	7" Sire	W9260P	1986	£15	£30	shaped pic disc
Causing A Commotion	7" Sire	W8224	1987	£5	£10	with badge
Causing A Commotion (Silver Screen Mix)	12" Sire	W8224TP	1987	£6	£15	pic disc
Cherish	12" Sire	W2883TP	1989	£4	£10	pic disc
Crazy For You	7" Geffen	WA6323	1985	£25	£50	shaped pic disc, Sleeve Pictured in guide
Crazy For You (Remix)	7" Sire	W0008P	1991	£1.50	£4	shaped pic disc with plinth
Dear Jessie	CD-s.. Sire	W2668CD	1989	£10	£25	pic disc
Dear Jessie	12" Sire	W2668T	1989	£2.50	£6	poster sleeve
Dear Jessie	12" Sire	W2668TP	1989	£2.50	£6	pic disc
Deeper And Deeper	12" Sire	W0146TP	199-	£2.50	£6	pic disc
Dress You Up	7" Sire	W8848P	1985	£10	£20	shaped pic disc
Dress You Up (Formal Mix)	12" Sire	W8848T	1985	£6	£15	poster sleeve
Erotica	12" Sire	W0138TP	1992	£330	£500	pic disc, gold insert
Everybody	7" Sire	W9899	1982	£20	£40	
Everybody	12" Sire	W9899T	1982	£35	£70	
Express Yourself	7" Sire	W2948W	1989	£4	£8	zipper sleeve
Express Yourself (Non-Stop Express Mix)	12" Sire	W2948TP	1989	£8	£20	pic disc
Gambler	7" Geffen	QA6585	1985	£6	£12	poster sleeve
Gambler	12" Geffen	A6585TA	1985	£4	£10	
Hanky Panky	12" Sire	W9789TP	1990	£6	£15	pic disc
Holiday	12" Sire	W0037T	1991	£2.50	£6	clear vinyl
Holiday (Edit)	7" Sire	W9405	1983	£2.50	£6	train PS
Holiday (Full Length Version)	12" Sire	W9405P	1985	£8	£20	pic disc
Holiday (Full Length Version)	12" Sire	W9405T	1983	£5	£12	train PS
Into The Groove	7" Sire	W8934P	1985	£7.50	£15	shaped pic disc
Into The Groove	12" Sire	W8934T	1985	£4	£10	with poster
La Isla Bonita (Extended Remix)	12" Sire	W8378TP	1987	£6	£15	with poster
Like A Prayer (3 mixes)	12" Sire	W7539TX	1989	£3	£8	
Like A Prayer (Extended Remix)	12" Sire	W7539TP	1989	£3	£8	pic disc
Like A Virgin	LP		1984	£25	£50	US, white vinyl
Like A Virgin	LP Sire	WX20P	1985	£15	£30	pic disc
Like A Virgin (US Dance Remix)	12" Sire	W9210T	1984	£6	£15	with poster
Live To Tell	12" Sire	W8717T	1986	£4	£10	with poster
Look Of Love	12" Sire	W8115TP	1987	£6	£15	pic disc
Lucky Star	7" Sire	W9522	1983	£15	£30	Sunglasses PS
Lucky Star (full length version)	12" Sire	W9522T	1983	£15	£30	Sunglasses PS
Lucky Star (full length version)	12" Sire	W9522T	1983	£4	£10	TV screen PS

Lucky Star (full length version)	12"	Sire	W9522T	1983	£10	£25	TV screen PS with poster
Lucky Star (US Remix)	12"	Sire	W9522TV	1983	£30	£60	plain sleeve
Material Girl	7"	Sire	W9083	1985	£15	£30	poster sleeve
Material Girl (Jellybean Dance Remix)	12"	Sire	W9083T	1985	£6	£15	with poster
Open Your Heart (Extended Version)	12"	Sire	W8480TP	1986	£6	£15	pic disc
Papa Don't Preach (Extended Remix)	12"	Sire	W8636TP	1986	£8	£20	pic disc
Papa Don't Preach (Extended Version)	12"	Sire	W8636T	1986	£4	£10	with poster
Royal Box (Immaculate Collection)	CD	Sire	7599264642	1990	£25	£50	CD,video,poster,cards - boxed
True Blue	LP	Sire		1986	£20	£40	US pic disc
True Blue	LP	Sire	WX54	1986	£20	£40	blue vinyl, poster
True Blue	LP	Sire	WX54	1986	£20	£40	clear vinyl
True Blue (Extended Dance Version)	12"	Sire	W8550TP	1986	£6	£15	pic disc
Vogue	7"	Sire	W9851P	1990	£6	£12	pic disc
Vogue	12"	Sire	W9851P	1990	£4	£10	pic disc
Vogue	12"	Sire	W9851TX	1990	£2.50	£6	with poster
Who's That Girl (Extended Version)	12"	Sire	W8341TP	1987	£15	£30	pic disc
You Can Dance	LP	Sire	PROMAD1	1987	£30	£60	promo pic disc

MADRIGAL
Beneath The Greenwood Tree	LP	private	MAD100	1973	£25	£50

MAESTRO, JOHNNY
Before I Loved Her	7"	United Artists	UP1004	1964	£4	£8	
Johnny Maestro Story	LP	Buddah	BDS5091	1971	£8	£20	US
Mr.Happiness	7"	HMV	POP909	1961	£7.50	£15	
What A Surprise	7"	HMV	POP875	1961	£7.50	£15	

MAGENTA
Canterbury Moon	LP	Cottage		1978	£30	£60

MAGIC
Enclosed	LP	Armadillo	8031	1970	£50	£100	US

MAGIC CARPET
Magic Carpet	LP	Mushroom	200MR20	1972	£60	£120	sleeve pictured in Guide

MAGIC CHRISTIANS
If You Want It	7"	Major Minor	MM673	1970	£4	£8

MAGIC LANTERNS
Auntie Grizelda	7"	CBS	202637	1967	£2	£5	
Country Woman	7"	Polydor	2058202	1972	£1.50	£4	
Excuse Me Baby	7"	CBS	202094	1966	£2	£5	chart single
Excuse Me Baby	7" EP	CBS	5798	1966	£10	£20	French
Knight In Rusty Armour	7"	CBS	202459	1967	£2	£5	
Let The Sunshine In	7"	Polydor	2058096	1971	£1.50	£4	
Lit Up With The Magic Lanterns	LP	CBS	62935	1969	£4	£10	
Melt All Your Troubles Away	7"	Camp	602009	1969	£2	£5	
Rumplestiltskin	7"	CBS	202250	1966	£7.50	£15	
Shame Shame	LP	Atlantic	SD8217	1969	£6	£15	US
Shame Shame	7"	Camp	602007	1969	£1.50	£4	
We'll Meet Again	7"	CBS	2750	1967	£1.50	£4	

MAGIC MIXTURE
This Is Magic Mixture	LP	Saga	FID2125	1968	£25	£50

MAGIC MUSHROOM BAND
Politics Of Ecstasy	LP	Pagan	PM003	1986	£25	£50	with poster
Process Of Illumination	LP	Fungus	FUN003	1990	£6	£15	with comic
Spaced Out	LP	Fungus	FUN005	1991	£5	£12	with booklet

MAGIC NOTES
Album Of Memory	7"	Blue Beat	BB9	1961	£5	£10

MAGIC SAM
Black Magic	LP	Delmark	DS620	1971	£8	£20
Magic Sam 1937-69	LP	Blue Horizon	763223	1969	£25	£50
Mean Mistreater	7" EP	Rooster	707	1969	£2.50	£6
Twenty-One Days In Jail	7"	Python	PEN701	1969	£10	£20
West Side Soul	LP	Delmark	DS615	1970	£8	£20

MAGIC VALLEY
Taking The Heart Out Of Love	7"	Penny Farthing	PEN701	1969	£4	£8

MAGICIANS
Liars	7"	Decca	F12374	1966	£1.50	£4
Painting On Wood	7"	MCA	MU1046	1968	£1.50	£4
Tarzan March	7"	Decca	F12602	1967	£1.50	£4
Wet Your Whistle	7"	Decca	F12361	1966	£1.50	£4

MAGISTRATES
After The Fox	7"	MGM	MGM1437	1968	£1.50	£4
Here Comes The Judge	7"	MGM	MGM1425	1968	£2	£5

MAGMA
1001 Centigrade	LP	Philips	6397031	1971	£4	£10
Kohn Tarkosz	LP	A&M	AMLH68260	1974	£4	£10

511

Live	LP	Utopia	CYL21245	1975	£6	£15	US double
Magma	LP	Philips	635951/2	1970	£6	£15	double
Mekanik Destructiw Kommandoh	LP	A&M	AMLH64397	1974	£4	£10	
Mekanik Machine	7"	A&M	AMS7119	1974	£1.50	£4	

MAGNA CARTA

In Concert	LP	Vertigo	6360068	1972	£5	£12	spiral label
Live	LP	Mercury	6304507	1978	£10	£25	Dutch
Lord Of The Ages	LP	Vertigo	6360093	1973	£4	£10	
Magna Carta	LP	Mercury	SMCL20166	1969	£10	£25	
Mid Winter	7"	Mercury	MF1096	1969	£4	£8	
Romeo Jack	7"	Fontana	TF1060	1969	£4	£8	
Seasons	LP	Vertigo	6360003	1970	£5	£12	spiral label, chart LP
Songs From Wasties Orchard	LP	Vertigo	6360040	1971	£8	£20	spiral label

MAGNIFICENT MEN

Peace Of Mind	7"	Capitol	CL15462	1966	£7.50	£15	
Save The Country	7"	Capitol	CL15570	1968	£4	£8	
Sweet Soul Medley	7"	Capitol	CL15530	1968	£1.50	£4	

MAGNUM

Midnight	12"	Polydor	POSPP833	1986	£2.50	£6	pic disc

MAGPIES

Blue Boy	7"	Doctor Bird	DB1132	1968	£5	£10	
Lulu	7"	Doctor Bird	DB1129	1968	£5	£10	

MAGUIRE, JOHN

Come Day, Go Day, God Send Sunday	LP	Leader	LEE4062	1973	£5	£12	

MAHAL, TAJ

Taj Mahal is in many ways the black equivalent of Ry Cooder. He has an archivist's approach to his musical culture, rediscovering old songs and presenting them as fresh pieces of music in order to encourage his audience to delve further. His earliest records are exclusively concerned with the blues, but he has ranged more widely since. In fact, Ry Cooder and Taj Mahal were both members of the cult sixties group, the Rising Sons, and Cooder is also a member of the band on the first Taj Mahal LP.

Eezee Rider	7"	Direction	584044	1969	£1.50	£4	
Everybody's Got To Change Sometime	7"	Direction	583547	1968	£2	£4	
Giant Step/De Ole Folks	LP	CBS	66226	1969	£6	£15	double
Give Your Woman What She Wants	7"	Direction	584586	1969	£1.50	£4	
Natch'l Blues	LP	Direction	863397	1968	£5	£12	
Real Thing	LP	CBS	66288	1971	£5	£12	double
Taj Mahal	LP	Direction	863279	1967	£6	£15	

MAHOGANY RUSH

Child Of The Novelty	LP	20th Century	S451	1973	£5	£12	US
Maxoom	LP	20th Century	S463	1975	£5	£12	US
Maxoom	LP	Nine	936	1972	£10	£25	US

MAIL

Omnibus	7"	Parlophone	R5916	1971	£1.50	£4	

MAIN ATTRACTION

And Now	LP	Tower	ST5117	1968	£5	£12	US

MAINEEAXE

Gonna Make You Rock	7"	Powerstation	OHM6	1984	£1.50	£4	

MAINHORSE

Mainhorse	LP	Polydor	2383049	1971	£6	£15	

MAINLAND

Exposure	LP	Christy	ACML0200	1979	£5	£12	

MAJAMOOD

Two Hundred Million Red Ants	7"	Doctor Bird	DB1052	1966	£5	£10	

MAJIC SHIP

Majic Ship	LP	Bel Ami	BA711	1968	£75	£150	US

MAJOR ACCIDENT

Warboots	7"	Massacred Melodies	MAME1001	1982	£6	£12	test pressing

MAJORITY

All Our Christmases	7"	Decca	F12727	1968	£2	£5	
I Hear A Rhapsody	7"	Decca	F12573	1967	£2	£5	
Little Bit Of Sunlight	7"	Decca	F12271	1965	£2.50	£6	
Pretty Little Girl	7"	Decca	F12186	1965	£2.50	£6	
Running Away With My Baby	7"	Decca	F12638	1967	£2	£5	
Simplified	7"	Decca	F12453	1966	£2	£5	
To Make Me A Man	7"	Decca	F12504	1966	£2	£5	
We Kiss in The Shadow	7"	Decca	F12313	1966	£2	£5	

MAJORS

Meet The Majors	LP	London	HAP8068	1963	£30	£60	
Meet The Majors	7" EP	London	REP1358	1963	£25	£50	
Ooh Wee Baby	7"	Liberty	LIB66009	1964	£7.50	£15	
She's A Troublemaker	7"	London	HLP9627	1962	£6	£12	
What In The World	7"	London	HLP9693	1963	£5	£10	
Wonderful Dream	7"	London	HLP9602	1962	£5	£10	

MAKEBA, MIRIAM

Click Song	7"	London	HL9747	1963	£1.50	£4
In Concert	LP	Reprise	RLP6253	1967	£5	£12
Keep Me In Mind	LP	Reprise	RSLP6381	1970	£5	£12
Makeba!	LP	Reprise	R(S)LP6310	1968	£5	£12
Miriam Makeba	LP	London	HA2332	1961	£6	£15

MAKEM, TOMMY

Bard Of Armagh	LP	CBS	64001	1970	£5	£12
Ever The Winds	LP	Polydor	2383328	1975	£5	£12
In The Dark Green Woods	LP	Polydor	2383280	1974	£5	£12
Sings Tommy Makem	LP	CBS	63112	1967	£6	£15

MAKEM, TOMMY & LIAM CLANCY

Makem And Clancy Concert	LP	CBS	88302	1977	£6	£15	
Tommy Makem And Liam Clancy	LP	Epic	EPC82081	1976	£5	£12	double

MAL & THE PRIMITIVES

Every Minute Of Every Day	7"	Pye	7N15915	1965	£20	£40

MALCOLM, CARLOS

Bonanza Ska	7"	Island	WI173	1965	£5	£10

MALCOLM, GEORGE

Bach Goes To Town	7"	Parlophone	MSP6058	1953	£1.50	£4

MALCOLM, HUGH

Good Time Rock	7"	Amalgamated	AMG827	1968	£4	£8	Lyn Taitt B side

MALICORNE

Almanach	LP	Hexagone	883007	1976	£4	£10	French
Malicorne	LP	Hexagone	883002	1974	£5	£12	French
Malicorne II	LP	Hexagone	883004	1975	£5	£12	French
Malicorne IV	LP	Hexagone	883015	1976	£4	£10	French
Quintessence	LP	Hexagone	883018	1977	£4	£10	French

MALLARD

In A Different Climate	LP	Virgin	V2077	1977	£4	£10
Mallard	LP	Virgin	V2045	1975	£4	£10

MALMKVIST, SIW

Man Who Took The Valise Off	7"	Atlantic	584229	1968	£1.50	£4

MALONE, CINDY

Weird Beard	7"	RCA	RCA1254	1961	£2	£5

MALONE, WIL

Wil Malone	LP	Fontana	STL5541	1970	£25	£50

MALTBY, RICHARD

Rat Race	7"	Columbia	DB4606	1961	£6	£12

MAMA CASS

Dream A Little Dream Of Me	7"	RCA	RCA1726	1968	£1.50	£4	chart single
It's Getting Better	7"	Stateside	SS8021	1969	£1.50	£4	chart single

MAMAS & PAPAS

California Dreamin'	LP	St.Michael	MO101225	1979	£4	£10	
California Dreamin'	7" EP	RCA	86902	1966	£7.50	£15	French
California Dreaming	7"	RCA	RCA1503	1966	£1.50	£4	chart single
Cass,John,Michelle,& Denny	LP	RCA	RD/SF7834	1966	£5	£12	chart LP
Creeque Alley	7"	RCA	RCA1613	1967	£1.50	£4	chart single
Dedicated To The One I Love	7"	RCA	RCA1576	1967	£1.50	£4	chart single
Dedicated To The One I Love	7" EP	RCA	86911	1967	£5	£10	French
Deliver	LP	RCA	RD/SF7880	1967	£5	£12	chart LP
For The Love Of Ivy	7"	RCA	RCA1744	1968	£1.50	£4	
Gathering Of Flowers	LP	Probe	SPB1003/4	1970	£5	£12	double
Glad To Be Unhappy	7"	RCA	RCA1649	1967	£1.50	£4	
Golden Era Vol.2	LP	Stateside	(S)SL5002	1968	£4	£10	
I Saw Her Again	7"	RCA	RCA1533	1966	£1.50	£4	chart single
I Saw Her Again	7" EP	RCA	86907	1966	£5	£10	French
If You Can Believe Your Eyes And Ears	LP	RCA	RD7803	1966	£5	£12	chart LP
Look Through My Window	7"	RCA	RCA1551	1966	£1.50	£4	
Look Through My Window	7" EP	RCA	86910	1966	£5	£10	French
Monday Monday	7"	RCA	RCA1516	1966	£1.50	£4	chart single
Monday Monday	7" EP	RCA	86905	1966	£5	£10	French
Monterey Pop Festival	LP	Dunhill	DS50100	1971	£6	£15	US
Papas And Mamas	LP	RCA	RD/SF7960	1968	£5	£12	
People Like Us	LP	Probe	SPB1048	1972	£4	£10	
Safe In My Garden	7"	RCA	RCA1710	1968	£1.50	£4	
Twelve Thirty	7"	RCA	RCA1630	1967	£1.50	£4	
Words Of Love	7"	RCA	RCA1564	1967	£1.50	£4	chart single
You've Got To Hide Your Love Away	7"	RCA	RCA1525	1966	£4	£8	Barry McGuire B side

MAMA'S BOYS

Silence Is Out Of Fashion	7"	Pussy			1981	£4	£8
Turn It Up/Too Little Of You To Love	LP	Spartan	SPLP001	1983	£6	£15	double

MAMMUT

Mammut	LP	Mouse	TTM5022	1971	£150	£250	German

MAN

2oz Of Plastic With A Hole In The Middle	LP	Dawn	DNLS3003	1969	£6	£15	
Back Into The Future	LP	United Artists	UAD60053/4	1973	£5	£12	double
Bananas	7" EP	United Artists	REM408	1976	£2	£5	
Be Good To Yourself	LP	United Artists	UAG29417	1972	£5	£12	Map of Wales cover
Christmas At The Patti	10" LP	United Artists	UDX205/6	1973	£6	£15	double
Daughter Of The Fireplace	7"	Liberty	LBF15448	1971	£4	£8	
Day And Night	7"	United Artists	UP35739	1974	£1.50	£4	
Do You Like It Here	LP	United Artists	UAG29236	1971	£5	£12	
Don't Go Away	7"	United Artists	UP35643	1974	£7.50	£15	
Live At The Padget Rooms	LP	United Artists	USP100	1972	£8	£20	
Man	LP	Liberty	LBS83464	1970	£5	£12	
Maximum Darkness	LP	United Artists	UAS29872	1975	£4	£10	
Revelation	LP	Pye	N(S)PL18275	1969	£6	£15	
Rhinos, Winos And Lunatics	LP	United Artists	UAS29631	1974	£4	£10	
Slow Motion	LP	United Artists	UAS29675	1974	£4	£10	
Sudden Life	7"	Pye	7N17684	1969	£5	£10	
Taking The Easy Way Out Again	7"	United Artists	UP35703	1974	£1.50	£4	

MAN FROM DELMONTE

Drive Drive Drive	7"	Ugly Man	UGLY3	1987	£2	£5
Water In My Eyes	7"	Ugly Man	UGLY5	1987	£1.50	£4
Water In My Eyes	12"	Ugly Man	UGLY5T	1987	£3	£8

MANASSAS

Manassas was the group formed by Steve Stills in the wake of the first disbanding of Crosby, Stills, & Nash. It was something of a supergroup itself, with various ex-members of the CSN rhythm section and of the Flying Burrito Brothers being involved. Steve Stills, however, remains firmly in control and the Manassas albums are very much a showcase for his talents. They include some of Stills' best songs.

Down The Road	LP	Atlantic	K40440	1973	£5	£12	chart LP
Manassas	LP	Atlantic	K60021	1972	£6	£15	double, chart LP

MANCE, JUNIOR

At The Village Vanguard	LP	Jazzland	JLP41	1961	£6	£15
Big Chief	LP	Jazzland	JLP(9)53	1961	£6	£15
Junior Mance And His Swinging Piano	LP	HMV	CLP1342	1959	£6	£15
Soulful Piano	LP	Jazzland	JLP30	1960	£6	£15

MANCHESTER MEKON

No Forgetting	7"	Newmarket	NEW102	1979	£2	£5

MANCHESTER MOB

Bony Maronie At The Hop	7"	Parlophone	R5552	1967	£7.50	£15

MANCHESTER PLAYBOYS

I Feel So Good	7"	Fontana	TF745	1966	£12.50	£25	
Wooly Bully	7" EP	Barclay	70852	1965	£15	£30	French

MANCHESTERS

Tribute To The Beatles	LP	Ember	FA2029	1966	£6	£15

MANCINI, HENRY

Music From Peter Gunn	LP	RCA	RD27123/SF5033	1959	£6	£15
Peter Gunn Theme	7"	RCA	RCA1134	1959	£1.50	£4
Pink Panther	7" EP	RCA	RCX7136	1964	£2.50	£6

MANCUSO, GUS

Introducing Gus Mancuso	LP	Vogue	LAE12069	1958	£5	£12

MANDALA BAND

Eye Of Wendor	LP	Chrysalis	CHR1181	1978	£4	£10
Mandala Band	LP	Chrysalis	CHR1095	1975	£4	£10

MANDEL, HARVEY

Baby Batter	LP	Dawn	DNLS3015	1971	£5	£12	
Cristo Redentor	LP	Philips	SBL7873	1968	£6	£15	
Feel The Sound Of Harvey Mandel	LP	Janus	3067	1974	£5	£12	US
Games Guitars Play	LP	Philips	SBL7915	1970	£6	£15	
Get Off In Chicago	LP	London	SHO8426	1972	£5	£12	
Righteous	LP	Philips	SBL7904	1969	£6	£15	
Shangrenade	LP	Janus	6499831	1973	£5	£12	
Snake	LP	Janus	6310210	1972	£5	£12	

MANDINGO

Medicine Man	7"	EMI	EMI2014	1973	£1.50	£4

MANDRAKE MEMORIAL

Mandrake Memorial	LP	Poppy	PYS40002	1968	£10	£25	US
Medium	LP	RCA	SF8028	1969	£15	£30	
Puzzle	LP	Poppy	PYS11003	1970	£10	£25	

MANDRAKE PADDLE STEAMER

Strange Walking Man	7"	Parlophone	R5780	1969	£25	£50

MANDRILL

Composite Truth	LP	Polydor	2391061	1973	£5	£12
Just Outside Of Town	LP	Polydor	2391092	1973	£5	£12
Mandrill	LP	Polydor	2489028	1970	£5	£12
Mandrill Is	LP	Polydor	2391030	1972	£5	£12

MANEATERS
Nine To Five .... 7" ...... Editions EG ...... EGO8 .... 1982 ... £12.50 .....£25 ......Adam & Toyah PS

MANHATTAN JAZZ SEPTET
Manhattan Jaz Septet .... LP ...... Vogue Coral .... LVA9053 .... 1957 ... £10 ....£25 ....

MANHATTANS
Baby I Need You .... 7" ...... Carnival .... CAR100 .... 1966 ... £4 ....£8 ....
I Wanna Be Your Everything .... 7" ...... Sue .... WI384 .... 1965 ... £7.50 .....£15 ....
That New Girl .... 7" ...... Carnival .... CAR101 .... 1966 ... £4 ....£8 ....

MANIAX
Out Of Reach .... 7" ...... White Label ..... WLR101/2 .... 196- ... £4 ....£8 ....

MANIC STREET PREACHERS
Feminine Is Beautiful .... 7" ...... Caff .... 15 .... 1991 ... £7.50 .....£15 ....
Generation Terrorists .... LP ...... Columbia .... 4710609 .... 1992 ... £6 ....£15 .... double pic disc
Motown Junk .... CD-s .. Heavenly .... HVN8CD .... 1991 ... £2.50 ....£6 ....
Motown Junk .... 12" .... Heavenly .... HVN8 .... 1991 ... £2.50 ....£6 ....
New Art Riot EP .... 12" .... Damaged   YUBB004 .... 1990 ... £2.50 ....£6 ...black & white label
                                                      Goods ....
New Art Riot EP .... 12" .... Damaged   YUBB004P .... 1990 ... £3 ....£8 .... pink vinyl
                                                      Goods ....
Suicide Alley .... 7" ...... SBS .... 002 .... 1989 ... £25 ....£50 ....no PS
Suicide Alley .... 7" ...... SBS .... 002 .... 1989 ... £35 ....£70 ....PS
UK Channel Boredom .... 7" ...... Hopelessly   1 .... 1990 ... £2 ....£5 .... flexi
                                                      Devoted ....

MANN, BARRY
Angelica .... 7" ...... Capitol .... CL15463 .... 1966 ... £2 ....£5 ....
Bless You .... 7" ...... HMV .... POP1108 .... 1963 ... £1.50 ....£4 ....
Hey Baby I'm Dancing .... 7" ...... HMV .... POP1084 .... 1962 ... £2 ....£5 ....
Little Miss USA .... 7" ...... HMV .... POP949 .... 1961 ... £2 ....£5 ....
Talk To Me Baby .... 7" ...... Colpix .... PX776 .... 1964 ... £2 ....£5 ....
Who Put The Bomp .... LP ...... HMV .... CLP1559 .... 1963 ... £60 ....£120 ....
Who Put The Bomp .... 7" ...... HMV .... POP911 .... 1961 ... £5 ....£10 ....
Young Electric Psychedelic Hippy... ... 7" ...... Capitol .... CL15538 .... 1968 ... £1.50 ....£4 ....

MANN, CARL
Like Mann .... LP ...... London .... HAS2277 .... 1960 ... £100 ....£200 ....
Like Mann .... LP ...... Philips .... 1960 .... 1960 ... £180 ....£300 ....US
Mona Lisa .... 7" ...... London .... HLS8935 .... 1959 ... £7.50 .....£15 ....
Pretend .... 7" ...... London .... HLS9006 .... 1959 ... £6 ....£12 ....
South Of The Border .... 7" ...... London .... HLS9170 .... 1960 ... £7.50 .....£15 ....

MANN, GLORIA
It Happened Again .... 7" ...... Brunswick .... 05610 .... 1956 ... £1.50 ....£4 ....
Why Do Fools Fall In Love .... 7" ...... Brunswick .... 05569 .... 1956 ... £5 ....£10 ....

MANN, HERBIE
And The Beat Goes On .... 7" ...... Atlantic .... 584112 .... 1967 ... £1.50 ....£4 ....
At Newport .... LP ...... Atlantic .... ATL5008 .... 1964 ... £4 ....£10 ....
At The Village Gate .... LP ...... Atlantic .... 587/588054 .... 1967 ... £4 ....£10 ....
East Coast Jazz No.4 Part 1 .... 7" EP.. London .... EZN19006 .... 1956 ... £2 ....£5 ....
Flute Fraternity .... 10" LP .. Top Rank .... 25015 .... 1960 ... £6 ....£15 ... with Buddy Colette
Free For All .... LP ...... Atlantic .... 590013 .... 1968 ... £4 ....£10 ....
Herbie Mann .... 7" EP.. Fontana .... TFE17113 .... 1958 ... £2 ....£5 ....
Herbie Mann-Sam Most Quintet .... LP ...... London .... LTZN15049 .... 1957 ... £8 ....£20 ....
Inspiration I Feel .... LP ...... Atlantic .... 588156 .... 1969 ... £4 ....£10 ....
Latin Mann .... LP ...... CBS .... (S)BPG62585 .... 1966 ... £4 ....£10 ....
Magic Flute Of Herbie Mann .... 7" EP.. Columbia .... SEB10102 .... 1959 ... £2 ....£5 ....
Memphis Underground .... LP ...... Atlantic .... 588200 .... 1969 ... £4 ....£10 ....
Memphis Underground .... 7" ...... Atlantic .... 584297 .... 1969 ... £1.50 ....£4 ....
Monday Night At The Village Gate ...... LP ...... Atlantic .... 587/588003 .... 1966 ... £4 ....£10 ....
Nirvana .... LP ...... Atlantic .... 587/588028 .... 1966 ... £4 ....£10 ....with Bill Evans
Philly Dog .... 7" ...... Atlantic .... 584052 .... 1966 ... £4 ....£8 ....Dave Pike B side
Right Now .... LP ...... London .... HAK/SHK8043 ...... 1963 ... £4 ....£10 ....
Roar Of The Grease Paint .... LP ...... Atlantic .... ATL/SAL5035 .... 1965 ... £4 ....£10 ....
Salute To The Flute .... LP ...... Fontana .... TFL5013 .... 1958 ... £5 ....£12 ....
Standing Ovation At Newport .... LP ...... Atlantic .... ATL/SAL5038 .... 1966 ... £4 ....£10 ....

MANN, JOHNNY SINGERS
Ballads Of The King .... 7" EP.. London .... REG1325 .... 1961 ... £2 ....£5 ....

MANN, MANFRED
When Manfred Mann decided to call a halt to his pop career, the result was one of the best albums of all to emerge from the interface between jazz and rock. Essentially the work of a big band, "Manfred Mann Chapter Three" showcased some fine playing - most notably from saxophonist Bernie Living, formerly with the Mike Westbrook band - and also demonstrated the excellence of the Mann-Hugg writing team. "Travelling Lady" was an update of "A B Side" - to be found on the reverse of the single "Ragamuffin Man" and itself the same piece of music as that used in a TV advert. The powerful brass riff that drives "Time", meanwhile, was adopted as the theme tune for a radio jazz programme. Manfred Mann had earlier indicated that he might have something like this up his sleeve when he released the "Instrumental Asylum" EP (whose tracks are also to be found on the LP 'Soul Of Mann"). Paul Jones had just left the group, so the others took advantage of their singerless condition to make a record of sparkling jazz versions of a few well-known rock tunes. The presence of Jack Bruce on bass, together with trumpeter Henry Lowther and saxophonist Lyn Dobson, was a distinct bonus. "Instrumental Assassination" attempted to repeat the formula, but somewhat less successfully, as new member Klaus Voorman was no substitute, in this kind of music, for the three jazzers he replaced.
5-4-3-2-1 .... 7" ...... HMV .... POP1252 .... 1964 ... £1.50 ....£4 ....chart single
As Is .... LP .... Fontana .... (S)TL5377 .... 1966 ... £6 ....£10 ....chart LP
As Is .... LP .... Fontana .... (S)TL5377 .... 1966 ... £8 ....£20 .... train cover
As Was .... 7" EP.. HMV .... 7EG8962 .... 1966 ... £7.50 .....£15 ....
Cock A Hoop .... 7" ...... HMV .... POP1225 .... 1963 ... £5 ....£10 ....

Title	Format	Label	Cat. No.	Year			Notes
Come Tomorrow	7"	Electrola	E22892	1965	£7.50	£15	sung in German
Come Tomorrow	7"	HMV	POP1381	1965	£1.50	£4	chart single
Do Wah Diddy Diddy	7"	HMV	POP1320	1964	£1.50	£4	chart single
Do Wah Diddy Diddy	7" EP	Pathe	EGF747	1964	£7.50	£15	French
Five Faces Of Manfred Mann	LP	Ascot	ALM13018/ ALS16018	1965	£6	£15	US
Five Faces Of Manfred Mann	LP	HMV	CLP1731	1964	£6	£15	chart LP
Fox On The Run	7"	Fontana	TF985	1968	£1.50	£4	chart single
Greatest Hits	LP	United Artists	UAL3551/ UAS6551	1966	£5	£12	US
Grooving With Manfred Mann	7" EP	HMV	7EG8876	1965	£5	£10	chart single
Ha Ha Said The Clown	7"	Fontana	TF812	1967	£1.50	£4	
Ha Ha Said The Clown	7"	Fontana	TF812	1967	£2.50	£6	PS
Ha Ha Said The Clown	7" EP	Fontana	465376	1966	£7.50	£15	French
Hits Of Manfred Mann	cass-s	Philips	MCF5002	1968	£4	£10	
Hits Of Manfred Mann & DDDBM&T	cass-s	Philips	MCF5005	1968	£4	£10	
Hubble Bubble	7"	HMV	POP1282	1964	£1.50	£4	chart single
If You Gotta Go, Go Now	7"	HMV	POP1466	1965	£1.50	£4	chart single
If You Gotta Go, Go Now	7" EP	Pathe	EGF853	1965	£7.50	£15	French
Instrumental Assassination	7" EP	Fontana	TE17483	1966	£2.50	£6	
Instrumental Asylum	7" EP	HMV	7EG8949	1966	£5	£10	
Just Like A Woman	7"	Fontana	TF730	1966	£1.50	£4	chart single
Just Like A Woman	7" EP	Fontana	465320	1966	£7.50	£15	French
Machines	7" EP	HMV	7EG8942	1966	£7.50	£15	
Manfred Mann	7" EP	HMV	7EG8848	1964	£6	£12	
Manfred Mann Album	LP	Ascot	ALM13015/ ALS16015	1964	£6	£15	US
Mann Made	LP	Ascot	ALM13024/ ALS16024	1966	£6	£15	US
Mann Made	LP	HMV	CLP1911/CSD1628	1964	£6	£15	chart LP
Mann Made Hits	LP	HMV	CLP3559	1966	£6	£15	chart LP
Maxwell House Shake	7"	Lyntone	LYN1981	1970	£1.50	£4	flexi
Michelin Theme	7"	Michelin	MIC1	1971	£4	£8	gatefold sleeve
Mighty Garvey	LP	Fontana	(S)TL5470	1968	£6	£15	
Mighty Quinn	LP	Mercury	SR61168	1968	£5	£12	US
Mighty Quinn	7"	Fontana	TF897	1968	£1.50	£4	chart single
My Little Red Book Of Winners	LP	Ascot	ALM13021/ ALS16021	1965	£15	£30	US
My Name Is Jack	7"	Fontana	TF943	1968	£1.50	£4	chart single
No Living Without Loving	7" EP	HMV	7EG8922	1965	£4	£10	
Oh No Not My Baby	7"	HMV	POP1413	1965	£1.50	£4	chart single
One In The Middle	7" EP	HMV	7EG8908	1965	£4	£8	
Pretty Flamingo	LP	United Artists	UAL3549/ UAS6549	1966	£5	£12	US
Pretty Flamingo	7"	HMV	POP1523	1966	£1.50	£4	chart single
Pretty Flamingo	7" EP	Pathe	EGF901	1966	£7.50	£15	French
Ragamuffin Man	7"	Fontana	TF1013	1969	£1.50	£4	chart single
Semi-Detached Suburban Mr.James	7"	Fontana	TF757	1966	£1.50	£4	chart single
Semi-Detached, Suburban Mr.James	7" EP	Fontana	465341	1966	£7.50	£15	French
Sha La La	7"	HMV	POP1346	1964	£1.50	£4	chart single
Sha La La	7" EP	Pathe	EGF781	1964	£7.50	£15	French
Ski 'Full-Of-Fitness' Theme	7"	Ski	SKI01	1970	£6	£12	PS
Ski 'Full-Of-Fitness' Theme	7"	Ski	SKI01	1971	£2	£5	
So Long Dad	7"	Fontana	TF862	1967	£2	£5	
Soul Of Mann	LP	HMV	CLP/CSD3594	1967	£6	£15	chart LP
Sweet Pea	7"	Fontana	TF828	1967	£2	£5	chart single
There's No Living Without Your Loving	7"	HMV	7XEA22017/8	1965	£6	£12	promo
Up The Junction	LP	Fontana	(S)TL5460	1968	£6	£15	
Up The Junction	7"	Fontana	TF908	1968	£2	£5	
Up The Junction	7"	Fontana	TF908	1968	£4	£8	PS
What A Man	LP	Fontana	SFL13003	1968	£6	£15	
Why Should We Not	7"	HMV	POP1189	1963	£5	£10	
You Gave Me Somebody To Love	7"	HMV	POP1541	1966	£2	£5	chart single

MANN, MANFRED CHAPTER THREE

Title	Format	Label	Cat. No.	Year			Notes
Happy Being Me	7"	Vertigo	6059012	1970	£1.50	£4	
Manfred Mann Chapter Three	LP	Vertigo	VO3	1969	£8	£20	spiral label
Manfred Mann Chapter Three Vol.2	LP	Vertigo	6360012	1970	£8	£20	spiral label

MANN, MANFRED EARTH BAND

Title	Format	Label	Cat. No.	Year			Notes
Glorified Magnified	LP	Philips	6308125	1972	£4	£10	
Manfred Mann's Earth Band	LP	Philips	6308086	1972	£4	£10	
Messin'	LP	Vertigo	6360087	1973	£4	£10	

MANN, SHADOW

Title	Format	Label	Cat. No.	Year		
Come Live With Me	7"	Roulette	RO504	1968	£1.50	£4

MANNE, SHELLY

Title	Format	Label	Cat. No.	Year		
2,3,4	LP	HMV	CLP1625	1962	£5	£12
At The Black Hawk Vol.1	LP	Contemporary	LAC12250/ SCA5015	1961	£5	£12
At The Black Hawk Vol.2	LP	Contemporary	LAC12255/ SCA5016	1961	£5	£12
At The Black Hawk Vol.3	LP	Contemporary	LAC12260/ SCA5017	1961	£5	£12
At The Black Hawk Vol.4	LP	Contemporary	LAC12265/ SCA5018	1961	£5	£12
Bells Are Ringing	LP	Contemporary	LAC12212	1960	£4	£10
My Fair Lady	LP	Contemporary	LAC12100	1958	£5	£12

Peter Gunne	LP	Contemporary.	LAC12193	1959	£5	£12	
Shelly Manne	10″ LP	London	LZC14019	1955	£20	£40	
Shelly Manne And Co.	LP	Stateside	SL10125	1965	£4	£10	
Shelly Manne And His Friends	LP	Contemporary.	LAC12075	1958	£6	£15	
Shelly Manne And His Men Vol.1	LP	Contemporary.	LAC12138	1959	£6	£15	
Shelly Manne And His Men Vol.1	10″ LP	Vogue	LDE072	1954	£20	£40	
Shelly Manne And His Men Vol.2	LP	Contemporary.	LAC12148	1959	£6	£15	
Shelly Manne And His Men Vol.2	10″ LP	Contemporary.	LDC143	1955	£20	£40	
Shelly Manne And Russ Freeman	10″ LP	Contemporary.	LDC192	1956	£20	£40	
Son Of Gunn	LP	Contemporary.	LAC12220	1960	£5	£12	
Songs Fom Li'l Abner	LP	Contemporary.	LAC12130	1958	£5	£12	
Three	10″ LP	Contemporary.	LDC190	1956	£20	£40	...with Shorty Rogers and Jimmy Giuffre
Three And The Two	LP	Contemporary.	LAC12276	1961	£5	£12	
Vol.4	LP	Contemporary.	LAC12062	1957	£6	£15	
Vol.7 - The Gambit	LP	Vogue	LAC12241	1961	£5	£12	
Volume 6	LP	Contemporary.	LAC12232	1960	£4	£10	

MANNING, BOB

It's All Right With Me	7″	Capitol	CL14190	1954	£1.50	£4	
Majorca	7″	Capitol	CL14256	1955	£1.50	£4	
Mission San Michel	7″	Capitol	CL14288	1955	£1.50	£4	
My Love Song To You	7″	Capitol	CL14234	1955	£1.50	£4	
Very Thought Of You	7″	Capitol	CL14220	1955	£1.50	£4	
What A Wonderful Way To Die	7″	Capitol	CL14318	1955	£1.50	£4	

MANNING, MARTY & THE CHEETAHS

Tarzan March	7″	CBS	2721	1967	£1.50	£4	

MANNION, EDDIE

Just Driftin'	7″	HMV	POP804	1960	£1.50	£4	

MANONE, WINGY

Go-Group	LP	London	HBU1063	1956	£6	£15	
Party Doll	LP	Brunswick	05655	1957	£5	£10	
Trumpet On The Wing	LP	Brunswick	LAT8236	1958	£6	£15	

MANSANO, JOE

Life On Reggae Planet	7″	Blue Cat	BS150	1968	£4	£8	Rico B side

MANSELL, TONY

Zambesi	7″	Parlophone	MSP6222	1956	£1.50	£4	

MANSFIELD, JAYNE

As Clouds Drift By	7″	London	HL10147	1967	£10	£20	Jimi Hendrix plays on B side
Busts Up Las Vegas	LP	20th Century			£8	£20	US
Shakespeare, Tchaikovsky And Me	LP	MGM	(S)E4204	1964	£5	£12	US

MANSON, CHARLES

It's Comin' Down Fast	7″	Fierce	FRIGHT012	1988	£4	£8	
Lie	LP	Awareness	22145	1970	£25	£50	US
Love And Terror Cult	LP	Fierce	FRIGHT001	198-	£10	£25	
Rise	7″	Fierce	FRIGHT006	1986	£4	£8	

MANTELL, JOHN

Remember Child	7″	CBS	201783	1965	£7.50	£15	

MANTLER, MIKE

Jazz Composers' Orchestra	LP	Virgin	JD3001	1974	£6	£15	double

MANUEL, IAN

Frosty Ploughshare	LP	Topic	12TS220	1972	£5	£12	

MAPHIA

Hans Im Gluck	LP	Alco	ALC80541	1974	£6	£15	German

MAPHIS, JOE

Fire On The Strings	LP	Columbia	CL1005	1957	£10	£25	US

MAPHIS, JOE & ROSE LEE

Mr.And Mrs.Country Music	LP	Starday	SLP286	1964	£4	£10	US
With The Blue Ridge Mountain Boys	LP	Capitol	(S)T1778	1962	£5	£12	US

MAPLE OAK

Maple Oak	LP	Decca	SKL5085	1971	£75	£150	
Son Of A Gun	7″	Decca	F13008	1970	£7.50	£15	

MAPP, LUCILLE

I'm Available	7″	Columbia	DB4040	1957	£1.50	£4	
Mangos	7″	Columbia	DB3916	1957	£1.50	£4	

MARA, TOMMY

Pledging My Love	7″	MGM	SP1128	1955	£1.50	£4	
Where The Blues Of The Night	7″	Felsted	AF109	1958	£1.50	£4	

MARATHONS

Peanut Butter	LP	Arvee	A428	1961	£25	£50	US
Peanut Butter	7″	Pye	7N25088	1961	£2.50	£6	
Peanut Butter	7″	Vogue	V9185	1961	£6	£12	

MARAUDERS

Baby	7"	Fontana	TF609	1965	£4	£8	
Check In	LP	no label		196-	£20	£40	US
Heart Full Of Tears	7"	Decca	F11748	1963	£2	£5	
Little Egypt	7"	Decca	F11836	1964	£2.50	£6	
That's What I Want	7"	Decca	F11695	1963	£2.50	£6	chart single

MARBLE PHROGG

Marble Phrogg	LP	Derrick	8868	1968	£180	£300	US

MARBLES

Marbles	LP	Cotillion	SD9029	1970	£6	£15	US
Only One Woman	7"	Polydor	56272	1968	£1.50	£4	chart single
Walls Fell Down	7"	Polydor	56310	1969	£1.50	£4	chart single

MARC & THE MAMBAS

Big Louise	12"	Some Bizarre	BZS1512	1982	£10	£25	
Bite Black And Blues	LP	Gutterheart	GH1	1984	£8	£20	fan club only
Black Heart	7"	Some Bizarre	BZS19	1983	£1.50	£4	with card
Black Heart	12"	Some Bizarre	BZS1912	1983	£4	£10	
Discipline	7"	Lyntone	LYN12505	1982	£2	£5	flexi
Sleaze	12"	Some Bizarre	BZS512	1982	£6	£15	fan club
Torment	12"	Some Bizarre	BZS2112	1983	£5	£12	
Untitled	LP	Some Bizarre	BZS13	1982	£4	£10	with 12', chart LP

MARCEL

Dream Consumed	LP	BASF	20210944	1971	£5	£12	German

MARCELLE, LYDIA

Another Kind Of Fellow	7"	Sue	WI4025	1966	£7.50	£15	

MARCELLINO, MUZZY

Mary Lou	7"	London	HLU8355	1956	£7.50	£15	Mr. Ford & Mr Goon-Bones B side

MARCELS

Blue Moon	LP	Pye	NPL28016	1961	£25	£50	
Blue Moon	7"	Pye	7N25073	1961	£2.50	£6	chart single
Heartaches	7"	Pye	7N25114	1961	£2.50	£6	
I Wanna Be The Leader	7"	Pye	7N25201	1963	£1.50	£4	
My Melancholy Baby	7"	Pye	7N25124	1962	£2	£5	
Summertime	7"	Pye	7N25083	1961	£1.50	£4	chart single
You Are My Sunshine	7"	Pye	7N25105	1961	£2	£5	

MARCH, GLORIA

Baby Of Mine	7"	London	HLB8568	1958	£5	£10	

MARCH, HAL

Hear Me Good	7"	London	HLD8534	1958	£7.50	£15	

MARCH HARE

Cry My Heart	7"	Chapter One	CH101	1968	£1.50	£4	
I Could Make It There With You	7"	Deram	DM258	1969	£1.50	£4	

MARCH, JO

Dormi, Dormi, Dormi	7"	London	HLR8696	1958	£1.50	£4	
Virgin Mary Had One Son	7"	London	HLR8763	1958	£1.50	£4	

MARCH, PEGGY

Hello Heartache Goodbye Love	7"	RCA	RCA1362	1963	£1.50	£4	
I Will Follow Him	LP	RCA	LPM/LSP2732	1963	£6	£15	US
I Will Follow Him	7"	RCA	RCA1338	1963	£1.50	£4	
If You Loved Me	7"	RCA	RCA1687	1968	£10	£20	
In Our Fashion	LP	RCA	LPM/LSP3408	1965	£6	£15	US
I've Been Here Before	7"	RCA	RCA1752	1968	£1.50	£4	
Let Her Go	7"	RCA	RCA1472	1965	£1.50	£4	
My Teenage Castle	7"	RCA	RCA1350	1963	£1.50	£4	
No Foolin'	LP	RCA	LSP3883	1968	£5	£12	US
Watch What You Do With My Baby	7"	RCA	RCA1426	1964	£1.50	£4	
What Am I Gonna Do With You	7"	RCA	RCA1809	1969	£1.50	£4	

MARCH VIOLETS

Grooving In Green	7"	Merciful Release	MR017	1982	£4	£8	
Religious As Hell	7"	Merciful Release	MR013	1982	£4	£8	

MARCHAN, BOBBY

Ain't No Reason For Girls To Be Lonely	7"	Action	ACT4533	1969	£1.50	£4	
Get Down With It	7"	Atlantic	584155	1968	£1.50	£4	
There's Something On Your Mind	LP	Sphere Sound	SSR7004	1964	£10	£25	U

MARCUS

Marcus	LP	United Artists	UAS30000	1976	£6	£15	

MARDEN, JANIE

Soldier Boy	7"	Decca	F10600	1955	£1.50	£4	
You Are My Love	7"	Decca	F10673	1955	£1.50	£4	

MARESCA, ERNIE

It's Their World	7"	London	HLU10008	1965	£1.50	£4
Love Express	7"	London	HLU9720	1963	£2.50	£6
Mary Jane	7"	London	HLU9579	1962	£5	£10
Rockin' Boulevard Street	7"	Stateside	SS560	1966	£4	£8
Rovin' Kind	7"	London	HLU9834	1964	£2.50	£6
Shout Shout	7"	London	HLU9531	1962	£4	£8
Shout! Shout! Knock Yourself Out	LP	Seville	SV7/87001	1962	£10	£25	US

MARGO & THE MARVETTES

Cherry Pie	7"	Parlophone	R5154	1964	£2.50	£6
Copper Kettle	7"	Parlophone	R5227	1965	£1.50	£4
Seven Letters	7"	Piccadilly	7N35387	1967	£1.50	£4
When Love Slips Away	7"	Pye	7N17423	1967	£1.50	£4

MARGRET, ANN

And Here She Is	LP	RCA	RD27239/SF5116	1962	£6	£15
Anne Margaret	LP	RCA	RD/SF7691	1964	£5	£12
Bachelors' Paradise	LP	RCA	RD/SF7649	1964	£5	£12
Beauty And The Beard	LP	RCA	RD/SF7632	1964	£5	£12
Bye Bye Birdie	LP	RCA	RD/SF7580	1963	£5	£12
Gimme Love	7"	RCA	RCA1267	1961	£1.50	£4
Just Don't Understand	7"	RCA	RCA1245	1961	£1.50	£4
Man's Favourite Sport	7"	RCA	RCA1396	1964	£1.50	£4
On The Way Up	LP	RCA	RD/SF7503	1962	£5	£12
Vivacious One	7" EP.	RCA	RCX7148	1964	£10	£20

MARGUERITA

Woman Come	7"	Black Swan	WI431	1964	£5	£10	Eric Morris B side

MARGULIS, CHARLIE

Gigi	7"	London	HLL8774	1959	£1.50	£4

MARIANNE

You Know My Name	7"	Columbia	DB8420	1968	£2.50	£6
You'd Better Change Your Evil Ways	7"	Columbia	DB8456	1968	£1.50	£4

MARIANO, CHARLIE

Beauties Of 1918	LP	Vogue	LAE12166	1959	£6	£15	with Jerry Dodgion
Charlie Mariano Quartet/Septet	LP	Parlophone	PMC1094	1959	£6	£15
Charlie Mariano Sextet	LP	London	LTZN15031	1957	£15	£30
Charlie Mariano Sextet	10" LP	London	LZN14032	1956	£25	£50

MARIAS, A.C.

Drop	7"	Dome	DOM451	1981	£2	£5

MARIE CELESTE

And Then Perhaps	LP	private		1971	£60	£120

MARILLION

The considerable success of an "old-fashioned" progressive group was one of the more surprising aspects of rock music in the eighties. Marillion achieved this, however, by gigging hard up and down the country and building a sizeable following before making any records at all. In common with other stars of the eighties, Marillion's recording career has been highlighted by a succession of picture disc releases, and it is these that now form the central axis of a Marillion collection.

Assassing	12"	EMI	12MARILP2	1984	£5	£12	pic disc
Clutching At Straws	LP	EMI	EMDP1002	1987	£4	£10	pic disc
Freaks	7"	EMI	MARILP9	1988	£2.50	£6	shaped pic disc
Fugazi	LP	EMI	MRLP1	1984	£6	£15	pic disc
Garden Party	7"	EMI	EMIP5393	1983	£5	£10	shaped pic disc
Garden Party	12"	EMI	12EMIS5393	1983	£3	£8	with poster
Heart Of Lothian	12"	EMI	12MARILP5	1985	£2.50	£6	pic disc
Incommunicado	CD-s	EMI	CDMARIL6	1987	£1.50	£4
Incommunicado	12"	EMI	12MARILP6	1987	£2.50	£6	pic disc
Kayleigh	7"	EMI	MARILP3	1985	£2.50	£6	pic disc
Kayleigh	12"	EMI	12MARILP3	1985	£4	£10	pic disc
Lavender Blue	12"	EMI	12MARILP4	1985	£3	£8	pic disc
Market Square Heroes	12"	EMI	12EMIP5351	1983	£20	£40	pic disc
Misplaced Childhood	LP	EMI	MRLP2	1985	£4	£10	pic disc
Punch And Judy	12"	EMI	12MARILP1	1984	£5	£12	pic disc
Real To Reel	LP	EMI	JESTP1	1984	£4	£10	pic disc
Script For A Jester's Tear	LP	EMI	EMCP3429	1984	£8	£20	pic disc
Sugar Mice	CD-s	EMI	CDMARIL7	1987	£3	£8
Sugar Mice	7"	EMI	MARILP7	1987	£2	£5	pic disc with poster
Sugar Mice	12"	EMI	12MARILP7	1987	£3	£8	pic disc
Warm Wet Circles	12"	EMI	12MARILP8	1987	£3	£8	pic disc

MARINE GIRLS

Beach Party	LP	Whaam!	COD1	1981	£4	£10
In My Mind	7"	In Phaze	COD2	1982	£4	£8

MARINERS

Love You Fair Dinkum	7"	London	HLA8201	1955	£7.50	£15
Spirituals	LP	London	HAA2007	1956	£6	£15

MARINI, MARINO

Ciao Ciao Bambina	7"	Durium	DC16636	1959	£1.50	£4	chart single
Come Prima	7"	Durium	DC16632	1958	£1.50	£4	chart single
Guitar Boogie	7"	Durium	DC16631	1958	£1.50	£4
Stella Stella	7"	Durium	DC16635	1958	£1.50	£4

MARIONETTES

At The End Of The Day	7"	Parlophone	R5374	1965	£1.50	£4	
Like A Man	7"	Parlophone	R5416	1966	£2	£5	
Raining It's Pouring	7"	Parlophone	R5356	1965	£1.50	£4	
Was It Me?	7"	Parlophone	R5300	1965	£1.50	£4	
Whirlpool Of Love	7"	Decca	F12056	1965	£1.50	£4	

MARK & JOHN

Walk Right Back	7"	Decca	F12044	1964	£2	£5	

MARK ALMOND

Mark Almond	LP	Harvest	SHSP4011	1971	£4	£10	

MARK FIVE

Baby What's Wrong	7"	Fontana	TF513	1964	£15	£30	

MARK FOUR

The Mark Four who recorded singles for Decca and Fontana were an early line-up of the Creation. The bass player was John Dalton, later a member of the Kinks.

Crazy Country Hop	7"	Mercury	MF825	1964	£10	£20	
Hurt Me If You Will	7"	Decca	F12204	1965	£15	£30	
Live At The Beat Scene Club	7"	Bam Caruso	OPRA037	1985	£4	£8	
Rock Around The Clock	7"	Mercury	MF815	1964	£10	£20	
Work All Day	7"	Fontana	TF664	1966	£15	£30	

MARK II

Night Theme	7"	Columbia	DB4549	1960	£1.50	£4	

MARK IV

I Got A Wife	7"	Mercury	AMT1025	1959	£4	£8	
Move Over Rover	7"	Mercury	AMT1045	1959	£4	£8	
Ring Ring Ring Those Bells	7"	Mercury	AMT1060	1959	£1.50	£4	

MARK, JON

All Neat In Black Stockings	7"	Philips	BF1772	1969	£1.50	£4	
Baby I Got A Long Way To Go	7"	Brunswick	05929	1965	£1.50	£4	
Paris Bells	7"	Brunswick	05952	1966	£1.50	£4	

MARKETTS

Balbao Blue	7"	Liberty	LIB55443	1962	£1.50	£4	
Batman	LP	Warner Bros	W1642	1966	£5	£12	
Batman Theme	7"	Warner Bros	WB5696	1966	£2.50	£6	
Out Of Limits	LP	Warner Bros	(S)T1537	1964	£6	£15	US
Out Of Limits	7"	Warner Bros	WB120	1964	£6	£12	
Surfer Stomp	LP	Liberty	LRP3226/LST7226	1962	£8	£20	US
Surfer Stomp	7"	Liberty	LIB55401	1962	£2.50	£6	
Surfing Scene	LP	Liberty	LRP3326/LST7326	1963	£6	£15	US
Take To Wheels	LP	Warner Bros	WM8140	1963	£6	£15	
Tarzan's March	7"	Warner Bros	WB5847	1967	£12.50	£25	
Vanishing Point	7"	Warner Bros	WB130	1964	£1.50	£4	

MARKEYS

Damnifiknow	LP	Stax	STS2025	1969	£6	£15	US
Do The Pop-Eye	LP	London	HAK8011	1962	£8	£20	
Foxy	LP	London	HLK9510	1962	£2.50	£6	
Great Memphis Sound	LP	Atlantic	587/588024	1966	£8	£20	US
Last Night	LP	Atlantic	(SD)8055	1961	£8	£20	
Last Night	7"	Atlantic	584074	1967	£1.50	£4	
Last Night	7"	London	HLK9399	1961	£4	£8	
Mellow Jelly	LP	Atlantic	587/588135	1968	£8	£20	
Morning After	7"	London	HLK9449	1961	£2	£5	
Philly Dog	7"	Atlantic	AT4079	1966	£5	£10	

MARKHAM, PIGMEAT

Pigmeat Markham was a black American comedian who might well be described as the James Brown of comedy for the way in which he kept his art in the ghetto, even when he himself had moved out of it. Markham invented the "Here Comes The Judge" by-line which featured on the TV show "Rowan And Martin's Laugh-In", although the song built around it was commandeered by Shorty Long for Tamla Motown.

Here Come The Judge	LP	Chess	LPS1523	1968	£8	£20	U
Here Comes The Judge	7"	Chess	CRS8077	1968	£2	£5	chart singl
Sock It To 'Em Judge	7"	Chess	CRS8085	1968	£1.50	£4	

MARKLEY

Markley: A Group	LP	Forward	STF1007	1969	£8	£20	U

MARKSMEN

Smersh	7"	Parlophone	R5075	1963	£4	£8	

MARLEY, BOB

African Herbsman	LP	Trojan	TRL62	1973	£8	£20	
African Herbsman	7"	Upsetter	US392	1972	£5	£10	
Baby We've Got A Date	7"	Blue Mountain	1021	1973	£2.50	£6	
Babylon By Bus	LP	Island	ISLD11	1978	£5	£12	with 12' (IPR2020
Burial	7"	Fab	FAB41	1968	£25	£50	test pressin
Burnin'	LP	Island	ILPS9256	1973	£5	£12	
Catch A Fire	LP	Island	ILPS9241	1972	£6	£15	lighter cove
Confrontation	LP	Island	ILPS9760	1983	£6	£15	pic dis
Confrontation	LP	Island	PILPS9760	1983	£10	£25	pic dis
Could You Be Loved	7"	Island	ISP210	1984	£1.50	£4	pic dis
Duppy Conqueror	7"	Unity	UN562	1972	£5	£10	Upsetters B sic
Duppy Conqueror	7"	Upsetter	US348	1971	£5	£10	Upsetters B sic
Freedom Train	7"	Summit	SUM8530	1971	£5	£10	

Get Up Stand Up	7"	Island	BMRM1	1973	£2	£5	1 sided promo
Guava Jelly	7"	Green Door	GD4025	1972	£5	£10	
Have Faith In The Lord	7"	Studio One	SO2010	1967	£12.50	£25	Joe Higgs B side
I Like It Like This	7"	Supreme	SUP216	196-	£15	£30	
I Shot The Sheriff	7"	Island	IDJ2	1974	£2.50	£6	promo
Jah Live	7"	Island	WIP6265	1974	£1.50	£4	
Johnny Was	7"	Island	WIP6296	1975	£1.50	£4	
Judge Not	7"	Island	WI088	1963	£35	£70	
Kaya	7"	Upsetter	US356	1971	£5	£10	Upsetters B side
Legend	LP	Island	PBMW1	1984	£4	£10	pic disc
Let Him Go	7"	Island	WI3009	1966	£15	£30	instrumental B side
Lick Samba	7"	Bullet	BU493	1971	£6	£12	
Lively Up Yourself	7"	Green Door	GD4002	1971	£6	£12	Tommy McCook B side
Lively Up Yourself	7"	Punch	PH102	1973	£5	£10	Tommy McCook B side
More Axe	7"	Upsetter	US369	1971	£5	£10	Upsetters B side
More Axe	7"	Upsetter	US372	1971	£5	£10	Upsetters B side
Mr.Brown	7"	Trojan	TR7926	1974	£2	£5	
Mr.Brown	7"	Upsetter	US354	1971	£5	£10	Upsetters B side
My Cup	7"	Upsetter	US340	1970	£6	£12	Lee Perry B side
Natty Dread	7"	Island	WIP6212	1974	£1.50	£4	
Oh My Darling	7"	Coxsone	CS7021	1967	£12.50	£25	Hamlins B side
One Cup Of Coffee	7"	Island	WI128	1963	£25	£50	Ernest Ranglin B side
One Love	12"	Island	12ISP169	1984	£2.50	£6	pic disc
Rasta Revolution	LP	Trojan	TRLS89	1974	£6	£15	
Roots Rock Reggae	7"	Island	WIP6309	1976	£1.50	£4	
Run For Cover	7"	Escort	ERT842	1970	£6	£12	
Screw Face	7"	Punch	PH101	1973	£5	£10	
Small Axe	7"	Punch	PH69	1971	£6	£12	Dave Barker B side
Small Axe	7"	Upsetter	US357	1971	£5	£10	
Soul Rebel	LP	Trojan	TBL126	1971	£8	£20	
Soul Shake Down Party	7"	Trojan	TR7759	1970		£12	Beverly Allstars B side
Soul Shake Down Party	7"	Trojan	TR7911	1974	£2	£5	
Soultown	7"	Bullet	BU464	1971	£5	£10	
Stir It Up	7"	Island	WIP6478	1976	£5	£10	demo
Stir It Up	7"	Trojan	TR617	1968	£10	£20	
Trenchtown Rock	7"	Green Door	GD4005	1971	£6	£12	
Trenchtown Rock	7"	Island	IDJ7	1974	£2.50	£6	promo

MARLEY, BOB & ROBERT PALMER

Record Shop Sampler	LP	Island	RSS1	197-	£6	£15	promo

MARLEY, RITA

Come To Me	7"	Island	WI3052	1967	£5	£10	Soul Boys B side
Pied Piper	7"	Rio	R108	1966	£4	£8	
You Lied	7"	Rio	R118	1966	£4	£8	Soul Brothers B side

MARLO, MICKI

Prize Of Gold	7"	Capitol	CL14271	1955	£2.50	£6	
That's Right	7"	London	HL8481	1957	£7.50	£15	B side with Paul Anka

MARLOWE, MARION

Hands Of Time	7"	London	HLA8306	1956	£20	£40

MARMALADE

The Marmalade were frequent visitors to the charts at the end of the sixties, but their good-humoured harmony pop is not the kind of thing to appeal to many collectors today. Nevertheless, the group's early single, "I See The Rain" is well worth hearing for the combination of harmony singing with a much heavier guitar sound than was the group's normal practice.

Best Of The Marmalade	LP	CBS	PB36	1969	£4	£10
I See The Rain	7"	CBS	2948	1967	£2.50	£6
There's A Lot Of It About	LP	CBS	63414	1968	£4	£10

MARQUIS OF KENSINGTON

Changing Of The Guards	7"	Immediate	IM052	1967	£6	£12

MARR, HANK

Tonk Game	7"	Blue Beat	BB26	1961	£5	£10

MARRIOTT, STEVE

Give Her My Regards	7"	Decca	F11619	1963	£25	£50

MARS, JOHNNY

Blues From Mars	LP	Polydor	2460168	1972	£5	£12

MARSDEN, BERYL

I Know	7"	Decca	F11707	1963	£2.50	£6
Music Talk	7"	Columbia	DB7797	1965	£4	£8
What's She Got	7"	Columbia	DB7888	1966	£4	£8
When The Lovelight Starts	7"	Decca	F11819	1964	£4	£8
Who You Gonna Hurt	7"	Columbia	DB7718	1965	£2.50	£6

MARSDEN, GERRY

In addition to the hunks of raw rock'n'roll, "You'll Never Walk Alone" and "Ferry Cross The Mersey", that he recorded with Gerry And The Pacemakers, the man who saw fit to lampoon Cliff Richard for his lack of rock'n'roll credibility (his filmed comments are included in the "Compleat Beatles" video), was also responsible for such roots classics as "I've Got My Ukelele" (not included here) and the B side of "Liverpool", which features a collaboration with that rock music giant, Derek Nimmo.

Gilbert Green		CBS	2946	1967	£2.50	£6
Liverpool	7"	CBS	3575	1968	£2.50	£6	B side with Derek Nimmo
Please Let Them Be	7"	CBS	2784	1967	£2.50	£6

MARSH, STEVIE

If You Were The Only Boy In The World	7"	Decca	F11181	1959	£1.50	£4	chart single

MARSH, WARNE

Jazz Of Two Cities	LP	London	LTZP15080	1957	£15	£30

MARSHALL, JACK

Eighteenth Century Jazz	LP	Capitol	T1108	1959	£4	£10
Soundsville	LP	Capitol	(S)T1194	1961	£4	£10
Thunder Road Chase	7"	Capitol	CL14888	1958	£4	£8

MARSHALL, LARRY

Move Your Feet	7"	Blue Beat	BB374	1965	£5	£10	
No One To Give Me Love	7"	Caltone	TONE126	1968	£4	£8	Phil Pratt B side
Suspicion	7"	Blue Beat	BB380	1965	£5	£10	

MARSHMALLOW HIGHWAY

I Don't Wanna Live This Way	7"	London	HLR10204	1968	£1.50	£4

MARSUPILAMI

Arena	LP	Transatlantic	TRA230	1971	£15	£30
Marsupilami	LP	Transatlantic	TRA213	1970	£15	£30

MARTELLS

Time To Say Goodnight	7"	Decca	F12463	1966	£2	£5

MARTERIE, RALPH

Cha-Hua-Hua	7"	Mercury	7MT232	1958	£1.50	£4
Guaglione	7"	Mercury	7MT138	1957	£1.50	£4
Music For A Private Eye	7" EP	Mercury	ZEP10068	1960	£2.50	£6
Night Stroll	7"	Mercury	7MT213	1958	£1.50	£4
Presenting	7" EP	Mercury	MEP9517	1957	£6	£12
Shish-kebab	7"	Mercury	7MT158	1958	£1.50	£4
Swinging Sound	7" EP	Mercury	ZEP10040	1959	£2	£5
Tequila	7"	Mercury	7MT204	1958	£1.50	£4

MARTERIE, RALPH & QUINCY JONES ORCHESTRAS

Big Band Sound	7" EP	Mercury	ZEP10024	1959	£2	£5

MARTHA & THE VANDELLAS

Bless You	7"	Tamla Motown	TMG794	1971	£1.50	£4	chart single
Come And Get These Memories	LP	Oriole	PS40052	1963	£30	£60	
Come And Get These Memories	7"	Oriole	CBA1819	1963	£30	£60	
Dance Party	LP	Tamla Motown	TML11013	1965	£17.50	£35	
Dancing In The Street	LP	Tamla Motown	(S)TML11099	1969	£5	£12	
Dancing In The Street	7"	Stateside	SS345	1964	£6	£12	chart single
Dancing In The Street	7"	Tamla Motown	TMG684	1969	£2	£5	chart single
Forget Me Not	7"	Tamla Motown	TMG762	1971	£2	£5	chart single
Greatest Hits	LP	Tamla Motown	(S)TML11040	1967	£4	£10	
Heat Wave	7"	Stateside	SS228	1963	£12.50	£25	
Heatwave	LP	Tamla Motown	TML11005	1965	£15	£30	
Hitting	7" EP	Tamla Motown	TME2017	1966	£20	£40	
Honey Chile	7"	Tamla Motown	TMG636	1968	£2.50	£6	chart single
I Can't Dance To The Music You're Playing	7"	Tamla Motown	TMG669	1968	£2	£5	
I Promise To Wait My Love	7"	Tamla Motown	TMG657	1968	£2	£5	
I'll Have To Let Him Go	7"	Oriole	CBA1814	1963	£180	£300	
I'm Ready For Love	7"	Tamla Motown	TMG582	1966	£2.50	£6	chart single
In My Lonely Room	7"	Stateside	SS305	1964	£12.50	£25	
Jimmy Mack	7"	Tamla Motown	TMG599	1967	£2	£5	chart single
Live	LP	Gordy	(GS)925	1967	£6	£15	US
Live Wire	7"	Stateside	SS272	1964	£10	£20	
Love Bug Leave My Heart Alone	7"	Tamla Motown	TMG621	1967	£4	£8	
Martha & The Vandellas	7" EP	Tamla Motown	TME2009	1965	£20	£40	
My Baby Loves Me	7"	Tamla Motown	TMG549	1966	£5	£10	
Nowhere to Run	7"	Tamla Motown	TMG502	1965	£5	£10	chart single
Nowhere To Run	7"	Tamla Motown	TMG694	1969	£1.50	£4	chart single
Quicksand	7"	Stateside	SS250	1964	£12.50	£25	
Ridin' High	LP	Tamla Motown	(S)TML11078	1968	£5	£12	
Watch Out	LP	Tamla Motown	(S)TML11051	1967	£8	£20	
What Am I Going To Do	7"	Tamla Motown	TMG567	1966	£4	£8	
Wild One	7"	Stateside	SS383	1965	£10	£20	
You've Been In Love Too Long	7"	Tamla Motown	TMG530	1965	£7.50	£15	

MARTIN & FINLEY

It's Another Sunday	7"	Tamla Motown	TMG867	1973	£30	£60	demo

MARTIN, ALAN

Days Are Lonely	7"	Rio	R94	1966	£4	£8	
Mother Brother	7"	Rio	R10	1963	£5	£10	
Must Know I Love You	7"	Rio	R66	1965	£5	£10	Vic Brown B side
Party	7"	Rio	R3	1963	£5	£10	
Rome Wasn't Built In A Day	7"	Rio	R96	1966	£4	£8	
Secretly	7"	Rio	R9	1963	£5	£10	
Since I Married Dorothy	7"	Rio	R74	1965	£5	£10	
Sweet Rosemarie	7"	Rio	R67	1965	£5	£10	Honey Duckers B side
Why Must I Cry	7"	Rio	R68	1965	£5	£10	
You Came Late	7"	Rio	R6	1963	£5	£10	

MARTIN, DAVE

All My Dreams	7"	Port-O-Jam	PJ4115	1964	£5	£10
Let Them Fight	7"	Port-O-Jam	PJ4112	1964	£5	£10

MARTIN, DEAN

Belle From Barcelona	7"	Capitol	CL14253	1955	£4	£8	
Capitol Presents	10" LP	Capitol	LC6590	1953	£15	£30	
Cha Cha D'Amor	7" EP	Capitol	EAP71702	1961	£2	£5	
Chee Chhe-oo Chee	7"	Capitol	CL14311	1955	£4	£8	
Dean Martin	7" EP	Capitol	EAP19123	1955	£6	£12	
Dean Martin And Jerry Lewis	7" EP	Capitol	EAP1033	1956	£2	£5	with Jerry Lewis
Dean Martin Sings, Nicolini Lucchesi Plays	10" LP	Britone	LP1002	1956	£20	£40	
Dino	LP	Capitol	(S)T1659	1962	£4	£10	
Everybody Loves Somebody	7" EP	Reprise	R30034	1964	£2	£5	
French Style	LP	Reprise	R(9)6021	1962	£4	£10	
Hey Brother Pour The Wine	7"	Capitol	CL14123	1954	£5	£10	
Hollywood Or Bust	7" EP	Capitol	EAP1806	1957	£2.50	£6	
How Do You Speak To An Angel?	7"	Capitol	CL14150	1954	£4	£8	chart single
If I Could Sing Like Bing	7"	Capitol	CL14180	1954	£4	£8	
I'm Yours	7" EP	Capitol	EAP120152	1961	£4	£8	
In Movieland	7" EP	Capitol	EAP120124	1961	£4	£8	
In Napoli	7"	Capitol	CL14370	1955	£4	£8	
Innamorata	7"	Capitol	CL14507	1956	£2	£5	chart single
Let Me Go Lover	7"	Capitol	CL14226	1955	£5	£10	chart single
Line And Dino	7" EP	Capitol	EAP120060	1961	£2.50	£6	with Line Renaud
Mambo Italiano	7"	Capitol	CL14227	1955	£5	£10	chart single
Man Who Plays The Mandolino	7"	Capitol	CL14690	1957	£1.50	£4	chart single
Memories Are Made Of This	7"	Capitol	CL14523	1956	£4	£8	chart single
Open Up The Doghouse	7"	Capitol	CL14215	1955	£5	£10	
Peddler Man	7"	Capitol	CL14170	1954	£4	£8	
Pretty Baby	LP	Capitol	T849	1957	£5	£12	
Relax-ay-voo	7"	Capitol	CL14356	1955	£4	£8	
Relaxing With Dean Martin	7" EP	Capitol	EAP120072	1961	£2.50	£6	
Return To Me	7"	Capitol	CL14844	1958	£1.50	£4	chart single
Return To Me	7" EP	Capitol	EAP1939	1957	£2	£5	
Rio Bravo	7"	Capitol	CL15015	1959	£1.50	£4	
Simpatico	7"	Capitol	CL14367	1955	£4	£8	
Sleep Warm	LP	Capitol	(S)T1150	1959	£4	£10	
Somebody Loves You	7" EP	Capitol	EAP61702	1961	£2	£5	
Sunny Italy	7" EP	Capitol	EAP1481	1955	£4	£8	
Sway	7"	Capitol	CL14138	1954	£6	£12	chart single
Swinging Down Yonder No.1	7" EP	Capitol	EAP1007	1956	£2.50	£6	
Swinging Down Yonder No.2	7" EP	Capitol	EAP1022	1956	£2.50	£6	
Swinging Down Yonder No.3	7" EP	Capitol	EAP1037	1956	£2.50	£6	
Ten Thousand Bedrooms	7" EP	Capitol	EAP1840	1957	£2.50	£6	
This Is Dean Martin	LP	Capitol	T1047	1958	£4	£10	
This Time I'm Swingin'	LP	Capitol	(S)T1442	1961	£4	£10	
Under The Bridges Of Paris	7"	Capitol	CL14255	1955	£4	£8	chart single
Volare	7"	Capitol	CL14910	1958	£1.50	£4	chart single
Volare	7" EP	Capitol	EAP11027	1958	£2	£5	
Watching The World Go By	7"	Capitol	CL14586	1956	£1.50	£4	
When You Pretend	7"	Capitol	CL14505	1956	£1.50	£4	
Winter Romance Pt.1	7" EP	Capitol	EAP11285	1960	£2.50	£6	
Winter Romance Pt.2	7" EP	Capitol	EAP21285	1960	£2.50	£6	
Winter Romance Pt.3	7" EP	Capitol	EAP31285	1960	£2.50	£6	
Young And Foolish	7"	Capitol	CL14519	1956	£2.50	£6	chart single

MARTIN, DEAN (TEX)

Country Star	LP	Reprise	R6061	1963	£5	£12
Rides Again	LP	Reprise	R6085	1964	£5	£12

MARTIN, DEREK

Daddy Rolling Stone	7"	Sue	WI308	1964	£6	£12	credited to Derak Martin
Soul Power	7"	Stax	601039	1968	£6	£12	
You Better Go	7"	Columbia	DB7694	1965	£7.50	£15	

MARTIN, DEWEY

Dewey Martin And Medicine Ball	LP	Uni	73088	1970	£6	£15	US

MARTIN, DON & DANDY

Got A Feelin'	7"	Giant	GN6	1967	£4	£8
Keep On Fighting	7"	Giant	GN24	1968	£4	£8

MARTIN, GEORGE

All My Loving	7"	Parlophone	R5135	1964	£2.50	£6
All Quiet On The Mersey Front	7"	Parlophone	R5222	1965	£2	£5
And I Love Her	LP	Studio Two	TWO141	1966	£6	£15
Beatles To Bond And Bach	LP	St.Michael	IMP105	1978	£6	£15
British Maid	LP	United Artists	(S)ULP1196	1968	£5	£12
I Feel Fine	7"	Parlophone	R5256	1965	£2	£5
Instrumentally Salutes Beatles Girls	LP	United Artists	(S)ULP1157	1966	£6	£15
Love In The Open Air	LP	United Artists	UP1165	1966	£10	£20
Music From A Hard Day's Night	7" EP	Parlophone	GEP8930	1965	£7.50	£15
Off The Beatles Track	LP	Parlophone	PMC1227/ PCS3057	1964	£8	£20
Plays Help	LP	Columbia	SX1775/TWO102	1965	£6	£15
Ringo's Theme	7"	Parlophone	R5166	1964	£2.50	£6
Theme One	7"	United Artists	UP1194	1967	£4	£8

Title	Format	Label	Catalogue	Year	Price	Price	Notes
Yesterday	7"	Parlophone	R5375	1965	£4	£8	

MARTIN, GRADY SLEW FOOT FIVE
Title	Format	Label	Catalogue	Year	Price	Price	Notes
Nashville	7"	Brunswick	05535	1956	£5	£10	

MARTIN, JANIS
Title	Format	Label	Catalogue	Year	Price	Price	Notes
Here Today & Gone Tomorrow Love	7"	Palette	PG9000	1960	£12.50	£25	

MARTIN, JEAN
Title	Format	Label	Catalogue	Year	Price	Price	Notes
Ain't Gonna Kiss Ya	7"	Decca	F11751	1963	£1.50	£4	
Will You Still Love Me Tomorrow	7"	Decca	F11897	1964	£1.50	£4	

MARTIN, JERRY
Title	Format	Label	Catalogue	Year	Price	Price	Notes
Shake A Take A	7"	London	HLU9692	1963	£1.50	£4	

MARTIN, KERRY
Title	Format	Label	Catalogue	Year	Price	Price	Notes
Stroll Me	7"	Parlophone	R4449	1958	£1.50	£4	

MARTIN, LUCIA
Title	Format	Label	Catalogue	Year	Price	Price	Notes
Big Jim	7"	Parlophone	R4915	1962	£4	£8	

MARTIN, MARK
Title	Format	Label	Catalogue	Year	Price	Price	Notes
Extraordinary Girl	7"	Page One	POF020	1967	£1.50	£4	

MARTIN, PAUL
Title	Format	Label	Catalogue	Year	Price	Price	Notes
Snake In The Grass	7"	Sue	WI4041	1967	£6	£12	

MARTIN, RAY
Title	Format	Label	Catalogue	Year	Price	Price	Notes
Blue Tango	7"	Columbia	SCM5001	1953	£2.50	£6	chart single
Carousel Waltz	7"	Columbia	SCM5264	1956	£1.50	£4	chart single
Swedish Rhapsody	7"	Columbia	SCM5063	1953	£2.50	£6	chart single
Waltzing Cat	7"	Columbia	SCM5002	1953	£1.50	£4	

MARTIN, RICKY & THE TYME MACHINE
Title	Format	Label	Catalogue	Year	Price	Price	Notes
Something Else	7"	Olga	OLE4	1968	£1.50	£4	

MARTIN, RODGE
Title	Format	Label	Catalogue	Year	Price	Price	Notes
When She Touches Me	7"	Polydor	56725	1967	£2.50	£6	

MARTIN, RON
Title	Format	Label	Catalogue	Year	Price	Price	Notes
Give Your Love To Me	7"	Doctor Bird	DB1151	1968	£5	£10	

MARTIN, SETH
Title	Format	Label	Catalogue	Year	Price	Price	Notes
Another Day Goes By	7"	Page One	POF073	1968	£1.50	£4	

MARTIN, SHANE
Title	Format	Label	Catalogue	Year	Price	Price	Notes
You're So Young	7"	CBS	3894	1969	£50	£100	

MARTIN, STEVE
Title	Format	Label	Catalogue	Year	Price	Price	Notes
Only You	7"	Columbia	SCM5212	1956	£1.50	£4	

MARTIN, TONY
Title	Format	Label	Catalogue	Year	Price	Price	Notes
All Of You	7"	HMV	POP282	1957	£1.50	£4	
Bigger Your Heart Is	7"	Tamla Motown	TMG537	1965	£20	£40	
Dream Music	10" LP	Mercury	MPT7516	1957	£6	£15	
Favourites	10" LP	Mercury	MPT7005	1956	£6	£15	
Golden Years	7"	HMV	7M136	1953	£2.50	£6	
I Could Write A Book	7"	HMV	7M203	1954	£2	£5	
I Love Paris	7"	HMV	7M258	1954	£1.50	£4	
It's Better In The Dark	7"	HMV	POP257	1956	£1.50	£4	
Love You Funny Thing	7"	HMV	7M376	1956	£1.50	£4	
My Bambina	7"	HMV	7M283	1955	£1.50	£4	
Please Please	7"	HMV	7M137	1953	£2.50	£6	
Sorta On The Border	7"	HMV	7M158	1953	£2.50	£6	
Speak To Me Of Love	10" LP	HMV	DLP1137	1957	£5	£12	
Stranger In Paradise	7"	HMV	7M302	1955	£5	£10	chart single
Talkin' To Your Picture	7"	Stateside	SS394	1965	£25	£50	
Tenement Symphony	7"	HMV	7M105	1953	£4	£8	
That's What A Rainy Day Is For	7"	HMV	7M210	1954	£1.50	£4	
Tony Martin Sings Vol.1	10" LP	Brunswick	LA8713	1955	£6	£15	
Uno	7"	HMV	7M254	1954	£1.50	£4	
Walk Hand In Hand	7"	HMV	7M414	1956	£2.50	£6	chart single
Walk Hand In Hand	7"	HMV	7MC41	1956	£4	£8	export
What's The Time In Nicaragua	7"	HMV	7M320	1955	£1.50	£4	

MARTIN, TRADE
Title	Format	Label	Catalogue	Year	Price	Price	Notes
Hula Hula Dancin' Doll	7"	London	HL9662	1963	£1.50	£4	

MARTIN, VINCE & THE TARRIERS
Title	Format	Label	Catalogue	Year	Price	Price	Notes
Cindy Oh Cindy	7"	London	HLN8340	1956	£10	£20	

MARTINDALE, WINK
Title	Format	Label	Catalogue	Year	Price	Price	Notes
Black Land Farmer	7"	London	HLD9419	1961	£1.50	£4	
Deck Of Cards	7"	London	HLD8962	1959	£2.50	£6	chart single
Deck Of Cards	7" EP	Dot	DEP20000	1965	£2.50	£6	
Deck Of Cards	7" EP	London	RED1370	1963	£6	£12	
Life Gets Teejus Don't It?	7"	London	HLD9042	1960	£1.50	£4	
Wink Martindale	LP	London	HAD2240	1960	£8	£20	

MARTINO, AL
Title	Format	Label	Catalogue	Year	Price	Price	Notes
Al Martino	LP	Top Rank	BUY030	1960	£4	£10	
Al Martino Sings	7" EP	Capitol	EAP1405	1955	£6	£12	

Come Close To Me	7"	Capitol	CL14379	1955	£5	£10
Darling I Love You	7"	Top Rank	JAR187	1959	£2	£5
Darling I Love You	7" EP	Ember	EMBEP4528	1963	£4	£8
Don't Go To Strangers	7"	Capitol	CL14224	1955	£6	£12
Girl I Left In Rome	7"	Capitol	CL14614	1956	£2.50	£6
Give Me Something To Go On With	7"	Capitol	CL14148	1954	£7.50	£15
I Can't Get You Out Of My Heart	7"	Top Rank	JAR108	1959	£2	£5
I Still Believe	7"	Capitol	CL14192	1954	£6	£12
I'm Sorry	7"	Capitol	CL14680	1957	£2.50	£6
Journey's End	7"	Capitol	CL14550	1956	£2.50	£6
Losing You	7" EP	Capitol	EAP120590	1964	£2	£5
Mama	7"	Top Rank	JAR337	1960	£1.50	£4
Man From Laramie	7"	Capitol	CL14343	1955	£7.50	£15 ... chart single
Not As A Stranger	7"	Capitol	CL14202	1954	£6	£12
Sings Of Love	7" EP	Capitol	EAP42107	1963	£2	£5
Snowy Snowy Mountains	7"	Capitol	CL14284	1955	£6	£12
Story Of Tina	7"	Capitol	CL14163	1954	£7.50	£15 ... chart single
Summertime	7"	Top Rank	JAR312	1960	£1.50	£4
Swing Along	LP	Top Rank	25035	1960	£4	£10
To Please My Lady	7" EP	Capitol	EAP120153	1961	£4	£8
Wanted	7"	Capitol	CL14128	1954	£7.50	£15 ... chart single
Why Do I Love You	7"	Top Rank	JAR418	1960	£1.50	£4

MARTIN'S MAGIC SOUNDS

Martin's Magic Sounds	LP	Deram	DML/SML1014	1968	£4	£10 ... credited to Irving Martin
Mon Amour Mon Amour	7"	Deram	DM141	1967	£1.50	£4

MARTYN, JOHN

John Martyn's first two albums are fairly conventional folk affairs, but his marriage to singer Beverley seemed to make him decide to experiment a little. The two LPs recorded by John and Beverley together are wonderful pieces of folk-rock with the strongly melodic, distinctive songs being enhanced by sympathetic playing from some well-known session names. Thereafter, John Martyn began to explore the sonic possibilities of the amplified guitar, coaxing a range of exciting and unusual sounds from his effects pedals, but without ever abandoning his love of melody. In live performance he was particularly impressive, as a dense wash of echoplexed sound would fill the hall - emanating from a man apparently playing nothing more than an acoustic guitar! This is brilliantly captured on the mock-bootleg "Live At Leeds", which was available in some European record shops, but could only be obtained by mail order from John Martyn himself in the UK.

Bless The Weather	LP	Island	ILPS9167	1971	£5	£12
Classic John Martyn	CD-s	Island	CID265	1986	£6	£15
Dancing	7"	Island	WIP6414	1978	£1.50	£4
Gun Money	7"	WEA	2599877	1982	£1.50	£4
Johnny Too Bad	7"	Island	WIP6547	1980	£1.50	£4
Johnny Too Bad	12"	Island	IPR2046	1981	£2.50	£6
Live At Leeds	LP	Island	ILPS9343	1975	£10	£25
Live At Leeds	LP	Island	ILPS9343	1975	£15	£30 ... autographed
London Conversation	LP	Island	ILP952	1967	£6	£15
May You Never	7"	Island	WIP6116	1971	£1.50	£4
Philentropy	LP	Body Swerve	JMLP001	1983	£4	£10
Tumbler	LP	Island	ILP991/ILPS9091	1968	£6	£15

MARTYN, JOHN & BEVERLEY

John The Baptist	7"	Island	WIP6076	1969	£2	£5
Road To Ruin	LP	Island	ILPS9133	1970	£6	£15
Stormbringer	LP	Island	ILPS9113	1970	£6	£15

MARTYN, KID

In New Orleans With Kid Sheik's Band	LP	77	LA1220	1962	£5	£12

MARVELETTES

As Long As I Know He's Mine	7"	Stateside	SS251	1964	£10	£20
Beechwood 45789	7"	Oriole	CBA1764	1962	£30	£60
Danger Heartbreak Dead Ahead	7"	Tamla Motown	TMG535	1965	£7.50	£15
Don't Mess With Bill	7"	Tamla Motown	TMG546	1966	£10	£20
Finders Keepers, Losers Weepers	7"	Tamla Motown	TMG1000	1975	£6	£12 ... Kim Weston B side
Here I Am Baby	7"	Tamla Motown	TMG659	1968	£2.50	£6
He's A Good Guy	7"	Stateside	SS273	1964	£12.50	£25
Hunter Gets Captured By The Game	7"	Tamla Motown	TMG594	1967	£6	£12
I'll Keep Holding On	7"	Tamla Motown	TMG518	1965	£12.50	£25
In Full Bloom	LP	Tamla Motown	(S)TML11145	1970	£6	£15
Locking Up My Heart	7"	Oriole	CBA1817	1963	£100	£200
Marvelettes	LP	Tamla Motown	(S)TML11052	1967	£15	£30
Marvelettes	7" EP	Tamla Motown	TME2003	1965	£30	£60
Marvellous Marvelettes	LP	Tamla Motown	TML11008	1965	£60	£120
My Baby Must Be A Magician	7"	Tamla Motown	TMG639	1968	£5	£10
Please Mr.Postman	7"	Fontana	H355	1961	£25	£60
Reaching For Something I Can't Have	7"	Tamla Motown	TMG701	1969	£2	£5
Reaching For Something I Can't Have	7"	Tamla Motown	TMG860	1973	£1.50	£4
Reaching For Something I Can't Have/ Magician	7"	Tamla Motown	TMG860	1973	£12.50	£25 ... demo
Sophisticated Soul	LP	Tamla Motown	(S)TML11090	1969	£8	£20
Too Many Fish In The Sea	7"	Stateside	SS369	1965	£10	£20
Twisting Postman	7"	Fontana	H386	1962	£25	£50
When You're Young And In Love	7"	Tamla Motown	TMG609	1967	£2.50	£6 ... chart single
You're My Remedy	7"	Stateside	SS334	1964	£10	£20
You're The One	7"	Tamla Motown	TMG562	1966	£7.50	£15

MARVELOWS

I Do	7"	HMV	POP1433	1965	£6	£12

MARVELS

Keep On Searching	7"	Columbia	DB8341	1968	£4	£8

MARVELS (2)

Angelo	7"	Dice	CC8	1962	£5	£10	
Don't Cry My Love	7"	Dice	CC17	1963	£5	£10	
Sonia	7"	Blue Beat	BB191	1963	£5	£10	

MARVELS FIVE

Don't Play That Song	7"	HMV	POP1452	1965	£1.50	£4	

MARVETTES

I Want A Revival	7"	Tabernacle	TS1001	196-	£2	£5	
It's Revival Time	LP	Coxsone	TLP1002	196-	£50	£100	
Sweet Jesus	7"	Tabernacle	TS1003	196-	£2	£5	

MARVIN & FARRAR

Marvin & Farrar	LP	EMI	EMA755	1973	£4	£10	
Music Makes My Day	7"	EMI	EMI2044	1973	£2	£5	
Small And Lonely Light	7"	EMI	EMI2335	1975	£1.50	£4	

MARVIN & JOHNNY

Cherry Pie	7"	Black Swan	WI467	1965	£5	£10	
Smack Smack	7"	Vogue	V9099	1958	£50	£100	
Yak Yak	7"	Vogue	V9074	1957	£60	£120	

MARVIN, BRETT & THE THUNDERBOLTS

Brett Marvin & The Thunderbolts	LP	Sonet	SNTF616	1970	£4	£10	

MARVIN, HANK

Break Another Dawn	7"	Columbia	DB8693	1970	£2.50	£6	
Goodnight Dick	7"	Columbia	DB8552	1969	£2.50	£6	
Hank Marvin	LP	Columbia	SCX6352	1969	£5	£12	chart LP
Hank Marvin	LP	Columbia	SX6352	1969	£6	£15	mono
London's Not Too Far	7"	Columbia	DB8326	1968	£2.50	£6	Shadows B side
Midnight Cowboy	7"	Columbia	DB8628	1969	£4	£8	Shadows B side
Sacha	7"	Columbia	DB8601	1969	£2.50	£6	

MARVIN, WELCH & FARRAR

Faithful	7"	Regal Zonophone	RZ3030	1971	£1.50	£4	
Lady Of The Morning	7"	Regal Zonophone	RZ3035	1971	£1.50	£4	
Marmaduke	7"	Regal Zonophone	RZ3048	1972	£1.50	£4	
Marvin, Welch & Farrar	LP	Regal Zonophone	SRZA8502	1971	£4	£10	chart LP
Second Opinion	LP	Regal Zonophone	4SRZA8504	1971	£6	£15	quad
Second Opinion	LP	Regal Zonophone	SRZA8504	1971	£5	£12	

MARY BUTTERWORTH

Mary Butterworth	LP	Breeder			£100	£200	US

MARZ & EPERJESSY

Marz And Eperjessy	LP	Bacillus	BLPS19072	1971	£4	£10	German

MARZ, RAINER

Drean Is Over	LP	Bacillus	BLPS19094	1972	£5	£12	German

MASAI

Across The Tracks	7"	Contempo	CS2007	1974	£2.50	£6	

MASCOTS

Hey Little Angel	7"	Pye	7N25189	1963	£2	£5	

MASEKELA, HUGH

Alive And Well At The Whiskey	LP	Uni	UNL(S)101	1968	£4	£10	
And The Union Of South Africa	LP	Rare Earth	SRE3002	1971	£4	£10	
Hugh Masekela	LP	Fontana	SFL13056	1969	£4	£10	

MASKED MARAUDERS

By 1969, if rock music was supposed to have matured into an art form, and its exponents were to be taken as serious musicians, then it went with the territory that the members of various star groups should, in the manner of jazz musicians, start playing on each other's albums. Al Kooper had shown the way by inviting Mike Bloomfield and Steve Stills to participate in the making of his "Super Session" album; Bloomfield had jammed on record with Moby Grape; and groups like Blind Faith and Crosby, Stills and Nash had been set up as a meeting place for star performers. It was against this background that Rolling Stone magazine printed a review of an album by the "Masked Marauders", a title that was apparently a thinly disguised cover for a collaboration between the Beatles, Mick Jagger, and Bob Dylan. The album really exists, too. Whether a joke on Rolling Stone's part inspired someone to actually make the record, or whether the magazine was simply happy to go along with a record comapny joke, is no longer clear. The album, however, is an interesting novelty, even if it becomes obvious fairly quickly that it is the work of impersonators. Despite this, the concept of such a stellar gathering being directed, amongst other tellingly inappropriate choices, towards the production of a version of "I Am The Japanese Sandman" is so delicious, that the record becomes an essential purchase despite itself!

Masked Marauders	LP	Reprise	RS6378	1969	£6	£15	US

MASKED PHANTOM

These Clogs Are Made For Waltzing	7"	Parlophone	R5437	1966	£1.50	£4	

MASKMAN & THE AGENTS

One Eye Open	7"	Direction	584059	1969	£1.50	£4	

MASON

Harbour	LP	Eleventh Hour .	1001	1971	£6	£15	US

| Mason | LP | Dawn | DNLS3050 | 1974 | £5 | £12 | |

MASON, BARBARA

Give Me Your Love	7"	Buddah	2011154	1972	£1.50	£4	
Love's The Thing	LP	Buddah	BDLP4032	1975	£4	£10	
Oh How It Hurts	LP	Action	ACLP6002	1969	£6	£15	
Oh How It Hurts	7"	Direction	583382	1968	£2.50	£6	
Slipping Away	7"	Action	ACT4542	1969	£5	£10	
Transition	LP	Buddah	BDLP4027	1975	£4	£10	
Yes I'm Ready	7"	London	HL9977	1965	£7.50	£15	

MASON, BARRY

| Over The Hills & Far Away | 7" | Deram | DM104 | 1966 | £15 | £30 | |

MASON, BONNIE JO

Cher recorded her tribute to Ringo Starr under this pseudonym.

| Ringo, I Love You | 7" | Annette | 1000 | 1964 | £30 | £60 | US |

MASON, CURTISS

| Monkberry Moon Delight | 7" | Columbia | DB8800 | 1971 | £1.50 | £4 | |

MASON, DAVE

Alone Together	LP	Blue Thumb	BTS19	1970	£5	£12	US, marbled vinyl
Little Woman	7"	Island	WIP6032	1968	£6	£12	
Only You Know And I Know	7"	Harvest	HAR5024	1970	£1.50	£4	
World In Changes	7"	Harvest	HAR5017	1970	£1.50	£4	

MASON, GLEN

Battle Of New Orleans	7"	Parlophone	R4562	1959	£1.50	£4	
Don't Forbid Me	7"	Parlophone	R4271	1957	£2	£5	
End	7"	Parlophone	R4485	1958	£1.50	£4	
Glendora	7"	Parlophone	R4203	1956	£2.50	£6	chart single
Green Door	7"	Parlophone	R4244	1956	£2.50	£6	chart single
Hot Diggity	7"	Parlophone	MSP6240	1956	£4	£8	
I May Never Pass This Way Again	7"	Parlophone	R4415	1958	£1.50	£4	
Round And Round	7"	Parlophone	R4291	1957	£1.50	£4	
That's What I Want	7"	Parlophone	R4723	1960	£1.50	£4	
Why Don't They Understand	7"	Parlophone	R4334	1957	£1.50	£4	
You Got What It Takes	7"	Parlophone	R4626	1960	£1.50	£4	

MASON, JAMES

| Tell Tale Heart | 7" EP | Brunswick | OE9444 | 1959 | £2 | £5 | |

MASON, MARLIN

| Don't Throw My Love Away | 7" | Vogue Coral | Q72168 | 1956 | £1.50 | £4 | |

MASON PROFFIT

| Moving Towards Happiness | LP | Happy Tiger | 1019 | 1970 | £5 | £12 | US |
| Wanted | LP | Happy Tiger | 1009 | 1969 | £6 | £15 | US |

MASON, SPENCER

| Flugel In Carnaby Street | 7" | Parlophone | R5555 | 1967 | £1.50 | £4 | |

MASQUERADERS

| I Ain't Got To Love Nobody Else | 7" | Bell | BLL1032 | 1968 | £1.50 | £4 | |
| Love, Peace And Happiness | 7" | Now | 1001 | 197- | £2 | £5 | |

MASS

| Labour Of Love | LP | 4AD | CAD107 | 1981 | £4 | £10 | |
| You And I | 7" | 4AD | AD14 | 1980 | £2 | £5 | with poster |

MASSED ALBERTS

| Goodbye Dolly | 7" | Parlophone | R5159 | 1964 | £2 | £5 | |

MASTERMINDS

| She Belongs To Me | 7" | Immediate | IM005 | 1965 | £6 | £12 | |

MASTERS

"Breaktime" was co-written by Frank Zappa.

| Breaktime | 7" | Emmy | 10082 | 1962 | £30 | £60 | US |

MASTER'S APPRENTICES

Choice Cuts	LP	Columbia	SCX07903	1971	£25	£50	
I'm Your Satisfier	7"	Regal Zonophone	RZ3031	1971	£10	£20	
Masterpiece	LP	Columbia	SCX07915	1972	£25	£50	
Master's Apprentices	LP	Regal Zonophone	SLRZ1016	1970	£40	£80	
Nickelodeon	LP	Regal Zonophone			£60	£120	
Toast To Panama Red	LP	Regal Zonophone	SLRZ1022	1971	£40	£80	

MASTERS, SAMMY

| Big Man Cried | 7" | London | HLR9949 | 1965 | £2 | £5 | |
| Rocking Red Wing | 7" | Warner Bros | WB10 | 1960 | £7.50 | £15 | chart single |

MASTERS, VALERIE

Christmas Calling	7"	Columbia	DB7426	1964	£5	£10	
Cow Cow Boogie	7"	Fontana	H253	1960	£1.50	£4	
Don't Ever Go	7"	Polydor	56056	1965	£1.50	£4	

MASTERSOUNDS

Title	Format	Label	Catalogue	Year			Notes
Ballads And Blues	LP	Vogue	LAE12223	1960	£4	£10	
In Concert	LP	Vogue	LAE12226	1960	£4	£10	

MATATA

Title	Format	Label	Catalogue	Year			Notes
Good Good Understanding	7"	President	PT438	1975	£1.50	£4	
I Feel Funky	7"	President	PT406	1973	£2.50	£6	
I Wanna Do My Thing	7"	President	PT380	1972	£1.50	£4	
Independence	LP	President	PTLS1057	1975	£10	£25	
Matata	LP	President	PTLS1052	1974	£5	£12	

MATCHING MOLE

Title	Format	Label	Catalogue	Year			Notes
Little Red Record	LP	CBS	65260	1973	£5	£12	
Matching Mole	LP	CBS	64850	1972	£4	£10	
O Caroline	7"	CBS	8101	1972	£2.50	£6	

MATHEWS, WILSON, DOONAN

Title	Format	Label	Catalogue	Year			Notes
Mathews, Wilson, Doonan	LP	Rola	R009	1981	£5	£12	

MATHIS, COUNTRY JOHNNY

Title	Format	Label	Catalogue	Year			Notes
Country And Western Express No.5	7" EP	Top Rank	JKP2064	1960	£7.50	£15	

MATHIS, JODI

Title	Format	Label	Catalogue	Year			Notes
Mama	7"	Capitol	CL15827	1975	£1.50	£4	

MATHIS, JOHNNY

Title	Format	Label	Catalogue	Year			Notes
Ave Maria	7" EP	Fontana	TFE17064	1958	£2.50	£6	
Away From Home	LP	HMV	CSD1638	1966	£15	£30	stereo
Best Of Everything	7"	Fontana	H218	1959	£1.50	£4	chart single
Certain Smile	LP	Columbia	CL1194	1958	£8	£20	US
Certain Smile	7"	Fontana	H142	1958	£1.50	£4	chart single
Chances Are	7"	Philips	JK1029	1957	£5	£10	
Christmas With Johnny Mathis	7" EP	Fontana	TFE17162	1958	£2.50	£6	
Come To Me	7" EP	Fontana	TFE17039	1958	£2.50	£6	
Eli Eli	7"	Fontana	TFE17282	1960	£2	£5	
Faithfully	LP	Fontana	STFL522	1960	£6	£15	stereo
Faithfully	LP	Fontana	TFL5084	1960	£5	£12	
Four Hits	7" EP	Fontana	TFE17275	1960	£2	£5	
Gina	7"	CBS	AAG117	1962	£1.50	£4	pic insert
Good Night Dear Lord	LP	Columbia	CL1119	1958	£8	£20	US
Greatest Hits	LP	Fontana	TFL5058	1959	£5	£12	
Handful Of Stars	7" EP	Fontana	TFE17091	1958	£2.50	£6	
Heavenly	LP	Fontana	TFL5023	1958	£6	£15	
I'll Be Seeing You	7" EP	Fontana	TFE17283	1960	£2	£5	
I'll Buy You A Star	LP	Fontana	TFL5134/STFL557	1961	£5	£12	chart LP
It's De Lovely	7" EP	Fontana	STFE8001	1960	£4	£8	stereo
It's De Lovely	7" EP	Fontana	TFE17194	1959	£2	£5	
Johnny Mathis	LP	Fontana	TFL5011	1957	£6	£15	
Johnny Mathis	7" EP	Fontana	TFE17011	1958	£2.50	£6	
Johnny Mathis	7" EP	Philips	BBE12156	1957	£5	£10	
Johnny's Moods	LP	Fontana	TFL5117/STFL545	1961	£5	£12	
Let Me Love You	7" EP	Fontana	TFE17025	1958	£2.50	£6	
Like Someone In Love	7" EP	Fontana	STFE8018	1960	£4	£8	stereo
Like Someone In Love	7" EP	Fontana	TFE17285	1960	£2	£5	
Live It Up	LP	Fontana	TFL5177/STFL589	1962	£5	£12	
Love Is Everything	LP	HMV	CLP/CSD3522	1966	£4	£10	
Meet Mister Mathis	7" EP	Fontana	TFE17177	1959	£2.50	£6	
Merry Christmas	LP	Fontana	TFL5031/STFL506	1958	£6	£15	
Misty	7"	Fontana	H219	1959	£1.50	£4	chart single
More Greatest Hits	LP	Fontana	STFL517	1960	£6	£15	stereo
More Greatest Hits	LP	Fontana	TFL5083	1960	£5	£12	
My Love For You	7"	Fontana	H267	1960	£1.50	£4	PS, chart single
Ole	LP	HMV	CSD1578	1965	£20	£40	stereo
Open Fire, Two Guitars	LP	Fontana	TFL5050/STFL515	1959	£6	£15	
Portrait Of Johnny	LP	Fontana	TFL5153/STFL571	1961	£5	£12	
Rhythms And Ballads Of Broadway	LP	Fontana	SET(S)101	1960	£8	£20	chart LP, double
Ride On A Rainbow	LP	Fontana	STFL516	1960	£6	£15	stereo
Ride On A Rainbow	LP	Fontana	TFL5061	1960	£5	£12	
Shadow Of Your Smile	LP	HMV	CLP/CSD3556	1966	£4	£10	
So Nice	7" EP	Fontana	STFE8000	1960	£4	£8	stereo
So Nice	7" EP	Fontana	TFE17215	1960	£2	£5	
Sounds Of Christmas	LP	HMV	CLP1696/CSD1521	1964	£4	£10	
Swing Low	7" EP	Fontana	TFE17089	1958	£2.50	£6	
Swing Softly	LP	Fontana	TFL5039/STFL500	1959	£6	£15	chart LP
Teacher Teacher	7"	Fontana	H130	1958	£1.50	£4	chart single
Tender Is The Night	LP	HMV	CLP1721	1964	£4	£10	
Tender Is The Night	LP	HMV	CSD1535	1964	£5	£12	stereo
Tenderly	7" EP	Fontana	TFE17281	1960	£2	£5	
There Goes My Heart	7" EP	Fontana	TFE17088	1958	£2.50	£6	
This Is Love	LP	HMV	CSD1600	1965	£6	£15	stereo
Twelfth Of Never	7" EP	Fontana	TFE17056	1958	£2.50	£6	
Warm	LP	Fontana	TFL5015/STFL510	1958	£6	£15	chart LP
While We're Young	7" EP	Fontana	TFE17047	1958	£2.50	£6	
Wild Is The Wind	LP	Columbia	CL1090	1957	£15	£30	US
Wild Is The Wind	7"	Fontana	H103	1957	£2	£5	
Winter Wonderland	7"	Fontana	H165	1958	£1.50	£4	chart single
Wonderful Wonderful	LP	Fontana	TFL5003	1957	£6	£15	
Wonderful World Of Make Believe	LP	HMV	CSD1553	1965	£8	£20	stereo
Your Teenage Dreams	7"	HMV	POP1217	1963	£2.50	£6	export, PS

MATTHEWS, IAN
If You Saw Through My Eyes	LP	Vertigo	6360034	1971	£6	£15	spiral label
Matthews Southern Comfort	LP	Uni	UNLS108	1970	£6	£15	
Tigers Will Survive	LP	Vertigo	6360056	1972	£6	£15	spiral label
Valley Hi	LP	Elektra	K42144	1973	£5	£12	

MATTHEWS, JOE
Sorry Ain't Good Enough	7"	Sue	WI4046	1968	£12.50	£25	

MATTHEWS' SOUTHERN COMFORT
Second Spring	LP	Uni	UNLS112	1970	£4	£10	chart LP

MATTHEWS, WINSTON
Sun Is Shining	7"	Banana	BA329	1971	£2	£5	Inn Keepers B side

MATUSOW, HARVEY JEWS HARP BAND
Afghan Red	7"	Head	HEAD4004	1969	£2	£5	
War Between The Fats And The Thins	LP	Head	HDLS6001	1969	£10	£25	

MAUDS
Hold On	LP	Mercury	MG2/SR61135	1967	£5	£12	US
Hold On	7"	Mercury	MF1000	1967	£2	£5	
Soul Drippin'	7"	Mercury	MF1062	1968	£1.50	£4	

MAUGHAN, SUSAN
Bobby's Girl	LP	Wing	WL1105	1965	£4	£10	
Bobby's Girl	7"	Philips	326544BF	1962	£1.50	£4	chart single
Cable Car For Two	7"	Philips	BF1713	1968	£1.50	£4	
Come And Get It	7"	Philips	BF1495	1966	£1.50	£4	
Don't Go Home	7"	Philips	BF1564	1967	£1.50	£4	
Effervescent Miss Maughan	7" EP	Philips	433621BE	1962	£5	£10	
Four Beaux And A Belle	7" EP	Philips	BE12549	1963	£6	£12	
Hand A Handkerchief To Helen	7"	Philips	326562BF	1963	£1.50	£4	
Hey Look Me Over	LP	Fontana	SFL13135	1969	£4	£10	chart single
Hey Lover	7"	Philips	BF1301	1964	£1.50	£4	
Hi I'm Susan Maughan & I Sing	7" EP	Philips	BBE12525	1962	£5	£10	
I Can't Make You Love Me	7"	Spark	SRL1049	1971	£1.50	£4	
I Didn't Mean What I Said	7"	Philips	326533BF	1962	£1.50	£4	
I Remember Loving You	7"	Philips	BF1679	1968	£1.50	£4	
I Wanna Be Bobby's Girl But...	LP	Philips	632300BL	1963	£8	£20	
Kiss Me Sailor	7"	Philips	BF1336	1964	£1.50	£4	
Make Him Mine	7"	Philips	BF1382	1964	£1.50	£4	
Mama Do The Twist	7"	Philips	BF1216	1961	£1.50	£4	
More Of Susan Maughan	7" EP	Philips	433641BE	1963	£6	£12	
Poor Boy	7"	Philips	BF1445	1965	£1.50	£4	
Sentimental Susan	LP	Philips	BL7637	1965	£5	£12	
She's New To You	7"	Philips	326586BF	1963	£1.50	£4	
Some Of These Days	7"	Philips	BF1236	1961	£1.50	£4	
Swingin' Susan	LP	Philips	BL7577	1964	£5	£12	
That Other Place	7"	Philips	BF1363	1964	£10	£20	
To Him	7"	Philips	BF1619	1967	£1.50	£4	
Verdict Is Guilty	7"	Philips	BF1266	1963	£1.50	£4	
We Really Go Together	7"	Philips	BF1824	1969	£1.50	£4	
When She Walks Away	7"	Philips	BF1417	1965	£1.50	£4	
Where The Bullets Fly	7"	Philips	BF1518	1966	£1.50	£4	
You Can Never Get Away From Me	7"	Philips	BF1399	1965	£1.50	£4	

MAUREENY WISHFUL
Maureeny Wishful	LP	Moonshine	WO2388	1968	£50	£100	

MAURICE & MAC
Why Don't You Try Me	7"	Chess	CRS8081	1968	£2.50	£6	
You Left The Water Running	7"	Chess	CRS8074	1968	£2.50	£6	

MAX CREEK
Drink The Stars	LP	Wranger			£15	£30	US double

MAX WEBSTER
High Class And Borrowed Shoes	LP	Anthem	ANR1007	1977	£5	£12	Canadian
Max Webster	LP	Anthem	ANR1006	1975	£5	£12	Canadian

MAXI
Do I Dream	7"	Decca	F13394	1973	£2	£5	

MAXIMILIAN
Snake	7"	London	HLX9356	1961	£12.50	£25	

MAXIM'S TRASH
Disco Girls	7"	Gimp	GIMP1	1979	£15	£30	

MAXIMUM BAND
Cupid	7"	Fab	FAB51	1968	£4	£8	

MAXIN, ERNEST
Four Walls	7"	Parlophone	R4319	1957	£1.50	£4	

MAXWELL, DIANE
Almost Seventeen	LP	Challenge	CHL607/CHS2501	1959	£5	£12	US

MAXWELL, HOLLY
Suffer	7"	Buddah	201056	1969	£1.50	£4	

MAY, BILLY

Arthur Murray Cha Cha Mambos Pt.1	7" EP	Capitol	EAP1578	1955	£2	£5	
Arthur Murray Cha Cha Mambos Pt.2	7" EP	Capitol	EAP2578	1955	£2	£5	
Dixieland Band	7" EP	Tempo	EXA4	1955	£2.50	£6	
Floater	7"	Capitol	CL14671	1956	£1.50	£4	
Hernando's Hideaway	7"	Capitol	CL14353	1955	£1.50	£4	
How Important Can It Be?	7"	Capitol	CL14266	1955	£1.50	£4	
It's Billy May Time	7" EP	Capitol	EAP1013	1956	£2.50	£6	
Making Whoopee	7" EP	Capitol	EAP20064	1960	£2	£5	
Man With The Golden Arm	7"	Capitol	CL14551	1956	£1.50	£4	chart single
More May	7" EP	Capitol	EAP1536	1955	£2	£5	
Nightmare	7"	Capitol	CL14609	1956	£2	£5	
Rudolph The Red Nosed Reindeer Mambo	7"	Capitol	CL14210	1954	£1.50	£4	
Shaner Maidel	7"	Capitol	CL14308	1955	£1.50	£4	
Sorta Dixie No.1	7" EP	Capitol	EAP1677	1957	£2	£5	
Sorta Dixie No.2	7" EP	Capitol	EAP2677	1957	£2	£5	
Sorta Dixie No.3	7" EP	Capitol	EAP3677	1957	£2	£5	
Sorta May Pt.1	7" EP	Capitol	EAP1562	1955	£2	£5	
Sorta May Pt.2	7" EP	Capitol	EAP2562	1955	£2	£5	
Sorta May Pt.3	7" EP	Capitol	EAP3562	1955	£2	£5	
Whatever Lola Wants	7"	Capitol	CL14713	1957	£1.50	£4	

MAY BLITZ

May Blitz	LP	Vertigo	6360007	1970	£15	£30	spiral label
Second Of May	LP	Vertigo	6360037	1971	£30	£60	spiral label

MAY, BRIAN

Driven By You	CD-s	Parlophone		1991	£10	£25	4 track promo
Starfleet	7"	EMI	EMI5436	1983	£2	£5	
Starfleet Project	LP	EMI	SFLT1078061	1983	£5	£12	
Who Wants To Live Forever	7"	Odeon	ODO112	1989	£2	£5	
Who Wants To Live Forever	12"	Odeon	12ODO112	1989	£6	£15	

MAY, PHIL

Phil May & The Fallen Angels	LP	Philips	6410969	1978	£4	£10	Dutch

MAYALL, JOHN

The various editions of the Bluesbreakers that John Mayall led during the sixties were an extraordinary training-ground for many of the more influential musicians of that time. Cream, Fleetwood Mac, the Aynsley Dunbar Retaliation, the Keef Hartley Band, Colosseum, Free, Mark-Almond, Stone The Crows, and even the Rolling Stones were all staffed by Mayall alumni. By placing a premium on instrumental prowess, but at the same time managing to place many of his albums among the best-sellers, John Mayall was of crucial importance in the growing maturity of rock music generally. He was never really a singles artist, however, and his original 45rpm releases have become quite scarce. All the songs are actually available on LP, but it should be noted that the version of "Double Trouble" included on the stereo pressing of "Looking Back" lacks the echo that helps to make the lead guitar part on the single into one of Peter Green's finest performances. (The mono "Looking Back" retains the echo in all its glory).

Back To The Roots	LP	Polydor	2657005	1971	£6	£15	double, chart LP
Banquet In Blues	LP	ABC	ABCL5187	1976	£4	£10	chart LP
Bare Wires	LP	Decca	LK/SKL4945	1968	£6	£15	chart LP
Bear	7"	Decca	F12846	1968	£2	£5	
Blues Alone	LP	Ace Of Clubs	ACL/SCL1243	1967	£4	£10	chart LP
Blues From Laurel Canyon	LP	Decca	LK/SKL4972	1969	£6	£15	chart LP
Bluesbreakers	LP	Decca	LK4804	1966	£6	£15	chart LP
Crawling Up A Hill	7"	Decca	F11900	1964	£10	£20	
Crocodile Walk	7"	Decca	F12120	1965	£7.50	£15	
Crusade	LP	Decca	LK/SKL4890	1967	£6	£15	chart LP
Diary Of A Band Vol.1	LP	Decca	LK/SKL4918	1968	£6	£15	chart LP
Diary Of A Band Vol.2	LP	Decca	LK/SKL4919	1968	£6	£15	chart LP
Don't Waste My Time	7"	Polydor	56544	1970	£2.50	£6	
Double Trouble	7"	Decca	F12621	1967	£5	£10	
Empty Rooms	LP	Polydor	583580	1970	£6	£12	
Hard Road	LP	Decca	LK/SKL4853	1967	£6	£15	chart LP
I'm Your Witchdoctor	7"	Immediate	IM012	1965	£10	£20	
I'm Your Witchdoctor	7"	Immediate	IM051	1967	£7.50	£15	
Jazz Blues Fusion	LP	Polydor	2425103	1972	£5	£12	
Jenny	7"	Decca	F12732	1968	£4	£8	
John Mayall Plays John Mayall	LP	Decca	LK4680	1965	£10	£25	
John Mayall's Bluesbreakers With Paul Butterfield	7" EP	Decca	DFER8673	1967	£6	£12	
Lonely Years	7"	Purdah	453502	1966	£25	£50	chart LP
Looking Back	LP	Decca	LK/SKL5010	1970	£5	£12	
Looking Back	7"	Decca	F12506	1966	£4	£8	
Looking Back	7" EP	Decca	457030	1964	£10	£20	French
Memories	LP	Polydor	2425085	1971	£6	£12	
No Reply	7"	Decca	F12792	1968	£2	£5	
Parchman Farm	7"	Decca	F12490	1966	£4	£8	
Sitting In The Rain	7"	Decca	F12545	1967	£4	£8	
So Many Roads	LP	Decca	SLK16590P	1970	£8	£20	
Suspicions	7"	Decca	F12684	1967	£4	£8	
Thinking Of My Woman	7"	Polydor	2066021	1971	£2	£5	
Through The Years	LP	Decca	SKL5086	1971	£5	£12	
Turning Point	LP	Polydor	583571	1970	£5	£12	chart LP
USA Union	LP	Polydor	2425020	1970	£5	£12	chart LP

MAYER, JOHN

Acka Raga	7"	Columbia	DB8037	1966	£4	£8	
Etudes	LP	Sonet	SNTF603	1969	£8	£20	
Indo-Jazz Fusions	LP	Columbia	SX/SCX6122	1967	£15	£30	
Indo-Jazz Fusions II	LP	Columbia	SX/SCX6215	1968	£15	£30	
Radha Krishna	LP	Columbia		1971	£15	£30	

MAYER, NATHANIEL

Going Back To The Village Of Love	LP	Fortune	8014	1964	£8	£20	US
Village Of Love	7"	HMV	POP1041	1962	£7.50	£15	

MAYFIELD, CURTIS

Back To The World	LP	Buddah	2318085	1973	£5	£12	
Curtis	LP	Buddah	2318015	1971	£6	£15	
Curtis Live	LP	Buddah	2659005	1971	£6	£15	double
Curtis Live	LP	Buddah	BDLP2001	1974	£5	£12	double
Early Years	LP	Probe	GTSP201	1973	£5	£12	
If There's A Hell Below	7"	Buddah	2011055	1970	£1.50	£4	
Keep On Keeping On	7"	Buddah	2011119	1972	£1.50	£4	
Move On Up	7"	Buddah	2011080	197-	£1.50	£4	black label
Move On Up	7"	Buddah	2011080	1971	£2	£5	multi-coloured label, chart single
Move On Up	7"	Buddah	BDS410	1974	£1.50	£4	
Roots	LP	Buddah	2318045	1972	£5	£12	
Superfly	LP	Buddah	2318065	1972	£5	£12	chart LP
Sweet Exorcist	LP	Buddah	2318099	1974	£5	£12	
We Got To Have Peace	7"	Buddah	2011101	1971	£1.50	£4	

MAYFIELD, PERCY

Bought Blues	LP	Tangerine	TRC1510	1969	£4	£10	
My Jug And I	LP	HMV	CLP/CSD3572	1967	£5	£12	
Percy Mayfield	LP	Tangerine	TRC1505	1969	£5	£12	
River's Invitation	7"	HMV	POP1185	1963	£4	£8	

MAYFIELD'S MULE

Mayfield's Mule included Andy Scott who was later a member of the Sweet.

Double Dealing Woman	7"	Parlophone	R5817	1969	£7.50	£15	
I See A River	7"	Parlophone	R5843	1970	£4	£8	
We Go Rollin'	7"	Parlophone	R5858	1970	£4	£8	

MAYHEM

Bloodrush	12"	Vigilante	VIG1T	1985	£2.50	£6	

MAYL, GENE

Dixieland Rhythm Kings	LP	London	LTZU15069	1957	£6	£15	
Dixieland Rhythm Kings	10" LP	London	HAPB1037	1955	£6	£15	

MAYPOLE

Maypole	LP	Colossus		1970	£8	£20	US

MAYTALS

54-46, That's My Number	7"	Trojan	TR7726	1969	£2	£5	
54-46 Was My Number	7"	Pyramid	PYR6030	1968	£4	£8	Roland Alphonso B side
Aldina	7"	Pyramid	PYR6070	1969	£2.50	£6	
Another Chance	7"	R&B	JB141	1964	£5	£10	Frankie Anderson B side
Bam Bam	7"	Doctor Bird	DB1038	1966	£5	£10	
Bim Today Bam Tomorrow	7"	Pyramid	PYR6050	1968	£4	£8	
Bla Bla Bla	7"	Trojan	TR7741	1970	£1.50	£4	
Christmas Feelings	7"	Ska Beat	JB174	1964	£5	£10	
Country Road	7"	Dragon	DRA1013	1973	£2	£5	
Do The Reggay	7"	Pyramid	PYR6057	1968	£4	£8	Beverley's Allstars B side
Dog War	7"	Blue Beat	BB231	1963	£5	£10	Rico B side
Don't Trouble Trouble	7"	Pyramid	6066	1969	£4	£8	
Don't Trouble Trouble	7"	Pyramid	PYR6066	1969	£2.50	£6	Beverley's Allstars
Everytime	7"	Island	WI102	1963	£5	£10	Tommy McCook B side
Fever	7"	Dragon	DRA1021	1974	£2	£5	
From The Roots	LP	Trojan	TRLS65	1973	£4	£10	
Funky Kingston	LP	Dragon	DRLS5002	1973	£4	£10	
Funky Kingston	LP	Island	ILPS9186	1973	£4	£10	
Give Me Your Love	7"	R&B	JB153	1964	£5	£10	
Hallelujah	7"	Blue Beat	BB176	1963	£5	£10	
He Is Real	7"	Blue Beat	BB215	1963	£5	£10	
Hurry Up	7"	R&B	JB130	1963	£5	£10	
In The Dark	LP	Dragon	DRLS5004	1974	£4	£10	
In The Dark	LP	Island	ILPS9231	1974	£4	£10	
In The Dark	7"	Dragon	DRA1016	1973	£2	£5	
I've Got A Pain	7"	Blue Beat	BB220	1963	£5	£10	Buster's Allstars B side
John And James	7"	Black Swan	WI464	1965	£4	£8	Theo Beckford B side
Joy And Jean	7"	Ska Beat	JB202	1965	£5	£10	
Judgement Day	7"	Blue Beat	BB255	1964	£5	£10	
Just Tell Me	7"	Pyramid	PYR6048	1968	£4	£8	
Light Of The World	7"	Blue Beat	BB299	1964	£5	£10	
Little Flea	7"	Blue Beat	BB245	1963	£5	£10	
Looking Down The Street	7"	Blue Beat	BB281	1964	£5	£10	Buster's Allstars B side
Louie Louie	7"	Trojan	TR7865	1972	£1.50	£4	
Man Who Knows	7"	R&B	JB161	1964	£5	£10	
Marching On	7"	Banana	BA340	1971	£2	£5	Roland Alphonso B side
Marching On	7"	R&B	JB150	1964	£5	£10	Lester Sterling B side
Matthew Mark	7"	R&B	JB103	1963	£5	£10	Don Drummond B side

531

Title	Format	Label	Cat No	Year			Notes
Millie	7"	Blue Beat	BB221	1963	£5	£10	
Monkey Man	LP	Trojan	TBL107	1970	£6	£15	
Monkey Man	7"	Trojan	TR7711	1969	£2.50	£6	chart single
My Darling	7"	Ska Beat	JB237	1966	£5	£10	Charmers B side
My New Name	7"	Island	WI213	1965	£5	£10	
Never Grow Old	LP	R&B	JBL1113	1964	£50	£100	
Never You Change	7"	Island	WI200	1965	£5	£10	
Original Golden Oldies Vol.3	LP	Prince Buster	PB11	1974	£6	£15	
Peeping Tom	7"	Summit	SUM8510	1970	£1.50	£4	Beverley's Allstars B side
Pressure Drop	7"	Pyramid	PYR6073	1969	£2.50	£6	Beverley's Allstars
Pressure Drop	7"	Trojan	TR7709	1969	£2.50	£6	Beverley's Allstars B side
Redemption Song	7"	Dynamic	DYN438	1972	£2.50	£6	
Sailing On	7"	Dragon	DRA1026	1974	£2	£5	
Scare Him	7"	Pyramid	PYR6064	1969	£2.50	£6	
Schooldays	7"	Pyramid	PYR6055	1968	£4	£8	
Sensational Maytals	LP	Doctor Bird	DLM5003	1966	£50	£100	
She's My Scorcher	7"	Trojan	TR7757	1970	£1.50	£4	
Shining Light	7"	R&B	JB155	1964	£5	£10	Lester Sterling B side
Sit Right Down	7"	Dragon	DRA1007	1973	£2	£5	
Ska War	7"	Blue Beat	BB306	1964	£5	£10	Skatalites B side
Struggle	7"	Pyramid	PYR6043	1968	£4	£8	Roland Alphonso B side
Sun, Moon And Stars	7"	Trojan	TR7768	1970	£1.50	£4	
Sweet And Dandy	7"	Pyramid	PYR6074	1969	£2.50	£6	
Tell Me The Reason	7"	Island	WI219	1965	£5	£10	Philip James B side
Time Tough	7"	Dragon	DRA1024	1974	£2	£5	
We Shall Overcome	7"	Pyramid	PYR6052	1968	£4	£8	Desmond Dekker B side
You Got Me Spinning	7"	Blue Beat	BB270	1964	£5	£10	

MAYTONES
Billy Goat	7"	Blue Cat	BS149	1968	£4	£8	
Botheration	7"	Blue Cat	BS165	1969	£4	£8	GG Rhythm Section B side
Copper Girl	7"	Blue Cat	BS166	1969	£4	£8	
Loving Reggae	7"	Blue Cat	BS152	1969	£4	£8	
Mi Nah Tek You Lick	7"	Blue Cat	BS173	1969	£4	£8	

MAZE
Ian Paice and Roger Evans of Maze were soon to experience a considerable change of fortune (albeit short-lived in the case of Evans), as they were recruited by Ritchie Blackmore as founder members of Deep Purple.

Catari Catari	7"	MGM	MGM1368	1967	£10	£20	
Hello Stranger	7"	Reaction	591009	1966	£25	£50	
In Special Danse Discotheque	7" EP.	Vogue	INT18136	1967	£50	£100	French

MAZE (2)
Armageddon	LP	MTA	5012	1971	£15	£30	US

MC5
Back In The USA	LP	Atlantic	2400016	1970	£8	£20	
Back In The USA	LP	Atlantic	K50346	1977	£4	£10	
High Time	LP	Atlantic	K40223	1971	£8	£20	
I Can Only Give You Everything	7"	AMG	1001	1966	£15	£30	US
Kick Out The Jams	LP	Elektra	EKL/EKS74042	1969	£8	£20	
Kick Out The Jams	LP	Elektra	EKS74042	1969	£20	£40	US, uncensored intro
Kick Out The Jams	LP	Elektra	K42027	1977	£4	£10	
Kick Out The Jams	7"	Elektra	EKSN45056	1968	£6	£12	
Looking At You	7"	A-Square	333	1967	£15	£30	US
Ramblin' Rose	7"	Elektra	EKSN45067	1969	£6	£12	

MCALOON, SEAN & JOHN REA
Drops Of Brandy	LP	Topic	12TS287	1976	£5	£12	

MCARTHUR, NEIL
Immediately after the demise of the Zombies, lead singer Colin Blunstone adopted a new stage name, Neil McArthur, and recorded a new version of the Zombies best known song, "She's Not There". The new interpretation is dramatically different from the original, even while keeping the same tempo. Few people were fooled by the name change, however, for Blunstone's breathy singing voice is very distinctive. Before long he was back using his own name.

Don't Try To Explain	7"	Deram	DM262	1969	£2	£5	
It's Not Easy	7"	Deram	DM275	1969	£2	£5	
She's Not There	7"	Deram	DM225	1969	£2	£5	chart single

MCAULEY, JACKIE
Jackie McAuley	LP	Dawn	DNLS3023	1971	£10	£25	
Rocking Shoes	7"	Dawn	DNS1020	1971	£2	£5	

MCAULIFF, LEON
Cozy Inn	LP	ABC	(S)394	1961	£6	£15	U
Take Off	LP	Dot	DLP3139	1958	£6	£15	U

MCBEATH, JIMMY
Come A'Ye Tramps And Hawkers	7" EP.	Collector	JES10	1961	£2	£5	
Wild Rover No More	LP	Topic	12T173	1967	£5	£12	

MCBRIDE, OWEN
Owen McBride	LP	Philo	1005	1973	£6	£15	U

MCCAFFERTY, DAN
Stay With Me Baby	7"	Mountain	DAN1	1978	£1.50	£4	P

MCCAIN, JERRY
Homogenised Love .... 7" .... Python .... 02 .... 1969 ... £10 ....£20

MCCALL, CASH
Anytime .... 7" .... Ember .... EMBS173 .... 1963 ... £4 ....£8
It's Wonderful .... 7" .... Chess .... CRS8056 .... 1967 ... £2.50 ....£6
Many Are The Words .... 7" .... Ember .... EMBS204 .... 1965 ... £4 ....£8

MCCALL, DARRELL
My Kind Of Lovin' .... 7" .... Capitol .... CL15196 .... 1961 ... £1.50 ....£4

MCCALL, TOUSSAINT
Nothing Takes The Place Of You .... 7" .... Pye .... 7N25420 .... 1967 ... £5 ....£10

MCCALLUM, DAVID
Communication .... 7" .... Capitol .... CL15439 .... 1966 ... £2.50 ....£6 ....chart single
In The Garden .... 7" .... Capitol .... CL15474 .... 1966 ... £1.50 ....£4
Music...A Bit More Of Me ..... LP .... Capitol .... (S)T2498 .... 1966 ... £5 ....£12
Music...A Part Of Me ..... LP .... Capitol .... (S)T2432 .... 1966 ... £5 ....£12

MCCALMANS
Audience With The McCalmans .... LP .... RCA .... LSA3179 .... 1973 ... £5 ....£12
McCalmans Folk .... LP .... One Up .... OU2161 .... 1968 ... £5 ....£12
Turn Again .... LP .... CBS .... 64145 .... 1970 ... £6 ....£15

MCCANDLESS, BILL
Jim .... 7" .... Decca .... F12008 .... 1964 ... £1.50 ....£4

MCCANN, JIM
McCanned! .... LP .... Polydor .... 2489053 .... 1973 ... £20 ....£40

MCCANN, LES
Bucket O'Grease .... 7" .... Mercury .... MF973 .... 1966 ... £2 ....£5
Much Les .... LP .... Atlantic .... 588176 .... 1969 ... £4 ....£10
Truth .... LP .... Vogue .... LAE12238 .... 1960 ... £6 ....£15

MCCANN, MARIE
Remember Me To Jimmy .... 7" .... Philips .... PB1211 .... 1961 ... £1.50 ....£4

MCCARTHY
In Purgatory .... 7" .... Wall Of Salmon .... MAC001 .... 1986 ... £6 ....£12

MCCARTHY, KEITH
Everybody Rude Now .... 7" .... Coxsone .... CS7014 .... 1967 ... £5 ....£10

MCCARTHY, LYN & GRAHAM
I Think It's Going To Rain .... 7" .... Columbia .... DB8422 .... 1968 ... £1.50 ....£4

MCCARTHY, MARY
Easy Kind Of Love .... 7" .... CBS .... 2832 .... 1967 ... £1.50 ....£4

MCCARTNEY, CECIL
Om .... LP .... Columbia .... SX/SCX6283 .... 1968 ... £5 ....£12

MCCARTNEY, PAUL
Some of Paul McCartney's more unusual records have been released under pseudonyms - The Country Hams, Suzy & The Redstripes, Percy "Thrills" Thrillington, and the Fireman. Rarities issued under his own name include a series of lavish packages promoting various of his album releases. Most collectable of these is the picture disc version of "Back To The Egg", which has aquired legendary status. (The regular issue of the album is, of course, quite common and not at all collectable). The rare version of the Apple single R5999, it should be mentioned, has 'Sally G' as the A side; there is nothing special about copies with 'Junior's Farm' on the A side. The first edition of the Price Guide included the LP "CHOBA B CCCP" in its McCartney section. This was a collection of rock'n'roll cover versions that Paul McCartney decided to issue in Russia only. The first copies to be seen in the UK were eagerly snapped up by collectors at a much higher price than they were worth. Over the succeeding months more and more copies turned up and the prices took a nose-dive - today one can hardly give copies of the record away. The album has now been issued in the UK, but on CD only.

Back To The Egg .... LP .... Parlophone ...... PCTC257 .... 1979 ... £100 ....£200 ....promo, boxed
Back To The Egg .... LP .... Parlophone ...... PCTCP257 .... 1979 ... £840 ......£1200 ....promo, pic disc
Band On The Run .... LP .... Capitol ...... SEAX11901 .... 1978 ... £10 ....£25 ....US pic disc
Band On The Run .... LP .... Columbia ...... HC36482 .... 1981 ... £8 ....£20 ....US audiophile
Band On The Run Interview Album ..... LP .... Apple ...... SPRO2955/6 .... 1974 ... £20 ....£40 ....US promo
Boxed Set Of 9 Promo Singles ..... 7" .... Parlophone ...... PMBOX1 .... 1986 ... £75 ....£150 numbered and signed
Brung To Ewe By Ram .... LP .... Apple ...... SPRO6210 .... 1971 ... £15 ....£30 ....US 1 sided interview promo
Give Ireland Back To The Irish .... 7" .... Apple ...... R5936 .... 1972 ... £2 ....£5 ....shamrock sleeve
Good Sign .... 12" .... Parlophone ...... GOOD1 .... 1989 ... £15 ....£30 ....promo
I've Had Enough .... 7" .... Parlophone ...... R6020 .... 1978 ... £2 ....£5 ....PS
McCartney .... r-reel . Apple ...... TAPMC7102 .... 1970 ... £20 ....£40 ....mono
McCartney .... r-reel . Apple ...... TDPCS7102 .... 1970 ... £8 ....£20 ....stereo
McCartney .... LP .... Apple ...... PCS7102 .... 1970 ... £20 ....£40 ....promo with interview sheets
McCartney Interview .... LP .... Columbia ...... A2S821 .... 1980 ... £50 ....£100 ....US promo double with book
Mull Of Kintyre .... 7" .... Capitol ...... R6018 .... 1977 ... £6 ....£12 ....blue vinyl test pressing
No More Lonely Nights .... 12" .... Parlophone ...... 12PR6080 .... 1984 ... £2.50 ....£6 ....pic disc
No More Lonely Nights (Arthur Baker Remix) ..... 12" .... Parlophone ...... 12RA6080 .... 1984 ... £10 ....£25
No More Lonely Nights (Mole Mix) ..... 12" .... Parlophone ...... 12R6080DJ .... 1984 ... £30 ....£60 ....1 sided promo
Once Upon A Long Ago .... CD-s .. Parlophone .... 1987 ... £30 ....£60 ....promo, different sleeve

One Upon A Long Ago (Extended Version)	12"	Parlophone	12RX6170	1987	£4	£10	
Party	12"	Parlophone	12RDJ6238	1989	£10	£25	promo
Paul McCartney & Bob Harris Talk About Buddy Holly	LP	MCA	BH1	1983	£10	£25	US promo
Sally G	7"	Apple	R5999	1975	£100	£200	demo
Spies Like Us	7"	Parlophone	RP6118	1985	£4	£8	shaped pic disc
Spies Like Us	12"	Parlophone	12RP6118	1985	£2.50	£6	pic disc
Temporary Secretary	7"	Parlophone	R6039	1980	£10	£20	demo only
Temporary Secretary	12"	Parlophone	12R6039	1980	£4	£10	
This One	7"	Parlophone	RX6223	1989	£2	£5	envelope pack with 6 cards
Tug Of War	LP	Parlophone	PCTC259	1982	£50	£100	promo, press pack, cassette interview
We All Stand Together	7"	Parlophone	RP6086	1984	£2.50	£5	shaped pic disc
Wings Over America	LP	Capitol	SWCO11593	1977	£30	£60	US promo, red white and blue vinyl

MCCARTNEY, PAUL & GEORGE MARTIN
Family Way	LP	Decca	LK/SKL4847	1966	£40	£80	

MCCHURCH SOUNDROOM
Delusion	LP	Pilz	20211037	1971	£30	£60	German

MCCLINTON, DELBERT
Hully Gully	7"	Decca	F11541	1962	£2.50	£6	

MCCLURE, BOBBY
Peak Of Love	7"	Chess	CRS8048	1966	£7.50	£15	

MCCLURE, CHRIS
Answer To Everything	7"	Polydor	56259	1968	£2	£5	
Dying Swan	7"	Decca	F12346	1966	£1.50	£4	
Hazy People	7"	Polydor	56227	1968	£4	£8	
Our Song Of Love	7"	RCA	RCA1849	1969	£1.50	£4	

MCCONNELL, CATHAL
Irish Jubilee	LP	Topic	12TS290	1976	£5	£12	with Robin Morton
On Lough Ernie's Shore	LP	Topic	12TS377	1978	£5	£12	

MCCOOK, TOMMY
Avengers	7"	Unity	UN506	1969	£2.50	£6	Laurel Aitken B side
Black Coffee	7"	Trojan	TR7706	1969	£2.50	£6	Vic Taylor B side
Bridge View	7"	R&B	JB163	1964	£5	£10	Naomi & Co B side
Buck And The Preacher	7"	Pyramid	PYR7002	1973	£2	£5	
Exodus	7"	Port-O-Jam	PJ4001	1964	£5	£10	Lee Perry B side
Indian Love Call	7"	Doctor Bird	DB1053	1966	£5	£10	Owen & Leon B side
Jam Session	7"	Doctor Bird	DB1058	1966	£5	£10	Lloyd & Glen B side
Jerk Time	7"	Rio	R100	1966	£4	£8	Uniques B side
Junior Jive	7"	Island	WI124	1963	£5	£10	Horace Seaton B side
Lock Jaw	7"	Trojan	TR7717	1969	£2.50	£6	Yardbrooms B side
Love Is A Treasure	7"	Duke	DU161	1973	£2	£5	
Moving	7"	Treasure Isle	TI7042	1968	£5	£10	Silvertones B side
Music Is My Occupation	7"	Ska Beat	JB179	1965	£5	£10	Mellodites B side
My Business	7"	Ska Beat	JB178	1965	£5	£10	Don Drummond B side
One Two Three	7"	Island	WI3047	1967	£5	£10	Treasure Isle Boys B side
Our Man Flint	7"	Treasure Isle	TI7039	1968	£5	£10	Silvertones B side
Out Of Space	7"	Rio	R101	1966	£4	£8	Uniques B side
Rub It Down	7"	Technique	TE927	1973	£2	£5	
Saboo	7"	Island	WI3049	1967	£5	£10	Movin Brothers B side
Saboo	7"	Treasure Isle	TI7018	1967	£5	£10	Moving Brothers B side
Saints	7"	Trojan	TR657	1969	£2.50	£6	Soul Ofrous B side
Sampson	7"	R&B	JB139	1964	£5	£10	Roy & Annette B side
Ska Jam	7"	Rio	R103	1966	£4	£8	
Two For One	7"	Black Swan	WI422	1964	£5	£10	Lascelle Perkins B side
Venus	7"	Treasure Isle	TI7032	1968	£5	£10	

MCCOOK, TOMMY & STRANGER COLE
Last Flight To Reggae City	7"	Unity	UN501	1968	£4	£8	Junior Smith B side

MCCORMICK BROTHERS
Authentic Bluegrass Hits	7" EP	Hickory	LPE1509	1966	£5	£10	
Red Hen Boogie	7"	Polydor	NH66986	1963	£15	£30	

MCCOY, BUDD
Hiawatha	7"	RCA	RCA1106	1959	£1.50	£4	

MCCOY, CLYDE
Dancing To The Blues	7" EP	Mercury	MEP9513	1957	£4	£8	

MCCOY, JOE
One In A Hundred	7"	Collector	JDL81	1959	£10	£20	

MCCOY, VAN
Hustle	7"	Avco	6105037	1975	£1.50	£4	

MCCOY, VIOLA

1923-1927	10" LP	Ristic	LP27	195-	£20	£40	

MCCOYS

Beat The Clock	7" EP..	Bang	770005	1966	£7.50	£15	French
Don't Worry Mother	7"	Immediate	IM028	1966	£2	£5	
Fever	7"	Immediate	IM021	1965	£2	£5	chart single
Fever	7" EP..	Atlantic	750007	1965	£7.50	£15	French
Hang On Sloopy	LP	Immediate	IMLP001	1965	£8	£20	
Hang On Sloopy	LP	Joy	JOYS196	1971	£5	£12	
Hang On Sloopy	7"	Immediate	IM001	1965	£2	£5	chart single
Hang On Sloopy	7"	Immediate	IM076	1969	£1.50	£4	
Hang On Sloopy	7" EP..	Barclay	70864	1965	£10	£20	French, B side by Strangeloves
Hang On Sloopy	7" EP..	Barclay	70864	1965	£12.50	£25	French, embossed sleeve, B side by Strangeloves
Human Ball	LP	Mercury	SR61207	1969	£6	£15	US
I Got To Go Back	7"	Immediate	IM046	1967	£2.50	£6	
Infinite McCoys	LP	Mercury	SR61163	1968	£6	£15	US
Jesse Brady	7"	Mercury	MF1067	1968	£2	£5	
McCoys Vol.1	7" EP..	Immediate	IMEP002	1966	£7.50	£15	
McCoys Vol.2	7" EP..	Immediate	IMEP003	1966	£7.50	£15	
Runaway	7"	Immediate	IM034	1966	£2	£5	
Say Those Magic Words	7"	London	HLZ10154	1967	£6	£12	
So Good	7"	Immediate	IM037	1966	£2	£5	
Up And Down	7"	Immediate	IM029	1966	£2	£5	
You Make Me Feel So Good	LP	Bang	BLP(S)213	1966	£6	£15	US

MCCRACKLIN, JIMMY

Best Of Jimmy McCracklin	LP	Minit	LP(2)4009	1967	£4	£10	US
Christmas Time	7"	Outasite	45120	1966	£12.50	£25	
Every Night Every Day	7"	Liberty	LIB66094	1965	£2	£5	
Every Night, Every Day	LP	Imperial	LP9285/12285	1965	£5	£12	US
How Do You Like Your Love	7"	Minit	MLF11003	1968	£2.50	£6	
I Got Eyes For You	7"	R&B	MRB5001	1965	£6	£12	
Just Gotta Know	LP	Stax	8506	1963	£10	£25	US
Jimmy McCracklin	7" EP..	Vocalion	VEP170160	1965	£25	£50	
Jimmy McCracklin Sings	LP	Chess	1464	1961	£15	£30	US
Just Got To Know	7"	Top Rank	JAR617	1962	£6	£12	
Let's Get Together	LP	Minit	LP24011	1968	£4	£10	US
My Answer	LP	Imperial	LP9306/12306	1966	£5	£12	US
New Soul	LP	Imperial	LP9316/12316	1966	£5	£12	US
Pretty Little Sweet Thing	7"	Minit	MLF11009	1968	£2.50	£6	
Stinger Man	LP	Minit	LP24017	1969	£4	£10	US
Think	LP	Imperial	LP9297/12297	1965	£5	£12	US
Think	7"	Liberty	LIB66129	1966	£2	£5	
Walk	7"	London	HL7035	1958	£7.50	£15	export
Walk	7"	London	HLM8598	1958	£15	£30	

MCCRAE, GWEN

It's Worth The Hurt	7"	President	PT416	1974	£1.50	£4	

MCCULLOCH, DANNY

Blackbird	7"	Capitol	CL15607	1969	£1.50	£4	
Wings Of A Man	LP	Capitol	E(S)T174	1969	£4	£10	

MCCULLOCH, GORDEANNA & THE CLUTHA

Sheath And Knife	LP	Topic	12TS370	1978	£5	£12	

MCCURN, GEORGE

I'm Just A Country Boy	7"	London	HLH9705	1963	£1.50	£4	

MCCUTCHEON, JOHN

Wind That Shakes The Barley	LP	June Appal	JA014	1977	£5	£12	US

MCDANIEL, MAISIE

Country Style	7" EP..	Fontana	TFE17398	1962	£2	£5	
Meet Maisie McDaniel	7" EP..	Fontana	TE17397	1963	£2	£5	

MCDANIELS, GENE

Anyone Else	7"	Liberty	LIB10130	1963	£1.50	£4	
Change Of Mood	7" EP..	Liberty	LEP2054	1962	£5	£10	
Chip Chip	7"	Liberty	LIB55405	1962	£1.50	£4	
Cry Baby Cry	7"	Liberty	LIB55541	1963	£1.50	£4	
Gene McDaniels	7" EP..	London	REG1298	1961	£12.50	£25	
Gene McDaniels Sings Movie Memories	LP	Liberty	LRP3204/LST7204	1962	£8	£20	US
Hit After Hit	LP	Liberty	LRP3258/LST7258	1962	£8	£20	US
Hundred Pounds Of Clay	LP	London	HAG2384/SAHG6184	1961	£10	£25	
Hundred Pounds Of Clay	7"	London	HLG9319	1961	£2	£5	
In Times Like These	LP	Liberty	LRP3146/LST7146	1960	£10	£25	US
In Times Like These	7"	Liberty	LIB55723	1964	£2.50	£6	
It's A Lonely Town	7"	Liberty	LIB55597	1963	£5	£10	
Point Of No Return	7"	Liberty	LIB55480	1962	£1.50	£4	
Sometimes I'm Happy	LP	Liberty	LBY1003	1962	£8	£20	
Spanish Lace	LP	Liberty	(S)LBY1128	1963	£8	£20	
Spanish Lace	7"	Liberty	LIB55510	1963	£1.50	£4	
Tear	7"	London	HLG9396	1961	£1.50	£4	

Tower Of Strength	LP	Liberty	LBY1021	1962	£8	£20
Tower Of Strength	7"	London	HLG9448	1961	£2	£5 ...chart single
Walk With A Winner	7"	Liberty	LIB55805	1965	£20	£40
Wonderful World Of Gene McDaniels	LP	Liberty	LRP3311/LST7311	1963	£6	£15 ...US

MCDEVITT, CHAS

Across The Bridge	7"	Oriole	CB1405	1958	£2.50	£6
Face In The Rain	7"	Oriole	CB1386	1957	£2.50	£6
Forever	7"	Top Rank	JAR338	1960	£1.50	£4
I Never Will Marry	7"	HMV	POP1151	1963	£1.50	£4
It Takes A Worried Man	7"	Oriole	CB1357	1957	£4	£8
I've Got A Thing About You	7"	HMV	POP928	1961	£1.50	£4
Johnny O	7"	Oriole	CB1403	1958	£2.50	£6
Juke Box Jumble	7"	Oriole	CB1457	1958	£2.50	£6
Naughty But Nice	7" EP	Columbia	SEG8471	1965	£2	£5
One Love	7"	HMV	POP845	1961	£1.50	£4
Sing Sing Sing	7"	Oriole	CB1395	1957	£2.50	£6
Six Big Folk Hits	7" EP	Columbia	SEG8468	1965	£2	£5
Teenage Letter	7"	Oriole	CB1511	1959	£1.50	£4 ...Shirley Douglas B side
Throwing Pebbles In A Pool	7"	HMV	POP999	1962	£1.50	£4

MCDEVITT, CHAS & NANCY WHISKEY

Chas And Nancy	7" EP	Oriole	EP7002	1957	£7.50	£15
Freight Train	7"	Oriole	CB1352	1957	£5	£10 ...chart single
Greenback Dollar	7"	Oriole	CB1371	1957	£5	£10 ...chart single

MCDONALD & GILES

McDonald & Giles	LP	Island	ILPS9126	1970	£6	£15

MCDONALD, ALISTAIR

Battle Ballads	LP	Major Minor	MMLP51	1969	£5	£12

MCDONALD, GAVIN

Lines	LP	Regal Zonophone	SLRZ1027	1972	£5	£12

MCDONALD, SHELAGH

Shelagh McDonald	LP	B&C	CAS1019	1970	£10	£25
Stargazer	LP	B&C	CAS1043	1971	£15	£30

MCDONALD, SKEETS

Country's Best	LP	Capitol	T1179	1959	£8	£20 ...US
Fallen Angel	7"	Capitol	CL14566	1956	£10	£20
Going Steady With The Blues	LP	Capitol	T1040	1958	£15	£30 ...US
Going Steady With The Blues	7" EP	Capitol	EAP11040	1959	£15	£30

MCDOWELL, MISSISSIPPI FRED

1904-72	LP	Xtra	XTRA1136	1974	£5	£12
Eight Years Rambling	LP	Revival	RVS1001	1971	£4	£10
Going Down South	LP	Polydor	236278	1969	£4	£10
I Do Not Play No Rock'n'Roll	LP	Capitol	EST409	1970	£6	£15
London 1	LP	Transatlantic	TRA194	1970	£4	£10
London 2	LP	Transatlantic	TRA203	1969	£4	£10
Long Way From Home	LP	CBS	63735	1970	£5	£12
Mississippi Delta Blues	LP	Fontana	688806ZL	1966	£5	£12
Mississippi Delta Blues	LP	Polydor	2460193	1972	£4	£10
My Home Is In The Delta	LP	Bounty	BY6022	1966	£5	£12

MCDUFF, BROTHER JACK

Carpetbaggers	7"	Stateside	SS328	1964	£2	£5
Change Is Gonna Come	LP	Atlantic	587030	1966	£6	£15
Concert McDuff	LP	Stateside	SL10165	1966	£6	£15
Down Home Style	LP	Blue Note	BST84322	1969	£5	£12
Down In The Valley	7"	Atlantic	584036	1966	£2	£5
Dynamic!	LP	Stateside	SL10101	1964	£6	£15
Live!	LP	Stateside	SL10060	1964	£6	£15
Live At The Jazz Workshop	LP	Stateside	SL10121	1965	£6	£15
Moon Rappin'	LP	Blue Note	BST84334	1969	£5	£12
Prelude	LP	Stateside	SL10142	1965	£6	£15
Rock Candy	7"	Stateside	SS302	1964	£2	£5
Sanctified Samba	7"	Stateside	SS275	1964	£2	£5
Screamin'	LP	Transatlantic	PR7259	1967	£6	£15
Silk And Soul	LP	Transatlantic	PR7404	1967	£6	£15
To Seek A New Home	LP	Blue Note	BST84348	1970	£4	£10
Who Knows What Tomorrow Brings	LP	Blue Note	BST84358	1970	£4	£10

MCELROY, WILLIE

Fair Of Enniskillen	LP	Outlet	OAS3001	1977	£6	£15 ...Iris

MCEVOY, JOHNNY

Sounds Like Johnny McEvoy	LP	Halpix	117	197-	£8	£20

MCEWEN, RORY & ALEX & ISLA CAMERON

Folksong Jubilee	LP	HMV	CLP1220	1958	£30	£60

MCFADDEN, BOB

Beat Generation	7"	Coral	Q72378	1959	£1.50	£4

MCGARRIGLE, KATE & ANNA

Complainte Pour Sainte Catherine	7"	Warner Bros	K16710	1976	£1.50	£4

| Love Over And Over | LP | Polydor | POLS1062 | 1982 | £5 | £12 | |

MCGARRIGLE, KATE AND ANNA

| Pronto Monto | LP | Warner Bros | K56561 | 1978 | £5 | £12 | |

MCGARRITY, LOU

| Salute To Louis | 10" LP | Parlophone | PMD1063 | 1958 | £4 | £10 | |

MCGEAR, MIKE

After various jokey performances as a member of the Scaffold and of Grimms, the solo recordings by Mike McGear find him in a relatively serious singer-songwriting mode. "McGear" is of considerable interest to Paul McCartney collectors as the album is virtually a Wings album with Mike McGear as guest star. McGear and McCartney are, of course, brothers.

McGear	LP	Centre Labs		198-	£15	£30	6 tracks, numbered & autographed
McGear	LP	Warner Bros	K56051	1974	£5	£12	
Woman	LP	Island	ILPS9191	1972	£5	£12	

MCGEEGAN, PAT

| Chance Of A Lifetime | 7" | Emerald | MD1096 | 1968 | £2 | £5 | |

MCGHEE, BROWNIE

At The Bunkhouse	LP	Smash	MGS27067	1965	£5	£12	US
Black Country Blues	LP	London	LTZC15144	1958	£8	£20	
Blues	10" LP	Folkways	2030		£6	£15	US
Bluest	7" EP	Pye	NJE1060	1957	£4	£8	with Dave Lee
Brownie McGhee	LP	Sharp	2003		£10	£25	US
Me And My Dog	78	Melodisc	1127	1951	£3	£8	

MCGHEE, HOWARD

Howard McGhee And Milt Jackson	LP	London	LTZC15062	1957	£10	£25	
Howard McGhee Sextet	10" LP	Vogue	LDE008	1952	£40	£80	
Jazz Concert West Coast	LP	London	LTZC15045	1957	£8	£20	
Maggie's Back In Town	LP	Contemporary	LAC12303	1961	£5	£12	
Return Of Howard McGhee	LP	London	LTZN15011	1956	£15	£30	
Together Again!	LP	Contemporary	LAC12291	1961	£6	£15	with Teddy Edwards
With The Frank Hunter Orchestra	LP	London	HAN2033	1957	£15	£30	

MCGHEE, STICKS & JOHN LEE HOOKER

| Highway Of Blues | LP | Audio Lab | AL1520 | 1959 | £17.50 | £35 | US |

MCGINN, MATT

| Little Ticks Of Time | LP | XTRA | XTRA1078 | 1969 | £5 | £12 | |

MCGOUGH & MCGEAR

It would be pleasing to imagine that the high value of the album recorded by two-thirds of the Scaffold was in some way a tribute to the song writing of Mike McGear or the inimitable poetic talents of Roger McGough. Sadly, the value has more to do with the cast of supporting musicians used on this poor-selling album, which includes Jimi Hendrix.

| McGough & McGear | LP | Parlophone | PCS7047 | 1968 | £100 | £200 | sleeve pictured in Guide |

MCGOUGH, ROGER

| Summer With Monika | LP | Island | ILPS9551 | 1978 | £5 | £12 | |

MCGOUGH, ROGER & BRIAN PATTEN

| British Poets Of Our Time | LP | Argo | ZPL1190 | 1975 | £8 | £20 | |

MCGRATH, BAT

| Introducing | LP | Epic | 26499 | 1969 | £5 | £12 | US |

MCGREGOR, CHRIS

African Sound	LP	Gallojazz		1963	£50	£100	
Kwela	LP	77		1968	£40	£80	
Up To Earth	LP	Polydor	583072	1968	£100	£200	test pressing
Very Urgent	LP	Polydor	184137	1968	£25	£50	

MCGREGOR, CHRIS & OTHERS

| Cold Castle Jazz Festival | LP | Gallojazz | | 1963 | £50 | £100 | |

MCGRIFF, EDNA

| Edna McGriff's The Name | 7" EP | Gala | 45XP1014 | 196- | £2.50 | £6 | |

MCGRIFF, JIMMY

All About My Girl	7"	Sue	WI303	1963	£6	£12	
At The Apollo	LP	London	HAC8242	1966	£8	£20	
Bag Full Of Soul	LP	United Artists	(S)ULP1158	1966	£5	£12	
Big Band	LP	United Artists	(S)ULP1170	1968	£5	£12	
Black Pearl	LP	Blue Note	BST84374	1970	£4	£10	
Blues For Mr.Jimmy	LP	London	HAC8247	1966	£8	£20	
Electric Funk	LP	Blue Note	BST84350	1970	£6	£15	
Gospel Time	LP	Sue	ILP908	1964	£15	£30	
Greatest Organ Hits	LP	United Artists	UAS29010	1969	£5	£12	
I've Got A Woman	LP	Sue	ILP907	1964	£15	£30	
I've Got A Woman	7"	Sue	WI317	1964	£6	£12	
Last Minute	7"	Sue	WI310	1964	£6	£12	
Round Midnight	7"	Sue	WI333	1964	£10	£20	
See See Rider	7"	United Artists	UP1170	1966	£2	£5	
Something To Listen To	LP	Blue Note	BST84364	1970	£4	£10	
Worm	LP	United Artists	UAS29004	1968	£5	£12	
Worm	7"	United Artists	UP35025	1969	£2.50	£6	

MCGUFFIE, BILL

Concerto For Boogie	7"	Parlophone	MSP6040	1953	£1.50	£4	
Fugue For Thought (Daleks:Invasion Earth)	7"	Philips	BF1550	1967	£1.50	£4	

MCGUINN, ROGER

Airplay Anthology	LP	Columbia	AS353	1975	£6	£15	US promo

MCGUIRE, BARRY

Eve Of Destruction	LP	ABC	ABCL5110	1965	£6	£15	
Eve Of Destruction	LP	RCA	RD7751	1965	£6	£15	
Eve Of Destruction	7"	RCA	RCA1469	1965	£2	£5	chart single
Eve Of Destruction	7" EP	RCA	86900	1965	£6	£12	French
Greenback Dollar	7"	Ember	EMBS224	1966	£1.50	£4	
Masters Of War	7"	RCA	RCA1638	1967	£1.50	£4	
So Long Stay Well	7"	Ember	EMBS208	1965	£1.50	£4	
This Precious Time	LP	Dunhill	D50005	1966	£6	£15	US, with Mamas & Papas
This Precious Time	7"	RCA	RCA1497	1966	£1.50	£4	
This Precious Time	7" EP	RCA	86904	1966	£6	£12	French
Upon A Painted Ocean	7"	RCA	RCA1493	1965	£1.50	£4	
Walking My Cat Named Dog	7"	RCA	RCA1508	1966	£1.50	£4	
World's Last Private Citizen	LP	Dunhill	D50033	1968	£5	£12	US

MCGUIRE SISTERS

Beginning To Miss You	7"	Vogue Coral	Q72265	1957	£1.50	£4	
By Request	10" LP	Coral	CRL56123	1955	£8	£20	US
Children's Holiday	LP	Vogue Coral	LVA9072	1957	£6	£15	
Delilah Jones	7"	Vogue Coral	Q72161	1956	£4	£8	chart single
Ding Dong	7"	Vogue Coral	Q72327	1958	£1.50	£4	
Do You Remember When?	LP	Vogue Coral	LVA9024	1956	£6	£15	
Endless	7"	Vogue Coral	Q72201	1956	£1.50	£4	
Forgive Me	7"	Vogue Coral	Q72296	1957	£1.50	£4	
Goodnight My Love, Pleasant Dreams	7"	Vogue Coral	Q72216	1957	£1.50	£4	
Greetings	LP	Coral	CRL57225	1958	£6	£15	US
He	LP	Coral	CRL57033	195-	£6	£15	US
He	7"	Vogue Coral	Q72108	1955	£2	£5	
Heart	7"	Vogue Coral	Q72238	1957	£1.50	£4	
His And Hers	LP	Coral	LVA9140	1961	£5	£12	
In The Alps	7"	Vogue Coral	Q72188	1956	£1.50	£4	
Interlude	7"	Vogue Coral	Q72272	1957	£1.50	£4	
Lonesome Polecat	7"	Vogue Coral	Q2028	1954	£2.50	£6	
May You Always	LP	Coral	LVA9115	1959	£6	£15	
May You Always	7"	Coral	Q72356	1959	£1.50	£4	chart single
May You Always	7" EP	Coral	FEP2033	1959	£7.50	£15	
McGuire Sisters	7" EP	Coral	FEP2001	1958	£7.50	£15	
Melody Of Love	7"	Vogue Coral	Q72052	1955	£2	£5	
Missing	7"	Vogue Coral	Q72145	1956	£2	£5	
Musical Magic	LP	Coral	CRL57180	1957	£6	£15	US
No More	7"	Vogue Coral	Q72050	1955	£5	£10	chart single
Our Golden Favorites	LP	Coral	LVA9133	1960	£5	£12	
Sincerely	LP	Coral	CRL57052	195-	£6	£15	US
Something's Gotta Give	7"	Vogue Coral	Q72082	1955	£2	£5	
Sugartime	LP	Coral	CRL57217	1958	£6	£15	US
Sugartime	7"	Coral	Q72305	1958	£2.50	£6	chart single
Teenage Party	LP	Coral	LVA9073	1957	£6	£15	
Tip Toe Through The Tulips	7"	Vogue Coral	Q72209	1956	£1.50	£4	
Volare	7"	Vogue Coral	Q72334	1958	£1.50	£4	
Volare	7" EP	Coral	FEP2006	1958	£7.50	£15	
When The Lights Are Low	LP	Coral	LVA9082	1958	£5	£12	
Without Him	7"	Vogue Coral	Q72249	1957	£1.50	£4	
Young And Foolish	7"	Vogue Coral	Q72117	1956	£2	£5	

MCKAY, FREDDIE

Picture On The Wall	LP	Attack	ATLP1013	1973	£5	£12	
Picture On The Wall	LP	Banana	BALPS01	1971	£10	£25	

MCKAY, SCOTT

Cold Cold Heart	7"	London	HLU9885	1964	£1.50	£4	
I Can't Make Your Way	7"	Columbia	DB8147	1967	£10	£20	

MCKEE, LONETTE

Save It	7"	Sussex	SXX4	1975	£1.50	£4	

MCKENNA MENDELSON MAINLINE

Better Watch Out	7"	Liberty	LBF15235	1969	£2.50	£6	
Don't Give Me No Goose For Christmas	7"	Liberty	LBF15276	1969	£2	£5	
Stink	LP	Liberty	LBS83251	1969	£6	£15	

MCKENNA, VAL

Mixed Up Shook Up Girl	7"	Piccadilly	7N35256	1965	£2.50	£6	

MCKENZIE, DOUG & BOB

Take Off	7"	Mercury	HOSER1	1982	£5	£10	

MCKENZIE, JUDY

Judy	LP	Key	KL005	1970	£8	£20	
Peace And Love And Freedom	LP	Key	KL009	1971	£8	£20	

MCKENZIE, MARLENE

Title	Format	Label	Cat No	Year			Notes
Left Me For Another	7"	Double D	DD106	1968	£4	£8	...Bobby Aitken B side

MCKENZIE, SCOTT

Title	Format	Label	Cat No	Year			Notes
San Francisco	7"	CBS	2816	1967	£1.50	£4	chart single
Voice Of Scott McKenzie	LP	CBS	(S)BPG63157	1967	£4	£10	

MCKENZIE, TOMMY

Title	Format	Label	Cat No	Year		
Fiddle Sticks	7"	Pama	PM720	1968	£2.50	£6

MCKINLEY, RAY & JOE MARSALA

Title	Format	Label	Cat No	Year		
Dixieland Jazz Battle	10" LP	Brunswick	LA8545	1952	£5	£12

MCKINLEYS

Title	Format	Label	Cat No	Year		
Give Him My Love	7"	Columbia	DB7583	1965	£4	£8
Someone Cares For Me	7"	Columbia	DB7230	1964	£1.50	£4
When He Comes Along	7"	Columbia	DB7310	1964	£1.50	£4

MCKUEN, ROD

Title	Format	Label	Cat No	Year			Notes
Happy Is A Boy Named Me	7"	London	HLU8390	1957	£7.50	£15	
Summer Love	LP	Decca	DL8714	1958	£8	£20	US
Two Brothers	7"	Brunswick	05828	1960	£5	£10	

MCKUSICK, HAL

Title	Format	Label	Cat No	Year		
East Coast Jazz	LP	London	LTZN15006	1956	£20	£40
Hal McKusick Quartet	LP	Parlophone	PMC1093	1959	£8	£20
Hal McKusick Quintet	LP	Voge Coral	LVA9062	1957	£10	£25
Jazz At The Academy	LP	Vogue Coral	LVA9054	1957	£10	£25

MCLAIN, TOMMY

Title	Format	Label	Cat No	Year			Notes
Sweet Dreams	7"	London	HL10065	1966	£4	£8	chart single
Think It Over	7"	London	HL10091	1966	£2.50	£6	

MCLAUGHLIN, DINNY

Title	Format	Label	Cat No	Year			Notes
Rake O'Reels And A Clatter Of Jigs	LP	Robin	ROBALM027	1971	£10	£25	Irish

MCLAUGHLIN, JOHN

John McLaughlin apparently spent much of the sixties driving a van for an amplification company, while playing his guitar where-ever and whenever he could. He was given the chance to make an album for the Marmalade label, but while "Extrapolation" is an above-average British jazz record of the period, it was almost immediately eclipsed by McLaughlin's good fortune in being invited to play with Miles Davis. As a player on the key albums to start electric jazz, it was therefore John McLaughlin who made highly amplified guitar respectable in jazz (although he had to work up to it - the tone on both "In A Silent Way" and "Bitches Brew" is quite mild).

Title	Format	Label	Cat No	Year			Notes
Devotion	LP	Douglas	DGL65075	1972	£4	£10	
Extrapolation	LP	Marmalade	608007	1969	£6	£15	
Extrapolation	LP	Polydor	2343012	1970	£5	£12	
My Goal's Beyond	LP	Douglas	DGL69014	1972	£4	£10	
Where Fortune Smiles	LP	Dawn	DNLS3018	1971	£6	£15	with John Surman and others

MCLEAN, FREDDIE

Title	Format	Label	Cat No	Year		
Go On Girl	7"	Blue Beat	BB386	1965	£5	£10

MCLEAN, JACKIE

Title	Format	Label	Cat No	Year		
Action Action Action	LP	Blue Note	BLP/BST84218	1965	£15	£30
Bluesnik	LP	Blue Note	BLP/BST84067	196-	£10	£25
'Bout Soul	LP	Blue Note	BST84284	1968	£6	£15
Capuchin Swing	LP	Blue Note	BLP/BST84038	196-	£10	£25
Demon's Dance	LP	Blue Note	BST84345	1969	£6	£15
Destination Out	LP	Blue Note	BLP/BST84165	1964	£10	£25
Fickle Sonance	LP	Blue Note	BLP/BST84089	1961	£20	£40
It's Time!	LP	Blue Note	BLP/BST84179	1964	£15	£30
Jackie's Bag	LP	Blue Note	BLP/BST84051	196-	£20	£40
Jackie's Pal	LP	Esquire	32111	1960	£10	£25
Let Freedom Ring	LP	Blue Note	BLP/BST84106	1962	£10	£25
Lights Out	LP	Esquire	32041	1958	£15	£30
New And Old Gospel	LP	Blue Note	BLP/BST84262	1967	£10	£25
One Step Beyond	LP	Blue Note	BLP/BST84137	1963	£10	£25
Right Now!	LP	Blue Note	BLP/BST84215	1965	£15	£30

MCLEAN, PHIL

Title	Format	Label	Cat No	Year		
Big Mouth Bill	7"	Top Rank	JAR613	1962	£1.50	£4
Small Sad Sam	7"	Top Rank	JAR597	1961	£1.50	£4

MCLOLLIE, OSCAR HONEYJUMPERS

Title	Format	Label	Cat No	Year		
Love Me Tonight	7"	London	HL8130	1955	£60	£120

MCLUHAN, MARSHALL

Title	Format	Label	Cat No	Year			Notes
Medium Is The Message	LP	Columbia	CL2701/CS9501	1967	£8	£20	US

MCLYNNS

Title	Format	Label	Cat No	Year		
Old Market Street	LP	CBS	63836	1970	£4	£10

MCMANUS, ROSS

Title	Format	Label	Cat No	Year		
I'm The Greatest	7"	HMV	POP1279	1964	£1.50	£4
Stop Your Playing Around	7"	HMV	POP1543	1966	£1.50	£4

MCMILLAN, RODDY

Title	Format	Label	Cat No	Year		
McPherson's Rant	7" EP	Beltona	SEP83	1960	£2	£5

MCNAIR, BARBARA

Title	Format	Label	Cat No	Year			Notes
Here I Am	LP	Motown	(S)644	1966	£8	£20	US

Title	Format	Label	Catalogue	Year			Notes
I Enjoy Being A Girl	LP	Warner Bros	W(S)1541	1964	£6	£15	US
I Enjoy Being A Girl	7" EP	Warner Bros	WEP6129	1964	£2.50	£6	
Livin' End	LP	Warner Bros	W(S)1570	1964	£6	£15	US
Real Barbara McNair	LP	Motown	S680	1969	£8	£20	US
You're Gonna Love My Baby	7"	Tamla Motown	TMG544	1966	£60	£120	

MCNAIR, HAROLD

Title	Format	Label	Catalogue	Year			Notes
Affectionate Funk	LP	Island	ILP926	1965	£15	£30	
Fence	LP	B&C	CAS1016	1970	£8	£20	
Harold McNair	LP	B&C	CAS1045	1971	£8	£20	
Harold McNair	LP	RCA	SF7969	1968	£10	£25	
Hipster	7"	RCA	RCA1742	1968	£4	£8	

MCNEELY, BIG JAY

Title	Format	Label	Catalogue	Year			Notes
Big Jay McNeely	LP	Warner Bros	W(S)1523	1963	£6	£15	US
Big Jay McNeely	10" LP	Federal	29596	1954	£50	£100	US
Big Jay McNeely In 3-D	LP	Federal	395530	1956	£37.50	£75	US
Big Jay McNeely In 3-D	LP	King	650	1959	£17.50	£35	US
Big Jay's Party	LP	Warner Bros	WM8143	1964	£6	£15	
Rhythm And Blues Concert	10" LP	Savoy	MG15045	1955	£37.50	£75	US
Something On Your Mind	7"	Sue	WI373	1965	£6	£12	
Something On Your Mind	7"	Top Rank	JAR169	1959	£5	£10	

MCNEIL, DAVID

Title	Format	Label	Catalogue	Year			Notes
Don't Let Your Chance Go By	7"	President	PT212	1968	£5	£10	

MCNEIL, PAUL

Title	Format	Label	Catalogue	Year			Notes
Contemporary Folk	LP	Decca	LK4699	1965	£10	£25	
Traditionally At The Troubadour	LP	Decca	LK4803	1966	£20	£40	

MCNEIL, PAUL & LINDA PETERS

Title	Format	Label	Catalogue	Year			Notes
You Ain't Goin' Nowhere	7"	MGM	MGM1408	1968	£4	£8	

MCPARTLAND, JIMMY

Title	Format	Label	Catalogue	Year			Notes
Dixieland At Carnegie Hall	LP	Columbia	33SX1122	1959	£5	£12	
Shades Of Bix	10" LP	Vogue Coral	LRA10006	1954	£6	£15	

MCPARTLAND, MARIAN

Title	Format	Label	Catalogue	Year			Notes
Marian McPartland	LP	Capitol	LCT6017	1955	£5	£12	
Marian McPartland	10" LP	Capitol	LC6828	1956	£6	£15	
Marian McPartland Trio	LP	Capitol	T785	1957	£5	£12	
With You In Mind	LP	Capitol	T895	1958	£5	£12	

MCPEAKE FAMILY

Title	Format	Label	Catalogue	Year			Notes
At Home With The McPeakes	LP	Fontana	STL5258	1965	£10	£25	
Delightful McPeakes	LP	Philips	6856017	1967	£10	£25	
Irish Folk!	LP	Fontana	TL5214	1964	£10	£25	
Irish To Be Sure	LP	Windmill	WMD151	1972	£10	£25	
McPeake	LP	Evolution			£30	£60	
McPeake Family Of Belfast	LP	Transatlantic	XTRA5012	1966	£6	£15	
Pleasant And Delightful	LP	Fontana	TL5433	1967	£10	£25	

MCPHATTER, CLYDE

Title	Format	Label	Catalogue	Year			Notes
Baby You Got It	7"	Deram	DM223	1969	£1.50	£4	
Best Of Clyde McPhatter	LP	Atlantic	ATL5001	1964	£15	£30	
Clyde	LP	Atlantic	8031	1959	£40	£80	US
Clyde McPhatter	7" EP	London	REE1202	1959	£40	£80	
Come What May	7"	London	HLE8707	1958	£20	£40	
Denver	7"	B&C	CB106	1969	£1.50	£4	
Everybody's Somebody's Fool	7"	Stateside	SS487	1966	£2	£5	
Golden Blues Hits	LP	Mercury	MG2/SR60655	1962	£6	£15	US
Greatest Hits	LP	Mercury	MG2/SR60783	1963	£6	£15	US
Greatest Hits	LP	MGM	(S)E3866	1960	£10	£25	US
Just Give Me A Ring	7"	London	HLE9079	1960	£10	£20	
Just To Hold Your Hand	7"	London	HLE8462	1957	£50	£100	
Lavender Lace	7"	Stateside	SS592	1967	£6	£12	
Let's Start Over Again	LP	MGM	(S)E3775	1959	£15	£30	US
Let's Try Again	7"	MGM	MGM1048	1959	£5	£10	
Little Bitty Pretty One	7"	Mercury	AMT1181	1962	£5	£10	
Live At The Apollo	LP	Mercury	MG2/SR60915	1964	£6	£15	US
Long Lonely Nights	7"	London	HLE8476	1957	£30	£60	
Love Ballads	LP	Atlantic	8024	1958	£60	£120	US
Lover Please	LP	Mercury	MMC14120	1963	£15	£30	
Lover Please	7"	Mercury	AMT1174	1962	£6	£12	
Lover's Question	7"	London	HLE8755	1958	£12.50	£25	
Lovey Dovey	7"	London	HLE8878	1959	£10	£20	
Masquerade Is Over	7"	MGM	MGM1014	1959	£6	£12	
McPhatter & Wilson Meet the Dominoes	LP	Ember	NR5001	1962	£50	£100	with Jackie Wilson
Only A Fool	7"	Deram	DM202	1968	£2	£5	
Rhythm And Soul	LP	Mercury	MG2/SR60750	1962	£15	£30	US
Rock And Cry	7"	London	HLE8525	1957	£30	£60	
Seven Days	7"	London	HL7006	1956	£30	£60	export
Seven Days	7"	London	HLE8250	1956	£100	£200	
Shot Of Rhythm & Blues	7"	Pama	PM705	1969	£1.50	£4	
Shot Of Rhythm & Blues	7"	Stateside	SS567	1966	£2.50	£6	
Since You've Been Gone	7"	London	HLE8906	1959	£10	£20	
Songs Of The Big City	LP	Mercury	MG2/SR60902	1964	£8	£20	US
Ta Ta	LP	Mercury	MG2/SR60597	1960	£15	£30	US
Ta Ta	7"	Mercury	AMT1108	1960	£4	£8	
Think Me A Kiss	7"	MGM	MGM1061	1960	£5	£10	

This Is Not Goodbye	7" EP.	MGM	MGMEP739	1960	£20	£40	
Tomorrow Is A-Comin'	7"	Mercury	AMT1136	1961	£4	£8	
Treasure Of Love	7"	London	HLE8293	1956	£60	£120	chart single
Tribute	LP	Atlantic	K30033	1973	£4	£10	
Twice As Nice	7"	MGM	MGM1040	1959	£5	£10	
Twice As Nice	7" EP.	MGM	MGMEP705	1959	£20	£40	
You Went Back On Your Word	7"	London	HLE9000	1959	£12.50	£25	
You're For Me	7"	Mercury	AMT1120	1960	£4	£8	

MCPHEE, TONY

I Asked For Water...But She Gave Me Gasoline	LP	Liberty	LBS83252	1969	£30	£60	with other artists
Me & The Devil	LP	Liberty	LBL/LBS83190	1968	£25	£50	
Pastoral Future	7"	United Artists	UP36177	1976	£1.50	£4	
Someone To Love Me	7"	Purdah	453501	1966	£30	£60	
Time Of Action	7"	Tony McPhee	TS001	198-	£2.50	£6	
Two Sides Of Tony McPhee	LP	WWA	WWA001	1973	£8	£20	

MCPHERSON, CHARLES

Bebop Revisited	LP	Stateside	SL10151	1965	£5	£12	

MCPHERSON, GILLIAN

Poets And Painters And Performers Of Blues	LP	RCA	SF8220	1971	£4	£10	

MCRAE, CARMEN

Afterglow	LP	Brunswick	LAT8257	1958	£5	£12	
Blue Moon	LP	Brunswick	LAT8147	1956	£5	£12	
Book Of Ballads	LP	London	HAR2185	1959	£5	£12	
By Special Request	LP	Brunswick	LAT8104	1956	£5	£12	
London's Girl Friends No.3	7" EP.	London	REN1094	1957	£5	£10	
Love Is Here To Stay	LP	Brunswick	05502	1955	£1.50	£4	
Play For Keeps	7"	London	HLR8837	1959	£2.50	£6	
So Much	7" EP.	Mercury	ZEP10132	1962	£2	£5	
Torchy	LP	Brunswick	LAT8133	1956	£5	£12	
Whatever Lola Wants	7"	Brunswick	05652	1957	£1.50	£4	

MCSHANN, JAY

Kansas City Memories	10" LP	Brunswick	LA8735	1956	£20	£40	

MCTELL, BLIND WILLIE

Atlanta Twelve String Guitar	LP	Atlantic	K40400	1973	£5	£12	
Blind Willie McTell	LP	Storyville	670186	1967	£6	£15	

MCTELL, RALPH

8 Frames A Second	LP	Transatlantic	TRA165	1968	£4	£10	
Kew Gardens	7"	Transatlantic	BIG131	1970	£1.50	£4	
My Side Of Your Window	LP	Transatlantic	TRA209	1969	£5	£12	
Spiral Staircase	LP	Transatlantic	TRA177	1969	£4	£10	
Summer Comes Along	7"	Transatlantic	BIG125	1969	£1.50	£4	

MCVAY, RAY

Genesis	7"	Parlophone	R5460	1966	£1.50	£4	
Kinda Kinky	7"	Pye	7N15816	1965	£6	£12	
Revenge	7"	Pye	7N15777	1965	£10	£20	

MCVOY, CARL

Tootsie	7"	London	HLU8617	1958	£60	£120	

MCWILLIAMS, DAVID

"The Days Of Pearly Spencer" by David McWilliams, with its telephone vocals and fountaining strings, was heavily promoted by the pirate radio stations and is, in consequence, particularly redolent of that era. The song is something of an oddity within McWilliams" recordings, however, as none of his other, folky material makes any attempt to match the inventiveness of Pearly Spencer's arrangement.

David McWilliams Vol.2	LP	Major Minor	MMLP10	1967	£5	£12	chart LP
David McWilliams Vol.3	LP	Major Minor	MMLP11	1968	£5	£12	chart LP
Days Of Pearly Spencer	LP	Starline	SRS5075	1971	£4	£10	
Days Of Pearly Spencer	7"	Major Minor	MM533	1968	£2	£5	
Days Of Pearly Spencer	7"	Parlophone	R5886	1971	£1.50	£4	
God And My Country	7"	CBS	202348	1966	£1.50	£4	
Lord Offaly	LP	Dawn	DNLS3039	1972	£4	£10	
Mama Are You My Friend?	7"	Major Minor	MM616	1969	£2	£5	
Singing Songs By David McWilliams	LP	Major Minor	MMLP2	1967	£5	£12	chart LP
Stranger	7"	Major Minor	MM592	1969	£2.50	£6	
This Side Of Heaven	7"	Major Minor	MM561	1968	£2	£5	

ME & THEM

Everything I Do Is Wrong	7"	Pye	7N15631	1964	£4	£8	
Feel So Good	7"	Pye	7N15596	1964	£4	£8	
Getaway	7"	Pye	7N15683	1964	£2.50	£6	

MEAN STREET DEALERS

Bent Needles	LP	Graduate	GRADLP1	1979	£8	£20	
Japanese Motorbikes	7"	Graduate	GRAD5	1980	£1.50	£4	

MEASLES

Casting My Spell	7"	Columbia	DB7531	1965	£7.50	£15	
Kicks	7"	Columbia	DB7875	1966	£7.50	£15	
Night People	7"	Columbia	DB7673	1965	£7.50	£15	
Walking In	7"	Columbia	DB8029	1966	£7.50	£15	

MEAT LOAF

Bat Out Of Hell	LP	Epic	EPC1182419	1982	£6	£15	pic disc
Bat Out Of Hell	LP	Epic	HE44974	1981	£4	£10	US audiophile
Dead Ringer	LP	Epic	EPC1183645	1981	£4	£10	pic disc
Live At Father's Place	LP	Epic	AS409	1978	£8	£20	US promo
Live At The El Mocambo	LP	CBS	CDN9	1978	£8	£20	Canadian promo
Modern Girl	7"	Arista	ARISDP585	1984	£1.50	£4	shaped pic disc with poster & plinth
More Than You Deserve	7"	RSO	RS407	1974	£10	£20	US
Stand By Me	7"	Ode	ODS66304	1975	£15	£30	
Stoney & Meatloaf	LP	Rare Earth	SRE3005	1972	£6	£15	
What You See Is What You Get	7"	Rare Earth	RES103	1971	£4	£8	Stoney And Meatloaf credit

MEAT WHIPLASH

Don't Slip Up	7"	Creation	CRE020	1985	£4	£8	sleeve photo of band by fence
Don't Slip Up	7"	Creation	CRE020	1985	£2	£5	sleeve photo of band in field

MEATBEAT MANIFESTO

I Got The Fear	12"	Sweatbox	SOX023R	1988	£2.50	£6	
Suck Hard	12"	Sweatbox	SOX023	1987	£3	£8	

MEATMEN

Blood Sausage	7"	Touch & Go		1982	£10	£20	
Crippled Children Suck	7"	Touch & Go		198-	£10	£20	

MEC OP SINGERS

Dies Irae	7" EP	DiscAZ	1071	1967	£6	£12	French

MEDDY EVILS

Find Somebody To Love	7"	Pye	7N15941	1965	£25	£50	
Ma's Place	7"	Pye	7N17091	1966	£25	£50	

MEDICINE HEAD

Coast To Coast	7"	Dandelion	5075	1970	£1.50	£4	
Dark Side Of The Moon	LP	Polydor	2310166	1971	£4	£10	
Heavy On The Drum	LP	Dandelion	DAN8005	1971	£6	£15	
His Guiding Hand	7"	Dandelion	4661	1970	£2.50	£6	
Kum On	7"	Polydor	2001276	1972	£2	£5	
New Bottles Old Medicine	LP	Dandelion	63757	1970	£6	£15	
Pictures In The Sky	7"	Dandelion	DAN7003	1971	£1.50	£4	chart single

MEDITATIONS

Transcendental Meditation	7"	Liberty	LBF15045	1968	£1.50	£4	

MEDIUM

Edward Never Lies	7"	CBS	3404	1968	£4	£8	
Medium	LP	Gamma	GS503		£6	£15	

MEDLEY, BILL

Peace Brother Peace	7"	MGM	MGM1456	1968	£2	£5	

MEDLIN, JOE

I Kneel At Your Throne	7"	Mercury	AMT1032	1959	£1.50	£4	

MEDWIN, MICHAEL

Army Game	7"	HMV	POP490	1958	£2	£5	chart single

MEEHAN, KEITH

Darkness Of My Life	7"	Marmalade	598016	1969	£4	£8	Tony Meehan B side

MEEHAN, TONY

Song Of Mexico	7"	Decca	F11801	1964	£1.50	£4	chart single

MEEK, JOE ORCHESTRA

Kennedy March	7"	Decca	F11796	1963	£10	£20	

MEGA CITY FOUR

Decoy	7"	Decoy	FART3	1989	£1.50	£4	with tracks by other artists
Miles Apart	7"	Primitive	PRIME009	1988	£5	£10	

MEGADETH

Anarchy In The UK	7"	Capitol	CLP480	1988	£1.50	£4	pic disc
Peace Sells...But Who's Buying?	LP	Capitol	ESTP2022	1986	£4	£10	pic disc
Wake Up Dead	7"	Capitol	CLP476	1987	£2.50	£6	pic disc

MEGATON

Megaton	LP	Decca	SLK16690P	1971	£30	£60	German
Megaton	LP	Deram	SMLR1086	1971	£180	£300	
Out Of Your Own Little World	LP	Deram	DM331	1971	£10	£20	

MEGATON (2)

Ging Gang Goolie	7"	Songbird	SB1010	1969	£1.50	£4	
I've Been Loving You	7"	Songbird	SB1009	1969	£1.50	£4	

MEGATONS

Shimmy Shimmy Walk	7"	Sue	WI325	1965	£6	£12	

MEGATRONS

Velvet Waters	7"	Top Rank	JAR146	1959	£1.50	£4
Whispering Winds	7"	Top Rank	JAR236	1959	£1.50	£4

MEHEGAN, JOHN

First Mehegan Vol.1	7" EP..	London	EZC19005	1956	£2	£5
First Mehegan Vol.2	7" EP..	London	EZC19015	1956	£2	£5

MEID, LOTHAR

Mensch Dieser Klaus	LP	Philips	6305283	1975	£4	£10	German

MEISENFLOO

Meisenfloo	LP	Lagua	60723	1972	£4	£10	German

MEL & TIM

Backfield In Motion	7"	Concord	CON004	1974	£1.50	£4

MELACHRINO ORCHESTRA

Autumn Concerto	7"	HMV	B10958	1956	£2	£5	chart single

MELANIE

Affectionately	LP	Buddah	203028	1969	£4	£10	
All The Right Noises	LP	Buddah	2318034	1971	£4	£10	
Beautiful People	7"	Buddah	201066	1969	£1.50	£4	
Bo Bo's Party	7"	Buddah	201028	1969	£1.50	£4	
Born To Be	LP	Buddah	203019	1969	£5	£12	
Candles In The Rain	LP	Buddah	2318009	1970	£4	£10	chart LP
Christopher Robin	7"	Buddah	201027	1968	£1.50	£4	
Four Sides Of Melanie	LP	Buddah	26590013	1974	£6	£15	double, chart LP
Garden In The City	LP	Buddah	2318054	1972	£4	£10	scratch & sniff sleeve
Gather Me	LP	Buddah	2322002	1971	£4	£10	chart LP
Gift From Honey	7"	Lyntone	2673/4	1973	£1.50	£4	flexi
Good Book	LP	Buddah	2322001	1971	£4	£10	chart LP
Leftover Wine	LP	Buddah	2318011	1970	£4	£10	chart LP
Stoneground Words	LP	Neighborhood	NHTC251	1972	£4	£10	
Tuning My Guitar	7"	Buddah	201063	1969	£5	£10	
What Have They Done To My Song Ma	7"	Buddah	2011038	1970	£1.50	£4	chart single

MELLE, GIL

Gil Melle Quintet	10" LP	Vogue	LDE141	1955	£25	£50

MELLEN, SUSAN

Mellen Bird	LP	Mam	MAMAS1014	1975	£8	£20

MELLOKINGS

Tonight Tonight	LP	Herald	H1013	1960	£50	£100	US

MELLO-LARKS

Just For A Lark	LP	Camden	CAL530	1959	£8	£20	US

MELLOTONES

Facts Of Life	7"	Camel	CA18	1969	£2.50	£6	Termites B side
Fat Girl In Red	7"	Amalgamated	AMG812	1968	£4	£8	Versatiles B side
Feel Good	7"	Amalgamated	AMG817	1968	£4	£8	
Let's Join Together	7"	Pyramid	PYR6060	1969	£2.50	£6	Beverley's Allstars B side
None Such	7"	Doctor Bird	DB1136	1968	£5	£10	Val Bennett B side
Uncle Charlie	7"	Trojan	TR612	1968	£4	£8	US

MELLOW CANDLE

Dan The Wing	7"	Deram	DM357	1972	£10	£20	
Feeling High	7"	SNB	553645	1968	£12.50	£25	
Swaddling Songs	LP	Deram	SDL7	1972	£180	£300	sleeve pictured in Guide

MELLOW CATS

Another Moses	7"	Blue Beat	BB54	1961	£5	£10	
Rock A Man Soul	7"	Blue Beat	BB68	1961	£5	£10	Monto & The Cyclones B side

MELLOW LARKS

Love You Baby	7"	Blue Beat	BB16	1961	£5	£10

MELLY, GEORGE

Abdul Abdul Amir	7"	Decca	F11115	1959	£1.50	£4
Abdul Abulbul Amir	7" EP..	Decca	DFE6557	1958	£2	£5
Black Bottom	7"	Decca	FJ10840	1957	£1.50	£4
Cemetery Blues	7"	Tempo	A147	1956	£1.50	£4
Frankie And Johnny	7"	Decca	F10457	1955	£1.50	£4
George Melly	7" EP..	Tempo	EXA47	1957	£4	£8
Heebie Jeebies	7"	Decca	FJ10806	1956	£1.50	£4
Ise A Muggin'	7"	Pye	7N15253	1960	£1.50	£4
Jenny's Ball	7"	Tempo	A144	1956	£1.50	£4
Kingdom Come	7"	Decca	F10763	1956	£1.50	£4
Michigan Water Blues	7" EP..	Decca	DFE6552	1958	£2	£5
Psychological Significance..	7" EP..	Columbia	SEG8093	1961	£2	£5
Waiting For A Train	7"	Decca	FJ10779	1956	£1.50	£4
With Mick Mulligan's Jazz Band	7" EP..	Tempo	EXA41	1957	£4	£8

MELODIANS

Come On Little Girl	7"	Treasure Isle....	TI7028	1968	£5	£10	Tommy McCook B side
Everbody Bawlin'	7"	Trojan	TR660	1969	£2	£5	Tommy McCook B side
Last Train To Expo '67	7"	Treasure Isle....	TI7023	1967	£5	£10	Tommy McCook B side
Lay It On	7"	Island	WI3014	1966	£5	£10	
Let's Join Together	7"	Studio One	SO2013	1967	£6	£12	Gaylads B side
Little Nut Tree	7"	Doctor Bird	DB1125	1968	£5	£10	
Rivers Of Babylon	7"	Summit	SUM8508	1970	£2.50	£6	
Sweet Rose	7"	Fab	FAB61	1968	£4	£8	
Sweet Sensation	LP	Trojan		1970	£5	£12	
Sweet Sensation	7"	Trojan	TR695	1969	£2	£5	chart single
Swing And Dine	7"	Doctor Bird	DB1139	1968	£5	£10	
You Don't Need Me	7"	Treasure Isle....	TI7006	1967	£5	£10	
You Have Caught Me	7"	Treasure Isle....	TI7022	1967	£5	£10	

MELODY ENCHANTERS

Blueberry Hill	7"	R&B	JB117	1963	£5	£10	
Enchanter's Ball	7"	Island	WI049	1963	£5	£10	

MELODY MAKER ALL STARS

Melody Maker All Stars	10" LP	Esquire	20001	1952	£15	£30	
Melody Maker All Stars	10" LP	Esquire	20008	1953	£15	£30	
Melody Maker All Stars	10" LP	Esquire	20031	1954	£15	£30	

MELODY MAKER MODERN GROUP

Melody Maker Modern Group	10" LP	Esquire	20030	1954	£15	£30	

MELSON, JOE

Hey Mister Cupid	7"	Polydor	NH66961	1961	£12.50	£25	
Oh Yeah	7"	Polydor	NH66959	1961	£15	£30	
Stay Away From Her	7"	Hickory	451229	1964	£1.50	£4	

MELTING BEER

It Makes No Difference	7"	Beggars Banquet	BEG144	1985	£2.50	£6	test pressing

MELTON, BARRY

We Are Like The Ocean	LP	Music Is Medicine	MIM9007	1977	£8	£20	US

MELTZER, TINA & DAVID

Poet Song	LP	Vanguard		196-	£10	£25	US

MEMBERS

Fear On The Streets	7"	XS		1977	£4	£8	
Offshore Banking Business	7"	Stiff	OFF3	1978	£1.50	£4	

MEMOS

My Type Of Girl	7"	Parlophone	R4616	1959	£20	£40	

MEMPHIS BEND

Ubangi Stomp	7"	United Artists..	UP36132	1976	£2	£5	

MEMPHIS HORNS

Get Up And Dance	7"	RCA	PB0836	1977	£2	£5	
Wooly Bully	7"	Atlantic	2091080	1971	£1.50	£4	

MEMPHIS JUG BAND

Memphis Jug Band	LP	Saydisc	RL33	1970	£5	£12	
Memphis Jug Band	7" EP	HMV	7EG8073	1955	£25	£50	
Memphis Jug Band Vol.2	LP	Saydisc	RL337	1971	£5	£12	

MEMPHIS MINNIE

1934-1936	LP	Limited Edition	no number	1969	£8	£20	
1934-1941	LP	Flyright	LP108	1974	£4	£10	
1934-1941	LP	Limited Edition	no number	1969	£8	£20	
1941-1949	LP	Flyright	LP109	1974	£4	£10	
1941-1949	LP	Sunflower	ET1400	1969	£8	£20	
Memphis Minnie	7" EP	Heritage	H103	1964	£7.50	£15	

MEMPHIS SLIM

All Kinds Of Blues	LP	Bluesville	BV(S)1053	1963	£5	£12	US
All Kinds Of Blues	LP	XTRA	XTRA5063	1970	£5	£12	
Alone With My Friends	LP	Battle	BM6118	1963	£5	£12	US
And The Real Honky Tonk	LP	Folkways	FG3535	1961	£6	£15	
At The Gate Of Horn	LP	Joy	JOYS143	1969	£4	£10	
At The Gate Of Horn	LP	Vee Jay	VJLP1012	1959	£15	£30	US
Big City Girl	7"	Storyville	A45055	1962	£2.50	£6	
Blue Memphis	LP	Barclay	920214	1972	£15	£30	with Peter Green
Blues In Europe	LP	Storyville	SLP188	1966	£5	£12	
Bluesingly Yours	LP	Polydor	623263	1968	£5	£12	
Boogie Woogie & The Blues	7" EP	Storyville	SEP385	1962	£7.50	£15	
Boogie Woogie Piano	LP	CBS	63470	1961	£6	£15	
Broken Soul Blues	LP	United Artists	UAL3137/ UAS6137	1961	£6	£15	US
Broken Soul Blues	LP	United Artists	ULP1042	1963	£6	£15	
Chicago Blues	LP	Folkways	FG3536	1961	£6	£15	
Chicago Blues	LP	XTRA	XTRA1085	1969	£5	£12	

Title	Format	Label	Catalog	Year	Price	Price	Notes
Clap Your Hands	LP	Fontana	TL5254	1965	£5	£12	
Frisco Bay Blues	LP	Fontana	688315ZL	1964	£6	£15	
Going To Kansas City	7" EP	Collector	JEN5	1961	£7.50	£15	
Just Blues	LP	Bluesville	BV(S)1018	1961	£6	£15	US
Legend Of The Blues	LP	Jubilee	JGM8003	1967	£5	£12	US
Memphis Slim	LP	Chess	LP1455	1961	£10	£25	US
Memphis Slim	LP	Collector	JGN1004	1961	£6	£15	
Memphis Slim	LP	Everest	215	1968	£4	£10	US
Memphis Slim	LP	King	LP885	1964	£6	£15	US
Memphis Slim	LP	World Record Club	T394	1962	£5	£12	
Memphis Slim	LP	XTRA	XTRA1008	1965	£6	£15	
Memphis Slim, USA	LP	Candid	9024	1962	£8	£20	US
Memphis Slim Vol.2	LP	Collector	JGN1005	1961	£6	£15	
Messin' Around With The Blues	LP	King	KS1082	1970	£4	£10	US
Mother Earth	LP	Buddah	BDS7505	1969	£4	£10	US
No Strain	LP	Fontana	688302ZL	1964	£6	£15	
Pinetop Blues	7"	Collector	JDN102	1960	£2.50	£6	
Pinetop's Blues	LP	Polydor	623211	1967	£5	£12	
Real Folk Blues	LP	Chess	1510	1966	£8	£20	US
Self Portrait	LP	Scepter	SM535	1966	£5	£12	US
Steady Rollin' Blues	LP	Bluesville	BV(S)1075	1964	£6	£15	US
Travellin' With The Blues	LP	Storyville	SLP118	1964	£5	£12	
Tribute To Big Bill Broonzy	LP	Candid	9023	1961	£8	£20	US
World's Foremost Blues Singer	LP	Fidelio	ATL4115	1964	£5	£12	
World's Foremost Blues Singer	7" EP	Summit	LSE2041	1963	£2.50	£6	

MEMPHIS THREE

Title	Format	Label	Catalog	Year	Price	Price	Notes
Wild Thing	7"	Page One	POF070	1968	£1.50	£4	

MEN

One of the Men was thinking of growing his hair long on one side only; the others were still working out how to get the best out of their new synthesizers. This was, in fact, the Human League.

Title	Format	Label	Catalog	Year	Price	Price	Notes
I Don't Depend On You	7"	Virgin	VS269	1979	£2.50	£6	
I Don't Depend On You	12"	Virgin	VS26912	1979	£2.50	£6	

MEN AT WORK

Title	Format	Label	Catalog	Year	Price	Price	Notes
Down Under	7"	Epic	EPCA1980	1983	£1.50	£4	shaped pic disc

MENDES, CARLOS

Title	Format	Label	Catalog	Year	Price	Price	Notes
Shadows	7"	Pye	7N25581	1972	£2	£5	

MENDES PREY

Title	Format	Label	Catalog	Year	Price	Price	Notes
Wonderland	7"	Wag	WAG2	1986	£2	£5	

MENZIES, IAN

Title	Format	Label	Catalog	Year	Price	Price	Notes
Have Tartan, Will Trad	LP	Pye	NJL23	1960	£4	£10	
Melody Maker All Stars	7" EP	Pye	NJE1049	1958	£2	£5	

MERCER, MARY MAE

Title	Format	Label	Catalog	Year	Price	Price	Notes
Mary Mae Mercer	7" EP	Decca	DFE8599	1965	£4	£8	

MERCURY, FREDDIE

Title	Format	Label	Catalog	Year	Price	Price	Notes
Barcelona	CD-s	Polydor	POCD887	1987	£3	£8	
Barcelona	CD-s	Polydor	POCD887	1987	£30	£60	signed
Barcelona	7"	Polydor	POSP887	1987	£1.50	£4	with Montserrat Caballe
Barcelona	12"	Polydor	POSPP887	1987	£8	£20	with Montserrat Caballe, pic disc
Barcelona	12"	Polydor	POSPX887	1987	£4	£10	with Montserrat Caballe, gatefold sleeve
Golden Boy	CD-s	Polydor	POCD23	1988	£4	£10	
Golden Boy	7"	Polydor	PO23	1988	£1.50	£4	with Montserrat Caballe
Golden Boy	12"	Polydor	PZ23	1988	£4	£10	with Montserrat Caballe
Great Pretender	7"	Parlophone	R6151	1987	£1.50	£4	
Great Pretender	7"	Parlophone	RP6151	1987	£15	£30	shaped pic disc & plinth
Great Pretender	12"	Parlophone	12R6151	1987	£3	£8	
Great Pretender	10"	Parlophone		1987	£5	£12	promo
How Can I Go On	CD-s	Polydor	PZCD29	1989	£3	£8	with Montserrat Caballe
How Can I Go On	7"	Polydor	POSX29	1988	£7.50	£15	with Montserrat Caballe, pic disc
How Can I Go On	12"	Polydor	PZ29	1989	£4	£10	with Montserrat Caballe
I Was Born To Love You	7"	CBS	A6019	1985	£1.50	£4	
I Was Born To Love You	7"	CBS	DA6019	1985	£10	£20	double
I Was Born To Love You	12"	CBS	TA6019	1985	£4	£10	
Living On My Own	7"	CBS	A6555	1985	£1.50	£4	
Living On My Own	12"	CBS	GTA6555	1985	£5	£12	gatefold sleeve
Living On My Own	12"	CBS	TA6555	1985	£3	£8	
Love Kills	7"	CBS	A4735	1984	£2	£5	Giorgio Moroder B side
Love Kills	7"	CBS	WA4735	1984	£20	£40	Giorgio Moroder B side, pic disc
Love Kills	12"	CBS	TA4735	1984	£5	£12	Giorgio Moroder B side
Love Me Like There's No Tomorrow	12"	CBS	TA6725	1985	£4	£10	

Made In Heaven	7"	CBS	A6413	1985	£2	£5	
Made In Heaven	7"	CBS	WA6413	1985	£15	£30	shaped pic disc
Made In Heaven	12"	CBS	TA6413	1985	£5	£12	
Mr.Bad Guy	LP	CBS	86312	1985	£4	£10	
Mr.Bad Guy	CD	CBS	CD86312	1985	£6	£15	
Time	12"	EMI	12EMI5559	1986	£3	£8	

MERION
I Go To Sleep	7"	Page One	POF041	1967	£1.50	£4	

MERKIN
Music From Merkin Manor	LP	Windi	1004	1969	£100	£200	US

MERLE, LOTTIE
Howlin' In The Moonlight	7"	Flyright	45001	1972	£1.50	£4	

MERMAN, ETHEL
Husband A Wife	7"	Brunswick	05346	1954	£1.50	£4	
There's No Business Like Show Business	7"	Brunswick	05381	1955	£1.50	£4	

MERRELL, RAY
Tears Of Joy	7"	Jayboy	BOY22	1970	£50	£100	

MERRICK, TONY
Lady Jane	7"	Columbia	DB7913	1966	£2	£5	chart single
Wake Up	7"	Columbia	DB7995	1966	£2	£5	

MERRILL, BOB
Nairobi	7"	Columbia	DB4086	1958	£1.50	£4	

MERRILL, BUDDY
Sweet September	7"	Vocalion	VN9261	1966	£4	£8	

MERRILL, HELEN
Date With The Blues	7" EP	MGM	MGMEP699	1959	£2	£5	
Nearness Of You	LP	Mercury	MMB12000	1959	£6	£15	

MERRY-GO-ROUND
Merry-Go-Round	LP	A&M	(SP)4132	1967	£5	£12	US

MERRYMEN
Big Bamboo	7"	Doctor Bird	DB1004	1966	£5	£10	
Caribbean Treasure Chest	LP	Island	ILP984	1968	£30	£60	

MERRYWEATHER, BIG MACEO
Big Maceo Merryweather And John Lee Hooker	LP	Fortune	3002		£10	£25	US

MERRYWEATHER, NEIL
Word Of Mouth	LP	Capitol	STBB278	1969	£6	£15	US double

MERSEYBEATS
Don't Let It Happen To Us	7"	Fontana	TF568	1965	£2.50	£6	
Don't Turn Around	7"	Fontana	TF459	1964	£1.50	£4	chart single
England's Best Sellers	LP	ARC International	834	1964	£15	£30	US
I Love You, Yes I Do	7"	Fontana	TF607	1965	£1.50	£4	chart single
I Stand Accused	7"	Fontana	TF645	1965	£1.50	£4	chart single
I Think Of You	7"	Fontana	TF431	1963	£1.50	£4	chart single
I Think Of You	7" EP	Fontana	465328	1966	£10	£20	French
I Think Of You	7" EP	Fontana	TE17423	1964	£10	£20	
It's Love That Really Counts	7"	Fontana	TF412	1963	£2	£5	chart single
Last Night	7"	Fontana	TF504	1964	£1.50	£4	chart single
Merseybeats	LP	Fontana	TL5210	1964	£30	£60	chart LP, sleeve pictured in Guide
Merseybeats	LP	Wing	WL1163	1965	£15	£30	
Merseybeats On Stage	7" EP	Fontana	TE17422	1964	£10	£20	
Wishin' And Hopin'	7"	Fontana	TF482	1964	£1.50	£4	chart single
Wishin' And Hopin'	7" EP	Fontana	TE17432	1964	£10	£20	

MERSEYBOYS
Fifteen Greatest Songs Of The Beatles	LP	Ace Of Clubs	ACL1169	1964	£6	£15	

MERSEYS
Cat	7"	Fontana	TF845	1967	£2.50	£6	
Lovely Loretta	7"	Fontana	TF955	1968	£2	£5	
Penny In My Pocket	7"	Fontana	TF916	1968	£2	£5	
Rhythm Of Love	7"	Fontana	TF776	1966	£1.50	£4	
Rhythm Of Love	7" EP	Fontana	465356	1966	£10	£20	French
So Sad About Us	7"	Fontana	TF732	1966	£2.50	£6	
Sorrow	7"	Fontana	TF694	1966	£1.50	£4	chart single

MERSEYSIPPI JAZZ BAND
Any Old Rags	10" LP	Esquire	20093	1958	£4	£10	
Merseysippi Jazz Band	10" LP	Esquire	20063	1956	£4	£10	
Merseysippi Jazz Band	10" LP	Esquire	20083	1957	£4	£10	
Merseysippi Jazz Band	10" LP	Esquire	20088	1957	£4	£10	

MERTON PARKAS
Flat Nineteen	7"	Well Suspect	BLAM002	1983	£1.50	£4	

MESMERIZING EYE
Psychedelia	LP	Smash	MGS27090	1967	£8	£20		US

MESSAGE
Dawn Anew Is Coming	LP	Bacillus	BLPS19081	1972	£5	£12	German

MESSENGER
Oy I Value Elation	7"	Anagram	A001	1967	£4	£8	

MESSENGERS
I'm Stealing Back	7"	Columbia	DB7344	1964	£2	£5
More Pretty Girls Than One	7"	Columbia	DB7495	1965	£1.50	£4

MESSINA, JIM
Dragsters	LP	Audio Fidelity	DF(S)7037	1964	£8	£20	US
Jim Messina And The Jesters	LP	Thimble	3	196-	£8	£20	US

METABOLIST
Dromm	7"	Dromm	DRO1	1979	£2.50	£6
Identity	7"	Dromm	DRO3	1979	£2	£5

METALLICA
Creeping Death	12"	Music For Nations	CV12KUT112	1987	£2.50	£6	blue vinyl
Creeping Death	12"	Music For Nations	CV12KUT112	1987	£15	£30	green or red vinyl
Creeping Death	12"	Music For Nations	GV12KUT112	1987	£6	£15	gold vinyl
Creeping Death	12"	Music For Nations	P12KUT112	1984	£4	£10	pic disc
Enter Sandman	CD-s	Vertigo	METCD7	1991	£15	£30	boxed
Enter Sandman	7"	Vertigo	METAL7	1991	£1.50	£4	pic disc
Enter Sandman	12"	Vertigo	METBX712	1991	£3	£8	boxed with 4 prints
Eye Of The Beholder	12"	Vertigo		1988	£8	£20	promo
Good, The Bad And The Live	12"	Vertigo	8754871	1990	£20	£40	6 x 12' plus EP
Harvester Of Sorrow	CD-s	Vertigo	METALCD2	1988	£3	£8	
Harvester Of Sorrow	7"	Vertigo	METAL2	1988	£10	£20	promo, special sleeve
Harvester Of Sorrow	12"	Vertigo	METAL212	1988	£10	£25	promo, special sleeve
Jump in The Fire	7"	Music For Nations	PKUT105	1986	£6	£12	shaped pic disc
Jump In The Fire	12"	Music For Nations	12KUT105	1984	£5	£12	red or gold vinyl
Kill 'em All	LP	Music For Nations	MFN7P	1986	£5	£12	pic disc
Master Of Puppets	LP	Music For Nations	MFN60P	1986	£5	£12	pic disc
Nothing Else Matters - Live	CD-s	Vertigo	METCL10	1992	£2.50	£6	
One	7"	Vertigo	MET5	1989	£15	£30	promo, special sleeve
One	10"	Vertigo	METPD510	1989	£4	£10	
One (Demo Version)	12"	Vertigo	METALG512	1989	£3	£8	gatefold PS
Ride The Lightning	LP	Music For Nations	MFN27	1984	£30	£60	green or blue vinyl
Ride The Lightning	LP	Music For Nations	MFN27P	1986	£5	£12	pic disc
Whiplash	12"	Megaforce	MRS04P	1987	£8	£20	pic disc
Whiplash Sampler	CD-s	Vertigo	METCD100	1988	£6	£15	promo

METEORS
Crazed	7"	Lost Soul	LOST101	1981	£2	£5	
Johnny Remember Me	7"	ID	EYE1P	1983	£1.50	£4	pic disc
Meteor Madness	7"	Ace	SW65	1981	£2	£5	blue vinyl
Meteor Madness	10"	Ace	SWT65	1981	£8	£20	test pressing
Radioactive Kid	7"	Ace	NS74	1981	£1.50	£4	clear vinyl

METEORS (2)
Get A Load Of This	7"	Polydor	NH52263	1964	£1.50	£4	

METERS
Cabbage Alley	LP	Reprise	K33242	1972	£5	£12	
Cissy Strut	LP	Island	ILPS9250	1974	£6	£15	
Fire On The Bayou	LP	Reprise	K54044	1975	£6	£15	
Look A Py-Py	7"	Direction	584751	1970	£6	£15	
Look-ka Py Py	LP	Josie	JOS4011	1970	£6	£15	US
Meters	LP	Josie	JOS4010	1969	£6	£15	US
Rejuvenation	LP	Reprise	K54027	1974	£6	£15	
Sophisticated Cissy	7"	Stateside	SS2140	1969	£2.50	£6	
Struttin'	LP	Josie	JOS4012	1970	£6	£15	US
Trick Bag	LP	Reprise	K54078	1976	£6	£15	

METHUSELAH
Matthew,Mark,Luke,& John	LP	Elektra	EKS74052	1969	£20	£40	

METIS, FRANK
Show Business	7" EP	London	REN1048	1956	£2.50	£6	

METROPHASE
In Black	7"	Neo London	MS01	1979	£2	£5	
New Age	7"	Neo London	MS02	1979	£2	£5	

METROTONES
Tops In Rock And Roll	10" LP	Columbia	6341	1955	£50	£100	US

MEV
Musica Elettronica Viva .... LP ..... Polydor .... 583769 .... 1969 ... £10 ....£25 ....

MEZA, LEE
If It Happens .... 7" .... Stateside ...... SS589 .... 1967 ... £15 ....£30 ....

MEZZROW, MEZZ
At The Schola Cantorum, Paris .... 10" LP	Ducretet-Thomson	TKL93092	1956	£8	£20	
King Jazz Story .... 7" EP..	Storyville	SEP394	1962	£2	£5	
Mezzrow-Bechet Quintet .... LP	Vogue	LAE12017	1956	£6	£15	
Pleyel Concert .... LP	Vogue	LAE12007	1955	£6	£15	

MGM STUDIO ORCHESTRA
Rock Around The Clock .... 7" .... MGM .... SP1144 .... 1955 ... £1.50 .....£4 ....

MICHAEL, GEORGE
Careless Whisper .... 7"	Epic	A4603	1984	£7.50	£15	poster PS
Careless Whisper .... 12"	Epic	WA4603	1984	£15	£30	pic disc
Careless Whisper (Wexler mix) .... 12"	Epic	QTA4603	1984	£20	£40	
Faith .... LP	Epic	EMUP3	1987	£15	£30	Australian, pic disc
Faith .... 12"	Epic	EMUP3	1987	£3	£8	pic disc
Father Figure .... 7"	Epic	EMUP4	1988	£2.50	£6	shaped pic disc
I Want Your Sex .... 12"	Epic	QT1	1987	£2.50	£6	
Listen Without Prejudice .... LP	Epic		1990	£20	£40	Brazilian, pic disc
Wembley .... cass..	Epic	XPC4060	1991	£6	£15	

MICHAELS, LEE
Heighty Hi .... 7" .... A&M .... AMS763 .... 1968 ... £1.50 .....£4 ....

MICHAELS, MARILYN
Tell Tommy I Miss Him .... 7" .... RCA .... RCA1208 .... 1960 ... £2 ....£5 ....

MICHIGAN RAG
Don't Run Away .... 7" .... Blue Horizon.... 2096009 .... 1972 ... £4 ....£8 ....

MICKEY & KITTY
Buttercup .... 7" .... London .... HLE9054 .... 1960 ... £6 ....£12 ....

MICKEY & SYLVIA
Bewildered .... 7"	RCA	RCA1064	1958	£10	£20	
Love Is Strange .... LP	RCA	CDN5133	1965	£40	£80	
Love Is Strange .... 7"	HMV	POP331	1957	£70	£140	
Love Is Strange .... 7"	RCA	RCA1487	1965	£7.50	£15	
New Sounds .... LP	Vik	LX1102	1958	£50	£100	US
Sweeter As The Day Goes By .... 7"	RCA	RCA1206	1960	£6	£12	

MIDDLETON, TONY
Don't Ever Leave Me .... 7"	Polydor	56704	1966	£75	£150	
My Little Red Book .... 7"	London	HLR9983	1965	£10	£20	with Burt Bacharach

MIDNIGHT AT NIXA GROUP
Midnight At Nixa .... LP ..... Nixa .... NJL3 .... £4 ....£10 ....

MIDNIGHT RAGS
Cars That Ate New York .... 7"	Velvet Moon....	VM1	1980	£2.50	£6	
Public Enemy .... 7"	Ace	ACE005	1980	£2	£5	

MIDNIGHT SHIFT
Saturday Jump .... 7" .... Decca .... F12487 .... 1966 ... £4 ....£8 ....

MIDNIGHT SUN
Midnight Dream .... LP	Sonet	SLPS1547	1974	£4	£10	
Midnight Sun .... LP	MCA	MCF2687	1973	£4	£10	
Midnight Sun .... LP	MCA	MKPS2019	1972	£6	£15	
Rainbow Band .... LP	Sonet	SLPS1523	1970	£6	£15	
Rainbow Band .... LP	Sonet	SLPS1523A	1971	£6	£15	different vocals
Walking Circles .... LP	MCA	MCF2691	1973	£4	£10	
Walking Circles .... LP	MCA	MKPS2024	1972	£6	£15	
Walking Circles .... LP	Sonet	SLPS1536	1972	£6	£15	

MIDNIGHTS
Midknights .... 7" EP..	private		196-	£50	£100	
Show Me Around .... 7"	Ember	EMBS220	1966	£2	£5	

MI5
You'll Never Stop Me Loving You .... 7" .... Parlophone..... R5486 .... 1966 ... £12.50 ...£25 ....

MIGHTY AVENGERS
Blue Turns To Grey .... 7"	Decca	F12085	1965	£5	£10	
Hide Your Pride .... 7"	Decca	F11891	1964	£5	£10	
Sleepy City .... 7"	Decca	F12198	1965	£6	£12	
So Much In Love .... 7"	Decca	F11962	1964	£5	£10	chart single

MIGHTY BABY
The group evolved out of the Action, but their music sounded little like that of the earlier group. With late arrivals Martin Stone (playing impressive lead guitar) and Ian Whiteman (keyboards and woodwinds) dominating the proceedings, Mighty Baby produced a floating, melodic kind of progressive rock that is amongst the most memorable of the genre. Remarkably, the best songs of all remained as forgotten out-takes until issued by Castle in 1985 ("Action Speaks Louder Than..."). Although credited to the Action, these five songs are actually the work of Mighty Baby and, despite their somewhat unsophisticated production, they emerge as classic recordings.
Devil's Whisper .... 7" .... Blue Horizon.... 2096003 .... 1971 ... £7.50 .....£15 ....

Egyptian Tomb	LP	Psycho	PSYCHO31	1985	£4	£10	
Jug Of Love	LP	Blue Horizon	2931001	1971	£35	£70	
Mighty Baby	LP	Head	HDLS6002	1969	£20	£40	

MIGHTY DOUGLAS

Laziest Man	7"	Jump Up	JU501	1967	£2.50	£6	
Teacher Teacher	7"	Jump Up	JU508	1967	£2.50	£6	
Ugliness	7"	Jump Up	JU509	1967	£2.50	£6	

MIGHTY MEN

No Way Out	7"	Salvo	SLO1804	1962	£5	£10	

MIGHTY MO

Ape Call	7"	Columbia	DB8851	1972	£1.50	£4	

MIGHTY POWER

You're Wasting Your Time	7"	Jump Up	JU513	1967	£2.50	£6	

MIGHTY SAM

Fannie Mae	7"	Stateside	SS544	1966	£2.50	£6	
Mighty Soul	LP	Soul City	SCM004	1970	£30	£60	
Mr.And Mrs.Untrue	7"	Hit And Run	5002	197-	£1.50	£4	
Papa True Love	7"	Soul City	SC115	1969	£2.50	£6	
Sweet Dreams	7"	Stateside	SS534	1966	£2.50	£6	
When She Touches Me	7"	Stateside	SS2076	1968	£2	£5	

MIGHTY SPARROW & BYRON LEE

Sparrow Meets The Dragon	LP	Trojan	TRLS8	1969	£5	£12	

MIGHTY TERROR

Kings Of Calypso No.1	7" EP	Pye	NEP24009	1956	£2	£5	
Kings Of Calypso No.5	7" EP	Pye	NEP24086	1958	£2	£5	

MIGHTY VIKINGS

Do Re Mi	7"	Island	WI3060	1967	£5	£10	
Rockitty Fockitty	7"	Island	WI3074	1967	£5	£10	

MIGIL FIVE

Boys And Girls	7"	Pye	7N15677	1964	£1.50	£4	
Come Dance	LP	Joy	JOYS138	1969	£4	£10	
If I Had My Way	7"	Jayboy	BOY4	1969	£2	£5	
Just Behind The Rainbow	7"	Pye	7N15757	1965	£1.50	£4	
Meet The Migil Five	7" EP	Pye	NEP24191	1964	£4	£8	
Mocking Bird Hill	7"	Pye	7N15597	1964	£1.50	£4	chart single
Mockingbird Hill	LP	Pye	NPL18093	1964	£6	£15	
Near You	7"	Pye	7N15645	1964	£1.50	£4	chart single
One Hundred Years	7"	Pye	7N15874	1965	£1.50	£4	
Pencil And Paper	7"	Pye	7N17023	1966	£1.50	£4	
Together	7"	Columbia	DB8196	1967	£4	£8	

MIGIL FOUR

Maybe	7"	Pye	7N15572	1963	£1.50	£4	

MIKE & THE MECHANICS

All I Need Is A Miracle	12"	WEA	U8765TP	1985	£2.50	£6	pic disc
Silent Running	7"	WEA	8908P	1985	£2.50	£6	shaped pic disc

MIKE & THE MODIFIERS

I Found Myself A Brand New Baby	7"	Oriole	CB1775	1962	£250	£400	

MIKI & GRIFF

Country Style	LP	Pye	NPL18074	1962	£4	£10	

MILANO, BOBBY

If Tears Could Bring You Back	7"	Capitol	CL14309	1955	£1.50	£4	
King Or A Slave	7"	Capitol	CL14252	1955	£1.50	£4	

MILBURN, AMOS

Blues Boss	LP	Motown	608	1963	£75	£150	US
Chicken Shack Boogie	LP	United Artists	UAS30203	1978	£4	£10	
Every Day Of The Week	7"	Vogue	V9064	1957	£30	£60	tri-centre
Let's Have A Party	LP	Score	LP4012	1957	£50	£100	US
Million Sellers	LP	Imperial	A9176	1962	£25	£50	US
One Scotch One Bourbon One Beer	7"	Vogue	V9163	1960	£37.50	£75	
Rock And Roll	7" EP	Vogue	VE170102	1957	£60	£120	
Rockin' The Boogie	LP	Aladdin	810	1958	£60	£120	US
Rockin' The Boogie	10" LP	Aladdin	704	1956	£100	£200	US
Rockin' The Boogie	10" LP	Aladdin	704	1956	£150	£250	US, red vinyl
Rum And Coca Cola	7"	Vogue	V9069	1957	£37.50	£75	
Thinking Of You Baby	7"	Vogue	V9080	1957	£30	£60	

MILBURN, AMOS JR.

Gloria	7"	London	HLU9795	1963	£4	£8	

MILEM, PERCY

Crying Baby, Baby, Baby	7"	Stateside	SS566	1966	£4	£8	

MILES, BUDDY

"Expressway To Your Skull" is exciting and dynamic big-band jazz-rock and it deserves to be very much more widely appreciated than it seems to be. This is the music that the Electric Flag were trying to create, without ever quite getting there - here Buddy Miles manages it without guitarist Mike Bloomfield's help. The sleeve notes to the album are by Jimi Hendrix, who knew a good thing when he heard it, although he does not play on the record. It is possible that he does play on the follow-up, "Electric Church", but in a surprisingly understated manner, if it is he.

Chapter VII	LP	Columbia	CQ32048	1973	£5	£12	US quad
Electric Church	LP	Mercury	SMCL20163	1969	£5	£12	
Expressway To Your Skull	LP	Mercury	SMCL20137	1968	£6	£15	
Miss Lady	7"	Mercury	MF1098	1969	£1.50	£4	
Them Changes	LP	Mercury	6338016	1970	£4	£10	
Them Changes	7"	Mercury	6052036	1971	£1.50	£4	
Train	7"	Mercury	MF1065	1968	£1.50	£4	
With Carlos Santana	LP	Columbia	CQ31308	1974	£5	£12	US quad

MILES, DICK

Cheating The Tide	LP	Greenwich Village	GVR227	1984	£5	£12	

MILES, GARRY

Look For A Star	7"	London	HLG9155	1960	£2.50	£6	
Looking For A Star	7" EP	London	REG1264	1960	£12.50	£25	

MILES, JOSIE

Josie Miles	7" EP	Poydras	103	196-	£2	£5	

MILES, LENNY

Don't Believe Him Donna	7"	Top Rank	JAR546	1961	£4	£8	

MILES, LIZZIE

Clambake On Bourbon Street	LP	Cook	1185	1957	£6	£15	US
Hot Songs	LP	Cook	1183	1956	£6	£15	US
Jazz	10" LP	Nixa	SLPY150	1954	£6	£15	
Lizzie Miles New Orleans Boys	7" EP	Melodisc	EPM755	1955	£7.50	£15	
Moans And Blues	LP	Cook	1182	1956	£6	£15	US
Night In New Orleans	LP	Capitol	T792	1957	£4	£10	
Torchy Lullabies	LP	Cook	1184	1956	£6	£15	US

MILES, LIZZIE & BILLY YOUNG

Blues They Sang	7" EP	HMV	7EG8178	1956	£6	£12	

MILKSHAKES

Please Don't Tell My Baby	7"	Bilko	BILK0	1982	£1.50	£4	

MILKWOOD

Many of the groups to emerge as "new wave" at the end of the seventies were not as new as all that. The Cars evolved from a group called Milkwood, who released a (fairly) hard rock LP as early as 1973.

How's The Weather	LP	Paramount	PAS6046	1973	£15	£30	US

MILLENIUM

Begin	LP	Columbia	CS9663	1968	£5	£12	US

MILLER

Baby I Got News For You	7"	Columbia	DB7735	1965	£40	£80	
Baby I Got News For You	7"	Oak	RGJ190	1965	£60	£120	

MILLER, BETTY

Jack O'Diamonds	7"	Top Rank	JAR127	1959	£1.50	£4	

MILLER, BOB & THE MILLERMEN

625 Special	7"	Polydor	BM56005	1965	£1.50	£4	
Dig This	7"	Fontana	H181	1959	£1.50	£4	
Get Smart	7"	Columbia	DB7877	1966	£1.50	£4	
In The Mood	7"	Fontana	H228	1959	£1.50	£4	
Little Dipper	7"	Fontana	H192	1959	£1.50	£4	
Manhunt	7"	Fontana	H245	1960	£1.50	£4	
My Guy's Back	7"	Fontana	H236	1960	£1.50	£4	
Night Theme	7"	Fontana	H284	1960	£1.50	£4	
No Goodbyes	7"	CBS	202299	1966	£1.50	£4	
Oliver Twist	7"	Parlophone	R4854	1961	£1.50	£4	
Scamp	7"	Columbia	DB4017	1957	£1.50	£4	
Square Bash	7"	Columbia	DB4140	1958	£1.50	£4	
Sweet Charity	7"	Columbia	DB8269	1967	£1.50	£4	
Trouble Shooter	7"	Parlophone	R4779	1961	£1.50	£4	
Uptown And Downtown	7"	Mercury	MF947	1965	£1.50	£4	

MILLER, BOBBIE

Every Beat Of My Heart	7"	Decca	F12252	1965	£2	£5	
Everywhere I Go	7"	Decca	F12354	1966	£20	£40	Ian Stewart B side
What A Guy	7"	Decca	F12064	1965	£12.50	£25	

MILLER, CHUCK

Auctioneer	7"	Mercury	7MT153	1958	£7.50	£15	
Auctioneer	7"	Mercury	AMT1026	1959	£5	£10	
Down The Road Apiece	7"	Mercury	7MT215	1958	£12.50	£25	
Going Going Gone	7" EP	Mercury	ZEP10058	1960	£15	£30	
No Baby Like You	7"	Capitol	CL14543	1956	£5	£10	

MILLER, FRANKIE

Country Music	7" EP	Top Rank	JKP3013	1962	£7.50	£15	
Popping Johnnie	7"	Melodisc	1529	1959	£4	£8	

| Rain Rain | 7" | Melodisc | 1552 | 1960 | £2.50 | £6 | |
| True Blue | 7" | Melodisc | 1519 | 1959 | £5 | £10 | |

MILLER, GARY

Gary Miller Hit Parade Vol.1	7" EP	Pye	NEP24047	1957	£7.50	£15	
Gary Miller Hit Parade Vol.2	7" EP	Pye	NEP24072	1958	£5	£10	
Gary On The Ball	LP	Pye	NPL18059	1961	£4	£10	
Lollipop	7"	Pye	7N15136	1958	£1.50	£4	
Marina	7"	Pye	7N15239	1959	£1.50	£4	
Meet Mister Miller Pt.1	7" EP	Pye	NEP24057	1957	£4	£8	
Meet Mister Miller Pt.2	7" EP	Pye	NEP24058	1957	£4	£8	
Meet Mister Miller Pt.3	7" EP	Pye	NEP24059	1957	£4	£8	
Meet Mr.Miller	LP	Pye	NPL18008	1957	£6	£15	
Stingray	7"	Pye	7N15698	1964	£5	£10	
Story Of My Life	7"	Pye	7N15120	1958	£1.50	£4	chart single
Yellow Rose Of Texas	7" EP	Pye	NEP24013	1956	£7.50	£15	

MILLER, GLEN

| Rocksteady Party | 7" | Doctor Bird | DB1128 | 1968 | £5 | £10 | |
| Where Is The Love | 7" | Doctor Bird | DB1089 | 1967 | £5 | £10 | |

MILLER, GLENN

Army Airforce Band	LP	HMV	RLS637	1956	£25	£50	5 LP set
Concert Vol.1	10" LP	HMV	DLP1012	1953	£6	£15	
Concert Vol.2	10" LP	HMV	DLP1013	1953	£6	£15	
Concert Vol.3	10" LP	HMV	DLP1021	1953	£6	£15	
Concert Vol.4	10" LP	HMV	DLP1081	1955	£4	£10	
Glenn Miller	10" LP	Philips	BBR8072	1955	£4	£10	
Glenn Miller	10" LP	Philips	BBR8092	1956	£4	£10	
Glenn Miller Story	10" LP	HMV	DLP1024	1954	£4	£10	
I Got Rhythm	7"	Columbia	SCM5086	1954	£2	£5	
Limited Edition	LP	HMV	RLS598	1954	£25	£50	5 LP set
Limited Edition Vol.2	LP	HMV	RLS599	1956	£25	£50	5 LP set
Little Brown Jug	7"	HMV	7M195	1954	£4	£8	
Miller Magic	10" LP	HMV	DLP1122	1956	£4	£10	
Orchestra Wives	10" LP	HMV	DLP1059	1954	£4	£10	
Polka Dots And Moonbeams	10" LP	HMV	DLP1145	1957	£4	£10	
Sun Valley Serenade	10" LP	HMV	DLP1104	1955	£4	£10	
Sunrise Serenade	10" LP	HMV	DLP1062	1955	£4	£10	
Time For Melody	10" LP	HMV	DLP1049	1954	£4	£10	

MILLER, JIMMY BARBECUES

| Jelly Baby | 7" | Columbia | DB4081 | 1958 | £12.50 | £25 | |
| Sizzling Hot | 7" | Columbia | DB4006 | 1957 | £12.50 | £25 | |

MILLER, JODY

| Home Of The Brave | 7" | Capitol | CL15415 | 1965 | £1.50 | £4 | chart single |
| If You Were A Carpenter | 7" | Capitol | CL15482 | 1966 | £1.50 | £4 | |

MILLER, KENNY

| Take My Tip | 7" | Stateside | SS405 | 1965 | £10 | £20 | |

MILLER, MANDY

| Children's Choice | 7" EP | Parlophone | GEP8776 | 1958 | £4 | £8 | |
| Nellie The Elephant | 7" | Parlophone | R4219 | 1956 | £2 | £5 | |

MILLER, MAX

Cheeky Chappie	7" EP	HMV	7EG8558	1959	£2	£5	
Max At The Met	7" EP	Pye	NEP24154	1961	£2	£5	
Max At The Met	10" LP	Pye	NPT19026	1958	£4	£10	
Max At The Met Vol.2	7" EP	Pye	NEP24162	1962	£2	£5	

MILLER, MITCH

| Lisbon Antigua | 7" EP | Philips | BBE12043 | 1956 | £4 | £8 | |

MILLER, NED

Do What You Do Do Well	7"	London	HL9937	1964	£1.50	£4	chart single
From A Jack To A King	LP	Fabor	FLP1001	1963	£20	£40	US, coloured vinyl
From A Jack To A King	LP	London	HA8072	1963	£8	£20	
From A Jack To a King	7"	London	HL9648	1963	£1.50	£4	chart single
Go On Back, You Fool	7"	Capitol	CL15301	1963	£1.50	£4	
Just Before Dawn	7"	London	HL9728	1963	£1.50	£4	
Ned Miller	7" EP	Capitol	EAP120492	1963	£5	£10	
Ned Miller	7" EP	London	RE1382	1963	£6	£12	

MILLER, ROGER

Chug-a-Lug	7"	Philips	BF1365	1964	£1.50	£4	
Dang Me	7"	Philips	BF1354	1964	£1.50	£4	
Engine Engine No.9	7"	Philips	BF1416	1965	£1.50	£4	
England Swings	7"	Philips	BF1456	1965	£1.50	£4	chart single
Kansas City Star	7"	Philips	BF1437	1965	£1.50	£4	chart single
King Of The Road	7"	Philips	BF1397	1965	£1.50	£4	chart single
King Of The Road	7" EP	Philips	BE12578	1965	£4	£8	
Return Of Roger Miller	LP	Philips	BL7669	1966	£4	£10	
Roger And Out	LP	Philips	BL7667	1965	£4	£10	
Songs I Have Written	LP	Camden	CDN5121	1965	£4	£10	
Third Time Around	LP	Philips	BL7676	1966	£4	£10	
Words And Music	LP	Philips	BL7748	1966	£4	£10	

MILLER, RUSS

| Sit In My Window | 7" | HMV | POP391 | 1957 | £10 | £20 | |

MILLER, STEPHEN

Story So Far	LP	Caroline	C1507	1974	£4	£10	

MILLER, STEVE BAND

Steve Miller could never quite decide whether he wanted to lead a progressive rock outfit or a blues band - so for much of the time the group's early records are both. Boz Scaggs was a member long enough to appear on the first two albums, while "My Dark Hour" features a rare guest appearance from Paul McCartney, on bass, drums, and backing vocals, at a time when he was still technically a member of the Beatles.

Anthology	LP	Capitol	ESTSP12	1972	£5	£12	double
Children Of The Future	LP	Capitol	(S)T2920	1968	£4	£10	
Fly Like An Eagle	LP	Mobile Fidelity	MFSL1021	1978	£5	£12	US audiophile
Going To The Country	7"	Capitol	CL15656	1970	£1.50	£4	
Little Girl	7"	Capitol	CL15618	1969	£2	£5	
Living In The USA	7"	Capitol	CL15564	1968	£2	£5	
My Dark Hour	7"	Capitol	CL15604	1969	£2	£5	
Revolution	LP	United Artists	UAS5185	1968	£5	£12	US, with other artists
Sailor	LP	Capitol	(S)T2984	1969	£4	£10	
Sittin' In Circles	7"	Capitol	CL15539	1968	£2.50	£6	

MILLER, SUZI

Ay Ay Senores	7"	Decca	F10677	1956	£1.50	£4	
Banjo's Back In Town	7"	Decca	F10593	1955	£1.50	£4	
Dance With Me Henry	7"	Decca	F10512	1955	£2.50	£6	
Get Up Get Up	7"	Decca	F10722	1956	£1.50	£4	
Happy Days And Lonely Nights	7"	Decca	F10389	1954	£4	£8	chart single, with Johnston Brothers
I Love My Baby	7"	Decca	F10848	1957	£1.50	£4	
Tweedle Dee	7"	Decca	F10475	1955	£4	£8	
Two Step Side Step	7"	Decca	F10423	1954	£1.50	£4	with The Johnston Brothers

MILLIE

Best Of Jackie & Millie Vol.2	LP	Trojan	TTL52	1970	£6	£15	
Best Of Millie Small	LP	Island	ILP953	1967	£30	£60	
Best Of Millie Small	LP	Trojan	TTL49	1969	£6	£15	
Bloodshot Eyes	7"	Fontana	TF617	1965	£5	£10	chart single
Chicken Feed	7"	Fontana	TF796	1967	£2.50	£6	
Don't You Know	7"	Fontana	TF425	1963	£4	£8	
How Can I Be Sure	7"	Blue Beat	BB96	1961	£5	£10	with Owen Gray
I Love The Way You Love	7"	Fontana	TF502	1964	£2.50	£6	
I've Fallen In Love With A Snowman	7"	Fontana	TF515	1965	£2.50	£6	
Killer Joe	7"	Fontana	TF740	1966	£2.50	£6	
Millie	7" EP	Bluebeat	BBEP302	1961	£15	£30	
Millie & Her Boyfriends	LP	Trojan	TTL17	1969	£6	£15	
Millie And Her Boyfriends	7" EP	Island	IEP705	1966	£12.50	£25	
Millie Sings Fats Domino	LP	Fontana	TL5276	1965	£15	£30	
More Millie	LP	Fontana	(S)TL5220	1964	£10	£25	
My Boy Lollipop	LP	Smash	MGS27055	1964	£10	£25	US
My Boy Lollipop	7"	Fontana	TF449	1964	£2	£5	chart single
My Boy Lollipop	7" EP	Fontana	TE17425	1964	£7.50	£15	
My Love And I	7"	Pyramid	PYR6080	1970	£2	£5	
My Street	7"	Brit	WI1002	1965	£5	£10	
My Street	7"	Fontana	TF591	1965	£2.50	£6	
Pledging My Love	7"	Trojan	TTL47	1970	£6	£15	with Jackie Edwards
Readin' Writin' Arithmetic	7"	Decca	F12948	1969	£2.50	£6	
See You Later Alligator	7"	Fontana	TF529	1965	£2.50	£6	
Sugar Plum	7"	Island	WI014	1962	£5	£10	with Owen Gray
Sweet William	7"	Fontana	TF479	1964	£2.50	£6	chart single
This World	7"	Island	WI050	1962	£5	£10	with Roy Panton
Time Will Tell	LP	Trojan	TBL108	1970	£6	£15	
When I Dance With You	7"	Fontana	TF948	1968	£2	£5	
You Better Forget	7"	Island	WIP6021	1967	£4	£8	

MILLIGAN, SPIKE

I'm Walking Out With A Mountain	7"	Parlophone	R4839	1961	£1.50	£4	
Milligan Preserved	LP	Parlophone	PMC1148	1961	£5	£12	chart LP
Muses With Milligan	LP	Decca	LK4701	1965	£5	£12	
Olympic Team	7"	Pye	7N15720	1964	£1.50	£4	
Purple Aeroplane	7"	Parlophone	R5513	1966	£1.50	£4	
Q5 Piano Tune	7"	Parlophone	R5771	1969	£1.50	£4	
Tower Bridge	7"	Parlophone	R5543	1966	£1.50	£4	
Will I Find My Love Today	7"	Parlophone	R4406	1958	£1.50	£4	
World Of Beachcomber	LP	Pye	NPL18271	1969	£4	£10	
Wormwood Scrubs Tango	7"	Parlophone	R4891	1962	£1.50	£4	

MILLINDER, LUCKY

Grape Vine	78	Vogue	V9021	1951	£3	£8	
I'm Waiting Just For You	78	Vogue	V9007	1951	£3	£8	
Ram Bunk Shush	78	Vogue	V2138	1952	£3	£8	

MILLIONAIRES

Chatterbox	7"	Decca	F12468	1966	£12.50	£25	

MILLIONAIRES (2)

Never For Me	7"	Mercury	6052301	1973	£4	£8	black label

MILLS, BARBARA

Queen Of Fools	7"	Hickory	451323	1965	£37.50	£75	
Queen Of Fools	7"	London	HLE10491	1975	£2	£5	
Try	7"	Hickory	451392	1965	£2.50	£6	

MILLS BROTHERS

Title	Format	Label	Cat. No.	Year	Price	Price	Notes
Barber Shop Harmony	LP	Decca	DL8890	195-	£5	£12	US
Best Of The Mills Brothers	LP	Decca	DXB193/ DXSB7193	195-	£5	£12	US
Dream Of You	7"	Brunswick	05550	1956	£1.50	£4	
End Of The World	LP	London	HAD/SAHD8092	1963	£4	£10	
Four Boys And A Guitar	10" LP	Brunswick	LA8702	1955	£5	£12	
Get A Job	7"	London	HLD8553	1958	£6	£12	
Glow	LP	Decca	DL8827	195-	£5	£12	US
Greatest Hits	LP	London	HAD2192/ SHD6046	1959	£5	£12	
Greatest Hits	LP	London	HAD2319	1961	£5	£12	
Gum Drop	7"	Brunswick	05487	1955	£7.50	£15	
Harmonizin'	LP	Decca	DL8892	195-	£5	£12	US
How Blue?	7"	Brunswick	05325	1954	£4	£8	
I Got You	7"	London	HAD9169	1960	£1.50	£4	
In Hi-Fi	LP	Decca	DL8664	195-	£5	£12	US
I've Changed My Mind A Thousand Times	7"	Brunswick	05522	1956	£2.50	£6	
Louis Armstrong And The Mills Brothers	10" LP	Brunswick	LA8681	1954	£5	£12	
Meet The Mills Brothers	10" LP	Brunswick	LA8664	1954	£6	£15	
Memory Lane	LP	Decca	DL8219	195-	£5	£12	US
Mills Brothers	7" EP	London	RED1215	1959	£4	£8	
Mills Brothers No.2	7" EP	Brunswick	OE9060	1955	£4	£8	
Ninety-Eight Cents	7"	Brunswick	05600	1956	£1.50	£4	
One Dozen Roses	LP	Decca	DL8491	195-	£5	£12	US
Paper Valentine	7"	Brunswick	05390	1955	£2.50	£6	
Presenting	7" EP	Brunswick	OE9014	1954	£6	£12	
San Antonio Rose	LP	London	HAD2383/ SAHD6183	1961	£4	£10	
Sing	LP	London	HAD2250/ SHD6074	1960	£5	£12	
Singin' And Swingin'	LP	Decca	DL8209	195-	£5	£12	US
Singing And Swinging Pt.1	7" EP	Brunswick	OE9239	1956	£4	£8	
Smack Dab In The Middle	7"	Brunswick	05439	1955	£5	£10	
Souvenir Album	LP	Decca	DL8148	195-	£5	£12	US
Souvenir Album	10" LP	Decca	DL5102	195-	£8	£20	US
Suddenly There's A Valley	7"	Brunswick	05488	1955	£2.50	£6	
That's Right	7"	Brunswick	05606	1956	£2.50	£6	
Wonderful Words	10" LP	Decca	DL5337	195-	£8	£20	US
Yes You Are	7"	Brunswick	05452	1955	£2.50	£6	

MILLS, GARY

Title	Format	Label	Cat. No.	Year	Price	Price	Notes
Bless You	7"	Decca	F11383	1961	£1.50	£4	
Comin' Down With Love	7"	Top Rank	JAR393	1960	£1.50	£4	
Hey Baby	7"	Top Rank	JAR119	1959	£4	£8	
I'll Step Down	7"	Decca	F11358	1961	£1.50	£4	
Look For A Star	7"	Top Rank	JAR336	1960	£1.50	£4	chart single
Looking For A Star	7" EP	Top Rank	JKP3001	1961	£10	£20	
Running Bear	7"	Top Rank	JAR301	1960	£1.50	£4	
Sad Little Girl	7"	Decca	F11415	1961	£1.50	£4	
Save A Dream For Me	7"	Decca	F11471	1962	£1.50	£4	
Seven Little Girls Sitting In The Back Seat	7"	Top Rank	JAR219	1959	£1.50	£4	
Top Teen Baby	7"	Top Rank	JAR500	1960	£1.50	£4	chart single
Top Teen Baby	7"	Top Rank	JAR500	1960	£4	£8	PS
Who's Gonna Take You Home Tonight	7"	Top Rank	JAR542	1961	£1.50	£4	

MILLS, GORDON

Title	Format	Label	Cat. No.	Year	Price	Price	Notes
Do It Yourself	LP	Ace Of Clubs	ACL1191	1965	£4	£10	

MILLS, HAYLEY

Title	Format	Label	Cat. No.	Year	Price	Price	Notes
Gypsy Girl	LP	Mainstream	6090	1966	£5	£12	US stereo
In Search Of The Castaways	LP	Disneyland	ST3916	1962	£5	£12	US stereo
Jeepers Creepers	7"	Decca	F21442	1962	£1.50	£4	
Let's Get Together	LP	Buena Vista	STER3311	1962	£5	£12	US stereo
Let's Get Together	7"	Decca	F21396	1961	£1.50	£4	chart single
Parent Trap	LP	Buena Vista	STER3309	1961	£5	£12	US stereo
Pollyanna	LP	Disneyland	ST1960	1960	£5	£12	US
Summer Magic	LP	MGM	(S)E4025	1963	£5	£12	US

MILLS, MAUDE

Title	Format	Label	Cat. No.	Year	Price	Price	Notes
Maude Mills	7" EP	Vintage Jazz	VEP34	196-	£7.50	£15	

MILLS, RUDY

Title	Format	Label	Cat. No.	Year	Price	Price	Notes
John Jones	7"	Big Shot	BI509	1968	£4	£8	
Lemi Li	7"	Explosion	EX2007	1969	£2.50	£6	
Reggae Hits	LP	Pama	SECO12	1969	£8	£20	
Tears On My Pillow	7"	Crab	CRAB24	1969	£1.50	£4	

MILLS, STEPHANIE

Title	Format	Label	Cat. No.	Year	Price	Price	Notes
This Empty Place/I See You For The First Time	7"	Tamla Motown	TMG1020	1976	£15	£30	demo

MILLSTONE GRIT

Title	Format	Label	Cat. No.	Year	Price	Price	Notes
Millstone Grit	LP	Box	488	1980	£6	£15	

MILLTOWN BROTHERS

Title	Format	Label	Cat. No.	Year	Price	Price	Notes
Coming From The Mill	CD-s	Big Round	BIGR101CD	1989	£4	£10	

Title	Format	Label	Cat. No.	Year	Price	Price	Notes
Coming From The Mill	12"	Big Round	BIGR101T	1989	£4	£10	
Roses	7"	Big Round	BIGR101	1989	£2.50	£6	
Which Way Should I Jump	7"	Big Round	BIGR104	1989	£1.50	£4	
Which Way Should I Jump	12"	Big Round	BIGR104T	1989	£2.50	£6	

MILSAP, RONNIE

Title	Format	Label	Cat. No.	Year	Price	Price	Notes
Ain't No Sole Left In These Ole Shoes	7"	Pye	7N25392	1966	£10	£20	
Ain't No Soul	7"	Wand	WN26	1972	£2	£5	

MILSAP, RONNIE & ROSCOE ROBINSON

Title	Format	Label	Cat. No.	Year	Price	Price	Notes
Soul Sensations	7" EP	Pye	NEP44078	1966	£5	£10	

MILTON, JOHNNY & THE CONDORS

Title	Format	Label	Cat. No.	Year	Price	Price	Notes
Cry Baby	7"	Fontana	TF488	1964	£2	£5	
Somethin' Else	7"	Decca	F11862	1964	£2	£5	

MILTON, ROY

Title	Format	Label	Cat. No.	Year	Price	Price	Notes
Great Roy Milton	LP	Kent	554	1963	£10	£25	US

MILTON, ROY & CHUCK HIGGINS

Title	Format	Label	Cat. No.	Year	Price	Price	Notes
Rock'n'Roll Versus Rhythm And Blues	LP	Dooto	DL223	1959	£25	£50	US

MIMMS, GARNETT

Title	Format	Label	Cat. No.	Year	Price	Price	Notes
All About Love	7"	United Artists	UP1172	1966	£4	£8	
As Long As I Have You	LP	United Artists	UAL3396/ UAS6396	1965	£10	£25	US
As Long As I Love You	7"	United Artists	UP1186	1967	£2.50	£6	
Cry Baby	LP	United Artists	ULP1067	1963	£15	£30	
Cry Baby	7"	United Artists	UP1033	1963	£2.50	£6	
For Your Precious Love	7"	United Artists	UP1038	1963	£2.50	£6	
I Can Hear My Baby Crying	7"	Verve	VS569	1968	£4	£8	
I'll Take Good Care Of You	LP	United Artists	UAL3498/ UAS6498	1965	£10	£25	US
I'll Take Good Care Of You	7"	United Artists	UP1130	1966	£40	£80	
It Was Easier To Hurt Her	7"	United Artists	UP1090	1965	£5	£10	
It's Been Such A Long Way Home	7"	United Artists	UP1147	1966	£5	£10	
Live	LP	United Artists	(S)ULP1174	1967	£10	£25	
My Baby	7"	United Artists	UP1153	1966	£2	£5	
Roll With The Punches	7"	United Artists	UP1181	1967	£4	£8	
Tell Me Baby	7"	United Artists	UP1048	1964	£2.50	£6	
Warm And Soulful	LP	United Artists	(S)ULP1145	1966	£10	£25	
We Can Find That Love	7"	Verve	VS574	1968	£2.50	£6	

MIND EXPANDERS

Title	Format	Label	Cat. No.	Year	Price	Price	Notes
What's Happening	LP	Dot	DLP25773	1967	£8	£20	US, stereo
What's Happening	LP	Dot	DLP3773	1967	£30	£60	US, mono

MINDBENDERS

Title	Format	Label	Cat. No.	Year	Price	Price	Notes
Ashes To Ashes	7"	Fontana	TF731	1966	£1.50	£4	chart single
Ashes To Ashes	7" EP	Fontana	465322	1966	£6	£12	French
Blessed Are The Lonely	7"	Fontana	TF910	1968	£2.50	£6	
Can't Live With You	7"	Fontana	TF697	1966	£1.50	£4	chart single
Groovy Kind Of Love	LP	Fontana	MGF2/SRF67554	1966	£6	£15	US
Groovy Kind Of Love	7"	Fontana	TF644	1966	£1.50	£4	chart single
I Want Her, She Wants Me	7"	Fontana	TF780	1966	£1.50	£4	
Letter	7"	Fontana	TF869	1967	£1.50	£4	chart single
Mindbenders	LP	Fontana	(S)TL5324	1966	£8	£20	chart LP
Mindbenders	LP	Fontana	SFL13045	1968	£8	£20	
Schoolgirl	7"	Fontana	TF877	1967	£2.50	£6	
Uncle Joe The Ice Cream Man	7"	Fontana	TF961	1968	£4	£8	
We'll Talk About It Tomorrow	7"	Fontana	TF806	1967	£1.50	£4	
We'll Talk About It Tomorrow	7" EP	Fontana	465378	1967	£6	£12	French
With Woman In Mind	LP	Fontana	(S)TL5403	1967	£10	£25	

MINEO, SAL

Title	Format	Label	Cat. No.	Year	Price	Price	Notes
Aladdin	LP	Columbia	CL1117	1958	£17.50	£35	US
Cutting In	7"	Fontana	H118	1958	£10	£20	
Sal	LP	Fontana	TFL5004	1958	£17.50	£35	
Seven Steps To Love	7"	Fontana	H135	1958	£7.50	£15	
Start Moving	7"	Philips	JK1024	1958	£10	£20	chart single

MINGUS, CHARLES

Title	Format	Label	Cat. No.	Year	Price	Price	Notes
Black Saint And The Sinner Lady	LP	HMV	CLP1694	1963	£6	£15	
Blues And Roots	LP	London	LTZK15194/ SAHK6087	1960	£6	£15	
Charles Mingus	7" EP	Philips	BBE12399	1960	£2.50	£6	
Charles Mingus Presents Charles Mingus	LP	Atlantic	SD8005	1962	£8	£20	
Charlie Mingus	LP	Atlantic	ATL/SAL5019	1965	£6	£15	
Charlie Mingus Quintet With Max Roach	LP	Vocalion	LAEF/SEAF591	1965	£6	£15	
Chazz	LP	Vocalion	LAE543	1963	£6	£15	
Clown	LP	London	LTZK15164	1959	£8	£20	
Duke's Choice	LP	Atlantic	545111	1970	£5	£12	
East Coasting	LP	Parlophone	PMC1092	1959	£10	£25	
East Coasting	LP	Polydor	623215	1968	£5	£12	
Jazz Composers Workshop	LP	Realm	RM211	1966	£5	£12	
Jazz Experiments	LP	London	LTZN15087	1957	£10	£25	
Jazz Makers	7" EP	Mercury	10021MCE	1965	£2.50	£6	
Jazz Portraits	LP	United Artists	ULP1004	1962	£8	£20	
Jazz Workshop Vol.2	10" LP	Vogue	LDE178	1956	£20	£40	

Title	Format	Label	Catalogue	Year			Notes
Mingus Ah Um	LP	CBS	52346	1969	£4	£10	
Mingus Ah Um	LP	Philips	BBL7352	1960	£6	£15	
Mingus At Monterey	LP	Liberty	LDS84002	1969	£6	£15	double
Mingus Dynasty	LP	CBS	(S)BPG62261	1966	£5	£12	
Mingus Dynasty	7″ EP	Philips	BBE12451/	1961	£2.50	£6	
			SBBE9050				
Mingus Mingus Mingus	LP	HMV	CLP1742/CSD1545	1965	£6	£15	
Mingus Plays Piano	LP	HMV	CLP1796	1964	£6	£15	
Mingus Revisited	LP	Mercury	SMWL21056	1969	£5	£12	
My Favourite Quintet	LP	Liberty	LBS83346	1970	£5	£12	
Oh Yeah	LP	London	HAK/SHK8007	1962	£6	£15	
Pithecanthropus Erectus	LP	Atlantic	587131	1968	£6	£15	
Pithecanthropus Erectus	LP	London	LTZK15052	1957	£10	£25	
Reincarnation Of A Lovebird	LP	Atlantic	587166	1969	£5	£12	
Scenes In The City	7″ EP	Parlophone	GEP8786	1963	£2.50	£6	
Things Ain't What They Used To Be	7″ EP	Philips	BBE12453/	1961	£2.50	£6	
			SBBE9052				
Tijuana Moods	LP	RCA	RD/SF7514	1962	£8	£20	
Town Hall Concert	LP	United Artists	ULP1068	1965	£8	£20	
Trio	LP	London	LTZJ15129	1958	£10	£25	

MINIM

Wrapped In A Union Jack	LP	Polydor	582011	1967	£30	£60	

MINISTRY

Cold Life	12″	Situation 2	SIT17T	1982	£2.50	£6	
Work For Love	7″	Arista	ARIST510	1983	£1.50	£4	with cassette

MINISTRY OF SOUND

White Collar Worker	7″	Decca	F12449	1966	£5	£10	

MINNELLI, LIZA

Middle Of The Street	7″	Capitol	CL15483	1966	£2	£5	

MINOGUE, KYLIE

Got To Be Certain	CD-s	PWL	PWCD12	1988	£2.50	£6	
Got To Be Certain (Extra Beat Boys Mix)	12″	PWL	PWLT12R	1988	£3	£6	
Hand On Your Heart (Heartache Mix)	12″	PWL	PWLT35R	1989	£4	£10	
I Should Be So Lucky (Bicentennial Mix)	12″	PWL	PWLT8R	1988	£2.50	£6	
Je Ne Sais Pas Pourquoi	7″	PWL	PWLP21	1988	£4	£8	poster PS
Locomotion (Sankie Mix)	12″	PWL	PWLT14R	1988	£2.50	£6	
Wouldn't Change A Thing (Espagna Mix)	12″	PWL	PWLT42R	1989	£3	£8	

MINOR THREAT

Filler	7″	Dischord	3	1981	£25	£50	with insert
In My Eyes	7″	Dischord	5	1981	£25	£50	red vinyl, with insert
Out Of Step	LP	Discord		198-	£10	£25	US

MINORBOPS

Need You Tonight	7″	Vogue	V9110	1958	£60	£120	

MINOTAURUS

Fly Away	LP	private		1971	£30	£60	
Rain Over Thessalia	LP	Thorofon		1970	£30	£60	

MINSTRELS

Miss Highty Tighty	7″	Studio One	SO2050	1968	£6	£12	Westmorelites B side

MINUTE MEN

Yankee Diddle	7″	Capitol	CL15206	1961	£1.50	£4	

MINUTEMEN

Buzz Or Howl Under The Influence Of The Heat	12″	SST	SST016	1984	£2.50	£6	
Paranoid Time	7″	SST	SST002	1983	£2.50	£6	

MIRACLES

Ain't It Baby	7″	London	HL9366	1961	£25	£50	
Away We A Go Go	LP	Tamla Motown	(S)TML11044	1967	£10	£25	
Christmas With The Miracles	LP	Tamla	236	1963	£50	£100	US
Come On Do The Jerk	7″	Stateside	SS377	1965	£10	£20	
Cookin' With The Miracles	LP	Tamla	223	1962	£50	£100	US
Doin' Mickey's Monkey	LP	Tamla	245	1963	£25	£50	US, mono
Doin' Mickey's Monkey	LP	Tamla	T2245	1963	£40	£80	US, stereo
Fabulous Miracles	LP	Stateside	SL10099	1964	£30	£60	
From The Beginning	LP	Tamla Motown	(S)TML11031	1966	£10	£25	
Going To A Go Go	LP	Tamla Motown	TML11024	1966	£15	£30	
Going To A Go-Go	7″	Tamla Motown	TMG547	1966	£5	£10	chart single
Hi We're The Miracles	LP	Oriole	PS40044	1963	£30	£60	
Hi We're The Miracles	LP	Tamla	220	1961	£60	£120	US
I Gotta Dance To Keep From Crying	7″	Stateside	SS263	1964	£12.50	£25	
I Like It Like That	LP	Tamla Motown	TML11003	1965	£17.50	£35	
I Like It Like That	7″	Stateside	SS324	1964	£10	£20	
I'll Try Something New	LP	Tamla	230	1962	£50	£100	US
I'm The One You Need	7″	Tamla Motown	TMG584	1966	£6	£12	chart single
Man In You	7″	Stateside	SS282	1964	£10	£20	
Mickey's Monkey	7″	Oriole	CBA1863	1963	£25	£50	
My Girl Has Gone	7″	Tamla Motown	TMG540	1965	£6	£12	

On Stage	LP	Tamla	241	1963	£25	£50	US
Ooh Baby Baby	7"	Tamla Motown	TMG503	1965	£12.50	£25	
Shop Around	LP	Tamla	224	1962	£50	£100	US
Shop Around	7"	London	HL9276	1961	£25	£50	
Shop Around	7" EP.	London	RE1295	1961	£30	£60	
That's What Love Is Made Of	7"	Stateside	SS353	1964	£10	£20	
Tracks Of My Tears	7"	Tamla Motown	TMG522	1965	£12.50	£25	
What's So Good About Goodbye	7"	Fontana	H384	1962	£30	£60	
Whole Lotta Shakin' In My Heart	7"	Tamla Motown	TMG569	1966	£6	£12	
You've Really Got A Hold On Me	7"	Oriole	CBA1795	1963	£27.50	£55	

MIRACLES & OTHERS

Nothing But A Man	LP	Motown	MT/S630	1965	£10	£25	US

MIRAGE

Carolyn	7"	Page One	POF111	1969	£1.50	£4
Go Away	7"	CBS	202007	1965	£6	£12
Hold On	7"	Philips	BF1554	1967	£4	£8
It's In Her Kiss	7"	CBS	201772	1965	£6	£12
Mystery Lady	7"	Page One	POF078	1968	£1.50	£4
Tomorrow Never Knows	7"	Philips	BF1534	1966	£10	£20
Wedding Of Ramona Blair	7"	Philips	BF1571	1967	£7.50	£15

MIRETTES

Real Thing	7"	Uni	UN505	1968	£1.50	£4
To Love Somebody	7"	Uni	UN501	1968	£1.50	£4

MIRKWOOD

Mirkwood	LP	Flams Ltd	PR1067	1971	£330	£500

MIRROR

Gingerbread Man	7"	Philips	BF1666	1968	£15	£30

MISFITS

Beware	12"	Cherry Red	PLP9	1981	£25	£50
Horror Business	7"	Plan 9	PL1009	198-	£25	£50
Night Of The Living Dead	7"	Plan 9		1980	£25	£50

MISFITS (2)

You Won't See Me	7"	Aberdeen Students	PRI101	196-	£4	£8

MISS JANE

Bad Mind People	7"	Pama	PM704	1968	£2.50	£6

MISS LAVELL

Everybody's Got Somebody	7"	Vocalion	VP9236	1965	£5	£10

MISS X

Christine	7"	Ember	EMBS175	1963	£1.50	£4	chart single

MISSING LINK

Nevergreen	LP	United Artists	UAS29439	1972	£6	£15	German

MISSING SCIENTISTS

Big City Bright Lights	7"	Rough Trade	RT057	1980	£2.50	£6

MISSION

Beyond The Pale (Armageddon Mix)	CD-s	Mercury	MYTHCD6	1988	£2.50	£6	
Garden Of Delight	12"	Chapter 22		1986	£5	£12	promo
Kingdom Come	12"	Mercury	MYTHX7	1988	£6	£15	promo
Like A Hurricane	12"	Chapter 22	L12CHAP7	1986	£4	£10	autographed
Stay With Me	7"	Mercury	MYSG1	1986	£2	£5	autographed, gatefold PS
Wasteland	7"	Mercury	MYTHB2	1987	£2	£5	2 singles, 5 photos, boxed
Wasteland	12"	Mercury	MYTHX22DJ	1987	£2.50	£6	promo with poster
Wasteland (Annivesay Mix)	12"	Mercury	MYTHX22	1987	£2.50	£6	

MISSION BELLES

Sincerely	7"	Decca	F12154	1965	£1.50	£4

MISSUS BEASTLY

Dr.Aftershave And The Mixed Pickles	LP	April	001	1976	£4	£10	German
Missus Beastly	LP	Nova	622030	1974	£6	£15	German
Nara Asst Incense	LP	Opp	532	1970	£15	£30	German

MISTY

Misty	LP	Cottage		1977	£15	£30

MISUNDERSTOOD

Children Of The Sun	7"	Fontana	TF998	1969	£12.50	£25	
I Can Take You To The Sun	7"	Fontana	TF777	1966	£12.50	£25	
Never Had A Girl Like You	7"	Fontana	TF1041	1969	£10	£20	
You're Tough Enough	7"	Fontana	TF1028	1969	£7.50	£15	
You're Tuff Enough	7"	Fontana	TF1028	1969	£12.50	£25	PS

MITCHELL, BLUE

Bantu Village	LP	Blue Note	BST84324	1969	£6	£15
Boss Horn	LP	Blue Note	BLP/BST84257	1967	£10	£25
Bring It Home To Me	LP	Blue Note	BLP/BST84228	1966	£10	£25

Collision In Black	LP	Blue Note	BST84300	1968	£6	£15	
Down With It	LP	Blue Note	BLP/BST84214	1965	£10	£25	
Heads Up!	LP	Blue Note	BST84272	1968	£10	£25	
Smooth As The Wind	LP	Riverside	RLP367	1961	£6	£15	
Thing To Do	LP	Blue Note	BLP/BST84178	1964	£6	£15	

MITCHELL, CHAD TRIO

Dona Dona Dona	7" EP	Kapp	KEV13015	1965	£7.50	£15	French
Lizzie Borden	7"	London	HLR9509	1962	£1.50	£4	
Paddy	7" EP	Colpix	CPS855	1965	£6	£12	French, no PS

MITCHELL, GUY

Alabam	7"	London	HLB10190	1968	£1.50	£4	
Before You Take Your Love FRom Me	7"	London	HLB10218	1968	£1.50	£4	
Best Of Guy Mitchell	LP	Realm	RM52336	1966	£5	£12	
Call Rosie On The Phone	7"	Philips	JK1027	1957	£5	£10	chart single
C'mon Let's Go	7"	Philips	PB766	1958	£2.50	£6	
Feet Up	7"	Columbia	SCM5018	1952	£7.50	£15	chart single
Go Tiger Go	7"	Pye	7N25179	1963	£5	£10	
Guy In Love	LP	Philips	BBL7246	1958	£8	£20	
Guy Mitchell	7" EP	Columbia	SEG7513	1954	£5	£10	
Guy Mitchell Sings	10" LP	Columbia	33S1028	1954	£15	£30	
Hangin' Around	7"	Philips	PB830	1958	£1.50	£4	
Have I Told You Lately That I Love You	7"	Pye	7N25185	1963	£1.50	£4	
Heartaches By The Number	7"	Philips	PB964	1959	£1.50	£4	chart single
Just Wish You'd Maybe Change Your Mind	7"	London	HLB10234	1968	£1.50	£4	
Knee Deep In The Blues	7"	Philips	JK1005	1957	£7.50	£15	
Let It Shine, Let It Shine	7"	Philips	PB858	1958	£1.50	£4	
My Heart Cries For You	7"	Philips	PB885	1958	£1.50	£4	
My Shoes Keep Walking Back To You	7"	Philips	PB1050	1960	£1.50	£4	
Pennies From Heaven	7" EP	Philips	BBE12215	1958	£6	£12	
Pretty Little Black Eyed Susie	7"	Columbia	SCM5037	1953	£7.50	£15	chart single
Pride O' Dixie	7"	Philips	PB915	1959	£1.50	£4	
Rock-a-Billy	7"	Philips	JK1015	1957	£7.50	£15	chart single
She Wears Red Feathers	7"	Columbia	SCM5032	1953	£7.50	£15	chart single
Showcase Of Hits	LP	Philips	BBL7265	1958	£8	£20	
Singing The Blues	7"	CBS	202238	1966	£5	£10	
Singing The Blues	7"	Philips	JK1001	1956	£7.50	£15	chart single
Singing The Blues	7" EP	Philips	BBE12112	1957	£6	£12	
Sings No.1	7" EP	Philips	BBE12008	1955	£5	£10	
Sings No.2	7" EP	Philips	BBE12093	1956	£6	£12	
Successes	7" EP	Columbia	SEG7598	1955	£5	£10	
Sunshine Guitar	LP	Philips	BBL7465	1961	£8	£20	
Sweet Stuff	7"	Philips	JK1023	1957	£5	£10	chart single
Train Of Love	7"	Columbia	SCM5022	1953	£7.50	£15	
Travelling Shoes	LP	London	HAB/SHB8364	1968	£5	£12	
Travelling Shoes	7"	London	HLB10173	1967	£1.50	£4	
Voice Of Your Choice	10" LP	Philips	BBR8031	1955	£10	£25	
Wonderful Guy	7" EP	Columbia	SEG7581	1955	£5	£10	
Wonderin' And Worryin'	7"	Philips	PB798	1958	£1.50	£4	

MITCHELL, JONI

Joni Mitchell's way with words, combined with an ear for an unusual melody, a love of musical change and adventure, and above all, a beautiful voice, has made her into one of the world's dozen or so truly essential rock artists. This Guide persists in listing her first LP as "Song To A Seagull", since although the label has only the more prosaic "Joni Mitchell", the cover has the more interesting title spelled out by seagulls, painted, as the majority of her album sleeves are, by Joni Mitchell herself.

Chelsea Morning		Reprise	RS23402	1969	£1.50	£4	
Chinese Cafe	7"	Geffen	DA3122	1983	£1.50	£4	with interview 7'
Clouds	LP	Reprise	RSLP6341	1969	£5	£12	
Court And Spark	LP	Asylum	EQ10001	1974	£6	£15	US quad
Court And Spark	LP	Nautilus	NR11	1981	£6	£12	US audiophile
Hissing Of Summer Lawns	LP	Asylum	EQ1051	1975	£6	£15	US quad
Hissing Of Summer Lawns	LP	Nimbus/ Asylum	K53018	1982	£5	£12	audiophile
Ladies Of The Canyon	LP	Reprise	RSLP6376	1970	£5	£12	chart LP
Night In The City	7"	Reprise	RS20694	1968	£1.50	£4	
Song To A Seagull	LP	Reprise	RSLP6293	1968	£5	£12	
Wild Things Run Fast	LP	Geffen	GHS2019	1982	£10	£25	US audiophile promo
You Turn Me On I'm A Radio	7"	Asylum	AYM511	1972	£2.50	£6	

MITCHELL, KEVIN

| Free And Easy | LP | Topic | 12TS314 | 1977 | £6 | £15 | |

MITCHELL, MCKINLEY

| Town I Live In | 7" | President | PT125 | 1968 | £1.50 | £4 | |

MITCHELL, PAT

| Uillean Pipes | LP | Topic | 12TS294 | 1976 | £5 | £12 | |

MITCHELL, PHILIP

| Free For All | 7" | Jayboy | BOY57 | 1972 | £1.50 | £4 | |
| I'm Gonna Build California | 7" | Jay Boy | BOY37 | 1971 | £1.50 | £4 | |

MITCHELL, RED

| Presenting Red Mitchell | LP | Contemporary | LAC12155 | 1959 | £8 | £20 | |
| Red Mitchell | LP | London | LTZN15041 | 1957 | £8 | £20 | |

MITCHELL, RONNIE

| How Many Times | 7" | London | HLU9220 | 1960 | £2 | £5 | |

MITCHELL, SINX
Weird Sensation .... 7" ...... Hickory .... 451248 .... 1964 ... £2.50 ....£6 ....

MITCHELL, WARREN
Alf Garnett - Sex And Other Thoughts . LP ..... Pye .... NPL18192 .... 1968 ... £4 ....£10 ....
Till Death Us Do Part .... LP ..... Pye .... NPL18154 .... 1966 ... £4 ....£10 ....with other artists

MITCHELL, WILLIE
20-75	7"	London	HLU9926	1964	£4	£8	
Bad Eye	7"	London	HLU10039	1966	£1.50	£4	
Driving Beat	LP	Hi	(S)HL32029	1966	£5	£12	US
Everything Is Gonna Be Alright	7"	London	HLU10004	1965	£5	£10	
Hit Sound Of Willie Mitchell	LP	London	HAU8319	1967	£5	£12	
Hold It	LP	Hi	(S)HL32021	1964	£5	£12	US
It's Dance Time	LP	Hi	(S)HL32026	1965	£5	£12	US
Live	LP	London	HAU/SHU8368	1968	£5	£12	
Mercy	7"	London	HLU10085	1966	£1.50	£4	
On Top	LP	London	HAU/SHU8388	1969	£5	£12	
Ooh Baby, You Turn Me On	LP	Hi	(S)HL32039	1967	£5	£12	US
Solid Soul	LP	London	HAU/SHU8372	1969	£5	£12	
Soul Bag	LP	London	HAU/SHU8408	1970	£5	£12	
Soul Serenade	LP	London	HAU/SHU8365	1968	£5	£12	
Soul Serenade	7"	London	HLU10186	1968	£1.50	£4	chart single
Sunrise Serenade	LP	Hi	(S)HL32010	1963	£5	£12	US

MITCHELLS
Get Those Elephants Outa Here .... LP ..... MGM .... C803 .... 1960 ... £8 ....£20 ....

MITCHUM, ROBERT
Calypso Is Like So	LP	Capitol	T853		£10	£25	US
Rachel And The Stranger	7" EP.	Brunswick	OE9197	1955	£5	£10	
What Is This Generation Coming To?	7"	Capitol	CL14701	1957	£1.50	£4	

MITHRANDIR
For You The Old Women .... LP ..... private .... 1976 ... £20 ....£40 .... US

MITTOO, JACKIE
Ba Ba Boom	7"	Coxsone	CS7009	1967	£5	£10	Slim Smith B side
Can I Change My Mind	7"	Bamboo	BAM31	1970	£2	£5	Brentford Allstars B side
Clean Up	7"	Bamboo	BAM15	1969	£2.50	£6	
Dancing Groove	7"	Bamboo	BAM51	1970	£2	£5	Black & George B side
Dark Of The Moon	7"	Bamboo	BAM17	1970	£2	£5	
Dark Of The Sun	7"	Doctor Bird	DB1177	1969	£5	£10	Matador Allstars B side
Evening Time	LP	Coxsone	CSL8014	1968	£50	£100	
Gold Dust	7"	Bamboo	BAM20	1970	£2	£5	Supertones B side
Holy Holy	7"	Bamboo	BAM315	1970	£2	£5	Larry Marshall B side
In London	LP	Coxsone	CSL8009	1967	£50	£100	
Keep On Dancing	LP	Coxsone	CSL8020	1969	£50	£100	
Killer Diller	7"	Island	WI293	1966	£5	£10	Patrick Hytton B side
Man Pon Spot	7"	Coxsone	CS7046	1968	£5	£10	Bop & The Beltones B side
Mission Impossible	7"	Coxsone	CS7075	1968	£5	£10	Heptones B side
Napoleon Solo	7"	Coxsone	CS7050	1968	£5	£10	Cannonball Bryan B side
Norwegian Wood	7"	Coxsone	CS7040	1968	£5	£10	Gaylads B side
Now	LP	Bamboo	BDLPS209	1970	£6	£15	
Our Thing	7"	Bamboo	BAM6	1969	£2.50	£6	C.Marshall B side
Peenie Wallie	7"	Bamboo	BAM320	1970	£2	£5	Roy Richards B side
Put It On	7"	Studio One	SO2043	1968	£6	£12	Soul Vendors B side
Ram Jam	7"	Coxsone	CS7019	1967	£5	£10	Summertaires B side
Somebody Help Me	7"	Coxsone	CS7002	1967	£5	£10	Gaylads B side
Somethin' Stupid	7"	Coxsone	CS7026	1967	£5	£10	Lyrics B side
Songbird	7"	Coxsone	CS7070	1968	£5	£10	
Sure Shot	7"	Coxsone	CS7042	1968	£5	£10	Octaves B side

MIXED BAG
Potiphar .... 7" ...... Decca .... F12880 .... 1969 ... £2 ....£5 ....
Round And Round .... 7" ...... Decca .... F12907 .... 1969 ... £1.50 ....£4 ....

MIXTURE
One By One .... 7" ...... Fontana .... TF640 .... 1965 ... £1.50 ....£4 ....

MIXTURES
Stompin' At The Rainbow .... LP ..... Linda .... 3301 .... 1962 ... £8 ....£20 .... US

MIZZY, VIC
Addams Family Main Theme .... 7" ...... RCA .... RCA1440 .... 1965 ... £1.50 ....£4 ....

MJ6
Private Eye .... 7" ...... Decca .... F11212 .... 1960 ... £1.50 ....£4 ....

MO & CO
You've Got A Friend .... LP ..... Cottage .... COT131 .... 1979 ... £6 ....£15 ....

MOB
I Dig Everything About You .... 7" ...... Polydor .... 2001127 .... 1971 ... £1.50 ....£4 ....

MOBLEY, HANK
All Stars .... LP ..... Blue Note .... BLP/BST81544 ...... 196- .... £15 ....£30 ....

Caddy For Daddy	LP	Blue Note	BLP/BST84230	1966	£8	£20
Dippin'	LP	Blue Note	BLP/BST84209	1965	£15	£30
Flip	LP	Blue Note	BST84329	1969	£5	£12
Hi Voltage	LP	Blue Note	BST84273	1968	£8	£20
Jazz Message No.2	LP	London	LTZC15099	1957	£15	£30
Mobley's Message	LP	Esquire	32029	1957	£15	£30
No Room For Squares	LP	Blue Note	BLP/BST84149	1963	£10	£25
Reach Out!	LP	Blue Note	BST84288	1968	£6	£15
Roll Call	LP	Blue Note	BLP/BST84058	1961	£15	£30
Soul Station	LP	Blue Note	BLP/BST84031	196-	£20	£40
Turnaround!	LP	Blue Note	BLP/BST84186	1964	£15	£30
Workout	LP	Blue Note	BLP/BST84080	1961	£15	£30

MOBY GRAPE

When Columbia records in America decided to try the marketing device of simultaneously releasing every track from Moby Grape's first LP on five singles, this was certainly recognition of the fact that every track is distinctive enough to withstand the treatment. The LP is frequently held up as San Francisco's best, an assessment that is not far from the truth. Thereafter, Moby Grape's career was one of decline, although "Wow" has its moments. The "Grape Jam" record that accompanied the US release is a wasted opportunity, however. Acquiring the services of a master guitarist like Mike Bloomfield and then sitting him in front of a piano is simply daft.

Can't Be So Bad	7"	CBS	3555	1968	£2.50	£6	
Moby Grape	LP	CBS	(S)BPG63090	1967	£15		
Moby Grape	LP	San Francisco Sound	04805	1983	£5	£12	US audiophile
Moby Grape '69	LP	CBS	63430	1969	£4	£10	
Omaha	7"	CBS	2935	1967	£5	£10	
Trucking Man	7"	CBS	3945	1969	£4	£8	
Truly Fine Citizen	LP	CBS	63698	1970	£4	£10	
Wow	LP	CBS	63271	1968	£6	£15	
Wow/Grape Jam	LP	Columbia	CS9613	1968	£8	£20	US double
Wow/Grape Jam	LP	San Francisco Sound	04801	1983	£8	£20	US audiophile double

MOCK TURTLES

And Then She Smiles	12"	Mirage	015	1989	£2.50	£6
Pomona	12"	Mirage	003	1987	£5	£12
Wicker Man	12"	Mirage	009	1989	£3	£8

MOCKINGBIRDS

How To Find A Lover	7"	Decca	F12510	1966	£10	£20
I Can Feel We're Parting	7"	Columbia	DB7565	1965	£12.50	£25
One By One	7"	Decca	F12434	1966	£10	£20
That's How It's Gonna Stay	7"	Columbia	DB7480	1965	£12.50	£25
You Stole My Love	7"	Immediate	IM015	1965	£25	£50

M.O.D.

M.O.D.	7"	Vertigo	6059233	1979	£2	£5

MODERN ART

Dreams To Live	7"	Color Disc	COLORS1	1985	£10	£20
Penny Valentine	7"	Color Disc	COLORS5	198-	£4	£8
Stereoland	LP	Color Disc	COLOR3	1987	£20	£40

MODERN ENGLISH

Drowning Man	7"	Limp	LMP2	1979	£6	£12
Gathering Dust	7"	4AD	AD15	1980	£2	£5
Smiles And Laughter	7"	4AD	AD110	1981	£1.50	£4
Swans On Glass	7"	4AD	AD6	1980	£2	£5

MODERN EON

Euthenics	7"	Inevitable	INEV003	1981	£2	£5
Pieces	7"	Modern Eon	EON001	1980	£6	£12

MODERN FOLK QUARTET

Changes	LP	Warner Bros	WM8157	1964	£4	£10	
Love Of A Clown	7"	Warner Bros	WB147	1964	£1.50	£4	
Modern Folk Quartet	LP	Warner Bros	WM/WS8135	1963	£4	£10	
Night Time Girl	7"	RCA	RCA1514	1966	£4	£8	
Palm Springs Weekend	LP	Warner Bros	W(S)1519	1963	£5	£12	US, with Connie Stevens

MODERN JAZZ QUARTET

All Of You	7" EP	Fontana	469204TE	195-	£2	£5	
At Music Inn	LP	London	LTZK15085	1957	£5	£12	
At Music Inn	LP	London	LTZK15173/ SAHK6050	1959	£5	£12	
At Music Inn	7" EP	London	REK1320	1961	£2	£5	
At The Opera House	LP	Columbia	33CX10128	1958	£8	£20	with Oscar Peterson
Best Of The Modern Jazz Quartet	LP	Stateside	SL10141	1965	£4	£10	
Comedy Suite	LP	London	HAK/SHK8046	1963	£4	£10	
Concorde	LP	Transatlantic	PR7005	196-	£6	£15	
European Concert	7" EP	London	REK1319	1961	£2	£5	
Five Ways Of Playing La Ronde	7" EP	Esquire	EP166	1958	£2	£5	
Fontessa	LP	London	LTZK15022/ SAHK6031	1957	£5	£12	
Gershwin Ballad Medley	7" EP	Esquire	EP116	195-	£2	£5	
Lonely Woman	LP	London	HAK/SHK8016	1963	£4	£10	
Lonely Woman	LP	Esquire	HAK8016	1962	£4	£10	
Looking Back	LP	Esquire	32124	1961	£5	£12	
Modern Jazz Quartet	LP	London	LTZK15136	1958	£5	£12	
Modern Jazz Quartet	7" EP	Esquire	EP106	195-	£2	£5	
Modern Jazz Quartet	7" EP	Esquire	EP109	195-	£2	£5	

Modern Jazz Quartet	7" EP..	London	EZK19047	1959	£2	£5	
Modern Jazz Quartet	7" EP..	London	REK1314	1961	£2	£5	
Modern Jazz Quartet	10" LP	Esquire	20038	1955	£20	£40	
Modern Jazz Quartet Vol.2	10" LP	Esquire	20069	1956	£20	£40	
Odds Against Tomorrow	LP	London	LTZK15181	1960	£5	£12	
One Never Knows	LP	London	LTZK15140/ SAHK6029	1958	£6	£15	
One Never Knows	7" EP..	London	EZK19046	1959	£2	£5	
Pyramid	LP	London	LTZK15193/ SAHK6086	1960	£5	£12	
Quartet	7" EP..	London	EZC19019	1957	£2	£5	
Quartet Is A Quartet Is A Quartet	LP	Atlantic	587044	1966	£4	£10	
Sheriff	LP	London	HAK/SHK8161	1964	£4	£10	
Space	LP	Apple	SAPCOR10	1969	£17.50	£35	single or gatefold sleeve, Sleeve pictured in Guide
Third Stream Music	LP	London	LTZK15207/ SAHK6124	1961	£5	£12	
Under The Jasmine Tree	LP	Apple	APCOR4	1968	£17.50	£35	mono
Under The Jasmine Tree	LP	Apple	SAPCOR4	1968	£15	£30	stereo

MODERN JAZZ SEXTET

Modern Jazz Sextet	LP	Columbia	33CX10048	1956	£20	£40	

MODERN JAZZ SOCIETY

Concert Of Contemporary Music	LP	Columbia	33CX10038	1956	£20	£40	

MODERNAIRES

April In Paris	7"	Vogue Coral	Q72169	1956	£1.50	£4	
At My Front Door	7"	Vogue Coral	Q72112	1955	£4	£8	
Birds And Puppies And Tropical Fish	7"	Vogue Coral	Q72069	1955	£2.50	£6	
Go On With The Wedding	7"	Vogue Coral	Q72158	1956	£1.50	£4	
Here Comes The Modernaires	LP	Coral	LVA9080	1958	£5	£12	
Let's Dance	7"	Vogue Coral	Q72135	1956	£1.50	£4	
Mood Indigo	7"	Vogue Coral	Q2024	1954	£2.50	£6	
New Juke Box Saturday Night	7"	Vogue Coral	Q2035	1954	£2.50	£6	
Sluefoot	7"	Vogue Coral	Q72084	1955	£2.50	£6	
Stop, Look And Listen	10" LP	Vogue Coral	LVC10012	1955	£6	£15	

MODS

Something On My Mind	7"	RCA	RCA1399	1964	£2	£5	

MODUGNO, DOMENICO

Ciao Ciao Bambina	7"	Oriole	CB1489	1959	£1.50	£4	chart single
Volare	7"	Oriole	CB1460	1958	£1.50	£4	
Volare	7"	Oriole	CB5000	1958	£1.50	£4	chart single

MODULATIONS

I Can't Fight Your Love	7"	Buddah	BDS406	1974	£1.50	£4	

MOFFAT ALLSTARS

Riot	7"	Jackpot	JP719	1969	£2.50	£6	Impersonators B side

MOGUL THRASH

Mogul Thrash	LP	RCA	SF8156	1971	£6	£15	
Sleeping In The Kitchen	7"	RCA	RCA2030	1970	£2	£5	

MOHAWK, ESSRA

Essra Mohawk	LP	Mooncrest	CREST24	1975	£5	£12	

MOHAWKS

Baby Hold On	7"	Pama	PM739	1968	£2.50	£6	
Champ	7"	Pama	PM719	1968	£5	£10	
Mony Mony	7"	Pama	PM757	1968	£2.50	£6	
Ride Your Pony	7"	Pama	PM758	1968	£2.50	£6	
Sweet Soul Music	7"	Pama	PM751	1968	£2.50	£6	

MOJO HANNAH

Six Days On The Road	LP	Kingdom	KVL9001	1972	£6	£15	

MOJO MEN

Dance With Me	7"	Pye	7N25336	1965	£4	£8	
Dance With Me	7" EP..	Vogue	INT18050	1965	£25	£50	French
Hanky Panky	7"	Reprise	RS20486	1966	£10	£20	
Me About You	7"	Reprise	RS20580	1967	£4	£8	
Sit Down I Think I Love You	7"	Reprise	RS20539	1967	£4	£8	

MOJOS

Comin' On To Cry	7"	Decca	F12127	1965	£5	£10	
Everything's Alright	7"	Decca	F11853	1964	£2.50	£6	chart single
Forever	7"	Decca	F11732	1963	£4	£8	
Goodbye Dolly Gray	7"	Decca	F12557	1967	£6	£12	
Mojos	7" EP..	Decca	DFE8591	1964	£20	£40	
Seven Daffodils	7"	Decca	F11959	1964	£2.50	£6	chart single
Until My Baby Comes Home	7"	Liberty	LBF15097	1968	£10	£20	
Wait A Minute	7"	Decca	F12231	1965	£7.50	£15	Stu James credit
Why Not Tonight	7"	Decca	F11918	1964	£2.50	£6	chart single

MOLES
Noting that the Moles' single was on the Parlophone label, and that it had moreover been produced by George Martin, many observers concluded that it must be a Beatles performance. In fact, "the Moles" was indeed a pseudonym, but for the rather less exciting Simon Dupree And The Big Sound.
We Are The Moles .... 7" ...... Parlophone...... R5743 .... 1968 ... £12.50 .....£25 ....

MOLLOY, MATT
Heathery Breeze .... LP ...... Polydor .... 2904018................ 1981 ... £5 ....£12 .... Irish
Matt Molloy .... LP ...... Mulligan .... LUN004 .... 1976 ... £5 ....£12 .... Irish

MOLLOY, MATT, PAUL BRADY, TOMMY PEOPLES
Matt Molloy, Paul Brady, Tommy .... LP ...... Mulligan .... LUN017 .... 1978 ... £5 ....£12 .... Irish
Peoples

MOLLY HATCHET
Beatin' The Odds .... LP ...... Epic .... AS99844 .... 1980 ... £10 ......£25 ..... US promo pic disc
Flirtin' With Disaster .... LP ...... CBS .... AL36110 .... 1979 ... £10 ......£25 ....US pic disc
Molly Hatchet .... LP ...... Epic .... 35347 .... 1978 ... £10 ......£25 ....US pic disc
Take No Prisoners .... LP ...... Epic .... AS991320 .... 1981 ... £10 ......£25 ..... US promo pic disc

MOLOCH
Moloch .... LP ...... Enterprise ...... ENS1002 .... £10 ......£25 .... US

MOLONEY, MICK
We Have Met Together .... LP ...... Transatlantic ... TRA263 .... 1973 ... £6 ....£15 ....

MOLONEY, PADDY & SEAN POTTS
Tin Whistles .... LP ...... Claddagh .... CC15 .... 1974 ... £6 ....£15 .... Irish

MOMENTS
Walk Right In .... 7" ...... London .... HLN9656 .... 1963 ... £1.50 ......£4 ....

MON DYH
Murderer .... LP ...... Elgenprod....... 6622192............... 1981 ... £5 ....£12 ....German

MONARCHS
Look Homeward Angel .... 7" ...... London .... HLU9862 .... 1964 ... £6 ....£12 ....

MONCUR III, GRACHAN
Evolution .... LP ...... Blue Note....... BLP/BST84153 ...... 1963 ... £8 ....£20 ....
Some Other Stuff .... LP ...... Blue Note....... BLP/BST84177 ...... 1964 ... £8 ....£20 ....

MONDAY, PAUL
Paul Monday was one of several names used by the man who found success as Gary Glitter.
Here Comes The Sun .... 7" ...... MCA................ MK5008 .... 1969 ... £4 ....£8 ....
Musical Man .... 7" ...... MCA................ MU1024 .... 1968 ... £5 ....£10 ....

MONEY
Breaking Of Her Heart .... 7" ...... Major Minor .... MM669 .... 1970 ... £1.50 ......£4 ....
Come Laughing Home .... 7" ...... Major Minor .... MM620 .... 1969 ... £2 ....£5 ....

MONEY, ZOOT
Big Time Operator .... 7" ...... Columbia........ DB7975 .... 1966 ... £4 ....£8 ....chart single
Big Time Operator .... 7" EP.. Columbia........ ESRF1801 .... 1966 ... £20 ......£40 ....French
Big Time Operator .... 7" EP.. Columbia........ SEG8519 .... 1966 ... £20 ......£40 ....
Good .... 7" ...... Columbia........ DB7518 .... 1965 ... £7.50 ...£15 ....
It Should Have Been Me .... LP ...... Columbia........ SX1734 .... 1965 ... £30 ......£60 ....
Let's Run For Cover .... 7" ...... Columbia........ DB7876 .... 1966 ... £5 ....£10 ....
Nick Knack .... 7" EP.. Columbia........ ESRF1874 .... 1967 ... £15 ......£30 ....French
Nick Nack .... 7" ...... Columbia........ DB8172 .... 1967 ... £6 ....£12 ....
No One But You .... 7" ...... Polydor .... 2058020............... 1970 ... £2.50 ...£6 ....
Please Stay .... 7" ...... Columbia........ DB7600 .... 1965 ... £5 ....£10 ....
Please Stay .... 7" EP.. Columbia........ ESRF1766 .... 1966 ... £15 ......£30 ....French
Something Is Worrying Me .... 7" ...... Columbia........ DB7697 .... 1965 ... £6 ....£12 ....
Star Of the Show .... 7" ...... Columbia........ DB8090 .... 1966 ... £6 ....£12 ....
Transition .... LP ...... Direction .... 863231................. 1968 ... £10 ......£25 ....
Uncle Willie .... 7" ...... Decca .... F11954................. 1964 ... £6 ....£12 ....
Welcome To My Head .... LP ...... Capitol .... 318....................... 1969 ... £8 ....£20 .... US
Zoot .... LP ...... Columbia........ SX/SCX6075 .... 1966 ... £10 ......£25 ....chart LP
Zoot Money .... LP ...... Polydor .... 2482019............... 1970 ... £6 ....£15 ....

MONGREL
Get Your Teeth Into This .... LP ...... Polydor .... 2383182............... 1973 ... £8 ....£20 ....

MONGRELS
I Long To Hear .... 7" ...... Decca .... F12003................. 1964 ... £10 ......£20 ....
My Love For You .... 7" ...... Decca .... F12086................. 1965 ... £10 ......£20 ....

MONITORS
Greetings We're The Monitors .... LP ...... Tamla Motown .. (S)TML11108 .... 1969 ... £20 ......£40 ....

MONK, THELONIOUS
Alone In San Francisco .... LP ...... Riverside .... RLP312 .... 1965 ... £5 ....£12 ....
Blue Monk .... 7" EP.. Esquire .... EP246 .... 1962 ... £2 ....£5 ....
Brilliant Corners .... LP ...... London .... LTZU15097 .... 1957 ... £10 ......£25 ....
Brilliant Corners .... LP ...... Riverside .... RLP12226 .... 1961 ... £8 ....£20 ....
Criss-Cross .... LP ...... CBS .... (S)BPG62173 ...... 1964 ... £4 ....£10 ....
Five By Monk By Five .... LP ...... Riverside .... RLP305 .... 1965 ... £5 ....£12 ....
Genius Of Modern Music Vol.1 .... LP ...... Blue Note....... BLP/BST81510 ...... 1964 ... £10 ......£25 ....
Genius Of Modern Music Vol.2 .... LP ...... Blue Note....... BLP/BST81511 ...... 1964 ... £10 ......£25 ....
Golden Monk .... LP ...... Stateside .... SL10152 .... 1965 ... £5 ....£12 ....

In Europe Vol.1	LP	Riverside	RLP002	1964	£5	£12	
In Europe Vol.2	LP	Riverside	RLP003	1965	£5	£12	
In Europe Vol.3	LP	Riverside	RLP004	1966	£5	£12	
It's Monk's Time	LP	CBS	(S)BPG62391	1965	£4	£10	
Misterioso	LP	CBS	(S)BPG62620	1966	£4	£10	
Misterioso	LP	Riverside	RLP279	1964	£5	£12	
Monk	LP	CBS	(S)BPG62497	1965	£4	£10	
Monk's Blues	LP	CBS	63609	1969	£4	£10	
Monk's Dream	LP	CBS	(S)BPG62135	1963	£4	£10	
Monk's Moods	LP	Esquire	32119	1961	£10	£25	
Monk's Moods	LP	Transatlantic	PR7159	1967	£4	£10	
Monk's Music	LP	Riverside	RLP12242	1962	£6	£15	
Nica's Tempo	LP	Realm	RM52223	1965	£4	£10	
Nutty	7" EP.	Riverside	REP3214	196-	£2	£5	with John Coltrane
Nutty Monk	7" EP.	Esquire	EP236	1961	£2	£5	
Quartet Plus Two At The Black Hawk	LP	Riverside	RLP12323	1962	£6	£15	
Ruby My Dear	7" EP.	Riverside	REP3217	196-	£2	£5	with John Coltrane
Solo	LP	CBS	(S)BPG62549	1965	£4	£10	
Straight, No Chaser	LP	CBS	(S)BPG63009	1967	£4	£10	
Thelonious Himself	LP	London	LTZU15120	1958	£10	£25	
Thelonious Himself	LP	Riverside	RLP12235	1963	£6	£15	
Thelonious In Action	LP	Riverside	RLP12262	1961	£6	£15	
Thelonious Monk	LP	CBS	(S)BPG62248	1964	£4	£10	
Thelonious Monk	7" EP.	Vogue	EPV1115	1956	£2	£5	
Thelonious Monk	10" LP	Esquire	20049	1955	£25	£50	
Thelonious Monk Orchestra At Town Hall	LP	Riverside	RLP12300	1962	£6	£15	
Thelonious Monk Plays	10" LP	Esquire	20075	1956	£25	£50	
Thelonious Monk Plays Duke Ellington	LP	London	LTZU15019	1957	£10	£25	
Thelonious Monk Plays Duke Ellington	LP	Riverside	RLP12201	1961	£8	£20	
Thelonious Monk Quintet	10" LP	Esquire	20039	1955	£25	£50	
Thelonious Monk Quintets	LP	Esquire	32109	1960	£10	£25	
Thelonious Monk Trio	7" EP.	Esquire	EP75	195-	£2	£5	
Thelonious Monk Vol.1	LP	Philips	BBL1510	1961	£6	£15	
Thelonious Monk Vol.2	LP	Philips	BBL1511	1962	£6	£15	
Thelonious Monk With John Coltrane	LP	Riverside	JLP(9)46	1963	£5	£12	
Unique Thelonious	LP	London	LTXU15071	1957	£10	£25	
Way Out!	LP	Fontana	FJL113	1965	£4	£10	
Work	LP	Esquire	32115	1961	£10	£25	
Work	LP	Transatlantic	PR7169	1967	£4	£10	

MONKEES

Alternate Title	7"	RCA	RCA1604	1967	£1.50	£4	chart single
Alternate Title	7" EP.	RCA	86956	1967	£6	£12	French
Barrel Full Of Monkees	LP	Colgems	SCOS1001	1971	£8	£20	US
Birds, The Bees And The Monkees	LP	RCA	RD/SF7948	1968	£5	£12	
Changes	LP	Colgems	COS119	1970	£10	£25	US
Daydream Believer	7"	RCA	RCA1645	1967	£1.50	£4	chart single
D.W.Washburn	7"	RCA	RCA1706	1968	£1.50	£4	chart single
Golden Hits	LP	RCA	PRS329	1972	£8	£20	US
Good Clean Fun	7"	RCA	RCA1887	1969	£2.50	£6	
Greatest Hits	LP	Colgems	COS115	1969	£6	£15	US
Head	LP	RCA	RD/SF8051	1969	£17.50	£35	
Headquarters	LP	Colgems	COM/COS103	1967	£6	£15	US, photo of 2 bearded Monkees chart LP
Headquarters	LP	RCA	RD/SF7886	1967	£5	£12	chart LP
I'm A Believer	7"	RCA	RCA1560	1966	£1.50	£4	chart single
I'm A Believer	7" EP.	RCA	86952	1966	£6	£12	French
Instant Replay	LP	RCA	RD/SF8016	1969	£6	£15	
Last Train To Clarksville	7"	RCA	RCA1547	1966	£1.50	£4	chart single
Last Train To Clarksville	7" EP.	RCA	86950	1966	£6	£12	French
Listen To The Band	7"	RCA	RCA1824	1969	£1.50	£4	
Little Bit Me, A Little Bit You	7"	RCA	RCA1580	1967	£1.50	£4	chart single
Little Bit Me, A Little Bit You	7" EP.	RCA	86955	1967	£6	£12	French
Monkees	LP	RCA	RD/SF7844	1967	£5	£12	chart LP
Monkees	LP	Readers Digest		197-	£5	£12	
Monkees Present	LP	Colgems	COS117	1969	£10	£25	US
More Of The Monkees	LP	RCA	RD/SF7868	1967	£5	£12	chart LP
Oh My My	7"	RCA	RCA1958	1970	£2.50	£6	
Pisces, Aquarius, Capricorn And Jones Ltd.	LP	RCA	RD/SF7912	1967	£5	£12	chart LP
Pleasant Valley Sunday	7"	RCA	RCA1620	1967	£1.50	£4	chart single
Porpoise Song	7"	RCA	RCA1862	1969	£2.50	£6	
Re-Focus	LP	Bell	6081	1973	£15	£30	US
Teardrop City	7"	RCA	RCA1802	1969	£1.50	£4	chart single
Tema Dei Monkees	7"	RCA	1546	1967	£7.50	£15	sung in Italian
Valleri	7"	RCA	RCA1679	1968	£1.50	£4	chart single

MONKS

It's Black Monk Time	LP	Polydor	2417129	1966	£60	£120	German

MONOGRAMS

Juke Box Cha Cha	7"	Parlophone	R4515	1959	£1.50	£4	

MONOPOLY

House Of Lords	7"	Polydor	56164	1967	£2	£5	
We're All Going To The Seaside	7"	Polydor	56188	1967	£2	£5	

MONOTONES

Book Of Love	7"	London	HLM8625	1958	£15	£30	

MONOTONES (2)

It's Great	7"	Pye	7N15640	1964	£2	£5
No Waiting	7"	Pye	7N15761	1965	£2	£5
Something's Hurting Me	7"	Pye	7N15814	1965	£2	£5
What Would I Do	7"	Pye	7N15608	1964	£2	£5

MONRO, MATT

Blue And Sentimental	10" LP	Decca	LF1276	1957	£8	£20	
Everybody Falls In Love With Someone	7"	Decca	F10816	1956	£4	£8	
From Russia With Love	7"	Parlophone	R5068	1963	£1.50	£4	chart single
From Russia With Love	7" EP	Parlophone	GEP8889	1963	£5	£10	
Garden Of Eden	7"	Decca	F10845	1957	£4	£8	
My House Is Your House	7"	Decca	F10870	1957	£4	£8	
Prisoner Of Love	7"	Fontana	H167	1958	£4	£8	
Story Of Ireland	7"	Fontana	H122	1958	£4	£8	
Yesterday	7"	Parlophone	R5348	1965	£1.50	£4	chart single

MONROE, BARRY

Never Again	7"	Polydor	56088	1966	£1.50	£4

MONROE, BILL

Blue Ridge Mountain Blues	7"	Brunswick	05960	1966	£1.50	£4	
Bluegrass Ramble	LP	Brunswick	LAT/STA8511	1963	£4	£10	
Bluegrass Special	LP	Brunswick	LAT/STA8579	1965	£4	£10	
Country Date	7" EP	Brunswick	OE9160	1955	£7.50	£15	
Country Waltz	7" EP	Brunswick	OE9195	1955	£7.50	£15	
Early Bluegrass	LP	Camden	CAL774	1963	£4	£10	US
Father Of Bluegrass Music	LP	Camden	CAL719	1962	£4	£10	US
Four Walls	7"	Brunswick	05681	1957	£2.50	£6	
Gotta Travel On	7"	Brunswick	05776	1959	£2.50	£6	
Great Bill Monroe	LP	Harmony	HL7290	1961	£4	£10	US
I Saw The Light	LP	Brunswick	LAT8338	1961	£4	£10	
I Saw The Light	LP	Decca	DL(7)8769	1959	£6	£15	US
Knee Deep In Bluegrass	LP	Decca	DL(7)8731	1958	£6	£15	US
Mr.Bluegrass	LP	Decca	DL(7)4080	1960	£6	£15	US
My All Time Country Favorites	LP	Decca	DL(7)4327	1962	£4	£10	US
New John Henry Blues	7"	Brunswick	05567	1956	£2.50	£6	

MONROE BROTHERS

Country Guitar Vol.14	7" EP	RCA	RCX7103	1963	£5	£10	
Country Guitar Vol.15	7" EP	RCA	RCX7104	1963	£5	£10	
Country Guitar Vol.16	7" EP	RCA	RCX7105	1963	£4	£8	with Bill Monroe

MONROE, MARILYN

Gentlemen Prefer Blondes	LP	MGM	E3231	1955	£15	£30	US
Gentlemen Prefer Blondes	10" LP	MGM	D116	1953	£25	£50	US
Heat Wave	78	HMV	B10847	1955	£6	£12	
I Wanna Be Loved By You	7"	London	HLT8862	1959	£6	£12	
I'm Gonna File My Claim	7"	HMV	7M232	1954	£7.50	£15	
Let's Make Love	LP	Columbia	CL1527/CS8327	1960	£10	£25	US
Let's Make Love	7" EP	Philips	BBE12414	1960	£7.50	£15	
Let's Make Love	7" EP	Philips	SBBE9031	1961	£10	£20	stereo
Marilyn	LP	20th Century	FXG/SXG5000	1959	£25	£50	US, with poster
Marilyn	LP	Stateside	(S)SL10048	1963	£6	£15	
Marilyn Monroe	LP	Ascot	ALM13008/ ALS16008	1964	£10	£25	US
Some Like It Hot	LP	London	HAT2176/ SHT6040	1959	£20	£40	
Some Like It Hot	7" EP	London	RET1231	1960	£12.50	£25	
There's No Business Like Show Business	7" EP	HMV	7EG8090	1955	£7.50	£15	
Unforgettable	LP	Movietone	72016	1967	£6	£15	US

MONROE, VAUGHN

Black Denim Trousers And Motorcycle Boots	7"	HMV	7M332	1955	£7.50	£15	
Butterscotch Mop	7"	HMV	7M287	1955	£1.50	£4	
Fiesta	7"	HMV	7M165	1953	£1.50	£4	
Greatest Hits	7" EP	RCA	RCX1043	1959	£6	£12	
Less Than Tomorrow	7"	HMV	7M144	1953	£1.50	£4	
Small World	7"	HMV	7M148	1953	£1.50	£4	
They Were Doin' The Mambo	7"	HMV	7M247	1954	£2	£5	

MONTANA SLIM

Dynamite Trail	LP	Decca	DL4092	1960	£8	£20	US
I'm Ragged But I'm Right	LP	Decca	DL8917	1959	£8	£20	US
Reminiscin'	LP	Camden	CAL668	1960	£4	£10	US
Wilf Carter As Montana Slim	LP	Starday	SLP300	1964	£4	£10	US
Wilf Carter/Montana Slim	LP	Camden	CAL527	1959	£5	£12	US

MONTANAS

All That Is Mine Can Be Yours	7"	Piccadilly	7N35262	1965	£2.50	£6	
Ciao Baby	7"	Pye	7N17282	1967	£1.50	£4	
Ciao Baby	7"	Pye	7N17729	1969	£1.50	£4	
Roundabout	7"	Pye	7N17697	1969	£2.50	£6	
Step In The Right Direction	7"	Pye	7N17499	1968	£2.50	£6	
Take My Hand	7"	Pye	7N17338	1967	£2.50	£6	
That's When Happiness Began	7"	Pye	7N17183	1966	£12.50	£25	
That's When Happiness Began	7" EP	Pye	PNV24179	1966	£55	£110	French

You're Making A Big Mistake	7"	Pye	7N17597	1968	£2.50	£6	
You've Got To Be Loved	7"	Pye	7N17394	1967	£2.50	£6	

MONTCLAIRS
Hung Up On Your Love	7"	Contempo	CS2036	1975	£2.50	£6	

MONTE, LOU
Darktwon Strutters' Ball	7"	HMV	7M190	1954	£1.50	£4	
Lazy Mary	7"	RCA	RCA1048	1958	£1.50	£4	

MONTE, VINNIE
Joannie Don't Be Angry	7"	Stateside	SS156	1963	£1.50	£4	
Summer Spree	7"	London	HL8947	1959	£4	£8	

MONTENEGRO, HUGO
Get Off The Moon	7"	Oriole	CBA1792	1963	£7.50	£15	
Man From UNCLE	LP	RCA	RD7758	1965	£8	£20	
More Music From The Man From UNCLE	LP	RCA	RD7832	1966	£8	£20	

MONTEZ, CHRIS
Chris Montez	7" EP	Pye	NEP44080	1966	£4	£8	
Let's Dance	7"	London	HLU9596	1962	£2	£5	chart single
Let's Dance	7" EP	London	REU1392	1963	£7.50	£15	
Let's Dance And Have Some Kinda Fun	LP	London	HAU8079	1963	£10	£25	
More I See You	LP	Pye	NPL23080	1966	£5	£12	
More I See You	7"	Pye	7N25369	1966	£1.50	£4	chart single
More I See You	7" EP	Pye	NEP44071	1966	£5	£10	
My Baby Loves To Dance	7"	London	HLU9764	1963	£1.50	£4	
Some Kinda Fun	7"	London	HLU9650	1963	£1.50	£4	chart single
Time After Time	LP	Pye	N(S)PL28187	1967	£4	£10	

MONTGOMERY BROTHERS
Montgomery Brothers Plus Five Others	LP	Vogue	LAE12137	1959	£8	£20	
Montgomeryland	LP	Vogue	LAE12246	1961	£5	£12	

MONTGOMERY, LITTLE BROTHER
1930-1969	LP	Saydisc	SDR213	1971	£5	£12	
Farro Street Jive	LP	XTRA	XTRA1115	1971	£4	£10	
Little Brother Montgomery	LP	Columbia	33SX1289	1960	£8	£20	
Little Brother Montgomery	LP	Decca	LK4664	1965	£6	£15	
Pinetop's Boogie Woogie	7"	Columbia	DB4595	1961	£5	£10	
Southside Blues	LP	Riverside	403	1960	£6	£15	US
Tasty Blues	LP	Bluesville	BV1012	1965	£5	£12	US

MONTGOMERY, LITTLE BROTHER & SUNNYLAND SLIM
Chicago Blues Session	LP	77	LA1221	1963	£6	£15	

MONTGOMERY, MARIAN
Love Makes Two People Sing	7"	Reaction	591018	1967	£2.50	£6	

MONTGOMERY, WES
Full House	LP	Riverside	RLP434	1962	£4	£10	
Go!	LP	Fontana	FJL109	1965	£4	£10	
Groove Yard	LP	Riverside	RLP12362	1961	£5	£12	with Buddy & Monk Montgomery
Incredible Jazz Guitar	LP	Riverside	RLP12320	1960	£5	£12	
Movin' Along	LP	Riverside	RLP12342	1960	£4	£10	
Wes Montgomery Trio	LP	Riverside	RLP12310	1959	£5	£12	

MONTROSE, JACK
Blues And Vanilla	LP	RCA	RD27023	1958	£6	£15	
Jack Montrose Sextet	LP	Vogue	LAE12042	1957	£10	£25	
Jack Montrose With Bob Gordon	LP	London	LTZK15043	1957	£10	£25	

MONTY & ROY
Tra La La Boogie	7"	Blue Beat	BB61	1961	£5	£10	

MONTY PYTHON
Brian	7"	Warner Bros	K17495PRO	1980	£2.50	£6	bleeped promo
Contractual Obligations Album	LP	Charisma	CAS1152	1981	£4	£10	with 'Farewell To John Denver'
Live At The City Center, April 1976	LP	Arista	AL4073	1976	£4	£10	US
Python On Song	7"	Charisma	MP001	1975	£2.50	£6	double
Flying Sheep	7"	BBC		1970	£8		

MONUMENT
First Monument	LP	Beacon	BEAS15	1971	£25	£50	

MOOCHE
Hot Smoke And Sasafrass	7"	Pye	7N17735	1969	£10	£20	

MOOD MOSAIC
Chinese Chequers	7"	Columbia	DB8149	1967	£2.50	£6	
Mood Mosaic	LP	Columbia	SX6153/TWO160	1967	£20	£40	
Touch Of Velvet, A Sting Of Brass	7"	Columbia	DB7801	1966	£4	£8	
Touch Of Velvet, A Sting Of Brass	7"	Columbia	DB8618	1969	£2	£5	
Yellow Spotted Capricorn	7"	Parlophone	R5716	1968	£1.50	£4	

(& see MARK WIRTZ)

MOOD OF HAMILTON
Why Can't There Be More Love?	7"	Columbia	DB8304	1967	£4	£8	

MOOD SIX
She's Too Far	7"	EMI	EMI5336	1982	£10	£20	test pressing

MOODIE, AMEIL
Mello Reggae	7"	Blue Cat	BS143	1968	£4	£8	
Ratchet Knife	7"	Blue Cat	BS164	1969	£4	£8	

MOODS
Duckwalk	7"	Starlite	ST45098	1963	£6	£12	

MOODY BLUES
Boulevard De La Madelaine	7"	Decca	F12498	1966	£1.50	£4	
Boulevard De La Madeleine	7" EP	Decca	457117	1966	£6	£12	French
Bye Bye Bird	7" EP	Decca	457117	1966	£6	£12	French
Days Of Future Passed	LP	Deram	DML707	1968	£4	£10	mono, chart LP
Days Of Future Passed	LP	Mobile Fidelity	MFSL1042	1980	£5	£12	US audiophile
Everyday	7"	Decca	F12266	1965	£1.50	£4	chart single
Fly Me High	7"	Decca	F12607	1967	£5	£10	
From The Bottom Of My Heart	7"	Decca	F12166	1965	£1.50	£4	chart single
Go Now	7"	Decca	F12022	1964	£1.50	£4	chart single
Go Now	7" EP	Decca	457057	1964	£6	£12	French
I Don't Want To Go On Without You	7"	Decca	F12095	1965	£1.50	£4	chart single
In Search Of The Lost Chord	LP	Deram	DML717	1968	£5	£12	mono, chart LP
Life's Not Life	7"	Decca	F12543	1967	£15	£30	
Lose Your Money	7"	Decca	F11971	1964	£12.50	£25	
Love And Beauty	7"	Decca	F12670	1967	£5	£10	
Magnificent Moodies	LP	Decca	LK4711	1966	£5	£12	
Moody Blues	7" EP	Decca	DFE8622	1965	£7.50	£15	
Moody Blues	7" EP	Decca	DFE8622	1968	£2.50	£6	boxed Decca logo
Never Comes The Day	7"	Deram	DM247	1969	£1.50	£4	
Octave	LP	Decca	TXS129	1978	£4	£10	blue vinyl
On The Threshold Of A Dream	LP	Deram	DML1035	1968	£5	£12	mono, chart LP
On The Threshold Of A Dream	LP	Nautilus	NR21	1981	£6	£15	US audiophile
Question	7"	Threshold	TH4	1970	£1.50	£4	chart single
Ride My See-Saw	7"	Deram	DM213	1968	£1.50	£4	chart single
Seventh Sojourn	LP	Mobile Fidelity	MFSL1151	1984	£5	£12	US audiophile
Talking Out Of Turn	7"	Threshold	THPD29	1981	£2	£5	pic disc
To Our Children's Children's Children	LP	Threshold	THM1	1969	£6	£15	mono, chart LP
Voices In The Sky	7"	Deram	DM196	1968	£1.50	£4	chart single
Watching And Waiting	7"	Threshold	TH1	1969	£1.50	£4	

MOODY, CLYDE
Best Of Clyde Moody	LP	King	891	1964	£6	£15	US

MOODY, JAMES
James Moody	10" LP	Esquire	20035	1955	£25	£50	
James Moody	10" LP	Esquire	20036	1955	£25	£50	
James Moody	10" LP	Esquire	20071	1956	£20	£40	
James Moody	10" LP	Esquire	20077	1956	£20	£40	
Moody's Workshop	LP	XTRA	XTRA5017	1966	£6	£15	

MOODY, JAMES & GEORGE WALLINGTON
Beginning And End Of Bop	LP	Blue Note	B6503	1969	£8	£20	

MOON
Pirate	7"	Liberty	LBF15333	1970	£1.50	£4	
Someday Girl	7"	Liberty	LIB15076	1968	£2	£5	
Without Earth	LP	Liberty	LBL/LBS83146	1968	£5	£12	

MOON, KEITH
Two Sides Of The Moon	LP	Polydor	2442134	1975	£5	£12	

MOONDOG
H'art Songs	LP	Kopf	RRF33016		£6	£15	German
Moondog	LP	CBS	63906	1969	£8	£20	
Moondog	LP	Esquire	32055	1958	£15	£30	
Moondog 2	LP	CBS	30897	1971	£8	£20	US
Moondog In Europe	LP	Kopf	RRF33014		£6	£15	German
On The Streets Of New York	7" EP	London	REP1010	1954	£10	£20	

MOONEY, ART
Giant	7"	MGM	MGM943	1957	£4	£8	
Rebel Without A Cause Theme	7"	MGM	MGM923	1957	£4	£8	
Rock And Roll Tumbleweed	7"	MGM	MGM951	1957	£7.50	£15	

MOONGLOWS
Best Of Bobby Lester & The Moonglows	LP	Chess	LP1471	1962	£30	£60	US
Collectors Showcase	LP	Constellation	CS2	1964	£6	£15	US
I Knew From The Start	7"	London	HLN8374	1957	£100	£200	US
Look It's The Moonglows	LP	Chess	LP1430	1958	£50	£100	US
Return Of The Moonglows	LP	RCA	LSP4722	1972	£4	£10	US

MOONGOONERS
This is a name used by Scott Walker in two of his many attempts to find success in the days before the Walker Brothers - this time in a duo with his fellow "brother", John Maus.
Moongoon Stomp	7"	Candix	335	1962	£10	£20	US
Moongoon Twist	7"	Donna	1373	1962	£7.50	£15	US

Moongoon Twist .... 7" ...... Essar .... 1007 .... 1962 ... £10 ....£20 .... US

MOONKYTE
Count Me Out .... LP ..... Mother .... SMOT1 .... 1971 ... £60 ....£120 ....

MOONLIGHTERS
Going Out .... 7" ...... Island .... WI043 .... 1963 ... £5 ....£10 ....

MOON'S TRAIN
Deed I Do .... 7" ...... MGM .... MGM1333 .... 1967 ... £4 ....£8 ....

MOONSHINE, MICKEY
Baby Blue .... 7" ...... Decca .... F13555 .... 1974 ... £2 ....£5 ....

MOONSHINERS
Hold Up .... LP ..... Page One .... POLS004 .... 1967 ... £6 ....£15 ....

MOONTREKKERS
Moondust .... 7" ...... Decca .... F11714 .... 1963 ... £4 ....£8 ....
Night Of The Vampire .... 7" ...... Parlophone..... R4814 .... 1961 ... £6 ....£12 ....chart single
There's Something At The Bottom ...... 7" ...... Parlophone..... R4888 .... 1962 ... £6 ....£12 ....

MOORCOCK, MICHAEL
Brothel In Rosenstrasse .... 7" ...... Flicknife .... 1982 ... £12.50 ..£25 ....
Dodgem Dude .... 7" ...... Flicknife .... FLEP200 .... 1980 ... £2 ....£5 ....
New World's Fair .... LP ..... United Artists .. UAG29732 .... 1975 ... £20 ....£40 ....with Deep Fix

MOORE, ALAN & DAVID J
V For Vendetta .... 12" ... Glass .... 12032 .... 1984 ... £3 ....£8 .....cartoon strip insert

MOORE, ANTHONY
Pieces From The Cloudland Ballroom .. LP ..... Polydor .... 2310162 .... 1971 ... £8 ....£20 ....
Secrets Of The Blue Bag .... LP ..... Polydor .... 2310179 .... 1972 ... £8 ....£20 ....

MOORE, BARRY
Treaty Stone .... LP ..... Mulligan .... LUN022 .... 1978 ... £10 ....£25 ....Irish

MOORE, BOB
Viva .... LP ..... Hickory .... 1968 ... £20 ....£40 .... US

MOORE, BOBBY
Searching For My Love .... LP ..... Chess .... CRL4521 .... 1966 ... £6 ....£15 ....
Searching For My Love .... 7" ...... Chess .... CRS8033 .... 1966 ... £4 ....£8 ....

MOORE, BREW
Quartet And Quintet .... LP ..... Vocalion .... LAE564 .... 1964 ... £5 ....£12 ....

MOORE, BUTCH
Walking The Streets In The Rain .... 7" ...... Pye .... 7N15832 .... 1965 ... £2 ....£5 ....

MOORE, CHRISTY
Anti Nuclear .... 12" ... Alt .... 101 .... 1978 ... £10 ....£25 ... with Barry Moore & The Early Grave Band
Christy Moore .... LP ..... Polydor .... 2383426 .... 1976 ... £6 ....£15 ....
Iron Behind The Velvet .... LP ..... Tara............... 2002 .... 1978 ... £5 ....£12 ....Irish
Paddy On The Road .... LP ..... Mercury .... 20170SMCL .... 1969 ... £25 ....£50 ....
Prosperous .... LP ..... Trailer .... LER3035 .... 1972 ... £10 ....£25 ....
Whatever Tickles Your Fancy .... LP ..... Polydor .... 2383344 .... 1975 ... £10 ....£25 ....

MOORE, CHRISTY, DONAL LUNNY & JIMMY FAULKNER
Live In Dublin .... LP ..... Tara................ 2005 .... 1978 ... £5 ....£12 ....Irish

MOORE, DUDLEY
Bedazzled .... LP ..... Decca .... LK/SKL4923 .... 1968 ... £5 ....£12 ....
Dudley Moore Trio .... LP ..... Decca .... LK/SKL4976 .... 1969 ... £8 ....£20 ....
Strictly For The Birds .... 7" ...... Parlophone..... R4772 .... 1961 ... £1.50 ......£4 ....

MOORE, GARY
Always Gonna Love You .... 7" ...... Virgin .... VSY528 .... 1982 ... £1.50 ......£4 ....pic disc
Back On The Streets .... 7" ...... MCA .... MCA386 .... 1978 ... £7.50 ......£15 ....PS
Falling In Love With You .... 7" ...... Virgin .... VSY564 .... 1983 ... £1.50 ......£4 ....pic disc
Grinding Stone .... LP ..... Columbia .... 65527 .... 1973 ... £4 ....£10 ....
Hold On To Your Love .... 7" ...... 10 .... TENS13 .... 1984 ... £4 ....£8 ....shaped pic disc
Over The Hills And Far Away .... 7" ...... 10 .... TENS134 .... 1986 ... £2 ....£5 ....shaped pic disc
Parisienne Walkways .... 7" ...... MCA .... MCA419 .... 1979 ... £2.50 ......£6 ....PS
Shapes Of Things .... 7" ...... 10 .... TENS19 .... 1984 ... £4 ....£8 ....shaped pic disc
Spanish Guitar .... 7" ...... MCA .... MCA534 .... 1979 ... £2.50 ......£6 ....PS

MOORE, GARY & PHIL LYNOTT
Out In The Fields .... 7" ...... 10 .... TENS49 .... 1985 ... £5 ....£10 .... shaped pic disc (2 different)

MOORE, GATEMOUTH
I'm A Fool To Care .... LP ..... King .... 684 .... 1960 ... £180 ......£300 .... US

MOORE, JACKIE
Precious, Precious .... 7" ...... Atlantic .... 2091054 .... 1971 ... £1.50 ......£4 ....
Sometimes It's Got To Rain .... 7" ...... Atlantic .... 2091095 .... 1971 ... £1.50 ......£4 ....

MOORE, JOHNNY
Big Big Boss .... 7" ...... Doctor Bird ...... DB1180................. 1969 ... £5 ....£10 ....Carl Bryan B side

MOORE, LATTIE
Best Of Lattie Moore .... LP ..... Audio Lab .... AL1555 .... 1960 ... £10 .... £25 .... US
Country Side .... LP ..... Audio Lab .... AL1573 .... 1962 ... £10 .... £25 .... US

MOORE, MERRILL
Bellyfull Of Blue Thunder .... LP .... Ember .... EMB3392 .... 1967 ... £4 .... £10
Hard Top Race .... 7" .... Capitol .... CL14369 .... 1955 ... £40 .... £80
Rough House 88 .... LP .... Ember .... EMB3394 .... 1968 ... £4 .... £10
Sweet Mama .... 7" .... B&C .... CB100 .... 1969 ... £2 .... £5

MOORE, MERRILL E.
Down The Road A-Piece .... 7" .... Ember .... EMBS253 .... 1968 ... £5 .... £10

MOORE, OSCAR
Oscar Moore Trio .... 10" LP London .... HAPB1035 .... 1955 ... £10 .... £25

MOORE, PHIL
Moore's Tour - An American In .... LP ..... MGM .... C790 .... 1959 ... £5 .... £12
England

MOORE, R.STEVIE
R.Stevie Moore is one of rock music's eccentrics, preferring to issue his records through his own mail order scheme than to tangle with record companies who would doubtless attempt to compromise Moore's quirky approach. The original issue of his first album, "Phonography", was produced in an edition of just ninety-nine copies and long ago sold out. The Zappa household has one, and so does UK collector Michael Gerzon, whose copy is likely to be the only one in the country.
Phonography .... LP ..... private .... US0001 .... 1976 ... £100 .... £200 .... US, sleeve pictured in Guide

MOORE, SCOTTY
Guitar That Changed The World .... LP ..... Columbia .... 33SX1680 .... 1964 ... £20 .... £40 .... identical US sleeve pictured in Guide

MOORE, SHELLEY
Where Is The Bluebird .... 7" ..... Starlite .... ST45003 .... 1958 ... £1.50 .... £4
You've Tied Me Up .... 7" ..... Starlite .... ST45002 .... 1958 ... £1.50 .... £4

MOORE, THURSTON, KIM GORDON, EPIC SOUNDTRACKS
Sitting On A Barbed Wire Fence .... 7" ..... Imaginary .... FREE003 .... 1992 ... £2 .... £5 .... promo

MOORE, WHISTLING ALEX
Whistling Alex Moore .... LP ..... 77 .... LA126 .... 1961 ... £8 .... £20

MOORS MURDERERS
The Moors Murderers, a punk group of which Steve Strange And Chrissie Hynde were both members, were supposed to have released a single called "Free Myra Hindley". Although acetates have turned up, however, it seems unlikely that regular vinyl copies exist.
Free Myra Hindley .... 7" ..... Pop Corn .... 1978 ... £700 .... £1000 .... existence doubtful

MOPED, JOHNNY
Basically The Original Johnny Moped .... 7" ..... Chiswick .... PROMO3 .... 1976 ... £4 .... £8 .... promo
Tape

MOPEDS
Whiskey And Soda .... 7" ...... Columbia .... DB108 .... 1968 ... £4 .... £8

MOQUETTES
Right String But Wrong Yo Yo .... 7" ...... Columbia .... DB7315 .... 1964 ... £12.50 .... £25

MORECOMBE & WISE
Boom Oo Yatta-Ta-Ta .... 7" ...... HMV .... POP1240 .... 1963 ... £1.50 .... £4
Bring Me Sunshine .... 7" ...... Columbia .... DB8646 .... 1969 ... £1.50 .... £4
Bring Me Sunshine .... 7" ...... Columbia .... DB8753 .... 1971 ... £1.50 .... £4
Mr.Morecombe Meets Mr.Wise .... LP ..... HMV .... CLP1682/CSD1522 1964 ... £4 .... £10

MOREL, TERRY
Songs Of A Woman In Love .... LP ..... Bethlehem .... 47 .... 1955 ... £8 .... £20 .... US

MORGAN
Nova Solis .... LP ..... RCA .... 1972 ... £10 .... £25

MORGAN & MARK SEVEN
I'm Gonna Turn My Life Around .... 7" ...... Polydor .... BM56083 .... 1966 ... £2 .... £5

MORGAN, AL
Jealous Heart .... 7" ...... London .... HLU8741 .... 1958 ... £2.50 .... £6
Jealous Heart .... 10" LP London .... HAPB1001 .... 1951 ... £5 .... £12
Little Red Book .... 10" LP London .... HAPB1003 .... 1951 ... £5 .... £12

MORGAN BROTHERS
Kissin' On The Red Light .... 7" ...... MGM .... MGM1026 .... 1959 ... £1.50 .... £4
Nola .... 7" ...... MGM .... MGM1007 .... 1959 ... £2.50 .... £6

MORGAN, DAVY
Tomorrow I'll Be Gone .... 7" ...... Columbia .... DB7624 .... 1965 ... £7.50 .... £15
True To Life .... 7" ...... Parlophone ...... R5692 .... 1968 ... £5 .... £10

MORGAN, DERRICK
Amelita .... 7" ...... Island .... WI289 .... 1966 ... £5 .... £10
Angel With Blue Eyes .... 7" ...... Island .... WI080 .... 1963 ... £5 .... £10
Are You Going To Marry Me? .... 7" ...... Blue Beat .... BB110 .... 1962 ... £5 .... £10 .... with Patsy Todd
Around The Corner .... 7" ...... Ska Beat .... JB188 .... 1965 ... £5 .... £10
Baby Please Don't Leave Me .... 7" ...... Blue Beat .... BB65 .... 1961 ... £5 .... £10 .... with Patsy Todd

567

Title	Format	Label	Cat. No.	Year	Price	Price	Notes
Balzing Fire	7"	Rio	R1	1963	£5	£10	
Be Still	7"	Blue Beat	BB76	1961	£5	£8	
Ben Johnson Day	7"	Pyramid	PYR6056	1968	£4	£8	Maytals B side
Best Of Derrick Morgan	LP	Doctor Bird	DLMB5014	1969	£50	£100	
Blazing Fire	7"	Island	WI051	1962	£5	£10	
Call My Name	7"	Blue Beat	BB171	1963	£5	£10	with Patsy Todd
Cherry Home	7"	Island	WI013	1962	£5	£10	
Cherry Pie	7"	Black Swan	WI425	1964	£5	£10	
Come Back My Love	7"	Blue Beat	BB121	1962	£5	£10	
Come On	7"	Island	WI024	1962	£5	£10	Monty & Cyclones B side
Come On Over	7"	Blue Beat	BB85	1961	£5	£10	
Conquering Ruler	7"	Island	WI3094	1967	£5	£10	Lloyd & Devon B side
Contented Wife	7"	Blue Beat	BB261	1964	£5	£10	
Cool Off Rudies	7"	Rio	R122	1966	£4	£8	
Copy Cat	7"	Bullet	BU419	1969	£2.50	£6	
Court Dismiss	7"	Pyramid	PYR6014	1967	£4	£8	Frederick McLean B side
Derrick Morgan And His Friends	LP	Island	ILP990	1969	£30	£60	
Derrick Top The Pop	7"	Unity	UN540	1969	£2.50	£6	
Do The Beng Beng	7"	Pyramid	PYR6025	1968	£4	£8	
Don't Cry	7"	Blue Beat	BB12	1961	£5	£10	
Don't Say	7"	Pyramid	PYR6063	1969	£2.50	£6	Basil Gabbidon B side
Don't You Know Little Girl	7"	Blue Beat	BB82	1961	£5	£10	with Patsy Todd
Eternity	7"	Blue Beat	BB318	1964	£5	£10	
Fat Man	7"	Blue Beat	BB7	1961	£5	£10	
Feel So Fine	7"	Blue Beat	BB57	1961	£5	£10	with Patsy Todd, Roland Alphonso B side
Forward March	LP	Island	ILP903	1963	£30	£60	
Forward March	LP	Trojan	TTL38	1970	£6	£15	
Gather Together	7"	Island	WI3010	1966	£5	£10	
Gimme Back	7"	Island	WI3101	1967	£5	£10	Viceroys B side
Give You My Love	7"	Nu Beat	NB027	1969	£4	£8	
Greedy Gal	7"	Pyramid	PYR6013	1967	£4	£8	Soul Brothers B side
Heart Of Stone	7"	Ska Beat	JB185	1965	£5	£10	with Naomi Campbell
Hey Boy, Hey Girl	7"	Nu Beat	NB008	1968	£4	£8	with Patsy Todd
Hold You Jack	7"	Island	WI3159	1968	£5	£10	
Hop	7"	Island	WI006	1962	£5	£10	
Housewive's Choice	7"	Island	WI018	1962	£5	£10	with Patsy Todd
I Am The Ruler	7"	Pyramid	PYR6029	1968	£4	£8	
I Found A Queen	7"	Island	WI288	1966	£5	£10	
I Love You	7"	Nu Beat	NB016	1968	£2.50	£6	Junior Smith B side
I Want A Lover	7"	Island	WI193	1965	£5	£10	with Naomi Campbell
I'm Sending This Message	7"	Island	WI091	1963	£5	£10	Larry Lawrence B side
In London	LP	Pama	ECO10	1969	£8	£20	
In My Heart	7"	Blue Beat	BB100	1962	£5	£10	Bell's Group B side
It's Alright	7"	Island	WI277	1966	£5	£10	
Jezebel	7"	Blue Beat	BB148	1962	£5	£10	
Johnny Grove	7"	Blue Beat	BB283	1964	£5	£10	Buster's Allstars B side
Joybells	7"	Blue Beat	BB141	1962	£5	£10	
Judge Dread In Court	7"	Pyramid	PYR6019	1967	£4	£8	
Katy Katy	7"	Blue Beat	BB268	1964	£5	£10	
Kill Me Dead	7"	Pyramid	PYR6021	1967	£4	£8	
King For Tonight	7"	Pyramid	PYR6046	1968	£4	£8	
Leave Earth	7"	Blue Beat	BB35	1961	£5	£10	
Leave Her Alone	7"	Island	WI037	1962	£5	£10	
Let Them Talk	7"	Blue Beat	BB233	1963	£5	£10	
Little Brown Girl	7"	Blue Beat	BB152	1962	£5	£10	with Patsy Todd
Look Before You Leap	7"	Island	WI055	1962	£5	£10	with Patsy Todd
Love And Leave Me	7"	Blue Beat	BB135	1962	£5	£10	with Lloyd Clarke
Love Not To Brag	7"	Blue Beat	BB97	1962	£5	£10	Drumbago B side
Lover Boy	7"	Blue Beat	BB207	1963	£5	£10	with Patsy Todd
Loverboy	7"	Blue Beat	BB18	1961	£5	£10	
Me Naw Give Up	7"	Pyramid	PYR6053	1968	£4	£8	Beverley's Allstars B side
Meekly Wait	7"	Blue Beat	BB94	1961	£5	£10	with Yvonne Harrison
Millie Girl	7"	Blue Beat	BB91	1961	£5	£10	
Miss Lulu	7"	Blue Beat	BB239	1963	£5	£10	with Patsy Todd
Moon Hop	LP	Pama	PSP1006	1969	£10	£25	
Moon Hop	7"	Crab	CRAB21	1970	£1.50	£4	chart single
National Dance	7"	Island	WI224	1965	£5	£10	with Patsy Todd, Desmond Dekker B side
Never Give Up	7"	Smash	SMA2339	1973	£1.50	£4	
No Dice	7"	Pyramid	PYR6024	1968	£4	£8	
No Raise, No Praise	7"	Island	WI053	1962	£5	£10	
Now We Know	7"	Blue Beat	BB31	1961	£5	£10	
Oh My Love	7"	Blue Beat	BB123	1962	£5	£10	with Patsy Todd
Oh Shirley	7"	Blue Beat	BB106	1962	£5	£10	with Patsy Todd
Patricia My Dear	7"	Blue Beat	BB177	1963	£5	£10	
Please Don't Talk About Me (with Eric Morris)	7"	Island	WI011	1962	£5	£10	
River To The Bank	7"	Crab	CRAB3	1968	£4	£8	Peter King B side
Send Me Some Loving	7"	Crab	CRAB23	1970	£2.50	£6	
Seven Letters	LP	Trojan	TTL5	1969	£6	£15	
Seven Letters	7"	Crab	CRAB8	1969	£2.50	£6	Tartans B side
Shake A Leg	7"	Blue Beat	BB62	1961	£5	£10	with Drumbago
Should Be Ashamed	7"	Blue Beat	BB130	1962	£5	£10	

Shower Of Rain	7"	Big Shot	BI506	1968	£4	£8	Val Bennett B side
Someone	7"	Island	WI3079	1967	£5	£10	
Starvation	7"	Island	WI225	1965	£5	£10	
Steal Away	7"	Blue Beat	BB224	1963	£5	£10	with Patsy Todd
Stir The Pot	7"	Blue Beat	BB280	1964	£5	£10	
Street Girl	7"	Black Swan	WI402	1964	£5	£10	
Sweeter Than Honey	7"	Blue Beat	BB329	1965	£5	£10	
Tears On My Pillow	7"	Blue Beat	BB187	1963	£5	£10	
Telephone	7"	Blue Beat	BB196	1963	£5	£10	
Throw Them Away	7"	Blue Beat	BB311	1964	£5	£10	
Times Are Going	7"	Blue Beat	BB48	1961	£5	£10	
Tougher Than Tough	7"	Pyramid	PYR6010	1967	£4	£8	Roland Alphonso B side
Travel On	7"	Island	WI004	1962	£5	£10	
Troubles	7"	Blue Beat	BB247	1964	£5	£10	with Patsy Todd
Try Me	7"	Pyramid	PYR6045	1968	£4	£8	
Trying To Make You Mine	7"	Blue Beat	BB160	1962	£5	£10	
Want More	7"	Pyramid	PYR6040	1968	£4	£8	Roland Alphonso B side
Weep No More	7"	Blue Beat	BB276	1964	£5	£10	
Woman A Grumble	7"	Pyramid	PYR6039	1968	£4	£8	
You I Love	7"	Blue Beat	BB291	1964	£5	£10	with Patsy Todd
You Never Miss Your Water	7"	Pyramid	PYR6027	1968	£4	£8	

MORGAN, FRANK

Frank Morgan	LP	Vogue	LAE12012	1956	£15	£30	

MORGAN, FREDDY

Side Saddle	7"	London	HL7077	export	£2	£5	

MORGAN, GEORGE

Morgan, By George	LP	Columbia	CL1044	1957	£6	£15	US

MORGAN, JANE

All The Way	LP	London	HAR2110	1958	£8	£20	
All The Way Part 1	7" EP	London	RER1161	1958	£5	£10	
All The Way Part 2	7" EP	London	RER1162	1958	£5	£10	
Around The World	7"	London	HLR8436	1957	£5	£10	
At The Coconut Grove	LP	London	HAR2430/ SAHR6226	1962	£6	£15	
Ballads Of Lady Jane	LP	London	HAR2316	1960	£6	£15	
Day The Rains Came	LP	London	HAR2158	1959	£8	£20	
Day The Rains Came	7"	London	HL7064	1958	£4	£8	export
Day The Rains Came	7"	London	HLR8751	1958	£2	£5	chart single
Day The Rains Came	7" EP	London	RER1204	1959	£6	£12	
Enchanted Island	7"	London	HLR8649	1958	£2.50	£6	
Fascination	LP	London	HAR2086	1957	£8	£20	
Fascination	7"	London	HLR8468	1957	£4	£8	
From The First Hello	7"	London	HLR8395	1957	£7.50	£15	
Great Songs From The Great Shows Vol.1	LP	London	HAR2136	1959	£6	£15	
Great Songs From The Great Shows Vol.2	LP	London	HAR2137	1959	£6	£15	
Happy Anniversary	7"	London	HLR8999	1959	£1.50	£4	
If I Could Only Live My Life Again	7"	London	HLR8810	1959	£2	£5	chart single
I'm New At The Game Of Romance	7"	London	HLR8539	1958	£4	£8	
In My Style	LP	Columbia	SX6010	1965	£6	£15	
I've Got Bells On My Heart	7"	London	HLR8611	1958	£4	£8	
Jane In Spain	LP	London	HAR2244	1960	£6	£15	
Jane Morgan	LP	Kapp	KL1023	195-	£6	£15	US
Jane Morgan	LP	Kapp	KL1098	1958	£6	£15	US
Jane Morgan	7" EP	London	RER1331	1961	£6	£12	
Jane Morgan Time	LP	London	HAR2371	1961	£6	£15	
Lord And Master	7"	London	HLR9210	1960	£1.50	£4	
Love Makes The World Go Around	LP	London	HAR/SHR8069	1963	£6	£15	
My Love Doesn't Love Me At All	7"	London	HLR9087	1960	£1.50	£4	
Romantica	7"	London	HLR9120	1960	£1.50	£4	chart single
Second Time Around	LP	London	HAR2377/ SAHR6177	1961	£6	£15	
Serenades The Victors	LP	Colpix	PXL460	1963	£6	£15	
Somebody	7"	London	HLR9249	1960	£1.50	£4	
Something Old, Something New	LP	London	HAR2133	1958	£8	£20	
What Now My Love	LP	London	HAR/SHR8042	1962	£6	£15	
Why Oh Why	7"	London	HL8148	1955	£10	£20	
With Open Arms	7"	London	HLR8925	1959	£1.50	£4	

MORGAN, JAYE P.

Are You Lonesome Tonight?	7"	MGM	MGM1005	1959	£1.50	£4	
Have You Ever Been Lonely	7"	Brunswick	05519	1956	£2.50	£6	
Jaye P Sings	7" EP	London	REP1013	1954	£7.50	£15	
Longest Walk	7"	HMV	7M327	1955	£2	£5	
Not One Goodbye	7"	HMV	7M365	1956	£1.50	£4	
Pepper Hot Baby	7"	HMV	7M348	1955	£7.50	£15	

MORGAN, JOHN

Records credited in the name of pianist John Morgan are listed in this Guide along with those by his group, Spirit Of John Morgan.

MORGAN, LEE

Another Monday Night At Birdland	LP	Columbia	33SX1181	1959	£6	£15	all star band
Birdland Story Vol.1	LP	Columbia	33SX1399	1961	£6	£15	
Caramba	LP	Blue Note	BST84289	1968	£5	£12	

569

Charisma	LP	Blue Note	BST84312	1969	£5	£12	
Cooker	LP	Blue Note	BLP/BST81578	196-	£10	£25	
Cornbread	LP	Blue Note	BLP/BST84222	1965	£8	£20	
Delightfulee Morgan	LP	Blue Note	BLP/BST84243	1966	£10	£25	
Expoobident	LP	Stateside	SL10016	1962	£6	£15	
Gigolo	LP	Blue Note	BLP/BST84212	1965	£8	£20	
Introducing Lee Morgan	LP	London	LTZC15101	1958	£20	£40	
Lee Morgan	LP	Blue Note	BST84381	1970	£4	£10	
Leeway	LP	Blue Note	BLP/BST84034	1965	£15	£30	
Live At The Lighthouse	LP	Blue Note	BST89906	1970	£4	£10	
Monday Night At Birdland	LP	Columbia	33SX1160	1959	£6	£15	all star band
Rumproller	LP	Blue Note	BLP/BST84199	1966	£10	£25	
Search For The New Land	LP	Blue Note	BLP/BST84169	1966	£10	£25	
Sidewinder	LP	Blue Note	BLP/BST84157	1965	£10	£25	
Sixth Sense	LP	Blue Note	BST84335	1969	£4	£10	

MORGAN, MACE THUNDERBIRDS
Shake And Swing	7" EP	Starlite	STEP36	1963	£7.50	£15	

MORGAN, PC ALEXANDER
Sussex By The Sea	7"	Columbia	DB8095	1966	£4	£8	

MORGAN, RUSS
Moonlight Music	7" EP	Brunswick	OE9068	1955	£2.50	£6	

MORGAN TWINS
Let's Get Going	7"	RCA	RCA1083	1958	£27.50	£55	

MORGEN
Morgen	LP	Probe	CPLP4507	1969	£25	£50	US

MORIN & WILSON
Peaceful Company	LP	Sovereign	SVNA7252	1972	£10	£25	

MORISETTE, JOHNNY
Meet Me At The Twisting Place	7"	Stateside	SS107	1962	£1.50	£4	

MORLY GREY
Only Truth	LP	Starshine		1969	£20	£40	US

MORMOS
Great Wall Of China	LP	CBS		1971	£40	£80	French
Magic Spell Of Mother's Wrath	LP	CBS		1972	£50	£100	French
Mormos	LP	CBS			£10	£25	French

MORNING
Morning	LP	Liberty	LBS83463	1970	£5	£12	

MORNING DEW
Morning Dew	LP	Roulette	R(S)41045	1967	£8	£20	US

MORNING GLORY
Morning Glory	LP	Island	ILPS9237	1973	£6	£15	

MORNING STAR
Morning Star	LP	CBS	35316	1978	£8	£20	US
Venus	LP	CBS	35713	1979	£8	£20	US

MORPHEUS
Rabenteuer	LP	private	34705	1976	£15	£30	German

MORRIS & MITCH
Cumberland Gap	7"	Decca	F10900	1957	£2.50	£6	
Highway Patrol	7"	Decca	F11086	1958	£2.50	£6	
Six Five Nothing Special	7" EP	Decca	DFE6486	1958	£7.50	£15	
What Is A Skiffler?	7"	Decca	F10929	1957	£2.50	£6	

MORRIS & THE MINORS
State The Obvious	7"	Round	MOR1	1980	£2	£5	

MORRIS, DERRICK
What's Your Grouse	7"	Pyramid	PYR6061	1969	£2.50	£6	Beverley's Allstars

MORRIS, ERIC
By The Sea	7"	Rio	R72	1965	£5	£10	
Children Of Today	7"	Island	WI234	1965	£5	£10	Baba Brooks B side
Country Girl	7"	Blue Beat	BB184	1963	£5	£10	
Fast Mouth	7"	Island	WI199	1965	£5	£10	
G.I. Lady	7"	Blue Beat	BB115	1962	£5	£10	
Home Sweet Home	7"	Black Swan	WI445	1965	£5	£10	Lester Sterling B side
Humpty Dumpty	7"	Blue Beat	BB53	1961	£5	£10	
If I Didn't Love You	7"	Doctor Bird	DB1056	1966	£5	£10	Tommy McCook B side
Little District	7"	Rio	R39	1964	£5	£10	
Live As A Man	7"	Rio	R48	1964	£5	£10	
Lonely Blue Boy	7"	Blue Beat	BB153	1962	£5	£10	Prince Buster B side
Love Can Break A Man	7"	Blue Beat	BB218	1963	£5	£10	
Love Can Make A Mansion	7"	Island	WI183	1965	£5	£10	
Mama No Fret	7"	Island	WI147	1964	£5	£10	Frankie Anderson B side
Miss Peggy's Grandmother	7"	Blue Beat	BB137	1962	£5	£10	Buster's Allstars B side

Money Can't Buy Life	7"	Blue Beat	BB83	1961	£5	£10	Alton Ellis B side
My Forty-Five	7"	Blue Beat	BB74	1961	£5	£10	
Oh My Dear	7"	Port-O-Jam	PJ4006	1964	£5	£10	
Over The Hills	7"	Blue Beat	BB128	1962	£5	£10	
Pack Up Your Troubles	7"	Blue Beat	BB105	1962	£5	£10	
Penny Reel	7"	Island	WI142	1964	£5	£10	Dotty & Bonnie B side
River Come Down	7"	Black Swan	WI439	1964	£5	£10	
Search The World	7"	Starlite	ST45052	1961	£5	£10	Buster's Group B side
Seven Long Years	7"	Blue Beat	BB140	1962	£5	£10	
Sinners Repent And Pray	7"	Blue Beat	BB81	1961	£5	£10	Alton Ellis B side
So You Shot Reds	7"	Blue Beat	BB193	1963	£5	£10	
Solomon Grundie	7"	Black Swan	WI414	1964	£5	£10	Baba Brooks B side
Stitch In Time	7"	Blue Beat	BB273	1964	£5	£10	
Suddenly	7"	Island	WI185	1965	£5	£10	
Supper In The Gutter	7"	Black Swan	WI433	1964	£5	£10	
What A Man Doeth	7"	Island	WI151	1964	£5	£10	Duke Reid B side

MORRIS, HEMSLEY

Love Is Strange	7"	Caltone	TONE104	1967	£4	£8	Don Drummond Jr. B side

MORRIS, JOE

Just Your Way Baby	78	London	HL8088	1954	£15	£30	
Travelin' Man	78	London	HL8098	1954	£3	£8	

MORRIS, LIBBY

When Liberace Winked At Me	7"	Parlophone	R4225	1956	£1.50	£4	

MORRIS, MILTON

No Bread And Butter	7"	Upsetter	US318	1969	£2	£5	Upsetters B side

MORRIS, MONTY

Can't Get No Peace	7"	Camel	CA12	1969	£2.50	£6	Upsetters B side
Deportation	7"	Big Shot	BI513	1969	£2.50	£6	
Last Laugh	7"	Doctor Bird	DB1162	1968	£5	£10	
Same Face	7"	Doctor Bird	DB1176	1969	£5	£10	
Say What You're Saying	7"	Pama	PM721	1968	£2.50	£6	

MORRIS, ROGER

First Album	LP	Regal Zonophone	SRZA8509	1972	£8	£20	

MORRIS, RUSSELL

Real Thing	7"	Decca	F22964	1969	£15	£30	

MORRIS, VICTOR

Now I'm Alone	7"	Amalgamated	AMG813	1968	£4	£8	

MORRISEY, PAT

I'm Pat Morrisey, I Sing	LP	Mercury	MG20197	1956	£8	£20	US

MORRISON, CURLEY JIM

Air Force Blues	7"	Starlite	ST45065	1961	£40	£80	

MORRISON, JAMES

Pure Genius Of James Morrison	LP	Shanachie	33004	1978	£5	£12	US

MORRISON, JAMES & TOM ENNIS

James Morrison And Tom Ennis	LP	Topic	12T390	1980	£5	£12	

MORRISON, TOM

Adventures Of Mighty Mouse & His Pals	7" EP	MGM	MGMEP709	1960	£4	£8	

MORRISON, VAN

Astral Weeks	LP	Warner Bros	WS1768	1968	£5	£12	
Blowin' Your Mind	LP	London	HAZ8346	1967	£6	£15	
Brown Eyed Girl	7"	London	HLM10453	1974	£1.50	£4	
Brown Eyed Girl	7"	London	HLZ10150	1967	£5	£10	
Caldonia	7"	Warner Bros	K16392	1974	£2.50	£6	
Come Running	7"	Warner Bros	WB7383	1970	£1.50	£4	
Domino	7"	Warner Bros	WB7434	1970	£2	£5	
Hard Nose The Highway	LP	Warner Bros	K46242	1973	£4	£10	
His Band And Street Choir	LP	Warner Bros	WS1884	1970	£5	£12	
It's Too Late To Stop Now	LP	Warner Bros	K86007	1974	£5	£12	double
Jackie Wilson Said	7"	Warner Bros	K16210	1972	£2.50	£6	
Joyous Sound	7"	Warner Bros	K16986	1977	£2.50	£6	
Live At The Roxy	LP	Warner Bros	WBMS102	1978	£15	£30	US promo
Moondance	LP	Nautilus	SD110	1981	£5	£12	US audiophile
Moondance	LP	Warner Bros	WS1835	1970	£5	£12	chart LP
Sense Of Wonder	LP	Mercury	MERH54	1985	£15	£30	test pressing with 'Crazy Jane On God'
St.Dominic's Preview	LP	Warner Bros	K46112	1972	£4	£10	green label
Tupelo Honey	LP	Warner Bros	K46114	1971	£4	£10	green label
Tupelo Honey	LP	Warner Bros	WS1950	1971	£5	£10	
Veedon Fleece	LP	Warner Bros	K56068	1974	£4	£10	

MORRISSEY

Every Day Is Like Sunday	CD-s	HMV	CDPOP1619	1988	£3	£8	
Interesting Drug	CD-s	HMV	CDPOP1621	1989	£3	£8	

Last Of The Famous International Playboys	CD-s ..	HMV	CDPOP1620	1989	£3	£8	
Ouija Board, Ouija Board	CD-s ..	HMV	CDPOP1622	1989	£2.50	£6	
Piccadilly Palare	CD-s ..	HMV	CDPOP1624	1990	£2.50	£6	
Sing Your Life	CD-s ..	HMV	CDPOP1626	1991	£2.50	£6	
Suedehead	CD-s ..	HMV	CDPOP1618	1988	£2.50	£6	

MORROW, BUDDY

Buddy Morrow And His Orchestra	7" EP	HMV	7EG8076	1955	£2	£5	
Dragnet	7"	HMV	7M162	1953	£1.50	£4	
Heap Big Beat	7"	HMV	7M151	1953	£1.50	£4	
Impact	7" EP	RCA	RCX174	1959	£2	£5	
Knock On Wood	7"	HMV	7M216	1954	£1.50	£4	
Staccato's Theme	7"	RCA	RCA1167	1960	£1.50	£4	

MORSE, ELLA MAE

Barrelhouse Boogie And The Blues	LP	Capitol	T513	1956	£15	£30	US
Barrelhouse Boogie And The Blues	7" EP..	Capitol	EAP1513	1955	£15	£30	
Barrelhouse Boogie And The Blues	10" LP	Capitol	LC6687	1954	£25	£50	
Birmingham	7"	Capitol	CL14376	1955	£10	£20	
Bring Back My Baby To Me	7"	Capitol	CL14223	1955	£15	£30	
Down In Mexico	7"	Capitol	CL14572	1956	£10	£20	
Heart Full Of Hope	7"	Capitol	CL14332	1955	£10	£20	
Hits Of Ella Mae Morse & Freddie Slack	LP	Capitol	T1802	1962	£8	£20	US
I'm Gone	7"	Capitol	CL14760	1957	£5	£10	
Morse Code	LP	Capitol	T898	1957	£10	£25	US
Razzle Dazzle	7"	Capitol	CL14341	1955	£25	£50	
Rockin' Brew	LP	Ember	SPE6605	1967	£6	£15	with Freddie Stack
Seventeen	7"	Capitol	CL14362	1955	£15	£30	
Smack Dab In The Middle	7"	Capitol	CL14303	1955	£12.50	£25	
What Good'll It Do Me	7"	Capitol	CL14726	1957	£5	£10	
When Boy Kiss Girl	7"	Capitol	CL14508	1956	£6	£12	

MORTIMER, AZIE

Lips	7"	London	HLX9237	1960	£1.50	£4	

MORTON, JELLY ROLL

Classic Jazz Piano Vol.1	10" LP	London	AL3534	1954	£10	£25	
Classic Jazz Piano Vol.2	10" LP	London	AL3559	1956	£10	£25	
Classic Piano Solos	LP	Riverside	RLP12111	1962	£6	£15	
Jazz Originators Vol.3	7" EP..	Collector	JE120	1959	£2	£5	
Jelly Roll Morton	LP	Fontana	TL5261	1965	£4	£10	
Jelly Roll Morton	7" EP..	RCA	RCX168	1955	£2	£5	
Jelly Roll Morton	7" EP..	Storyville	SEP379	1961	£2	£5	
Jelly Roll Morton	7" EP..	Vogue	EPV1126	1956	£2	£5	
Jelly Roll Morton & His Red Hot Peppers	10" LP	HMV	DLP1016	1953	£10	£25	
Jelly Roll Morton No.2	7" EP..	RCA	RCX207	1960	£2	£5	
King Of New Orleans Jazz	LP	RCA	RD27113	1959	£8	£20	
King Of New Orleans Jazz Vol.2	LP	RCA	RD27184	1961	£8	£20	
Kings Of Jazz	10" LP	London	AL3520	1954	£10	£25	
Morton Sixes And Sevens	LP	Fontana	TL5415	1967	£4	£10	
Morton's Red Hot Peppers	10" LP	HMV	DLP1044	1954	£10	£25	
Morton's Red Hot Peppers No.3	10" LP	HMV	DLP1071	1955	£10	£25	
Mr.Jelly Lord	LP	Riverside	RLP12132	1961	£6	£15	
New Orleans Memories	10" LP	Vogue	LDE080	1954	£10	£25	
Solos	10" LP	London	AL3519	1954	£10	£25	
Treasures Of North American Negro Music Vol.4	7" EP..	Fontana	TFE17263	1960	£2	£5	

MORTON, JELLY-ROLL

Burnin' The Iceberg	7"	HMV	7M256	1954	£2	£5	
Fat Frances	7"	HMV	7M178	1954	£2	£5	
Jungle Blues	7"	HMV	7M207	1954	£2	£5	
Smoke House Blues	7"	HMV	7M187	1954	£2	£5	
Tank Town Bump	7"	HMV	7M132	1953	£2	£5	

MORTON, MANDY

Magic Lady	LP	Banshee	BAN1001	1978	£75	£150	with Spriguns
Magic Lady	LP	Banshee	BAN1001	1979	£100	£200	blue vinyl
Sea Of Storms	LP	Polydor	2382101	1980	£8	£20	German
Song For Me (Music Prince)	7"	Banshee	BANS791	1979	£5	£10	with Spriguns
Valley Of The Light	LP	Banshee		1978	£15	£30	

MORTON, ROBIN & CATHAL MCCONNEL

Irish Jubilee	LP	Mercier	IRL10	1970	£15	£30	Irish

MOSAICS

Let's Go Drag Racing	7"	Columbia	DB7990	1966	£6	£12	

MOSELEY, REVEREND

Treasures Of North American Negro Music Vol.6	7" EP..	Fontana	TFE17265	1960	£2	£5	

MOSES & JOSHUA

Get Out Of My Heart	7"	Bell	BELL1018	1968	£2	£5	
Get Out Of My Heart	7"	Bell	BLL1018	1968	£2	£5	

MOSKOW

Man From UNCLE	7"	Moskow	SRS2103	1982	£2	£5	

MOSS, BILL
Sock It To Em Soul Brother .... 7" ..... Pama .... PM765 .... 1969 ... £1.50 ....£4 ....

MOSS, BUDDY
Georgia Blues Vol.2 .... LP ..... Kokomo .... K1003 .... 196- ... £20 ....£40 ....

MOSS, JENNY
Hobbies .... 7" ..... Columbia .... DB7061 .... 1963 ... £10 ....£20 ....

MOST, ABE OCTET
Presenting The Abe Most Octet .... 7" EP.. London .... REP1028 .... 1955 ... £5 ....£10 ....

MOST BROTHERS
Dottie .... 7" ..... Decca .... F11040 .... 1958 ... £2.50 ....£6 ....
Teen Angel .... 7" ..... Decca .... F10998 .... 1958 ... £4 ....£8 ....
Whistle Bait .... 7" ..... Decca .... F10968 .... 1957 ... £4 ....£8 ....

MOST, MICKIE
Feminine Look .... 7" ..... Columbia .... DB7117 .... 1963 ... £5 ....£10 ....
Money Honey .... 7" ..... Columbia .... DB7245 .... 1964 ... £4 ....£8 ....
Sea Cruise .... 7" ..... Columbia .... DB7180 .... 1963 ... £4 ....£8 ....
That's Alright .... 7" EP.. Columbia .... ESRF1588 .... 1964 ... £12.50 .....£25 ....
Yes Indeed I Do .... 7" ..... Decca .... F11664 .... 1963 ... £4 ....£8 .... French

MOST, SAM
Plays Bird, Bud, Monk And Miles .... LP ..... Parlophone ..... PMC1087 .... 1959 ... £8 ....£20 ....
Sam Most .... LP ..... London .... LTZN15063 .... 1957 ... £8 ....£20 ....
Sam Most Sextet .... 10" LP Vanguard .... PPT12009 .... 1956 ... £8 ....£20 ....

MOTEN, BENNY
Plays Kay-Cee Jazz .... 10" LP HMV .... DLP1057 .... 1954 ... £8 ....£20 ....

MOTHER EARTH
Bring Me Home .... LP ..... Reprise .... K44133 .... 1971 ... £5 ....£12 ....
I Did My Part .... 7" ..... Mercury .... MF1081 .... 1969 ... £2.50 ....£6 ....
Living With The Animals .... LP ..... Mercury .... SMCL20143 .... 1968 ... £6 ....£15 ....
Make A Joyful Noise .... LP ..... Mercury .... SMCL20173 .... 1969 ... £6 ....£15 ....
Satisfied .... LP ..... Mercury .... 6338023 .... 1970 ... £6 ....£15 ....
Temptation Took Control .... 7" ..... Reprise .... K14089 .... 1972 ... £1.50 ....£4 ....
Tracy Nelson Country .... LP ..... Mercury .... SMCL20179 .... 1969 ... £6 ....£15 ....

MOTHER MALLARD'S PORTABLE MASTERPIECE COMPANY
Like A Duck To Water .... LP ..... Earthquack ...... 0002 .... 1973 ... £5 ....£12 .... US
Mother Mallard's Portable Masterpiece LP ..... Earthquack ...... 0001 .... 1973 ... £5 ....£12 .... US
Company ....

MOTHER TUCKER'S YELLOW DUCK
Home Grown Stuff .... LP ..... Capitol .... 1969 ... £20 ....£40 .... Canadian
Starting A New Day .... LP ..... Capitol .... 197- ... £20 ....£40 .... Canadian

MOTHERHOOD
I Feel So Free .... LP ..... United Artists .. UAS69173 .... 1969 ... £6 ....£15 .... German

MOTHERLIGHT
Bobak Jons Malone .... LP ..... Morgan Blue .... BT5003 .... 1969 ... £50 ....£100 ....
Town

MOTHER'S RUIN
Say It's Not True .... 7" ..... Spectra .... SPC7 .... 1982 ... £2 ....£5 ....
Street Lights .... 7" ..... Spectra .... SPC6 .... 1982 ... £2 ....£5 ....

MOTHMEN
Show Me Your House And Car .... 7" ..... Do It .... DUN12 .... 1981 ... £2 ....£5 ....
Show Me Your House And Car .... 12" ... Do It .... DUNIT12 .... 1981 ... £2.50 ....£6 ....

MOTIONS
Every Step I Take .... 7" ..... Pye .... 7N25390 .... 1966 ... £1.50 ....£4 ....
Every Step I Take .... 7" EP.. Vogue .... INT18097 .... 1966 ... £7.50 ....£15 .... French
I've Waited So Long .... 7" EP.. Vogue .... INT18017 .... 1965 ... £7.50 ....£15 .... French
Wasted Words .... 7" EP.. Vogue .... INT18069 .... 1966 ... £7.50 ....£15 .... French

MOTIVATION
Come On Down .... 7" ..... Direction .... 583248 .... 1968 ... £1.50 ....£4 ....

MOTLEY CRUE
Dr.Feelgood .... 7" ..... Elektra .... EKR97P .... 1989 ... £2.50 ....£6 .... shaped pic disc
Girls Girls Girls .... 7" ..... Elektra .... EKR59 .... 1987 ... £2 ....£5 .... X-rated PS
Girls Girls Girls .... 7" ..... Elektra .... EKR59P .... 1987 ... £2 ....£5 .... poster sleeve
Girls Girls Girls .... 12" ... Elektra .... EKR59TB .... 1987 ... £3 ....£8 ...... with patch, boxed
Girls Girls Girls .... 12" ... Elektra .... EKR59TP .... 1987 ... £3 ....£8 .... pic disc
Helter Skelter .... 12" ... Elektra .... 198- ... £8 ....£20 .... US promo pic
disc, with poster
Looks That Kill .... 7" ..... Elektra .... E9756 .... 1984 ... £2.50 ....£6 ....
Looks That Kill .... 12" ... Elektra .... E9756T .... 1984 ... £3 ....£8 .... with transfer
Shout At The Devil .... LP ..... Elektra .... 9602 .... 1983 ... £6 ....£15 .. pic disc with poster
Smokin' In The Boys' Room .... 7" ..... Elektra .... EKR33P .... 1986 ... £10 ....£20 ....interlocking
shaped pic disc
Smokin' In The Boys' Room .... 7" ..... Elektra .... EKR33P .... 1986 ... £7.50 ....£15 .mask shaped pic disc
Smokin' In The Boys' Room .... 12" ... Elektra .... EKR33T .... 1986 ... £3 ....£8 ... with patch & poster
Too Fast For Love .... LP ..... Leathur .... LR123 .... 1981 ... £30 ....£60 .... US
Too Young To Fall In Love .... LP ..... Elektra .... E9732 .... 1984 ... £2.50 ....£6 ....

Too Young To Fall In Love	12"	Elektra	E9732T	1984	£3	£8	with poster
You're All I Need	12"	Elektra	EKR65TB	1988	£2.50	£6	with patch & poster, boxed
You're All I Need	12"	Elektra	EKR65TP	1988	£3	£8	pic disc

MOTORHEAD

When Lemmy left Hawkwind, he covered over the psychedelic designs on his equipment with black paint and thereby defined the image for his new group. Motorhead managed to become popular among fans of punk at a time when heavy metal was distinctly out of fashion. Of course, the group's approach to heavy metal was a bit different - short pieces played very fast, the emphasis being on energy rather than on displays of vituosity - and they very much anticipated the thrash metal style of the late eighties. The first edition of the Price Guide gave the information that only ten copies of the "Motohead" single on white vinyl exist - information that has since been repeated elsewhere. In fact, it turns out that the single was not at all limited - and the author was inundated with phone calls from collectors telling him so!

Ace Of Spades	LP	Bronze	BRON531	1980	£5	£12	gold vinyl
Ace Of Spades	7"	GWR	GWR15	1988	£5	£10	
Ace Of Spades	12"	Bronze	BROX106	1980	£2.50	£6	
Beerdrinkers And Hellraisers	7"	Big Beat	NS61	1980	£2	£5	Radio Play Edition
Beerdrinkers And Hellraisers	12"	Big Beat	SWT61	1980	£2.50	£6	orange or blue vinyl
Bomber	LP	Bronze	BRON523	1979	£5	£12	blue vinyl
Bomber	7"	Bronze	BRO85	1979	£2	£5	blue vinyl
Iron Fist	7"	Bronze	BRO146	1982	£4	£8	blue vinyl
Iron Fist	7"	Bronze	BRO146	1982	£2	£5	red vinyl
Killed By Death	7"	Bronze	BROP185	1984	£6	£12	shaped pic disc
Louie Louie	7"	Bronze	BRO60	1978	£1.50	£4	chart single
Motorhead	LP	Big Beat	WIK2	1977	£4	£10	red or clear vinyl
Motorhead	7"	Chiswick	WIK2	1977	£10	£25	silver sleeve
Motorhead	7"	Big Beat	NSP13	1980	£2.50	£6	pic disc (2 versions)
Motorhead	7"	Chiswick	S13	1977	£2	£5	
Motorhead	12"	Chiswick	S13	1977	£3	£8	
Motorhead (Live)	7"	Bronze	BROP124	1981	£4	£8	pic disc
No Class	7"	Bronze	BRO78	1979	£1.50	£4	3 PS's, chart single
No Remorse	LP	Bronze	PROLP5	1984	£5	£12	double, 'leather' sleeve
No Sleep Till Hammersmith	LP	Bronze	BRON535	1981	£5	£12	gold vinyl
Overkill	LP	Bronze	BRON515	1979	£5	£12	green vinyl
Overkill	7"	Bronze	BRO67	1979	£1.50	£4	with badge
Overkill	12"	Bronze	12BRO67	1979	£2.50	£6	
Stand By Your Man	7"	Bronze	BRO151	1982	£1.50	£4	with Wendy O.Williams
White Line Fever	7"	Stiff	BUY9	1977	£5	£10	PS

MOTORHEAD & GIRLSCHOOL

| St.Valentine's Massacre EP | 10" | Bronze | BROX116 | 1981 | £2.50 | £6 | |

MOTOWN SPINNERS

| It's A Shame | 7" | Tamla Motown | TMG755 | 1970 | £2 | £5 | chart single |
| Together We Can Make Such Sweet Music | 7" | Tamla Motown | TMG766 | 1970 | £1.50 | £4 | |

MOTT THE HOOPLE

Brain Capers	LP	Island	ILPS9178	1971	£5	£12	
Downtown	7"	Island	WIP6112	1971	£2.50	£6	chart single
Mad Shadows	LP	Island	ILPS9119	1970	£5	£12	
Midnight Lady	7"	Island	WIP6105	1971	£4	£8	PS
Mott The Hoople	LP	Island	ILPS9108	1969	£6	£15	chart LP
Mott The Hoople	LP	Island	ILPS9108	1969	£15	£30	with 'Road To Birmingham'
Rock And Roll Queen	7"	Island	WIP6072	1969	£6	£12	
The Hoople	LP	Columbia	PCQ32871	1974	£5	£12	US quad
Wild Life	LP	Island	ILPS9144	1971	£5	£12	chart LP

MOULE, KEN

| Jazz At Toad Hall | LP | Decca | LK4261/SKL4042 | 1958 | £8 | £20 | |
| Ken Moule | LP | Decca | LK4192 | 1957 | £10 | £25 | |

MOULTRIE, MATTIE

| That's How Strong My Love Is | 7" | CBS | 202547 | 1967 | £4 | £8 | |

MOUND CITY BLUE BLOWERS

| Blues Blowing Jazz Vol.1 | 7" EP | Collector | JEL1 | 1959 | £4 | £8 | |
| Mound City Blue Blowers | 7" EP | HMV | 7EG8096 | 1955 | £2.50 | £6 | |

MOUNT RUSHMORE

| Stone Free | 7" | Dot | 115 | 1968 | £2 | £5 | |

MOUNTAIN

Mountain was formed by Felix Pappalardi in a deliberate attempt to capture some of the market that had been opened up by Cream. Pappalardi had, of course, worked with Cream on both "Disraeli Gears" and "Wheels Of Fire". Guitarist Leslie West was not in Eric Clapton's league, but Mountain nevertheless had its momemts - most notably on "Nantucket Sleighride", a section of which was made familiar to Sunday TV viewers in the London area as the theme tune to "Weekend World".

Avalanche	LP	Columbia	CQ33088	1974	£5	£12	US quad
Best Of Mountain	LP	Columbia	CQ32079	1973	£5	£12	US quad
Dreams Of Milk And Honey	7"	Bell	BLL1078	1970	£4	£8	
Flowers Of Evil	LP	Island	ILPS9179	1971	£5	£12	
Mississippi Queen	7"	Bell	BLL1112	1970	£2	£5	
Mountain Climbing	LP	Bell	SBLL133	1970	£5	£12	
Nantucket Sleighride	LP	Island	ILPS9148	1971	£5	£12	chart LP
Road Goes Ever On	LP	Island	ILPS9199	1972	£5	£12	chart LP
Sittin' On A Rainbow	7"	Bell	BLL1125	1970	£2	£5	
Twin Peaks	LP	CBS	88095	1974	£5	£12	double

MOUNTAIN ASH
Hermit .... LP ..... Witches Bane .. LKLP6036 .... 1975 ... £65 ....£130 ....

MOUNTAIN BUS
Sundance .... LP ..... Good .... 101 .... 1971 ... £25 ....£50 .... US

MOUNTAIN, VALERIE
Go It Alone .... 7" ..... Columbia .... DB4660 .... 1961 ... £1.50 ......£4
Some People .... 7" ..... Pye .... 7N15450 .... 1962 ... £1.50 ......£4

MOUNTAIN, VALERIE & THE EAGLES
Some People .... 7" EP.. Pye .... NEP24158 .... 1962 ... £4 ....£8

MOUSE
All The Fallen Teen Angels .... 7" ..... Sovereign .... SOV127 .... 1974 ... £6 ....£12
Lady Killer .... LP ..... Sovereign .... SVNA7262 .... 1974 ... £75 ....£150
We Can Make It .... 7" ..... Sovereign .... SOV122 .... 1973 ... £6 ....£12

MOUSE & THE TRAPS
L.O.V.E. .... 7" ..... President .... PT174 .... 1968 ... £6 ....£12
Sometimes You Just Can't Win .... 7" ..... President .... PT210 .... 1968 ... £2.50 ......£6

MOUSEFOLK
Don't Let It Slip Away .... 7" .... Tea Time .... 01 .... 1988 ... £2.50 ......£6 ....flexi with PS
Surf's Up ....

MOVE
The Move could never quite decide whether they wished to become part of the burgeoning progressive rock scene or whether they just wanted to be a pop group. In the event, much of the group's music is an uneasy compromise between the two, with the series of hit singles receiving the most care and invention in their construction. The most interesting Move release is possibly the live EP "Something Else", where the group powers its way through an assortment of dynamic cover versions. They turn Spooky Tooth's "Sunshine Help Me" into something of a showcase for Roy Wood's squally lead guitar, but the fact that the melodic bass playing is given at least as much prominence in the mix makes the music sound remarkably fresh.

Blackberry Way .... 7" .... Regal RZ3015 .... 1969 ... £1.50 ......£4 ....chart single
Zonophone.....
Brontosaurus .... 7" .... Regal RZ3026 .... 1970 ... £1.50 ......£4 ....chart single
Zonophone.....
Cherry Blossom Clinic .... 7" .... Regal .... 1968 ... £25 ....£50 ....test pressing
Zonophone.......
Chinatown .... 7" .... Harvest .... HAR5043 .... 1971 ... £1.50 ......£4 ....chart single
Curly .... 7" .... Regal RZ3021 .... 1969 ... £1.50 ......£4 ....chart single
Zonophone.....
Fire Brigade .... 7" .... MagniFly .... ECHO104 .... 1972 ... £2.50 ......£6 ....PS
Fire Brigade .... 7" .... Regal RZ3005 .... 1968 ... £1.50 ......£4 ....chart single
Zonophone.....
Flowers In The Rain .... 7" .... Regal RZ3001 .... 1967 ... £1.50 ......£4 ....chart single
Zonophone....
I Can Hear The Grass Grow .... 7" .... Deram .... DM117 .... 1967 ... £1.50 ......£4 ....chart single
I Can Hear The Grass Grow .... 7" EP.. Deram .... 15002 .... 1967 ... £10 ....£20 ....French
Looking On .... LP ..... Fly .... FLY1 .... 1971 ... £4 ....£10
Message From The Country .... LP ..... Harvest .... SHSP4013 .... 1971 ... £4 ....£10
Move .... LP ..... Regal (S)LRZ1002 .... 1968 ... £6 ....£15 ....chart LP
Zonophone.....
Move/Shazam .... LP ..... Cube .... TOOFA5/6 .... 1972 ... £5 ....£12 ....double
Night Of Fear .... 7" .... Deram .... DM109 .... 1966 ... £1.50 ......£4 ....chart single
Shazam .... LP ..... Regal SLRZ1012 .... 1970 ... £6 ....£15
Zonophone.....
Something Else .... 7" EP. Regal TRZ2001 .... 1968 ... £12.50 ....£25
Zonophone.....
Something Else From The Move .... 7" .... EMI.................. PSRS315 .... 1968 ... £15 ....£30 .... 1 sided
promo sampler
Tonight .... 7" .... Harvest .... HAR5038 .... 1971 ... £1.50 ......£4 ....chart single
When Alice Comes Back To The Farm .. 7" .... Fly .... BUG2 .... 1970 ... £1.50 ......£4
Wild Tiger Woman .... 7" .... Regal RZ3012 .... 1968 ... £2 ....£5
Zonophone.....

MOVEMENT
Head For The Sun .... 7" .... Transatlantic .. BIG112 .... 1968 ... £15 ....£30
Something You've Got .... 7" .... Pye .... 7N17443 .... 1968 ... £25 ....£50

MOVING FINGER
Higher And Higher .... 7" .... Mercury .... MF1077 .... 1969 ... £4 ....£8
Jeremy The Lamp .... 7" .... Mercury .... MF1051 .... 1968 ... £6 ....£12
So Many People .... 7" .... Decca .... F13406 .... 1973 ... £4 ....£8

MOVING GELATINE PLATES
Moving Gelatine Plates .... LP ..... CBS .... 64399 .... 1971 ... £35 ....£70
World Of Genius Hans .... LP ..... CBS .... 64146 .... 1971 ... £35 ....£70

MOVING HEARTS
Live Hearts .... LP ..... WEA .... IR0203 .... 1983 ... £5 ....£12
Moving Hearts .... LP ..... WEA .... K583387 .... 1981 ... £5 ....£12

MOVING SIDEWALKS
Flash .... LP ..... Tantara .... TYS6919 .... 1968 ... £50 ....£100 .... US

MOZART, MICKEY
Little Dipper .... 7" .... Columbia .... DB4308 .... 1959 ... £1.50 ......£4

MR.CLEAN
Both sides of the Mr.Clean single are the work of Frank Zappa, who wrote and produced the songs and played guitar on them.

Mr.Clean	7"	Original Sound 40	1964	£30	£60		US

MR.DYNAMITE
Sh'mon	7"	Sue	WI4027	1967	£10	£20	

MR.FLOOD'S PARTY
Compared To What	7"	Bulldog	BD6	1975	£2	£5	
Compared To What	7"	Ember	EMBS312	1970	£5	£10	
Mr.Flood's Party	LP	Cotillion	9003	1969	£6	£15	US

MR.FOUNDATION
Time-oh	7"	Studio One	SO2061	1968	£6	£12	Dudley Sibley & Peter Austin B side

MR.FOX
Complete Mr.Fox	LP	Transatlantic	TRA303	1975	£10	£25	double
Gypsy	LP	Transatlantic	TRA236	1971	£15	£30	
Little Woman	7"	Transatlantic	BIG135	1970	£2	£5	
Mr.Fox	LP	Transatlantic	TRA226	1970	£10	£25	

MR.GASSER & THE WEIRDOS
Hot Rod Hootenanny	LP	Capitol	(S)T2010	1963	£6	£15	US
Rods 'N' Ratfinks	LP	Capitol	(S)T2057	1963	£6	£15	US
Surfink!	LP	Capitol	(S)T2114	1964	£8	£20	US

MR.MO'S MESSENGERS
Feelin' Good	7"	Columbia	DB8133	1967	£2.50	£6

MR.TWISTER & THE TORNADOES
Big Twist	7"	Starlite	ST45099	1963	£1.50	£4

MU
Lemurian Music	LP	United Artists	UAG29709	1975	£8	£20	
Mu	LP	RTV	300	1972	£20	£40	US

MUCKRAM WAKES
Map Of Derbyshire	LP	Trailer	LER2085	1973	£10	£25
Muckram Wakes	LP	Trailer	LER2093	1976	£6	£15
Warbles, Jangles And Reeds	LP	Highway	SHY7009	1980	£6	£15

MUCKY DUCK
Jefferson	7"	Deram	DM314	1970	£1.50	£4

MUD
Flower Power	7"	CBS	203002	1967	£6	£12	
Flower Power	7"	CBS	203002	1967	£10	£20	PS
Jumping Jehosaphat	7"	Philips	6006022	1970	£5	£10	
Shangri-La	7"	Philips	BF1775	1969	£5	£10	
Up The Airy Mountain	7"	CBS	3355	1968	£6	£12	

MUDCRUTCH
The songs issued by Mudcrutch are the earliest recordings to feature Tom Petty.
Depot Street	7"	Shelter	40357	1975	£7.50	£15	US
Up In Mississippi	7"	Pepper	9449	1971	£100	£200	US

MUDLARKS
Book Of Love	7"	Columbia	DB4133	1958	£2.50	£6	chart single
Lollipop	7"	Columbia	DB4099	1958	£2.50	£6	chart single
Love Game	7"	Columbia	DB4250	1959	£1.50	£4	chart single
Mudlarks	7" EP	Columbia	SEG7854	1958	£6	£12	
New Love	7"	Columbia	DB4064	1958	£2	£5	
There's Never Been A Night	7"	Columbia	DB4190	1958	£1.50	£4	
Which Witch Doctor	7"	Columbia	DB4210	1958	£1.50	£4	

MUGWUMPS
Historical Recording	LP	Valiant	VS134	1967	£4	£10	
I Don't Wanna Know	7"	Warner Bros	WB144	1964	£2.50	£6	
Mugwumps	LP	Warner Bros	W1697	1967	£6	£15	

MUIR, BOBBY
Baby What You Done Me Wrong	7"	Blue Beat	BB20	1961	£5	£10	
Spanish Town Twist	7"	Blue Beat	BB77	1961	£5	£10	
That's My Girl	7"	Blue Beat	BB44	1961	£5	£10	

MULCAYS
Harbour Lights	7"	London	HLF8188	1955	£10	£20	
Harmonics By The Mulcays	7" EP	London	REF1046	1956	£6	£12	
Merry Christmas	7" EP	London	REP1016	1954	£5	£10	

MULDAUR, GEOFF
Geoff Muldaur	LP	Prestige	14004	1964	£6	£15	US
Sleepy Man Blues	LP	Prestige	7727	1965	£6	£15	US

MULDAUR, GEOFF & MARIA
Pottery Pie	LP	Reprise	RS6350	1970	£5	£12	US
Sweet Potatoes	LP	Warner Bros	MS2073	1972	£5	£12	US

MULDOONS
I'm Lost Without You	7"	Decca	F12164	1965	£10	£20

MULESKINNERS
Back Door Man	7"	Fontana	TF527	1965	£30	£60

Title	Format	Label	Catalog	Year			Notes
Muleskinners	7" EP	Keepoint	KEEEP7104	196-	£150	£250	

MULLICAN, MOON

Title	Format	Label	Catalog	Year			Notes
Cherokee Boogie	78	Vogue	V9013	1951	£6	£12	
Country Round Up	7" EP	Parlophone	GEP8794	1959	£12.50	£25	
His All-Time Greatest Hits	LP	King	555	1958	£25	£50	US
I'll Sail My Ship Alone	LP	Sterling	ST601	196-	£10	£25	US
Instrumentals	LP	Audio Lab	AL1568	1962	£20	£40	US
Many Moods Of Moon Mullican	LP	King	681	1960	£25	£50	US
Moon Over Mullican	LP	Coral	CRL57235	1958	£75	£150	US
Mr.Piano Man	LP	Starday	SLP267	1964	£6	£15	US
Piano Breakdown	7" EP	Parlophone	CGEP15	195-	£10	£20	export
Seven Nights To Rock	7"	Parlophone	MSP6254	1956	£150	£250	with Boyd Bennett
Sixteen Of His Favorite Tunes	LP	King	628	1959	£25	£50	US
Twenty-Four Of His Favorite Tunes	LP	KIng	937	1965	£5	£12	US
Unforgettable Moon Mullican	LP	Starday	SLP398	1967	£5	£12	US

MULLIGAN, GERRY

Title	Format	Label	Catalog	Year			Notes
At The Village Vanguard	LP	HMV	CLP1488/CSD1396	1962	£6	£15	
Concert In Jazz	LP	HMV	CLP1549/CSD1432	1962	£5	£12	
Concert Jazz Band	LP	HMV	CLP1432/CSD1351	1961	£6	£15	
Concert Jazz Band	LP	Verve	VLP9037	1963	£5	£12	
Genius Of Gerry Mulligan	LP	Vocalion	LAE12268	1960	£6	£15	
Gerry Mulligan Allstars	LP	Esquire	32014	1956	£10	£25	
Gerry Mulligan Allstars	10" LP	Esquire	20032	1954	£25	£50	
Gerry Mulligan And Paul Desmond Quartet	LP	Columbia	33CX10113	1958	£6	£15	
Gerry Mulligan Meets Ben Webster	LP	HMV	CLP1373	1960	£6	£15	
Gerry Mulligan Meets Johnny Hodges	LP	HMV	CLP1465/CSD1372	1962	£6	£15	
Gerry Mulligan Quartet	LP	Vogue	LAE12006	1956	£10	£25	
Gerry Mulligan Quartet	LP	Vogue	LAE12015	1956	£10	£25	
Gerry Mulligan Quartet	LP	Vogue	LAE12050	1957	£8	£20	
Gerry Mulligan Quartet	LP	Vogue	LAE12080	1958	£8	£20	
Gerry Mulligan Quartet	10" LP	Vogue	LDE075	1954	£25	£50	
Gerry Mulligan Quartet Vol.1	10" LP	Vogue	LDE029	1953	£25	£50	
Gerry Mulligan Quartet Vol.2	10" LP	Vogue	LDE030	1953	£25	£50	
Gerry Mulligan Quartet Vol.3	10" LP	Vogue	LDE031	1953	£25	£50	
Gerry Mulligan Quartet Vol.4	10" LP	Vogue	LDE083	1954	£25	£50	
Gerry Mulligan Quartet With Lee Konitz	10" LP	Vogue	LDE156	1955	£25	£50	
Gerry Mulligan Tentette	10" LP	Capitol	LC6621	1953	£25	£50	
Getz Meets Mulligan In Hi-Fi	LP	Columbia	33CX10120	1958	£6	£15	with Stan Getz
I Want To Live	LP	London	LTZT15161/SAHT6023	1959	£6	£15	with Shelly Manne
Mainstream Of Jazz	LP	Emarcy	EJL1259	1957	£10	£25	
Mainstream Vol.1	7" EP	Emarcy	ERE1574	1958	£2	£5	
Mainstream Vol.2	7" EP	Emarcy	ERE1575	1958	£2	£5	
Mulligan Mania	7" EP	Mercury	ZEP10071	1960	£2	£5	
Mulligan Meets Monk	LP	London	LTZU15127	1958	£8	£20	with Thelonious Monk
Mulligan Meets Monk	LP	Riverside	RLP12247	1962	£6	£15	
On Tour	LP	HMV	CLP1585	1962	£5	£12	with Zoot Sims
Phil Sunkel's Jazz Concerto Grosso	LP	HMV	CLP1204	1958	£8	£20	with Bob Brookmeyer
Presenting Gerry Mulligan & His Tentette	7" EP	Capitol	EAP1439	1955	£2	£5	
Presenting Gerry Mulligan & His Tentette	7" EP	Capitol	EAP2439	1955	£2	£5	
Presenting The Gerry Mulligan Sextet	LP	Emarcy	EJL101	1956	£10	£25	
Presenting The Gerry Mulligan Sextet	7" EP	Emarcy	ERE1553	1958	£2	£5	
Presenting The Gerry Mulligan Sextet Vol.2	7" EP	Emarcy	ERE1556	1958	£2	£5	
Presenting The Gerry Mulligan Sextet Vol.3	7" EP	Emarcy	ERE1560	1958	£2	£5	
Relax	LP	Fontana	FJL105	1964	£4	£10	
Reunion With Chet Baker	LP	Vogue	LAE12185/SEA5007	1959	£8	£20	
Songbook Vol.1	LP	Vogue	LAE12128/SEA5006	1959	£10	£25	
What Is There To Say?	LP	Philips	BBL7320	1959	£4	£10	
What Is There To Say?	LP	Philips	SBBL552	1959	£5	£12	

MULLIGAN, MICK

Title	Format	Label	Catalog	Year			Notes
Jazz At The Railway Arms	LP	Tempo	TAP14	1957	£6	£15	with George Melly
Meet Mick Mulligan	LP	Pye	NJL21	1959	£5	£12	
Mick Mulligan's Jazz Band	7" EP	Tempo	EXA25	1955	£2	£5	
Saints Meet The Sinners	LP	Parlophone	PMC1103/PCS3005	1959	£5	£12	with George Melly

MUMFORD, GENE

Title	Format	Label	Catalog	Year			Notes
More Than You Know	7"	Philips	PB862	1958	£1.50	£4	

MUNGO JERRY

Title	Format	Label	Catalog	Year			Notes
Lady Rose	7"	Dawn	DNX2510	1971	£1.50	£4	PS

MUNRO, HAL

Title	Format	Label	Catalog	Year			Notes
Breathless	7"	Embassy	WB284	1958	£1.50	£4	
C'mon Everybody	7"	Embassy	WB336	1959	£1.50	£4	

MUNSTERS

Title	Format	Label	Catalog	Year			Notes
Munsters	LP	Decca	DL4588	1964	£8	£20	US

MURE, BILLY

Supersonics In Flight	7" EP..	RCA	RCX158/SRC7032 .	1959 ...	£7.50 ....£15	
Versatile Billy Mure	7" EP..	Felsted	GEP1006	1959 ...	£2.50 ....£6	

MURMAIDS

Popsicles And Icicles	7"	Stateside	SS247	1963 ...	£4 ......£8	
Popsicles And Icicles	7" EP..	Columbia	ESRF1487	1964 ...	£6 ....£12	French

MURPHEY, MICHAEL

Geronimo's Cadillac	LP	Regal Zonophone	ZONO8512	1972 ...	£4 ......£10	

MURPHY BLEND

First Loss	LP	Kuckuck	2375005	1970 ...	£6 ......£15	German

MURPHY, DENIS & JULIA CLIFFORD

Star Above The Garter	LP	Claddagh	CC5	1969 ...	£5 ......£12	Irish

MURPHY, MARK

Hit Parade	LP	Capitol	(S)T5011	1960 ...	£5 ......£12	
Mark Time!	LP	Fontana	(S)TL5217	1964 ...	£5 ......£12	
Meet Mark Murphy	LP	Brunswick	LAT8172	1957 ...	£5 ......£12	
This Could Be The Start Of Something	LP	Capitol	T1177	1959 ...	£5 ......£12	
Who Can I Turn To	LP	Immediate	IMLP/IMSP004	1966 ...	£15 ......£30	

MURPHY, NOEL

Another Round	LP	Fontana	STL5496	1969 ...	£5 ......£12	
Murf	LP	Village Thing	VTS25	1973 ...	£5 ......£12	
Nya-a-a-a-h!	LP	Fontana	(S)TL5450	1967 ...	£5 ......£12	

MURPHY, ROSE

Songs By Rose Murphy	10" LP	Mercury	MG10004	1953 ...	£5 ......£12	

MURPHY, TURK

Music Of Jelly Roll Morton	LP	Philips	BBL7051	1955 ...	£5 ......£12	
New Orleans Shuffle	LP	Philips	BBL7145	1957 ...	£4 ......£10	
Turk Murphy Jazz Band	LP	Philips	BBL7088	1956 ...	£5 ......£12	
Turk Murphy Jazz Band	LP	Philips	BBL7095	1956 ...	£5 ......£12	
Turk Murphy Jazz Band	10" LP	Good Time Jazz	LDG037	1954 ...	£5 ......£12	
Turk Murphy Jazz Band	10" LP	Good Time Jazz	LDG078	1954 ...	£5 ......£12	
Turk Murphy Jazz Band	10" LP	Good Time Jazz	LDG180	1956 ...	£5 ......£12	
Turk Murphy Jazz Band	10" LP	Good Time Jazz	LDG186	1956 ...	£5 ......£12	

MURRAY, ALEX

Teen Angel	7"	Decca	F11203	1960 ...	£1.50 ......£4	

MURRAY, LARRY

Sweet Country Suite	LP	Verve		1969 ...	£8 ......£20	US

MURRAY, MISTER

Down Came The Rain	7"	Fontana	TF623	1965 ...	£1.50 ......£4	

MURRAY, MITCH CLAN

Skyliner	7"	Clan	597001	1966 ...	£1.50 ......£4	

MURRAY, PETE/PASCAL FRUITS

TV Themes	7" EP..	ATV	ATV1	1969 ...	£2.50 ......£6	

MURRAY, RUBY

Ain't That A Grand And Glorious Feeling	7"	Columbia	DB4042	1957 ...	£1.50 ......£4	
Endearing Young Charms	7" EP..	Columbia	SEG7952	1959 ...	£2.50 ......£6	
Endearing Young Charms	10" LP	Columbia	33S1135	1958 ...	£8 ......£20	
Evermore	7"	Columbia	SCM5180	1955 ...	£5 ......£10	chart single
Everybody's Sweetheart No.1	7" EP..	Columbia	SEG7620	1956 ...	£2.50 ......£6	
Everybody's Sweetheart No.2	7" EP..	Columbia	SEG7631	1956 ...	£2.50 ......£6	
Everybody's Sweetheart No.3	7" EP..	Columbia	SEG7636	1956 ...	£4 ......£8	
Forgive Me My Darling	7"	Columbia	DB4075	1958 ...	£1.50 ......£4	
From The First Hello	7"	Columbia	DB3911	1957 ...	£2.50 ......£6	
Goodbye Jimmy Goodbye	7"	Columbia	DB4305	1959 ...	£1.50 ......£4	chart single
If Anyone Finds This, I Love You	7"	Columbia	SCM5169	1955 ...	£5 ......£10	chart single
In Love	7"	Columbia	DB3852	1956 ...	£2.50 ......£6	
In My Life	7"	Columbia	DB4108	1958 ...	£1.50 ......£4	
It Only Hurts For A Little While	7"	Columbia	DB3810	1956 ...	£4 ......£8	
Little White Lies	7"	Columbia	DB3994	1957 ...	£1.50 ......£4	
Love's Old Sweet Song	7" EP..	Columbia	ESG7830	1960 ...	£5 ......£10	stereo
Love's Old Sweet Song	7" EP..	Columbia	SEG8052	1960 ...	£2.50 ......£6	
Mr.Wonderful	7"	Columbia	DB3933	1957 ...	£2.50 ......£6	
Oh Please Make Him Jealous	7"	Columbia	SCM5225	1956 ...	£4 ......£8	
Real Love	7"	Columbia	DB4192	1958 ...	£1.50 ......£4	chart single
Ruby	LP	Columbia	33SX1201/ SCX3289	1960 ...	£5 ......£12	
Ruby Is A Gem	7" EP..	Columbia	SEG7588	1955 ...	£6 ......£12	
Scarlet Ribbons	7"	Columbia	DB3955	1957 ...	£2.50 ......£6	
Softly Softly	7"	Columbia	SCM5162	1955 ...	£7.50 ......£15	chart single
True Love	7"	Columbia	DB3849	1956 ...	£2.50 ......£6	
When Irish Eyes Are Smiling	10" LP	Columbia	33S1079	1955 ...	£6 ......£15	

MUSHROOM
Devil Among The Tailors	7"	Hawk	HASP320	1975	£10	£20	
Early One Morning	LP	Hawk	HALPX116	1973	£150	£250	
Early One Morning	LP	Hawk	HALPX116	1973	£210	£350	with poster

MUSIC BOX
Songs Of Sunshine	LP	Westwood	MRS013	1972	£8	£20	

MUSIC DOCTORS
Reggae In The Summertime	LP	Trojan	TBL117	1970	£5	£12	

MUSIC EMPORIUM
Music Emporium	LP	Psycho	PSYCHO11	1983	£6	£15	
Music Emporium	LP	Sentinel	1000	1969	£700	£1000	US

MUSIC EXPLOSION
Little Bit O'Soul	LP	Laurie	(S)LLP2040	1967	£6	£15	US
Little Bit O'Soul	7"	Stateside	SS2028	1967	£2.50	£6	
Little Bit O'Soul	7" EP	Vogue	INT18140	1967	£10	£20	French
Little Black Egg	7"	Philips	BF1547	1967	£2.50	£6	
Sunshine Games	7"	Stateside	SS2054	1967	£2	£5	

MUSIC MACHINE
Bonniwell Music Machine	LP	Warner Bros	WS1732	1968	£8	£20	US
People In Me	LP	Pye	7N25414	1967	£7.50	£15	demo
Talk Talk	7"	Pye	7N25407	1967	£10	£20	
Talk Talk	7" EP	Vogue	INT18121	1967	£25	£50	French
Turn On The Music Machine	LP	Original Sound	5015/8875	1966	£15	£30	US

MUSICA URBANA
Musica Urbana	LP	Edigsa	UM2033	1976	£8	£20	Spanish

MUSKETEER GRIPWEED
The single credited to Musketeer Gripweed is taken from the soundtrack of the film "How I Won The War" and is an often overlooked rarity from the oeuvre of the man who played the character in the film - John Lennon. As it happens, Lennon's contribution to the record is fairly minimal. His role in the film was not a singing one and on the record he merely contributes a fragment of speech to a basically instrumental piece.

How I Won The War	7"	United Artists	UP1196	1966	£20	£40	

MUSSELWHITE, CHARLIE
Charlie Musselwhite	LP	Vanguard	VSD79287	1968	£6	£15	US
Stand Back, Here Comes Charlie Musslewhite	LP	Vanguard	VSD79232	1967	£6	£15	US
Stone Blues	LP	Vanguard	SVRL19012	1968	£6	£15	US
Tennessee Woman	LP	Vanguard	VSD6528	1969	£5	£12	US

MUSSULLI, BOOTS
Diga Diga Doo	7"	Capitol	KC65002	1954	£1.50	£4	
Kenton Presents Jazz	10" LP	Capitol	KPL106	1955	£10	£25	

MUSTANG
Why	7"	Parlophone	R5579	1967	£7.50	£15	

MUSTANGS
Dartell Stomp	LP	Providence	PLP001	1963	£8	£20	US

MUSTWANGS
Rock Lomond	7"	Mercury	AMT1140	1961	£2.50	£6	

MUTE DRIVERS
Mute Drivers	LP	Mute Drivers	MD001	198-	£5	£12	

MUTT'N'JEFF
Don't Nag Me Ma	7"	Decca	F12335	1966	£4	£8	

MY BLOODY VALENTINE
After a shaky start (as represented by many of their early collectable records), My Bloody Valentine achieved greatness with the release of their "Isn't Anything" album. Decades after the invention of the electric guitar, they managed to find entirely new ways of making it sound - and added this to a melodic strength in a combination that is frequently exhilarating.

Ecstasy	mini LP	Lazy	LAZY08	1987	£10	£25	
Feed Me With Your Kiss	7"	Creation	CRE061	1988	£1.50	£4	
Geek!	12"	Fever	FEV5	1986	£6	£15	
Isn't Anything	LP	Creation	CRELP040	1988	£5	£12	with 7' (CREFRE4)
New Record By My Bloody Valentine	12"	Kaleidoscope Sound	KS101	1986	£8	£20	
No Place To Go	7"	Fever	FEV5X	1986	£4	£8	
Strawberry Wine	12"	Lazy	LAZY07T	1987	£6	£15	
Sunny Sundae Smile	7"	Lazy	LAZY04	1987	£6	£12	
Sunny Sundae Smile	12"	Lazy	LAZY04T	1987	£6	£15	
This Is Your Bloody Valentine	mini LP	Tycoon	ST7501	1985	£25	£50	German
You Made Me Realise	7"	Creation	CRE055	1988	£1.50	£4	

MY CAPTAINS
History	7"	4AD	AD103	1981	£1.50	£4	

MY DEAR WATSON
Elusive Face	7"	Parlophone	R5687	1968	£7.50	£15	
Have You Seen Your Saviour	7"	DJM	DJS224	1970	£4	£8	
Stop Stop I'll Be There	7"	Parlophone	R5737	1968	£7.50	£15	

MY LORDE SHERIFFE'S COMPLAINTE
My Lorde Sheriffe's Complainte .... LP ...... Frog .... FROG1 .... 1979 ... £10 ....£25 ....

MY SOLID GROUND
My Solid Ground .... LP ...... Bacillus .... BLPS19071 .... 1971 ... £35 ....£70 ....

MYERS, DAVE
| Greatest Racing Themes | LP | Carole | CAR(S)8002 | 1967 | £5 | £12 | US |
| Hangin' Twenty | LP | Del-Fi | DFLP/DFST1239 | 1963 | £6 | £15 | US |

MYLES, BILLY
Joker .... 7" ...... HMV .... POP423 .... 1957 ... £7.50 ....£15 ....

MYNEDIAD AM DDIM
Mae'r Grwp Yn Talu	LP	Sain	1064M	1976	£6	£15
Mynediad Am Ddim	LP	Sain	1021M	1975	£10	£25
Rhwng Saith Stol	LP	Sain	1083M	1977	£6	£15
Torth O Fara	LP	Sain	1137M	1978	£5	£12

MYRTELLES
Don't Wanna Cry Again .... 7" ...... Oriole .... CB1805 .... 1963 ... £1.50 ....£4 ....

MYSTERIES
Give Me Rhythm And Blues .... 7" ...... Decca .... F11919 .... 1964 ... £12.50 ....£25 ....

MYSTERY MAKER
Mystery Maker .... LP ...... Caves .... UHC3 .... 1977 ... £40 ....£80 ....

MYSTIC ASTROLOGICAL CRYSTAL BAND
| Clip Out, Put On Book | LP | Carole | S8003 | 1968 | £6 | £15 | US |
| Mystic Astrological Crystal Band | LP | Carole | (S)8001 | 1967 | £6 | £15 | US |

MYSTIC MOODS ORCHESTRA
Cosmic Force	LP	Mobile Fidelity	1002	1981	£8	£20	US audiophile
Emotions	LP	Mobile Fidelity	1001	1981	£8	£20	US audiophile
Stormy Weekend	LP	Mobile Fidelity	1003	1981	£8	£20	US audiophile

MYSTIC SIVA
Mystic Siva .... LP ...... Vo .... 19713 .... 1970 ... £90 ....£180 .... US

MYSTICS
| Adam And Eve | 7" | HMV | POP646 | 1959 | £12.50 | £25 |
| Don't Take The Stars | 7" | Top Rank | JAR243 | 1959 | £5 | £10 |

MYTHOS
Dreamlab	LP	Kosmische	KM58016	1975	£4	£10	German
Mythos	LP	Ohr	OMM556019	1972	£8	£20	German
Strange Guys	LP	Venus	MYF1003	1977	£4	£10	German

MYTHRA
| Death And Destiny | 7" | Streetbeat | LAMP2 | 1980 | £2.50 | £6 |
| Killer | 12" | Streetbeat | LAMP2T | 1980 | £10 | £25 |

N

N BETWEENS
The N Betweens' sole single, a version of the Young Rascals' American hit, "You Better Run", was produced by the legendary Kim Fowley. Success did not come to the group until a few years later, however, when it had changed its name to Slade.

NA FILI
Chanter's Tune	LP	Transatlantic	TRA353	1977	£5	£12	
Farewell To Connacht	LP	Outlet	SOLP1010	1971	£6	£15	Irish
Kindly Welcome	LP	Dolphin	DOL1008	1974	£5	£12	Irish
Na Fili 3	LP	Outlet	SOLP1017	1973	£6	£15	Irish
One Day For Recreation (with Sean O Se)	LP	Circa	003	1980	£5	£12	Irish

NABAY
Believe It Or Not	7"	Grapevine	GRP143	1979	£1.50	£4	

NAKED TRUTH
Two Little Rooms	7"	Deram	DM287	1970	£2	£5	

NAMYSLOWSKI, ZBIGNIEW
Lola	LP	Decca	LK4644	1964	£5	£12	

NANETTE
Nanette	LP	Columbia	SCX6398	1970	£6	£15	

NANGLE, ED
Whipping The Prince	7"	Coxsone	CS7038	1968	£5	£10	Heptones B side

NANTOS, NICK & THE FIREBALLERS
Guitars On Fire	LP	Summit	ATL4114	1964	£5	£12	
Guitars On Fire	7" EP	Summit	LSE2042	1963	£2	£5	

NAPOLEON XIV
I'm In Love With My Little Red Tricycle	7"	Warner Bros	WB5853	1966	£2.50	£6	
They're Coming To Take Me Away	LP	Warner Bros	W(S)1661	1966	£25	£50	US
They're Coming To Take Me Away	7" EP	Warner Bros	WB108	1966	£7.50	£15	French
They're Coming To Take Me Away Ha Ha	7"	Warner Bros	WB5831	1966	£2	£5	chart single

NARNIA
Narnia	LP	Myrrh	MYR1007	1974	£50	£100	

NASH, BILLY
Madison Step	7"	Philips	370406BF	1963	£1.50	£4	
Sunset	7"	Philips	PB1181	1961	£1.50	£4	

NASH, GENE
Ja Ja Ja	7"	Capitol	CL15042	1959	£4	£8	

NASH, JOHNNY
As Time Goes By	7"	HMV	POP620	1959	£1.50	£4	
Baby Baby Baby	7"	HMV	POP651	1959	£1.50	£4	
Cigareets, Whiskey, And Wild Wild Women	7"	Warner Bros	WB93	1963	£1.50	£4	
Cupid	7"	Major Minor	MM603	1969	£1.50	£4	chart single
Don't Take Away Your Love	7"	Warner Bros	WB65	1962	£1.50	£4	
From Both Sides Now	7"	Major Minor	MM619	1969	£1.50	£4	with Kim Weston
Glad You're My Baby	7"	MGM	MGM1480	1969	£2.50	£6	
Goodbye	7"	HMV	POP746	1960	£1.50	£4	
Groovy Feeling	7"	Major Minor	MM701	1970	£1.50	£4	
Hold Me Tight	7"	Regal Zonophone	RZ3010	1968	£1.50	£4	chart single
I Got Rhythm	LP	HMV	CLP1325/CSD1288	1960	£4	£10	
Imagination	7"	HMV	POP673	1959	£1.50	£4	
Johnny Nash	LP	HMV	CLP1251	1959	£4	£10	
Johnny Nash And Kim Weston	LP	Major Minor	MMLP/SMLP54	1969	£4	£10	
Ladder Of Love	7"	HMV	POP402	1957	£1.50	£4	
Let's Get Lost	LP	Encore	ENC2005	1962	£4	£10	
Let's Move And Groove	7"	Pye	7N25353	1966	£1.50	£4	
Love Ain't Nothing	7"	Pye	7N25250	1964	£7.50	£15	
Love And Peace	7"	Major Minor	MM630	1969	£1.50	£4	
Love Me Tender	7"	Major Minor	MM646	1969	£1.50	£4	
Midnight Moonlight	7"	HMV	POP553	1958	£1.50	£4	
My Pledge To You	7"	HMV	POP475	1958	£1.50	£4	
Ol' Man River	7"	Warner Bros	WB76	1962	£1.50	£4	
One More Time	7"	Pye	7N25363	1966	£1.50	£4	
Presenting Johnny Nash	7" EP	RCA	RCX7163	1964	£10	£20	
Prince Of Peace	LP	Major Minor	MMLP/SMLP63	1969	£4	£10	
Quiet Hour	LP	HMV	CLP1299	1959	£4	£10	
Roots Of Heaven	7"	HMV	POP597	1959	£1.50	£4	
Somebody	7"	HMV	POP822	1960	£1.50	£4	
Soul Folk	LP	Major Minor	MMLP/SMLP56	1969	£4	£10	

Stir It Up	7"	CBS	7800	1972	£1.50	£4	chart single
Strange Feeling	7"	Chess	CRS8005	1965	£5	£10	
Very Special Love	7"	HMV	POP435	1958	£1.50	£4	
You Got Soul	LP	Major Minor	MMLP/SMLP47	1969	£4	£10	
You Got Soul	7"	Major Minor	MM586	1969	£1.50	£4	chart single

NASHVILLE FIVE

Brainwave	7"	Decca	F11484	1962	£2	£5	
Like Nashville	7" EP	Decca	DFE6706	1962	£7.50	£15	
Stand Up And Say That	7"	Decca	F11427	1962	£2	£5	

NASHVILLE TEENS

All Along The Watchtower	7"	Decca	F12754	1968	£4	£8	
Biggest Night Of Her Life	7"	Decca	F12657	1967	£4	£8	
Ella James	7"	Parlophone	R5925	1971	£5	£10	
Find My Way Back Home	7"	Decca	F12089	1965	£1.50	£4	chart single
Find My Way Back Home	7" EP	Decca	457074	1965	£25	£50	French
Forbidden Fruit	7"	Decca	F12458	1966	£2	£5	
Google Eye	7"	Decca	F12000	1964	£1.50	£4	chart single
Hard Way	7"	Decca	F12316	1966	£1.50	£4	chart single
I'm Coming Home	7"	Decca	F12580	1967	£2.50	£6	
Lament Of The Cherokee Reservation Indian	7"	Major Minor	MM599	1969	£5	£10	
Lawdy Miss Clawdy	7"	Enterprise	ENT001	1972	£1.50	£4	
Nashville Teens	LP	New World	NW6002	1975	£10	£25	
Nashville Teens	7" EP	Decca	DFE8600	1965	£15	£30	
Soon Forgotten	7"	Decca	F12255	1965	£2	£5	
That's My Woman	7"	Decca	F12542	1966	£2	£5	
This Little Bird	7"	Decca	F12143	1965	£1.50	£4	chart single
Tobacco Road	LP	London	LL3407/PS407	1964	£25	£50	US
Tobacco Road	7"	Decca	F11930	1964	£1.50	£4	chart single
Tobacco Road	7" EP	Decca	457047	1964	£15	£30	French

NATIONAL HEAD BAND

Albert One	LP	Warner Bros	K46094	1971	£6	£15	

NATIONAL PINION POLE

Make Your Mark Little Mark	7"	Planet	PLF111	1966	£5	£10	

NATURALS

Blue Roses	7"	Parlophone	R5257	1965	£2.50	£6	
Daisy Chain	7"	Parlophone	R5116	1964	£1.50	£4	
I Should Have Known Better	7"	Parlophone	R5165	1964	£1.50	£4	chart single
It Was You	7"	Parlophone	R5202	1964	£1.50	£4	

NAVARRO, FATS

Memorial	10" LP	London	LZC14015	1955	£25	£50	
Memorial Vol.1	LP	Realm	RM52192	1965	£4	£10	
Memorial Vol.2	LP	Realm	RM52208	1965	£4	£10	
Trumpet Giants	LP	Stateside	SL10103	1964	£4	£10	with tracks by Miles Davis & Dizzy Gillespie

NAYLOR, JERRY

Stop Your Crying	7"	Top Rank	JAR591	1961	£2.50	£6	

NAYLOR, SHEL

How Deep Is The Ocean	7"	Decca	F11776	1963	£7.50	£15	
One Fine Day	7"	Decca	F11856	1964	£30	£60	

NAZARETH

Bad Bad Boy	7"	Mooncrest	MOON9	1973	£2	£5	PS
Broken Down Angel	7"	Mooncrest	MOON1	1973	£1.50	£4	
Dear John	7"	Pegasus	PGS2	1972	£7.50	£15	
Exercises	LP	Pegasus	PEG14	1972	£5	£12	
If You See My Baby	7"	Pegasus	PGS5	1972	£7.50	£15	
Morning Dew	7"	Pegasus	PGS4	1972	£7.50	£15	
Nazareth	LP	Mooncrest	CREST10	1972	£4	£10	
Nazareth	LP	Pegasus	PEG10	1971	£6	£15	
Whatever You Want Babe	7"	Mountain	NAZ4	1979	£2.50	£6	purple vinyl, PS

NAZZ

Hello It's Me	7"	Screen Gems	SGC219002	1969	£5	£10	
Nazz	LP	Screen Gems	SGC22001	1968	£10	£25	
Nazz 3	LP	Screen Gems	SGC22004	1969	£10	£25	
Nazz 3	LP	Screen Gems	SGC22004	1969	£15	£30	green vinyl
Nazz Nazz	LP	Screen Gems	SGC22002	1969	£10	£25	
Nazz Nazz	LP	Screen Gems	SGC22002	1969	£15	£30	red vinyl
Not Wrong Long	7"	Screen Gems	SGC219003	1969	£6	£12	
Open My Eyes	7"	Atlantic	584024	1968	£20	£40	demo
Open My Eyes	7"	Screen Gems	SGC219001	1968	£5	£10	

NAZZ (2)

Presumably to avoid confusion with Todd Rundgren's (then) more successful group, this Nazz subsequently changed its name to Alice Cooper.

Lay Down And Die, Goodbye	7"	Very	001	1967	£330	£500	US

NEAL, JOHNNY & THE STARLINERS

And I Will Love You	7"	Pye	7N15388	1961	£15	£30	

NEAL, TOMMY
Goin' To A Happening	7"	Vocalion	VP9290	1968	£4	£8	

NEAT CHANGE
I Lied To Auntie May	7"	Decca	F12809	1968	£6	£12	

NECROMANDUS
Quicksand Dream	LP	Reflection	MM09	1990	£5	£12	

NECROMONICON
Tips Zum Selbsmord	LP	Best Prehodi	F60634	1972	£470	£700	German

NECROS
I.Q.32	7"	Dischord	4	1981	£12.50	£25	with insert
Sex Drive	7"	Touch & Go		1981	£15	£30	

NED & NELDA
This typically irreverent parody was the work of Frank Zappa and Ray Collins.
Hey Nelda	7"	Vigah	002	1963	£37.50	£75	US

NEE, BERNIE
Medal Of Honour	7"	Philips	PB794	1958	£4	£8	

NEEFS, LOUIS
Jennifer Jennings	7"	Columbia	DB8561	1969	£6	£12	

NEELY, ELGIN
Four Walls	7"	Vogue	V9240	1965	£1.50	£4	

NEIGHBORHOOD CHILDREN
Neighborhood Children	LP	Acta	38005	1968	£8	£20	US

NEIL & JACK
Neil Diamond began his recording career here.
I'm Afraid	7"	Duel	517	1961	£75	£150	US
You Are My Love At Last	7"	Duel	508	1960	£75	£150	US

NEIL, FRED
Bleecker & MacDonald	LP	Elektra	EKL/EKS7293	1965	£6	£15	US
Candy Man	7"	Elektra	EKSN45036	1968	£1.50	£4	US
Everybody's Talkin'	LP	Capitol	ST2665	1969	£6	£15	US
Everybody's Talkin'	7"	Capitol	CL15616	1969	£1.50	£4	US
Hootenanny Live At The Bitter End	LP	FM	FM309	1964	£6	£15	US
Little Bit Of Rain	LP	Elektra	EKS74073	1970	£5	£12	US
Other Side Of This Life	LP	Capitol	ST657	1971	£5	£12	US
Sessions	LP	Capitol	ST2862	1971	£5	£12	US
Tear Down The Walls	LP	Elektra	EKL/EKS7248	1964	£6	£15	US
World Of Folk Music	LP	FM	FM319	1964	£6	£15	US

NEKTAR
Down To Earth	LP	United Artists	UAG29680	1974	£4	£10	
Journey To The Centre Of The Eye	LP	Bellaphon	BLPS19064	1972	£5	£12	German
Live At The Roundhouse	LP	Bellaphon	BLPS19182	1974	£4	£10	German
Nektar	LP	Bellaphon	BLPS19224	1976	£4	£10	German
Remember The Future	LP	United Artists	UAS29545	1973	£4	£10	
Sounds Like This	LP	United Artists	UAD60041/2	1973	£5	£12	double
Tab In The Ocean	LP	United Artists	UAS29499	1972	£4	£10	

NELSON, BILL
Northern Dream	LP	Smile	LAF2182	1971	£4	£10	no booklet
Northern Dream	LP	Smile	LAF2182	1971	£10	£25	with booklet

NELSON, DAVID
Somebody Loves Me	7"	Philips	BF1321	1964	£2.50	£6	

NELSON, EARL
No Time To Cry	7"	London	HLW8950	1959	£4	£8	

NELSON, OLIVER
Blues And The Abstract Truth	LP	HMV	CLP1528	1961	£6	£15	

NELSON, OZZIE & HARRIET
Ozzie And Harriet Nelson	LP	London	HAP2145	1959	£8	£20	

NELSON, RICK
Album Seven	LP	London	HAP2445	1962	£10	£25	mono
Album Seven	LP	London	SAHP6236	1962	£15	£30	stereo
Another Side Of Rick	LP	MCA	MUP(S)302	1968	£5	£12	
Be Bop Baby	7"	London	HLP8499	1957	£10	£20	
Believe What You Say	7"	London	HLP8594	1958	£6	£12	
Best Always	LP	Brunswick	LAT/STA8615	1965	£8	£20	
Bright Lights,Country Music	LP	Brunswick	LAT/STA8657	1966	£8	£20	
Come Out Dancin'	7"	Brunswick	05939	1965	£2.50	£6	
Country Fever	LP	Brunswick	LAT/STA8680	1967	£10	£25	
Everlovin'	7"	London	HLP9440	1961	£1.50	£4	chart single
Fools Rush In	7"	Brunswick	05895	1963	£1.50	£4	chart single
For You	7"	Brunswick	05900	1964	£1.50	£4	chart single
For Your Sweet Love	LP	Brunswick	LAT8545	1963	£8	£20	mono
For Your Sweet Love	LP	Brunswick	STA8545	1963	£10	£25	stereo
Happy Guy	7"	Brunswick	05924	1964	£1.50	£4	
Happy Guy	7" EP	Brunswick	OE9512	1965	£7.50	£15	

Title	Format	Label	Catalogue	Year	Price	Price	Notes
Hello Mary Lou	7"	London	HLP9347	1961	£1.50	£4	chart single
I Got A Feeling	7" EP	London	REP1238	1960	£10	£20	
I Got A Woman	7"	Brunswick	05885	1963	£1.50	£4	
I Need You	7"	Liberty	LIB12033	1966	£1.50	£4	
I Wanna Be Loved	7"	London	HLP9021	1960	£2.50	£6	chart single
I'm In Love Again	7" EP	Liberty	LEP4028	1965	£12.50	£25	
I'm Walking	7"	HMV	POP355	1957	£40	£80	gold label
In Concert	LP	MCA	MUPS409	1970	£4	£10	
It's A Young World	7" EP	London	REP1339	1962	£7.50	£15	
It's Up To You	LP	London	HAP8066	1963	£10	£25	
It's Up To You	7"	London	HLP9648	1963	£1.50	£4	chart single
It's Up To You	7" EP	London	REP1362	1963	£7.50	£15	
Just A Little Too Much	7"	London	HLP8927	1959	£2.50	£6	chart single
Lonely Corner	7"	Brunswick	05918	1964	£1.50	£4	
Long Vacation	LP	Imperial	LP9244/12244	1963	£10	£25	US
Love And Kisses	LP	Brunswick	LAT/STA8630	1965	£8	£20	
Milkcow Blues	7"	London	HLP9260	1961	£4	£8	
Million Sellers	LP	Liberty	LBY3027	1963	£6	£15	
More Songs By Ricky	LP	Imperial	LP12059	1960	£75	£150	US, blue vinyl
More Songs By Ricky	LP	London	HAP2290	1960	£10	£25	mono
More Songs By Ricky	LP	London	SAHP6102	1960	£15	£30	stereo
My Babe	7"	London	HLP8738	1958	£4	£8	
Never Be Anyone Else But You	7"	London	HLP8817	1959	£4	£8	chart single
On The Flip Side	LP	Decca	DL(7)4836	1967	£8	£20	US, with Joanie Sommers
One Boy Too Late	7" EP	Brunswick	OE9502	1963	£7.50	£15	
Perspective	LP	Decca	DL75014	1968	£6	£15	US
Poor Little Fool	7"	London	HLP8670	1958	£4	£8	chart single
Rick Is 21	LP	London	HAP2379	1961	£10	£25	mono
Rick Is 21	LP	London	SAHP6179	1961	£15	£30	stereo
Rick Nelson Country	LP	MCA	24004	1973	£4	£10	US
Rick Sings Nelson	LP	MCA	MUPS422	1970	£4	£10	
Ricky	LP	London	HAP2080	1957	£20	£40	
Ricky Nelson	LP	London	HAP2119	1958	£15	£30	
Ricky Nelson No.1	7" EP	London	REP1168	1959	£10	£20	
Ricky Nelson No.2	7" EP	London	REP1169	1959	£10	£20	
Ricky Nelson No.3	7" EP	London	REP1170	1959	£10	£20	
Ricky Nelson No.4	7" EP	London	REP1300	1961	£12.50	£25	
Ricky No.1	7" EP	London	REP1141	1958	£10	£20	
Ricky No.2	7" EP	London	REP1142	1958	£10	£20	
Ricky No.3	7" EP	London	REP1143	1958	£10	£20	
Ricky No.4	7" EP	London	REP1144	1958	£10	£20	
Ricky Sings Again	LP	London	HAP2159	1959	£15	£30	
Ricky Sings Again Pt.1	7" EP	London	REP1200	1959	£10	£20	
Ricky Sings Again Pt.2	7" EP	London	REP1201	1959	£10	£20	
Ricky Sings Spirituals	7" EP	London	REP1249	1960	£7.50	£15	
Rudy The Fifth	LP	MCA	MUPS440	1971	£4	£10	
Sings For You	LP	Brunswick	LAT8562	1964	£8	£20	mono
Sings For You	LP	Brunswick	STA8562	1964	£10	£25	stereo
Sings For You	7" EP	Liberty	LEP4001	1964	£7.50	£15	
Someday	7"	London	HLP8732	1958	£2.50	£6	chart single
Songs By Ricky	LP	London	HAP2206	1959	£15	£30	
Spotlight On Rick	LP	Brunswick	LAT/STA8596	1964	£8	£20	
Stood Up	7"	London	HLP8542	1958	£7.50	£15	chart single
String Along	7"	Brunswick	05889	1963	£2	£5	
Teen Time	LP	Verve	V2083	1957	£60	£120	US
Teenage Idol	7"	London	HLP9583	1962	£1.50	£4	chart single
That's All	7" EP	Liberty	LEP4019	1964	£12.50	£25	
Today's Teardrops	7"	Liberty	LIB66004	1964	£2.50	£6	
Very Thought Of You	LP	Brunswick	LAT/STA8581	1964	£8	£20	
Very Thought Of You	7"	Brunswick	05908	1964	£1.50	£4	
Yes Sir That's My Baby	7"	London	HLP9188	1960	£2.50	£6	
You Are My One And Only Love	7"	HMV	POP390	1957	£25	£50	Barney Kessel B side
You Can't Just Quit	7"	Brunswick	05964	1966	£4	£8	
Young Emotions	7"	London	HLP9121	1960	£2.50	£6	chart single
Young World	7"	London	HLP9524	1962	£1.50	£4	chart single

NELSON, SANDY

Title	Format	Label	Catalogue	Year	Price	Price	Notes
And Then There Were Drums	7"	London	HLP9612	1962	£1.50	£4	
Bouncy	7"	London	HLP9214	1960	£2	£5	
Compelling Percussion	LP	London	HAP/SHP8029	1963	£5	£12	
Drum Party	7"	London	HLP9015	1959	£2.50	£6	
Drummin' Up A Storm	LP	London	HAP/SHP8009	1962	£6	£15	
Drummin' Up A Storm	7"	London	HLP9558	1962	£1.50	£4	chart single
Drums A Go-go	LP	Liberty	LBY3061	1965	£4	£10	
Drums Are My Beat	7"	London	HLP9521	1962	£1.50	£4	
Get With It	7"	London	HLP9377	1961	£2	£5	
In The Mood	7" EP	London	REP1371	1963	£7.50	£15	
Let There Be Drums	LP	London	HAP2425/ SAHP6221	1961	£6	£15	
Let There Be Drums	7"	London	HLP9466	1961	£1.50	£4	chart single
Let There Be Drums	7" EP	London	REP1337	1962	£7.50	£15	
Live In Las Vegas	LP	Liberty	LBY3035	1965	£4	£10	
Ooh Poo Pah Doo	7"	London	HLP9717	1963	£1.50	£4	
Sandy Nelson Plays	LP	Liberty	LBY3007	1964	£4	£10	
Sandy Nelson Plays	7" EP	Liberty	LEP4033	1965	£5	£10	
Superdrums	LP	Liberty	(S)LBY3080	1967	£4	£10	
Teen Beat	LP	London	HAP2260/ SAHP6082	1960	£6	£15	
Teen Beat	7"	Top Rank	JAR197	1959	£2	£5	chart single

| Teen Beat '65 | 7" | Liberty | LIB66060 | 1964 | £1.50 | £4 | |
| Teenage House Party | LP | London | HAP/SHP8051 | 1963 | £6 | £15 | |

NELSON, TERRY

Bulldog Push	7"	Dice	CC25	1964	£5	£10	
Love On Saturday Night	7"	Dice	CC22	1963	£5	£10	
My Blue Eyed Baby	7"	Dice	CC27	1964	£5	£10	
Run Baby Run	7"	Dice	CC23	1963	£5	£10	

NELSON TRIO

| All In Good Time | 7" | London | HLL9019 | 1960 | £2 | £5 | |
| Tear It Up | 7" | Oriole | CB1360 | 1957 | £1.50 | £4 | |

NELSON, WILLIE

And Then I Wrote	LP	Liberty	(S)LBY1240	1966	£5	£12	
And Then I Wrote	LP	Liberty	LRP3238/LST7238	1962	£6	£15	US
Country Willie	LP	RCA	RD7749	1965	£4	£10	
Half A Man	7"	Liberty	LIB55532	1963	£1.50	£4	
Here's Willie Nelson	LP	Liberty	LRP3308/LST7308	1963	£6	£15	US
River Boy	7"	Liberty	LIB55697	1964	£1.50	£4	
Texas In My Soul	LP	RCA	RD7997	1969	£4	£10	

NEO MAYA

| I Won't Hurt You | 7" | Pye | 7N17371 | 1967 | £20 | £40 | |

NEOGY, CHIITRA

| Perfumed Garden | LP | Gemini | GMX5030 | 1970 | £4 | £10 | |
| Perfumed Garden | LP | Morgan | M1003L | 1968 | £6 | £15 | |

NEON HEARTS

| Regulations | 7" | Neon Hearts | NEON1 | 1977 | £2 | £5 | |

NEON ROSE

| Neon Rose | LP | Vertigo | 6316250 | 1973 | £10 | £25 | German |
| Reload | LP | Vertigo | | 1974 | £10 | £25 | German |

NEP-TUNES

| Surfer's Holiday | LP | Family | (S)FLP552 | 1963 | £6 | £15 | US |

NEPTUNE'S EMPIRE

| Neptune's Empire | LP | Polymax | PXX01 | 1971 | £40 | £80 | sleeve pictured in Guide |

NERO & THE GLADIATORS

Czardas	7"	Decca	F11413	1961	£5	£10	
Entry Of The Gladiators	7"	Decca	F11329	1961	£5	£10	chart single
In The Hall Of The Mountain King	7"	Decca	F11367	1961	£5	£10	chart single

NERVE

It Is	7"	Page One	POF081	1968	£5	£10	
Magic Spectacles	7"	Page One	POF055	1968	£5	£10	
Piece By Piece	7"	Page One	POF097	1968	£4	£8	
Ten Downing Street	7"	Page One	POF019	1967	£2.50	£6	

NERVOUS NORVUS

Ape Call	7"	London	HLD8338	1956	£30	£60	gold label
Bullfrog Hop	7"	London	HLD8383	1957	£40	£80	gold label
Does A Chinese Chicken Have A Pigtail	7"	Salvo	SLO1812	1962	£7.50	£15	Rod Barton B side

NESMITH, MICHAEL

And The First National Band	7" EP.	Island	IEP4	1976	£2	£5	
And The Hits Just Keep On Comin'	LP	Island	ILPS9439	1977	£4	£10	
And The Hits Just Keep On Coming	LP	RCA	LSP4695	1972	£5	£12	US
Best Of Michael Nesmith	LP	RCA	RS1064	1976	£4	£10	US
Compilation	LP	Island	ILPS9425	1977	£4	£10	
From A Radio Engine To The Photon Wing	LP	Island	ILPS9486	1977	£4	£10	
Infinite Rider On The Big Dogma	LP	Pacific Arts	PAC7130	1979	£4	£10	US
Just A Little Love	7"	Edan	1001	197-	£25	£50	US
Live At The Palais	LP	Pacific Arts	PAC7118	1978	£4	£10	US
Loose Salute	LP	RCA	LSP4415	1970	£5	£12	US
Magnetic South	LP	RCA	SF8136	1970	£5	£12	
Mike Nesmith Radio Special	LP	Pacific Arts	PAC71300	1976	£6	£15	US promo
Nevada Fighter	LP	RCA	SF8209	1971	£5	£12	
Pretty Much Your Standard Ranch Stash	LP	RCA	APL10164	1973	£5	£12	US
Prison	LP	Island	ILPS9428	1975	£6	£15	
Prison	LP	Pacific Arts	PAC7101	1975	£8	£20	US, boxed with booklet
Tantamount To Treason	LP	RCA	SF8276	1972	£5	£12	
Tapioca Tundra	7"	Dot	17152	1968	£5	£10	US
Wichita Train Whistle Sings	LP	Dot	(S)LDP516	1968	£8	£20	

NEU

Neu	LP	United Artists	UAS29396	1972	£5	£12	
Neu 2	LP	United Artists	UAS29500	1973	£5	£12	
Neu '75	LP	United Artists	UAS29782	1975	£5	£12	

NEVILLE, AARON

| Here 'Tis | LP | Liberty | LBY3089 | 1967 | £6 | £15 | |

Title	Format	Label	Cat No	Year	Price1	Price2	Notes
Tell It Like It Is	LP	Par-Lo	LP1	1967	£8	£20	US
Tell It Like It Is	7"	B&C	CB107	1969	£1.50	£4	
Tell It Like It Is	7"	Stateside	SS584	1967	£5	£10	

NEW AGE STEPPERS
| Fade Away | 7" | ONU Sound | ONU1 | 1980 | £1.50 | £4 | B side by The London Underground |

NEW BREED
| Friends And Lovers Forever | 7" | Decca | F12295 | 1965 | £7.50 | £15 | |

NEW CHRISTS
| Face A New God | 7" | Green | LRS076 | 1981 | £20 | £40 | |
| Living Eyes | LP | Trafalgar | | 1981 | £5 | £12 | |

NEW CHRISTY MINSTRELS
Green Green	7"	CBS	AAG160	1963	£1.50	£4	
Three Wheels On My Wagon	7"	CBS	201328	1965	£1.50	£4	
Three Wheels On My Wagon	7" EP	CBS	EP6057	1965	£2	£5	

NEW COLONY SIX
At The River's Edge	7"	Stateside	SS522	1966	£25	£50	
Attacking A Strawman	LP	Mercury	SR61228	1970	£6	£15	US
Breakthrough	LP	Sentar	LP101	1966	£75	£150	US
Colonization	LP	Sentar	(S)ST3001	1967	£6	£15	US
I Confess	7"	London	HLZ10033	1966	£12.50	£25	
I Will Always	7"	Mercury	MF1030	1968	£2	£5	
Revelations	LP	Mercury	SR61165	1969	£5	£12	US
Things I'd Like To Say	7"	Mercury	MF1086	1969	£2	£5	

NEW DEAL STRING BAND
| New Deal String Band | LP | Argo | ZDA104 | 1969 | £6 | £15 | |

NEW DIMENSIONS
Deuces And Eights	LP	Sutton	(SSU)331	1963	£5	£12	US
Soul Surf	LP	Sutton	(SSU)336	1964	£5	£12	US
Surf'n'Bongos	LP	Sutton	(SSU)332	1963	£5	£12	US

NEW FACES
| Like A Man | 7" | Pye | 7N17029 | 1966 | £1.50 | £4 | |

NEW FORMULA
| Stay Indoors | 7" | Pye | 7N17818 | 1969 | £7.50 | £15 | |

NEW GENERATION
Police Is Here	7"	Spark	SRL1019	1970	£1.50	£4	
Sadie And Her Magic Mr.Garland	7"	Spark	SRL1000	1969	£2	£5	
Smokey Blues Away	7"	Spark	SRL1007	1969	£2	£5	chart single

NEW HEAVENLY BLUE
| Educated Homegrown | LP | RCA | SF8189 | 1971 | £5 | £12 | |
| New Heavenly Blue | LP | Atlantic | SD7247 | 1972 | £5 | £12 | US |

NEW JUMP BAND
| Only Kind Of Girl | 7" | Domain | D1 | 1968 | £2 | £5 | |

NEW LORDS
| New Lords | LP | Columbia | 1C06229429 | 1971 | £4 | £10 | German |

NEW MODEL
| Chilean Warning | 7" | Mr.Clean | MRC1 | 1983 | £2 | £5 | in folder |

NEW MODEL ARMY
Aries Enterprises	cass			1981	£8	£20	with other artists
Better Than Them	7"	EMI	NMAD2	1985	£2	£5	double
Better Than Them	12"	EMI	12NMA2	1985	£3	£8	
Bittersweet	7"	Quiet!	QS002	1983	£5	£10	with flexi
Brave New World	12"	EMI	12NMAD3	1985	£4	£10	double
Fifty-First State	12"	EMI	12NMAD4	1986	£4	£10	double
Great Expectations	7"	Abstract	ABS0020	1983	£7.50	£15	
Never Mind The Jacksons, Here's The Pollocks	12"	Abstract	12ABS030	1985	£2.50	£6	with tracks by other artists
No Rest	12"	EMI	12NMAD1	1985	£4	£10	double
Poison Street	7"	EMI	NMA5	1987	£7.50	£15	red vinyl
Poison Street	12"	EMI	12NMAD5	1987	£4	£10	double
Price	7"	Abstract	ABS0028	1984	£4	£8	
White Coats	7"	EMI	NMA6	1987	£5	£10	red vinyl

NEW MONITORS
| Fence Around Your Heart | 7" | Buddah | 2011118 | 1971 | £1.50 | £4 | |

NEW ORDER
Blue Monday	CDV single	Factory	FACDV73R	1988	£2.50	£6	
Gatefold Substance	LP	Factory	FACT200S	1987	£8	£20	numbered g/f sleeve
Hacienda Christmas Flexi	7"	Factory	FAC51B	1982	£2.50	£6	flexi
Power, Corruption And Lies	LP	Factory		1983	£37.50	£75	German, multi-coloured vinyl
Round And Round (Ben Grosse remix)	12"	Factory	FAC263DJ	1989	£2.50	£6	promo
Run 2	12"	Factory	FAC273	1989	£4	£10	
Substance	cass	Factory	FACT200C	1987	£6	£15	box set

NEW ORDER (2)
Bradford Red Light District .... LP ...... Come .... CARA12 .... 1981 ... £6 ....£15 ....

NEW ORDER (3)
You've Got Me High .... 7" EP.. Warner Bros .... WB113 .... 1966 ... £10 ....£20 ....French

NEW ORLEANS ALL STAR JAZZ BAND
New Orleans All Star Jazz Band .... LP ...... Vogue .... LAE12013 .... 1956 ... £5 ....£12

NEW ORLEANS BOOTBLACKS
Flat Foot .... 7" .... Columbia .... SCM5090 .... 1954 ... £1.50 ....£4

NEW ORLEANS RHYTHM KINGS
New Orleans Rhythm Kings .... 10" LP London .... AL3552 .... 1956 ... £6 ....£15

NEW TWEEDY BROTHERS
New Tweedy Brothers .... LP ...... Ridon .... 234 .... £330 .....£500 .... US

NEW VAUDEVILLE BAND
Finchley Central	LP	Fontana	(S)TL5430	1967	£4	£10	
Finchley Central	7"	Fontana	TF824	1967	£1.50	£4	chart single
Finchley Central	7" EP.	Fontana	465381	1967	£4	£8	French
Green Street Green	7"	Fontana	TF853	1967	£1.50	£4	chart single
New Vaudeville Band	7" EP.	Fontana	TFE17497	1968	£4	£8	
Peek-A-Boo	7"	Fontana	TF784	1967	£1.50	£4	chart single
Peek-A-Boo	7" EP.	Fontana	465362	1966	£4	£8	French
Winchester Cathedral	LP	Fontana	886408TY	1966	£4	£10	
Winchester Cathedral	7"	Fontana	TF741	1966	£1.50	£4	chart single
Winchester Cathedral	7" EP.	Fontana	465342	1966	£4	£8	French

NEW VICTORY BAND
One More Dance And Then .... LP ...... Topic .... 12TS382 .... 1978 ... £6 ....£15

NEW YORK ART QUARTET
Mohawk .... LP ...... Fontana .... 681009ZL .... 1967 ... £8 ....£20

NEW YORK BLONDES
The "Madam X" featured on the New York Blondes' single is Debbie Harry, who was highly annoyed at the record's release. She had in fact recorded her vocal part purely as a demo for US DJ Rodney Bigenheimer to follow when making his own record (and the single's B side is indeed by him).
Little GTO .... 7" .... London .... HL10574 .... 1979 ... £2 ....£5 ....PS

NEW YORK DOLLS
Jet Boy	7"	Mercury	6052402	1973	£1.50	£4	
New York Dolls	LP	Mercury	6338270	1973	£5	£12	
Stranded In The Jungle	7"	Mercury	6052615	1974	£1.50	£4	
Too Much Too Soon	LP	Mercury	6338498	1974	£5	£12	

NEW YORK PUBLIC LIBRARY
Got To Get Away	7"	MCA	MU1025	1968	£2.50	£6	
I Ain't Gonna Eat Out My Heart Anymore	7"	Columbia	DB7948	1966	£7.50	£15	
Love Me Two Times	7"	MCA	MU1045	1968	£2	£5	

NEW YORK ROCK & ROLL ENSEMBLE
Faithful Friends	LP	Atco	228032	1969	£4	£10	
New York Rock & Roll Ensemble	LP	Atco	33240	1968	£5	£12	US
Reflections	LP	Atco	33312	1970	£4	£10	US

NEWBEATS
Ain't That Lovin' You Baby	7" EP.	Hickory	LPE1506	1965	£5	£10	
Big Beat Sounds	LP	Hickory	LP(S)122	1965	£6	£15	US
Birds Are For The Bees	7"	Hickory	451305	1965	£1.50	£4	
Birds Are For The Bees	7" EP.	CBS	6095	1965	£5	£10	French
Bread And Butter	LP	Hickory	LPM120	1965	£6	£15	
Bread And Butter	7"	Hickory	451269	1964	£2	£5	chart single
Bread And Butter	7" EP.	CBS	5916	1964	£5	£10	French
Break Away	7"	Hickory	451290	1965	£1.50	£4	
Crying My Heart Out	7"	Hickory	451387	1965	£6	£12	
Everything's Alright	7"	Hickory	451282	1964	£1.50	£4	
I Can't Hear You No More	7"	Hickory	451320	1965	£1.50	£4	
My Yesterday Love	7"	Hickory	451422	1965	£1.50	£4	
Newbeats	7" EP.	Hickory	LPE1503	1964	£4	£8	
Oh Girls Girls	7" EP.	Hickory	LPE1510	1966	£6	£12	
Run Baby Run	LP	Hickory	LP(S)128	1965	£6	£15	US
Run Baby Run	7"	Hickory	451332	1965	£5	£10	
Run Baby Run	7"	London	HL10341	1971	£1.50	£4	chart single
Run Baby Run	7" EP.	CBS	6209	1965	£5	£10	French
Too Sweet To Be Forgotten	7"	Hickory	451366	1965	£4	£8	

NEWBORN, PHINEAS
Phineas Newborn .... LP ...... London .... LTZK15057 .... 1957 ... £8 ....£20

NEWCASTLE BIG BAND
The Newcastle Big Band was a semi-professional sixteen-piece jazz band whose privately produced LP would mean little to anyone who had not actually seen the band live, were it not for the fact that the bass player just happened to go by the name of Sting.
Newcastle Big Band .... LP ...... Impulse .... ISSNBB106 .... 1972 ... £75 ....£150

NEWEY, DENNIS
Border Patrol	7"	Philips	PB1198	1961	£1.50	£4	
Checkpoint	7"	Philips	PB1134	1961	£1.50	£4	

Nightriders .... 7" ...... Philips .... 326538BF .... 1962 ... £1.50 ....£4 ....

NEWLEY, AMTHONY

In My Solitude	LP	Decca	LK4600	1964 ... £4 ....£10		
Newley Delivered	LP	Decca	LK4654	1965 ... £4 ....£10		
Newley Recorded	LP	RCA	RD/SF7837	1967 ... £4 ....£10		
Who Can I Turn To	LP	RCA	RD/SF7737	1966 ... £4 ....£10		

NEWLEY, ANTHONY

And The Heavens Cried	7" ...... Decca	F11331	1961 ... £1.50 .....£4		....chart single
Do You Mind	7" ...... Decca	F11220	1960 ... £1.50 .....£4		....chart single
Idle On Parade	7" ...... Decca	F11137	1959 ... £2 ....£5		
Idle On Parade	7" EP.. Decca	DFE6566	1959 ... £7.50 .....£15		....chart single
If She Should Come To You	7" ...... Decca	F11254	1960 ... £1.50 .....£4		....chart single
I've Waited So Long	7" ...... Decca	F11127	1959 ... £1.50 .....£4		....chart single
Love Is A Now And Then Thing	LP ..... Decca	LK4343	1960 ... £4 ....£10		.........chart LP
More Hits From Tony	7" EP.. Decca	DFE6655	1960 ... £4 ....£8		
Personality	7" ...... Decca	F11142	1959 ... £1.50 .....£4		....chart single
Pop Goes the Weasel	7" ...... Decca	F11362	1961 ... £1.50 .....£4		....chart single
Someone To Love	7" ...... Decca	F11163	1959 ... £1.50 .....£4		
Strawberry Fair	7" ...... Decca	F11295	1960 ... £1.50 .....£4		....chart single
This Time The Dream's On Me	7" EP.. Decca	DFE6687	1961 ... £2.50 .....£6		
Tony	LP ..... Decca	LK4406	1961 ... £4 ....£10		.........chart LP
Tony's Hits	7" EP.. Decca	DFE6629	1960 ... £5 ....£10		
What Kind Of Fool Am I	7" ...... Decca	F11376	1961 ... £1.50 .....£4		....chart single
Why	7" ...... Decca	F11194	1960 ... £1.50 .....£4		....chart single

NEWLEY, ANTHONY, PETER SELLERS & JOAN COLLINS

Fool Brittania .... 7" EP.. Ember .... EMBEP4530 .... 1963 ... £2.50 .....£6 ....

NEWMAN, ANDY

Rainbow .... LP ..... Track .... 2406103.............. 1971 ... £5 ....£12 ....

NEWMAN, BRAD

Candy Lips	7" ...... Fontana	267220TF	1962 ... £1.50 .....£4		
Get A Move On	7" ...... Fontana	H369	1962 ... £1.50 .....£4		
I'll Find You Another Baby	7" ...... Fontana	267273TF	1963 ... £1.50 .....£4		
Please Don't Cry	7" ...... Piccadilly	7N35174	1964 ... £1.50 .....£4		
Point Of No Return	7" ...... Fontana	267243TF	1962 ... £1.50 .....£4		
Somebody To Love	7" ...... Fontana	H357	1962 ... £1.50 .....£4		....chart single

NEWMAN, COLIN

We Means We Starts .... 7" ...... 4AD .... AD209 .... 1982 ... £1.50 .....£4 ....

NEWMAN, JIMMY

Fallen Star	7" ...... London	HLD8460	1957 ... £7.50 .....£15		
Grin And Bear It	7" ...... MGM	MGM1037	1959 ... £2 ....£5		
Grin And Bear It	7" EP.. MGM	MGMEP706	1959 ... £10 ....£20		
What About Me	7" ...... MGM	MGM1085	1960 ... £1.50 .....£4		
Whatcha Gonna Do	7" ...... MGM	MGM1009	1959 ... £2.50 .....£6		

NEWMAN, JOE

I Feel Like A Newman	LP ..... Vogue	LAE12049	1957 ... £15 ....£30		
Joe Newman And His Band	10" LP Vanguard........	PPT12001	1955 ... £20 ....£40		
Joe Newman And The Boys In The Band	10" LP Vogue	LDE126	1955 ... £20 ....£40		
Joe Newman Octet	10" LP HMV	DLP1114	1956 ... £15 ....£30		
Joe Newman Sextet	LP ..... Vogue Coral	LVA9052	1957 ... £8 ....£20		
Locking Horns	LP ..... Columbia	33SX1064	1957 ... £6 ....£15		...with Zoot Sims
Soft Swingin' Jazz	LP ..... Coral	LVA9106	1959 ... £8 ....£20		.....with Shirley Scott
With Woodwinds	LP ..... Columbia	33SX1143	1959 ... £6 ....£15		

NEWMAN, LIONEL ORCHESTRA

Hey Eula .... 7" ...... Columbia .... DB4150 .... 1958 ... £1.50 ....£4 ....

NEWMAN, PAUL

Ain't You Got A Heart .... 7" ...... Mercury .... MF969 .... 1966 ... £4 ....£8 ....

NEWMAN, RANDY

12 Songs	LP ..... Reprise	RSLP6373	1970 ... £5 ....£12		
Creates Something New Under The Sun	LP ..... Reprise	R(S)LP6286	1968 ... £6 ....£15		
Gone Dead Train	7" ...... Reprise	RS20945	1970 ... £1.50 .....£4		
Good Old Boys	LP ..... Reprise	MS42193	1974 ... £4 ....£10		.............US quad
I Think It's Gonna Rain Today	78 ...... Reprise	0284	1968 ... £5 ....£10		.............US promo
Live	LP ..... Reprise	K44151	1971 ... £4 ....£10		
Love Story	7" ...... Reprise	RS20692	1968 ... £1.50 .....£4		

NEWMAN, TOM

Faerie Symphony	LP ..... Decca	TXS123	1977 ... £6 ....£15		
Fine Old Tom	LP ..... Virgin	V2022	1975 ... £5 ....£12		
Live At The Argonaut	LP ..... Virgin	V2042	1975 ... £40 ....£80		.....test pressing only

NEWMAN, TONY

Soul Thing	7" ...... Decca	F12795	1968 ... £4 ....£8		
Soul Thing	7" ...... Decca	F13041	1970 ... £4 ....£8		

NEWPORT JAZZ FESTIVAL ALL STARS

Newport Jazz Festival All Stars .... LP ..... London .... LTZK15202............ 1961 ... £4 ....£10 ....

NEWPORTERS
Having achieved little success as the Moongooners, Scott Engel and John Maus next tried the name "Newporters".
Adventures In Paradise .... 7" .... Scotchtown ..... 500....................... 1963 ... £15 ....£30 .... US

NEWS
Entertainer .... 7" .... Decca .... F12356 .... 1966 ... £2.50 ....£6 ....
This Is The Moment .... 7" .... Decca .... F12477 .... 1966 ... £2.50 ....£6 ....

NEWTON, WAYNE
Summer Wind .... 7" .... Capitol .... CL15410 .... 1965 ... £1.50 ....£4 ....

NEWTON-JOHN, OLIVIA
If Not For You .... LP ..... Polydor .... 2310136 .... 1976 ... £6 ....£15 ....German
If Not For You .... LP ..... Uni .... 73117..................... 1971 ... £6 ....£15 ....US
Magic .... 7" ...... Jet .... P196 .... 1980 ... £1.50 ....£4 ....pic disc
Music Makes My Day .... LP ..... Pye .... NSPL28185 .... 1974 ... £4 ....£10 ....chart LP
Olivia .... LP ..... Pye .... NSPL28168 .... 1972 ... £4 ....£10 ....
Olivia Newton-John .... LP ..... Pye .... NSPL28155 .... 1971 ... £4 ....£10 ....
Till You Say You'll Be Mine .... 7" ...... Decca .... F12396................... 1966 ... £40 ....£80 ....
Totally Hot .... LP ..... EMI .... EMAP789 .... 1978 ... £5 ....£12 ....pic disc
Xanadu .... 10" .... Jet .... 10185.................... 1980 ... £2.50 ....£6 ....pink vinyl, with E.L.O.

NEWTOWN NEUROTICS
Hypocrite .... 7" ...... No Wonder...... SRTS79CUS363.... 1979 ... £2.50 ....£6 ....
When The Oil Runs Out .... 7" ...... No Wonder...... NOW4 .... 1980 ... £2 ....£5 ....with insert

NI DHOMHNAILL, MAIREAD
Mairead Ni Dhomhnaill .... LP ..... Gael-Linn .... CEF055 .... 1976 ... £5 ....£12 ....Irish

NI DHOMHNAILL, TRIONA
Triona .... LP ..... Gael Linn .... CEF043 .... 1975 ... £5 ....£12 ....Irish

NI GHUAIRIM, SORCHA
Sings Traditional Irish Songs .... LP ..... Folkways .... FW6861 .... 1966 ... £6 ....£15 ....US

NIAGARA
Niagara .... LP ..... United Artists .. UAS29232 .... 1971 ... £4 ....£10 ....German
S.U.B. .... LP ..... United Artists .. UAS29343 .... 1972 ... £4 ....£10 ....German

NICE
America .... 7" ...... Immediate .... IM068 .... 1968 ... £1.50 ....£4 ....chart single
America .... 7" ...... Immediate .... IM068 .... 1968 ... £4 ....£8 ....PS
Ars Longa Vita Brevis .... LP ..... Immediate .... IMSP020 .... 1968 ... £4 ....£10 ....
Brandenburger .... 7" ...... Immediate .... IM072 .... 1968 ... £2 ....£5 ....
Country Pie .... 7" ...... Charisma .... CB132 .... 1971 ... £1.50 ....£4 ....
Nice .... LP ..... Immediate .... IMSP026 .... 1969 ... £4 ....£10 ....chart LP
She Belongs To Me .... 7" ...... Immediate .... AS4........................ 1969 ... £10 ....£20 ....promo
Thoughts Of Emerlist Davjack .... LP ..... Immediate .... IMLP/IMSP016 ...... 1967 ... £5 ....£12 ....
Thoughts Of Emerlist Davjack .... 7" ...... Immediate .... AS2........................ 1967 ... £15 ....£30 ....promo with
                                                                                                                                                        John Peel interview

Thoughts Of Emerlist Davjack .... 7" ...... Immediate .... IM059 .... 1967 ... £2 ....£5 ....

NICELY, NICK
DCT Dreams .... 7" ...... Voxette .... VOX1001 .... 1980 ... £2.50 ....£6 ....
Hillyfields .... 7" ...... EMI .... EMI5256 .... 1981 ... £2.50 ....£6 ....

NICHOLLS, BILLY
Would You Believe .... LP ..... Immediate .... IMLP009 .... 1967 ... £50 ....£100 ....
Would You Believe .... 7" ...... Immediate .... IM063 .... 1968 ... £5 ....£10 ....

NICHOLLS, JANICE
Janice Nicholls was a regular member of the teenage panel called upon every week to mark selected new singles out of five on TV's Thank Your Lucky Stars. In those innocent days, a Birmingham accent was considered a novelty, and Ms.Nicholls' cry of "Oi'll give it foive" was greeted with enthusiastic applause.
Oi'll Give It Five .... 7" ...... Decca .... F11586................... 1963 ... £2 ....£5 ....

NICHOLS, RED
Jazz Time .... 10" LP Capitol .... LC6534 .... 1951 ... £8 ....£20 ....

NICHOLSON, LEA
Horsemusic .... LP ..... Trailer .... LER3010 .... 1971 ... £8 ....£20 ....

NICHOLSON, ROGER
Gentle Sound Of The Dulcimer .... LP ..... Argo .... ZDA204 .... 1974 ... £5 ....£12 ....

NICHOLSON, ROGER, JAKE WALTON, ANDREW CRONSHAW
Times And Traditions For Dulcimer ..... LP ..... Trailer .... LER2094 .... 1976 ... £5 ....£12 ....

NICKS, STEVIE
Bella Donna .... LP ..... Mobile Fidelity MFSL1121 .... 1982 ... £5 ....£12 ...... US audiophile
I Can't Wait .... 12" .... Parlophone...... 12R6110 .... 1986 ... £2.50 ....£6 ....
Stand Back .... 12" .... WEA .... U9870T .... 1983 ... £3 ....£8 ....

NICO
Chelsea Girl .... LP ..... MGM................ 2353025................. 1968 ... £6 ....£15 ....
Desert Shore .... LP ..... Reprise .... RSLP6424 .... 1971 ... £6 ....£15 ....
End .... LP ..... Island .... ILPS9311 .... 1974 ... £4 ....£10 ....
I'm Not Saying .... 7" ...... Immediate .... IM003 .... 1965 ... £12.50 ....£25 ....
Marble Index .... LP ..... Elektra............. EKL/EKS74029 ..... 1968 ... £8 ....£20 ....
Vegas .... 7" ...... Flicknife .... FLS206 .... 1981 ... £2 ....£5 ....

NICOL, JIMMY

Baby Please Don't Go	7"	Pye	7N15699	1964	£10	£20	
Clementine	7"	Decca	F12107	1965	£5	£10	
Humpty Dumpty	7"	Pye	7N15623	1964	£6	£12	
Husky	7"	Pye	7N15666	1964	£5	£10	

NICOLL, WATT

Nice To Be Nice	LP	XTRA	XTRA1122	1971	£5	£12	

NIEHAUS, LENNIE

Lennie Niehaus	10" LP	Contemporary.	LDC150	1955	£20	£40	
Lennie Niehaus Quintet	LP	Contemporary.	LDC120	1955	£20	£40	
Vol.1 The Quintet	LP	Vogue	LAC12167	1960	£8	£20	
Vol.3 - The Octet No.2	LP	Contemporary.	LAC12054	1957	£10	£25	
Vol.5 The Sextet	LP	Contemporary.	LAC12151	1959	£8	£20	
Zounds!	LP	Contemporary.	LAC12222	1960	£8	£20	

NIGHT OWLS

Twisting The Oldies	LP	Valmor	79	1962	£8	£20	US

NIGHT SHADES

Be My Guest	7"	CBS	201763	1965	£1.50	£4	
Fell So Fast	7"	CBS	201817	1965	£1.50	£4	

NIGHT SHADOWS

Square Root Of Two	LP	Hottrax	1414	1968	£50	£100	US

NIGHT SUN

Mournin'	LP	Polydor	2459094	1976	£4	£10	German
Mournin'	LP	Zebra	2949004	1972	£8	£20	German

NIGHTBIRDS

Cat On A Hot Tin Roof	7"	Oriole	CB1490	1959	£1.50	£4	

NIGHTBLOOMS

Crystal Eyes	7"	Fierce	FRIGHT041	1990	£4	£8	

NIGHTCAPS

Wine Wine Wine	LP	Vandan	VRLP8124	1961	£20	£40	US

NIGHTCRAWLERS

Little Black Egg	LP	Kapp	KL1520/KS3520	1967	£15	£30	US
Little Black Egg	7"	London	HLR10109	1967	£10	£20	

NIGHTHAWK, ROBERT

Robert Nighthawk	7" EP.	XX	MIN718	196-	£2.50	£6	

NIGHTHAWKS

Rock And Roll	LP	Aladdin	101	195-	£37.50	£75	US

NIGHTINGALE, MAXINE

Don't Push Me Baby	7"	Pye	7N17798	1969	£1.50	£4	

NIGHTINGALES

This Package	7"	Vindaloo	VILP2X	1985	£4	£8	

NIGHTMARES IN WAX

Birth Of A Nation	7"	Inevitable.	INEV002	1979	£6	£12	
Black Leather	12"	KY	KY91/2	1985	£5	£12	3 tracks
Black Leather	12"	KY	KY9	1984	£5	£12	2 tracks

NIGHTRIDERS

It's Only The Dog	7"	Polydor	56116	1966	£17.50	£35	
Love Me Right Now	7"	Polydor		1966	£25	£50	demo

NIGHTROCKERS

Dance To The Rock	7" EP.	Golf Drouot	71014	1967	£6	£12	French
I Can Tell	7" EP.	Golf Drouot	71013	1967	£6	£12	French

NIGHTSHIFT

Corrine Corrina	7"	Piccadilly	7N35243	1965	£5	£10	
That's My Story	7"	Piccadilly	7N35264	1965	£5	£10	

NIGHT-TIMERS

Music Played On	7"	Parlophone	R5355	1965	£7.50	£15	

NIHILIST SPASM BAND

IX - X = X	LP	United Dairies	UD016	1985	£5	£12	

NILE, BILL & HIS GOODTIME BAND

I Try Not To Laugh	7"	Deram	DM290	1970	£2	£5	

NILSSON, HARRY

Aerial Ballet	LP	RCA	RD/SF7973	1968	£5	£12	
Point	LP	RCA	LPSX1004	1972	£5	£12	US, with book
Scatalogue	LP	RCA	SP33567	1974	£6	£15	US promo compilation
Spotlight On Nilsson	LP	Tower	(D)T5095	1967	£6	£15	US

NILSSON, HARRY & JOHN LENNON

Pussy Cats	LP	RCA	APD10570	1974	£5	£12	US quad

NIMOY, LEONARD

Mr.Spock's Music From Outer Space ...	LP	Dot	DLP3794/25794	1967	£10	£25	US
New World Of Leonard Nimoy	LP	Dot	DLP25966	1969	£6	£15	US
Outer Space/Inner Mind	LP	Paramount	1030	197-	£8	£20	US
Touch Of Leonard Nimoy	LP	Dot	DLP25910	1969	£6	£15	US
Two Sides Of Leonard Nimoy	LP	Dot	DLP25835	1968	£6	£15	US
Way I Feel	LP	Dot	DLP25883	1968	£6	£15	US

NINA

Do You Know How Christmas Trees Are Grown?	7"	CBS	4681	1970	£5	£10

NINA & FREDERICK

Nina And Frederick	LP	Columbia	33SX1314	1958	£4	£10

NINE DAYS WONDER

Nine Days Wonder	LP	Harvest	SHSP4014	1971	£10	£25	
Only The Dancers	LP	Bacillus	BLPS19200	1975	£4	£10	German
Sonnet To Billy Frost	LP	Bacillus	BLPS19234	1975	£4	£10	German
We Never Lost Control	LP	Bacillus	BLPS19163	1973	£5	£12	German

999

Action	12"	Labritian	12FREE10	1978	£2.50	£6	
I'm Alive	7"	Labritian	LAB999	1977	£2	£5	
Nasty Nasty	78	United Artists	FREE7	1977	£10	£20	promo

NINE SENSE

Happy Daze	LP	Ogun	OG910	1977	£5	£12
Oh! For The Edge	LP	Ogun	OG900	1976	£5	£12

1910 FRUITGUM COMPANY

1,2,3, Red Light	7"	Pye	7N25468	1968	£1.50	£4	
Hard Ride	LP	Buddah	2359006	1970	£4	£10	
May I Take A Giant Step	7"	Pye	7N25458	1968	£1.50	£4	
Pop Goes The Weasel	7"	Pye	7N25478	1968	£1.50	£4	
Red Light	LP	Buddah	BDS5022	1968	£4	£10	US
Simon Says	LP	Pye	N(S)PL28115	1968	£4	£10	
Simon Says	7"	Pye	7N25447	1968	£1.50	£4	chart single

NINE-THIRTY FLY

Nine-Thirty Fly	LP	Ember	NR5062	1972	£60	£120

NING

Machine	7"	Decca	F23114	1971	£2.50	£6

NINO & THE EBBTIDES

Those Oldies But Goodies	7"	Top Rank	JAR572	1961	£12.50	£25

NIPPLE ERECTORS

The Pogues' Shane MacGowan began his recording career with the punk Nipple Erectors, later abbreviated to the less controversial Nips.

King Of The Bop	7"	Soho	SH1	1978	£5	£10	glossy PS
King Of The Bop	7"	Soho	SH1	1978	£4	£8	matt PS

NIPS

All The Time In The World	7"	Soho	SH4	1978	£6	£12	
Gabrielle	7"	Chiswick	CHIS119	1979	£2.50	£6	
Gabrielle	7"	Soho	SH9	1979	£2	£5	
Gabrielle	7"	Soho	SH9	1980	£10	£20	licensed to cool stamp
Happy Song	7"	Burning Rome	TP5	1981	£5	£10	
Only At The End Of The Beginning	LP	Soho	HOHO1	1980	£6	£15	

NIRVANA

The original Nirvana had long since ceased recording when Kurt Kobain arrived on the scene with a band of the same name, but it was clearly very much in Patrick Campbell-Lyons' interest to claim copyright infringement. He received an out-of-court financial settlement, although there is little possibility of confusion between the adventurous psychedelic pop of Campbell-Lyons' band and the agonised guitar mayhem of the American newcomers.

All Of Us	LP	Island	ILP987/ILPS9087	1968	£15	£30	
All Of Us	7"	Island	WIP6045	1968	£5	£10	
Dedicated To Markos III	LP	Pye	NSPL28132	1970	£25	£50	
Girl In The Park	7"	Island	WIP6038	1968	£5	£10	
Local Anaesthetic	LP	Vertigo	6360031	1971	£15	£30	spiral label
Nirvana	LP	Metromedia	1018	1970	£10	£25	US
Oh! What A Performance	7"	Island	WIP6057	1969	£5	£10	
Pentecost Hotel	7"	Island	WIP6020	1967	£5	£10	
Pentecost Hotel	7"	Philips	6006127	1971	£2	£5	
Pentecost Hotel	7" EP	Fontana	460236	1967	£7.50	£15	French
Rainbow Chaser	7"	Island	WIP6029	1968	£4	£8	chart single
Rainbow Chaser	7"	Island	WIP6180	1976	£1.50	£4	
Rainbow Chaser	7"	Philips	6006129	1972	£2	£5	
Saddest Day Of My Life	7"	Vertigo	6059035	1970	£5	£10	
Simon Simopath	LP	Island	ILP959/ILPS9059	1967	£20	£40	
Songs Of Love And Praise	LP	Philips	6308089	1972	£15	£30	
Stadium	7"	Philips	6006166	1972	£2	£5	
Tiny Goddess	7"	Island	WIP6016	1967	£5	£10	
Wings Of Love	7"	Island	WIP6052	1968	£5	£10	
World Is Cold Without You	7"	Pye	7N25525	1970	£5	£10	

NIRVANA (2)

Although his approach to music was not very similar, Kurt Kobain became a Jimi Hendrix for the nineties rock generation when he chose the ultimate escape from the unwelcome pressures of stardom. It may well be the case that Nirvana had already passed their best - but sadly, we shall never know. It remains the case, however, that "Nevermind" seems more like one of the all-time classic rock albums with every month that passes.

Bleach	LP	Sub Pop	SP34	1989	£20	£40	US, white vinyl
Bleach	LP	Sub Pop	SP34	1989	£6	£15	US, with poster
Bleach	LP	Tupelo	TUPLP6	1989	£15	£30	green vinyl
Bleach	LP	Tupelo	TUPLP6	1989	£30	£60	white vinyl
Blew	CD-s	Tupelo	TUPCD8	1989	£4	£10	
Blew	12"	Tupelo	TUPEP8	1989	£4	£10	
Come As You Are	12"	Geffen	DGCTP7	1992	£2.50	£6	pic disc
Hormoaning	LP	Geffen	GEF21711	1991	£8	£20	burgundy vinyl
In Bloom	12"	Geffen	GFSTP34	1992	£2.50	£6	pic disc
In Utero	LP	Geffen	GEF24536	1993	£6	£15	clear vinyl
Lithium	12"	Geffen	DGCTP9	1992	£2.50	£6	pic disc
Love Buzz	7"	Sub Pop	SP23	1988	£50	£100	US, 'Guitars' matrix message
Molly's Lips	7"	Sub Pop	SP97	1991	£10	£20	US, black vinyl
Molly's Lips	7"	Sub Pop	SP97	1991	£15	£30	US, green vinyl
Oh, The Guilt	7"	Touch & Go	TG83	1993	£1.50	£4	blue vinyl
Oh, The Guilt	7"	Touch & Go	TG83	1993	£2.50	£6	blue vinyl, with poster
Sliver	7"	Sub Pop	SP73	1990	£7.50	£15	US, blue vinyl, foldover PS
Sliver	7"	Tupelo	TUP25	1991	£7.50	£15	green vinyl
Smells Like Teen Spirit	12"	Geffen	DGCTP5	1991	£2.50	£6	pic disc

NITE PEOPLE

Is This A Dream	7"	Page One	POF159	1969	£2.50	£6
Love, Love, Love	7"	Page One	POF149	1969	£5	£10
Morning Sun	7"	Fontana	TF919	1968	£5	£10
P.M.	LP	Page One	POLS025	1969	£50	£100
Season Of The Rain	7"	Page One	POF174	1970	£2.50	£6
Summertime Blues	7"	Fontana	TF885	1967	£12.50	£25
Sweet Tasting Wine	7"	Fontana	TF747	1966	£4	£8
Trying To Find Another Man	7"	Fontana	TF808	1967	£2.50	£6

NITE ROCKERS

Ooh Baby	7"	RCA	RCA1079	1958	£30	£60

NITTY GRITTY DIRT BAND

Alive	LP	Liberty	LST7615	1969	£5	£12	US
Buy For My The Rain	7" EP.	Liberty	LEP2279	1967	£10	£20	French
Dead And Alive	LP	Liberty	LBS83286	1969	£4	£10	
Nitty Gritty Dirt Band	LP	Liberty	LRP3501/LST7501	1967	£5	£12	US
Pure Dirt	LP	Liberty	LBL/LBS83122	1968	£5	£12	
Rare Junk	LP	Liberty	LST7611	1967	£5	£12	US
Ricochet	LP	Liberty	LRP3516/LST7516	1967	£5	£12	US
Uncle Charlie And His Dog Teddy	LP	Liberty	LBG83345	1970	£4	£10	
Will The Circle Be Unbroken	LP	United Artists	UAT9801	1973	£10	£25	US triple

NITZER EBB

Warsaw Ghetto	12"	P.O.V.C.	NEP/NEBX2	1986	£4	£10	double

NITZSCHE, JACK

Jack Nitzsche was Phil Spector's arranger during the sixties and hence due to as much credit as Spector himself for the invention of the "wall of sound" that is so characteristic of Spector's productions. Nitzsche made a number of instrumental records in a series of attempts to take advantage of contemporary music fads, but his masterpiece is "St.Giles Cripplegate", recorded in 1972. This is a suite of short pieces scored for a small group of strings and is essentially a classical work made contemporary by its use of acid harmonies.

Chopin '66	LP	Reprise	R(S)6200	1966	£6	£15	US
Hits Of The Beatles	LP	Reprise	R(S)6115	1964	£8	£20	US
Lonely Surfer	LP	Reprise	R(S)6101	1963	£8	£20	US
Lonely Surfer	7"	Reprise	R20202	1963	£5	£10	
Lonely Surfer	7" EP.	Reprise	RVEP60036	1963	£12.50	£25	French
Night Walker	7"	Reprise	R20337	1964	£4	£8	
St.Giles Cripplegate	LP	Reprise	MS2092	1972	£5	£12	US

NIVENS

Let Loose Of My Knee	7"	Woosh	WOOSH1	1988	£2.50	£6	flexi, B side by Holidaymakers

NIX NOMADS

You're Nobody Till Somebody Loves You	7"	HMV	POP1354	1964	£25	£50

NNB

Slack	7"	Wave Seven	WSNNB	1978	£10	£20

NO INTRODUCTION

No Introduction	LP	Spark		1968	£8	£20

NO QUARTER

Survivors	12"	Reel	REEL1	1983	£2.50	£6

NOAKES, RAB

Do You See The Light	LP	Decca	SKL5061	1970	£6	£15
Never Too Late	LP	Warner Bros	K56114	1975	£4	£10
Rab Noakes	LP	A&M	AMLS68119	1972	£5	£12
Red Pump Special	LP	Warner Bros	K46284	1974	£4	£10
Restless	LP	Ring O	2339201	1978	£4	£10

NOBLE, LISA
It's A Boy .... 7" ...... Decca .... F11051 .... 1958 ... £1.50 ....£4 ....
Maggie .... 7" ...... Decca .... F11006 .... 1958 ... £1.50 ....£4 ....

NOBLE, PATSY ANN
Don't You Ever Change Your Mind ...... 7" .... Columbia........ DB4956 .... 1963 ... £1.50 ....£4 ....

NOBLEMEN
Thunder Wagon .... 7" .... Top Rank .... JAR155 .... 1959 ... £2 ....£5 ....

NOBLES, CLIFF
Horse .... LP ..... Direction......... 863477 .... 1969 ... £5 ....£12 ....
Horse .... 7" ...... Direction......... 583518 .... 1968 ... £1.50 ....£4 ....
Judge Baby, I'm Back .... 7" ...... Direction......... 583738 .... 1968 ... £1.50 ....£4 ....
Switch It On .... 7" ...... Direction......... 584205 .... 1969 ... £1.50 ....£4 ....

NOCTURNAL EMISSIONS
Befehlsnotstand .... LP ..... Sterile .... SR5 .... 1984 ... £20 ....£40 ....
Beyond Logic .... LP ..... Earthly   EARTH05 .... 1989 ... £5 ....£12 ....
                                                           Delights ....
Chaos - Live At The Ritzy .... 7" ...... CFC .... LP2 .... 1984 ... £20 ....£40 ....
Drowning In A Sea Of Bliss .... LP ..... Sterile .... SR4 .... 1984 ... £25 ....£50 ....
Fruiting Body .... LP ..... Sterile .... ION2 .... 1984 ... £20 ....£40 ....
Mouth Of The Babes .... LP ..... Earthly   EARTH06 .... 1990 ... £5 ....£12 ....
                                                           Delights ....
No Sacrifice .... 12" ... Sterile .... SR6 .... 1984 ... £4 ....£10 ....
Shake Those Chains, Rattle Those ...... LP ..... Sterile .... SR9 .... 1986 ... £5 ....£12 ....
Cages
Songs Of Love And Revolution .... LP ..... Sterile .... SR7 .... 1985 ... £6 ....£15 ....
Spiritflesh .... LP ..... Earthly   EARTH04 .... 1988 ... £8 ....£20 ....
                                                           Delights ....
Tissue Of Lies .... LP ..... Sterile .... EMISS001 .... 1984 ... £15 ....£30 ....
Tissue Of Lies .... LP ..... Sterile .... EMISS001 .... 1984 ... £30 ....£60 .... Numbered
Viral Shedding .... LP ..... Illuminated ..... JAMSLP33 .... 1984 ... £6 ....£15 ....
World Is My Womb .... LP ..... Earthly   EARTH02 .... 1987 ... £6 ....£15 ....
                                                           Delights ....

NOCTURNES
Troika .... 7" ...... Solar .... SRP102 .... 1964 ... £2.50 ....£6 ....

NOCTURNES (2)
Carpet Man .... 7" ...... Columbia........ DB8453 .... 1968 ... £1.50 ....£4 ....
I Wish You Would Show Me Your .... 7" ...... Columbia........ DB8158 .... 1967 ... £1.50 ....£4 ....
Mind
Montage .... 7" ...... Columbia........ DB8493 .... 1968 ... £1.50 ....£4 ....
New Man .... 7" ...... Columbia........ DB8332 .... 1968 ... £1.50 ....£4 ....
Nocturnes .... LP ..... Columbia........ SX/SCX6223 .... 1968 ... £5 ....£12 ....
Wanted Alive .... LP ..... Columbia........ SX/SCX6315 .... 1968 ... £6 ....£15 ....
Why .... 7" ...... Columbia........ DB8219 .... 1967 ... £2 ....£5 ....

NOCTURNS
Carrying On .... 7" ...... Decca .... F12002 .... 1964 ... £2.50 ....£6 ....

NODE, PROFESSOR ERNEST
Egg Plant That Ate Chicago .... 7" ...... Columbia........ DB8100 .... 1967 ... £1.50 ....£4 ....

NOEL, DICK
Birds And The Bees .... 7" ...... London .... HLH8295 .... 1956 ... £7.50 ....£15 ....

NOIR
We Had To Let You Have It .... LP ..... Dawn .... DNLS3029 .... 1971 ... £8 ....£20 ....

NOLAN SISTERS
Blackpool .... 7" ...... Nevis .... NEVS007 .... 1972 ... £5 ....£10 ....
But I Do .... 7" ...... EMI.................. EMI2209 .... 1974 ... £4 ....£8 ....
Don't Make Waves .... 7" ...... Epic .... EPC8349 .... 1980 ... £1.50 ....£4 ....
Medley .... 7" ...... Target .... SAM84 .... 1978 ... £2 ....£5 .... promo
Nolan Sisters .... LP ..... Hanover   HG19751 .... 1977 ... £10 ....£25 ....
                                                           Grand.............
Rain .... 7" ...... Target .... TGT108 .... 1976 ... £1.50 ....£4 ....
Silent Night .... 7" EP.. Nevis .... NEVEP005 .... 1972 ... £2 ....£5 ....
Singing Nolans .... LP ..... Nevis .... NEVR009 .... 1972 ... £6 ....£15 ....

NOLAND, TERRY
Oh Baby Look At Me .... 7" ...... Coral .... Q72311 .... 1958 ... £30 ....£60 ....
Terry Noland .... LP ..... Brunswick........ BL54041 .... 1958 ... £60 ....£120 .... US

NOMADI
Interpretano .... LP ..... Columbia........ 06417990 .... 1974 ... £4 ....£10 .... Italian

NOONE, JIMMY
Jimmy Noone Orchestra .... 10" LP Vogue Coral .... LRA10026 .... 1955 ... £5 ....£12 ....

NORDINE, KEN
Classic Collection .... LP ..... Dot .... DLP25880 .... 1968 ... £6 ....£15 .... US
Colors .... LP ..... Philips .... 2/600224 .... 196- ... £6 ....£15 .... US
Concert In The Sky .... LP ..... Decca .... DL8550 .... 1957 ... £10 ....£25 .... US
Ken Nordine Reads .... 7" EP.. London .... RED1091 .... 1957 ... £10 ....£20 .... US
Love Words .... LP ..... Dot .... DLP3115/ .... 1958 ... £6 ....£15 .... US
                                                                              DLP25115 ....

Title	Format	Label	Catalogue	Year	Low	High	Notes
My Baby	LP	Dot	DLP3142/ DLP25142	1958	£6	£15	US
Next!	LP	Dot	DLP3196/ DLP25196	1959	£6	£15	US
Shifting Whispering Sands	7"	London	HLD8205	1955	£7.50	£15	gold label, chart single
Ship That Never Sailed	7"	London	HLD8417	1957	£2.50	£6	
Son Of Word Jazz	LP	London	LTZD15145	1959	£8	£20	
Twink	LP	Philips	2/600258	196-	£6	£15	US
Word Jazz	LP	London	LTZD15131	1958	£10	£25	
Word Jazz	7" EP	London	EZD19040	1959	£6	£12	
Word Jazz Vol.2	LP	Dot	DLP3301/25301	1960	£6	£15	US

NORMAN & THE INVADERS

Title	Format	Label	Catalogue	Year	Low	High	Notes
Night Train To Surbiton	7"	United Artists	UP1077	1965	£6	£12	
Our Wedding Day	7"	United Artists	UP1031	1964	£1.50	£4	

NORMAN CONQUEST

Title	Format	Label	Catalogue	Year	Low	High	Notes
Two People	7"	MGM	MGM1376	1968	£15	£30	

NORMAN, LARRY

Title	Format	Label	Catalogue	Year	Low	High	Notes
Bootleg	LP	One Way	JC900	1971	£5	£12	US
So Long Ago/The Garden	LP	MGM	SE4942	1973	£6	£15	US
Street Level	LP	One Way	JC7937	1970	£5	£12	US
Upon This Rock	LP	Key	DOVE6	1969	£5	£12	

NORMAN, MONTY

Title	Format	Label	Catalogue	Year	Low	High	Notes
Dr.No	LP	United Artists	SULP1097	1965	£6	£15	
Dr.No	LP	United Artists	ULP1097	1965	£5	£12	mono
Dr.No	7" EP	United Artists	UEP1010	1965	£7.50	£15	
Garden Of Eden	7"	HMV	POP281	1957	£2.50	£6	

NORMAN, OLIVER

Title	Format	Label	Catalogue	Year	Low	High	Notes
Down In The Basement	7"	Polydor	56176	1967	£1.50	£4	

NORTH, ROY

Title	Format	Label	Catalogue	Year	Low	High	Notes
Blues In Three	7"	Oak	RGJ107	1963	£7.50	£15	

NORTH STARS

Title	Format	Label	Catalogue	Year	Low	High	Notes
She's So Far Out She's In	7"	Fontana	TF726	1966	£5	£10	

NORTHERN LIGHTS

The singles credited to Northern Lights were actually by the Hootenanny Singers and are therefore of considerable interest to Abba collectors.

Title	Format	Label	Catalogue	Year	Low	High	Notes
No Time	7"	United Artists	UP1123	1966	£10	£20	
Through Darkness Light	7"	United Artists	UP1161	1966	£10	£20	

NORTHWIND

Title	Format	Label	Catalogue	Year	Low	High	Notes
Sister Brother Lover	LP	Regal Zonophone	SLRZ1020	1971	£100	£200	

NORVBO, RED

Title	Format	Label	Catalogue	Year	Low	High	Notes
Hi-Five	LP	RCA	RD27013	1957	£5	£12	

NORVO, RED

Title	Format	Label	Catalogue	Year	Low	High	Notes
Ad Lib	LP	London	LTZD15116	1958	£5	£12	
Move!	LP	Realm	RM158	1964	£5	£12	
Red Norvo	10" LP	London	LZU14039	1957	£10	£25	
Red Norvo All Stars	LP	Philips	BBL7077	1956	£8	£20	
Red Norvo Nine	10" LP	Vogue	LDE061	1954	£20	£40	
Red Norvo Trio	10" LP	Brunswick	LA8718	1955	£20	£40	
Red Norvo Trio	10" LP	Vogue	LDE115	1955	£20	£40	
Windjammer City Style	LP	London	HAD2134	1958	£4	£10	

NOSFERATU

Title	Format	Label	Catalogue	Year	Low	High	Notes
Nosferatu	LP	Vogue	LDVS17178	1970	£150	£250	German

NOTATIONS

Title	Format	Label	Catalogue	Year	Low	High	Notes
Need Your Love	7"	Chapter One	SCH174	1974	£5	£10	
Notations	LP	Curtom	K56212	1976	£8	£20	

NOTES, FREDDIE & THE RUDIES

Title	Format	Label	Catalogue	Year	Low	High	Notes
Montego Bay	LP	Trojan	TBL152	1970	£6	£15	
Montego Bay	7"	Trojan	TR7791	1970	£1.50	£4	chart single
Unity	LP	Trojan	TBL109	1970	£6	£15	

NOTSENSIBLES

Title	Format	Label	Catalogue	Year	Low	High	Notes
Margaret Thatcher	7"	Redball	RR021	1979	£2	£5	

NOTTS ALLIANCE

Title	Format	Label	Catalogue	Year	Low	High	Notes
Cheerful 'Orn	LP	Tradition	TSR011	1972	£5	£12	

NOVA LOCAL

Title	Format	Label	Catalogue	Year	Low	High	Notes
Nova 1	LP	MCA	MUPS377	1968	£4	£10	

NOVALIS

Title	Format	Label	Catalogue	Year	Low	High	Notes
Banished Bridge	LP	Brain	0001029	1973	£4	£10	German

NOVAS

Title	Format	Label	Catalogue	Year	Low	High	Notes
Push A Little Harder	7"	RCA	RCA1360	1963	£1.50	£4	

NOVAS (2)
Crusher	7"	London	HLU9940	1965	£7.50	£15	

NOW
Development Corporations	7"	Ultimate	ULT401	1978	£2.50	£6	blue vinyl, PS

NOWY, RALF
Escalation	LP	Atlantic	K40556	1974	£4	£10	German
Lucifer's Dream	LP	Intercord	260158	1973	£5	£12	German
Nowy 2	LP	Atlantic	ATL50205	1975	£4	£10	German

NOYS OF US
He's Alright Jill	7"	KRS	KRS502	196-	£12.50	£25	

NRBQ
NRBQ	LP	CBS	63653	1969	£4	£10	

NSU
Turn On Or Turn Me Down	LP	Stable	SLE8002	1969	£50	£100	

NU NOTES
Hall Of Mirrors	7"	HMV	POP1232	1963	£12.50	£25	
Kathy	7"	HMV	POP1311	1964	£2.50	£6	

NU TORNADOS
Philadelphia USA	7"	London	HLU8756	1958	£5	£10	

NUBBIT, GUITAR
Guitar Nubbit	7" EP	XX	MIN705	196-	£2.50	£6	

NUCLEUS
Awakening	LP	Mood	24000	1980	£8	£20	
Belladonna	LP	Vertigo	6360076	1972	£8	£20	spiral label
Belladonna	LP	Vertigo	6360076	1973	£5	£12	
Elastic Rock	LP	Vertigo	6360008	1970	£8	£20	spiral label, chart LP
Elastic Rock	LP	Vertigo	6360008	1973	£4	£10	
Labyrinth	LP	Vertigo	6360091	1973	£5	£12	
Solar Plexus	LP	Vertigo	6360039	1971	£6	£15	spiral label
Solar Plexus	LP	Vertigo	6360039	1973	£4	£10	
We'll Talk About It Later	LP	Vertigo	6360027	1970	£8	£20	spiral label
We'll Talk About It Later	LP	Vertigo	6360027	1973	£4	£10	

NUCLEUS (2)
Nucleus	LP	Mainstream	6120	1967	£6	£15	US

NUGENT, TED
State Of Shock	LP	Epic	AS99607	1979	£4	£10	US pic disc

NUGGETS
Quirl Up In My Arms	7"	Capitol	CL14216	1955	£6	£12	
Shtiggy Boom	7"	Capitol	CL14267	1955	£5	£10	

NUMAN, GARY
America	7"	IRS	ILPD1004	1988	£1.50	£4	pic disc
America	7"	IRS	ILPD1004	1988	£7.50	£15	pic disc, Gary pic both sides
Cars	12"	Intercord	INT126502	1979	£5	£12	German
Cars (E Reg Model)	7"	Beggars Banquet	BEG199P	1987	£1.50	£4	pic disc
Fury	LP	Numa	NUMAP1003	1986	£10	£25	pic disc with Your Fascination pic
Fury	CD	Numa	CDNUMA1003	1986	£10	£25	
Ghost	LP	Numa	NUMAD1007	1987	£6	£15	double
I Die: You Die	7"	Beggars Banquet	BEG26A1	1980	£7.50	£15	test pressing, different mix
Images Five And Six	LP	Fan Club	GNFCDA3	1987	£6	£15	double
Images Nine And Ten	LP	Fan Club	GNFCDA5	1989	£5	£12	double
Images One And Two	LP	Fan Club	GNFCDA1	1986	£8	£20	double
Images Seven And Eight	LP	Fan Club	GNFCDA4	1987	£6	£15	double
Images Three And Four	LP	Fan Club	GNFCDA2	1987	£8	£20	double
Metal Rhythm	LP	IRS	ILPX035	1988	£4	£10	pic disc
New Anger	CD-s	IRS	ILSCD1003	1988	£3	£8	
Photograph	LP	Intercord	INT146606		£37.50	£75	German
Plan	LP	Beggars Banquet	BEGA55P	1985	£4	£10	pic disc
Remember I Was Vapour	12"	Intercord	INT126600	1980	£4	£10	German
Strange Charm	CD	Numa	CDNUMA1005	1986	£20	£40	
Telekon	LP	Beggar's Banquet	BEGA19	1980	£5	£12	green vinyl
Telekon	LP	Beggars Banquet	BEGA19	1980	£20	£40	clear or white vinyl
Telekon	LP	Beggars Banquet	BEGA19	1980	£8	£20	red, yellow, blue, or orange vinyl
This Is Love	12"	Numa	NUMX16	1986	£2.50	£6	double
Warriors	7"	Beggars Banquet	BEG95P	1983	£7.50	£15	shaped pic disc
Your Fascination	7"	Numa	NUP9	1985	£1.50	£4	pic disc
Your Fascination	12"	Numa	NUMP9	1985	£2.50	£6	pic disc

NUMBER NINE BREAD STREET
Number Nine Bread Street .... LP ...... Holyground ..... HG112 .... 1967 ... £180 ......£300 ....

NURSE WITH WOUND
Alas The Madonna Does Not Function	12"	United Dairies .	UD027	1986 ...	£3	............£8	
Automating Vol.1	LP	United Dairies .	UD019	1986 ...	£5	............£12	
Automating Vol.2	LP	United Dairies .	UD030	1989 ...	£5	............£12	
Chance Meeting On A Dissecting Table...	LP	United Dairies .	UD1	1979 ...	£40	............£80	
Crank	7"	Wisewound	WW01	1987 ...	£2.50	............£6	...... B side by Termite Queen
Drunk With The Old Man Of The Mountains	LP	United Dairies .	UD025	1987 ...	£20	............£40	
Faith's Favourites	12"	Yankhi.................	YANKHI02	1988 ...	£2.50	........£6	...B side by Current 93
Homotopy To Marie	LP	United Dairies .	UD012	1985 ...	£10	............£25	
Insect And Individual Silenced	LP	United Dairies .	UD08	1981 ...	£20	............£40	
Merzbild Schwet	LP	United Dairies .	UD04	1980 ...	£30	............£60	
Missing Sense	LP	United Dairies .	UD020	1986 ...	£5	............£12	... B side by Organum
Ostranenie	LP	Third Mind......	YMR03	1984 ...	£10	............£25	
Ostranenie 1913	LP	Third Mind......	TMR03..................	1984 ...	£15	............£30	
Soliloquy For Lilith	LP	Idle Hole	MIRRORONE	1988 ...	£15	............£30	............3 LPs, boxed
To The Quiet Man From A Tiny Girl	LP	United Dairies .	UD03	1980 ...	£30	............£60	

NUTRONS
Very Best Things .... 7" ...... Melodisc .... 1593 .... 1964 ... £6 ....£12

NUTTER, MAY'F
Head Shrinker .... 7" .... Vocalion .... VP9282 .... 1966 ... £1.50 ......£4

NUTTY SQUIRRELS
Uh! Oh! .... 7" ...... Pye .... 7N25044 .... 1959 ... £1.50 ......£4

NYMAN, MICHAEL
Decay Music .... LP ...... Obscure .... OBS6 .... 1976 ... £4 ....£10

NYRO, LAURA
Laura Nyro is a singer-songwriter with soul - and it is that quality that makes her records so distinctive. The trilogy begun by "Eli And The Thirteenth Confession" represents her best work, with "Eli" perhaps having the edge. Any album that can take the listener from the bleakest despair ("Poverty Train"), through the wistfully romantic ("Emmie"), to uplifting joy ("Eli's Comin'") can only be described as special.

Christmas & The Beads Of Sweat	LP	CBS	64157.................	1970 ...	£5	............£12
Eli & The 13th Confession	LP	CBS	63346.................	1968 ...	£5	............£12
Eli's Coming	7"	CBS	3604.................	1968 ...	£1.50	............£4
First Songs	LP	CBS	64991.................	1973 ...	£4	............£10
First Songs	LP	Verve	SVLP6022............	1969 ...	£8	............£20
Gonna Take A Miracle	LP	CBS	64770.................	1971 ...	£5	............£12
More Than A New Discovery	LP	Verve	FTS3020............	1966 ...	£8	............£20
New York Tendaberry	LP	CBS	63510.................	1969 ...	£5	............£12
Once It Was Alright Now	7"	CBS	4031.................	1968 ...	£1.50	............£4
Time And Love	7"	CBS	4719.................	1969 ...	£1.50	............£4
Up On The Roof	7"	CBS	5218.................	1970 ...	£1.50	............£4
Wedding Bell Blues	7"	Verve	VS1502.................	1967 ...	£1.50	............£4
When I Was A Freeport	7"	CBS	7028.................	1971 ...	£1.50	............£4

O

O LEVEL

Title	Format	Label	Cat#	Year	Price	Price	Notes
East Sheen	7"	Psycho	PSYCHO1	1978	£7.50	£15	2 PS's
Malcolm McLaren	7"	King's Road	KR002	197-	£4	£8	2 PS's

OAK

Title	Format	Label	Cat#	Year	Price	Price	Notes
Welcome To Our Fair	LP	Topic	12TS212	1971	£25	£50	

OBERON

Title	Format	Label	Cat#	Year	Price	Price	Notes
Midsummer Night's Dream	LP	Acorn		1971	£75	£150	

O'BRIEN, HUGH

Title	Format	Label	Cat#	Year	Price	Price	Notes
Wyatt Earp Sings	LP	ABC	203	1957	£10	£25	US

OCCASIONAL WORD ENSEMBLE

Title	Format	Label	Cat#	Year	Price	Price	Notes
Year Of The Great Leap Sideways	LP	Dandelion	63753	1969	£8	£20	

OCCULT CHEMISTRY

Title	Format	Label	Cat#	Year	Price	Price	Notes
Water Earth Fire Air	7"	Bikini Girl		1980	£2.50	£6	clear flexi

OCHS, PHIL

Title	Format	Label	Cat#	Year	Price	Price	Notes
All The News That's Fit To Sing	LP	Elektra	EKL269	1964	£8	£20	
Chords Of Fame	LP	A&M	AMLM64599	1974	£6	£15	double
Greatest Hits	LP	A&M	AMLS973	1970	£6	£15	
Gunfight At Carnegie Hall	LP	A&M	SP9010	1971	£8	£20	Canadian
I Ain't Marchin' Anymore	LP	Elektra	EKL287	1965	£8	£20	
I Ain't Marching Anymore	7"	Elektra	EKSN45002	1965	£2	£5	
In Concert	LP	Elektra	EKL310	1966	£8	£20	
Interviews With Phil Ochs	LP	Folkways	FB5321	1971	£8	£20	US
Pleasures Of The Harbour	LP	A&M	AML(S)913	1967	£6	£15	
Rehearsals For Retirement	LP	A&M	AMLS934	1969	£6	£15	
Small Circle Of Friends	7"	A&M	AMS716	1968	£2	£5	
Tape From California	LP	A&M	AMLS919	1968	£6	£15	

O'CONNOR, DES

Title	Format	Label	Cat#	Year	Price	Price	Notes
Moonlight Swim	7"	Columbia	DB4011	1957	£1.50	£4	

O'CONNOR, SINEAD

Title	Format	Label	Cat#	Year	Price	Price	Notes
Mandinka	CD-s	Ensign	ENYCD611	1987	£3	£8	
Mandinka (Jake's Remix)	12"	Ensign	ENYXR611	1987	£2.50	£6	
Nothing Compares 2 U	7"	Ensign	ENYPB630	1990	£1.50	£4	boxed with poster and badge

O'CONNOR, SINEAD & THE EDGE

Title	Format	Label	Cat#	Year	Price	Price	Notes
Heroine	7"	Virgin	VS897	1986	£1.50	£4	
Heroine	12"	Virgin	VS89712	1986	£3	£8	

OCTOBER, JOHNNY

Title	Format	Label	Cat#	Year	Price	Price	Notes
Growin' Prettier	7"	Capitol	CL15070	1959	£1.50	£4	
There'll Always Be A Feeling	7"	Capitol	CL15121	1960	£1.50	£4	

OCTOPUS

Title	Format	Label	Cat#	Year	Price	Price	Notes
Hey Na Na	7"	Mooncrest	MOON7	1973	£1.50	£4	
Laugh At The Poor Man	7"	Penny Farthing	PEN705	1970	£10	£20	
Restless Nights	LP	Penny Farthing	PELS508	1970	£85	£170	
River	7"	Penny Farthing	PEN716	1970	£5	£10	

OCTOPUS (2)

Title	Format	Label	Cat#	Year	Price	Price	Notes
Octopus	LP	ESP	2000	1969	£6	£15	US

OCTOPUS (3)

Title	Format	Label	Cat#	Year	Price	Price	Notes
Keep Smiling	7" EP	Vogue	EPL8167	1963	£4	£8	French

O'DAY, ANITA

Title	Format	Label	Cat#	Year	Price	Price	Notes
And Billy May Swing Rodgers And Hart	LP	HMV	CLP1436/CSD1354	1961	£6	£15	
Anita	LP	HMV	CLP1085	1956	£8	£20	
Anita O'Day Collates	10" LP	Columbia	33C9020	1956	£20	£40	
Anita Sings The Most	LP	Columbia	33CX10125	1958	£6	£15	
At Mister Kelly's	10" LP	HMV	DLP1203	1959	£6	£15	
Evening With Anita O'Day	LP	Columbia	33CX10068	1957	£15	£30	
Pick Yourself Up	10" LP	HMV	DLP1169	1958	£8	£20	
Swings Cole Porter With Billy May	LP	HMV	CLP1332	1960	£6	£15	

O'DAY, PAT

Title	Format	Label	Cat#	Year	Price	Price	Notes
Earth Angel	7"	MGM	SP1129	1955	£5	£10	
Soldier Boy	7"	MGM	SP1142	1955	£4	£8	

ODDIE, BILL

Title	Format	Label	Cat#	Year	Price	Price	Notes
Can't Get Through	7"	Parlophone	R5433	1966	£1.50	£4	
Knitting Song	7"	Parlophone	R5346	1965	£1.50	£4	
On Ilkla Moor Baht'at	7"	Dandelion	4786	1970	£2	£5	
We Love Jimmy Young	7"	Decca	F12903	1969	£1.50	£4	

ODDSOCKS
Men Of The Moment .... LP ..... Sweet Folk & .... SFA030................ 1975 ... £5 ....£12 ....
Country...........

ODELL, ANN
A Little Taste .... LP ..... DJM .... DJLPS434 .... 1973 ... £6 ....£15 ....

O'DELL, MAC
Hymns For The Country Folk .... LP ..... Audio Lab .... AL1544 .... 1960 ... £10 ....£25 ....US
Stone Has Rolled Away .... 7" ...... Parlophone...... CMSP25 .... 1954 ... £2.50 ....£6 ....export

O'DELL, RONNIE
Melody Of Napoli .... 7" ...... London .... HLD8439 .... 1957 ... £2.50 ....£6 ....

ODIN
Odin .... LP ..... Vertigo .... 6360608............ 1972 ... £5 ....£12 ....

O'DONNELL, AL
Al O'Donnell .... LP ..... Trailer .... LER2073 .... 1972 ... £10 ....£25 ....
Al O'Donnell 2 .... LP ..... Transatlantic ... LTRA501 .... 1978 ... £5 ....£12 ....

O'DONNELL, JOE
Gaodhal's Vision .... LP ..... Polydor .... 2383465............. 1977 ... £8 ....£20 ....

ODYSSEY
Odyssey .... LP ..... private .... £400 ......£600 ....US

ODYSSEY (2)
Beware .... 7" EP.. Jag .... 232001............... 1967 ... £7.50 ....£15 ....French, B side
by Jimmy Powell

ODYSSEY (3)
Odyssey .... LP ..... Mowest........... MWS7002 .... 1973 ... £8 ....£20 ....

ODYSSEY (4)
How Long Is Time .... 7" ...... Strike .... JH312 .... 1966 ... £4 ....£8 ....

O'HALLORAN BROTHERS
Men Of The Island .... LP ..... Topic............... 12TS305............. 1976 ... £6 ....£15 ....

O'HARA'S PLAYBOYS
Ballad Of The Soon Departed .... 7" ...... Fontana .... TF872 .... 1967 ... £2 ....£5 ....
Get Ready .... LP ..... Fontana .... (S)TL5461 .... 1968 ... £6 ....£15 ....
I Started A Joke .... 7" ...... Fontana .... TF974 .... 1968 ... £2 ....£5 ....
In The Shelter Of My Heart .... 7" ...... Fontana .... TF924 .... 1968 ... £2 ....£5 ....
Island In The Sun .... 7" ...... Fontana .... TF893 .... 1967 ... £2 ....£5 ....
Party No.1 .... LP ..... Decca .... 1964 ... £15 ....£30 ....German
Spicks And Specks .... 7" ...... Fontana .... TF793 .... 1967 ... £2 ....£5 ....
Start All Over .... 7" ...... Fontana .... TF763 .... 1966 ... £2 ....£5 ....
Voices .... 7" ...... Fontana .... TF949 .... 1968 ... £2 ....£5 ....

OHIO EXPRESS
Beg Borrow & Steal .... LP ..... Cameo .... CS20000 .... 1968 ... £5 ....£12 ....US
Down At Lulu's .... 7" ...... Pye .... 7N25469............ 1968 ... £1.50 ....£4 ....
Yummy Yummy Yummy .... 7" ...... Pye .... 7N25459............ 1968 ... £1.50 ....£4 ....chart single

OHIO PLAYERS
Here Today And Gone Tomorrow .... 7" ...... Capitol .... CL15587 .... 1969 ... £1.50 ....£4 ....

OHO
Okinawa .... LP ..... private .... £17.50 .....£35 ....US

OISIN
Bealoideas .... LP ..... ID.................... IDLP2011 .... 1979 ... £5 ....£12 ....Irish
Jeannie C .... LP ..... Tara................. 2013................ 1982 ... £5 ....£12 ....Irish
Oisin .... LP ..... ID.................... IDLP2006 .... 1976 ... £5 ....£12 ....Irish
Over The Moor To Maggie .... LP ..... Tara................. 2012................ 1980 ... £5 ....£12 ....Irish

O'JAYS
Back On Top .... LP ..... Bell .... 6014................ 1968 ... £6 ....£15 ....US
Backstabbers .... LP ..... CBS .... 65257.............. 1973 ... £4 ....£10 ....
Choice .... 7" ...... Bell .... BLL1033 .... 1968 ... £2 ....£5 ....
Comin' Through .... LP ..... Imperial .... LP9290/12290 ... 1965 ... £6 ....£15 ....US
Don't You Know A True Love .... 7" ...... Now .... 1002................ 1970 ... £2 ....£5 ....
I'll Be Sweeter Tomorrow .... 7" ...... Stateside .... SS2073 .... 1967 ... £15 ....£30 ....
Lipstick Traces .... 7" ...... Liberty .... LIB66102 .... 1965 ... £12.50 .....£25 ....
Look Over Your Shoulder .... 7" ...... Bell .... BLL1020 .... 1968 ... £4 ....£8 ....
Soul Sounds .... LP ..... Minit .... LP40008 .... 1967 ... £6 ....£15 ....US
Stand In For Love .... 7" ...... Liberty .... LIB66197 .... 1966 ... £5 ....£10 ....

OKAYSIONS
Girl Watcher .... 7" ...... Stateside .... SS2126.............. 1969 ... £7.50 ....£15 ....

O'KEEFE, JOHNNY
Real Wild Child .... 7" ...... Coral .... Q72330 .... 1958 ... £30 ....£60 ....
Tell the Blues So Long .... 7" ...... Zodiac .... ZR0016 .... 196- ... £5 ....£10 ....

O'KEEFE, PADRAIG, DENIS MURPHY, JULIA CLIFFORD
Kerry Fiddles .... LP ..... Topic............... 12T309 .... 1977 ... £5 ....£12 ....

OKEEFENOKEE JUG BAND
Okeefenokee Jug Band .... 7" EP.. Vogue .... EPV1188 .... 1958 ... £2.50 ....£6 ....

OKIN, EARL

Stop And You'll Become Aware	7"	CBS	4495	1968	£2.50	£6	

OKKO

Sitar And Electronics	LP	BASF	20211177	1971	£4	£10	German

OKTOBER

Uhrsprung	LP	Trikont	US0024	1976	£4	£10	German

OLA & THE JANGLERS

Alex Is The Man	7" EP.	Pathe	EGF975	1966	£7.50	£15	French
I Can Wait	7"	Decca	F12646	1967	£2.50	£6	
Patterns	LP	Metronome		1967	£8	£20	German
Surprise Surprise	LP	Sonet		1968	£8	£20	Swedish
That's When	7" EP.	Pathe	EGF924	1966	£7.50	£15	French
Twelve Big Hits	LP	Sonet		1969	£6	£15	Swedish
What A Way To Die	7"	Transatlantic	BIG108	1968	£2.50	£6	

OLD MAN & THE SEA

Old Man & The Sea	LP	Sonet		1972	£150	£250	

OLD SWAN BAND

No Reels	LP	Free Reed	FRR011	1976	£6	£15	
Old Swan Band	LP	Free Reed	FRR028	1978	£8	£20	

OLDFIELD, MIKE

Interesting variations exist with regard to the quadraphonic version of Mike Oldfield's "Tubular Bells". All copies of the picture disc are a stereo remix of the quadraphonic version, the same as first appeared in the four album "Boxed" compilation. The first forty thousand copies of the black vinyl edition are not a true quadraphonic recording at all, but merely a doctored version of the stereo issue. Thereafter, the records are a true quadraphonic mix, but there is no indication on the cover or label of the record that the substitution has been made.

Don Alfonso	7"	Virgin	VS117	1975	£4	£8	PS
Family Man	7"	Virgin	VSY489	1982	£1.50	£4	pic disc
Five Miles Out	7"	Virgin	VSY464	1982	£1.50	£4	pic disc
Hergest Ridge	LP	Virgin	QV2013	1975	£6	£15	quad
Hergest Ridge	7"	Virgin		1974	£4	£8	1 sided promo sampler
Impressions	LP	Tellydisc	TEL4	1979	£10	£25	
Mike Oldfield's Single	7"	Virgin	VS101	1974	£2	£5	PS
Mistake	7"	Virgin	VSY541	1982	£1.50	£4	pic disc
Moonlight Shadow	7"	Virgin	VSY586	1983	£1.50	£4	pic disc
Ommadawn	LP	Virgin	QV2043	1976	£6	£15	quad
Ommadawn	12"	Virgin	VDJ9	1975	£4	£10	promo sampler
Orchestral Tubular Bells	7"	Virgin	VDJ1	1975	£4	£8	promo sampler
Shine	7"	Virgin	VSS863	1986	£6	£12	shaped pic disc
Spanish Tune	7"	Virgin	VS112	1974	£25	£50	promo
Tubular Bells	LP	Virgin	QV2001	1974	£5	£12	quad
Tubular Bells	LP	Virgin	VP2001	1978	£5	£12	pic disc
William Tell Overture	7"	Virgin	VS167	1977	£1.50	£4	PS

OLDHAM, ANDREW ORCHESTRA

16 Hip Hits	LP	Ace Of Clubs	ACL1180	1964	£17.50	£35	
365 Rolling Stones	7"	Decca	F11878	1964	£7.50	£15	US
East Meets West	LP	Parrot	PA6/PAS71003	1965	£10	£25	US
Funky And Fleopatra	7"	Decca	F11829	1964	£7.50	£15	B side by Jeannie & Her Redheads
Maggie May	LP	Decca	LK4636	1964	£8	£20	
Right Of Way	7"	Decca	F11987	1964	£7.50	£15	
Rolling Stones Songbook	LP	Decca	LK/SKL4796	1966	£15	£30	
There Are But Five Rolling Stones	7"	Decca	F11817	1964	£7.50	£15	B side by Cleo

OLDHAM TINKERS

Best O'T Bunch	LP	Topic	12TS237	1974	£5	£12	
For Old Time's Sake	LP	Topic	12TS276	1975	£6	£15	
Oldham's Burning Sands	LP	Topic	12TS206	1971	£6	£15	
Sit Thee Down	LP	Topic	12TS323	1977	£6	£15	
That Lancashire Band	LP	Topic	12TS399	1979	£6	£15	

O'LEARY, JOHN

Music For The Set	LP	Topic	12TS357	1977	£5	£12	

OLENN, JOHNNY

Born Reckless	7"	Mercury	AMT1050	1959	£15	£30	
Just Rollin'	LP	Liberty	LRP3029	1958	£50	£100	US
My Idea Of Love	7"	London	HLU8388	1957	£60	£120	

O'LIST, DAVID

Fallout Love	7"	Underground Music	UMA004	1982	£1.50	£4	

OLIVER

Good Morning Starshine	7"	CBS	4435	1969	£1.50	£4	chart single

OLIVER & THE TWISTERS

Look Who's Twistin' Everybody	LP	Colpix	CP423	1961	£8	£20	US

OLIVER (2)

Standing Stone	LP	private	OL1	1974	£100	£200	

OLIVER, JOHNNY

Chain Gang	7"	MGM	SP1165	1956	£2	£5	

What A Kiss Won't Do	7"	Mercury	AMT1095	1960	£1.50	£4

OLIVER, KING

Creole Jazz Band	10" LP	London	AL3504	1954	£10	£25
In Harlem	10" LP	HMV	DLP1609	1955	£10	£25
King Oliver	LP	Philips	BBL7181	1957	£6	£15
King Oliver Jazz Band	10" LP	Columbia	33S1065	1955	£10	£25
Louis Armstrong 1923	LP	Riverside	RLP12122	1961	£4	£10
Oliver Dixie Syncopators	10" LP	Vogue Coral	LRA10020	1955	£10	£25
Plays The Blues	10" LP	London	AL3510	1954	£10	£25

OLIVER, PAUL

Conversation With The Blues	LP	Decca	LK4664	1965	£15	£30

OLLIE & THE NIGHTINGALES

You're Leaving Me	7"	Stax	STAX109	1969	£2	£5

OLSSON, NIGEL

Drum Orchestra And Chorus	LP	DJM	DJLPS417	1972	£5	£12

OLYMPICS

Baby Do The Philly Dog	7"	Action	ACT4539	1969	£2.50	£6	
Baby Do The Philly Dog	7"	Fontana	TF778	1966	£4	£8	
Baby It's Hot	7"	Vogue	V9204	1962	£4	£8	
Dance By The Light Of The Moon	LP	Vocalion	VAH8059	1961	£20	£40	
Dance With A Dolly	7"	Vogue	V9181	1961	£4	£8	
Dance With The Teacher	7"	HMV	POP564	1958	£6	£12	
Do The Bounce	LP	Tri-Disc	1001	1963	£10	£25	US
Doin' The Hully Gully	LP	Arvee	A423	1960	£30	£60	US
Good Lovin'	7"	Warner Bros	WB157	1965	£6	£12	
I Wish I Could Shimmy	7"	Vogue	V9174	1960	£5	£10	chart single
I'll Do A Little Bit More	7"	Action	ACT4556	1969	£2	£5	
Little Pedro	7"	Vogue	V9184	1961	£4	£8	B side Cappy Lewis
Nothing	7"	HMV	POP1155	1963	£2.50	£6	
Party Time	LP	Arvee	A429	1961	£25	£50	US
Private Eye	7"	Columbia	DB4346	1959	£6	£12	
Something Old, Something New	LP	Fontana	TL5407	1967	£6	£15	
Stomp	7"	Vogue	V9198	1962	£4	£8	
The Bounce	7"	Sue	WI348	1964	£6	£12	
Twist	7"	Vogue	V9196	1962	£4	£8	
We Go Together	7"	Fontana	TF678	1966	£4	£8	
Western Movies	7"	HMV	POP528	1958	£5	£10	chart single

O.M.D.

The rarest Orchestral Manoeuvres In The Dark record is not one that a collector of the group's music is ever likely to find. As a mispressing, however, it is arguably only of interest to the completist in any case - the song "Souvenir" replaces "Love Action" as the A side on forty copies of the Human League single. Thirty-five of these were destroyed, which leaves a grand total of five copies available for collectors. In the circumstances, it is not realistic to quote a price for these.

Constructive Conversation With OMD	LP	Epic	AS1408	198-	£6	£15	US promo
Dreaming	CD-s	Virgin	VSCDX987	1988	£2.50	£6	
Electricity	7"	Factory	FAC6	1979	£5	£10	
La Femme Accident	7"	Virgin	VSS811	1985	£1.50	£4	square pic disc
Locomotion	7"	Virgin	VSY660	1984	£1.50	£4	shaped pic disc
Never Turn Away	7"	Virgin	VSY727	1984	£1.50	£4	pic disc
Sailing On The Seven Seas	CD-s	Virgin	VSCDT1310	1991	£3	£8	
Shame	CD-s	Virgin	MIKE93812	1987	£2.50	£6	
Talking Loud And Clear	7"	Virgin	VSY685	1984	£1.50	£4	pic disc
We Love You	7"	Virgin	VSC911	1986	£2	£5	with cassette

OMEGA

Omega	LP	Bellaphon	BLPS19147	1973	£5	£12	German
Omega III	LP	Bellaphon	BLPS19191	1974	£4	£10	German
Two Hundred Years After The Last War	LP	Bellaphon	BLPS19175	1974	£5	£12	German

OMEGA (2)

Prophet	LP	Rock Machine	MACH1	1985	£8	£20

ONE

One	LP	Fontana	STL5539	1969	£25	£50

ONE IN A MILLION

Double Sight	7"	MGM	MGM1370	1968	£60	£120
Use Your Imagination	7"	CBS	202513	1967	£25	£50

1000 MEXICANS

Art Of Love	7"	Whaam!	WHAAM12	1983	£1.50	£4

1000 VIOLINS

Halcyon Days	12"	Dreamworld	DREAM2	1985	£2.50	£6

ONE TWO & THREE

Black Pearl	7"	Decca	F12093	1965	£2.50	£6
Black Pearls And Green Diamonds	LP	Decca	LK4682	1965	£40	£80

O'NEIL, MATTY

Don't Sell Daddy Any More Whisky	7"	London	L1037	1954	£12.50	£25	gold label

O'NEILL, JOHNNY

Wagon Train	7"	RCA	RCA1114	1959	£1.50	£4

101'ERS

Elgin Avenue Breakdown	LP	Andalucia	AND101	1981	£4	£10	
Key To Your Heart	7"	Chiswick	S3	1976	£2.50	£6	PS

ONES

The lead guitarist with The Ones was Edgar Froese, later to play in an entirely different style as leader of Tangerine Dream.

Lady Greengrass	7"	Star Club	148593STF	1966	£100	£200	German

ONES (2)

Ones	LP	Ashwood House	1105	1966	£60	£120	US

ONLOOKERS

You And I	7"	Demon	D1012	1982	£5	£10	

ONLY ONES

Many of the punk musicians to emerge in the late seventies were far from being the brash youngsters they were painted. Skulking at the back of the Only Ones' line-up was the familiar face of Mike Kellie, formerly the drummer with Spooky Tooth. The pedigree of the group's bass player went back even further - he was a member of Scottish beat group, the Beatstalkers. This experience was no doubt the reason the Only Ones were able to deliver such convincing interpretations of Peter Perrett's material. "Another Girl Another Planet" in particular is a classic rock recording by any standard.

Another Girl, Another Planet	7"	CBS	6228	1978	£2.50	£6	PS
Another Girl, Another Planet	7"	CBS	6576	1978	£2.50	£6	demo
Another Girl, Another Planet	12"	CBS	126576	1978	£2.50	£6	
Baby's Got A Gun	LP	CBS	84089	1980	£4	£10	
Even Serpents Shine	LP	CBS	83451	1979	£4	£10	
Lovers Of Today	7"	Vengeance	VEN001	1977	£2.50	£6	
Lovers Of Today	12"	Vengeance	VEN001	1977	£3	£8	
Only Ones	LP	CBS	82830	1978	£4	£10	
Out There In The Night	7"	CBS	7285	1979	£1.50	£4	PS
Trouble In The World	7"	CBS	7963	1979	£25	£50	black & red PS

ONO, YOKO

Approximately Infinite Universe	LP	Apple	SAPDO1001	1973	£15	£30	double
Death Of Samantha	7"	Apple	47	1973	£7.50	£15	
Feeling The Space	LP	Apple	SAPCOR26	1973	£15	£30	
Fly	LP	Apple	SPTU101/2	1971	£15	£30	double
Mind Train	7"	Apple	41	1972	£2	£5	
Mind Train	7"	Apple	41	1972	£7.50	£15	PS
Mrs.Lennon	7"	Apple	38	1971	£4	£8	
Plastic Ono Band	LP	Apple	SAPCOR17	1970	£15	£30	
Run Run Run	7"	Apple	48	1973	£7.50	£15	
Walking On Thin Ice	12"	WEA	PROA934	1981	£6	£15	promo
Welcome (The Many Sides Of Yoko Ono)	LP	Apple	PRP18026	1974	£150	£250	Japanese promo

ONYX

Air	7"	Parlophone	R5888	1971	£2	£5	
My Son John	7"	Pye	7N17622	1968	£4	£8	
Next Stop Is Mine	7"	Parlophone	R5906	1971	£2	£5	
Tamaris Khan	7"	Pye	7N17668	1969	£10	£20	
Time Off	7"	CBS	4635	1969	£6	£12	
You've Gotta Be With Me	7"	Pye	7N17477	1968	£4	£8	

OPAL BUTTERFLY

Beautiful Beige	7"	CBS	3576	1968	£10	£20	
Mary Anne With The Shakey Hand	7"	CBS	3921	1969	£25	£50	
You're A Groupie Girl	7"	Polydor	2058041	1970	£6	£12	

OPEL, JACKIE

Cry Me A River	7"	King	KG1011	1965	£5	£10	
Done With A Friend	7"	Ska Beat	JB190	1965	£5	£10	
Go Whey	7"	Island	WI209	1965	£5	£10	
I Am What I Am	7"	Rio	R117	1966	£4	£8	Jackie Mittoo B side
Little More	7"	Ska Beat	JB227	1965	£5	£10	
Old Rockin' Chair	7"	Island	WI227	1965	£5	£10	Skatalites B side
Pity The Fool	7"	R&B	JB160	1964	£5	£10	
Solid Rock	7"	R&B	JB138	1964	£5	£10	
TV In Jamaica	7"	Jump Up	JU512	1967	£4	£8	
Wipe Those Tears	7"	Island	WI203	1965	£5	£10	
You're No Good	7"	Black Swan	WI421	1964	£5	£10	

OPEN MIND

Horses And Chariots	7"	Philips	BF1790	1969	£12.50	£25	
Magic Potion	7"	Philips	BF1805	1969	£30	£60	
Open Mind	LP	Antar	ANTAR2	1986	£6	£15	
Open Mind	LP	Philips	SBL7893	1969	£150	£250	sleeve pictured in Guide

OPEN ROAD

Swamp Fever	7"	Greenwich	GSS102	1972	£4	£8	
Windy Daze	LP	Greenwich	GSLP1001	1971	£10	£25	

OPUS

Baby Come On	7"	Columbia	DB8675	1970	£7.50	£15	

O'QUIN, GENE

Boogie Woogie Fever	78	Capitol	CL13600	1951	£2.50	£6	

ORA

Ora	LP	Tangerine	DPLP002S	1969	£100	£200	sleeve pictured in Guide

ORANGE BICYCLE

Carry That Weight	7"	Parlophone	R5811	1969	£6	£12	
Early Pearly Morning	7"	Columbia	DB8352	1968	£6	£12	
Goodbye Stranger	7"	Regal Zonophone	RZ3029	1971	£6	£12	
Hyacinth Threads	7"	Columbia	DB8259	1967	£6	£12	
Hyacinth Threads	7" EP	Impact	200013	1967	£15	£30	French
Jelly On The Bread	7"	Parlophone	R5854	1970	£6	£12	
Jenskadajka	7"	Columbia	DB8413	1968	£6	£12	
Laura's Garden	7"	Columbia	DB8311	1967	£6	£12	
Orange Bicycle	LP	Parlophone	PCS7108	1970	£30	£60	sleeve pictured in Guide
Sing This All Together	7"	Columbia	DB8483	1968	£6	£12	
Take Me To The Pilot	7"	Parlophone	R5827	1970	£6	£12	
Tonight I'll Be Staying Here	7"	Parlophone	R5789	1969	£6	£12	

ORANGE JUICE

One feature of the punk explosion was the emergence of a number of independently run record labels. Only a lucky few have survived, but one of the most fondly regarded of those that have not is Postcard records. Much of this regard has to do with the label's sponsoring of Orange Juice.The group's series of sparkling singles are amongst the delights of the immediate post-punk years and they possess a drive and a liveliness somewhat lacking in the new versions of the same songs recorded for the first Polydor LP. These singles are rightly highly prized.

Blue Boy	7"	Postcard	80-2	1980	£10	£20	hand coloured sleeve
Blue Boy	7"	Postcard	80-2	1980	£2	£5	white or brown sleeve
Falling And Laughing	7"	Postcard	80-0	1980	£20	£40	pic in bag, Felicity flexi
Falling And Laughing	7"	Postcard	80-0	1980	£25	£50	pic in bag, Felicity flexi, postcard
Poor Old Soul	7"	Postcard	81-2	1981	£1.50	£4	
Poor Old Soul	7"	Postcard	81-2	1981	£2.50	£6	with postcard
Simply Thrilled Honey	7"	Postcard	80-6	1980	£1.50	£4	
Simply Thrilled Honey	7"	Postcard	80-6	1980	£7.50	£15	colour insert in bag

ORANGE MACHINE

Three Jolly Little Dwarfs	7"	Pye	7N17559	1968	£15	£30	
You Can All Join In	7"	Pye	7N17680	1969	£15	£30	

ORANGE PEEL

I Got No Time	7"	Reflection	R55	1970	£4	£8	
Orange Peel	LP	Bellaphon	BLPS19036	1972	£10	£25	German

ORANGE SEAWEED

Stay Awhile	7"	Pye	7N17515	1968	£7.50	£15	

ORB

The success of the Orb has been achieved despite (or because of?) breaking so many of the rules governing the methods of most rock artists that it becomes impossible not to be fascinated by their career. Within a critical climate that still reviles the progressive rock of the seventies, the Orb have nevertheless managed to achieve acclaim by working within an approach that is indistinguishable from one of the major progressive strands. (Emphasised by the Orb's use of Pink Floyd quotes and imagery, and the collaborations with Steve Hillage). At the same time, the Orb have managed to persuade people that a music based on texture and sound-sculpture - music that seems to call for its listeners to be sitting or lying down in a blissed out condition - is actually a kind of dance music. Along the way, the Orb have sold a large number of records, including several multiple-album sets and singles playing for vastly longer than than the norm. One of the group's biggest hits so far is "Blue Room", a single playing at just two seconds under the forty minute time-span ruled by Gallup to be the maximum length for an item to qualify for inclusion in the singles charts.

Adventures Beyond The Underworld	LP	Big Life	BLRDLP5	1991	£5	£12	double
Assassin	CD-s	Big Life	ORBPROMOCD5	1992	£2.50	£6	promo
Assassin	12"	Big Life	ORBPROMO5	1992	£5	£12	promo, turquoise vinyl
Aubrey Mixes: The Ultraworld Excursions	LP	Big Life	BLRLP14	1991	£6	£15	
Aubrey Mixes: The Ultraworld Excursions	CD	Big Life	BLRCD14	1991	£8	£20	
Blue Room	CD-s	Big Life	BLRDA75	1992	£2.50	£6	with postcard
Blue Room	7"	Big Life	BLR81D	1992	£7.50	£15	jukebox issue
Blue Room	12"	Big Life	ORBPROMO4	1992	£3	£8	promo
Huge Ever Growing Pulsating Brain	CD-s	Big Life	BLR27CD	1990	£6	£15	
Huge Ever Growing Pulsating Brain	12"	Big Life	BLR27T	1990	£6	£15	
Huge Ever Growing Pulsating Brain (Orbital Dance Mix)	12"	Wau! Mr.Modo	MWS017T	1990	£10	£25	
Huge Ever Growing Pulsating Brain (Orbital Dance Mix)	12"	Wau! Mr.Modo	MWS017R	1990	£20	£40	
Huge Ever Growing Pulsating Brain (remixes)	CD-s	Big Life	BLR27CD	1990	£8	£20	
Huge Ever Growing Pulsating Brain (remixes)	12"	Big Life	BLR27T	1990	£8	£20	
Huge Ever Growing Pulsating Remix	12"	Big Life	ORBPROMO1	1990	£6	£15	promo
Huge Ever Growing Pulsating Remix	12"	Wau! Mr.Modo	MWS017T	1990	£20	£40	promo
Kiss	12"	Wau! Mr.Modo	MWS010T	1989	£20	£40	
Little Fluffy Clouds	CD-s	Big Life	BLR33CD	1990	£4	£10	
Little Fluffy Clouds (Dance Mix)	12"	Big Life	BLR33T	1990	£4	£10	
Little Fluffy Clouds (Dance Mix)	12"	Big Life	ORBPROMO2	1990	£6	£15	promo
Little Fluffy Clouds (Drums And Vox Version)	12"	Big Life	BLR33R	1990	£6	£15	
Orb In Dub	12"	Big Life	BLRR46	1991	£10	£25	
Perpetual Dawn	CD-s	Big Life	BLR46CD	1991	£5	£12	

Perpetual Dawn	12"	Big Life	BLRT46	1991	£3	£8	
Perpetual Dawn: Ultrabass	12"	Big Life	ORBPROMO3	1991	£5	£12	promo
Perpetual Dawn: Ultrabass II	12"	Big Life	ORBPICTURE3	1991	£15	£30	promo pic disc
Perpetual Dawn: Ultrabass II	12"	Big Life	ORBPICTURE3	1991	£20	£40	promo pic disc - plays Towers Of Dub
UFOrb	LP	Big Life	BLRLP18	1992	£6	£15	double
UFOrb	LP	Big Life	BLRLP18	1992	£10	£25	triple

ORBIDOIG

Nocturnal Operation	7"	Situation 2	SIT15	1981	£2	£5	

ORBISON, ROY

At The Rockhouse	LP	Sun	LP1260	1961	£50	£100	US
Big O	LP	London	HAU/SHU8406	1970	£6	£15	
Blue Angel	7"	London	HLU9207	1960	£2	£5	chart single
Blue Bayou	7"	London	HLU9777	1963	£1.50	£4	chart single
Born To Be Loved By You	7"	London	HLU10176	1968	£1.50	£4	
Borne On The Wind	7"	London	HLU9845	1964	£1.50	£4	chart single
Break My Mind	7"	London	HLU10294	1969	£1.50	£4	
Breakin' Up Is Breakin' My Heart	7"	London	HLU10015	1966	£1.50	£4	chart single
Classic	LP	London	HAU/SHU8297	1966	£5	£12	chart LP
Crawling Back	7"	London	HLU10000	1965	£1.50	£4	chart single
Crowd	7"	London	HLU9561	1962	£1.50	£4	chart single
Cry Softly Lonely One	LP	London	HAU/SHU8357	1968	£6	£15	
Cry Softly Lonely One	7"	London	HLU10143	1967	£1.50	£4	
Crying	LP	London	HAU2437/ SHU6229	1962	£6	£15	chart LP
Crying	7"	London	HLU9405	1961	£1.50	£4	chart single
Devil Doll	7" EP	Ember	EMBEP4570	1965	£12.50	£25	
Dream Baby	7"	London	HLU9511	1962	£1.50	£4	chart single
Early Orbison	LP	Monument	LMO/SMO5013	1967	£5	£12	
Exciting Sounds	LP	Ember	NR5013	1964	£5	£12	chart LP
Falling	7"	London	HLU9727	1963	£1.50	£4	chart single
Fastest Guitar Alive	LP	London	HAU/SHU8358	1968	£8	£20	
God Loves You	7"	London	HLU10358	1972	£1.50	£4	
Goodnight	7"	London	HLU9951	1965	£1.50	£4	chart single
Greatest Hits	LP	Monument	LMO/SMO5007	1967	£4	£10	
Hank Williams The Roy Orbison Way	LP	MGM	SE4683	1970	£5	£12	US
Heartache	7"	London	HLU10222	1968	£1.50	£4	chart single
Hillbilly Rock	7" EP	London	RES1089	1957	£50	£100	gold label
I'm Hurtin'	7"	London	HLU7108	1961	£6	£12	export
I'm Hurtin'	7"	London	HLU9307	1961	£1.50	£4	
In Dreams	LP	London	HAU/SHU8108	1963	£6	£15	chart LP
In Dreams	7"	London	HLU9676	1963	£1.50	£4	chart single
In Dreams	7" EP	London	REU1373	1963	£4	£10	
It's Over	7"	London	HLU9882	1964	£1.50	£4	chart single
It's Over	7" EP	London	REU1435	1964	£5	£10	
Laminar Flow	LP	Asylum	K53092	1979	£4	£10	
Lana	7"	London	HLU10051	1966	£1.50	£4	chart single
Last Night	7"	London	HLU10339	1971	£1.50	£4	
Lonely And Blue	LP	London	HAU2342	1961	£6	£15	chart LP
Love Hurts	7" EP	London	REU1440	1965	£6	£12	
Memphis	LP	London	SHU8445	1973	£5	£12	
Memphis Tennessee	7"	London	HLU10388	1972	£2	£5	
More Greatest Hits	LP	Monument	LMO/SMO5014	1968	£4	£10	
My Friend	7"	London	HLU10261	1969	£1.50	£4	chart single
Oh Pretty Woman	LP	London	HAU8207	1964	£6	£15	chart single
Oh Pretty Woman	7"	London	HLU9919	1964	£1.50	£4	chart single
Oh Pretty Woman	7" EP	London	REU1437	1964	£5	£10	
Only The Lonely	78	London	HLU9149	1960	£50	£100	
Only The Lonely	7"	London	HLU9149	1960	£2	£5	chart single
Only The Lonely	7" EP	London	REU1274	1960	£5	£10	
Ooby Dooby	7"	Sun	6094001	1972	£1.50	£4	
Orbison Way	LP	London	HAU/SHU8279	1966	£6	£15	chart LP
Orbisongs	LP	Monument	LMO/SMO5004	1966	£5	£12	chart LP
Penny Arcade	7"	London	HLU10285	1969	£4	£8	chart single
Pretty Paper	7"	London	HLU9930	1964	£1.50	£4	chart single
Ride Away	7"	London	HLU9986	1965	£1.50	£4	chart single
Roy Orbison Sings	LP	London	SHU8435	1972	£5	£12	
Roy Orbison's Stage Show Hits	7" EP	London	REU1439	1965	£5	£10	
Runnin' Scared	7"	London	HLU9342	1961	£1.50	£4	chart single
She	7"	London	HLU10159	1967	£1.50	£4	
Sings Don Gibson	LP	London	HAU/SHU8318	1967	£6	£15	
So Good	7"	London	HLU10113	1967	£1.50	£4	chart single
So Young	7"	London	HLU10310	1970	£1.50	£4	
Special Delivery	LP	Camden	CAL/CAS820	1964	£5	£12	US
Sweet And Easy To Love	7"	Ember	EMBS209	1965	£2	£5	
Sweet And Easy To Love	7"	Ember	EMBS209	1965	£5	£10	PS
Sweet And Easy To Love	7" EP	Ember	EMBEP4546	1964	£12.50	£25	
There Is Only One	LP	London	HAU/SHU8252	1965	£6	£15	chart LP
There Won't Be Many Coming Home	7"	London	HLU10096	1966	£1.50	£4	chart single
This Kind Of Love	7"	Ember	EMBS200	1964	£2	£5	
This Kind Of Love	7"	Ember	EMBS200	1964	£5	£10	PS
Too Soon To Know	7"	London	HLU10067	1966	£1.50	£4	chart single
Trying To Get To You	7" EP	Ember	EMBEP4563	1964	£12.50	£25	
Twinkle Toes	7"	London	HLU10034	1966	£1.50	£4	chart single
Uptown	7" EP	London	REU1354	1963	£5	£10	
Walk On	7"	London	HLU10206	1968	£1.50	£4	chart single
Wild Hearts	7"	ZTT	DZTAS9	1985	£7.50	£15	double
Workin' For The Man	7"	London	HLU9607	1962	£1.50	£4	chart single

| You're My Baby | 7" | Ember | EMBS197 | 1964 | £2 | £5 | |
| You're My Girl | 7" | London | HLU9978 | 1965 | £1.50 | £4 | chart single |

ORBIT FIVE

| I Wanna Go To Heaven | 7" | Decca | F12799 | 1968 | £5 | £10 | |
| I Wanna Go To Heaven | 7" | Decca | F12799 | 1968 | £7.50 | £15 | PS |

ORCHIDS

Gonna Make Him Mine	7"	Decca	F11743	1963	£4	£8	
I've Got That Feeling	7"	Decca	F11861	1964	£4	£8	
Love Hit Me	7"	Decca	F11785	1963	£4	£8	

ORCHIDS (2)

| From This Day | 7" | Sha La La | 005 | 1988 | £2 | £5 | flexi, B side by Sea Urchins |
| I've Got A Habit | 7" | Sarah | 002 | 1988 | £6 | £12 | with poster |

ORE

| Halcyon Days | LP | Akashic | | 1979 | £15 | £30 | US pic disc |
| Your Time Will Come | 7" | Bandit | BR003 | 1982 | £6 | £12 | |

ORGANAIRE, CHARLES

| Little Village | 7" | R&B | JB149 | 1964 | £5 | £10 | |
| Little Village | 7" | Rio | R28 | 1964 | £5 | £10 | |

ORGANISATION

| Tone Float | LP | RCA | SF8111 | 1970 | £40 | £80 | |

ORGANISERS

| Lonesome Road | 7" | Pye | 7N17022 | 1966 | £20 | £40 | |

ORGANUM

| Pulp | 7" | Aeroplane | AR7 | 198- | £10 | £20 | |

O'RIADA, SEAN

Ceol Na Nuasal	LP	Gael Linn	CEF015	1967	£6	£15	Irish
O'Riada's Farewell	LP	Claddagh	CC12	1972	£5	£12	Irish
Reacaireacht An Riadaigh	LP	Gael Linn	CEF010	1965	£6	£15	Irish

ORIGINAL BARNSTORMERS SPASM BAND

| That's All There Is | 7" | Tempo | A168 | 195- | £1.50 | £4 | |

ORIGINAL CHECKMATES

Checkmate Twist	7"	Pye	7N15442	1962	£4	£8	
Hot Toddy	7"	Pye	7N15428	1962	£2.50	£6	
Union Pacific	7"	Decca	F11688	1963	£7.50	£15	

ORIGINAL DIXIELAND JAZZ BAND

Historic Records Of The First Recorded Jazz	10" LP	HMV	DLP1065	1955	£8	£20	
In England	10" LP	Columbia	33S1087	1956	£8	£20	
In England No.2	10" LP	Columbia	33S1133	1957	£8	£20	

ORIGINAL DOWNTOWN SYNCOPATORS

| It's Jass | 7" EP | Columbia | SEG8293 | 1964 | £5 | £10 | |
| Original Downtown Syncopators | 7" EP | VJM | VEP14 | 1962 | £5 | £10 | |

ORIGINAL DYAKS

| Gotta Get A Good Thing Going | 7" | Columbia | DB8184 | 1967 | £2.50 | £6 | |

ORIGINAL FIVE BLIND BOYS

| Original Five Blind Boys | 7" EP | Vogue | EPV1159 | 1957 | £5 | £10 | |

ORIGINAL NEW ORLEANS RHYTHM KINGS

| Golden Leaf Strut | 7" | Columbia | SCM5113 | 1954 | £2 | £5 | |

ORIGINAL TORNADOES

| Telstar | 7" | SRT | SRTS75350 | 1965 | £2 | £5 | |

ORIGINALS

Baby I'm For Real	7"	Tamla Motown	TMG733	1970	£2	£5	
Down To Love Town	7"	Tamla Motown	TMG1038	1976	£1.50	£4	
Down To Love Town	12"	Tamla Motown	TMGT1038	1976	£2.50	£6	
God Bless Whoever Sent You	7"	Tamla Motown	TMG822	1972	£1.50	£4	
Good Night Irene	7"	Tamla Motown	TMG592	1967	£12.50	£25	
Green Grow The Lilacs	LP	Tamla Motown	(S)TML11116	1969	£5	£12	
Green Grow The Lilacs	7"	Tamla Motown	TMG702	1969	£4	£8	

ORIGINALS (2)

| Gimme A Little Kiss Will Ya | 7" | Top Rank | JAR600 | 1962 | £4 | £8 | |

ORIGINELLS

| My Girl | 7" | Columbia | DB7259 | 1964 | £5 | £10 | |
| Nights | 7" | Columbia | DB7388 | 1964 | £4 | £8 | |

ORIOLES

Crying In The Chapel	78	London	L1201	1953	£20	£40	
Hold Me, Thrill Me, Kiss Me	78	London	L1180	1953	£20	£40	
In The Mission Of St.Augustine	78	London	HL8001	1954	£20	£40	

ORION, P.J. & THE MAGNATES

| P.J.Orion & The Magnates | LP | Magnate | 122459 | 1961 | £8 | £20 | US |

ORION THE HUNTER

Orion The Hunter	LP	Portrait	PRT25906	1984	£6	£15	
Orion The Hunter	CD	Portrait	PRT25906	1984	£10	£25	

ORLANDO

Am I The Same Guy	7"	NEMS	564159	1969	£1.50	£4	

ORLANDO, TONY

Beautiful Dreamer	7"	Columbia	DB4954	1963	£1.50	£4	
Bless You	LP	Fontana	STFL582	1963	£20	£40	stereo
Bless You	LP	Fontana	TFL5167	1963	£15	£30	mono
Bless You	7"	Fontana	H330	1961	£2	£5	chart single
Bless You	7" EP	Columbia	SEG8238	1963	£12.50	£25	
Chills	7"	Columbia	DB4871	1962	£1.50	£4	
Halfway To Paradise	7"	Fontana	H308	1961	£2.50	£6	
Happy Times	7"	Fontana	H350	1961	£2	£5	
Joannie	7"	Columbia	DB4991	1963	£1.50	£4	
Talking About You	7"	Fontana	H366	1962	£1.50	£4	
Tell Me What I Can Do	7"	Columbia	DB7288	1964	£1.50	£4	

ORLONS

All The Hits	LP	Cameo Parkway	C1033	1962	£10	£25	
Biggest Hits	LP	Cameo Parkway	C1061	1963	£8	£20	
Bon Doo Wah	7"	Cameo Parkway	C287	1963	£4	£8	
Crossfire	7"	Cameo Parkway	C273	1963	£2.50	£6	
Don't Hang Up	7"	Cameo Parkway	C231	1962	£2	£5	chart single
Down Memory Lane	LP	Cameo	C1073	1963	£8	£20	US
Knock Knock	7"	Cameo Parkway	C332	1964	£4	£8	
Not Me	LP	Cameo	C1054	1963	£8	£20	US
Not Me	7"	Cameo Parkway	C257	1963	£2	£5	
Rules Of Love	7"	Cameo Parkway	C319	1964	£4	£8	
Shimmy Shimmy	7"	Cameo Parkway	C295	1963	£2	£5	
South Street	LP	Cameo	C1041	1963	£10	£25	US
South Street	7"	Cameo Parkway	C243	1963	£2	£5	
Spinning Top	7"	Mojo	2092029	1972	£1.50	£4	
Spinning Top	7"	Planet	PLF117	1966	£15	£30	
Wah Watusi	LP	Cameo	C1020	1962	£10	£25	US
Wah Watusi	7"	Columbia	DB4865	1962	£4	£8	

ORLONS & DOVELLS

Golden Hits	LP	Cameo	C1067	1963	£8	£20	US

ORNANDEL, CYRIL

King Of Kings	7"	MGM	SP 1141	1955	£1.50	£4	

ORPHAN EGG

Orphan Egg	LP	Carole	CARS8004	1968	£5	£12	US

ORPHEUS

My Life	7"	Red Bird	RB10041	1966	£4	£8	

ORPHEUS (2)

Orpheus	LP	MGM	C(S)8072	1968	£4	£10	

ORY, KID

Dance With Kid Ory - Or Just Listen	LP	HMV	CLP1395/CSD1325	1960	£5	£12	
In The Beginning	7" EP	Collector	JE117	1960	£2	£5	
In The Mood	LP	HMV	CLP1329	1960	£5	£12	
Kid From New Orleans	LP	HMV	CLP1303	1959	£6	£15	
Kid Ory	7" EP	Philips	BBE12275	1959	£2	£5	
Kid Ory In Europe	7" EP	Storyville	SEP317	195-	£2	£5	
Kid Ory Plays W.C.Handy	LP	Columbia	33CX10116	1958	£6	£15	
Kid Ory	LP	HMV	CLP1364	1960	£5	£12	
Kid Ory's Creole Jazz Band	LP	Good Time Jazz	LAG12064	1957	£6	£15	
Kid Ory's Creole Jazz Band	LP	Good Time Jazz	LAG12104	1958	£5	£12	
Kid Ory's Creole Jazz Band	7" EP	Good Time Jazz	EPG1006	195-	£2	£5	
Kid Ory's Creole Jazz Band	7" EP	Tempo	EXA5	1955	£2	£5	
Kid Ory's Creole Jazz Band	7" EP	Vogue	EPV1035	1955	£2	£5	
Kid Ory's Creole Jazz Band 1944-1945	10" LP	Philips	BBR8088	1956	£5	£12	
Kid Ory's Creole Jazz Band 1944-1945 Vol.2	10" LP	Goodtime Jazz	LDG055	1954	£6	£15	
Kid Ory's Creole Jazz Band 1944-1945 Vol.3	10" LP	Goodtime Jazz	LDG093	1954	£6	£15	
	10" LP	Goodtime Jazz	LDG184	1956	£6	£15	
Kid Ory's Creole Jazz Band 1954	LP	Good Time Jazz	LAG12004	1955	£5	£12	

Title		Format	Label	Cat. No.	Year			Notes
Legendary Kid 1956		LP	Good Time Jazz	LAG12084	1958	£5	£12	
Song Of The Wanderer		LP	Columbia	33CX10134	1959	£6	£15	
We've Got Rhythm		LP	HMV	CLP1422/CSD1342	1961	£6	£15	with Henry Allen

OS MUNDI
Title		Format	Label	Cat. No.	Year			Notes
43 Minuten		LP	Brain	0001015	1972	£6	£15	German
Latin Mass		LP	Metronome	15381	1970	£6	£15	German

OSANNA
Title		Format	Label	Cat. No.	Year			Notes
Landscape Of Life		LP	Fonit	LPX32	1974	£8	£20	Italian
L'Uomo		LP	Fonit	LPX10	1971	£8	£20	Italian
Milano Calibro 9		LP	Fonit	LPX14	1972	£8	£20	Italian
Palepoli		LP	Fonit	LPX19	1972	£8	£20	Italian
Uno		LP	Fonit	LPX26	1974	£8	£20	Italian

OSBORNE BROTHERS
Title		Format	Label	Cat. No.	Year			Notes
Banjo Boys		7"	MGM	MGM1184	1962	£2.50	£6	
Country Picking & Hillside Singing		7" EP	MGM	MGMEP691	1959	£7.50	£15	

OSBORNE, MIKE
Title		Format	Label	Cat. No.	Year			Notes
Outback		LP	Turtle	TUR300	1971	£25	£50	sleeve pictured in Guide

OSBOURNE, JOHNNY
Title		Format	Label	Cat. No.	Year			Notes
Come Back Darling		LP	Trojan	TTL29	1970	£6	£15	

OSBOURNE, OZZY
Title		Format	Label	Cat. No.	Year			Notes
Bark At The Moon		12"	Epic	TA3915	1983	£6	£15	silver vinyl
Bark At The Moon		12"	Epic	WA3915	1983	£5	£12	pic disc
Diary Of A Madman		LP	Jet		1981	£15	£30	US promo pic disc
Miracle Man		7"	Epic	6530639	1988	£2	£5	shaped pic disc
Mr.Crowley		7"	Jet	JET7003	1980	£2	£5	chart single
Mr.Crowley		12"	Jet	JETP12003	1980	£5	£12	pic disc
So Tired		12"	Epic	WA4452	1984	£4	£10	gold vinyl
Symptom Of The Universe		7"	Jet	JETP7030	1982	£4	£8	pic disc

OSBURN, BOB
Title		Format	Label	Cat. No.	Year			Notes
Bound To Happen		7"	London	HLD9869	1964	£4	£8	

OSCAR
Title		Format	Label	Cat. No.	Year			Notes
Club Of Lights		7"	Reaction	591003	1966	£7.50	£15	
Holiday		7"	Reaction	591016	1967	£7.50	£15	
Join My Gang		7"	Reaction	591006	1966	£7.50	£15	
Open Up The Skies		7"	Polydor	56257	1968	£7.50	£15	
Over The Wall We Go		7"	Reaction	591012	1967	£10	£20	

OSCAR BICYCLE
Title		Format	Label	Cat. No.	Year			Notes
On A Quiet Night		7"	CBS	3237	1968	£7.50	£15	

OSIBISA
Title		Format	Label	Cat. No.	Year			Notes
Osibisa		LP	MCA	MDKS8001	1971	£4	£10	chart LP
Woyaya		LP	MCA	MDKS8005	1971	£4	£10	chart LP

O'SULLIVAN, BERNARD & TOMMY MCMAHON
Title		Format	Label	Cat. No.	Year			Notes
Play Irish Traditional Music From County Clare		LP	Free Reed	FRS505	1976	£5	£12	

OSWALD, LEE HARVEY
Title		Format	Label	Cat. No.	Year			Notes
Self Portrait In Red		LP	Inca	1001	1967	£6	£15	US
Speaks		LP	Truth	2265	1967	£6	£15	US

OTHER BROTHERS
Title		Format	Label	Cat. No.	Year			Notes
Let's Get Together		7"	Pama	PM785	1969	£2.50	£6	

OTHER HALF
Title		Format	Label	Cat. No.	Year			Notes
Mr.Pharmacist		7" EP	Vogue	INT18112	1966	£25	£50	French
Other Half		LP	Acta	A38004	1968	£8	£20	US

OTHER TWO
Title		Format	Label	Cat. No.	Year			Notes
Don't You Wanna Love Me		7"	RCA	RCA1465	1965	£1.50	£4	
I Wanna Be With You		7"	Decca	F11911	1964	£2.50	£6	
I'll Never Let You Go		7"	RCA	RCA1531	1966	£1.50	£4	

OTHERS
Title		Format	Label	Cat. No.	Year			Notes
Oh Yeah		7"	Fontana	TF501	1964	£20	£40	

OTIS, JOHNNY
Title		Format	Label	Cat. No.	Year			Notes
All I Want Is Your Love		7"	Capitol	CL14837	1958	£4	£8	
Baby I Got News For You		7"	Ember	EMBS192	1964	£2	£5	
Bye Bye Baby		7"	Capitol	CL14817	1958	£5	£10	chart single
Casting My Spell		7"	Capitol	CL15018	1959	£4	£8	
Crazy Country Hop		7"	Capitol	CL14941	1958	£5	£10	
Cuttin' Up		LP	Epic	BN26524	1970	£4	£10	US
Formidable		LP	Ember	SPE6604	196-	£6	£15	
Harlem Nocturne		78	Parlophone	R3291	1950	£7.50	£15	B side Slim Gaillard
Johnny Otis		7" EP	Vocalion	VEP170162	1965	£25	£50	
Johnny Otis Show		LP	Capitol	T940	1958	£25	£50	
Johnny Otis Show		7" EP	Capitol	EAP11134	1959	£15	£30	
Live At Monterey		LP	Epic	66295	1971	£5	£12	
Ma He's Making Eyes At Me		7"	Capitol	CL14794	1957	£2.50	£6	chart single

Mumbling Mosie	7"	Capitol	CL15112	1960	£4	£8	
Pioneers Of Rock Vol.3	LP	Starline	SRS5129	1973	£4	£10	
Ring A Ling	7"	Capitol	CL14875	1958	£5	£10	
Rock And Roll Hit Parade Vol.1	LP	Dig	104	1957	£50	£100	US
Three Girls Named Molly	7"	Capitol	CL15057	1959	£2.50	£6	
Well Well Well Well	7"	Capitol	CL14854	1958	£2.50	£6	
You	7"	Capitol	CL15008	1959	£2.50	£6	

OTIS, SHUGGIE

Here Comes Shuggie Otis	LP	CBS	63996	1970	£5	£12	

OTWAY, JOHN

Beware Of The Flowers	7"	Viking	no number	1975	£7.50	£15	
Deep And Meaningless	LP	Polydor	2383501	1978	£4	£10	with 7' (OT1)
Gypsy	7"	County	COUN215	1972	£7.50	£15	

OTWAY, JOHN & WILD WILLY BARRETT

John Otway & Wild Willie Barrett	LP	Extracted	ELP1	1977	£5	£12	
Murder Man	7"	Track	2094111	1973	£1.50	£4	

OUGENWEIDE

All Die Weill Ich Mag	LP	Polydor	2371517	1974	£4	£10	German
Eulenspiegel	LP	Polydor	2371714	1976	£4	£10	German
Fryheit	LP	Polydor	2437576	1978	£4	£10	German
Ohrenschmaus	LP	Polydor	2371700	1975	£4	£10	German
Ougenweide	LP	Polydor	2371678	1974	£4	£10	German
Ougenweide	LP	Zebra	2949009	1973	£5	£12	German
Ungezwungen	LP	Polydor	2634091	1977	£5	£12	German double

OUR PLASTIC DREAM

Little Bit Of Shangrila	7"	Go	AJ11411	1967	£25	£50	

OUT OF DARKNESS

Out Of Darkness	LP	Key	KL006	1970	£100	£200	sleeve pictured in Guide

OUT OF FOCUS

Four Letter Monday Afternoon	LP	Kuckuck	2640101	1972	£15	£30	German double
Out Of Focus	LP	Kuckuck	2375010	1972	£10	£25	German
Wake Up	LP	Kuckuck	2375006	1971	£10	£25	German

OUTCASTS

Frustration	7"	It	IT4	1978	£2.50	£6	
Just Another Teenage Rebel	7"	Good Vibrations	GOT3	1978	£2	£5	2 different PS's
Self Conscious Over You	LP	Good Vibrations	BIG1	1979	£4	£10	

OUTER LIMITS

Dark Side Of The Moon	7"	Decca	F13176	1971	£4	£8	
Great Train Robbery	7"	Instant	IN001	1968	£7.50	£15	
Just One More Chance	7"	Deram	DM125	1967	£6	£12	
When The Work Is Thru'	7"	Elephant	LUR100	1967	£12.50	£25	5 Man Cargo B side

OUTLAW BLUES BAND

Breaking In	LP	Stateside	SSL10290	1969	£5	£12	
Outlaw Blues Band	LP	Bluesway	BLS6021	1968	£5	£12	US

OUTLAWS

The Outlaws were employed as session men by producer Joe Meek and therefore appear on records by the likes of Mike Berry, John Leyton, and Heinz. Between October 1962 and April 1964 the lead guitarist was Ritchie Blackmore. He can be heard on the four Outlaws singles issued in 1963-4, but not on the Outlaws album. This record, which contains cowboy-oriented instrumentals, has been highly sought after since the early days of record collecting.

Ambush	7"	HMV	POP877	1961	£5	£10	chart single
Dream Of The West	LP	HMV	CLP1484	1961	£50	£100	sleeve pictured in Guide
Keep A Knocking	7"	HMV	POP1277	1964	£10	£20	
Last Stage West	7"	HMV	POP990	1962	£5	£10	
Law And Order	7"	HMV	POP1241	1963	£6	£12	
Return Of The Outlaws	7"	HMV	POP1124	1963	£6	£12	
Sioux Serenade	7"	HMV	POP1074	1962	£6	£12	
Swinging Low	7"	HMV	POP844	1961	£5	£10	chart single
That Set The Wild West Free	7"	HMV	POP1195	1963	£6	£12	
Valley Of The Sioux	7"	HMV	POP927	1961	£5	£10	

OUTRIGGERS

Surrender	7" EP	Warner Bros	WSEP2027	1961	£2.50	£6	stereo

OUTSIDERS

Album No.2	LP	Capitol	(S)T2568	1966	£8	£20	US
Girl In Love	7"	Capitol	CL15450	1966	£6	£12	
Happening Live	LP	Capitol	(S)T2745	1967	£8	£20	US
Help Me Girl	7"	Capitol	CL15480	1966	£5	£10	
Help Me Girl	7" EP	Capitol	EAP120879	1966	£12.50	£25	French
I'll Give You Time	7"	Capitol	CL15495	1967	£5	£10	
I'll Give You Time	7" EP	Capitol	EAP120948	1967	£12.50	£25	French
Outsiders In	LP	Capitol	(S)T2636	1967	£8	£20	US
Respectable	7"	Capitol	CL15468	1966	£6	£12	
Time Won't Let Me	LP	Capitol	(S)T2501	1966	£8	£20	US
Time Won't Let Me	7"	Capitol	CL15435	1966	£7.50	£15	
Time Won't Let Me	7" EP	Capitol	EAP120804	1966	£12.50	£25	French

OUTSIDERS (2)
Calling On Youth	LP	Raw Edge	RER001	1977	£4	£10	
Close Up	LP	Raw Edge	RER003	1978	£4	£10	
One To Infinity	7"	Raw Edge	RER002	1977	£2	£5	
Vital Hours	7"	Xciting Plastic		1978	£5	£10	

OUTSIDERS (3)
Keep On Doing It	7"	Decca	F12213	1965	£4	£8	

OUTSKIRTS OF INFINITY
Lord Of The Dark Skies	LP	Woronzow	WOO7	1987	£5	£12	

OVARY LODGE
Ovary Lodge	LP	Ogun	OG600	1976	£6	£15	
Ovary Lodge	LP	RCA	SF83724	1973	£15	£30	

OVERLANDERS
Along Came Jones	7"	Pye	7N15804	1965	£1.50	£4	
Don't It Make You Feel Good	7" EP	Pye	PNV24124	1964	£7.50	£15	French
Michelle	LP	Pye	NPL18138	1966	£6	£15	
Michelle	7"	Pye	7N17034	1966	£1.50	£4	chart single
Michelle	7" EP	Pye	NEP24245	1966	£6	£12	
Michelle	7" EP	Pye	PNV24161	1966	£7.50	£15	French

OVERMAN, RUNE
Big Bass Boogie	7"	Decca	F11605	1963	£1.50	£4	

OVERTAKERS
That's The Way You Like It	7"	Amalgamated	AMG803	1968	£4	£8	

OWEN & LEON
Fits Is On Me	7"	Island	WI164	1964	£5	£10	Skatalites B side
My Love For You	7"	Island	WI163	1964	£5	£10	
Running Around	7"	Island	WI165	1964	£5	£10	Skatalites B side

OWEN B
Owen B	LP	Musicol		197-	£40	£80	US

OWEN, RAY
Ray Owen's Moon	LP	Polydor	2325061	1971	£5	£12	
Tonight I'll Be Staying Here With You	7"	Fontana	TF1045	1969	£1.50	£4	

OWEN, REG
Manhattan Spiritual	7"	Pye	7N25009	1959	£1.50	£4	chart single

OWENS, BUCK
Act Naturally	7" EP	Capitol	EAP120602	1964	£5	£10	
Before You Go	LP	Capitol	(S)T2353	1966	£4	£10	
Best Of Buck Owens	LP	Capitol	(S)T2105	1964	£4	£10	
Buck Owens Sings Harlan Howard	LP	Capitol	(S)T1482	1961	£5	£12	US
Carnegie Hall Concert	LP	Capitol	(S)T2556	1967	£4	£10	
Everlasting Love	7"	Capitol	CL15009	1959	£1.50	£4	
Fabulous Country Music Sound	LP	Starday	SLP172	1962	£4	£10	US
Foolin' Around	7" EP	Capitol	EAP11550	1961	£4	£8	
It Takes People Like You To Make People Like Me	LP	Capitol	(S)T2841	1968	£4	£10	
I've Got A Tiger By The Tail	LP	Capitol	(S)T2283	1966	£4	£10	
Roll Out The Red Carpet	LP	Capitol	(S)T2443	1966	£4	£10	
Together Again	LP	Capitol	T2135	1965	£4	£10	
Under Your Spell Again	LP	Capitol	(D)T1489	1961	£5	£12	US
Your Tender Loving Care	LP	Capitol	(S)T2760	1968	£4	£10	
Yours, Country Style	LP	Capitol	(S)T20861	1966	£4	£10	

OWENS, DONNIE
Need You	7"	London	HL8747	1958	£4	£8	

OWL
Run To The Sun	7"	United Artists	UP2240	1968	£6	£12	

OXLEY, TONY
Baptised Traveller	LP	CBS	52664	1969	£20	£40	
Four Compositions For Sextet	LP	CBS	64071	1970	£20	£40	
Ichnos	LP	RCA	SF8215	1971	£20	£40	

OXYM
Music Power	7"	Cargo	CRS3	1981	£2.50	£6	

OZZ II
Assassin	LP	Zebra	ZEB2	1984	£5	£12	

610

P

PABLO, AUGUSTUS
Title		Label	Cat No	Year			Notes
East Of The River Nile	7"	Big Shot	BI579	1971	£1.50	£4	Herman B side
Reggae In The Fields	7"	Duke	DU122	1971	£1.50	£4	Tommy McCook B side
Snowball And Pudding	7"	Ackee	ACK138	1971	£1.50	£4	Aquarians B side
Still Yet	7"	Ackee	ACK134	1971	£1.50	£4	Aquarians B side

PACIFIC DRIFT
| Feelin' Free | LP | Nova | (S)DN13 | 1970 | £8 | £20 | |
| Water Woman | 7" | Deram | DM304 | 1970 | £2 | £5 | |

PACIFIC GAS & ELECTRIC
| Get It On | LP | B&C | CAS1003 | 1969 | £4 | £10 | |
| Pacific Gas & Electric | LP | CBS | 63822 | 1969 | £4 | £10 | |

PACIFIC SHOWBAND
| Distant Drums | 7" | Pye | 7N15728 | 1964 | £1.50 | £4 | |
| No One Will Ever Know | 7" | Pye | 7N15780 | 1965 | £1.50 | £4 | |

PACIFIC SOUND
| Forget Your Dream | LP | Splendid | | 1972 | £250 | £400 | Swiss |

PACK
| Do You Believe In Magic | 7" | Columbia | DB7702 | 1965 | £10 | £20 | |

PACK (2)
Brave New Soldiers	7"	SS	PAK1	1979	£4	£8	
King Of Kings	7"	Rough Trade	RT025	1979	£2.50	£6	
Kirk Brandon And The Pack Of Lies	7"	SS	SS1N2/SS2N1	1980	£5	£10	
Long Live The Past	7"	Cyclops	CYCLOPS1	1982	£1.50	£4	

PACKABEATS
Dream Lover	7"	Pye	7N15549	1963	£4	£8	
Evening In Paris	7"	Pye	7N15480	1962	£4	£8	
Gypsy Beat	7"	Parlophone	R4729	1961	£1.50	£4	chart single

PACKERS
Hole In The Wall	LP	Soul City	SCM003	1970	£15	£30	
Hole In The Wall	7"	Pye	7N25343	1966	£5	£10	
Hole In The Wall	7"	Soul City	SC111	1969	£2.50	£6	

PAC-KEYS
| Stone Fox | 7" | Speciality | SPE1003 | 1967 | £2.50 | £6 | |

PADDY, KLAUS & GIBSON
I Wanna Know	7"	Pye	7N15906	1965	£4	£8	
No Good Without You Baby	7"	Pye	7N17060	1966	£7.50	£15	
Teresa	7"	Pye	7N17112	1966	£4	£8	

PAGE BOYS
| You're My Kind Of Girl | 7" | Whaam! | WHAAM10 | 1983 | £2 | £5 | |

PAGE, CHRIS
| Wait And See | 7" | Cameo Parkway | CP751 | 1963 | £1.50 | £4 | |

PAGE FIVE
| Let Sleeping Dogs Lie | 7" | Parlophone | R5426 | 1966 | £7.50 | £15 | |

PAGE, HAL & THE WHALERS
| Going Back To My Home Town | 7" | Melodisc | 1553 | 1960 | £10 | £20 | chart single |

PAGE, JIMMY
She Just Satisfies	CD-s	Fontana	TFCD533	1991	£2.50	£6	Led Zeppelin pack
She Just Satisfies	7"	Fontana	TF533	1965	£120	£220	
Wasting My Time	7"	Geffen	GEF41	1988	£2	£5	

PAGE, LARRY
Big Blon' Baby	7"	Saga	SAG452902	1959	£2	£5	
Cool Shake	7"	Columbia	DB3965	1957	£5	£10	
How Am I Doing, Hey, Hey	7"	Saga	SAG452903	1959	£2	£5	
Kinky Music	LP	Decca	LK4692	1965	£30	£60	
Little Old Fashioned Love	7"	Saga	SAG452904	1959	£1.50	£4	
Sings His Personal Choice	7" EP	Saga	STP1024	1963	£2	£5	
That'll Be The Day	7"	Columbia	DB4012	1957	£5	£10	
Theme From Peyton Place	7"	Decca	F12368	1966	£1.50	£4	
Under Control	7"	Columbia	DB4080	1958	£2.50	£6	
Waltzing To Jazz	7"	Decca	F12320	1966	£2	£5	

PAGE, MALLY
| Life And Soul Of The Party | 7" | Pye | 7N17105 | 1966 | £1.50 | £4 | |

PAGE, PATTI
Title	Format	Label	Cat No	Year			Notes
Bring Us Together	7"	Mercury	7MT200	1958	£1.50	£4	
Christmas With Patti Page	10" LP	Mercury	MPT7510	1956	£5	£12	
Folk Song Favourites	10" LP	Mercury	MG25101	1954	£5	£12	
I'm Getting Sentimental Over You	10" LP	Mercury	MPT7531	1957	£5	£12	
In The Land Of Hi-Fi	LP	Emarcy	EJL1252	1957	£4	£10	
Lady Is A Tramp	7" EP	Mercury	SEZ19008	1961	£2.50	£6	stereo
Left Right Out Of Your Heart	7"	Mercury	7MT223	1958	£2	£5	
My, How The Time Goes By	7"	Mercury	7MT184	1958	£1.50	£4	
My Kinda Love	7" EP	Mercury	SEZ19020	1961	£2.50	£6	stereo
Patti Page	7" EP	Mercury	MEP9502	1956	£4	£8	
Patti Page No.1	7" EP	Mercury	ZEP10006	1959	£4	£8	
Patti Page No.2	7" EP	Mercury	ZEP10017	1959	£2.50	£6	
Patti Page No.3	7" EP	Mercury	ZEP10032	1959	£2.50	£6	
Patti Page No.4	7" EP	Mercury	ZEP10045	1959	£2.50	£6	
Patti's Songs	10" LP	Mercury	MG25197	1955	£5	£12	
Patti's Songs	10" LP	Mercury	MPT7535	1957	£4	£10	
These Worldly Wonders	7"	Mercury	7MT206	1958	£1.50	£4	

PAGE TEN
Boutique	7"	Decca	F12248	1965	£5	£10	

PAGEBOYS
When I Meet A Girl Like You	7"	London	HLU9948	1965	£1.50	£4	

PAICH, MARTY
Marty Paich Quartet	10" LP	London	LZU14040	1957	£8	£20	

PAIGE, JOEY
Cause I'm In Love With You	7"	Fontana	TF554	1965	£6	£12	

PAIGE, ROSALIND
Love, Oh Careless Love	7"	MGM	MGM937	1957	£2	£5	
When The Saints	7"	London	HL8120	1955	£6	£12	

PAINTBOX
Get Ready For Love	7"	Youngblood	YB1013	1971	£1.50	£4	

PAINTED SHIP
Frustration	7"	Mercury	MF988	1967	£15	£30	

PAISLEYS
Cosmic Mind At Play	LP	Audio City	70	1968	£35	£70	US
Cosmic Mind At Play	LP	Peace		1970	£30	£60	US
Cosmic Mind At Play	LP	Psycho	PSYCHO7	1983	£5	£12	

PALADIN
Charge	LP	Bronze	ILPS9190	1972	£8	£20	
Paladin	LP	Bronze	ILPS9150	1971	£6	£15	

PALE SAINTS
Children Break	7"	Panic		198-	£5	£10	flexi, B side by Savlons & Kerry Fiddles

PALEY, TOM
Sue Cow	LP	Argo	ZFB3	1969	£6	£15	

PALEY, TOM & PEGGY SEEGER
Who's Going To Shoe Your Pretty Little Foot?	LP	Topic	12T113	1964	£15	£30	

PALLAS
Arrive Alive	LP	Cool King	CKLP002	1983	£5	£12	
Arrive Alive	7"	Granite Wax	GWS1	1982	£12.50	£25	
Knightmoves	12"	Harvest	12PLSD3	1985	£6	£15	with Mad Machine 7"
Pallas	7"	Sueicide	PAL101	1978	£20	£40	
Paris Is Burning	12"	Cool King	12CK010	1983	£2.50	£6	
Sentinel	LP	Harvest	SHSP2400121	1984	£4	£10	with poster

PALMER, BRUCE
Cycle Is Complete	LP	Verve	VRF3086	1971	£6	£15	US

PALMER, CLIVE
Just Me	LP	Autogram	ALLP258	1979	£25	£50	German

PALMER, EARL
Drum Village	7"	Capitol	CL14859	1958	£2.50	£6	

PALMER, EARL & BILLY MAY
Swingin' Drums	7" EP	Capitol	EAP11026	1958	£4	£8	

PALMER, ROBERT
I Didn't Mean To Turn You On	CD-s	Island	CID283	1986	£6	£15	
Live In Boston	LP	Warner Bros	WBMS111	1979	£8	£20	US promo
Secrets	LP	Island		1979	£8	£20	US promo pic disc

PALMER, ROY & THE STATE STREET RAMBLERS
Chicago Skiffle Session	10" LP	London	AL3518	1954	£6	£15	

PALMETTO KINGS
Ten Rum Bottles .... 7" ...... Starlite .... ST45021 .... 1960 ... £1.50 ....£4 ....

PAN
Pan .... LP ..... Sonet .... 1970 ... £100 ......£200

PANAMA LTD.JUG BAND
Indian Summer .... LP ...... Harvest .... SHVL779 .... 1970 ... £15 ....£30 ....
Lady Of Shallott .... 7" ...... Harvest .... HAR5010 .... 1969 ... £4 ....£8 ....
Panama Ltd.Jug Band .... LP ...... Harvest .... SHVL753 .... 1969 ... £15 ....£30 ....
Round And Round .... 7" ...... Harvest .... HAR5022 .... 1970 ... £4 ....£8 ....

PANCAKE
Roxy Elephant .... LP ..... Offers .... OMP7602 .... 1975 ... £4 ....£10 ....German

PANCHO, GENE
I Like Sweet Music .... 7" ...... Giant .... GN21 .... 1968 ... £4 ....£8 ....

PANDAMONIUM
Chocolate Buster Dan .... 7" ...... CBS .... 3451 .... 1968 ... £20 ....£40 ....
No Presents For Me .... 7" ...... CBS .... 2664 .... 1967 ... £25 ....£50 ....
Season Of The Witch .... 7" ...... CBS .... 202462 .... 1967 ... £20 ....£40 ....

PANHANDLE
Panhandle .... LP ..... Decca .... SKL5105 .... 1972 ... £6 ....£15 ....

PANTA REI
.... LP ..... Harvest .... 197- .... £20 ....£40 ....

PANTER, JAN
Scratch My Back .... 7" ...... Pye .... 7N17097 .... 1966 ... £10 ....£20 ....

PANTHER
Wir Wollen Alles .... LP ..... Panther .... 2667 .... 1974 ... £10 ....£25 ....German

PANTHERS
Baby .... 7" EP.. Polydor .... 60118 .... 196- ... £25 ....£50 ....French

PANTON, ROY
Cherita .... 7" ...... Rio .... R19 .... 1964 ... £5 ....£10 ....
Forty Four .... 7" ...... Blue Beat .... BB117 .... 1962 ... £5 ....£10 .. Leon & Owen B side
Hell Gate .... 7" ...... Blue Beat .... BB219 .... 1963 ... £5 ....£10 ....
Mighty Ruler .... 7" ...... Blue Beat .... BB182 .... 1963 ... £5 ....£10 ....
You Don't Know Me .... 7" ...... Rio .... R33 .... 1964 ... £5 ....£10 ....Edward's
Allstars B side

PANZA DIVISION
We'll Rock The World .... 7" ...... Panza Trax........ PTO1 .... 1982 ... £4 ....£8 ....

PAOLA
Bonjour Bonjour .... 7" ...... Decca .... F22916 .... 1969 ... £1.50 ....£4 ....

PAPAS, NIKKI
By The River .... 7" ...... Parlophone..... R4652 .... 1960 ... £2.50 ....£6 ....
Forty-Nine State Rock .... 7" ...... Parlophone..... R4590 .... 1959 ... £4 ....£8 ....

PAPER BLITZ TISSUE
Boy Meets Girl .... 7" ...... RCA .... RCA1652 .... 1967 ... £30 ....£60 ....

PAPER BUBBLE
Scenery Dream .... LP ..... Deram .... DML/SML1059 ...... 1970 ... £6 ....£15 ....

PAPER GARDEN
Paper Garden .... LP ..... Musicor .... MS3175 .... 1970 ... £8 ....£20 ....

PAPER WINGED DREAMS
Paper Winged Dreams .... LP ..... Brimstone....... .... 1970 ... £20 ....£40 ....US

PARADIS, VANESSA
Coupe Coupe .... 7" ...... Polydor .... 8719427 .... 1989 ... £4 ....£8 ....French
Joe Le Taxi .... 7" ...... Polydor .... POSPG902 .... 1988 ... £7.5 ....£15 ....poster PS
La Magie Des Surprises Parties .... 7" ...... Polydor .... 1985 ... £40 ....£80 ....French
Manolo Manolete .... CD-s .. Polydor .... 8873082 .... 1988 ... £20 ....£40 ....French
Manolo Manolete .... 7" ...... Polydor .... 8872657 .... 1988 ... £7.50 ....£15 ....French
Manolo Manolete .... 12" ...... Polydor .... 8872651 .... 1988 ... £15 ....£30 ....French
Marilyn And John .... 7" ...... Polydor .... PO16 .... 1988 ... £1.50 ....£4 ....
Marilyn And John .... 12" ...... Polydor .... PZ16 .... 1988 ... £2.50 ....£6 ....
Maxou .... 7" ...... Polydor .... PO38 .... 1988 ... £1.50 ....£4 ....
Maxou .... 12" ...... Polydor .... PZ38 .... 1988 ... £3 ....£8 ....
Mosquito .... 7" ...... Polydor .... 8730747 .... 1989 ... £4 ....£8 ....
Tandem .... 7" ...... Polydor .... 8773027 .... 1990 ... £4 ....£8 ....French
Tandem .... 12" ...... Polydor .... 8773022 .... 1990 ... £7.50 ....£15 ....French
Tandem (remix) .... CD-s .. Polydor .... 1990 ... £25 ....£50 ....French
Tandem (remix) .... 12" ...... Polydor .... 8773031 .... 1990 ... £12.50 ....£25 ....French
Variations Sur Le Meme T'aime .... LP ..... Polydor .... 1990 ... £8 ....£20 ....French

PARADONS
Diamonds And Pearls .... 7" ...... Top Rank .... JAR514 .... 1960 ... £12.50 ....£25 ....

PARADOX
Changing The Changes .... 7" ...... Polydor .... 56275 .... 1968 ... £27.50 ....£55 ....

613

PARAFFIN JACK FLASH LTD.
Movers And Groovers .... LP ...... Pye .... NSPL18252 .... 1968 ... £6 ....£15 ....

PARAGONS
Paragons Meet The Jesters .... LP ...... Jubilee .... JLP1098 .... 1959 ... £25 ....£50 .... US
Paragons Meet The Jesters .... LP ...... Jubilee .... JLP1098 .... 1959 ... £50 ....£100 ... US, coloured viny
Paragons Vs.The Harptones .... LP ...... Musicnote .... M8001 .... 1964 ... £10 ....£25 .... US

PARAGONS (2)
Happy Go Lucky Girl .... 7" ..... Doctor Bird ...... DB1060.................. 1966 ... £5 ....£10
Have You Ever Been In Love .... 7" ..... Studio One .... SO2081 .... 1969 ... £6 ....£12
Left With A Broken Heart .... 7" ..... Duke .... DU7 .... 1968 ... £4 ....£8
Memories By The Score .... 7" ..... Island .... WI3138 .... 1968 ... £5 ....£10
Mercy Mercy Mercy .... 7" ..... Treasure Isle.... TI7011 .... 1967 ... £5 ....£10
On The Beach .... LP ..... Doctor Bird ...... DLM5010.............. 1967 ... £50 ....£100
On The Beach .... 7" ..... Island .... WI3045 .... 1967 ... £5 ....£10 .... Tommy
                                                                                                                                                      McCook B side
Same Song .... 7" ..... Treasure Isle.... TI7013 .... 1967 ... £5 ....£10 .... Tommy
                                                                                                                                                      McCook B side
Silver Bird .... 7" ..... Treasure Isle.... TI7034 .... 1968 ... £5 ....£10
So Depressed .... 7" ..... Island .... WI3093 .... 1967 ... £5 ....£10
Talking Love .... 7" ..... Island .... WI3067 .... 1967 ... £5 ....£10
Tide Is High .... 7" ..... Treasure Isle.... TI7009 .... 1967 ... £5 ....£10
Wear You To The Ball .... 7" ..... Treasure Isle.... TI7025 .... 1967 ... £5 ....£10

PARAMOR, NORRIE ORCHESTRA
Dance Of The Warriors .... 7" ..... Columbia .... DB7446 .... 1965 ... £1.50 .....£4
Randall And Hopkirk (Deceased) .... 7" ..... Polydor .... 56375................... 1970 ... £4 ....£8
Z Cars .... 7" ..... Columbia .... DB4789 .... 1962 ... £1.50 .....£4

PARAMOUNTS
*The Paramounts are yet another R&B group who gigged hard through the sixties without ever gaining very much success and who made
several singles that essentially serve to emphasise why this was. Arguably, however, the group was capable of very much more, for the
handful of unreleased tracks included on the Edsel compilation of the Paramounts singles are easily the most impressive. And later, the
original line-up of the group made two LPs which did so much more to realise its potential - but these, "Home" and "Broken Barricades", came ou
under a different name; that of Procol Harum.*
Bad Blood .... 7" ...... Parlophone..... R5187 .... 1964 ... £5 ....£10
Blue Ribbons .... 7" ...... Parlophone..... R5272 .... 1965 ... £5 ....£10
Draw Me Closer .... 7" EP.. Odeon .... SOE3774 .... 1965 ... £50 ....£100 .... French
I'm The One Who Loves You .... 7" ...... Parlophone..... R5155 .... 1964 ... £7.50 .....£15
Little Bitty Pretty One .... 7" ...... Parlophone..... R5107 .... 1964 ... £5 ....£10
Paramounts .... 7" EP.. Parlophone..... GEP8908 .... 1964 ... £80 ....£160
Poison Ivy .... 7" ...... Parlophone..... R5093 .... 1963 ... £5 ....£10 .... chart singl
You've Never Had It So Good .... 7" ...... Parlophone..... R5351 .... 1965 ... £6 ....£12

PARCHMENT
Hollywood Sunset .... LP ..... Pye .... NSPL18409 .... 1973 ... £6 ....£15
Light Up The Fire .... LP ..... Pye .... NSPL18388 .... 1972 ... £6 ....£12
Rehearsal For A Reunion .... LP ..... Pilgrim .... 1977 ... £6 ....£15
Shamblejam .... LP ..... Myrrh .... MYR1028 .... 1975 ... £8 ....£20

PARENTI, TONY
Ragtime .... LP ...... London .... LTZU15072 .... 1957 ... £6 ....£15

PARFITT, PAULA
I'm Gonna Give Back Your Ring .... 7" ...... Beacon............. BEA145 .... 1969 ... £17.50 ....£35

PARIS, BOBBY
I Walked Away .... 7" ...... Capitol .... CL16067 .... 1979 ... £1.50 .....£4 ....H.B.Barnam B sid
Night Owl .... 7" ...... London .... HLU10553 .... 1977 ... £1.50 .....£4 ..Yvonne Baker B sid
Personally .... 7" ...... Polydor .... 56747.................. 1968 ... £20 ....£40

PARIS, MICA
*After 4th & Broadway had sent out two hundred promotional copies of Mica Paris' "A Stand 4 Love EP", they discovered that they ha
inadvertently included Prince's original demo of "If I Love U 2 Nite" on the record. The DJ's who had received it were asked to return th
offending article, but one wonders how many actually did!*
If I Love U 2 Nite .... 12" ... 4th & .... 12BRWDJ207........ 1991 ... £37.50 .....£75 .... prom
                                                        Broadway ....

PARIS SISTERS
Dream Lover .... 7" ...... MGM............... MGM1240 .... 1964 ... £7.50 .....£15
I Love How You Love Me .... 7" ...... Top Rank .... JAR588................. 1961 ... £15 ....£30

PARISH HALL
Parish Hall .... LP ...... Liberty .... LBS83374 .... 1970 ... £5 ....£12

PARKER, BENNY & THE DYNAMICS
Boys And Girls .... 7" ...... Decca .... F11944 .... 1964 ... £10 ....£20

PARKER, BILLY
Thanks A Lot .... 7" ...... Decca .... F11668 .... 1963 ... £1.50 .....£4

PARKER, BOBBY
It's Hard But It's Fair .... 7" ...... Blue Horizon.... 573151 .... 1969 ... £7.50 .....£15
Watch Your Step .... 7" ...... London .... HLU9393 .... 1961 ... £7.50 .....£15
Watch Your Step .... 7" ...... Sue .... WI340 .... 1964 ... £7.50 .....£15

PARKER, CHARLIE
All Star Quintet/Sextet .... 7" EP.. Vogue .... EPV1264 .... 1960 ... £2 ....£5
April In Paris .... LP ...... Columbia .... 33CX10081 .... 1957 ... £25 ....£50
Bird And Diz .... 10" LP Columbia .... 33C9026 .... 1956 ... £40 ....£80 ....with Dizzy Gillesp

Title	Format	Label	Cat. No.	Year			Notes
Bird At St.Nick's	LP	Melodisc	MLP12105	1955	£20	£40	
Bird Is Free	LP	Esquire	32157	1962	£6	£15	
Charlie Parker Big Band	LP	Columbia	33CX10004	1955	£40	£80	
Charlie Parker Big Band	7" EP	HMV	7EG8626	1960	£2	£5	
Charlie Parker Plays	7" EP	Vogue	EPV1011	1955	£2	£5	
Charlie Parker Plays Cole Porter	LP	Columbia	33CX10089	1957	£20	£40	
Charlie Parker Quintet	7" EP	Esquire	EP57	195-	£2	£5	
Charlie Parker Vol.1	10" LP	Vogue	LDE004	1952	£50	£100	
Charlie Parker Vol.2	10" LP	Vogue	LDE016	1953	£50	£100	
Essential Charlie Parker	LP	HMV	CLP1538	1961	£5	£12	
Immortal Charlie Parker Vol.1	LP	London	LTZC15104	1958	£10	£25	
Immortal Charlie Parker Vol.2	LP	London	LTZC15105	1958	£10	£25	
Immortal Charlie Parker Vol.3	LP	London	LTZC15106	1958	£10	£25	
Immortal Charlie Parker Vol.4	LP	London	LTZC15107	1958	£10	£25	
Immortal Charlie Parker Vol.5	LP	London	LTZC15108	1958	£10	£25	
In Sweden	LP	Collector	JGN1002	1960	£6	£15	
In Sweden 1950	LP	Storyville	SLP27	1962	£5	£12	
Jazz Perennial	LP	Columbia	33CX10117	1958	£10	£25	
Magnificent Charlie Parker No.1	7" EP	Columbia	SEB10002	1955	£2	£5	
Magnificent Charlie Parker No.2	7" EP	Columbia	SEB10038	1956	£2	£5	
Magnificent Charlie Parker No.3	7" EP	Columbia	SEB10053	1957	£2	£5	
Now's The Time	7" EP	Columbia	SEB10026	1956	£2	£5	
Parker's Mood	7" EP	Realm	REP4008	1964	£2	£5	
Plays South Of The Border	7" EP	Columbia	SEB10032	1956	£2	£5	
Portrait Of The Bird	LP	Columbia	33SX1555	1963	£4	£10	

PARKER, DAVID

Title	Format	Label	Cat. No.	Year			Notes
David Parker	LP	Polydor	2460101	1971	£30	£60	

PARKER, DEAN & THE REDCAPS

Title	Format	Label	Cat. No.	Year			Notes
Stormy Evening	7"	Decca	F11555	1962	£10	£20	

PARKER, DYON

Title	Format	Label	Cat. No.	Year			Notes
Out On The Highway	LP	Marble Arch	MAL787	1968	£6	£15	

PARKER, EULA

Title	Format	Label	Cat. No.	Year			Notes
Silhouettes	7"	Oriole	CB1411	1957	£2.50	£6	

PARKER, FESS

Title	Format	Label	Cat. No.	Year			Notes
Wringle Wrangle	7"	Oriole	CB1378	1957	£2.50	£6	
Yaller Yaller Gold	7"	Philips	PB654	1957	£2.50	£6	

PARKER, GRAHAM

Title	Format	Label	Cat. No.	Year			Notes
Live At Marble Arch	LP	Vertigo	GP1	1977	£5	£12	promo
Live Sparks	LP	Arista	SP63	1979	£5	£12	US promo

PARKER, JIMMY

Title	Format	Label	Cat. No.	Year			Notes
We Gonna	7"	Top Rank	JAR608	1962	£2	£5	

PARKER, JUNIOR

Title	Format	Label	Cat. No.	Year			Notes
Annie Get Your Yo Yo	7"	Vogue	V9193	1962	£5	£10	
Driving Wheel	LP	Duke	DLP76	1962	£15	£30	US
Goodbye Little Girl	7"	Vocalion	V9275	1966	£5	£10	
Like It Is	LP	Mercury	SMCL20097	1967	£6	£15	
Memorial	LP	Vogue	LDM30163	1973	£4	£10	
Stand By Me	7"	Vogue	V9179	1961	£6	£12	
These Kind Of Blues	7"	Vocalion	VP9256	1966	£6	£12	

PARKER, KEN

Title	Format	Label	Cat. No.	Year			Notes
Change Is Gonna Come	7"	Giant	GN34	1968	£4	£8	Val Bennett B side
Down Low	7"	Island	WI3096	1967	£5	£10	
Help Me Make It Through The Night	7"	Treasure Isle	TI7073	1972	£2	£5	Tommy McCook B side
I Can't Hide	7"	Duke	DU79	1970	£2	£5	Tommy McCook B side
It's Alright	7"	Amalgamated	AMG847	1969	£4	£8	Cobbs B side
Jimmy Brown	LP	Trojan	TRLS80	1974	£5	£12	
Jimmy Brown	7"	Duke Reid	DR2521	1971	£2.50	£6	
Lonely Man	7"	Island	WI3105	1967	£5	£10	Errol Dunkley B side
My Whole World Is Falling Down	7"	Bamboo	BAM1	1969	£2.50	£6	
Only Yesterday	7"	Amalgamated	AMG853	1969	£4	£8	Cobbs B side
See Them A Come	7"	Studio One	SO2001	1967	£6	£12	Mr.Foundation B side

PARKER, KNOCKY

Title	Format	Label	Cat. No.	Year			Notes
Knocky Parker	LP	London	HAU2008	1956	£5	£12	
Knocky Parker Trio	10" LP	London	HBU1044	1956	£5	£12	

PARKER, LEO

Title	Format	Label	Cat. No.	Year			Notes
Let Me Tell You 'Bout It	LP	Blue Note	BLP/BST84087	1961	£20	£40	

PARKER, RAY

Title	Format	Label	Cat. No.	Year			Notes
Ghostbusters	7"	Arista	ARISD580	1984	£4	£8	shaped pic disc
Ghostbusters	12"	Arista	ARIPD12580	1984	£3	£8	luminous pic disc

PARKER, RAYMOND

Title	Format	Label	Cat. No.	Year			Notes
Ring Around The Roses	7"	Sue	WI4024	1966	£6	£12	

PARKER, ROBERT

Title	Format	Label	Cat. No.	Year			Notes
Barefootin'	LP	Island	ILP942	1966	£10	£25	
Barefootin'	7"	Island	WI286	1966	£2.50	£6	chart single
Happy Feet	7"	Island	WI3008	1966	£5	£10	

PARKER, SONNY
My Soul's On Fire .... 7" .... Vogue .... V2392 .... 1956 ... £60 ....£120 ....

PARKER, WINFIELD
Stop Her On Sight .... 7" .... Mojo .... 2093019 .... 1972 ... £1.50 ....£4 ....

PARKING LOT
World Spinning Sadly .... 7" .... Parlophone...... R5779 .... 1969 ... £15 ....£30 ....

PARKINSON, JIMMY
But You	7"	Columbia	DB3876	1957	£1.50	£4	
Great Pretender	7"	Columbia	SCM5236	1956	£6	£12	chart single
In The Middle Of The House	7"	Columbia	DB3833	1956	£5	£10	chart single
Lover's Quarrel	7"	Columbia	DB3808	1956	£5	£10	
Solo	10" LP	Columbia	33S1109	1957	£6	£15	
Walk Hand In Hand	7"	Columbia	SCM5267	1956	£5	£10	chart single
Whatever Lola Wants	7"	Columbia	DB3912	1957	£1.50	£4	

PARKS, BERNICE
Only Love Me .... 7" .... Vogue Coral .... Q72056 .... 1955 ... £4 ....£8

PARKS, SONNY
New Boy In Town .... 7" .... Warner Bros .... WB100 .... 1963 ... £1.50 ....£4

PARKS, VAN DYKE
Number Nine	7"	MGM	MGM1301	1966	£2	£5	
Song Cycle	LP	Warner Bros	WS1727	1968	£5	£12	US

PARLAN, HORACE
Headin' South	LP	Blue Note	BLP/BST84062	1961	£20	£40
Movin' & Groovin'	LP	Blue Note	BLP/BST84028	196-	£25	£50
On The Spur Of The Moment	LP	Blue Note	BLP/BST84074	1961	£20	£40
Speakin' My Piece	LP	Blue Note	BLP/BST84043	196-	£20	£40
Up And Down	LP	Blue Note	BLP/BST84082	1961	£15	£30
Us Three	LP	Blue Note	BLP/BST84037	196-	£20	£40

PARLET
Invasion Of The Booty Snatchers .... LP ...... Casablanca ...... CAL2052 .... 1979 ... £6 ....£15

PARLIAMENT
Chocolate City	LP	Casablanca	CAL2012	1975	£4	£10	
Chocolate City	LP	Casablanca	NBLP7014	1975	£5	£12	
Clones Of Dr.Funkenstein	LP	Casablanca	CAL2003	1976	£5	£12	
Come In Out Of The Rain	7"	Invictus	INV522	1972	£2	£5	
Funkentelechy Vs. The Placebo Syndrome	LP	Casablanca	CALH2021	1978	£4	£10	
Gloryhallastoopid	LP	Casablanca	NBLP7195	1979	£4	£10	US
Live/Funk Earth Tour	LP	Casablanca	CALD5002	1977	£6	£15	double
Mothership Connection	LP	Casablanca	CAL2013	1977	£4	£10	
Mothership Connection	LP	Casablanca	CBC4009	1976	£5	£12	
Motor Booty Affair	LP	Casablanca	CALN2044	1979	£5	£12	
Motor Booty Affair	LP	Casablanca	NBPIX7125	1978	£5	£12	US pic disc
Osmium	LP	Invictus	SVT1004	1971	£25	£50	
Silent Boatman	7"	Invictus	INV513	1971	£2	£5	
Trombipulation	LP	Casablanca	NBLP7294	1981	£4	£10	US
Up For The Down Stroke	LP	Casablanca	CAL2011	1974	£5	£12	
Up For The Down Stroke	LP	Casablanca	NBLP7002	1974	£8	£20	

PARLIAMENTS
I Wanna Testify	7"	Track	604013	1967	£5	£10
I Wanna Testify	7"	Track	604032	1969	£2	£5

PARLOPHONE POPS ORCHESTRA
Rock Around The Clock .... 7" .... Parlophone...... R4250 .... 1956 ... £1.50 ....£4

PARLOUR BAND
Is A Friend .... LP ...... Deram .... SDL10 .... 1972 ... £50 ....£100

PARNELL, JACK
Jack Parnell And His Orchestra	7" EP	Parlophone	GEP8532	1955	£2.50	£6
Jack Parnell Quartet	10" LP	Decca	LF1065	1952	£4	£10
Night Train	7"	Parlophone	MSP6031	1953	£1.50	£4
Trip To Mars	10" LP	Parlophone	PMD1053	1958	£4	£10
Waltzing The Blues	7"	Parlophone	MSP6009	1953	£1.50	£4

PARR, CATHERINE
You Belong To Me .... 7" .... Decca .... F12210 .... 1965 ... £2.50 ....£6

PARRISH & GURVITZ
Parrish & Gurvitz .... LP ...... Regal Zonophone...... SRZA8506 .... 1971 ... £4 ....£10

PARRISH, DEAN
Determination	7"	Stateside	SS550	1966	£15	£30
I'm On My Way	7"	UK	USA2	1975	£1.50	£4
Skate	7"	Stateside	SS580	1967	£7.50	£15
Tell Her	7"	Stateside	SS531	1966	£10	£20

PARRY, SAM
If Sadness Could Sing .... LP ...... Argo .... ZDA155 .... 1972 ... £25 ....£50

PARSONS, ALAN PROJECT

Best Of The Alan Parsons Project	LP	Mobile Fidelity	MFSL1175	1984	£4	£10	US audiophile
I, Robot	LP	Mobile Fidelity	MFSL1084	1982	£4	£10	US audiophile
I, Robot	LP	Mobile Fidelity	MFSL1084	1982	£6	£15	US audiophile (UHQR)
Turn Of A Friendly Card	LP	Arista		1980	£4	£10	US audiophile
Vulture Culture	LP	Arista		1984	£6	£15	US promo pic disc

PARSONS, BILL

All American Boy	7"	London	HL8798	1959	£6	£12	chart single

PARSONS, GRAM

G.P.	LP	Reprise	K44228	1973	£4	£10	
Grievous Angel	LP	Reprise	K54018	1974	£4	£10	
New Soft Shoe	7"	Reprise	K14245	1973	£1.50	£4	

PARTON, DOLLY

Hello I'm Dolly	LP	Monument	MLP8085/ SLP18085	1967	£5	£12	US

PARTON, DOLLY & GEORGE JONES

Dolly Parton And George Jones	LP	Starday	SLP429	1968	£4	£10	US

PARTRIDGE, DON

Blue Eyes	7"	Columbia	DB8416	1968	£1.50	£4	chart single
Breakfast On Pluto	7"	Columbia	DB8538	1969	£1.50	£4	chart single
Colour My World	7"	Columbia	DB8583	1969	£1.50	£4	
Don Partridge	LP	Columbia	SX/SCX6280	1968	£4	£10	
Going To Germany	7"	Columbia	DB8617	1969	£1.50	£4	
Rosie	7"	Columbia	DB8330	1968	£1.50	£4	chart single
Singing Soho Style	7" EP	CFP	CFP001/002	196-	£4	£8	
We Have Ways Of Making You Laugh	7"	Columbia	DB8484	1968	£1.50	£4	
We're All Happy Together	7"	Columbia	DB8723	1970	£1.50	£4	

PARZIVAL

Barock	LP	Telefunken	SLE14685	1972	£4	£10	German
Legend	LP	Teldec	14635	1971	£6	£15	German

PASCALIS, MARIANNA, ROBERT & BESSY

Music Lesson	7"	Power Exchange	PX254	1977	£2	£5	

PASHA

Someone Shot The Lollipop Man	7"	Liberty	LBF15199	1968	£35	£70	

PASSING FANCY

Passing Fancy	LP	Boo	6801	196-	£37.50	£75	US

PASSIONS

I Only Want You	7"	Top Rank	JAR313	1960	£10	£20	
Jackie Brown	7"	Capitol	CL14874	1958	£7.50	£15	
Just To Be With You	7"	Top Rank	JAR224	1959	£10	£20	

PASSPORT

Doldinger Jubilee	LP	Atlantic	K60073	1973	£8	£20	triple

PAST SEVEN DAYS

Raindance	7"	4AD	AD102	1981	£1.50	£4	

PASTEL SIX

Cinnamon Cinder	LP	Zen	1001	1963	£8	£20	US
Cinnamon Cinder	7"	London	HLU9651	1963	£2	£5	
Golden Oldies	LP	Mark56	MLP511	1963	£6	£15	US

PASTELS

Heavens Above	7"	Villa 21	VILLA3	1985	£10	£20	
Heavens Above	7"	Whaam!	WHAAM5	1982	£7.50	£15	
I Wonder Why	7"	Rough Trade	RT137	1983	£6	£12	
I'm Alright With You	12"	Creation	CRE023T	1985	£2.50	£6	
Something Going On	7"	Creation	CRE005	1984	£6	£12	
Truck Train Tractor	12"	Glass	PASTEL001	1987	£2.50	£6	double

PASTIES & CREAM

Pasties & Cream	LP	Sentinel		1971	£6	£15	

PASTORAL SYMPHONY

Love Machine	7"	President	PT202	1968	£4	£8	

PAT & MARIE

I Try Not To Tell You	7"	Ska Beat	JB234	1966	£5	£10	
You're Really Leaving	7"	Ska Beat	JB235	1966	£5	£10	

PAT & ROXIE

Sing To Me	7"	Caribou	CRC2	1965	£2	£5	

PATCHES

Living In America	7"	Warner Bros	K16201	1972	£5	£10	

PATCHWORK

Patchwork	LP	Canon			£50	£100	

PATE, JOHNNY
Jazz Goes Ivy League	10" LP	Parlophone	PMD1057	1958	£10	£25	
Swingin' Flute	10" LP	Parlophone	PMD1072	1959	£10	£25	

PATHETIX
Aleister Crowley	7"	No Records	001	1978	£1.50	£4	

PATHFINDERS
I Love You Caroline	7"	Decca	F12038	1964	£2.50	£6	

PATHFINDERS (2)
Don't You Believe It	7"	Parlophone	R5372	1965	£2	£5	

PATHWAY TO YOUR MIND
Pathway To Your Mind	LP	Major Minor	MM/SMLP19	1968	£25	£50	

PATIENCE & PRUDENCE
Dreamers' Bay	7"	London	HLU8425	1957	£6	£12	
Gonna Get Alomg Without Ya Now	7"	London	HL7017	1957	£2	£5	export
Gonna Get Along Without You Now	7"	London	HLU8369	1957	£7.50	£15	chart single
Smile And A Song	7" EP	London	REU1087	1957	£10	£20	
Tom Thumb's Tune	7"	London	HLU8773	1958	£2.50	£6	
Tonight You Belong To Me	7"	London	HLU8321	1956	£7.50	£15	chart single
You Tattletale	7"	London	HLU8493	1957	£4	£8	

PATRICK, BOBBY BIG SIX
Monkey Time	7"	Decca	F12030	1964	£5	£10	
Shake It Easy Baby	7"	Decca	F11898	1964	£6	£12	
Tenbeat From Star Club Hamburg	7" EP	Decca	DFE8570	1964	£25	£50	

PATRICK, DAN
Tiger Lee	7"	Stateside	SS2004	1967	£2.50	£6	

PATRICK, KENTRICK
Don't Stay Out Late	7"	Island	WI079	1963	£5	£10	
End Of The World	7"	Island	WI104	1963	£5	£10	
Golden Love	7"	Island	WI119	1963	£5	£10	
Goodbye Peggy Darling	7"	Island	WI137	1964	£5	£10	Baba Brooks B side
I Am Wasting Time	7"	Island	WI140	1964	£5	£10	
Man To Man	7"	Island	WI066	1963	£5	£10	
Take Me To The Party	7"	Island	WI132	1963	£5	£10	

PATRON OF THE ARTS
Eleanor Rigby	7"	Page One	POF012	1966	£7.50	£15	

PATSY
Little Flea	7"	Doctor Bird	DB1122	1968	£5	£10	

PATTEN, BRIAN
Brian Patten	LP	Caedmon	TC1300	1970	£10	£25	
Sly Cormorant	LP	Argo	ZSW607	1977	£6	£15	
Vanishing Trick	LP	Tangent	TGS116	1971	£20	£40	

PATTERSON, BOBBY
Broadway Ain't Funky No More	7"	Pama	PM735	1968	£2.50	£6	
Busy Busy Bee	7"	Pama	PM754	1968	£2	£5	
Good Old Days	7"	Pama	PM743	1968	£2	£5	
I'm In Love With You	7"	Action	ACT4604	1972	£4	£8	
My Thing Is Your Thing	7"	Pama	PM773	1969	£2	£5	
T.C.B. Or T.Y.A.	7"	Pama	PM763	1969	£2.50	£6	
Virginia Reel	LP	Leader	LED2053	1973	£5	£12	

PATTERSON, OTTILIE
3000 Years With Ottilie	LP	Marmalade	608011	1969	£6	£15	
Baby Please Don't Go	7"	Columbia	DB7208	1964	£7.50	£15	
Beale Street Blues	7"	Pye	7NJ2015	1958	£1.50	£4	
Bitterness Of Death	7"	Marmalade	598020	1969	£4	£8	
Blues	7" EP	Decca	DFE6303	1956	£4	£8	
I Hate A Man Like You	7"	Decca	F10472	1955	£1.50	£4	
Kay-Cee Rider	7"	Pye	7N15109	1957	£1.50	£4	
Nobody Knows You When You're Down And Out	7"	Decca	F10621	1955	£1.50	£4	
Ottilie	7" EP	Columbia	SEG7915	1959	£2	£5	
That Patterson Girl	7" EP	Polygon	JTE102	1956	£7.50	£15	
That Patterson Girl	7" EP	Pye	NJE1012	1956	£4	£8	
That Patterson Girl Vol.2	7" EP	Pye	NJE1023	1956	£4	£8	
Trombone Cholly	7"	Pye	7NJ2025	1958	£1.50	£4	

PATTERSON'S PEOPLE
Shake Hands With The Devil	7"	Mercury	MF913	1966	£5	£10	

PATTO
Patto's original take on jazz-rock never quite managed to achieve the wide acclaim that it deserved, despite the band having a singer (Mike Patto) possessing one of the classic rock voices and a guitarist (Ollie Halsall) whose blend of technical expertise and imagination made him into the kind of player that other guitarists looked up to. The album "Hold Your Fire" is an oddity in that it exists with two different versions of the A side. The songs are the same, but on one they have a much rougher, rawer sound than on the other. There do not appear to be any visual differences between the two versions of the album, unfortunately.

Hold Your Fire	LP	Vertigo	6360032	1971	£40	£80	spiral label, sleeve pictured in Guide
Patto	LP	Vertigo	6360016	1970	£15	£30	spiral label
Roll Em Smoke Em	LP	Island	ILPS9210	1972	£8	£20	

PATTO, MIKE
Can't Stop Talking About My Baby	7"	Columbia	DB8091	1966	£20	£40

PATTON, ALEXANDER
Li'l Lovin' Sometimes	7"	Capitol	CL15461	1966	£25	£50

PATTON, CHARLIE
Charlie Patton	7" EP.	Heritage	REU4	195-	£7.50	£15

PATTON, JIMMY
Blue Darlin'	LP	Sims	127	1965	£8	£20	US
Make Room For The Blues	LP	Moon	101	196-	£8	£20	US

PATTON, JOHN
Accent On The Blues	LP	Blue Note	BST84340	1969	£10	£25
Along Came John	LP	Blue Note	BLP/BST84130	1963	£20	£40
Got A Good Thing Goin'	LP	Blue Note	BLP/BST84229	1966	£15	£30
Let 'Em Roll	LP	Blue Note	BLP/BST84239	1966	£15	£30
Oh Baby!	LP	Blue Note	BLP/BST84192	1964	£25	£50
That Certain Feeling	LP	Blue Note	BST84281	1968	£10	£25
Understanding	LP	Blue Note	BST84306	1968	£10	£25
Way I Feel	LP	Blue Note	BLP/BST84174	1964	£15	£30

PATTY & THE EMBLEMS
Mixed Up Shook Up Girl	7"	Stateside	SS322	1964	£6	£12

PAUL
Will You Follow Me	7"	Polydor	BM56045	1965	£4	£8

PAUL & PAULA
First Day Back At School	7"	Philips	BF1281	1963	£1.50	£4	
First Quarrel	7"	Philips	BF1256	1963	£1.50	£4	
Hey Paula	7"	Philips	304012BF	1963	£1.50	£4	chart single
Holiday For Teens	LP	Philips	BL7587	1964	£6	£15	
No Other Baby	7"	Philips	BF1380	1964	£1.50	£4	
Sing For Young Lovers	LP	Philips	652026BL	1963	£6	£15	
Something Old Something New	7"	Philips	BF1269	1963	£1.50	£4	
We Go Together	LP	Philips	BL7573	1963	£6	£15	
Young Lovers	7"	Philips	304016BF	1963	£1.50	£4	chart single
Young Lovers	7" EP.	Philips	BBE12539	1963	£10	£20	

PAUL & RITCHIE & THE CRYIN' SHAMES
C'mon Back	7"	Decca	F12483	1966	£30	£60

PAUL & THE JETLINERS
Great Pretender	7"	Rainbow	RAI102	1966	£4	£8
Something On My Mind	7"	Rainbow	RAI105	1966	£4	£8

PAUL, BUNNY
Lovey Dovey	7"	Columbia	SCM5131	1954	£2.50	£6
New Love	7"	Columbia	SCM5102	1954	£2	£5
Please Have Mercy	7"	Capitol	CL14279	1955	£2.50	£6
Song Of The Dreamer	7"	Capitol	CL14368	1955	£1.50	£4
Such A Night	7"	Columbia	SCM5112	1954	£4	£8
Two Castanets	7"	Capitol	CL14304	1955	£1.50	£4
You Came A Long Way From St.Louis	7"	Columbia	SCM5151	1954	£1.50	£4

PAUL, DARLENE
Act Like Nothing Happened	7"	Capitol	CL15344	1964	£5	£10

PAUL, EUGENE
Farewell My Darling	7"	Pama	PS317	1971	£1.50	£4

PAUL, JOHN E.
I Wanna Know	7"	Decca	F12685	1967	£20	£40

PAUL, LES & MARY FORD
Although guitarist Les Paul gained his many hits by playing a bouncy, light pop with his singer wife, Mary Ford, he has an importance in the history of rock that entirely transcends the actual sound of his music. He was a fearless experimentalist in the studio, pioneering the use of multiple over-dubbing and speeded-up tape effects and building the first eight-track tape recorder as early as 1954. And if that was not enough, he also designed the electric guitar that still bears his name and which has played such a major role in the development of blues and heavy rock - persuading the Gibson company to begin mass production of the instrument at a time when the only other commercially available elctric guitar was the Fender Telecaster.

Amukiriki	7"	Capitol	CL14521	1956	£2.50	£6	
At The Save A Penny Super Store	7"	Philips	PB906	1959	£2	£5	
Bewitched	7"	Capitol	CL14839	1958	£2	£5	
Bye Bye Blues	LP	Capitol	T356	1953	£8	£20	US
Bye Bye Blues	10" LP	Capitol	LC6806	1956	£8	£20	
Cimarron	7"	Capitol	CL14593	1956	£2	£5	
Cinco Robles	7"	Capitol	CL14710	1957	£2	£5	
Genuine Love	7"	Capitol	CL14300	1955	£6	£12	
Hitmakers	LP	Capitol	T416	195-	£6	£15	
Hits Of Les And Mary	LP	Capitol	T1476	1960	£5	£12	
Hummin' And Waltzin'	7"	Capitol	CL14738	1957	£1.50	£4	
Hummingbird	7"	Capitol	CL14342	1955	£6	£12	
Jazz Me Blues	7" EP.	Capitol	EAP120740	1965	£4	£8	
Jealous Heart	7"	Philips	PB882	1959	£2	£5	
Jura	7"	Philips	PB1155	1961	£1.50	£4	
Les And Mary	LP	Capitol	T577	195-	£6	£15	US
Les And Mary	10" LP	Capitol	LC6704	1955	£8	£20	
Les Paul And Mary Ford	10" LP	Capitol	LC6701	1955	£8	£20	

Title	Format	Label	Catalogue	Year			Notes
Les Paul Now	LP	Decca	LK4924/PFS4138...	1968	£4	£10	
Lover	LP	Capitol	T1276	1959	£5	£12	
Lover's Luau	LP	Philips	BBL7306	1959	£5	£12	
Mandolino	7"	Capitol	CL14185	1954	£6	£12	
Mister Sandman	7"	Capitol	CL14212	1954	£10	£20	
Mr. And Mrs. Music	7" EP	Capitol	EAP20048	1959	£5	£10	
New Sound Vol.1	LP	Capitol	T226	195-	£8	£20	US
New Sound Vol.1	10" LP	Capitol	LC6514	1951	£10	£25	
New Sound Vol.2	LP	Capitol	T286	195-	£8	£20	US
New Sound Vol.2	10" LP	Capitol	LC6581	1953	£10	£25	
Nola	7" EP	Capitol	EAP120145	1961	£2.50	£6	
Pair Of Fools	7"	Capitol	CL14809	1957	£2.50	£6	
Presenting Les Paul And Mary Ford	7" EP	Capitol	EAP19121	1955	£4	£8	
Put A Ring On My Finger	7"	Philips	PB873	1958	£5	£10	
Runnin' Wild	7"	Capitol	CL14665	1956	£2.50	£6	
Say The Words I Love To Hear	7"	Capitol	CL14577	1956	£2	£5	
Sitting On Top Of The World	7" EP	Capitol	EAP1540	1955	£5	£10	
Small Island	7"	Capitol	CL14858	1958	£1.50	£4	
Song In Blue	7"	Capitol	CL14233	1955	£6	£12	
Strollin' Blues	7"	Capitol	CL14776	1957	£2.50	£6	
Texas Lady	7"	Capitol	CL14502	1956	£4	£8	
Theme From The Threepenny Opera	7"	Capitol	CL14534	1956	£2.50	£6	
Time To Dream	LP	Capitol	T802	1957	£6	£15	

PAULETTE SISTERS

Title	Format	Label	Catalogue	Year			Notes
Dream Boat	7"	Capitol	CL14294	1955	£4	£8	
Ring-A-Dang-A-Do	7"	Capitol	CL14310	1955	£4	£8	
You Win Again	7"	Capitol	CL14347	1955	£4	£8	

PAUL'S DISCIPLES

Title	Format	Label	Catalogue	Year			Notes
See That My Grave Is Kept Clean	7"	Decca	F12081	1965	£7.50	£15	

PAUL'S TROUBLES

Title	Format	Label	Catalogue	Year			Notes
You'll Find Out	7"	Ember	EMBS233	1967	£7.50	£15	

PAUPERS

Title	Format	Label	Catalogue	Year			Notes
Ellis Island	LP	Verve	SVLP6017	1968	£4	£10	
Magic People	LP	Verve	3026	1967	£5	£12	US
Southdown Road	7"	Verve	VS1520	1969	£1.50	£4	
Think I Care	7"	Verve	VS1514	1968	£1.50	£4	

PAVILION, PERCY (CAPTAIN SENSIBLE)

Title	Format	Label	Catalogue	Year			Notes
Cricket EP	7"	Pavilioned In Splendour	PIS1	1983	£1.50	£4	

PAVLOV'S DOG

Title	Format	Label	Catalogue	Year			Notes
St.Louis Hounds	LP	private		197-	£37.50	£75	US

PAX ETERNAL

Title	Format	Label	Catalogue	Year			Notes
Second Chance Mr.Jones	7"	Decca	F13167	1971	£2.50	£6	

PAXTON, GARY

Title	Format	Label	Catalogue	Year			Notes
Stop Twisting Baby	7"	Liberty	LIB55485	1962	£1.50	£4	

PAXTON, TOM

Title	Format	Label	Catalogue	Year			Notes
Ain't That News	LP	Elektra	EKL/EKS7289	1965	£5	£12	
Compleat Tom Paxton Recorded Live	LP	Elektra	EKD2003	1971	£6	£15	double
Crazy John	7"	Elektra	EKSN45064	1969	£1.50	£4	
Jennifer's Rabbit	7"	Elektra	EKSN45021	1967	£1.50	£4	
Last Thing On My Mind	7"	Elektra	EKSN45001	1965	£1.50	£4	
Leaving London	7"	Elektra	EKSN45006	1967	£1.50	£4	
Morning Again	LP	Elektra	EKL/EKS74019	1968	£4	£10	
New Songs For Old Friends	LP	Reprise	K44237	1973	£5	£12	
Number Six	LP	Elektra	EKS74066	1970	£4	£10	chart LP
One Time And One Time Only	7"	Elektra	EKSN45003	1967	£1.50	£4	
Outward Bound	LP	Elektra	EKL/EKS7317	1966	£5	£12	
Ramblin' Boy	LP	Elektra	EKL/EKS7277	1964	£5	£12	
Things I Notice Now	LP	Elektra	EKS74043	1969	£4	£10	
Tom Paxton	7" EP	Elektra	EPK802	1967	£2.50	£6	
Victoria Dines Alone	7"	Elektra	EKSN45045	1969	£1.50	£4	

PAYNE, BENNY

Title	Format	Label	Catalogue	Year			Notes
Sunny Side Up	LP	London	LTZR15103	1957	£10	£25	

PAYNE, CECIL

Title	Format	Label	Catalogue	Year			Notes
Connection	LP	Summit	AJS16	1962	£8	£20	

PAYNE, FREDA

Title	Format	Label	Catalogue	Year			Notes
Band Of Gold	LP	Invictus	SVT1001	1971	£5	£12	
Band Of Gold	7"	Invictus	INV502	1970	£1.50	£4	chart single
Band Of Gold	7"	Invictus	INV533	1973	£4	£8	
Contact	LP	Invictus	SVT1005	1972	£4	£10	
He Who Laughs Last	7"	HMV	POP1091	1962	£4	£8	

PAYNE, LEON

Title	Format	Label	Catalogue	Year			Notes
Americana	LP	Starday	SLP236	1963	£5	£12	US
Leon Payne	LP	Starday	SLP231	1963	£5	£12	US

PEABODY, DAVE

Title	Format	Label	Catalogue	Year			Notes
Peabody Hotel	LP	Village Thing	VTS22	1973	£6	£15	

PEACE, DAVE QUARTET

Good Morning Mr.Blues	LP	Saga	FID2155	1969	£6	£15

PEACHES & HERB

Close Your Eyes	7"	CBS	2711	1967	£1.50	£4
For Your Love	LP	CBS	63119	1967	£4	£10
For Your Love	7"	CBS	2866	1967	£6	£12
Golden Duets	LP	Direction	863263	1968	£4	£10
Let It Be Me	7"	Direction	583415	1968	£2	£5
Let's Fall In Love	LP	CBS	62966	1967	£4	£10
Let's Fall In Love	7"	CBS	202509	1967	£6	£12
Let's Make A Promise	7"	Direction	583829	1968	£1.50	£4
Love Is Strange	7"	Direction	583096	1967	£1.50	£4
Satisfy My Hunger	7"	Direction	584909	1970	£1.50	£4
Soothe Me With Your Love	7"	Direction	585249	1970	£2.50	£6
United	7"	Direction	583548	1968	£1.50	£4
When He Touches Me	7"	Direction	584085	1969	£1.50	£4

PEACOCK, ANNETTE

I'm The One	LP	RCA	SF8255	1972	£6	£15
Live In Paris	LP	Aura		1981	£25	£50

PEACOCK, ANNETTE & PAUL BLEY

Dual Unity	LP	Freedom	2383105	1972	£8	£20
Improvisie	LP	America	30AM6121	197-	£8	£20
Revenge	LP	Polydor	2425043	1971	£20	£40

PEAK FOLK

Peak Folk	LP	Folk Heritage		197-	£8	£20

PEANUT

Peanut was a teenage American girl singer (at least she sounds like a teenager - she features in no rock reference books) whose version of "Home Of The Brave" was played on the radio a few times without becoming a chart hit. Nevertheless, her singing conveys such a sense of angst, of youthful hopes and wishes and love - and frustration in the face of blind adult unreason - that the song is an absolute classic, even if an unheralded one.

Home Of The Brave	7"	Pye	7N15963	1965	£2.50	£6
I Didn't Love Him Anyway	7"	Columbia	DB8104	1967	£1.50	£4
I'm Waiting For The Day	7"	Columbia	DB8032	1966	£1.50	£4
Thank You For The Rain	7"	Pye	7N15901	1965	£1.50	£4

PEANUT BUTTER CONSPIRACY

The Peanut Butter Conspiracy added Mamas and Papas-style harmony vocals on to the instrumental sound of Jefferson Airplane. The combination works brilliantly and the group's best songs are quite delightful, although somehow the group failed to find the success that they should have.

Back In L.A.	7"	London	HLH10290	1969	£4	£8	
For Children Of All Ages	LP	Challenge	2000	1968	£8	£20	US
Great Conspiracy	LP	CBS	63277	1968	£8	£20	
Is Spreading	LP	Columbia	CL2654/CS9495	1967	£8	£20	US
It's A Happening Thing	7"	CBS	2981	1967	£2.50	£6	
Turn On A Friend	7"	CBS	3543	1968	£2.50	£6	

PEARCE, BOB BLUES BAND

Blues Crusade	LP	Avenue	BEV1054	1968	£5	£12

PEARL JAM

Ten	LP	Epic	4688840	1992	£4	£10	pic disc

PEARLS BEFORE SWINE

Balaklava	LP	Fontana	STL5503	1968	£8	£20
Beautiful Lies You Could Live	LP	Reprise	RSLP6467	1971	£6	£15
City Of Gold	LP	Reprise	RSLP6442	1971	£6	£15
One Nation Underground	LP	Fontana	STL5505	1967	£8	£20
These Things Too	LP	Reprise	RSLP6364	1969	£6	£15
Use Of Ashes	LP	Reprise	RSLP6405	1970	£6	£15

PEARSE, JOHN

John Pearse	LP	XTRA	XTRA1056	1968	£5	£12
Teach Yourself Folk Guitar	LP	Saga	XID5503	1963	£6	£15

PEARSON, BUSTER

Big Funky	7"	Action	ACT4612	1973	£1.50	£4

PEARSON, DUKE

How Insensitive	LP	Blue Note	BST84344	1969	£5	£12
Introducing Duke Pearson's Big Band	LP	Blue Note	BST84276	1968	£6	£15
Merry Ole Soul	LP	Blue Note	BST84323	1969	£6	£15
Now Hear This	LP	Blue Note	BST84308	1969	£5	£12
Phantom	LP	Blue Note	BST84293	1968	£5	£12
Right Touch	LP	Blue Note	BST84267	1968	£6	£15
Sweet Honey Bee	LP	Blue Note	BLP/BST84252	1967	£10	£25
Tender Feelin's	LP	Blue Note	BLP/BST84035	196-	£20	£40
Wahoo	LP	Blue Note	BLP/BST84191	1965	£10	£25

PEARSON, JOHNNY

Rat Catcher's Theme	7"	Columbia	DB7851	1966	£2.50	£6

PEARSON, KEITH

Right Hand Band	LP	Eron	014	1976	£4	£10

PEARSON, RONNIE

Teenage Fancy	7"	HMV	POP489	1958	£75	£150

PEASANTS
Got Some Lovin' For You Baby .... 7" ...... Columbia .... DB7642 .... 1965 ... £25 .... £50 ....

PEBBLES
First Time Loving .... 7" ...... Parlophone..... R5921 .... 1971 ... £2 .... £5 ....
Goodnight Ma .... 7" ...... Parlophone..... R5900 .... 1971 ... £2.50 .... £6 ....
Incredible George .... 7" ...... Decca .... F22944 .... 1969 ... £4 .... £8 ....
Stand Up And Be Counted .... 7" ...... Deram .... DM305 .... 1970 ... £2 .... £5 ....

PEBBLES (2)
Huma La La La La .... 7" EP.. President .... PRC512 .... 196- ... £4 .... £8 .... French

PEDDLERS
Birthday .... LP ..... CBS .... 63682 .... 1969 ... £4 .... £10 .... chart LP
Free Wheelers .... LP ..... CBS .... (S)BPG63183 ... 1968 ... £4 .... £10 .... chart LP
Georgia On My Mind .... LP ..... Philips .... 6386066 .... 1971 ... £4 .... £10 ....
Live At The Pickwick .... LP ..... Philips .... (S)BL7768 .... 1967 ... £8 .... £20 ....
Suite London .... LP ..... Philips .... 6308102 .... 1972 ... £4 .... £10 ....
Three For All .... LP ..... Philips .... 6308028 .... 1970 ... £5 .... £12 ....
Three In A Cell .... LP ..... CBS .... 63411 .... 1968 ... £4 .... £10 ....

PEDECIN, MIKE QUINTET
Musical Medicine .... LP ..... Apollo .... LP484 .... 1957 ... £25 .... £50 .... US
When The Cats Come Twistin' In .... 7" ...... HMV .... POP1001 .... 1962 ... £1.50 .... £4 ....

PEDRICKS, BOBBY
White Bucks And Saddle Shoes .... 7" ...... London .... HLX8740 .... 1958 ... £12.50 .... £25 ....

PEEBLES, ANN
I Can't Stand The Rain .... LP ..... London .... SHU8468 .... 1974 ... £5 .... £12 ....
Part Time Love .... LP ..... Hi .... HL32059 .... 1971 ... £6 .... £15 .... US
Straight From The Heart .... LP ..... London .... SHU8434 .... 1972 ... £5 .... £12 ....
Tellin' It .... LP ..... London .... SHU8490 .... 1976 ... £4 .... £10 ....
This Is .... LP ..... Hi .... HL32053 .... 1969 ... £6 .... £15 .... US

PEEL, DAVID & LOWER EAST SIDE
American Revolution .... LP ..... Elektra .... EKS74069 .... 1970 ... £6 .... £15 ....
American Revolution .... LP ..... Elektra .... K42074 .... 1972 ... £4 .... £10 ....
Have A Marijuana .... LP ..... Elektra .... EKL/EKS74032 ... 1968 ... £6 .... £15 ....
Pope Smokes Dope .... LP ..... Apple .... SW3391 .... 1972 ... £8 .... £20 .... US

PEEL, JOHN
John Peel has made many cameo appearances on other people's records - the odd spoken line, the occasional burst of jew's harp - but "Archive Things", which is credited to him, contains not a single sound of Peel. Instead, the record is a compilation of short world music extracts that were included in John Peel's wide-ranging "Night Ride" radio programme. There are some fascinating noises to be heard here, and as a sixties artefact, the record is almost as essential as "Sgt.Pepper", if rather less celebrated.
Archive Things .... LP ..... BBC .... REC68M .... 1970 ... £8 .... £20 ....

PEELERS
Banished Misfortune .... LP ..... Polydor .... 2460165 .... 1972 ... £100 .... £200 ....

PEELS
Juanita Banana .... LP ..... Karate .... 5402 .... 1966 ... £8 .... £20 .... US
Juanita Banana .... 7" ...... Stateside .... SS513 .... 1966 ... £2.50 .... £6 ....
Time Marches On .... 7" ...... Audio Fidelity.. AFSP527 .... 196- ... £5 .... £10 ....

PEENUTS
Theme From The Monkees .... 7" ...... Ember .... EMBS242 .... 1967 ... £1.50 .... £4 ....

PEEP SHOW
Esprit De Corps .... 7" ...... Polydor .... BM52226 .... 1968 ... £5 .... £10 ....
Mazy .... 7" ...... Polydor .... 56196 .... 1967 ... £30 .... £60 ....

PEEPS
Gotta Get A Move On .... 7" ...... Philips .... BF1478 .... 1966 ... £4 .... £8 ....
Now Is The Time .... 7" ...... Philips .... BF1421 .... 1965 ... £5 .... £10 ....
Tra La La .... 7" ...... Philips .... BF1509 .... 1966 ... £4 .... £8 ....
What Can I Say .... 7" ...... Philips .... BF1443 .... 1965 ... £5 .... £10 ....

PEG LEG SAM
Last Medicine Show .... LP ..... Flyright .... LP507/8 .... 1974 ... £5 .... £12 .... double

PEGG, BOB
Ancient Maps .... LP ..... Transatlantic ... TRA299 .... 1975 ... £6 .... £15 ....
Bob Pegg & Nick Strutt .... LP ..... Transatlantic ... TRA265 .... 1973 ... £6 .... £15 ....
Shipbuilder .... LP ..... Transatlantic ... TRA280 .... 1974 ... £6 .... £15 ....

PEGG, BOB & CAROLANNE
He Came From The Mountains .... LP ..... Trailer .... LER3016 .... 1971 ... £8 .... £20 ....

PEGG, CAROLANNE
Carolanne Pegg .... LP ..... Transatlantic ... TRA266 .... 1973 ... £35 .... £70 ....

PEGGY'S LEG
Grinilla .... LP ..... Bunch .... BAN2001 .... 1973 ... £100 .... £200 ....
William Tell Overture .... 7" ...... Bunch .... 1973 ... £10 .... £20 ....

PEIFFER, BERNARD
Bernard Peiffer .... LP ..... Felsted .... PDL85022 .... 1956 ... £5 .... £12 ....
Bernard Peiffer Trio .... LP ..... Top Rank .... 30025 .... 1960 ... £4 .... £10 ....
Bernard Peiffer Trio .... 10" LP Felsted .... EDL87016 .... 1955 ... £10 .... £25 ....

Orchestra	10" LP	Felsted	EDL87011	1955	£10	£25	
Piano A La Mood	LP	Brunswick	LAT8262	1958	£5	£12	
Trio	10" LP	Felsted	EDL87013	1955	£10	£25	

PELL, DAVE

Dave Pell Octet	LP	London	HAK2021	1957	£5	£12	
I Had The Craziest Dream	LP	Capitol	T925	1958	£4	£10	
Irving Berlin Gallery	10" LP	London	HAPB1020	1954	£20	£40	
Love Story	LP	London	LTZK15082	1957	£10	£25	
Rodgers And Hart Gallery	10" LP	London	HAPB1034	1955	£15	£30	

PELL MELL

From The New World	LP	Philips	6305193	1975	£4	£10	German
Marburg	LP	Bacillus	BLPS19090	1972	£5	£12	German
Marburg	LP	Bellaphon	BAC2008	1974	£4	£10	German
Rhapsody	LP	Venus	VB761PMAB	1976	£4	£10	German

PEMBROKE, JIM

Corporal Cauliflower's Mental Functions	LP	Love	LRLP214	1977	£8	£20	Swedish
Hot Thumbs O'Riley	LP	Charisma	CAS1071	1973	£8	£20	
Pigworm	LP	Love	LRLP103	1974	£8	£20	Swedish
Wicked Ivory	LP	Love	LRLP52	1972	£8	£20	Swedish

PENDARVIS, TRACY

South Bound Line	7"	London	HLS9213	1960	£6	£12	
Thousand Guitars	7"	London	HLS9059	1960	£6	£12	

PENDLEFOLK

Pendlefolk	LP	Folk Heritage	FHR007	1970	£6	£15	

PENETRATION

Race Against Time	LP	Clifdayn	PEN1	1979	£4	£10	

PENETRATION (2)

Aquarian Symphony	LP	Higher Key	33071	1974	£30	£60	US

PENGUIN CAFE ORCHESTRA

Music From The Penguin Cafe	LP	Obscure	OBS7	1976	£4	£10	

PENGUINS

The Penguins' "Earth Angel" is arguably the definitive doo wop performance, although the UK sales of the original issue were minimal. In consequence, this is now one of the most valuable London recordings of all. The later "Memories Of El Monte" is collectable largely on account of its having been written by Frank Zappa and Ray Collins.

Cool Cool Penguins	LP	Dooto	DTL242	1959	£75	£150	US
Earth Angel	7"	London	HL8114	1955	£700	£1000	gold label
Memories Of El Monte	7"	Original Sound	27	1962	£20	£40	US

PENN, DAWN

Long Days, Short Nights	7"	Rio	R113	1967	£4	£8	
You Don't Love Me	7"	Studio One	SO2030	1967	£6	£12	

PENN, TONY

That's What I Like	7"	Starlite	ST45083	1962	£10	£20	

PENNY, HANK

Bloodshot Eyes	7"	Parlophone	MSP6202	1956	£12.50	£25	

PENNY PEEPS

I See The Morning	7"	Liberty	LBF15114	1968	£4	£8	
Model Village	7"	Liberty	LBF15053	1968	£4	£30	

PENROSE, CHARLES

Adventures Of A Laughing Policeman	7" EP	Columbia	SEG7743	1957	£2	£5	
Laughing Policeman	7"	Columbia	DB8959	1972	£1.50	£4	

PENTAD

Don't Throw It All Away	7"	Parlophone	R5368	1965	£4	£8	
It Better Be Me	7"	Parlophone	R5424	1966	£4	£8	
Silver Dagger	7"	Parlophone	R5288	1965	£7.50	£15	

PENTAGONS

To Be Loved	7"	London	HLU9333	1961	£12.50	£25	

PENTANGLE

Basket Of Light	LP	Transatlantic	TRA205	1969	£4	£10	chart LP
Cruel Sister	LP	Transatlantic	TRA228	1970	£5	£12	chart LP, gatefold sleeve
Light Flight	7"	Transatlantic	BIG128	1969	£1.50	£4	chart single
Once I Had A Sweetheart	7"	Transatlantic	BIG124	1969	£1.50	£4	chart single
Pentangle	LP	Transatlantic	TRA162	1968	£6	£15	chart LP
Reflections	LP	Transatlantic	TRA240	1971	£5	£12	gatefold sleeve
Solomon's Seal	LP	Reprise	K44197	1972	£15	£30	
Sweet Child	LP	Transatlantic	TRA178	1968	£8	£20	double
Travellin' Song	7"	Transatlantic	BIG109	1968	£2	£5	

PEOPLE

Both Sides Of People	LP	Capitol	ST151	1969	£10	£25	US
I Love You	LP	Capitol	ST2924	1968	£10	£25	US
In Ancient Times	7"	Deram	DM346	1971	£4	£8	
Somebody Tell Me My Name	7"	Capitol	CL15553	1968	£2.50	£6	

623

There Are People And There Are People	LP	Paramount	PAS5013	1970	£8	£20	US
Ulla	7"	Capitol	CL15599	1969	£2.50	£6	

PEOPLE BAND
People Band	LP	Transatlantic	TRA214	1970	£8	£20

PEOPLE'S CHOICE
I Like To Do It	7"	Mojo	2092024	1971	£2	£5

PEOPLES, TOMMY
Tommy Peoples	LP	Eireann	CL13	1976	£8	£20

PEOPLES, TOMMY & DAITHI SPROULE
Iron Man	LP	Shanachie	79044	1985	£5	£12	US

PEOPLES, TOMMY & PAUL BRADY
High Part Of The Road	LP	Shanachie	29003	1976	£5	£12	US

PEPPER
We'll Make It Together	7"	Pye	7N17569	1968	£4	£8

PEPPER, ART
Art Pepper Quartet	LP	London	LZU14038	1956	£15	£30
Art Pepper Quartet	10" LP	Vogue	LDE067	1954	£25	£50
Gettin' Together	LP	Contemporary	LAC12262	1961	£8	£20
Meets The Rhythm Section	LP	Contemporary	LAC12066	1958	£8	£20
Modern Jazz Classics	LP	Contemporary	LAC12229	1960	£8	£20

PEPPER, JIM
Pepper's Pow Wow	LP	Atlantic	2400149	1971	£6	£15

PEPPER, KEN
Just A Little At A Time	7"	Top Rank	JAR535	1961	£1.50	£4

PEPPERMINT CIRCUS
All The King's Horses	7"	Olga	OLE007	1967	£1.50	£4
Let Me Go	7"	A&M	AMS778	1970	£1.50	£4
One Thing Can Lead To Another	7"	A&M	AMS765	1969	£2	£5

PEPPERMINT, DANNY
Maybe Tomorrow	7"	London	HLL9614	1962	£1.50	£4	
One More Time	7"	London	HLL9516	1962	£1.50	£4	
Peppermint Twist	7"	London	HLL9478	1961	£2	£5	chart single
Twist With Danny Peppermint	LP	London	HAL2438	1962	£4	£10	

PEPPERMINT RAINBOW
Pink Lemonade	7"	MCA	MU1034	1968	£2.50	£6
Rosemary	7"	MCA	MU1091	1969	£2	£5
Will You Be Staying After Sunday	7"	MCA	MU1076	1969	£2	£5

PEPPERMINT TROLLEY COMPANY
Peppermint Trolley Company	LP	Acta	A38007	1968	£8	£20	US

PEPPI
I Never Danced Before	7"	Decca	F11638	1963	£1.50	£4
Pistol Packin' Mama	7"	Decca	F11991	1964	£2	£5
Skip	7"	Decca	F12055	1965	£1.50	£4

PERCELLS
Cheek To Cheek	7"	HMV	POP1154	1963	£1.50	£4

PERCEWOOD'S ONAGRAM
Ameurope	LP	Onagram	PO1004	1974	£4	£10	German
Lessons For Virgins	LP	Virgin	AR6601	1971	£8	£20	German
Percewood's Onagram	LP	Virgin	PO1	1970	£4	£10	German
Tropical Brainforest	LP	Virgin	AR6602	1972	£4	£10	German

PERCIVAL, LANCE
Shame And Scandal In The Family	7"	Parlophone	R5335	1965	£1.50	£4	chart single

PERE UBU
Art Of Walking	LP	Rough Trade	ROUGH14	1980	£4	£10	with 'Miles' & 'Arabia'
Fabulous Sequel	7"	Chrysalis	CHS2372	1979	£2	£5	
Final Solution	7"	Hearthan	HR102	1976	£37.50	£75	US
Modern Dance	LP	Blank	001	1978	£6	£15	
Modern Dance	LP	Mercury	910052	1978	£4	£10	
Modern Dance	7"	Hearthan	HR104	1977	£15	£30	US
Street Waves	7"	Hearthan	HR103	1976	£7.50	£15	US
Thirty Seconds Over Tokyo	7"	Hearthan	HR101	1975	£25	£50	US
Thirty Seconds Over Tokyo	7"	Hearthan	HR101	1975	£12.50	£25	US, without PS

PEREGRINE
Songs Of Mine	LP	Westwood		197-	£35	£70

PERFECT, CHRISTINE
Christine Perfect was pianist and vocalist with Chicken Shack and since the songs that she led were always the best that the group produced, it is not surprising that her solo LP is a particularly good example of British blues. When Peter Green left Fleetwood Mac, Christine Perfect was drafted in as his replacement, when she began to use her married name, Christine McVie.

Christine Perfect	LP	Blue Horizon	763860	1970	£15	£30
I'm Too Far Gone	7"	Blue Horizon	573172	1970	£4	£8
When You Say	7"	Blue Horizon	573165	1969	£2.50	£6

PERFECT PEOPLE
House In The Country .... 7" ...... MCA .... MU1079 .... 1969 ... £4 .... £8 ....

PERFORMERS
I Can't Stop You .... 7" ...... Action .... ACT4552 .... 1969 ... £2.50 ...... £6 ....

PERIGEO
Abbiamo Tutti Un Blues Da Plangere ...	LP	RCA		1973 ...	£8	£20	Italian
Attraverso Il Parigeo	LP	RCA	NL33039	1977 ...	£6	£15	Italian
Azimut	LP	RCA	PSL10555	1972 ...	£8	£20	Italian
Genealogia	LP	RCA		1974 ...	£8	£20	Italian
La Valle Del Tepli	LP	RCA		1975 ...	£6	£15	Italian
Non E Poi Cosi Lontano	LP	RCA		1976 ...	£6	£15	Italian

PERISHERS
How Does It Feel .... 7" ...... Fontana .... TF965 .... 1968 ... £7.50 ...... £15 ....

PERKINS, BILL
Just Friends .... LP ..... Vogue .... LAE12088 .... 1958 ... £10 ...... £25 ....
On Stage .... LP ..... Vogue .... LAE12078 .... 1958 ... £8 ...... £20 ....

PERKINS, CARL
All Mama's Children	7"	CBS	4991	1970 ...	£1.50 ...	£4	
Any Way The Wind Blows	7"	Philips	PB1179	1961 ...	£5 ...	£10	
Big Bad Blues	7"	Brunswick	05909	1964 ...	£2 ...	£5	...... with The Nashville Teens
Blue Suede Shoes	7"	London	HLS10192	1968 ...	£2 ...	£5	
Blue Suede Shoes	7"	London	HLU8271	1956 ...	£50 ...	£100	...... chart single
Boppin' The Blues	7"	CBS	63826	1970 ...	£4 ...	£10	...... with NRBQ
Country Boy's Dream	LP	London	HAP/SHP8366	1968 ...	£5 ...	£12	
Country Boy's Dream	7"	London	HLP7125	1968 ...	£5 ...	£10	...... export
Country Boy's Dream	7"	Stateside	SS599	1967 ...	£2.50 ...	£6	
Dance Album	LP	Sun	LP1225	1957 ...	£150 ...	£250	...... US
Dance Album (Teen Beat)	LP	London	HAS2202	1959 ...	£30 ...	£60	...... sleeve pictured in Guide
Dixie Fried	7"	London	HLS10192	1968 ...	£30 ...	£60	...... demo
Glad All Over	7"	London	HLS8527	1957 ...	£30 ...	£60	
Gone, Gone, Sone	7"	Sun	224	1955 ...	£25 ...	£50	...... US
Help Me Find My Baby	7"	Brunswick	05905	1964 ...	£2.50 ...	£6	
King Of Rock	LP	CBS	63309	1968 ...	£5 ...	£12	
Lake County Cotton Country	7"	Spark	SRL1009	1968 ...	£2.50 ...	£6	
Matchbox	7"	London	HLS8408	1957 ...	£50 ...	£100	
Monkeyshine	7"	Brunswick	05923	1964 ...	£4 ...	£8	
Movie Magg	7"	Flip	501	1955 ...	£150 ...	£250	...... US
One Ticket To Loneliness	7"	Philips	PB983	1959 ...	£5 ...	£10	
Restless	7"	CBS	3932	1969 ...	£2 ...	£5	
Teen Beat	LP	Sun	LP1225	1961 ...	£75 ...	£150	...... US
That's Right	7"	London	HLS8608	1958 ...	£30 ...	£60	
Whole Lotta Carl Perkins	LP	CBS	52305	1962 ...	£5 ...	£12	
Whole Lotta Shakin'	LP	Columbia	CL1234	1958 ...	£50 ...	£100	...... US

PERKINS, GEORGE
Keep On Trying .... 7" ...... Hit And Run .... 5003 .... 197- ... £1.50 ...... £4 ....

PERKINS, JOE
Little Eefin Annie .... 7" ...... London .... HLU9794 .... 1963 ... £1.50 ...... £4 ....
Wrapped Up In Your Love .... 7" ...... Mojo .... 2092047 .... 1972 ... £1.50 ...... £4 ....

PERKINS, LASCELLES
Creation	7"	Blue Beat	BB41	1961 ...	£5 ...	£10	
I'm So Grateful	7"	Ska Beat	JB175	1964 ...	£5 ...	£10	
Tango Lips	7"	Island	WI038	1963 ...	£5 ...	£10	
Tell It All Brothers	7"	Banana	BA317	1970 ...	£2.50 ...	£6	...... Sound Dimension B side

PERKINS, POLLY
Girls Are At It Again .... 7" ...... Decca .... F11583 .... 1963 ... £1.50 ...... £4 ....

PERMANENTS
O Dear, What Can The Matter Be ..... 7" ...... London .... HLU9803 .... 1963 ... £1.50 ...... £4 ....

PERRIN, PAT
Over You .... 7" ...... Island .... WI3115 .... 1968 ... £5 .... £10 .... Lloyd Terrell B side

PERRINE, PEP
Live And In Person .... LP ..... Hideout .... 1004 .... 1968 ... £50 ...... £100 .... US

PERRI'S
Perri-Lee .... 7" ...... Oriole .... CB1481 .... 1959 ... £1.50 ...... £4 ....

PERRY, JEFF
Love Don't Come No Stronger .... 7" ...... Arista .... ARIST51 .... 1976 ... £2 ...... £5 ....

PERRY, LEE
Africa Blood	LP	Trojan	TRL166	1979 ...	£5 ...	£12	
Bad Minded People	7"	Port-O-Jam	PJ4003	1964 ...	£5 ...	£10	...... Tommy McCook B side
Chatty Chatty Woman	7"	Port-O-Jam	PJ4010	1964 ...	£5 ...	£10	...... Tommy McCook B side
Country Girl	7"	Island	WI223	1965 ...	£5 ...	£10	
Doctor Dick	7"	Island	WI292	1966 ...	£6 ...	£12	.. Soul Brothers B side

Just Keep It Up	7"	Island	WI259	1965	£6	£12	Roland Alphonso B side
Kill Them All	7"	Upsetter	US325	1970	£2	£5	
Man And Wife	7"	R&B	JB106	1963	£6	£12	
Never Get Weary	7"	Island	WI118	1963	£6	£12	Tommy McCook B side
Old For New	7"	R&B	JB104	1963	£6	£12	
Open Up	7"	Ska Beat	JB215	1965	£5	£10	Roland Alphonso B side
People Funny Boy	7"	Doctor Bird	DB1146	1968	£5	£10	Burt Walters B side
Please Don't Go	7"	Island	WI210	1965	£6	£12	
Prince In The Dark	7"	R&B	JB102	1963	£6	£12	
Revolution Dub	LP	Cactus	CTLP112	1979	£5	£12	
Roast Duck	7"	Ska Beat	JB201	1965	£5	£10	
Royalty	7"	R&B	JB135	1964	£6	£12	
Rub And Squeeze	7"	Island	WI298	1966	£5	£10	Soul Brothers B side
Run For Cover	7"	Doctor Bird	DB1073	1967	£5	£10	
Trial And Crosses	7"	Ska Beat	JB203	1965	£5	£10	
Uncle Desmond	7"	Trojan	TR644	1968	£4	£8	
Upsetter	LP	Trojan	TTL13	1969	£8	£20	
Upsetter	7"	Amalgamated	AMG808	1968	£4	£8	
Upsetter Again	LP	Trojan	TTL28	1970	£8	£20	
Whop Whop Man	7"	Doctor Bird	DB1098	1967	£5	£10	
Wishes Of The Wicked	7"	Ska Beat	JB212	1965	£5	£10	
Woodman	7"	Ska Beat	JB251	1966	£5	£10	
Yakety Yak	7"	Upsetter	US324	1969	£2.50	£6	

PERRY, MAL
That's When Your Heartaches Begin	7"	Fontana	H133	1958	£1.50	£4
Things I Didn't Say	7"	Fontana	H157	1958	£1.50	£4
Too Young To Love	7"	Fontana	H149	1958	£1.50	£4

PERRY SISTERS
Willie Boy	7"	Brunswick	05802	1959	£7.50	£15

PERRY, STEVE
Crooked Little Man	7"	Decca	F11895	1964	£1.50	£4	
Ginny Come Lately	7"	Decca	F11462	1962	£1.50	£4	
My Dad	7"	Decca	F11656	1963	£1.50	£4	
Step By Step	7"	HMV	POP745	1960	£1.50	£4	chart single
Young And In Love	7"	Decca	F11526	1962	£1.50	£4	

PERSEPHONE, BILLY
Billy Persephone	LP	Orion		1972	£15	£30	US

PERSIANS
I Only Have Eyes For You	7"	Pama	PM772	1969	£1.50	£4

PERSIMMON'S PECULIAR SHADES
Watchmaker	7"	Major Minor	MM554	1968	£6	£12

PERSONALITIES
Hey Little Girl	7"	Ska Beat	JB222	1965	£5	£10
Push It Down	7"	Blue Beat	BB354	1965	£5	£10
Suffering	7"	Dice	CC30	1965	£5	£10

PERSUADERS
Surfer's Nightmare	LP	Saturn	SAT(S)5000	1963	£20	£40	US

PERSUADERS (2)
Thin Line Between Love And Hate	7"	Atlantic	2091164	1971	£1.50	£4

PERSUASIONS
Acappella	LP	Straight	STS1062	1970	£10	£25	
Party In The Woods	7"	Minit	MLF11017	1969	£2.50	£6	
Street Corner Symphony	LP	Island	ILPS9201	1972	£5	£12	
We Came To Play	LP	Capitol	ST791	1971	£5	£12	US

PERSUASIONS (2)
Big Brother	7"	Columbia	DB7700	1965	£7.50	£15
I'll Go Crazy	7"	Columbia	DB7560	1965	£6	£12
La La La La La	7"	Columbia	DB7859	1966	£7.50	£15

PERT, MORRIS
Book Of Love/ Fragmenti I/ Ultimate Decay	LP	Chantry	CHT007	1982	£25	£50
Luminos/ Chromosphere/ 4 Japanese Verses	LP	Chantry	ABM21	1975	£30	£60
Luminos/ Chromosphere/ 4 Japanese Verses	LP	Chantry	CHT001	198-	£25	£50

PERTH COUNTY CONSPIRACY
Alive	LP	Columbia	GES90037		£6	£15	US double
Does Not Exist	LP	Columbia	ELS375	1969	£10	£25	Canadia

PERTWEE, JON
Who Is The Doctor?	7"	Purple	PUR111	1972	£2.50	£6

PESKY GEE
Exclamation Mark	LP	Pye	NSPL18293	1969	£20	£40
Where Is My Mind	7"	Pye	7N17708	1969	£7.50	£15

PET SHOP BOYS

Title	Format	Label	Cat. No.	Year			Notes
Actually	LP	Parlophone	PCSD104	1987	£25	£50	blue vinyl
Actually	LP	Parlophone	PCSD104	1987	£20	£40	clear vinyl
Always On My Mind	CD-s	Parlophone	CDR6171	1987	£2.50	£6	
Always On My Mind (Dance Mix)	12"	Parlophone	12RS6171	1987	£4	£10	gatefold PS
Always On My Mind (Phil Harding Remix)	12"	Parlophone	12RX6171	1987	£4	£10	
Domino Dancing	CD-s	Parlophone	CDR6190	1988	£4	£10	
Domino Dancing (Remix)	12"	Parlophone	12RX6190	1988	£4	£10	
Heart	CD-s	Parlophone	CDR6177	1988	£2.50	£6	
Heart (Julian Mendelsohn Remix)	12"	Parlophone	12RX6177	1988	£4	£10	
It's A Sin	CD-s	Parlophone	CDR6158	1987	£2.50	£6	
It's A Sin	cass-s	Parlophone	TCR6158	1987	£2.50	£6	
It's A Sin	12"	Parlophone	12R6158	1987	£3	£8	double sleeve
It's A Sin (Ian Levine Remix)	12"	Parlophone	12RX6158	1987	£4	£10	
It's Alright	10"	Parlophone	10R6220	1989	£2.50	£6	with poster
Left To My Own Devices	CD-s	Parlophone	CDR6198	1988	£2.50	£6	
Love Comes Quickly	10"	Parlophone	10R6116	1986	£15	£30	with poster
Love Comes Quickly (Dance Mix)	12"	Parlophone	12R6116	1986	£2.50	£6	
Love Comes Quickly (Dance Mix)	12"	Parlophone	12R6116	1986	£4	£10	cut out sleeve
Opportunities	7"	Parlophone	R6097	1985	£7.50	£15	2 different mixes
Opportunities	12"	Parlophone	12R6097	1985	£8	£20	
Opportunities (Version Latina)	12"	Parlophone	12RA6097	1985	£15	£30	
Paninaro	12"	Parlophone	2015626	1987	£15	£30	Italian
Rent	CD-s	Parlophone	CDR6168	1987	£3	£8	
Suburbia	cass-s	Parlophone	TCR6140	1986	£3	£8	2 versions
Suburbia	7"	Parlophone	RD6140	1986	£4	£8	double
Suburbia	12"	Parlophone	12R6140	1986	£3	£8	double sleeve
West End Girls	7"	Epic	A4292	1984	£12.50	£25	
West End Girls	12"	Epic	TA4292	1984	£20	£40	
West End Girls (Dance Mix)	12"	Parlophone	12R6115	1985	£3	£8	cut-out sleeve with pic labels
West End Girls (Shep Pettibone Mastermix)	12"	Parlophone	12RA6115	1986	£4	£10	2 sleeves
West End Girls (Untitled Remix)	10"	Parlophone	10R6115	1985	£15	£30	round sleeve
What Have I Done To Deserve This	CD-s	Parlophone	CDR6163	1987	£3	£8	

PETARDS

Title	Format	Label	Cat. No.	Year			Notes
Deeper Blue	LP	Europa	E313	1968	£8	£20	German
Hitshock	LP	Liberty	LBS83325	1969	£8	£20	German
Pet Arts	LP	Liberty	LBS83481/2	1971	£8	£20	German double
Petards	LP	Liberty	LBS83204	1969	£8	£20	German

PETER & GORDON

Title	Format	Label	Cat. No.	Year			Notes
Baby I'm Yours	7"	Columbia	DB7729	1965	£1.50	£4	chart single
Chantent En Francais	7" EP	Columbia	ESRF1726	1965	£10	£20	French
Hits Of Nashville	LP	Capitol	(S)T2430	1966	£5	£12	US
Hot, Cold & Custard	LP	Capitol	(S)T2882	1968	£5	£12	US
Hurtin' 'n' Lovin'	LP	Columbia	33SX1761/ SCX3565	1965	£5	£12	
I Can Remember	7"	Columbia	DB8585	1969	£1.50	£4	
I Don't Want To See You Again	LP	Capitol	(S)T2220	1964	£5	£12	US
I Don't Want To See You Again	7"	Columbia	DB7356	1964	£1.50	£4	
I Don't Want To See You Again (Cilla Black B side)	7"	Capitol	PRO2720	1964	£15	£30	US promo - Paul McCartney & John Lennon intros
I Feel Like Going Out	7"	Columbia	DB8398	1968	£1.50	£4	
I Go To Pieces	LP	Capitol	(S)T2324	1965	£5	£12	US
I Go To Pieces	LP	Columbia	SCXC25	1965	£8	£20	export
I Go To Pieces	7"	Columbia	DB7407	1964	£1.50	£4	
I Go To Pieces	7" EP	Columbia	ESRF1677	1965	£6	£12	French
In London For Tea	LP	Capitol	(S)T2747	1967	£5	£12	US
In Touch	LP	Columbia	33SX1660/ SCX3532	1964	£5	£12	
Jokers	7"	Columbia	DB8198	1967	£1.50	£4	
Knight In Rusty Armour	LP	Capitol	(S)T2729	1967	£5	£12	US
Knight In Rusty Armour	7"	Columbia	DB8075	1966	£1.50	£4	
Lady Godiva	LP	Capitol	(S)T2664	1967	£5	£12	US
Lady Godiva	LP	Columbia	SCXC33	1966	£8	£20	export
Lady Godiva	7"	Columbia	DB8003	1966	£1.50	£4	chart single
Lady Godiva	7" EP	Columbia	ESRF1824	1966	£6	£12	French
Nobody I Know	7"	Columbia	DB7292	1964	£1.50	£4	chart single
Nobody I Know	7" EP	Columbia	ESRF1566	1964	£6	£12	French
Nobody I Know	7" EP	Columbia	SEG8348	1964	£5	£10	
Peter & Gordon	LP	Columbia	33SX1630/ SCX3518	1964	£5	£12	
Peter & Gordon	LP	Columbia	SX/SCX6045	1966	£5	£12	
Somewhere	LP	Columbia	SX/SCX6097	1966	£5	£12	
Sunday For Tea	7"	Columbia	DB8159	1967	£1.50	£4	
Sunday For Tea	7" EP	Columbia	ESRF1858	1967	£6	£12	French
To Know You Is To Love You	7"	Columbia	DB7617	1965	£1.50	£4	chart single
To Show I Love You	7"	Columbia	DB7951	1966	£1.50	£4	
True Love Ways	LP	Capitol	(S)T2368	1965	£5	£12	US
True Love Ways	7"	Columbia	DB7524	1965	£1.50	£4	chart single
Woman	LP	Capitol	(S)T2477	1966	£5	£12	US
Woman	LP	Columbia	SCXC29	1965	£8	£20	export
Woman	7"	Columbia	DB7834	1966	£1.50	£4	chart single
World Without Love	LP	Capitol	(S)T2115	1964	£5	£12	US
World Without Love	7"	Columbia	DB7225	1964	£1.50	£4	chart single
World Without Love	7" EP	Columbia	ESRF1533	1964	£6	£12	French

You've Had Better Times	7"	Columbia	DB8451	1968	£1.50	£4

PETER & PAUL
Schoolgirl	7"	Blue Beat	BB364	1965	£5	£10

PETER & THE HEADLINES
Don't Cry Little Girl	7"	Decca	F11980	1964	£5	£10
I've Got My Reasons	7"	Decca	F12035	1964	£5	£10

PETER & THE PERSUADERS
Wanderer	7" EP.	Oak	RGJ197	196-	£10	£20

PETER & THE WOLVES
Julie	7"	MGM	MGM1397	1968	£2	£5
Lanternlight	7"	MGM	MGM1374	1968	£2	£5
Little Girl Lost And Found	7"	MGM	MGM1352	1967	£2	£5

PETER B'S
Each member of this instrumental group went on to further success. Initially, they all formed the backing group for Shotgun Express; later bassist Dave Ambrose joined the Brian Auger Trinity, organist Peter Bardens formed Camel, while guitarist Peter Green and drummer Mick Fleetwood became half of Fleetwood Mac.

If You Wanna Be Happy	7"	Columbia	DB7862	1966	£15	£30

PETER, PAUL & MARY
Big Boat	7"	Warner Bros	WB87	1963	£1.50	£4	
Blowing In The Wind	7"	Warner Bros	WB104	1963	£1.50	£4	chart single
Don't Think Twice, It's Alright	7"	Warner Bros	WB110	1963	£1.50	£4	
Early Morning Rain	7"	Warner Bros	WB5659	1965	£1.50	£4	
For Lovin' Me	7"	Warner Bros	WB152	1965	£1.50	£4	
House Song	7"	Warner Bros	WB5798	1967	£1.50	£4	
Hurry Sundown	7"	Warner Bros	WB5883	1967	£1.50	£4	
I Dig Rock'n'Roll Music	7"	Warner Bros	WB7067	1967	£1.50	£4	
If I Had A Hammer	7"	Warner Bros	WB74	1962	£1.50	£4	
In Concert	LP	Warner Bros	(W)W21555	1964	£6	£15	double, chart LP
In The Wind	LP	Warner Bros	(W)W1507	1963	£4	£10	chart LP
In The Wind Vol.1	7" EP.	Warner Bros	WEP6135	1964	£2	£5	
In The Wind Vol.2	7" EP.	Warner Bros	WEP6137	1964	£2	£5	
Lemon Tree	7"	Warner Bros	WB66	1962	£1.50	£4	
Moving	LP	Warner Bros	(W)W1473	1962	£4	£10	
Moving	7" EP.	Warner Bros	WEP6119	1964	£2	£5	
Oh Rock My Soul	7"	Warner Bros	WB136	1964	£1.50	£4	
Other Side Of This Life	7"	Warner Bros	WB5849	1966	£1.50	£4	
Peter, Paul & Mary	LP	Warner Bros	(W)W1449	1962	£4	£10	chart LP
Peter, Paul & Mary	7" EP.	Warner Bros	WEP6114	1963	£2	£5	
Peter, Paul & Mary	7" EP.	Warner Bros	WEP6122	1964	£2	£5	
Puff The Magic Dragon	7"	Warner Bros	WB95	1963	£1.50	£4	
Stewball	7"	Warner Bros	WB121	1964	£1.50	£4	
Tell It On The Mountain	7"	Warner Bros	WB127	1964	£1.50	£4	chart single
Times They Are A Changing	7"	Warner Bros	WB142	1964	£1.50	£4	chart single
Too Much Of Nothing	7"	Warner Bros	WB7092	1968	£1.50	£4	
When The Ship Comes In	7"	Warner Bros	WB162	1965	£1.50	£4	

PETER'S FACES
De-Boom-Lay-Boom	7"	Piccadilly	7N35225	1965	£2	£5
Wait	7"	Piccadilly	7N35205	1964	£2.50	£6
Why Did You Bring Him To The Dance	7"	Piccadilly	7N35178	1964	£1.50	£4

PETERS, JANICE
This Little Girl's Gone Rocking	7"	Columbia	DB4222	1958	£7.50	£15
You're The One	7"	Columbia	DB4276	1959	£6	£12

PETERS, MARK
Candy's Gonna Cry	7"	Oriole	CB1909	1964	£6	£12
Don't Cry For Me	7"	Piccadilly	7N35207	1964	£2.50	£6
Janie	7"	Oriole	CB1836	1963	£6	£12

PETERS, WENDY
Morning Dew	7"	Saga	OPP1	1968	£6	£12

PETERSEN, PAUL
Amy	7"	Pye	7N25196	1963	£1.50	£4	
Keep Your Love Locked	7"	Pye	7N25153	1962	£1.50	£4	
Lollipops And Roses	7"	Pye	7N25163	1962	£1.50	£4	
My Dad	7"	Pye	7N25173	1963	£1.50	£4	
She Can't Find Her Keys	7"	Pye	7N25133	1962	£1.50	£4	with Shelley Fabares

PETERSON, BOBBY
Hunch	7"	Top Rank	JAR232	1959	£6	£12
Piano Rock	7"	Sue	WI346	1965	£6	£12
Rocking Charlie	7"	Sue	WI342	1964	£5	£10

PETERSON, OSCAR
At The Cocertgebouw	LP	HMV	CLP1317	1959	£6	£15
In Romantic Mood	LP	HMV	CLP1086	1956	£6	£15
Jazz Soul	LP	HMV	CLP1429	1961	£6	£15
Keyboard	LP	Columbia	33CX10062	1957	£6	£15
My Fair Lady	LP	HMV	CLP1278	1959	£6	£15
Newport Jazz Festival 1957	LP	Columbia	33CX10109	1958	£6	£15
Night On The Town	LP	Columbia	33CX10135	1959	£6	£15
Night Train	LP	Verve	VLP9052	1963	£4	£10
O Lady Be Good	10" LP	Columbia	33C9025	1956	£10	£25

Oscar Peterson	LP	Columbia	33CX10024	1956	£8	£20	
Oscar Peterson	7" EP	Columbia	SEB10005	1955	£2	£5	
Oscar Peterson No.2	7" EP	Columbia	SEB10022	1956	£2	£5	
Oscar Peterson Quartet	10" LP	Columbia	33C1038	1955	£20	£40	
Oscar Peterson Quartet	10" LP	Columbia	33C9013	1955	£15	£30	
Oscar Peterson Sings	10" LP	Columbia	33C1039	1955	£20	£40	
Oscar Peterson Sings	10" LP	Columbia	33C9014	1955	£15	£30	
Plays Cole Porter	LP	Columbia	33CX10016	1955	£10	£25	
Plays Count Basie	LP	Columbia	33CX10039	1956	£10	£25	
Plays Duke Ellington	LP	Columbia	33CX10012	1955	£10	£25	
Plays Harold Arlen	LP	Columbia	33CX10073	1957	£6	£15	
Plays Pretty	10" LP	Columbia	33C1037	1955	£20	£40	
Plays Pretty	10" LP	Columbia	33C9012	1955	£15	£30	
Plays Richard Rogers	LP	Columbia	33CX10028	1956	£10	£25	
Stratford	LP	Columbia	33CX10096	1958	£6	£15	
Swinging Brass	LP	HMV	CLP1403/CSD1326	1960	£6	£15	

PETERSON, PAUL

Little Bit Of Sandy	7"	Tamla Motown	TMG670	1968	£5	£10	

PETERSON, RAY

Answer Me	7"	RCA	RCA1175	1960	£2.50	£6	chart single
Corrine Corrina	7"	London	HLX9246	1960	£2.50	£6	chart single
Corrine Corrina	7" EP	London	REX1293	1961	£12.50	£25	
Give Us Your Blessing	7"	London	HLX9746	1963	£2.50	£6	
I Could Have Loved You So Well	7"	London	HLX9489	1962	£2	£5	
If You Were Here	7"	MGM	MGM1249	1964	£1.50	£4	
Other Side Of Ray Peterson	LP	MGM	(S)E4277	1965	£6	£15	US
Shirley Purly	7"	RCA	RCA1154	1959	£4	£8	
Sweet Little Kathy	7"	London	HLX9332	1961	£2.50	£6	
Tell Laura I Love Her	LP	RCA	LPM/LSP2297	1960	£20	£40	US
Tell Laura I Love Her	7"	RCA	RCA1195	1960	£2.50	£6	
Very Best Of Ray Peterson	LP	MGM	(S)E4250	1964	£6	£15	US
Wonder Of You	7"	RCA	RCA1131	1959	£4	£8	chart single
You Didn't Care	7"	London	HLX9569	1962	£2	£5	
You Thrill Me	7"	London	HLX9379	1961	£2	£5	

PETITES

Get Your Daddy's Car Tonight	7"	Philips	PB1035	1960	£1.50	£4	

PETS

Beyond The Sea	7"	Pye	7N25004	1959	£1.50	£4	
Cha Hua Hua	7"	London	HL8652	1958	£7.50	£15	

PETTI, MARY

Hey Lawdy Lawdy	7"	RCA	RCA1239	1961	£7.50	£15	

PETTIFORD, OSCAR

In Hi Fi No.2	10" LP	HMV	DLP1197	1958	£15	£30	
Oscar Pettiford Group	LP	London	LTZN15035	1957	£15	£30	
Oscar Pettiford Group	10" LP	London	LZN14023	1956	£20	£40	
Oscar Pettiford Orchestra	LP	HMV	CLP1171	1958	£15	£30	
Oscar Pettiford Sextet	10" LP	Vogue	LDE098	1954	£40	£80	

PETTY, NORMAN

Corsage	LP	Vik	1073	1959	£10	£25	US
Mood Indigo	7"	HMV	7M274	1954	£5	£10	
Moondreams	LP	Columbia	CL1092	1958	£30	£60	US
Petty For Your Thoughts	LP	Top Rank	RS639	1960	£8	£20	US

PETTY, TOM

Damn The Torpedoes	LP	MCA	MCA5105	1980	£5	£12	Canadian audiophile
Hard Promises	LP	MCA	BSR5162	1981	£5	£12	Canadian audiophile
Official Bootleg	LP	Shelter	IDJ24	1977	£5	£12	promo

PFM

Per Un Amico	LP	Numero Uno	ZSLN55155	1972	£5	£12	Italian
Storia Di Un Minoto	LP	Numero Uno	ZSLN55055	1972	£5	£12	Italian

PHANTOMS

Great Guitar Hits	LP	Arc		1964	£15	£30	
Phantom Guitar	7"	Palette	PG9014	1961	£4	£8	

PHAROAHS

Pharoahs	7" EP	Decca	DFE6522	1958	£100	£200	

PHASE FOUR

Man Am I Worried?	7"	Fab	FAB6	1967	£10	£20	
What Do You Say About That	7"	Decca	F12327	1966	£2.50	£6	
What Do You Say About That	7"	Fab	FAB1	1966	£2.50	£6	

PHELPS, JAMES

Check Yourself	7"	Paramount	3019	1971	£2.50	£6	

PHILLIPS, ANTHONY

Anthony Phillips was an original member of Genesis, playing guitar on both the debut album and its follow-up, "Trespass" - his successor was Steve Hackett.

Anthem From Tarka	CD-s	PRT	PYD18	1988	£4	£10	
Anthem From Tarka	7"	PRT	PYS18	1988	£2.50	£6	
Collections	7"	Philips	6837406	1977	£10	£20	PS
Prelude '84	7"	RCA	RCA102	1981	£2	£5	PS

Private Parts And Pieces	LP	Arista	AFLP1	1979	£4	£10	
Sally	12"	Street Tunes	JJ10212	1984	£2.50	£6	
Um And Aargh	7"	Arista	ARIST252	1978	£2	£5	PS
We're All As We Lie	7"	Arista	ARIST192	1978	£2.50	£6	
Wise After The Event	LP	Passport	PB9828	1978	£5	£12	US pic disc

PHILLIPS, CONFREY
Shotgun Rock And Roll	7"	Decca	F10866	1957	£4	£8

PHILLIPS, ESTHER
Am I That Easy To Forget	7"	Ember	EMBS174	1963	£2	£5	
And I Love Him	LP	Atlantic	(SD)8102	1965	£6	£15	US
And I Love Him	LP	Atlantic	584103	1967	£1.50	£4	
And I Love Him	7"	Atlantic	AT4028	1965	£2	£5	
Chains	7"	Sue	WI395	1965	£5	£10	
Country Side Of Esther Phillips	LP	Atlantic	(SD)8130	1966	£5	£12	US
Esther	LP	Atlantic	(SD)8122	1966	£5	£12	US
From A Whisper To A Scream	LP	Kudu	KUL2	1973	£6	£15	
Home Is Where The Hatred Is	7"	Kudu	KUS4000	1973	£2	£5	
I Could Have Told You	7"	Atlantic	AT4077	1966	£10	£20	
I'm Sorry	7"	Atlantic	584126	1967	£1.50	£4	
I've Never Found A Man	7"	Kudu	KUS4002	1973	£1.50	£4	
Let Me Know When It's Over	7"	Atlantic	AT4048	1965	£2	£5	
Memory Lane	LP	King	LP622	1956	£400	£600	US
Reflections Of Great Country And Western Standards	LP	Ember	CW103	1963	£5	£12	
Release Me	LP	Lenox	227	1962	£10	£25	US
Release Me	7"	Ember	EMBS221	1966	£1.50	£4	
Release Me	7"	Stateside	SS140	1962	£2.50	£6	
Sings	LP	Atlantic	587/588010	1966	£5	£12	
Somebody Else Is Taking My Place	7"	Atlantic	584062	1967	£1.50	£4	
Tonight I'll Be Staying Here With You	7"	Roulette	RO508	1968	£1.50	£4	
Too Late To Worry, Too Blue To Cry	7"	Roulette	RO505	1968	£1.50	£4	
When A Woman Loves A Man	7"	Atlantic	584013	1966	£1.50	£4	

PHILLIPS, FLIP
Flip Phillips	10" LP	Columbia	33C9003	1955	£25	£50

PHILLIPS, GREGORY
Angie	7"	Pye	7N15546	1963	£1.50	£4
Don't Bother Me	7"	Pye	7N15633	1964	£1.50	£4
Down In The Boondocks	7"	Immediate	IM004	1965	£4	£8
Everybody Knows	7"	Pye	7N15583	1963	£1.50	£4

PHILLIPS, JOHN
Mississippi	7"	Stateside	SS8046	1970	£1.50	£4
Wolfking Of L.A.	LP	Stateside	SSL5027	1970	£4	£10

PHILLIPS, PHIL
I Love To Love You	7"	Mercury	AMT1139	1961	£5	£10
Sea Of Love	7"	Mercury	AMT1059	1959	£6	£12
Take This Heart	7"	Mercury	AMT1072	1960	£2.50	£6
Your True Love Once More	7"	Mercury	AMT1093	1960	£4	£8

PHILLIPS, SHAWN
I'm A Loner	LP	Columbia	33SX1748	1965	£37.50	£75
Little Tin Soldier	7"	Columbia	DB7789	1965	£2.50	£6
Nobody Listens	7"	Columbia	DB7699	1965	£4	£8
Shawn	LP	Columbia	SCX6006	1966	£30	£60
Solitude	7"	Columbia	DB7611	1965	£2.50	£6
Stargazer	7"	Parlophone	R5606	1967	£7.50	£15
Summer Came	7"	Columbia	DB7956	1966	£2.50	£6

PHILLIPS, STU
Champlain & St.Lawrence Line	7"	London	HL8673	1958	£2	£5	
Strangers When We Meet	7"	Pye	7N25062	1960	£1.50	£4	Bob Merse Orchestra B sid

PHILLIPS, TEDDY
Ridin' To Tennessee	7"	London	HL8032	1954	£10	£20

PHILLIPS, TOM, GAVIN BRYARS & FRED ORTON
Irma	LP	Obscure	OBS9	1978	£4	£10

PHILLIPS, WARREN & THE ROCKETS (SAVOY BROWN)
World Of Rock And Roll	LP	Decca	(S)PA43	1969	£6	£15

PHILOSOPHERS
After Sundown	LP	PS		196-	£15	£30	U

PHILPOTT, VINCE & THE DRAGS
Cramp	7"	Decca	F11997	1964	£7.50	£15

PHILWIT & PEGASUS
Philwit & Pegasus	LP	Chapter One	CHS805	1970	£10	£25

PHLUPH
Phluph	LP	Verve	V65054	1968	£5	£12	U

PHOENIX, PAT
Rovers Chorus	7"	HMV	POP1030	1962	£2	£5

PHOTOGRAPHED BY LIGHTNING
Sleeps Terminator	7"	Fierce	FRIGHT008	1986	£10	£20	

PIAF, EDITH
Great Piaf	7" EP	Columbia	SEG8220	1963	£2	£5	
No Regrets	7"	Columbia	DB4642	1961	£1.50	£4	
Non Je Ne Regrette Rien	7"	Columbia	DB4596	1961	£1.50	£4	
Non Je Ne Regrette Rien	7" EP	Columbia	SEG8308	1964	£2	£5	
Qu'il Etait Triste	7" EP	Columbia	SEG8387	1965	£2	£5	

PIANO RED
Bouncin' With Red	78	HMV	B10316	1952	£10	£20	
Hey Good Lookin'	78	HMV	B10246	1952	£10	£20	
In Concert	LP	Groove	1002	1964	£50	£100	US
Jump Man Jump	LP	Groove	1001	1964	£50	£100	US
Rhythm & Blues Vol.2	7" EP	RCA	RCX7138	1964	£10	£20	
Rocking With Red	7"	HMV	7M108	1953	£40	£80	

PIC & BILL
All I Want Is You	7"	Page One	POF024	1967	£2.50	£6	
Sad World Without You	7"	Page One	POF052	1968	£4	£8	
This Is It	7"	Page One	POF037	1967	£1.50	£4	

PICCADILLY LINE
At The Third Stroke	7"	CBS	2785	1967	£4	£8	
Emily Small	7"	CBS	2958	1967	£4	£8	
Evenings With Corrina	7"	CBS	3743	1968	£1.50	£4	
Huge World Of Emily Small	LP	CBS	(S)BPG63129	1967	£10	£25	
Yellow Rainbow	7"	CBS	3595	1968	£1.50	£4	

PICKENS, BUSTER
Texas Piano	LP	Heritage	HLP1008	196-	£15	£30	

PICKETT, BOBBY & THE CRYPT KICKERS
Monster Mash	LP	Garpax	(S)GP67001	1962	£10	£25	US
Monster Mash	7"	London	HLU9597	1962	£4	£8	

PICKETT, DAN
Dan Pickett	7" EP	XX	MIN710	196-	£2.50	£6	

PICKETT, KENNY
Got A Gun	7"	F-Beat	PRO2	1980	£2.50	£6	promo

PICKETT, NICK
Silversleeves	LP	Reprise	K44172	1972	£8	£20	

PICKETT, WILSON
634-5789	7"	Atlantic	AT4072	1966	£2.50	£6	chart single
99 & A Half Won't Do	7"	Atlantic	584023	1966	£2	£5	
Best Of Wilson Pickett	LP	Atlantic	587/588092	1968	£5	£12	
Call My Name, I'll Be There	7"	Atlantic	2091153	1971	£1.50	£4	
Don't Fight It	7"	Atlantic	AT4052	1965	£4	£8	chart single
Don't Knock My Love	7"	Atlantic	2091124	1971	£1.50	£4	
Engine No.9	LP	Atlantic	2400026	1971	£5	£12	
Engine No.9	7"	Atlantic	2091032	1970	£1.50	£4	
Everybody Needs Somebody To Love	7"	Atlantic	584101	1967	£2	£5	
Exciting Wilson Pickett	LP	Atlantic	587/588029	1966	£6	£15	
Fire And Water	7"	Atlantic	2091086	1971	£1.50	£4	
Funky Broadway	7"	Atlantic	584130	1967	£1.50	£4	chart single
Hey Joe	7"	Atlantic	584281	1969	£1.50	£4	
Hey Jude	LP	Atlantic	588170	1969	£5	£12	
Hey Jude	7"	Atlantic	584236	1969	£1.50	£4	chart single
I Found A True Love	7"	Atlantic	584221	1968	£1.50	£4	
If You Need Me	LP	Joy	JOYS181	1971	£5	£12	
I'm A Midnight Mover	7"	Atlantic	584203	1968	£1.50	£4	chart single
I'm In Love	LP	Atlantic	587/588107	1968	£5	£12	
In The Midnight Hour	LP	Atlantic	587032	1966	£6	£15	
In The Midnight Hour	LP	Atlantic	ATL5037	1965	£8	£20	
In The Midnight Hour	7"	Atlantic	584150	1968	£1.50	£4	
In The Midnight Hour	7"	Atlantic	AT4036	1965	£4	£8	chart single
It's Too Late	LP	Double-L	DL2300/SDL8300	1963	£10	£25	US
It's Too Late	7"	Liberty	LIB10115	1963	£6	£12	
Land Of 1000 Dances	7"	Atlantic	584039	1966	£2	£5	chart single
Midnight Mover	LP	Atlantic	587/588111	1968	£5	£12	
Mini-Skirt Minnie	7"	Atlantic	584261	1969	£1.50	£4	
Mustang Sally	7"	Atlantic	584066	1966	£2	£5	chart single
My Heart Belongs To You	7"	MGM	MGM1286	1965	£10	£20	
New Orleans	7"	Atlantic	584107	1967	£2	£5	
Right On	LP	Atlantic	2465002	1970	£4	£10	
She's Looking Good	7"	Atlantic	584183	1968	£1.50	£4	
Sound Of Wilson Pickett	LP	Atlantic	587/588080	1967	£6	£15	
Stag-o-lee	7"	Atlantic	584142	1967	£1.50	£4	
Sugar Sugar	7"	Atlantic	2091005	1970	£1.50	£4	
That Kind Of Love	7"	Atlantic	584173	1968	£1.50	£4	
Wicked Pickett	LP	Atlantic	587/588057	1967	£6	£15	
You Keep Me Hanging On	7"	Atlantic	584313	1970	£1.50	£4	

PICKFORD, ED
Facing The Crowd	LP	Rip Off	ROF002	1982	£5	£12	
Songwriter	LP	Rip Off	ROF001	1976	£6	£15	

PICKFORD-HOPKINS, GARY

Why?	7"	Spartan	SP143	1983	£4	£8	
Why?	12"	Spartan	SP143T	1983	£4	£10	

PICKWICKS

Apple Blossom Time	7"	Decca	F11901	1964	£4	£8	
Little By Little	7"	Warner Bros	WB151	1965	£12.50	£25	
You're Old Enough	7"	Decca	F11957	1964	£4	£8	

PIED PIPERS

Kissin' Drive Rock	7"	Parlophone	CMSP21	1954	£2.50	£6	export
Ragamuffin	7"	Columbia	DB7883	1966	£2.50	£6	

PIERCE, BILLY & DEDE

Jazz At Preservation Hall Vol.2	LP	London	HAK/SHK8163	1964	£5	£12	

PIERCE, NAT

Chamber Music For Moderns	LP	Vogue Coral	LVA9060	1957	£5	£12	
Kansas City Memories	LP	Vogue Coral	LVA9050	1957	£5	£12	

PIERCE, WEBB

Bound For The Kingdom	LP	Decca	DL(7)8889	1959	£6	£15	US
Bye Bye Love	7"	Brunswick	05682	1957	£12.50	£25	
Country & Western Favourites Vol.1	7" EP	Ember	EMBEP4520	1962	£4	£8	
Country Round Up	7" EP	Parlophone	GEP8792	1959	£10	£20	
Cross Country	LP	Brunswick	LAT8551	1965	£5	£12	
Drifting Texas Sands	7"	Brunswick	05842	1960	£2.50	£6	
Hideaway Heart	LP	Brunswick	LAT8540	1965	£6	£15	
I Ain't Never	7"	Brunswick	05809	1959	£4	£8	
In The Jailhouse Now	LP	MCA	MUPS364	1969	£4	£10	
Just Imagination	LP	Decca	DL8728	1957	£8	£20	US
No Love Have I	7"	Brunswick	05820	1960	£4	£8	
One And Only Webb Pierce	LP	King	648	1959	£6	£15	US
Teenage Boogie	7"	Brunswick	05630	1956	£60	£120	
That Wondering Boy	LP	Decca	DL8295	1956	£8	£20	US
That Wondering Boy	10" LP	Brunswick	LA8716	1955	£10	£25	
Webb	LP	Brunswick	LAT8324	1959	£6	£15	
Webb Pierce	LP	Decca	DL8129	1955	£8	£20	US
Webb Pierce Pt.1	7" EP	Brunswick	OE9253	1956	£5	£10	
Webb Pierce Pt.2	7" EP	Brunswick	OE9254	1956	£5	£10	
Webb Pierce Pt.3	7" EP	Brunswick	OE9255	1956	£5	£10	
Webb Pierce Story	LP	Decca	DX(S)B(7)181	1964	£6	£15	US, with booklet

PIGG, BILLY

Border Minstrel	LP	Leader	LEA4006	1971	£6	£15	

PIGGLESWICK FOLK

Pig In The Middle	LP	Acorn	CF256	197-	£6	£15	

PIGSTY HILL LIGHT ORCHESTRA

Cushion Foot Stomp	LP	Village Thing	VTS1	1970	£4	£10	
Piggery Jokery	LP	Village Thing	VTS8	1971	£4	£10	

PIIRPAUKE

Live	LP	Love	LRLP251	1977	£8	£20	Swedish
Piirpauke I	LP	Love	LRLP148	1975	£10	£25	Swedish
Piirpauke II	LP	Love	LRLP192	1976	£10	£25	Swedish

PILTDOWN MEN

Gargantua	7"	Capitol	CL15211	1961	£2.50	£6	
Goodnight Mrs.Flintstone	7"	Capitol	CL15186	1961	£1.50	£4	chart single
Goodnight Mrs.Flintstone/Piltdown Rides Again	7" EP	Capitol	EAP120155	1961	£10	£20	
McDonald's Cave	7"	Capitol	CL15149	1960	£1.50	£4	chart single
Piltdown Rides Again	7"	Capitol	CL15175	1961	£1.50	£4	chart single
Pretty Girl Is Like A Melody	7"	Capitol	CL15245	1962	£2	£5	

PIMM, SIR HUBERT

Goodnight And Cheerio	7"	London	HL8155	1955	£12.50	£25	
Pimm's Party	7" EP	London	REU1032	1955	£2	£5	

PINEAPPLE CHUNKS

Drive My Car	7"	Mercury	MF922	1965	£4	£8	

PINEWOOD TOM & TALL TOM

Male Blues Vol.4	7" EP	Collector	JEL5	1959	£5	£10	

PINGUIN

Der Grosse Rote Vogel	LP	Zebra	2949001	1971	£8	£20	German

PINHAS, RICHARD

Rhizosphere	LP	Cobra	COB37005	1977	£4	£10	French

PINK FAIRIES

Kings Of Oblivion	LP	Polydor	2383212	1973	£6	£15	with poster
Never Never Land	LP	Polydor	2383045	1971	£6	£15	
Never Never Land	LP	Polydor	2383045	1971	£10	£25	plastic cover
Never Never Land	LP	Polydor	2383045	1971	£75	£150	red vinyl
Snake	7"	Polydor	2058089	1970	£7.50	£15	
Well Well Well	7"	Polydor	2058302	1972	£5	£10	

PINK FLOYD

In their early days, Pink Floyd epitomised what British psychedelic music was all about and their first two albums are rightly prized as crucially important documents of the period. Like many LPs recorded in the second half of the sixties, there are many differences between the mono and stereo versions, this being particularly noticeable on the often densely arranged "Saucerful Of Secrets" record. The Columbia singles are also much in demand, especially since the only vinyl reissue of the last three consists of a German compilation LP. Promotional copies of the 1967 singles were issued in picture sleeves, which are extremely scarce today.

Title	Format	Label	Cat. No.	Year			Notes
Animals	LP	Columbia	PCQ34474	1977	£10	£25	US quad
Another Brick In The Wall Pt.2 (live)	12"	EMI	12PF1	1988	£4	£10	promo only
Apples And Oranges	7"	Columbia	DB8310	1967	£10	£20	
Apples And Oranges	7"	Columbia	DB8310	1967	£150	£250	promo, PS
Arnold Layne	7"	Columbia	DB8156	1967	£7.50	£15	chart single
Arnold Layne	7"	Columbia	DB8156	1967	£150	£250	promo, PS
Arnold Layne	7" EP	Columbia	ESRF1857	1967	£150	£250	French
Atom Heart Mother	LP	Harvest	Q4SHVL781	1973	£10	£25	quad
Collection Of Great Dance Songs	LP	Columbia	HC47680	1983	£8	£20	US audiophile
Dark Side Of The Moon	LP	Capitol	SEAX11902	1978	£8	£20	US pic disc
Dark Side Of The Moon	LP	Harvest	Q4SHVL804	1973	£10	£25	quad
Dark Side Of The Moon	LP	Mobile Fidelity	MFSL1017	1978	£8	£20	US audiophile
Dark Side Of The Moon (UHQR)	LP	Mobile Fidelity	MFSL1017	1982	£60	£120	US audiophile
First XI	LP	Harvest	PF11	1979	£60	£120	9LPs & 2pic discs, boxed
It Would Be So Nice	7"	Columbia	DB8401	1968	£12.50	£25	
Learning To Fly	7"	EMI	EMP26	1987	£1.50	£4	pink vinyl
Money	7"	Harvest	HAR5217	1981	£7.50	£15	pink vinyl
More	LP	Columbia	SCX6346	1969	£5	£12	green photo rear sleeve, chart LP
Nice Pair	LP	Harvest	SHDW403	1973	£6	£15	double, Mr.Phang sleeve
Off The Wall	LP	Columbia	AS756	1979	£8	£20	US promo sampler
On The Turning Away	7"	EMI	EMP34	1987	£1.50	£4	pink vinyl
Piper At The Gates Of Dawn	LP	Columbia	SCX6157	1967	£8	£20	stereo, chart LP
Piper At The Gates Of Dawn	LP	Columbia	SX6157	1967	£15	£30	mono, chart LP
Point Me At The Sky	7"	Columbia	DB8511	1968	£12.50	£25	
Saucerful Of Secrets	LP	Columbia	SCX6258	1968	£10	£25	stereo, chart LP
Saucerful Of Secrets	LP	Columbia	SX6258	1968	£17.50	£35	mono, chart LP
See Emily Play	7"	Columbia	DB8214	1967	£7.50	£15	chart single
See Emily Play	7"	Columbia	DB8214	1967	£150	£250	promo, PS
Tonight Let's All Make Love In London	LP	Instant	INLP002	1968	£30	£60	with other artists
Tour '75	LP	Capitol	SPRO8116/7	1975	£15	£30	US promo compilation
Wall	LP	Columbia	H2C46183	1983	£25	£50	US audiophile
Wall In Store	LP	Columbia	XDAP93012	1979	£30	£60	US promo
Wish You Were Here	LP	Columbia	HC43453	1982	£8	£20	US audiophile
Wish You Were Here	LP	Harvest	Q4SHVL814	1976	£10	£25	quad
Zabriskie Point	LP	MGM	2315002	1970	£6	£15	with other artists
Zabriskie Point	LP	MGM	CS8120	1970	£8	£20	with other artists

PINK MICE

Title	Format	Label	Cat. No.	Year			Notes
In Action	LP	Europa	E456	1971	£4	£10	German
In Synthesizer	LP	Europa	E1011	1973	£4	£10	German

PINK MILITARY

Title	Format	Label	Cat. No.	Year			Notes
Buddha Waking Disney Sleeping	7"	Last Trumpet	LT001	1979	£2	£5	

PINK PEOPLE

Title	Format	Label	Cat. No.	Year			Notes
Indian Hate Call	7"	Philips	BF1356	1964	£6	£12	
Psychologically Unsound	7"	Philips	BF1355	1964	£10	£20	

PINKERTON'S ASSORTED COLOURS

Title	Format	Label	Cat. No.	Year			Notes
Don't Stop Lovin' Me Baby	7"	Decca	F12377	1966	£1.50	£4	chart single
Magic Rocking Horse	7"	Decca	F12493	1966	£5	£10	
Mirror Mirror	7"	Decca	F12307	1966	£1.50	£4	chart single
Mirror Mirror	7" EP	Decca	457113	1966	£10	£20	French

PINKY

Title	Format	Label	Cat. No.	Year			Notes
All Cried Out	7"	Polydor	BM56009	1965	£2.50	£6	

PINNACLE

Title	Format	Label	Cat. No.	Year			Notes
Assassin	LP	Stag	HP125	1974	£50	£100	

PIONEERS

Title	Format	Label	Cat. No.	Year			Notes
Alli Button	7"	Amalgamated	AMG850	1969	£4	£8	Hippy Boys B side
Bad To Be Good	7"	Trojan	TR7897	1973	£1.50	£4	
Battle Of The Giants	LP	Trojan	TBL139	1970	£6	£15	
Black Bud	7"	Trojan	TR685	1969	£1.50	£4	
Catch The Beat	7"	Amalgamated	AMG828	1968	£4	£8	Sir Gibbs' Allstars B side
Don't You Know	7"	Amalgamated	AMG833	1969	£4	£8	
Easy Come Easy Go	7"	Pyramid	PYR6062	1969	£2.50	£6	Beverley's Allstars B side
Freedom Feeling	LP	Trojan	TRLS64	1973	£4	£10	
Give And Take	7"	Trojan	TR7846	1972	£1.50	£4	chart single
Give It To Me	7"	Blue Cat	BS103	1968	£4	£8	Leaders B side
Give Me A Little Loving	7"	Amalgamated	AMG811	1968	£4	£8	
Give Up	7"	Rio	R106	1966	£4	£8	
Good Nannie	7"	Rio	R102	1966	£4	£8	
Greetings From The Pioneers	LP	Amalgamated	AMGLP2003	1968	£30	£60	
Honey Bee	7"	Trojan	TR7923	1974	£1.50	£4	
I Believe In Love	LP	Trojan	TRLS48	1972	£4	£10	
I Love No Other Girl	7"	Caltone	TONE119	1968	£4	£8	Milton Boothe B side

Jackpot	7"	Amalgamated	AMG821	1968	£4	£8	Creators B side
Let Your Yeah Be Yeah	7"	Trojan	TR7825	1971	£1.50	£4	chart single
Long Shot	7"	Amalgamated	AMG814	1968	£4	£8	
Long Shot Kick The Bucket	7"	Trojan	TR672	1969	£2	£5	chart single, Rico B side
Longshot	LP	Trojan	TBL103	1969	£6	£15	
Love Love Every Day	7"	Amalgamated	AMG846	1969	£4	£8	Moon Boys B side
Mama Look Deh	7"	Amalgamated	AMG835	1969	£4	£8	Blenders B side
No Dope Me Pony	7"	Amalgamated	AMG823	1968	£4	£8	Lord Salmons B side
Pee Pee Cluck Cluck	7"	Pyramid	PYR6065	1969	£2.50	£6	Beverley's Allstars B side
Poor Rameses	7"	Trojan	TR698	1969	£1.50	£4	Beverley's Allstars B side
Reggae Beat	7"	Blue Cat	BS139	1968	£4	£8	
Shake It Up	7"	Blue Cat	BS100	1968	£4	£8	
Sweet Dreams	7"	Amalgamated	AMG830	1968	£4	£8	Don Drummond Jr. B side
Tickle Me For Days	7"	Amalgamated	AMG826	1968	£4	£8	Versatiles B side
Whip Them	7"	Blue Cat	BS105	1968	£4	£8	
Who The Cap Fits	7"	Amalgamated	AMG840	1969	£4	£8	
Yeah	LP	Trojan	TRL24	1971	£5	£12	

PIPKINS
Gimme Dat Ding	7"	Columbia	DB8662	1970	£1.50	£4	chart single

PIPS
Every Beat Of My Heart	7"	Top Rank	JAR574	1961	£6	£12	

PIRANHAS
Somethin' Fishy	LP	Custom Fidelity	1452	1969	£37.50	£75	US

PIRATES
My Babe	7"	HMV	POP1250	1964	£6	£12	
Shades Of Blue	7"	Polydor	56712	1966	£7.50	£15	

PISCES
Pisces	LP	Trailer	LER2025	1971	£8	£20	

PITNEY, GENE
Backstage	7"	Stateside	SS490	1966	£1.50	£4	chart single
Backstage	7" EP	Stateside	SE1040	1966	£2.50	£6	
Being Together	LP	Stateside	(S)SL10181	1966	£4	£10	with Melba Montgomery
Big Sixteen	LP	Stateside	SL10118	1964	£4	£10	
Big Sixteen	LP	United Artists	ULP1073	1964	£6	£15	
Big Sixteen Vol.3	LP	Stateside	(S)SL10199	1967	£4	£10	
Blue Gene	LP	United Artists	ULP1061	1964	£5	£12	
Cold Light Of Day	7"	Stateside	SS597	1967	£1.50	£4	chart single
Donna Means Heartbreak	7"	United Artists	UP1030	1964	£1.50	£4	
Every Breath I Take	7"	HMV	POP933	1961	£5	£10	
Gene Italiano	7" EP	Stateside	SE1032	1965	£4	£8	
Gene Pitney Sings Just For You	7" EP	Stateside	SE1036	1966	£2.50	£6	
Half Heaven Half Heartache	7"	United Artists	UP1012	1964	£1.50	£4	
I Must Be Seeing Things	7"	Stateside	SS390	1965	£1.50	£4	chart single
I Must Be Seeing Things	7" EP	Stateside	SE1030	1965	£2.50	£6	
I Wanna Love My Life Away	7"	London	HL9270	1961	£4	£8	chart single
I'm Gonna Be Strong	LP	Stateside	SL10120	1965	£4	£10	
I'm Gonna Be Strong	7"	Stateside	SS358	1964	£1.50	£4	chart single
I'm Gonna Find Me A Girl	7"	United Artists	UP1055	1964	£1.50	£4	
It Hurts To Be In Love	7"	Stateside	SS365	1964	£1.50	£4	chart single
It Hurts To Be In Love	7"	United Artists	UP1063	1964	£1.50	£4	chart single
Just One Smile	LP	Stateside	(S)SL10212	1967	£4	£10	
Just One Smile	7"	Stateside	SS558	1966	£1.50	£4	chart single
Looking Thru The Eyes Of Love	LP	Stateside	SL10148	1965	£4	£10	
Looking THru The Eyes Of Love	7"	Stateside	SS420	1965	£1.50	£4	
Love Grows	7"	Stateside	SS2118	1968	£1.50	£4	
Man Who Shot Liberty Valance	7"	HMV	POP1018	1962	£4	£8	
Many Sides Of Gene Pitney	LP	HMV	CLP1566	1961	£8	£20	
Maria Elena	7"	Stateside	SS2142	1969	£1.50	£4	chart single
Mecca	7"	United Artists	UP1021	1964	£1.50	£4	
Meets The Fair Young Ladies Of Folkland	LP	United Artists	ULP1064	1964	£5	£12	
More Big Sixteen	LP	Stateside	SL10132	1965	£4	£10	
Nobody Needs Your Love	LP	Stateside	(S)SL10183	1966	£4	£10	
Nobody Needs Your Love	7"	Stateside	SS518	1966	£1.50	£4	chart single
Only Love Can Break A Heart	LP	United Artists	(S)ULP1028	1963	£5	£12	
Only Love Can Break A Heart	7"	United Artists	UP1005	1964	£1.50	£4	
Pitney Sings Just For You	LP	United Artists	ULP1043	1963	£5	£12	
Pitney Today	LP	Stateside	(S)SL10242	1968	£4	£10	
Princess In Rags	7"	Stateside	SS471	1965	£1.50	£4	chart single
San Remo Winners And Others	7" EP	Stateside	SE1041	1967	£4	£8	
Shady Lady	7"	Stateside	SS2177	1970	£1.50	£4	chart single
She Lets Her Hair Down	7"	Stateside	SS2157	1969	£1.50	£4	
Sings The Great Songs Of Our Time	LP	Stateside	SL10156	1965	£4	£10	
Something's Gotten Hold Of My Heart	7"	Stateside	SS2060	1967	£1.50	£4	chart single
Somewhere In The Country	7"	Stateside	SS2103	1968	£1.50	£4	chart single
Street Called Hope	7"	Stateside	SS2164	1970	£1.50	£4	chart single
That Girl Belongs To Yesterday	7"	United Artists	UP1045	1964	£1.50	£4	chart single
That Girl Belongs To Yesterday	7" EP	Stateside	SE1028	1965	£2.50	£6	

Title	Format	Label	Catalogue	Year	Price	Price	Notes
That Girl Belongs To Yesterday	7" EP..	United Artists ..	UEP1002	1964	£2.50	£6	
There's No Living Without Your Love ..	7" EP..	Stateside	SE1045	1967	£2.50	£6	
Town Without Pity	7"....	HMV	POP952	1962	£4	£8	chart single
Town Without Pity	7" EP..	HMV	7EG8832	1963	£10	£20	
Twenty Four Hours From Tulsa	7"....	United Artists ..	UP1035	1963	£1.50	£4	chart single
Twenty Four Hours From Tulsa	7" EP..	Stateside	SE1027	1965	£7.50	£15	
Twenty Four Hours From Tulsa	7" EP..	United Artists ..	UEP1001	1964	£2.50	£6	
Young, Warm And Wonderful	LP	Stateside	(S)SL10194	1967	£4	£10	
Yours Until Tomorrow	7"....	Stateside	SS2131	1968	£1.50	£4	chart single

PIXIES
Live	LP	4AD		1989	£15	£30	promo

PIXIES THREE
Birthday Party	7"	Mercury	AMT1214	1963	£1.50	£4	
Party With The Pixies Three	LP	Mercury	MG2/SR60912	1964	£20	£40	US

PLAGUE
Looking For The Sun	7"	Decca	F12730	1968	£25	£50	

PLAINSONG
In Search Of Amelia Earhart	LP	Elektra	K42120	1972	£6	£15	
Plainsong II	LP	Elektra		197-	£37.50	£75	demo only

PLANETS
Chunky	7"	HMV	POP818	1960	£1.50	£4	
Jam Roll	7"	HMV	POP832	1961	£2.50	£6	
Jungle Street	7"	HMV	POP895	1961	£4	£8	
Like Party	7"	Palette	PG9008	1960	£4	£8	
Like Party	7"	Palette	PG9008	1960	£6	£12	PS

PLANT, RICHARD
Better Be Sane	LP	Tradition	TSR022	1975	£5	£12	

PLANT, ROBERT
Long Time Coming	7"	CBS	202858	1966	£60	£120	
Our Song	7"	CBS	202656	1966	£60	£120	
Pictures At Eleven	LP	Swan Song	SAM154	1982	£4	£10	interview promo
Principal Of Moments	LP	Es Paranza	SAM169	1983	£4	£10	interview promo

PLANXTY
Cold Blow And Rainy Night	LP	Polydor	2383301	1974	£5	£12	
Planxty	LP	Polydor	2383186	1973	£5	£12	
Planxty Collection	LP	Polydor	2383397	1974	£5	£12	
Time Dance	12"	WEA	IR28207	1981	£15	£30	Irish
Well Below The Valley	LP	Polydor	2383232	1973	£5	£12	

PLASTIC CLOUD
Plastic Cloud	LP	Allied		196-	£75	£150	Canadian

PLASTIC GANGSTERS
Plastic Gangsters	7"	Secret	SHH144	198-	£5	£10	promo

PLASTIC PENNY
Currency	LP	Page One	POLS014	1969	£20	£40	
Everything I Am	7"	Page One	POF051	1967	£1.50	£4	chart single
Heads I Win, Tails You Lose	LP	Page One	POLS611	1970	£20	£40	
Hound Dog	7"	Page One	POF107	1969	£2	£5	
Nobody Knows It	LP	Page One	POF062	1968	£2	£5	
She Does	7"	Page One	POF146	1969	£2	£5	
Two Sides Of Plastic Penny	LP	Page One	POL(S)005	1968	£20	£40	
Your Way To Tell Me Go	7"	Page One	POF079	1968	£2	£5	

PLASTIC PEOPLE OF THE UNIVERSE
Egon Bondy's Happy Heart Club Banned	LP	Invisible	SCOPA10001	1979	£6	£15	French

PLATFORM SIX
Girl Down Town	7"	Piccadilly	7N35255	1965	£6	£12	

PLATTERS
Are You Sincere	7"	Mercury	7MT205	1958	£7.50	£15	
Around The World	LP	Mercury	MMC14009	1959	£10	£25	
Best Of The Platters	LP	Ember	EMB3339	1962	£4	£10	
Ebb Tide	7"	Mercury	AMT1098	1960	£1.50	£4	
Enchanted	7"	Mercury	AMT1039	1959	£1.50	£4	
Fabulous Platters	7" EP.	Mercury	MEP9504	1956	£7.50	£15	
Fabulous Platters Vol.2	7" EP.	Mercury	MEP9514	1957	£6	£12	
Fabulous Platters Vol.3	7" EP.	Mercury	MEP9524	1957	£6	£12	
Flying Platters	LP	Mercury	MPL6528	1957	£10	£25	
Flying Platters	7" EP.	Mercury	MEP9526	1958	£6	£12	
Flying Platters No.2	7" EP.	Mercury	MEP9528	1958	£6	£12	
Going Back To Detroit	LP	Stateside	(S)SL10208	1967	£4	£10	
Golden Hits	LP	Mercury	MMC14091	1962	£4	£10	
Great Pretender	78	Mercury	MT117	1956	£1.50	£4	chart single
Great Pretender	7"	Mercury	MT117	1956	£10	£20	export
Harbour Lights	7"	Mercury	AMT1081	1960	£1.50	£4	chart single
Harbour Lights	7" EP.	Mercury	ZEP10112	1961	£6	£12	
Helpless	7"	Mercury	7MT197	1958	£12.50	£25	
I Love You A Thousand Times	7"	Stateside	SS511	1966	£6	£12	
I Wish	7"	Mercury	AMT1001	1958	£5	£10	

If I Didn't Care	7"	Mercury	AMT1128	1961	£1.50	£4	
I'll Be Home	7"	Stateside	SS568	1966	£2	£5	
I'll Never Smile	7"	Mercury	AMT1154	1961	£1.50	£4	
Life Is Just A Bowl Of Cherries	LP	Mercury	MMC14072	1961	£6	£15	
Magic Touch	78	Mercury	MT107	1956	£3	£8	
My Blue Heaven	7"	Mercury	AMT1066	1959	£2	£4	
My Prayer	78	Mercury	MT120	1956	£1.50	£4	chart single
My Secret	7"	Mercury	AMT1076	1960	£1.50	£4	
Only You	7"	Ember	JBS701	1962	£60	£120	
Pick Of The Platters No.1	7" EP	Mercury	ZEP10000	1959	£6	£12	
Pick Of The Platters No.2	7" EP	Mercury	ZEP10008	1959	£6	£12	
Pick Of The Platters No.3	7" EP	Mercury	ZEP10025	1959	£6	£12	
Pick Of The Platters No.4	7" EP	Mercury	ZEP10031	1959	£6	£12	
Pick Of The Platters No.5	7" EP	Mercury	ZEP10042	1959	£6	£12	
Pick Of The Platters No.6	7" EP	Mercury	ZEP10056	1960	£7.50	£15	
Pick Of The Platters No.7	7" EP	Mercury	ZEP10070	1960	£7.50	£15	
Platters	LP	Federal	395549	1955	£180	£300	US
Platters	LP	King	LP549	1956	£100	£200	US
Platters	LP	Mercury	MPL6504	1956	£15	£30	
Platters	7" EP	Mercury	MEP9537	1958	£7.50	£15	
Platters	10" LP	Parlophone	PMD1058	1958	£60	£120	
Platters On A Platter	7" EP	Mercury	ZEP10126	1962	£7.50	£15	
Platters On Parade	LP	Mercury	MMC14010	1959	£10	£25	
Platters Vol.2	LP	Mercury	MPL6511	1957	£15	£30	
Red Sails In The Sunset	7"	Mercury	AMT1106	1960	£1.50	£4	
Reflections	LP	Mercury	MMC14045	1960	£6	£15	
Remember When	LP	Mercury	MMC14014	1959	£8	£20	
Remember When	7"	Mercury	AMT1053	1959	£1.50	£4	chart single
Sing Latino	LP	Mercury	MCL20000	1964	£4	£10	
Smoke Gets In Your Eyes	7"	Mercury	AMT1016	1958	£2.50	£6	chart single
Sweet Sweet Lovin'	7"	Stateside	SS2067	1967	£4	£8	
Tenth Anniversary Album	LP	Wing	WL1174	1967	£4	£10	
To Each His Own	7"	Mercury	AMT1118	1960	£1.50	£4	
Twilight Time	7"	Mercury	7MT214	1958	£5	£10	chart single
Washed Ashore	7"	Stateside	SS2042	1967	£4	£8	
With This Ring	7"	Stateside	SS2007	1967	£2.50	£6	
With This Ring	7"	Stateside	SS2150	1969	£2	£5	
You're Making A Mistake	7"	Mercury	7MT227	1958	£6	£12	

PLAY DEAD

Poison Takes A Hold	7"	Fresh	FRESH29	1981	£1.50	£4	
This Side Of Heaven	7"	Tanz	TANZ1	1985	£2	£5	promo only
TV Eye	7"	Fresh	FRESH38	1981	£1.50	£4	

PLAYBOYS

Over The Weekend	7"	London	HLU8681	1958	£12.50	£25	

PLAYERS

Mockingbird	7"	Oriole	CB1861	1963	£4	£8	

PLAYGIRLS

Hey Sport	7"	RCA	RCA1133	1959	£4	£8	

PLAYGIRLS (2)

Looks Are Deceiving	7"	Black Swan	WI456	1965	£5	£10	

PLAYGROUND

At The Zoo	7"	MGM	MGM1351	1967	£1.50	£4	
Rain, The Wind And Other Things	7"	Decca	F13011	1970	£1.50	£4	

PLAYMATES

At Play With The Playmates	7" EP	Columbia	SEG7864	1958	£2.50	£6	
Barefoot Girl	7"	Columbia	DB3941	1957	£1.50	£4	
Beep Beep	7"	Columbia	DB4224	1958	£2	£5	
Darling It's Wonderful	7"	Columbia	DB4033	1957	£1.50	£4	
Day I Died	7"	Columbia	DB4207	1958	£1.50	£4	
Don't Go Home	7"	Columbia	DB4151	1958	£1.50	£4	
Jo-Ann	7"	Columbia	DB4084	1958	£1.50	£4	
Let's Be Lovers	7"	Columbia	DB4127	1958	£1.50	£4	
Party Playmates	7" EP	Columbia	SEG7949	1959	£2.50	£6	
Party Playmates No.2	7" EP	Columbia	SEG7966	1960	£2.50	£6	
Star Love	7"	Columbia	DB4288	1959	£1.50	£4	
What Is Love	7"	Columbia	DB4338	1959	£2.50	£6	

PLAYTHINGS

Stop What You're Doing To Me	7"	Pye	7N45212	1970	£1.50	£4	

PLEASE, BOBBY

Your Driver's License Please	7"	London	HLB8507	1957	£75	£150	demo

PLEASURE FAIR

Morning Glory Days	7"	Uni	UN500	1968	£1.50	£4	
Pleasure Fair	LP	UNI	UNL(S)100	1967	£5	£12	

PLEASURE, KING

Golden Days	LP	Vogue	LAE12258	1961	£5	£12	
King Pleasure	7" EP	Vocalion	EPVH1285	1964	£2.50	£6	
King Pleasure	10" LP	Esquire	20066	1956	£25	£50	

PLEASURE SEEKERS

Suzi Quatro was just fifteen when she formed the Pleasure Seekers - an all-girl group that also included her sister Patti, who later turned up as a member of Fanny.

Good Kind Of Hurt	7"	Mercury	72800	1968	£7.50 .....£15	US
Never Thought You'd Leave Me	7"	Hideout	1006	1967	£30 ......£60	US

PLEASURES

Music City	7"	Sue	WI357	1965	£5 ....£10

PLEBS

Bad Blood	7"	Decca	F12006	1964	£10 ......£20

PLEXUS

Plexus	LP	Look	LKLP6175	1978	£6 ....£15

PLUMMERS

Litle Stars	7"	Blue Beat	BB260	1964	£5 ....£10

PLUS

Seven Deadly Sins	LP	Probe	SPB1009	1970	£8 ....£20

PLUTO

I Really Want It	7"	Dawn	DNS1026	1972	£7.50 .....£15
Pluto	LP	Dawn	DNLS3030	1972	£40 ......£80
Rag A Bone Joe	7"	Dawn	DNS1017	1971	£7.50 .....£15

POACHER, CYRIL

Broomfield Wager	LP	Topic	12TS252	1975	£5 ....£12

POCO

Cantamos	LP	Epic	PEQ33192	1974	£5 ....£12	US quad
Crazy Eyes	LP	Epic	EQ32354	1973	£5 ....£12	US quad
Deliverin'	LP	Epic	EQ30209	1971	£5 ....£12	US quad
Legend	LP	Mobile Fidelity	MFSL1020	1978	£5 ....£12	US audiophile

POET & THE ONE MAN BAND

Poet & The One Man Band featured neither a poet nor a one man band, but instead was the home for some subsequently well known musicians - notably guitarists Albert Lee and Jerry Donahue and bass player Pat Donaldson. The group was not able to survive the collapse of its record company, but eventually metamorphosed into Heads, Hands And Feet.

Poet & The One Man Band	LP	Verve	SVLP6012	1969	£15 ......£30

POETS

Alone Am I	7"	Pye	7N17668	1968	£35 ......£70	
Baby Don't You Do It	7"	Immediate	IM024	1966	£20 ......£40	
Call Again	7"	Immediate	IM006	1965	£20 ......£40	
Heyla Hola	7"	Strike Cola	SC1	1971	£10 ......£20	
I Am So Blue	7"	Decca	F12195	1965	£7.50 .....£15	
Now We're Thru	7"	Decca	F11995	1964	£4 ....£8	chart single
That's The Way It's Got To Be	7"	Decca	F12074	1965	£15 ......£30	
Wooden Spoon	7"	Decca	F12569	1967	£35 ......£70	

POETS (2)

She Blew A Good Thing	7"	United Artists	UP35308	1971	£1.50 .....£4

POGUE MAHONE

Dark Streets Of London	7"	Rough Trade	PM1	1984	£2 ....£5 ....no PS

POGUES

Boys From The County Hell	7"	Stiff	BUY212	1984	£4 ....£8	
Dark Streets Of London	7"	Stiff	BUY207	1984	£2 ....£5	no PS
Dirty Old Town	7"	Stiff	PBUY229	1985	£2 ....£5	pic disc
Dirty Old Town	12"	Stiff	BUYIT229	1985	£4 ....£10	
Dirty Old Town	12"	Stiff	BUYIT229	1985	£6 ....£15	with poster
Dirty Old Town	12"	Stiff	MAIL3	1985	£4 ....£10	mail order
Haunted	12"	MCA	MCAT1084	1986	£2.50 .....£6	with poster
Pair Of Brown Eyes	7"	Stiff	DBUY220	1985	£5 ....£10	pic disc
Pair Of Brown Eyes	12"	Stiff	BUYIT220	1985	£4 ....£10	
Poguetry In Motion	7"	Stiff	PBUY243	1986	£1.50 .....£4	
Sally MacLennane	7"	Stiff	BUY224	1985	£2.50 .....£6	green vinyl, wraparound PS
Sally MacLennan	7"	Stiff	DBUY224	1985	£4 ....£8	shaped pic disc
Sally MacLennan	12"	Stiff	BUYIT224	1985	£3 ....£8	

POLICE

In addition to the various coloured vinyl releases, picture discs, and other limited edition rarities issued by the Police, there is an American version of "Ghost In The Machine" too rare to be given a realistic value. This is a picture disc, with red LED lights set into the vinyl, along with the (small!) batteries to operate them. Whether it was ever intended to issue this commercially is not clear, but in the event only ten copies were actually produced.

Can't Stand Losing You	7"	A&M	AM214	1979	£7.50 .....£15	US badge shaped pic disc
Can't Stand Losing You	7"	A&M	AMS7381	1978	£4 ....£8	red, yellow, or green vinyl
Can't Stand Losing You	7"	A&M	AMS7381	1979	£2.50 .....£6	white vinyl
Don't Stand So Close To Me	7"	A&M	SP3720	1981	£7.50 .....£15	US star shaped pic disc
Every Breath You Take	7"	A&M	AM117	1983	£4 ....£8	double
Every Breath You Take	7"	A&M	AMSP117	1983	£2 ....£5	pic disc
Fall Out	7"	Illegal	IL001	1977	£4 ....£8	black & white PS
Ghost In The Machine	LP	Nautilus	NR40	1982	£6 ....£15	US audiophile
Message In A Bottle	7"	A&M		1979	£7.50 .....£15	US badge shaped pic disc

Title	Format	Label	Cat. No.	Year	Price	Price	Notes
Message In A Bottle	7"	A&M	PR4400	1980	£7.50	£15	US star shaped pic disc
Outlandos D'Amour	LP	A&M	AMLH68502	1978	£5	£12	blue vinyl
Police Enquiry	LP	A&M	SAMP13	1981	£4	£10	interview promo
Police Pack	7"	A&M	AMPP6001	1980	£10	£20	6x7', blue vinyl
Regatta De Blanc	10" LP	A&M	AMLT64792	1979	£6	£15	double
Roxanne	7"	A&M	2096/2147	1979	£7.50	£15	US badge shaped pic disc
Roxanne	7"	A&M	AMS7348	1978	£1.50	£4	telephone PS
Roxanne	12"	A&M	AMS7348	1978	£4	£10	telephone PS
Spirits In The Material World	7"	A&M	AMS8194	1981	£2	£5	poster sleeve, badge
Wrapped Around Your Finger	7"	A&M	AMP127	1983	£2.50	£6	pic disc (Stewart or Andy)
Wrapped Around Your Finger	7"	A&M	AMP127	1983	£1.50	£4	pic disc (Sting)
Zenyatta Mondatta	LP	Nautilus	NR19	1981	£6	£15	US audiophile

POLITICIANS

Politicians	7"	Hot Wax	SHW5007	1972	£6	£12	

POLK, FRANK

Trying To Keep Up With The Joneses	7"	Capitol	CL15389	1965	£7.50	£15	

POLLACK, BEN

Dixieland	LP	London	LTZC15081	1957	£5	£12	

POLLARD, RAY

Drifter	7"	United Artists	UP1111	1965	£50	£100	
It's A Sad Thing	7"	United Artists	UP1133	1966	£25	£50	

POLYPHONY

Polyphony	LP	Zella		1973	£75	£150	

POLYROCK

The album made by Polyrock in 1980 is destined for rediscovery as soon as people realise that it represents a surprising foray by minimalist composer Philip Glass into the world of rock music (predating his better known collaboration with the likes of Paul Simon and Linda Ronstadt, "Songs From Liquid Days" by some six years). Glass's role with Polyrock is akin to that of Brian Eno on the early Talking Heads albums - he produces and plays keyboards and generally leaves his aesthetic sensibilities to permeate through the music. The result is quite like the music of Talking Heads, in fact, but with a distinctly original slant.

Polyrock	LP	RCA	PL43502	1980	£4	£10	

POMEROY, HERB

Life Is A Many-Splendoured Gig	LP	Columbia	33SX1091	1958	£10	£25	

PONI-TAILS

Born Too Late	7"	HMV	POP516	1958	£2.50	£6	chart single
Close Friends	7"	HMV	POP558	1958	£2	£5	
Early To Bed	7"	HMV	POP596	1959	£2.50	£6	chart single
I'll Be Seeing You	7"	HMV	POP663	1959	£2	£5	
Moody	7"	HMV	POP644	1959	£2	£5	
Poni-Tails	7" EP	HMV	7EG8427	1957	£12.50	£25	

PONTY, JEAN-LUC

Ponty is a rather fine jazz violinist, who during the course of a long career has played with both Frank Zappa and John McLaughlin (and managed to annoy both of them, apparently). The "King Kong" album is effectively part of Frank Zappa's oeuvre - he produced the record and plays guitar on the one track he did not actually write.

Astrorama	LP	Far East	65016	1970	£5	£12	
Electric Connection	LP	Liberty	LBL/LBS83262	1969	£5	£12	
Experience	LP	Pacific Jazz	PJ20168	1969	£5	£12	US
King Kong	LP	Liberty	LBS83375	1970	£5	£12	
Open Strings	LP	MPS	68088	1972	£4	£10	German
Sunday Walk	LP	MPS	0068226	197-	£4	£10	German
Sunday Walk	LP	MPS	15045	1967	£6	£15	German

POOGY

She Looked Me In The Eye	7"	EMI	EMI2136	1974	£5	£10	

POOH STICKS

1-2-3 Red Light	7"	Fierce	FRIGHT021	1988	£6	£12	
Alan McGee	CD-s	Fierce	FRIGHT026	1988	£5	£12	
Alan McGee	CD-s	Fierce	FRIGHT026	1988	£6	£15	boxed, booklet
Dying For It	7"	Fierce	FRIGHT034	1989	£6	£12	
Dying For It	7"	Fierce	FRIGHT034	1989	£2.50	£6	1 sided
Dying For It	7"	Fierce	FRIGHT034	1989	£7.50	£15	autographed
Fierce Box Set	7"	Fierce	FRIGHT021-025	1988	£25	£50	5 one-sided singles
Go Go Girl	7"	Cheree	3	1989	£1.50	£4	flexi
Hard On Love	7"	Woosh	WOOSH7	1989	£4	£8	yellow flexi with fanzine
Million Seller	7"	Fierce	FRIGHT42	1992	£7.50	£15	1 sided
On Tape	7"	Fierce	FRIGHT011	1988	£20	£40	
Orgasm	LP	53rd & 3rd	AGAMC5	1989	£8	£20	pink vinyl
Pooh Sticks	LP	Fierce	FRIGHT025	1989	£5	£12	
Trade Mark Of Quality	LP	Fierce	FRIGHT035	1990	£8	£20	

POOLE, BRIAN

Everything I Touch Turns To Tears	7"	CBS	202349	1966	£5	£10	
Hey Girl	7"	Decca	F12402	1966	£1.50	£4	
Just How Loud	7"	CBS	3005	1967	£2.50	£6	
Send Her To Me	7"	President	PT239	1969	£1.50	£4	
That Reminds Me Baby	7"	CBS	202661	1967	£1.50	£4	
What Do Women Most Desire	7"	President	PT264	1969	£1.50	£4	

POOLE, BRIAN & THE TREMELOES

After A While	7"	Decca	F12124	1965	£1.50	£4	
Big Hits Of 1962	LP	Ace Of Clubs	ACL1146	1963	£15	£30	
Brian Poole & The Tremeloes	7" EP	Decca	DFE8566	1964	£7.50	£15	
Brian Poole & The Tremeloes Vol.2	7" EP	Decca	DFE8610	1965	£7.50	£15	
Brian Poole Is Here	LP	Audio Fidelity	2151/6151	1966	£8	£20	US
Candy Man	7"	Decca	F11823	1964	£1.50	£4	chart single
Candy Man	7" EP	Decca	457027	1964	£7.50	£15	French
Do You Love Me	7"	Decca	F11739	1963	£1.50	£4	chart single
Do You Love Me	7" EP	Decca	457017	1963	£7.50	£15	French
Good Lovin'	7"	Decca	F12274	1965	£1.50	£4	
I Can Dance	7"	Decca	F11771	1963	£1.50	£4	chart single
I Want Candy	7"	Decca	F12197	1965	£1.50	£4	chart single
It's About Time	LP	Decca	LK4685	1965	£8	£20	
Keep On Dancing	7"	Decca	F11616	1963	£2	£5	
Meet Me Where We Used To Meet	7"	Decca	F11567	1963	£2	£5	
Someone Someone	7"	Decca	F11893	1964	£1.50	£4	chart single
That Ain't Right	7"	Decca	F11515	1962	£2	£5	
Three Bells	7"	Decca	F12037	1964	£1.50	£4	chart single
Time Is On My Side	7" EP	Decca	457064	1965	£7.50	£15	French
Tremeloes Are Here	LP	Audio Fidelity	2177/6177	1967	£8	£20	US
Twelve Steps To Love	7"	Decca	F11951	1964	£1.50	£4	chart single
Twenty Miles	7" EP	Decca	457034	1964	£7.50	£15	French
Twist And Shout	LP	Decca	LK4550	1963	£15	£30	
Twist And Shout	7"	Decca	F11694	1963	£1.50	£4	chart single
Twist Little Sister	7"	Decca	F11455	1962	£2	£5	

POOLE, LOU & LAURA

Only You And I Know	7"	Jay Boy	BOY63	1972	£1.50	£4	

POOR SOULS

Love Me	7"	Alp	595004	1966	£12.50	£25	
When My Baby Cries	7"	Decca	F12183	1965	£6	£12	

POP GROUP

For How Much Longer Do We Tolerate Mass Murder	LP	Rough Trade	ROUGH9	1980	£4	£10	with 4 posters
Y	LP	Radar	RAD20	1979	£5	£12	with poster

POP, IGGY

Five Foot One	7"	Arista	ARIST274	1979	£1.50	£4	pic disc

POP, IGGY & THE STOOGES

Fun House	LP	Elektra	2410009	1970	£5	£12	
Fun House	LP	Elektra	EKS74071	1970	£10	£25	
Fun House	LP	Elektra	K42051	1971	£5	£12	
Metallic K.O.	LP	Skydog	SGIS008	1976	£4	£10	French
Raw Power	LP	CBS	65586	1973	£6	£15	with inner sleeve
Stooges	LP	Elektra	EKS74051	1969	£15	£30	
Stooges	LP	Elektra	K42032	1971	£5	£12	

POP RIVITS

Empty Sounds From Anarchy Ranch	LP	Hipocrite	HIP0	1979	£6	£15	
Greatest Hits	LP	Hipocrite	HIP007	1979	£5	£12	
Fun In THe UK	7"	Hypocrite	JIM1	1979	£4	£8	double
Pop Rivits	7"	Hypocrite	HEP002	1979	£1.50	£4	
Pop Rivits EP	7"	Hypocrite	HEP001	1979	£2	£5	

POP TOPS

Oh Lord, Why Lord	7" EP	Princess	745001	196-	£4	£8	French

POP WILL EAT ITSELF

Beaver Patrol	7"	Chapter 22	LCHAP16	1987	£2	£5	pink or clear vinyl
Love Missile F1-11 (Designer Grebo Mix)	12"	Chapter 22	L12CHAP13	1987	£3	£8	
Poppies Say Grrr	7"	Desperate	DAN1	1986	£1.50	£4	orange sleeve
Poppies Say Grrr	7"	Desperate	SRT1	1986	£7.50	£15	brown paper sleeve
There Is No Love Between Us Anymore	12"	Chapter 22	L12CHAP20	1988	£2.50	£6	
There Is No Love Between Us Anymore (High Mix)	12"	Chapter 22	CLUBCHAP20	1988	£3	£8	

POP WORKSHOP

Fairyland	7"	Page One	POF091	1968	£1.50	£4	
Punch And Judy Man	7"	Page One	POF129	1969	£2	£5	

POPCORN BLIZZARD

The "Once Upon A Time" single marks the recording debut of Marvin Aday, better known by his stage name, Meat Loaf.

Once Upon A Time	7"	Magenta		1967	£15	£30	US

POPCORNS

Zero Zero	7"	Columbia	DB4968	1963	£1.50	£4	

POPE, TIM

I Want To Be A Tree	7"	Fiction	FICS21	1984	£4	£8	
I Want To Be A Tree	12"	Fiction	FICSX21	1984	£6	£15	

POPOL VUH

Affenstunde	LP	Liberty	LBS83460	1971	£6	£15	German
Aguirre	LP	Barclay	840103	1975	£5	£12	French
Bruder Des Schattens	LP	Brain	0060167	1978	£4	£10	German

Das Hohelied Salomos	LP	United Artists	UAS29781	1975	£5	£12	German
Einsjager Und Siebenjager	LP	Komische	KM58017	1975	£5	£12	German double
Herz Aus Glas	LP	Brain	0060079	1977	£4	£10	German
Hosanna Mantra	LP	Pilz	20291431	1973	£8	£20	German
In Der Garten Pharaos	LP	Pilz	20212769	1972	£8	£20	German
Letzte Tage Letzte Nachte	LP	United Artists	UAS29916	1976	£5	£12	German
Nosferatu	LP	Egg	900573	1978	£4	£10	French
Perlenklanged	LP	PDU	6073	1977	£4	£10	Italian
Seligpreisung	LP	Komische	KM58009	1974	£5	£12	German
Tantric Songs	LP	Brain	0060242	1979	£4	£10	German
Yoga	LP	PDU	6060	1976	£5	£12	Italian

POPOL VUH (2)

Popol Vuh	LP	Polydor	2923009	1972	£8	£20	Norwegian
Quiche Maya	LP	Polydor	2382038	1973	£8	£20	Norwegian

POPPIES

Lullaby Of Love	7"	Columbia	DB7879	1966	£6	£12

POPPYHEADS

Cremation Town	7"	Sarah	006	1988	£2	£5	with poster
Postcard For Flossy	7"	Sha La La	004	1988	£2	£5	flexi

POPULAR FIVE

I'm A Lovemaker	7"	Minit	MLF11011	1968	£4	£8

PORTER & CALYPSO STAR BAND

Cinemascope	7"	Kalypso	XX11	1960	£2	£5

PORTER, NOLAN

If I Could Only Be Sure	7"	Probe	PRO580	1972	£2	£5

PORTION CONTROL

Hit The Pulse	LP	In Phaze	EZ2	1983	£5	£12
Raise The Pulse	12"	Illuminated	ILL2612	1984	£2.50	£6
Rough Justice	12"	Illuminated	ILL3212	1984	£2.50	£6
Step Forward	LP	Illuminated	JAMS44	1984	£4	£10
Surface And Be Seen	12"	In Phaze	PORCON006	1982	£4	£10

PORTOBELLO EXPLOSION

We Can Fly	7"	Carnaby	CNS4001	1969	£10	£20

POSEY, SANDY

Best Of Sandy Posey	LP	MGM	CS8060	1968	£4	£10	
Born A Woman	LP	MGM	C(S)8035	1967	£5	£12	
Born A Woman	7"	MGM	MGM1321	1966	£1.50	£4	chart single
Looking At You	LP	MGM	C(S)8073	1968	£4	£10	
Sandy Posey	LP	MGM	C(S)8051	1968	£4	£10	
Single Girl	LP	MGM	C(S)8042	1967	£4	£10	
Single Girl	7"	MGM	MGM1330	1966	£1.50	£4	chart single

POSITIVELY THIRTEEN O'CLOCK

Psychotic Reaction	7" EP	Vogue	INT18099	1966	£25	£50	French, B side by TV & The Tribesmen

POST, HOWIE & THE SWIFTIES

Tom Swift	7"	Fontana	TF421	1963	£2.50	£6

POSTER, ADRIENNE

He Doesn't Love Me	7"	Decca	F12079	1965	£5	£10
Only Fifteen	7"	Decca	F11797	1963	£1.50	£4
Shang A Doo Lang	7"	Decca	F11864	1964	£2.50	£6
Something Beautiful	7"	Decca	F12329	1966	£4	£8
They Long To Be Close To You	7"	Decca	F12455	1966	£1.50	£4
Winds That Blow	7"	Decca	F12181	1965	£4	£8

POTATOES

Bend	7"	Fontana	TF756	1966	£2	£5

POTEMKINE

Foetus	LP	Tapioca	TP10008	1976	£6	£15	French
Nicolas II	LP	Phaeton	7801	1978	£4	£10	French

POTLIQUOR

First Taste	LP	Dawn	DNLS3016	1971	£30	£60

POTTER, PHIL

My Song Is Love Unknown	LP	Genesis	GEN10	197-	£8	£20
Restorer	LP	Dove	DOVE61	1979	£4	£10

POUND HOUNDS

Home Sweet Home	7"	Brunswick	05484	1955	£1.50	£4	Mellomen B side

POUNDS, ALAN GET RICH

Searching In The Wilderness	7"	Parlophone	R5532	1966	£75	£150

POWELL, BOBBY

Peace Begins Within	7"	Mojo	2092034	1972	£2	£5

POWELL, BUD

Amazing Bud Powell Vol.1	LP	Blue Note	BLP/BST81503	1963	£10	£25
Amazing Bud Powell Vol.2	LP	Blue Note	BLP/BST81504	1964	£10	£25

At The Blue Note Cafe	LP	Fontana	SFJL924	1969	£4	£10
Blues For Bouffemont	LP	Fontana	SFJL901	1968	£4	£10
Blues For Bud	LP	Columbia	33CX10123	1958	£10	£25
Bouncing With Bud	LP	XTRA	XTRA1011	1965	£4	£10
Bud Powell	7" EP	Columbia	SEB10013	1955	£2	£5
Bud Powell Trio	7" EP	Vogue	EPV1030	1955	£2	£5
Bud Powell Trio	7" EP	Vogue	EPV1036	1955	£2	£5
Bud Powell Trio	10" LP	Columbia	33C9016	1956	£20	£40
Bud Powell Trio	10" LP	Vogue	LDE010	1952	£30	£60
Bud Powell Trio Featuring Max Roach	LP	Columbia	33SX1575	1963	£6	£15
Bud Powell's Modernists	7" EP	Vogue	EPV1033	1955	£2	£5
Genius Of Bud Powell	7" EP	Columbia	SEB10074	1957	£2	£5
Genius Of Bud Powell No.2	7" EP	Columbia	SEB10094	1958	£2	£5
Jazz At Massey Hall	LP	Vogue	LAE558	1964	£6	£15
Jazz Original	LP	Columbia	33CX10069	1957	£20	£40
Lonely One	LP	HMV	CLP1294	1959	£8	£20
Return Of Bud Powell	LP	Columbia	33SX1701	1965	£5	£12
Scene Changes	LP	Blue Note	BLP/BST84009	196-	£10	£25
Time Waits	LP	Blue Note	BLP/BST81598	196-	£10	£25
Vintage Years	LP	Verve	VLP9075	1964	£4	£10

POWELL, JANE

Jane Powell	LP	HMV	CLP1131	1957	£5	£12
Jane Powell Sings	7" EP	MGM	MGMEP701	1959	£5	£10
King And I	7" EP	MGM	MGMEP584	1957	£2	£5
Three Sailors And A Girl	10" LP	Capitol	LC6665	1954	£5	£12
True Love	7"	HMV	POP267	1956	£1.50	£4

POWELL, JIMMY

I Can Go Down	7"	Strike	JH309	1966	£2.50	£6
I Just Can't Get Over You	7"	Decca	F12751	1968	£4	£8
Remember Then	7"	Decca	F11570	1963	£2	£5
Sugar Babe	7"	Decca	F11447	1962	£2	£5
Sugar Babe	7"	Decca	F12793	1968	£2	£5
Sugar Babe	7"	Pye	7N15735	1964	£6	£12
That's Alright	7"	Pye	7N15663	1964	£12.50	£25
Tom Hark	7"	Decca	F11544	1962	£2	£5
Unexpected Mirrors	7"	Decca	F12664	1967	£4	£8

POWELL, KEITH

Answer Is No	7"	Columbia	DB7116	1963	£4	£8
Come Here Baby	7"	Piccadilly	7N35249	1965	£1.50	£4
Goodbye Girl	7"	Piccadilly	7N35275	1966	£1.50	£4
I Should Know Better	7"	Columbia	DB7366	1964	£7.50	£15
It Keeps Rainin'	7"	Piccadilly	7N35353	1966	£2.50	£6
People Get Ready	7"	Piccadilly	7N35235	1965	£2	£5
Tore Up	7"	Columbia	DB7229	1964	£4	£8
Victory	7"	Piccadilly	7N35300	1966	£1.50	£4

POWELL, KEITH & BILLIE DAVIS

Swingin' Tight	7"	Piccadilly	7N35340	1966	£1.50	£4
When You Move You Lose	7"	Piccadilly	7N35288	1966	£2	£5
You Don't Know Like I Know	7"	Piccadilly	7N35321	1966	£2.50	£6

POWELL, MARILYN

All My Loving	7"	Fontana	TF448	1964	£2	£5

POWELL, MEL

Borderline	LP	Vanguard	PPL11001	1956	£6	£15
Thingamagig	LP	Vanguard	PPL11000	1956	£6	£15

POWELL, SELDON

Seldon Powell Plays	LP	Vogue	LAE12184	1959	£6	£15
Seldon Powell Sextet	LP	Vogue	LAE12201	1959	£8	£20

POWELL, SPECS

Movin' In	LP	Columbia	33SX1083	1958	£5	£12

POWER, DUFFY

Davy O'Brien	7"	Parlophone	R5631	1967	£1.50	£4
Dream Lover	7"	Fontana	H194	1959	£4	£8
Duffy Power	LP	GSF	GS502	1973	£5	£12
Duffy Power	LP	Spark	SRLM2005	1973	£5	£12
Hey Girl	7"	Parlophone	R5059	1963	£2.50	£6
I Saw Her Standing There	7"	Parlophone	R5024	1963	£10	£20
Innovations	LP	Transatlantic	TRA229	1971	£6	£15
It Ain't Necessarily So	7"	Parlophone	R4992	1963	£5	£10
I've Got Nobody	7"	Fontana	H302	1961	£1.50	£4
Kissing Time	7"	Fontana	H214	1959	£2.50	£6
No Other Love	7"	Fontana	H344	1961	£1.50	£4
Starry Eyed	7"	Fontana	H230	1959	£2.50	£6
Tired Broke And Busted	7"	Parlophone	R5111	1964	£4	£8
Where Am I	7"	Parlophone	R5169	1964	£2.50	£6
Whole Lotta Shaking Going On	7"	Fontana	H279	1960	£4	£8

POWER, JIMMY

Irish Fiddle Player	LP	Topic	12TS306	1976	£5	£12

POWERHOUSE

Chain Gang	7"	Decca	F12471	1966	£6	£12
Raindrops	7"	Decca	F12507	1966	£2.50	£6

POWERPACK

Title	Format	Label	Cat#	Year			Notes
I'll Be Anything For You	7"	CBS	202551	1967	£2.50	£6	
It Hurts Me So	7"	CBS	202335	1966	£7.50	£15	
Oh Calcutta	7"	Polydor	2001077	1970	£1.50	£4	

POWERS, JOEY

Title	Format	Label	Cat#	Year			Notes
Midnight Mary	7"	Stateside	SS236	1963	£1.50	£4	

PRADO, PEREZ

Title	Format	Label	Cat#	Year			Notes
Cherry Pink And Apple Blossom White	7"	HMV	7M295	1955	£2.50	£6	chart single
Patricia	7"	RCA	RCA1067	1958	£1.50	£4	chart single

PRANNATH, PANDIT

Title	Format	Label	Cat#	Year			Notes
Earth Groove	LP	Transatlantic	TRA193	1969	£6	£15	

PRATT, GRAHAM & EILEEN

Title	Format	Label	Cat#	Year			Notes
Clear Air Of The Day	LP	Cottage	811	1977	£10	£25	

PRATT, PHIL

Title	Format	Label	Cat#	Year			Notes
Sweet Song	7"	Jolly	JY008	1968	£4	£8	Thrillers B side

PRAYING MANTIS

Title	Format	Label	Cat#	Year			Notes
All Day And All Of The Night	7"	Arista	ARIST397	1981	£2	£5	
Soundhouse Tapes	7" EP	Ripper		1980	£4	£8	
Tell Me The Nightmare's Wrong	7"	Jet	JET7026	1982	£1.50	£4	
Time Tells No Lies	LP	Arista	SPART1153	1981	£6	£15	

PREACHERS

Title	Format	Label	Cat#	Year			Notes
Hole In My Soul	7"	Columbia	DB7680	1965	£12.50	£25	
Zeke	7" EP	Barclay	70890	1965	£50	£100	French

PRECIOUS FEW

Title	Format	Label	Cat#	Year			Notes
Young Girl	7"	Pye	7N17510	1968	£1.50	£4	

PRECISIONS

Title	Format	Label	Cat#	Year			Notes
If This Is Love	7"	Track	604014	1967	£4	£8	

PREFAB SPROUT

Title	Format	Label	Cat#	Year			Notes
Lions In My Own Garden	7"	Candle	1	1982	£7.50	£15	no PS
Lions In My Own Garden	7"	Kitchenware	SK4	1983	£2	£5	

PREGNANT INSOMNIA

Title	Format	Label	Cat#	Year			Notes
Wallpaper	7"	Direction	583132	1967	£15	£30	

PREMIERS

Title	Format	Label	Cat#	Year			Notes
Farmer John	LP	Warner Bros	W(S)1565	1964	£15	£30	US
Farmer John	7"	Warner Bros	WB134	1964	£6	£12	
Farmer John	7" EP	Warner Bros	WEP1437	1964	£15	£30	French

PREMO & HOPETON

Title	Format	Label	Cat#	Year			Notes
Your Safekeep	7"	Rio	R139	1967	£4	£8	

PRESELI FOLK

Title	Format	Label	Cat#	Year			Notes
Preseli Folk	LP	private	PRE001	1979	£25	£50	

PRESIDENTS

Title	Format	Label	Cat#	Year			Notes
Candy Man	7"	Decca	F11826	1964	£10	£20	

PRESLEY, ELVIS

Elvis Presley's position as the most popular rock solo artist ever is indisputable and the list of collectable records made by him is correspondingly long. Although American singles are generally outside the scope of the present volume, Presley's Sun singles were felt to be of such historical importance that they have been included. For the same reason, the legendary "Elvis And Janis" South African release is also included. As far as Presley's earliest records in the UK are concerned, the HMV issues are not that rare: they were all enormous sellers at the time of their release. What are rare, however, are copies in anything like mint condition. The values quoted are for these rarities. For records in less than mint condition, the drop in value with deteriorating condition is dramatic - one of the HMV albums, with its cover torn and repaired with selotape and with its playing surface displaying an impressive network of scratches and scars, would be worth a nominal few pounds only, if anything at all. Meanwhile, it should be noted that, with the exception of the last issued records whose sales were quite small in the format, 78rpm releases are worth considerably less than their 45rpm equivalents. Of course, not everything by Elvis Presley is automatically valuable - one example that is not, despite appearances to the contrary, is the double hits compilation, "Elvis's 40 Greatest", pressed on pink vinyl. The record cover proclaims "special pink pressing", but in fact all copies are like this, and the set is very common. Other non-rarities include the picture disc versions of the "Legendary Performer" albums, which are attractive items but not valuable, and any of the vast number of Elvis repackages on RCA's cheap Camden label.

Title	Format	Label	Cat#	Year			Notes
Ain't That Lovin' You Baby	7"	RCA	RCA1422	1964	£1.50	£4	chart single
All Shook Up	78	HMV	POP359	1957	£6	£12	
All Shook Up	78	RCA	RCA1088	1958	£17.50	£35	
All Shook Up	7"	HMV	JO473	1957	£75	£150	export
All Shook Up	7"	HMV	POP359	1957	£37.50	£75	gold label chart single
All Shook Up	7"	HMV	POP359	1957	£12.50	£25	silver label
All Shook Up	7"	RCA	RCA1088	1958	£10	£20	tri-centre
All That I Am	7"	RCA	RCA1545	1966	£1.50	£4	chart single
Aloha From Hawaii Via Satellite	LP	RCA	DPS2040	1973	£5	£12	double
Aloha From Hawaii Via Satellite	LP	RCA	R4P5035	1973	£8	£20	quad double
Aloha From Hawaii Via Satellite	LP	RCA	VPSX6089	1973	£530	£800	US, with 'Chicken of the Sea' sticker
Are You Lonesome Tonight	7"	RCA	RCA1216	1961	£1.50	£4	chart single
Baby I Don't Care	7"	RCA	RCAP332	1983	£2	£5	pic disc
Best Of Elvis	10" LP	HMV	DLP1159	1956	£100	£200	sleeve pictured in Guide
Big Boss Man	7"	RCA	RCA1642	1967	£2.50	£6	
Big Hunk Of Love	78	RCA	RCA1136	1959	£15	£30	

Title	Format	Label	Catalogue	Year	Price	Price	Notes
Big Hunk Of Love	7"	RCA	RCA1136	1959	£5	£10	tri-centre, chart single
Blue Christmas	7"	RCA	RCA1430	1964	£1.50	£4	chart single
Blue Hawaii	LP	RCA	LPM2426	1961	£8	£20	US, black label, 'Long 33 1/3 Play'
Blue Hawaii	LP	RCA	LPM2426	1961	£22.50	£45	US, black label, 'Long 33 1/3 Play', 'Contains The Twist Special'
Blue Hawaii	LP	RCA	LSP2426	1961	£15	£30	US, black label, 'Living Stereo'
Blue Hawaii	LP	RCA	LSP2426	1961	£25	£50	US, black label, 'Living Stereo', 'Contains The Twist Special'
Blue Hawaii	LP	RCA	RD27238	1961	£5	£12	mono, chart LP
Blue Hawaii	LP	RCA	SF5115	1961	£8	£20	stereo
Blue Moon	78	HMV	POP272	1956	£6	£12	
Blue Moon	7"	HMV	POP272	1956	£75	£150	gold label, chart single
Blue Moon	7"	HMV	POP272	1956	£50	£100	silver label
Blue Moon	7"	RCA	RCA2601	1975	£2.50	£6	
Blue River	7"	RCA	RCA1504	1966	£1.50	£4	chart single
Blue Suede Shoes	78	HMV	POP213	1956	£7.50	£15	
Blue Suede Shoes	7"	HMV	7M405	1956	£75	£150	gold label, chart single
Blue Suede Shoes	7"	HMV	7M405	1956	£50	£100	silver label
Bossa Nova Baby	7"	RCA	RCA1374	1963	£1.50	£4	chart single
Californian Holiday	LP	RCA	RD7820	1966	£5	£12	mono, chart LP
Californian Holiday	LP	RCA	SF7820	1966	£6	£15	stereo
Canadian Tribute	LP	RCA	KKL17065	1978	£4	£10	US, yellow vinyl
Christmas Album	LP	RCA	LOC1035	1957	£150	£250	US, black label, 'Long 33 1/3 Play'
Christmas Album	LP	RCA	LPM1951	1958	£25	£50	US, black label, 'Long 33 1/3 Play'
Christmas Album	LP	RCA	RD27052	1957	£30	£60	glossy cover
Christmas Album	LP	RCA	RD27052	1958	£20	£40	matt cover
Clambake	LP	RCA	LPM3893	1967	£37.50	£75	US, black label, 'Monaural'
Clambake	LP	RCA	LPM3893	1967	£45	£90	US, black label, 'Monaural', with photo
Clambake	LP	RCA	LSP3893	1967	£8	£20	US, black label, 'Stereo'
Clambake	LP	RCA	LSP3893	1967	£17.50	£35	US, black label, 'Stereo', with photo
Clambake	LP	RCA	RD7917	1967	£5	£12	mono, chart LP
Clambake	LP	RCA	SF7917	1967	£6	£15	stereo
Clean Up Your Own Backyard	7"	RCA	RCA1869	1969	£1.50	£4	chart single
Collectors' Gold	7" EP	RCA	RCX3	1983	£4	£8	
Crying In The Chapel	7"	RCA	RCA1455	1965	£1.50	£4	chart single
Date With Elvis	LP	RCA	LPM2011	1959	£25	£50	US, black label, 'Long 33 1/3 Play'
Date With Elvis	LP	RCA	LPM2011	1959	£50	£100	US, black label, 'Long 33 1/3 Play', titles on sticker
Date With Elvis	LP	RCA	RD27128	1959	£15	£30	chart LP
Devil In Disguise	7"	RCA	RCA1355	1963	£1.50	£4	chart single
Do The Clam	7"	RCA	RCA1443	1965	£1.50	£4	chart single
Don't	78	RCA	RCA1043	1958	£6	£12	
Don't	7"	RCA	RCA1043	1958	£5	£10	tri-centre, chart single
Don't Cry Daddy	7"	RCA	RCA1916	1970	£1.50	£4	PS, chart single
Double Trouble	LP	RCA	LPM3787	1967	£10	£25	US, black label, 'Monaural'
Double Trouble	LP	RCA	LPM3787	1967	£20	£40	US, black label, 'Monaural', with photo
Double Trouble	LP	RCA	LSP3787	1967	£8	£20	US, black label, 'Stereo'
Double Trouble	LP	RCA	LSP3787	1967	£17.50	£35	US, black label, 'Stereo', with photo
Double Trouble	LP	RCA	RD7892	1967	£5	£12	mono, chart LP
Double Trouble	LP	RCA	SF7892	1967	£6	£15	stereo
Easy Come Easy Go	7" EP	RCA	RCX7187	1967	£12.50	£25	
Elvis	LP	RCA	LPM1382	1956	£25	£50	US, black label, 'Long 33 1/3 Play'
Elvis	LP	RCA	LPM1382	1956	£37.50	£75	US, black label, 'Long 33 1/3 Play', album ads on cover
Elvis	LP	RCA	LPM1382	1956	£470	£700	US, black label, 'Long 33 1/3 Play', alternate 'Old Shep'
Elvis	LP	RCA	LPM1382	1956	£75	£150	US, black label, 'Long 33 1/3 Play', tracks listed as 'band'
Elvis	LP	RCA	LPM1382	1957	£100	£200	US mispress - same song 6 times on one side
Elvis	LP	RCA	LPM1382	1957	£100	£200	US mispress - unbanded
Elvis	LP	RCA	RD8011	1968	£4	£10	mono, chart LP

Title	Format	Label	Cat. No.	Year	Low	High	Notes
Elvis	LP	RCA	SF8378	1973	£4	£10	
Elvis - A Golden Celebration	LP	RCA	PL85172	1985	£15	£30	6 LPs, boxed
Elvis - For LP Fans Only	LP	RCA	RD27120	1959	£15	£30	
Elvis Aron Presley	LP	RCA	CPL83699	1980	£20	£40	8 LPs, booklet, boxed
Elvis Aron Presley Radio Station Sampler	LP	RCA	DJL13781	1980	£8	£20	promo
Elvis Aron Presley Sampler	LP	RCA	DJL13729	1980	£8	£20	promo
Elvis For Everyone	LP	RCA	LPM3450	1965	£8	£20	US, black label, 'Monaural'
Elvis For Everyone	LP	RCA	LSP3450	1965	£10	£25	US, black label, 'Stereo'
Elvis For Everyone	LP	RCA	RD7752	1965	£5	£12	mono, chart LP
Elvis For Everyone	LP	RCA	SF7752	1965	£6	£15	stereo
Elvis For You Vol.1	7" EP	RCA	RCX7142	1964	£12.50	£25	
Elvis For You Vol.2	7" EP	RCA	RCX7143	1964	£12.50	£25	
Elvis In Tender Mood	7" EP	RCA	RCX135	1959	£7.50	£15	tri-centre
Elvis Is Back	LP	RCA	LPM2231	1960	£20	£40	US, black label, 'Long 33 1/3 Play'
Elvis Is Back	LP	RCA	LPM2231	1960	£30	£60	US, black label, 'Long 33 1/3 Play', titles on sticker
Elvis Is Back	LP	RCA	LSP2231	1960	£25	£50	US, black label, 'Living Stereo'
Elvis Is Back	LP	RCA	LSP2231	1960	£37.50	£75	US, black label, 'Living Stereo', song titles on sticker
Elvis Is Back	LP	RCA	RD27171	1960	£6	£15	gatefold mono, chart LP
Elvis Is Back	LP	RCA	SF5060	1960	£10	£25	gatefold stereo
Elvis Now	LP	RCA	SF8266	1972	£4	£10	
Elvis Presley	LP	RCA	LPM1254	1956	£25	£50	US, black label, 'Long 33 1/3 Play', dark pink 'Elvis' on cover
Elvis Presley	LP	RCA	LPM1254	1956	£37.50	£75	US, black label, 'Long 33 1/3 Play', light pink 'Elvis' on cover
Elvis Presley	LP	St.Michael	IMP113	1978	£15	£30	
Elvis Presley	7" EP	RCA	RCX104	1957	£7.50	£15	tri-centre
Elvis Presley Interview Record	LP	RCA	PL80835		£8	£20	promo
Elvis Presley Story	LP	Watermark Inc.	EPS1A13B	1977	£330	£500	promo 13 LP boxed set
Elvis Sails	7" EP	RCA	RCX131	1959	£10	£20	tri-centre
Elvis Sings Christmas Songs	7" EP	RCA	RCX121	1958	£30	£60	round centre, gatefold sleeve
Elvis Sings Christmas Songs	7" EP	RCA	RCX121	1958	£10	£20	tri-centre
Elvis Today	LP	RCA	APD11039	1975	£20	£40	US quad (black label)
Elvis Today	LP	RCA	APD11039	1975	£40	£80	US quad (orange label)
EP Collection	7" EP	RCA	EP1	1982	£25	£50	11 EP set
EP Collection Vol.2	7" EP	RCA	EP2	1983	£25	£50	11 EP set
Flaming Star & Summer Kisses	LP	RCA	RD7723	1965	£10	£25	chart LP
Follow That Dream	7" EP	RCA	RCX211	1962	£4	£8	chart single
Follow That Dream	7" EP	RCA	RCX211	1962	£40	£80	mispressed 2nd side
Fool Such As I	78	RCA	RCA1113	1959	£12.50	£25	
Fool Such As I	7"	RCA	RCA1113	1959	£5	£10	tri-centre, chart single
For LP Fans Only	LP	RCA	LPM1990	1959	£37.50	£75	US, black label, 'Long 33 1/3 Play'
Frankie And Johnny	LP	RCA	LPM3553	1966	£8	£20	US, black label, 'Monaural'
Frankie And Johnny	LP	RCA	LPM3553	1966	£17.50	£35	US, black label, 'Monaural', with photo
Frankie And Johnny	LP	RCA	LSP3553	1966	£8	£20	US, black label, 'Stereo'
Frankie And Johnny	LP	RCA	LSP3553	1966	£17.50	£35	US, black label, 'Stereo', with photo
Frankie And Johnny	LP	RCA	RD7793	1966	£5	£12	mono, chart LP
Frankie And Johnny	LP	RCA	SF7793	1966	£6	£15	stereo
Frankie And Johnny	7"	RCA	RCA1509	1966	£2	£5	chart single
From Elvis In Memphis	LP	Mobile Fidelity	MFSL1059	1980	£5	£12	US audiophile
From Elvis In Memphis	LP	RCA	RD8029	1969	£6	£15	mono
From Elvis In Memphis	LP	RCA	SF8029	1969	£4	£10	stereo
From Memphis To Vegas - From Vegas To Memphis	LP	RCA	SF8080/1	1970	£5	£12	double
Fun In Acapulco	LP	RCA	LPM2756	1963	£8	£20	US, black label, 'Mono'
Fun In Acapulco	LP	RCA	LSP2756	1963	£10	£25	US, black label, 'Living Stereo'
Fun In Acapulco	LP	RCA	RD7609	1963	£5	£12	mono, chart LP
Fun In Acapulco	LP	RCA	SF7609	1963	£6	£15	stereo
GI Blues	LP	RCA	LPM2256	1960	£8	£20	US, black label, 'Long 33 1/3 Play'
GI Blues	LP	RCA	LSP2256	1960	£15	£30	US, black label, 'Living Stereo'
GI Blues	LP	RCA	RD27192	1960	£5	£12	mono, chart LP
GI Blues	LP	RCA	SF5078	1960	£10	£25	stereo
G.I.Blues: The Alternate Takes	7" EP	RCA	RCX1	1982	£5	£10	
G.I.Blues: The Alternate Takes Vol.2	7" EP	RCA	RCX2	1982	£4	£8	

Title	Format	Label	Catalogue	Year	Low	High	Notes
Girl Happy	LP	RCA	LPM3338	1965	£8	£20	US, black label, 'Monaural'
Girl Happy	LP	RCA	LSP3338	1965	£10	£25	US, black label, 'Stereo'
Girl Happy	LP	RCA	RD7714	1965	£5	£12	mono, chart LP
Girl Happy	LP	RCA	SF7714	1965	£6	£15	stereo
Girl Of My Best Friend	78	RCA	RCA1194	1960	£180	£300	
Girl Of My Best Friend	7"	RCA	RCA1194	1960	£2	£5	chart single
Girls Girls Girls	LP	RCA	LPM2621	1962	£8	£20	US, black label, 'Long 33 1/3 Play'
Girls Girls Girls	LP	RCA	LPM2621	1962	£30	£60	US, black label, 'Long 33 1/3 Play', with calendar
Girls Girls Girls	LP	RCA	LSP2621	1962	£15	£30	US, black label, 'Living Stereo'
Girls Girls Girls	LP	RCA	LSP2621	1962	£35	£70	US, black label, 'Living Stereo', with calendar
Girls Girls Girls	LP	RCA	RD7534	1963	£5	£12	mono, chart LP
Girls Girls Girls	LP	RCA	SF7534	1963	£6	£15	stereo
Gold 16 Series	7"	RCA	RCA2694-2709	1977	£20	£40	16 x 7" in cardboard carrier
Golden Records	LP	RCA	LPM1707	1958	£30	£60	US, black label, 'Long 33 1/3 Play', title in blue print
Golden Records	LP	RCA	RB16069	1958	£20	£40	gatefold sleeve, 4 photo pages, chart LP
Golden Records	LP	RCA	RD16069	1958	£10	£25	gatefold sleeve, 2 photo pages
Golden Records	LP	RCA	RD16069	1958	£6	£15	single sleeve, chart LP
Golden Records	LP	RCA	SF8129	1963	£5	£12	stereo
Golden Records Vol.2	LP	RCA	LPM2075	1960	£25	£50	US, black label, 'Long 33 1/3 Play'
Golden Records Vol.2	LP	RCA	RD27159	1959	£10	£25	chart LP
Golden Records Vol.3	LP	RCA	LPM2765	1963	£8	£20	US, black label, 'Mono'
Golden Records Vol.3	LP	RCA	LPM2765	1963	£22.50	£45	US, black label, 'Mono', with book
Golden Records Vol.3	LP	RCA	LSP2765	1963	£10	£25	US, black label, 'Living Stereo'
Golden Records Vol.3	LP	RCA	LSP2765	1963	£25	£50	US, black label, 'Living Stereo', with book
Golden Records Vol.3	LP	RCA	RD7630	1964	£5	£12	mono, chart LP
Golden Records Vol.3	LP	RCA	SF7630	1964	£6	£15	stereo
Golden Records Vol.4	LP	RCA	LPM3921	1968	£180	£300	US, black label, 'Monaural'
Golden Records Vol.4	LP	RCA	LPM3921	1968	£210	£350	US, black label, 'Monaural', with photo
Golden Records Vol.4	LP	RCA	LSP3921	1968	£8	£20	US, black label, 'Stereo'
Golden Records Vol.4	LP	RCA	LSP3921	1968	£35	£70	US, black label, 'Stereo', with photo
Golden Records Vol.4	LP	RCA	RD/SF7924	1968	£6	£15	
Golden Records Vol.4	LP	RCA	RD/SF7924	1968	£8	£20	Never Ending listed on sleeve
Good Luck Charm	7"	RCA	RCA1280	1962	£1.50	£4	chart single
Good Rockin' Tonight	78	Sun	210	1954	£100	£200	US
Good Rockin' Tonight	7"	Sun	210	1954	£250	£400	US
Good Times	LP	RCA	APL10475	1974	£4	£10	
Got A Lot Of Living To Do	78	RCA	RCA1020	1957	£6	£12	
Got A Lot Of Living To Do	7"	RCA	RCA1020	1957	£5	£10	tri-centre, chart single
Greatest Hits	LP	RCA/Readers Digest	GELV6A	1975	£10	£25	7 LPs, booklet, boxed
Guitar Man	7"	RCA	RCA1663	1968	£1.50	£4	chart single
Hard Headed Woman	78	RCA	RCA1070	1958	£7.50	£15	
Hard Headed Woman	7"	RCA	RCA1070	1958	£5	£10	tri-centre, chart single
Harem Holiday	LP	RCA	RD7767	1965	£5	£12	mono, chart LP
Harem Holiday	LP	RCA	SF7767	1965	£6	£15	stereo
Harum Scarum	LP	RCA	LPM3468	1965	£8	£20	US, black label, 'Monaural'
Harum Scarum	LP	RCA	LPM3468	1965	£17.50	£35	US, black label, 'Monaural', with photo
Harum Scarum	LP	RCA	LSP3468	1965	£8	£20	US, black label, 'Stereo'
Harum Scarum	LP	RCA	LSP3468	1965	£17.50	£35	US, black label, 'Stereo', with photo
Having Fun On Stage	LP	Boxcar		1974	£37.50	£75	US
Having Fun On Stage	LP	RCA	APM10818	1974	£5	£12	
He Touched Me	LP	RCA	SF8275	1972	£4	£10	
Heartbreak Hotel	78	HMV	POP182	1956	£6	£12	
Heartbreak Hotel	7"	HMV	7M385	1956	£75	£150	gold label, chart single
Heartbreak Hotel	7"	HMV	7M385	1956	£50	£100	silver label, chart single
Heartbreak Hotel	7"	RCA	RCAMAXI2104	1971	£2	£5	chart single

Title	Format	Label	Catalogue	Year	Price	Price	Notes
His Hand In Mine	LP	RCA	LPM2328	1961	£10	£25	US, black label 'Long 33 1/3 Play
His Hand In Mine	LP	RCA	LSP2328	1961	£17.50	£35	US, black label, 'Living Stereo
His Hand In Mine	LP	RCA	RD27211	1960	£6	£15	mono, chart LP
His Hand In Mine	LP	RCA	SF5094	1960	£10	£25	stereo
His Latest Flame	7"	RCA	RCA1258	1961	£1.50	£4	chart single
Hound Dog	78	HMV	POP249	1956	£6	£12	
Hound Dog	78	RCA	RCA1095	1958	£25	£50	export
Hound Dog	7"	HMV	7MC50	1957	£90	£180	export
Hound Dog	7"	HMV	POP249	1956	£75	£150	gold label, chart single
Hound Dog	7"	HMV	POP249	1956	£50	£100	silver label
Hound Dog	7"	RCA	RCA1095	1958	£12.50	£25	tri-centre
How Great Thou Art	LP	RCA	LPM3758	1967	£10	£25	US, black label, 'Monaural
How Great Thou Art	LP	RCA	LSP3758	1967	£8	£20	US, black label, 'Stereo
How Great Thou Art	LP	RCA	RD/SF7867	1967	£6	£15	chart LP
I Can Help	10"	RCA	RCAP369	1983	£2.50	£6	pic disc
I Want You I Need You I Love You	78	HMV	POP235	1956	£6	£12	
I Want You I Need You I Love You	7"	HMV	7M424	1956	£75	£150	gold label, chart single
I Want You I Need You I Love You	7"	HMV	7M424	1956	£50	£100	silver label
I Want You I Need You I Love You	7"	HMV	7MC45	1957	£90	£180	export
If Every Day Was Like Christmas	7"	RCA	RCA1557	1966	£1.50	£4	chart single
If I Can Dream	7"	RCA	RCA1795	1969	£2	£5	chart single
I'm Left You're Right She's Gone	78	HMV	POP428	1958	£6	£12	
I'm Left You're Right She's Gone	78	Sun	217	1955	£100	£200	US
I'm Left You're Right She's Gone	7"	HMV	POP428	1957	£25	£50	chart single
I'm Left You're Right She's Gone	7"	Sun	217	1955	£250	£400	US
In The Ghetto	7"	RCA	RCA1831	1969	£1.50	£4	chart single
Indescribably Blue	7"	RCA	RCA1565	1967	£2	£5	chart single
International Hotel, Las Vegas, Presents Elvis Presley	LP	RCA	LSP6020	1970	£330	£500	US double LP, 7 various inserts, boxed
It Happened At The World's Fair	LP	RCA	LPM2697	1963	£10	£25	US, black label 'Long 33 1/3 Play
It Happened At The World's Fair	LP	RCA	LPM2697	1963	£50	£100	US, black label, 'Long 33 1/3 Play', with photo
It Happened At The World's Fair	LP	RCA	LSP2697	1963	£15	£30	US, black label, 'Living Stereo
It Happened At The World's Fair	LP	RCA	LSP2697	1963	£60	£120	US, black label, 'Living Stereo with photo
It Happened At The World's Fair	LP	RCA	RD7565	1963	£5	£12	mono, chart LP
It Happened At The World's Fair	LP	RCA	SF7565	1963	£6	£15	stereo
It's Now Or Never	7"	RCA	RCA1207	1960	£1.50	£4	chart single
Jailhouse Rock	LP	MGM		1957	£50	£100	US red vinyl promo with Leiber & Stoller interview
Jailhouse Rock	78	RCA	RCA1028	1958	£6	£12	
Jailhouse Rock	7"	RCA	RCA1028	1958	£5	£10	tri-centre, chart single
Jailhouse Rock	7"	RCA	RCAMAXI2153	1971	£2.50	£6	chart single
Jailhouse Rock	7"	RCA	RCAP1028	1983	£4	£8	B side credits 'Hound Dog
Jailhouse Rock	7"	RCA	RCAP1028	1983	£2.50	£6	pic disc
Jailhouse Rock	7" EP	RCA	RCX106	1958	£6	£12	tri-centre, chart single
Jailhouse Rock (B side not Elvis)	78	Decca		1958	£40	£80	promo
Kentucky Rain	7"	RCA	RCA1949	1970	£1.50	£4	PS, chart single
Kid Galahad	7" EP	RCA	RCX7106	1963	£5	£10	
King Creole	LP	RCA	LPM1884	1958	£30	£60	US, black label 'Long 33 1/3 Play
King Creole	LP	RCA	LPM1884	1958	£60	£120	US, black label 'Long 33 1/3 Play with bonus photo
King Creole	LP	RCA	RD27088	1958	£10	£25	mono, chart LP
King Creole	LP	RCA	SF8231	1963	£8	£20	stereo
King Creole	78	RCA	RCA1081	1958	£7.50	£15	
King Creole	7"	RCA	RCA1081	1958	£6	£12	tri-centre, chart single
King Creole Vol.1	7" EP	RCA	RCX117	1958	£6	£12	tri-centre, black label
King Creole Vol.1	7" EP	RCA	RCX117	1969	£5	£10	orange label
King Creole Vol.2	7" EP	RCA	RCX118	1958	£6	£12	tri-centre
Kiss Me Quick	7"	RCA	RCA1375	1963	£1.50	£4	chart single
Kissin' Cousins	LP	RCA	LPM2894	1964	£22.50	£45	US, black label, 'Mono', no photo on cover
Kissin' Cousins	LP	RCA	LPM2894	1964	£8	£20	US, black label, 'Mono', with photo on cover
Kissin' Cousins	LP	RCA	LSP2894	1964	£25	£50	US, black label 'Living Stereo', no photo on cover
Kissin' Cousins	LP	RCA	LSP2894	1964	£10	£25	US, black label, 'Living Stereo photo on cover
Kissin' Cousins	LP	RCA	RD7645	1964	£5	£12	mono, chart LP
Kissin' Cousins	LP	RCA	SF7645	1964	£6	£15	stereo
Kissin' Cousins	7"	RCA	RCA1404	1964	£1.50	£4	chart single

Title	Format	Label	Catalogue	Year	Low	High	Notes
Lawdy Miss Clawdy	78	HMV	POP408	1957	£7.50	£15	
Lawdy Miss Clawdy	7"	HMV	POP408	1957	£20	£40	chart single
Legend	CD	RCA	PD89000	1983	£90	£180	3 gold discs, boxed
Legend	CD	RCA	PD89000	1983	£25	£50	3 silver discs, boxed
Little Less Conversation	7"	RCA	RCA1768	1968	£2.50	£6	
Live In Memphis	LP	RCA	APD10430	1973	£60	£120	US quad
Long Legged Girl	7"	RCA	RCA1616	1967	£2.50	£6	chart single
Love In Las Vegas	7" EP	RCA	RCX7141	1964	£6	£12	
Love Letters	7"	RCA	RCA1526	1966	£1.50	£4	chart single
Love Letters From Elvis	LP	RCA	SF8202	1971	£4	£10	
Love Machine	7"	RCA	RCA1593	1967	£2.50	£6	chart single
Love Me Tender	78	HMV	POP253	1956	£6	£12	
Love Me Tender	7"	HMV	JO465	1957	£90	£180	export
Love Me Tender	7"	HMV	POP253	1956	£75	£150	gold label, chart single
Love Me Tender	7"	HMV	POP253	1956	£50	£100	silver label
Love Me Tender	7" EP	HMV	7EG8199	1957	£40	£80	
Loving You	LP	RCA	LPM1515	1957	£30	£60	US, black label, 'Long 33 1/3 Play'
Loving You	78	RCA	RCA1013	1957	£6	£12	
Loving You	7"	RCA	RCA1013	1957	£6	£12	tri-centre, chart single
Loving You	10" LP	RCA	RC24001	1957	£20	£40	
Milkcow Blues Boogie	78	Sun	215	1955	£100	£200	US
Milkcow Blues Boogie	7"	Sun	215	1955	£330	£500	US
Moody Blue	LP	RCA	AFL12428	1977	£50	£100	US, black vinyl
Mystery Train	78	HMV	POP295	1957	£10	£20	
Mystery Train	78	Sun	223	1955	£100	£200	US
Mystery Train	7"	HMV	7MC42	1957	£100	£200	export
Mystery Train	7"	HMV	POP295	1957	£75	£150	gold label, chart single
Mystery Train	7"	HMV	POP295	1957	£50	£100	silver label
Mystery Train	7"	Sun	223	1955	£250	£400	US
O Sole Mio	7"	RCA	479314	1961	£7.50	£15	sung in Italian
On Stage February 1970	LP	RCA	SF8128	1970	£4	£10	
One Broken Heart For Sale	7"	RCA	RCA1337	1963	£1.50	£4	chart single
One Night	78	RCA	RCA1100	1959	£7.50	£15	
One Night	7"	RCA	RCA1100	1959	£2.50	£6	tri-centre, chart single
Paradise Hawaiian Style	LP	RCA	LPM3643	1966	£8	£20	US, black label, 'Monaural'
Paradise Hawaiian Style	LP	RCA	LSP3643	1966	£8	£20	US, black label, 'Stereo'
Paradise Hawaiian Style	LP	RCA	RD7810	1966	£5	£12	mono, chart LP
Paradise Hawaiian Style	LP	RCA	SF7810	1966	£6	£15	stereo
Paralyzed	78	HMV	POP378	1957	£6	£12	
Paralyzed	7"	HMV	POP378	1957	£35	£70	gold label, chart single
Paralyzed	7"	HMV	POP378	1957	£25	£50	silver label
Peace In The Valley	7" EP	RCA	RCX101	1957	£10	£20	tri-centre
Pot Luck	LP	RCA	RD27265	1962	£5	£12	mono, chart LP
Pot Luck	LP	RCA	SF5135	1962	£8	£20	stereo
Pot Luck With Elvis	LP	RCA	LPM2523	1962	£15	£30	US, black label, 'Long 33 1/3 Play'
Pot Luck With Elvis	LP	RCA	LSP2523	1962	£20	£40	US, black label, 'Living Stereo'
Promised Land	LP	RCA	APD10873	1974	£20	£40	US quad (black label)
Promised Land	LP	RCA	APD10873	1974	£40	£80	US quad (orange label)
Promised Land	LP	RCA	APL10873	1975	£4	£10	
Pure Elvis	LP	RCA	DJL13455	1980	£100	£200	US promo
Rags To Riches	7"	RCA	RCA2084	1971	£1.50	£4	PS, chart single
Raised On Rock	7"	RCA	APL10388	1973	£4	£10	
Return To Sender	7"	RCA	RCA1320	1962	£1.50	£4	chart single
Rip It Up	78	HMV	POP305	1957	£12.50	£25	
Rip It Up	7"	HMV	POP305	1957	£75	£150	gold label, chart single
Rip It Up	7"	HMV	POP305	1957	£50	£100	silver label
Rock-A-Hula Baby	7"	RCA	RCA1270	1962	£1.50	£4	
Rock'n'Roll	LP	HMV	CLP1093	1956	£100	£200	chart LP, sleeve pictured in Guide
Rock'n'Roll No.2	LP	HMV	CLP1105	1956	£100	£200	sleeve pictured in Guide
Rock'n'Roll No.2	LP	RCA	RD7528	1962	£6	£15	mono, chart LP
Rock'n'Roll No.2	LP	RCA	SF7528	1962	£8	£20	stereo
Roustabout	LP	RCA	LPM2999	1964	£10	£25	US, black label, 'Mono'
Roustabout	LP	RCA	LSP2999	1964	£150	£250	US, black label, 'Living Stereo'
Roustabout	LP	RCA	LSP2999	1964	£10	£25	US, black label, 'Stereo'
Roustabout	LP	RCA	RD7678	1965	£5	£12	mono, chart LP
Roustabout	LP	RCA	SF7678	1965	£6	£15	stereo
Santa Bring My Baby Back	78	RCA	RCA1025	1957	£6	£12	
Santa Bring My Baby Back	7"	RCA	RCA1025	1957	£7.50	£15	tri-centre, chart single
She's Not You	7"	RCA	RCA1303	1962	£1.50	£4	chart single
Singer Presents Elvis	LP	RCA	PRS279	1968	£6	£15	US
Singer Presents Elvis	LP	RCA	PRS279	1968	£8	£20	US, with photo
Sings The Wonderful World Of Christmas	LP	RCA	SF8221	1971	£4	£10	
Something For Everybody	LP	RCA	LPM2370	1961	£10	£25	US, black label, 'Long 33 1/3 Play'

Title	Format	Label	Catalogue	Year	Price	Price	Notes
Something For Everybody	LP	RCA	LSP2370	1961	£17.50	£35	US, black label, 'Living Stereo'
Something For Everybody	LP	RCA	RD27244	1961	£6	£15	mono, chart LP
Something For Everybody	LP	RCA	SF5106	1961	£8	£20	stereo
Sound Of Your Cry	7"	RCA	RCAP232	1982	£2	£5	pic disc
Special Palm Sunday Programme	LP	RCA	SP33461	1967	£400	£600	US promo
Speedway	LP	RCA	LPM3989	1968	£250	£400	US, black label, 'Monaural'
Speedway	LP	RCA	LPM3989	1968	£250	£400	US, black label, 'Monaural', with photo
Speedway	LP	RCA	LSP3989	1968	£8	£20	US, black label, 'Stereo'
Speedway	LP	RCA	LSP3989	1968	£22.50	£45	US, black label, 'Stereo', with photo
Speedway	LP	RCA	RD7957	1968	£6	£15	mono
Speedway	LP	RCA	SF7957	1968	£8	£20	stereo
Spinout	LP	RCA	LPM3702	1966	£8	£20	US, black label, 'Monaural'
Spinout	LP	RCA	LPM3702	1966	£17.50	£35	US, black label, 'Monaural', with photo
Spinout	LP	RCA	LSP3702	1966	£8	£20	US, black label, 'Stereo'
Spinout	LP	RCA	LSP3702	1966	£17.50	£35	US, black label, 'Stereo', with photo
Strictly Elvis	7" EP	RCA	RCX175	1959	£6	£12	tri-centre, chart single
Stuck On You	78	RCA	RCA1187	1960	£50	£100	
Stuck On You	7"	RCA	RCA1187	1960	£2	£5	chart single
Such A Night	7"	RCA	RCA1411	1964	£2	£5	chart single
Such A Night	7" EP	RCA	RCX190	1960	£6	£12	
Surrender	7"	RCA	RCA1227	1961	£1.50	£4	chart single
Suspicious Minds	7"	RCA	RCA1900	1969	£1.50	£4	PS, chart single
Take Good Care Of Her	7"	RCA	APBO0196	1974	£50	£100	
Tell Me Why	7"	RCA	RCA1489	1965	£2.50	£6	chart single
That's All Right	78	Sun	209	1954	£150	£250	US
That's All Right	7"	Sun	209	1954	£330	£500	US
There Goes My Everything	7"	RCA	RCA2060	1971	£1.50	£4	PS, chart single
There's Always Me	7"	RCA	RCA1628	1967	£10	£20	
Tickle Me Vol.1	7" EP	RCA	RCX7173	1965	£6	£12	
Tickle Me Vol.2	7" EP	RCA	RCX7174	1965	£6	£12	
Today	LP	RCA	RS1011	1975	£4	£10	
Too Much	78	HMV	POP330	1957	£6	£12	
Too Much	7"	HMV	JO466	1957	£90	£180	export
Too Much	7"	HMV	POP330	1957	£50	£100	gold labe
Too Much	7"	HMV	POP330	1957	£37.50	£75	silver labe
Torna A Surrento	7"	RCA	1160	1960	£7.50	£15	sung in Italiar
Touch Of Gold	7" EP	RCA	RCX1045	1959	£7.50	£15	tri-centre
Touch Of Gold Vol.2	7" EP	RCA	RCX1048	1960	£12.50	£25	tri-centre
Truth About Me	78	Weekend Mail		1957	£50	£100	cardboard folder
TV Guide Presents Elvis Presley		RCA	GBMW8705	1956	£2500	£3500	promo
Until It's Time For You To Go	7"	RCA	RCA2188	1972	£1.50	£4	PS, chart single
U.S. Male	7"	RCA	RCA1688	1968	£1.50	£4	chart single
Viva Las Vegas	7"	RCA	RCA1390	1964	£1.50	£4	chart single
Wear My Ring Around Your Neck	78	RCA	RCA1058	1958	£6	£12	
Wear My Ring Around Your Neck	7"	RCA	RCA1058	1958	£5	£10	tri-centre, chart single
Wild In The Country	7"	RCA	RCA1244	1961	£1.50	£4	chart single
Wonder Of You (B side not Elvis)	7"	RCA	LB1	1979	£2	£5	intro by Noel Edmonds
Wonderful World Of Elvis Presley	LP	St.Michael	IMP204	1978	£25	£50	
Wooden Heart	7"	RCA	RCA1226	1961	£1.50	£4	chart single
World 50 Gold Hits Vol.1	LP	RCA	LPM6401	1970	£10	£25	4 LPs booklet, boxed, char L
World 50 Gold Hits Vol.2	LP	RCA	LPM6402	1971	£15	£30	4 LPs, piec of cloth, boxe
You'll Never Walk Alone	7"	RCA	RCA1747	1968	£2.50	£6	chart single
Your Time Hasn't Come Yet Baby	7"	RCA	RCA1714	1968	£1.50	£4	chart single

PRESLEY, ELVIS & JANIS MARTIN

Title	Format	Label	Catalogue	Year	Price	Price	Notes
Elvis And Janis	10" LP	Teal		1958	£1400	£2000	South Africa

PRESLEY, REG

Title	Format	Label	Catalogue	Year	Price	Price	Notes
It's Down To You Marianne	7"	CBS	1478	1973	£1.50	£4	
Lucinda Lee	7"	Page One	POF131	1969	£1.50	£4	

PRESLEY, SID EXPERIENCE

Title	Format	Label	Catalogue	Year	Price	Price	Notes
Cold Turkey	12"	Sid Presley Experience	SPE41	1984	£2.50	£6	
Hup 234	7"	I.D.	EYE4	1984	£2	£5	

PRESS GANG

Title	Format	Label	Catalogue	Year	Price	Price	Notes
Press Gang	LP	Hawk	HALP135	1976	£6	£15	Iris

PRESTIGE BLUES SWINGERS

Title	Format	Label	Catalogue	Year	Price	Price	Notes
Outskirts Of Town	LP	Esquire	32110	1961	£8	£20	

PRESTON, BILLY

Title	Format	Label	Catalogue	Year	Price	Price	Notes
All That I've Got	7"	Apple	21	1970	£1.50	£4	
All That I've Got	7"	Apple	21	1970	£7.50	£15	P

Billy's Bag	7"	President	PT263	1969	£1.50	£4	
Billy's Bag	7"	Sue	WI4012	1966	£5	£10	
Encouraging Words	LP	Apple	SAPCOR14	1969	£8	£20	
Everything's Alright	LP	Apple	19	1969	£2	£5	
Greazee	7"	Soul City	SC107	1969	£4	£8	
Greazee Soul	LP	Soul City	SCM002	1969	£4	£10	
In The Midnight Hour	7"	Capitol	CL15458	1966	£2.50	£6	
Most Exciting Organ Ever	LP	Sue	ILP935	1966	£15	£30	
Sunny	7"	Capitol	CL15471	1966	£1.50	£4	
That's The Way God Planned It	LP	Apple	SAPCOR9	1969	£6	£15	
That's The Way God Planned It	LP	Apple	ST3359	1969	£10	£25	US, face close-up on cover
That's The Way God Planned It	LP	Apple	ST3359	1969	£5	£12	US, multiple Prestons on cover
That's The Way God Planned It	7"	Apple	12	1969	£2	£5	chart single
That's The Way God Planned It	7"	Apple	12	1969	£4	£10	PS
Wildest Organ In Town	LP	Capitol	(S)T2532	1966	£5	£12	

PRESTON, DON

Bluse	LP	A&M	SP4155	1969	£6	£15	US

PRESTON, EARL

That's For Sure	7"	Fontana	TF481	1964	£4	£8	
Watch Your Step	7"	Fontana	TF406	1963	£5	£10	

PRESTON, JOHNNY

Big Chief Heartache	7"	Mercury	AMT1145	1961	£1.50	£4	
Charming Billy	7"	Mercury	AMT1114	1960	£1.50	£4	chart single
Come Rock With Me	LP	Mercury	MG2/SR60609	1961	£15	£30	US
Cradle Of Love	7"	Mercury	AMT1092	1960	£1.50	£4	chart single
Free Me	7"	Mercury	AMT1167	1961	£1.50	£4	
I'm Starting To Go Steady	7"	Mercury	AMT1104	1960	£2.50	£6	chart single
Leave My Kitten Alone	7"	Mercury	AMT1129	1961	£5	£10	
Ring Tail Tooter	7" EP	Mercury	ZEP10098	1960	£17.50	£35	
Rock And Roll Guitar	7"	Mercury	AMT1164	1961	£2.50	£6	
Running Bear	LP	Mercury	MMC14051	1960	£25	£50	
Running Bear	7"	Mercury	AMT1079	1960	£2	£5	chart single
Running Bear	7" EP	Mercury	ZEP10078	1960	£12.50	£25	
Token Of Love	7" EP	Mercury	ZEP10116	1961	£20	£40	

PRESTON, MIKE

As If I Didn't Know	7"	Decca	F11385	1961	£1.50	£4	
Cry Baby	7"	Decca	F11754	1963	£1.50	£4	
Forgive Me	7"	Emerald	MD1028	1964	£1.50	£4	
Four Songs By Ray Noble	7" EP	Decca	DFE6635	1960	£4	£8	
Girl Like You	7"	Decca	F11222	1960	£1.50	£4	
I'd Do Anything	7"	Decca	F11255	1960	£1.50	£4	chart single
In Surabaya	7"	Decca	F11120	1959	£1.50	£4	
Innocent Eyes	7"	Decca	F11440	1962	£1.50	£4	
It's A Sin To Tell A Lie	7"	Decca	F11498	1962	£1.50	£4	
It's All Happening	7"	Decca	F11366	1961	£1.50	£4	
Marry Me	7"	Decca	F11335	1961	£1.50	£4	chart single
Marry Me	7" EP	Decca	DFE6679	1961	£4	£8	
Mr.Blue	7"	Decca	F11167	1959	£1.50	£4	
My First Love Affair	7"	Decca	F11461	1962	£1.50	£4	
My Lucky Love	7"	Decca	F11053	1958	£2	£5	
No Strings	7"	Decca	F11810	1964	£1.50	£4	
Punish Her	7"	Decca	F11613	1963	£1.50	£4	
Till Then My Love	7"	Decca	F12092	1965	£1.50	£4	
Togetherness	7"	Decca	F11287	1960	£1.50	£4	chart single
Why Why Why	7"	Decca	F11087	1958	£1.50	£4	

PRETENDERS

Adultress	7"	Real		1981	£2	£5	promo only
Pretenders	LP	Nautilus	NR38	1981	£6	£15	US audiophile
Pretenders	LP	Real	RAL3	1980	£6	£15	autographed

PRETTY THINGS

The Pretty Things always seemed to suffer from too much labouring in the shadow of the Rolling Stones (Dick Taylor had, of course, been an early member of the Stones), but they nevertheless achieved a fair degree of success and, despite numerous comings and goings on the part of various of the group's members, they are still around and playing. "S.F.Sorrow" has received a fair amount of acclaim for being a kind of rock opera pre-dating the Who's "Tommy", but the group's best work has always been found on their singles. The early Fontana singles are tough, gritty R&B that easily stand comparison with the likes of Them, or even the Rolling Stones. Later, the Columbia singles "Defecting Grey" and "Talkin' About The Good Times" are superb pieces of psychedelia and should definitely be included on any list of the essential recordings of the period.

Children	7"	Fontana	TF829	1967	£5	£10	
Come See Me	7"	Fontana	TF688	1966	£2.50	£6	chart single
Cry To Me	7"	Fontana	TF585	1965	£2	£5	chart single
Defecting Grey	7"	Columbia	DB8300	1967	£6	£12	
Don't Bring Me Down	7"	Fontana	TF503	1964	£2	£5	chart single
Don't Bring Me Down	7" EP	Fontana	465253	1964	£15	£30	French
Emotions	LP	Fontana	(S)TL5425	1967	£10	£25	
Emotions	LP	Fontana	SFL13140	1969	£6	£15	
Freeway Madness	LP	Warner Bros	K46190	1972	£4	£10	
Get The Picture	LP	Fontana	TL5280	1965	£15	£30	
Good Mr.Square	7"	Harvest	HAR5016	1970	£4	£8	
Honey I Need	7"	Fontana	TF537	1965	£2	£5	chart single
House In The Country	7"	Fontana	TF722	1966	£2.50	£6	chart single
I Can Never Say	7" EP	Fontana	465296	1965	£15	£30	French
Midnight To Six Man	7"	Fontana	TF647	1966	£2.50	£6	chart single
Midnight To Six Man	7" EP	Fontana	465310	1966	£15	£30	French

October 26	7"	Harvest	HAR5031	1970	£2.50	£6	
On Film	7" EP..	Fontana	TE17472	1966	£35	£70	
Parachute	LP	Harvest	SHVL774	1970	£6	£15	chart LP
Pretty Things	LP	Fontana	TL5239	1965	£15	£30	chart LP
Pretty Things	LP	Wing	WL1167	1967	£6	£15	
Pretty Things	7" EP..	Fontana	TE17434	1964	£10	£20	
Private Sorrow	7"	Columbia	DB8494	1968	£5	£10	
Progress	7"	Fontana	TF773	1966	£4	£8	
Progress	7" EP..	Fontana	465353	1966	£15	£30	French
Raining In My Heart	7" EP..	Fontana	TE17442	1965	£7.50	£15	
Rosalyn	7"	Fontana	TF1024	1969	£1.50	£4	
Rosalyn	7"	Fontana	TF469	1964	£4	£8	chart single
S.F.Sorrow	LP	Columbia	SCX6306	1968	£10	£25	
S.F.Sorrow/Parachute	LP	Harvest	SHDW406	1975	£6	£15	double
Stone Hearted Mama	7"	Harvest	HAR5037	1971	£2.50	£6	
Talkin' About The Good Times	7"	Columbia	DB8353	1968	£7.50	£15	

PREVIN, ANDRE

Andre Previn	LP	Brunswick	LAT8093	1956	£6	£15	
Double Play	LP	Contemporary.	LAC12142/ SCA5004	1959	£6	£15	with Russ Freeman
Modern Jazz Performances Of Songs From Gigi	LP	Contemporary.	LAC12144	1959	£4	£10	
Pal Joey	LP	Contemporary.	LAC12126	1958	£4	£10	

PREVIN, DORY

Dory Previn	LP	Warner Bros	K56066	1974	£4	£10	
Live At Carnegie Hall	LP	United Artists ..	UAD60045	1973	£6	£15	double
Mary C.Brown And The Hollywood Sign	LP	United Artists ..	UAG29435	1972	£4	£10	
On My Way To Where	LP	United Artists ..	UAG29176	1973	£4	£10	
Reflections In A Mud Puddle	LP	United Artists ..	UAG29346	1972	£4	£10	
We're Children Of Coincidence	LP	Warner Bros	K56213	1976	£4	£10	

PREVOST, EDDIE

Live Vol.1	LP	Matchless	MR1	1978	£5	£12	

PRICE, ALAN

Amazing Alan Price	7" EP..	Decca	DFE8677	1967	£4	£8	
Any Day Now	7"	Decca	F12217	1965	£1.50	£4	
Barefootin'	7" EP..	Decca	457129	1966	£5	£10	French
Don't Stop The Carnival	7"	Decca	F12731	1968	£1.50	£4	chart single
Hi Lili Hi Lo	7"	Decca	F12442	1966	£1.50	£4	chart single
House That Jack Built	7"	Decca	F12641	1967	£1.50	£4	chart single
I Put A Spell On You	7"	Decca	F12367	1966	£1.50	£4	chart single
I Put A Spell On You	7" EP..	Decca	457109	1966	£5	£10	French
Love Story	7"	Decca	F12808	1968	£1.50	£4	US
Price Is Right	LP	Parrot	PAS71018	1968	£4	£10	
Price On His Head	LP	Decca	LK/SKL4907	1967	£5	£12	
Price To Pay	LP	Decca	LK4839	1966	£6	£15	
Shame	7"	Decca	F12691	1967	£1.50	£4	chart single
Simon Smith & His Amazing Dancing Bear	7"	Decca	F12570	1967	£1.50	£4	chart single
Simon Smith And The Amazing Dancing Bear	7" EP..	Decca	457143	1967	£5	£10	French
Trimdon Grange Explosion	7"	Deram	DM263	1969	£1.50	£4	
When I Was A Cowboy	7"	Decca	F12774	1968	£1.50	£4	
Willow Weep For Me	7"	Decca	F12518	1966	£1.50	£4	

PRICE, LLOYD

Another Fairy Tale	7"	HMV	POP983	1962	£1.50	£4	
Boo-Hoo	7"	HMV	POP926	1961	£2	£5	
Come Into My Heart	7"	HMV	POP672	1959	£1.50	£4	
Cookin'	LP	HMV	CLP1519	1962	£6	£15	mono
Cookin'	LP	HMV	CSD1413	1962	£10	£25	stereo
Exciting Lloyd Price	LP	HMV	CLP1285	1959	£10	£25	
Exciting Lloyd Price	7" EP..	HMV	7EG8538	1959	£12.50	£25	
Exciting Lloyd Price	7" EP..	HMV	GES5784	1959	£25	£50	stereo
Fantastic Lloyd Price	LP	HMV	CLP1393	1960	£8	£20	mono
Fantastic Lloyd Price	LP	HMV	CSD1323	1960	£10	£25	stereo
I'm Gonna Get Married	7"	HMV	POP650	1959	£1.50	£4	chart single
Just Because	7"	London	HL8438	1957	£25	£50	
Just Call Me	7"	HMV	POP799	1960	£2	£5	
Know What You're Doing	7"	HMV	POP826	1961	£2	£5	
Lady Luck	7"	HMV	POP712	1960	£1.50	£4	chart single
Lloyd Price	LP	London	HAU2213	1960	£10	£25	
Lloyd Price Now	LP	Major Minor	SMLP57	1969	£5	£12	
Lloyd Price Orchestra	LP	Double-L	D2301/SDL8301	1963	£6	£15	US
Lloyd Swings For Sammy	LP	Monument	MLP8032/ SMP18032	1965	£5	£12	US
Love Music	7"	GSF	GSZ5	1973	£2.50	£6	
Misty	LP	Double-L	D2303/SDL8303	1963	£6	£15	US
Mr.Personality	LP	HMV	CLP1314	1959	£10	£25	
Mr.Personality Sings The Blues	LP	HMV	CLP1361	1960	£8	£20	
Mr.Personality's Big 15	LP	ABC	(S)324	1960	£8	£20	US
No Ifs No Ands	7"	HMV	POP741	1960	£1.50	£4	
Personality	7"	HMV	POP626	1959	£2	£5	chart single
Question	7"	HMV	POP772	1960	£2	£5	
Sings The Million Dollar Sellers	LP	Encore	ENC2004	1963	£5	£12	
Stagger Lee	LP	Joy	JOYS202	1971	£5	£12	

Stagger Lee	7"	HMV	POP580	1959	£4	£8	chart single
Under Your Spell Again	7"	HMV	POP1100	1962	£1.50	£4	
Where Were You On Our Wedding Day	7"	HMV	POP598	1959	£2	£5	chart single

PRICE, MALCOLM

Country Session	LP	Decca	LK4627	1964	£5	£12	
His Songs, His Guitars	LP	Saga		1969	£4	£10	
Pickin' On The Country Strings	7" EP	Oak	RGJ106	196-	£7.50	£15	
Then We All Got Up And Walked Away	LP	Sweet Folk And Country	SFA017	1975	£4	£10	
Way Down Town	LP	Decca	LK4665	1965	£5	£12	

PRICE, RAY

Greatest Hits	LP	Columbia	CL1566	1961	£6	£15	US
Ray Price	7" EP	Philips	BBE12137	1957	£5	£10	
Ray Price Sings Heart Songs	LP	Columbia	CL1015	1957	£8	£20	US
Talk To Your Heart	LP	Columbia	CL1148	1958	£6	£15	US

PRICE, RED

Danger Man	7"	Parlophone	R4789	1961	£4	£8	
Rocky Mountain Gal	7"	Decca	F10822	1956	£1.50	£4	
Weekend	7"	Pye	7N15169	1958	£1.50	£4	
Wow	7"	Pye	7N15262	1960	£1.50	£4	

PRICE, RED (2)

Blue Beat's Over	7"	Blue Beat	BB209	1963	£5	£10	

PRICE, RICK

Talking To The Flowers	LP	Gemini	GME1017	1971	£6	£15	

PRICE, RIKKI

Rikki Price	7" EP	Fontana	TFE17100	1958	£4	£8	

PRICE, SAMMY

Blues Ain't Nothin'	LP	London	LTZR15240/ SAHR6234	1962	£6	£15	
Boogieing With Big Sid	7"	Storyville	A45068	196-	£7.50	£15	
Original Sammy Blues	7" EP	Columbia	SEG7679	1957	£4	£8	
Sammy Price	7" EP	Vogue	EPV1146	1956	£12.50	£25	
Sammy Price's Bluesicians	7" EP	Vogue	EPV1151	1956	£12.50	£25	
Swingin' Paris Style	LP	Vogue	LAE12027	1957	£6	£15	

PRICE, VINCENT

Vincent Price	LP	Columbia	33SX1141	1959	£5	£12	

PRIDE, DICKIE

Betty Betty	7"	Columbia	DB4403	1960	£4	£8	
Midnight Oil	7"	Columbia	DB4296	1959	£5	£10	
Pride Without Prejudice	LP	Columbia	33SX1307	1960	£30	£60	
Pride Without Prejudice	LP	Columbia	SCX3369	1961	£40	£80	stereo
Primrose Lane	7"	Columbia	DB4340	1959	£7.50	£15	chart single
Sheik Of Shake	7" EP	Columbia	SEG7937	1959	£40	£80	
Slipping And Sliding	7"	Columbia	DB4283	1959	£10	£20	
You're Singing Our Love Song	7"	Columbia	DB4451	1960	£1.50	£4	

PRIMA, LOUIS

Angelina	7"	Prima	PR1009	1964	£1.50	£4	
Buona Sera	7"	Capitol	CL14821	1958	£5	£10	chart single
Call Of The Wildest	LP	Capitol	T836	1958	£8	£20	
Doin' The Twist	LP	Dot	DLP3410/25410	1961	£5	£12	US
Fee Fie Fo O	7"	Prima	PR1001	1964	£1.50	£4	
Five Months, Two Weeks, Two Days	7"	Capitol	CL14669	1956	£10	£20	
Fun With Louis Prima	7" EP	Philips	BBE12290	1959	£2	£5	
Louis Prima	LP	Rondo	842	1959	£8	£20	US
Ol' Man Moses	7"	London	HLD9230	1960	£2.50	£6	
Stay Awake	7"	Prima	PR1006	1964	£1.50	£4	
Strictly Prima	LP	Capitol	T1132	1959	£8	£20	
Strictly Prima	7" EP	Capitol	EAP11132	1959	£4	£8	
Swings	LP	Ember	EMB3348	1962	£4	£10	
Wildest	LP	Capitol	T755	1957	£6	£15	
Wildest Comes Home	LP	Capitol	(S)T1723	1962	£5	£12	US
Wonderland By Night	LP	Dot	DLP3352/25352	1960	£5	£12	US

PRIMA, LOUIS & KEELY SMITH

Bei Mir Bist Du Schon	7"	London	HLD8923	1959	£2	£5	
Hits	LP	Capitol	T1531	1962	£4	£10	
I'm Confessin'	7"	London	HLD9084	1960	£2	£5	
Las Vegas Prima Style	LP	Capitol	T1010	1958	£5	£12	
Louis And Keely	LP	London	HAD2243	1960	£5	£12	
On Stage	LP	London	HAD2350/ SAHD6149	1961	£5	£12	
Take A Little Walk Around The Block	7"	Columbia	SCM5092	1954	£4	£10	

PRIMAL SCREAM

All Fall Down	7"	Creation	CRE17	1985	£6	£12	
Crystal Crescent	7"	Creation	CRE26	1986	£4	£8	
Gentle Tuesday/Imperial	7"	Elevation		1987	£5	£10	promo
Imperial	12"	Elevation	ACIDT5	1987	£2.50	£6	poster sleeve
Primal Scream	LP	Creation	CRELP054	1989	£5	£12	with 7' (Split Wide Open)

PRIMARY INDUSTRY

At Gunpoint	7"	Temps Modernes	CSBTVV	1986	£4	£8	

PRIMATES

Hot Tamalas	7"	Action	ACT4530	1969	£2	£5	

PRIMETTES

"Looking Back With The Primettes" consists of early material recorded by the Supremes under their original name. Only one US single was actually released prior to the group signing with Tamla records.

Looking Back With The Primettes	LP	Ember	EMBS3398	1968	£15	£30	
Roots Of Diana Ross	LP	Windmill	WMD192	1973	£5	£12	
Tears Of Sorrow	7"	Lupine	120	1960	£50	£100	US

PRIMITIVES

Blow Up	LP	Arc		1967	£75	£150	Italian
Help Me	7"	Pye	7N15721	1964	£50	£100	
Ho Mary	7" EP	Vogue	INT18093	1966	£75	£150	French
You Said	7"	Pye	7N15755	1965	£75	£150	

PRIMITIVES (2)

Ocean Blue	7"	Lazy	LAZY5	1987	£2.50	£6	no PS
Really Stupid	7"	Lazy	LAZY2	1986	£1.50	£4	
Really Stupid	12"	Lazy	LAZYT2	1986	£3	£8	
Stop Killing Me	7"	Lazy	LAZY3	1986	£2	£5	with badge
Stop Killing Me	12"	Lazy	LAZYT3	1986	£2.50	£6	
Thru The Flowers	12"	Head	HEAD010	1986	£10	£25	test pressing
Thru The Flowers	12"	Lazy	LAZY1	1986	£4	£10	

PRIMITIVES (3)

During 1964, Lou Reed was employed as a song-writer and performer by a company specialising in quick cash-in records. "The Ostrich" was one of these, but it managed to gain sufficient attention to be made to appear on Dick Clark's TV show. The group put together for the purpose was almost a prototype Velvet Underground, consisting of Lou Reed, John Cale, and fellow avant-garde enthusiast Tony Conrad.

Ostrich	7"	Pickwick	1001	1964	£30	£60	US

PRIMROSE CIRCUS

P.S. Call Me Lulu	7"	President	PT314	1970	£2	£5	

PRINCE

All the major stars of the eighties have had their recording careers boosted by a proliferation of picture disc and other limited edition releases, and Prince is no exception. Most critics would have it that the legendary "Black Album" contains music of unparalleled splendour and that its last minute withdrawal was an act of typically idiosyncratic and wilful behaviour on the part of its maker. Original copies are rare (though not as rare as to justify some of the extreme prices that are quoted on occasion - the thousand pound figure quoted here is a maximum), but bootleg versions, with a variety of cover designs, are in common circulation. These enable anyone not over-awed by the record's reputation to hear that the Black Album lacks entirely the sense of surprise that is present in the best of Prince's work.

1999	LP	WEA	9238091	1983	£5	£12	single LP
1999	7"	WEA	W9896	1983	£5	£10	chart single
1999	7"	WEA	W9896C	1983	£7.50	£15	with cassette
1999	12"	WEA	W9896T	1983	£6	£15	
Alphabet Street	CD-s	WEA	W7900CD	1988	£4	£10	
Anotherloverholenyohead	7"	WEA	W8521W	1986	£2	£5	poster sleeve
Anotherloverholenyohead	7"	WEA	W8521F	1986	£4	£8	double
Anotherloverholenyohead	12"	WEA	W8521T	1986	£4	£10	poster sleeve
Arms Of Orion	CD-s	WEA	W2757CDX	1989	£2.50	£6	tri-fold sleeve
Batdance	CD-s	WEA	W2924CDX	1989	£3	£8	batpack box
Batdance	12"	WEA	W2924TP	1989	£3	£8	pic disc
Batman	LP	WEA	WX281P	1989	£4	£10	pic disc
Black Album	LP or CD	Paisley Park	WX147	1988	£700	£1000	promo only
Controversy	7"	WEA	K17866	1981	£10	£20	
Controversy	12"	WEA	K17866T	1981	£17.50	£35	
Crown Jewels	CD	WEA	SAM1037	1992	£15	£30	promo
D.M.S.R.	12"	WEA		1983	£20	£40	promo
Do It All Night	7"	WEA	K17768	1981	£7.50	£15	no PS
Do It All Night	12"	WEA	K17768T	1981	£25	£50	no PS
For You	LP	WEA	BSK3150	1978	£5	£12	US
Girls And Boys	7"	WEA	W8586F	1986	£4	£8	double
Girls And Boys	7"	WEA	W8586P	1986	£12.50	£25	shaped pic disc
Girls And Boys	12"	WEA	W8586T	1986	£4	£10	with poster
Glam Slam	CD-s	WEA	W7806CD	1988	£4	£10	
Gotta Stop Messin' About	7"	WEA	K17819	1981	£30	£60	2 different B sides
Gotta Stop Messin' About	12"	WEA	LV47	1981	£65	£130	2 different B sides
I Could Never Take The Place Of Your Man	12"	WEA	W8288TP	1987	£6	£15	pic disc
I Wanna Be Your Lover	7"	WEA	K17537	1979	£4	£8	no PS, chart single
I Wanna Be Your Lover	12"	WEA	K17527T	1979	£6	£15	no PS
I Wish U Heaven	CD-s	WEA	W7745CD	1988	£4	£10	
I Wish U Heaven	7"	WEA	W7745	1988	£2	£5	poster sleeve
I Would Die 4 U (US Remix)	12"	WEA	W9121TE	1984	£10	£25	
If I Was Your Girlfriend	7"	WEA	W8334E	1987	£4	£8	peach vinyl, cards & stickers
If I Was Your Girlfriend	7"	WEA	W8334W	1987	£2	£5	poster sleeve
If I Was Your Girlfriend	12"	WEA	W8334TP	1987	£6	£15	pic disc
Kiss	7"	WEA	W8751TP	1986	£5	£10	shaped pic disc
Kiss	7"	WEA	W8751TP	1986	£10	£20	shaped pic disc, stand
Kiss	12"	WEA	W8751T	1986	£4	£10	with poster
Let's Go Crazy	12"	WEA	W2000T	1985	£2.50	£6	with poster & sticker
Let's Work	7"	WEA	K17922	1982	£12.50	£25	
Let's Work	12"	WEA	K17922T	1982	£50	£100	
Little Red Corvette	7"	WEA	W9436	1983	£12.50	£25	poster sleeve

Title	Format	Label	Cat No	Year	Price	Price	Notes
Little Red Corvette	7"	WEA	W9688	1983	£2.50	£6	chart single
Little Red Corvette	12"	WEA	W9436T	1983	£15	£30	
Little Red Corvette	12"	WEA	W9436T	1983	£40	£80	with calendar
Little Red Corvette	12"	WEA	W9436T	1983	£25	£50	with poster
Little Red Corvette	12"	WEA	W9688T	1983	£8	£20	
Little Red Corvette	12"	WEA	W9688T	1983	£20	£40	with poster & sticker
Little Red Corvette/1999	7"	Warner Bros	201290	1983	£10	£20	US pic disc
Mountains	12"	WEA	W8711T	1986	£4	£10	with poster
Mountains	10"	WEA	W8711TW	1986	£8	£20	white vinyl
Paisley Park	7"	WEA	W9052P	1985	£12.50	£25	shaped pic disc
Paisley Park	12"	WEA	W9052T	1985	£2.50	£6	
Paisley Park	12"	WEA	W9052TP	1985	£4	£10	with poster
Parade	LP	WEA	WX39P	1986	£15	£30	pic disc
Partyman	12"	WEA	W2814TP	1989	£4	£10	pic disc
Pop Life	12"	WEA	W8858T	1985	£3	£8	
Purple Rain	LP	WEA	9251101	1984	£10	£25	purple vinyl, poster
Purple Rain	7"	WEA	W9174P	1984	£20	£40	shaped pic disc
Purple Rain	12"	WEA	W9174T	1984	£2.50	£6	
Purple Rain	12"	WEA	W9174T	1984	£4	£10	with poster
Raspberry Beret	12"	WEA	W8929T	1985	£2.50	£6	
Sexy Dancer	7"	WEA	K17590	1980	£10	£20	no PS
Sexy Dancer	12"	WEA	K17590T	1980	£30	£60	no PS
Sexy MF	12"	Paisley Park	W0123P	1992	£2.50	£6	pic disc
Sign O The Times	12"	WEA	W8399TP	1987	£10	£25	pic disc
Thunder	12"	Paisley Park	W0113TP	1992	£2.50	£6	pic disc
U Got The Look	12"	WEA	W8289TP	1987	£6	£15	pic disc
When Doves Cry	12"	WEA	W9296T	1984	£2.50	£6	
When Doves Cry/1999	12"	WEA	W9296T	1984	£8	£20	shrinkwrapped double

PRINCE & PRINCESS

Title	Format	Label	Cat No	Year	Price	Price	Notes
Ready Steady Go	7"	Island	WI609	1965	£5	£10	

PRINCE BUSTER

Title	Format	Label	Cat No	Year	Price	Price	Notes
Aguar Fumar	7"	Blue Beat	BB293	1964	£5	£10	
Al Capone	7"	Blue Beat	BB324	1964	£5	£10	chart single
All My Loving	7"	Fab	FAB35	1968	£4	£8	
All On My Mind	7"	Blue Beat	BB400	1965	£5	£10	
Ambition	7"	Blue Beat	BB328	1965	£5	£10	Ivanhoe Martin B side
Baldhead Pum Pum	7"	Prince Buster	PB47	1972	£1.50	£4	
Big Fight	7"	Blue Beat	BB282	1964	£5	£10	
Big Fight	7"	Blue Beat	BB338	1965	£5	£10	
Big Five	LP	Melodisc	MLP12157	1972	£5	£12	
Big Five	7"	Fab	FAB150	1970	£2.50	£6	
Big Five	7"	Prince Buster	PB1	1967	£5	£10	
Big Sister Stuff	7"	Prince Buster	PB14	1972	£1.50	£4	
Black Organ	7"	Fab	FAB141	1970	£2.50	£6	
Black Soul	7"	Fab	FAB102	1969	£4	£8	Caledonians B side
Blackhead Chinaman	7"	Dice	CC11	1963	£5	£10	
Blood Pressure	7"	Blue Beat	BB278	1964	£5	£10	
Blue Beat Spirit	7"	Blue Beat	BB211	1963	£5	£10	
Bonanza	7"	Blue Beat	BB307	1964	£5	£10	
Bull Buck	7"	Fab	FAB118	1969	£4	£8	Roland Alphonso B side
Burning Creation	7"	Blue Beat	BB173	1963	£5	£10	
Bye Bye Baby	7"	Fab	FAB16	1967	£4	£8	
Captain Burke	7"	Blue Beat	BB333	1965	£5	£10	
Cincinatti Kid	7"	Blue Beat	BB342	1965	£5	£10	
Come And Do It With Me	7"	Fab	FAB32	1968	£4	£8	
Come Home	7"	Blue Beat	BB317	1964	£5	£10	
Congo Revolution	7"	Blue Beat	BB325	1965	£5	£10	Little Darling B side
Dallas Texas	7"	Fab	FAB37	1968	£4	£8	
Dallas, Texas	7"	Blue Beat	BB266	1964	£5	£10	
Dance Cleopatra	7"	Blue Beat	BB388	1965	£5	£10	
Dark End Of The Street	7"	Blue Beat	BB377	1965	£5	£10	
Doctor Rodney	7"	Fab	FAB82	1969	£4	£8	
Don't Throw Stones	7"	Blue Beat	BB343	1965	£5	£10	
Drunkard's Psalm	7"	Blue Beat	BB378	1965	£5	£10	
Everybody Ska	7"	Stateside	SS335	1964	£5	£10	
Everybody Yeah Yeah	7"	Blue Beat	BB313	1964	£5	£10	
Eye For An Eye	7"	Blue Beat	BB294	1964	£5	£10	
Fabulous Greatest Hits	LP	Melodisc	MS1	1968	£5	£12	
Fishey	7"	Prince Buster	PB4	1971	£2.50	£6	
Float Like A Butterfly	7"	Blue Beat	BB314	1964	£5	£10	
Fowl Thief	7"	Blue Beat	BB186	1963	£5	£10	
Free Love	7"	Fab	FAB38	1968	£4	£8	Daltons B side
Ganja Plant	7"	Fab	FAB132	1970	£2.50	£6	
Ghost Dance	7"	Blue Beat	BB289	1965	£5	£10	Sweethearts B side
Glory Of Love	7"	Fab	FAB36	1968	£4	£8	
Glory Of Love	7"	Fab	FAB49	1968	£4	£8	
Going To Ethiopia	7"	Fab	FAB47	1968	£4	£8	
Going To The River	7"	Fab	FAB26	1967	£4	£8	
Going West	7"	Blue Beat	BB277	1964	£5	£10	
Green Green Grass Of Home	7"	Fab	FAB57	1968	£4	£8	Soul Makers B side
Here Comes The Bride	7"	Blue Beat	BB309	1964	£5	£10	
Hey Jude	7"	Fab	FAB94	1969	£4	£8	
Hit Me Back	7"	Fab	FAB140	1970	£2.50	£6	
Hypocrite	7"	Fab	FAB80	1968	£4	£8	
I Feel The Spirit	LP	Blue Beat	BBLP802	1963	£50	£100	

653

Title	Format	Label	Cat No	Year			Notes
I Feel The Spirit	LP	Fab	MS2	1970	£5	£12	
I May Never Love You Again	7"	Blue Beat	BB274	1964	£5	£10	
I Wish Your Picture Was You	7"	Prince Buster	PB7	1971	£2.50	£6	
I Won't Let You Cry	7"	Blue Beat	BB357	1965	£5	£10	
Independence Day	7"	Blue Beat	BB116	1962	£5	£10	
Intensified Dirt	7"	Fab	FAB56	1968	£4	£8	
It's Burke's Law	LP	Blue Beat	BBLP806	1965	£50	£100	
It's Too Late	7"	Blue Beat	BB352	1965	£5	£10	
Jealous	7"	Blue Beat	BB243	1963	£5	£10	
Johnny Cool	7"	Fab	FAB11	1967	£5	£10	
Johnny Dark	7"	Blue Beat	BB290	1964	£5	£10	Owen Gray B side
Johnny Dollar	7"	Blue Beat	BB326	1965	£5	£10	Terry Nelson B side
Judge Dread	LP	Blue Beat	BBLP809	1967	£50	£100	
Judge Dread	7"	Blue Beat	BB387	1965	£5	£10	Fitzroy Campbell B side
King Duke Sir	7"	Blue Beat	BB163	1962	£5	£10	
Kings Of Old	7"	Fab	FAB31	1968	£4	£8	
Knock On Wood	7"	Blue Beat	BB373	1965	£5	£10	
Land Of Imagination	7"	Blue Beat	BB391	1965	£5	£10	
Ling Ting Tang	7"	Rainbow	RAI110	1966	£4	£8	
Love Each Other	7"	Blue Beat	BB170	1963	£5	£10	
Madness	7"	Prince Buster	PB19	1972	£2.50	£6	
Money	7"	Blue Beat	BB162	1962	£5	£10	School Boys B side
Mules Mules Mules	7"	Blue Beat	BB279	1964	£5	£10	Charmers B side
My Girl	7"	Blue Beat	BB321	1964	£5	£10	
My Happiness	7"	Prince Buster	PB9	1971	£2.50	£6	
My Heart Is Gone	7"	Prince Buster	PB16	1972	£2.50	£6	
Nice Nice	7"	Fab	FAB64	1968	£4	£8	
No Knowledge In College	7"	Blue Beat	BB271	1964	£5	£10	
Ob La Di Ob La Da	7"	Fab	FAB93	1969	£4	£8	
Old Lady	7"	Blue Beat	BB262	1964	£5	£10	
One Hand Washes The Other	7"	Blue Beat	BB138	1962	£5	£10	
Open Up Bartender	7"	Blue Beat	BB158	1962	£5	£10	
Original Golden Oldies Vol.1	LP	Prince Buster	PB9	1973	£5	£12	
Outlaw	LP	Blue Beat	BBLP822	1969	£50	£100	sleeve pictured in Guide
Pharaoh House Crash	7"	Fab	FAB92	1969	£4	£8	
Picket Line	7"	Blue Beat	BB349	1965	£5	£10	Eric Morris B side
Police Trim Rasta	7"	Fab	FAB176	1971	£2.50	£6	
Prince Buster On Tour	LP	Blue Beat	BBLP808	1967	£50	£100	
Prince Royal	7"	Blue Beat	BB244	1963	£5	£10	Cosmo B side
Prophet	7"	Blue Beat	BB359	1965	£5	£10	
Protection	7"	Prince Buster	PB15	1972	£1.50	£4	
Pum Pum A Go Kill You	7"	Fab	FAB101	1969	£4	£8	
Quiet Place	7"	Blue Beat	BB393	1965	£5	£10	
Rat Trap	7"	Fab	FAB142	1970	£2.50	£6	
Rat Trap	7"	Prince Buster	PB2	1971	£2.50	£6	
Rebel	7"	Fab	FAB124	1969	£2.50	£6	
Repect	7"	Blue Beat	BB335	1965	£5	£10	
Rock And Shake	7"	Fab	FAB20	1967	£4	£8	Hortense Ellis B side
Rolling Stones	7"	Blue Beat	BB192	1963	£5	£10	Rico B side
Rough Rider	7"	Fab	FAB40	1968	£4	£8	
Rum And Coca Cola	7"	Blue Beat	BB330	1965	£5	£10	
Run Man Run	7"	Blue Beat	BB150	1962	£5	£10	
Shakin' Up Orange Street	7"	Fab	FAB10	1967	£5	£10	
Shanty Town Get Scanty	7"	Blue Beat	BB370	1965	£5	£10	
She Loves You	7"	Blue Beat	BB234	1963	£5	£10	
She Pon Top	7"	Blue Beat	BB232	1963	£5	£10	
She Was A Rough Rider	LP	Blue Beat	BBLP820	1967	£50	£100	with Teddy King
Shepherd Beng	7"	Fab	FAB41	1968	£4	£8	
Sister's Big Stuff	LP	Melodisc	MLP12156	1972	£6	£15	
Sit And Wonder	7"	Blue Beat	BB382	1965	£5	£10	Roland Alphonso B side
Sit Down And Cry	7"	Blue Beat	BB389	1965	£5	£10	
Ska-Lip-Soul	LP	Blue Beat	BBLP805	1965	£50	£100	
Sons Of Zion	7"	Prince Buster	PB8	1971	£1.50	£4	Ansell Collins B side
Soul Dance	7"	Blue Beat	BB398	1965	£5	£10	
Soul Serenade	7"	Blue Beat	BB390	1965	£5	£10	
Sounds And Pressure	7"	Blue Beat	BB372	1965	£5	£10	
South Of The Border	7"	Prince Buster	PB36	1972	£1.50	£4	
Spider And The Fly	7"	Blue Beat	BB199	1963	£5	£10	
Stand Up	7"	Fab	FAB122	1969	£2.50	£6	
Still	7"	Prince Buster	PB32	1972	£2.50	£6	
Sugar Pop	7"	Blue Beat	BB316	1964	£5	£10	
Take It Easy	7"	Blue Beat	BB384	1965	£5	£10	
Talkin' 'Bout My Girl	7"	Blue Beat	BB355	1965	£5	£10	
Ten Commandments	LP	RCA	LPM/LSP3792	1967	£6	£15	US
Ten Commandments	7"	Blue Beat	BB167	1963	£5	£10	
Ten Commandments	7"	Blue Beat	BB334	1965	£5	£10	
Ten Commandments	7"	Philips	BF1552	1967	£4	£8	
That's All	7"	Fab	FAB131	1970	£2.50	£6	
They Got To Come	7"	Dice	CC6	1962	£5	£10	
They Got To Go	7"	Blue Beat	BB101	1962	£5	£10	
Thirty Pieces Of Silver	7"	Blue Beat	BB248	1964	£5	£10	
Thirty Pieces Of Silver	7"	Unity	UN522	1969	£2.50	£6	
This Gun For Hire	7"	Blue Beat	BB395	1965	£5	£10	
Three Blind Mice	7"	Blue Beat	BB225	1963	£5	£10	
Three More Rivers To Cross	7"	Blue Beat	BB180	1963	£5	£10	Raymond Harper B side

Title		Label	Cat#	Year			Notes
Tickler	7"	Blue Beat	BB269	1964	£5	£10	Cosmo B side
Tie The Donkey's Tail	7"	Fab	FAB119	1969	£4	£8	
Time Longer Than Rope	7"	Blue Beat	BB133	1962	£5	£10	
To Be Loved	7"	Blue Beat	BB362	1965	£5	£10	
Train To Girls Town	7"	Fab	FAB25	1967	£4	£8	
Tutti Frutti	LP	Fab	MS6	1970	£6	£15	
Under Arrest	7"	Blue Beat	BB339	1965	£5	£10	
Vagabond	7"	Blue Beat	BB402	1965	£5	£10	
Wash All Your Troubles Away	7"	Blue Beat	BB200	1963	£5	£10	Rico B side
Wash All Your Troubles Away	7"	Blue Beat	BB210	1963	£5	£10	Rico B side
Watch It Blackhead	7"	Blue Beat	BB189	1963	£5	£10	
We Shall Overcome	7"	Fab	FAB58	1968	£4	£8	
Welcome To Jamaica	LP	Blue Beat	BBLP821	1968	£50	£100	
What A Hard Man Fe Dead	LP	Blue Beat	BBLP807	1967	£50	£100	
What A World	7"	Blue Beat	BB144	1962	£5	£10	
Window Shopping	7"	Blue Beat	BB197	1963	£5	£10	
Wine And Grind	7"	Fab	FAB108	1969	£4	£8	
Wine And Grind	7"	Fab	FAB81	1968	£4	£8	
Wings Of A Dove	7"	Blue Beat	BB254	1964	£5	£10	Maytals B side
World Peace	7"	Dice	CC18	1963	£5	£10	
You'll Be Lonely And Blue	7"	Blue Beat	BB383	1965	£5	£10	
Young Gifted And Black	7"	Fab	FAB127	1970	£2.50	£6	
Your Turn	7"	Rainbow	RAI107	1966	£4	£8	
You're Mine	7"	Blue Beat	BB216	1963	£5	£10	

PRINCE CHARLIE

Hit And Run	7"	Coxsone	CS7101	1969	£5	£10

PRINCE HAROLD

Forget About Me	7"	Mercury	MF952	1966	£4	£8

PRINCE OF DARKNESS

Burial Of Longshot	7"	Down Town	DT441	1969	£1.50	£4

PRINCE PATO EXPEDITION

Firebird	LP	Beacon	BEAS18	197-	£8	£20

PRINCE, VIV

Light Of The Charge Brigade	7"	Columbia	DB7960	1966	£7.50	£15

PRINCESS & THE SWINEHERD

Princess And The Swineherd	LP	Oak	RGJ633	1968	£10	£25

PRINCIPAL EDWARD'S MAGIC THEATRE

Principal Edward's Magic Theatre were the first, and perhaps the only group ever to receive an Arts Council Grant. They were a large organisation, incorporating dancers and light-show operators as well as musicians, so that their records do not entirely succeed in conveying what they did. "Soundtrack", however, is an interesting record, crossing folk with rock and poetry so well that one is never quite sure what is coming next. The music also features a cameo appearance from John Peel, who delivers one spoken line (in the role of a child!). The second album, meanwhile, includes a welcome antidote to all those hymns of praise to various American cities, in the form of a song dedicated to the town of Kettering.

Asmoto Running Band	LP	Dandelion	DAN8002	1971	£8	£12
Ballad Of The Big Girl Now	7"	Dandelion	K4405	1970	£2.50	£6
Round One	LP	Deram	SML1108	1974	£6	£15
Soundtrack	LP	Dandelion	63752	1969	£8	£20

PRIOR, MADDY

Changing Winds	LP	Chrysalis	CHR1203	1978	£6	£15
Woman In The Wings	LP	Chrysalis	CHR1185	1978	£6	£15

PRIOR, MADDY & JUNE TABOR

Silly Sisters	LP	Chrysalis	CHR1101	1976	£5	£12

PRISONAIRES

Just Walkin' In The Rain	7"	Sun	186	1953	£30	£60	US
My God Is Real	7"	Sun	189	1953	£50	£100	US
Prisoner's Prayer	7"	Sun	191	1953	£30	£60	US
There Is Love In You	7"	Sun	207	1954	£2100	£3000	US

PROBY, P.J.

All four members of Led Zeppelin appear on one track of the P.J.Proby album "Three Week Hero", and the record has long been a collectors' item for this reason. Proby's career is dotted with moments like this: he was the lucky recipient of an unreleased Beatles song (although his mannered voice is not actually ideal for making the best of "That Means A Lot"); he managed to land the starring role in the "Elvis" stage show (and is accordingly central in the collectable album that was only ever available at the theatre); and was later to be found recording in an unlikely partnership with the group Focus. (The resulting album is listed within their entry. Cynics should resist making too much of its title, however, for "Focus Con Proby" is Italian in origin!).

Believe It Or Not	LP	Liberty	LBL/LBS83087	1968	£8	£20	
California License	LP	Liberty	LBL83320	1969	£30	£60	credited to Jet Powers, sleeve pictured in Guide
Christmas With P.J.Proby	7" EP	Liberty	LEP2239	1965	£6	£12	
Day That Lorraine Came Down	7"	Liberty	LIB15152	1968	£4	£8	
Elvis	LP	Astoria	1	1978	£10	£25	with other artists
Enigma	LP	Liberty	LBL/LBS83032	1967	£4	£10	
Enigma	LP	Liberty	LBY1361	1966	£6	£15	
Go Go P.J.Proby	LP	Liberty	LRP3406/LST7406	1965	£6	£15	US
Hanging From Your Loving Tree	7"	Liberty	LIB15245	1969	£4	£8	
Hero	LP	Palm	7007	1981	£6	£15	with other artists
Hold Me	7"	Decca	F11904	1964	£1.50	£4	chart single
Hold Me	7" EP	Decca	457044	1964	£10	£20	French
I Am P.J.Proby	LP	Liberty	LBY1235	1964	£6	£15	chart LP
I Apologise	7"	Liberty	LIB10188	1965	£1.50	£4	chart single

Title	Format	Label	Cat. No.	Year			Notes
I Can't Make It Alone	7"	Liberty	LIB10250	1966	£1.50	£4	chart single
I Can't Make It Alone	7" EP	Liberty	LEP2274	1967	£7.50	£15	French
I'm Yours	LP	Ember	NR5069	1973	£5	£12	
It's Goodbye	7"	Liberty	LIB15386	1970	£4	£8	
It's Your Day Today	7"	Liberty	LIB15046	1968	£1.50	£4	chart single
Let The Water Run Down	7"	Liberty	LIB10206	1965	£1.50	£4	chart single
Maria	7"	Liberty	LIB10218	1965	£1.50	£4	chart single
My Prayer	7" EP	Liberty	LEP2253	1966	£7.50	£15	French
Niki Hoeky	7"	Liberty	LIB55936	1967	£4	£8	
Phenomenon	LP	Liberty	LBL/LBS83045	1967	£8	£20	
P.J.Proby	7"	Liberty	LBY1264	1965	£6	£15	
P.J.Proby	7" EP	Liberty	LEP2192	1965	£4	£8	
P.J.Proby Again	7" EP	Liberty	LEP2267	1966	£7.50	£15	
P.J.Proby Hits	7" EP	Liberty	LEP2251	1966	£7.50	£15	
P.J.Proby's In Town	LP	Liberty	LBL/LBS83018	1967	£4	£10	
P.J.Proby's In Town	LP	Liberty	LBY1291	1965	£6	£15	
Somewhere	7"	Liberty	LIB10182	1964	£1.50	£4	chart single
Somewhere	7" EP	Liberty	LEP2220	1965	£7.50	£15	French
Somewhere	7" EP	Liberty	LEP2229	1965	£4	£8	
That Means A Lot	7"	Liberty	LIB10215	1965	£2.50	£6	chart single
That Means A Lot	7" EP	Liberty	LEP2240	1965	£7.50	£15	French
Three Week Hero	LP	Liberty	LBS83219	1969	£20	£40	
To Make A Big Man Cry	7"	Liberty	LIB10236	1966	£1.50	£4	chart single
Today I Killed A Man	7"	Liberty	LIB15280	1970	£4	£8	
Together	7"	Decca	F11967	1964	£1.50	£4	chart single
Try To Forget Her	7"	Liberty	LIB55361	1964	£2.50	£6	
We'll Meet Again	7"	Columbia	DB8874	1972	£1.50	£4	
What's Wrong With My World	LP	Liberty	LST7561	1968	£5	£12	US
What's Wrong With My World	7"	Liberty	LIB15085	1968	£1.50	£4	
Work With Me Annie	7"	Liberty	LIB55974	1967	£2.50	£6	
You Got Me Cryin'	7"	Melodisc	FAB2	1966	£2	£5	
You Got Me Cryin'	7"	Melodisc	FAB2	1966	£5	£10	PS
You've Come Back	7"	Liberty	LIB10223	1966	£1.50	£4	chart single

PROCESSION

Title	Format	Label	Cat. No.	Year			Notes
Every American Citizen	7"	Mercury	MF1053	1968	£1.50	£4	

PROCOL HARUM

Title	Format	Label	Cat. No.	Year			Notes
Broken Barricades	LP	Chrysalis	ILPS9158	1971	£6	£15	chart LP
Homburg	7"	Regal Zonophone	RZ3003	1967	£1.50	£4	chart single
Home	LP	Regal Zonophone	SLRZ1014	1970	£6	£15	chart LP
Il Tuo Diamente	7"	IL	IL9005	1969	£5	£10	sung in Italian
Lives	LP	A&M	SP8053	1972	£8	£20	US interview promo
Procol Harum	LP	Regal Zonophone	LRZ1001	1967	£6	£15	
Quite Rightly So	7"	Regal Zonophone	RZ3007	1968	£1.50	£4	chart single
Salty Dog	LP	Regal Zonophone	SLRZ1009	1969	£6	£15	chart LP
Salty Dog	7"	Regal Zonophone	RZ3019	1969	£1.50	£4	chart single
Shine On Brightly	LP	Regal Zonophone	(S)LRZ1004	1969	£6	£15	
Shine On Brightly/Home	LP	Cube	TOOFA10	1972	£6	£15	double
Whiter Shade Of Pale	7"	Deram	DM126	1967	£1.50	£4	chart single
Whiter Shade Of Pale	7"	MagniFly	ECHO10	1972	£2	£5	PS
Whiter Shade/A Salty Dog	LP	Cube	TOOFA7/8	1972	£6	£15	double, chart LP

PROCOPE, RUSSELL

Title	Format	Label	Cat. No.	Year			Notes
Persuasive Sax	LP	London	HAD2013	1956	£5	£12	

PROCTOR, JUDD

Title	Format	Label	Cat. No.	Year			Notes
Better Late	7"	Parlophone	R5126	1964	£1.50	£4	
Guitars Galore	LP	Morgan	MR103P	196-	£5	£12	
It's Bluesy	7"	Parlophone	R4920	1962	£1.50	£4	
Nola	7"	Parlophone	R4809	1961	£1.50	£4	
Plainsman	7"	Parlophone	R4769	1961	£1.50	£4	
Speakeasy	7"	Parlophone	R4841	1961	£1.50	£4	
Turk	7"	Parlophone	R4885	1962	£1.50	£4	

PROCTOR, MIKE

Title	Format	Label	Cat. No.	Year			Notes
Mr.Commuter	7"	Columbia	DB8254	1967	£12.50	£25	

PROFESSOR LONGHAIR

Title	Format	Label	Cat. No.	Year			Notes
Baby Let Me Hold Your Hand	7"	Sue	WI397	1965	£7.50	£15	
Live On The Queen Mary	LP	Harvest	SHSP4086	1978	£4	£10	
Mess Around	7"	Harvest	HAR5154	1978	£1.50	£4	
New Orleans 88	10" LP	Speakeasy	1078	1972	£15	£30	
New Orleans Piano	LP	Atlantic	K40402	1972	£6	£15	
Professor Longhair	7" EP	XX	MIN708	196-	£7.50	£15	

PROFESSOR WOLFF

Title	Format	Label	Cat. No.	Year			Notes
Professor Wolff	LP	Metronome	MLP15422	1972	£15	£30	German

PROFILE

Title	Format	Label	Cat. No.	Year			Notes
Got To Find A Way	7"	Mercury	MF891	1965	£1.50	£4	
Haven't They Got Better Things To Do	7"	Mercury	MF875	1965	£2.50	£6	

PROLES
Proles Go To The Seaside	7"	Can't Play		1978	£6	£12	

PROPAGANDA
13th Life Of Dr.Mabuse	12"	ZTT	12ZTAS2 (2A2U)	1985	£5	£12	
Bejewelled Duel	12"	ZTT	12ZTAS8	1985	£2.50	£6	white label promo
Complete Machinery	cass-s	ZTT	CTIS12	1985	£4	£10	
Das Testaments Des Mabuse	cass-s	ZTT	CTIS101	1985	£3	£8	
Das Testaments Des Mabuse	12"	ZTT	12ZTAS2	1985	£3	£8	dark PS
Das Testaments Des Mabuse	12"	ZTT	12ZTAS2	1985	£3	£8	white PS
Do Well	cass-s	ZTT	CTIS108	1985	£3	£8	
Dr.Mabuse (Remix)	12"	ZTT	12ZTAS2DJ	1985	£4	£10	promo
Duel	12"	ZTT	DUAL1	1985	£2	£5	double
Duel	7"	ZTT	PZTAS8	1985	£2	£5	shaped pic disc
P Machinery (Beta)	12"	ZTT	12XZTAS12	1985	£4	£10	
P Machinery (Beta)	12"	ZTT	12ZTAST12	1985	£3	£8	double, poster
P Machinery (Beta Wrap Around Of)	12"	ZTT	12ZTAS21	1985	£2.50	£6	
P Machinery (Polish)	12"	ZTT	12PZTAS12	1985	£2.50	£6	clear vinyl
Wishful Thinking	CD	ZTT	ZCIDQ20	1985	£15	£30	

PROPELLER
Let Us Live Together	LP	Philips	6305114	1971	£5	£12	German

PROPHET, ORVAL
Run Run Run	7"	London	HLL9729	1963	£2.50	£6	

PROPHET, REX
Canadian Plowboy	7" EP	Brunswick	OE9144	1955	£4	£8	

PROPHETS
I Got The Fever	7"	Mercury	MF1097	1969	£7.50	£15	

PROTOS
One Day A New Horizon	LP	Airship	AP391	1982	£50	£100	

PROVIDENCE
Ever Sense The Dawn	LP	Threshold	THS9	1972	£10	£25	

PROVINE, DOROTHY
Crazy Words Crazy Tune	7"	Warner Bros	WB70	1962	£1.50	£4	chart single
Don't Bring Lulu	7"	Warner Bros	WB53	1961	£1.50	£4	chart single
Hard Hearted Hannah	7"	Warner Bros	WB58	1962	£1.50	£4	
Music Music Music	7"	Warner Bros	WB101	1963	£1.50	£4	

PRYSOCK, ARTHUR
Again	7" EP	CBS	EP6076	1966	£7.50	£15	
I Worry About You	LP	Old Town	LP102	1962	£6	£15	US
It's Too Late Baby Too Late	7"	CBS	201820	1965	£2.50	£6	

PRYSOCK, RED
Battle Royal	LP	Mercury	MG20106	1956	£15	£30	US
Beat	LP	Mercury	MPL6535	1958	£15	£30	
Blow Your Horn	78	Mercury	MB3158	1954	£7.50	£15	
Chop Suey	7"	Mercury	AMT1028	1959	£4	£8	
First Rock'n'Roll Party	10" LP	Mercury	MPT7512	1957	£20	£40	
Fruit Boots	LP	Mercury	MPL6550	1958	£15	£30	
Jump Red, Jump	10" LP	Mercury	MPT7517	1957	£20	£40	
Rock'n'Roll	LP	Mercury	MG20088	1955	£20	£40	US
Swing Softly Red	LP	Mercury	MG20188	1956	£15	£30	US
Teen Age Rock	78	Mercury	MT154	1957	£5	£10	

PSYCHEDELIC FURS
Interchords	LP	Columbia	AS1296	1981	£8	£20	US interview promo
We Love You	7"	Epic	8005DJ	1979	£2	£5	censored promo

PSYCHEDELIC PSOUL
Freak Scene	LP	Columbia	CS9456	1968	£4	£10	US

PSYCHIC TV

When Throbbing Gristle split apart, the pieces flew off into three directions, one of which led to the group Psychic TV. Genesis P.Orridge retained a similar record release policy to that of Throbbing Gristle, with a plethora of limited edition issues that were inevitably destined to rise in value. The music is considerably more commercial on the whole, but with a sardonic streak reminiscent of Frank Zappa's irreverent approach.

Album Ten	LP	Temple	TOPY032	1988	£6	£15	pic disc
Allegory And Self	LP	Temple	TOPY038	1988	£5	£12	pic disc
Dreams Less Sweet	LP	CBS	25737	1983	£5	£12	with 12'
Force The Hand Of Chance	LP	Some Bizarre	PSY1	1982	£6	£15	double, with insert
Godstar	12"	Temple	TOPIC009	1986	£2.50	£6	pic disc
Good Vibrations	12"	Temple	TOPY023	1987	£2.50	£6	
Jack The Tab	12"	DC	DC23	1988	£2.50	£6	
Just Drifting	7"	Some Bizarre	PTV1	1982	£2.50	£6	
Just Drifting	12"	Some Bizarre	PTV1T	1982	£5	£12	
Live At Thee Pyramid NYC 1988	LP	Temple	TOPY047	1989	£5	£12	pic disc
Love War Riot	10"	Temple	TOPY048T	1989	£2.50	£6	
Magick Defends Itself	12"	Temple	TOPY022	1987	£2.50	£6	
Mouth Of The Night	LP	Temple	TOPY010	1985	£5	£12	pic disc
Pagan Day	LP	Temple	TOPY003	1984	£6	£15	pic disc
Psychick TV Themes Vol.2	LP	Temple	TOPY004	1985	£5	£12	
Psychick TV Themes Vol.3	LP	Temple	TOPY008	1985	£5	£12	
Rev.Jim Jones	LP				£10	£25	US pic disc

Roman P		7"	Sordide Sentimental	SS33009	1984	£5	£10
Those Who Do Not		LP	Gramm/ Temple	GRAMM23	1984	£8	£20 ....double
Unclean		12"	Temple	TOPY001	1984	£3	£8

PUBLIC ENEMY

Rebel Without A Pause		7"	Def Jam	6512450	1987	£2	£5 ....pic disc

PUBLIC FOOT THE ROMAN

Public Foot The Roman		LP	Sovereign	SVNA7259	1973	£10	£25

PUBLIC IMAGE LTD.

Commercial Zone		LP	XYZ	007	1984	£4	£10 ....US
Metal Box		LP	Virgin	METAL1	1979	£6	£15 ....3x12' in can

PUCKETT, GARY & UNION GAP

Incredible		LP	CBS	63429	1968	£5	£12
Woman Woman		LP	Columbia	CS9612	1968	£5	£12 ....US
Young Girl		LP	CBS	63342	1968	£5	£12 ....chart LP

PUDDING

Magic Bus		7"	Decca	F12603	1967	£10	£20

PUGSLEY MUNION

Just Like You		LP	J&S	SLP0001		£17.50	£35 ....US

PULLINS, LEROY

I'm A Nut		7"	London	HLR10056	1966	£4	£8

PULP

Pulp's "His'n'Hers" was one of the highlights of 1994, the confident swagger and sleaze of Jarvis Cocker's song-writing being matched by a scintillating performance from the whole group and recalling some of the best moments of an imaginary meeting between Soft Cell and David Bowie. An album as fresh as this might have been expected to be the group's debut, but in fact, Pulp had been around for nearly a dozen years, so that there are numerous early recordings for collectors to seek out (although none is in the same league as "His'n'Hers"). Unless Jarvis Cocker once performed under the name of "Ann Bean", who is the singer on "Low Flying Aircraft", then the 1979 Pulp is a different group.

Countdown		CD-s	Fire	BLAZE051CD	1991	£3	£8
Countdown		12"	Fire	BLAZE051T	1991	£3	£8
Dogs Are Everywhere		12"	Fire	BLAZE10S	1986	£4	£10
Everybody's Problem		7"	Red Rhino	RED37	1983	£5	£10
Freaks		LP	Fire	FIRELP5	1987	£6	£15
It		LP	Red Rhino	REDLP29	1984	£5	£12
Little Girl With Blue Eyes		12"	Fire	FIRE5	1985	£4	£10
Master Of The Universe		7"	Fire	BLAZE21S	1987	£2.50	£6
Master Of The Universe		12"	Fire	BLAZE21T	1987	£4	£10
My Legendary Girlfriend		7"	Caff	CAFF17	1992	£4	£8
My Legendary Girlfriend		12"	Fire	BLAZE44044	1991	£3	£8
My Lighthouse		7"	Red Rhino	RED32	1983	£2.50	£6
They Suffocate At Night		7"	Fire	BLAZE17S	1987	£2.50	£6
They Suffocate At Night		12"	Fire	LAZE17T	1987	£4	£10

PULP (2)

Low Flying Aircraft		7"	Pulp	PB1	1979	£2	£5

PULSAR

Halloween		LP	CBS	82477	1977	£6	£15 ....French
Pollen		LP	Decca	SKLR5228	1976	£8	£20
Strands Of The Future		LP	Decca	TXS119	1976	£8	£20

PULSE

Pulse		LP	Major Minor	SMLP64	1970	£25	£50

PUMA, JOE

Joe Puma Quintet		10" LP	London	LZN14033	1956	£25	£50

PUMPKIN PIE

Down The Cut		LP	Saydisc	SDL272	1976	£10	£25

PUMPKINHEAD

Pumpkinhead		LP	Mulligan	LUN001	1976	£6	£15 ....Irish

PUNCHIN' JUDY

Punchin' Judy		LP	Transatlantic	TRA272	1973	£5	£12

PUPILS

Tribute To The Rolling Stones		LP	Fontana	SFL13087	1969	£8	£20
Tribute To The Rolling Stones		LP	Wing	WL1150	1966	£40	£80

PUPPETS

Baby Don't Cry		7"	Pye	7N15634	1964	£6	£12
Everybody's Talking		7"	Pye	7N15556	1963	£6	£12
Shake With Me		7"	Pye	7N15625	1964	£6	£12

PURDIE, BERNARD 'PRETTY'

Funky Donkey		7"	Direction	583301	1968	£1.50	£4
Soul Clappin'		7"	Direction	583628	1968	£1.50	£4
Soul Drums		LP	Direction	863290	1968	£4	£10

PURIFY, JAMES & BOBBY

Do Unto Me		7"	Bell	BLL1067	1969	£1.50	£4
Do Unto Me		7"	Stateside	SS2093	1968	£2	£5

Help Yourself To All My Lovin'	7"	Bell	BLL1024	1968	£1.50	£4	
I Can't Remember	7"	Bell	BLL1008	1968	£1.50	£4	
I Take What I Want	7"	Stateside	SS2039	1967	£1.50	£4	
I'm Your Puppet	7"	Mojo	2092056	1972	£1.50	£4	
I'm Your Puppet	7"	Stateside	SS547	1966	£2	£5	
James And Bobby Purify	LP	Stateside	SL10206	1967	£5	£12	
Let Love Come Between Us	7"	Stateside	SS2049	1967	£4	£8	
Pure Sound Of James And Bobby Purify	LP	Bell	MBLL/SBLL101	1967	£6	£15	
Shake A Tail Feather	7"	Bell	BLL1056	1969	£2	£5	
Shake A Tail Feather	7"	Stateside	SS2016	1967	£5	£10	
Untie Me	7"	Bell	BLL1043	1969	£1.50	£4	
Wish You Didn't Have To Go	7"	Stateside	SS595	1967	£2	£5	

PURPLE FOX

Tribute To Jimi Hendrix	LP	Stereo Gold Award	MER340	1971	£5	£12	

PURPLE GANG

Granny Takes A Trip	7"	Transatlantic	BIG101	1967	£4	£8	
Kiss Me Goodnight Sally Green	7"	Transatlantic	BIG111	1968	£2	£5	
Purple Gang Strikes	LP	Transatlantic		1968	£10	£25	

PUSSY

Plays	LP	Morgan Blue Town	BT5002	1969	£180	£300	

PUSSY (2)

Feline Woman	7"	Deram	DM368	1972	£7.50	£15	

PUSSYFOOT

Freeloader	7"	Decca	F12474	1966	£4	£8	
Good Times	7"	Pye	7N17520	1968	£4	£8	
Mr.Hyde	7"	Decca	F12561	1967	£4	£8	

PUTHLI, ASHA

Asha Puthli	LP	CBS	65804	1973	£8	£20	
Devil Is Loose	LP	CBS	81443	1976	£8	£20	
She Loves To Hear The Music	LP	CBS	80978	1975	£6	£15	

PUZZLE

Hey Medusa	7"	Stateside	SS2146	1969	£1.50	£4	
Puzzle	LP	Motown	768	1973	£5	£12	US

PYRAMID

The lead singer on the Pyramid's impressive Deram single was Ian Matthews, subsequently a member of Fairport Convention before embarking on a solo career.

Summer Of Last Year	7"	Deram	DM111	1967	£7.50	£15	

PYRAMIDS

Penetration	LP	Best	LPM1001/ BRS36501	1964	£20	£40	US
Penetration	7"	London	HLU9847	1964	£6	£12	

PYRAMIDS (2)

Pyramids	LP	President	PTL1021	1968	£8	£20	
Train Tour To Rainbow City	7"	President	PT161	1967	£2	£5	chart single

PYRAMIDS (3)

Stay With Him	7"	Doctor Bird	DB1307	1969	£5	£10	

Q

Q65
Afghanistan	LP	Negram		1969	£50	£100	Dutch
Greatest Hits	LP	Decca	6454409	1969	£25	£50	Dutch
Revolution	LP	Decca	6440675	1966	£30	£60	Dutch

QUAITE, CHRISTINE
Guilty Eyes	7"	Oriole	CB1739	1962	£1.50	£4	
Here She Comes	7"	Oriole	CB1921	1963	£1.50	£4	
If You've Got A Heart	7"	Stateside	SS435	1965	£1.50	£4	
In The Middle Of The Floor	7"	Oriole	CB1876	1963	£1.50	£4	
Long After Tonight Is All Over	7"	Stateside	SS482	1966	£7.50	£15	
Mister Heartache	7"	Oriole	CB1845	1963	£1.50	£4	
Will You Be The Same Tomorrow	7"	Oriole	CB1945	1964	£2	£5	
Your Nose Is Gonna Grow	7"	Oriole	CB1772	1962	£1.50	£4	

QUAKER CITY BOYS
Teasin'	7"	London	HLU8796	1959	£2.50	£6	

QUAKERS
I'm Ready	7"	Oriole	CB1992	1965	£25	£50	
She's Alright	7"	Studio 36	KSP109/110	1965	£50	£100	

QUARTER NOTES
Ten Minutes To Midnight	7"	Parlophone	R4365	1957	£1.50	£4	

QUARTERMAN, JOE & FREE SOUL
Joe Quarterman And Free Soul	LP	GSF	GS504	1973	£20	£40	

QUARTZ
Against All Odds	LP	Heavy Metal	HMRPD9	1983	£4	£10	pic disc
Live Count Dracula	LP	Reddington	001	1980	£4	£10	
Nantucket Sleighride	7"	Reddingtons	DAN1	1980	£2	£5	white vinyl
Quartz	LP	Pye	NSPL28261	1978	£4	£10	
Quartz	LP	United Artists	UAG30081	1977	£4	£10	

QUATERMASS
Quatermass	LP	Harvest	SHVL775	1970	£20	£40	

QUEBEC, IKE
Blue And Sentimental	LP	Blue Note	BLP/BST84098	1963	£10	£25	
Bossa Nova - Soul Samba	LP	Blue Note	BLP/BST84114	1964	£10	£25	
Buzzard Lope	7"	Blue Note	451749	1964	£2	£5	
Heavy Soul	LP	Blue Note	BLP/BST84093	1961	£15	£30	
It Might As Well Be Spring	LP	Blue Note	BLP/BST84105	1964	£10	£25	

QUEEN
When EMI were given the Queen's Award To Industry, they were in a position to make an appropriate memento of the occasion and, accordingly, they pressed up a small number of copies of the group Queen's "Bohemian Rhapsody" on royal blue vinyl. The choice has become doubly appropriate since then, for Queen went on to become one of EMI's best selling acts. Since Freddie Mercury's death in November 1991, the values of Queen rarities have inevitably increased rapidly, as indeed have the solo records made by all four members. In addition to those items listed below, there have been coloured vinyl pressings of several Queen LPs issued in various countries and selling for £40-£50. The red vinyl UK pressing of "Sheer Heart Attack" that appears on several dealers' and collectors' wants lists, however, would appear never to have been released.

Another One Bites The Dust	CD-s	Parlophone	QUECD8	1988	£3	£8	
Another One Bites The Dust	7"	EMI	EMI5102	1980	£2	£5	PS
Back Chat	7"	EMI	EMI5325	1982	£2.50	£6	
Back Chat	12"	EMI	12EMI5325	1982	£10	£25	
Bicycle Race	7"	EMI	EMI2870	1978	£1.50	£4	chart single, PS
Bicycle Race	7"	EMI	EMI2870	1978	£5	£10	mispressed B side - plays Crystal Gale or Dollar
Body Language	7"	EMI	EMI5293	1982	£1.50	£4	
Body Language	12"	EMI	12EMI5293	1982	£6	£15	
Bohemian Rhapsody	CD-s	Parlophone	QUECD3	1988	£3	£8	
Bohemian Rhapsody	7"	EMI	EMI2375	1975	£700	£1000	blue vinyl, PS
Bohemian Rhapsody	7"	EMI	EMI2375	1975	£12.50	£25	PS
Bohemian Rhapsody	7"	EMI	EMI2375	1975	£12.50	£25	PS
Bohemian Rhapsody	7"	EMI	EMI2378	1975	£5	£10	misprinted number
Breakthru	CD-s	EMI	CDQUEEN11	1989	£5	£12	
Breakthru	7"	EMI	QUEENPD11	1989	£7.50	£15	shaped pic disc, uncut disc pictured in Guide
Breakthru'	12"	Parlophone	12QUEEN11	1989	£2.50	£6	
Complete Works	LP	EMI	QB1	1985	£50	£100	13 LP boxed set
Complete Works	LP	EMI	QB1	1985	£210	£350	13 LP boxed set, autographed
Crazy Little Thing Called Love	CD-s	Parlophone	QUECD7	1988	£3	£8	
Crazy Little Thing Called Love	7"	EMI	EMI5001	1979	£1.50	£4	chart single, PS
Crazy Little Thing Called Love	7"	EMI	EMI5001	1979	£5	£10	mispressed with 2 B sides
Don't Stop Me Now	7"	EMI	EMI2910	1979	£1.50	£4	chart single, PS

Title	Format	Label	Cat No	Year			Notes
Flash	7"	EMI	EMI5126	1980	£1.50	£4	PS
Friends Will Be Friends	7"	EMI	QUEEN8	1986	£2	£5	
Friends Will Be Friends	7"	EMI	QUEENP8	1986	£10	£20	pic disc
Friends Will Be Friends	12"	EMI	12QUEEN8	1986	£3	£8	
Greatest Hits	LP	EMI	EMTV30	1981	£6	£15	mispress - side 2 plays Anne Murray
Hammer To Fall	7"	EMI	QUEEN4	1984	£40	£80	live PS
Hammer To Fall	7"	EMI	QUEEN4	1984	£1.50	£4	red PS
Hammer To Fall (Headbangers Mix)	12"	EMI	12QUEEN4	1984	£60	£120	live PS, sleeve pictured in Guide
Hammer To Fall (Headbangers Mix)	12"	EMI	12QUEEN4	1984	£3	£8	red PS
Headlong	CD-s	EMI	CDQUEEN18	1991	£3	£8	
Headlong	12"	Parlophone	12QUEENPD18	1991	£6	£15	pic disc
Highlander	CDV	EMI	EMCDV2	1986	£60	£120	pic disc
I Want It All	CD-s	EMI	CDQUEEN10	1989	£6	£15	pic disc
I Want It All	12"	Parlophone	12QUEEN10	1989	£2.50	£6	
I Want To Break Free	CD-s	EMI	QUECD11	1988	£3	£8	
I Want To Break Free	7"	EMI	QUEEN2	1984	£2.50	£6	4 different PS's
I Want To Break Free	12"	EMI	12QUEEN2	1984	£4	£10	
I'm Going Slightly Mad	7"	Parlophone	QUEENPD17	1991	£7.50	£15	shaped pic disc
I'm Going Slightly Mad	12"	EMI	12QUEENG17	1991	£3	£8	gatefold PS
Innuendo	12"	Parlophone	12QUEENPD16	1991	£8	£20	pic disc
Invisible Man	CD-s	Parlophone	CDQUEEN16	1989	£8	£20	
Invisible Man	7"	EMI	QUEENX12	1989	£5	£10	clear vinyl
Invisible Man	12"	EMI	12QUEENX12	1989	£6	£15	clear vinyl
Invisible Man	12"	Parlophone	12QUEEN12	1989	£2.50	£6	
It's A Hard Life	7"	EMI	QUEEN3	1984	£2	£5	
It's A Hard Life	12"	EMI	12QUEEN3	1984	£5	£12	no PS
It's A Hard Life	12"	EMI	12QUEENP3	1984	£15	£30	French pic disc
Jazz	LP	EMI	PIC3	1978	£75	£150	promo
Jealousy	7"	EMI	EMI2036	1979	£7.50	£15	
Keep Yourself Alive	7"	EMI	EMI2036	1973	£15	£30	
Killer Queen	CD-s	Parlophone	QUECD2	1988	£3	£8	
Killer Queen	7"	EMI	EMI2229	1974	£1.50	£4	chart single
Kind Of Magic	CD-s	Parlophone	QUECD12	1988	£3	£8	
Kind Of Magic	7"	EMI	QUEEN7	1986	£1.50	£4	
Kind Of Magic	12"	EMI	12QUEEN7	1986	£4	£10	
Kind Of Magic	12"	EMI	12QUEENP7	1986	£20	£40	pic disc
Las Palabras De Amor	7"	EMI	EMI5316	1982	£5	£10	
Love Of My Life	7"	EMI	EMI2959	1979	£10	£20	
Miracle	CD-s	Parlophone	QUEENCD15	1989	£5	£12	
Miracle	7"	Parlophone	QUEEN15	1989	£1.50	£4	
Miracle	7"	Parlophone	QUEENH15	1989	£5	£10	hologram PS
Miracle	12"	Parlophone	12QUEEN15	1989	£3	£8	yellow PS
Miracle	12"	Parlophone	12QUEENP15	1989	£5	£12	turquoise PS, insert
News Of The World	LP	EMI	EMA784	1977	£75	£150	promo, boxed
Night At The Opera	LP	Mobile Fidelity	MFSL1067	1980	£8	£20	US audiophile
Now I'm Here	7"	EMI	EMI2256	1975	£1.50	£4	chart single
One Vision	7"	EMI	QUEEN6	1985	£2.50	£6	lyric inner sleeve
One Vision	12"	EMI	12QUEEN6	1985	£2.50	£6	
One Vision	12"	EMI	12QUEEN6	1985	£10	£25	PVC cover, red inner
One Vision	12"	EMI	12QUEEN6	1985	£4	£10	with inner sleeve
Play The Game	7"	EMI	EMI5076	1980	£5	£10	mispressed with 2 B sides
Play The Game	7"	EMI	EMI5076	1980	£1.50	£4	PS, chart single
Queen	LP	Elektra	EQ5064	1973	£8	£20	US quad
Queen	LP	EMI	EMC3006	1973	£25	£50	EMI conference copy, unfinished sleeve
Queen's First EP	CD-s	Parlophone	QUECD5	1988	£3	£8	
Queen's First EP	7" EP	EMI	EMI2623	1977	£4	£8	chart single
Radio Ga Ga	CD-s	Parlophone	QUECD10	1988	£3	£8	
Radio Ga Ga	12"	EMI	12QUEEN1	1984	£2.50	£6	
Save Me	7"	EMI	EMI5022	1980	£1.50	£4	PS, chart single
Scandal	CD-s	Parlophone	CDQUEEN14	1989	£6	£15	
Scandal	7"	Parlophone	QUEENP14	1989	£4	£8	poster PS
Scandal	12"	Parlophone	12QUEEN14	1989	£2.50	£6	
Scandal	12"	Parlophone	12QUEENS14	1989	£8	£20	1 side etched with signatures
Seven Seas Of Rhye	7"	EMI	EMI2121	1974	£2	£5	chart single
Seven Seas Of Rye	CD-s	EMI	QUECD1	1988	£3	£8	
Show Must Go On	CD-s	Parlophone	CDQUEENG19	1991	£8	£20	boxed with poster
Show Must Go On	12"	Parlophone	12QUEENSG19	1991	£6	£15	1 side etched with signatures
Somebody To Love	CD-s	Parlophone	QUECD4	1988	£3	£8	
Somebody To Love	7"	EMI	EMI2565	1976	£4	£8	PS
Spread Your Wings	7"	EMI	EMI2757	1978	£2.50	£6	PS, chart single
Thank God It's Christmas	7"	EMI	QUEEN5	1984	£2.50	£6	
Thank God It's Christmas	12"	EMI	12QUEEN5	1984	£6	£15	
Under Pressure	CD-s	Parlophone	QUECD9	1988	£3	£8	
Under Pressure (Live)	7"	EMI		1986	£10	£20	promo
We Are The Chamnpions	CD-s	Parlophone	QUECD6	1988	£3	£8	
We Are The Champions	7"	EMI	EMI2708	1977	£1.50	£4	PS, chart single
Who Wants To Live Forever	7"	EMI	QUEEN9	1986	£2.50	£6	
Who Wants To Live Forever	12"	EMI	12QUEEN9	1986	£5	£12	
Works	7"	EMI		1984	£2.50	£6	promo flex
You're My Best Friend	7"	EMI	EMI2494	1976	£12.50	£25	chart single, PS

QUEENSRYCHE

| Eyes Of A Stranger | 12" | EMI | 12MTG65 | 1989 | £3 | £8 | gatefold PS |

Gonna Get Close To You	7"	EMI	EA22	1986	£2	£5	
Gonna Get Close To You	7"	EMI	EAD22	1986	£5	£10	double
Gonna Get Close To You	12"	EMI	12EA22	1986	£4	£10	
Overseeing The Operation	10"	EMI	10QR1	1988	£3	£8	
Queen Of The Reich	12"	EMI	12EA162	1983	£4	£10	
Take Hold Of The Flame	7"	EMI	EA183	1984	£4	£8	

QUESTION MARK & THE MYSTERIANS

96 Tears	LP	Cameo	C(S)2004	1966	£15	£30	US
96 Tears	7"	Cameo Parkway	C428	1966	£6	£12	chart single
96 Tears	7" EP.	Columbia	ESRF1825	1966	£12.50	£25	French
Action	LP	Cameo	C(S)2006	1966	£15	£30	US
Can't Get Enough Of You Baby	7"	Cameo Parkway	C467	1967	£2	£5	
Can't Get Enough Of You baby	7" EP.	Stateside	FSE105	1967	£12.50	£25	French
Do Something To Me	7"	Cameo Parkway	C496	1967	£5	£10	
Girl	7" EP.	Stateside	FSE1006	1967	£12.50	£25	French
I Need Somebody	7"	Cameo Parkway	C441	1966	£5	£10	
You Captivate Me	7"	Cameo Parkway	C479	1967	£5	£10	

QUESTIONS

We Got Love	7"	Decca	F22740	1968	£5	£10	

QUICKLY, TOMMY

Humpty Dumpty	7"	Pye	7N15748	1964	£4	£8	
Kiss Me Now	7"	Piccadilly	7N35151	1963	£2.50	£6	
Prove It	7"	Piccadilly	7N35167	1964	£2.50	£6	
Tip Of My Tongue	7"	Piccadilly	7N35137	1963	£15	£30	
Wild Side Of Life	7"	Pye	7N15708	1964	£2	£5	chart single
You Might As Well Forget Him	7"	Piccadilly	7N35183	1964	£2.50	£6	

QUICKSAND

Home Is Where I Belong	LP	Dawn	DNLS3056	1974	£20	£40	

QUICKSILVER MESSENGER SERVICE

Anthology	LP	Capitol	ESTSP13	1978	£5	£12	double
Comin' Thru'	LP	Capitol	ST11002	1972	£4	£10	
Happy Trails	LP	Capitol	E(S)T120	1969	£6	£15	
Just For Love	LP	Capitol	EAST498	1970	£5	£12	
Maiden Of The Cancer Moon	LP	Psycho	PSYCHO10	1983	£10	£25	double
Quicksilver	LP	Capitol	SW819	1972	£4	£10	
Quicksilver Messenger Service	LP	Capitol	(S)T2904	1968	£8	£20	
Shady Grove	LP	Capitol	EST391	1969	£5	£12	
What About Me	LP	Capitol	EAST630	1971	£5	£12	

QUIET FIVE

Homeward Bound	7"	Parlophone	R5421	1966	£2	£5	chart single
Honeysuckle Rose	7"	Parlophone	R5302	1965	£2	£5	
I Am Waiting	7"	Parlophone	R5470	1966	£2	£5	
When Morning Sun Dries The Dew	7"	Parlophone	R5273	1965	£2	£5	chart single

QUIET WORLD

Love Is Walking	7"	Dawn	DNS1005	1970	£7.50	£15	
Rest Comfortably	7"	Pye	7N45005	1970	£7.50	£15	
Road	LP	Dawn	DNLS3007	1970	£25	£50	

QUIK

I Can't Sleep	7"	Deram	DM155	1967	£12.50	£25	
King Of The World	7"	Deram	DM139	1967	£6	£12	
Love Is A Beautiful Thing	7"	Deram	DM121	1967	£12.50	£25	

QUILL, GENE

Three Bones And A Quill	LP	Vogue	LAE12204	1959	£8	£20	

QUINCICASM

Quincicasm	LP	Saydisc	SDL249	1973	£5	£12	

QUINICHETTE, PAUL

Basie Reunion	LP	Esquire	32087	1960	£8	£20	
For Basie	LP	Esquire	32067	1959	£10	£25	

QUINN, MIKE

Someone Slipping Into My Mind	7"	Fontana	TF761	1966	£2	£5	

QUINTESSENCE

Quintessence seem to epitomise hippiedom - living communally, radiating peace and love, and above all being obsessed with Eastern religion and music. The group's albums are a smooth blend of Indian chanting and English electric guitar, the two being held together by Raja Ram's fluid, melodic flute playing. They are among the most successful attempts to fuse Eastern and Western musics, although the hippy context will inevitably make the music sound rather dated to modern listeners.

Dive Deep	LP	Island	ILPS9143	1970	£5	£12	chart LP
In Blissful Company	LP	Island	ILPS9110	1969	£6	£15	
Indweller	LP	RCA	SF8317	1972	£4	£10	
Notting Hill Gate	7"	Island	WIP6075	1970	£2	£5	
Quintessence	LP	Island	ILPS9128	1970	£6	£15	chart LP
Self	LP	RCA	SF8273	1971	£4	£10	chart LP
Sweet Jesus	7"	Neon	NE1003	1971	£2	£5	
Sweet Jesus	7"	Neon	NE1003	1971	£6	£12	PS

QUINTET OF THE YEAR

Jazz At Massey Hall	LP	Vogue	LAE12031	1957	£50	£100
Jazz At Massey Hall Vol.1	10" LP	Vogue	LDE040	1954	£50	£100
Jazz At Massey Hall Vol.2	10" LP	Vogue	LDE053	1954	£50	£100
Jazz At Massey Hall Vol.3	10" LP	Vogue	LDE087	1954	£50	£100

QUIST, DARYL

Above And Beyond	7"	Pye	7N15605	1964	£4	£8
Goodbye To You	7"	Pye	7N15563	1963	£2	£5
Keep Moving	7"	Pye	7N15538	1963	£2	£5
Put Away Your Teardrops	7"	Decca	F12058	1965	£1.50	£4
When She Comes To You	7"	Pye	7N15656	1964	£2	£5

QUO VARDIS

100 Mph	7"	Redball	RB001	1979	£5	£10

QUODLING'S DELIGHT

Among The Leaves So Green	LP	Fanfare	FR2179	197-	£6	£15
Among The Leaves So Green	LP	Volta	Q121	197-	£6	£15

QUOTATIONS

Imagination	7"	HMV	POP975	1962	£15	£30

QUOTATIONS (2)

Alright Baby	7"	Decca	F11907	1964	£5	£10
Cool It	7"	CBS	3710	1968	£1.50	£4

R

RABBIT
Broken Arrows	LP	Island	ILPS9238	1973	£4	£10	
Dark Saloon	LP	Island	ILPS9289	1974	£4	£10	

RABBLE
Rabble	LP	Roulette		1969	£15	£30	US
Rabble Album	LP	Transworld	6700	1966	£15	£30	US

RABIN, MIKE
Head Over Heels	7"	Columbia	DB7350	1964	£12.50	£25	
If I Were You	7"	Polydor	BM56007	1965	£6	£12	

RACHEL & THE REVOLVERS
"The Revo-Lution" is one of several early Brian Wilson productions.
Revo-Lution	7"	Dot	16392	1962	£150	£250	US

RACHELL, YANK TENNESSEE JUG BUSTERS
Mandolin Blues	LP	77	LA1223	1964	£6	£15

RADCLIFFE, JIMMY
Long After Tonight Is All Over	7"	Stateside	SS374	1965	£10	£20	chart single

RADHA KRISHNA TEMPLE
Govinda	7"	Apple	25	1970	£2.50	£6	chart single
Govinda	7"	Apple	25	1970	£7.50	£15	PS
Hare Krishna Mantra	7"	Apple	15	1969	£2.50	£6	chart single
Hare Krishna Mantra	7"	Apple	15	1969	£7.50	£15	PS
Radha Krishna Temple	LP	Apple	SAPCOR18	1971	£10	£25	

RADIANTS
Hold On	7"	Chess	CRS8073	1968	£5	£10
Voice Your Choice	7"	Chess	CRS8002	1965	£5	£10

RADIATORS FROM SPACE
Song Of The Faithful Departed	7"	Chiswick	CHIS144	1979	£2	£5	Irish
Sunday World	7"	CBS	5572	1977	£10	£20	Irish
Teenager In Love	7"	Chiswick	NS24	1978	£7.50	£15	test pressing
Walkin' Home Alone Again	7"	Chiswick	NS45	1979	£7.50	£15	test presing

RADICE, MARK
Hey My Love	7"	Paramount	PARA3024	1972	£1.50	£4	
New Day	7"	Paramount	PARA3025	1972	£1.50	£4	

RADIO ACTORS
Nuclear Waste	7"	Charly	CYS1058	1979	£1.50	£4	PS
Nuclear Waste	7"	DB	DBS5	1979	£1.50	£4	PS

RADIO BIRDMAN
Aloha Steve And Danno	7"	Trafalgar	TRS12	1978	£5	£10
Alone In The Endzone	7"	WEA	100160	1981	£25	£50
Burn My Eye	7"	Trafalgar	ME109	1976	£50	£100
Living Eyes	LP	WEA	600085	1981	£6	£15
New Race	7"	Trafalgar	TRS11	1977	£25	£50
Radios Appear	LP	Sire	9103332	1978	£8	£20
Radios Appear (Second Version)	LP	Sire	SRK6050	1978	£8	£20
What Gives?	7"	Sire	6078617	1978	£5	£10

RADIO HEART
London Times	7"	GFM	GFMX112	1987	£1.50	£4	shaped pic disc
Radio Heart	LP	NBR	NBRL1	1987	£5	£12	
Radio Heart	CD	NBR		1987	£20	£40	European
Radio Heart	7"	GFM	GFMG109	1987	£2.50	£6	shaped pic disc
Radio Heart	7"	GFM	GFMX109	1987	£2.50	£6	pic disc

RADIO STARS
Songs For Swinging Lovers	LP	Chiswick	WIK5	1977	£4	£10	with 7' (PROMO2)

RAEBURN, BOYD
Teen Rock	LP	Columbia	CL1073	1957	£10	£25	US

RAELETS
One Hurt Deserves Another	7"	HMV	POP1591	1967	£1.50	£4	

RAFFERTY, GERRY
City To City	LP	Mobile Fidelity	MFSL1058	1980	£4	£10	US audiophile

RAG DOLLS
Dusty	7"	Stateside	SS398	1965	£1.50	£4
My Old Man's A Groovy Old Man	7"	Columbia	DB8378	1968	£1.50	£4
Never Had So Much Loving	7"	Columbia	DB8289	1967	£1.50	£4
Society Girl	7"	Cameo Parkway	P921	1964	£1.50	£4

RAGING STORMS
Dribble .... 7" ..... London .... HLU9556 .... 1962 ... £5 ....£10 ....

RAGLAND, LOU
Since You Said You'd Be Mine .... 7" ...... Warner Bros .... K16312 .... 1973 ... £4 ....£8 ....

RAGNAROK
Fata Morgana	LP	Silence	SRS4666	1981 ...	£5	...£12	...........Swedish
Fjarliar I Magen	LP	Silence	SRS4655	1980 ...	£5	...£12	...........Swedish
Ragnarok	LP	Silence	SRS4633	1977 ...	£6	...£15	...........Swedish
Three Signs	LP	Silence	SRS126704	1984 ...	£4	...£10	...........Swedish
Undertakers Circus	LP	Polydor	2382025	1973 ...	£8	...£20	...........Swedish

RAILWAY CHILDREN
Music From The East Zone .... 7" ...... Gross Product . OBCT1 .... 1983 ... £2 ....£5 .... with tracks
by other artists

RAIN
Once .... 7" ...... Jive Alive........ JA002 .... 1985 ... £1.50 ....£4 ....

RAINBEAUS
That's All I'm Asking Of You .... 7" .... Vogue .... V9161 .... 1960 ... £4 ....£8 ....

RAINBOW
L.A.Connection .... 7" ...... Polydor .... 2066968 .... 1978 ... £2 ....£5 ....red vinyl
Street Of Dreams .... 7" ...... Polydor .... POSPP631........... 1983 ... £2.50 ....£6 ....pic disc

RAINBOW FFOLLY
Drive My Car .... 7" ...... Parlophone..... R5701 .... 1968 ... £10 ....£20 ....
Sallies Forth .... LP ...... Parlophone..... PMC/PCS7050...... 1967 ... £55 ....£110 ....sleeve
pictured in Guide

RAINBOW PEOPLE
Dream Time .... 7" ...... Pye .... 7N17582 .... 1968 ... £5 ....£10 ....
Living In A Dream World .... 7" ...... Pye .... 7N17759 .... 1969 ... £1.50 ....£4 ....
Sailing Song .... 7" ...... Pye .... 7N17624 .... 1968 ... £1.50 ....£4 ....

RAINCHECKS
How Are You Baby .... 7" ...... R&B .... MRB5002 .... 1965 ... £10 ....£20 ....
Something About You .... 7" ...... Solar .... SRP104........... 1964 ... £1.50 ....£4 ....

RAINDROPS
Kind Of Boy You Can't Forget .... 7" ...... London .... HL9769 .... 1963 ... £5 ....£10 ....
Raindrops .... LP ...... London .... HA8140 .... 1964 ... £15 ....£30 ....
That Boy John .... 7" ...... London .... HL9825 .... 1964 ... £5 ....£10 ....
What A Guy .... 7" ...... London .... HL9718 .... 1963 ... £6 ....£12 ....
What A Guy .... 7" EP.. London .... RE1415 .... 1964 ... £10 ....£20 ....

RAINDROPS (2)
Along Came Jones .... 7" ...... Parlophone..... R4559 .... 1959 ... £1.50 ....£4 ....
Banjo Boy .... 7" ...... Oriole .... CB1555 .... 1960 ... £1.50 ....£4 ....
Book Of Love .... 7" ...... Fontana .... TF463 .... 1964 ... £1.50 ....£4 ....
If I Had My Life To Live Over .... 7" ...... Oriole .... CB1544 .... 1960 ... £1.50 ....£4 ....
Will You Love Me Tomorrow .... 7" ...... Oriole .... CB1595 .... 1961 ... £1.50 ....£4 ....

RAINE, LORRY
Love Me Tonight .... 7" ...... London .... HL8132 .... 1955 ... £10 ....£20 ....
You Broke My Broken Heart .... 7" ...... London .... HL8043 .... 1954 ... £10 ....£20 ....

RAINEY, MA
Ma Rainey	LP	Milestone	M47021	1975 ...	£5	...£12	...........double
Ma Rainey	10" LP	Ristic	LP13	195- ...	£10	...£25	....
Ma Rainey	10" LP	Ristic	LP19	195- ...	£10	...£25	....
Ma Rainey Vol.3	10" LP	London	AL3558	1956 ...	£8	...£20	....
Sings The Blues	LP	Riverside	RL12108	1962 ...	£6	...£15	....
Vol.1	10" LP	London	AL3502	1953 ...	£8	...£20	....
Vol.2	10" LP	London	AL3538	1955 ...	£8	...£20	....

RAINEY, MA & TRIXIE SMITH
Female Blues Vol.3 .... 7" EP.. Collector ...... JEL22 .... 1964 ... £5 ....£10 ....

RAINMAN
Rainman .... LP ...... Negram .... NQ20038 .... 1971 ... £40 ....£80 ....Dutch

RAINWATER, MARVIN
Country & Western Favourites Vol.2 ...	7" EP..	Ember	EMBEP4521	1962 ...	£6	...£12	....
Dance Me Daddy	7"	MGM.....	MGM988	1958 ...	£4	...£8	....
Gonna Find Me A Bluebird	LP	MGM.....	E4046	1962 ...	£15	...£30	...........US
Gonna Find Me A Bluebird	7"	MGM.....	MGM961	1957 ...	£6	...£12	....
Half Breed	7"	MGM.....	MGM1030	1959 ...	£2.50	...£6	....
I Can't Forget	7"	London	HLU9447	1961 ...	£37.50	...£75	....
I Dig You Baby	7"	MGM.....	MGM980	1958 ...	£2.50	...£6	...........chart single
Marvin Rainwater	7" EP..	MGM.....	MGMEP685	1958 ...	£12.50	...£25	....
Meet Marvin Rainwater	7" EP..	MGM.....	MGMEP647	1958 ...	£12.50	...£25	....
Nothin' Needs Nothin'	7"	MGM.....	MGM1052	1960 ...	£4	...£8	....
Songs By Marvin Rainwater	LP	MGM.....	E3534	1957 ...	£30	...£60	...........US
Songs By Marvin Rainwater	10" LP	MGM.....	D152	1957 ...	£30	...£60	....
Tennessee Hound Dog Yodel	7"	MGM.....	SP1150	1955 ...	£12.50	...£25	....
What Am I Supposed To Do	7"	MGM.....	MGM929	1956 ...	£7.50	...£15	....
Whole Lotta Marvin	7" EP..	MGM.....	MGMEP662	1958 ...	£12.50	...£25	....
Whole Lotta Woman	7"	MGM.....	MGM974	1958 ...	£2.50	...£6	...........chart single

With A Heart, With A Beat	LP	MGM	E3721	1958	£20	£40		US

RAINY DAY
Painting Pictures	7"	EMI	EMI5472	1984	£4	£8	

RAINY DAZE
Autumn Leaves	7"	CBS	3200	1967	£5	£10	
Blood Of Oblivion	7"	Polydor	BM56737	1968	£5	£10	
That Acapulco Gold	LP	Uni	(7)3002	1967	£6	£15	US
That Acapulco Gold	7"	Polydor	56731	1968	£4	£8	

RAISINS
Ain't That Lovin' You Baby	7"	Major Minor	MM540	1968	£2	£5	
I Thank You	7"	Major Minor	MM602	1969	£2	£5	

RALFI
Wonderful Thing	7"	Island	USA003	1974	£2.50	£6	

RALLY ROUNDERS
Bike Beat	7"	Lyntone	LYN574	196-	£15	£30	

RAM
Where? In Conclusion	LP	Polydor		1972	£8	£20	US

RAM, BUCK
Benfica	7"	London	HLU9677	1963	£2	£5	
Magic Touch	LP	Mercury	MG2/SR60392	1960	£5	£12	US

RAM JAM BAND
Shake Shake Senora	7"	Columbia	DB7621	1965	£4	£8	

RAMASES
Crazy One	7"	CBS	3717	1968	£30	£60	
Glass Top Coffin	LP	Vertigo	6360115	1975	£5	£12	
Space Hymns	LP	Vertigo	6360046	1971	£10	£25	spiral label
Space Hymns	LP	Vertigo	6360046	1973	£5	£12	

RAMATAM
In April Came The Dawning	LP	Atlantic	SD7261	1973	£4	£10	US

RAMBLERS
Dodge City	7"	Decca	F11775	1963	£6	£12	

RAMONES
Blitzkrieg Bop	7"	Sire	6078601	1976	£20	£40	PS
I Remember You	7"	Sire	6078603	1977	£4	£8	PS
I Wanna Be Sedated	7"	RSO	RSO70	1981	£2	£5	
Meltdown With The Ramones	7"	Sire	SREP1	1980	£1.50	£4	
Ramones Leave Home	LP	Sire	9103254	1977	£5	£12	with 'Carbona Not Glue'
Rockaway Beach	12"	Sire	6078611	1977	£2.50	£6	with poster
Sheena Is A Punk Rocker	7"	Sire	6078606	1977	£2	£5	
Sheena Is A Punk Rocker	12"	Sire	6078606	1977	£3	£8	
She's The One	7"	Sire	SIR4009	1979	£2	£5	
Swallow My Pride	7"	Sire	6078607	1977	£2	£5	
Time Has Come Today	7"	Sire	W9606	1983	£4	£8	
Time Has Come Today	12"	Sire	WT9606	1983	£4	£10	

RAMPART STREET PARADERS
Rampart And Vine	LP	Philips	BBL7194	1958	£6	£15	
Rampart Street Paraders	LP	Philips	BBL7112	1957	£6	£15	

RAMRODS
Loch Lomond Rock	7"	London	HLU9355	1961	£2.50	£6	
Riders In The Sky	7"	London	HLU9282	1961	£2	£5	chart single
Riders In The Sky	7" EP	London	REU1292	1961	£15	£30	

RAMRODS (2)
Overdrive	7"	United Artists	UP1113	1965	£2.50	£6	

RAMSEY, BILL
Go Man Go	7"	Polydor	NH66812	1962	£2.50	£6	

RANALDO, LEE
From Here To Infinity	12"	Blast First	BFFP9	1987	£2.50	£6	clear vinyl

RANCHERS
American Sailor At The Cavern	7"	Cavern Sound	IMSTL2	1965	£4	£8	

RANDALL, FREDDY
Dr.Jazz	10" LP	Parlophone	PMD1046	1957	£4	£10	

RANDAZZO, TEDDY
Big Wide World	LP	Copix	CP445	1963	£8	£20	US
Dance To The Locomotion	7"	HMV	POP1062	1962	£1.50	£4	
Hey, Let's Twist	LP	Roulette	R25168	1962	£8	£20	US
I'm Confessin'	LP	Vik	LX1121	1960	£10	£25	US
Journey To Love	LP	HMV	CLP1527/CSD1421	1962	£6	£15	
Twists	LP	HMV	CLP1601	1963	£8	£20	

RANDELL, LYNNE
Ciao Baby	7"	CBS	2847	1967	£50	£100	

That's A Hoe Down	7"	CBS	2927	1967	£4	£8	

RANDELLS

Martian Hop	7"	London	HLU9760	1963	£7.50	£15	

RANDI, DON

Live At The Discotheque	7" EP	Reprise	RVEP6102	1967	£5	£10	French

RANDOLPH, BARBARA

I Got A Feeling	7"	Tamla Motown	TMG628	1967	£12.50	£25	
I Got A Feeling	7"	Tamla Motown	TMG788	1971	£2	£5	

RANDOLPH, BOOTS

Hey Mr.Sax Man	7"	London	HLU9891	1964	£1.50	£4	
More Yakety Sax	LP	London	HAU8280	1966	£5	£12	
Shadow Of Your Smile	7"	Monument	MON1001	1967	£1.50	£4	
These Boots Were Made For Walking	7"	London	HLU10028	1966	£4	£8	
Yakety Sax	LP	London	HAU8106	1963	£5	£12	
Yakety Sax	7"	London	HLU9685	1963	£2.50	£6	
Yakety Sax Of Boots Randolph	7" EP	London	REU1365	1963	£6	£12	

RANDOM BLUES BAND

Winchester Cathedral	7" EP	Vogue	INT18103	1966	£4	£8	French

RANDY & THE RAINBOWS

Denise	7"	Stateside	SS214	1963	£10	£20	

RANEE & RAJ

Don't Tell Me I Must Go	7"	Fontana	TF941	1968	£1.50	£4	
Feel Like A Clown	7"	Fontana	TF920	1968	£2.50	£6	

RANEY, JIMMY

In Three Attitudes	LP	HMV	CLP1264	1959	£8	£20	
Jimmy Raney 1955	10" LP	Esquire	20054	1955	£20	£40	
Visits Paris	10" LP	Vogue	LDE071	1954	£20	£40	
Visits Paris Vol.2	10" LP	Vogue	LDE097	1955	£20	£40	

RANEY, SUE

When Your Lover Has Gone	7" EP	Capitol	EAP1964	1958	£2.50	£6	

RANEY, WAYNE

Adam	7"	Parlophone	CSMP20	1954	£5	£10	export
Country And Western	7" EP	Parlophone	GEP8746	1958	£10	£20	

RANGLERS

You Never Said Goodbye	7"	Trend	TRE1007	1968	£2.50	£6	

RANGLIN, ERNEST

Harmonica Twist	7"	Island	WI015	1962	£5	£10	
Reflections	LP	Island	ILP915	1964	£20	£40	
Soho	7" EP	Black Swan	IEP704	1966	£10	£20	
Swing-A-Ling	7"	Black Swan	WI417	1964	£5	£10	
Wranglin'	LP	Island	ILP909	1964	£20	£40	

RANKIN, KENNY

Mind Dusters	LP	Mercury	20145SMCL	1968	£5	£12	

RAPEMAN

Hated Chinee	7"	Fierce	FRIGHT031	1988	£2	£5	

RAPHAEL, JOHNNY

We're Only Young Once	7"	Vogue	V9104	1958	£10	£20	

RAPIERS

Vol.1	7"	Red Door	RA001	1983	£2.50	£6	
Vol.2	7"	Twang	RA002	1984	£2	£5	
Vol.3	7"	Twang	RA003	1985	£1.50	£4	

RAPKIN, BRIAN & KELVIN JONES

Dreams Of The Blue Beast	LP	MSR		197-	£15	£30	

RAPP, TOM

Stardancer	LP	Blue Thumb	BTS44	1972	£6	£15	US
Sunforest	LP	Blue Thumb	BTS56	1973	£6	£15	US
Tom Rapp	LP	Reprise	MS2069	1972	£6	£15	US

RARE AMBER

Malfunction Of The Engine	7"	Polydor	56309	1969	£5	£10	sleeve
Rare Amber	LP	Polydor	583046	1969	£40	£80	pictured in Guide

RARE BIRD

As Your Mind Flies By	LP	Charisma	CAS1011	1970	£6	£15	
Epic Forest	LP	Polydor	2442101	1972	£8	£20	with 7' (2814011)
Rare Bird	LP	Charisma	CAS1005	1969	£6	£15	
Sympathy	7"	Charisma	CB120	1970	£1.50	£4	chart single
Sympathy	7"	Charisma	CB179	1972	£1.50	£4	PS

RARE BREED

Beg Borrow And Steal	7"	Strike	JH316	1966	£5	£10	

RARE EARTH

Title	Format	Label	Cat No	Year	Price	Price	Notes
Dream Answers	LP	Verve	5056	1968	£4	£10	US
Ecology	LP	Tamla Motown	STML11180	1971	£4	£10	
Get Ready	LP	Tamla Motown	STML11165	1970	£4	£10	
Get Ready	7"	Tamla Motown	TMG742	1970	£2.50	£6	

RAS MICHAEL & THE SONS OF NEGUS

Title	Format	Label	Cat No	Year	Price	Price	Notes
Nyahbinghi	LP	Trojan	TRS113	1975	£4	£10	
Tribute	LP	Trojan	TRS132	1976	£4	£10	

RASCALS

Title	Format	Label	Cat No	Year	Price	Price	Notes
Beautiful Morning	7"	Atlantic	584182	1968	£1.50	£4	
Carry Me Back	7"	Atlantic	584292	1969	£1.50	£4	
Collection	LP	Atlantic	587060	1967	£6	£15	
Come On Up	7"	Atlantic	584050	1966	£4	£8	
Freedom Suite	LP	Atlantic	588183	1969	£4	£10	
Freedom Suite Narration	LP	Atlantic		1969	£6	£15	US promo
Girl Like You	7"	Atlantic	584128	1967	£1.50	£4	chart single
Glory Glory	7"	Atlantic	2091029	1970	£1.50	£4	
Good Lovin'	7"	Atlantic	AT4082	1966	£2	£5	
Good Lovin'	7" EP	Atlantic	750011	1966	£6	£12	French
Greatest Hits	LP	Atlantic	587/588120	1968	£4	£10	
Groovin'	LP	Atlantic	587/588074	1967	£6	£15	
Groovin'	7"	Atlantic	584111	1967	£1.50	£4	chart single
Heaven	7"	Atlantic	584255	1969	£1.50	£4	
Hold On	7"	Atlantic	584307	1970	£1.50	£4	
How Can I Be Sure	7"	Atlantic	584138	1967	£1.50	£4	
I Ain't Gonna Eat Out My Heart	7"	Atlantic	584085	1967	£1.50	£4	
I Ain't Gonna Eat Out My Heart	7"	Atlantic	AT4059	1965	£2	£5	
It's Wonderful	7"	Atlantic	584161	1968	£2	£5	
I've Been Lonely Too Long	7"	Atlantic	584081	1967	£4	£8	
I've Been Lonely Too Long	7" EP	Atlantic	750021	1967	£6	£12	French
Love Is A Beautiful Thing	7"	Atlantic	584024	1966	£4	£8	
Once Upon A Dream	LP	Atlantic	587/588098	1968	£4	£10	
People Got To Be Free	7"	Atlantic	584210	1968	£1.50	£4	
Search And Nearness	LP	Atlantic	2400113	1971	£4	£10	
See	LP	Atlantic	588210	1969	£4	£10	
See	7"	Atlantic	584274	1969	£1.50	£4	
Sentirai La Pioggla	7" EP	Atlantic	NP3124	1968	£5	£10	sung in Italian
Sueno	7" EP	Atlantic	750027	1967	£6	£12	French
Too Many Fish In The Sea	7"	Atlantic	584067	1966	£1.50	£4	
Young Rascals	LP	Atlantic	587012	1966	£8	£20	

RASPBERRIES

Title	Format	Label	Cat No	Year	Price	Price	Notes
Fresh	LP	Capitol	ST11123	1972	£5	£12	
Raspberries	LP	Capitol	ST11036	1972	£5	£12	
Side Three	LP	Capitol	ST11220	1973	£5	£12	

RATIP, ARMAN

Title	Format	Label	Cat No	Year	Price	Price	Notes
Introducing	LP	Columbia	SCX6432	1970	£8	£20	
Spy From Istanbul	LP	Regal Zonophone	SLRZ1038	1973	£8	£20	

RATS

The Rats, whose recording career had begun and ended a little earlier, were the group taken on by David Bowie and renamed The Spiders From Mars. The assumption is that Mick Ronson is to be heard playing on the singles, but in fact he did not join the Rats until the late sixties. His recording debut is therefore not to be found on any of the singles by the Rats, but on the 1969 album by Michael Chapman, "Fully Qualified Survivor".

Title	Format	Label	Cat No	Year	Price	Price	Notes
Every Day I Have The Blues	7"	Oriole	CB1967	1964	£20	£40	
I Gotta See My Baby	7"	Columbia	DB7607	1965	£15	£30	
Spoonful	7"	Columbia	DB7483	1965	£30	£60	
Spoonful	7"	Oak	RGJ145	1964	£75	£150	1 sided

RATS (2)

Title	Format	Label	Cat No	Year	Price	Price	Notes
Sack Of Woe	7"	CBS	201740	1965	£15	£30	

RATT

Title	Format	Label	Cat No	Year	Price	Price	Notes
Lay It Down	7"	Atlantic	A9546P	1985	£1.50	£4	shaped pic disc
You're In Love	7"	Atlantic	A9502P	1986	£2	£5	shaped pic disc

RATTLES

Title	Format	Label	Cat No	Year	Price	Price	Notes
Au Star Club De Hambourg	7" EP	Barclay	70656	1964	£20	£40	French
Bye Bye Johnny	7"	Decca	F11873	1964	£5	£10	
Come On And Sing	7"	Fontana	TF618	1965	£2.50	£6	
Gin Mill	LP	RCA	PPL14016	1974	£4	£10	German
Greatest Hits	LP	Mercury	MG1127	1967	£10	£25	
Hurra, Die Rattles Kommen	LP	Star Club		1966	£30	£60	German
Rattles	LP	Decca	SKL5088	1971	£8	£20	
Remember Final Ligure	LP	Star Club	158031	1967	£35	£70	German
Say All Right	7"	Fontana	TF724	1966	£2.50	£6	
Sha-La-La-Le-Lee	7" EP	Barclay	466030	1967	£20	£40	French
Stomp	7"	Philips	BF1277	1963	£2.50	£6	
Teenbeat From the Star Club Hamburg	7" EP	Decca	DFE8568	1964	£20	£40	
Tell Me What Can I Do	7"	Decca	F11936	1964	£4	£8	
Tonight Starring Edna	LP	Philips	6305176	1972	£4	£10	German
Twist At The Star Club	LP	Philips	BL7614	1964	£37.50	£75	
Witch	LP	Philips	6305072	1971	£6	£15	German
Witch	7"	Decca	F23058	1970	£1.50	£4	chart single
You Can't Have Sunshine Every Day	7"	Decca	F23119	1971	£1.50	£4	

RAVEL, CHRIS & THE RAVERS
Chris Ravel was Chris Andrews, later a moderately successful solo artist and a more successful songwriter and producer - most notably for Sandie Shaw.

| I Do | 7" | Decca | F11696 | 1963 | £4 | £8 | |

RAVEN
Children At Our Feet	7"	CBS	5043	1970	£2	£5	
Live At The Inferno	LP	Discovery	36133	196-	£6	£15	US
Raven	LP	Columbia	CS9903	1969	£6	£15	US

RAVEN, JON
| Ballad Of The Black Country | LP | Broadside | BRO116 | 1975 | £6 | £15 | |
| Harvest | LP | Broadside | BRO117 | 1976 | £6 | £15 | |

RAVEN, JON, JOHN KIRKPATRICK, SUE HARRIS
| English Canals | LP | Broadside | BRO118 | 1976 | £6 | £15 | |

RAVEN, JON, MIKE RAVEN, PETE SAGE, JEAN WARD
| Kate Of Coalbrookdale | LP | Argo | ZFB29 | 1971 | £8 | £20 | |

RAVEN, JON, NIC JONES, TONY ROSE
| Songs Of A Changing World | LP | Trailer | LER2083 | 1973 | £10 | £25 | |

RAVEN, MIKE
Mike Raven was a disc jockey on pirate radio and then on Radio One. He used to present a specialist programme of soul and blues and the two LPs listed here are to some extent re-creations of the blues part. The "Blues Show" provides a necessarily brief, but effective history of the blues. Mike Raven introduces each track and his comments are relevant enough - and his voice soothing enough - to prevent the introductions becoming irritating on successive hearings. The "Blues Sampler" is similar, but attempts to show the range of blues styles rather than following a historical approach.

| Mike Raven Blues Sampler | LP | Transatlantic | TRASAM5 | 1969 | £5 | £12 | |
| Mike Raven Blues Show | LP | XTRA | XTRA1047 | 1966 | £6 | £15 | |

RAVEN, PAUL
It is astonishing to realise that the earliest record made by Gary Glitter dates from as early as 1960! The man who was born Paul Gadd adopted the Raven surname for most of the sixties, and has a starring role on the original "Jesus Christ Superstar" album under this name.

Soul Thing	7"	MCA	MU1035	1968	£5	£10	
Stand	7"	MCA	MKS5053	1970	£4	£8	
Too Proud	7"	Decca	F11202	1960	£10	£20	
Tower Of Strength	7"	Parlophone	R4842	1961	£6	£12	
Walk On Boy	7"	Parlophone	R4812	1961	£6	£12	

RAVEN, SIMON
| I Wonder If She Remembers Me | 7" | Piccadilly | 7N35301 | 1966 | £10 | £20 | |

RAVENS
Begin The Beguine	78	Oriole	CB1149	1953	£6	£12	
I Just Wanna Hear You Say	7"	Oriole	CB1910	1964	£4	£8	
Rock Me All Night Long	78	Oriole	CB1148	1953	£6	£12	
Who'll Be The Fool?	78	Oriole	CB1258	1954	£6	£12	
Write Me A Letter	LP	Regent	MG6062	195-	£30	£60	US

RAVENS (2)
| Career Girl | 7" | Pye | 7N25077 | 1961 | £1.50 | £4 | |

RAVERS
| Badam Bam | 7" | Upsetter | US312 | 1969 | £1.50 | £4 | Upsetters B side |

RAVING SAVAGES
| Everybody Surf | 7" EP | Decca | DFE8546 | 1963 | £20 | £40 | |
| Surfin' USA | 7" EP | Decca | 457020 | 1963 | £15 | £30 | French |

RAW HERBS
| Old Joe | 7" | Medium Cool | MC002 | 1986 | £1.50 | £4 | flexi |

RAW MATERIAL
Hi There Allelujah	7"	Evolution	E2445	1970	£10	£20	
Raw Material Album	LP	Evolution	Z1006	1970	£85	£170	
Time And Illusion	7"	Evolution	E2441	1969	£10	£20	
Time Is	LP	Neon	NE8	1971	£85	£170	sleeve pictured in Guide
Traveller Man	7"	Evolution	E24495	1970	£10	£20	

RAWLS, LOU
I Don't Love You Anymore	7"	Capitol	CL15515	1967	£2	£5	
It's You	7"	Capitol	CL15583	1969	£1.50	£4	
Lost And Looking	7" EP	Capitol	EAP120646	1964	£2.50	£6	
Love Is A Hurting Thing	7"	Capitol	CL15465	1966	£1.50	£4	
My Ancestors	7"	Capitol	CL15533	1968	£1.50	£4	
Show Business	7"	Capitol	CL15507	1967	£1.50	£4	
Soul Serenade	7"	Capitol	CL15548	1968	£1.50	£4	
Yes It Hurts Doesn't It	7"	Capitol	CL15499	1967	£1.50	£4	
You Can Bring Me All Your Heartaches	7"	Capitol	CL15488	1967	£1.50	£4	
Your Good Thing	7"	Capitol	CL15611	1969	£1.50	£4	

RAY, JAMES
If You Gotta Make A Fool Of Somebody	LP	Caprice	(S)LP1002	1962	£8	£20	US
If You Gotta Make A Fool Of Somebody	7"	Pye	7N25126	1962	£4	£8	
Itty Bitty Pieces	7"	Pye	7N25147	1962	£2.50	£6	

RAY, JAMES (2)

Mexican Sundown Blues	7"	Merciful Release	MRAY52	1986	£1.50	£4
Mexican Sundown Blues	12"	Merciful Release	MRAY52	1986	£2.50	£6

RAY, JOHNNIE

At The London Palladium	10" LP	Philips	BBR8001	1953	£10	£25	
Best Of Johnnie Ray	LP	Realm	RM52317	1966	£4	£10	
Big Beat	LP	Philips	BBL7148	1957	£10	£25	
Build Your Love	7"	Philips	JK1025	1957	£7.50	£15	chart single
Here And Now	7"	Philips	PB918	1959	£1.50	£4	
How Many Nights How Many Days	7"	HMV	POP902	1961	£2.50	£6	
I Believe	7"	London	HLG9484	1962	£2.50	£6	Timi Yuro B side
I'll Never Fall In Love Again	7"	Philips	PB952	1959	£1.50	£4	chart single
I'm Just A Shadow Of Myself	7"	Columbia	SCM5122	1954	£7.50	£15	
In Las Vegas	LP	Philips	BBL7254	1958	£10	£25	
In The Heart Of A Fool	7"	London	HLA9216	1960	£1.50	£4	
Johnnie Ray	LP	Liberty	LBY1020	1962	£6	£15	
Johnnie Ray	7" EP	Columbia	SEG7511	1954	£7.50	£15	
Johnnie Ray	7" EP	Philips	BBE12006	1955	£7.50	£15	
Johnnie Ray	7" EP	Philips	BBE12217	1958	£4	£8	
Lonely For A Letter	7"	Philips	PB829	1958	£1.50	£4	
Look Homeward Angel	7"	Philips	JK1004	1957	£10	£20	chart single
Miss Me Just A Little	7"	Philips	PB785	1958	£2	£5	
Nobody's Sweetheart	7"	Columbia	SCM5111	1954	£7.50	£15	
On The Trail	LP	Philips	BBL7363	1961	£6	£15	
On The Trail	7" EP	Philips	BBE12460	1961	£5	£10	
Pink Sweater Angel	7"	Philips	JK1033	1957	£7.50	£15	
Please Don't Talk About Me	7"	Columbia	SCM5074	1953	£7.50	£15	
Showcase Of Hits	LP	Philips	BBL7264	1959	£8	£20	
Sinner Man Am I	LP	Philips	BBL7348	1960	£8	£20	
So Long	7"	Philips	JK1011	1957	£7.50	£15	
Strollin' Girl	7"	Philips	PB808	1958	£2	£5	
Tales From The Vienna Woods	LP	Ace Of Clubs	ACL1059	1961	£4	£10	
Tell The Lady I Said Goodbye	7"	Columbia	SCM5041	1953	£7.50	£15	
Till Morning	LP	Philips	BBL7285/SBBL555	1959	£6	£15	
Up Until Now	7"	Philips	PB849	1958	£1.50	£4	
Voice Of Your Choice	10" LP	Philips	BBR8062	1955	£10	£25	
Walkin' My Baby Back Home	7"	Columbia	SCM5015	1953	£10	£20	chart single
Walking And Crying	7" EP	Philips	BBE12115	1957	£7.50	£15	
What More Can I Say	7"	Philips	PB884	1958	£1.50	£4	
When's Your Birthday Baby	7"	Philips	PB901	1959	£1.50	£4	
Yes Tonight Josephine	7"	Philips	JK1016	1957	£7.50	£15	chart single
Yes Tonight Josephine	7" EP	Philips	BBE12192	1958	£5	£10	

RAY, RICARDO

Nitty Gritty	7"	Roulette	RO501	1967	£4	£8

RAY, WADE

Burning Desire	7"	London	HL9700	1963	£4	£8

RAYBURN, MARGIE

I Would	7"	London	HLU8648	1958	£5	£10
I'm Available	7"	London	HLU8515	1957	£5	£10
Wedding Song	7"	Capitol	CL14532	1956	£1.50	£4

RAYE, SOL

While I'm Here	7"	Deram	DM154	1967	£1.50	£4

RAYMOND, TONY

Infant King	7"	Oriole	CB1777	1962	£1.50	£4

RAYNOR, MARTIN & THE SECRETS

Candy To Me	7"	Columbia	DB7563	1965	£4	£8

RAYNOR, MIKE

Is She A Woman Now	7"	Decca	F22690	1967	£1.50	£4
Ob La Di Ob La Da	7"	Decca	F22864	1969	£1.50	£4
Turn Your Head	7"	Decca	F12605	1967	£2	£5
Wonderful Day	7"	Decca	F22790	1968	£1.50	£4

RAYS

Silhouettes	7"	London	HLU8505	1957	£15	£30

RAZORCUTS

Big Pink Cake	7"	Subway Organisation	SUBWAY5	1986	£2.50	£6
Sometimes I Worry About You	7"	Caff	CAFF10	198-	£4	£8

RAZOR'S EDGE

Let's Call It A Day Girl	7"	Stateside	SS532	1966	£2	£5

REA, CHRIS

Bombolini	12"	Magnet	MAGT259	1984	£6	£15	
I Don't Know What It Is But I Love It	12"	Magnet	MAGT255	1984	£2.50	£6	
Josephine	12"	Magnet	MAGT280	1985	£2.50	£6	
Let It Loose	12"	Magnet	12MAG233	1982	£3	£8	with 7" (CHRIS1)
Let's Dance (Rea Mix)	12"	Magnet	MAGT299R	1987	£2.50	£6	
So Much Love	7"	Magnet	MAG10	1974	£10	£20	

REA, JOHN
Traditional Music On The Hammer Dulcimer	LP	Topic	12TS373	1978	£5	£12	

REACTA
Stop The World	7"	Battery Operated	WAC1	1979	£7.50	£15	

REACTION
Oh Me Oh My	7"	Columbia	DB119	1970	£4	£8	Rico B side

REACTION (2)
Reaction	LP	Polydor	2371251	1972	£15	£30	German

REACTION (3)
I Can't Resist	7"	Island	WIP6437	1978	£2	£5	

READER, PAT
Cha Cha On The Moon	7"	Piccadilly	7N35077	1962	£7.50	£15	
Helpless	7"	Oriole	CB1903	1963	£1.50	£4	
Ricky	7"	Triumph	RGM1024	1960	£7.50	£15	

READING, BERTICE
Jazz Train Girl	7" EP	Parlophone	GEP8537	1955	£2	£5	
My Big Best Shoes	7"	Parlophone	R4487	1958	£4	£8	
No Flowers By Request	7"	Decca	F10965	1957	£4	£8	
Rock Baby Rock	7"	Parlophone	R4462	1958	£7.50	£15	

READING, WILMA
Two Can Have A Party	7"	Pye	7N45380	1974	£2	£5	

REAL MCCOY
This Is The Real McCoy	LP	Marble Arch	MAL1251	1970	£8	£20	

REALIZATION OF ETERNITY
Beyond The End	LP	Narco		197-	£20	£40	US

REALLY RED
Crowd Control	7"	CIA	CIA001	1979	£15	£30	
Despise Moral Majority	7"	CIA	CIA003	1981	£15	£30	
Modern Needs	7"	CIA	CIA002	1980	£15	£30	
Teaching You The Fear	LP	CIA	CIA006	1981	£20	£40	

REALM
Hard Time Loving You	7"	CBS	202044	1966	£7.50	£15	

REBEL ROUSERS
Should I	7"	Fontana	TF973	1968	£6	£12	

REBELS
Hard To Love You	7"	Page One	POF017	1967	£7.50	£15	

REBENACK, MAC
Mac Rebenack achieved early notoriety as the only white musician to find employment on R&B sessions in New Orleans. Later he re-invented himself as the voodoo singer Dr.John, although it is as Rebenack that he continues to play as a highly-respected boogie pianist.
Good Times	7"	Ace	611	1961	£7.50	£15	US
Storm Warning	7"	Rex	1008	196-	£7.50	£15	US

REBIRTH
Rebirth	LP	Avantgarde		1968	£20	£40	US

REBOUNDS
Help Me	7"	Fontana	TF461	1964	£6	£12	

REBS
Bunky	7"	Capitol	CL14932	1958	£2.50	£6	

RECO, EZO & THE LAUNCHERS
Jamaica Blue Beat	7" EP	Columbia	SEG8326	1964	£10	£20	
King Of Kings	7"	Columbia	DB7217	1964	£4	£8	chart single
Little Girl	7"	Columbia	DB7222	1964	£4	£8	
Please Come Back	7"	Columbia	DB7290	1964	£4	£8	

RECREATION
Recreation	LP	Bellaphon	BLPS19006	1970	£4	£10	German

RED CRAYOLA
God Bless The Red Crayola	LP	International Artists	IALP7	1968	£8	£20	US
Parable Of Arable Land	LP	International Artists	IALP2	1967	£22.50	£45	US mono
Parable Of Arable Land	LP	International Artists	IALP2	1967	£10	£25	US stereo

RED DIRT
Red Dirt	LP	Fontana	STL5540	1970	£180	£300	

RED HOT CHILI PEPPERS
Abbey Road EP	12"	EMI	12MTPD41	1988	£4	£10	pic disc
Fight Like A Brave	12"	EMI	12EAP241	1988	£4	£10	pic disc
Hollywood (Africa)	7"	EMI	EA205	1985	£2	£5	
Hollywood (Africa)	12"	EMI	12EA205	1985	£3	£8	

| Knock Me Down | 7" | EMI | MTPD70 | 1989 | £4 | £8 | pic disc |

RED LIGHTS
| Never Wanna Leave | 7" | Free Range | PF5 | 1978 | £1.50 | £4 | |

RED LORRY YELLOW LORRY
Beating My Head	7"	Red Rhino	RED20	1982	£4	£8	
He's Read	7"	Red Rhino	RED39	1983	£2	£5	
Take It All	7"	Red Rhino	RED28	1983	£2.50	£6	

RED ONION JAZZ BABIES
| New Orleans Encore | 10" LP | London | HAPB1025 | 1954 | £6 | £15 | |

RED ONION JAZZ BAND
| Dance Off Both Your Shoes | LP | London | LTZU15138 | 1958 | £6 | £15 | |

RED, SONNY
| Out Of The Blue | LP | Blue Note | BLP/BST84032 | 196- | £20 | £40 | |

RED SQUARES
| Mountain's High | 7" | Columbia | DB8160 | 1967 | £4 | £8 | |
| True Love Story | 7" | Columbia | DB8247 | 1967 | £2.50 | £6 | |

RED TELEVISION
| Red Television | LP | Brecht Times | | 1971 | £100 | £200 | |

REDCAPS
Mighty Fine Girl	7"	Decca	F11903	1964	£4	£8	
Shout	7"	Decca	F11716	1963	£4	£8	
Talking About You	7"	Decca	F11789	1963	£5	£10	

REDD, FREDDIE
Get Happy	LP	Nixa	NJL19	1958	£8	£20	
Music From The Connection	LP	Blue Note	BLP/BST84027	196-	£15	£30	
Shades Of Redd	LP	Blue Note	BLP/BST84045	196-	£20	£40	

REDD, GENE & THE GLOBE TROTTERS
| Red River Valley Rock | 7" | Parlophone | R4584 | 1959 | £4 | £8 | |

REDDING, OTIS
Champagne And Wine	7"	Atlantic	584220	1968	£1.50	£4	
Come To Me	7"	London	HLK9876	1964	£6	£12	
Day Tripper	7"	Stax	601005	1967	£2	£5	chart single
Dictionary Of Soul	LP	Atlantic	587/588050	1967	£8	£20	chart LP
Dock Of The Bay	LP	Atco	228022	1969	£5	£12	
Dock Of The Bay	LP	Stax	230/231001	1968	£6	£15	chart LP
Dock Of The Bay	7"	Atlantic	2091112	1971	£1.50	£4	
Dock Of The Bay	7"	Stax	601031	1968	£1.50	£4	chart single
Early Otis Redding	7" EP	Sue	IEP710	1966	£25	£50	
Fa Fa Fa Fa Fa Song	7"	Atlantic	584049	1966	£2	£5	chart single
Free Me	7"	Atco	226002	1969	£1.50	£4	
Glory Of Love	7"	Stax	601017	1967	£2	£5	
Happy Song	7"	Stax	601040	1968	£1.50	£4	chart single
Hard To Handle	7"	Atlantic	584199	1968	£1.50	£4	chart single
History Of Otis Redding	LP	Atco	228001	1969	£5	£12	
History Of Otis Redding	LP	Volt	418	1968	£6	£15	chart LP
I Can't Turn You Loose	LP	Atlantic	584030	1966	£2	£5	chart single
Immortal Otis Redding	LP	Atlantic	587/588113	1968	£6	£15	chart LP
In Person At The Whiskey	LP	Atlantic	587/588148	1968	£6	£15	
I've Been Loving You Too Long	7"	Atlantic	2091062	1971	£1.50	£4	
I've Been Loving You Too Long	7"	Atlantic	AT4029	1965	£15	£30	demo only
Let Me Come On Home	7"	Stax	601007	1967	£1.50	£4	chart single
Live In Europe	LP	Atco	228017	1969	£5	£12	
Live In Europe	LP	Stax	589016	1968	£6	£15	chart LP
Look At The Girl	7"	Atco	226012	1970	£1.50	£4	
Love Man	LP	Atco	228025	1969	£6	£15	
Love Man	7"	Atco	226001	1969	£1.50	£4	chart single
Lover's Question	7"	Atlantic	584249	1969	£1.50	£4	
Mr.Pitiful	7"	Atlantic	AT4024	1965	£4	£8	
My Girl	7"	Atlantic	584092	1967	£2	£5	chart single
My Girl	7"	Atlantic	AT4050	1965	£2.50	£6	chart single
My Lover's Prayer	7"	Atlantic	584019	1966	£2	£5	chart single
Otis Blue	LP	Atlantic	587/588036	1966	£6	£15	chart LP
Otis Blue	LP	Atlantic	ATL5041	1966	£8	£20	chart LP
Pain In My Heart	LP	Atlantic	587042	1967	£8	£20	chart LP
Pain In My Heart	7"	London	HLK9833	1964	£6	£12	
Papa's Got A Brand New Bag	7"	Atlantic	584234	1968	£1.50	£4	
Remembering	LP	Atlantic	2464003	1970	£4	£10	
Respect	7"	Atlantic	584091	1967	£2	£5	
Respect	7"	Atlantic	AT4039	1965	£2.50	£6	
Satisfaction	7"	Atlantic	AT4080	1966	£2.50	£6	chart single
Satisfaction	7"	Stax	601027	1967	£1.50	£4	
Shake	7"	Stax	601011	1967	£2	£5	chart single
She's Alright	7"	Evolution	E2442	1969	£2.50	£6	
She's Alright	7"	Pye	7N25463	1968	£2.50	£6	
Shout Bamalama	7"	Sue	WI362	1965	£10	£20	
Sings Soul Ballads	LP	Atlantic	587035	1966	£6	£15	
Sings Soul Ballads	LP	Atlantic	ATL5029	1965	£8	£20	chart LP
Soul Album	LP	Atlantic	587011	1966	£6	£15	chart LP
Tell The Truth	LP	Atco	2400018	1971	£6	£15	
Try A Little Tenderness	7"	Atlantic	584070	1967	£2	£5	chart single

Wonderful World	7"	Atlantic	2091020	1970	£1.50	£4	

REDDING, OTIS & CARLA THOMAS

King And Queen	LP	Atlantic	589007	1967	£8	£20	chart LP
Knock On Wood	7"	Stax	601021	1967	£1.50	£4	chart single
Lovey Dovey	7"	Stax	601033	1968	£1.50	£4	
Tramp	7"	Stax	601012	1967	£1.50	£4	chart single

REDDING, OTIS & JIMI HENDRIX

Historic Performances Recorded At Monterey	LP	Reprise	MS2029	1970	£5	£12	US, 1 side each artist

REDE, EMMA

Just Like A Man	7"	Columbia	DB8136	1967	£5	£10	

REDELL, TEDDY

Judy	7"	London	HLK9140	1960	£15	£30	

REDGRAVE, VANESSA

Hanging Fom A Tree	7"	Topic	STOP111	1964	£1.50	£4	

REDMAN, GEORGE

George Redman Group	10" LP	London	HAPB1036	1955	£10	£25	

REDMOND, ROY

Good Day Sunshine	7"	Warner Bros	WB2075	1967	£1.50	£4	

REDPATH, JEAN

Ballad Folk	LP	BBC	REC293	1977	£6	£15	
Love, Lilt And Laughter	LP	Bounty	BY6004	1966	£6	£15	
There Were Minstrels	LP	Trailer	LER2106	1977	£5	£12	

REDSKINS

Lev Bronstein	7"	CNT	CNT007	1982	£6	£12	

REDWAY, MIKE

Have No Fear, Bond Is Here	7"	Deram	DM124	1967	£2	£5	

REDWOODS

Please Mister Scientist	7"	Columbia	DB4859	1962	£4	£8	

REECE, DIZZY

Progress Report	LP	Tempo	TAP9	1957	£10	£25	
Soundin' Off	LP	Blue Note	BLP/BST84033	196-	£15	£30	

REED, CHUCK

Let's Put Our Hearts Together	7"	Columbia	DB4113	1958	£5	£10	
Talking No Trash	7"	Stateside	SS108	1962	£1.50	£4	
Whispering Heart	7"	Brunswick	05646	1957	£2.50	£6	

REED, DENNY

Teenager Feels It Too	7"	London	HLK9274	1961	£1.50	£4	

REED, FRED

Northumbrian Voice	LP	White Meadow	01	1978	£5	£12	

REED, JERRY

Bessie Baby	7"	Capitol	CL14851	1958	£40	£80	

REED, JIMMY

At Carnegie Hall	LP	Joy	JOY(S)120	1969	£4	£10	
At Carnegie Hall	LP	Stateside	SL10012	1962	£8	£20	
At Soul City	LP	Joy	JOYS127	1969	£4	£10	
At Soul City	LP	Vee Jay	LP1095	1964	£8	£20	US
Baby What You Want Me To Do	7"	Top Rank	JAR333	1960	£5	£10	
Best Of Jimmy Reed	LP	Joy	JOYS155	1969	£4	£10	
Best Of Jimmy Reed	LP	Vee Jay	LP/SR1039	1962	£8	£20	US
Big Boss Man	LP	BluesWay	BLS6013	1968	£6	£15	US
Big Boss Man	LP	DJM	DJD28033	1976	£5	£12	double
Blues Of Jimmy Reed	7" EP	Stateside	SE1016	1964	£7.50	£15	
Boss Man Of The Blues	LP	Stateside	SL10091	1964	£6	£15	
Down In Virginia	LP	Action	ACLP6011	1969	£6	£15	
Found Love	LP	Vee Jay	LP1022	1960	£10	£25	US
Found Love	7"	Top Rank	JAR394	1960	£4	£8	
Hush Hush	7"	Top Rank	JAR533	1961	£4	£8	
I'm Jimmy Reed	LP	Vee Jay	LP1004	1958	£25	£50	US
I'm Jimmy Reed	7" EP	Stateside	SE1026	1964	£7.50	£15	
Just Jimmy Reed	LP	Joy	JOYS146	1969	£4	£10	
Just Jimmy Reed	LP	Stateside	SL10055	1963	£8	£20	
Legend, The Man	LP	Joy	JOY(S)111	1969	£4	£10	
Legend, The Man	LP	Vee Jay	VJ(S)8501	1965	£6	£15	US
More Of The Best Of Jimmy Reed	LP	Vee Jay	LP/SR1080	1964	£6	£15	US
New Jimmy Reed	LP	HMV	CLP/CSD3611	1967	£6	£15	
Now Appearing	LP	Vee Jay	LP1025	1960	£10	£25	US
Odds And Ends	7"	Sue	WI4004	1966	£6	£12	
Plays 12 String Guitar Blues	LP	Joy	JOYS132	1969	£4	£10	
Plays 12 String Guitar Blues	LP	Stateside	SL10086	1964	£6	£15	
Rockin' With Reed	LP	Joy	JOYS141	1969	£4	£10	
Rockin' With Reed	LP	Vee Jay	LP1008	1959	£20	£40	US
Shame Shame Shame	7"	Stateside	SS205	1963	£4	£8	
Shame Shame Shame	7"	Stateside	SS330	1964	£2	£5	chart single

Sings The Best Of The Blues	LP	Joy	JOYS151	1969	£4	£10	
Sings The Best Of The Blues	LP	Stateside	SL10069	1964	£6	£15	
Soulin'	LP	Stateside	(S)SL10221	1968	£6	£15	
T'Ain't No Big Thing	LP	Vee Jay	LP1067	1963	£8	£20	US
Things Ain't What They Used To Be	LP	Fontana	688514ZL	1965	£6	£15	
Two Ways To Skin A Cat	7"	HMV	POP1579	1967	£4	£8	

REED, JIMMY & EDDIE TAYLOR

Jimmy Reed & Eddie Taylor	7" EP	XX	MIN704	196-	£4	£8

REED, LOU

The battle of the formats was won by the compact disc the moment that a reissue of Lou Reed's "Metal Machine Music" was released on CD. The disturbing electronic hubbub that the album contains may be an interesting insight into Reed's early association with minimalist avant-garde composer LaMonte Young, but it does not make for a listening experience that many Reed fans would wish to endure even once. It has been suggested that the album was Reed's ironic way of fulfilling a contract, but tapes exist of the Velvet Underground playing music not very dissimilar to this. More indicative of cynicism are the live recordings of the Velvet Underground's 1993 tour, which show Reed to be performing some of the old material with an alarming lack of enthusiasm. (The shame of this being heightened all the more by the knowledge that much of Reed's solo material from recent years has been rather fine).

Blue Mask	LP	RCA	DJL14266	1981	£5	£12	US interview promo
Metal Machine Music	LP	RCA	CPD21101	1975	£17.50	£35	US quad
Metal Machine Music	LP	RCA	CPL21101	1975	£15	£30	
No Money Down	12"	RCA		1986	£2.50	£6	promo, green vinyl
Nowhere At All	7"	RCA	PB9135		£4	£8	French, 1 sided

REED, LULU

Blue And Moody	LP	King	604	1959	£100	£200	US
Troubles On Your Mind	7"	Parlophone	CMSP34	1955	£5	£10	export

REED, LULU & FREDDY KING

Lulu Reed & Freddy King	7" EP	Ember	EMBEP4536	1963	£10	£20

REED, LULU & SYL JOHNSON

Lulu Reed & Syl Johnson	7" EP	Ember	EMBEP4535	1963	£12.50	£25

REED, NEHEMIAH

Family War	7"	Island	WI3102	1968	£5	£10

REED, OLIVER

Wild One	7"	Decca	F11390	1961	£1.50	£4

REED, TAWNY

Needle In A Haystack	7"	Pye	7N15935	1965	£4	£8
You Can't Take It Away	7"	Pye	7N17078	1966	£4	£8

REED, VIVIAN

I Wanna Be Free	7"	Direction	583574	1968	£1.50	£4

REEGAN, VALA & THE VALARONS

Fireman	7"	Atlantic	584009	1966	£45	£90

REESE, DELLA

Della	LP	RCA	RD27167/SF5057	1960	£4	£10	
Della Della Cha-Cha-Cha	LP	RCA	RD27208/SF5091	1961	£4	£10	
Home	7"	HMV	POP1504	1966	£1.50	£4	
I Cried For You	7"	London	HL7024	1957	£1.50	£4	export
It Wasn't A Very Good Year	7"	HMV	POP1553	1966	£1.50	£4	
On Stage	LP	RCA	RD/SF7508	1963	£4	£10	
Sermonette	7"	London	HLJ8814	1959	£2	£5	
Special Delivery	LP	RCA	RD27234/SF5112	1962	£4	£10	
Story Of The Blues	LP	London	LTZJ15163/ SAHJ6021	1959	£4	£10	
You Gotta Love Everybody	7"	London	HLJ8687	1958	£2	£5	

REEVES, EDDIE

Cry Baby	7"	London	HL9548	1962	£4	£8

REEVES, JIM

Bimbo	LP	London	HAU8015	1962	£8	£20	
Bimbo	7"	London	HL8014	1954	£40	£80	
Bimbo Boy	7" EP	London	REP1015	1954	£20	£40	
Bimbo Vol.2	7" EP	London	REP1033	1955	£17.50	£35	
Blue Boy	7"	RCA	RCA1074	1958	£6	£12	
Butterfly Love	7"	London	HL8055	1954	£40	£80	
Drinking Tequila	7"	London	HL8159	1955	£55	£110	
Echo Bonita	7"	London	HL8064	1954	£40	£80	
Four Walls	7"	RCA	RCA1005	1957	£10	£20	
Gentleman Jim	LP	RCA	RD7541	1962	£4	£10	
Girls I Have Known	LP	RCA	LPM1685	1958	£8	£20	US
God Be With You	LP	RCA	LPM/LSP1950	1958	£6	£15	US
He'll Have To Go	7"	RCA	RD27176	1960	£5	£12	
He'll Have To Go	7"	RCA	RCA1168	1960	£1.50	£4	chart single
International Jim Reeves	LP	RCA	RD7577	1962	£4	£10	
Intimate Jim Reeves	7"	RCA	RCA1144	1961	£5	£12	
Jim Reeves	LP	RCA	RD27193/SF5079	1961	£5	£12	US
Jim Reeves	LP	RCA	LPM1576	1957	£10	£25	US
Jim Reeves Sings	LP	Abbott	LP5001	1956	£210	£350	US
Jimbo	LP	RCA	LPM1410	1957	£15	£30	US
Mexican Joe	7"	London	HL8030	1954	£40	£80	
Padre Of Old San Antone	7"	London	HL8105	1954	£30	£60	
Partners	7"	RCA	RCA1144	1959	£2	£5	
Penny Candy	7"	London	HL8118	1955	£37.50	£75	
Singing Down The Lane	LP	RCA	LPM1256	1956	£25	£50	US

Songs To Warm Your Heart	LP	RCA	LPM/LSP2001	1959	£6	£15	US
Tahiti	7"	London	HLU8185	1955	£30	£60	
Talkin' To Your Heart	LP	RCA	LPM/LSP2339	1961	£5	£12	US
Tall Tales And Short Tempers	LP	RCA	LPM/LSP2284	1961	£5	£12	US
Touch Of Velvet	LP	RCA	RD7521	1962	£4	£10	
Twelve Songs Of Christmas	LP	RCA	RD7663	1965	£4	£10	
Wilder Your Heart Beats	7"	London	HLU8351	1956	£30	£60	

REFLECTION

Present Tense	LP	Reflection	RL3015	1968	£10	£25	

REFLECTIONS

Just Like Romeo And Juliet	LP	Golden World	300	1964	£20	£40	US
Just Like Romeo And Juliet	7"	Stateside	SS294	1964	£7.50	£15	
Just Like Romeo And Juliet	7"	Tamla Motown	TMG907	1974	£1.50	£4	
Poor Man's Son	7"	Stateside	SS406	1965	£4	£8	
Poor Man's Son	7" EP	Stateside	SE1034	1965	£10	£20	

REFUGEE

Refugee	LP	Charisma	CAS1087	1974	£4	£10	

REGAN, JOAN

Cross Of Gold	7"	Decca	F10659	1956	£4	£8	chart single
Danger Heartbreak Ahead	7"	Decca	F10505	1955	£2	£5	
Don't Take Me For Granted	7"	Decca	F10710	1956	£1.50	£4	
Don't Talk To Me About Love	7"	CBS	202100	1966	£12.50	£25	
Girl Next Door	10" LP	Decca	LF1182	1954	£8	£20	
Gone	7"	Decca	F10801	1956	£1.50	£4	
Honestly	7"	Decca	F10742	1956	£1.50	£4	
If I Give My Heart To You	7"	Decca	F10373	1954	£4	£8	chart single
Just Joan	LP	Decca	LK4153	1956	£5	£12	
Just Say You Love Her	7"	Decca	F10521	1955	£2	£5	
No One Beside You	7"	CBS	2657	1967	£5	£10	
Open Up Your Heart	7"	Decca	F10474	1955	£4	£8	chart single
Prize Of Gold	7"	Decca	F10432	1955	£4	£8	chart single
Shepherd Boy	7"	Decca	F10598	1955	£2	£5	
Successes	7" EP	Decca	DFE6235	1955	£2.50	£6	
Successes Vol.2	7" EP	Decca	DFE6278	1956	£6	£12	
Sweet Heartaches	7"	Decca	F10757	1956	£1.50	£4	
This Ole House	7"	Decca	F10397	1954	£5	£10	
Wait For Me Darling	7"	Decca	F10362	1954	£4	£8	chart single

REGENTS

Barbara Ann	LP	Gee	(S)GLP708	1961	£20	£40	US
Barbara Ann	7"	Columbia	DB4666	1961	£4	£8	
Live At The Am/Pm Discotheque	LP	Capitol	(S)KAO2153	1964	£8	£20	US
Runaround	7"	Columbia	DB4694	1961	£5	£10	

REGENTS (2)

Bye Bye Johnny	7"	Oriole	CB1912	1964	£6	£12	

REGENTS (3)

Words	7"	CBS	202247	1966	£6	£12	

REGENTS (4)

Seventeen	7"	Rialto	TREB111	1979	£2	£5	

REGGAE BOYS

Me No Born Ya	7"	Amalgamated	AMG841	1969	£4	£8	
Pupa Live On Eye Top	7"	Bullet	BU431	1970	£2	£5	
Reggae Train	7"	Amalgamated	AMG843	1969	£4	£8	
Walk By Day Fly By Night	7"	Pressure Beat	PB5503	1970	£2	£5	Joe Gibbs B side

REICH, STEVE

Come Out	LP	Odyssey	32160160		£4	£10	
Four Organs	LP	Angel	S36059		£4	£10	
Four Organs	LP	Shandar	83511		£4	£10	
It's Gonna Rain	LP	Columbia	MS7265		£4	£10	US

REICHEL, ACHIM

A.R.3	LP	Zebra	2949006	1973	£4	£10	German
A.R.4	LP	Zebra	2949008	1973	£4	£10	German
Autovision	LP	Zebra	2949016	1974	£4	£10	German
Die Grune Reise	LP	Polydor	2371128	1971	£5	£12	German
Echo	LP	Polydor	2633003	1972	£6	£15	German double
Erholung	LP	Brain	0001068	1975	£4	£10	German

REID, BERYL

Love Makes The World Go Around	7"	HMV	POP1489	1965	£2	£5	

REID, CARLTON

Leave Me To Cry	7"	Blue Cat	BS162	1969	£4	£8	
Turn On The Lights	7"	Ska Beat	JB254	1966	£5	£10	

REID, CLARENCE

I'm Gonna Tear You A New Heart	7"	Atlantic	584301	1969	£1.50	£4	
Nobody But You Babe	7"	Atlantic	584290	1969	£1.50	£4	

REID, DUKE

Duke's Cookies	7"	Blue Beat	BB24	1961	£5	£10	Jiving Juniors B side
Hurt	7"	Duke Reid	DR2522	1971	£2.50	£6	

| Mood I Am In | 7" | Blue Beat | BB165 | 1963 | £5 | £10 | .. Stranger Cole B side |
| True Confession | 7" | Doctor Bird | DB1028 | 1966 | £5 | £10 | Tommy McCook B side |

REID, LEROY

| Fiddler | 7" | Blue Cat | BS125 | 1968 | £4 | £8 | Lovelettes B side |

REID, P.

| Redeemed | 7" | Ska Beat | JB197 | 1965 | £5 | £10 | |

REID, TERRY

Bang Bang, You're Terry Reid	LP	Epic	BN26427	1968	£6	£15	US
Better By Far	7"	Columbia	DB8409	1968	£5	£10	
Hand Don't Fit The Glove	7"	Columbia	DB8166	1967	£5	£10	
River	LP	Warner Bros	K40340	1973	£5	£12	
Superlungs	7"	Columbia	PSRS323	1969	£7.50	£15	1 sided demo
Terry Reid	LP	Columbia	SCX6370	1969	£6	£15	

REIGN

| Line Of Least Resistance | 7" | Regal Zonophone | RZ3028 | 1970 | £20 | £40 | |

REIGN GHOST

| Allied | LP | | | | £100 | £200 | Canadian |

REILLY, JOHN

| Bonny Green Tree | LP | Topic | 12T359 | 1978 | £6 | £15 | |

REILLY, TOMMY

| Blow Man Blow | 7" | Philips | 326543BF | 1962 | £1.50 | £4 | |
| S.O.S. | 7" | Oriole | CB1833 | 1963 | £1.50 | £4 | |

REILLY, VINI & MORRISSEY

| I Know Very Well How I Got My Note Wrong | 7" | Factory | FACT244& | 1989 | £2 | £5 | |

REINCARNATION

| Fat City | LP | Probe | | 1969 | £6 | £15 | |

REINHARDT, DJANGO

Art Of Django	LP	HMV	CLP1340	1960	£6	£15	
Django	LP	HMV	CLP1249	1959	£8	£20	
Django	10" LP	Mercury	MG10019	1957	£20	£40	
Django - The Unforgettable	LP	HMV	CLP1389	1960	£6	£15	
Django Reinhardt	7" EP	HMV	7EG8132	1955	£2	£5	
Django Reinhardt	10" LP	HMV	DLP1045	1954	£20	£40	
Django Reinhardt Vol.1	10" LP	Vogue	LDE049	1954	£20	£40	
Django Reinhardt Vol.2	10" LP	Vogue	LDE084	1954	£20	£40	
Django Reinhardt Vol.3	10" LP	Vogue	LDE106	1954	£20	£40	
Improvisation	7" EP	Collector	JEN8	1962	£2	£5	
Memorial	LP	Vogue	LAE12251	1961	£4	£10	
Nuages	10" LP	Felsted	EDL87005	1954	£20	£40	
Requiem For A Jazzman	LP	Ember	CJS810	196-	£5	£12	
Swing From Paris	10" LP	Decca	LF1139	1953	£20	£40	
Swing Guitars	7" EP	Collector	JEN6	1961	£2	£5	

REISMAN, JOE

| Guns Of Navarone | 7" | Pye | 7N25087 | 1961 | £1.50 | £4 | PS |

REIVERS

| Work Of The Reivers Vol.2 | 7" EP | Top Rank | JKP2062 | 1960 | £2 | £5 | |

REJOICE

| November Snow | 7" | Stateside | SS8010 | 1969 | £1.50 | £4 | |

RELEASE MUSIC ORCHESTRA

Garuda	LP	Brain	0001072	1975	£4	£10	German
Get The Ball	LP	Brain	0001083	1975	£4	£10	German
Life	LP	Brain	0001056	1974	£5	£12	German

RELF, JANE

| Without A Song From You | 7" | Decca | F13231 | 1971 | £6 | £12 | |

RELF, KEITH

| Mr.Zero | 7" | Columbia | DB7920 | 1966 | £7.50 | £15 | chart single |
| Shapes In My Mind | 7" | Columbia | DB8084 | 1966 | £12.50 | £25 | |

R.E.M.

Academy Fight Song	7"	fan club		1989	£35	£70	
Baby Baby	7"	fan club	122591	1991	£20	£40	
Can't Get There From Here	12"	IRS	IRT102	1985	£3	£6	
Chronic Town	mini LP	IRS	SP70502	1982	£8	£20	US, gargoyle label
Fall On Me	12"	IRS	IRMT121	1986	£2.50	£6	
Femme Fatale	7"	Evatone		198-	£7.50	£15	US, flexi, PS
Ghost Reindeer In The Sky	7"	fan club		1990	£25	£50	
It's The End Of The World As We Know It	CD-s	IRS	DIRMX180	1992	£4	£10	4 tracks
Losing My Religion	CD-s	Warner Bros	W0015CDX	1991	£2.50	£6	with poster
Orange Crush	7"	Warner Bros	W2960B	1989	£1.50	£4	boxed with poster

Out Of Time	CD	Warner Bros	7599264962	1991	£8	£20	black 'leather' cover, with 10 cards
Parade Of The Wooden Soldiers	7"	fan club	U23528M	1988	£40	£80	
Radio Free Europe	7"	Hibtone	HT0001	1981	£50	£100	US
Radio Free Europe	7"	IRS	PFP1017	1983	£12.50	£25	
Rockville	7"	IRS	IRS107	1984	£7.50	£15	
Rockville	12"	IRS	IRSX107	1984	£6	£15	
South Central Rain	7"	IRS	IRS105	1984	£6	£12	
South Central Rain	12"	IRS	IRSX105	1984	£6	£15	
Talk About The Passion	7"	IRS	PFP1026	1983	£5	£10	promo only
Talk About The Passion	12"	IRS	PFSX1026	1983	£8	£20	
Tighten Up	7"	Bucketfull Of Brains	BOB5	1985	£2.50	£6	flexi
Wendell Gee	7"	IRS	IRMD105	1985	£5	£10	double
Wendell Gee	12"	IRS	IRT105	1985	£2.50	£6	
Wolves Lower	7"	Trouser Press		1982	£10	£20	US, flexi

REMAINS

Remains	LP	Epic	LN24214/BN26214	1966	£40	£80	US

REMO FOUR

Attention	LP	Phonogram	6434158	1973	£5	£12	German
Live Like A Lady	7"	Fontana	TF787	1967	£15	£30	
Peter Gunn	7"	Piccadilly	7N35175	1964	£5	£10	
Sally Go Round The Roses	7"	Piccadilly	7N35186	1964	£5	£10	
Smile	LP	Starclub	158034	1967	£30	£60	German

RENAISSANCE

The history of Renaissance is complicated by the fact that the name covers what, in effect, are two entirely different groups. The first eponymous LP was made by ex-Yardbirds Keith Relf and Jim McCarty and represented the results of a conscious attempt to broaden their music beyond the Yardbirds' blues-based material. It is Beethoven, rather than Jimmy Reed, who is the major influence here. While making the second LP, however (eventually given a limited release as "Illusion"), the group fell apart, with only pianist John Hawken prepared to carry on. He found a new group of musicians to complete the line-up, then decided to leave himself! The immediate result was a stage set consisting of songs from the first LP played by a set of musicians, none of whom had played on the record! Somewhat later, most of the original members got back together, but now had to issue their records under the name Illusion, as the second Renaissance had become quite successful in their own right during the intervening years.

Ashes Are Burning	LP	Sovereign	SVNA7261	1973	£4	£10	
Illusion	LP	Island	6339017	1972	£8	£20	European
Illusion	LP	Island	HELP27	1971	£20	£40	test pressing only
Jekyll And Hyde	7"	Sire	SIR4019	1979	£5	£10	
Northern Lights	7"	Sire	SRE1022	1978	£7.50	£15	export pic disc
Prologue	LP	Sovereign	SVNA7253	1972	£4	£10	
Prologue/Ashes Are Burning	LP	Sovereign	CAPACK3	1979	£6	£15	double
Renaissance	LP	Island	ILPS9114	1969	£6	£15	chart LP
Scheherazade	LP	Mobile Fidelity	MFSL1099	1982	£5	£12	US audiophile
Sea	7"	Island	WIP6079	1970	£2.50	£6	

RENAUD, HENRI

Henri Renaud All Stars	10" LP	Vogue	LDE088	1955	£15	£30	
Henri Renaud Band	10" LP	Vogue	LDE111	1955	£15	£30	
Henri Renaud-Al Cohn Quartet	10" LP	Vogue	LDE103	1954	£15	£30	
Henri Renaud-Bobby Jaspar Quintet	10" LP	Vogue	LDE096	1955	£15	£30	

RENAUD, LINE

If I Love You	7"	Capitol	CL14230	1955	£4	£8	

RENAY, DIANE

Kiss Me Sailor	7"	Stateside	SS290	1964	£1.50	£4	
Navy Blue	LP	Twentieth Century	TF(S)3133	1964	£6	£15	US
Unbelievable Guy	7"	Stateside	SS270	1964	£1.50	£4	

RENBOURN, JOHN

Another Monday	LP	Transatlantic	TRA149	1966	£6	£15	
Enchanted Garden	LP	Transatlantic	TRA356	1980	£5	£12	
Faro Annie	LP	Transatlantic	TRA247	1971	£6	£15	
Heads And Tails	LP	Transatlantic	TRASAM18	1974	£4	£10	with Stefan Grossman
Hermit	LP	Transatlantic	TRA336	1976	£10	£25	
John Renbourn	LP	Transatlantic	TRA135	1965	£6	£15	
Lady & The Unicorn	LP	Transatlantic	TRA224	1970	£6	£15	
Maid In Bedlam	LP	Transatlantic	TRA348	1977	£5	£12	
Sir John Alot Of Merrie England	LP	Transatlantic	TRA167	1968	£6	£15	

RENBOURN, JOHN & STEFAN GROSSMAN

John Renbourn And Stefan Grossman	LP	Sonet	SNTF139	1978	£5	£12	

RENDELL, DON

As one of the British jazz musicians to emerge after the War, saxophonist Don Rendell's earliest records are not especially remarkable. Unlike the majority of his contemporaries, however, Rendell was interested in the way jazz in America was moving forwards. "Roarin"" is a good hard bop recording which stands up well against the American competition. It also features the playing of a young Graham Bond on alto saxophone. Later Don Rendell formed a quintet with trumpeter Ian Carr and the pair proceeded to create an English version of what Miles Davis was doing in America. When Davis went electric, Ian Carr did the same, founding the group Nucleus. For Rendell, however, this was a step too far. His contribution to rock-influenced jazz is limited to membership of the jazz orchestra used on Neil Ardley's "Symphony Of Amaranths".

Don Rendell Jazz Six	7" EP	Pye	NJE1044	1957	£10	£20	
Don Rendell Presents The Jazz Six	LP	Nixa	NJL7	1957	£20	£40	
Don Rendell Quartet	7" EP	Tempo	EXA11	1955	£10	£20	
Don Rendell Quintet	7" EP	Tempo	EXA20	1956	£10	£20	
Don Rendell Sextet	7" EP	Tempo	EXA12	1955	£10	£20	
Don Rendell Sextet	7" EP	Tempo	EXA16	1955	£10	£20	2 tracks b* Damian Robinson

In Paris	10" LP	Vogue	LDE144	1955	£25	£50		
Jazz Britannia	7" EP	MGM	MGMEP615	1957	£10	£20	2 tracks by Joe Harriott
Meet Don Rendell	10" LP	Tempo	LAP1	1955	£25	£50	
Packet Of Blues	7" EP	Decca	DFE6501	1958	£10	£20	
Playtime	LP	Decca	LK4265	1958	£20	£40	
Roarin'	LP	Jazzland	JLP51	1962	£30	£60	
Spacewalk	LP	Columbia	SCX6491	1971	£20	£40	

RENDELL, DON & IAN CARR QUINTET

Change Is	LP	Columbia	SCX6368	1969	£25	£50	
Dusk Fire	LP	Columbia	SX6064	1966	£25	£50	
Live	LP	Columbia	SX/SCX6316	1969	£25	£50	
Phase III	LP	Columbia	SX/SCX6214	1968	£25	£50	
Shades Of Blue	LP	Columbia	33SX1733	1965	£25	£50	

RENE & RENE

Loving You Could Hurt Me So	7"	Island	WIP6001	1967	£5	£10	

RENE & THE ALLIGATORS

She Broke My Heart	7"	Decca	F22324	1966	£2.50	£6	

RENE, GOOGIE

Chica Boo	7"	Atlantic	584015	1966	£2	£5	
Forever	7"	London	HLY9056	1960	£5	£10	
Smokey Joe's Lala	7"	Atlantic	AT4076	1966	£7.50	£15	

RENEGADE SOUNDWAVE

Cocaine Sex	12"	Rhythm King	LEFT20T	1988	£8	£20	
Kray Twins	12"	Rhythm King	LEFT8T	1987	£3	£8	

RENEGADES

Cadillac	7"	Polydor	56508	1970	£7.50	£15	
Cadillac	7" EP	Riviera	231113	1965	£30	£60	French
No Man's Land	7"	Columbia	DB8383	1968	£7.50	£15	
Take A Message	7"	Parlophone	R5592	1967	£7.50	£15	
Thirteen Women	7"	President	PT106	1968	£15	£30	

RENIA

First Offenders	LP	Transatlantic	TRA261	1973	£8	£20	

RENNARD, JON

Brimbledon Fair	LP	Tradition	TSR003	1970	£5	£12	
Parting Glass	LP	Tradition	TSR010	1971	£5	£12	

RENO, DON & RED SMILEY

Country And Western	7" EP	Parlophone	GEP8777	1958	£7.50	£15	

RENO, GERRY

Don't Ever Change	7"	Decca	F11477	1962	£1.50	£4	
It Only Happens In The Movies	7"	Decca	F11774	1963	£1.50	£4	
Who's Fooling Who	7"	Decca	F11516	1962	£1.50	£4	

RENTAL, ROBERT

Bridge	LP	Industrial	IR0007	1979	£4	£10	with Thomas Leer
Live	12"	Rough Trade	ROUGH17	1980	£2.50	£6	1 sided
Paralysis	7"	Regular	ER102	1978	£2	£5	

REPARATA & THE DELRONS

Captain Of Your Ship	7"	Bell	BLL1002	1968	£1.50	£4	chart single
Saturday Night It Didn't Happen	7"	Bell	BLL1014	1968	£12.50	£25	
Tommy	7"	Stateside	SS414	1965	£2.50	£6	
Whenever A Teenager Cries	LP	World Artists	2/3006	1965	£8	£20	US
Whenever A Teenager Cries	7"	Stateside	SS382	1965	£2	£5	

RESIDENTS

The Residents' gimmick of keeping the individual members' identities completely secret has, amazingly, been successfully maintained since the early seventies. Their music is extremely eccentric, a quality that is emphasised by their record release policy. The proliferation of limited edition cover designs, coloured vinyls, and so forth, listed here does not include such ultra-rarities as a one-sided clear vinyl 12" of "Duck Stab", of which just six copies were made.

Babyfingers	7"	Ralph	RR0377	1977	£50	£100	US
Big Bubble	LP	Ralph	RZ8552	198-	£25	£50	US pink marbled vinyl
Blorp Esette	LP	LAFMS	005	1975	£25	£50	US
Census Taker	LP	Episode	ED21	1985	£15	£30	US
Commercial Album	LP	Ralph	RZ8052	1980	£6	£15	US
Commercial Single	7"	Pre	PRE009	1980	£5	£10	
Duck Stab/Buster And Glen	LP	Ralph	RR0278	1978	£4	£10	US
Earth Vs. The Flying Saucers	7"	Ralph	SP1		£10	£20	US green vinyl, 1 sided
Eskimo	LP	Ralph	ESK7906	1979	£6	£15	US
Eskimo	LP	Ralph	ESK7906	1979	£10	£25	US, white vinyl
Eskimo	LP	Ralph	ESK7906	1983	£8	£20	US, pic disc
Fingerprince	LP	Ralph	RR1276	1977	£25	£50	US, brown sleeve
Fingerprince	LP	Ralph	RR1276	1978	£6	£15	US, black & pink sleeve
Fingerprince	LP	Ralph	RR1276	1978	£8	£20	US, sienna sleeve
George And James	LP	Korova	KODE9	1984	£6	£15	
George And James	LP	Ralph	RZ8402	1984	£15	£30	US
George And James	LP	Ralph	RZ8402	1984	£25	£50	US, clear vinyl
Hit The Road Jack	7"	Torso	70032	1987	£1.50	£4	pic disc
Hit The Road Jack	12"	Torso	TORSO120032	1987	£2.50	£6	

Title	Format	Label	Catalogue	Year	Price	Price	Notes
Intermission	LP	Ralph	RZ8522	1982	£6	£15	US
Intermission	12"	London	RALPH1	1983	£2.50	£6	
It's A Man's Man's Man's World	7"	Korova	KOW36	1984	£1.50	£4	
It's A Man's Man's Man's World	7"	Ralph	RZ8422	198-	£5	£10	US pic disc
Kaw-Liga	7"	Ralph	RZ8621	198-	£5	£10	US pic disc
Mark Of The Mole	LP	Ralph	RZ8152	1981	£6	£15	US
Mark Of The Mole	LP	Ralph	RZ8152	1981	£10	£25	US, brown vinyl
Meet The Residents	LP	Ralph	RR0274	1974	£40	£80	US
Meet The Residents	LP	Ralph	RR0677	1985	£8	£20	US, pic disc
Meet The Residents (remixed)	LP	Ralph	RR0677	1977	£4	£10	US
Mole Show	LP	Ralph	RZ0001	1983	£8	£20	US
Mole Show	LP	Ralph	RZ0001	1983	£10	£25	US, pic disc
Nibbles	LP	Virgin	VR3	1979	£4	£10	
Not Available	LP	Ralph	RR1174	1978	£4	£10	US
Not Available	LP	Ralph	RR1174	1978	£25	£50	US, purple label
Pal TV LP	LP	Doublevision	DVR17	1985	£4	£10	red vinyl
Picnic Boy - The Commercial Album	LP	Pre	PREX2	1980	£5	£12	
Please Do Not Steal It	LP	Ralph	DJ7901	1979	£8	£20	US
Ralph Before '84 Vol.1	LP	Korova	KODE10	1984	£6	£15	
Ralph Before '84 Vol.2	LP	Korova	KODE12	1985	£6	£15	
Residents Play The Beatles	7"	Ralph	RR0577	1977	£50	£100	US, hand coloured PS
Residents Radio Special	LP	Ralph	173	1977	£10	£25	US promo
Santa Dog	7"	Ralph	RR1272	1972	£75	£150	US double, hand coloured PS
Satisfaction	7"	Ralph	RR0776	1976	£50	£100	US, hand coloured PS
Stars And Hank Forever	LP	Ralph			£25	£50	US green vinyl
Subterranean Modern	LP	Ralph	SM7908	1979	£6	£15	
Ten Years In Twenty Minutes	LP	Ralph	RR8205D	198-	£25	£50	US clear vinyl, 1 sided, no sleeve
Third Reich And Roll	LP	Ralph	RR1075	1976	£25	£50	US, orange & green carrot on sleeve
Third Reich And Roll	LP	Ralph	RR1075	1978	£4	£10	US
Third Reich And Roll	LP	Ralph	RR1075	1978	£8	£20	US, censored sleeve
Thirteenth Anniversary Edition	LP	Ralph			£8	£20	US pic disc
Tunes Of Two Cities	LP	Ralph	RR8202	1982	£6	£15	US
Vileness Fats	LP	Ralph	RZ8452	1984	£25	£50	US, red vinyl

RESTIVO, JOHNNY

Title	Format	Label	Catalogue	Year	Price	Price	Notes
I Like Girls	7"	RCA	RCA1159	1959	£5	£10	
Oh Johnny	LP	RCA	LPM/LSP2149	1959	£15	£30	US
Shape I'm In	7"	RCA	RCA1143	1959	£7.50	£15	tri-centre
Sweet Sweet Loving	7"	Ember	EMBS135	1961	£2	£5	

RETREADS

Title	Format	Label	Year	Price	Price
Would You Listen Girl	7"	Eddi Cosmo	1980	£4	£8

REVELL, DIGGER & THE DENVER MEN

Title	Format	Label	Catalogue	Year	Price	Price
Surfside	7"	Decca	F11657	1963	£2.50	£6

REVELLS

Title	Format	Label	Catalogue	Year	Price	Price
Mind Party	7"	CBS	7050	1971	£4	£8

REVELS

Title	Format	Label	Catalogue	Year	Price	Price
Midnight Stroll	7"	Top Rank	JAR235	1959	£6	£12

REVELS (2)

Title	Format	Label	Catalogue	Year	Price	Price	Notes
Revels On A Rampage	LP	Impact	LPM1	1964	£25	£50	US

REVERE, PAUL & THE RAIDERS

Title	Format	Label	Catalogue	Year	Price	Price	Notes
Alias Pink Puzz	LP	Columbia	CS9905	1969	£4	£10	US
Christmas Past And Present	LP	Columbia	CL2755/CS9555	1967	£5	£12	US
Cinderella Sunshine	7"	CBS	3757	1968	£2	£5	
Don't Take It So Hard	7"	CBS	3586	1968	£2.50	£6	
Goin' To Memphis	7"	CBS	63265	1968	£4	£10	
Good Thing	LP	CBS	(S)BPG62963	1969	£6	£15	
Good Thing	7"	CBS	202502	1967	£4	£8	
Great Airplane Strike	7"	CBS	202411	1966	£4	£8	
Greatest Hits	LP	Columbia	KCL2662/KCS9462	1967	£4	£10	US
Hard 'n' Heavy	LP	CBS	63649	1969	£4	£10	
Here They Come	LP	Columbia	CL2307/CS9107	1965	£6	£15	US
Him Or Me - Who's It Gonna Be?	7"	CBS	2737	1967	£4	£8	
Hungry	7"	CBS	202253	1966	£4	£8	
In The Beginning	LP	Jerden	JRL/JRS7004	1966	£6	£15	US
Indian Reservation	LP	Columbia	CQ30768	1973	£5	£12	US quad
Just Like Me	7"	CBS	202027	1966	£1.50	£4	
Just Like Us	LP	CBS	(S)BPG62406	1966	£6	£15	
Kicks	7"	CBS	202205	1966	£4	£8	
Let Me	7"	CBS	4260	1969	£2.50	£6	
Like Long Hair	7"	Gardena	G1000	1961	£75	£150	US
Like Long Hair	7"	Sue	WI344	1966	£5	£10	
Like Long Hair	7"	Top Rank	JAR557	1961	£6	£12	
Midnight Ride	LP	CBS	(S)BPG62397	1966	£6	£15	
Moreen	7"	CBS	3186	1967	£2.50	£6	
Paul Revere & The Raiders	LP	Sande	1001	1962	£100	£200	US
Paul Revere & The Raiders	LP	Sears	SPS439	1970	£25	£50	US
Revolution	7"	CBS	(S)BPG63095	1967	£4	£10	
Something Happening	LP	Columbia	CS9665	1968	£4	£10	US
Spirit Of '67	LP	Columbia	CL2595/CS9395	1967	£5	£12	US
Steppin' Out	7"	CBS	202003	1965	£2	£5	
Steppin' Out	7" EP	CBS	5930	1966	£12.50	£25	French

Ups And Downs .... 7" ...... CBS .... 202610 .... 1967 ... £4 ....£8

REVEREND BLACK & THE ROCKIN' VICARS
Zing Went The Strings Of My Heart ..... 7" ...... Decca .... 1963 ... £25 ....£50 .... Irish

REVILLOS
Attack .... LP ...... Superville .... SV4001 .... 1982 ... £10 ....£25

REVOLUTION
Hallelujah .... 7" ...... Piccadilly .... 7N35289 .... 1966 ... £10 ....£20

REVOLUTIONARY BLUES BAND
Revolutionary Blues Band .... LP ..... MCA .... MUPS402 .... 1970 ... £6 ....£15

REVOLVING PAINT DREAM
Flowers In The Sky .... 7" ...... Creation .... CRE2 .... 1984 ... £7.50 .....£15

REX & THE MINORS
Chicken Sax .... 7" ...... Triumph.......... RGM1023 .... 1960 ... £7.50 .....£15

REXROTH, KENNETH
Poetry And Jazz At The Blackhawk .... LP ..... Fantasy ...... 7008 .... 1958 ... £8 ....£20 .... US

REY, ALVINO
Original Mama Blues .... 7" ...... London .... HLD9431 .... 1961 ... £2 ....£5

REY, LITTLE BOBBY
Rockin' J Bells .... 7" ...... Top Rank ...... JAR525 .... 1960 ... £1.50 .....£4

REYNARD
Fresh From The Earth .... LP ..... Pilgrim .... GRA102 .... 1976 ... £15 ....£30

REYNOLDS, DEBBIE
Am I That Easy To Forget?	LP	London	HAD2294/ SAHD6106	1960	£5 ...£12	
Athena	LP	Mercury	MG25202	1954	£25 ...£50	US
Bundle Of Joy	LP	RCA	LPM1339	1956	£15 ...£30	US
Carolina In The Morning	7"	MGM	SP1127	1955	£2.50 ...£6	
Debbie	LP	London	HAD2200/ SHD6051	1959	£5 ...£12	
Debbie Reynolds	7" EP	MGM	MGMEP670	1958	£4 ...£8	
Delightful	7" EP	MGM	MGMEP694	1959	£4 ...£8	
Fine And Dandy	LP	London	HAD2326	1961	£5 ...£12	
From Debbie With Love	7" EP	MGM	MGMEP725	1960	£4 ...£8	
Great Folk Hits	LP	London	HAD/SHD8075	1963	£5 ...£12	
I Love Melvin	10" LP	MGM	D114	1953	£15 ...£30	
Love Is The Tender Trap	7"	MGM	SP1155	1956	£1.50 ...£4	
Say One For Me	LP	Columbia	CL1337/CS8137	1959	£6 ...£15	US
Tammy	LP	Vogue Coral	LVA9070	1957	£10 ...£25	
Tammy	7"	Vogue Coral	Q72274	1957	£2.50 ...£6	chart single
This Happy Feeling	7"	Coral	Q72324	1958	£1.50 ...£4	
Two Weeks With Love	LP	MGM	E3233	1955	£6 ...£15	US
Two Weeks With Love	10" LP	MGM	E530	1950	£10 ...£25	US

REYNOLDS, JODY
Endless Sleep .... 7" ...... London .... HL8651 .... 1958 ... £10 ....£20

REYNOLDS, STAN
Missouri .... 7" ...... Decca ...... F11510 .... 1962 ... £1.50 .....£4

REYNOLDS, TIMMY
Lullaby Of Love .... 7" ...... Ember .... EMBS133 .... 1962 ... £2 ....£5 .... B side Jeff Mills

REYS, RITA
Cool Voice Of Rita Reys .... 10" LP .. Philips............ BBR8120 .... 1958 ... £8 ....£20

REZILLOS
Can't Stand My Baby	7"	Sensible	FAB1	1977	£1.50 ...£4	PS, chart single
Can't Stand The Rezillos	LP	Sire	K56530	1978	£4 ...£10	chart LP
Cold Wars	7"	Sire	SIR4014	1979	£1.50 ...£4	PS
Flying Saucer Attack	7"	Sensible	FAB2	1977	£12.50 ...£25	
Flying Saucer Attack	7"	Sire	6078612	1977	£1.50 ...£4	PS
Top Of The Pops	7"	Sire	SIR4001	1978	£1.50 ...£4	PS, chart single

RHINO 39
Xerox .... 7" ...... Dangerhouse .. RH39 .... 1979 ... £10 ....£20

RHINOCEROS
Apricot Brandy	7"	Elektra	EKSN45051	1968	£1.50 ...£4
Back Door	7"	Elektra	EKSN45080	1969	£2 ...£5
I Will Serenade You	7"	Elektra	EKSN45058	1969	£2 ...£5
Rhinoceros	LP	Elektra	EKL/EKS74030	1969	£4 ...£10

RHODEN, PAT
Jezebel .... 7" ...... Ska Beat........ JB195 .... 1965 ... £5 ....£10
Woman Is Greedy .... 7" ...... Trojan .... TR606 .... 1968 ... £2.50 .....£6

RHODEN, WINSTON
Make Believe .... 7" ...... Blue Beat ...... BB360 .... 1965 ... £5 ....£10

RHODES, TODD
Specks .... 7" ...... Parlophone...... MSP6171.............. 1955 ... £5 ....£10

RHUBARB RHUBARB
Rainmaker .... 7" ..... President .... PT229 .... 1968 ... £7.50 ....£15 ....

RHYTHM & BLUES INC.
Honey Don't .... 7" ..... Fontana .... TF524 .... 1965 ... £12.50 .....£25

RHYTHM ACES
Christmas .... 7" ..... Island .... WI032 .... 1962 ... £5 ....£10
I'll Be There .... 7" ..... Blue Beat .... BB134 .... 1962 ... £5 ....£10
Please Don't Go Away .... 7" ..... Starlite .... ST45066 .... 1961 ... £5 ....£10
Thousand Teardrops .... 7" ..... Starlite .... ST45061 .... 1961 ... £6 ....£12

RHYTHM KINGS
Blue Soul .... 7" ...... Vogue .... V9212 .... 1963 ... £5 ....£10

RHYTHM OF LIFE
Soon .... 7" ...... Rhythm Of Life RHYTHM001 .... 1982 ... £1.50 ....£4

RHYTHM ROCKERS
Soul Surfin' .... LP ...... Challenge .... CHL617 .... 1963 ... £6 ....£15 .... US

RHYTHMETTES
I'll Be With You In Apple Blossom 7" ...... Coral .... Q72358 .... 1959 ... £1.50 ....£4
Time ....

RIBA, PAU
Jo, La Donya I El Gripau .... LP ...... Edigsa .... 1971 ... £30 ....£60 .... US

RICE, MACK
Love's A Mother Brother .... 7" ...... Atlantic .... 584250 .... 1969 ... £1.50 ....£4

RICE-DAVIES, MANDY
Introducing Mandy .... 7" EP.. Ember .... EMBEP4537 .... 1963 ... £7.50 ....£15

RICH, BUDDY
Buddy And Sweets .... LP ...... Columbia .... 33CX10080 .... 1957 ... £6 ....£15 ..... with Harry Edison
Buddy Rich .... 7" EP.. Columbia .... SEB10024 .... 195- ... £2 ....£5
In Miami .... LP ...... Columbia .... 33CX10138 .... 1959 ... £6 ....£15
Just Sings .... LP ...... HMV .... CLP1185 .... 1958 ... £6 ....£15
Rich Versus Roach .... LP ...... Mercury .... MMC14031 .... 1960 ... £6 ....£15 ..... with Max Roach
Sings Johnny Mercer .... LP ...... HMV .... CLP1092 .... 1956 ... £6 ....£15
Swinging Buddy Rich .... 7" EP.. Columbia .... SEB10071 .... 1957 ... £2 ....£5
This One's For Basie .... LP ...... Columbia .... 33CX10071 .... 1957 ... £6 ....£15
Wailing Buddy Rich .... LP ...... Columbia .... 33CX10052 .... 1956 ... £6 ....£15

RICH, CHARLIE
Big Boss Man .... LP ...... RCA .... LPM/LSP3537 ...... 1966 ... £6 ....£15 .... US
Charlie Rich .... LP ...... Groove .... G(S)1000 .... 1964 ... £6 ....£15 .... US
Just A Little Bit Sweet .... 7" ...... London .... HLS9482 .... 1962 ... £5 ....£10
Lonely Weekends .... LP ...... Philips .... 1970 .... 1960 ... £150 ....£250 .... US
Lonely Weekends .... 7" ...... London .... HLU9107 .... 1960 ... £7.50 ....£15
Love Is After Me .... 7" ...... London .... HLU10104 .... 1967 ... £5 ....£10
Many New Sides Of Charlie Rich LP ...... Philips .... BL7695 .... 1966 ... £6 ....£15
Mohair Sam .... 7" ...... Mercury .... MF1109 .... 1969 ... £2 ....£5
Mohair Sam .... 7" ...... Philips .... BF1432 .... 1965 ... £2 ....£5
That's Rich .... LP ...... RCA .... RD7719 .... 1965 ... £10 ....£25
Too Many Teardrops .... 7" ...... RCA .... RCA1433 .... 1965 ... £1.50 ....£4

RICH, DAVE
City Lights .... 7" ...... RCA .... RCA1092 .... 1958 ... £2.50 ....£6

RICH, LEWIS
Everybody But Me .... 7" ...... Parlophone ...... R5283 .... 1965 ... £1.50 ....£4
I Don't Want To Hear It Anymore 7" ...... Parlophone ...... R5434 .... 1966 ... £2.50 ....£6

RICH MOUNTAIN TOWER
Rich Mountain Tower .... LP ...... London .... SHO8427 .... 1972 ... £6 ....£15

RICHARD & THE YOUNG LIONS
Open Up Your Door .... 7" ...... Philips .... BF1520 .... 1966 ... £12.50 .....£25

RICHARD, CLIFF
Cliff Richard's first two LPs were issued in mono only and yet stereo mixes of some of the tracks can be found on EPs. These are consequently much sought after. Cliff's 78rpm releases are also scarce and break the usual maxim that 78's are much less valuable than their 45rpm equivalents. Few of the religious records he has made over the years have sold particularly well and many of these now fetch quite high prices. Becoming increasingly hard to find, too, is the single "Honky Tonk Angel", which was withdrawn at Cliff Richard's insistence, despite being a likely chart hit, after someone told him what a honky tonk angel actually was (a prostitute). The most desirable Cliff Richard collectors' item of all, however (apart from unreleased acetates which are too scarce to be a realistic collectors' goal for most people), is likely to be one of the complete film soundtrack albums that were presented to all the people involved in the making of "Summer Holiday" and "Wonderful Life".
21 Today .... LP ...... Columbia .... 33SX1368 .... 1961 ... £8 ....£20 ..... mono, chart LP
21 Today .... LP ...... Columbia .... SCX3409 .... 1961 ... £20 ....£40 .... stereo
31st Of February Street .... LP ...... EMI .... EMC3048 .... 1974 ... £8 ....£20
32 Minutes 17 Seconds .... LP ...... Columbia .... 33SX1431 .... 1962 ... £8 ....£20 ..... mono, chart LP
32 Minutes 17 Seconds .... LP ...... Columbia .... SCX3436 .... 1962 ... £20 ....£40 .... stereo
About That Man .... LP ...... Columbia .... SCX6408 .... 1970 ... £40 ....£80
Aladdin & His Wonderful Lamp .... LP ...... Columbia .... 33SX1676 .... 1964 ... £5 ....£12 ..... mono, chart LP
Aladdin & His Wonderful Lamp .... LP ...... Columbia .... SCX3522 .... 1964 ... £6 ....£15 .... stereo
All My Love .... 7" ...... Columbia .... DB8293 .... 1967 ... £1.50 ....£4 .... chart single
Angel .... 7" ...... Columbia .... DC762 .... 1965 ... £20 ....£40 ....export
Angel .... 7" EP.. Columbia .... SEG8444 .... 1965 ... £7.50 ....£15

Title	Format	Label	Catalogue	Year	Low	High	Notes
Best Of Cliff Richard	LP	Columbia	SX/SCX6343	1969	£4	£10	chart LP
Best Of Cliff Richard And The Shadows	LP	Readers Digest	GRICA140	1984	£25	£50	8 LPs, boxed
Best Of Cliff Richard And The Shadows	7"	Lyntone	LYN14745	197-	£4	£8	flexi
Big Ship	7"	Columbia	DB8581	1969	£1.50	£4	chart single
Blue Turns To Grey	7"	Columbia	DB7866	1966	£1.50	£4	chart single
Boyfriend flexi	7"	Boyfriend		196-	£7.50	£15	flexi
Brand New Song	7"	Columbia	DB8957	1972	£1.50	£4	
Carnival	7"	Columbia	23060	1965	£7.50	£15	German import
Carol Singers	7" EP	Columbia	SEG8533	1967	£12.50	£25	
Carols	LP	Word	WRDR3034	1988	£10	£25	
Cinderella	LP	Columbia	SX/SCX6103	1967	£8	£20	chart LP
Cinderella	7" EP	Columbia	SEG8527	1967	£30	£60	
Cliff	LP	Columbia	33SX1147	1959	£8	£20	blue & black label
Cliff	LP	Columbia	33SX1147	1959	£15	£30	chart LP, green label
Cliff En Espania	7" EP	HMV		196-	£15	£30	sung in Spanish
Cliff In Japan	LP	Columbia	SX/SCX6244	1968	£10	£25	chart LP, blue & black label
Cliff In Japan	LP	Columbia	SX/SCX6244	1968	£6	£15	white & black label
Cliff No.1	7" EP	Columbia	ESG7754	1959	£20	£40	stereo
Cliff No.1	7" EP	Columbia	SEG7903	1959	£10	£20	
Cliff No.2	7" EP	Columbia	ESG7769	1959	£20	£40	stereo
Cliff No.2	7" EP	Columbia	SEG7910	1959	£10	£20	
Cliff Richard	LP	Columbia	33SX1709	1965	£10	£25	mono, chart LP
Cliff Richard	LP	Columbia	SCX3546	1965	£15	£30	stereo
Cliff Richard	LP	World Record Club	STP1051	1966	£17.50	£35	
Cliff Richard In Spain	7" EP	Columbia	SEG8151	1962	£7.50	£15	
Cliff Richard No.2	LP	Epic	LN24115/BN26115	1964	£10	£25	US
Cliff Richard No.2	7" EP	Columbia	SEG8168	1962	£7.50	£15	
Cliff Richard Singles Sampler	LP	EMI	PSLP350	1982	£10	£25	promo
Cliff Richard Songbook	LP	World Record Club	ALBUM26	1980	£15	£30	6 LPs, boxed
Cliff Richard Story	LP	World Record Club	SM255-260	1972	£15	£30	6 LPs, boxed
Cliff Richard Story	7"	Lyntone	LYNSF1218	1973	£2.50	£6	sampler flexi with interview
Cliff Sings	LP	ABC	(S)321	1960	£15	£30	US
Cliff Sings	LP	Columbia	33SX1192	1959	£8	£20	blue & black label
Cliff Sings	LP	Columbia	33SX1192	1959	£15	£30	chart LP, green label
Cliff Sings No.1	7" EP	Columbia	ESG7788	1960	£20	£40	stereo
Cliff Sings No.1	7" EP	Columbia	SEG7979	1960	£7.50	£15	
Cliff Sings No.2	7" EP	Columbia	ESG7794	1960	£20	£40	stereo
Cliff Sings No.2	7" EP	Columbia	SEG7987	1960	£7.50	£15	
Cliff Sings No.3	7" EP	Columbia	ESG7808	1960	£20	£40	stereo
Cliff Sings No.3	7" EP	Columbia	SEG8005	1960	£7.50	£15	
Cliff Sings No.4	7" EP	Columbia	ESG7816	1960	£20	£40	stereo
Cliff Sings No.4	7" EP	Columbia	SEG8021	1960	£10	£20	
Cliff's Hit Parade	7" EP	Columbia	SEG8133	1962	£6	£12	
Cliff's Hits	7" EP	Columbia	SEG8203	1962	£6	£12	
Cliff's Hits From Aladdin	7" EP	Columbia	SEG8395	1965	£6	£12	
Cliff's Lucky Lips	7" EP	Columbia	SEG8269	1963	£6	£12	
Cliff's Palladium Successes	7" EP	Columbia	SEG8320	1964	£7.50	£15	
Cliff's Rock Party	7"	Serenade		196-	£7.50	£15	flexi
Cliff's Silver Discs	7" EP	Columbia	SEG8050	1960	£5	£10	
Congratulations	7" EP	Columbia	SEG8540	1968	£10	£20	
Constantly	7"	Columbia	DB7272	1964	£1.50	£4	chart single
Das Gluck Ist Rosarot	7"	Columbia	C23371	1966	£7.50	£15	German import
Das Ist Die Frage Aller Fragen	7"	Columbia	22811	1964	£7.50	£15	German import
Day I Met Marie	7"	Columbia	DB8245	1967	£1.50	£4	chart single
Don't Forget To Catch Me	7"	Columbia	DB8503	1968	£1.50	£4	chart single
Don't Stop Me Now	LP	Columbia	SX/SCX6133	1967	£8	£20	chart LP
Don't Talk To Him	7"	Columbia	DB7150	1963	£1.50	£4	chart single
Don't Talk To Him	7" EP	Columbia	SEG8299	1964	£7.50	£15	
Dream	7" EP	Columbia	ESG7867	1961	£12.50	£25	stereo
Dream	7" EP	Columbia	SEG8119	1961	£6	£12	
Du Bist Mein Erster Gedanke	7"	EMI	23211	1967	£7.50	£15	sung in German
Ein Girl Wiedu	7"	Columbia	C23510	196-	£7.50	£15	sung in German
Es War Keine So Wunderbar Wie Du	7"	Columbia	22962	1964	£7.50	£15	German import
Established 1958	LP	Columbia	SX/SCX6282	1968	£6	£15	chart LP
Every Face Tells A Story	7"	EMI	PSR410	1977	£10	£20	promo sampler
Expresso Bongo	7" EP	Columbia	ESG7783	1960	£15	£30	stereo
Expresso Bongo	7" EP	Columbia	SEG7971	1960	£6	£12	chart single
Fall In Love With You	7"	Columbia	DB4431	1960	£5	£10	black label
Fall In Love With You	7"	Columbia	DB4431	1960	£1.50	£4	chart single
Finders Keepers	LP	Columbia	SX/SCX6079	1966	£5	£12	chart LP
Finders Keepers	7"	EMI	PSR304	1967	£6	£12	1 sided promo
Flying Machine	7"	Columbia	DB8797	1971	£2	£5	chart single
Forever Kind Of Love	7" EP	Columbia	SEG8347	1964	£7.50	£15	
Forty Greatest Hits	7"	EMI	PSR414/5	1977	£7.50	£15	double promo sampler
From A Distance	7"	EMI	EMPD155	1990	£1.50	£4	pic disc
Gee Whiz It's You	7"	Columbia	DC756	1961	£2.50	£6	export, chart single
Girl Like You	7"	Columbia	DB4667	1961	£4	£8	black label
Girl Like You	7"	Columbia	DB4667	1961	£1.50	£4	chart single
Good News	LP	Columbia	JSX6167	1967	£17.50	£35	export
Good News	LP	Columbia	SX/SCX6167	1967	£6	£15	chart LP
Good Times (Better Times)	7"	Columbia	DB8548	1969	£1.50	£4	chart single
Goodbye Sam Hello Samantha	7"	Columbia	DB8685	1970	£1.50	£4	chart single

Title	Format	Label	Catalogue No.	Year	Price	Price	Notes
Green Light	7"	EMI	EMI2920	1979	£10	£20	PS
Gut Dasses Freunde Gibt	7"	Electrola		196-	£7.50	£15	sung in German
Heart User	12"	EMI	12RICH2	1985	£2.50	£6	poster PS
Help It Along	LP	EMI	EMA768	1974	£6	£15	
Help It Along	7"	EMI	EMI2022	1973	£4	£8	PS, chart single
High Class Baby	78	Columbia	DB4203	1958	£7.50	£15	
High Class Baby	7"	Columbia	DB4203	1958	£10	£20	black label
High Class Baby	7"	Columbia	DB4203	1958	£4	£8	chart single
His Land	LP	Columbia	SCX6443	1970	£25	£50	
Hit Album	LP	Columbia	33SX1512	1963	£4	£10	chart LP
Hits From Summer Holiday	7" EP	Columbia	ESG7896	1963	£12.50	£25	stereo
Hits From Summer Holiday	7" EP	Columbia	SEG8250	1963	£5	£10	
Hits From The Young Ones	7" EP	Columbia	SEG8159	1963	£6	£12	different mixes
Hits From When In Rome	7" EP	Columbia	SEG8478	1966	£17.50	£35	
Hits From Wonderful Life	7" EP	Columbia	ESG7906	1964	£15	£30	stereo
Hits From Wonderful Life	7" EP	Columbia	SEG8376	1964	£6	£12	
Holiday Carnival	7" EP	Columbia	ESG7892	1963	£12.50	£25	stereo
Holiday Carnival	7" EP	Columbia	SEG8246	1963	£6	£12	
Honky Tonk Angel	7"	EMI	EMI2344	1975	£10	£20	
How Wonderful To Know	LP	World Record Club	(S)T643	1964	£8	£20	
Hymns And Inspirational Songs	LP	Word	WRDR3017	1986	£10	£25	
I Ain't Got Time Anymore	7"	Columbia	DB8708	1970	£1.50	£4	chart single
I Could Easily Fall	7"	Columbia	DB7420	1964	£1.50	£4	chart single
I Just Don't Have The Heart	12"	EMI	12EMP101	1989	£2.50	£6	pic disc
I Love You	7"	Columbia	DB4547	1960	£5	£10	black label
I Love You	7"	Columbia	DB4547	1960	£1.50	£4	chart single
Ich Bin Verliebt In Dich	7"	Odeon	C21703	1961	£7.50	£15	Sung In German
Ich Traume Deine Traume	7"	Columbia		196-	£7.50	£15	sung in German
I'll Come Running	7"	Columbia	DB8210	1967	£1.50	£4	chart single
I'll Love You Forever Today	7"	Columbia	DB8437	1968	£2.50	£6	chart single
I'm Lookin' Out The Window	7"	Columbia	DB4828	1962	£4	£8	black label
I'm Looking Out The Window	7"	Columbia	DB4828	1962	£1.50	£4	chart single
I'm The Lonely One	7"	Columbia	DB7203	1964	£1.50	£4	chart single
In The Country	7"	Columbia	DB8094	1966	£1.50	£4	chart single
It'll Be Me	7"	Columbia	DB4886	1962	£4	£8	black label
It'll Be Me	7"	Columbia	DB4886	1962	£1.50	£4	chart single
It's A Small World	LP	Myrrh	MYRR1209	1988	£15	£30	
It's All In The Game	LP	Epic	LN24089/BN26089	1964	£8	£20	US
It's All In The Game	7"	Columbia	DB7089	1963	£1.50	£4	chart single
It's All Over	7"	Columbia	DB8150	1967	£1.50	£4	chart single
It's Only Me You've Left Behind	7"	EMI	EMI2279	1975	£4	£8	
Japan Tour 1974	LP	EMI	EMS67037	1975	£50	£100	Japanese
Jesus	7"	Columbia	DB8864	1972	£2.50	£6	chart single
Kinda Latin	LP	Columbia	SCX6039	1966	£15	£30	stereo
Kinda Latin	LP	Columbia	SX6039	1966	£10	£25	mono, chart LP
La La La La La	7" EP	Columbia	SEG8517	1966	£10	£20	
Lean On You	7"	EMI	EMP105	1989	£1.50	£4	pic disc
Leave My Woman Alone	7"	Columbia	DB8657	1970	£1.50	£4	with Hank Marvin, chart single
Listen To Cliff	LP	ABC	(S)391	1961	£10	£25	US
Listen To Cliff	LP	Columbia	33SX1320	1961	£8	£20	mono, chart LP
Listen To Cliff	LP	Columbia	SCX3375	1961	£20	£40	stereo
Listen To Cliff No.1	7" EP	Columbia	ESG7858	1961	£12.50	£25	stereo
Listen To Cliff No.1	7" EP	Columbia	SEG8105	1961	£7.50	£15	
Listen To Cliff No.2	7" EP	Columbia	ESG7870	1961	£12.50	£25	stereo
Listen To Cliff No.2	7" EP	Columbia	SEG8126	1961	£7.50	£15	
Little Town	7"	EMI	EMIP5348	1982	£2	£5	pic disc
Live At The Talk Of The Town	LP	Starline	SRS5031	1970	£4	£10	
Live In Japan '72	LP	EMI	EOP930773B	1972	£60	£120	Japanese
Livin' Lovin' Doll	78	Columbia	DB4249	1959	£15	£30	
Livin' Lovin' Doll	7"	Columbia	DB4249	1959	£12.50	£25	black label
Livin' Lovin' Doll	7"	Columbia	DB4249	1959	£7.50	£15	chart single
Living Doll	78	Columbia	DB4306	1959	£10	£20	
Living Doll	7"	Columbia	DB4306	1959	£7.50	£15	black label
Living Doll	7"	Columbia	DB4306	1959	£1.50	£4	chart single
Living In Harmony	7"	Columbia	DB8917	1972	£1.50	£4	chart single
Look In My Eyes Maria	7" EP	Columbia	SEG8405	1965	£7.50	£15	
Love Is Forever	LP	Columbia	SX1769/SCX3569	1965	£8	£20	chart LP
Love Is Forever	7" EP	Columbia	SEG8488	1966	£10	£20	
Love Songs	7" EP	Columbia	ESG7900	1963	£17.50	£35	stereo
Love Songs	7" EP	Columbia	SEG8272	1963	£6	£12	
Lucky Lips	7"	Columbia	DB7034	1963	£1.50	£4	chart single
Man Gratuliert Mir	7"	Columbia		196-	£7.50	£15	sung in German
Maria No Mas	7"	Columbia		196-	£7.50	£15	sung in Spanish
Marianne	7"	Columbia	DB8476	1968	£1.50	£4	chart single
Me And My Shadows	LP	Columbia	33SX1261	1960	£8	£20	mono, chart LP
Me And My Shadows	LP	Columbia	SCX3330	1960	£20	£40	stereo
Me And My Shadows	LP	Regal	SREG1120	1960	£25	£50	export
Me And My Shadows No.1	7" EP	Columbia	ESG7837	1961	£12.50	£25	stereo
Me And My Shadows No.1	7" EP	Columbia	SEG8065	1961	£7.50	£15	
Me And My Shadows No.2	7" EP	Columbia	ESG7841	1961	£12.50	£25	stereo
Me And My Shadows No.2	7" EP	Columbia	SEG8071	1961	£7.50	£15	
Me And My Shadows No.3	7" EP	Columbia	ESG7843	1961	£12.50	£25	stereo
Me And My Shadows No.3	7" EP	Columbia	SEG8078	1961	£7.50	£15	
Mean Streak	78	Columbia	DB4290	1959	£15	£30	
Mean Streak	7"	Columbia	DB4290	1959	£10	£20	black label
Mean Streak	7"	Columbia	DB4290	1959	£4	£8	chart single
Minute You're Gone	7"	Columbia	DB7496	1965	£1.50	£4	chart single
Mistletoe And Wine	12"	EMI	12EMX78	1988	£2.50	£6	with Advent calendar

Title	Format	Label	Cat No	Year	Price1	Price2	Notes
More Hits	LP	Columbia	SCX3555	1965	£6	£15	stereo
More Hits	LP	Columbia	SX1737	1965	£5	£12	mono, chart LP
More Hits From Summer Holiday	7" EP	Columbia	ESG7898	1963	£12.50	£25	
More Hits From Summer Holiday	7" EP	Columbia	SEG8263	1963	£7.50	£15	stereo
Move It	78	Columbia	DB4178	1958	£7.50	£15	
Move It	7"	Columbia	DB4178	1958	£10	£20	black label
Move It	7"	Columbia	DB4178	1958	£5	£10	chart single
Music And Life Of Cliff Richard	cass	EMI	TCEXSP1601	1974	£15	£30	6 tapes, boxed
Music From America	7"	Rainbow	196-		£7.50	£15	flexi
My Italian Friends	LP	Columbia	CCMQ8024	196-	£25	£50	sung in Italian
Next Time	7"	Columbia	DB4950	1962	£1.50	£4	chart single
Nine Times Out Of Ten	7"	Columbia	DB4506	1960	£6	£12	black label
Nine Times Out Of Ten	7"	Columbia	DB4506	1960	£2	£5	chart single
Non Dimenti Care Chitiama	7"	HMV		196-	£7.50	£15	sung in Italian
Non L'Ascoltare	7"	Columbia	SCMQ1860	196-	£7.50	£15	sung in Italian
Nothing To Remind Me	7"	EMI		1967	£7.50	£15	promo
O Mio Signore	7" EP	Columbia	2221	196-	£15	£30	sung in Italian
On My Word	7"	Columbia	DB7596	1965	£1.50	£4	chart single
On The Beach	7"	Columbia	DB7305	1964	£1.50	£4	chart single
Per Un Bacio Diamour	LP	Columbia	CCMQ8081	196-	£25	£50	sung in Italian
Personal Message To You	7"	Serenade		1960	£10	£20	blue flexi
Please Don't Tease	7"	Columbia	DB4479	1960	£5	£10	black label
Please Don't Tease	7"	Columbia	DB4479	1960	£1.50	£4	chart single
Power To All Our Friends	7"	EMI		196-	£7.50	£15	sung in Spanish
Rote Lippen Soll Man Kussen	7"	Columbia	C22563	196-	£7.50	£15	sung in German
Schon Wie Ein Traume	7"	Columbia	C21843	196-	£7.50	£15	sung in German
Serious Charge	7" EP	Columbia	SEG7895	1959	£10	£20	
Shooting From The Heart	7"	EMI	RICHP1	1984	£4	£8	shaped pic disc
Silvery Rain	7"	Columbia	DB8774	1971	£2.50	£6	chart single
Sincerely	LP	Columbia	SCX6537	1969	£6	£15	stereo, chart LP
Sincerely	LP	Columbia	SX6537	1969	£8	£20	mono
Sing A Song Of Freedom	7"	Columbia	DB8836	1971	£1.50	£4	chart single
Small Corners	LP	Word	WRDR3036	1988	£10	£25	
Some People	7"	EMI	EMP18	1987	£2	£5	shaped pic disc
Star Souvenir Greetings	7"	New Spotlight		196-	£6	£12	flexi
Summer Holiday	LP	Columbia	33SX1472	1963	£5	£12	mono, chart LP
Summer Holiday	LP	Columbia	SCX3462	1963	£5	£12	blue & black label
Summer Holiday	LP	Columbia	SCX3462	1963	£8	£20	stereo, green label
Summer Holiday	LP	Elstree Studios		1962	£330	£500	Original soundtrack, double
Summer Holiday	LP	Epic	LN24063/BN26063	1963	£8	£20	US
Summer Holiday	7"	Columbia	DB4977	1963	£1.50	£4	chart single
Sunny Honey Girl	7"	Columbia	DB8747	1971	£2	£5	chart single
Swinger's Paradise	LP	Epic	LN24145/BN26145	1965	£8	£20	US
Take Four	7" EP	Columbia	SEG8450	1965	£7.50	£15	
Take Me High	LP	EMI	EMC3016	1973	£5	£12	chart LP
Take Me High	LP	EMI	EMC3016	1973	£8	£20	with poster
Take Me High	7"	EMI	EMI2088	1973	£1.50	£4	chart single
Theme For A Dream	7"	Columbia	DB4593	1961	£5	£10	black label
Theme For A Dream	7"	Columbia	DB4593	1961	£1.50	£4	chart single
Thirtieth Anniversary Picture Record Collection	LP	EMI	SMPLC1	1989	£6	£15	double pic disc
This Was My Special Day	7"	Columbia	DB7435	1964	£12.50	£25	demo only
Throw Down A Line	7"	Columbia	DB8615	1969	£1.50	£4	with Hank Marvin, chart single
Thunderbirds Are Go	7" EP	Columbia	SEG8510	1966	£17.50	£35	
Time Drags By	7"	Columbia	DB8017	1966	£1.50	£4	chart single
Time For Cliff And The Shadows	7" EP	Columbia	ESG7887	1963	£17.50	£35	stereo
Time For Cliff And The Shadows	7" EP	Columbia	SEG8228	1963	£7.50	£15	
Time In Between	7"	Columbia	DB7660	1965	£1.50	£4	chart single
Tracks And Grooves	LP	Columbia	SCX6435	1970	£8	£20	chart LP
Travellin' Light	78	Columbia	DB4351	1959	£17.50	£35	
Travellin' Light	7"	Columbia	DB4351	1959	£5	£10	black label
Travellin' Light	7"	Columbia	DB4351	1959	£1.50	£4	chart single
Twelfth Of Never	7"	Columbia	DB7372	1964	£1.50	£4	chart single
Two A Penny	LP	Columbia	SX/SCX6262	1968	£8	£20	blue & black label
Two A Penny	LP	Columbia	SX/SCX6262	1968	£6	£15	white & black label
Two Hearts	7"	EMI	EMP42	1987	£1.50	£4	shaped pic disc
Un Saludo De Cliff	7" EP	HMV	13955	196-	£15	£30	sung in Spanish
Visions	7"	Columbia	DB7968	1966	£1.50	£4	chart single
Voice In The Wilderness	78	Columbia	DB4398	1960	£17.50	£35	
Voice In The Wilderness	7"	Columbia	DB4398	1960	£5	£10	black label
Voice In The Wilderness	7"	Columbia	DB4398	1960	£1.50	£4	chart single
Walking In The Light	LP	Myrrh	MYR1176	1985	£10	£25	
Walking In The Light	CD	Myrrh	MYRCD1176	1985	£6	£15	
We Don't Talk Anymore (2 versions)	12"	EMI	SPRO9252	1979	£4	£10	US promo
What'd I Say	7"	Columbia	DC758	1963	£100	£200	export
When In France	LP	EMI	4C06206234	1977	£8	£20	Belgian
When In France	7" EP	Columbia	SEG8290	1964	£7.50	£15	
When In Rome	LP	Columbia	SX1762	1965	£10	£25	
When In Spain	LP	Columbia	33SX1541	1963	£6	£15	mono, chart LP
When In Spain	LP	Columbia	SCX3488	1963	£10	£25	stereo
When The Girl In Your Arms	7"	Columbia	DB4716	1961	£4	£8	black label
When The Girl In Your Arms	7"	Columbia	DB4716	1961	£1.50	£4	chart single
Why Don't They Understand	7" EP	Columbia	SEG8384	1965	£7.50	£15	
Wind Me Up	7"	Columbia	DB7745	1965	£1.50	£4	chart single
Wind Me Up	7" EP	Columbia	SEG8474	1966	£7.50	£15	
With The Eyes Of A Child	7"	Columbia	DB8641	1969	£1.50	£4	chart single
Wonderful Life	LP	Columbia	33SX1628	1964	£5	£12	mono, chart LP
Wonderful Life	LP	Columbia	SCX3515	1964	£8	£20	stereo

Wonderful Life	LP	Elstree Studios		1963	£330	£500	Original soundtrack, double
Wonderful Life No.1	7" EP	Columbia	ESG7902	1964	£12.50	£25	stereo
Wonderful Life No.1	7" EP	Columbia	SEG8338	1964	£6	£12	
Wonderful Life No.2	7" EP	Columbia	ESG7903	1964	£12.50	£25	stereo
Wonderful Life No.2	7" EP	Columbia	SEG8354	1964	£6	£12	
Wonderful To Be Young	LP	Dot	DLP3474/25474	1962	£10	£25	US
Yes He Lives	7"	EMI	EMI2730	1978	£2	£5	
Young Ones	LP	Columbia	33SX1384	1961	£6	£15	mono, chart LP
Young Ones	LP	Columbia	SCX3397	1961	£10	£25	stereo
Young Ones	7"	Columbia	DB4761	1962	£4	£8	black label
Young Ones	7"	Columbia	DB4761	1962	£1.50	£4	chart single
Zuviel Allein	7"	Odeon	C22707	1964	£7.50	£15	Sung In German

RICHARD, CLIFF/QUEEN

We Don't Talk Anymore	7"	EMI	EMI2975	1979	£5	£10	mispress - plays Bohemian Rhapsody

RICHARDS, CYNTHIA

Foolish Fool	LP	Trojan	TBL123	1970	£6	£15	

RICHARDS, JOHNNY

Experiments In Sound	LP	Capitol	T981	1959	£4	£10	
Rites Of Diablo	LP	Esquire	32076	1959	£4	£10	
Something Else	LP	London	LTZN1511	1958	£5	£12	
Walk Softly - Run Wild	LP	Coral	LVA9122	1960	£4	£10	
Wide Range	LP	Capitol	T885	1958	£5	£12	

RICHARDS, KEITH

Before They Make Me Run	7"	Rolling Stones		1979	£4	£8	promo
Run Rudolph Run	7"	Rolling Stones	RSR102	1979	£2.50	£6	PS
Talk Is Cheap	LP	Virgin		1988	£25	£50	promo album on 4 x 7"

RICHARDS, LISA

Mean Old World	7"	Vocalion	VP9244	1965	£7.50	£15	

RICHARDS, LLOYD

Be Good	7"	Port-O-Jam	PJ4004	1964	£5	£10	

RICHARDS, ROY

Contact	7"	Doctor Bird	DB1012	1966	£5	£10	Fitzy & Freddy B side
Double Trouble	7"	Island	WI283	1966	£5	£10	Delroy Wilson B side
Hopeful Village	7"	Island	WI3037	1967	£5	£10	
Rub-A-Dub	7"	Island	WI3027	1967	£5	£10	
South Vietnam	7"	Island	WI3000	1966	£5	£10	
Summertime	7"	Coxsone	CS7061	1968	£5	£10	Righteous Flames B side
Western Standard Time	7"	Island	WI299	1966	£5	£10	Eagles B side

RICHARDS, TRUDY

Wishbone	7"	Capitol	CL14728	1957	£1.50	£4	

RICHARDS, WENDY & DIANA BERRY

We Had A Dream	7"	Decca	F11680	1963	£2	£5	

RICHARDS, WINSTON

Green Coolie	7"	Island	WI297	1966	£5	£10	Marcia Griffiths B side
Studio Blitz	7"	Rio	R124	1967	£4	£8	

RICHMOND

Frightened	LP	Dart	ARTS65371	1973	£8	£20	

RICK & THE KEENS

Peanuts	7"	Mercury	AMT1150	1961	£7.50	£15	

RICKETTS & ROWE

Hold Me Tight	7"	Starlite	ST45048	1961	£5	£10	

RICKETTS, BERESFORD

Baby Baby	7"	Starlite	ST45029	1960	£2	£5	
Cherry Baby	7"	Starlite	ST45025	1960	£5	£10	
I'm Going To Cry	7"	Starlite	ST45079	1962	£5	£10	
Jailer Bring Me Water	7"	Blue Beat	BB350	1965	£5	£10	
O Jean	7"	Dice	CC12	1963	£5	£10	
You Better Be Gone	7"	Blue Beat	BB107	1962	£5	£10	

RICO

Baby Face	7"	Doctor Bird	DB1302	1969	£5	£10	Rudies B side
Blow Your Horn	7"	Trojan	TTL12	1969	£8	£20	
Blues From The Hills	7"	Blue Beat	BB195	1963	£5	£10	Stranger Cole B side
Bullet	7"	Blue Cat	BS160	1969	£4	£8	
In Reggae Land	LP	Pama	ECO14	1969	£8	£20	
Jingle Bells	7"	Fab	FAB12	1967	£4	£8	
Lion Speaks	7"	Treasure Isle	TI7052	1969	£4	£8	Andy Capp B side
Luke Lane Shuffle	7"	Blue Beat	BB56	1961	£5	£10	Prince Buster B side
Planet Rock	7"	Planetone	RC4	197-	£1.50	£4	
Quando Quando	7"	Downtown	DT417	1969	£2	£5	
Reco's Farewell	7"	Island	WI022	1962	£5	£10	Bunny & Skitter B side
Soul Man	7"	Pama	PM706	1968	£4	£8	

Tender Foot Ska	7"	Pama	PM715	1968	£4	£8	
Tribute To Don Drummond	7"	Bullet	BU407	1969	£1.50	£4	
Youth Boogie	7"	Planetone	RC5	197-	£1.50	£4	

RICOTTI, FRANK

Our Point Of View	LP	CBS	52668	1969	£6	£15	

RIDDLE, NELSON

Batman	LP	Stateside	(S)SL10179	1966	£5	£12	
Pendulum Song	7"	Capitol	CL14262	1955	£1.50	£4	
Route Sixty-Six	7" EP	Capitol	EAP41771	1961	£2	£5	
Run For Cover	7"	Capitol	CL14305	1955	£1.50	£4	
Supercar	7"	Capitol	CL15309	1963	£4	£8	
Vera Cruz	7"	Capitol	CL14241	1955	£1.50	£4	

RIDDLERS

Batman Theme	7"	Polydor	56716	1966	£4	£8	

RIDE

Taste	7"	Creation	CRE087P	1990	£2	£5	1 sided promo

RIDING, JACKIE

Wave	7"	Melodisc	FAB4	1966	£1.50	£4	

RIFF RAFF

Original Man	LP	RCA	LPL15023	1974	£4	£10	
Riff Raff	LP	RCA	SF8351	1973	£4	£10	

RIFFS

Oh What A Feeling	7"	Blue Beat	BB242	1963	£5	£10	

RIFKIN

Continental Hesitation	7"	Page One	POF071	1968	£15	£30	

RIFKIN, JOSHUA

Baroque Beatles	LP	Elektra		1968	£10	£25	US

RIGBY, ELEANOR

I Want To Sleep With You	7"	Waterloo Sunset	RUSS101	1985	£4	£8	with condom & sticker
Take Another Shot Of My Heart	7"	Waterloo Sunset	RUSS102	1985	£2.50	£6	with signed story

RIGG, BRAM SET

Take The Time To Be Yourself	7"	Stateside	SS2020	1967	£20	£40	

RIGG, DIANA

Sentimental Journey	7"	RCA	RCA2179	1972	£2	£5	

RIGGS, JACKIE

Great Pretender	7"	London	HLF8244	1956	£10	£20	

RIGHTEOUS BROTHERS

Back To Back	LP	London	HA8278	1966	£8	£20	
Bring Your Love To Me	7"	Pye	7N25297	1965	£1.50	£4	
Ebb Tide	7"	London	HL10011	1965	£1.50	£4	chart single
Ebb Tide	7"	Verve	VS576	1968	£1.50	£4	
Ebb Tide	7" EP	Barclay	070915	1965	£6	£12	French
For Your Love	7"	Pye	7N25334	1965	£1.50	£4	
Georgia On My Mind	7"	Pye	7N25358	1966	£1.50	£4	
Go Ahead And Cry	7"	Verve	VS542	1966	£1.50	£4	
He	7"	Verve	VS537	1966	£1.50	£4	
In Action	LP	Sue	ILP937	1966	£15	£30	
Island In The Sun	LP	Verve	VS547	1966	£1.50	£4	chart single
Just Once In My Life	LP	London	HA8245	1965	£8	£20	
Just Once In My Life	7"	London	HL9962	1965	£20	£40	demo only
Just Once In My Life	7"	London	HLU10066	1966	£1.50	£4	
Let The Good Times Roll	7"	Pye	7N25323	1964	£2.50	£6	
Little Latin Lupe Lu	7"	London	HL9743	1963	£2.50	£6	
My Babe	7"	London	HL9814	1963	£2.50	£6	
One For The Road	LP	Verve	(S)VLP9228	1968	£4	£10	
Right Now	LP	Pye	NPL28059	1965	£6	£15	
Righteous Brothers	7" EP	Pye	NEP44043	1965	£5	£10	
Righteous Brothers	7" EP	Verve	VEP5024	1966	£4	£10	
Some Blue Eyed Soul	LP	Pye	NPL28056	1965	£8	£20	
Something's Got A Hold On Me	7"	Pye	7N25304	1965	£1.50	£4	
Soul And Inspiration	LP	Verve	(S)VLP9131	1966	£6	£15	
Soul And Inspiration	7"	Verve	VS535	1966	£1.50	£4	chart single
Soul And Inspiration	7" EP	Verve	26501	1966	£6	£12	French
Souled Out	LP	Verve	(S)VLP9190	1967	£4	£10	
Stranded In The Middle Of No Place	7"	Verve	VS560	1967	£2	£5	
Unchained Melody	7"	London	HL9975	1965	£1.50	£4	chart single
Unchained Melody	7" EP	Barclay	70860	1965	£6	£12	French
White Cliffs Of Dover	7"	London	HL10086	1966	£1.50	£4	chart single
You Can Have Her	7"	Sue	WI4018	1966	£4	£8	
You've Lost That Lovin' Feelin'	LP	London	HA8226	1965	£8	£20	
You've Lost That Lovin' Feelin'	7"	London	HL9943	1965	£2	£5	chart single
You've Lost That Lovin' Feeling	7" EP	Barclay	70766	1965	£6	£12	French

RIGHTEOUS FLAMES

Gimme Some Sign Girl	7"	Fab	FAB18	1967	£4	£8	

RIGHTEOUS TWINS
If I Could Hear My Master .... 7" .... Blue Cat .... BS174 .... 1969 ... £4 ....£8 ....

RIKKI & THE LAST DAYS OF EARTH
City Of The Damned .... 7" .... DJM .... DJS10814 .... 1977 ... £2 ....£5 ....

RILEY, BILLY LEE
Harmonica Beatlemania .... LP ..... Mercury .... SR60974 .... 1964 ... £5 ....£12 .... US
I've Been Searchin' .... 7" .... King .... KG1015 .... 1965 ... £4 ....£8 ....

RILEY, BOB
Midnight Line .... 7" .... MGM .... MGM977 .... 1958 ... £12.50 .....£25 ....

RILEY, HOWARD
Angle .... LP ..... CBS .... 52669 .... 1969 ... £10 ....£25 ....
Day Will Come .... LP ..... CBS .... 64077 .... 1970 ... £6 ....£15 ....
Discussions .... LP ..... Opportunity ...... CP2500 .... 1967 ... £75 ....£150 ....
Flight .... LP ..... Turtle .... TUR301 .... 1970 ... £15 ....£30 ....

RILEY, JEANNIE C.
Harper Valley P.T.A. .... 7" .... Polydor .... 56748 .... 1968 ... £1.50 ....£4 ....chart single

RILEY, TERRY
Composer Terry Riley pioneered the use of tape-loops to create a dense, meditational sound and was a direct influence on the Soft Machine school of rock music. His "Church Of Anthrax" is co-credited to John Cale, and the well-known ex-member of the Velvet Underground gets the star billing. Really, however, the music is all Riley's, with Cale essentially sitting at the feet of the master and following as best as he can.
Happy Ending .... LP ..... Warner Bros. ... 46125 .... 1972 ... £6 ....£15 ....
In 'C' .... LP ..... CBS .... 64565 .... 1970 ... £4 ....£10 ....
Keyboard Studies .... LP ..... Byg .... 1969 ... £15 ....£30 ....French
Le Secret De La Vie .... LP ..... Philips .... 9120037 .... 1975 ... £4 ....£10 ....
Persian Surgery Dervishes .... LP ..... Shandar .... 83501 .... 1972 ... £10 ....£25 ....double
Reed Streams .... LP ..... Mass Art Inc .... M131 .... 1967 ... £15 ....£30 .... US

RIMMER, SHANE
Three Bells .... 7" .... Columbia .... DB4343 .... 1959 ... £1.50 ....£4 ....

RINGS & THINGS
Strange Things Are Happening .... 7" .... Fontana .... TF987 .... 1968 ... £20 ....£40 ....

RINKY DINKS
Choo Choo Cha Cha .... 7" .... Capitol .... CL14999 .... 1959 ... £2.50 ....£6 ....

RIO, BOBBY
Ask The Lonely .... 7" .... Piccadilly .... 7N35303 .... 1966 ... £2.50 ....£6 ....
Boy Meets Girl .... 7" .... Pye .... 7N15790 .... 1965 ... £7.50 ....£15 ....
Don Diddly .... 7" .... Stateside .... SS211 .... 1963 ... £1.50 ....£4 ....
Everything In The Garden .... 7" .... Pye .... 7N15897 .... 1965 ... £7.50 ....£15 ....
Value For Love .... 7" .... Pye .... 7N15958 .... 1965 ... £7.50 ....£15 ....

RIO GRANDES
Soldiers Take Over .... 7" .... Pyramid .... PYR6001 .... 1966 ... £4 ....£8 ....

RIOT SQUAD
Any Time .... 7" .... Pye .... 7N15752 .... 1965 ... £7.50 ....£15 ....
Cry Cry Cry .... 7" .... Pye .... 7N17041 .... 1966 ... £7.50 ....£15 ....
Gotta Be A First Time .... 7" .... Pye .... 7N17237 .... 1967 ... £7.50 ....£15 ....
I Take It We're Through .... 7" .... Pye .... 7N17092 .... 1966 ... £10 ....£20 ....
I Wanna Talk About My Baby .... 7" .... Pye .... 7N15817 .... 1965 ... £10 ....£20 ....
I Wanna Talk About My Baby .... 7" EP.. Pye .... PNV24134 .... 1965 ... £50 ....£100 ....French
It's Never Too Late to Forgive .... 7" .... Pye .... 7N17130 .... 1966 ... £7.50 ....£15 ....
Not A Great Talker .... 7" .... Pye .... 7N15869 .... 1965 ... £7.50 ....£15 ....

RIOTS
I Am In Love .... 7" .... Island .... WI197 .... 1965 ... £5 ....£10 ....
Telling Lies .... 7" .... Island .... WI176 .... 1965 ... £5 ....£10 ....

RIPCHORDS
Gone .... 7" .... CBS .... AAG162 .... 1963 ... £2.50 ....£6 ....
Here I Stand .... 7" .... CBS .... AAG143 .... 1963 ... £2.50 ....£6 ....
Hey Little Cobra .... LP ..... CBS .... BPG62228 .... 1964 ... £10 ....£25 ....
Hey Little Cobra .... 7" .... CBS .... AAG181 .... 1964 ... £5 ....£10 ....
Hey Little Cobra .... 7" EP.. CBS .... 5682 .... 1964 ... £7.50 ....£15 ....French
Three Window Coupe .... LP ..... CBS .... CL2216/CS9016 ... 1965 ... £10 ....£25 .... US
Three Window Coupe .... 7" .... CBS .... AAG202 .... 1964 ... £7.50 ....£15 ....

RIPPERS
Honestly .... LP ..... Saga .... FID2142 .... 1968 ... £5 ....£12 ....

RISING MOON
Rising Moon .... LP ..... Theatre .... 1974 ... £15 ....£30 ....
                                                            Projects...........

RISING SONS
The bright blues-based music of the Rising Sons, of which the two original singles listed comprise just a part of what was recorded, has recently been gathered together on to CD. The result shows the band to be one of the great lost sixties units, with a timeless quality that allows the music to easily transcend its decade. The Rising Sons were driven by the combined talents of Taj Mahal and Ry Cooder, both of whose careers can be seen to proceed logically from this starting point.
Candy Man .... 7" .... Columbia .... 43534 .... 1966 ... £10 ....£20 .... US
You're My Girl .... 7" .... Stateside .... SS426 .... 1965 ... £5 ....£10 ....

RISING STORM
Title	Format	Label	Cat No	Year	Price	Price	Notes
Calm Before The Rising Storm	LP	Remnant	BBA3571	1968	£700	£1000	US

RITA
Title	Format	Label	Cat No	Year	Price	Price	Notes
Erotica	7"	Major Minor	MM6533	1969	£2.50	£6	

RITCHIE, JEAN
Title	Format	Label	Cat No	Year	Price	Price	Notes
Child Ballads Vol.1	LP	Folkways	FA2301	1960	£5	£12	US
Child Ballads Vol.2	LP	Folkways	FA2302	1961	£5	£12	US
Songs From Kentucky	10" LP	Argo	ARS1009	1953	£8	£20	

RITTER, TEX
Title	Format	Label	Cat No	Year	Price	Price	Notes
Blood On The Saddle	LP	Capitol	(S)T1292	1960	£4	£10	
Cowboy Favourites	10" LP	Capitol	LC6552	1952	£15	£30	
Deck Of Cards	7" EP	Capitol	EAP11323	1960	£2.50	£6	
Hillbilly Heaven	LP	Capitol	(S)T1623	1961	£4	£10	US
Is There A Santa Claus?	7"	Capitol	CL14175	1954	£2.50	£6	
Last Frontier	7"	Capitol	CL14536	1956	£1.50	£4	
Last Wagon	7"	Capitol	CL14660	1956	£1.50	£4	
Lincoln Hymns	LP	Capitol	(S)W1562	1961	£4	£10	US
Marshall Of Wichita	7"	Capitol	CL14335	1955	£2.50	£6	
Psalms	LP	Capitol	T1100	1959	£6	£15	
Searchers	7"	Capitol	CL14605	1956	£1.50	£4	
Songs From The Western Screen	LP	Capitol	T971	1958	£10	£25	US
Wayward Wind	7"	Capitol	CL14581	1956	£5	£10	chart single
Whale Of A Tale	7"	Capitol	CL14277	1955	£2.50	£6	

RIVERS, BLUE & THE MAROONS
Title	Format	Label	Cat No	Year	Price	Price	Notes
Blue Beat In My Soul	LP	Columbia	SX6192	1967	£30	£60	
Witchcraft Man	7"	Columbia	DB103	1967	£4	£8	

RIVERS, BOYD & CLIFF AUNGIER
Title	Format	Label	Cat No	Year	Price	Price	Notes
Wanderin'	LP	Decca	LK4696	1965	£8	£20	

RIVERS, CLIFF
Title	Format	Label	Cat No	Year	Price	Price	Notes
True Lips	7"	London	HLU9739	1963	£5	£10	

RIVERS, DANNY
Title	Format	Label	Cat No	Year	Price	Price	Notes
Can't You Hear My Heart	7"	Decca	F11294	1960	£4	£8	chart single
Hawk	7"	Top Rank	JAR408	1960	£2.50	£6	
Moving In	7"	HMV	POP1000	1962	£7.50	£15	
My Baby's Gone Away	7"	Decca	F11357	1961	£4	£8	
There Will Never Be Anyone	7"	Decca	F11865	1964	£1.50	£4	

RIVERS, DEKE
Title	Format	Label	Cat No	Year	Price	Price	Notes
Outsider	7"	Oriole	CB1735	1962	£2.50	£6	

RIVERS, JOHNNY
Title	Format	Label	Cat No	Year	Price	Price	Notes
And I Know You Wanna Dance	LP	Imperial	LP9307/12307	1966	£4	£10	US
At The Whisky A Go Go	LP	Liberty	LBY3031	1964	£5	£12	
Back At The Whisky	LP	Imperial	LP9284/12284	1965	£5	£12	US
Blue Skies	7"	Pye	7N25118	1962	£1.50	£4	
Changes	LP	Liberty	(S)LBY3087	1967	£4	£10	
Go Johnny Go	LP	United Artists	UAL3386/ UAS6386	1964	£5	£12	
Golden Hits	LP	Imperial	LP9324/12324	1966	£4	£10	US
He Don't Love You	7"	Liberty	LIB12021	1965	£1.50	£4	
Here We Go Go Again	LP	Liberty	LBY3036	1964	£5	£12	
I Washed My Hands In Muddy Water	7"	Liberty	LIB66175	1966	£1.50	£4	
In Action	LP	Imperial	LP9280/12280	1965	£5	£12	US
Maybellene	7"	Liberty	LIB66056	1964	£1.50	£4	
Meanwhile Back At The Whisky A Go-Go	LP	Liberty	LBY3056	1965	£4	£10	
Memphis	7"	Liberty	LIB66032	1964	£1.50	£4	
Midnight Special	7"	Liberty	LIB66087	1965	£1.50	£4	
More Johnny Rivers	7" EP	Liberty	LEP4049	1966	£2.50	£6	
Mountain Of Love	7"	Liberty	LIB66075	1964	£1.50	£4	
Rocks The Folk	LP	Liberty	LBY3064	1965	£4	£10	
Sensational Johnny Rivers	LP	Capitol	(S)T2161	1964	£5	£12	US
Seventh Son	7"	Liberty	LIB66112	1965	£1.50	£4	
Tom Dooley	7"	Liberty	LIB12023	1965	£1.50	£4	
Tracks Of My Tears	7"	Liberty	LIB66244	1966	£1.50	£4	
Under Your Spell Again	7"	Liberty	LIB66155	1966	£1.50	£4	

RIVERS, SAM
Title	Format	Label	Cat No	Year	Price	Price	Notes
Contours	LP	Blue Note	BLP/BST84206	1965	£8	£20	
Fuchsia Swing Song	LP	Blue Note	BLP/BST84184	1964	£8	£20	
New Conception	LP	Blue Note	BLP/BST84249	1966	£8	£20	

RIVERS, TONY & THE CASTAWAYS
Title	Format	Label	Cat No	Year	Price	Price	Notes
Come Back	7"	Columbia	DB7536	1965	£2	£5	
Girl Don't Tell Me	7"	Immediate	IM027	1966	£5	£10	
God Only Knows	7"	Columbia	DB7971	1966	£2	£5	
I Can Guarantee Your Love	7"	Polydor	56245	1968	£2.50	£6	
I Love The Way You Walk	7"	Columbia	DB7224	1964	£4	£8	
Life's Too Short	7"	Columbia	DB7336	1964	£2.50	£6	
Nowhere Man	7"	Parlophone	R5400	1966	£2.50	£6	
Shake Shake Shake	7"	Columbia	DB7135	1963	£4	£8	
She	7"	Columbia	DB7448	1965	£2	£5	

RIVIERAS

California Sun	7"	Pye	7N25237	1964	£6	£12	
California Sun	7" EP	Columbia	ESRF1523	1964	£12.50	£25	French
Campus Party	LP	Riviera	701	1964	£8	£20	US
Let's Have A Party	LP	USA	102	1964	£8	£20	US

RIVIERAS (2)

Blessings Of Love	7"	HMV	POP773	1960	£4	£8	

RIVINGTONS

Bird's The Word	7"	Liberty	LIB55553	1963	£7.50	£15	
Doin' The Bird	LP	Liberty	LRP3282/LST7282	1963	£15	£30	US
Pappa Oom Mow Mow	7"	Liberty	LIB55427	1962	£7.50	£15	
Rose Growing In The Ruins	7"	CBS	202088	1966	£6	£12	

RO RO

Blackbird	7"	Regal Zonophone	RZ3076	1973	£7.50	£15	
Down On The Road	7"	Regal Zonophone	RZ3056	1972	£7.50	£15	
Here I Go Again	7"	Parlophone	R5920	1971	£7.50	£15	
Meet At The Water	LP	Regal Zonophone	SRZA8510	1972	£75	£150	

ROACH, FREDDIE

All That's Good	LP	Blue Note	BLP/BST84190	1965	£15	£30	
Brown Sugar	LP	Blue Note	BLP/BST84168	1964	£15	£30	
Down To Earth	LP	Blue Note	BLP/BST84113	1962	£15	£30	
Good Move	LP	Blue Note	BLP/BST84158	1964	£17.50	£35	
Mo' Greens Please	LP	Blue Note	BLP/BST84128	1963	£15	£30	

ROACH, MAX

At Newport	LP	Emarcy	MMB12005	1959	£8	£20	
Best Of Max Roach & Clifford Brown In Concert	LP	Vocalion	LAE12036	1957	£15	£30	
I Remember Clifford	LP	Mercury	MMC14041	1960	£6	£15	
Jazz In 3/4 Time	LP	Emarcy	EJL1282	1958	£15	£30	
Max Roach And Clifford Brown	7" EP	Vogue	EPV1074	1956	£2	£5	
Max Roach And Clifford Brown	7" EP	Vogue	EPV1083	1956	£2	£5	
Max Roach And Clifford Brown	7" EP	Vogue	EPV1091	1956	£2	£5	
Max Roach And Clifford Brown In Concert Vol.1	10" LP	Vogue	LDE117	1955	£20	£40	
Max Roach And Clifford Brown In Concert Vol.2	10" LP	Vogue	LDE128	1955	£20	£40	sleeve pictured in Guide
Max Roach Plus Four	LP	Emarcy	MMB12009	1959	£10	£25	
Percussion Bitter Suite	LP	HMV	CLP1522	1962	£5	£12	
Quiet As It's Kept	LP	Mercury	MMC14054	1961	£8	£20	

ROAD

Road	LP	Rare Earth	SRE3006	1972	£5	£12	

ROADRUNNERS

Pantomania	7" EP	Cavern Sound	2BSNL7	1965	£12.50	£25	

ROADSTERS

Joy Ride	7"	Stateside	SS293	1964	£5	£10	

ROARING JELLY

Golden Greats	LP	Free Reed	FRR013	1976	£5	£12	

ROARING SIXTIES

The group who made a single in defence of the pirate radio stations were actually the Farinas - later to evolve into Family.

We Love The Pirates	7"	Marmalade	598001	1966	£12.50	£25	

ROBAN'S SKIFFLE GROUP

Careless Love	7"	Storyville	A45062	1962	£5	£10	
Roban's Skiffle Group	7" EP	Storyville	SEP507	195-	£7.50	£15	
Roban's Skiffle Group	7" EP	Storyville	SEP509	195-	£7.50	£15	
Roban's Skiffle Group	7" EP	Storyville	SEP511	195-	£7.50	£15	

ROBB, E.G.

Jezebel	7"	Columbia	DB7100	1963	£1.50	£4	

ROBBINS, MARTY

Ballad Of The Alamo	7"	Fontana	H270	1960	£2	£5	PS
Big Iron	7"	Fontana	H229	1959	£1.50	£4	chart single
Carl, Lefty, & Marty	10" LP	Columbia	CL2544	1956	£50	£100	US
Christmas With Marty Robbins	LP	CBS	63354	1968	£4	£10	
Devil Woman	LP	CBS	(S)BPG62113	1963	£5	£12	
Devil Woman	7"	CBS	AAG114	1962	£1.50	£4	chart single
Drifter	LP	CBS	(S)BPG62782	1966	£4	£10	
El Paso	7"	Fontana	H233	1959	£1.50	£4	chart single
Greatest Hits	LP	Columbia	CL1325	1959	£6	£15	US
Gunfighter	7" EP	Fontana	TFE17224	1960	£2.50	£6	
Gunfighter Ballads And Trail Songs	LP	Fontana	TFL5063	1959	£6	£15	
Hanging Tree	7"	Fontana	H184	1959	£2	£5	
Hawaii's Calling Me	LP	CBS	(S)BPG62169	1963	£5	£12	
Heart Of Marty Robbins	LP	Columbia	STS2016	1969	£6	£15	US
I'm Not Ready Yet	7"	CBS	AAG151	1963	£1.50	£4	
Island Woman	LP	CBS	(S)BPG62297	1964	£5	£12	
Jimmy Martinez	7"	Fontana	H324	1961	£1.50	£4	

Just A Little Sentimental	LP	Fontana	TFL5162/STFL579.	1961	£6	£15	
Just A Little Sentimental	7" EP..	CBS	AGG20004	1962	£2.50	£6	
Just A Little Sentimental Vol.2	7" EP..	CBS	AGG20013	1962	£2.50	£6	
Long Tall Sally	78	Philips	PB590	1956	£2.50	£6	
Marty After Midnight	LP	CBS	(S)BPG62041	1962	£5	£12	
Marty Robbins	LP	Columbia	CL1189	1958	£8	£20	US
Marty Robbins	7" EP..	CBS	AGG20049	1964	£2.50	£6	
Marty's Big Hits	7" EP..	Fontana	TFE17161	1959	£10	£20	
More Greatest Hits	LP	Fontana	TFL5145/STFL565.	1961	£5	£12	
More Gunfighter Ballads And Trail Songs	LP	Fontana	TFL5113/STFL541.	1961	£6	£15	
My Kind Of Country	LP	CBS	(S)BPG62962	1967	£4	£10	
Portrait Of Marty	LP	CBS	66211	1968	£5	£12	double
Portrait Of Marty	LP	Columbia	CL1855/CS8655	1962	£5	£12	US
Return Of The Gunfighter	LP	CBS	(S)BPG62190	1964	£4	£10	
R.F.D.	LP	CBS	(S)BPG62437	1965	£5	£12	
Rock'n'Roll'n'Robbins	10" LP	Columbia	CL2601	1956	£210	£350	US
Sittin' In A Tree House	7"	Fontana	H150	1958	£4	£8	
Song Of Robbins	LP	Columbia	CL2621/CS9421	1967	£4	£10	US
Song Of Robbins	LP	Columbia	CL976	1957	£10	£25	US
Song Of The Islands	LP	Columbia	CL1087	1957	£10	£25	US
Song Of The Islands	LP	Columbia	CL2625	1967	£4	£10	US
Song Of The Islands	7" EP..	Fontana	TFE17167	1959	£2.50	£6	
Stairway Of Love	7"	Fontana	H128	1958	£6	£12	
Teenagers' Dad	7"	CBS	AAG141	1963	£1.50	£4	
Tonight Carmen	LP	CBS	(S)BPG63116	1967	£4	£10	
Turn The Lights Down Low	LP	CBS	(S)BPG62499	1965	£4	£10	
Wedding Bells	7" EP..	Fontana	TFE17168	1959	£2.50	£6	
What God Has Done	LP	CBS	(S)BPG62689	1966	£4	£10	
White Sports Coat	7"	Philips	JK1019	1957	£7.50	£15	

ROBBINS, MEL

Save It	7"	London	HLM8966	1959	£100	£200	tri-centre

ROBBINS, SYLVIA

Frankie And Johnny	7"	London	HLJ9118	1960	£5	£10	

ROBBS

Robbs	LP	Mercury	MG2/SR61130	1966	£6	£15	US

ROBERTS, ANDY

Andy Roberts & The Great Stampede	LP	Elektra	K42151	1973	£5	£12	
Home Grown	LP	B&C	CAS1034	1971	£4	£10	
Home Grown	LP	RCA	SF8086	1970	£5	£12	
Nina And The Dream Tree	LP	Pegasus	PEG5	1971	£6	£15	
Urban Cowboy	LP	Elektra	K42139	1973	£5	£12	

ROBERTS, BOB

Songs From The Sailing Barges	LP	Topic	12TS361	1978	£5	£12	
Stormy Weather Boys	7" EP..	Collector	JEB6	1961	£2	£5	

ROBERTS, HOWARD

Mr.Roberts Plays Guitar	10" LP	Columbia	33C9038	1957	£6	£15	

ROBERTS, JOHN

I'll Forget About You	7"	Action	ACT4511	1968	£4	£8	
Sockin' 1,2,3,4	7"	Sue	WI4042	1967	£5	£10	

ROBERTS, KEITH

Pier Of The Realm	LP	Trailer	LER3031	1972	£6	£15	

ROBERTS, KENNY

Run Like The Devil	7"	Pye	7N17054	1966	£10	£20	

ROBERTS, KIM

I'll Prove It	7"	Decca	F11813	1964	£15	£30	

ROBERTS, PADDY

Strictly For Grown-Ups	10" LP	Decca	LF1322	1959	£4	£10	

ROBERTSON, DALE

Presents His Album Of Western Classics	LP	RCA	SF5064	1960	£4	£10	

ROBERTSON, DON

Happy Whistler	7"	Capitol	CL14575	1956	£2.50	£6	chart single

ROBERTSON, JEANNIE

Cuckoo's Nest & Other Scottish Folk Songs	LP	XTRA	XTRA5037	1968	£5	£12	
Gallowa' Hills	7" EP..	Collector	JES1	1960	£2	£5	
I Ken Where I'm Going	7" EP..	Collector	JES8	1960	£2	£5	
I Ken Where I'm Going	10" LP	Topic	10T52	1960	£8	£20	
Jeannie Robertson	LP	Topic	12T96	1963	£8	£20	
Jeannie's Merry Muse	7" EP..	HMV	7EG8534	1960	£2	£5	
Lord Donald	LP	Collector	JFS4001	1960	£8	£20	
Twa Brothers	7" EP..	Collector	JES4	1960	£2	£5	

ROBIC, IVO

Morgen	7"	Polydor	NH23923	1959	£1.50	£4	chart single

ROBIN, TINA

Everyday	7"	Vogue Coral	Q72309	1958	£2.50	£6	
Get Out Of My Life	7"	Mercury	AMT1199	1962	£1.50	£4	
Lady Fair	7"	Vogue Coral	Q72284	1957	£5	£10	
Never In A Million Years	7"	Vogue Coral	Q72294	1957	£2.50	£6	
No School Tomorrow	7"	Coral	Q72323	1958	£4	£8	

ROBINS

Cherry Lips	7"	Vogue	V9168	1960	£30	£60	
Just Like That	7"	Vogue	V9173	1960	£20	£40	
Rock'n'Roll With The Robins	LP	Whippet	WLP703	195-	£75	£150	US

ROBINS, JIMMY

I Can't Please You	7"	President	PT118	1968	£20	£40	

ROBINSON, ALVIN

Down Home Girl	7"	Red Bird	RB10010	1964	£6	£12	
Something You Got	7"	Pye	7N25248	1964	£4	£8	
You Brought My Heart Right Down	7"	Strike	JH307	1966	£5	£10	

ROBINSON, BROTHER CLEOPHUS

Negro Spirituals	7" EP	Vogue	EPV1196	1958	£5	£10	

ROBINSON, FLOYD

Floyd Robinson	LP	RCA	RD27166	1960	£10	£25	
Makin' Love	7"	RCA	RCA1146	1959	£1.50	£4	chart single

ROBINSON, HARRY XV

Heavy Date	7"	Decca	F11319	1961	£1.50	£4	

ROBINSON, JACKIE

Let The Little Girl Dance	7"	Amalgamated	AMG824	1968	£4	£8	Derrick Morgan B side
Over And Over	7"	Amalgamated	AMG819	1968	£4	£8	

ROBINSON, LLOYD

Cuss Cuss	7"	Duke	DU5	1968	£4	£8	
When You Walk	7"	Blue Beat	BB122	1962	£5	£10	
Worm	7"	Camel	CA41	1970	£2.50	£6	
You Told Me	7"	Blue Beat	BB159	1962	£5	£10	

ROBINSON, M.

Who Are You	7"	Port-O-Jam	PJ4114	1964	£5	£10	

ROBINSON, ROSCOE

That's Enough	7"	Pye	7N25385	1966	£10	£20	
That's Enough	7"	Wand	WN27	1972	£2	£5	

ROBINSON, SMOKEY & THE MIRACLES

Baby Baby Don't Cry	7"	Tamla Motown	TMG687	1969	£1.50	£4	
Greatest Hits	LP	Tamla Motown	(S)TML11072	1968	£4	£10	
I Don't Blame You At All	7"	Tamla Motown	TMG774	1971	£1.50	£4	chart single
I Second That Emotion	7"	Tamla Motown	TMG631	1967	£2	£5	chart single
If You Can Want	7"	Tamla Motown	TMG648	1968	£2	£5	chart single
I'm The One You Need	7"	Tamla Motown	TMG761	1971	£1.50	£4	chart single
Love I Saw In You Was Just A Mirage	7"	Tamla Motown	TMG598	1967	£6	£12	
Make It Happen	LP	Tamla Motown	(S)TML11067	1968	£5	£12	
More Love/Come Spy With Me	7"	Tamla Motown	TMG614	1967	£30	£60	
More Love/Swept For You Baby	7"	Tamla Motown	TMG614	1967	£4	£8	
My Girl Is Gone	7"	Tamla Motown	TMG811	1972	£1.50	£4	
Special Occasion	LP	Tamla Motown	(S)TML11089	1969	£4	£10	
Special Occasion	7"	Tamla Motown	TMG673	1968	£2	£5	chart single
Tears Of A Clown/Who's Gonna Take The Blame	7"	Tamla Motown	TMG745	1970	£1.50	£4	
Tears Of A Clown/You Must Be Love	7"	Tamla Motown	TMG745	1970	£10	£20	
Tracks Of My Tears	7"	Tamla Motown	TMG696	1969	£1.50	£4	chart single
Yester-Love	7"	Tamla Motown	TMG661	1968	£2.50	£6	

ROBINSON, SUGAR CHILE

Capitol Presents	10" LP	Capitol	LC6586	1953	£15	£30	

ROBINSON, TOM

All Right All Night	7"	EMI	EMI2946	1978	£2.50	£6	demo
Good To Be Gay	7"	Chebel	SRT/CUS015	1975	£7.50	£15	
Pre-Album Sampler	LP	Harvest	SPRO8791	1978	£6	£15	US

ROBISON, CARSON

Eight Square Dances	10" LP	MGM	D101	1952	£5	£12	
Jitterbug	7"	MGM	SP1024	1953	£5	£10	
Lady Round	7"	MGM	SP1004	1953	£2.50	£6	
Life Gets Teejus	7" EP	MGM	MGMEP669	1958	£5	£10	
Square Dance - With Calls	7" EP	MGM	MGMEP755	1961	£4	£8	

ROBSON, NICKY

Stars	7"	Scratch	SCR6	1980	£7.50	£15	
Stars	12"	Scratch	SCRT6	1980	£10	£25	

ROCCO, TONY

Keep A Walking	7"	Parlophone	R4886	1962	£4	£8	

ROCK BROTHERS

Dungaree Doll	7"	Parlophone	MSP6201	1956	£12.50	£25	

ROCK, DICKIE
Boys	7"	Piccadilly	7N35154	1963	£2	£5
Come Back To Stay	7"	Pye	7N17063	1965	£5	£10
Twenty Flight Rock	7"	Piccadilly	7N35202	1964	£2	£5

ROCK, JOHNNY
Johnny Rock	7" EP	Vogue	VE170112	1958	£2.50	£6

ROCK SHOP
Rock Shop	LP	Lee		1969	£30	£60	US

ROCK WORKSHOP
Rock Workshop	LP	CBS	64075	1970	£6	£15
Very Last Time	LP	CBS	64394	1971	£6	£15

ROCKADROME
Rockadrome	LP	private			£37.50	£75	Canadian

ROCK-A-TEENS
Woo Hoo	LP	Roulette	(S)R25109	1960	£20	£40	US
Woo Hoo	7"	Columbia	DB4361	1959	£7.50	£15	

ROCKERS
Get Cracking	7"	Oriole	CB1501	1959	£2	£5

ROCKETS
Gibraltar Rock	7"	Philips	PB982	1959	£5	£10
Warrior	7"	Zodiac	ZR0010	196-	£5	£10

ROCKETS (2)
Neil Young became friendly with The Rockets while still a member of Buffalo Springfield. When later he was looking for a permanent backing band, the Rockets were an obvious choice. Young renamed the group Crazy Horse, recording a "Requiem For The Rockets" on the first album they made together ("Everybody Knows This Is Nowhere").

Hole In My Pocket	7"	White Whale	270	1967	£6	£12	US
Rockets	LP	White Whale	S7116	1968	£8	£20	US

ROCKETS (3)
Plasteroid	LP	Rockland	RKL20137	1977	£6	£15	French pic disc

ROCKIN' BERRIES
Black Gold	LP	Satril	SATL4002	1976	£5	£12	
Dawn Go Away	7"	Pye	7N17411	1967	£2.50	£6	
Happy To Be Blue	7" EP	Piccadilly	NEP34045	1965	£7.50	£15	
He's In Town	7"	Piccadilly	7N35203	1964	£1.50	£4	chart single
He's In Town	7" EP	Pye	PNV24128	1964	£7.50	£15	French
I Could Make You Fall In Love	7"	Piccadilly	7N35304	1966	£2	£5	
I Didn't Mean To Hurt You	7"	Piccadilly	7N35197	1964	£2	£5	chart single
I Didn't Mean To Hurt You	7" EP	Piccadilly	NEP34039	1965	£6	£12	
In Town	LP	Piccadilly	NPL38013	1964	£25	£50	chart LP, sleeve pictured in Guide
Itty Bitty Pieces	7"	Decca	F11760	1963	£5	£10	
Life Is Just A Bowl Of Berries	LP	Piccadilly	NPL38022	1964	£25	£50	
Midnight Mary	7"	Piccadilly	7N35327	1966	£2.50	£6	
Mr.Blue	7"	Pye	7N17589	1968	£1.50	£4	
New From The Berries	7" EP	Piccadilly	NEP34043	1965	£6	£12	
Poor Man's Son	7"	Piccadilly	7N35236	1965	£1.50	£4	chart single
Smiles	7"	Piccadilly	7N35400	1967	£2	£5	
Sometimes	7"	Piccadilly	7N35373	1967	£2	£5	
Wah Wah Woo	7"	Decca	F11698	1963	£5	£10	
Water Is Over My Head	7"	Piccadilly	7N35270	1965	£1.50	£4	chart single
What In The World's Come Over You	7"	Piccadilly	7N35217	1965	£1.50	£4	chart single
When I Reach The Top	7"	Pye	7N17519	1968	£1.50	£4	
You're My Girl	7"	Piccadilly	7N35254	1965	£1.50	£4	chart single

ROCKIN' FOO
Rockin' Foo	LP	Stateside	SSL10303	1970	£5	£12

ROCKIN' HORSE
Yes It Is	LP	Philips	6308075	1970	£20	£40

ROCKIN' RAMRODS
Don't Fool With Fu Manchu	7"	Polydor	56512	1970	£6	£12

ROCKIN' REBELS
Rockin' Crickets	7"	Stateside	SS187	1963	£2.50	£6	
Wild Weekend	LP	Swan	SLP509	1962	£25	£50	US
Wild Weekend	7"	Stateside	SS162	1963	£2.50	£6	

ROCKIN' R'S
Crazy Baby	7"	London	HL8872	1959	£12.50	£25

ROCKIN' SAINTS
Cheat On Me Baby	7"	Brunswick	05843	1960	£20	£40

ROCKIN' STRINGS
Red Sails In The Sunset	7"	Columbia	DB4349	1959	£2	£5

ROCKIN' VICKERS
Dandy	7"	CBS	202241	1966	£10	£20
I Go Ape	7"	Decca	F11993	1964	£7.50	£15
It's Alright	7"	CBS	202051	1966	£15	£30

ROCK'N'ROLL REVIVAL SHOW
Midnight Train	7"	Decca	F12752	1968	£1.50	£4	

ROCKSTEADYS
Squeeze And Freeze	7"	Giant	GN2	1967	£4	£8	

ROCKY HORROR SHOW
Rocky Horror Box Set	LP	Pacific	RHBX1	1983	£10	£25	LP Box Set
Rocky Horror Picture Show	LP	Ode	ODE78332	1975	£5	£12	
Rocky Horror Show	LP	UK	UKAL1015	1973	£5	£12	
Rocky Horror Show (US Roxy Cast)	LP	Ode	ODE77026	1974	£5	£12	
Rocky Horror Show (US Roxy Cast)	LP	Ode	OSVP77026	1983	£5	£12	pic disc
Time Warp	7"	Ode	ODS66305	1975	£2	£5	

ROCKYFELLERS
Ching A Ling Baby	7"	Pye	7N25225	1963	£1.50	£4	
Killer Joe	LP	Scepter	SP(S)512	1963	£6	£15	US
Killer Joe	7"	Stateside	SS175	1963	£1.50	£4	
Like The Big Guys Do	7"	Stateside	SS212	1963	£1.50	£4	

ROCOMARS
All In Black Woman	7"	King	KG1031	1965	£15	£30	

ROD & THE COBRAS
At A Drag Race At Surf City	LP	Somerset	20500	1963	£5	£12	US

ROD, KEN & THE CAVALIERS
Magic Wheel	7"	Triumph	RGM1001	1960	£12.50	£25	

RODDENBERRY, GENE
Star Trek Theme	7"	CBS	4692	1976	£2	£5	

RODGERS, CLODAGH
Believe Me I'm No Fool	7"	Decca	F11534	1962	£1.50	£4	
Every Day Is Just The Same	7"	Columbia	DB7926	1966	£1.50	£4	
Mister Heartache	7"	Decca	F11812	1964	£1.50	£4	
Sometime Kind Of Love	7"	Decca	F11607	1963	£1.50	£4	
Stormy Weather	7"	Columbia	DB8038	1966	£1.50	£4	
To Give My Love To You	7"	Decca	F11667	1963	£1.50	£4	
Wanting You	7"	Columbia	DB7468	1965	£1.50	£4	

RODGERS, EILEEN
Careful, Careful	7"	Fontana	H136	1958	£2	£5	
Sailor	7"	London	HLR9271	1961	£5	£10	
Treasure Of Your Love	7"	Fontana	H156	1958	£2	£5	

RODGERS, IKE
Ike Rodgers	10" LP	London	AL3512	1954	£5	£12	

RODGERS, JIMMIE
Best Of Jimmie Rodgers	LP	RCA	LPM/LSP3315	1965	£5	£12	US
Country Music Hall Of Fame	LP	RCA	RD7505	1962	£5	£12	US
Jimmie Rodgers	7" EP.	HMV	7EG8163	1956	£10	£20	
Jimmie The Kid	LP	RCA	RD27241	1961	£5	£12	
Legendary Jimmie Rodgers	7" EP.	RCA	RCX1058	1960	£7.50	£15	
Memorial Album Vol.1	10" LP	RCA	LPT3037	1952	£10	£25	US
Memorial Album Vol.2	10" LP	RCA	LPT3038	1952	£10	£25	US
Memorial Album Vol.3	10" LP	RCA	LPT3039	1952	£10	£25	US
My Rough And Rowdy Ways	LP	RCA	RD27203	1961	£5	£12	
My Time Ain't Long	LP	RCA	RD7644	1964	£5	£12	
Never No Mo' Blues	LP	RCA	RD27138	1960	£6	£15	
Short But Brilliant Life Of Jimmie Rodgers	LP	RCA	RD7562	1963	£5	£12	
Train Whistle Blues	LP	RCA	RD27110	1959	£6	£15	
Travellin' Blues	10" LP	RCA	LPT3073	1952	£10	£25	US

RODGERS, JIMMIE (2)
Because You're Young	7"	Columbia	DB4281	1959	£1.50	£4	
Bimbombey	7"	Columbia	DB4235	1959	£1.50	£4	
Come Along Julie	7"	Columbia	DB7014	1963	£1.50	£4	
English Country Garden	7"	Columbia	DB4847	1962	£1.50	£4	chart single
English Country Garden	7" EP.	Columbia	SEG8253	1963	£2.50	£6	
English Country Garden	7" EP.	Dot	DEP20002	1965	£2	£5	
Face In A Crowd	7"	London	HLD9697	1963	£1.50	£4	
Favourites	LP	Columbia	33SX1176	1959	£4	£10	
Folk Songs And Readings	LP	Roulette	R25020	1958	£5	£12	US
Fox And The Goose	7"	Columbia	DB4904	1962	£1.50	£4	
His Golden Year	LP	Roulette	R25057	1959	£5	£12	US
Honeycomb	7"	Columbia	DB3986	1957	£6	£12	chart single
I Forgot More Than You'll Ever Know	7"	London	HLD9664	1964	£1.50	£4	
I Forgot More Than You'll Ever Know	7"	Pye	7N25253	1964	£1.50	£4	
I'm Gonna Be The Winner	7"	London	HLD9752	1963	£1.50	£4	
It's Over	7"	Dot	DS16761	1966	£1.50	£4	
Jimmie Rodgers	LP	Columbia	33SX1082	1958	£6	£15	
Jimmie Rodgers	7" EP.	Columbia	SEG7770	1958	£7.50	£15	
Jimmie Rodgers Favourites	7" EP.	Dot	DEP20007	1965	£4	£8	
Jimmie Rodgers No.2	7" EP.	Columbia	SEG7911	1959	£5	£10	
Jimmie Rodgers Sings	7" EP.	Columbia	SEG7811	1958	£5	£10	
Joshua Fit The Battle Of Jericho	7"	Columbia	DB4447	1960	£1.50	£4	
Kisses Sweeter Than Wine	7"	Columbia	DB4052	1957	£2.50	£6	chart single
Little Shepherd Of Kingdom Come	7"	Columbia	DB4617	1961	£1.50	£4	

Title	Format	Label	Catalogue	Year	Price	Price	Notes
Long Hot Summer	LP	Roulette	R25026	1958	£6	£15	US
No One Will Ever Know	7"	London	HLD9582	1962	£1.50	£4	
Number One Ballads	LP	Columbia	33SX1097	1958	£5	£12	
Oh Oh, I'm Falling In Love Again	7"	Columbia	DB4078	1958	£2.50	£6	chart single
Rhumba Boogie	7"	London	HLD9654	1963	£1.50	£4	
Secretly	7"	Columbia	DB4130	1958	£1.50	£4	
Sings Folk Songs	LP	Columbia	33SX1144	1959	£4	£10	
Soldier, Won't You Marry Me?	7"	Columbia	DB4327	1959	£1.50	£4	
Strangers	7"	Dot	DS16694	1964	£1.50	£4	
Tucumcari	7"	Columbia	DB4362	1959	£1.50	£4	
Twilight On The Trail	LP	Columbia	33SX1217/ SCX3302	1960	£4	£10	
Waltzing Matilda	7"	Columbia	DB4401	1960	£1.50	£4	
Wizard	7"	Columbia	DB4175	1958	£1.50	£4	
Woman From Liberia	7"	Columbia	DB4206	1958	£1.50	£4	chart single

ROE, TOMMY

Title	Format	Label	Catalogue	Year	Price	Price	Notes
Ballads And Beat	LP	HMV	CLP1860	1965	£6	£15	
Be A Good Girl	7"	HMV	POP1290	1964	£1.50	£4	
Come On	7"	HMV	POP1259	1963	£1.50	£4	
Diane From Manchester Square	7"	HMV	POP1386	1965	£1.50	£4	
Dizzy	LP	Stateside	(S)SL10282	1969	£5	£12	
Dizzy	7"	Stateside	SS2143	1969	£1.50	£4	chart single
Doesn't Anybody Know My Name	7"	HMV	POP1469	1965	£1.50	£4	
Don't Cry Donna	7"	HMV	POP1117	1963	£1.50	£4	
Everybody	7"	HMV	POP1207	1963	£1.50	£4	chart single
Everybody Likes Tommy Roe	LP	HMV	CLP1074	1965	£8	£20	
Folk Singer	7"	HMV	POP1138	1963	£1.50	£4	chart single
Folk Singer	7" EP	HMV	7EG8806	1963	£6	£12	
Heather Honey	7"	Stateside	SS2152	1969	£1.50	£4	chart single
Hooray For Hazel	7"	HMV	POP1556	1966	£1.50	£4	
It's Now Winter's Day	LP	ABC	(S)594	1967	£5	£12	US
It's Now Winter's Day	7"	HMV	POP1574	1967	£1.50	£4	
Jam Up Jelly Tight	7"	Stateside	SS2156	1969	£1.50	£4	
Kiss And Run	7"	HMV	POP1174	1963	£1.50	£4	
Little Miss Heartbreak	7"	HMV	POP1364	1964	£1.50	£4	
Melancholy Mood	7"	HMV	POP1611	1967	£1.50	£4	
Pearl	7"	Stateside	SS2174	1970	£1.50	£4	
Phantasy	LP	ABC	(S)610	1967	£5	£12	US
Sheila	LP	HMV	CLP1614	1963	£8	£20	
Sheila	7"	HMV	POP1060	1962	£2	£5	chart single
Something For Everybody	LP	ABC	(S)467	1964	£6	£15	US
Stir It Up And Serve It	7"	Stateside	SS2165	1970	£1.50	£4	
Susie Darlin'	7"	HMV	POP1092	1962	£1.50	£4	chart single
Sweet Pea	LP	ABC	(S)575	1966	£6	£15	US
Sweet Pea	7"	HMV	POP1539	1966	£1.50	£4	
Town Crier	7"	HMV	POP1116	1963	£5	£10	demo only

ROGERS, DEAN

Title	Format	Label	Catalogue	Year	Price	Price
Keep The Miracle Going	7"	Parlophone	R4732	1961	£1.50	£4
Timber	7"	Parlophone	R4835	1961	£1.50	£4

ROGERS, JULIE

Title	Format	Label	Catalogue	Year	Price	Price
Contrasts	LP	Mercury	20086(S)MCL	1966	£4	£10
Julie Rogers	7" EP	Mercury	10023MCE	1964	£2.50	£6
Songs Of Inspiration	LP	Mercury	20100(S)MCL	1967	£4	£10
Sound Of Julie	LP	Mercury	20048(S)MCL	1965	£4	£10
Sound Of Julie	7" EP	Mercury	10028MCE	1965	£2.50	£6

ROGERS, LINCOLN

Title	Format	Label	Catalogue	Year	Price	Price
Let Love Come Between Us	7"	Phoenix	NIX137	1973	£2	£5

ROGERS, MARK & THE MARKSMEN

Title	Format	Label	Catalogue	Year	Price	Price
Hold It	7"	Parlophone	R5045	1963	£5	£10

ROGERS, PAULINE

Title	Format	Label	Catalogue	Year	Price	Price
Spinning The Blues	7"	Columbia	SCM5106	1954	£1.50	£4

ROGERS, PIERCE & THE OVERLANDERS

Title	Format	Label	Catalogue	Year	Price	Price
Do You Still Love Me?	7"	Parlophone	R4838	1961	£1.50	£4

ROGERS, ROY

Title	Format	Label	Catalogue	Year	Price	Price	Notes
Bible Tells Me So	LP	Capitol	(S)T1745	1962	£5	£12	US
Christmas Is Always	LP	Capitol	(S)T2818	1967	£5	£12	US
Happy Trails	7" EP	HMV	7EG8182	1956	£7.50	£15	US
Hymns Of Faith	10" LP	RCA	LPT3168	1954	£8	£20	US
Jesus Loves Me	7"	Bluebird	LBY1022	1959	£5	£12	US
Roy Rogers	7" EP	HMV	7EG8145	1955	£5	£10	
Souvenir Album	10" LP	RCA	LPT3041	1952	£10	£25	US
Sweet Hour Of Prayer	LP	RCA	LPM1439	1957	£6	£15	US

ROGERS, SHORTY

Title	Format	Label	Catalogue	Year	Price	Price	Notes
Chances Are It Swings	LP	RCA	RD27149/SF5048	1960	£5	£12	
Cool And Crazy	10" LP	HMV	DLP1030	1954	£25	£50	
Courts The Count	LP	HMV	CLP1041	1955	£10	£25	
Eight Shorty Rogers Numbers	10" LP	HMV	DLP1058	1954	£25	£50	
Modern Sounds	LP	Capitol	T2025	1963	£5	£12	with Gerry Mulligan
Modern Sounds	10" LP	Capitol	LC6549	1952	£25	£50	
Shorty Rogers And His Giants	LP	London	LTZK15023	1957	£10	£25	
Shorty Rogers And His Giants	LP	London	LTZK15056	1957	£10	£25	
Shorty Rogers And His Orchestra	LP	MGM	C820	1960	£4	£10	

Title	Format	Label	Cat#	Year			Notes
Shorty Rogers And His Orchestra	7" EP..	HMV	7EG8044	1954	£2	£5	
Shorty Rogers Plays Richard Rodgers	LP	RCA	RD27018	1958	£8	£20	
Swingin' Nutcracker	LP	RCA	RD27199/SF5084	1961	£5	£12	
Way Up There	LP	London	LTZK15179	1960	£6	£15	
Wherever The Five Winds Blow	LPL	HMV	CLP1129	1957	£10	£25	

ROGERS, TIMMIE

Title	Format	Label	Cat#	Year			Notes
Back To School Again	7"	London	HLU8510	1957	£12.50	£25	
Take Me To Your Leader	7"	London	HLU8601	1958	£17.50	£35	

ROGERS, VERN & THE HI-FI'S

Title	Format	Label	Cat#	Year			Notes
Anna	7"	Oriole	CB1923	1963	£1.50	£4	
He's New To You	7"	Oriole	CB1826	1963	£1.50	£4	
I Will	7"	Oriole	CB1885	1963	£1.50	£4	
That Ain't Right	7"	Oriole	CB1785	1962	£1.50	£4	

ROGUES

Title	Format	Label	Cat#	Year			Notes
Memories Of Missy	7"	Decca	F12718	1967	£2.50	£6	
Rogue's Reef	7"	CBS	201731	1965	£4	£8	

ROHDE, JAN

Title	Format	Label	Cat#	Year			Notes
Come Back Baby	7"	Qualiton	PSP7128	1960	£1.50	£4	

ROKES

Title	Format	Label	Cat#	Year			Notes
Hold My Hand	7"	RCA	RCA1646	1967	£7.50	£15	
Let's Live For Today	7"	RCA	RCA1587	1967	£6	£12	
Let's Live For Today	7" EP..	RCA	86577	1967	£10	£20	French
Rokes	LP	RCA	SA4	196-	£20	£40	Italian
Rokes Vol.2	LP	RCA	SA8	196-	£20	£40	Italian
When The Wind Arises	7"	RCA	RCA1694	1968	£12.50	£25	

ROLAND, CHERRY

The unknown Cherry Roland was lucky enough to be chosen for the leading role in "Just For Fun". This British film, along with its predecessor "It's Trad Dad" (starring Helen Shapiro and Craig Douglas) served, in the pre-video age, as an extended promotional feature for the music of a number of new pop stars. The actual plot of the film was fairly minimal, which may be the reason for Miss Roland's failure to develop a career in pop subsequently.

Title	Format	Label	Cat#	Year			Notes
Boys	7"	Fontana	TF420	1963	£1.50	£4	
Handy Sandy	7"	Decca	F11579	1963	£1.50	£4	
Just For Fun	7"	Decca	F11648	1963	£1.50	£4	

ROLAND, JOE

Title	Format	Label	Cat#	Year			Notes
Joe Roland Quintet	LP	London	LTZN15005	1956	£8	£20	

ROLAND, PAUL

Title	Format	Label	Cat#	Year			Notes
Blades Of Battenburg	12"	Aftermath	AEP12011	1983	£2.50	£6	
Demon In A Glass Case	7"	Imaginary	MIRAGE002	1986	£1.50	£4	

ROLAND, WALTER & GEORGIA SLIM

Title	Format	Label	Cat#	Year			Notes
Male Blues Vol.1	7" EP..	Collector	JEL2	1959	£5	£10	

ROLL MOVEMENT

Title	Format	Label	Cat#	Year			Notes
I'm Out On My Own	7"	Go	AJ11410	1967	£4	£8	

ROLLERS

Title	Format	Label	Cat#	Year			Notes
Continental Walk	7"	London	HLG9340	1961	£4	£8	

ROLLING STONES

It is easily forgotten how the Rolling Stones had some of the role of tougher alter egos for the Beatles during the sixties. As the Beatles started to become more and more experimental in their approach, so the Rolling Stones did the same. When eventually the Beatles came up with "Sgt.Pepper" and "Strawberry Fields For Ever", the Rolling Stones responded with "Their Satanic Majesties Request" and "We Love You". Critics do not like these records very much, seeing them as being apart from what the Rolling Stones are all about, but they quite clearly achieve everything that psychedelic music tried to do. The death of Brian Jones, who loved to experiment with different instruments, apparently robbed the Rolling Stones of their ambition, for little of what the group has played since has extended much beyond a diet of the blues and Chuck Berry. The mono pressing of "Satanic Majesties" attracts a premium, especially in America, but for once, the mix does not actually sound any different in detail to the stereo version. The LP "Sticky Fingers", with its Andy Warhol zip cover, just scrapes into the collectors' list - this was not a limited edition and is very much more common than some people believe. Bootleg copies of the notorious "Cocksucker Blues", recorded to fulfill the Stones' Decca contract, have long been available. The German Teldec boxed set is remarkable, however, for including a copy of the single as a bonus, issued for the first and only time as an official release.

Title	Format	Label	Cat#	Year			Notes
12 X 5	LP	London	LL3402	1964	£8	£20	US
12 X 5	LP	London	LL3402	1964	£700	£1000	US, blue vinyl
19th Nervous Breakdown	7"	Decca	F12331	1966	£2	£5	chart single
19th Nervous Breakdown	7"	Decca	F12331	1966	£12.50	£25	export, Dutch PS
19th Nervous Breakdown	7" EP..	Decca	450206	1966	£40	£80	French
2000 Light Years From Home	7"	Decca	F22706	1967	£10	£20	export
Aftermath	LP	Decca	LK/SKL4786	1966	£10	£25	chart LP
Aftermath	LP	London	LL3476	1966	£8	£20	US
Angie	7"	Rolling Stones.	RS19105	1973	£1.50	£4	chart single
Around And Around	LP	Decca	SLK16315P	1965	£15	£30	German
As Tears Go By	7" EP..	Decca	457104	1966	£7.50	£15	French
Beggar's Banquet	LP	Decca	LK4955	1968	£15	£30	mono
Beggar's Banquet	LP	Decca	SKL4955	1968	£5	£12	chart LP
Between The Buttons	LP	Decca	6835207		£8	£20	Dutch, yellow vinyl
Between The Buttons	LP	Decca	LK/SKL4852	1967	£8	£20	chart LP
Between The Buttons	LP	London	LL3499	1967	£8	£20	US
Brown Sugar	7"	Atlantic	K19107	1974	£7.50	£15	
Brown Sugar	7"	Rolling Stones.	RS19100	1971	£1.50	£4	chart single
Brown Sugar	7"	Rolling Stones.	RS19100	1971	£5	£12	PS
Brown Sugar	7"	Rolling Stones.	SUGARP1	1984	£5	£10	shaped pic disc
Carol	7" EP..	Decca	457036	1964	£7.50	£15	French
Come On	7"	Decca	F11675	1963	£4	£8	chart single
Con Le Mie La Crime	7"	Decca	F22270	1965	£15	£30	sung in Italian

Title	Format	Label	Cat. No.	Year	Price	Price	Notes
Could You Walk On The Waters	LP	Decca		1966	£150	£250	
December's Children	LP	London	LL3451	1965	£8	£20	US
Ed Rudy Interview Album	LP	INS Radio	1003	1965	£25	£50	US
Emotional Rescue	7"	Rolling Stones.		1980	£2	£5	interview promo, blue flexi
Empty Heart	7"	Decca	AT15035	1964	£40	£80	export
Exile On Main Street	LP	Rolling Stones.	COC69100	1972	£6	£15	double, with postcards, chart LP
Fan Club Single	7"	Rolling Stones.	R8370/1	1983	£2	£5	interview disc
First Eight Studio Albums	LP	Decca	ROLL1	1983	£40	£80	8 LPs, book, boxed
Five By Five	7" EP.	Decca	DFE8590	1964	£2.50	£6	
Flowers	LP	Decca	LK/SKL4888	1967	£30	£60	export, sleeve pictured in Guide
Flowers	LP	Decca	SKL4888	197-	£15	£30	boxed Decca logo
Flowers	LP	London	LL3509	1967	£8	£20	
Get Off My Cloud	7"	Decca	F12263	1965	£2	£5	chart single, demo pictured in Guide
Get Off My Cloud	7"	Decca	F22265	1965	£10	£20	export
Get Off My Cloud	7"	Decca	F22265	1965	£20	£40	export, PS
Get Off My Cloud	7" EP.	Decca	457092	1965	£7.50	£15	French
Get Off My Cloud	7" EP.	Decca	457092	1965	£40	£80	French, PS on stage at Olympia
Get Yer Ya-Ya's Out	LP	Decca	SKL5065	1970	£5	£12	chart LP
Gimme Shelter	LP	Decca	SKL5101	1971	£4	£10	
Golden B Sides	LP	Decca	SKL5165	1973	£100	£200	test pressing only
Got Live If You Want It	LP	London	LL3493	1966	£8	£20	US
Got Live If You Want It	7" EP.	Decca	457081	1965	£6	£12	French
Got Live If You Want It	7" EP.	Decca	DFE8620	1965	£2.50	£6	
Got Live If You Want It	7" EP.	Decca	DFE8620	1965	£25	£50	export, red label
Got Live If You Want It	7" EP.	Decca	SDE7502	1965	£20	£40	export
Great Years	LP	Reader's Digest		1983	£15	£30	5 LPs, boxed
Greatest Hits	LP	RCA	SP0268	1972	£15	£30	US
Happy	7"	Rolling Stones.	SAM4	1971	£10	£20	promo
Have You Seen Your Mother Baby	7"	Decca	F12497	1966	£2	£5	chart single
Have You Seen Your Mother Live!	LP	Decca	SKL4838	197-	£15	£30	boxed Decca logo
Have You Seen Your Mother, Live	LP	Decca	LK/SKL4838	1966	£30	£60	export
Heart Of Stone	7"	Decca	F22180	1965	£10	£20	export
Heart Of Stone	7"	Decca	F22180	1965	£20	£40	export, PS
Heart Of Stone	7" EP.	Decca	457066	1965	£7.50	£15	French
Hightide And Green Grass	LP	Decca	TXL/TXS101	1966	£6	£15	chart LP, pic booklet
Hightide And Green Grass	LP	London	NP1	1966	£8	£20	US
Hits Live	LP	Decca	SKL4495	1965	£75	£150	export promo
Honky Tonk Women	7"	Decca	F12952	1969	£1.50	£4	chart single
Honky Tonk Women	7"	Decca	F12952	1969	£12.50	£25	export, PS
Hot Stuff	12"	Rolling Stones.		1976	£8	£20	promo, black & blue vinyl
Hot Stuff	12"	Rolling Stones.		1976	£10	£25	promo, clear vinyl
I Don't Know Why	7"	Decca	F13584	1975	£6	£12	Jagger/Richard writing credit
I Don't Know Why	7"	Decca	F13584	1975	£4	£8	Stevie Wonder writing credit
I Wanna Be Your Man	7"	Decca	AT15005	1963	£10	£20	export
I Wanna Be Your Man	7"	Decca	F11764	1963	£2.50	£6	chart single
I Wanna Be Your Man	7" EP.	Decca	457026	1963	£20	£40	French, PS with 4 titles listed
I Wanna Be Your Man	7" EP.	Decca	457026	1963	£12.50	£25	French, PS with main title only
I Wanna Be Your Man/Stones	7"	Decca	F11764	1963	£6	£12	
If You Need Me	7" EP.	Decca	457043	1964	£6	£12	French
Interview With Mick Jagger By Tom Donahue	LP	Rolling Stones.	PR164	1971	£15	£30	US promo
It's All Over Now	7"	Decca	F11934	1964	£2	£5	chart single
It's All Over Now	7"	Decca	F13517	1974	£40	£80	
It's All Over Now	7" EP.	Decca	457039	1964	£7.50	£15	French
It's Only Rock'n'Roll	7"	Rolling Stones.	RS19114	1974	£1.50	£4	chart single
Jumpin' Jack Flash	7"	Decca	F12782	1968	£1.50	£4	chart single
Last Time	7"	Decca	F12104	1965	£2	£5	chart single
Last Time	7"	Decca	F12104	1965	£15	£30	export, Dutch PS
Let It Bleed	LP	Decca	LK5025	1969	£15	£30	mono
Let It Bleed	LP	Decca	LK5025	1969	£17.50	£35	mono, with sticker and poster
Let It Bleed	LP	Decca	SKL5025	1969	£5	£12	with inner sleeve, chart LP
Let It Bleed	LP	Decca	SKL5025	1969	£10	£25	with sticker, inner sleeve and poster
Let's Spend The Night Together	7"	Decca	F12546	1967	£2	£5	chart single
Let's Spend The Night Together	7"	Decca	F12546	1967	£15	£30	export, PS
Little Queenie	7"	Decca	F13126	1971	£7.50	£15	export
Little Queenie	7"	Decca	F13126	1971	£15	£30	export, PS
Little Red Rooster	7"	Decca	AT15040	1965	£40	£80	export
Little Red Rooster	7"	Decca	F12014	1964	£2	£5	chart single
Miss You	12"	Rolling Stones.	12EMI2802	1978	£2.50	£6	pink vinyl
Mother's Little Helper	7" EP.	Decca	457122	1966	£7.50	£15	French
Not Fade Away	7"	Decca	AT15008	1964	£10	£20	export
Not Fade Away	7"	Decca	F11845	1964	£2	£5	chart single
Not Fade Away	7" EP.	Decca	457031	1964	£12.50	£25	French

Title	Format	Label	Catalogue	Year			Notes
Out Of Our Heads	LP	Decca	LK/SKL4725	1965	£35	£70	export, US format
Out Of Our Heads	LP	Decca	LK/SKL4733	1965	£10	£25	chart LP
Out Of Our Heads	LP	Decca	SKL4733	196-	£5	£12	boxed Decca logo
Out Of Our Heads	LP	London	LL3429	1965	£8	£20	US
Out Of Time	7"	Decca	F13597	1975	£1.50	£4	chart single
Paint It Black	7"	Decca	F12395	1966	£2	£5	chart single
Poison Ivy	7"	Decca	F11742	1963	£100	£200	
Promotional LP	LP	Decca	RSM1	1969	£330	£500	promo compilation
Rest Of The Best Of The Rolling Stones	LP	Teldec	630125FX	1984	£50	£100	4 LPs, boxed, with 7", German
Rock And A Hard Place	CD-s	Rolling Stones	RSR6554482	1989	£8	£20	boxed with poster
Rock And A Hard Place	CD-s	Rolling Stones	RSR6554485	1989	£8	£20	tongue-shaped sleeve
Rocks Off	7"	Rolling Stones	SAM3	1971	£10	£20	promo
Rolling Stones	LP	Decca	LK4605	196-	£5	£12	red label, no flaps on rear sleeve
Rolling Stones	LP	Decca	LK4605	1964	£10	£25	chart LP
Rolling Stones	LP	Decca	LK4605	1964	£20	£40	with 2.52 version of Tell Me
Rolling Stones	LP	London	LL3375	1964	£8	£20	US
Rolling Stones	LP	London	LL3375	1964	£50	£100	US, maroon label, 'London/ffrr' in box, bonus photo - advertised
Rolling Stones	7" EP	Decca	DFE8560	1964	£2.50	£6	
Rolling Stones	7" EP	Decca	SDE7260	1964	£25	£50	export
Rolling Stones	7" EP	Decca	SDE7503	1966	£40	£80	export
Rolling Stones No.2	LP	Decca	LK4661	1965	£10	£25	chart LP
Rolling Stones No.2	LP	Decca	LK4661	1965	£5	£12	red label, no flaps on rear sleeve
Rolling Stones Now!	LP	London	LL3420	1965	£8	£20	US
Rolling Stones Vol.2	7" EP	Decca	SDE7501	1964	£20	£40	export
Sad Day	7"	Decca	F13404	1973	£2	£5	
Satisfaction	7"	Decca	AT15043	1965	£40	£80	export, PS
Satisfaction	7"	Decca	F12220	1965	£2	£5	chart single
Satisfaction	7" EP	Decca	457086	1965	£7.50	£15	French, B.Jones in centre of group pic
Satisfaction	7" EP	Decca	457086	1965	£40	£80	French, K.Richard in centre of group pic
Satisfaction/Under Assistant West Coast...	7"	Decca	F12220	1965	£7.50	£15	export
Satisfation/Under Assistant West Coast...	7"	Decca	F12220	1965	£15	£30	export, PS
She Was Hot	7"	Rolling Stones	RSRP114	1984	£5	£10	shaped pic disc
Single Stones	7"	Decca	STONE1-12	1981	£20	£40	mail order box set with poster & badge
Some Girls	LP	Decca	DC2	1978	£8	£20	French, red vinyl
Some Girls	LP	Mobile Fidelity	MFSL1087	1982	£6	£15	US audiophile
Songs Of The Rolling Stones	LP	ABKCO	MPD1	1973	£50	£100	US promo
Songs Of The Rolling Stones Vol.2	LP	ABKCO		197-	£50	£100	US promo
Sticky Fingers	LP	Mobile Fidelity	MFSL1060	1980	£8	£20	US audiophile
Sticky Fingers	LP	Rolling Stones	COC59100	1971	£4	£10	insert, chart LP
Still Life	LP	Rolling Stones	CUNP39115	1982	£5	£12	pic disc
Stones On CD	CD	CBS	SAMP1103	198-	£40	£80	promo
Street Fighting Man	7"	Decca	F13195	1971	£1.50	£4	chart single
Street Fighting Man	7"	Decca	F13195	1971	£12.50	£25	export, PS
Street Fighting Man	7"	Decca	F13203	1971	£6	£12	
Street Fighting Man	7"	Decca	F13204	1971	£7.50	£15	export
Street Fighting Man	7"	Decca	F13204	1971	£15	£30	export, PS
Street Fighting Man	7"	Decca	F22825	1968	£12.50	£25	export, PS
Tell Me	7"	Decca	AT15032	1964	£40	£80	export
Terrifying	CD-s	Rolling Stones	RSR6551225	1990	£8	£20	in tin
Their Satanic Majesties Request	LP	Decca	TXL103	1967	£15	£30	3D Cover, mono
Their Satanic Majesties Request	LP	Decca	TXS103	1967	£10	£25	3D cover, chart LP
Their Satanic Majesties Request	LP	Decca	TXS103	198-	£6	£15	reissue with 3D sleeve
Their Satanic Majesties Request	LP	London	NP2	1967	£37.50	£75	US, mono
Through The Past Darkly	LP	Decca	LK5019	1969	£8	£20	octagonal Cover, mono
Through The Past Darkly	LP	Decca	SKL5019	1969	£6	£15	octagonal cover, chart LP
Time Is On My Side	7"	Decca	AT15039	1965	£40	£80	export
Time Is On My Side	7" EP	Decca	457050	1964	£7.50	£15	French
Trident Mixes	LP	ABKCO	PR164	197-	£330	£500	US promo double
Tumbling Dice	7"	Rolling Stones	RS19103	1972	£1.50	£4	chart single
We Love You	7"	Decca	F12654	1967	£2	£5	chart single
We Love You	7"	Decca	F12654	1967	£15	£30	export, PS

ROLLING STONES & OTHERS

Title	Format	Label	Catalogue	Year			Notes
Jamming With Edward	LP	Rolling Stones	COC39100	1972	£4	£10	

ROLLINS, SONNY

Title	Format	Label	Catalogue	Year			Notes
Alfie	LP	HMV	CLP/CSD3529	1967	£4	£10	
At Music Inn	LP	MGM	C818	1960	£8	£20	side 2 by Teddy Edwards
Blow!	LP	Fontana	FJL124	1965	£5	£12	
Bridge	LP	RCA	RD/SF7504	1962	£6	£15	
East Broadway Rundown	LP	HMV	CLP/CSD3610	1967	£4	£10	
Freedom Suite	LP	Riverside	RLP12258	1962	£8	£20	
Movin' Out	LP	Esquire	32155	1962	£8	£20	
Newk's Time	LP	Blue Note	BLP/BST84001	1964	£10	£25	
Night At The Village Vanguard	LP	Blue Note	BLP/BST81581	1964	£10	£25	

Title	Format	Label	Catalogue	Year			Notes
Now's The Time	LP	RCA	RD7670	1965	£6	£15	
On Impulse	LP	HMV	CLP1915	1966	£5	£12	
Our Man In Jazz	LP	RCA	RD/SF7546	1963	£5	£12	
Perspectives	LP	Esquire	32035	1957	£10	£25	with MJQ
Rollins And Brownie	7" EP	Esquire	EP238	1961	£2	£5	with Clifford Brown
Saint Thomas	7" EP	Esquire	EP248	1962	£2	£5	
Saxophone Colossus	LP	Esquire	32045	1958	£10	£25	
Saxophone Colossus	LP	Stateside	SL10164	1966	£4	£10	
Sonny Boy	LP	Esquire	32175	1963	£6	£15	
Sonny Meets Hawk	LP	RCA	RD/SF7593	1964	£8	£20	with Coleman Hawkins
Sonny Rollins	LP	Blue Note	BLP/BST81542	1961	£10	£25	
Sonny Rollins & Co.	LP	RCA	RD/SF7626	1964	£5	£12	
Sonny Rollins And The Big Brass	LP	MGM	C776	1959	£8	£20	
Sonny Rollins And The Contemporary Leaders	LP	Contemporary	LAC12213	1960	£8	£20	
Sonny Rollins And The Contemporary Leaders	LP	Contemporary	SCA5013	1960	£8	£20	
Sonny Rollins And The Modern Jazz Quartet	7" EP	Esquire	EP94	195-	£2	£5	
Sonny Rollins Plus Four	LP	Esquire	32025	1957	£10	£25	
Sonny Rollins Quartet	LP	Esquire	32038	1958	£10	£25	
Sonny Rollins Quartet	10" LP	Esquire	20050	1955	£25	£50	
Sonny Rollins Quintet	LP	Esquire	32075	1959	£10	£25	
Sonny Rollins Quintet	10" LP	Esquire	20080	1957	£25	£50	
Sonny Rollins Vol.2	LP	Blue Note	BLP/BST81558	1961	£10	£25	
Sonny Rollins With Thelonious Monk	7" EP	Esquire	EP148	1957	£2	£5	
Sound Of Sonny	LP	Riverside	RLP12241	1961	£8	£20	
Standard Sonny Rollins	LP	RCA	RD/SF7736	1967	£4	£10	
Tenor Madness	LP	Esquire	32058	1958	£10	£25	
Tour De Force	LP	Esquire	32085	1959	£10	£25	
Valse Hot	7" EP	Esquire	EP228	1960	£2	£5	
Wailing Mr.Rollins	7" EP	Esquire	EP198	1958	£2	£5	
Way Out West	LP	Contemporary	LAC12118	1958	£8	£20	
What's New	LP	RCA	RD/SF7524	1963	£5	£12	

ROMAN, MARK

Title	Format	Label	Catalogue	Year			Notes
Cuddly Toy	7"	Columbia	DB8360	1968	£1.50	£4	

ROMAN, MIMI

Title	Format	Label	Catalogue	Year			Notes
Johnny Will	7"	Warner Bros	WB55	1962	£1.50	£4	

ROMAN, MURRAY

Title	Format	Label	Catalogue	Year			Notes
Blind Man's Movie	LP	Track	613015	1969	£5	£12	
You Can't Beat People Up...	LP	Track	613007	1969	£5	£12	

ROMAN, RON

"Love Of My Life" was written by Frank Zappa and was later recorded by him on the LP "Cruising With Ruben And The Jets".

Title	Format	Label	Catalogue	Year			Notes
Love Of My Life	7"	Daani	101	1963	£30	£60	US

ROMAN, TONY

Title	Format	Label	Catalogue	Year			Notes
Shadows On A Foggy Day	7" EP	Festival	CEP19101	196-	£6	£12	French

ROMEO, MAX

Title	Format	Label	Catalogue	Year			Notes
Belly Woman	7"	Unity	UN507	1969	£2.50	£6	Paulett & The Lovers B side
Blowing In The Wind	7"	Nu Beat	NB022	1969	£4	£8	Larry Marshall B side
Clap Clap	7"	Unity	UN545	1969	£2.50	£6	
Don't Want To Let You Go	7"	Caltone	TONE106	1967	£4	£8	
Dream	LP	Pama	PMLP11	1969	£8	£20	
It's Not The Way	7"	Blue Cat	BS163	1969	£4	£8	Al Reid B side
Let The Power Fall	LP	Pama	PMP2010	1971	£8	£20	
Me Want Man	7"	Blue Cat	BS161	1969	£4	£8	
Put Me In The Mood	7"	Island	WI3104	1968	£5	£10	
Sweet Chariot	7"	Trojan	TR656	1969	£2.50	£6	
Twelfth Of Never	7"	Island	WI3124	1967	£5	£10	Val Bennett B side
Twelfth Of Never	7"	Unity	UN511	1969	£2.50	£6	Tartons B side
Walk Into The Room	7"	Island	WI3111	1968	£5	£10	Dawn Penn B side
War In A Babylon	7"	Island	WIP6283	1976	£1.50	£4	
Wet Dream	7"	Unity	UN503	1969	£1.50	£4	chart single
Wine Her Goosie	7"	Unity	UN516	1969	£2.50	£6	King Cannon B side

ROMEOS

Title	Format	Label	Catalogue	Year			Notes
Precious Memories	LP	Mark II	1001	1967	£5	£12	US

ROMERO, CHAN

Title	Format	Label	Catalogue	Year			Notes
Hippy Hippy Shake	7"	Columbia	DB4341	1959	£20	£40	
My Little Ruby	7"	Columbia	DB4405	1960	£25	£50	

ROMNEY, HUGH 'WAVY GRAVY'

Title	Format	Label	Catalogue	Year			Notes
Third Stream Humor	LP	World Pacific	WP1805	1962	£6	£15	US

RONALD & RUBY

Title	Format	Label	Catalogue	Year			Notes
Lollipop	7"	RCA	RCA1053	1958	£5	£10	

RONALDE, RONNIE

Title	Format	Label	Catalogue	Year			Notes
Ave Maria	7"	Columbia	SCM5141	1954	£1.50	£4	
Ballad Of Davy Crockett	7"	Columbia	SCM5214	1956	£2.50	£6	
Christmastide	7"	Columbia	SCM5205	1955	£1.50	£4	
Happy Whistler	7"	Columbia	SCM5275	1956	£1.50	£4	
In A Monastery Garden	7"	Columbia	SCM5007	1953	£2.50	£6	

My Starlight Lullaby	7"	Columbia	SCM5116	1954	£1.50	£4	
Robin Hood	7"	Columbia	SCM5241	1956	£2.50	£6	
Song Of The Mountains	7"	Columbia	SCM5006	1953	£2.50	£6	
We'll Always Remember	7"	Columbia	SCM5101	1954	£1.50	£4	
Yarmouth Song	7"	Columbia	SCM5262	1956	£1.50	£4	

RONDELLS
Backbeat Number One	7"	London	HLU9404	1961	£6	£12	
Good Good	7"	London	HLU8716	1958	£15	£30	

RONDO, DON
Blonde Bombshell	7"	London	HLJ8641	1958	£2	£5	
City Lights	7"	London	HLJ8749	1958	£1.50	£4	
Don't	7"	Columbia	DB3909	1957	£1.50	£4	
Dormi, Dormi, Dormi	7"	London	HLJ8695	1958	£1.50	£4	
I've Got Bells On My Heart	7"	London	HLJ8610	1958	£2	£5	
King Of Holiday Island	7"	London	HLL9217	1960	£1.50	£4	
Rondo Part One	7" EP.	London	REJ1154	1958	£4	£8	
Rondo Part Two	7" EP.	London	REJ1155	1958	£4	£8	
Song From The Geisha Boy	7"	London	HLJ8808	1959	£1.50	£4	
Two Different Worlds	7"	Columbia	DB3854	1956	£1.50	£4	
What A Shame	7"	London	HLJ8567	1958	£2	£5	
White Silver Sands	7"	London	HLJ8466	1957	£2	£5	

RONDO, GENE
Ben Nevis	7"	Giant	GN39	1968	£4	£8	

RONETTES
Baby I Love You	7"	London	HLU9826	1964	£2.50	£6	chart single
Be My Baby	7"	London	HLU9793	1963	£2.50	£6	chart single
Best Part Of Breaking Up	7"	London	HLU9905	1964	£4	£8	chart single
Born To Be Together	7"	London	HLU9952	1965	£4	£8	
Do I Love You	7"	London	HLU9922	1964	£2.50	£6	chart single
Good Girls	7"	May	138	1962	£12.50	£25	US
He Did It	7"	Dimension	1046	1964	£15	£30	US
I Can Hear Music	7"	London	HLU10087	1966	£12.50	£25	
I'm Gonna Quit While I'm Ahead	7"	Colpix	646	1962	£7.50	£15	US
Is This What I Get For Loving You	7"	London	HLU9976	1965	£4	£8	
Presenting The Fabulous Ronettes	LP	London	HAU8212	1964	£15	£30	black label
Presenting The Fabulous Ronettes	LP	London	HAU8212	1964	£35	£70	plum label
Presenting The Fabulous Ronettes	LP	Philles	PHLP4006	1964	£35	£70	US, mono
Presenting The Fabulous Ronettes	LP	Philles	PHLPST4006	1964	£50	£100	US, stereo
Ronettes	LP	Colpix	PXL486	1965	£25	£50	sleeve pictured in Guide
Silhouettes	7"	May	114	1962	£12.50	£25	US
Walking In The Rain	7"	London	HLU9931	1964	£2.50	£6	
You Came You Saw You Conquered	7"	A&M	AMS748	1969	£1.50	£4	

RONNIE & ROY
Big Fat Sally	7"	Capitol	CL15028	1959	£30	£60	

RONNIE & THE DEL AIRES
Drag	7"	Coral	Q72473	1964	£2.50	£6	

RONNIE & THE HI-LITES
Twistin' And Kissin'	7"	Pye	7N25140	1962	£4	£8	

RONNIE & THE POMONA CASUALS
Interest in this group revolves around the fact that Arthur Lee sang lead vocal on the track "Slow Jerk", which was also written by him. The music, however, bears no resemblance to that of any of the incarnations of Lee's better-known group - Love.
Everybody Jerk	LP	Donna	2112	1965	£25	£50	US
Slow Jerk	7"	Donna	1405	1965	£12.50	£25	US

RONNIE & THE RAINBOWS
Loose Ends	7"	London	HL9345	1961	£2.50	£6	

RONNIE & THE RELATIVES
After making these two singles, the group shortened their name to the Ronettes.
I'm Gonna Quit While I'm Ahead	7"	May	111	1962	£12.50	£25	US
Sweet Sixteen	7"	Colpix	481	1961	£12.50	£25	US

RONNO
The single credited to Ronno was recorded by the musicians who featured on David Bowie's "Ziggy Stardust" album (led by much-missed guitarist Mick Ronson), with the former singer from the Rats, Benny Marshall.
Fourth Hour Of My Sleep	7"	Vertigo	6059029	1970	£10	£20	

RONNY & THE DAYTONAS
Beach Boy	7"	Stateside	SS432	1965	£4	£8	
Bucket T	7"	Stateside	SS391	1965	£4	£8	
Bucket T	7" EP.	Columbia	ESRF1641	1964	£7.50	£15	French
California Bound	7"	Stateside	SS367	1964	£2.50	£6	
GTO	LP	Mala	4001	1964	£10	£25	US
GTO	7"	Stateside	SS333	1964	£4	£8	
Sandy	LP	Mala	4002(S)	1964	£10	£25	US
Sandy	7"	Stateside	SS484	1966	£4	£8	

RONSON, MICK
Play Don't Worry	LP	RCA	APL10681	1975	£4	£10	chart LP
Slaughter On Tenth Avenue	LP	RCA	APL10353	1974	£4	£10	chart LP

ROOFTOP SINGERS

Mama Don't Allow It	7"	Fontana	TF411	1963	£1.50	£4	
Tom Cat	7"	Fontana	271702TF	1963	£1.50	£4	
Walk Right In	LP	Fontana	680999TL	1963	£4	£10	
Walk Right In	7"	Fontana	271700TF	1963	£1.50	£4	chart single

ROOM

Pre-Flight	LP	Deram	SML1073	1970	£90	£180	

ROOM 13

Murder Mystery	12"	Woronzow	WOO2	1982	£8	£20	

ROOM TEN

I Love My Love	7"	Decca	F12249	1965	£1.50	£4	

ROOT BOYS

Please Don't Stop The Wedding	7"	Columbia	DB115	1970	£4	£8	

ROSA, LISA

Mama He Treats Your Daughter Mean	7"	Ember	EMBS168	1963	£2	£5	

ROSANO, ROSITA

Queer Things	7"	Melodisc	1436	1957	£1.50	£4	

ROSE, ANDY

Just Young	7"	London	HLU8761	1958	£7.50	£15	

ROSE, DAVID ORCHESTRA

Stripper	7"	MGM	MGM1158	1962	£1.50	£4	

ROSE, DUSTY

Birds And The Bees	7"	London	HLU8162	1955	£20	£40	
Country Songs	7" EP	London	REU1078	1957	£20	£40	

ROSE GARDEN

Next Plane To London	7"	Atlantic	584163	1968	£2	£5	
Rose Garden	LP	Atco	SD33225	1968	£6	£15	US

ROSE, JOHNNY

Linda Lea	7"	Capitol	CL15166	1960	£1.50	£4	

ROSE OF AVALANCHE

L.A. Rain	12"	L.I.L.	12LIL1	1985	£2.50	£6	

ROSE, TIM

I Guess It's Over	7"	CBS	3478	1968	£1.50	£4	
Love - A Kind Of Hate Story	LP	Capitol	673	1970	£6	£15	US
Morning Dew	7"	CBS	202631	1967	£2.50	£6	
Musician	LP	Atlantic	K50183	1975	£5	£12	
Roanoke	7"	CBS	4209	1969	£1.50	£4	
Through Rose Coloured Glasses	LP	CBS	63636	1969	£6	£15	
Tim Rose	LP	CBS	(S)BPG63168	1967	£8	£20	
Tim Rose	LP	Dawn	DNLS3062	1974	£6	£12	
Tim Rose	LP	Playboy	101	1972	£6	£15	US

ROSE, TONY

On Banks Of Green Willow	LP	Trailer	LER2101	1976	£5	£12	
Under The Greenwood Tree	LP	Trailer	LER2024	1971	£5	£12	
Young Hunting	LP	Trailer	LER2013	1970	£6	£15	

ROSENMAN, LEONARD

Lord Of The Rings	LP	Fantasy	LORPD2	1978	£8	£20	US double pic disc

ROSIE

Lonely Blue Nights	7"	Coral	Q72426	1961	£4	£8	

ROSIE & THE ORIGINALS

Angel Baby	7"	London	HLU9266	1961	£12.50	£25	

ROSOLINO, FRANK

I Play Trombone	LP	London	LTZN15067	1957	£8	£20	
That Old Black Magic	7"	Capitol	KC65001	1954	£1.50	£4	

ROSS, ANNIE

Annie By Candlelight	10" LP	Nixa	NJT504	1957	£8	£20	
Fish	LP	Decca	F10514	1955	£2.50	£6	
Gasser	LP	Vogue	LAE12233	1960	£8	£20	with Zoot Sims
Go To The Wall	7" EP	Transatlantic	TRAEP112	1964	£2	£5	
Nocturne For Vocalist	7" EP	Pye	NJE1035	1957	£2	£5	
Only You	7"	Decca	F10680	1956	£2	£5	
Sings A Song With Mulligan	LP	Vogue	LAE12203	1959	£8	£20	with Gerry Mulligan
With The Teacho Wiltshire Group	7" EP	Esquire	EP1	1954	£2	£5	
With The Tony Crombie Fourtet	7" EP	Pieces Of Eight	PEP604	195-	£2	£5	
With The Tony Kinsey Quintet	LP	XTRA	XTRA1049	1966	£4	£10	

ROSS, ANNIE & PONY POINDEXTER

Annie Ross And Pony Poindexter	LP	Polydor	583711	1968	£5	£12	

ROSS, DAVE

Everybody's Got A Girl But Tino	7"	Oriole	CB1416	1958	£1.50	£4	

ROSS, DIANA

Ain't No Mountain High Enough	7"	Tamla Motown	TMG751	1970	£1.50	£4	chart single
Theme From Mahogany	7"	Tamla Motown	TMG1010	1976	£4	£8	demo, PS

ROSS, DIANA & THE SUPREMES

Forever Came Today	7"	Tamla Motown	TMG650	1968	£2	£5	chart single
I'm Living In Shame	7"	Tamla Motown	TMG695	1969	£2	£5	chart single
In And Out of Love	7"	Tamla Motown	TMG632	1967	£2	£5	chart single
Live At The Talk Of The Town	LP	Tamla Motown	(S)TML11070	1968	£5	£12	chart LP
Love Child	LP	Tamla Motown	(S)TML11095	1969	£4	£10	chart LP
Love Child	7"	Tamla Motown	TMG677	1968	£1.50	£4	chart single
No Matter What Sign You Are	7"	Tamla Motown	TMG704	1969	£1.50	£4	chart single
Reflections	LP	Tamla Motown	(S)TML11073	1968	£5	£12	chart LP
Reflections	7"	Tamla Motown	TMG616	1967	£2	£5	chart single
Sing And Perform Funny Girl	LP	Tamla Motown	(S)TML11088	1969	£4	£10	
Some Day We'll Be Together	7"	Tamla Motown	TMG721	1969	£1.50	£4	chart single
Some Things You Never Get Used To	7"	Tamla Motown	TMG662	1968	£2	£5	chart single

ROSS, DIANA & THE SUPREMES & THE TEMPTATIONS

I Second That Emotion	7"	Tamla Motown	TMG709	1969	£1.50	£4	chart single
I'm Gonna Make You Love Me	7"	Tamla Motown	TMG685	1969	£1.50	£4	chart single
Why	7"	Tamla Motown	TMG730	1970	£1.50	£4	

ROSS, DR.ISAIAH

Call The Doctor	LP	Bounty	BY6020	1966	£6	£15	
Doctor Ross	LP	XTRA	XTRA1038	1966	£8	£20	
Flying Eagle	LP	Blue Horizon	LP1	1966	£400	£600	
Live At Montreux	LP	Polydor	2460169	1972	£4	£10	

ROSS, GENE

Endless Sleep	7"	Parlophone	R4434	1958	£7.50	£15	

ROSS, JACKIE

Jerk And Twine	7"	Chess	CRS8003	1965	£5	£10	
Selfish One	7"	Pye	7N25259	1964	£10	£20	

ROSS, RONNIE

Double Event	LP	Parlophone	PMC1079	1959	£8	£20	

ROSSELSON, LEON

Palaces Of Gold	LP	Acorn	CF249	197-	£8	£20	

ROSSELSON, LEON & ADRIAN MITCHELL

Laugh, A Song, And A Hand Grenade	LP	Transatlantic	TRA171	1968	£6	£15	

ROSSELSON, LEON & ROY BAILEY

That's Not The Way It's Got To Be	LP	Acorn	CF251	1975	£5	£12	

ROSSELSON, LEON, ROY BAILEY, MARTIN CARTHY

Word Is Hugga Mugga Chugga Humbugga Boom Chit	LP	Trailer	LER3015	1971	£5	£12	

ROSSI & SCOTT

Jealousy	12"	Vertigo	VERX24	1985	£2.50	£6	
Modern Romance	12"	Vertigo	VERX17	1985	£3	£8	

ROSSI, NITA

Daddy Christmas Song	7"	Piccadilly	7N35354	1966	£1.50	£4	
Here I Go Again	7"	Piccadilly	7N35307	1966	£6	£12	
Misty Blue	7"	Piccadilly	7N35384	1967	£4	£8	
Untrue Unfaithful	7"	Piccadilly	7N35258	1965	£4	£8	

ROSSO, NINI

Il Silenzio	7"	Durium	DRS54000	1965	£1.50	£4	chart single

ROSTILL, JOHN

Funny Old World	7"	Columbia	DB8794	1971	£20	£40	

ROTARY CONNECTION

Aladdin	LP	Chess	CRLS4547	1969	£5	£12	
Dinner Music	LP	Cadet	LPS328	1970	£4	£10	US
Hey Love	LP	Cadet	50006	1971	£4	£10	US
Peace At Last	LP	Cadet	LPS318	1969	£4	£10	US
Rotary Connection	LP	Chess	CRL4538	1968	£4	£10	
Songs	LP	Chess	CRLS4551	1969	£4	£10	
Soul Man	7"	Chess	CRS8072	1968	£1.50	£4	

ROTATIONS

"Heavies" is one of several early Frank Zappa productions.

Heavies	7"	Original Sound	41	1964	£25	£50	US

ROTH, DAVE LEE

Yankee Rose	7"	Warner Bros	W8656	1986	£2	£5	shaped pic disc
Sensible Shoes	5"	Warner Bros	W0016P	1991	£2.50	£6	shaped pic disc

ROTHCHILDS

Artificial City	7"	Decca	F12488	1966	£5	£10	
You've Made Your Choice	7"	Decca	F12411	1966	£4	£8	

ROULETTES

The Roulettes were formed as a backing group for Adam Faith, when the singer attempted to meet the challenge of the Beatles head-on by adopting the beat style himself. The Roulettes tried very hard to establish an independent career for themselves as well, but little of the group's material was sufficiently distinctive. The closest they came to a hit was with "Long Cigarette", which is a memorable song for all that it is closely modelled on a John Lennon performance, but a BBC ban put a stop to its progress up the charts.

Bad Time	7"	Parlophone	R5110	1964	£4	£8
Help Me Help Myself	7"	Fontana	TF876	1967	£5	£10
Hully Gully Slip And Slide	7"	Pye	7N15467	1962	£5	£10
I Can't Stop	7"	Oak	RGJ205	1965	£20	£40
I Can't Stop	7"	Parlophone	R5461	1966	£4	£8
I Hope He Breaks Your Heart	7"	Parlophone	R5278	1965	£4	£8
I'll Remember Tonight	7"	Parlophone	R5148	1964	£4	£8
Long Cigarette	7"	Parlophone	R5382	1965	£4	£8
Rhyme Boy Rhyme	7"	Fontana	TF822	1967	£5	£10
Soon You'll Be Leaving	7"	Parlophone	R5072	1963	£4	£8
Stakes And Chips	LP	Parlophone	PMC1257	1965	£180	£300
Stubborn Kind Of Fellow	7"	Parlophone	R5218	1964	£4	£8
Tracks Of My Tears	7"	Parlophone	R5419	1966	£4	£8

ROUND ROBIN

Kick That Little Foot Sally Ann	7"	London	HLU9908	1964	£7.50	£15

ROUSE, CHARLIE

Bossa Nova Bacchanal	LP	Blue Note	BLP/BST84119	1962	£10	£25	
Chase Is On	LP	Parlophone	PMC1090	1959	£6	£15	with Paul Quinichette
Takin' Care Of Business	LP	Jazzland	JLP19	1960	£8	£20	

ROUTERS

A Ooga	7"	Warner Bros	WB108	1963	£2	£5	
Charge!	LP	Warner Bros	WM/WS8162	1964	£8	£20	
Let's Go	7"	Warner Bros	WB77	1962		£5	chart single
Let's Go	7" EP.	Warner Bros	WEP1418	1962	£6	£12	French
Let's Go With The Routers	LP	Warner Bros	WM/WS8126	1963	£8	£20	
Make It Snappy	7"	Warner Bros	WB91	1963	£2	£5	
Play 1963's Great Instrumentals	LP	Warner Bros	WM/WS8144	1964	£8	£20	
Stamp And Shake	7"	Warner Bros	WB139	1964	£2	£5	
Stingray	7"	Warner Bros	WB97	1963	£2	£5	

ROUTH, JONATHAN

Candid Mike	7" EP.	Pye	NEP24128	1960	£2	£5
Candid Mike	10" LP	Pye	NPT19016	1957	£4	£10

ROVERS

Ichi Bon Tami Dachi	7"	Capitol	CL14283	1955	£7.50	£15

ROWAN & MARTIN

Rowan & Martin's Laugh-In	LP	CBS	63490	1969	£4	£10

ROWDIES

She's No Angel	7"	Teenage Depression	TD1/2	1979	£1.50	£4

ROWELY, MAJOR

There's A Riot Going On	7"	Stateside	SS438	1965	£1.50	£4

ROWENA, JEFF

Ambush	7"	Pye	7N15365	1961	£1.50	£4
Dance Baby Dance	7"	Oriole	CB1787	1963	£1.50	£4
Dance Baby Dance	7"	Oriole	CB1797	1963	£1.50	£4
Diddle De Dum	7"	Oriole	CB1810	1963	£1.50	£4
Eleanor	7"	CBS	202460	1967	£1.50	£4
La Cucuracha	7"	Pye	7N15423	1962	£1.50	£4
Peanut Vendor	7"	Pye	7N15328	1961	£1.50	£4

ROWLAND, STEVE

So Sad	7"	Fontana	TF844	1967	£2.50	£6

ROWSOME, LEO

Classics Of Irish Piping Vol.1	LP	Topic	12T259	1976	£5	£12	
Classics Of Irish Piping Vol.3	LP	Topic	12T322	1977	£5	£12	
Ri Na Bpiobari	LP	Claddagh	CC1	1959	£15	£30	Irish

ROXETTE

Dressed For Success	CD-s	EMI	CDEM162	1990	£4	£10	
Dressed For Success	CD-s	EMI	CDEM96	1989	£8	£20	
Dressed For Success	12"	EMI	12EM96	1989	£2.50	£6	
It Must Have Been Love	CD-s	EMI	CDEM141	1990	£2.50	£6	
Listen To Your Heart	CD-s	EMI	CDEM108	1990	£8	£20	
Listen To Your Heart	CD-s	EMI	CDEM149	1990	£4	£10	
Listen To Your Heart	12"	EMI	12EM108	1990	£2.50	£6	
Look	CD-s	EMI	CDEM87	1989	£8	£20	
Look	7"	EMI	EM87	1989	£10	£20	red vinyl
Look	12"	EMI	12EM87	1989	£6	£15	
Look	12"	EMI	12EM87	1989	£20	£40	red vinyl
Look Sharp	LP	EMI		1989	£25	£50	European pic disc

ROXY MUSIC

Love Is The Drug	12"	EG	EGOX26	1986	£3	£8	promo
Over You/Eight Miles High	12"	Polydor	POSPX93	1980	£3	£8	promo
Trash	12"	Polydor	POSPX32	1978	£3	£8	promo
Virginia Plain	7"	Island	WIP6144	1972	£6	£12	PS

ROY & ANNETTE
Title	Format	Label	Cat#	Year			Notes
My Baby	7"	R&B	JB107	1963	£5	£10	

ROY & ENID
Title	Format	Label	Cat#	Year			Notes
He'll Have To Go	7"	Coxsone	CS7069	1968	£5	£10	
Reggae For Days	7"	Coxsone	CS7088	1969	£5	£10	
Rockin' Time	7"	Coxsone	CS7063	1968	£5	£10	

ROY & MILLIE
Title	Format	Label	Cat#	Year			Notes
Cherry I Love You	7"	Black Swan	WI409	1964	£5	£10	
Oh Merna	7"	Black Swan	WI410	1964	£5	£10	Don Drummond B side
Oh Shirley	7"	Black Swan	WI427	1964	£5	£10	
Over And Over	7"	Blue Beat	BB154	1962	£5	£10	
There'll Come A Day	7"	Island	WI090	1963	£5	£10	
We'll Meet	7"	Island	WI005	1962	£5	£10	Roland Alphonso B side

ROY & PATSY
Title	Format	Label	Cat#	Year			Notes
In Your Arms Dear	7"	Blue Beat	BB118	1962	£5	£10	

ROY & PAULINE
Title	Format	Label	Cat#	Year			Notes
Have You Seen My Baby	7"	Island	WI067	1963	£5	£10	

ROY & THE DUKE ALL STARS
Title	Format	Label	Cat#	Year			Notes
Pretty Blue Eyes	7"	Blue Cat	BS113	1968	£4	£8	
Train	7"	Blue Cat	BS117	1968	£4	£8	

ROY & YVONNE
Title	Format	Label	Cat#	Year			Notes
Little Girl	7"	Blue Beat	BB258	1964	£5	£10	
Two Roads	7"	Black Swan	WI436	1964	£5	£10	

ROY, I
Title	Format	Label	Cat#	Year			Notes
Blackman Time	7"	Downtown	DT503	1973	£2	£5	
Dread Baldhead	LP	Klik	KLP9020	1976	£4	£10	
Hell And Sorrow	LP	Trojan	TRLS71	1973	£4	£10	
I Roy	LP	Trojan	TRLS91	1974	£4	£10	
Monkey Fashion	7"	Technique	TE930	1973	£1.50	£4	
Musical Drum Sound	7"	Harry J	HJ6655	1973	£1.50	£4	
Musical Shark Attack	LP	Virgin	V2075	1977	£4	£10	
Outformer Parker	7"	Attack	ATT8102	1975	£1.50	£4	
Presenting I Roy	LP	Trojan	TRLS63	1973	£4	£10	
Welding	7"	Philips	6006479	1975	£1.50	£4	
Yaha Ma Ride	7"	Atra	ATRA17	1974	£1.50	£4	

ROY, LEE
Title	Format	Label	Cat#	Year			Notes
Oh Ee Baby	7"	Island	WI251	1965	£5	£10	

ROY, U
U Roy is the major pioneer where the art of Jamaican DJ music is concerned. It was U Roy who first scored a series of successes with singles that used the stripped down backing tracks from other people's hits as a springboard for his spoken rants. This "toasting" style rapidly became all-pervasive in reggae and was undoubtedly a significant influence on the later American rapping scene.

Title	Format	Label	Cat#	Year			Notes
Festival Wise	7"	Dynamic	DYN448	1972	£2.50	£6	
Flashing My Whip	7"	Duke Reid	DR2519	1971	£4	£8	
Hard Feeling	7"	Gay Feet	GS210	1973	£1.50	£4	
Love I Tender	7"	Duke	DU105	1970	£2.50	£6	Joya Landis B side
Rule The Nation	7"	Duke Reid	DR2510	1970	£4	£8	Nora Dean B side
Tom Drunk	7"	Duke Reid	DR2517	1971	£4	£8	
True True	7"	Duke Reid	DR2518	1971	£4	£8	
U Roy	LP	Attack	ATLP1006	1973	£6	£15	
Version Galore	LP	Trojan	TBL161	1971	£8	£20	
Version Galore	7"	Duke Reid	DR2515	1970	£4	£8	Tommy McCook B side
Wake The Town	7"	Duke Reid	DR2509	1970	£4	£8	
Wear You To The Ball	7"	Duke Reid	DR2513	1970	£4	£8	Earl Lindo B side
You'll Never Get Away	7"	Duke Reid	DR2514	1970	£4	£8	Tommy McCook B side

ROYAL, BILLY JOE
Title	Format	Label	Cat#	Year			Notes
Billy Joe Royal	LP	Columbia	CL2781/CS9581	1967	£4	£10	US
Down In The Boondocks	7"	CBS	201802	1965	£1.50	£4	chart single
Down In The Boondocks	7" EP	CBS	6206	1965	£6	£12	French
Heart's Desire	7"	CBS	202087	1966	£15	£30	
Introducing Billy Joe Royal	LP	CBS	BPG62590	1966	£5	£12	
Never In A Hundred Years	7"	Atlantic	584002	1966	£1.50	£4	
Never In A Hundred Years	7"	Oriole	CB1751	1962	£4	£8	
Yo Yo	7"	CBS	202548	1967	£2	£5	

ROYAL GUARDSMEN
Title	Format	Label	Cat#	Year			Notes
Baby Let's Wait	7"	London	HLP10235	1968	£1.50	£4	
I Say Love	7"	London	HLP10182	1968	£1.50	£4	
Return Of The Red Baron	LP	London	HAP/SHP8351	1968	£5	£12	
Return Of The Red Baron	7"	Stateside	SS2010	1967	£1.50	£4	chart single
Snoopy And His Friends	LP	Laurie	(S)LLP2042	1967	£5	£12	US
Snoopy For President	LP	Laurie	SLLP2046	1968	£5	£12	US
Snoopy For President	7"	London	HLP10211	1968	£1.50	£4	
Snoopy Vs. The Red Baron	7"	Stateside	SS574	1967	£1.50	£4	chart single
Snoopy Vs. The Red Baron	7" EP	Vogue	INT18118	1967	£10	£20	French
Snoopy Vs.The Red Baron	LP	Stateside	(S)SL10202	1967	£5	£12	
Snoopy's Christmas	7"	London	HLP10171	1967	£1.50	£4	
Wednesday	7"	Stateside	SS2051	1967	£5	£10	

ROYAL HOLIDAYS

Title	Format	Label	Cat No	Year	Price 1	Price 2	Notes
Margaret	7"	London	HLU8722	1958	£17.50	£35	

ROYAL, JAMES

Title	Format	Label	Cat No	Year	Price 1	Price 2	Notes
Call My Name	LP	CBS	63780	1967	£5	£12	
Call My Name	7"	CBS	202525	1967	£1.50	£4	
Hey Little Boy	7"	CBS	3450	1968	£6	£12	
Light And Shade	LP	Carnaby	CNLS6008	1971	£4	£10	
Send Out Love	7"	CBS	4463	1969	£4	£8	
She's About A Mover	7"	Parlophone	R5290	1965	£4	£8	
Woman Called Sorrow	7"	CBS	3624	1968	£4	£8	
Work Song	7"	Parlophone	R5383	1965	£5	£10	

ROYAL JOKERS

Title	Format	Label	Cat No	Year	Price 1	Price 2	Notes
Rock And Roll Spectacular	LP	Dawn	1119	195-	£10	£25	US

ROYAL PLAYBOYS

Title	Format	Label	Cat No	Year	Price 1	Price 2	Notes
Spirituals And Jubilees	10" LP	Waldorf	33136	195-	£8	£20	US

ROYAL, ROBBIE

Title	Format	Label	Cat No	Year	Price 1	Price 2	Notes
Only Me	7"	Mercury	MF923	1965	£2.50	£6	

ROYAL ROCKERS

Title	Format	Label	Cat No	Year	Price 1	Price 2	Notes
Jet II	7"	Top Rank	JAR329	1960	£2.50	£6	

ROYAL TEENS

Title	Format	Label	Cat No	Year	Price 1	Price 2	Notes
Little Cricket	7"	Capitol	CL15068	1959	£6	£12	
Short Shorts	7"	HMV	POP454	1958	£10	£20	

ROYALETTES

Title	Format	Label	Cat No	Year	Price 1	Price 2	Notes
Elegant Sound Of The Royalettes	LP	MGM	C8028	1966	£8	£20	
I Want To Meet Him	7"	MGM	MGM1292	1965	£4	£8	
It's A Big Mistake	7"	MGM	MGM1324	1966	£4	£8	
It's Gonna Take A Miracle	LP	MGM	(S)E4332	1965	£8	£20	US
It's Gonna Take A Miracle	7"	MGM	MGM1279	1965	£7.50	£15	
Poor Boy	7"	MGM	MGM1272	1965	£5	£10	
River Of Tears	7"	Transatlantic	BIG106	1968	£2	£5	
You Bring Me Down	7"	MGM	MGM1302	1966	£6	£12	

ROYALS

Title	Format	Label	Cat No	Year	Price 1	Price 2	Notes
Never Gonna Give You Up	7"	Duke	DU29	1969	£2.50	£6	
Never See Come See	7"	Amalgamated	AMG831	1968	£4	£8	Cannonball Bryan B side
Pick Out Me Eye	7"	Trojan	TR662	1969	£4	£8	
Save Mama	7"	Blue Beat	BB259	1964	£5	£10	

ROYALTONES

Title	Format	Label	Cat No	Year	Price 1	Price 2	Notes
Flamingo Express	7"	London	HLU9296	1961	£4	£8	
Holy Smokes	7"	Stateside	SS309	1964	£4	£8	
Poor Boy	7"	London	HLJ8744	1958	£6	£12	

ROYCE, EARL & THE OLYMPICS

Title	Format	Label	Cat No	Year	Price 1	Price 2	Notes
Guess Things Happen That Way	7"	Parlophone	R5261	1965	£5	£10	
Que Sera Sera	7"	Columbia	DB7433	1964	£5	£10	

ROZA, LITA

Title	Format	Label	Cat No	Year	Price 1	Price 2	Notes
Bell Bottom Blues	7"	Decca	F10269	1954	£2.50	£6	
Between The Devil And The Deep Blue Sea	LP	Decca	LK4218	1957	£6	£15	
Between The Devil And The Deep Blue Sea	7" EP	Decca	DFE6443	1957	£5	£10	
But Love Me	7"	Decca	F10761	1956	£1.50	£4	
Changing Partners	7"	Decca	F10240	1954	£2	£5	
Heartbeat	7"	Decca	F10427	1954	£2	£5	
Hey There	7"	Decca	F10611	1955	£4	£8	chart single
Innismore	7"	Decca	F10792	1956	£1.50	£4	
Jimmy Unknown	7"	Decca	F10679	1956	£4	£8	chart single
Julie	7"	Decca	F10830	1956	£1.50	£4	
Let Me Go Lover	7"	Decca	F10431	1955	£2	£5	
Listening In The After Hours	10" LP	Decca	LF1243	1956	£8	£20	
Lita Roza	7" EP	Decca	DFE6399	1957	£5	£10	
Love Is The Answer	LP	Decca	LK4171	1957	£6	£15	
Lucky Lips	7"	Decca	F10861	1957	£2	£5	
Mama Doll Song	7"	Decca	F10393	1954	£1.50	£4	
Man In The Raincoat	7"	Decca	F10541	1955	£1.50	£4	
Me On A Carousel	LP	Pye	NPL18020/ NSPL83003	1958	£4	£10	
Presenting	10" LP	Decca	LF1187	1954	£8	£20	
Secret Love	7"	Decca	F10277	1954	£2	£5	
Selection	7" EP	Decca	DFE6386	1956	£5	£10	
Tomorrow	7"	Decca	F10479	1955	£2	£5	
Tonight My Heart She Is Crying	7"	Decca	F10884	1957	£1.50	£4	
Too Young To Go Steady	7"	Decca	F10728	1956	£1.50	£4	
Two Hearts, Two Kisses	7"	Decca	F10536	1955	£2	£5	

RUB-A-DUBS

Title	Format	Label	Cat No	Year	Price 1	Price 2	Notes
Without Love	7"	Blue Beat	BB304	1964	£5	£10	

RUBBER BAND

Title	Format	Label	Cat No	Year	Price 1	Price 2	Notes
Cream Song Book	LP	Major Minor	SMLP5045	1969	£4	£10	
Hendrix Song Book	LP	Major Minor	SMLP5048	1969	£4	£10	

RUBBER BOOTZ
Joy Ride .... 7" ...... Deram .... DM134.................. 1967 ... £2 .... £5

RUBBER BUCKET
The Rubber Bucket single is actually the work of Gary Glitter.
We Are Living In One Place .... 7" ... MCA .... MK5006 .... 1969 ... £7.50 .... £15

RUBBER MEMORY
Welcome .... LP ... RPC .... 69401 .... 1966 ... £10 .... £25 .... US

RUBEN & THE JETS
Con Safos .... LP ..... Mercury .... SRM1694 .... 1973 ... £5 .... £12 .... US
For Real .... LP ..... Mercury .... SRM1659 .... 1973 ... £6 .... £15 .... US

RUBIAYATS
Omar Khayam .... 7" ...... Action .... ACT4516 .... 1968 ... £1.50 .... £4

RUBIN
You've Been Away .... 7" ... MCA .... MCA196 .... 1975 ... £2 .... £5

RUBY & THE ROMANTICS
Baby Come Home	7"	London	HLR9916	1964	£5	£10	
Greatest Hits	LP	London	HAR8282	1966	£8	£20	
Hey There Lonely Boy	7"	London	HLR9771	1963	£2	£5	
Hey There Lonely Boy	7" EP.	London	RER1427	1964	£7.50	£15	
More Than Yesterday	LP	ABC	S638	1968	£6	£15	US
My Summer Love	7"	London	HLR9734	1963	£2	£5	
Our Day Will Come	LP	London	HAR8078	1963	£10	£25	
Our Day Will Come	7"	London	HLR9679	1963	£2.50	£6	chart single
Our Day Will Come	7" EP.	London	RER1389	1963	£7.50	£15	
Our Everlasting Love	7"	London	HLR9881	1964		£8	
Ruby And The Romantics	LP	Kapp	KL1526/KS3526	1967	£6	£15	US
Till Then	LP	Kapp	KL1341/KS3341	1963	£8	£20	US
When You're Young And In Love	7"	London	HLR9935	1964	£2	£5	
Young Wings Can Fly	7"	London	HLR9801	1963	£2	£5	
Your Baby Doesn't Love You Anymore	7"	London	HLR9972	1965	£2	£5	

RUDE BOYS
Rock Steady Massachusetts .... 7" ...... Island .... WI3088 .... 1967 ... £5 .... £10

RUDIES
7-11	7"	Blue Cat	BS107	1968	£4	£8	
Brixton Market	7"	Fab	FAB104	1969	£2	£5	
Cupid	7"	Blue Cat	BS109	1968	£4	£8	Rico B side
Engine 59	7"	Nu Beat	NB005	1968	£2.50	£6	
Give Me The Rights	7"	Fab	FAB70	1968	£2.50	£6	
I Wanna Go Home	7"	Fab	FAB46	1968	£4	£8	
Mighty Meaty	7"	Fab	FAB71	1968	£2.50	£6	
Train To Vietnam	7"	Nu Beat	NB001	1968	£4	£8	

RUDIMENTARY PENI
Media Person .... 7" ...... Outer Himalayan ...... OH003 .... 1981 ... £2 .... £5

RUDY & SKETTO
ABC Boogie	7"	Dice	CC2	1962	£5	£10	
Hold The Fire	7"	Dice	CC16	1963	£5	£10	
Little Schoolgirl	7"	Dice	CC7	1962	£5	£10	
Minna	7"	Blue Beat	BB252	1964	£5	£10	
Mr.Postman	7"	Dice	CC10	1963	£5	£10	
Oh Dolly	7"	Blue Beat	BB310	1964	£5	£10	
See What You Done	7"	Blue Beat	BB297	1964	£5	£10	
Show Me The Way To Go Home	7"	Blue Beat	BB208	1963	£5	£10	
Summer Is Just Around The Corner	7"	Dice	CC5	1962	£5	£10	
Ten Thousand Miles From Home	7"	Blue Beat	BB230	1963	£5	£10	
Was It Me	7"	Blue Beat	BB198	1963	£5	£10	
We Are So Happy	7"	Dice	CC19	1963	£5	£10	

RUFF, RAY & THE CHECKMATES
I Took A Liking To You .... 7" ...... London .... HLU9889 .... 1964 ... £6 .... £12

RUFFIN, BRUCE
Rain .... LP ..... Trojan .... TRL23 .... 1971 ... £5 .... £12

RUFFIN, DAVID
Feelin' Good	LP	Tamla Motown	(S)TML11139	1970	£5	£12	
Heavy Love	7"	Tamla Motown	TMG1022	1976	£1.50	£4	
I've Lost Everything I Ever Loved	7"	Tamla Motown	TMG711	1969	£1.50	£4	
My Whole World Ended	LP	Tamla Motown	(S)TML11118	1969	£5	£12	
Whole World Ended	7"	Tamla Motown	TMG689	1969	£1.50	£4	

RUFFIN, DAVID & JIMMY
I Am My Brother's Keeper .... LP ..... Tamla Motown ... STML11176 ...... 1971 ... £4 .... £10

RUFFIN, JIMMY
Don't Let Him Take Your Love From Me	7"	Tamla Motown	TMG664	1968	£2	£5	
Don't You Miss Me A Little Bit Baby	7"	Tamla Motown	TMG617	1967	£2.50	£6	
Farewell Is A Lonely Sound	7"	Tamla Motown	TMG726	1970	£1.50	£4	chart single
Gonna Give Her All The Love I Got	7"	Tamla Motown	TMG603	1967	£2.50	£6	chart single

I'll Say Forever My Love	7"	Tamla Motown	TMG649	1968	£2	£5	
I'll Say Forever My Love	7"	Tamla Motown	TMG740	1970	£1.50	£4	chart single
It's Wonderful	7"	Tamla Motown	TMG753	1970	£1.50	£4	chart single
I've Passed This Way Before	7"	Tamla Motown	TMG593	1967	£2.50	£6	chart single
I've Passed This Way Before	7"	Tamla Motown	TMG703	1969	£1.50	£4	chart single
Jimmy Ruffin Way	LP	Tamla Motown	(S)TML11048	1967	£6	£15	chart LP
Let's Say Goodbye Tomorrow	7"	Tamla Motown	TMG767	1971	£1.50	£4	
On The Way Out	7"	Tamla Motown	TMG784	1971	£1.50	£4	
Ruff 'n' Ready	LP	Tamla Motown	(S)TML11106	1969	£6	£15	
What Becomes Of The Broken Hearted	7"	Tamla Motown	TMG577	1966	£2	£5	chart single

RUFUS

Rags To Rufus	LP	ABC	ABCL5052	1974	£4	£10	
Rufus	LP	ABC	ABCL5114	1973	£4	£10	
Rufus With Chaka Khan	LP	ABC	ABCL5151	1975	£4	£10	
Rufusized	LP	ABC	ABCL5063	1974	£4	£10	

RUFUS ZUPHALL

Phallobst	LP	Pilz	20210995	1971	£6	£15	German
Weiss Der Teufel	LP	Good Will	GLS10001	1969	£40	£80	German

RUGOLO, PETE

Adventures In Rhythm	LP	Philips	BBL7035	1955	£5	£12	
Behind Brigitte Bardot	LP	Warner Bros	WM4001/WS8001	1960	£4	£10	
Music From Richard Diamond	LP	Mercury	MMC14034/ CMS18025	1960	£5	£12	
Out On A Limb	LP	Emarcy	EJL1274	1958	£4	£10	
Percussion At Work	LP	Mercury	MMB12004	1959	£4	£10	
Pete Rugolo	LP	Philips	BBL7069	1956	£5	£12	
Pete Rugolo And His Orchestra	10" LP	Philips	BBR8024	1954	£4	£10	
Pete Rugolo Orchestra	LP	Emarcy	EJL1254	1957	£5	£12	
Reeds In Hi Fi	LP	Mercury	MMC14012	1959	£4	£10	
Rugolo Plays Kenton	LP	Mercury	BMS17000	1959	£6	£15	
Rugolo Plays Kenton	LP	Mercury	MMB12011	1959	£4	£10	

RULERS

Copasetic	7"	Rio	R107	1966	£5	£10	
Don't Be A Rude Boy	7"	Rio	R105	1966	£4	£8	
Got To Be Free	7"	Trojan	TR696	1969	£2.50	£6	
Well Covered	7"	Rio	R135	1967	£4	£8	Carl Dawkins B side
Wrong Embryo	7"	Rio	R132	1967	£4	£8	

RUMBLERS

Boss	7"	London	HLD9684	1963	£6	£12	
Bossounds	LP	London	HAD/SHD8081	1963	£15	£30	
Bossounds	7" EP	London	RED1396	1963	£12.50	£25	
Soulful Jerk	7"	King	KG1021	1965	£17.50	£35	

RUMBOLD, EDWICK

Shades Of Grey	7"	Parlophone	R5622	1967	£15	£30	
Specially When	7"	CBS	202393	1966	£15	£30	

RUMPELSTILTSKIN

Rumpelstiltskin	LP	Bell	6047	1969	£6	£15	US

RUMSEY, HOWARD

Howard Rumsey's Lighthouse All Stars	LP	Contemporary	LAC12055	1957	£8	£20	
Howard Rumsey's Lighthouse All Stars	10" LP	Contemporary	LDC187	1956	£10	£25	
Howard Rumsey's Lighthouse All-Stars	10" LP	Vogue	EPC1175	1953	£10	£25	
Jazz Rolls Royce	LP	Colrich	XSD5	1959	£4	£10	
Lighthouse All Stars	10" LP	Contemporary	LDC146	1955	£10	£25	
Lighthouse All Stars	10" LP	Contemporary	LDC152	1955	£10	£25	
Lighthouse All Stars Vol.3	LP	Contemporary	LAC12182	1960	£5	£12	
Lighthouse At Laguna	LP	Contemporary	LAC12125	1959	£6	£15	
Music For Lighthousekeeping	LP	Contemporary	LAC12086	1958	£6	£15	
Oboe - Flute	LP	Contemporary	LAC12146	1959	£6	£15	
Sunday Jazz A La Lighthouse Vol.1	LP	Contemporary	LAC12120	1958	£6	£15	

RUN 229

Soho	7"	MM	JR7040S	1980	£4	£8	

RUNAWAYS

And Now...The Runaways	LP	Cherry Red	ARED38	1979	£4	£10	blue vinyl
Little Lost Girls	12"	Rhino		1981	£3	£8	US pic disc
Runaways	LP	Mercury	9100029	1976	£4	£10	orange vinyl

RUNDGREN, TODD

Ballad Of Todd Rundgren	LP	Bearsville	K45506	1971	£5	£12	
I Saw The Light	7"	Bearsville	K15506	1972	£1.50	£4	chart single
Runt	LP	Bearsville	K45505	1970	£5	£12	
Something Anything	LP	Bearsville	2BR2066	1972	£40	£80	US double promo, 1 red, 1 blue vinyl
Something Anything	LP	Bearsville	K65501	1972	£5	£12	double
Todd	LP	Bearsville	K85501	1974	£5	£12	double
Todd Rundgren Radio Show	LP	Bearsville	PRO524	1972	£15	£30	US promo
Todd Rundgren Radio Show	LP	Bearsville	PRO597	1974	£10	£25	US promo
Wizard A True Star	LP	Bearsville	K45513	1973	£4	£10	

RUNDGREN, TODD & PATTI SMITH
Back To The Bars	LP	Bearsville	PROA788	1978	£10	£25	US promo

RUNNING, JUMPING & STANDING STILL
Aye O	7"	Liberty	LBF15209	1969	£2	£5	

RUNNING MAN
Running Man	LP	Neon	NE11	1972	£70	£140	

RUNRIG
Loch Lomond	7"	Ridge	RRS003	1982	£4	£8	
Runrig Play Gaelic	LP	Neptune	NA105	1978	£6	£15	
Skye	7"	Simple	SIM8	1984	£1.50	£4	

RUPERT & DAVID
Sound Of Silence	7"	Decca	F12306	1965	£1.50	£4	

RUPERT'S PEOPLE
I Can Show You	7"	Columbia	DB8362	1968	£12.50	£25	
Prologue To A Magic World	7"	Columbia	DB8278	1967	£12.50	£25	
Reflections Of Charles Brown	7"	Columbia	DB8226	1967	£7.50	£15	

RUSH
All The World's A Stage	LP	Mercury	6672015	1977	£6	£15	double with photo page
Body Electric	12"	Vertigo	RUSH1112	1984	£8	£20	
Body Electric	10"	Mercury	RUSH1110	1984	£2.50	£6	red vinyl
Countdown	7"	Mercury	RUSHP10	1982	£6	£12	shaped pic disc
Everything You Always Wanted To Hear	LP	Mercury	MK32	1975	£8	£20	US promo
Hemispheres	LP	Mercury	9100059	1978	£5	£12	pic disc
Not Fade Away	7"	Moon	MN001	1973	£100	£200	Canadian
Power Windows	LP	Vertigo	VERHP31	1985	£5	£12	pic disc
Prime Mover	CD-s	Vertigo	RUSHCD14	1988	£2.50	£6	
Rush	LP	Moon			£60	£120	Canadian
Rush Through Time	LP	Mercury	001	1978	£10	£25	US promo pic disc
Rush'n'Roulette	12"	Mercury		1982	£6	£15	US promo, 6 tracks running simultaneously
Subdivisions	7"	Mercury	RUSHP9	1982	£1.50	£4	pic disc

RUSH (2)
Happy	7"	Decca	F12614	1967	£2	£5	
Make Mine Music	7"	Decca	F12635	1967	£2	£5	

RUSH, MERRILEE
Angel Of The Morning	LP	Bell	SBLL109	1968	£4	£10	

RUSH, OTIS
All Your Love	7"	Blue Horizon	573159	1969	£5	£10	
Groaning The Blues	LP	Python	KM3	1970	£8	£20	
Homework	7"	Vocalion	VP9260	1966	£7.50	£15	
Mourning In The Morning	LP	Atlantic	588188	1969	£8	£20	
Mourning In The Morning	LP	Atlantic	K40495	1972	£5	£12	
This One's A Good Un	LP	Blue Horizon	763222	1968	£20	£40	
Troubles, Troubles	LP	Sonet	SNTF756	1978	£4	£10	

RUSH, TOM
Blues And Folk	LP	XTRA	XTRA5024	1966	£6	£15	
Circle Game	LP	Elektra	EKL/EKS74018	1968	£6	£15	
Classic Rush	LP	Elektra	EKL/EKS74062	1969	£5	£12	
I Got A Mind To Ramble	LP	XTRA	XTRA5053	1968	£6	£15	
Long John	7" EP	Vogue	INT18040	1965	£6	£12	French
Merrimack County	LP	CBS	64887	1972	£4	£10	
Mind Ramblin'	LP	Prestige	14003	1963	£6	£15	US
No Regrets	7"	Elektra	EKSN45025	1968	£1.50	£4	
On The Road Again	7"	Elektra	EKSN45015	1967	£2	£5	
Something In The Way She Moves Me	7"	Elektra	EKSN45032	1968	£1.50	£4	
Something In The Way She Moves Me	7"	Elektra	EKSN45718	1970	£1.50	£4	
Take A Little Walk With Me	LP	Elektra	EKL/EKS7308	1966	£6	£15	
Tom Rush	LP	CBS	63940	1970	£4	£10	
Tom Rush	LP	Elektra	EKL288	1965	£6	£15	
Who Do You Love	7"	Elektra	EKSN45005	1967	£2	£5	
Wrong End Of A Rainbow	LP	CBS	64268	1970	£4	£10	

RUSHING, JIMMY
And The Big Brass	LP	Philips	BBL7252/SBBL524	1958	£6	£15	
Blues I Love To Sing	LP	Ace Of Hearts	AH119	1966	£5	£12	
Cat Meets Chick	LP	Philips	BBL7105	1957	£6	£15	with Ada Moore
Cat Meets Chick	7" EP	Philips	BBE12150	1957	£5	£10	with Ada Moore
Every Day I Have The Blues	LP	HMV	CLP/CSD3632	1967	£5	£12	
Five Feet Of Soul	LP	Golden Guinea	GGL0384	1967	£4	£10	
If This Ain't The Blues	LP	Vanguard	PPL11008	1958	£6	£15	
Jazz Odyssey	LP	Philips	BBL7166	1957	£6	£15	
Jimmy Rushing	7" EP	Ember	EMBEP4523	1962	£2.50	£6	
Jimmy Rushing	7" EP	Parlophone	GEP8597	1957	£4	£8	
Listen To The Blues	LP	Fontana	FJL405	1967	£5	£12	
Little Jimmy All Star Band	7" EP	Vanguard	EPP14003	1957	£4	£8	
Little Jimmy Rushing And The Big Brass	LP	Philips	BBL7252	1958	£5	£12	
Rushing Lullabies	LP	Philips	BBL7360	1960	£6	£15	

Showcase	10" LP	Vanguard	PPT12016	1957	£8	£20	
Sings The Blues	10" LP	Vanguard	PPT12002	1955	£10	£25	
Smith Girls - Bessie, Clara	LP	Philips	BBL7484/SBBL631	1961	£6	£15	
Way I Feel	7" EP	Parlophone	GEP8695	1958	£4	£8	

RUSKIN, BARBARA
Halfway To Paradise	7"	Piccadilly	7N35224	1965	£1.50	£4	

RUSSAL, THANE
Drop Everything And Run	7"	CBS	202403	1966	£15	£30	
Security	7"	CBS	202049	1966	£20	£40	
Security	7"	CBS	202049	1966	£55	£110	PS

RUSSELL, CONNIE
Ayuh Ayuh	7"	Capitol	CL14236	1955	£4	£8	
Farewell Farewell	7"	Capitol	CL14268	1955	£1.50	£4	
Foggy Night In San Francisco	7"	Capitol	CL14214	1955	£2.50	£6	
Green Fire	7"	Capitol	CL14246	1955	£2	£5	
Love Me	7"	Capitol	CL14197	1954	£2.50	£6	
No One But You	7"	Capitol	CL14171	1954	£4	£8	

RUSSELL, DOROTHY
You're The One I Love	7"	Duke Reid	DR2524	1971	£2.50	£6	

RUSSELL FAMILY
Of Doolin County Clare	LP	Topic	12TS251	1975	£5	£12	

RUSSELL, GEORGE
Ezz-thetics	LP	Riverside	RLP375	1961	£6	£15	
Jazz Workshop	LP	RCA	RD7511	1962	£6	£15	
New York, N.Y.	LP	Brunswick	LAT8333	1960	£8	£20	
Outer View	LP	Fontana	688705ZL	1964	£4	£10	
Stratus Seekers	LP	Riverside	RLP(9)412	1962	£5	£12	

RUSSELL, JANE
If You Wanna See Mamie Tonight	7"	Capitol	CL14590	1956	£1.50	£4	
Jane Russell	7" EP	MGM	MGMEP702	1959	£7.50	£15	
Please Do It Again	7"	Columbia	SCM5043	1953	£2.50	£6	

RUSSELL, JOHNNY
Lonesome Boy	7"	MGM	MGM1074	1960	£2	£5	

RUSSELL, LEON
Everybody's Talkin' 'Bout The Young	7"	Pye	7N16771	1965	£4	£8	
Leon Russell	LP	A&M	AMLS982	1970	£4	£10	
Leon Russell	LP	Shelter	SHE1001	1968	£5	£12	US, extra track
Looking Inside The Asylum Choir	LP	Mercury	SMCL21041	1968	£4	£10	

RUSSELL, RAY
Dragon Hill	LP	CBS	52663	1969	£10	£25	
June 11th 1971	LP	RCA	SF8214	1971	£8	£20	
Rites And Rituals	LP	CBS	64271	1971	£10	£25	
Secret Asylum	LP	Black Lion	BLP12100	1973	£8	£20	
Turn Circle	LP	CBS	52586	1968	£10	£25	

RUSSELL, ROLAND
Rhythm Hips	7"	Nu Beat	NB019	1968	£2.50	£6	

RUSSO, WILLIAM
Three Pieces For Blues Band & Symphony Orchestra	LP	Deutsche Grammophon	2530309	197-	£6	£15	with Siegel-Schwall Band

RUSTIKS
I'm Not The Loving Kind	7"	Decca	F12059	1965	£2	£5	
What A Memory Can Do	7"	Decca	F11960	1964	£4	£8	

RUSTLERS
High Strung	7"	Pye	7N15398	1961	£1.50	£4	

RUSTY & DOUG
Cajun Joe	7"	Fontana	267238TF	1962	£5	£10	
Hey Mae	7"	Oriole	CB1510	1959	£40	£80	
Hey Mae	7"	Polydor	NH66970	1962	£10	£20	
Like You	7"	London	HL8972	1959	£7.50	£15	

RUTHERFORD, MIKE
Time And Time Again/End Of The Day	7"	Charisma	CB364	1980	£2.50	£6	PS
Time And Time Again/Overnight Job	7"	Charisma	CB364	1980	£1.50	£4	PS
Time And Time Again/Overnight Job	7"	Charisma	CB364	1980	£1.50	£4	PS, B side labelled 'End Of The Day'

RUTLES
The Rutles album and its accompanying television program is an affectionate parody by Neil Innes and Eric Idle of the career of the Beatles. The cover of the LP is almost better than the music inside - it displays numerous photographs of album sleeves and group portraits that exactly mirror originals featuring the Beatles. The music is cleverly constructed to be reminiscent of key songs by the Beatles, although ultimately Neil Innes' recreations are rather less skillful than those put together by XTC on their Dukes Of Stratosfear albums.

Rutles	LP	Warner Bros	K56459	1978	£5	£12	chart LP
Rutles Sampler	12"	Warner Bros	PROA723	1978	£4	£10	US promo, yellow vinyl

RUTS
Babylon's Burning	7"	RSO	RSO71	1980	£1.50	£4	XTC B side

Title	Format	Label	Cat No	Year	Price	Price	Notes
Babylon's Burning	7"	Virgin	VS271	1979	£1.50	£4	PS
Stepping Bondage	7"	Bohemian	BO4	1983	£2.50	£6	

RYAN, BARRY

Title	Format	Label	Cat No	Year	Price	Price	Notes
Barry Ryan	LP	Polydor	583067	1969	£4	£10	
Eloise	7"	MGM	MGM1442	1968	£1.50	£4	chart single
Hunt	7"	Polydor	56348	1969	£1.50	£4	
Love Is Love	7"	MGM	MGM1464	1968	£1.50	£4	
Sings Paul Ryan	LP	MGM	CS8106	1968	£5	£12	

RYAN, CHARLIE

Title	Format	Label	Cat No	Year	Price	Price	Notes
Hot Rod	LP	King	751	1961	£8	£20	US

RYAN, KRIS & THE QUESTIONS

Title	Format	Label	Cat No	Year	Price	Price	Notes
Marie Marie	7"	Mercury	MF852	1964	£1.50	£4	
Miss Ann	7"	Mercury	MF818	1964	£1.50	£4	
On The Right Track	7" EP	Mercury	10024MCE	1965	£7.50	£15	
Tell Me Now	7"	Mercury	MF877	1965	£1.50	£4	

RYAN, MARION

Title	Format	Label	Cat No	Year	Price	Price	Notes
Better Use Your Head	7"	Philips	BF1721	1968	£5	£10	
Hit Parade	7" EP	Pye	NEP24079	1958	£6	£12	
Jo-Jo The Dog Faced Boy	7"	Pye	7N15200	1959	£1.50	£4	
Lady Loves	LP	Pye	NPL18030	1959	£8	£20	mono
Lady Loves	LP	Pye	NSPL18030	1959	£10	£25	stereo
Love Me Forever	7"	Pye	7N15121	1958	£1.50	£4	chart single
Oh Oh I'm Falling In Love Again	7"	Pye	7N15130	1958	£1.50	£4	
Stairway Of Love	7"	Pye	7N15138	1958	£1.50	£4	
That Ryan Gal	7" EP	Pye	NEP24041	1957	£4	£8	
World Goes Around And Around	7"	Pye	7NSR15157	1958	£2	£5	stereo

RYAN, PAUL & BARRY

Title	Format	Label	Cat No	Year	Price	Price	Notes
Claire	7"	Decca	F12633	1967	£1.50	£4	chart single
Don't Bring Me Your Heartaches	7"	Decca	F12260	1965	£1.50	£4	chart single
Have Pity On The Boy	7"	Decca	F12319	1966	£1.50	£4	chart single
Have You Ever Loved Somebody	7"	Decca	F12494	1966	£1.50	£4	chart single
Heartbreaker	7"	MGM	MGM1354	1967	£1.50	£4	
I Love Her	7"	Decca	F12391	1966	£1.50	£4	chart single
I Love How You Love Me	7"	Decca	F12445	1966	£1.50	£4	chart single
Keep It Out Of Sight	7"	Decca	F12567	1967	£1.50	£4	chart single
Missy Missy	7"	Decca	F12520	1966	£1.50	£4	chart single
Paul And Barry Ryan	LP	MGM	C(S)8081	1968	£5	£12	
Pictures Of Today	7"	MGM	MGM1385	1968	£1.50	£4	
Two Of A Kind	LP	Decca	LK4878	1967	£6	£15	

RYAN, PHIL & THE CRESCENTS

Title	Format	Label	Cat No	Year	Price	Price	Notes
Gypsy Woman	7"	Columbia	DB7574	1965	£5	£10	
Mary Don't You Weep	7"	Columbia	DB7406	1964	£2	£5	

RYDELL, BOBBY

Title	Format	Label	Cat No	Year	Price	Price	Notes
All The Hits	LP	Cameo Parkway	C1019	1962	£5	£12	
All The Hits Vol.2	LP	Cameo Parkway	C1040	1963	£5	£12	
At The Copa	LP	Columbia	33SX1425	1962	£5	£12	
Best Of Bobby Rydell	7" EP	Summit	LSE2036	1963	£4	£8	
Biggest Hits	LP	Cameo	C1009	1961	£6	£15	US, gatefold
Biggest Hits Vol.2	LP	Cameo	C1028	1962	£5	£12	US
Bobby Rydell	7" EP	Cameo Parkway	CPE553	1963	£6	£12	
Butterfly Baby	7"	Cameo Parkway	C242	1963	£1.50	£4	
Bye Bye Birdie	LP	Cameo Parkway	C1043	1963	£5	£12	
Cha Cha Cha	7"	Cameo Parkway	C228	1962	£1.50	£4	
Childhood Sweetheart	7"	Cameo Parkway	C272	1963	£1.50	£4	
Ciao Ciao Bambino	7"	Cameo Parkway	C361	1965	£1.50	£4	
Fish	7"	Columbia	DB4690	1961	£1.50	£4	
Forget Him	7"	Cameo Parkway	C108	1963	£1.50	£4	chart single
Forget Him	7"	Cameo Parkway	C108	1963	£2.50	£6	PS
Good Time Baby	7"	Columbia	DB4600	1961	£1.50	£4	chart single
I Can't Say Goodbye	7"	Capitol	CL15371	1965	£1.50	£4	
I Wanna Thank You	7"	Columbia	DB4731	1961	£1.50	£4	
I'll Never Dance Again	7"	Columbia	DB4858	1962	£1.50	£4	
It's Time We Parted	7"	Cameo Parkway	C129	1962	£1.50	£4	
I've Got Bonnie	7"	Columbia	DB4785	1962	£1.50	£4	
Kissin' Time	7"	Top Rank	JAR181	1959	£2.50	£6	
Lovingest	7" EP	Top Rank	JKP2059	1960	£10	£20	
Make Me Forget	7"	Cameo Parkway	C309	1964	£1.50	£4	
Salutes The Great Ones	LP	Columbia	33SX1352	1961	£6	£15	
Sings And Swings	LP	Columbia	33SX1308	1960	£8	£20	
Somebody Loves You	LP	Capitol	T2281	1965	£4	£10	
Stranger In The World	7"	Capitol	CL15381	1965	£1.50	£4	
Sway	7"	Columbia	DB4545	1960	£1.50	£4	chart single

Sway With Bobby Rydell	7" EP..	Cameo Parkway	CPE551	1963	£6	£12	
Swinging School	7"	Columbia	DB4471	1960	£1.50	£4	chart single
That Old Black Magic	7"	Columbia	DB4651	1961	£1.50	£4	
Until I Met You	7"	Cameo Parkway	CP601	1966	£1.50	£4	
Volare	7"	Columbia	DB4495	1960	£1.50	£4	chart single
We Got Love	LP	Cameo	C1006	1959	£8	£20	US
We Got Love	7"	Top Rank	JAR227	1959	£2.50	£6	
When I See That Girl Of Mine	7"	Capitol	CL15424	1965	£2	£5	
Wild One	LP	Columbia	33SX1243	1960	£10	£25	
Wild One	7"	Columbia	DB4429	1960	£1.50	£4	chart single
Wild (Wood) Days	LP	Cameo	C1055	1963	£5	£12	

RYDER, MAL

Cry Baby	7"	Decca	F11669	1963	£5	£10	
Lonely Room	7"	Piccadilly	7N35234	1965	£6	£12	
See The Funny Little Clown	7"	Vocalion	V9219	1964	£20	£40	
Your Friend	7"	Piccadilly	7N35209	1964	£7.50	£15	

RYDER, MITCH

All Mitch Ryder Hits!	LP	Bell	MBLL/SBLL114	1968	£5	£12	
Breakout	LP	Stateside	(S)SL10189	1967	£6	£15	
Breakout	7"	Stateside	SS521	1966	£7.50	£15	
Devil With A Blue Dress On	7"	Stateside	SS549	1966	£2.50	£6	
Jenny Take A Ride	7"	Stateside	SS481	1966	£4	£8	chart single
Jenny Take A Ride	7" EP.	Columbia	ESRF1745	1966	£7.50	£15	French
Joy	7"	Stateside	SS2037	1967	£2	£5	
Little Latin Lupe Lu	7"	Stateside	SS498	1966	£2.50	£6	
Little Latin Lupe Lu	7" EP.	Columbia	ESRF1804	1966	£7.50	£15	French
Mitch Ryder Sings The Hits	LP	New Voice	S2005	1968	£5	£12	US
Personality	7"	Stateside	SS2096	1968	£2	£5	
Ridin'	7" EP.	Stateside	SE1039	1966	£7.50	£15	
Sock It To Me	LP	Stateside	(S)SL10204	1967	£6	£15	
Sock It To Me Baby	7"	Stateside	SS596	1967	£2.50	£6	
Sock It To Me Baby	7" EP.	Columbia	ESRF1849	1967	£7.50	£15	French
Take A Ride	LP	Stateside	(S)SL10178	1966	£6	£15	
Too Many Fish In The Sea	7"	Stateside	SS2023	1967	£2.50	£6	
Too Many Fish In The Sea	7" EP.	Stateside	FSE1005	1967	£7.50	£15	French
What Now My Love	LP	Stateside	(S)SL10229	1967	£5	£12	
What Now My Love	7"	Stateside	SS2063	1967	£5	£10	
You Are My Sunshine	7"	Stateside	SS2075	1968	£2	£5	

RYE & QUARTERBOYS

Fantasy	7"	Replay	REPLAY001	1982	£2	£5	

RYLES & DALLAS

Blowin' In The Wind	7" EP.	Riviera	231125	1965	£4	£8	French

RYPDAL, TERJE

Bleak House	LP	Polydor	2915053	196-	£6	£15	Swedish

SABLE, PAUL & THE JUNGLE 'N' BEATS
Rave On ... 7" ... Fontana ... TF457 ... 1964 ... £10 ... £20

SABLES, BILL
Bill Sables ... LP ... Westwood ... WRS027 ... 1972 ... £15 ... £30

SABRE
Miracle Man ... 7" ... Neat ... NEAT23 ... 1983 ... £1.50 ... £4

SABRES
Roly Poly ... 7" ... Decca ... F12528 ... 1966 ... £4 ... £8

SACRED ALIEN
Legends ... 7" ... Neon ... SADX1 ... 1984 ... £4 ... £8
Spiritual Planet ... 7" ... Greenwood ... GW1 ... 198- ... £7.50 ... £15

SACRED MUSHROOM
Sacred Mushroom ... LP ... Parallax ... P4001 ... 1969 ... £20 ... £40 ... US

SAD LOVERS & GIANTS
Colourless Dream ... 7" ... Last Movement ... LM005 ... 1981 ... £2.50 ... £6
Imagination ... 7" ... Last Movement ... LM003 ... 1981 ... £4 ... £8
Lost In A Moment ... 7" ... Midnight Music ... DING1 ... 1982 ... £1.50 ... £4

SADI, FATS
Fats Sadi ... 10" LP ... Vogue ... LDE133 ... 1955 ... £40 ... £80
Fats Sadi-Martial Solal Quartet ... LP ... Vogue ... LAE12043 ... 1957 ... £10 ... £25

SAFARIS
Image Of A Girl ... 7" ... Top Rank ... JAR424 ... 1960 ... £7.50 ... £15
Summer Nights ... 7" ... Top Rank ... JAR528 ... 1961 ... £1.50 ... £4

SAGAR, MIKE & THE CRESTERS
Deep Feeling ... 7" ... HMV ... POP819 ... 1960 ... £1.50 ... £4 ... chart single
Set Me Free ... 7" ... HMV ... POP988 ... 1961 ... £1.50 ... £4

SAGITTARIUS
Another Time ... 7" ... CBS ... 3276 ... 1968 ... £2 ... £5
Blue Marble ... LP ... Together ... STT1002 ... 1969 ... £10 ... £25 ... US
My World Fell Down ... 7" ... CBS ... 2867 ... 1967 ... £4 ... £8
Present Tense ... LP ... Columbia ... CS9644 ... 1968 ... £8 ... £20 ... US

SAGRAM
Pop Explosion Sitar Style ... LP ... Windmill ... WMD118 ... 1972 ... £10 ... £25

SAHARA
Sunrise ... LP ... Dawn ... DNLS3068 ... 1973 ... £4 ... £10

SAHM, DOUG
Return Of Doug Saldana ... LP ... Philips ... PHS600353 ... 1971 ... £6 ... £15 ... US
Rough Edges ... LP ... Mercury ... SRM1655 ... 1973 ... £6 ... £15 ... US

SAINT ETIENNE
Only Love Can Break Your Heart ... 12" ... Heavenly ... HVN212R ... 1990 ... £2.50 ... £6

SAINT JUST
La Casa Del Lago ... LP ... Harvest ... 1974 ... £50 ... £100 ... Italian
Saint Just ... LP ... Harvest ... 1973 ... £50 ... £100 ... Italian

SAINT STEVEN
Saint Steven ... LP ... Probe ... 1968 ... £8 ... £20

SAINTE-MARIE, BUFFY
Best Of Buffy Sainte-Marie ... LP ... Vanguard ... VSD3/4 ... 1973 ... £5 ... £12 ... double
Best Of Buffy Sainte-Marie Vol.2 ... LP ... Vanguard ... VSD33/34 ... 1974 ... £5 ... £12 ... double
Fire,Fleet & Candle Light ... LP ... Vanguard ... VSD79250 ... 1967 ... £4 ... £10
Illuminations ... LP ... Vanguard ... VSD79300 ... 1969 ... £4 ... £10
I'm Gonna Be A Country Girl Again ... LP ... Vanguard ... VSD79280 ... 1968 ... £4 ... £10
It's My Way ... LP ... Fontana ... TFL6040 ... 1964 ... £5 ... £12
It's My Way ... LP ... Vanguard ... VSD79142 ... 1969 ... £4 ... £10
Little Wheel Spin And Spin ... LP ... Fontana ... (S)TFL6071 ... 1966 ... £5 ... £12
Little Wheel Spin And Spin ... LP ... Vanguard ... SVRL19023 ... 1969 ... £4 ... £10
Many A Mile ... LP ... Fontana ... TFL6047 ... 1965 ... £5 ... £12
Many A Mile ... LP ... Vanguard ... SVRL19031 ... 1969 ... £4 ... £10
Moonshot ... LP ... Vanguard ... VSD79312 ... 1972 ... £4 ... £10
Native North American Child ... LP ... Vanguard ... VSD79340 ... 1974 ... £4 ... £10
Quiet Places ... LP ... Vanguard ... VSD79330 ... 1973 ... £4 ... £10
She Used To Wanna Be A Ballerina ... LP ... Vanguard ... VSD79311 ... 1971 ... £4 ... £10
Sweet America ... LP ... ABC ... ABCL5168 ... 1976 ... £5 ... £12

Timeless Love	7"	Fontana	H695	1966	£1.50	£4	
Universal Soldier	7"	Fontana	TF614	1965	£1.50	£4	
Until It's Time For You To Go	7"	Fontana	TF574	1965	£1.50	£4	

SAINTS

Eternally Yours	LP	Harvest	SHSP4078	1978	£4	£10	
I'm Stranded	LP	Harvest	SHSP4065	1977	£4	£10	
I'm Stranded	7"	Power Exchange	PX242	1976	£1.50	£4	

SAINTS (2)

Husky Team	7"	Pye	7N15582	1963	£5	£10	
Wipe Out	7"	Pye	7N15548	1963	£5	£10	

SAINTS (3)

Alive	LP	MJB	BEVLP127/8	1964	£120	£220	
Saints	10" LP	MJB	BEV73/4	196-	£120	£220	

SAINTY, RUSS

Don't Believe Him Donna	7"	Decca	F11325	1961	£1.50	£4	
Happy Go Lucky Me	7"	Top Rank	JAR381	1960	£1.50	£4	
It Ain't That Easy	7"	Columbia	DB7521	1965	£1.50	£4	
Keep Your Love Locked	7"	HMV	POP1055	1962	£1.50	£4	
Lonesome Town	7"	Parlophone	R5168	1964	£1.50	£4	
Race With The Devil	7"	Decca	F11270	1960	£1.50	£4	
Saving My Tears	7"	Columbia	DB7708	1965	£1.50	£4	
Send Me The Pillow That You Dream On	7"	HMV	POP1069	1962	£1.50	£4	
This Is My Lovely Day	7"	Columbia	DB7394	1964	£1.50	£4	
Unforgettable Love	7"	HMV	POP1181	1963	£1.50	£4	

SAITHESWAITE, SIR SIDNEY

Our Mabel	7"	Parlophone	R5636	1967	£1.50	£4	
Tea Lovely Tea	7"	Parlophone	R5591	1967	£1.50	£4	

SAKAMOTO, KYU

Sukiyaki	LP	Capitol	(D)T10349	1963	£5	£12	US
Sukiyaki	7"	HMV	POP1171	1963	£1.50	£4	chart single

SAKER

Even Though We Ain't Got Money	7"	CBS	7399	1971	£2	£5	
Foggy Tuesday	7"	Parlophone	R5740	1968	£4	£8	
Hey Joe	7"	Parlophone	R5752	1969	£4	£8	
Still Got You	7"	Polydor	BM56231	1968	£1.50	£4	
What A Beautiful World	7"	CBS	7010	1971	£2	£5	

SALAMANDER

Crystal Ball	7"	CBS	5102	1970	£5	£10	
Ten Commandments	LP	Youngblood	SSYB14	1972	£60	£120	

SALES, SOUPY

Mouse	7"	HMV	POP1432	1965	£1.50	£4	

SALLY & THE ALLEYCATS

Is It Something I Said	7"	Parlophone	R5183	1964	£2.50	£6	

SALLYANGIE

The Sallyangie was a folky duo comprising Sally Oldfield and her young brother Michael. Their one LP was re-released in the seventies, in a vain attempt on the part of Transatlantic records to gain some spin-off benefit from the success of "Tubular Bells" and its successors. The new cover, however, is completely different to the original, which shows a close-up of the two Oldfields, so distinguishing the two versions is no problem.

Child Of Allah	7"	Philips	6006259	1972	£7.50	£15	
Children Of The Sun	LP	Transatlantic	TRA176	1968	£20	£40	
Children Of The Sun	LP	Transatlantic	TRA176	1973	£6	£15	reissue, different sleeve
Two Ships	7"	Transatlantic	BIG126	1969	£7.50	£15	

SALMA, DOUG

Highland Fling	7"	Philips	BF1279	1963	£1.50	£4	

SALT & PEPPER

High Noon	7"	London	HLU9338	1961	£1.50	£4	

SALVADOR, SAL

Sal Salvador Quartet	10" LP	Capitol	KPL105	1955	£15	£30	

SALVATION

Cinderella	7"	United Artists	UP35048	1969	£1.50	£4	
Salvation	LP	United Artists	UAS29062	1969	£6	£15	

SALVATION (2)

Girlsoul	7"	Merciful Release	MR025	1983	£2.50	£6	
Girlsoul	12"	Merciful Release	MRX025	1983	£3	£8	
Jessica's Crime	12"	Batfish	USS104	1986	£2.50	£6	

SALVO, SAMMY

Afraid	7"	London	HLP8997	1959	£2.50	£6	
Billy Blue	7"	Polydor	NH66974	1962	£2.50	£6	
Say Yeah	7"	RCA	RCA1032	1958	£6	£12	

SAM & BILL

Fly Me To The Moon	7"	Pye	7N25355	1966	£5	£10
I Feel Like Tryin'	7"	Brunswick	05973	1967	£7.50	£15

SAM & DAVE

Baby Baby Don't Stop Now	7"	Atlantic	584324	1970	£1.50	£4	
Best Of Sam And Dave	LP	Atlantic	587/588155	1969	£4	£10	
Can't You Find Another Way	7"	Atlantic	584211	1968	£1.50	£4	
Double Dynamite	LP	Atlantic	588181	1969	£6	£15	
Double Dynamite	LP	Stax	589003	1967	£8	£20	chart LP
Everybody Got To Believe	7"	Atlantic	584228	1968	£1.50	£4	
Hold On I'm Comin'	LP	Atlantic	587/588045	1966	£6	£15	chart LP
Hold On I'm Comin'	7"	Atlantic	584003	1966	£2.50	£6	
I Thank You	LP	Atlantic	587/588154	1968	£6	£15	
I Thank You	7"	Stax	601030	1968	£1.50	£4	chart single
If You Got The Loving	7"	Atlantic	584047	1966	£1.50	£4	
No More Pain	7"	King	KG1041	1966	£2.50	£6	
Ooh Ooh Ooh	7"	Atlantic	584303	1969	£1.50	£4	
Sam And Dave	LP	Major Minor	MCP5000	1968	£4	£10	
Sam And Dave	LP	Roulette	(S)R25323	1966	£6	£15	US
Soothe Me	7"	Stax	601004	1967	£2	£5	chart single
Soul Man	7"	Stax	601023	1967	£2	£5	chart single
Soul Men	LP	Atlantic	588185	1969	£6	£15	
Soul Men	LP	Stax	589015	1967	£8	£20	chart LP
Soul Sister Brown Sugar	7"	Atlantic	584237	1969	£2	£5	chart single
When Something Is Wrong With My Baby	7"	Stax	601006	1967	£2	£5	
You Don't Know Like I Know	7"	Atlantic	584086	1967	£2	£5	
You Don't Know Like I Know	7"	Atlantic	584247	1969	£2	£5	
You Don't Know Like I Know	7"	Atlantic	AT4066	1966	£4	£8	
You Don't Know What You Mean To Me	7"	Atlantic	584192	1968	£1.50	£4	
You Got Me Hummin'	7"	Atlantic	584064	1967	£1.50	£4	

SAM APPLE PIE

Call Me Boss	7"	DJM	DJS274	1973	£2	£5	
East 17	LP	DJM	DJLPS429	1973	£8	£20	
Sam Apple Pie	LP	Decca	LKR/SKLR5005	1969	£35	£70	
Sometime Girl	7"	Decca	F22932	1969	£5	£10	

SAM, ERV & TOM

Soul Teacher	7"	Direction	583339	1968	£1.50	£4

SAM THE SHAM & THE PHARAOHS

Best Of Sam The Sham	LP	MGM	(S)E4422	1967	£6	£15	US
Hair On My Chinny Chin Chin	7"	MGM	MGM1326	1966	£1.50	£4	
Hair On My Chinny Chin Chin	7" EP	MGM	63639	1966	£6	£12	French
How Do You Catch A Girl	7"	MGM	MGM1331	1966	£1.50	£4	
Ju Ju Hand	7"	MGM	MGM1278	1965	£2.50	£6	
Ju Ju Hand	7" EP	MGM	63624	1965	£6	£12	French
Li'l Red Riding Hood	LP	MGM	C(S)8032	1966	£6	£15	
Li'l Red Riding Hood	7"	MGM	MGM1315	1966	£2.50	£6	chart single
Lil' Red Riding Hood	7" EP	MGM	63637	1966	£6	£12	French
Nefertiti	LP	MGM	(S)E4479	1967	£5	£12	US
Oh That's Bad No That's Good	7"	MGM	MGM1337	1967	£1.50	£4	
On Tour	LP	MGM	(S)E4347	1966	£6	£15	US
Red Hot	7"	MGM	MGM1298	1966	£2.50	£6	
Red Hot	7" EP	MGM	63631	1966	£6	£12	French
Red Hot	7" EP	MGM	MGMEP794	1966	£7.50	£15	
Ring Dang Doo	7"	MGM	MGM1285	1965	£2.50	£6	
Ring Dang Doo	7" EP	MGM	63626	1965	£6	£12	French
Ten Of Pentacles	LP	MGM	SE4526	1968	£5	£12	US
Their Second Album	LP	MGM	(S)E4314	1965	£6	£15	US
Wooly Bully	LP	MGM	C1007	1965	£6	£15	
Wooly Bully	7"	MGM	MGM1269	1965	£4	£8	chart single
Wooly Bully	7"	MGM	MGM1473	1969	£1.50	£4	
Wooly Bully	7" EP	MGM	63623	1965	£10	£20	French, group PS
Wooly Bully	7" EP	MGM	63623	1965	£7.50	£15	French, sphinx PS
Yakety Yak	7"	MGM	MGM1379	1968	£1.50	£4	

SAMAIN

Vibrations Of Doom	LP	Roadrunner			£35	£70	Canada

SAME

Wild About You	7"	Wessex	WEX267	1979	£1.50	£4

SAMETI

Hungry For Love	LP	Warner Bros	56074	1974	£4	£10	German
Sameti	LP	Brain	0001020	1972	£8	£20	German

SAMMLA MAMMAS MANNA

For Aldre Nybegynnare	LP	Silence	SRS4640	1978	£4	£10	Swedish
Klossa Knapitatet	LP	Silence	SRS4627	1974	£6	£15	Swedish
Maltid	LP	Silence	SRS4621	1973	£8	£20	Swedish
Samla Mammas Manna	LP	Silence	SRS4604	1971	£8	£20	Swedish
Snorungarnas Symfoni	LP	Musiknatet Wax	MNW70P	1976	£5	£12	Swedish

SAMMY

Sammy	LP	Philips	6308136	1972	£8	£20

SAMPSON, DAVE & THE HUNTERS

Dave	7" EP..	Columbia	ESG7853	1961	£37.50	£75	stereo
Dave	7" EP..	Columbia	SEG8095	1961	£25	£50	
Easy To Dream	7"	Columbia	DB4625	1961	£4	£8	
If You Need Me	7"	Columbia	DB4502	1960	£5	£10	chart single
Sweet Dreams	7"	Columbia	DB4449	1960	£5	£10	
Why The Chicken	7"	Columbia	DB4597	1961	£2.50	£6	
Wide Wide World	7"	Fontana	H361	1962	£2.50	£6	

SAMPSON, EDGAR

Swing Softly Sweet Sampson	LP	Vogue Coral	LVA9039	1957	£6	£15	

SAMPSON, TOMMY & HIS STRONGMEN

Rockin'	7"	Melodisc	1411	1958	£2.50	£6	

SAMSON

Are You Samson	LP	Instant	INSP004	1969	£15	£30	Sleeve pictured in guide
Venus	7"	Parlophone	R5867	1970	£4	£8	

SAMSON (2)

Riding With The Angels	7"	RCA	RCA67	1981	£1.50	£4	pic disc
Samson	LP	Gem	GEMLP113	1981	£4	£10	
Survivors	LP	Laser	LAP1	1979	£4	£10	
Telephone	7"	Lightning	GIL547	1978	£7.50	£15	
Vice Versa	7"	EMI	EMI5061	1980	£2.50	£6	

SAMUEL PRODY

Samuel Prody	LP	Global	6306906	1974	£40	£80	German

SAMUELS, JERRY

Puppy Love	7"	HMV	7M411	1956	£1.50	£4	

SAMUELS, WINSTON

Be Prepared	7"	Ska Beat	JB196	1965	£5	£10	
Follow	7"	Rio	R26	1964	£5	£10	
Greatest	7"	Island	WI3051	1967	£5	£10	
I Won't Be Discouraged	7"	Island	WI3053	1967	£5	£10	
Luck Will Come My Way	7"	Black Swan	WI419	1964	£5	£10	Lloyd Brevitt B side
My Angel	7"	Ska Beat	JB214	1965	£5	£10	
Time Will Tell	7"	Ska Beat	JB244	1966	£5	£10	
Up And Down	7"	Ska Beat	JB241	1966	£5	£10	
What Have I Done	7"	Ska Beat	JB238	1966	£5	£10	
You Are The One	7"	Black Swan	WI426	1964	£5	£10	
You Are The One	7"	Columbia	DB7405	1964	£2.50	£6	

SAMURAI

Samurai	LP	Greenwich	GSLP1003	1971	£40	£80	

SAN FRANCISCO EARTHQUAKE

Fairy Tales Can Come True	7"	Mercury	MF1036	1968	£4	£8	

SAN REMO STRINGS

Festival Time	7"	Tamla Motown	TMG795	1971	£1.50	£4	chart single
Reach Out And I'll Be There	7"	Tamla Motown	TMG807	1972	£1.50	£4	
San Remo Strings Swing	LP	Tamla Motown	STML11216	1973	£5	£12	

SAND

Sand	LP	Barnaby	BR15006	1973	£8	£20	US double

SANDELLS

Scramblers	LP	World Pacific	(ST)1818	1964	£5	£12	US
Scramblers	LP	World Pacific	ST1818	1964	£10	£25	US red vinyl

SANDERS, ALEX

Witch Is Born	LP	A&M	AMLS984	1970	£15	£30	

SANDERS, GARY

Ain't No Beatle	7"	Warner Bros	WB5676	1966	£1.50	£4	

SANDERS, PHARAOH

These days, Pharaoh Sanders has matured into a tranquil elder statesman of jazz. Originally, however, he was the angry young saxophonist with the flame-thrower technique, who was brought in by John Coltrane to help push his own playing towards a new peak of intensity. Sanders" own first album on ESP has become very scarce, although the music represents the uneasy compromise that results when a fiery, avant-garde player is provided with a rhythm section whose idea of an appropriate support derives from a politer, earlier time.

Black Unity	LP	Impulse	AS9219	1973	£4	£10	
Deaf, Dumb, Blind	LP	Impulse	AS9199	1973	£4	£10	
Live At The East	LP	Impulse	AS9227	1973	£4	£10	
Pharaoh	LP	ESP	1003	1965	£25	£50	

SANDERS, RAY

World So Full Of Love	7"	London	HLG7106	1960	£2.50	£6	export

SANDFORD, CHRIS

I Wish They Wouldn't Always Say	7"	Fontana	TF633	1965	£1.50	£4	
Not Too Little Not Too Much	7"	Decca	F11778	1963	£1.50	£4	chart single
You're Gonna Be My Girl	7"	Decca	F11842	1964	£1.50	£4	

SANDON, JOHNNY

Blizzard	7"	Pye	7N15717	1964	£4	£8	
Donna Means Heartbreak	7"	Pye	7N15665	1964	£4	£8	

Lies	7"	Pye	7N15542	1963	£4	£8	
Magic Potion	7"	Pye	7N15559	1963	£4	£8	
Sixteen Tons	7"	Pye	7N15602	1964	£4	£8	

SANDPEBBLES

If You Didn't Hear Me The First Time	7"	Toast	TT505	1968	£1.50	£4	
Love Power	7"	Track	604015	1967	£2.50	£6	
Love Power	7"	Track	604028	1969	£2	£5	

SANDPIPERS

Guantanamera	7"	Pye	7N25380	1966	£1.50	£4	chart single
Guantanamera	7" EP	Pye	NEP44081	1966	£2	£5	
Louie Louie	7"	Pye	7N25396	1966	£1.50	£4	

SANDRA

I'll Never Be Maria Magdalena	12"	10	TENY7812	1986	£3	£8	pic disc

SANDROSE

Sandrose	LP	Polydor	2480137	1972	£65	£130	sleeve pictured in Guide

SANDS

Mrs.Gillespie's Refrigerator	7"	Reaction	591017	1967	£37.50	£75	
Venus	7"	Major Minor	MM681	1970	£5	£10	

SANDS (2)

Dance Dance Dance	7"	Tribune	TRS122	197-	£2	£5	
Sand Doin's	LP	Tribune		197-	£10	£25	

SANDS, CLIVE

Hooked On A Feeling	7"	SNB	554058	1969	£2.50	£6	
Witchi Tai To	7"	SNB	554431	1969	£5	£10	

SANDS, DAVEY & THE ESSEX

Advertising Girl	7"	CBS	202620	1967	£4	£8	
Please Be Mine	7"	Decca	F12170	1965	£5	£10	

SANDS, EVIE

Picture Me Gone	7"	Cameo Parkway	C413	1966	£20	£40	
Take Me For A Little While	7"	Red Bird	BC118	1965	£7.50	£15	

SANDS FAMILY

First Day And Second Day	LP	Autogram	FLLP501	1974	£6	£15	German
Folk From The Mournes	LP	Outlet	OAS3004	1968	£6	£15	Irish
Real Irish Folk	LP	Emerald	GES1201	1979	£6	£15	
Third Day	LP	Autogram	ALLP233	1974	£6	£15	German
You'll Be Well Looked After	LP	Leaf	7005	1975	£5	£12	Irish

SANDS, JODIE

All I Ask Of You	7"	Starlite	ST45005	1958	£1.50	£4	
Please Don't Tell Me	7"	London	HL8530	1957	£2	£5	
Someday	7"	HMV	POP533	1958	£1.50	£4	chart single
With All My Heart	7"	London	HL8456	1957	£2	£5	

SANDS, TOMMY

Big Date	7"	Capitol	CL14889	1958	£1.50	£4	
Blue Ribbon Baby	7"	Capitol	CL14925	1958	£5	£10	
Connie	7"	HMV	POP1193	1963	£1.50	£4	
Dream With Me	LP	Capitol	T1426	1961	£8	£20	
Going Steady	7"	Capitol	CL14745	1957	£2.50	£6	
Hawaiian Rock	7"	Capitol	CL14872	1958	£5	£10	
Is It Ever Gonna Happen	7"	Capitol	CL15013	1959	£5	£10	
Let Me Be Loved	7"	Capitol	CL14781	1957	£1.50	£4	
Love In A Goldfish Bowl	7"	Capitol	CL15219	1961	£1.50	£4	
Man Like Wow	7"	Capitol	CL14811	1957	£4	£8	
Old Oaken Bucket	7"	Capitol	CL15143	1960	£1.50	£4	chart single
Only 'Cos I'm Lonely	7"	HMV	POP1247	1963	£1.50	£4	
Ring A Ding Ding	7"	Capitol	CL14724	1957	£2.50	£6	
Sands At The Sands	LP	Capitol	(S)T1364	1960	£8	£20	US
Sands Storm	LP	Capitol	T1081	1959	£8	£20	
Sands Storm Part 1	7" EP	Capitol	EAP11081	1959	£10	£20	
Sands Storm Part 2	7" EP	Capitol	EAP21081	1959	£12.50	£25	
Sands Storm Part 3	7" EP	Capitol	EAP31081	1959	£12.50	£25	
Sing Boy Sing	LP	Capitol	T929	1958	£10	£25	
Sing Boy Sing	7"	Capitol	CL14834	1958	£2.50	£6	
Sinner Man	7"	Capitol	CL15047	1959	£1.50	£4	
Statue	7"	Liberty	LIB55842	1966	£10	£20	
Steady Date	LP	Capitol	T848	1957	£10	£25	
Steady Date Part 1	7" EP	Capitol	EAP1848	1957	£10	£20	
Steady Date Part 2	7" EP	Capitol	EAP2848	1957	£10	£20	
Steady Date Part 3	7" EP	Capitol	EAP3848	1957	£10	£20	
Teenage Crush	7"	Capitol	CL14695	1957	£5	£10	
Teenage Crush	7" EP	Capitol	EAP1851	1957	£10	£20	
Teenage Rock	LP	Capitol	T1109	1959	£8	£20	US
That's The Way I Am	7"	Capitol	CL15071	1959	£1.50	£4	
This Thing Called Love	LP	Capitol	T1123	1959	£6	£15	
This Thing Called Love	7" EP	Capitol	EAP11123	1959	£6	£12	
When I'm Thinking Of You	LP	Capitol	(S)T1239	1960	£6	£15	
Worrying Kind	7"	Capitol	CL14971	1959	£7.50	£15	
You Hold The Future	7"	Capitol	CL15109	1960	£1.50	£4	

SANDS, TONY & THE DRUMBEATS
Shame Shame Shame .... 7" ...... Studio 36 .... NSRSEP1/2 .... 196- .... £50 ....£100 ....

SANDS, WES
There's Lots More Where This Came | 7" ...... Columbia .... DB4996 .... 1963 ... £7.50 ......£15 ....
From ....

SANDY
Solitary Man .... 7" ...... Columbia .... DB7938 .... 1966 ... £1.50 ....£4 ....

SANDY COAST
Blackboard Jungle Lady .... 7" ...... Polydor .... 2001457 .... 1973 ... £10 ....£20
From The Stereo Workshop .... LP ..... Page One .... POLS020 .... 1969 ... £60 ....£120
Shipwreck .... LP ..... Page One .... MORS201 .... 1969 ... £60 ....£120
Stone Wall .... LP ..... Polydor .... 2310277 .... 1973 ... £10 ....£25

SANSOM, BOBBY
There's A Place .... 7" ...... Oriole .... CB1837 .... 1963 ... £2.50 ....£6
Where Have You Been .... 7" ...... Oriole .... CB1888 .... 1963 ... £1.50 ....£4

SANSON, VERONIQUE
French singer-songwriter Veronique Sanson composed "Amoureuse", which was a big hit for Kiki Dee. Her own version is the lead track of an excellent album which was released in two versions, one with French lyrics and one with English. One would not have thought that it would make much difference, but the French version is far superior. The way in which Ms.Sanson's voice takes on an attractive soft vibrato at the end of the lines is ideally matched to the soft endings of the French words. In English she sounds a little ordinary, but in French the record stands revealed as a superb example of the singer-songwriting genre. Veronique Sanson is a considerable star in France these days, but "Amoureuse" remains her only success outside that country.
Amoureuse .... LP ..... Elektra .... K42106 .... 1972 ... £5 ....£12 .... English vocals
Veronique Sanson .... LP ..... Elektra .... K42106 .... 1972 ... £5 ....£12 .... French vocals

SANTAMARIA, MONGO
25 Miles .... 7" ...... Direction .... 584430 .... 1969 ... £2 ....£5
Black Eyed Peas And Rice .... 7" ...... CBS .... 201766 .... 1965 ... £1.50 ......£4
Cloud Nine .... 7" ...... Direction .... 584086 .... 1969 ... £2 ....£5
El Pussycat .... 7" ...... CBS .... 201766 .... 1965 ... £1.50 ......£4
Sherry .... 7" ...... Oriole .... 1963 ... £7.50 ......£15
Watermelon Man .... 7" ...... Riverside .... RIF106909 .... 1963 ... £2 ....£5
Working On A Groovy Thing .... LP ..... CBS .... 63904 .... 1971 ... £4 ....£10

SANTANA
Abraxas .... LP ..... CBS .... Q64087 .... 1974 ... £5 ....£12 ....quad
Abraxas .... LP ..... Columbia .... HC40130 .... 1981 ... £5 ....£12 .... US audiophile
Amigos .... LP ..... Columbia .... PCQ33576 .... 1975 ... £5 ....£12 ....US quad
Barboletta .... LP ..... CBS .... Q69084 .... 1974 ... £5 ....£12 ....quad
Caravanserai .... LP ..... CBS .... Q65299 .... 1974 ... £5 ....£12 ....quad
Festival .... LP ..... Columbia .... PCQ34423 .... 1977 ... £5 ....£12 ....US quad
Greatest Hits .... LP ..... CBS .... Q69081 .... 1974 ... £5 ....£12 ....quad
Illuminations .... LP ..... Columbia .... PCQ32900 .... 1974 ... £5 ....£12 ....US quad
Santana .... LP ..... CBS .... 63815 .... 1970 ... £4 ....£10 .... laminated cover
Santana .... LP ..... Columbia .... PCQ32964 .... 1974 ... £5 ....£12 ....US quad
Santana III .... LP ..... CBS .... Q69015 .... 1974 ... £5 ....£12 ....quad
Solo Guitar Of Devadip Carlos Santana LP ..... Columbia .... AS573 .... 1979 ... £8 ....£20 .... US promo
Welcome .... LP ..... CBS .... Q69040 .... 1974 ... £5 ....£12 ....quad
Zebop .... LP ..... Columbia .... HC47158 .... 1981 ... £5 ....£12 .... US audiophile

SANTELLS
So Fine .... 7" ...... Sue .... WI4020 .... 1966 ... £6 ....£12

SANTO & JOHNNY
Beatles' Greatest Hits .... LP ..... Canadian Am. . (S)1017 .... 1964 ... £8 ....£20 .... US
Birmingham .... 7" ...... Parlophone ...... R4865 .... 1962 ... £1.50 ......£4 ....
Brilliant Guitar Sounds .... LP ..... Imperial .... LP9363/12363 ..... 1967 ... £4 ....£10 .... US
Bullseye .... 7" ...... Parlophone ...... R4844 .... 1961 ... £2 ....£5 ....
Caravan .... 7" ...... Parlophone ...... R4844 .... 1960 ... £1.50 ......£4 ....
Come On In .... LP ..... Canadian Am. . (S)1006 .... 1962 ... £6 ....£15 .... US
Come September .... 7" ...... Pye .... 7N25111 .... 1961 ... £1.50 ......£4 ....
Encore .... LP ..... Canadian Am. . (S)1002 .... 1960 ... £6 ....£15 .... US
Golden Guitars .... LP ..... Imperial .... LP12366 .... 1968 ... £4 ....£10 .... US
Hawaii .... LP ..... Stateside .... (S)SL1008 .... 1964 ... £6 ....£15 ....
In The Still Of The Night .... LP ..... Canadian Am. . (S)1014 .... 1963 ... £6 ....£15 .... US
In The Still Of The Night .... 7" ...... Stateside .... SS292 .... 1964 ... £1.50 ......£4 ....
Mona Lisa .... LP ..... Philips .... (S)BL7760 .... 1967 ... £4 ....£10 ....
Mucho .... LP ..... Canadian Am. . (S)1018 .... 1965 ... £5 ....£12 .... US
Off Shore .... LP ..... Canadian Am. . (S)1011 .... 1963 ... £6 ....£15 .... US
On The Road Again .... LP ..... Imperial .... LP12418 .... 1968 ... £4 ....£10 .... US
Pulcinella .... LP ..... Philips .... (S)BL7759 .... 1967 ... £4 ....£10 ....
Santo & Johnny No.1 .... 7" EP.. Parlophone ...... GEP8806 .... 1960 ... £7.50 ......£15 ....
Santo & Johnny No.2 .... 7" EP.. Parlophone ...... GEP8813 .... 1960 ... £7.50 ......£15 ....
Santo And Johnny .... LP ..... Canadian Am. . 1001 .... 1959 ... £8 ....£20 .... US
Sleepwalk .... 7" ...... Pye .... 7N25037 .... 1959 ... £2 ....£5 ....chart single
Spanish Harlem .... 7" ...... Stateside .... SS110 .... 1962 ... £1.50 ......£4 ....
Teardrop .... 7" ...... Parlophone ...... R4619 .... 1960 ... £2 ....£5 ....chart single
Three Caballeros .... 7" ...... Stateside .... SS253 .... 1964 ... £1.50 ......£4 ....
Wish You Were Here .... LP ..... Canadian Am. . (S)1016 .... 1964 ... £6 ....£15 .... US

SAPPHIRES
Evil One .... 7" ...... HMV .... POP1461 .... 1965 ... £35 ....£70 ....
Gotta Have Your Love .... 7" ...... HMV .... POP1441 .... 1965 ... £40 ....£80 ....
Who Do You Love .... LP ..... Swan .... LP513 .... 1964 ... £25 ....£50 .... US
Who Do You Love .... 7" ...... Stateside .... SS267 .... 1964 ... £10 ....£20

Your True Love	7"	Stateside	SS223	1963	£10	£20

SARABAND
| Close To It All | LP | Folk Heritage | FHR050 | 1973 | £10 | £25 |

SARACEN
Heroes Saints And Fools	LP	Nucleus	NEAT492	1982	£6	£15
No More Lonely Nights	7"	Nucleus	SAR1	1982	£2	£5
We Have Arrived	7"	Nucleus	NEAT30	1983	£2	£5

SARGENT, DON
| Gypsy Boots | 7" | Vogue | V9160 | 1960 | £40 | £80 |

SARI & THE SHALIMARS
| It's So Lonely Being Together | 7" | United Artists | UP2235 | 1968 | £5 | £10 |

SARJEANT, DEREK
Derek Sarjeant Folk Trio	LP	Assembly	JP3001	1971	£20	£40
Folk Songs	7" EP	Oak	RGJ101	196-	£10	£20
Folk Songs Vol.2	7" EP	Oak	RGJ105	196-	£10	£20
Man Of Kent	7" EP	Oak	RGJ117	1963	£10	£20
Songs We Like To Sing	7" EP	Oak	RGJ103	196-	£7.50	£15

SARNE, MIKE
Code Of Love	7"	Parlophone	R5010	1963	£1.50	£4	chart single
Come Outside	LP	Parlophone	PMC1187	1962	£8	£20	
Come Outside	7"	Parlophone	R4902	1962	£1.50	£4	chart single
Hello Lover Boy	7"	Parlophone	R5090	1963	£1.50	£4	
Just For Kicks	7"	Parlophone	R4974	1962	£1.50	£4	chart single
Love Me Please	7"	Parlophone	R5170	1964	£1.50	£4	
Mike Sarne Hit Parade	7" EP	Parlophone	GEP8879	1963	£7.50	£15	
Out And About	7"	Parlophone	R5129	1964	£1.50	£4	
Please Don't Say	7"	Parlophone	R5060	1963	£1.50	£4	
Will I What	7"	Parlophone	R4932	1962	£1.50	£4	chart single

SAROFEEN & SMOKE
| Do It | LP | Pye | NSPL28153 | 1971 | £4 | £10 |

SAROLTA
| Open Your Hands | 7" | Island | WIP6035 | 1968 | £2 | £5 |

SARSTEDT, PETER
| Where Do You Go To | 7" | United Artists | UP2262 | 1968 | £1.50 | £4 | chart single |

SASPARELLA
| Spooky | 7" | Decca | F12892 | 1969 | £2 | £5 |

SASSAFRAS
| Expecting Company | LP | Polydor | 2383245 | 1973 | £5 | £12 |

SASSENACHS
| That Don't Worry Me | 7" | Fontana | TF518 | 1964 | £5 | £10 |

SATAN & THE DE-CIPLES
| Underground | LP | Goldband | 7750 | 1969 | £50 | £100 | US |

SATANIC RITES
| Live To Ride | 7" | Heavy Metal | HEAVY8 | 1981 | £4 | £8 |

SATAN'S RATS
In My Love For You	7"	DJM	DJS10819	1977	£4	£8
Year Of The Rats	7"	DJM	DJS10821	1978	£5	£10
You Make Me Sick	7"	DJM	DJS10840	1978	£5	£10

SATCHMO, PAT
| Hello Dolly | 7" | Upsetter | US316 | 1969 | £1.50 | £4 |

SATIN BELLS
| Baby You're So Right For Me | 7" | Pye | 7N17531 | 1968 | £2 | £5 |
| I Stand Accused | 7" | Decca | F22937 | 1969 | £1.50 | £4 |

SATIN WHALE
| Desert Places | LP | Brain | 0001049 | 1974 | £4 | £10 | German |

SATINS FOUR & THE CINNAMON ANGELS
| Mixed Soul | LP | B.T.Puppy | S1010 | 1970 | £6 | £15 | US |

SATISFACTION
| Satisfaction | LP | Decca | SKL5075 | 1971 | £5 | £12 |

SATISFIERS
| Where'll I Be Tomorrow Tonight? | 7" | Vogue Coral | Q72247 | 1957 | £5 | £10 |

SATTIN, LONNIE
High Steel	7"	Capitol	CL14638	1956	£1.50	£4
I'll Never Stop Loving You	7"	Capitol	CL14771	1957	£1.50	£4
Ring Around The Moon	7"	Capitol	CL14831	1958	£1.50	£4
Trapped	7"	Capitol	CL14552	1956	£1.50	£4

SATURNALIA

Like the other early rock LP picture disc (Curved Air's "Airconditioning"), "Magical Love" looks rather better than it sounds, for only a few playings are enough to make the sound quality begin to seriously deteriorate. And unlike the situation with Curved Air, Saturnalia's record was never issued in the more conventional form. As a result, it is hard to be fair to the music: it sounds like third division progressive fare - a bit like Principal Edward's Magic Theatre on an off day - but listening through the welter of background hiss one cannot be sure. To be complete, by the way, the record should come with a booklet, although few copies of this seem to have survived.

Magical Love	LP	Matrix	TRIX1	1969	£10	£25	pic disc with centre pattern & booklet
Magical Love	LP	Matrix	TRIX1	1969	£25	£50	test pressing, not pic disc
Magical Love	LP	Matrix	TRIX1SP	1980	£4	£10	pic disc

SAUNDERS, LARRY

On The Real Side	7"	London	HLU10469	1974	£2.50	£6

SAUTER-FINEGAN ORCHESTRA

Inside Sauter-Finegan	LP	HMV	CLP1027	1955	£10	£25
Memories Of Goodman And Miller	LP	RCA	RD27093/SF5029	1959	£5	£12

SAVAGE, EDNA

Arrivederci Darling	7"	Parlophone	MSP6189	1955	£5	£10	chart single
Candlelight	7"	Parlophone	MSP6181	1955	£4	£8	
Let Me Be Loved	7"	Parlophone	R4360	1957	£1.50	£4	
Me Head's In De Barrel	7"	Parlophone	R4301	1957	£1.50	£4	
My Prayer	7"	Parlophone	R4226	1956	£2.50	£6	
Never Leave Me	7"	Parlophone	R4253	1957	£1.50	£4	
Please Hurry Home	7"	Parlophone	MSP6217	1956	£2.50	£6	
Stars Shine In Your Eyes	7"	Parlophone	MSP6175	1955	£4	£8	

SAVAGE, JOAN

Five Oranges, Four Apples	7"	Columbia	DB3929	1957	£1.50	£4
Left Right Out Of My Heart	7"	Columbia	DB4159	1958	£1.50	£4
Love Letters In The Sand	7"	Columbia	DB3968	1957	£1.50	£4
Shake Me I Rattle	7"	Columbia	DB4039	1957	£5	£10

SAVAGE RESURRECTION

Savage Resurrection	LP	Mercury	SMCL20123	1968	£10	£25
Thing In E	7"	Mercury	MF1027	1968	£6	£12

SAVAGE ROSE

In The Plain	LP	Polydor	46292	1968	£5	£12
Savage Rose	LP	Polydor	184144	1968	£5	£12
Travellin'	LP	Polydor	184316	1969	£5	£12

SAVAGES

Live And Wild	LP	Drone		196-	£50	£100	US

SAVARIN, JULIAN JAY

I Am You	7"	Lyntone	LYN3426	197-	£2.50	£6
Waiters On The Dance	LP	Birth	RAB2	1971	£50	£100

SAVILLE, JIMMY

Ahab The Arab	7"	Decca	F11493	1962	£1.50	£4
Bossa Nova	7"	Decca	F11576	1963	£1.50	£4

SAVOY BROWN

Savoy Brown passed through numerous line-ups, in which the presence of guitarist Kim Simmonds was the only constant factor. Simmonds and his companions lacked the imagination to break very far out of the constraints of playing the blues, although they tried hardest on "Blue Matter", which includes the memorable "Train To Nowhere".

Blue Matter	LP	Decca	LK/SKL4994	1968	£8	£20	
Boogie Brothers	LP	Decca	SKL5186	1974	£4	£10	
Getting To The Point	LP	Decca	LK/SKL4925	1968	£15	£30	
Hard Way To Go	7"	Decca	F13019	1970	£1.50	£4	
Hellbound Train	LP	Decca	TXS107	1972	£4	£10	
I Tried	7"	Purdah	453503	1966	£30	£60	
I'm Tired	7"	Decca	F12978	1969	£2	£5	
Jack The Toad	LP	Decca	TXS112	1973	£4	£10	
Lion's Share	LP	Decca	SKL5152	1973	£4	£10	
Looking In	LP	Decca	SKL5066	1970	£5	£12	chart LP
Poor Girl	7"	Decca	F13098	1970	£1.50	£4	
Raw Sienna	LP	Decca	LK5030	1970	£6	£15	mono
Raw Sienna	LP	Decca	SKL5030	1970	£5	£12	stereo
Shake Down	LP	Decca	LK/SKL4883	1967	£15	£30	
Skin 'n' Bone	LP	London	PS670	1976	£4	£10	US
Step Further	LP	Decca	LK/SKL5013	1969	£6	£15	
Street Corner Talking	LP	Decca	TXS104	1970	£4	£10	
Taste And Try Before You Buy	7"	Decca	F12702	1967	£4	£8	
Tell Mama	7"	Decca	F13247	1971	£1.50	£4	
Train To Nowhere	7"	Decca	F12843	1969	£2	£5	
Walking By Myself	7"	Decca	F12797	1968	£2.50	£6	
Wire Fire	LP	London	PS659	1975	£4	£10	US

SAXON

And The Bands Played On	7"	Carrere	CAR180P	1981	£1.50	£4	pic disc
Back On The Streets	7"	Parlophone	RP6103	1985	£2	£5	shaped pic disc
Power And The Glory	7"	RCA	SAXONP1	1983	£1.50	£4	signed pic disc
Rock The Nations	7"	EMI	EMIP5587	1986	£1.50	£4	shaped pic disc

SAXON, AL

Battle Of The Sexes	7" EP	Fontana	TFE17271	1960	£5	£10

Big Deal	7" EP..	Fontana	TFE17202	1959	£5	£10	
Only Sixteen	7"	Fontana	H205	1959	£1.50	£4	chart single
Those You've Never Heard	7" EP.	Fontana	TFE17014	1958	£5	£10	
You're The Top Cha	7"	Fontana	H164	1958	£1.50	£4	chart single

SAXON, SKY

Dog=God	7"	Fierce	FRIGHT029	1987	£4	£8	various inserts
They Say	7"	Conquest	777	196-	£10	£20	US

SAXONS

Meet The Saxons	LP	Ace Of Clubs	ACL1173	1963	£30	£60	
Saxon War Cry	7"	Decca	F12179	1965	£12.50	£25	

SAXONS (2)

Love Minus Zero	LP	Mirrosonic	AS1017	1966	£10	£25	US

SAYLES, JOHNNY

Deep Down In Your Heart	7"	Liberty	LIB12042	1966	£4	£8	

SCAFFOLD

1-2-3	7"	Parlophone	R5703	1968	£1.50	£4	
2 Day's Monday	7"	Parlophone	R5443	1966	£1.50	£4	
All The Way Up	7"	Parlophone	R5847	1970	£1.50	£4	
Busdreams	7"	Parlophone	R5866	1970	£1.50	£4	
Charity Bubbles	7"	Parlophone	R5784	1969	£1.50	£4	
Do The Albert	7"	Parlophone	R5922	1971	£1.50	£4	
Do You Remember?	7"	Parlophone	R5679	1968	£1.50	£4	chart single
Evening With The Scafold	LP	Parlophone	PMC/PCS7051	1968	£6	£15	
Fresh Liver	LP	Island	ILPS9234	1973	£4	£10	
Gin Gan Goolie	7"	Parlophone	R5812	1969	£1.50	£4	chart single
Goodbat Nightman	7"	Parlophone	R5548	1966	£4	£8	
L The P	LP	Parlophone	PMC/PCS7077	1969	£5	£12	
Lily The Pink	7"	Parlophone	R5734	1968	£1.50	£4	chart single
Thank U Very Much	7"	Parlophone	R5643	1967	£1.50	£4	chart single

SCAGGS, BOZ

Boz	LP	Polydor	LPHM46253	1965	£20	£40	
Boz Scaggs	LP	Atlantic	588205	1969	£4	£10	
Boz Scaggs	LP	Columbia	AS203	1974	£8	£20	US promo sampler
Silk Degrees	LP	Columbia	HC43920	1980	£5	£12	US audiophile
Still Falling For You	LP	Columbia		1978	£8	£20	US early version of 'Two Down Then Left'

SCALES, HARVEY & THE SOUND

Get Down	7"	Atlantic	584146	1967	£1.50	£4	

SCAMPS

Petite Fleur	7"	London	HLW8827	1959	£2	£5	

SCARECROW

Scarecrow	LP	Spilt Milk	SMFM11278	1978	£30	£60	numbered

SCARLETS

Let's Go	7"	Philips	BF1376	1964	£1.50	£4	

SCENE

Hey Girl	7"	Hole In The Wall	HS1	1980	£1.50	£4	

SCHAEFER, HAL ORCHESTRA

March Of THe Vikings	7"	London	HLT8692	1958	£1.50	£4	

SCHAUBROECK, ARMAND

I Came To Visit	LP	Mirror		1977	£6	£15	US
Shakin' Shakin'	LP	Mirror	5	1978	£8	£20	US

SCHICKERT, GUNTER

Samtvogel	LP	Brain	0040176	1975	£4	£10	German
Samtvogel	LP	SCH	33003	1974	£10	£25	German

SCHIFRIN, LALO

Mission Impossible	LP	Dot	(S)LPD503	1968	£6	£15	
Mission Impossible	7"	Dot	DOT103	1968	£2.50	£6	

SCHMETTERLINGE

Boom Boom Boomerang	7"	Pye	7N25743	1977	£2.50	£6	

SCHMIDT, IRMIN

Film Musik Vols 3 & 4	LP	Spoon	SPOON018/019	1984	£5	£12	double

SCHMIDT, ZAPPATA

It's Gonna Get You	LP	President	PTLS1041	1971	£4	£10	

SCHMITT, OLIVER LINDSEY

Graffenstadden	LP	private		1972	£22.50	£45	

SCHNITZLER, CONRAD

Auf Dem Schwarzen Kanal	LP	RCA	5908	1980	£4	£10	German
Black Cassette	cass	private		1974	£6	£15	German
Blau	LP	Block	KS1003	1972	£10	£25	German
Con	LP	Paragon	66052	1978	£4	£10	German

Con 3	LP	Sky	SKY061	1981	£4	£10	German
Conal	LP	Uniton	U002	1981	£4	£10	Norwegian
Conrad Und Sohn	LP	private	GS1001	1981	£4	£10	German
Contempora	LP	private	CT1001	1981	£4	£10	German
Control	LP	Dys	DYS04	1981	£4	£10	US
Convex	LP	private	GS1002	1982	£4	£10	German
Conzequenz	LP	Block	KS1004	1980	£6	£15	German
Gelb	LP	Block	EB110	1983	£4	£10	German
Grun	LP	Block	EB111	1983	£4	£10	German
Red Cassette	cass	private		1974	£6	£15	German
Rot	LP	Block	KS1002	1971	£10	£25	German
Schwarz	LP	Block	KS1001	1971	£10	£25	German

SCHOENER, EBERHARD

Bali Agung	LP	Horzu	29647	1976	£4	£10	German
Bastien Und Bastienne	LP	EMI	30231	1977	£4	£10	German
Book	LP	Ariola	28706	1978	£4	£10	German
Day's Lullaby	LP	Reprise	REP44143	1971	£6	£15	German
Der Schauspieldirektor	LP	EMI	30230	1977	£4	£10	German
Destruction Of Harmony	LP	Ariola	808471U	1971	£8	£20	German
Die Schachtel	LP	Reprise		1971	£10	£25	of synthesisers.
Events	LP	Harvest	45879	1980	£4	£10	German
Flash Back	LP	Harvest	32839	1978	£4	£10	German
Meditation	LP	Ariola	87131	1974	£6	£15	German
Spurensicherung	LP	Phonogram	814167	1983	£4	£10	German
Trance Formation	LP	Harvest	32526	1977	£4	£10	German
Video Magic	LP	Harvest	45234	1978	£4	£10	German
Windows	LP	EMI	95634	1974	£4	£10	German

SCHOOL BOYS

Dream Lover	7"	Port-O-Jam	PJ4000	1964	£5	£10	
Little Dilly	7"	Blue Beat	BB174	1963	£5	£10	Prince Buster B side

SCHOOL GIRLS

Last Time	7"	Blue Beat	BB214	1963	£5	£10	
Live Up To Justice	7"	Blue Beat	BB185	1963	£5	£10	
Love Another Love	7"	Blue Beat	BB168	1963	£5	£10	
Never Let You Go	7"	Blue Beat	BB263	1964	£5	£10	Skatalites B side

SCHOOLBOYS

Beatle Mania	LP	Palace	778	1964	£8	£20	US

SCHROEDER, JOHN ORCHESTRA

Agent OO Soul	7"	Piccadilly	7N35271	1965	£4	£8	
Fugitive Theme	7"	Piccadilly	7N35240	1965	£2	£5	PS
Hungry For Love	7"	Piccadilly	7N35285	1966	£4	£8	
Soul For Sale	7"	Piccadilly	7N35362	1967	£5	£10	
Virgin Soldiers March	7"	Pye	7N17862	1969	£4	£8	
Working In The Soulmine	LP	Piccadilly	N(S)PL38025	1966	£5	£12	
You've Lost That Lovin' Feeling	7"	Piccadilly	7N35253	1965	£1.50	£4	

SCHULLER, GUNTHER

Jazz Abstractions	LP	Atlantic	587/588043	1966	£6	£15	

SCHULMAN, IVY & THE BOWTIES

Rock Pretty Baby	7"	London	HLN8372	1957	£30	£60	

SCHULTZ, ERNST

Paranoia Picknick	LP	Kuckuck	2375014	1972	£10	£25	German

SCHULZE, KLAUS

Although Schulze started his recording career as a drummer with Tangerine Dream (he appears on the group's debut, "Electronic Meditation"), all his own albums, of which there are a large number, contain music performed by a bank of synthesisers. Schulze's music, which has a kinship with that of Tangerine Dream, tends nevertheless to sound starker and more experimental. His records vary considerably in their effectiveness, but at their best, they show Schulze to be the finest synthesiser artist of all. "Irrlicht" is available in two different versions - the one listed here has the added benefit of a real orchestra blended with the electronics.

Cyborg	LP	Komische	KM258005	1973	£6	£15	German double
Irrlicht	LP	Ohr	OMM556022	1972	£6	£15	German

SCHUMANN, WALTER

Haunted House	7"	HMV	7M229	1954	£1.50	£4	
Man From Laramie	7"	HMV	7M323	1955	£1.50	£4	

SCHUNGE

Ballad Of A Simple Love	LP	Regal Zonophone	SLRZ1033	1972	£8	£20	
Ballad Of A Simple Love	7"	Regal Zonophone	RZ3077	1973	£2.50	£6	
Misty	7"	Regal Zonophone	RZ3066	1972	£2.50	£6	

SCHWUMP

Aphids In The Wall	7"	Ralph	RRX0776	1976	£50	£100	US

SCIENCE POPTION

You've Got Me High	7"	Columbia	DB8106	1967	£15	£30	

SCIENTIST

Professor In Action	7"	Amalgamated	AMG848	1969	£4	£8	

SCI-FI SEX STARS

Title	Format	Label	Cat No	Year			Notes
Rock It Miss USA	12"	Sputnicko	WMI001	1986	£2.50	£6	

SCOBEY, BOB

Title	Format	Label	Cat No	Year			Notes
Bob Scobey Band	LP	Columbia	33CX10058	1956	£5	£12	
Bob Scobey Band	10" LP	Good Time Jazz	LDG155	1955	£6	£15	
Bob Scobey's Frisco Band	LP	Good Time Jazz	LAG12116	1958	£6	£15	
Bob Scobey's Frisco Band	LP	Good Time Jazz	LAG12180	1959	£5	£12	
Bob Scobey's Frisco Jazz Band	10" LP	HMV	DLP1146	1957	£5	£12	
Scobey And Clancy	LP	Good Time Jazz	LAG12145	1959	£5	£12	with Clancy Hayes
Swingin' On The Golden Gate	LP	RCA	RD27031	1958	£5	£12	

SCORCHED EARTH

Title	Format	Label	Cat No	Year			Notes
Tomorrow Never Comes	7"	Carrere	CAR342	1985	£4	£8	
Tomorrow Never Comes	12"	Carrere	CART342	1985	£8	£20	

SCORCHERS

Title	Format	Label	Cat No	Year			Notes
Ugly Man	7"	Doctor Bird	DB1170	1968	£5	£10	

SCORE

Title	Format	Label	Cat No	Year			Notes
Please Please Me	7"	Decca	F12527	1966	£30	£60	

SCORPIONS

Title	Format	Label	Cat No	Year			Notes
Lonesome Crow	LP	Brain	0040023	1972	£4	£10	German
Lonesome Crow	LP	Heavy Metal	MHIPD2	1982	£6	£15	pic disc

SCORPIONS (2)

Title	Format	Label	Cat No	Year			Notes
Riders In The Sky	7"	Parlophone	R4740	1961	£2	£5	
Scorpio	7"	Parlophone	R4768	1961	£2.50	£6	

SCOT, COLIN

Title	Format	Label	Cat No	Year			Notes
Colin Scot With Friends	LP	United Artists	UAG29154	1971	£4	£10	

SCOTS OF ST.JAMES

Title	Format	Label	Cat No	Year			Notes
Gypsy	7"	Go	AJ111404	1966	£30	£60	
Timothy	7"	Spot	JW1	1967	£25	£50	

SCOTT, ANDY

Title	Format	Label	Cat No	Year			Notes
Invisible	12"	Static	TAK3112	1984	£2.50	£6	clear vinyl
Invisible	12"	Static	TAK31	1984	£1.50	£4	clear vinyl
Krugerrands	12"	Statik	TAK1012	1983	£2.50	£6	
Lady Starlight	7"	RCA	RCA2629	1975	£2.50	£6	
Let Her Dance	7"	Static	TAK24	1984	£2.50	£6	
Let Her Dance	12"	Static	TAK2412	1984	£2.50	£6	

SCOTT, BILLY

Title	Format	Label	Cat No	Year			Notes
Carole	7"	Top Rank	JAR270	1960	£1.50	£4	
You're The Greatest	7"	London	HLU8565	1958	£5	£10	

SCOTT, BOBBY

Title	Format	Label	Cat No	Year			Notes
Bobby Scott Trio	7" EP	London	EZC19008	1956	£5	£10	
Bobby Scott Trio	10" LP	London	LZN14001	1955	£10	£25	
Chain Gang	7"	London	HL8254	1956	£10	£20	
Compositions	10" LP	London	LZN14018	1956	£10	£25	
Great Scott	10" LP	Bethlehem	1004	1954	£8	£20	US

SCOTT, CECIL

Title	Format	Label	Cat No	Year			Notes
Harlem Washboard	LP	Columbia	33SX1232	1960	£4	£10	

SCOTT, FREDDIE

Title	Format	Label	Cat No	Year			Notes
Am I Grooving You	7"	London	HLZ10139	1967	£4	£8	
Are You Lonely For Me	LP	Shout	SLP(S)501	1967	£6	£15	US
Are You Lonely For Me	7"	London	HLZ10103	1967	£5	£10	
Cry To Me	7"	London	HLZ10123	1967	£4	£8	
Everything I Have Is Yours	LP	Columbia	CL2258/CS9058	1964	£6	£15	US
Freddie Scott Sings	LP	Colpix	(S)CP461	1964	£6	£15	US
Great If	7"	Upfront	UP1	197-	£1.50	£4	
He Ain't Gonna Give You None	7"	London	HLZ10172	1967	£2.50	£6	
Hey Girl	7"	Colpix	PX692	1963	£6	£12	
I Got A Woman	7"	Colpix	PX709	1963	£6	£12	
Lonely Man	LP	Columbia	CL2660/CS9460	1967	£6	£15	US
Sugar Sunday	7"	Roulette	RO509	1969	£2.50	£6	

SCOTT, HAZEL

Title	Format	Label	Cat No	Year			Notes
Late Show	10" LP	Capitol	LC6607	1953	£6	£15	

SCOTT, JACK

Title	Format	Label	Cat No	Year			Notes
All I See Is Blue	7"	Capitol	CL15302	1963	£5	£10	
Burning Bridges	LP	Capitol	(S)T2035	1964	£20	£40	
Burning Bridges	7"	Top Rank	JAR375	1960	£1.50	£4	chart single
Burning Bridges	7" EP	Capitol	EAP20035	1959	£25	£50	demo
Cool Water	7"	Top Rank	JAR419	1960	£4	£8	
Goodbye Baby	7"	London	HLU8804	1959	£6	£12	
I Can't Hold Your Letters In My Arms	7"	Capitol	CL15261	1962	£5	£10	
I Never Felt Like This	7"	London	HLL8851	1959	£6	£12	
I Remember Hank Williams	LP	Top Rank	BUY034	1960	£20	£40	chart LP
I Remember Hank Williams	7" EP	Top Rank	JKP3011	1961	£10	£20	

Title	Format	Label	Catalogue	Year	Price	Price	Notes
Is There Something On Your Mind	7"	Top Rank	JAR547	1961	£2.50	£6	
Jack Scott	LP	London	HAL2156	1958	£37.50	£75	
Little Feeling	7"	Capitol	CL15200	1961	£2.50	£6	
My Dream Come True	7"	Capitol	CL15216	1961	£4	£8	
My True Love	7"	London	HLU8626	1958	£6	£12	chart single
My True Love	7" EP	London	REI1205	1959	£25	£50	tri-centre
Patsy	7"	Top Rank	JAR524	1960	£2.50	£6	
Spirit Moves Me	LP	Top Rank	35109	1961	£25	£50	
Steps One And Two	7"	Capitol	CL15236	1962	£4	£8	
There Comes A Time	7"	London	HLL8970	1959	£6	£12	
Way I Walk	7"	London	HLL8912	1959	£7.50	£15	chart single
What Am I Living For	LP	Carlton	(ST)LP12122	1958	£30	£60	US
What In The World's Come Over You	LP	Top Rank	25024	1960	£25	£50	chart LP
What In The World's Come Over You	7"	Top Rank	JAR280	1960	£2	£5	chart single
What In The World's Come Over You	7" EP	Top Rank	JKP3002	1961	£12.50	£25	
With Your Love	7"	London	HLU8765	1958	£7.50	£15	

SCOTT, JAY & TOMMY

Angela	7"	Decca	F11474	1962	£1.50	£4	

SCOTT, JOHN

Hi-Fluting Boogie	7"	Parlophone	R4697	1960	£1.50	£4	

SCOTT, JUDI

Billy Sunshine	7"	Page One	POF066	1968	£4	£8	

SCOTT, LINDA

Composer	7"	CBS	4528	1969	£2	£5	
Count Every Star	7"	Columbia	DB4829	1961	£1.50	£4	
Don't Bet Money Honey	7"	Columbia	DB4692	1961	£1.50	£4	chart single
Great Scott	LP	Columbia		1961	£20	£40	
Greatest Hits	LP	Canadian Am.	(S)1007	1962	£10	£25	US
Hey Look At Me Now	LP	Kapp	KL1424/KS3424	1965	£6	£15	US
It's All Because	7"	Columbia	DB4748	1961	£1.50	£4	
I've Told Every Little Star	7"	Columbia	DB4638	1960	£1.50	£4	chart single
Let's Fall In Love	7"	London	HLR9802	1963	£1.50	£4	
Linda	LP	Congress	(S)3001	1962	£8	£20	US
Never In A Million Years	7"	Pye	7N25146	1962	£1.50	£4	
Starlight, Starbright	LP	Canadian Am.	(S)1005	1961	£10	£25	US

SCOTT, MARSHALL ETC.

Goin' Where The Lovin' Is	7"	HMV	POP1585	1967	£1.50	£4	
Same Old Feeling	7"	HMV	POP1536	1966	£1.50	£4	

SCOTT, MIKE

I Am A Rock	7"	Mercury	MF906	1965	£1.50	£4	

SCOTT, NICKY

Back Street Girl	7"	Immediate	IM045	1967	£5	£10	
Big City	7"	Immediate	IM044	1967	£7.50	£15	

SCOTT, PEGGY

Every Little Bit Hurts	7"	Polydor	56772	1969	£1.50	£4	

SCOTT, RAMBLIN' TOMMY

Ain't Love Grand	7"	Parlophone	CMSP15	1954	£2	£5	export

SCOTT, ROBIN

Sailor	7"	Head	HEAD4003	1969	£5	£10	
Woman From The Warm Grass	LP	Head	HDLS6003	1969	£50	£100	sleeve pictured in Guide

SCOTT, RONNIE

At The Royal Festival Hall	10" LP	Decca	LF1261	1956	£10	£25	
Live At Ronnie Scott's	LP	CBS	52661	1969	£5	£12	
Night Is Scott And You're So Swingable	LP	Fontana	TL5332	1966	£5	£12	
Presenting The Ronnie Scott Sextet	LP	Philips	BBL7153	1957	£8	£20	
Ronnie Scott Jazz Club Vol.1	LP	Esquire	32001	1954	£8	£20	
Ronnie Scott Jazz Club Vol.2	LP	Esquire	32002	1954	£8	£20	
Ronnie Scott Jazz Club Vol.3	LP	Esquire	32003	1954	£8	£20	
Ronnie Scott Jazz Club Vol.4	LP	Esquire	32006	1954	£8	£20	
Ronnie Scott Quartet	10" LP	Esquire	20006	1953	£15	£30	

SCOTT, SIMON & THE LEROYS

Move It Baby	7"	Parlophone	R5164	1964	£4	£8	chart single
My Baby's Got Soul	7"	Parlophone	R5207	1964	£4	£8	
Tell Him I'm Not Home	7"	Parlophone	R5298	1965	£2.50	£6	

SCOTT, TERRY

My Brother	7"	Parlophone	R4967	1962	£4	£8	

SCOTT, TOMMY

Who Will It Be?	7"	Decca	F11839	1964	£1.50	£4	
Wrap Your Troubles In Dreams	7"	Decca	F11942	1964	£1.50	£4	

SCOTT, TONY

Fifty-Second Street Scene	LP	Coral	LVA9109	1959	£8	£20	
South Pacific Jazz	LP	HMV	CLP1190	1958	£5	£12	
Tony Scott Quartet	10" LP	Vogue Coral	LRA10034	1955	£15	£30	
Tony Scott Quartet	10" LP	Vogue Coral	LRA10037	1955	£15	£30	

SCOTT-HERON, GIL

Title	Format	Label	Catalogue	Year	Price	Price	Notes
B Movie	7"	Arista	ARIST452	1981	£1.50	£4	
B Movie	7"	Arista	ARIST573	1984	£1.50	£4	
B Movie	12"	Arista	ARIST573	1984	£2.50	£6	
B Movie	10"	Arista	ARIST10643	1985	£2.50	£6	
Bottle	LP	Audio Fidelity	1017	197-	£5	£12	US
Bottle	7"	Arista	ARIST169	1978	£1.50	£4	
Bottle	7"	Inferno	HEAT23	1979	£1.50	£4	
Bottle	12"	Arista	ARIST169	1978	£2.50	£6	
Bottle	12"	Inferno	HEAT2312	1979	£2.50	£6	
Bridges	LP	Arista	SPARTY1031	1977	£6	£15	
First Minute Of A New Day	LP	Arista	ARTY106	1975	£8	£20	
Free Will	LP	Flying Dutchman	10153	1972	£15	£30	US
From South Africa To South Carolina	LP	Arista	ARTY121	1976	£5	£12	
It's Your World	LP	Arista	DARTY1	1976	£10	£25	
Lady Day And John Coltrane	7"	Philips	6073705	1971	£1.50	£4	
Pieces Of a Man	LP	Philips	6369415	1973	£10	£25	
Real Eyes	LP	Arista	9540	1980	£6	£15	US
Revolution Will Not Be Televised	LP	RCA	SF8428	1975	£8	£20	
Secrets	LP	Arista	SPARTY1073	1978	£6	£15	
Small Talk At 125th And Lennox	LP	Flying Dutchman		1972	£15	£30	US
Winter In America	LP	Strata East	19742	1975	£10	£25	US

SCOTTY

Title	Format	Label	Catalogue	Year	Price	Price	Notes
Schooldays	LP	Trojan	TRL33	1971	£8	£20	

SCRAMBLERS

Title	Format	Label	Catalogue	Year	Price	Price	Notes
Cycle Psychos	LP	Crown	384	1964	£8	£20	US

SCREAMING GYPSY BANDITS

Title	Format	Label	Catalogue	Year	Price	Price	Notes
Screaming Gypsy Bandits	LP	BRBQ		1973	£25	£50	US

SCRITTI POLITTI

Title	Format	Label	Catalogue	Year	Price	Price	Notes
Absolute	12"	Virgin	VSY68012	1984	£2.50	£6	pic disc
Skank Bloc	7"	St.Pancras	SCRIT1	1978	£2	£5	
Work In Progress	7"	Rough Trade	RT034	1979	£1.50	£4	

SCROTUM POLES

Title	Format	Label	Catalogue	Year	Price	Price	Notes
Revelation	7"	Scrotum Poles	ERECT1	1980	£1.50	£4	

SCRUGG

Title	Format	Label	Catalogue	Year	Price	Price	Notes
I Wish I Was Five	7"	Pye	7N17451	1968	£10	£20	
Lavender Popcorn	7"	Pye	7N17551	1968	£10	£20	
Will The Real Geraldine Please Stand Up	7"	Pye	7N17656	1969	£7.50	£15	

SEA URCHINS

Title	Format	Label	Catalogue	Year	Price	Price	Notes
30.10.88	7"	Fierce	FRIGHT032	1989	£2.50	£6	
Pristine Christine	7"	Sarah	001	1987	£7.50	£15	with poster
Solace	7"	Sarah	008	1988	£2	£5	

SEA-DERS

Title	Format	Label	Catalogue	Year	Price	Price	Notes
Thanks A Lot	7"	Decca	F22576	1967	£12.50	£25	

SEAMAN, PHIL

Title	Format	Label	Catalogue	Year	Price	Price	Notes
Meets Eddie Gomez	LP	Saga	OPP102	1968	£15	£30	
Phil Seaman Now	LP	Verve	(S)VLP9220	1968	£15	£30	
Phil Seaman Story	LP	Decibel	BSN103	196-	£20	£40	

SEARCHERS

Title	Format	Label	Catalogue	Year	Price	Price	Notes
Ain't Gonna Kiss Ya	7" EP	Pye	NEP24177	1963	£4	£8	
Bumble Bee	7" EP	Pye	NEP24218	1965	£4	£8	
Bumble Bee	7" EP	Pye	PNV24137	1965	£10	£20	French
Chantent En Francais	7" EP	Pye	PNV24121	1964	£50	£100	French
Desdemona	7"	RCA	RCA2057	1971	£6	£12	
Don't Make Promises	7"	private		197-	£5	£10	
Don't Throw Your Love Away	7"	Pye	7N15630	1964	£1.50	£4	chart single
Don't Throw Your Love Away	7" EP	Pye	PNV24120	1964	£10	£20	French
Four By Four	7" EP	Pye	NEP24228	1965	£5	£10	
Four Strong Winds	7"	private		197-	£5	£10	
Goodbye My Love	7"	Pye	7N15794	1965	£1.50	£4	chart single
Have You Ever Loved Somebody	7"	Pye	7N17170	1966	£1.50	£4	chart single
Hear Hear	LP	Mercury	MG2/SR60914	1964	£10	£25	US
He's Got No Love	7"	Pye	7N15878	1965	£1.50	£4	chart single
Hungry For Love	7" EP	Pye	NEP24184	1964	£4	£8	
It's The Searchers	LP	Pye	NPL18092	1964	£6	£15	chart LP
It's Too Late	7"	Sire	SIR4036	1980	£1.50	£4	
Kinky Kathy Abernathy	7"	Liberty	LBF15340	1969	£10	£20	
Love Is Everywhere	7"	RCA	RCA2139	1971	£2.50	£6	
Meet The Searchers	LP	Golden Guinea	GGL0349	1965	£4	£10	
Meet The Searchers	LP	Kapp	KL1363/KS3363	1964	£6	£15	US
Meet The Searchers	LP	Pye	NPL18086	1963	£6	£15	chart LP
Needles And Pins	7"	Ariola		1964	£10	£20	sung in German
Needles And Pins	7"	Pye	7N15594	1964	£1.50	£4	chart single
Needles And Pins	7"	Pye		1964	£10	£20	sung in French
Needles And Pins	7"	RCA	RCA2248	1972	£2	£5	
Needles And Pins	7" EP	Pye	PNV24118	1964	£10	£20	French
New Searchers LP	LP	Kapp	KL1412/KS3412	1965	£6	£15	US

Title	Format	Label	Catalogue	Year			Notes
Play The System	7" EP	Pye	NEP24201	1964	£5	£10	
Popcorn Double Feature	7"	Pye	7N17225	1967	£2.50	£6	
Searchers	LP	private		1962	£75	£150	French
Searchers '65	7" EP	Pye	NEP24222	1965	£4	£8	
Searchers Meet The Rattles	LP	Mercury	MG2/SR60994	1965	£15	£30	US
Searchers No.4	LP	Kapp	KL1449/KS3449	1965	£6	£15	US
Second Take	LP	RCA	SF8289	1972	£4	£10	
Secondhand Dealer	7"	Pye	7N17424	1967	£5	£10	
Sing Singer Sing	7"	RCA	RCA2231	1972	£2.50	£6	
Solitaire	7"	RCA	RCA2330	1973	£2	£5	
Some Day We're Gonna Love Again	7"	Pye	7N15670	1964	£1.50	£4	chart single
Someday We're Gonna Love Again	7" EP	Pye	PNV24123	1964	£10	£20	French
Sounds Like The Searchers	LP	Pye	NPL18111	1964	£6	£15	chart LP
Sub Ist Sie	7"	Vogue	14116	1963	£10	£20	sung in German
Sugar And Spice	LP	Pye	NPL18089	1963	£6	£15	chart LP
Sugar And Spice	7"	Pye	7N15566	1963	£1.50	£4	chart single
Surf Encore	7" EP	Pye	PNV24114	1963	£10	£20	French
Surfin' With The Searchers	7" EP	Pye	PNV24112	1963	£10	£20	French
Sweet Nothings	7"	Philips	BF1274	1963	£2.50	£6	chart single
Sweets For My Sweet	7"	Pye	7N15533	1963	£1.50	£4	chart single
Sweets For My Sweet	7" EP	Pye	NEP24183	1963	£4	£8	
Sweets For My Sweet	7" EP	Pye	PNV24108	1963	£10	£20	French
Take It Or Leave It	7"	Pye	7N17094	1966	£1.50	£4	chart single
Take Me For What I'm Worth	LP	Kapp	KL1477/KS3477	1966	£6	£15	US
Take Me For What I'm Worth	LP	Pye	NPL18120	1965	£6	£15	
Take Me For What I'm Worth	7"	Pye	7N15992	1965	£1.50	£4	chart single
Take Me For What I'm Worth	7"	Pye	7N15992	1965	£10	£20	export PS
Take Me For What I'm Worth	7" EP	Pye	NEP24263	1966	£35	£70	
Tausend Nadelstiche	7"	Vogue	14130	1963	£10	£20	sung in German
This Is Us	LP	Kapp	KL1409/KS3409	1964	£6	£15	US
Umbrella Man	7"	Liberty	LBF15159	1968	£6	£12	
Vahevala	7"	RCA	RCA2288	1972	£2	£5	
Verzeih My Love	7"	Vogue	14338	1965	£10	£20	sung in German
Western Union	7"	Pye	7N17308	1967	£4	£8	
What Have They Done To The Rain	7"	Pye	7N15739	1964	£1.50	£4	chart single
When I Get Home	7"	Pye	7N15950	1965	£1.50	£4	chart single
When You Walk In The Room	7"	Pye	7N15694	1964	£1.50	£4	chart single
When You Walk In The Room	7" EP	Pye	NEP24204	1964	£6	£12	

SEASTONE

| Mirrored Dreams | LP | Plankton | PKN101 | 1978 | £50 | £100 | sleeve pictured in Guide |

SEATHROUGH

| Lala Lapla | LP | private | | 197- | £25 | £50 | |

SEATON, B.B.

Hold On	7"	R&B	JB143	1964	£5	£10	Lester Sterling B side
I'm So Glad	7"	Island	WI123	1963	£5	£10	
Thin Line Between Love And Hate	LP	Trojan	TRLS59	1973	£4	£10	

SEATRAIN

Seatrain evolved out of The Blues Project, following the departure of founder members Danny Kalb, Steve Katz, and Al Kooper. The new sounds of violin and saxophone aquired a dominant role and for the first Seatrain LP the musicians are clearly inspired by the novelty of their new line-up. Unfortunately, this inspiration was short lived and the two LPs that followed are rather ordinary.

| Seatrain | LP | A&M | AMLS941 | 1969 | £6 | £15 | |

SEAWIND

| One Sweet Night | 7" | CTI | CTSP13 | 1978 | £4 | £8 | |

SEBASTIAN, JOHN

John B.Sebastian	LP	Reprise	K44086	1971	£4	£10	
John B.Sebastian	LP	Reprise	RSLP6379	1970	£5	£12	
Live	LP	MGM	SE4720	1970	£6	£15	US

SEBASTIAN, JOHN (2)

| Inca Dance | 7" | London | HL8029 | 1954 | £6 | £12 | |
| Stranger In Paradise | 7" | London | HL8131 | 1955 | £6 | £12 | |

SECOND CITY JAZZMEN

| Tribute To Madge | LP | Esquire | 32053 | 1958 | £4 | £10 | |

SECOND CITY SOUND

| Tchaikovsky One | 7" | Decca | F12310 | 1965 | £1.50 | £4 | chart single |
| Touch Of Velvet, Sting Of Brass | 7" | Major Minor | MM600 | 1969 | £1.50 | £4 | |

SECOND COMING

| Second Coming | LP | Mercury | 6338030 | 1970 | £6 | £15 | |

SECOND HAND

Second Hand revolved around keyboard virtuoso Ken Elliott and drummer Kieran O'Connor, who subsequently recorded as Seventh Wave. Their music is an interesting blend of classical and avant garde influences within a sound that is nevertheless rock based - rather like the better-known Egg, in fact. "Death May Be Your Santa Claus" is that rare thing, an expensive progressive album that is actually something or a forgotten masterpiece.

| Death May Be Your Santa Claus | LP | Mushroom | 200MR6 | 1972 | £50 | £100 | sleeve pictured in Guide |
| Reality | LP | Polydor | 583045 | 1968 | £30 | £60 | |

SECOND LAYER

| Flesh As Property | 7" | Fresh | FRESH5 | 1979 | £2.50 | £6 | |
| Flesh As Property | 7" | Tortch | TOR001 | 1979 | £4 | £8 | |

| State Of Emergency | 7" | Tortch | TOR006 | 1980 | £2 | £5 | |

SECOND LIFE
| Second Life | LP | Metronome | MLP15409 | 1971 | £8 | £20 | German |

SECOND MOVEMENT
| Blind Man's Mirror | LP | Castle | 1003 | 1976 | £5 | £12 | German |

SECOND VISION
| First Steps | LP | Chrysalis | CHR1289 | 1980 | £5 | £12 | |

SECRET OYSTER
| Secret Oyster | LP | CBS | 65769 | 1973 | £6 | £15 | Danish |
| Vidunderlige Kalling | LP | CBS | 81044 | 1975 | £6 | £15 | Dutch |

SECRETS
| Boy Next Door | 7" | Philips | BF1298 | 1964 | £1.50 | £4 | |
| Other Side Of Town | 7" | Philips | BF1318 | 1964 | £1.50 | £4 | |

SECRETS (2)
I Intend To Please	7"	CBS	2818	1967	£1.50	£4	
Infatuation	7"	CBS	202585	1967	£1.50	£4	
Such A Pity	7"	CBS	202466	1967	£1.50	£4	

SEDAKA, NEIL
Bad Girl	7"	RCA	RCA1368	1963	£1.50	£4	
Breaking Up Is Hard To Do	7"	RCA	RCA1298	1962	£1.50	£4	chart single
Calendar Girl	7"	RCA	RCA1220	1961	£1.50	£4	chart single
Circulate	LP	RCA	RD27207/SF5090	1960	£10	£25	
Circulate	7"	RCA	RCA1331	1963	£1.50	£4	
Dreamer	7"	RCA	RCA1359	1963	£1.50	£4	
Greatest Hits	LP	RCA	LPM/LSP2627	1962	£6	£15	US
Happy Birthday Sweet Sixteen	7"	RCA	RCA1266	1961	£1.50	£4	chart single
I Go Ape	7"	RCA	RCA1115	1959	£2.50	£6	chart single
King Of Clowns	7"	RCA	RCA1282	1962	£1.50	£4	chart single
Let's Go Steady Again	7"	RCA	RCA1343	1963	£1.50	£4	chart single
Little Devil	7"	RCA	RCA1236	1961	£1.50	£4	chart single
Little Devil And His Other Hits	LP	RCA	LPM/LSP2421	1961	£8	£20	US
Neil Sedaka	LP	RCA	RD27140	1959	£20	£40	
Neil Sedaka	7" EP	RCA	RCX166	1959	£7.50	£15	
Neil Sedaka No.2	7" EP	RCA	RCX186	1960	£7.50	£15	
Neil Sedaka No.3	7" EP	RCA	RCX212	1962	£7.50	£15	
Next Door To An Angel	7"	RCA	RCA1319	1962	£1.50	£4	chart single
No Vacancy	7"	RCA	RCA1099	1959	£6	£12	
Oh Carol	7"	RCA	RCA1152	1959	£4	£8	tri-centre, chart single
Oh Delilah	7"	Stateside	SS105	1962	£4	£8	Marvels B side
Ring A Rocking	7"	London	HLW8961	1959	£12.50	£25	
Rock With Sedaka	LP	RCA	LPM/LSP2035	1959	£20	£40	US
Stairway To Heaven	7"	RCA	RCA1178	1960	£1.50	£4	chart single
Sweet Little You	7"	RCA	RCA1250	1961	£1.50	£4	
With The Tokens	LP	Vernon	518	1963	£6	£15	US
World Through A Tear	7"	RCA	RCA1475	1965	£1.50	£4	
You Mean Everything To Me	7"	RCA	RCA1198	1960	£1.50	£4	chart single
You've Got To Learn Your Rhythm And Blues	7"	RCA	RCA1130	1959	£6	£12	

SEEDORF, RUDY
| One Million Stars | 7" | Island | WI189 | 1965 | £5 | £10 | |

SEEDS
Can't Seem To Make You Mine	7"	Vocalion	VN9287	1967	£7.50	£15	
Farmer	7" EP	Vogue	INT18125	1967	£15	£30	French
Full Spoon Of Seedy Blues	LP	GNP Crescendo	(S)2040	1967	£10	£25	US red label
Future	LP	Vocalion	VAN/SAVN8070	1967	£10	£25	
Merlin's Music Box	LP	GNP Crescendo	(S)2043	1967	£10	£25	US red label
No Escape	7" EP	Vogue	INT18022	1966	£25	£50	French
Psych-Out	LP	Sidewalk	ST5913	1968	£8	£20	US, with other artists
Pushin' Too Hard	7"	Vocalion	VN9277	1966	£7.50	£15	
Seeds	LP	GNP Crescendo	(S)2023	1966	£10	£25	US red label
Try To Understand	7" EP	Vogue	INT18077	1966	£15	£30	French
Web Of Sound	LP	Vocalion	VAN8062	1966	£10	£25	

SEEGER, MIKE
| Mike Seeger | LP | Fontana | TFL6039 | 1965 | £8 | £20 | |

SEEGER, PEGGY
Best Of Peggy Seeger	LP	Pre	PRE13005	1961	£8	£20	
Early In The Spring	7" EP	Topic	TOP73	1962	£4	£8	
Peggy Alone	LP	Argo	(Z)DA63	1969	£8	£20	
Pretty Little Baby	7"	Decca	F12282	1965	£2.50	£6	
Troubled Love	7" EP	Topic	TOP72	1962	£4	£8	

SEEGER, PEGGY & GUY CARAWAN
| America At Play | LP | HMV | CLP1174 | 1958 | £8 | £20 | |

SEEGER, PEGGY & MIKE
| Peggy 'n' Mike | LP | Argo | (Z)DA80 | 1968 | £8 | £20 | |
| Peggy 'n' Mike | LP | Argo | ZFB62 | 1972 | £5 | £12 | |

SEEGER, PETE

Broadsides	LP	XTRA	XTRA1016	1964	£5	£12	
Careless Love	7"	Top Rank	TR5020	1960	£1.50	£4	... B side by Leon Bibb
Guitar Guide	LP	XTRA	XTRA1034	1965	£6	£15	with book
Guitar Guide For Folksingers	LP	Topic	12T20	1958	£8	£20	with booklet
I Can See A New Day	LP	CBS	(S)BPG62462	1964	£6	£12	
In Concert	LP	Folklore	FLAUT1	1963	£4	£10	
In Concert	7" EP.	CBS	AGG20055	1964	£2	£5	
In Concert Vol.2	LP	Folklore	FLAUT2	1963	£4	£10	
In Person	LP	Verve	(S)VLP5004	1965	£5	£12	
Little Boxes	7"	CBS	201743	1965	£1.50	£4	
Little Boxes	7"	CBS	AAG187	1963	£1.50	£4	
Pete And Five Strings	7" EP.	Topic	TOP33	1959	£4	£8	
Story Songs	LP	Philips	BBL7507	1961	£4	£10	
Tribute To Leadbelly	7" EP.	Melodisc	EPM778	1958	£4	£8	
We Shall Overcome	LP	CBS	(S)BPG62209	1963	£6	£15	

SEEKERS

Chilly Winds	7"	Decca	F22167	1965	£1.50	£4	
With A Swag On My Shoulder	7"	Oriole	CB1935	1965	£2	£5	

SEEMON & MARIJKE

Son Of America	LP	A&M	SP4309	1970	£6	£15	US

SEFTONES

I Can See Through You	7"	CBS	202491	1966	£5	£10	

SEGER, BOB

Against The Wind	LP	Mobile Fidelity	MFSL1127	1983	£4	£10	US audiophile
Bob Seger Story	LP	Capitol		1981	£6	£15	US promo
Brand New Morning	LP	Capitol	ST731	1971	£6	£15	US
Lucifer	7"	Capitol	CL15642	1970	£2.50	£6	
Mongrel	LP	Capitol	SKAO499	1970	£4	£10	US gatefold
Night Moves	LP	Mobile Fidelity	MFSL1034	1979	£6	£15	US audiophile
Noah	LP	Capitol	ST236	1969	£6	£15	US
Ramblin' Gamblin' Man	LP	Capitol	ST172	1969	£5	£12	US
Ramblin' Gamblin' Man	7"	Capitol	CL15574	1968	£2.50	£6	
Seger Classics	LP	Capitol	PSLP271/2	1977	£10	£25	promo double
Smokin' OP's	LP	Reprise	K44214	1972	£4	£10	
Stranger In Town	LP	Capitol	EAST11698	1978	£4	£10	grey vinyl
Stranger In Town	LP	Capitol	SEAX11904	1978	£4	£10	US pic disc

SELAH JUBILEE QUARTET

Spirituals	10" LP	Remington	1023	195-	£10	£25	US

SELF, FREDDIE

Don't Cry	7"	Mercury	MF839	1964	£1.50	£4	

SELF, RONNIE

Bop-a-Lena	78	Philips	PB810	1958	£12.50	£25	

SELLERS, BROTHER JOHN

Big Beat Up The River	LP	Monitor	505		£8	£20	US
Blues & Spirituals	7" EP.	Columbia	SEG7740	1957	£5	£10	
Blues & Spirituals	7" EP.	Vanguard	EPP14002	1956	£5	£10	
In London	LP	Decca	LK4197	1957	£6	£15	
In London	7" EP.	Decca	DFE6457	1957	£4	£8	
Jack Of Diamonds	10" LP	Vanguard	PPT12017	1957	£5	£12	
Sings Blues And Folk Songs	10" LP	Vanguard	PPT12008	1956	£5	£12	

SELLERS, PETER

Any Old Iron	7"	Parlophone	R4337	1957	£1.50	£4	chart single
Best Of Sellers	10" LP	Parlophone	PMD1069	1958	£5	£12	chart LP
Drop Of The Hard Stuff	7"	Parlophone	R4491	1958	£1.50	£4	
Hard Day's Night	7"	Parlophone	R5393	1965	£2	£5	chart single
Putting on The Smile	7"	Parlophone	R4605	1959	£1.50	£4	
Songs For Swingin' Sellers	7" EP.	Parlophone	GEP8822	1960	£2	£5	
Songs For Swingin' Sellers	7" EP.	Parlophone	SGE2013	1960	£2.50	£6	stereo
Songs For Swingin' Sellers No.2	7" EP.	Parlophone	SGE2016	1960	£2	£5	stereo
Songs For Swingin' Sellers No.3	7" EP.	Parlophone	SGE2019	1961	£2	£5	stereo
Songs For Swingin' Sellers No.4	7" EP.	Parlophone	SGE2020	1961	£2	£5	stereo
Voice Behind The Mask	LP	Guild	62002	196-	£5	£12	

SELLERS, PETER & SOPHIA LOREN

Bangers And Mash	7"	Parlophone	R4724	1961	£1.50	£4	chart single
Goodness Gracious Me	7"	Parlophone	R4702	1960	£1.50	£4	chart single
Peter And Sophia	LP	Parlophone	PMC1131/ PCS3012	1960	£4	£10	chart LP
Peter And Sophia No.1	7" EP.	Parlophone	SGE2021	1961	£2	£5	
Peter And Sophia No.2	7" EP.	Parlophone	SGE2022	1961	£2	£5	
Peter And Sophia No.3	7" EP.	Parlophone	SGE2023	1961	£2	£5	

SELLERS, PETER, SPIKE MILLIGAN & HARRY SECOMBE

How To Win An Election	LP	Philips	AL3464	1964	£4	£10	chart LP

SEMA FOUR

Four From Sema Four	7"	Pollen	PBM022	1979	£2	£5	
Up And Down	7"	Pollen	PBM024	1979	£2.50	£6	

SENATE

I Can't Stop	7"	Columbia	DB8110	1967	£2.50	£6	

SENATOR BOBBY
Wild Thing	7"	Cameo Parkway	P127	1962	£1.50	£4		

SENATORS
Breakdown	7"	Oriole	CB1957	1964	£6	£12	
She's A Mod	7"	Dial	DSP7001	1964	£10	£20	
Tables Are Turning	7"	CBS	201768	1965	£6	£12	

SENDIT, RAY & HIS ROCKY TEAM
Rocket 0869	7"	Felsted	SD80052	1957	£1.50	£4	

SENSATION FIX
Boxes Paradise	LP	Polydor	2448068	1977	£5	£12	Italian
Finest Finger	LP	Polydor	2448048	1976	£6	£15	Italian
Flying Tapes	LP	Polydor	2448074	1978	£5	£12	Italian
Fragment Of Light	LP	Polydor	2448023	1974	£6	£15	Italian
Portable Madness	LP	Polydor	2448034	1974	£6	£15	Italian
Vision's Fugitives	LP	All Ears	SF11478	1977	£5	£12	US

SENSATIONAL CREED
Nocturnal Operations	7"	Beggars Banquet	BEG125	1984	£2	£5	
Nocturnal Operations	12"	Beggars Banquet	BEG125T	1984	£2.50	£6	

SENSATIONS
Let Me In	LP	Argo	LP4022	1963	£15	£30	US
Let Me In	7"	Pye	7N25128	1962	£4	£8	
Music Music Music	7"	Pye	7N25110	1961	£4	£8	

SENSATIONS (2)
Born To Love You	7"	Doctor Bird	DB1102	1967	£5	£10	
Right On Time	7"	Doctor Bird	DB1100	1967	£5	£10	
Thing Called Soul	7"	Doctor Bird	DB1074	1967	£5	£10	
Those Guys	7"	Duke	DU2	1968	£4	£8	
Warrior	7"	Camel	CA31	1969	£1.50	£4	

SENSATIONS (3)
Look At My Baby	7"	Decca	F12392	1966	£4	£8	

SENSELESS THINGS
Andi In A Karma	12"	What Goes On.	GOESON37	1990	£6	£15	test pressing
I'm Moving	7"	Yo Jo Jo	3	1988	£4	£8	flexi
Up And Coming	CD-s ..	Way Cool	WC006CD	1991	£4	£10	
Up And Coming	12"	Red	RED001T	1988	£6	£15	two versions
Up And Coming	12"	Way Cool	WC006	1991	£3	£8	

SENTINELS
Big Surf	LP	Del-Fi	LP/ST1232	1963	£5	£12	US
Surfer Girl	LP	Del-Fi	LP/ST1241	1963	£5	£12	US
Vegas Go-Go	LP	Sutton	SU338	1964	£5	£12	US

SEPULTURA
Arise	LP	Roadracer	RO93288	1991	£5	£12	pic disc
Bestial Devastation	LP	Gogumelo	803248	1985	£20	£40	Brazilian, B side by Overdose

SERENDIPITY
Castles	7"	CBS	4428	1969	£15	£30	
Through With You	7"	CBS	3733	1968	£30	£60	

SERFS
Early Bird Cafe	LP	Capitol		1969	£6	£15	US

SERPENT POWER
Serpent Power	LP	Vanguard	VSD79252	1967	£10	£25	US

SETTLERS
Alive	LP	Columbia	SCX6381	1969	£6	£15	
As Long As There's Love	7"	Columbia	DB8424	1968	£1.50	£4	
Early Morning Rain	7"	Pye	7N17104	1966	£1.50	£4	
Early Settlers	LP	Island	ILP947	1967	£8	£20	
Keep Moving On	7"	Columbia	DB8750	1971	£1.50	£4	
Lightning Tree	LP	Decca	622082AF	1975	£5	£12	German
Lightning Tree	7"	York	SYK505	1971	£1.50	£4	chart single
Major To Minor	7"	Pye	7N17375	1967	£1.50	£4	
Nowhere Man	7"	Pye	7N17065	1966	£2	£5	
On The Other Side	7"	Pye	7N17213	1966	£1.50	£4	
Settle Down	7"	Decca	F11938	1964	£2	£5	
Settlers	LP	York	FYK405	1972	£6	£15	
Sing Out	LP	Decca	LK4645	1964	£6	£15	
Till Winter Follows Spring	7"	Pye	7N17171	1966	£2	£5	
When's It Gonna Be My Turn	7"	Decca	F12123	1965	£2	£5	
Woman Called Freedom	7"	Pye	7N15965	1965	£1.50	£4	
World Of The Settlers	LP	Decca	SPA343	1974	£4	£10	

SEVEN AGES OF MAN
Seven Ages Of Man	LP	Rediffusion	ZS115	1972	£20	£40	

SEVEN LETTERS

Bam Bam Baji	7"	Doctor Bird	DB1209	1969	£5	£10	
Flour Dumpling	7"	Doctor Bird	DB1195	1969	£5	£10	
Fung Sure	7"	Doctor Bird	DB1306	1969	£5	£10	
La Bella Jig	7"	Treasure Isle	TI7055	1969	£4	£8	
Mama Me Want Girl	7"	Doctor Bird	DB1206	1969	£5	£10	
Parsons Corner	7"	Treasure Isle	TI7054	1969	£4	£8	
People Get Ready	7"	Doctor Bird	DB1189	1969	£5	£10	
Please Stay	7"	Doctor Bird	DB1194	1969	£5	£10	
Soul Crash	7"	Doctor Bird	DB1207	1969	£5	£10	
There Goes My Heart	7"	Doctor Bird	DB1208	1969	£5	£10	

SEVEN SECONDS

Skins, Brains, And Guts	7"	Alternative Tentacles	VIRUS15	1982	£1.50	£4	

SEVENTEEN

Don't Let Go	7"	Vendetta	VD001	1980	£15	£30	

SEVERIN

Chance In Time	7"	CBS	7280	1971	£2	£5	

SEVILLE, DAVID

Armen's Theme	7"	London	HLU8359	1957	£6	£12	gold label
Bird On My Head	7"	London	HLU8659	1958	£2	£5	
Bonjour Tristesse	7"	London	HLU8582	1958	£1.50	£4	
David Seville & His Orchestra	7" EP	London	REU1085	1957	£5	£10	
Gift	7"	London	HLU8411	1957	£2	£5	
Got To Get To Your House	7"	London	HLU8485	1957	£4	£8	
Take Five	7"	London	HLU8736	1958	£1.50	£4	
Witch Doctor	LP	London	HAU2153	1959	£5	£12	
Witch Doctor	7"	London	HLU8619	1958	£2	£5	chart single
Witch Doctor & His Friends	7" EP	London	REU1219	1959	£5	£10	

SEX PISTOLS

What was revolutionary about the Sex Pistols was not so much their music or their image, but the way in which they (or rather their manager, Malcolm McLaren) saw rock music as an institution out of which it was possible to make a considerable amount of money. The strategy of signing to a label for a large advance, which was retained when the record company became too outraged by the group's behaviour to honour its side of the contract, worked supremely well. The Sex Pistols found themselves wealthy almost before they had recorded anything. Curiously, when Sigue Sigue Sputnik demonstrated a similarly mercenary attitude to music making, they found themselves vilified, rather than lauded as the Sex Pistols had been. Meanwhile, the Sex Pistols' early carryings-on have left us with one of the most valuable of modern collectors' items: the version of "God Save The Queen" that was very briefly available on the A&M label.

Anarchie Pour L'UK	7"	Barclay	640162	1979	£2	£5	French, PS
Anarchy In The UK	7"	Barclay	640112	1977	£2	£5	French, PS
Anarchy In The UK	7"	EMI	EMI2566	1976	£4	£8	chart single, Dave Goodman production credit on B side
Anarchy In The UK	7"	EMI	EMI2566	1976	£7.50	£15	Chris Thomas production credit on B side
Anarchy In The UK	12"	Barclay	740501	1977	£2.50	£6	French
Biggest Blow	12"	Virgin	VS22012	1978	£3	£8	with Interview
Filth And The Fury	LP	McDonald Brothers	JOCKBOX	1987	£10	£25	6 LP boxed set
Frigging In The Rigging	7"	Barclay	640159	1979	£5	£10	French, PS
Frigging In The Rigging	7"	Virgin	VS240	1979	£7.50	£15	mispress, A side plays 'Silly Thing'
God Save The Queen	7"	A&M	AMS7284	1977	£530	£800	
God Save The Queen	7"	Barclay	640106	1977	£2.50	£6	French, PS
God Save The Queen	7"	Virgin	VS181	1977	£1.50	£4	chart single, PS
Great Rock'N'Roll Swindle	LP	Virgin	VD2510	1979	£5	£12	with 'Whatcha Gonna Do About It'
Great Rock'n'Roll Swindle	7"	Virgin	VS290	1979	£1.50	£4	credit card PS
Great Rock'n'Roll Swindle	7"	Virgin	VS290	1979	£5	£10	with bonus 'telephone call' track
Heyday	cass	Factory	FACT30	1980	£5	£12	satin pouch, Xmas card
Holidays In The Sun	7"	Barclay	640116	1977	£2	£5	French, PS
Holidays In The Sun	7"	Virgin	VS191	1977	£2	£5	PS
My Way	7"	Barclay	640154	1978	£2.50	£6	French, PS
My Way	7"	Virgin	VS220	1978	£7.50	£15	mispress, other side plays The Motors
My Way	12"	Barclay	740509	1979	£3	£8	French
Never Mind The Bollocks	LP	Virgin	V2086	1977	£6	£15	no track listing on sleeve
Never Mind The Bollocks	LP	Virgin	V2086	1977	£10	£25	with poster & 1 sided 7' (VDJ24)
Never Mind The Bollocks	LP	Virgin	VP2086	1978	£8	£20	pic disc
Pistols Pack	7"	Virgin	SEX1	1980	£10	£20	6x7', plastic wallet
Pretty Vacant	7"	Barclay	640109	1977	£2	£5	French, PS
Pretty Vacant	7"	Virgin	VS184	1977	£1.50	£4	chart single, PS
Stepping Stone	7"	Virgin	VS339	1980	£6	£12	mispress, plays Gillan
Submission	7"	Barclay	640137	1977	£2	£5	French, PS
Submission	7"	Chaos	DICK1	1985	£2.50	£6	blue, pink, or yellow vinyl
Submission	12"	Chaos	EXPORT1	1985	£2.50	£6	6 different coloured vinyls
Who Killed Bambi	7"	Barclay	640160	1979	£4	£8	French, PS
You Need Hands	7"	Barclay	640161	1979	£2	£5	French, PS

SEXY GIRLS
Pom-Pom Song	7"	Fab	FAB100	1969	£2	£5	Little Joe B side

SEYTON, DENNY
Just A Kiss	7"	Parlophone	R5363	1965	£6	£12	

SEYTON, DENNY & THE SABRES
It's The Gear (14 Hits)	LP	Wing	WL1032	1965	£10	£25	
Short Fat Fanny	7"	Mercury	MF814	1964	£7.50	£15	
Tricky Dicky	7"	Mercury	MF800	1964	£7.50	£15	
Way You Look Tonight	7"	Mercury	MF824	1964	£10	£20	chart single

SHADE JOEY & THE NIGHT OWLS
Blue Birds Over The Mountain	7"	Parlophone	R5180	1964	£10	£20	

SHADES
Sun Glasses	7"	London	HLX8713	1958	£10	£20	B side Knott Sisters

SHADES (2)
Weird Walk	7"	Starlite	ST45074	1962	£6	£12	

SHADES OF BLUE
Happiness Is The Shades Of Blue	LP	Impact	IM101/1001	1966	£8	£20	US
Oh How Happy	7"	Sue	WI4022	1966	£5	£10	

SHADES OF BLUE (2)
Voodoo Blues	7"	Parlophone	R5270	1965	£7.50	£15	
Where Did All The Good Times Go	7"	Pye	7N15988	1965	£4	£8	

SHADES OF JOY
Shades Of Joy	LP	Fontana	STL5498	1969	£5	£12	

SHADOWS
Alice In Sunderland	7" EP	Columbia	SEG8445	1965	£7.50	£15	
Apache	7"	Columbia	DB4484	196-	£5	£10	black label
Apache	7"	Columbia	DB4484	1960	£1.50	£4	chart single
Atlantis	7"	Columbia	DB7047	1963	£1.50	£4	chart single
Atlantis	7" EP	Columbia	ESDF1480	1963	£6	£12	French
Be Bop A Lula	7" EP	Columbia	ESRF20002	196-	£6	£12	French
Boys	7" EP	Columbia	ESG7881	1962	£10	£20	stereo
Boys	7" EP	Columbia	SEG8193	1962	£4	£8	
Chelsea Boot	7"	Columbia	PSR310	1967	£5	£10	promo
Dance On	7"	Columbia	DB4948	1962	£1.50	£4	chart single
Dance On	7" EP	Columbia	ESDF1457	1963	£6	£12	French
Dance On With The Shadows	7" EP	Columbia	SEG8233	1963	£5	£10	
Dance With The Shadows	LP	Columbia	33SX1619	1964	£4	£10	chart LP
Dance With The Shadows	LP	Columbia	SCX3511	1964	£5	£12	stereo
Dance With The Shadows No.1	7" EP	Columbia	SEG8342	1964	£5	£10	
Dance With The Shadows No.2	7" EP	Columbia	SEG8375	1964	£6	£12	
Dance With The Shadows No.3	7" EP	Columbia	SEG8408	1965	£6	£12	
Dear Old Mrs.Bell	7"	Columbia	DB8372	1968	£2	£5	
Don't Cry For Me Argentina	12"	EMI	12EMI2890	1978	£2.50	£6	double groove
Don't Make My Baby Blue	7"	Columbia	DB7650	1965	£1.50	£4	chart single
Dreams I Dream	7"	Columbia	DB8034	1966	£2	£5	chart single
F.B.I.	7"	Columbia	DB4580	196-	£4	£8	black label
F.B.I.	7"	Columbia	DB4580	1961	£1.50	£4	chart single
Foot Tapper	7"	Columbia	DB4984	1963	£1.50	£4	chart single
Foot Tapping With The Shadows	7" EP	Columbia	SEG8268	1963	£5	£10	
Frightened City	7"	Columbia	DB4637	196-	£4	£8	black label
Frightened City	7"	Columbia	DB4637	1961	£1.50	£4	chart single
From Hank,Bruce,Brian,& John	LP	Columbia	SX/SCX6199	1967	£4	£10	
Genie With The Light Brown Lamp	7"	Columbia	DB7416	1964	£1.50	£4	chart single
Geronimo	7"	Columbia	DB7163	1963	£1.50	£4	chart single
Guitar Tango	7"	Columbia	DB4870	196-	£4	£8	black label
Guitar Tango	7"	Columbia	DB4870	1962	£1.50	£4	chart single
Guitar Tango	7" EP	Columbia	ESDF1437	1963	£6	£12	French
I Met A Girl	7"	Columbia	DB7853	1966	£2	£5	chart single
It'll Be Me Babe	7"	EMI	EMI2451	1976	£1.50	£4	
Jigsaw	LP	Columbia	SX/SCX6148	1967	£5	£12	chart LP
Kon-Tiki	7"	Columbia	DB4698	196-	£4	£8	black label
Kon-Tiki	7"	Columbia	DB4698	1961	£1.50	£4	chart single
Little B	7" EP	Columbia	ESDF1447	1963	£6	£12	French
Los Shadows	7" EP	Columbia		1964	£10	£20	export
Los Shadows	7" EP	Columbia	SEG8278	1963	£5	£10	
Love De Luxe	7"	EMI	EMI2838	1978	£1.50	£4	
Magical Mrs.Clamps	7"	EMI	PSR316	1968	£6	£12	promo, B side by Cliff Richard
Man Of Mystery	7"	Columbia	DB4530	196-	£5	£10	black label
Man Of Mystery	7"	Columbia	DB4530	1960	£1.50	£4	chart single
Maroc 7	7"	Columbia	DB8170	1967	£1.50	£4	chart single
Maroc 7	7"	Columbia	PSR304	1967	£6	£12	promo, spoken intro
Mary Anne	7"	Columbia	DB7476	1965	£1.50	£4	chart single
More Hits	LP	Columbia	33SX1791/ SCX3578	1965	£4	£10	
Naughty Nippon Nights	7"	Columbia	PSR313	1967	£5	£10	promo
On Stage And Screen	7" EP	Columbia	SEG8528	1967	£7.50	£15	
Out Of The Shadows	LP	Columbia	33SX1458	1962	£4	£10	chart LP
Out Of The Shadows	LP	Columbia	SCX3449	1962	£5	£12	stereo
Out Of The Shadows	7" EP	Columbia	ESG7883	1963	£10	£20	stereo
Out Of The Shadows	7" EP	Columbia	SEG8218	1963	£5	£10	

Title	Format	Label	Catalogue	Year	Price	Price	Notes
Out Of The Shadows No.2	7" EP..	Columbia	ESG7895	1963	£10	£20	stereo
Out Of The Shadows No.2	7" EP..	Columbia	SEG8249	1963	£5	£10	
Place In The Sun	7"	Columbia	DB7952	1966	£2	£5	chart single
Rhythm And Greens	7"	Columbia	DB7342	1964	£1.50	£4	chart single
Rhythm And Greens	7" EP.	Columbia	ESG7904	1964	£10	£20	stereo
Rhythm And Greens	7" EP.	Columbia	SEG8362	1964	£5	£10	
Rise And Fall Of Flingel Bunt	7"	Columbia	DB7261	1964	£1.50	£4	chart single
Rise And Fall Of Flingel Bunt	7"	Columbia	DB7261	1964	£5	£10	mispress, 2 A sides
Rockin' With Curly Leads	LP	EMI	EMA762	1973	£5	£12	
Run Billy Run	7"	EMI	EMI2310	1975	£1.50	£4	
Saturday Dance	7"	Columbia	DB4387	1959	£12.50	£25	
Saturday Dance	7"	Columbia	DB4387	196-	£6	£12	black label
Savage	7"	Columbia	DB4726	196-	£4	£8	black label
Savage	7"	Columbia	DB4726	1961	£1.50	£4	chart single
Shadow Music	LP	Columbia	33SX/SCX6041	1966	£4	£10	chart LP
Shadows	LP	Columbia	33SX1374	1962	£5	£12	chart LP
Shadows	LP	Columbia	SCX3414	1962	£8	£20	stereo
Shadows	LP	World Record Club	ALBUM72	1972	£15	£30	6 LPs, boxed
Shadows	7"	Lyntone	LYN10099	1972	£2	£5	promo flexi
Shadows	7" EP.	Columbia	ESG7834	1961	£10	£20	stereo
Shadows	7" EP.	Columbia	SEG8061	1961	£4	£8	
Shadows Know	LP	Atlantic	(SD)8097	1964	£10	£25	US
Shadows No.2	7" EP.	Columbia	SEG8148	1962	£5	£10	
Shadows No.3	7" EP.	Columbia	SEG8166	1962	£5	£10	
Shadows To The Fore	7" EP.	Columbia	SEG8094	1961	£4	£8	
Shazam	7" EP..	Columbia	ESRF1402	1963	£6	£12	French
Shindig	7"	Columbia	DB7106	1963	£1.50	£4	chart single
Shindig With The Shadows	7" EP.	Columbia	SEG8286	1963	£5	£10	
Sleepwalk	7" EP.	Columbia	ESDF1434	1963	£6	£12	French
Sound Of The Shadows	LP	Columbia	33SX1736	1965	£4	£10	chart LP
Sound Of The Shadows	LP	Columbia	SCX3554	1965	£5	£12	stereo
Sound Of The Shadows No.1	7" EP.	Columbia	SEG8459	1965	£6	£12	
Sound Of The Shadows No.2	7" EP.	Columbia	SEG8473	1966	£6	£12	
Sound Of The Shadows No.3	7" EP.	Columbia	SEG8494	1966	£6	£12	
Spotlight On The Shadows	7" EP.	Columbia	SEG8135	1962	£4	£8	
Stingray	7"	Columbia	DB7588	1965	£1.50	£4	chart single
Surfing With The Shadows	LP	Atlantic	(SD)8089	1963	£10	£25	US
Theme For Young Lovers	7"	Columbia	DB7231	1964	£1.50	£4	chart single
Themes From Aladdin	7" EP.	Columbia	SEG8396	1965	£6	£12	
Those Brilliant Shadows	7" EP.	Columbia	SEG8321	1964	£5	£10	
Those Talented Shadows	7" EP.	Columbia	SEG8500	1966	£6	£12	
Thunderbirds Are Go	7"	EMI	PSR305	1967	£5	£10	1 sided promo
Tomorrow's Cancelled	7"	Columbia	DB8264	1967	£4	£8	
Treat Me Nice	7"	Polydor	POSP439	1982	£1.50	£4	
Twenty Golden Greats	LP	EMI	EMTV3	1977	£5	£12	mispress, Pink Floyd on side 2
Twenty Golden Greats	7"	EMI		1977	£2	£5	promo sampler
Warlord	7"	Columbia	DB7769	1965	£1.50	£4	chart single
Wonderful Land	7"	Columbia	DB4790	1962	£1.50	£4	chart single
Wonderful Land Of The Shadows	7" EP.	Columbia	SEG8171	1962	£4	£8	
Wonderful Lnad	7"	Columbia	DB4726	196-	£2.50	£6	black label

SHADOWS (2)

Under Stars Of Love	7"	HMV	POP563	1958	£12.50	£25	

SHADOWS OF KNIGHT

Back Door Men	LP	Dunwich	(S)667	1966	£15	£30	US
Bad Little Woman	7"	Atlantic	584045	1966	£6	£12	
Gloria	LP	Dunwich	(S)666	1966	£15	£30	US
Gloria	7"	Atlantic	AT4085	1966	£6	£12	
Oh Yeah	7"	Atlantic	584021	1966	£6	£12	
Oh Yeah	7" EP.	Atco	113	1966	£25	£50	French
Shadows Of Knight	LP	Super K	SKS6002	1969	£8	£20	US
Shake	7"	Buddah	201024	1968	£4	£8	
Someone Like Me	7"	Atlantic	584136	1967	£6	£12	

SHADRACK CHAMELEON

Shadrack Chameleon	LP	Iglus		1969	£60	£120	US

SHADROCKS

Go Go Special	7"	Island	WI3061	1967	£5	£10	

SHAFTESBURY

Lull Before The Storm	LP	OK Records	OKA001	1980	£15	£30	
We Are The Boys	LP	OK	OKO002	1981	£8	£20	

SHAFTO, BOBBY

How Could You	7"	Parlophone	R5252	1965	£1.50	£4	
I Haven't Got A Girl	7"	Parlophone	R4958	1962	£1.50	£4	
Love Love Love	7"	Parlophone	R5167	1964	£1.50	£4	
Over And Over	7"	Parlophone	R4870	1962	£1.50	£4	
Same Old Room	7"	Parlophone	R5403	1966	£1.50	£4	
See Me Cry	7"	Parlophone	R5403	1966	£1.50	£4	
She's My Girl	7"	Parlophone	R5130	1964	£1.50	£4	
Who Wouldn't Love A Girl Like You	7"	Parlophone	R5184	1964	£1.50	£4	

SHAGGS

Philosophy Of The World	LP	Third World	3001		£50	£100	US

SHAKEOUTS
Every Little Once In A While	7"	Columbia	DB7613	1965	£10	£20	

SHAKERS (2)
Break It All	LP	Audio Fidelity	(S)2155	1966	£8	£20	US

SHAKERS (KINGSIZE TAYLOR & DOMINOES)
Hippy Hippy Shake	7"	Polydor	NH66991	1963	£7.50	£15	
Let's Do The Madison, Twist, Locomotion..	LP	Polydor	46639	1963	£15	£30	German
Memphis Tennessee	7" EP	Polydor	50025	1963	£15	£30	French
Money	7"	Polydor	NH52158	1963	£6	£12	
Whole Lotta Loving	7"	Polydor	NH52272	1964	£6	£12	
Hippy Hippy Shake	7"	Polydor	NH52213	1963	£5	£10	
Money	7"	Polydor	NH52258	1963	£5	£10	

SHAKESPEARE, CHRIS GLOBE SHOW
Ob La Di, Ob La Da	7"	Page One	POF113	1969	£5	£10	

SHAKESPEARS
Saint	7" EP	Barclay	070981	1966	£10	£20	French
Summertime	7" EP	Barclay	071036	1966	£10	£20	French

SHAKEY JAKE
Further On Up The Road	LP	Liberty	LBL83217E	1969	£5	£12	

SHAKEY VICK
Little Woman You're So Sweet	LP	Pye	NSPL18276	1969	£15	£30	

SHAM 69
I Don't Wanna	7"	Step Forward	SF4	1977	£2	£5	
I Don't Wanna	12"	Step Forward	SF4	1977	£2.50	£6	
Sons Of The Streets	7"	no label	no number	1977	£2	£5	1 sided
What Have We Got	7"	Brick Wall	no number	1978	£2.50	£6	1 sided

SHAM, SAM
Drumbago's Dead	7"	Blue Cat	BS157	1969	£4	£8	Sparters B side

SHAME
Don't Go Away Little Girl	7"	MGM	MGM1349	1967	£15	£30	

SHAME (2)
Real Tears	7"	Fierce	FRIGHT003	1985	£10	£20	test pressing

SHAMEN
Progen (C-Mix F&)	12"	One Little Indian	36TP12L	1990	£3	£8	
They May Be Right	12"	One Big Guitar	OBG003T	1986	£3	£8	
Wayward Wednesday In May Affair	7"	Skipping Kitten		1986	£2.50	£6	1 sided flexi
Young Till Yesterday	7"	Moksha	SOMA1	1986	£1.50	£4	
Young Till Yesterday	12"	Moksha	SOMA1T	1986	£2.50	£6	

SHAMES
Greenburg Glickstein Charles	7"	CBS	3820	1968	£4	£8	
I Wanna Meet You	7"	CBS	202450	1966	£4	£8	
Mr.Unreliable	7"	CBS	2704	1967	£4	£8	
Sugar And Spice	7"	CBS	202344	1966	£7.50	£15	

SHAMROCKS
Cadillac	7" EP	Polydor	60122	196-	£6	£12	French
Don't Say	7" EP	Polydor	60124	196-	£10	£20	French
In Paris	LP	Polydor	658032	1966	£20	£40	French
Shamrocks	LP	Ariola	72151	1965	£30	£60	German
Smoke Rings	LP	Polydor		1966	£15	£30	German

SHANE & THE SHANE GANG
Whistle Stop	7"	Pye	7N15662	1964	£2.50	£6	

SHANE, VALERIE
One Billion Seven Million Thirty-Three	7"	Philips	PB879	1958	£2.50	£6	

SHANES
I Don't Want Your Love	7"	Columbia	DB7601	1965	£15	£30	

SHANGRI-LAS
Give Him A Great Big Kiss	7"	Red Bird	RB10018	1965	£4	£8	
Give Him A Great Big Kiss	7" EP	Red Bird	RBEV28007	1965	£12.50	£25	French
Give Us Your Blessings	7"	Red Bird	RB10030	1965	£2.50	£6	
Golden Hits	LP	Mercury	MCL20096	1966	£6	£15	
He Cried	7"	Red Bird	RB10053	1966	£2.50	£6	
I Can Never Go Home Any More	7"	Red Bird	RB10043	1966	£2	£5	
I Can Never Go Home Any More	7" EP	Red Bird	RB40004	1966	£15	£30	demo
I Can Never Go Home Any More	7" EP	Red Bird	RBEV28009	1966	£12.50	£25	French
I Can Never Go Home Anymore	7"	Red Bird	RB20104	1965	£25	£50	US
Leader Of The Pack	LP	Red Bird	RB20101	1964	£25	£50	
Leader Of The Pack	7"	Red Bird	RB10014	1964	£2	£5	chart single
Leader Of The Pack	7" EP	Red Bird	RBEV28005	1964	£12.50	£25	French, B side by The Jelly Beans
Long Live Our Love	7"	Red Bird	RB10048	1966	£2.50	£6	
Out In The Streets	7"	Red Bird	RB10025	1965	£2.50	£6	

Past Present And Future	7"	Red Bird	RB10068	1966	£4	£8	
Remember	7" EP	Red Bird	RBEV28004	1964	£12.50	£25	French, B side
							by The Butterflies
Remember Walking In The Sand	7"	Red Bird	RB10008	1964	£2	£5	chart single
Right Now And Not Later	7"	Red Bird	RB10036	1965	£10	£20	
Shangri-Las	7" EP	Red Bird	RB40002	1965	£12.50	£25	
Shangri-Las '65	LP	Red Bird	RB20104	1965	£17.50	£35	US
Shangri-Las Sing	LP	Post	4000		£5	£12	US
Sweet Sound Of Summer	7"	Mercury	MF962	1967	£2	£5	
Take Your Time	7"	Mercury	MF979	1967	£2	£5	

SHANK, BUD

Bud Shank Group	10" LP	Vogue	LDE157	1955	£15	£30	
Bud Shank Quartet	LP	Vogue	LAE12113	1958	£10	£25	
Bud Shank Quintet	LP	Vogue	LAE12020	1956	£10	£25	
Bud Shank-Bob Brookmeyer Group	10" LP	Vogue	LDE181	1956	£15	£30	
Flute 'n Oboe	LP	Vogue	VA160104	1958	£6	£15	with Bob Cooper
Holiday In Brazil	LP	Vogue	LAE12215	1960	£6	£15	
Jazz At Cal-Tech	LP	Vogue	LAE12095	1958	£8	£20	
New Groove	LP	Vogue	LAE12288	1961	£5	£12	
Swing's To TV	LP	Vogue	VA160134	1959	£8	£20	with Bob Cooper

SHANKAR, L.

Touch Me There	LP	Zappa	SRZ11602	1979	£5	£12	US

SHANKAR, RAVI

At The Woodstock Festival	LP	United Artists	UAG29379	1970	£6	£15	
Four Raga Moods	LP	Mushroom	300MR8	1971	£15	£30	double
In Concert 1972	LP	Apple	SAPDO1002	1973	£50	£100	double
In New York	LP	Fontana	TL5424	1967	£5	£12	
In San Francisco	LP	Columbia	SCX6382	1970	£4	£10	
India's Master Musician	LP	Fontana	TL5253	1965	£5	£12	
India's Master Musician	LP	Vogue	VA160156	1959	£6	£15	
Joi Bangla	7"	Apple	37	1971	£2	£5	
Joi Bangla	7"	Apple	37	1971	£6	£12	PS
Live At The Monterey Pop Festival	LP	Columbia	SX/SCX6273	1968	£4	£10	
Music Of India	LP	HMV	ASD463	1962	£5	£12	
Portrait Of Genius	LP	Fontana	TL5285	1966	£5	£12	
Raga	LP	Apple	SWAO3384	1971	£8	£20	US
Song From The Hills	7"	Fontana	TF712	1966	£2	£5	
Sound Of The Sitar	LP	Fontana	TL5357	1966	£5	£12	

SHANNON, CHICK

Tears On The Console	LP	Holyground	HG120	1975	£100	£200	
Tears On The Console	LP	Magic Mixture	MM3	1990	£5	£12	

SHANNON, DEAN

Jezebel	7"	HMV	POP820	1960	£4	£8	
Ubangi Stomp	7"	HMV	POP1103	1962	£6	£12	

SHANNON, DEL

1,661 Seconds	LP	Amy	S8006	1965	£17.50	£35	US, stereo
1,661 Seconds	LP	Stateside	SL10140	1965	£8	£20	
Best Of Del Shannon	LP	Dot	DLP3834	1967	£4	£10	US
Big Hurt	7"	Liberty	LIB55866	1966	£2.50	£6	
Break Up	7"	Stateside	SS430	1965	£1.50	£4	
Comin' Back To Me	7"	Stateside	SS8025	1969	£2.50	£6	
Cry Myself To Sleep	7"	London	HLX9587	1962	£1.50	£4	chart single
Del Shannon	7" EP	London	REX1332	1962	£7.50	£15	
Del Shannon No.2	7" EP	London	REX1346	1963	£7.50	£15	
Del Shannon's Hits	7" EP	Stateside	SE1029	1965	£6	£12	
Del's Own Favourites	7" EP	London	REX1383	1963	£7.50	£15	
Do You Want To Dance	7"	Stateside	SS349	1964	£1.50	£4	
For A Little While	7"	Liberty	LIB55889	1966	£2.50	£6	
From Del To You	7" EP	London	REX1387	1963	£7.50	£15	
From Me To You	7"	Big Top	3152	1963	£10	£20	US
Further Adventures Of C.Westover	LP	Liberty	LBL/LBS83114	1968	£6	£15	
Gemini	7"	Liberty	LBF15079	1968	£2.50	£6	
Handy Man	LP	Stateside	SL10115	1965	£6	£15	
Handy Man	7"	Stateside	SS317	1964	£1.50	£4	chart single
Hats Off To Del Shannon	7"	London	HAX8071	1963	£8	£20	chart LP
Hats Off To Larry	7"	London	HLX9402	1961	£1.50	£4	chart single
Hey Little Girl	7"	London	HLX9515	1962	£1.50	£4	chart single
I Can't Believe My Ears	7"	Stateside	SS494	1966	£2.50	£6	
Keep Searchin'	7"	Stateside	SS368	1965	£1.50	£4	chart single
Little Town Flirt	LP	Big Top	S121308	1963	£25	£50	US, stereo
Little Town Flirt	LP	London	HAX8091	1963	£8	£20	chart LP
Little Town Flirt	7"	London	HLX9653	1963	£1.50	£4	chart single
Live In England	LP	United Artists	UAS29474	1973	£4	£10	
Mary Jane	7"	Stateside	SS269	1964	£1.50	£4	chart single
Mind Over Matter	7"	Liberty	LIB10277	1967	£2	£5	
Move It On Over	7"	Stateside	SS452	1965	£4	£8	
New Del Shannon	7" EP	Liberty	LEP2272	1967	£12.50	£25	
Runaway	LP	Big Top	123003	1961	£17.50	£35	US, mono
Runaway	LP	Big Top	S123003	1961	£150	£250	US, stereo
Runaway	7"	London	HAX2402	1961	£10	£25	
Runaway	7"	London	HLX9317	1961	£6	£12	B side mispress
							- plays 'Snake'
Runaway	7"	London	HLX9317	1961	£2	£5	chart single
Runaway '67	7"	Liberty	LBF15020	1967	£2	£5	

She	7"	Liberty	LIB55939	1967	£2.50	£6	
Sings Hank Williams	LP	Stateside	SL10130	1965	£6	£15	
Sister Isabelle	7"	Stateside	SS8040	1970	£2.50	£6	
So Long Baby	7"	London	HLX9462	1961	£1.50	£4	chart single
Stranger In Town	7"	Stateside	SS395	1965	£1.50	£4	chart single
Sue's Gonna Be Mine	7"	London	HLX9800	1963	£1.50	£4	chart single
Swiss Maid	7"	London	HLX9609	1962	£1.50	£4	chart single
That's The Way Love Is	7"	London	HLX9858	1964	£1.50	£4	
Thinkin' It Over	7"	Liberty	LBF15061	1968	£2.50	£6	
This Is My Bag	LP	Liberty	(S)LBY1320	1966	£8	£20	
Total Commitment	LP	Liberty	(S)LBY1335	1966	£8	£20	
Two Kinds Of Teardrops	7"	London	HLX9719	1963	£1.50	£4	chart single
Two Silhouettes	7"	London	HLX9761	1963	£1.50	£4	chart single
What's A Matter Baby	7"	United Artists	UP35460	1972	£1.50	£4	

SHANNON, HUGH

Hugh Shannon Sings	10" LP	Atlantic	406		£8	£20	US

SHAPE OF THE RAIN

Riley, Riley, Wood & Waggett	LP	Neon	NE7	1971	£15	£30	

SHAPES & SIZES

Little Lovin' Somethin'	7"	Decca	F12441	1966	£1.50	£4	

SHAPIRO, HELEN

Brickyard Blues	7"	Oval	OVAL26	1984	£1.50	£4	
Don't Treat Me Like A Child	7"	Columbia	DB4589	1961	£1.50	£4	chart single
Even More Hits From Helen	7" EP	Columbia	SEG8209	1962	£4	£8	
Fever	7"	Columbia	DB7190	1964	£1.50	£4	chart single
Forget About The Bad Things	7"	Columbia	DB7810	1966	£1.50	£4	
He Knows How To Love Me	7"	Columbia	DB7340	1964	£1.50	£4	
Helen	7" EP	Columbia	ESG7872	1961	£5	£10	stereo
Helen	7" EP	Columbia	SEG8128	1961	£2.50	£6	
Helen Hits Out	LP	Columbia	33SX1661	1964	£6	£15	
Helen Hits Out	LP	Columbia	SCX3533	1964	£10	£25	stereo
Helen In Nashville	LP	Columbia	33SX1561	1963	£8	£20	
Helen's Hit Parade	7" EP	Columbia	SEG8136	1961	£4	£8	
Helen's Sixteen	LP	Columbia	33SX1494	1963	£6	£15	
Helen's Sixteen	LP	Columbia	SCX3470	1963	£10	£25	stereo
Here In Your Arms	7"	Columbia	DB7587	1965	£1.50	£4	
I Wish I'd Never Loved You	7"	Columbia	DB7395	1964	£1.50	£4	
In My Calendar	7"	Columbia	DB8073	1966	£1.50	£4	
Keep Away From Other Girls	7"	Columbia	DB4908	1962	£1.50	£4	chart single
Let's Talk About Love	7"	Columbia	DB4824	1962	£1.50	£4	chart single
Little Miss Lonely	7"	Columbia	DB4869	1962	£1.50	£4	chart single
Look Over Your Shoulder	7"	Columbia	DB7266	1964	£1.50	£4	
Look Who It Is	7"	Columbia	DB7130	1963	£1.50	£4	chart single
Make Me Belong To You	7"	Columbia	DB8148	1967	£1.50	£4	
More Hits From Helen	7" EP	Columbia	SEG8174	1962	£4	£8	
Not Responsible	7"	Columbia	DB7072	1963	£1.50	£4	
Queen For Tonight	7"	Columbia	DB4966	1963	£1.50	£4	chart single
Something Wonderful	7"	Columbia	DB7690	1965	£1.50	£4	
Stop & You'll Become Aware	7"	Columbia	DB8256	1967	£37.50	£75	
Take Down A Note Miss Smith	7"	Pye	7N17893	1970	£1.50	£4	
Teenager In Love	LP	Epic	LN24/BN26075	1963	£8	£20	US
Teenager Sings The Blues	7" EP	Columbia	ESG7880	1962	£7.50	£15	stereo
Teenager Sings The Blues	7" EP	Columbia	SEG8170	1962	£4	£8	
Tell Me What He Said	7"	Columbia	DB4782	1962	£1.50	£4	chart single
Today Has Been Cancelled	7"	Pye	7N17714	1969	£1.50	£4	
Tomorrow Is Another Day	7"	Columbia	DB7517	1965	£1.50	£4	
Tops With Me	LP	Columbia	33SX1397	1962	£5	£12	chart LP
Tops With Me	LP	Columbia	SCX3428	1962	£8	£20	stereo
Tops With Me No.1	7" EP	Columbia	ESG7888	1962	£12.50	£25	stereo
Tops With Me No.1	7" EP	Columbia	SEG8229	1963	£7.50	£15	
Tops With Me No.2	7" EP	Columbia	ESG7891	1962	£12.50	£25	stereo
Tops With Me No.2	7" EP	Columbia	SEG8243	1963	£7.50	£15	
Twelve Hits And A Miss	LP	Encore	ENC209	1967	£5	£12	
Waiting On The Shores Of Nowhere	7"	Pye	7N17975	1970	£1.50	£4	
Walking Back To Happiness	7"	Columbia	DB4715	1961	£1.50	£4	chart single
Woe Is Me	7"	Columbia	DB7026	1963	£1.50	£4	chart single
You Don't Know	7"	Columbia	DB4670	1961	£1.50	£4	chart single
You'll Get Me Loving You	7"	Pye	7N17600	1968	£1.50	£4	
You've Guessed It	7"	Pye	7N17785	1969	£4	£8	

SHARADES

Dumbhead	7"	Decca	F11811	1964	£15	£30	

SHARAE, BILLY

Do It	7"	Action	ACT4602	1971	£2	£5	

SHARKS

Goodbye Lorene	7"	RCA	RCA1776	1968	£2	£5	

SHARON, MARIE

These songs were produced by Brian Wilson, who used the same tune for "Thinkin' 'Bout You Baby" as he later re-worked for the Beach Boys' own song, "Darlin".

Run-Around Lover	7"	Capitol	5064	1963	£30	£60	US
Thinkin' 'Bout You Baby	7"	Capitol	5195	1964	£30	£60	US

SHARON, RALPH

Around The World In Jazz	LP	Columbia	33SX1090	1958	£6	£15	

SHARON, SUE & RALPH

Title	Format	Label	Catalog	Year			Notes
Mr. And Mrs. Jazz	LP	London	LTZN15102	1958	£5	£12	

SHARONS

Title	Format	Label	Catalog	Year			Notes
Someone To Turn To	LP	Emblem	JDR325	1970	£40	£80	

SHARP, DEE DEE

Title	Format	Label	Catalog	Year			Notes
All The Hits	LP	Cameo	(S)C1032	1962	£8	£20	US
Biggest Hits	LP	Cameo	C1062	1963	£6	£15	US
Do The Bird	LP	Cameo	(S)C1050	1963	£8	£20	US
Do The Bird	7"	Cameo Parkway	C244	1963	£4	£8	chart single
Down Memory Lane	LP	Cameo	C1074	1963	£6	£15	US
Eighteen Golden Hits	LP	Cameo	(S)C2002	1966	£6	£15	US
Gravy For My Mashed Potatoes	7"	Columbia	DB4874	1962	£2.50	£6	
I Really Love You	7"	Cameo Parkway	C375	1965	£15	£30	
It's A Funny Situation	7"	Cameo Parkway	C382	1965	£15	£30	demo
It's Mashed Potato Time	LP	Cameo	C1018	1962	£8	£20	US
Mashed Potato Time	7"	Columbia	DB4818	1962	£2.50	£6	
My Best Friend's Man	7"	Atlantic	584056	1966	£4	£8	
Ride	7"	Cameo Parkway	C230	1962	£2	£5	
Rock Me In The Cradle Of Love	7"	Cameo Parkway	C260	1963	£2.50	£6	
Songs Of Faith	LP	Cameo	C1022	1962	£6	£15	US
What Kinda Lady	7"	Action	ACT4522	1969	£10	£20	
Wild	7"	Cameo Parkway	C274	1963	£2	£5	

SHARP, STEVIE & CLEANCUTS

Title	Format	Label	Catalog	Year			Notes
We Are The Mods	7"	Happy Face	MM122	1980	£15	£30	no PS

SHARPE & NUMAN

Title	Format	Label	Catalog	Year			Notes
New Thing From London Town	12"	Numa	NUMP19	1986	£2.50	£6	pic disc
Voices	12"	Polydor	POPX894	1988	£2.50	£6	pic disc

SHARPE, BILL

Title	Format	Label	Catalog	Year			Notes
Change Your Mind	7"	Polydor	POSPP722	1985	£2.50	£6	pic disc
Change Your Mind	12"	Polydor	POPX722	1985	£4	£10	pic disc

SHARPE, RAY

Title	Format	Label	Catalog	Year			Notes
Hey Little Girl	7"	United Artists	UP1032	1963	£6	£12	
Linda Lu	7"	London	HLW8932	1959	£12.50	£25	

SHARPEES

Title	Format	Label	Catalog	Year			Notes
Tired Of Being Lonely	7"	President	PT399	1974	£1.50	£4	
Tired Of Being Lonely	7"	Stateside	SS495	1966	£17.50	£35	

SHARPLES, BOB

Title	Format	Label	Catalog	Year			Notes
Hurricane Boogie	7"	Decca	F10707	1956	£1.50	£4	

SHARPS

Title	Format	Label	Catalog	Year			Notes
Lock My Heart	7"	Vogue	V9086	1957	£60	£120	
Shuffling	7"	Vogue	V9096	1958	£50	£100	

SHATNER, WILLIAM

Title	Format	Label	Catalog	Year			Notes
Transformed Man	LP	Decca	DL75043	1968	£8	£20	US

SHAVERS, CHARLIE

Title	Format	Label	Catalog	Year			Notes
Charlie Shavers Quintet	10" LP	London	LZN14009	1956	£10	£25	
Gershwin, Shavers And Strings	10" LP	London	HBU1053	1956	£8	£20	
With The Sy Oliver Orchestra	10" LP	London	HBN1047	1956	£10	£25	

SHAW, ARTIE

Title	Format	Label	Catalog	Year			Notes
Any Old Time	LP	RCA	RD27065	1958	£6	£15	
Artie Shaw And His Gramercy Five	10" LP	Columbia	33C9006	1955	£8	£20	
Speak To Me Of Love	10" LP	Brunswick	LA8677	1954	£8	£20	

SHAW, ARVELL

Title	Format	Label	Catalog	Year			Notes
Skin Tight And Cymbal Wise	LP	Columbia	33SX1076	1958	£4	£10	

SHAW, GEORGIE

Title	Format	Label	Catalog	Year			Notes
Banjo Woogie	7"	Brunswick	05476	1955	£1.50	£4	

SHAW, MARLENA

Title	Format	Label	Catalog	Year			Notes
Mercy, Mercy, Mercy	7"	Chess	CRS8054	1967	£2.50	£6	

SHAW, NINA

Title	Format	Label	Catalog	Year			Notes
Woven In My Soul	7"	CBS	3239	1968	£2.50	£6	

SHAW, RICKY

Title	Format	Label	Catalog	Year			Notes
No Love But Your Love	7"	London	HLU9606	1962	£1.50	£4	

SHAW, ROLAND

Title	Format	Label	Catalog	Year			Notes
I Spy	7" EP	Decca	DFE8670	1966	£5	£10	

SHAW, ROLAND ORCHESTRA

Title	Format	Label	Catalog	Year			Notes
James Bond In Action	LP	Decca	LK4730	1965	£5	£12	

SHAW, SANDIE

Always Something There To Remind Me	7"	Pye	7N15704	1964	£1.50	£4	chart single
Always Something There To Remind Me	7" EP	Pye	NEP24208	1964	£4	£8	
As Long As You're Happy Baby	7"	Pye	7N15671	1964	£7.50	£15	
Girl Don't Come	7"	Pye	7N15743	1964	£1.50	£4	chart single
Golden Hits	LP	Golden Guinea	GGL0360	1966	£4	£10	
Hand In Glove	12"	Rough Trade	RTT130	1984	£2.50	£6	
How Can You Tell	7"	Pye	7N15987	1965	£1.50	£4	chart single
I Don't Need Anything	7"	Pye	7N17239	1967	£1.50	£4	chart single
I'll Stop At Nothing	7"	Pye	7N15783	1965	£1.50	£4	chart single
Long Live Love	7"	Pye	7N15841	1965	£1.50	£4	chart single
Long Live Love	7" EP	Pye	NEP24220	1965	£2.50	£6	
Love Me, Please Love Me	LP	Pye	N(S)PL18205	1967	£4	£10	
Me	LP	Pye	NPL18121	1965	£5	£12	
Message Understood	7"	Pye	7N15940	1965	£1.50	£4	chart single
Message Understood	7" EP	Pye	NEP24236	1966	£2.50	£6	
Nothing Comes Easy	7"	Pye	7N17086	1966	£1.50	£4	chart single
Nothing Comes Easy	7" EP	Pye	NEP24254	1966	£2.50	£6	
Puppet On A String	LP	Pye	N(S)PL18182	1967	£4	£10	
Reviewing The Situation	LP	Pye	N(S)PL18323	1969	£4	£10	
Run	7"	Pye	7N17163	1966	£1.50	£4	chart single
Run With Sandie Shaw	7" EP	Pye	NEP24264	1966	£6	£12	
Sandie	LP	Pye	NPL18110	1965	£5	£12	chart LP
Sandie	7" EP	Pye	NEP24232	1965	£4	£8	
Sandie Shaw In French	7" EP	Pye	NEP24271	1967	£7.50	£15	
Sandie Shaw In Italian	7" EP	Pye	NEP24273	1967	£7.50	£15	
Sandie Shaw Supplement	LP	Pye	N(S)PL18232	1968	£4	£10	
Show Me	7"	Pye	7N17564	1968	£1.50	£4	
Tell The Boys	7" EP	Pye	NEP24281	1967	£6	£12	
Think Sometimes About Me	7"	Pye	7N17212	1966	£1.50	£4	chart single
Together	7"	Pye	7N17587	1968	£1.50	£4	
Tomorrow	7"	Pye	7N17036	1966	£1.50	£4	chart single
Tomorrow	7" EP	Pye	NEP24247	1966	£6	£12	

SHAW, THOMAS

Thomas Shaw	LP	XTRA	XTRA1132	1972	£5	£12	

SHAW, TIMMY & THE STERNPHONES

Gonna Send You Back To Georgia	7"	Pye	7N25239	1964	£4	£8	

SHAYNE, LISA

Don't Ever Change	7"	Fontana	TF563	1965	£1.50	£4	

SHE TRINITY

Across The Street	7"	CBS	2819	1967	£1.50	£4	
Hair	7"	President	PT283	1969	£1.50	£4	
Have I Sinned	7"	Columbia	DB7943	1966	£2	£5	
He Fought The Law	7"	Columbia	DB7874	1966	£2.50	£6	
Wild Flower	7"	Columbia	DB7959	1966	£2	£5	
Yellow Submarine	7"	Columbia	DB7992	1966	£4	£8	

SHEARING, GEORGE

Black Satin	LP	Capitol	(S)T858	1958	£4	£10	
Blue Chiffon	LP	Capitol	T1124	1959	£4	£10	
Burnished Brass	LP	Capitol	T1038	1959	£4	£10	
George Shearing And The Montgomery Brothers	LP	Jazzland	JLP55	1961	£6	£15	
I Hear Music	10" LP	MGM	D118	1953	£6	£15	
In The Night	LP	Capitol	T1003	1959	£5	£12	with Dakota Staton
Jazz Conception	LP	MGM	C769	1958	£4	£10	
Latin Escapade	LP	Capitol	T737	1957	£4	£10	
Latin Lace	LP	Capitol	(S)T1082	1959	£4	£10	
Nearness Of You	10" LP	Decca	LF1036	1951	£6	£15	
On Stage	LP	Capitol	(S)T1187	1960	£4	£10	
Shearing Caravan	LP	MGM	C767	1958	£4	£10	
Shearing Piano	LP	Capitol	T909	1958	£4	£10	
Shearing Spell	10" LP	Capitol	LC6803	1956	£6	£15	
Touch Of Genius	10" LP	MGM	D129	1954	£6	£15	
Velvet Carpet	LP	Capitol	T720	1956	£4	£10	
Very First Session	10" LP	Vogue	LDE188	1956	£6	£15	
You're Hearing George Shearing	10" LP	MGM	D103	1952	£6	£15	

SHED, HENRY

Bend Me Shape Me	7"	Stateside	SS2198	1971	£1.50	£4	

SHEEN, BOBBY

Dr.Love	7"	Capitol	CL15455	1966	£20	£40	
Dr.Love	7"	Capitol	CL15713	1972	£2	£5	

SHEEP

Hide And Seek	7"	Stateside	SS493	1966	£6	£12	

SHEEP (2)

Sheep	LP	Myrrh	MYR1000	1973	£15	£30	

SHEFFIELDS

Bag's Groove	7"	Pye	7N15767	1965	£25	£50	
Got My Mojo Working	7"	Pye	7N15627	1964	£25	£50	

It Must Be Love .... 7" .... Pye .... 7N15600 .... 1964 ... £25 .... £50 ....

SHEIKS
Missing You .... 7" .... Parlophone ...... R5500 .... 1966 ... £4 .... £8 ....
Missing You .... 7" EP.. Odeon .... MEO123 .... 1966 ... £7.50 .... £15 .... French
Tears Are Coming .... 7" EP.. Odeon .... MEO131 .... 1966 ... £7.50 .... £15 .... French

SHEIKS (2)
Tres Chic .... 7" .... London .... HLW9012 .... 1959 ... £2 .... £5

SHELDON, DOUG
Big Big Baby .... 7" .... Decca .... F11463 .... 1962 ... £1.50 .... £4
Book Of Love .... 7" .... Decca .... F11368 .... 1961 ... £1.50 .... £4
Here I Stand .... 7" EP.. Decca .... DFE8527 .... 1963 ... £10 .... £20
I Saw Linda Yesterday .... 7" .... Decca .... F11564 .... 1963 ... £1.50 .... £4 .... chart single
I Was Alone .... 7" .... Decca .... F11654 .... 1963 ... £1.50 .... £4
It's Because Of You .... 7" .... Pye .... 7N17011 .... 1965 ... £1.50 .... £4
Live Now Pay Later .... 7" .... Decca .... F11529 .... 1962 ... £1.50 .... £4
Lollipops And Roses .... 7" .... Decca .... F11514 .... 1962 ... £1.50 .... £4
Mickey's Monkey .... 7" .... Decca .... F11790 .... 1963 ... £1.50 .... £4
Runaround Sue .... 7" .... Decca .... F11398 .... 1961 ... £1.50 .... £4 .... chart single
Take It Like A Man .... 7" .... Sue .... WI332 .... 1965 ... £4 .... £8
You Never Had It So Good .... 7" .... Decca .... F11433 .... 1962 ... £1.50 .... £4
Your Ma Said You Cried In Your Sleep 7" .... Decca .... F11416 .... 1961 ... £1.50 .... £4 .... chart single

SHELDON, SANDI
You're Gonna Make Me Love You .... 7" .... Epic .... EPC4186 .... 1976 ... £2 .... £5

SHELL
Goodbye Little Girl .... 7" .... Columbia .... DB8082 .... 1966 ... £4 .... £8

SHELLEY
I Will Be Wishing .... 7" .... Pye .... 7N15711 .... 1964 ... £4 .... £8

SHELLEY, LIZ
Make Me Your Baby .... 7" .... Brunswick .... 05940 .... 1965 ... £2 .... £5

SHELLEY, PETE
Sky Yen .... 12" ..... Groovy .... STP2 .... 1980 ... £4 .... £10

SHELLS
Baby Oh Baby .... 7" .... London .... HLU9288 .... 1961 ... £10 .... £20
It's A Happy Holiday .... 7" .... London .... HLU9644 .... 1962 ... £6 .... £12

SHELLY, ALAN
Lady Black Wife .... 7" .... Philips .... BF1709 .... 1969 ... £5 .... £10

SHELTON, ANNE
Absent Friends .... 7" .... Philips .... JK1012 .... 1957 ... £2 .... £5
Anne Shelton .... LP ..... Philips .... BBL7188 .... 1957 ... £5 .... £12
Anne Shelton .... 7" EP.. Philips .... BBE12090 .... 1956 ... £6 .... £12
Answer Me .... 7" .... HMV .... 7M164 .... 1953 ... £2 .... £5
Book .... 7" .... HMV .... 7M186 .... 1954 ... £2 .... £5
Cross Over The Bridge .... 7" .... HMV .... 7M197 .... 1954 ... £2 .... £5
Favourites .... 10" LP Decca .... LF1023 .... 1952 ... £6 .... £15
Favourites Vol.2 .... 10" LP Decca .... LF1106 .... 1953 ... £6 .... £15
Four Standards .... 7" EP.. Decca .... DFE6321 .... 1956 ... £2.50 .... £6
Goodnight, Well It's Time To Go .... 7" .... HMV .... 7M240 .... 1954 ... £2 .... £5
My Gypsy Heart .... 7" .... HMV .... 7M279 .... 1954 ... £2 .... £5
Songs From The Heart .... LP ..... Philips .... BBL7291 .... 1959 ... £4 .... £10

SHELTON, ROSCOE
Question .... 7" .... Sue .... WI354 .... 1965 ... £6 .... £12
Roscoe Shelton .... LP ..... Excello .... 8002 .... 1961 ... £20 .... £40 .... US

SHENDERY, DEANNA
Comin' Home Baby .... 7" .... Decca .... F12090 .... 1965 ... £4 .... £8

SHENLEY & ANNETTE
Million Dollar Baby .... 7" .... Blue Beat .... BB72 .... 1961 ... £5 .... £10

SHENLEY & HYACINTH
World Is On A Wheel .... 7" .... Rio .... R80 .... 1966 ... £4 .... £8

SHEP & THE LIMELITES
Daddy's Home .... 7" .... Pye .... 7N25090 .... 1961 ... £20 .... £40
Our Anniversary .... LP ..... Hull .... 1001 .... 1962 ... £100 .... £200 .... US
Our Anniversary .... LP ..... Roulette .... R25350 .... 1967 ... £10 .... £25 .... US
Ready For Your Love .... 7" .... Pye .... 7N25112 .... 1961 ... £12.50 .... £25 .... US

SHEPARD, JEAN
Lonesome Love .... LP ..... Capitol .... T1126 .... 1959 ... £5 .... £12 .... US
Songs Of A Love Affair .... LP ..... Capitol .... T728 .... 1956 ... £8 .... £20 .... US
This Is Jean Shepard .... LP ..... Capitol .... T1253 .... 1959 ... £4 .... £10

SHEPARD, TOMMY
Shepard's Flock .... LP ..... Vogue Coral .... LVA9046 .... 1957 ... £10 .... £25

SHEPHERD, BILL
Big Guitar .... 7" .... Pye .... 7N15137 .... 1958 ... £1.50 .... £4
Whistling Sailor .... 7" .... Island .... WIP6013 .... 1967 ... £2.50 .... £6

SHEPHERD BOYS
Title	Format	Label	Catalog	Year			Notes
Summer Sweetheart	7"	Columbia	DB3816	1956	£1.50	£4	
Teenage Love	7"	Columbia	SCM5282	1956	£1.50	£4	

SHEPHERD SISTERS
Title	Format	Label	Catalog	Year			Notes
Alone	7"	HMV	POP411	1957	£2	£5	chart single
Dancing Baby	7"	Mercury	AMT1005	1958	£1.50	£4	
Eating Pizza	7"	Mercury	7MT218	1958	£1.50	£4	
Gettin' Ready For Freddy	7"	Mercury	7MT196	1958	£2.50	£6	
Talk Is Cheap	7"	London	HLK9758	1963	£2	£5	
What Makes Little Girls Cry	7"	London	HLK9681	1963	£2	£5	

SHEPLEY, TOM
Title	Format	Label	Catalog	Year			Notes
How Do You Do?	LP	Tradition	TSR031	1978	£5	£12	

SHEPP, ARCHIE
Title	Format	Label	Catalog	Year			Notes
And The New York Contemporary Five	LP	Polydor	623235	1967	£5	£12	
And The New York Contemporary Five Vol.2	LP	Polydor	623267	1968	£5	£12	
Four For Trane	LP	HMV	CLP/CSD3524	1966	£5	£12	
Live In San Francisco	LP	HMV	CLP/CSD3600	1967	£5	£12	
Magic Of Ju-Ju	LP	Impulse	MIPL/SIPL512	1969	£5	£12	
Mama Too Tight	LP	Impulse	MIPL/SIPL508	1968	£5	£12	
On This Night	LP	HMV	CLP/CSD3561	1966	£5	£12	
One For The Trane	LP	Atlantic	583732	1969	£5	£12	
Rufus	LP	Fontana	681014ZL	1967	£5	£12	
Three For A Quarter, One For A Dime	LP	Impulse	SIPL520	1969	£5	£12	
Way Ahead	LP	Impulse	MIPL/SIPL516	1969	£5	£12	

SHEPPARDS
Title	Format	Label	Catalog	Year			Notes
Sheppards	LP	Constellation	CS4	1964	£8	£20	US

SHEPPERTON FLAMES
Title	Format	Label	Catalog	Year			Notes
Take Me For What I Am	7"	Deram	DM257	1969	£5	£10	

SHERIDAN, DANI
Title	Format	Label	Catalog	Year			Notes
Guess I'm Dumb	7"	Planet	PLF106	1966	£5	£10	

SHERIDAN, MIKE & THE NIGHTRIDERS
Title	Format	Label	Catalog	Year			Notes
Here I Stand	7"	Columbia	DB7462	1965	£6	£12	
No Other Guy	7"	Columbia	DB7141	1963	£7.50	£15	
Please Mister Postman	7"	Columbia	DB7183	1963	£6	£12	
What A Sweet Thing That Was	7"	Columbia	DB7302	1964	£6	£12	

SHERIDAN, MIKE LOT
Title	Format	Label	Catalog	Year			Notes
Don't Turn Your Back On Me	7"	Columbia	DB7798	1966	£7.50	£15	
Take My Hand	7"	Columbia	DB7677	1965	£7.50	£15	

SHERIDAN, TONY
Title	Format	Label	Catalog	Year			Notes
Skinnie Minnie	7"	Polydor	NH52927	1964	£6	£12	
Skinnie Minnie	7" EP	Polydor	21978	1964	£15	£30	French
Tony Sheridan	LP	Polydor	46612/237112	1963	£15	£30	German
Will You Still Love Me Tomorrow	7"	Polydor	NH52315	1964	£6	£12	

SHERIDAN-PRICE
Title	Format	Label	Catalog	Year			Notes
Sometimes I Wonder	7"	Gemini	GMS009	1979	£4	£8	
This Is To Certify That	LP	Gemini	GME1002	1970	£5	£12	

SHERLOCK, ROGER
Title	Format	Label	Catalog	Year			Notes
Memories Of Sligo	LP	Inchecronin	INC7419	1978	£6	£15	

SHERMAN, ALLAN
Title	Format	Label	Catalog	Year			Notes
Crazy Downtown	7"	Warner Bros	WB160	1965	£1.50	£4	
End Of A Symphony	7"	RCA	RCA1419	1964	£1.50	£4	
Hello Muddah Hello Fadduh	7"	Warner Bros	WB106	1963	£1.50	£4	chart single
Hello Muddah Hello Fadduh	7"	Warner Bros	WB140	1964	£1.50	£4	
It's A Most Unusual Play	7"	Warner Bros	WB5741	1966	£1.50	£4	
Me Come Back To Sorrento	7"	Warner Bros	WB122	1964	£1.50	£4	
My Son The Nut Vol.1	7" EP	Warner Bros	WSEP6120	1964	£2	£5	stereo
Second Hand Nose	7"	Warner Bros	WB5749	1966	£1.50	£4	
Shine On Harvey Bloom	7"	Warner Bros	WB5725	1965	£1.50	£4	
Skin	7"	Warner Bros	WB131	1964	£1.50	£4	
Twelve Gifts Of Christmas	7"	Warner Bros	WB5736	1965	£1.50	£4	
Won't You Come Home Disraeli	7"	Warner Bros	WB115	1963	£1.50	£4	

SHERRILL, BILLY
Title	Format	Label	Catalog	Year			Notes
Like Making Love	7"	Mercury	AMT1131	1961	£1.50	£4	

SHERRYS
Title	Format	Label	Catalog	Year			Notes
At The Hop With The Sherrys	LP	Guyden	GLP503	1962	£25	£50	US
Do The Popeye	7" EP	London	RE1363	1963	£12.50	£25	
Pop Pop Popeye	7"	London	HLW9625	1962	£2	£5	
Slop Time	7"	London	HL9686	1963	£2.50	£6	

SHERWOOD, BOBBY
Title	Format	Label	Catalog	Year			Notes
Bobby Sherwood Orchestra	10" LP	Capitol	LC6632	1954	£6	£15	

SHERWOOD, TONY
Title	Format	Label	Catalog	Year			Notes
Piano Boogie Twist	7"	Zodiac	ZR010	196-	£2.50	£6	

SHERWOODS

El Scorpion	7"	Pye	7N25097	1961	£1.50	£4	
Memories	7"	Solar	SRP105	1964	£1.50	£4	

SHEVELLES

Ooh Poo Pah Do	7"	Oriole	CB1915	1963	£2	£5	

SHEVELLS

Big City Lights	7"	Polydor	56239	1968	£4	£8	
Come On Home	7"	United Artists	UP1125	1966	£10	£20	
I Could Conquer The World	7"	United Artists	UP1059	1964	£5	£10	
Walking On The Edge	7"	United Artists	UP1076	1965	£2.50	£6	
Watermelon Man	7"	United Artists	UP1081	1965	£2.50	£6	

SHEVETON, TONY

Excuses	7"	Oriole	CB1975	1964	£1.50	£4	
Hey Little Girl	7"	Oriole	CB1766	1962	£1.50	£4	
Lonely Heart	7"	Oriole	CB1726	1962	£1.50	£4	
Lullaby Of Love	7"	Oriole	CB1705	1962	£1.50	£4	
Million Drums	7"	Oriole	CB1895	1963	£1.50	£4	chart single
Runaround Sue Is Getting Married	7"	Oriole	CB1788	1963	£1.50	£4	

SHIELD, TREVOR

Moon is Playing A Trick	7"	Trojan	TR664	1969	£2.50	£6	

SHIELDS

You Cheated	7"	London	HLD8706	1958	£10	£20	

SHIELDS, KEITH

Hey Gyp	7"	Decca	F12572	1967	£15	£30	
So Hard Living Without You	7"	Decca	F12666	1967	£6	£12	
Wonder Of You	7"	Decca	F12609	1967	£5	£10	

SHIFRIN, SUSAN

25 Miles	7"	Decca	F13145	1971	£1.50	£4	

SHILOH

Shiloh	LP	Amos	AAS7015	1970	£4	£10	US

SHINDIGS

Little While Back	7"	Parlophone	R5377	1965	£10	£20	
One Little Letter	7"	Parlophone	R5316	1965	£10	£20	

SHINDOGS

Who Do You Think You Are	7"	Fontana	TF790	1967	£2.50	£6	

SHINES, JOHNNY

Country Blues	LP	XTRA	XTRA1142	1974	£5	£12	
Last Night's Dream	LP	Blue Horizon	763212	1969	£25	£50	

SHINN, DON

Departures	LP	Columbia	SCX6355	1969	£8	£20	
Temples With Prophets	LP	Columbia	SX/SCX6319	1969	£10	£25	

SHIRALEE

I'll Stay By Your Side	7"	Fontana	TF855	1967	£2.50	£6	

SHIRELLES

Are You Still My Baby	7"	Pye	7N25288	1965	£2	£5	
Baby It's You	LP	Stateside	SL10006	1962	£20	£40	
Baby It's You	7"	Top Rank	JAR601	1962	£2.50	£6	
Big John	7"	Top Rank	JAR590	1961	£2.50	£6	
Dedicated To The One I Love	7"	Top Rank	JAR549	1961	£2.50	£6	
Don't Say Goodnight	7"	Stateside	SS213	1963	£2	£5	
Everybody Loves A Lover	7"	Stateside	SS152	1963	£2	£5	
Foolish Little Girl	LP	Scepter	S(PS)511	1963	£15	£30	US
Foolish Little Girl	7"	Stateside	SS181	1963	£2	£5	chart single
Greatest Hits	LP	Stateside	SL10041	1963	£10	£20	
Greatest Hits Vol.2	LP	Scepter	S(PS)560	1967	£6	£15	US
Here And Now	LP	Pricewise	P4002	197-	£5	£12	US
I Met Him On A Sunday	7"	Brunswick	05746	1958	£12.50	£25	
It's A Mad, Mad, Mad, Mad World	LP	Scepter	S(PS)514	1963	£10	£25	US
It's A Mad, Mad, Mad, Mad World	7"	Pye	7N25229	1963	£2	£5	
It's Love That Really Counts	7"	Stateside	SS129	1962	£2.50	£6	
Mama Said	7"	Top Rank	JAR567	1961	£2.50	£6	
Maybe Tonight	7"	Pye	7N25279	1964	£5	£10	
Sha La La	7"	Pye	7N25240	1964	£2	£5	
Shades of Blue	7"	Pye	7N25386	1966	£1.50	£4	
Shirelles Sing The Golden Oldies	LP	Scepter	S(PS)516	1964	£8	£20	US
Shirelles Sound	7" EP	Top Rank	JKP3012	1961	£15	£30	
Sing To Trumpet & Strings	LP	Top Rank	35115	1961	£30	£60	
Soldier Boy	7"	HMV	POP1019	1962	£2.50	£6	chart single
Spontaneous Combustion	LP	Scepter	S(PS)562	1967	£6	£15	US
Swing The Most	LP	Pricewise	P4001	197-	£5	£12	US
There's A Storm Going On In My Heart	7"	Mercury	MF1093	1969	£5	£10	
Tonight You're Gonna Fall In Love	7"	Pye	7N25233	1964	£2	£5	
Tonight's The Night	LP	Scepter	S(PS)501	1961	£20	£40	US
Tonight's The Night	7"	London	HL9233	1960	£5	£10	
Too Much Of A Good Thing	7"	Pye	7N25425	1967	£4	£8	
Welcome Home Baby	7"	Stateside	SS119	1962	£2.50	£6	

What A Difference A Day Made	7"	Top Rank	JAR578	1961	£2	£5	
What Does A Girl Do	7"	Stateside	SS232	1963	£2	£5	
Will You Still Love Me Tomorrow	7"	Top Rank	JAR540	1960	£2.50	£6	chart single

SHIRELLES & KING CURTIS

Twist Party	LP	Scepter	S(PS)505	1962	£10	£25	US

SHIRLEY & ALFRED

Kid Games And Nursery Rhymes	7"	Liberty	LBF15120	1968	£1.50	£4

SHIRLEY & LEE

Come On And Have Your Fun	7"	Vogue	V9129	1959	£12.50	£25	
Everybody's Rocking	7"	Vogue	V9118	1958	£20	£40	
I Feel Good	7"	Vogue	V9063	1957	£17.50	£35	
I Want To Dance	7"	Vogue	V9088	1957	£12.50	£25	
I'll Do It	7"	Vogue	V9137	1959	£12.50	£25	
I'll Thrill You	7"	Vogue	V9103	1958	£12.50	£25	
I've Been Loved Before	7"	London	HLI9186	1960	£7.50	£15	
Legendary Masters	LP	United Artists	LA026G2	1974	£5	£12	US
Let The Good Times Roll	LP	Aladdin	807	1956	£100	£200	US
Let The Good Times Roll	LP	Imperial	A9179	1962	£25	£50	US
Let The Good Times Roll	LP	Score	SLP4023	1957	£37.50	£75	US
Let The Good Times Roll	LP	Warwick	(WST)2028	1961	£30	£60	US
Let The Good Times Roll	7"	Island	WI257	1965	£6	£12	
Let The Good Times Roll	7"	London	HLI9209	1960	£7.50	£15	
Let The Good Times Roll	7"	Vogue	V9059	1956	£22.50	£45	
Little Word	7"	Vogue	V9135	1959	£12.50	£25	
Rock All Nite	7"	Vogue	V9072	1957	£25	£50	
Rock 'N' Roll	7" EP	Vogue	VE170101	1957	£75	£150	
Rocking With The Clock	7"	Vogue	V9084	1957	£25	£50	
Shirley And Lee	7" EP	Vogue	VE170145	1960	£75	£150	
That's What I Wanna Do	7"	Vogue	V9067	1957	£15	£30	
True Love	7"	Vogue	V9156	1959	£12.50	£25	
You'd Be Thinking Of Me	7"	Vogue	V9094	1957	£17.50	£35	

SHIRLEY & THE RUDE BOYS

Gently Set Me Free	7"	Blue Beat	BB375	1965	£5	£10

SHIRLEY & THE SHIRELLES

Look What You've Done	7"	Bell	BLL1049	1969	£2	£5

SHIRLEY, DON

Improvisations	LP	London	HAA2046	1957	£4	£10	with Richard Davis

SHIRLEY, ROY

Dance Arena	7"	Giant	GN32	1968	£4	£8	
Dance The Reggae	7"	Doctor Bird	DB1168	1968	£5	£10	
Facts Of Life	7"	Island	WI3168	1968	£5	£10	
Get On The Ball	7"	Caltone	CAL101	1967	£4	£8	Johnny Moore B side
Get On The Ball	7"	Caltone	TONE101	1967	£4	£8	Johnny Moore B side
Good Is Better Than Bad	7"	Island	WI3118	1967	£5	£10	
Hold Them	7"	Doctor Bird	DB1068	1966	£5	£10	
Hush A Bye	7"	Doctor Bird	DB1165	1968	£5	£10	
If I Did Know	7"	Island	WI3125	1967	£5	£10	
I'm The Winner	7"	Doctor Bird	DB1079	1967	£5	£10	
Life	7"	Duke	DU18	1969	£2.50	£6	
Million Dollar Baby	7"	Island	WI3110	1967	£5	£10	Sensations B side
Move All Day	7"	Island	WI3108	1967	£5	£10	
Musical Field	7"	Doctor Bird	DB1093	1967	£5	£10	Lee Perry B side
Musical War	7"	Island	WI3071	1967	£5	£10	
Paradise	7"	Ska Beat	JB253	1966	£5	£10	
Prophet	7"	Doctor Bird	DB1088	1967	£5	£10	
Thank You	7"	Doctor Bird	DB1108	1967	£5	£10	
Thank You	7"	Island	WI3098	1967	£5	£10	
Think About The Future	7"	Fab	FAB54	1968	£4	£8	
Warming Up The Scene	7"	Giant	GN33	1968	£4	£8	Glen Adams B side
World Needs Love	7"	Amalgamated	AMG815	1968	£4	£8	

SHIRLEY, SUSAN

Imagine	7"	Columbia	DB8937	1972	£1.50	£4
Jealous Guy	7"	Columbia	DB8835	1971	£1.50	£4
Really Into Something Good	7"	Philips	6006037	1970	£6	£12

SHIVA'S HEADBAND

Coming To A Head	LP	Armadillo	None	1969	£15	£30	US
Psychedelic Yesterday	LP	Ape	1001	1981	£6	£15	US
Take Me To The Mountains	LP	Capitol	ST538	1970	£8	£20	US

SHIVEL, BUNNY

You'll Never Find Another Love Like Mine	7"	Capitol	CL15487	1967	£4	£8

SHIVER

Walpurgis	LP	Maris	20501	1969	£50	£100	German

SHOCKING BLUE

With a lead singer who sounded not unlike Grace Slick, Shocking Blue would have loved to have been taken seriously as the Dutch Jefferson Airplane. Unfortunately, their material was cast a little too firmly in the light-weight pop mould, but this stood the group in good stead in the case of their hit single "Venus", whose absurdly catchy melody and rhythm have made the song into a perennial favourite.

At Home	LP	Penny Farthing	PELS500	1969	£5	£12	
Inkpot	7"	Polydor	2001299	1972	£1.50	£4	chart single

Mighty Joe	7"	Penny Farthing	PEN713	1970	£1.50	£4	
Never Marry A Railroad Man	7"	Penny Farthing	PEN721	1970	£1.50	£4	
Out Of Sight Out Of Mind	7"	Polydor	2001266	1972	£1.50	£4	
Sally Was A Good Old Girl	7"	Penny Farthing	PEN744	1970	£1.50	£4	
Scorpio's Dance	LP	Penny Farthing	PELS510	1970	£5	£12	
Shocking You	7"	Penny Farthing	PEN758	1971	£1.50	£4	
Venus	7"	Penny Farthing	PEN702	1969	£1.50	£4	chart single

SHOES
Un Dans Versailles	LP	private		1974	£50	£100	US

SHOES (2)
Farewell In The Rain	7"	Polydor	56739	1968	£1.50	£4	

SHONDELL, TROY
I Got A Woman	7"	London	HL9668	1963	£2.50	£6	
Many Sides Of Troy Shondell	LP	London	HAY8128	1964	£20	£40	
Tears From An Angel	7"	Liberty	LIB55398	1962	£1.50	£4	
This Time	7"	London	HLG9432	1961	£2.50	£6	chart single

SHONDELLS
At The Saturday Hop	LP	La Louisianne	109	1964	£20	£40	US
Don't Cry My Soldier Boy	7"	Ember	EMBS191	1964	£1.50	£4	

SHOOT
On The Frontier	LP	Capitol	SMAS11229	1972	£4	£10

SHOP ASSISTANTS
All Day Long	7"	Subway Organisation	SUBWAY1	1985	£4	£8	red PS
Something To Do	7"	Villa 21	002	1985	£15	£30	

SHORE, DINAH
Changing Partners	7"	HMV	7M183	1954	£2	£5
Come Back To My Arms	7"	HMV	7M221	1954	£2	£5
Holding Hands At Midnight	LP	RCA	RD27072	1958	£4	£10
If I Give My Heart To You	7"	HMV	7M250	1954	£2.50	£6
Keep It A Secret	7"	HMV	7M119	1953	£4	£8
Love And Marriage	7"	HMV	7M352	1956	£1.50	£4
Sweet Thing	7"	HMV	7M139	1953	£2	£5
Three Coins In The Fountain	7"	HMV	7M236	1954	£2.50	£6

SHORT, BOBBY
Bobby Short	LP	London	HAK2123	1958	£5	£12

SHORT, BRIAN
Anything For A Laugh	LP	Transatlantic	TRA245	1971	£5	£12

SHORT CROSS
Arising	LP	Breeder			£75	£150

SHORTER, WAYNE
Adam's Apple	LP	Blue Note	BLP/BST84232	1966	£8	£20
All Seeing Eye	LP	Blue Note	BLP/BST84219	1965	£8	£20
Ju Ju	LP	Blue Note	BLP/BST84182	1964	£10	£25
Night Dreamer	LP	Blue Note	BLP/BST84173	1964	£10	£25
Schizophrenia	LP	Blue Note	BST84297	1968	£6	£15
Speak No Evil	LP	Blue Note	BLP/BST84194	1965	£8	£20
Super Nova	LP	Blue Note	BST84332	1969	£5	£12

SHORTKUTS
Your Eyes May Shine	7"	United Artists	UP2233	1968	£5	£10

SHORTY & THEM
Pills	7"	Fontana	TF460	1964	£7.50	£15

SHOTGUN EXPRESS
Funny 'Cos Neither Could I	7"	Columbia	DB8178	1967	£10	£20	
I Could Feel The Whole World	7"	Columbia	DB8025	1966	£10	£20	
I Could Feel The Whole World Turn Round	7" EP	Columbia	ESRF1864	1967	£50	£100	Frenc

SHOTS
Keep A Hold Of What You've Got	7"	Columbia	DB7713	1965	£10	£20

SHOUTS
She Was My Baby	7"	React	EA101	1964	£4	£8

SHOWBIZ KIDS
I Don't Want To Discuss That	7"	Top Secret	CON1	198-	£5	£10

SHOWMEN
Action	7"	Pama	PM767	1969	£1.50	£4
It Will Stand	7"	London	HLP9481	1962	£12.50	£25
Wrong Girl	7"	London	HLP9571	1962	£25	£50

SHOWSTOPPERS
Ain't Nothing But A House Party	7"	Beacon	3100	1968	£2.50	£6	chart singl
Ain't Nothing But A House Party	7"	Beacon	BEA100	1968	£1.50	£4	
Shake Your Mini	7"	Beacon	3106	1968	£1.50	£4	

SHOX
No Turning Back	7"	Axis	AXIS4	1980	£4	£8	
No Turning Back	7"	Beggars Banquet	BEG33	1980	£2	£5	

SHRIEVE, MICHAEL
Transfer Station Blue	LP	Fortuna		1984	£15	£30	US

SHUBERT
Until The Rains Come	7"	Fontana	TF942	1968	£5	£10	

SHUMAN, MORT
Cry A Little	7"	Fontana	H685	1966	£2	£5	
I'm A Man	7"	Decca	F11184	1959	£15	£30	tri-centre
Monday Monday	7"	Immediate	IM048	1967	£5	£10	

SHUSHA
From East To West	LP	Tangent	TGS138	1978	£5	£12	
Persian Love Songs And Mystic Chants	LP	Tangent	TGS108	1970	£5	£12	
Shusha	LP	United Artists	UAS29575	1974	£4	£10	
Song Of Long Time Lovers	LP	Tangent	TGS114	1972	£5	£12	

SHUTDOWN DOUGLAS
Twin Cut Outs	7" EP	Capitol	EAP41997	1964	£6	£12	French

SHUTDOWNS
Four In The Floor	7"	Colpix	PX11016	1963	£5	£10	

SHY
Once Bitten Twice Shy	LP	Ebony	EBON15	1983	£6	£15	

SHY LIMBS
Lady In Black	7"	CBS	4624	1969	£15	£30	
Reputation	7"	CBS	4190	1969	£15	£30	

SHY ONES
La Route	7"	Oriole	CB1924	1964	£5	£10	
Nightcap	7"	Oriole	CB1848	1963	£6	£12	

SHYSTER
Tick Tock	7"	Polydor	56202	1968	£40	£80	

SIBLEY, DUDLEY
Gun Man	7"	Island	WI3034	1967	£5	£10	
Run Boy Run	7"	Coxsone	CS7010	1967	£5	£10	

SIDEKICKS
Suspicions	7"	RCA	RCA1538	1966	£4	£8	

SIEGEL-SCHWALL BAND
The Siegel-Schwall Band so accurately epitomise the worst aspects of the late sixties fascination with the blues on the part of white rock performers, that it is amazing how the group managed to make such a large number of albums. Each is characterised by an entirely routine approach to the blues in which the form is reproduced without any genuine understanding or feeling. Composer William Russo was able to use this to interesting effect, however, when he incorporated the group within his "Three Pieces For Blues Band And Symphony Orchestra". Here it is vital that the blues group play cliches, so that they can be subverted by the oblique lines superimposed by the orchestra. It is an unusual approach to the combination of rock and classical styles, but it works superbly well.

953 West	LP	Teldec	10121	1973	£4	£10	German
Best Of The Siegel-Schwall Band	LP	Vanguard	VSD79336	1974	£4	£10	US
Live Last Summer	LP	Wooden Nickel	WNS1288	1974	£4	£10	US
RIP Siegel-Schwall	LP	Wooden Nickel	WNS1554	1974	£4	£10	US
Say Siegel-Schwall	LP	Vanguard	VRS/VSD79249	1967	£5	£12	US
Shake	LP	Vanguard	SVRL19044	1968	£5	£12	
Siegel-Schwall '70	LP	Vanguard	VSD6562	1970	£5	£12	US
Siegel-Schwall Band	LP	RCA	SF8246	1971	£4	£10	
Siegel-Schwall Band	LP	Vanguard	VRS/VSD79235	1966	£5	£12	US
Sleepy Hollow	LP	RCA	LSP10394	1972	£4	£10	

SIFFRE, LABI
It Must Be Love	7"	Pye	7N25572	1971	£1.50	£4	

SIGHT & SOUND
Alley Alley	7"	Fontana	TF982	1968	£5	£10	
Our Love Is In The Pocket	7"	Fontana	TF927	1968	£5	£10	

SIGLER, BUNNY
Let The Good Times Roll	LP	Parkway	P(S)50000	1967	£6	£15	US
Let The Good Times Roll	7"	Cameo Parkway	P153	1962	£5	£10	
Let The Good Times Roll	7"	London	HLU10518	1976	£1.50	£4	

SIGNATURES
Prepare To Flip	LP	Warner Bros	W1353	1959	£5	£12	US
Sing In	LP	Warner Bros	W1250	1959	£5	£12	US
Their Voices And Instruments	LP	Whippet	702	1957	£6	£15	US

SIGNS
Ain't You Got A Heart	7"	Decca	F12522	1966	£5	£10	

SILBERBART
Four Times Sound Razing	LP	Philips	6305095	1971	£30	£60	German

SILENT PARTNER
Hung By A Thread .... LP ...... Lucky Boy .... £75 ....£150 .... US

SILHOUETTES
Get A Job .... LP ...... Goodway .... GLP100 .... 195- .... £50 ....£100 .... US
Get A Job .... 7" ...... Parlophone ..... R4407 .... 1958 .... £12.50 ....£25 ....
Heading For The Poorhouse .... 7" ...... Parlophone ..... R4425 .... 1958 .... £15 ....£30 ....

SILK
Smooth As Raw Silk .... LP ...... ABC .... 1969 .... £8 ....£20 .... US

SILK, ERIC
Silken Touch .... 10" LP Esquire .... 20095 .... 1958 ... £6 ....£15 ....

SILKIE
Blood Red River .... 7" ...... Fontana .... TF556 .... 1965 ... £1.50 .....£4 ....
Born To Be With You .... 7" ...... Fontana .... TF709 .... 1966 ... £1.50 .....£4 ....
Born To Be With You .... 7" EP.. Fontana .... 465306 .... 1966 ... £6 ....£12 ....French
Keys To My Soul .... 7" ...... Fontana .... TF659 .... 1966 ... £1.50 .....£4 ....
Sing Dylan .... LP ...... Fontana .... TL5256 .... 1965 ... £6 ....£15 ....
You've Got To Hide Your Love Away ... LP ...... Fontana .... MGF2/SRF67548... 1965 ... £8 ....£20 .... US
You've Got To Hide Your Love Away ... 7" ...... Fontana .... TF603 .... 1965 ... £2 ....£5 ....chart single
You've Got To Hide Your Love Away ... 7" EP.. Fontana .... 465294 .... 1965 ... £10 ....£20 ....French

SILL, JUDEE
Heart Food .... LP ...... Asylum .... SYL9006 .... 1973 ... £4 ....£10 ....
Judee Sill .... LP ...... Asylum .... SYLA8751 .... 1971 ... £5 ....£12 ....

SILLY SURFERS
Sounds Of The Silly Surfers .... LP ...... Mercury .... MG2/SR60977 .... 1965 ... £5 ....£12 .... US

SILLY WIZARD
Silly Wizard .... LP ...... XTRA .... XTRA1158 .... 1976 ... £6 ....£15 ....

SILOAH
Saureadler .... LP ...... Car .... 1558015 .... 1970 ... £150 ......£250 ....German
Sukram Gurk .... LP ...... German Blues . 1558025 .... 1972 ... £150 ......£250 ....German

SILVER
Change Has Got To Come .... 7" ...... Fab .... FAB163 .... 1971 ... £2.50 .....£6 ....
Love Me Forever .... 7" ...... Columbia .... DB117 .... 1970 ... £4 ....£8 ....
Things .... 7" ...... Jolly .... JY012 .... 1968 ... £4 ....£8 ....

SILVER, ANDEE
Boy I Used To Know .... 7" ...... HMV .... POP1344 .... 1964 ... £1.50 .....£4 ....
Handful Of Silver .... LP ...... Decca .... SKL5059 .... 1970 ... £5 ....£12 ....
Only Your Love Can Save Me .... 7" ...... Fontana .... TF666 .... 1966 ... £1.50 .....£4 ....
Too Young To Go Steady .... 7" ...... HMV .... POP1297 .... 1964 ... £1.50 .....£4 ....

SILVER APPLES
Contracts .... LP ...... Kapp .... 3584 .... 1969 ... £10 ....£25 .... US
Silver Apples .... LP ...... Kapp .... 3562 .... 1968 ... £6 ....£15 .... US

SILVER BIRCH
Silver Birch .... LP ...... Brayford .... BR02 .... 1974 ... £150 ......£250 ....sleeve
pictured in Guide

SILVER BULLITT
Willpower Weak, Temptation Strong ... 7" ...... Philips .... 6073808 .... 197- ... £2 ....£5 ....

SILVER BYKE
Who Needs Tomorrow .... 7" ...... London .... HLZ10200 .... 1968 ... £1.50 .....£4 ....

SILVER EAGLE
Theodore .... 7" ...... MGM .... MGM1345 .... 1967 ... £6 ....£12 ....

SILVER, EDDIE
Rockin' Robin .... 7" ...... Parlophone ..... R4483 .... 1958 ... £2.50 .....£6 ....
Seven Steps To Love .... 7" ...... Parlophone ..... R4439 .... 1958 ... £5 ....£10 ....

SILVER, HORACE
Best Of Horace Silver .... LP ...... Blue Note .... BST84325 .... 1969 ... £5 ....£12 ....
Blowin' The Blues Away .... LP ...... Blue Note .... BLP/BST84017 ...... 196- ... £15 ....£30 ....
Cape Verdean Blues .... LP ...... Blue Note .... BLP/BST84220 ...... 1965 ... £10 ....£25 ....
Doin' The Thing At The Village Gate ... LP ...... Blue Note .... BLP/BST84076 ...... 196- ... £15 ....£30 ....
Finger Poppin' .... LP ...... Blue Note .... BLP/BST84008 ...... 196- ... £15 ....£30 ....
Horace Silver And The Jazz .... LP ...... Blue Note .... BLP/BST81518 ...... 196- ... £10 ....£25 ....
Messengers
Horace Silver Trio .... 10" LP Vogue .... LDE065 .... 1954 ... £25 ....£50 ....
Horace-Scope .... LP ...... Blue Note .... BLP/BST84042 ...... 196- ... £15 ....£30 ....
Jody Grind .... LP ...... Blue Note .... BLP/BST84250 ...... 1966 ... £8 ....£20 ....
Let's Get To The Nitty Gritty .... 7" ...... Blue Note .... 451902 .... 1963 ... £2 ....£5 ....
Serenade To A Soul Sister .... LP ...... Blue Note .... BST84277 .... 1968 ... £8 ....£20 ....
Silver's Blue .... LP ...... Philips .... BBL7183 .... 1957 ... £10 ....£25 ....
Silver's Serenade .... LP ...... Blue Note .... BLP/BST84131 ...... 1963 ... £15 ....£30 ....
Sister Sadie .... 7" ...... Blue Note .... 451750 .... 1961 ... £2 ....£5 ....
Six Pieces Of Silver .... LP ...... Blue Note .... BLP/BST81539 ...... 196- ... £20 ....£40 ....
Song For My Father .... LP ...... Blue Note .... BLP/BST84185 ...... 1964 ... £10 ....£25 ....
Stylings Of Silver .... LP ...... Blue Note .... BLP/BST81562 ...... 196- ... £15 ....£30 ....
Sweet Sweetie Dee .... 7" ...... Blue Note .... 451903 .... 1964 ... £2 ....£5 ....
That Healin' Feelin' .... LP ...... Blue Note .... BST84352 .... 1970 ... £5 ....£12 ....

Tokyo Blues	LP	Blue Note	BLP/BST84110	1962	£15	£30	
Too Much Sake	7"	Blue Note	451873	1963	£2	£5	
United States Of Mind	LP	Blue Note	BST84368	1970	£5	£12	
You Gotta Take A Little Love	LP	Blue Note	BST84309	1969	£6	£15	

SILVER, LORRAINE
| Happy Faces | 7" | Pye | 7N17055 | 1966 | £12.50 | £25 | |
| Lost Summer Love | 7" | Pye | 7N15922 | 1965 | £20 | £40 | |

SILVER METRE
| Silver Metre | LP | National General | NG2000 | 1969 | £6 | £15 | US |

SILVER SISTERS
| Waiting For The Stars To Shine | 7" | Parlophone | R4669 | 1960 | £1.50 | £4 | |

SILVER STARS STEEL BAND
| Silver Stars Steel Band | LP | Island | ILP904 | 1963 | £15 | £30 | |

SILVERS
| What A Way To Start A Day | 7" | Polydor | 56094 | 1966 | £2 | £5 | |

SILVERSPOON, DOOLEY
| Game Players | 7" | Seville | SEV1022 | 1976 | £1.50 | £4 | |

SILVERSTARS
| Old Man Say | 7" | Trojan | TR646 | 1968 | £4 | £8 | |

SILVERSTEIN, SHEL
Crouching On The Outside	LP	Janus	2JLS3052	1970	£5	£12	US
Hairy Jazz	LP	Elektra	EKL/EKS7176	1959	£6	£15	US
Inside Folk Songs	LP	Atlantic	(SD)8072	1963	£5	£12	US

SILVERTONES
Cool Down	7"	Treasure Isle	TI7020	1967	£5	£10	Tommy McCook B side
Intensified Change	7"	Trojan	TR7705	1969	£2.50	£6	
It's Real	7"	Doctor Bird	DB1041	1966	£5	£10	Lyn Taitt B side
Midnight Hour	7"	Treasure Isle	TI7027	1968	£5	£10	Tommy McCook B side
Silver Bullets	LP	Trojan	TRLS69	1971	£6	£15	
That's When It Hurts	7"	Technique	TE924	1973	£1.50	£4	

SILVESTER, VICTOR
| Alligator Roll | 7" | Columbia | DB3907 | 1957 | £2.50 | £6 | |
| Rockin' Rhythm Roll | 7" | Columbia | DB3888 | 1957 | £2.50 | £6 | |

SILVO, JOHNNY & DAVE MOSES
| Live From London | LP | Bus Stop | BUSLP5001 | 1973 | £5 | £12 | |

SIMEON, OMER
| Omer Simeon | 10" LP | Vogue | LDE174 | 1956 | £25 | £50 | |

SIMMONS, BEVERLY
| Remember Otis | LP | Pama | PMLP/PMSP9 | 1969 | £6 | £15 | |
| Mr.Pitiful | 7" | Pama | PM716 | 1968 | £2.50 | £6 | |

SIMMONS, CARL
| King Of Rock'n'Roll | 7" | Atlantic | K10421 | 1974 | £1.50 | £4 | |

SIMMONS, JEFF
Lucille Has Messed Up My Mind	LP	Reprise	RS6391	1969	£20	£40	
Lucille Has Messed Up My Mind	LP	Straight	STS1057	1969	£20	£40	
Naked Angels Soundtrack	LP	Straight	STS1056	1969	£15	£30	US

SIMMONS, JUMPIN' GENE
Haunted House	7"	London	HLU9913	1964	£4	£8	
Jump	7"	London	HLU9933	1964	£5	£10	
Jumpin' Gene Simmons	LP	Hi	(S)HL12018	1964	£8	£20	US

SIMMONS, LITTLE MAC
| Blues From Chicago | 7" EP | Outasite | OSEP1 | 1966 | £25 | £50 | |

SIMMS, JASON
| It's Got To Be Mellow | 7" | Domain | D5 | 1968 | £1.50 | £4 | |

SIMON & GARFUNKEL
At The Zoo	7"	CBS	202608	1967	£2	£5	
At The Zoo	7" EP	CBS	6339	1967	£5	£10	French
Bridge Over Troubled Waters	LP	CBS	Q63699	1973	£5	£12	quad
Bridge Over Troubled Waters	LP	Columbia	HC49914	1981	£6	£15	US audiophile
Bridge Over Troubled Waters	LP	Mobile Fidelity	MFSL1173	1981	£6	£15	US audiophile
Dangling Conversation	7"	CBS	202285	1966	£4	£8	
Fakin' It	7"	CBS	2911	1967	£2	£5	
Feelin' Groovy	7" EP	CBS	EP6360	1967	£2	£5	
Greatest Hits	LP	Columbia	HC41350	1981	£6	£15	US audiophile
Hazy Shade Of Winter	7"	CBS	202378	1966	£1.50	£4	
Hit Sounds Of Simon And Garfunkel	LP	Pickwick	SPC3059	1966	£6	£15	US
Homeward Bound	7"	CBS	202045	1966	£1.50	£4	chart single
I Am A Rock	7"	CBS	202303	1966	£1.50	£4	chart single
I Am A Rock	7" EP	CBS	EP6074	1966	£2	£5	
Mrs.Robinson	7" EP	CBS	EP6400	1968	£2.50	£6	chart single

Simon & Garfunkel	LP	Sears	SP435	1969	£6	£15	US
Simon And Garfunkel	LP	Allegro	ALL836	1967	£6	£15	
Sound Of Silence	7"	CBS	201977	1965	£1.50	£4	
Sounds Of Silence	7" EP	CBS	5655	1965	£5	£10	French
Wednesday Morning 3 a.m.	7" EP	CBS	EP6053	1965	£2	£5	

SIMON, JOE

My Special Prayer	7"	Monument	MON1004	1967	£1.50	£4	
Nine Pound Steel	7"	Monument	MON1010	1968	£1.50	£4	
No Sad Songs	7"	Monument	MON1014	1968	£1.50	£4	
Teenager's Prayer	7"	London	HLU10057	1966	£4	£8	
That's The Way I Want Our Love	7"	Monument	MON1051	1970	£2	£5	
Whole Lotta Lovin'	7"	Monument	MON1049	1970	£1.50	£4	

SIMON, PAUL

Early Songs	LP	Crest	EBM7172	196-	£15	£30	US promo
Greatest Hits, Etc.	LP	Columbia	HC45032	1981	£6	£15	US audiophile
I Am A Rock	7"	CBS	201797	1965	£5	£10	
I Am A Rock	7" EP	CBS	6211	1965	£6	£12	French, no PS
Kodakchrome	7"	CBS	1545	1973	£5	£10	
Paul Simon	LP	CBS	Q69007	1972	£5	£12	quad
Paul Simon Plus	LP	MCP	8027	1966	£8	£20	US, with Neil Sedaka & 4 Seasons
Paul Simon Songbook	LP	CBS	(S)BPG62579	1965	£6	£15	
Still Crazy After All These Years	LP	CBS	Q86001	1975	£5	£12	quad
Still Crazy After All These Years	LP	Columbia	HC43540	1981	£6	£15	US audiophile
There Goes Rhymin' Simon	LP	CBS	Q69035	1973	£5	£12	quad

SIMON, PLUG & GRIMES

Is This A Dream?	7"	Deram	DM296	1970	£4	£8	

SIMON SISTERS

The Simon Sisters made a number of records of mainly children's songs, before sister Lucy got married and decided to leave the music business. Younger sister Carly carried on by herself and eventually became rather successful.

Cuddlebug	LP	Kapp	KL1397/KS3397	1964	£6	£15	US
Cuddlebug	7"	London	HLR9984	1965	£1.50	£4	
Lobster Quadrille	LP	Columbia	CS24506	1969	£5	£12	US
Simon Sisters	LP	Kapp	KL1359/KS3359	1964	£6	£15	US
Winkin' Blinkin' And Nod	7"	London	HLR9893	1964	£2.50	£6	

SIMON, TONY

Gimme A Little Sign	7"	Track	604012	1967	£2.50	£6	

SIMONE, NINA

Ain't Got No - I Got Life	7"	RCA	RCA1743	1968	£1.50	£4	chart single
Amazing	LP	Colpix	(S)CP407	1959	£5	£12	US
And Her Friends	LP	Bethlehem	BCP6041	1959	£5	£12	US
At Carnegie Hall	LP	Colpix	(S)CP455	1963	£5	£12	US
At Newport	LP	Colpix	(S)CP412	1960	£5	£12	US
At The Town Hall	LP	Pye	NPL28014	1962	£5	£12	
At The Village Gate	LP	Colpix	PXL421	1965	£5	£12	
Best Of Nina Simone	LP	Philips	SBL7895	1969	£4	£10	
Black Gold	LP	RCA	SF8142	1971	£4	£10	
Broadway, Blues, Ballads	LP	Philips	BL7662	1965	£4	£10	
Do I Move You?	7"	RCA	RCA1583	1967	£1.50	£4	
Do What You Gotta Do	7"	RCA	RCA1961	1970	£1.50	£4	
Don't Let Me Be Misunderstood	7"	Philips	BF1388	1965	£2	£5	
Don't Let Me Be Misunderstood	7"	Philips	BF1736	1968	£1.50	£4	
Don't Let Me Be Misunderstood	7" EP	Philips	BE12585	1965	£2.50	£6	
Either Way I Lose	7"	Philips	BF1465	1966	£2	£5	
Exactly Like You	7"	Colpix	PX799	1964	£2	£5	
Fine And Mellow	7" EP	Colpix	PXE303	1964	£2.50	£6	
Folksy Nina	LP	Colpix	PXL465	1964	£5	£12	
Forbidden Fruit	LP	Colpix	PXL419	1965	£4	£10	
Forbidden Fruit	LP	Pye	NJL36	1961	£6	£15	
Gimme Some	7"	Philips	BF1785	1969	£1.50	£4	
Here Comes The Sun	LP	RCA	SF8192	1971	£4	£10	
High Priestess Of Soul	LP	Philips	BL7764	1967	£4	£10	
I Love To Love	7" EP	Colpix	PXE307	1966	£2.50	£6	
I Loves You Porgy	7"	Parlophone	R4583	1959	£1.50	£4	
I Put A Spell On You	LP	Philips	BL7671	1965	£4	£10	chart LP
I Put A Spell On You	7"	Philips	BF1415	1965	£2	£5	chart single
In Concert	LP	Philips	BL7678	1965	£4	£10	
In The Morning	7"	RCA	RCA1879	1969	£1.50	£4	
Intimate Nina Simone	7" EP	Parlophone	GEP8864	1962	£4	£8	
Just Say I Love Him	7" EP	Colpix	PXE306	1966	£2.50	£6	
Let It All Out	LP	Philips	(S)BL7722	1966	£4	£10	
Little Girl Blue	LP	Bethlehem	BCP6028	1959	£6	£15	US
My Baby Just Cares For Me	7" EP	Parlophone	GEP8844	1961	£7.50	£15	
Nina Simone	LP	Polydor	623214	1969	£4	£10	
Nina With Strings	LP	Colpix	(S)CP496	1966	£4	£10	US
Nina's Choice	LP	Colpix	(S)CP443	1963	£5	£12	US
Nuff Said	LP	RCA	SF7979	1969	£4	£10	chart LP
Original	LP	Bethlehem	BCP(S)6028	1961	£5	£12	US
Other Woman	7"	Pye	7N25466	1968	£1.50	£4	
Pastel Blues	LP	Philips	BL7683	1966	£4	£10	
Revolutin'	7"	RCA	RCA1805	1969	£1.50	£4	
Save Me	7"	RCA	RCA1903	1969	£1.50	£4	
Silk And Soul	LP	RCA	RD/SF7967	1968	£4	£10	
Sings Ellington	LP	Colpix	(S)CP425	1962	£5	£12	US

Sings The Blues	LP	RCA	RD/SF7883	1967	£4	£10	
Solitaire	7"	Pye	7N25029	1959	£1.50	£4	
Strange Fruit	7" EP.	Philips	BE12589	1965	£2.50	£6	
Tell Me More	LP	Fontana	SFJL954	1968	£5	£12	
To Love Somebody	7"	RCA	RCA1779	1968	£1.50	£4	chart single
Why?	7"	RCA	RCA1697	1970	£1.50	£4	
Why Must Your Love Well Be So Dry	7"	RCA	RCA1968	1970	£1.50	£4	
Wild Is The Wind	LP	Philips	BL7726	1966	£4	£10	
You Can Have Him	7"	Colpix	PX200	1963	£2	£5	

SIMONE, SUGAR

Black Is Gold	7"	Doctor Bird	DB1192	1969	£5	£10	
Boom Biddy Boom	7"	Fab	FAB106	1969	£2	£5	Rudies B side
Come And Try	7"	Doctor Bird	DB1201	1969	£5	£10	
I Love My Baby	7"	Rainbow	RAI114	1967	£4	£8	
I Need A Witness	7"	Fab	FAB107	1969	£2	£5	
Is It Because	7"	Rainbow	RAI103	1966	£4	£8	
It's Alright	7"	Go	AJ11409	1967	£2	£5	
Squeeze Is On	7"	Doctor Bird	DB1193	1969	£5	£10	
Suddenly	7"	Sue	WI4029	1967	£5	£10	
Vow	7"	CBS	3250	1968	£2.50	£6	

SIMON'S SECRETS

I Know What Her Name Is	7"	CBS	3056	1967	£5	£10	
Naughty Boy	7"	CBS	3406	1968	£5	£10	

SIMPLE MINDS

Celebrate	7"	Arista	ARIST394	1981	£2.50	£6	
Celebrate	12"	Arista	ARIST12394	1981	£3	£8	
Changeling	7"	Zoom	ARIST325	1980	£4	£8	
Chelsea Girl	7"	Zoom	ZUM11	1979	£1.50	£4	
Don't You Forget About Me	7"	Virgin	VSS749	1985	£7.50	£15	shaped pic disc
Ghostdancing	CD-s	Virgin	MIKE90712	1986	£2.50	£6	
I Travel	7"	Arista	ARIST372	1980	£5	£10	with blue flexi 7'
I Travel	12"	Arista	ARIST12372	1980	£3	£8	
I Travel	12"	Arista	ARIST12448	1982	£2.50	£6	
Life In A Day	7"	Zoom	ZUM10	1979	£2	£5	chart single
Live In The City Of Light	LP	Virgin	SMDL1	1987	£5	£12	double, booklet, gold embossed sleeve
Once Upon A Time	LP	Virgin	V2364	1985	£5	£12	pic disc
Someone Somewhere In Summertime	7"	Virgin	VS538	1982	£2	£5	poster sleeve
Someone Somewhere In Summertime	7"	Virgin	VSY538	1982	£4	£8	pic disc
Sons And Fascination/Sister Feelings Call	LP	Virgin	V2207	1981	£6	£15	double
Sparkle In The Rain	LP	Virgin	V2300	1984	£5	£12	white vinyl
Speed Your Love To Me	7"	Virgin	VSY649	1984	£4	£8	pic disc
Street Fighting Years	CD	Virgin	SMBXD1	1989	£10	£25	boxed with book & interview cassettes
Street Fighting Years	cass	Virgin	SMBXC1	1989	£6	£15	boxed with book & interview cassettes
Up On The Catwalk	7"	Virgin	VSY661	1984	£4	£8	pic disc

SIMPLY RED

Every Time We Say Goodbye	12"	WEA	YZ161TW	1987	£3	£8	with sheet music & 4 cards
Holding Back The Years	7"	Elektra	EKR29P	1985	£7.50	£15	shaped pic disc
Infidelity	12"	Elektra	YZ114TP	1987	£2	£10	pic disc
Money's Too Tight To Mention	7"	Elektra	EKR9P	1985	£2	£5	pic disc
Open Up The Red Box	7"	WEA	YZ75B	1986	£2	£5	box sleeve
Open Up The Red Box	7"	WEA	YZ75F	1986	£2	£5	double
Picture Book	LP	Elektra	EKT27P	1985	£5	£12	pic disc
Right Thing	12"	WEA	YZ103TP	1987	£2.50	£6	pic disc
Something's Burning	7"	Lyntone	LYN15914	1985	£1.50	£4	flexi, 10000 Maniacs B side

SIMPSON, DANNY

Outa Sight	7"	Trojan	TR653	1969	£2.50	£6	

SIMPSON, DUDLEY

Moonbase 3	7"	BBC	RESL13	1973	£1.50	£4	

SIMPSON, FRANK

Four Star Hits	LP	Audio Lab	1552	1960	£10	£25	US

SIMPSON, HOKE

I Finally Found You	7"	HMV	POP442	1958	£1.50	£4	

SIMPSON, JEANETTE

My Baby Just Cares For Me	7"	Giant	GN29	1968	£4	£8	
Rain	7"	Giant	GN16	1967	£4	£8	
Through Loving You	7"	Giant	GN35	1968	£4	£8	

SIMPSON, LEO

I Love Her So	7"	Blue Beat	BB351	1965	£5	£10	
Waxy Doodle	7"	Pyramid	PYR7004	1973	£2	£5	

SIMPSON, LIONEL

Eight People	7"	Ska Beat	JB221	1965	£5	£10	

Title	Format	Label	Cat #	Year			Notes
Give Over	7"	Ska Beat	JB233	1966	£5	£10	
Love Is A Game	7"	Ska Beat	JB205	1965	£5	£10	

SIMPSON, MARTIN

Title	Format	Label	Cat #	Year			Notes
Golden Vanity	LP	Trailer	LER2099	1976	£8	£20	

SIMS, CHUCK

Title	Format	Label	Cat #	Year			Notes
Little Pigeon	7"	London	HLR8577	1958	£50	£100	

SIMS, FRANKIE LEE

Title	Format	Label	Cat #	Year			Notes
Lucy Mae Blues	LP	Speciality	SNTF5004	1971	£4	£10	

SIMS, ZOOT

Title	Format	Label	Cat #	Year			Notes
Choice	LP	Vogue	LAE12309	1961	£6	£15	
Cookin!	LP	Fontana	FJL123	1965	£4	£10	
George Handy Compositions	LP	HMV	CLP1165	1958	£10	£25	
Goes To Town	10" LP	Vogue	LDE056	1954	£25	£50	
Plays Four Altos	LP	HMV	CLP1188	1958	£10	£25	
Trotting	LP	XTRA	XTRA5001	1966	£5	£12	
Zoot!	LP	London	LTZU15135	1958	£10	£25	
Zoot Sims Allstars	10" LP	Esquire	20010	1953	£25	£50	
Zoot Sims Quartet/Quintet	10" LP	Esquire	20002	1952	£25	£50	
Zoot Sims Quartet/Quintet	10" LP	Esquire	20018	1953	£25	£50	
Zoot Sims Quartet/Quintet	10" LP	Esquire	20040	1955	£25	£50	

SIMS, ZOOT (2)

Title	Format	Label	Cat #	Year			Notes
Please Don't Do It	7"	Port-O-Jam	PJ4007	1964	£5	£10	with Lloyd Robinson
Press Along	7"	Blue Beat	BB183	1963	£5	£10	Prince Buster B side
Searching	7"	Blue Beat	BB143	1962	£5	£10	with Lloyd Robinson
Tit For Tat	7"	Coxsone	CS7095	1969	£5	£10	

SINATRA, FRANK

Title	Format	Label	Cat #	Year			Notes
Adventures Of The Heart	LP	Fontana	TFL5006	1958	£6	£15	
All The Way	LP	Capitol	W(S)1538	1962	£4	£10	
Among My Souvenirs	7" EP	Fontana	TFE17272	1960	£2	£5	
Anchors Aweigh	7" EP	Fontana	TFE17043	1958	£2	£5	
Birth Of The Blues	7"	Columbia	SCM5052	1953	£5	£10	
Broadway Kick	LP	Fontana	TFL5054	1959	£6	£15	
Bye Baby	7" EP	Fontana	TFE17273	1960	£2	£5	
Christmas Dreaming	10" LP	Philips	BBR8114	1957	£6	£15	
Christmas Songs	10" LP	Columbia	CL6019	195-	£6	£15	US
Christmas Waltz	7"	Capitol	CL14174	1954	£4	£8	
Close To You	LP	Capitol	LCT6130	1957	£5	£12	
Come Back To Sorrento	LP	Fontana	TFL5082	1960	£5	£12	
Come Dance With Me	LP	Capitol	(S)LCT6179	1959	£5	£12	
Come Swing With Me	LP	Capitol	W(S)1594	1962	£4	£10	
Conducts The Music Of Alex Wilder	10" LP	Columbia	ML4271	195-	£6	£15	US
Conducts Tone Poems Of Colour	LP	Capitol	LCT6111	1956	£5	£12	
Dedicated To You	10" LP	Columbia	CL6096	195-	£6	£15	US
Don't Change Your Mind About Me	7"	Capitol	CL14270	1955	£4	£8	
Dream	7" EP	Fontana	TFE17158	1959	£2	£5	
Embraceable You	7" EP	Fontana	TFE17286	1960	£2	£5	
Fabulous Frank	10" LP	Philips	BBR8038	1955	£6	£15	
Fairy Tale	7"	Capitol	CL14373	1955	£4	£8	
Five Minutes More	7" EP	Fontana	TFE17280	1960	£2	£5	
Flowers Mean Forgiveness	7"	Capitol	CL14564	1956	£1.50	£4	
Fools Rush In	7" EP	Fontana	TFE17037	1958	£2	£5	
Francis A.Sinatra And Edward K.Ellington	LP	Reprise	R(S)LP1024	1968	£4	£10	
Frank Sinatra	7" EP	Columbia	SEG7565	1955	£2.50	£6	
Frank Sinatra	7" EP	HMV	7EG8070	1954	£4	£8	
Frankie	LP	Philips	BBL7168	1957	£6	£15	
Frankie	7" EP	Fontana	TFE17182	1959	£2	£5	
Frankie And Tommy (with Tommy Dorsey)	LP	RCA	RD27069	1958	£6	£15	
Frankie's Favourites	7" EP	Columbia	SEG7597	1955	£2.50	£6	
Frankly Sentimental	10" LP	Columbia	CL6059	195-	£6	£15	US
Gal That Got Away	7"	Capitol	CL14221	1955	£4	£8	
Great Years	LP	Capitol	W1/2/31762	1963	£6	£15	triple
High Hopes	7" EP	Capitol	EAP11224	1959	£2	£5	
I Am Loved	7" EP	Fontana	TFE17038	1958	£2	£5	
I Dream Of You	7" EP	Fontana	TFE17284	1960	£2	£5	
If I Forget You	7"	Fontana	H140	1958	£1.50	£4	
In The Wee Small Hours Of The Morning	7"	Capitol	CL14360	1955	£4	£8	
In The Wee Small Hours Vol.1	10" LP	Capitol	LC6702	1955	£6	£15	
In The Wee Small Hours Vol.2	10" LP	Capitol	LC6705	1955	£6	£15	
It's D-Lovely	10" LP	HMV	DLP1123	1956	£8	£20	with Tommy Dorsey
I've Got A Crush On You	7" EP	Fontana	TFE17254	1960	£2	£5	
I've Got A Crush On You	10" LP	Columbia	CL6290	195-	£6	£15	US
Jolly Christmas	LP	Capitol	LCT6144	1957	£4	£10	
Learnin' The Blues	7"	Capitol	CL14296	1955	£5	£10	chart single
London By Night	LP	Capitol	T20389	1962	£5	£12	
Look To Your Heart	LP	Capitol	LCT6181	1959	£5	£12	
Love And Marriage	7"	Capitol	CL14503	1956	£2.50	£6	chart single
Love Is A Kick	LP	Fontana	TFL5074	1960	£5	£12	
Lover	7" EP	Fontana	TFE17012	1958	£2	£5	
Mad About You	7" EP	Fontana	TFE17023	1958	£2	£5	
Man And His Music	LP	Reprise	R(9)1016	1966	£5	£12	double
Melancholy Baby	7" EP	Fontana	TFE17274	1960	£2	£5	

Title	Format	Label	Catalogue	Year			Notes
Melody Of Love	7"	Capitol	CL14238	1955	£4	£8	
Melody Of Love	7" EP	Capitol	EAP1590	1956	£2	£5	
Moonlight Sinatra	LP	Reprise	R(9)1018	1966	£5	£12	
Moonlight Sinatra	7" EP	HMV	7EG8128	1955	£4	£8	
My Funny Valentine	LP	Capitol	T20577	1964	£5	£12	
My Funny Valentine	7"	Capitol	CL14352	1955	£4	£8	
Nearness Of You	7" EP	Philips	BBE12182	1958	£2	£5	
New Orleans (with Jo Stafford)	10" LP	Columbia	CL6268	195-	£6	£15	US
Nice 'n' Easy	LP	Capitol	W(S)1417	1961	£4	£10	
No One Cares	LP	Capitol	(S)LCT6185	1959	£4	£10	
No One Cares	7" EP	Capitol	SEP11221	1961	£5	£10	stereo
No One Cares No.2	7" EP	Capitol	SEP21221	1961	£5	£10	stereo
No One Cares No.3	7" EP	Capitol	SEP31221	1961	£5	£10	stereo
Not As A Stranger	7"	Capitol	CL14326	1955	£5	£10	chart single
Out Town	7" EP	Capitol	EAP1025	1956	£2.50	£6	
Pal Joey	LP	Capitol	LCT6148	1958	£4	£10	
Point Of No Return	LP	Capitol	W(S)1676	1962	£5	£12	
Put Your Dreams Away	LP	Fontana	TFL5048	1959	£8	£20	
Reflections	LP	Fontana	TFL5107	1960	£5	£12	
Ring-A-Ding-Ding	LP	Reprise	R1001	1961	£4	£10	
Robin And The Seven Hoods	LP	Reprise	R2021	1964	£25	£50	
Santa Claus Is Comin' To Town	7"	Columbia	SCM5076	1953	£5	£10	
Session With Sinatra	7" EP	Capitol	EAP1629	1956	£2.50	£6	
Sinatra '65	LP	Reprise	R(9)6167	1965	£4	£10	
Sinatra And Company	LP	Reprise	RSLP1033	1971	£4	£10	
Sinatra And Strings	LP	Reprise	R(9)1004	1962	£4	£10	
Sinatra Family Wish You A Happy Christmas	LP	Reprise	R(S)LP1026	1969	£5	£12	
Sinatra Plus	LP	Fontana	SET303	1961	£5	£12	double
Sinatra Serenade	7" EP	Columbia	SEG7582	1955	£2.50	£6	
Sinatra Souvenir	LP	Fontana	TFL5138	1961	£5	£12	
Sinatra,Bailey & James (with Pearl Bailey & Harry James)	7" EP	Fontana	TFE17028	1958	£2	£5	
Sing And Dance	10" LP	Philips	BBR8003	1954	£8	£20	
Sing And Dance No.1	7" EP	Philips	BBE12016	1956	£2	£5	
Sing And Dance No.2	7" EP	Philips	BBE12058	1956	£2	£5	
Sing Is You	7" EP	Fontana	TFE17253	1960	£2	£5	
Sings For Only The Lonely	LP	Capitol	(S)LCT6168	1958	£5	£12	
Sings Great Songs From Great Britain	LP	Reprise	R1006	1962	£8	£20	
Sings Great Songs From Great Britain	LP	Reprise	R91006	1962	£15	£30	stereo
Sings Of Love And Things	LP	Capitol	W(S)1729	1963	£4	£10	
Sings Rodgers And Hart	LP	Capitol	W1825	1963	£4	£10	
Sings Songs From Carousel	7" EP	Philips	BBE12152	1957	£2	£5	
Songs By Sinatra Vol.1	10" LP	Columbia	CL6087	195-	£6	£15	US
Songs For Swingin' Lovers	LP	Capitol	LCT6106	1956	£6	£15	
Songs For Young Lovers	10" LP	Capitol	LC6654	1954	£6	£15	
Songs For Young Lovers No.1	7" EP	Capitol	EAP1488	1955	£2	£5	
Songs For Young Lovers No.2	7" EP	Capitol	EAP2488	1955	£2	£5	
Songs From Young At Heart	7" EP	Capitol	EAP1571	1955	£2.50	£6	
S'posin'	7"	Columbia	SCM5167	1955	£5	£10	
Story	LP	Fontana	TFL5030	1958	£6	£15	
Summit (with Crosby,Davis Jr,Martin)	LP	Reprise	R5031	1966	£25	£50	
Swing Easy	LP	Capitol	W587	1960	£4	£10	
Swing Easy	10" LP	Capitol	LC6689	1954	£6	£15	
Swingin' Affair	LP	Capitol	LCT6135	1957	£5	£12	
Swingin' Session	LP	Capitol	W(S)1491	1961	£4	£10	
Tender Trap	7"	Capitol	CL14511	1956	£2.50	£6	chart single
That Old Feeling	LP	Philips	BBL7180	1957	£6	£15	
They Say It's Wonderful	7" EP	Fontana	TFE17255	1960	£2	£5	
This Is Sinatra	LP	Capitol	LCT6123	1957	£5	£12	
This Is Sinatra Vol.2	LP	Capitol	LCT6155	1958	£5	£12	
Three Coins In The Fountain	7"	Capitol	CL14120	1954	£5	£10	chart single
Two Hearts, Two Kisses	7"	Capitol	CL14292	1955	£5	£10	
Voice	LP	Fontana	TFL5000	1958	£6	£15	
Voice No.1 - Four Star	7" EP	Fontana	TFE17181	1959	£2	£5	
Voice Of Sinatra	10" LP	Columbia	CL6001	195-	£6	£15	US
Watertown	LP	Reprise	RSLP1031	1970	£4	£10	
We're In Love	7" EP	Fontana	TFE17042	1958	£2	£5	
When I Stop Loving You	7"	Capitol	CL14188	1954	£4	£8	
Where Are You?	LP	Capitol	(S)LCT6152	1958	£5	£12	stereo
Who Wants To Be A Millionaire	7"	Capitol	CL14644	1956	£1.50	£4	
You Do Something To Me	7"	Columbia	SCM5060	1953	£5	£10	
You Go To My Head	7" EP	Fontana	TFE17256	1960	£2	£5	
You My Love	7"	Capitol	CL14240	1955	£5	£10	chart single
Young At Heart	7"	Capitol	CL14064	1954	£6	£12	chart single

SINATRA, NANCY

Title	Format	Label	Catalogue	Year			Notes
Boots	LP	Reprise	R(S)LP6202	1966	£5	£12	chart LP
Country My Way	LP	Reprise	R(S)LP6251	1967	£4	£10	
Cuff Links And A Tie Clip	7"	Reprise	R20017	1961	£1.50	£4	
Friday's Child	7"	Reprise	RS20491	1966	£1.50	£4	
Greatest Hits	LP	Reprise	RSLP6409	1970	£4	£10	chart LP
How Does That Grab You?	LP	Reprise	R6207	1966	£5	£12	chart LP
How Does That Grab You Darlin'	7"	Reprise	R20461	1966	£1.50	£4	chart single
Hundred Years	7"	Reprise	RS20670	1968	£1.50	£4	
I Move Around	7" EP	Reprise	REP30072	1966	£5	£10	
In Our Time	7"	Reprise	RS20514	1966	£1.50	£4	
Lightning's Girl	7"	Reprise	RS20620	1967	£1.50	£4	
Love Eyes	7"	Reprise	RS20559	1967	£1.50	£4	
Movin' With Nancy	LP	Reprise	R(S)LP6277	1968	£4	£10	

Title	Format	Label	Cat. No.	Year			Notes
Nancy	LP	Reprise	RSLP6333	1969	£4	£10	
Nancy In London	LP	Reprise	R(S)6221	1966	£5	£12	US
Nashville Nancy	7" EP	Reprise	REP30086	1967	£5	£10	
Put Your Head On My Shoulder	7"	Reprise	R20144	1963	£1.50	£4	
Run For Your Life	7" EP	Reprise	REP30069	1966	£5	£10	
So Long Babe	7"	Reprise	R20407	1965	£1.50	£4	
Something Stupid	7" EP	Reprise	REP30082	1967	£2.50	£6	
Sorry 'Bout That	7" EP	Reprise	REP30080	1967	£5	£10	
Sugar	LP	Reprise	RLP6239	1966	£4	£10	
Sugar Town	7"	Reprise	RS20527	1967	£1.50	£4	chart single
These Boots Are Made For Walking	7"	Reprise	R20432	1966	£1.50	£4	chart single
To Know Him Is To Love Him	7"	Reprise	R20045	1962	£1.50	£4	
True Love	7"	Reprise	R20335	1964	£1.50	£4	
Woman	LP	RCA	SF8331	1972	£4	£10	
You Only Live Twice	7"	Reprise	RS20595	1967	£1.50	£4	chart single

SINATRA, NANCY & LEE HAZELWOOD

Title	Format	Label	Cat. No.	Year			Notes
Jackson	7" EP	Reprise	REP30083	1967	£4	£8	
Ladybird	7"	Reprise	RS20629	1967	£1.50	£4	chart single
Nancy And Lee	LP	Reprise	R(S)LP6273	1968	£4	£10	chart LP
Nancy And Lee Again	LP	RCA	LSP4645	1972	£4	£10	US
Did You Ever?	LP	RCA	SF8240	1972	£4	£10	
Some Velvet Morning	7"	Reprise	RS23215	1967	£1.50	£4	

SINCLAIR, JIMMY

Title	Format	Label	Cat. No.	Year			Notes
Verona	7"	Blue Beat	BB47	1961	£5	£10	

SINDELFINGEN

Title	Format	Label	Cat. No.	Year			Notes
Odgipig	LP	Medway		1973	£330	£500	
Odgipig/Triangle	LP	Cenotaph	CEN111	1990	£10	£25	double

SINFIELD, PETE

Title	Format	Label	Cat. No.	Year			Notes
Still	LP	Manticore	K43501	1973	£5	£12	

SINGER, RAY

Title	Format	Label	Cat. No.	Year			Notes
What's Been Done	7"	Ember	EMBS231	1967	£5	£10	

SINGER, SUSAN

Title	Format	Label	Cat. No.	Year			Notes
Autumn Leaves	7"	Oriole	CB1778	1962	£1.50	£4	
Hello First Love	7"	Oriole	CB1703	1962	£1.50	£4	
I Know	7"	Oriole	CB1882	1963	£1.50	£4	
Johnny Summertime	7"	Oriole	CB1741	1962	£1.50	£4	
Lock Your Heart Away	7"	Oriole	CB1802	1963	£1.50	£4	

SINGING BELLES

Title	Format	Label	Cat. No.	Year			Notes
Someone Loves You Joe	7"	Top Rank	JAR350	1960	£1.50	£4	

SINGING DOGS

Title	Format	Label	Cat. No.	Year			Notes
Singing Dogs	7" EP	Pye	NEP24029	1957	£7.50	£15	

SINGING NUN

Title	Format	Label	Cat. No.	Year			Notes
Dominique	7"	Philips	BF1293	1963	£1.50	£4	chart single

SINGING POSTMAN

Title	Format	Label	Cat. No.	Year			Notes
First Delivery	7" EP	Parlophone	GEP8956	1966	£2.50	£6	
Mind How You Go	7"	Parlophone	R5584	1967	£1.50	£4	
Roundabout	7"	Parlophone	R5505	1966	£1.50	£4	
Sound Barrier	7"	Parlophone	R5632	1967	£1.50	£4	

SINGLETON, MARGIE

Title	Format	Label	Cat. No.	Year			Notes
Eyes Of Love	7"	Melodisc	1544	1960	£1.50	£4	
Magic Star	7"	Mercury	AMT1197	1962	£2	£5	

SINISTER DUCKS

Title	Format	Label	Cat. No.	Year			Notes
March Of The Sinister Ducks	7"	Situation 2	SIT25	1983	£5	£10	

SINK, EARL

Title	Format	Label	Cat. No.	Year			Notes
Little Suzie Parker	7"	Warner Bros	WB51	1961	£2	£5	
Looking For Love	7"	Capitol	CL15310	1963	£4	£8	
Supermarket	7"	Warner Bros	WB38	1961	£2	£5	

SINNERS

Title	Format	Label	Cat. No.	Year			Notes
I Can't Stand It	7"	Columbia	DB7158	1963	£4	£8	
It's So Exciting	7"	Columbia	DB7295	1964	£5	£10	

SINNERS (2)

Title	Format	Label	Cat. No.	Year			Notes
Sinneresmes	LP	Jupiter		1974	£50	£100	Canadian
Vox Populi	LP			197-	£20	£40	Canadian

SIOUXSIE & THE BANSHEES

Title	Format	Label	Cat. No.	Year			Notes
Candyman	7"	Wonderland	SHEDP10	1986	£2	£5	double, gatefold PS
Head Cut	7"	Fan Club	FILE1	1983	£15	£30	
Hong Kong Garden	7"	Polydor	2059052	1978	£6	£12	gatefold sleeve
Israel	12"	Polydor	POSPX205	1980	£4	£10	no PS
Mittageisen	7"	Polydor	2059151	1979	£2	£5	PS, chart single
Playground Twist	7"	Polydor	POSP59	1979	£1.50	£4	chart single, red paper label
This Wheel's On Fire	7"	Wonderland	SHEG11	1987	£2	£5	double, gatefold PS, numbered

Through The Looking Glass	LP	Wonderland	SHELP4	1987	£5	£12	mispress, 1 side plays Jimi Hendrix
Through The Looking Glass	7"	Wonderland		1987	£7.50	£15	3 x 7' in plastic wallet, promo
Voices	7"	Wonderland		1984	£2	£5	promo

SIR COLLINS BAND

Collins And The Boys	7"	Collins Downbeat	CR0011	1968	£2	£5	
Soul Feelings	7"	Collins Downbeat	CR0017	1968	£2	£5	

SIR DOUGLAS QUINTET

1&1&1=4	LP	Philips	PHS600344	1970	£5	£12	US
Best Of The Sir Douglas Quintet	LP	London	HAU8311	1965	£25	£50	
Dynamite Woman	7"	Mercury	MF1129	1969	£2	£5	
Honky Blues	LP	Smash	SRS67108	1968	£6	£15	US
Mendocino	LP	Mercury	SMCL20160	1969	£5	£12	
Mendocino	7"	Mercury	MF1079	1969	£2	£5	
Rains Came	7"	London	HLU10019	1966	£2.50	£6	
She's About A Mover	7"	London	HLU10248	1969	£2	£5	
She's About A Mover	7"	London	HLU9964	1965	£2.50	£6	chart single
She's About A Mover	7" EP.	London	REU10171	1965	£10	£20	French
Story Of John Hardy	7"	London	HLU10001	1965	£2.50	£6	
Together After Five	LP	Mercury	SMCL20186	1970	£5	£12	
Tracker	7"	London	HLU9982	1965	£4	£8	

SIR HENRY & HIS BUTLERS

Let's Go	LP	Polydor	623003	1965	£25	£50	German
Let's Go	7" EP.	Polydor	60101	196-	£10	£20	French
Pretty Style	7"	Columbia	DB8497	1968	£6	£12	

SIR HORACE & HIS MERRY KNIGHTS

Mambo Jamaica	7"	Kalypso	XX03	1960	£1.50	£4	

SIR LORD COMIC

Great Wuga Wuga	7"	Doctor Bird	DB1070	1967	£5	£10	
Jack Of My Trade	7"	Pressure Beat	PB5506	1969	£2	£5	Cynthia Richards B side
Rhythm Rebellion	7"	Bamboo	BAM66	1970	£2	£5	Roy Richards B side
Ska-ing West	7"	Doctor Bird	DB1019	1966	£5	£10	Maytals B side

SIREN

Originally named Coyne-Clague after the lead singer and guitarist, the group had settled on the rather more wieldy Siren by the time of their first recording for John Peel's Dandelion label. Kevin Coyne has made Siren's bluesy style into the basis of a still continuing solo career, gaining a considerable cult following, while Dave Clague has opted to temper his music making with the financial security of being a teacher.

Siren	LP	Dandelion	63755	1969	£6	£15	
Strange Locomotion	LP	Dandelion	DAN8001	1971	£6	£15	
Strange Locomotion	7"	Dandelion	DAN7002	1971	£2	£5	

SISTER MARY GERTRUDE

My Auld Killarney Hat	7"	Pye	7N15787	1965	£1.50	£4	

SISTERS LOVE

Bigger You Love	7"	A&M	AMS808	1970	£1.50	£4	
I'm Learning To Trust My Man	7"	Mowest	MW3009	1973	£2	£5	
Mr.Fix-It Man	7"	Tamla Motown	TMG828	1972	£1.50	£4	

SISTERS OF MERCY

Alice	7"	Merciful Release	MR015	1982	£5	£10	white background
Body And Soul	7"	Merciful Release	MR029	1984	£2	£5	
Body Electric	7"	CNT	002	1982	£30	£60	
Damage Done	7"	Merciful Release	MR007	1980	£40	£80	
Doctor Jeep	12"	Merciful Release	MR51TX	1990	£2.50	£6	3 tracks
First And Last And Always	LP	Merciful Release	MR337L	1985	£6	£15	gatefold sleeve
More	CD-s	Merciful Release	MR47CDX	1990	£2.50	£6	12' sleeve
No Time To Cry	7"	Merciful Release	MR035	1985	£2	£5	
No Time To Cry	12"	Merciful Release	MR035T	1985	£2.50	£6	
Reptile House	12"	Merciful Release	MR023	1983	£2.50	£6	with lyric sheet
This Corrosion	CD-s	Merciful Release	MR039CD	1987	£4	£10	no WEA logo on back
This Corrosion	7"	Merciful Release	MR039	1987	£2.50	£6	boxed with 3 postcards
This Corrosion	12"	Merciful Release	MR039T	1987	£10	£25	promo with video
Walk Away	7"	Merciful Release	MR033	1984	£2	£5	
Walk Away	7"	Merciful Release	MR033	1984	£5	£10	with flexi
Walk Away	12"	Merciful Release	MR033T	1984	£4	£10	with flexi (SAM218)

SITTING BULL
Trip Away	LP	CBS	64697	1971	£5	£12	German

SITUATION
Situation	7"	CBS	202392	1966	£4	£8

SIX
Six	LP	London	LTZN15042	1957	£10	£25
Six	10" LP	Columbia	33C9028	1956	£10	£25
View From Jazzbo's Head	LP	London	LTZN15066	1957	£10	£25

SIX TEENS
Casual Look	7"	London	HLU8345	1956	£100	£200

SIXPENCE
You're The Love	7"	London	HLJ10124	1967	£7.50	£15

SIXTY-NINE
Circle Of The Crayfish	LP	Philips	6305164	1972	£5	£12	German
Live	LP	Philips	6623046	1974	£6	£15	German double

SIZE SEVEN
Crying My Heart Out	7"	Rendezvous	PR5020	196-	£1.50	£4
In Time	7"	Mercury	MF896	1965	£1.50	£4
It's Got To Be Love	7"	Mercury	MF854	1965	£1.50	£4
Where Do We Go From Here	7"	Mercury	MF845	1965	£1.50	£4

SKA CHAMPIONS
My Tears	7"	Blue Beat	BB305	1964	£5	£10

SKA KINGS
Oil In My Lamp	7"	Atlantic	AT4003	1964	£4	£8
Skasville	7"	Parlophone	R5338	1965	£2.50	£6

SKATALITES
Ball 'O' Fire	7"	Island	WI207	1965	£5	£10	Linval Sparker B side
Beardman Ska	7"	Island	WI228	1965	£5	£10	Bonnie & Rita B side
Confucius	LP	Doctor Bird	DLM5000	1966	£40	£80	
Cos You're The One I Love	7"	Spark	SRL1034	1971	£2.50	£6	
Dick Tracy	7"	Island	WI226	1965	£5	£10	Soulettes B side
Don't Knock It	7"	Decca	F12743	1968	£4	£8	
Dragon Weapon	7"	Island	WI175	1965	£5	£10	Desmond Dekker B side
Dr.Kildare	7"	Island	WI191	1965	£5	£10	
Guns Of Navarone	7"	Island	WI168	1965	£5	£10	chart single
Latin Goes Ska	7"	Ska Beat	JB177	1965	£5	£10	Lord Tanamo B side
Ska Authentic	LP	Studio One	SOL9006	1967	£50	£100	
Timothy	7"	Ska Beat	JB206	1965	£5	£10	King Scratch B side

SKELETAL FAMILY
Night	7"	Red Rhino	RED36	1983	£2	£5
Trees	7"	Luggage	RRP00724	1983	£4	£8

SKI PATROL
Agent Orange	7"	Malicious Damage	MD2	1980	£2	£5

SKID ROW
A modern band calling itself Skid Row cannot detract from the fact that the name truly belongs to the Irish band with whom the seventeen year old Gary Moore made his first recordings.

34 Hours	LP	CBS	64411	1971	£5	£12	
New Places, Old Faces	7"	Song	SO0002	1969	£15	£30	Irish
Night Of The Warm Witch	7"	CBS	7181	1971	£2	£5	
Sandie's Gone	7"	CBS	4893	1970	£2	£5	
Saturday Morning Man	7"	Song	SO0003	1969	£15	£30	Irish
Skid	LP	CBS	63965	1970	£5	£12	chart LP

SKID ROW (2)
Eighteen And Life	7"	Atlantic	A8883P	1990	£1.50	£4	shaped pic disc

SKIDMORE, ALAN
Jazz In Britain 1968-69	LP	Decca	ECS2114	1972	£8	£20	with other artists
Once Upon A Time	LP	Nova	SDN11	1969	£20	£40	sleeve pictured in Guide
TCB	LP	Philips	6308041	1970	£20	£40	

SKIFS, BJORN
Haunted By A Dream	7"	EMI	EMI5172	1981	£2	£5

SKIN ALLEY
Skin Alley	LP	CBS	63847	1969	£20	£40
Skintight	LP	Transatlantic	TRA273	1973	£6	£15
To Pagham & Beyond	LP	CBS	64140	1970	£8	£20
Two Quid Deal	LP	Transatlantic	TRA260	1972	£6	£15

SKIN, FLESH & BONES
Butter Te Fish	7"	Pyramid	PYR7014	1974	£2	£5

SKINNER, JIMMIE
Country Singer	LP	Decca	DL(7)4132	1961	£6	£15	US
I'm A Lot More Lonesome Now	7"	Mercury	AMT1117	1960	£1.50	£4	

John Wesley Hardin	7"	Mercury	AMT1062	1959	£1.50	£4	
Kentucky Colonel Vol.1	7" EP.	London	REB1421	1964	£4	£8	
Kentucky Colonel Vol.2	7" EP.	London	REB1422	1964	£4	£8	
Kentucky Colonel Vol.3	7" EP.	London	REB1423	1964	£4	£8	
Riverboat Gambler	7"	Mercury	AMT1088	1960	£1.50	£4	
Songs That Make The Juke Box Play	LP	Mercury	MG20352	1957	£8	£20	US
Walking My Blues Away	7"	Mercury	AMT1030	1959	£1.50	£4	

SKIP & FLIP

Cherry Pie	7"	Top Rank	JAR358	1960	£2.50	£5	
Fancy Nancy	7"	Top Rank	JAR248	1959	£2	£5	
It Was I	7"	Top Rank	JAR156	1959	£2.50	£6	

SKIP & THE CREATIONS

Mobam	LP	Justice		196-	£75	£150	US

SKIP BIFFERTY

The album made by Skip Bifferty is something of a forgotten sixties classic, to file next to the debut albums by Family and Traffic. The group never managed to build on its encouraging start, however. Four years later, the follow-up was finally made and issued under the name of Bell And Arc. Sadly, by this time, much of the group's inspiration seemed to have evaporated.

Happy Land	7"	RCA	RCA1648	1967	£5	£10	
Man In Black	7"	RCA	RCA1720	1968	£5	£10	
On Love	7"	RCA	RCA1621	1967	£6	£12	
Skip Bifferty	LP	RCA	RD/SF7941	1967	£37.50	£75	black label, sleeve pictured in Guide
Skip Bifferty	LP	RCA	RD/SF7941	1967	£25	£50	orange label

SKREWDRIVER

All Skrewed Up	LP	Chiswick	CH3	1977	£5	£12	plays at 45rpm
All Skrewed Up	LP	Chiswick	WIK3	1977	£5	£12	German, 3 extra tracks
Anti-Social	7"	Chiswick	NS18	1977	£2	£5	PS
Back With A Bang	12"	Skrewdriver	SKREW1T	1982	£4	£10	
Built Up	7"	TJM	TJM4	1980	£6	£12	
Hards	7"	White Noise	WN3	1983	£7.50	£15	
Streetfight	7"	Chiswick	NS28	1978	£20	£40	test pressing
Voice Of Britain	7"	White Noise	WN2	1983	£6	£12	
White Power	7"	White Noise	WN1	1983	£7.50	£15	
You're So Dumb	7"	Chiswick	S11	1977	£2	£5	PS

SKULLFLOWER

In The Bottomless Pit	7"	Shock	SX001	1989	£5	£10	
Rotten Sun	7"	Toe Jam		1990	£1.50	£4	
Xaman	7"	Shock	SX008	1989	£2.50	£6	

SKULLSNAPS

My Hang Up Is You	7"	GSF	GSZ7	1973	£5	£10	

SKUNKS

Gettin' Started	LP	Teen Town	101	196-	£8	£20	US

SKY, PATRICK

Harvest Of Gentle Clang	LP	Vanguard	SVRL19054	1970	£6	£15	
Patrick Sky	LP	Vanguard	VSD79179	1965	£6	£15	
Photographs	LP	Verve	FTS3079	1969	£5	£12	US
Reality Is Bad Enough	LP	Verve	FTS3052	1968	£6	£15	US

SKYBIRD

Summer Of '73	LP	Holyground	HGS118	1973	£20	£40	

SKYLINERS

I'll Close My Eyes	7"	Pye	7N25091	1961	£5	£10	
It Happened Today	7"	London	HLU8971	1959	£12.50	£25	
Pennies From Heaven	7"	Polydor	NH66951	1960	£5	£10	
Since I Don't Have You	LP	Original Sound	(S)8873	1963	£15	£30	US
Since I Don't Have You	7"	London	HLB8829	1959	£50	£100	
Skyliners	LP	Calico	LP3000	1959	£60	£120	US
This I Swear	7"	London	HLU8924	1959	£25	£50	

SLACK ALICE

Slack Alice	LP	Philips	6308214	1974	£4	£10	

SLACK, FREDDIE

Boogie Woogie	10" LP	Capitol	LC6529	1951	£10	£25	
Boogie Woogie On The 88	10" LP	Wing	MGW60003	195-	£10	£25	US
Boogie Woogie On The 88	10" LP	Wing	MGW60003		£8	£20	US

SLADE

Alive At Reading '80	7"	Cheapskate	CHEAP5	1980	£1.50	£4	
Alive Vol.2	LP	Barn	2314106	1978	£6	£15	
All Join Hands	12"	RCA	RCAT455	1984	£4	£10	
Bangin' Man	7"	Polydor	2058492	1974	£10	£20	PS
Burning In The Heat Of Love	7"	Barn	2014106	1977	£5	£10	
Cum On Feel The Noize	12"	Polydor	POSPX399	1981	£2.50	£6	
Do You Believe In Miracles	7"	RCA	PB40449	1985	£4	£8	double
Do You Believe In Miracles	12"	RCA	PT40450D	1985	£4	£10	double
Do You Believe In Miracles	12"	RCA	RCAPT40449D	1985	£4	£10	double
Far Far Away	7"	Lyntone	LYN3156/7	1975	£2.50	£6	flexi
Get Down And Get With It	7"	Polydor	2058112	1971	£2	£5	chart single
Ginny Ginny	7"	Barn	002	1979	£10	£20	black vinyl promo

753

Ginny Ginny	7"	Barn	002	1979	£4	£8	yellow vinyl
Give Us A Goal	7"	Barn	2014121	1978	£1.50	£4	
Gypsy Road Hog	7"	Barn	2014105	1977	£1.50	£4	chart single
Hear Me Calling	7"	Polydor	2814008	1970	£25	£50	promo
Hokey Cokey	7"	Speed	SPEED201P	1982	£2	£5	pic disc
In For A Penny	7"	Polydor	2058663	1975	£2	£5	PS
Know Who You Are	7"	Polydor	2058054	1970	£25	£50	
Knuckle Sandwich	7"	Cheapskate	CHEAP24	1981	£1.50	£4	
Merry Xmas Everybody	7"	Cheapskate	CHEAP11	1980	£2	£5	PS, chart single
Merry Xmas Everybody	7"	Polydor	2058422	1973	£10	£20	PS
My Baby Left Me/That's Alright Mama	7"	Barn	2014114	1977	£2.50	£4	chart single
Myzsterious Mizster Jones	7"	RCA	PB40027	1985	£2	£5	pic disc
Night Starvation	7"	S.O.T.B.	SUPER3	1980	£10	£20	demo
Nobody's Fool	7"	Polydor	2058716	1976	£1.50	£4	
Nobody's Fools	LP	Polydor	2383377	1976	£4	£10	
Okey Cokey	7"	Barn	011	1979	£2.50	£6	
Okey Cokey	7"	Speed	SPEED201	1982	£2.50	£6	no PS
Play It Loud	LP	Polydor	2383026	1970	£4	£10	
Return To Base	LP	Barn	NARB003	1979	£10	£25	
Rock'n'Roll	7"	Barn	2014127	1978	£4	£8	
Ruby Red	7"	RCA	RCA191	1982	£2.50	£6	
Ruby Red	7"	RCA	RCAD191	1982	£2	£5	double
Shape Of Things To Come	7"	Fontana	TF1079	1970	£20	£40	
Sign Of The Times	7"	Barn	010	1979	£5	£10	
Six Of The Best	12"	S.O.T.B.	SUPER453	1980	£3	£8	
Slade Talk To 19 Readers	7"	Lyntone	LYN2797	1973	£2	£5	flexi
Slade Talk To Melanie Readers	7"	Lyntone	LYN2645	1973	£2	£5	flexi
Slade Talk To Melanie/19 Readers	7"	Lyntone	LYN2645/2797	1975	£4	£8	flexi
Still The Same	7"	RCA	PB41147	1987	£2.50	£6	double
Thanks For The Memory	7"	Polydor	2058585	1975	£12.50	£25	promo, different lyrics
We'll Bring The House Down	7"	Cheapskate	CHEAP16	1981	£1.50	£4	
Whatever Happened To Slade	LP	Barn	2314103	1977	£6	£15	
Wheels Ain't Comin' Down	7"	Cheapskate	CHEAP21	1981	£1.50	£4	
Whole World's Going Crazy	7"	Polydor	SFI122	1972	£2	£5	flexi, Mike Hugg B side
Wild Winds Are Blowing	7"	Fontana	TF1056	1969	£20	£40	
You Boyz Make Big Noize	7"	Cheapskate	BOYZ1	1987	£2	£5	

SLADE, PRENTIS

I Can Tell	7"	Parlophone	R4850	1961	£2	£5	

SLAM CREEPERS

Saturday	7"	Olga	OLE009	1968	£5	£10	

SLAPP HAPPY

Desperate Straights	LP	Virgin	V2024	1974	£5	£12	with Henry Cow
Slapp Happy	LP	Virgin	V2014	1974	£5	£12	
Sort Of	LP	Polydor	2310204	1972	£20	£40	with insert
Sort Of	LP	Recommended	RRS5	1986	£5	£12	

SLAUGHTER & THE DOGS

Do It Dog Style	LP	Decca	SKL5292	1978	£6	£15	
Live Slaughter Rabid Dogs	LP	Rabid	HAT23	1978	£4	£10	

SLAUGHTER JOE

I'll Follow You Down	7"	Creation	CRE019	1985	£2.50	£6	
I'll Follow You Down	12"	Creation	CRET019	1985	£2.50	£6	

SLAY, FRANK ORCHESTRA

Flying Circle	7"	Top Rank	JAR599	1962	£1.50	£4	

SLAYER

Criminally Insane	7"	London	LON133	1987	£5	£10	cross sleeve, red vinyl

SLEDGE, F.

Red Eye Girl	7"	Blue Beat	BB386	1965	£5	£10	

SLEDGE, PERCY

Any Day Now	7"	Atlantic	584264	1969	£1.50	£4	
Baby Help Me	7"	Atlantic	584080	1967	£2.50	£6	
Best Of Percy Sledge	LP	Atlantic	587/588153	1969	£4	£10	
Come Softly To Me	7"	Atlantic	584225	1968	£1.50	£4	
Heart Of A Child	7"	Atlantic	584055	1966	£2.50	£6	
It Tears Me Up	7"	Atlantic	584071	1967	£1.50	£4	
Kind Woman	7"	Atlantic	584286	1969	£1.50	£4	
Out Of Left Field	7"	Atlantic	584108	1967	£1.50	£4	
Percy Sledge Way	LP	Atlantic	587/588081	1967	£6	£15	
Pledging My Love	7"	Atlantic	584140	1967	£1.50	£4	
Take Time To Know Her	LP	Atlantic	SD8180	1968	£6	£15	US
Take Time To Love Her	7"	Atlantic	584177	1968	£1.50	£4	
True Love Travels On A Gravel Road	7"	Atlantic	584300	1969	£1.50	£4	
Warm And Tender Love	7"	Atlantic	584034	1966	£1.50	£4	chart single
Warm And Tender Soul	LP	Atlantic	587/588048	1967	£6	£15	
When A Man Loves A Woman	LP	Atlantic	587/588105	1968	£6	£15	
When A Man Loves A Woman	7"	Atlantic	584001	1966	£2	£5	chart single

SLEDGEHAMMER

In The Queue	7"	Illuminated	ILL33	1985	£5	£10	shaped pic disc
Sledgehammer	7"	Slammer	SRTS79/CUS395	1979	£2	£5	

SLEEPWALKERS
Sleepwalk	7"	Parlophone	R4580	1959	£2	£5	

SLEEPY
Love's Immortal Fire	7"	CBS	3592	1968	£6	£12	
Rosie Can't Fly	7"	CBS	3838	1968	£6	£12	

SLENDER PLENTY
Silver Tree Top School For Boys	7"	Polydor	56189	1967	£7.50	£15	

SLEVIN, JIMI
Freeflight	LP	Claddagh	CCF7	1982	£20	£40	

SLICK, GRACE
And Through The Hoop	LP	RCA	DJL13544	1979	£6	£15	US interview promo
Welcome To The Wrecking Ball	LP	RCA	DJL13922	1981	£6	£15	US interview promo

SLICKEE BOYS
Separated Vegetables	LP	Dacoit	1001	1977	£30	£60	US
Separated Vegetables	LP	Limp	10003	1980	£25	£50	US

SLICKERS
Frying Pan	7"	Blue Cat	BS154	1969	£4	£8	Rarfield Williams B side
Johnny Too Bad	7"	Dynamic	DYN406	1970	£4	£8	Roland Alphonso B side
Man Beware	7"	Amalgamated	AMG852	1969	£4	£8	
Money Reaper	7"	Amalgamated	AMG866	1969	£4	£8	
Nana	7"	Blue Cat	BS134	1968	£4	£8	Martin Riley B side
Run Fattie	7"	Trojan	TR7719	1969	£2	£5	
Wala Wala	7"	Blue Cat	BS133	1968	£4	£8	Lester Sterling B side

SLITS
Return Of The Giant Slits	LP	CBS	85269	1981	£4	£10	with 7' (XPS125)

SLOAN, P.F.
12 More Times	LP	Dunhill	D50007	1966	£5	£12	US
Man Behind The Red Balloon	7" EP	RCA	86903	1966	£4	£8	French
Measure Of Pleasure	LP	Atco	33268	1968	£4	£10	US
Sins Of The Family	7"	RCA	RCA1482	1965	£1.50	£4	
Sins Of The Family	7" EP	RCA	86901	1965	£4	£8	French
Songs Of Our Time	LP	Dunhill	D50004	1965	£5	£12	US

SLOAN, SAMMI
Yes I Would	7"	Columbia	DB8480	1968	£2	£5	

SLY & THE FAMILY STONE
Dance To The Music	LP	Direction	863412	1968	£6	£15	
Dance To The Music	7"	Columbia	DB8369	1968	£12.50	£25	
Dance To The Music	7"	Direction	583568	1968	£1.50	£4	chart single
Everyday People	7"	Direction	583938	1969	£1.50	£4	chart single
Family Affair	7"	Epic	EPC1148	1973	£1.50	£4	
Family Affair	7"	Epic	EPC1148	1973	£2.50	£6	PS
Family Affair	7"	Epic	EPC7632	1971	£1.50	£4	chart single
Fresh	LP	Epic	EPC69039	1973	£4	£10	
Greatest Hits	LP	CBS	Q69002	1973	£6	£15	quad
Greatest Hits	LP	Epic	EPC69002	1970	£4	£10	
High Energy	LP	Epic	EPC22004	1975	£6	£15	double
High On You	LP	Epic	PEQ33835	1975	£5	£12	US quad
Hot Fun In The Summertime	7"	Direction	584471	1969	£1.50	£4	
I Want To Take You Higher	7"	CBS	5054	1970	£1.50	£4	
Life	LP	Epic	BN26397	1968	£6	£15	US
M'Lady	LP	Direction	863461	1968	£6	£15	
M'Lady	7"	Direction	583707	1968	£1.50	£4	chart single
Running Away	7"	Epic	EPC7810	1972	£1.50	£4	chart single
Small Talk	LP	Epic	EPC69070	1974	£4	£10	
Small Talk	LP	Epic	PEQ32930	1974	£5	£12	US quad
Stand	LP	Epic	863655	1969	£6	£15	
Stand	7"	Direction	584279	1969	£1.50	£4	
Thank You	7"	Direction	584782	1970	£1.50	£4	
There's A Riot Going On	LP	Epic	EPC64613	1971	£6	£15	chart LP
Whole New Thing	LP	Epic	LN24/BN26324	1967	£6	£15	US

SMALL FACES
	7"	Immediate	AS1	1967	£15	£30	promo
Afterglow Of Your Love	7"	Immediate	IM077	1969	£2	£5	chart single
All Or Nothing	7"	Decca	F12470	1966	£1.50	£4	chart single
All Or Nothing	7" EP	Decca	457123	1966	£12.50	£25	French
Autumn Stone	LP	Immediate	IMA101/2	1969	£10	£25	double
From The Beginning	LP	Decca	LK4879	1967	£15	£30	chart LP
Here Come The Nice	7" EP	Columbia	ESRF1876	1967	£12.50	£25	French
Here Comes The Nice	7"	Immediate	IM050	1967	£1.50	£4	chart single
Hey Girl	7"	Decca	F12393	1966	£1.50	£4	chart single
I Can't Make It	7"	Decca	F12565	1967	£2.50	£6	chart single
I Can't Make It	7" EP	Decca	457144	1967	£12.50	£25	French
In Memoriam	LP	Immediate	IMSP022	1970	£10	£25	German
Itchycoo Park	7"	Immediate	IM057	1967	£1.50	£4	chart single
Itchycoo Park	7" EP	Columbia	ESRF1882	1967	£12.50	£25	French
I've Got Mine	7"	Decca	F12276	1965	£2	£5	
Lazy Sunday	7"	Immediate	IM064	1968	£1.50	£4	chart single
My Mind's Eye	7"	Decca	F12500	1967	£1.50	£4	chart single

Title	Format	Label	Catalog#	Year	Price	Price	Notes
My Mind's Eye	7" EP..	Decca	457133	1967	£12.50	£25	French
Ogden's Nut Gone Flake	LP	Immediate	IMLP/IMSP012	1967	£8	£20	round cover, chart LP
Patterns	7"	Decca	F12619	1967	£5	£10	
Sha-La-La-La-Lee	7"	Decca	F12317	1966	£1.50	£4	chart single
Sha-La-La-La-Lee	7" EP..	Decca	457106	1966	£7.50	£15	French
Small Faces	LP	Decca	LK4790	1966	£10	£25	chart LP
Small Faces	LP	Immediate	IMLP/IMSP008	1967	£15	£30	chart LP
There Are But Four Small Faces	LP	Immediate	Z1252002	1968	£8	£20	US
Tin Soldier	7"	Immediate	IM062	1967	£1.50	£4	chart single
Tin Soldier	7"	Immediate	IM062	1967	£5	£10	PS
Universal	7"	Immediate	IM069	1968	£1.50	£4	chart single
Whatcha Gonna Do About it	7"	Decca	F12208	1965	£1.50	£4	chart single
Whatcha Gonna Do About It	7" EP..	Decca	457091	1965	£12.50	£25	French

SMALL HOURS

Title	Format	Label	Catalog#	Year	Price	Price
Kid	7"	Automatic	K17708	1980	£10	£20
Kid	10"	Automatic	K17708X	1980	£6	£15

SMALL, JOAN

Title	Format	Label	Catalog#	Year	Price	Price
You Can't Say I Love You	7"	Parlophone	R4269	1957	£2	£5

SMALL, KAREN

Title	Format	Label	Catalog#	Year	Price	Price
To Get You Back Again	7"	Vocalion	VP9281	1966	£4	£8

SMALL WORLD

Title	Format	Label	Catalog#	Year	Price	Price
Love Is Dead	7"	Whaam!	WHAAM3	1982	£6	£12

SMILE

Smile included Brian May and Roger Taylor who, not long after the release of the group's only single, left in order to help found Queen. Red vinyl copies of the single, incidentally, are counterfeits.

Title	Format	Label	Catalog#	Year	Price	Price	Notes
Earth	7"	Mercury	72977	1969	£60	£120	US, possibly promo only

SMILIN' JOE

Title	Format	Label	Catalog#	Year	Price	Price
ABC's	78	London	HL8106	1954	£25	£50

SMITH, ADAM

Title	Format	Label	Catalog#	Year	Price	Price
I Wonder Why	7"	Island	WI057	1962	£5	£10

SMITH, ARTHUR 'GUITAR BOOGIE'

Title	Format	Label	Catalog#	Year	Price	Price	Notes
Arthur 'Guitar Boogie' Smith And His Crackerjacks	7" EP..	MGM	MGMEP510	1954	£7.50	£15	
Arthur 'Guitar Boogie' Smith And His Crackerjacks	7" EP..	MGM	MGMEP695	1959	£10	£20	
Express Boogie	7"	MGM	SP1039	1953	£7.50	£15	
Fingers On Fire	LP	MGM	E3525	1958	£8	£20	US
Fingers On Fire	10" LP	MGM	D111	1953	£10	£25	
Five String Banjo Boogie	7"	MGM	SP1021	1953	£7.50	£15	
Foolish Questions	10" LP	MGM	D131	1954	£10	£25	
Guitar Boogie	7"	MGM	SP1008	1953	£10	£20	
Hi Lo Boogie	7"	MGM	SP1122	1955	£7.50	£15	
I Get So Lonely	7"	MGM	SP1096	1954	£7.50	£15	
Mister Guitar	7" EP..	Stateside	SE1005	1963	£7.50	£15	
Original Guitar Boogie	LP	Dot	DLP5600	1964	£5	£12	US
Red Headed Stranger	7"	MGM	SP1110	1954	£7.50	£15	
Specials	10" LP	MGM	E3301	195-	£10	£25	US

SMITH, BARRY

Title	Format	Label	Catalog#	Year	Price	Price
Hold On To It	7"	People	PEO119	1975	£7.50	£15

SMITH, BEASLEY

Title	Format	Label	Catalog#	Year	Price	Price
Goodnight Sweet Dreams	7"	London	HLD8235	1956	£10	£20
My Foolish Heart	7"	London	HLD8273	1956	£10	£20

SMITH, BESSIE

Title	Format	Label	Catalog#	Year	Price	Price	Notes
Any Woman's Blues	LP	CBS	66262	1971	£5	£12	double
Bessie Smith	7" EP..	Philips	BBE12360	1960	£2.50	£6	
Bessie Smith Story Vol.1	LP	CBS	BPG62377	1966	£5	£12	
Bessie Smith Story Vol.1	LP	Philips	BBL7019	1955	£8	£20	
Bessie Smith Story Vol.2	LP	CBS	BPG62378	1966	£5	£12	
Bessie Smith Story Vol.2	LP	Philips	BBL7020	1955	£8	£20	
Bessie Smith Story Vol.3	LP	CBS	BPG62379	1966	£5	£12	
Bessie Smith Story Vol.3	LP	Philips	BBL7042	1955	£8	£20	
Bessie Smith Story Vol.4	LP	CBS	BPG62380	1966	£5	£12	
Bessie Smith Story Vol.4	LP	Philips	BBL7049	1955	£8	£20	
Bessie's Blues	LP	Philips	BBL7513	1962	£6	£15	
Empress	LP	CBS	66264	1971	£5	£12	double
Empress Of The Blues	7" EP..	Philips	BBE12202	1958	£2.50	£6	
Empress Of The Blues No.2	7" EP..	Philips	BBE12231	1959	£2.50	£6	
Empress Of The Blues No.3	7" EP..	Philips	BBE12233	1959	£2.50	£6	
Empty Bed Blues	LP	CBS	66273	1971	£5	£12	double
Nobody's Blues But Mine	LP	CBS	67232	1972	£5	£12	double
World's Greatest Blues Singer	LP	CBS	66258	1971	£5	£12	double

SMITH, BETTY

Title	Format	Label	Catalog#	Year	Price	Price
Betty Smith Quintet	7" EP..	Decca	DFE6446	1957	£7.50	£15
Betty's Blues	7"	Decca	F11031	1958	£2.50	£6
Bewitched	7"	Decca	F10986	1958	£2.50	£6
Sweet Georgia Brown	7"	Tempo	A163	1957	£4	£8
There's A Blue Ridge Mountain	7"	Tempo	A162	1957	£4	£8

SMITH, BETTY QUINTET

Title	Format	Label	Cat. No.	Year			Notes
Begin The Beguine	7"	Decca	F11071	1958	£1.50	£4	
Song Of India	7"	Decca	F11124	1959	£1.50	£4	

SMITH, BOB

Title	Format	Label	Cat. No.	Year			Notes
Visit	LP	Kent	KST551	1969	£25	£50	US

SMITH, BUSTER

Title	Format	Label	Cat. No.	Year			Notes
Legendary Buster Smith	LP	London	LTZK15206	1960	£6	£15	

SMITH, CARL

Title	Format	Label	Cat. No.	Year			Notes
Carl Smith	10" LP	Columbia	HL2579	1956	£8	£20	US
Carl Smith Touch	LP	Philips	BBL7437	1960	£5	£12	
Let's Live A Little	LP	Columbia	CL1172	1958	£6	£15	US
Sentimental Songs	10" LP	Columbia	HL9023	195-	£8	£20	US
Smith's The Name	LP	Columbia	CL1022	1957	£6	£15	US
Softly And Tenderly	10" LP	Columbia	HL9026	195-	£8	£20	US
Sunday Down South	LP	Columbia	CL959	1957	£6	£15	US
Ten Thousand Drums	7"	Philips	PB943	1959	£2.50	£6	

SMITH, CLARA

Title	Format	Label	Cat. No.	Year			Notes
Blues	7" EP	Philips	BBE12491	1961	£5	£10	
Volume 1	LP	VJM	VLP15	1969	£5	£12	
Volume 2	LP	VJM	VLP16	1969	£5	£12	
Volume 3	LP	VJM	VLP17	1969	£5	£12	

SMITH, DAVE & THE ASTRONAUTS

Title	Format	Label	Cat. No.	Year			Notes
Lover Like You	7"	Columbia	DB104	1967	£4	£8	

SMITH, EDDIE

Title	Format	Label	Cat. No.	Year			Notes
Silver Star Stomp	7"	Parlophone	MSP6186	1955	£5	£10	
Upturn	7"	Top Rank	JAR285	1960	£4	£8	

SMITH, EDGEWOOD & FABULOUS TAILFEATHERS

Title	Format	Label	Cat. No.	Year			Notes
Ain't That Lovin' You	7"	Sue	WI4037	1967	£5	£10	

SMITH, EFFIE

Title	Format	Label	Cat. No.	Year			Notes
Dial That Phone	7"	Sue	WI4010	1966	£5	£10	

SMITH, ELSON

Title	Format	Label	Cat. No.	Year			Notes
Flip Flop	7"	Fontana	H291	1961	£4	£8	

SMITH, GEORGE HARMONICA

Title	Format	Label	Cat. No.	Year			Notes
Arkansas Trap	LP	Deram	SML1082	1971	£15	£30	
Blues In The Dark	7"	Blue Horizon	451002	1966	£15	£30	
Blues With A Feeling	LP	Liberty	LBS83218	1970	£6	£15	
No Time To Jive	LP	Blue Horizon	763856	1970	£25	£50	
Someone You're Gonna Learn	7"	Blue Horizon	573170	1970	£5	£10	

SMITH, GLORIA

Title	Format	Label	Cat. No.	Year			Notes
Playmates	7"	London	HLU8903	1959	£2.50	£6	

SMITH, GORDON

Title	Format	Label	Cat. No.	Year			Notes
Long Overdue	LP	Blue Horizon	763211	1968	£20	£40	
Too Long	7"	Blue Horizon	573156	1969	£5	£10	

SMITH, HAROLD MAJESTIC CHOIR

Title	Format	Label	Cat. No.	Year			Notes
We Can All Walk A Little Bit Prouder	7"	Chess	CRS8100	1969	£1.50	£4	

SMITH, HUEY 'PIANO'

Title	Format	Label	Cat. No.	Year			Notes
Don't You Know Yokomo	7"	Top Rank	JAR282	1960	£7.50	£15	
For Dancing	LP	Ace	LP1015	1961	£30	£60	US
Having A Good Time	LP	Ace	LP1004	1959	£30	£60	US
High Blood Pressure	7"	Columbia	DB4138	1958	£20	£40	
If It Ain't One Thing It's Another	7"	Sue	WI364	1965	£6	£12	
Popeye	7"	Top Rank	JAR614	1962	£6	£12	
Rock 'n' Roll Revival	LP	Ace	LP2021	196-	£25	£50	US
Rockin' Pneumonia	7"	Sue	WI380	1965	£6	£12	
Rockin' Pneumonia And Boogie Woogie Flu	LP	Sue	ILP917	1965	£20	£40	
T'was The Night Before Christmas	LP	Ace	LP1027	1962	£25	£50	US

SMITH, HURRICANE

Title	Format	Label	Cat. No.	Year			Notes
Don't Let It Die	7"	Columbia	DB8785	1971	£1.50	£4	chart single

SMITH, JIMMY

Title	Format	Label	Cat. No.	Year			Notes
Any Number Can Win	LP	Verve	VLP9057	1963	£4	£10	
At Club Baby Grand, Wilmington, Delaware Vol.1	LP	Blue Note	BLP/BST81528	1966	£10	£25	
At Club Baby Grand, Wilmington, Delaware Vol.2	LP	Blue Note	BLP/BST81529	1966	£10	£25	
At Small's Paradise Vol.1	LP	Blue Note	BLP/BST81585	196-	£10	£25	
At Small's Paradise Vol.2	LP	Blue Note	BLP/BST81586	196-	£10	£25	
At The Organ Vol.1	LP	Blue Note	BLP/BST81512	196-	£10	£25	
At The Organ Vol.2	LP	Blue Note	BLP/BST81513	196-	£10	£25	
Back At The Chicken Shack	LP	Blue Note	BLP/BST84117	1964	£10	£25	
Bashin'	LP	Verve	CLP1596/CSD1462	1962	£4	£10	
Bucket	LP	Blue Note	BLP/BST84235	1966	£6	£15	
Can Heat	7"	Blue Note	451905	1964	£4	£8	
Cat	LP	Verve	(S)VLP9079	1964	£4	£10	
Cat	7"	Verve	VS523	1964	£1.50	£4	

Cat In A Tree	7"	Verve	VS551	1967	£1.50	£4	
Christmas Cookin'	LP	Verve	(S)VLP9231	1968	£4	£10	
Crazy Baby	LP	Blue Note	BLP/BST84030	1961	£10	£25	
Creeper	7" EP	Verve	VEP5021	1965	£2	£5	
Date With Jimmy Smith Vol.1	LP	Blue Note	BLP/BST81547	196-	£10	£25	
Date With Jimmy Smith Vol.2	LP	Blue Note	BLP/BST81548	196-	£10	£25	
Dynamic Duo	LP	Verve	(S)VLP9160	1967	£4	£10	with Wes Montgomery
Further Adventures Of Jimmy And Wes	LP	Verve	(S)VLP9241	1969	£4	£10	with Wes Montgomery
Got My Mojo Working	LP	Verve	(S)VLP9123	1966	£4	£10	
Got My Mojo Working	7"	Verve	VS536	1966	£2	£5	chart single
Greatest Hits	LP	Blue Note	BST89901	1970	£4	£10	
Hobo Flats	LP	Verve	(S)VLP9039	1963	£4	£10	
Hobo Flats	7"	Verve	VS509	1965	£1.50	£4	
Home Cookin'	LP	Blue Note	BLP/BST84050	1961	£10	£25	
Hoochie Coochie Man	LP	Verve	(S)VLP9142	1966	£4	£10	
House Party	LP	Blue Note	BLP/BST84002	1964	£10	£25	
I'm Movin' On	LP	Blue Note	BLP/BST84255	1967	£6	£15	
I'm Your Hoochie Coochie Man	7"	Verve	VS540	1966	£1.50	£4	
Incredible Jimmy Smith Vol.1	LP	Blue Note	BLP/BST81551	1964	£10	£25	
Incredible Jimmy Smith Vol.2	LP	Blue Note	BLP/BST81552	1965	£10	£25	
Jimmy Smith Vol.3	LP	Blue Note	BLP/BST81525	196-	£10	£25	
Livin' It Up	LP	Verve	(S)VLP9227	1968	£4	£10	
Mickey Mouse	7"	Verve	VS562	1967	£1.50	£4	
Midnight Special	LP	Blue Note	BLP/BST84078	1962	£10	£25	
Monster	LP	Verve	(S)VLP9093	1965	£4	£10	
Open House	LP	Blue Note	BST84269	1968	£6	£15	
Organ Grinder Swing	LP	Verve	(S)VLP9108	1966	£4	£10	
Organ Grinder's Swing	7"	Verve	VS531	1965	£1.50	£4	
Peter And The Wolf	LP	Verve	(S)VLP9159	1966	£4	£10	
Plain Talk	LP	Blue Note	BST84296	1968	£5	£12	
Plays Fats Waller	LP	Blue Note	BLP/BST84100	1964	£8	£20	
Plays Pretty For You	LP	Blue Note	BLP/BST81563	196-	£10	£25	
Plays The Blues	7" EP	Verve	VEP5016	1965	£2	£5	
Prayer Meetin'	LP	Blue Note	BLP/BST84164	1964	£10	£25	
Respect	LP	Verve	(S)VLP9182	1967	£4	£10	
Rockin' The Boat	LP	Blue Note	BLP/BST84141	1964	£8	£20	
Sermon	LP	Blue Note	BLP/BST84011	1966	£10	£25	
Sermon	7"	Blue Note	451879	1964	£4	£8	
Softly As A Summer Breeze	LP	Blue Note	BLP/BST84200	1966	£8	£20	
Sounds Of Jimmy Smith	LP	Blue Note	BLP/BST81556	196-	£10	£25	
Stay Loose	LP	Verve	(S)VLP9218	1968	£4	£10	
Swinging With The Incredible Jimmy Smith	7" EP	Verve	VEP5022	1965	£2	£5	
Walk On The Wild Side	7"	HMV	POP1025	1962	£2	£5	
Walk On The Wild Side	7" EP	Verve	VEP5008	1964	£2	£5	
When My Dreamboat Comes Home	7"	Blue Note	451904	1963	£4	£8	
Where The Spies Are	7"	Verve	VS534	1966	£1.50	£4	
Who's Afraid Of Virginia Wolf	7"	Verve	VS521	1964	£1.50	£4	
Who's Afraid Of Virginia Woolf	LP	Verve	VLP9068	1964	£4	£10	

SMITH, JOEY & BABA BROOKS
Maybe Once	7"	R&B	JB131	1964	£5	£10

SMITH, JOHNNY
Johnny Smith And His New Quartet	LP	Vogue	LAE12202	1960	£4	£10
Johnny Smith Quartet	LP	Vogue	LAE12221	1960	£4	£10
Moods	LP	Vogue	LAE12198	1961	£6	£15
Moonlight In Vermont	LP	Vogue	LAE12189	1959	£8	£20
Plays Jimmy Van Heusen	LP	Vogue	LAE12169	1959	£8	£20

SMITH, JUDI
Leaves Come Tumbling Down	7"	Decca	F12132	1965	£5	£10

SMITH, JUNIOR
Come Cure Me	7"	Giant	GN25	1968	£4	£8
Cool Down Your Temper	7"	Giant	GN1	1967	£4	£8
I'm Gonna Leave You Girl	7"	Giant	GN18	1968	£4	£8

SMITH, KEELY
Don't Take Your Love From Me	7"	Capitol	CL14994	1959	£1.50	£4
Here In My Heart	7"	London	HLD9240	1960	£1.50	£4
If I Knew I'd Find You	7"	London	HLD8984	1959	£2	£5
That Old Black Magic	7"	Capitol	CL14948	1958	£1.50	£4

SMITH, LONNIE
Drives	LP	Blue Note	BST84351	1970	£6	£15
Move Your Hand	LP	Blue Note	BST84326	1969	£6	£15
Think	LP	Blue Note	BST84290	1968	£6	£15
Turning Point	LP	Blue Note	BST84313	1969	£6	£15

SMITH, LONNIE LISTON
Lonnie Liston Smith is a jazz keyboard player who was briefly a part of the Miles Davis band during the time in the early seventies when the trumpeter was engaged in some of his most experimental work with densely constructed rhythms. Smith's own records contain a very much more commercial form of jazz-funk, the track "Expansions" having aquired some of the status of a disco classic.

Chance For Peace	7"	RCA	RCA2668	1976	£1.50	£4
Expansions	LP	RCA	SF8434	1975	£6	£15
Expansions	7"	RCA	PB9450	1975	£1.50	£4
Expansions	7"	RCA	RCA2568	1975	£2	£5
Expansions	12"	RCA	PC9450	1979	£3	£8

Get Down Everybody .... 7" .... RCA .... RCA2727 .... 1976 ... £1.50 ....£4 ....

SMITH, LORENZO
Firewater .... 7" .... Outasite .... 45503 .... 1966 ... £12.50 .....£25 ....

SMITH, MARVIN
Time Stopped .... 7" .... Coral .... Q72486 .... 1966 ... £10 ....£20 ....

SMITH, MICHAEL
Mi Cyaan Believe It .... LP ..... Island .... ILPS .... 1982 ... £5 ....£12 ....

SMITH, O.C.
Dynamic O.C.Smith .... LP ..... CBS .... 63147 .... 1968 ... £4 ....£10 ....
Son Of Hickory Holler's Tramp .... 7" .... CBS .... 3343 .... 1968 ... £1.50 ....£4 ....chart single

SMITH, OCIE
Lighthouse .... 7" .... London .... HLA8480 .... 1957 ... £20 ....£40 ....

SMITH, PATTI
Brian Jones .... 7" .... Fierce .... FRIGHT017 .... 1988 ... £5 ....£10 ....
Hey Joe .... 7" .... Mer .... 601 .... 1974 ... £20 ....£40 .... US
Horses .... LP ..... Arista .... S4066 .... 1975 ... £8 ....£20 ....US grey vinyl

SMITH, PAUL
Big Men .... LP ..... HMV .... CLP1356 .... 1960 ... £5 ....£12 ....
Delicate Jazz .... LP ..... Capitol .... T1017 .... 1959 ... £5 ....£12 ....
Paul Smith .... 10" LP Capitol .... LC6820 .... 1956 ... £8 ....£20 ....
Paul Smith Quartet .... 10" LP Vogue .... LDE168 .... 1956 ... £8 ....£20 ....

SMITH, RAY
Best Of Ray Smith .... LP ..... T. .... 56062 .... 196- ... £8 ....£20 .... US
Greatest Hits .... LP ..... Columbia .... CL1937/CS8737 .... 1963 ... £6 ....£15 .... US
Rocking Little Angel .... 7" .... London .... HL9051 .... 1960 ... £15 ....£30 .... US
Travellin' With Ray .... LP ..... Judd .... JLPA701 .... 1960 ... £50 ....£100 .... US

SMITH, SLIM
Everybody Needs Love .... LP ..... Pama .... ECO9 .... 1969 ... £8 ....£20 ....
Everybody Needs Love .... 7" .... Unity .... UN504 .... 1969 ... £2.50 ....£6 ... Junior Smith B side
Greatest Hits .... LP ..... Trojan .... TBL198 .... 1973 ... £5 ....£12 ....
I've Got Your Number .... 7" .... Island .... WI3023 .... 1966 ... £5 ....£10 ....
Just A Dream .... LP ..... Trojan .... TBL186 .... 1972 ... £6 ....£15 ....
Rougher Yet .... 7" .... Coxsone .... CS7034 .... 1968 ... £5 ....£10 ....
Slim Smith .... LP ..... Lord Koos .... KLP1 .... 197- ... £8 ....£20 ....
Watch This Sound .... 7" .... Trojan .... TR619 .... 1968 ... £4 ....£8 ....

SMITH, SOMETHIN' & THE REDHEADS
Don't Want To Set The World On Fire 7" .... Fontana .... H154 .... 1958 ... £1.50 ....£4 ....

SMITH, STUART
My Head Goes Round .... 7" .... Polydor .... 563336 .... 1969 ... £2 ....£5 ....

SMITH, STUFF
Stuff Smith .... LP ..... Columbia .... 33CX10093 .... 1957 ... £6 ....£15 ....

SMITH, TAB
All My Life .... 7" .... Vogue .... V2299 .... 1962 ... £1.50 ....£4 ....
Jump Time .... 7" .... Vogue .... V2410 .... 1956 ... £5 ....£10 ....
Music Styled By Tab Smith .... 10" LP United .... LP001 .... 195- ... £25 ....£50 .... US
My Happiness Cha-Cha .... 7" .... London .... HLM8801 .... 1959 ... £2 ....£5 ....
Red Hot And Cool Blues .... 10" LP United .... LP003 .... 195- ... £25 ....£50 .... US

SMITH, TERRY
Fall Out .... LP ..... Philips .... SBL7871 .... 1969 ... £10 ....£25 ....
Terry Smith .... LP ..... Lambert .... LAM002 .... 1977 ... £10 ....£25 ....

SMITH, TRIXIE
Freight Train Blues .... 78 ...... Vocalion .... V1006 .... 1952 ... £3 ....£8 ....
He Likes It Slow .... 78 ...... Tempo .... R42 .... 1951 ... £2.50 ....£6 ....
My Daddy Rocks Me .... 78 ...... Vocalion .... V1017 .... 1952 ... £3 ....£8 ....
Trixie Smith .... 10" LP Audubon .... 195- ... £8 ....£20 ....
Trixie Smith .... 10" EP Poydras .... 101 .... 195- ... £4 ....£10 ....
Trixie Smith .... 10" EP Ristic .... 12 .... 195- ... £4 ....£10 ....

SMITH, TRULY
Boy From Chelsea .... 7" .... Decca .... F12700 .... 1967 ... £1.50 ....£4 ....
I Wanna Go Back There Again .... 7" .... Decca .... F12645 .... 1967 ... £4 ....£8 ....
Love Is Me Love Is You .... 7" EP.. Decca .... 457115 .... 1966 ... £4 ....£8 ....French
My Smile Is Just A Frown Turned .... 7" .... Decca .... F12373 .... 1966 ... £7.50 ....£15 ....
Upside Down
This Is The First Time .... 7" .... MGM .... MGM1431 .... 1968 ... £2.50 ....£6 ....

SMITH, T.V. EXPLORERS
Servant .... cass-s Kaleidoscope .. KRLA401162 .... 1981 ... £8 ....£20 ....

SMITH, VERDELLE
Don't Need Anything .... 7" .... Capitol .... CL15481 .... 1966 ... £4 ....£8 ....
In My Room .... 7" .... Capitol .... CL15434 .... 1966 ... £2 ....£5 ....
Tar And Cement .... 7" .... Capitol .... CL15456 .... 1966 ... £2.50 ....£6 ....
There's So Much Love Around Me .... 7" .... Capitol .... CL15514 .... 1967 ... £2 ....£5 ....

SMITH, WARREN
First Country Collection .... LP ..... Liberty .... LRP3199/LST7199 1961 ... £10 ....£25 .... US

I Don't Believe I'll Fall In Love	7"	London	HL7101	1960	£10	£20	export
Judge And Jury	7"	Liberty	LIB55699	1964	£4	£8	
Odds And Ends	7"	London	HLG7110	1961	£10	£20	

SMITH, WHISPERING

Over Easy	LP	Blue Horizon	2431015	1971	£15	£30	

SMITH, WHISTLING JACK

Around The World	LP	Deram	DML1009	1967	£4	£10	
Hey There Little Miss Mary	7" EP.	Deram	15005	1967	£4	£8	French
I Was Kaiser Bill's Batman	7"	Deram	DM112	1967	£1.50	£4	chart single
I Was Kaiser Bill's Batman	7" EP.	Deram	15001	1967	£4	£8	French

SMITH, WILLIE

And His Friends	10" LP	Mercury	MG26000	1954	£20	£40	

SMITH, WILLIE 'THE LION'

Legend Of Willie 'The Lion' Smith	LP	Top Rank	RX3015	1959	£6	£15	
Willie 'The Lion' Smith	10" LP	London	HAPB1017	1954	£10	£25	
Willie 'The Lion' Smith	10" LP	Vogue	LDE177	1956	£8	£20	

SMITHEREENS

Beauty And Sadness	LP	Little Ricky		1983	£8	£20	US
Blue Period	CD-s	Enigma	UNVCD21	1990	£3	£8	with Belinda Carlisle

SMITHS

The Smiths remained with Rough Trade for the major part of their career and saw the record company's fortunes rise along with their own, so that there are no obscure early singles for the Smiths collector to seek out. The single "This Charming Man", available in three versions, has, however, become quite scarce, despite gaining a respectable position in the lower reaches of the charts. The original cover of "What Difference Does It Make", showing a film still of Terence Stamp in "The Collector" is not particularly rare. One suspects that its withdrawal in favour of a cover with Morrisey in identical pose was designed solely to illustrate the song's title.

Ask	cass-s	Rough Trade	RT194C	1986	£2.50	£6	
Ask	12"	Rough Trade	RTT194	1986	£4	£10	clear vinyl
Girlfriend In A Coma	cass-s	Rough Trade	RTT197C	1987	£2.50	£6	
Hand In Glove	7"	Rough Trade	RT131	1983	£2.50	£6	Rough Trade logo on label
Hand In Glove	7"	Rough Trade	RT131	1987	£20	£40	blue sleeve, silver photo
Hatful Of Hollow	CD	Rough Trade	ROUGHCD76	1988	£6	£15	
Meat Is Murder	7"	Rough Trade	RT186	1985	£15	£30	test pressing
Meat Is Murder	12"	Rough Trade	RTT186	1985	£20	£40	test pressing
Panic	7"	Rough Trade	RT193	1986	£2.50	£6	'Hang the DJ' stickers
Panic	12"	Rough Trade	RTT193	1986	£3	£8	'Hang the DJ' stickers
Panic	12"	Rough Trade	RTT193	1986	£3	£8	blue vinyl
Queen Is Dead	LP	Rough Trade		1986	£8	£20	German, green vinyl
Reel Around The Fountain	7"	Rough Trade	RT136	1983	£50	£100	test pressing
Shoplifters Of The World Unite	12"	Rough Trade	RTT195	1987	£2.50	£6	with carrier bag
Smiths	LP	Rough Trade	RTD25	1984	£50	£100	German multi-coloured vinyl
Still Ill	7"	Rough Trade	RT161DJ	1984	£7.50	£15	promo
Strangeways Here We Come	LP	Rough Trade	RTD60	1987	£6	£15	German blue-grey vinyl
This Charming Man	7"	Rough Trade	RT136	1983	£5	£10	chart single
This Charming Man	12"	Rough Trade	RTT136	1983	£5	£12	
This Charming Man (New York remix)	12"	Rough Trade	RTT136NY	1983	£6	£15	
What Difference Does It Make	12"	Rough Trade	RTT146	1984	£2.50	£6	Terence Stamp sleeve
William, It Was Really Nothing	7"	Rough Trade	RT166	1984	£2.50	£6	
William, It Was Really Nothing	12"	Rough Trade	RTT166	1984	£3	£8	
You Just Haven't Earned It Yet Baby	12"	Rough Trade	RTT195	1987	£20	£40	mispressing

SMOKE

The English Smoke managed to maintain a surprisingly long career (including making records under the name of Chords Five) for a group that were essentially a one-hit wonder. That one hit, however, "My Friend Jack", is something of a psychedelic classic, driven by viciously reverbed and fuzzed guitars.

Dreams Of Dreams	7"	Revolution	REVP1002	1970	£5	£10	
If The Weather's Sunny	7"	Columbia	DB8252	1967	£6	£12	
It Could Be Wonderful	7"	Island	WIP6023	1967	£12.50	£25	
It's Just Your Way Of Lovin'	7" EP.	Impact	200012	1967	£15	£30	French
It's Smoke Time	LP	Metronome		1967	£25	£50	German
My Friend Jack	7"	Columbia	DB8115	1967	£6	£12	chart single
My Friend Jack	7" EP.	Impact	200010	1967	£15	£30	French
My Lullaby	7"	Decca	FR13514	1974	£2	£5	
Ride Ride Ride	7"	Pageant	SAM101	1971	£5	£10	
Shagalagalu	7"	Decca	FR13484	1974	£2	£5	
Smoke	LP	BASF		1968	£15	£30	German
Sugar Man	7"	Regal Zonophone	RZ3071	1972	£5	£10	
Utterly Simple	7"	Island	WIP6031	1968	£100	£200	demo

SMOKE (2)

At George's Coffee Shop	LP	Uni	73065	1970	£6	£15	US
Smoke	LP	Sidewalk	ST5912	1968	£8	£20	US
Smoke	LP	Uni	73052	1969	£6	£15	US

SMOKESTACK LIGHTNIN'

Although the name would suggest a blues group, Smokestack Lightnin' actually played blue-eyed soul, though without very much ambition or even very much soulfulness. The long version of the song after which the group was named is used as a climax to the "Off The Wall" album. The piece becomes stretched out as each member delivers a solo on his instrument - but none is in the least memorable.

Light In My Window	7"	Bell	BLL1046	1969	£2	£5	
Off The Wall	LP	Bell	MBLL/SBLL116	1969	£8	£20	

SMOKEY BABE

Smokey Babe And His Friends	LP	77	LA1212	1962	£6	£15	

SMOKEY CIRCLES

Smokey Circles' Album	LP	Carnaby	CNLS6006	1970	£20	£40	

SMOTHERS, SMOKEY

Backporch Blues	LP	King	779	1962	£50	£100	US
Driving Blues Of Smokey Smothers	LP	Polydor	623239	1966	£20	£40	

SNAFU

Situation Normal	LP	WWA	013	1974	£4	£10	
Snafu	LP	WWA	003	1974	£4	£10	

SNAKEHIPS

Snakehips Arnold And The King Of Boogie	LP	Spaceward	3S2/EDENLP75	1975	£8	£20	

SNAPPERS

If There Were	7"	Top Rank	JAR167	1959	£4	£8	

SNAPPERS (2)

Upside Down Inside Out	7"	CBS	2719	1967	£4	£8	

SNEAKERS

In The Red	LP	Car	0398	1978	£8	£20	US

SNEAKY PETES

Savage	7"	Decca	F11199	1960	£2	£5	

SNEEKERS

I Just Can't Get To Sleep	7"	Columbia	DB7385	1964	£20	£40	

SNIDER, LEN

Everyone Knows	7"	London	HLU9790	1963	£1.50	£4	

SNIVELLING SHITS

Isgodaman?	7"	Damaged Goods	FNARR4B	1989	£1.50	£4	box set, pink vinyl
Terminal Stupid	7"	Ghetto Rockers	PRE2	1977	£4	£8	

SNOBS

Buckle Shoe Stomp	7"	Decca	F11867	1964	£10	£20	

SNOOKY & MOODY

Snooky And Moody's Blues	7"	Blue Horizon	451003	1966	£12.50	£25	

SNOW, HANK

Big Country Hits	LP	RCA	LPM/LSP2458	1961	£6	£15	US
Country & Western Jamboree	LP	RCA	LPM1419	1957	£10	£25	US
Country Classics	LP	RCA	LPM1233	1955	£10	£25	US
Country Classics	10" LP	RCA	LPT3026	1952	£15	£30	US
Country Guitar No.4	7" EP.	RCA	RCX116	1958	£4	£8	
Country Guitar No.7	7" EP.	RCA	RCX142	1959	£4	£8	
Hank Snow Salutes Jimmie Rodgers	10" LP	RCA	LPT3131	1953	£15	£30	US
Hank Snow Sings	10" LP	RCA	LPT3070	1952	£15	£30	US
Hank Snow Sings Jimmie Rodgers Songs	LP	RCA	LPM/LSP2043	1959	£6	£15	US
Hank Snow Sings Sacred Songs	LP	RCA	LPM1638	1958	£8	£20	US
Hank Snow's Country Guitar	LP	RCA	LPM1435	1957	£10	£25	US
Hank Snow's Country Guitar	10" LP	RCA	LPT3267	1954	£15	£30	US
Hits, Hits And More Hits	LP	RCA	LPM/LSP3965	1968	£4	£10	US
I've Been Everywhere	LP	RCA	RD/SF7607	1964	£5	£12	
Just Keep A-Movin'	LP	RCA	LPM1113	1955	£10	£25	US
My Arabian Baby	7"	HMV	7MC24	1954	£2.50	£6	export
My Religion's Not Old-Fashioned	7"	HMV	7MC25	1954	£2.50	£6	export
Old Doc Brown	LP	RCA	LPM1156	1955	£15	£30	US
One And Only Hank Snow	LP	Camden	CDN5102	1963	£4	£10	
Railroad Man	LP	RCA	RD/SF7579	1963	£5	£12	
Sings Your Favourite Country Hits	LP	RCA	RD7741	1966	£4	£10	
Songs Of Tragedy	LP	RCA	RD7658	1964	£4	£10	
Souvenirs	LP	RCA	LPM/LSP2285	1961	£6	£15	US
Spanish Fireball	7"	HMV	7MC15	1954	£2.50	£6	export
That Country Gentleman	7" EP.	RCA	RCX7154	1964	£5	£10	
Together Again	LP	RCA	LPM/LSP2580	1962	£5	£12	US
When Tragedy Struck	LP	RCA	RD27115	1959	£6	£15	
When Tragedy Struck	7" EP.	RCA	RCX7125	1963	£2	£5	
Why Do You Punish Me	7"	HMV	7MC7	1954	£2.50	£6	export
Yellow Roses	7"	HMV	7MC31	1954	£2.50	£6	export

SNYDER, BILL

Bewitched	7" EP.	London	REP1011	1954	£2.50	£6	
Bewitched	10" LP	London	HAPB1004	1951	£4	£10	

S.O.A. (STATE OF ALERT)

No Policy	7"	Dischord	2 (NR12554)	1981	£15	£30	with insert
No Policy	7"	Dischord	2 (NR12554)	1981	£35	£70	with insert, green vinyl

SOCIALITES
Jive Jimmy .... 7" ...... Warner Bros .... WB148 .... 1964 ... £6 ....£12 ....

SOCIETIE
Bird Has Flown .... 7" ...... Deram .... DM162 .... 1967 ... £7.50 ....£15 ....

SOCOLOW, FRANK
Sounds By Socolow .... LP ...... London .... LTZN15090 .... 1957 ... £10 ....£25

SOCRATES
On The Wings .... LP ..... Peters .... PILPS9002 .... 1976 £8 ....£20 .... US
Phos .... LP ..... Peters .... PILPS9013 .... 1977 £8 ....£20 .... US

SOFT BOYS
Anglepoise Lamp .... 7" ...... Radar .... ADA8 .... 1978 ... £4 ....£8 ....PS
Can Of Bees .... LP ..... Two Crabs ...... CLAW1001 .... 1979 ... £6 ....£15 ...white & black labels
Give It To The Soft Boys .... 7" ...... Raw .... RAW5 .... 1977 ... £6 ....£12 ....
He's A Reptile .... 7" ...... Midnight   DING4 .... 1983 ... £1.50 .....£4
                                                                        Music ....
I Wanna Destroy You .... 7" ...... Armageddon ... AS005 .... 1980 ... £2.50 .....£6
Love Poisoning .... 7" ...... Bucketfull Of   BOB1 .... 1982 ... £1.50 .....£4
                                                                        Brains ....
Near The Soft Boys .... 7" ...... Armageddon ... AEP002 .... 1980 ... £4 ....£8
Only The Stones Remain .... 7" ...... Armageddon ... AS029 .... 1981 ... £4 ....£5
Wading Through The Ventilator .... 12" ..... Delorean .... SOFT1P .... 1985 ... £2.50 .....£6 ....pic disc

SOFT CELL
The combination of a singer with a limited, rather tuneless voice and a keyboard player still struggling with the opening chapter of his synthesizer instruction manual was an unlikely recipe for the creation of some of the finest single releases of the eighties. Soft Cell proved that rock music's perennial reliance on the inspired amateur can sometimes strike gold.
12' Singles .... 12" ..... Some Bizarre... CELBX1 .... 1982 ... £30 ....£60 .... 6x12', boxed
A Man Can Get Lost .... 7" ...... Some Bizarre... HARD1 .... 1981 ... £4 ....£8
Down In The Subway (Remix) .... 12" ..... Some Bizarre... BZSR2212 .... 1984 ... £5 ....£12
Ghostrider (live) .... 7" ...... fan club .... 1984 ... £4 ....£8 .... flexi
Memorabilia .... 12" ..... Some Bizarre... HARD12 .... 1981 ... £4 ....£10
Mutant Moments .... 7" ...... Big Frock .... ABF1 .... 1980 ... £30 ....£60 ....with insert
Say Hello Wave Goodbye (live) .... 7" ...... fan club .... 1983 ... £5 ....£10 .... flexi
Soul Inside .... 7" ...... Some Bizarre... BZS2020 .... 1983 ... £2 ....£5 ....double
Tainted Love/Memorabilia .... 12" ..... Some Bizarre... BZS212 .... 1981 ... £2.50 .....£6

SOFT MACHINE
Alive And Well .... LP ..... Harvest .... SHSP4083 .... 1978 ... £4 ....£10
Bundles .... LP ..... Harvest .... SHSP4044 .... 1975 ... £4 ....£10
Fifth .... LP ..... CBS .... 64806 .... 1972 ... £4 ....£10
Fourth .... LP ..... CBS .... 64280 .... 1971 ... £5 ....£12 ....chart LP
Love Makes Sweet Music .... 7" ...... Polydor .... 56151 .... 1967 ... £25 ....£50
Seven .... LP ..... CBS .... 65799 .... 1973 ... £4 ....£10
Sixth .... LP ..... CBS .... 68214 .... 1973 ... £4 ....£10
Soft Machine .... LP ..... Probe .... 4500 .... 1968 ... £8 ....£20 ...... US, wheel cover
Softs .... LP ..... Harvest .... SHSP4056 .... 1976 ... £4 ....£10
Third .... LP ..... CBS .... 66246 .... 1970 ... £6 ....£15 ...... double, chart LP
Triple Echo .... LP ..... Harvest .... SHTW800 .... 1977 ... £10 ....£25 ....triple
Volume 2 .... LP ..... Probe .... SPB1002 .... 1969 ... £6 ....£15
Volumes 1 & 2 .... LP ..... ABC .... ABCL5004 .... 1974 ... £6 ....£15 ....double

SOFT SHOE
For Those Alone .... LP ..... Aardvark .... AARD1 .... 1978 ... £37.50 ...£75

SOFTLEY, MICK
Am I The Red One .... 7" ...... CBS .... 202469 .... 1967 ... £12.50 ...£25
Any Mother Doesn't Grumble .... LP ..... CBS .... 64841 .... 1972 ... £10 ....£25
Can You Hear Me Now .... 7" ...... CBS .... 5130 .... 1970 ... £1.50 .....£4
I'm So Confused .... 7" ...... Immediate ...... IM014 .... 1965 ... £4 ....£8
Lady Willow .... 7" ...... CBS .... 8269 .... 1972 ... £1.50 .....£4
Songs For Swingin' Survivors .... LP ..... Columbia .... 33SX1781 .... 1965 ... £50 ....£100
Street Singer .... LP ..... CBS .... 64395 .... 1971 ... £10 ....£25
Sunrise .... LP ..... CBS .... 64098 .... 1970 ... £8 ....£20

SOHO SKIFFLE GROUP
Soho Skiffle Group .... 7" EP.. Melodisc .... EPM772 .... 1957 ... £7.50 ....£15

SOL INVICTUS
Looking For Europe .... 7" ...... World Serpent. WS7002 .... 1991 ... £2 ....£5 .... 1 sided
See The Dove Fall .... 7" ...... Shock .... SX016 .... 1991 ... £2 ....£5

SOLAL, MARTIAL
Martial Solal Trio .... 10" LP Vogue .... LDE105 .... 1954 ... £10 ....£25

SOLAR PLEXUS
Concerto Grosso (English) .... LP ..... Odeon .... 34684/5 .... 1972 ... £8 ....£20 .... Swedish double
Concerto Grosso (Swedish) .... LP ..... Odeon .... 34573/4 .... 1972 ... £8 ....£20 .... Swedish double
Det Er Inte Baten .... LP ..... Harvest .... 06234975 .... 1974 ... £5 ....£12 .... European
Hellrre Gycklare An Hycklare .... LP ..... Harvest .... 06235166 .... 1975 ... £5 ....£12 .... European
Solar Plexus .... LP ..... Polydor .... 2383222 .... 1973 ... £6 ....£15
Solar Plexus 2 .... LP ..... Odeon .... 34797 .... 1973 ... £6 ....£15 ....Swedish

SOLDIER
Sheralee .... 7" ...... Heavy Metal .... HEAVY12 .... 1982 ... £2 ....£5

SOLID GOLD CADILLAC

In common with most British jazz musicians of the time, Mike Westbrook incorporated many elements of rock music within his compositions, while many of the members of his band were equally at home whether playing jazz, rock, or somewhere in between. Solid Gold Cadillac was the closest that Westbrook came to leading a straight rock group, although the music is inevitably suffused with a jazz sensibility.

Brain Damage	LP	RCA	SF8365	1973	£6	£15
Solid Gold Cadillac	LP	RCA	SF8311	1972	£6	£15

SOLITAIRES

Walking Along	7"	London	HLM8745	1958	£50	£100

SOLO

Solo	LP			197-	£30	£60 ... US

SOLSTICE

Marillion managed to pull off a considerable feat when they managed to get progressive rock into the album and singles charts at a time when the music was supposed to be deeply unfashionable. A number of other bands were actually working in the same area at the time, one of the best being Solstice - for all that they sounded strongly reminiscent of mid-seventies Yes. Bass player Mark Hawkins was invited to join Marillion in the early days - sadly, he turned the offer down on the grounds that Solstice were more likely to be successful.

Silent Dance	LP	Equinox	EQRLP001	1984	£10	£25

SOME CHICKEN

Arabian Daze	7"	Raw	RAW13	1978	£2	£5	
Arabian Daze	7"	Raw	RAW13	1978	£25	£50	PS, coloured vinyl
New Religion	7"	Raw	RAW7	1977	£1.50	£4	PS

SOMEONE'S BAND

Someone's Band	LP	Deram	SML1068	1970	£40	£80
Story	7"	Deram	DM313	1970	£5	£10

SOMERS, GORDON

Sound Of The Beatles	7" EP	Top Ten	TPSX101	1964	£4	£8

SOMERS, VIRGINIA

Lovin' Spree	7"	Decca	F10301	1954	£2	£5

SOMETHING HAPPENS!

Burn Clear	7"	Cooking Vinyl	WILD001	1986	£4	£8

SOMMERS, JOANNIE

Be My Love	7"	Warner Bros	WB23	1960	£1.50	£4	
Behind Closed Doors	LP	Warner Bros	B1348	1960	£6	£15	US, boxed with booklet
Come Alive	LP	Columbia	CL2495/CS9295	1966	£4	£10	US
For Those Who Think Young	LP	Warner Bros	WM4062/WS8062	1962	£6	£15	
Goodbye Joey	7"	Warner Bros	WB85	1963	£1.50	£4	
If You Love Him	7"	Warner Bros	WB150	1965	£1.50	£4	
Johnny Get Angry	LP	Warner Bros	WM/WS8107	1963	£6	£15	
Johnny Get Angry	7"	Warner Bros	WB71	1962	£1.50	£4	
Johnny Get Angry Vol.1	7" EP	Warner Bros	WEP6121	1964	£5	£10	
Johnny Get Angry Vol.1	7" EP	Warner Bros	WSEP6121	1964	£7.50	£15	stereo
Johnny Get Angry Vol.2	7" EP	Warner Bros	WEP6123	1964	£5	£10	
Johnny Get Angry Vol.2	7" EP	Warner Bros	WSEP6123	1964	£7.50	£15	stereo
Let's Talk About Love	LP	Warner Bros	WM/WS8119	1964	£5	£12	
Little Girl Bad	7"	Warner Bros	WB105	1963	£1.50	£4	
Lively Set	LP	Decca	DL(7)9119	1964	£5	£12	US
One Boy	7"	Warner Bros	WB44	1961	£1.50	£4	
Passing Strangers	7"	Warner Bros	WB78	1962	£1.50	£4	
Positively The Most	LP	Warner Bros	W(S)1346	1960	£6	£15	US
Positively The Most	7" EP	Warner Bros	WEP6013	1960	£4	£8	
Positively The Most	7" EP	Warner Bros	WSEP2013	1960	£7.50	£15	stereo
Ruby Duby Du	7"	Warner Bros	WB31	1961	£1.50	£4	
Softly, The Brazilian Sound	LP	Warner Bros	W(S)1575	1965	£5	£12	US
Sommers' Seasons	LP	Warner Bros	W(S)1504	1964	£6	£15	US
Voice Of The Sixties	LP	Warner Bros	WM4045/WS8045	1961	£6	£15	
Voice Of The Sixties	7" EP	Warner Bros	WEP6047	1961	£4	£8	
Voice Of The Sixties	7" EP	Warner Bros	WSEP2047	1961	£7.50	£15	stereo

SONGSTERS

Bahama Buggy Ride	7"	London	HL8100	1954	£10	£20

SONIC BOOM

Since the acrimonious split between Pete Kember and Jason Pierce put an end to the career of cult favourites, Spacemen 3, Kember has worked under his solo identity, Sonic Boom. Sadly, his continuation of Spacemen 3's characteristic drone style seems very pedestrian in comparison with the flights of fancy created by Pierce's group, Spiritualised. Meanwhile, his attempts to forge a more avant-garde version of the approach lack the sense of excitement and power of the group that should be a major influence - Sonic Youth. (The impact of the guitar drones on "Octaves" compares very poorly with Lee Ranaldo's earlier "From Here To Infinity" experimental creation).

Octaves	10"	Silvertone	SONIC1	1990	£3	£8	orange vinyl
Soul Kiss (Glide Divine)	LP	Silvertone	OREZLP518	1992	£6	£15	oil filled cover
Spectrum	LP	Silvertone	OREZLP506	1990	£4	£10	rotating disc sleeve
To The Moon And Back	7"	Silvertone	SONIC2	1991	£2	£5	
To The Moon And Back	7"	Silvertone	SONIC2	1991	£4	£8	PS

SONIC YOUTH

Confusion Is Sex	LP	Neutral	ND02	1983	£5	£12	US
Daydream Nation	LP	Blast First	BFFP34	1988	£5	£12	double, with signed poster
Death Valley '69	7"	Iridescence	112	1984	£5	£10	US
Flower	7"	Blast First	BFFP3	1985	£5	£10	promo
Flower	12"	Blast First	BFFP3	1986	£4	£10	yellow vinyl
Flower (censored version)/Rewolf	12"	Blast First	BFFP3	1985	£6	£15	promo

Making The Nature Scene	7"	Forced Exposure	FE001	1985	£15	£30		US
Marilyn Moore	7"	Chemical Imbalance	CT1	1986	£5	£10		US
Savage Pencil	12"	Blast First	BFFP3P	1986	£4	£10		
Savage Pencil	12"	Blast First	BFFP3P	1986	£15	£30	signed by S.Pencil	
Sonic Death	cass	Ecstatic Peace		1984	£6	£15		US
Sonic Youth	LP	Neutral	ND01	1982	£5	£12		US
Starpower	7"	Blast First	BFFP7	1986	£4	£8	with badge & poster	
Stick Me Donna Magick Momma	7"	Fierce	FRIGHT015/6	1988	£5	£10		
Stick Me Donna Magick Momma	7"	Fierce	FRIGHT015/6	1988	£10	£20	2 x 1 sided 7'	
Walls Have Ears	LP	NOT	NOT1	1986	£25	£50	double	

SONICS

Explosives	LP	Buckshot	BSR001	1974	£8	£20		US
Here Are The Sonics	LP	Etiquette	LP024	1965	£25	£50		US
Introducing The Sonics	LP	Jerden	JRL7007	1967	£20	£40		US
Sonics Boom	LP	Etiquette	LP(S)027	1966	£20	£40		US

SONICS & WAILERS

Merry Christmas	LP	Etiquette	ALB02	196-	£50	£100		US

SONIC'S RENDEZVOUS BAND

City Slang	7"	Orchide	OR1002	1978	£25	£50

SONN, LARRY

Larry Sonn Orchestra	LP	Vogue Coral	LVA9040	1957	£6	£15

SONNY

Inner Views	LP	Atco		1967	£6	£15		US
Laugh At Me	7"	Atlantic	AT4038	1965	£1.50	£4	chart single	
Laugh At Me	7" EP	Atco	107	1965	£5	£10	French	
Revolution Kind	7"	Atlantic	AT4060	1965	£1.50	£4		

SONNY & CHER

Baby Don't Go	7"	Reprise	R20309	1964	£1.50	£4	chart single	
Baby Don't Go	7" EP	Reprise	RVEP60076	1965	£6	£12	French, B side by Jerry Keller	
Beat Goes On	7"	Atlantic	584078	1967	£1.50	£4	chart single	
Beat Goes On	7" EP	Atco	118	1967	£6	£12	French	
Best Of Sonny And Cher	LP	Atlantic	587/588083	1967	£4	£10		
But You're Mine	7"	Atlantic	AT4047	1965	£1.50	£4	chart single	
Circus	7"	Atlantic	584168	1968	£1.50	£4		
Get It Together	7"	Atlantic	2091021	1970	£1.50	£4		
Good Combination	7"	Atlantic	584162	1968	£1.50	£4		
Good Times	LP	Atco	(SD)33214	1967	£4	£10		US
Have I Stayed Too Long	7"	Atlantic	584018	1966	£1.50	£4	chart single	
I Got You Babe	7"	Atlantic	AT4035	1965	£1.50	£4	chart single	
I Got You Babe	7" EP	Atco	101	1965	£6	£12	French	
In Case You're In Love	LP	Atlantic	587/588052	1967	£5	£12		
It's The Little Things	7"	Atlantic	584129	1967	£1.50	£4		
Je M'En Balance Car Je L'Aime	7" EP	Atco	108	1965	£6	£12	French	
Just You	7" EP	Atco	102	1965	£6	£12	French	
Letter	7"	Vocalion	VL9247	1965	£1.50	£4		
Little Man	7"	Atlantic	584040	1966	£1.50	£4	chart single	
Living For You	7"	Atlantic	584057	1966	£1.50	£4		
Look At Us	LP	Atlantic	ATL/STL5036	1964	£5	£12	chart LP	
Petit Homme	7" EP	Atco	117	1966	£6	£12	French	
Plastic Man	7" EP	Atco	125	1967	£5	£10	French	
Podunk	7"	Atlantic	584110	1967	£1.50	£4		
Sonny And Cher And Caesar And Cleo	7" EP	Reprise	R30056	1965	£5	£10		
What Now My Love	7"	Atlantic	AT4069	1966	£1.50	£4	chart single	
What Now My Love	7" EP	Atco	112	1966	£6	£12	French	
Wondrous World Of Sonny And Cher	LP	Atlantic	587006	1966	£5	£12	chart LP	
You've Got To Have A Thing	7"	Atlantic	584215	1968	£1.50	£4		

SONNY & THE CASCADES

Exciting New Liverpool Sound	LP	Columbia	CL2172	1964	£8	£20		US

SONNY & THE DAFFODILS

Sonny And The Daffodils	7" EP	Ember	EMBEP4538	1963	£10	£20

SONS & LOVERS

Happiness Is Love	7"	Beacon	3107	1968	£1.50	£4
Help Me	7"	Beacon	3101	1968	£1.50	£4
Matters	7"	Camp	602002	1967	£2	£5

SONS OF CHAMPLIN

Follow Your Heart	LP	Capitol	ST675	1971	£5	£12		US
Loosen Up Naturally	LP	Capitol	SWBB200	1969	£10	£25	US double	
Sons	LP	Capitol	SKAO322	1969	£6	£15		US
Welcome To The Dance	LP	CBS	65663	1973	£4	£10		

SONS OF FRED

I, I, I	7"	Parlophone	R5391	1965	£15	£30
Sweet Love	7"	Columbia	DB7605	1965	£30	£60
You Told Me	7"	Parlophone	R5415	1966	£20	£40

SONS OF MAN

Sons Of Man	7" EP	Oak	RGJ612	1967	£100	£200

SONS OF PILTDOWN MEN
Mad Goose .... 7" .... Pye .... 7N25206 .... 1963 ... £4 ....£8 ....

SONS OF SOUL
Yea Yea Baby .... 7" .... Doctor Bird ...... DB1037 .... 1966 ... £5 ....£10 ....

SONS OF THE PIONEERS
Cowboy Classics	10" LP	RCA	LPM3032	1952	£15	£30	US
Cowboy Hymns And Spirituals	10" LP	RCA	LPM3095	1952	£15	£30	US
Favorite Cowboy Songs	LP	RCA	LPM1130	1955	£6	£15	US
How Great Thou Art	LP	RCA	LPM1431	1957	£5	£12	US
One Man's Songs	LP	RCA	LPM1483	1957	£6	£15	US
Sons Of The Pioneers	LP	RCA	RD27016	1957	£6	£15	
Sons Of The Pioneers	7" EP	HMV	7EG8069	1954	£5	£10	
Western Classics	10" LP	RCA	LPM3162	1953	£15	£30	US

SOPHOMORES
Sophomores .... LP ..... Seeco .... CELP451 .... £8 ....£20 .... US

SOPWITH CAMEL
Hello Hello	LP	Kama Sutra	KSBS2063	1973	£5	£12	US
Hello Hello	7"	Kama Sutra	KAS205	1966	£2.50	£6	
Miraculous Hump Returns From The Moon	LP	Reprise	K44251	1973	£5	£12	
Postcard From Jamaica	7" EP	Kama Sutra	617109	1967	£12.50	£25	French
Sopwith Camel	LP	Kama Sutra	KLP(S)8060	1967	£8	£20	US

SORROWS
Baby	7"	Piccadilly	7N35230	1965	£7.50	£15	
I Don't Wanna Be Free	7"	Piccadilly	7N35219	1965	£10	£20	
Let Me In	7"	Piccadilly	7N35336	1966	£7.50	£15	
Let Me In	7" EP	Pye	PNV24168	1966	£30	£60	French
Let The Love Live	7"	Piccadilly	7N35309	1966	£7.50	£15	
Old Songs New Songs	LP	Miura		1968	£50	£100	Italian
Pink, Purple, Yellow, Red	7"	Piccadilly	7N35385	1967	£20	£40	
Take A Heart	LP	Pye	NPL38023	1965	£40	£80	
Take A Heart	7"	Piccadilly	7N35260	1965	£2.50	£6	chart single
Take A Heart	7" EP	Pye	PNV24150	1965	£30	£60	French
You've Got What I Want	7"	Piccadilly	7N35277	1966	£6	£12	
You've Got What I Want	7"	Piccadilly	7N35277	1966	£10	£20	export PS

SORT SOL
Marble Station .... 7" .... 4AD .... AD101 .... 1981 ... £2.50 ......£6 ....

SOUL AGENTS
Don't Break It Up .... 7" .... Pye .... 7N15768 .... 1965 ... £15 ....£30 ....
I Just Want To Make Love To You .... 7" .... Pye .... 7N15660 .... 1964 ... £15 ....£30 ....
Seventh Son .... 7" .... Pye .... 7N15707 .... 1964 ... £15 ....£30 ....

SOUL AGENTS (2)
For Your Education .... 7" .... Coxsone .... CS7018 .... 1967 ... £5 ....£10 . Summertaires B side
Lecture .... 7" .... Coxsone .... CS7027 .... 1967 ... £5 ....£10 ...... Soul Boys B side

SOUL BROTHERS
Carib Soul	LP	Coxsone	CSL8002	1967	£50	£100	
Green Moon	7"	Island	WI282	1966	£5	£10	
Hi Life	7"	Island	WI3039	1967	£5	£10	Delroy Wilson B side
Hot Shot Ska	LP	Coxsone	CSL8001	1967	£50	£100	
James Bond Girl	7"	Ska Beat	JB258	1967	£5	£10	Summertaires B side
Our Man Flint	7"	Island	WI3016	1967	£5	£10	
Ska Shuffle	7"	Rio	R119	1966	£4	£8	Hortense & Delroy B side
Sound One	7"	Island	WI296	1966	£5	£10	Emillo Straker B side

SOUL BROTHERS (2)
Good Lovin' Never Hurt .... 7" .... Mercury .... MF916 .... 1965 ... £2.50 ......£6 ....
I Can't Believe It .... 7" .... Parlophone .... R5321 .... 1965 ... £6 ....£12 ....
I Keep Ringing My Baby .... 7" .... Decca .... F12116 .... 1965 ... £4 ....£8 .... chart single

SOUL BROTHERS SIX
Some Kind Of Wonderful .... 7" .... Atlantic .... 584118 .... 1967 ... £7.50 ......£15 ....
Some Kind Of Wonderful .... 7" .... Atlantic .... 584256 .... 1969 ... £1.50 ......£4 ....

SOUL CHILDREN
Friction .... LP ..... Stax .... STX1005 .... 1974 ... £5 ....£12 ....
Genesis .... LP ..... Stax .... 2325076 .... 1972 ... £4 ....£10 ....

SOUL CITY
Everybody Dance Now .... 7" .... Cameo Parkway .... C103 .... 1962 ... £15 ....£30 ....

SOUL CITY EXECUTIVES
Happy Chatter .... 7" .... Soul City .... SC109 .... 1969 ... £2 ....£5 ....

SOUL CLAN
Soul Meeting .... 7" .... Atlantic .... 584202 .... 1968 ... £1.50 ......£4 ....
Soul Meeting .... 7" .... Atlantic .... 584202 .... 1968 ... £4 ....£8 .... PS

SOUL DEFENDERS
Way Back Home .... 7" .... Banana .... BA354 .... 1971 ... £2 ....£5 ..... Soul Rebels B side

SOUL FLAMES
Mini Really Fit Dem .... 7" ...... Nu Beat .... NB020 .... 1968 ... £2.50 ....£6 ....

SOUL, HORATIO
Ten White Horses .... 7" ...... Island .... WI3132 .... 1968 ... £4 ....£8 ....

SOUL, JIMMY
I Hate You Baby	7"	Stateside	SS274	1964 ...	£2.50 ....£6	
If You Wanna Be Happy	LP	SPQR	E16001	1963 ...	£10 ....£25	.... US
If You Wanna Be Happy	7"	Stateside	SS178	1963 ...	£2.50 ....£6	..........chart single
If You Wanna Be Happy	7" EP..	Stateside	SE1010	1964 ...	£6 ....£12	
Jimmy Soul And The Belmonts	LP	Spinorama	123	1963 ...	£6 ....£15	.... US
Twisting Mathilda	7"	Stateside	SS103	1962 ...	£2.50 ....£6	

SOUL, JUNIOR
Chattie Chattie	7"	Big Shot	BI503	1968 ...	£4 ....£8	
Hustler	7"	Big Shot	BI527	1969 ...	£2.50 ....£6	
Miss Cushie	7"	Doctor Bird	DB1112	1967 ...	£5 ....£10	.........Lyn Taitt B side

SOUL KINGS
Magnificent Seven .... 7" ...... Blue Cat .... BS169 .... 1969 ... £4 ....£8 Rupie Edwards B side

SOUL LEADERS
Pour On The Sauce .... 7" ...... Rio.................. R134 .... 1967 ... £4 ....£8 ....

SOUL PURPOSE
Hummin' .... 7" ...... Island .... WIP6040 .... 1968 ... £5 ....£10 ....

SOUL RUNNERS
Grits 'n' Cornbread .... 7" ...... Polydor .... 56732 .... 1967 ... £2.50 ....£6 ....

SOUL SEARCHERS
Salt Of The Earth .... LP ..... Sussex .... LPSX4 .... 1974 ... £6 ....£15 ....

SOUL, SHARON
How Can I Get To You? .... 7" ...... Stateside .... SS411 .... 1965 ... £17.50 ....£35 ....

SOUL SISTERS
Good Time Tonight	7"	London	HLC9970..........	1965 ...	£7.50 ....£15	
I Can't Stand It	7"	Sue	WI312	1964 ...	£7.50 ....£15	
Loop De Loop	7"	Sue	WI336	1964 ...	£10 ....£20	
Soul Sisters	LP	Sue	ILP913	1964 ...	£15 ....£30	

SOUL SISTERS (2)
Wreck A Buddy .... 7" ...... Amalgamated . AMG839 .... 1969 ... £4 ....£8 ....

SOUL SOUNDS
"Soul Survival" is an album of R&B instrumentals played by various ex-Savages and Rebel Rousers. Soul Sounds was not a working group, but the musicians could play this kind of music with one arm tied behind their backs (well, perhaps not quite!) and the record is a convincing addition to the genre, if a little out-of-date for 1967.
Soul Survival .... LP ..... Columbia......... SX6158................... 1967 ... £6 ....£15 ....

SOUL STIRRERS
Soul Stirrers Featuring Sam Cooke ...... LP ..... London .... HAU8232 .... 1965 ... £8 ....£20 ....

SOUL SURVIVORS
Explosion	7"	Stateside	SS2094............	1968 ...	£2 ....£5	
Expressway To Your Heart	7"	Stateside	SS2057............	1967 ...	£5 ....£10	
Mama Soul	7"	Atlantic	584275............	1969 ...	£1.50 ....£4	

SOUL VENDORS
Captain Cojoe	7"	Studio One	SO2070	1968 ...	£6 ....£12	...Jackie Mittoo B side
Drum Song	7"	Coxsone	CS7031	1967 ...	£5 ....£10	..... Cool Spoon B side
Evening Time	7"	Studio One	SO2048	1968 ...	£6 ....£12	... Righteous Flames
Fat Fish	7"	Coxsone	CS7029	1967 ...	£5 ....£10	Marcia Griffiths B side
Grooving Steady	7"	Coxsone	CS7037	1968 ...	£5 ....£10	... Roy Richards B side
Hot Rod	7"	Studio One	SO2034	1967 ...	£6 ....£12	......Gaylads B side
On Tour	LP	Coxsone	CSL8010	1967 ...	£50 ....£100	
Real Rock	7"	Coxsone	CS7057	1968 ...	£5 ....£10	....Al Campbell B side
Rocking Sweet Pea	7"	Studio One	SO2018	1967 ...	£6 ....£12	.... Joe Higgs B side
Sixth Figure	7"	Coxsone	CS7084	1969 ...	£5 ....£10	.....Denzil Laing B side
Soul Joint	7"	Studio One	SO2066	1968 ...	£6 ....£12	
To Sir With Love	7"	Blue Cat	BS112	1968 ...	£4 ....£8	.... Righteous Flames B side
You Troubled Me	7"	Coxsone	CS7028	1967 ...	£5 ....£10	..........Bop & The Beltones B side

SOULE, GEORGE
Get Involved .... 7" ...... United Artists .. UP35771................ 1975 ... £2.50 ....£6 ....

SOULETTES
My Desire .... 7" ...... Jackpot .... JP766 .... 1971 ... £2.50 ....£6 ....

SOULFUL STRINGS
Burning Spear	7"	Chess	CRS8068	1967 ...	£5 ....£10	
Groovin' With The Soulful Strings	LP	Chess	CRLS4534	1969 ...	£5 ....£12	
I Wish It Would Rain	7"	Chess	CRS8094	1969 ...	£2 ....£5	

SOULMATES
Bring Your Love Back Home	7"	Parlophone	R5407	1966 ...	£2.50 ....£6	
Is That You	7"	Parlophone	R5601	1967 ...	£2.50 ....£6	

| Mood Melancholy | 7" | Parlophone | R5506 | 1966 | £4 | £8 | |
| Too Late To Say You're Sorry | 7" | Parlophone | R5334 | 1965 | £2.50 | £6 | |

SOULMATES (2)

| On The Move | 7" | Amalgamated | AMG842 | 1969 | £4 | £8 | |
| Them A Laugh And A Ki Ki | 7" | Amalgamated | AMG836 | 1969 | £4 | £8 | |

SOUND

| Physical World | 7" | Tortch | TOR003 | 1979 | £7.50 | £15 | |
| Sound | LP | Tortch | TOR008 | 1979 | £8 | £20 | |

SOUND DIMENSION

Baby Face	7"	Bamboo	BAM7	1969	£2.50	£6	Gladiators B side
Black Onion	7"	Bamboo	BAM14	1969	£2.50	£6	
Doctor Sappa Too	7"	Bamboo	BAM5	1969	£2.50	£6	
In The Summertime	7"	Banana	BA313	1970	£1.50	£4	
Jamaica Rag	7"	Bamboo	BAM9	1969	£2.50	£6	C.Marshall B side
More Scorcia	7"	Coxsone	CS7093	1969	£5	£10	Lennie Hibbert B side
My Sweet Lord	7"	Banana	BA338	1970	£1.50	£4	Dennis Brown B side
Poison Ivy	7"	Bamboo	BAM18	1970	£2	£5	
Scorcia	7"	Coxsone	CS7083	1969	£5	£10	Cecil & Jackie B side
Soulful Strut	7"	Coxsone	CS7090	1969	£5	£10	
Time Is Tight	7"	Coxsone	CS7097	1969	£5	£10	Barry Llewellyn B side
Whoopee	7"	Bamboo	BAM13	1969	£2.50	£6	Norma Fraser B side

SOUND NETWORK

| Watching | 7" | Mercury | MF944 | 1965 | £5 | £10 | |

SOUND SIXTY-SIX

| Flight 4864 | 7" | Decca | F12323 | 1966 | £2 | £5 | |

SOUNDGARDEN

Hands All Over	CD-s	A&M	AMCD560	1990	£2.50	£6	
Hands All Over	10"	A&M	AMX560	1990	£2.50	£6	
Louder Than Love	12"	A&M	AMY574	1989	£2.50	£6	1 side etched

SOUNDS AROUND

| Red White And You | 7" | Piccadilly | 7N35396 | 1967 | £1.50 | £4 | |
| What Does She Do? | 7" | Piccadilly | 7N35345 | 1966 | £4 | £8 | |

SOUNDS INCORPORATED

Emily	7"	Parlophone	R4815	1961	£2.50	£6	
Go	7"	Decca	F11590	1963	£2	£5	
How Do You Feel	7"	Polydor	56209	1967	£1.50	£4	
I'm Coming Through	7"	Columbia	DB7737	1965	£5	£10	
Keep Moving	7"	Decca	F11723	1963	£5	£10	
My Little Red Book	7"	Columbia	DB7676	1965	£1.50	£4	
Original	LP	MFP	MFP1132	1966	£4	£10	
Rinky Dink	LP	Regal	SREG1071	1965	£4	£10	
Sounds Incorporated	LP	Columbia	SX/SCX3531	1964	£5	£12	
Sounds Incorporated	LP	Studio Two	TWO1449	1966	£5	£12	
Sounds Like Locomotion	LP	Decca	F11540	1962	£1.50	£4	
Spanish Harlem	7"	Columbia	DB7321	1964	£1.50	£4	chart single
Spartans	7"	Columbia	DB7239	1964	£1.50	£4	chart single
Time For You	7"	Columbia	DB7545	1965	£1.50	£4	
Top Gear	7" EP.	Columbia	SEG8360	1964	£5	£10	
Twist At The Star Club Hamburg	LP	Philips	P48036L	1964	£8	£20	German
William Tell	7"	Columbia	DB7404	1964	£1.50	£4	

SOUNDS NICE

| Love At First Sight | LP | Parlophone | PMC/PCS7089 | 1969 | £8 | £20 | |
| Love At First Sight | 7" | Parlophone | R5797 | 1969 | £1.50 | £4 | chart single |

SOUNDS ORCHESTRAL

| Cast Your Fate To The Wind | 7" | Piccadilly | 7N35206 | 1964 | £1.50 | £4 | chart single |

SOUNDS SENSATIONAL

| Love In The Open Air | 7" | HMV | POP1584 | 1967 | £4 | £8 | |

SOUP

| Soup | LP | Arf Arm | 1 | 1970 | £10 | £25 | US, insert but no cover |

SOUP DRAGONS

| Deep Trash (Lovegod) | cass | Raw TV Products | | 1989 | £4 | £10 | |
| Sun Is In The Sky | 7" | Subway | SUBWAY2 | 1986 | £6 | £12 | |

SOUP GREENS

| Like A Rolling Stone | 7" | Stateside | SS457 | 1965 | £10 | £20 | |

SOUTH COAST SKA STARS

| South Coast Rumble | 7" | Safari | SAFE27 | 1980 | £2 | £5 | |

SOUTH FORTY

| Live At The Someplace Else | LP | Metrobeat | MBS1000 | 1964 | £5 | £12 | US |

SOUTH, JOE

Birds Of A Feather	7"	Capitol	CL15535	1968	£1.50	£4	
Birds Of A Feather	7"	Capitol	CL15602	1969	£1.50	£4	
Clock Up On The Wall	7"	Capitol	CL15636	1970	£1.50	£4	

Concrete Jungle	7"	MGM	MGM1267	1965	£2	£5	
Don't It Make You Wanna Go Home	7"	Capitol	CL15608	1969	£2.50	£6	
Don't Throw Your Love To The Wind	7"	Capitol	CL15568	1968	£1.50	£4	
Games People Play	7"	Capitol	CL15579	1969	£1.50	£4	chart single
Hush	7"	Capitol	CL15666	1970	£1.50	£4	
I Want To Be Somebody	7"	HMV	POP1474	1965	£2	£5	
Introspect	LP	Capitol	E(S)T108	1969	£4	£10	
Leanin' On You	7"	Capitol	CL15594	1969	£1.50	£4	
Masquerade	7"	Oriole	CB1752	1962	£2.50	£6	
Walk A Mile In My Shoes	7"	Capitol	CL15625	1970	£4	£8	

SOUTHERN DEATH CULT

Moya	7"	Situation 2	SIT19	1982	£1.50	£4	poster sleeve

SOUTHERN, JERI

At The Crescendo	LP	Capitol	(S)T1278	1960	£5	£12	
Caresses	7" EP	Brunswick	OE9438	1959	£4	£8	
Coffee, Cigarettes And Memories	LP	Columbia	33SX1134	1958	£5	£12	
Fire Down Below	7"	Brunswick	05665	1957	£1.50	£4	chart single
I Waited So Long	7"	Brunswick	05737	1958	£1.50	£4	
Jeri Gently Jumps	LP	Brunswick	LAT8209	1957	£6	£15	
Man That Got Away	7"	Brunswick	05367	1955	£2.50	£6	
Meets Cole Porter	LP	Capitol	(S)T1173	1959	£5	£12	
Meets Johnny Smith	LP	Columbia	33SX1155	1959	£5	£12	
Occasional Man	7"	Brunswick	05490	1955	£2.50	£6	
Prelude To A Kiss	LP	Decca	DL8745	1958	£5	£12	US
Remind Me	7"	Brunswick	05343	1954	£2.50	£6	
Ridin' High	7" EP	Columbia	SEG7935	1959	£4	£8	
Scarlet Ribbons	7"	Brunswick	05709	1957	£1.50	£4	
Southern Breeze	LP	Columbia	33SX1110	1958	£5	£12	
Southern Hospitality	LP	Decca	DL8761	1958	£5	£12	US
Southern Style	LP	Brunswick	LAT8100	1956	£6	£15	
Warm	10" LP	Brunswick	LA8699	1955	£8	£20	
When Your Heart's On Fire	LP	Decca	DL8394	1957	£6	£15	US
Where Walks My True Love	7"	Brunswick	05529	1956	£1.50	£4	
You Better Go Now	LP	Decca	DL8214	1956	£6	£15	US

SOUTHERN, JOHNNY

She's Long, She's Tall	7"	Melodisc	1434	1957	£1.50	£4	
We Will Make Love	7"	Melodisc	1413	1958	£1.50	£4	

SOUTHERN SOUND

Just The Same As You	7"	Columbia	DB7982	1966	£60	£120	

SOUTHERN TONES

Waiting On The Lord	7" EP	Collector	JEN10	1962	£2	£5	

SOUTHLANDERS

Ain't That A Shame	7"	Parlophone	MSP6182	1955	£7.50	£15	
Alone	7"	Decca	F10946	1957	£1.50	£4	chart single
Choo-Choo-Choo Cha-Cha-Cha	7"	Decca	F11067	1958	£2	£5	
Down Deep	7"	Decca	F11014	1958	£1.50	£4	
Hush A Bye Rock	7"	Parlophone	MSP6236	1956	£5	£10	
Peanuts	7"	Decca	F10958	1957	£2	£5	
Put A Light In The Window	7"	Decca	F10982	1958	£6	£12	
Southlanders No.1	7" EP	Decca	DFE6508	1958	£10	£20	
Torero	7"	Decca	F11032	1958	£5	£10	

SOUTHSIDE JOHNNY & THE ASBURY DUKES

Little Girl So Fine	7"	Epic	EPC5230	1977	£5	£10	
Live At The Bottom Line	LP	Epic	AS275	1976	£6	£15	US promo

SOUTHWEST F.O.B.

Smell Of Incense	LP	Hip	HIS7001	1969	£6	£15	US
Smell Of Incense	7"	Stax	STAX107	1968	£1.50	£4	

SOUTHWIND

Boogie Woogie Country Girl	7"	Harvest	HAR5019	1970	£2	£5	

SOUVENIRS

How Many Teardrops	7"	Decca	F11731	1963	£1.50	£4	

SOVEREIGNS

Bring Me Home Love	7"	King	KG1050	1966	£2.50	£6	

SOVIET FRANCE

Soviet France	12"	Red Rhino	RED12	1982	£4	£10	hessian sleeve

SOVINE, RED

Country Music	7" EP	Top Rank	JKP3015	1962	£5	£10	
Giddy-Up Go	LP	London	HAB8288	1966	£4	£10	
I Didn't Jump The Fence	LP	London	HAB8343	1967	£5	£12	
One And Only Red Sovine	LP	Starday	SLP132	1961	£6	£15	US
Red Sovine	LP	MGM	E3465	1957	£8	£20	US
Sixteen Tons	7"	Brunswick	05513	1956	£15	£30	

SOXX, BOB B. & THE BLUE JEANS

Not Too Young To Get Married	7"	London	HLU9754	1963	£6	£12	
Why Do Lovers Break Each Others' Hearts	7"	London	HLU9694	1963	£5	£10	

Zip A Dee Doo Dah	LP	London	HAU8121	1963	£30	£60	sleeve pictured in Guide
Zip A Dee Doo Dah	LP	Philles	PHLP4002	1963	£40	£80	US
Zip A Dee Doo Dah	7"	London	HLU9646	1963	£4	£8	chart single

SPACE
Just Blue	LP	Pye	NSPH28275	1979	£6	£15	pic disc

SPACE (2)
Space	LP	KLF	SPACELP1	1990	£8	£20	
Space	CD	KLF	SPACECD1	1990	£10	£25	

SPACE ART
Space Art	LP	Ariola	AHAL8001	1977	£4	£10	German

SPACEMEN
Clouds	7"	Top Rank	JAR228	1959	£2.50	£6	
Music For Batman And Robin	LP	Roulette	MG/SR25322	1966	£6	£15	US
Rockin' In The 25th Century	LP	Roulette	MG/SR25275	1964	£6	£15	US

SPACEMEN 3
First Genesis and then Spacemen 3 emerged to prove public schools as an effective, if unlikely breeding ground for innovative rock music. Spacemen 3 developed rapidly from the first album catalogue of their sixties influences, finding a variety of imaginative ways of texturing electric guitar drones. Though not all of the songs are equally successful, at their best (such as on the album length 12" single "Transparent Radiation" and on all of the records of the group's main successor, Spiritualised) the result is music that is both moving and magisterial. The demise of the Glass label has ensured that original pressings of the group's records are rising in value, even though album reissues on the Fire label are readily available.

Big City (remix)/I Love You	12"	Fire	BLAZE41TR	1991	£25	£50	test pressing
Dreamweapon	LP	Fierce	FRIGHT042	1990	£5	£12	
Dreamweapon	CD	Fierce	FRIGHT042CD	1990	£6	£15	
Extract From A Contemporary Sitar Evening	7"	Cheree	CHEREE5	1989	£5	£10	flexi, B side by Bark Psychosis & Fury Things
Perfect Precription	LP	Glass	GLALP026	1987	£6	£15	
Performance	LP	Glass	GLALP030	1988	£6	£15	
Performance	CD	Glass	GLACD030	1988	£6	£15	
Revolution	12"	Fire	THREEBIE3	1989	£8	£20	
Sound Of Confusion	LP	Glass	GLALP018	1986	£6	£15	
Take Me To The Other Side	12"	Glass	GLASS12054	1988	£6	£15	
Transparent Radiation	12"	Glass	GLAEP108	1987	£30	£60	sleeve pictured in Guide
Walkin' With Jesus	12"	Glass	GLAEP105	1986	£20	£40	lyric insert

SPADES
Subsequent issues of "You're Gonna Miss Me" were credited to the group's new name - the Thirteenth Floor Elevators.

You're Gonna Miss Me	7"	Zero	10002	1966	£75	£150	US

SPAGHETTI JUNCTION
Work's Nice - If You Can Get It	7"	Columbia	DB8935	1972	£2.50	£6	

SPANIELS
Goodnite, It's Time To Go	LP	Vee Jay	LP1002	1958	£100	£200	US
Spaniels	LP	Joy	JOYS197	1971	£5	£12	
Spaniels	LP	Vee Jay	LP1024	1960	£50	£100	US

SPANIER, MUGGSY
Broadcasts This Is Is Jazz	10" LP	Vogue	LDE015	1953	£8	£20	
Gem Of The Ocean	LP	MGM	C936	1963	£4	£10	
Great Sixteen	LP	RCA	RD27132	1959	£8	£20	
Muggsy Spanier And His Band	10" LP	Brunswick	LA8722	1955	£8	£20	
Muggsy Spanier And His Dixieland Band	LP	Mercury	MPL6516	1957	£6	£15	
Muggsy Spanier And His Ragtime Band	10" LP	HMV	DLP1031	1954	£8	£20	
Muggsy Spanier And The Bucktown Five	10" LP	London	AL3528	1954	£8	£20	

SPANISH BOYS
I Am Alone	7"	Blue Beat	BB331	1965	£5	£10	

SPANISHTOWN SKABEATS
Solomon	7"	Blue Beat	BB320	1964	£5	£10	

SPANKY & OUR GANG
Lazy Day	7"	Mercury	MF1010	1967	£1.50	£4	
Like To Get To Know You	LP	Mercury	SMCL20121	1968	£5	£12	
Like To Get To Know You	7"	Mercury	MF1023	1968	£1.50	£4	
Live	LP	Mercury	SR61326	1970	£5	£12	US
Spank's Greatest Hits	LP	Mercury	SR61227	1970	£4	£10	US
Spanky & Our Gang	LP	Mercury	(S)MCL20114	1967	£5	£12	
Sunday Morning	7"	Mercury	MF1018	1968	£1.50	£4	
Without Rhyme Or Reason	LP	Mercury	SR61183	1968	£5	£12	US

SPANN, OTIS
Biggest Thing Since Colossus	LP	Blue Horizon	763217	1969	£25	£50	with Fleetwood Mac
Blues Are Where It's At	LP	HMV	CLP/CSD3609	1963	£8	£20	
Blues Never Die	LP	Stateside	SL10169	1966	£6	£15	
Blues Of Otis Spann	LP	Decca	LK4615	1964	£6	£15	
Bottom Of The Blues	LP	Stateside	(S)SL10255	1968	£6	£15	
Can't Do Me No Good	7"	Blue Horizon	573142	1968	£5	£10	
Cracked Spanner Head	LP	Deram	DML/SML1036	1969	£15	£30	

Title	Format	Label	Cat#	Year			Notes
Cryin' Time	LP	Vanguard	VSD6514	1970	£5	£12	
Fathers And Sons	LP	Chess	CRLS4556	1969	£6	£15	
Good Morning Mr.Blues	LP	Storyville	SLP157	1964	£6	£15	
Nobody Knows My Troubles	LP	Bounty	BY6037	1967	£6	£15	
Nobody Knows My Troubles	LP	Polydor	545030	1967	£6	£15	
Otis Spann Is The Blues	LP	Candid	CJS9001	1960	£20	£40	US
Piano Blues	LP	Storyville	SLP168	1965	£6	£15	with Memphis Slim
Portraits In Blues Vol.3	LP	Storyville	670157	1967	£5	£12	
Raised In Mississippi	LP	Python	KM4	1969	£8	£20	
Stirs Me Up	7"	Decca	F11972	1964	£4	£8	
Sweet Giant Of The Blues	LP	Flying Dutchman	BT29006	1969	£5	£12	US
Walkin'	7"	Blue Horizon	573155	1969	£7.50	£15	with Fleetwood Mac
Walking Blues	LP	Epic	64888	1972	£5	£12	

SPARKERS
Dip It Up	7"	Blue Cat	BS155	1969	£4	£8	

SPARKLES
Tell Me	7" EP	DMF		196-	£10	£20	French

SPARKS
Girl From Germany	7"	Bearsville	K15516	1974	£1.50	£4	
I Like Girls	7"	Island	WIP6377	1976	£1.50	£4	
I Want To Hold Your Hand	7"	Island	WIP6282	1976	£4	£8	
Introducing Sparks	LP	Columbia	PC34901	1976	£15	£30	US red vinyl promo
Wonder Girl	7"	Bearsville	K15505	1972	£4	£8	

SPARKS, RANDY
Birmingham Train	7"	HMV	POP683	1959	£1.50	£4	

SPARROW
Carnival Boycott	7"	Kalypso	XX10	1960	£2.50	£6	
Clara Honey Bunch	7"	Melodisc	CAL17	1964	£2.50	£6	
Goaty	7"	Melodisc	CAL18	1964	£2.50	£6	
Hotter Than Ever	LP	Trojan	TRL49	1972	£4	£10	
Leading Calypsonians	7"	Melodisc	CAL15	1964	£2.50	£6	
Mighty Sparrow	7" EP	Kalypso	XXEP1	1961	£4	£8	
Mr.Herbert	7"	Kalypso	XX22	196-	£2.50	£6	
Mr.Walker	7"	Nems	3558	196-	£2.50	£6	
Party With The Sparrow	7" EP	Kalypso	XXEP3	196-	£4	£8	
Sack	7"	Kalypso	XX17	1960	£2.50	£6	
Slave	LP	Island	ILP902	1963	£20	£40	
Sparrow Come Back	LP	RCA	SF7516	1962	£10	£25	
Village Ram	7"	Jump Up	JU523	1967	£2.50	£6	

SPARROW (2)
This is the first recording of the group that became better known as Steppenwolf.
Tomorrow's Ship	7"	CBS	202342	1966	£10	£20	

SPARROW, JACK
Ice Water	7"	Doctor Bird	DB1005	1966	£5	£10	
More Ice Water	7"	Doctor Bird	DB1027	1966	£5	£10	

SPARROWS
Mersey Sound	LP	Elkay	3009	1964	£6	£15	US

SPARTANS
Can You Waddle?	7"	Stateside	SS117	1962	£1.50	£4	

SPEAR OF DESTINY
Prisoner Of Love	7"	Epic	DA4068	1984	£1.50	£4	double
Was That You	CD-s	10	TENZ173	1987	£2.50	£6	
Wheel	7"	Epic	WA3372	1983	£2	£5	pic disc

SPEAR, ROGER RUSKIN
Electric Shocks	LP	United Artists	UAS29508	1972	£6	£15	
I Love To Bumpity Bump	7"	United Artists	UP35720	1974	£1.50	£4	
On Her Doorstep Last Night	7"	United Artists	UP35683	1974	£1.50	£4	
Rebel Trouser	7"	United Artists	UP35221	1971	£2	£5	
Unusual	LP	United Artists	UAG29381	1972	£6	£15	

SPECIALS
Gangsters	7"	2-Tone	TT1/TT2	1979	£1.50	£4	paper label, chart single

SPECKLED RED
Dirty Dozens	LP	Esquire	32190	1963	£10	£25	
Dirty Dozens	LP	Storyville	SLP117	1964	£4	£10	
Oh Red	LP	VJM	LC11	1971	£5	£12	
Storyville Blues Anthology Vol.4	7" EP	Storyville	SEP384	1962	£7.50	£15	

SPECTOR, PHIL
Despite the growing importance in the late eighties of record producers as artists, Phil Spector is still the only producer with the status of a star. His Christmas album, released a number of times over the years, is the perfect seasonal recording. Various of the artists associated with Spector are given traditional songs to peform (none of them carols, interestingly) and surrounded by dense arrangements that stay just on the right side of mawkishness.
Christmas Album	LP	Apple	APCOR24	1972	£8	£20	chart LP
Christmas Gift For You	LP	London	HAU8141	1963	£25	£50	
Christmas Gift For You	LP	Philles	PHLP4005	1963	£25	£50	US blue label
Christmas Gift For You	LP	Philles	PHLP4005	1964	£8	£20	US yellow label

Presents Today's Hits	LP	Philles	PHLP4004	1963	£30	£60	US

SPECTOR, RONNIE
Try Some Buy Some	7"	Apple	33	1971	£2.50	£6	
Try Some Buy Some	7"	Apple	33	1971	£6	£12	PS

SPECTORS THREE
The Spector is, of course, Phil of that name.
I Really Do	7"	Trey	3001	1959	£5	£10	US
My Heart Stood Still	7"	Trey	3005	1960	£6	£12	US

SPECTRES
The three singles recorded by the Spectres are the first releases by the group that was eventually to gain international success as Status Quo.
Hurdy Gurdy Man	7"	Piccadilly	7N35352	1966	£75	£150	
I Who Have Nothing	7"	Piccadilly	7N35339	1966	£75	£150	
We Ain't Got Nothin' Yet	7"	Piccadilly	7N35368	1967	£75	£150	

SPECTRUM
Free	7"	RCA	RCA1853	1969	£2	£5	
Glory	7"	RCA	RCA1883	1969	£2	£5	
Headin' For A Heatwave	7"	RCA	RCA1651	1967	£2	£5	
I'll Be Gone	7"	Parlophone	R5908	1971	£4	£8	
Light Is Dark Enough	LP	RCA	INTS1118	1970	£15	£30	
Little Girl	7"	Columbia	DB7742	1965	£2	£5	
Little Red Boat By The River	7"	RCA	RCA1753	1968	£1.50	£4	
Ob La Di, Ob La Da	7"	RCA	RCA1775	1968	£2	£5	
Portobello Road	7"	RCA	RCA1619	1967	£2	£5	
Portobello Road	7"	RCA	RCA1976	1970	£1.50	£4	
Saturday's Child	7"	RCA	RCA1589	1967	£2	£5	
Tables And Chairs	7"	RCA	RCA1700	1968	£2	£5	

SPEDDING, CHRIS
Backwoods Progression	LP	Harvest	SHSP4004	1970	£6	£15	
Only Lick I Know	LP	Harvest	SHSP4017	1972	£6	£15	
Rock And Roll Band	7"	Harvest	HAR5013	1970	£4	£8	B side by Battered Ornaments

SPEED GLUE SHINKI
	LP				£330	£500	Japanese

SPEEDBALL
No Survivor	7"	Dirty Dick	DD1/2	1980	£5	£10	
No Survivor	7"	Dirty Dick	DD1/2	1980	£7.50	£15	printed sleeve

SPELLBINDERS
Chain Reaction	7"	CBS	202622	1967	£6	£12	
Chain Reaction	7"	Direction	583970	1969	£4	£8	
Help Me	7"	CBS	202453	1966	£6	£12	
Since I Don't Have You	7"	CBS	2776	1967	£2	£5	
Sweet Sweet Lovin'	7"	CBS	202435	1967	£4	£8	

SPELLMAN, BENNY
Fortune Teller	7"	London	HLP9570	1962	£12.50	£25	

SPENCE, JOHNNY
Doctor Kildare Theme	7"	Parlophone	R4872	1962	£1.50	£4	chart single

SPENCE, SKIP
Oar	LP	Columbia	CS9831	1968	£8	£20	US

SPENCE, TRENTON
Matty Belly	7"	Kalypso	XX04	1960	£2.50	£6	

SPENCER, DON
Busy Doing Nothing	7"	HMV	POP1186	1963	£1.50	£4	
Fireball	7"	HMV	POP1087	1962	£4	£8	chart single
Fireball & Other Titles	7" EP.	HMV	7EG8802	1963	£10	£20	
In My Life	7"	Fontana	TF701	1966	£1.50	£4	
Why Don't They Understand	7"	Page One	POF006	1966	£1.50	£4	

SPENCER, EDDIE
If This Is Love	7"	Power Exchange	PX207	1976	£1.50	£4	

SPENCER, JEREMY
Jeremy Spencer	LP	Reprise	K44105	1971	£10	£25	
Jeremy Spencer	LP	Reprise	RSLP9002	1970	£15	£30	
Jeremy Spencer And The Children	LP	CBS	65387	1973	£4	£10	
Linda	7"	Reprise	RS27002	1970	£2	£5	

SPENCER, SONNY
Oh Boy	7"	Parlophone	R4611	1959	£6	£12	

SPERMULL
Spermull	LP	Brain		1973	£25	£50	German

SPHYNKTA
Death And Violence	7"	Sultanic	SUL999	1983	£2.50	£6	red vinyl
In The Shade Of The Gods	7"	Sultanic	SUL666	1983	£5	£10	red vinyl

SPICE
Union Jack	7"	Olga	OLE013	1968	£15	£30	

What About The Music	7"	United Artists	UP2246	1968	£12.50	£25	

SPICER, GEORGE
Blackberry Fold	LP	Topic	12T235	1974	£5	£12	

SPIDELLS
Find Out What's Happening	7"	Sue	WI4019	1966	£7.50	£15	

SPIDER
Comedown Song	7"	Decca	F12430	1966	£6	£12	

SPIDER (2)
Children Of The Street	7"	Alien	ALIEN14	1980	£1.50	£4	

SPIDERS
I Didn't Wanna Do It	LP	Imperial	LP9140	1961	£50	£100	US
I'm Slippin' In	78	London	HL8086	1954	£15	£30	

SPIDERS (2)
The Spiders were led by Vincent Furnier - later to adopt the stage name of Alice Cooper.
Don't Blow Your Mind	7"	Santa Cruz	003	1966	£210	£350	US
Why Don't You Love Me?	7"	Nascot	112	1965	£470	£700	US

SPINNERS
Heebie Jeebies	7"	Columbia	DB4693	1961	£50	£100	
Original Spinners	LP	Motown	639	1967	£6	£15	US
Party My Pad	LP	Time	52092	1963	£25	£50	US
Sweet Thing	7"	Tamla Motown	TMG514	1965	£45	£90	demo only

SPIRAL STAIRCASE
Baby What I Mean	7"	CBS	3507	1968	£5	£10	
More Today Than Yesterday	7"	CBS	4187	1969	£10	£20	
No One For Me To Turn To	7"	CBS	4524	1969	£7.50	£15	

SPIRALS
Rocking Cow	7"	Capitol	CL14958	1958	£5	£10	

SPIRIT
12 Dreams Of Dr.Sardonicus	LP	Epic	EPC64191	1970	£4	£10	
1984	7"	CBS	4773	1970	£2.50	£6	
Animal Zoo	7"	CBS	5149	1970	£2.50	£6	
Clear	LP	CBS	63729	1969	£5	£12	
Dark Eyed Woman	7"	CBS	4511	1969	£2	£5	
Dark Eyed Woman	7"	CBS	4565	1969	£2	£5	
Family That Plays Together	LP	CBS	63523	1968	£5	£12	
Highlights Of Spirit Of '76	LP	Mercury	001	1976	£5	£12	promo
I Got A Line On You	7"	CBS	3880	1969	£2.50	£6	
Potatoland	LP	Beggars Banquet	BEGA23	1981	£4	£10	with cartoon book
Spirit	LP	CBS	63278	1968	£5	£12	
Spirit Of '76	LP	Mercury	6672012	1975	£5	£12	double
Uncle Jack	7"	CBS	3523	1968	£2.50	£6	

SPIRIT OF JOHN MORGAN
Age Machine	LP	Carnaby	CNLS6007	1970	£25	£50	
Age Machine	7"	Carnaby	CNS4019	1970	£4	£8	
Kaleidoscope	LP	Carnaby	6302010	1972	£25	£50	
Live At Durrant House	LP	SWP	1007	197-	£50	£100	
Spirit Of John Morgan	LP	Carnaby	6437503	1971	£6	£15	
Spirit Of John Morgan	LP	Carnaby	CNLS6002	1969	£25	£50	
Train For All Reasons	7"	Carnaby	CNS4005	1969	£4	£8	

SPIRIT OF MEMPHIS QUARTET
Negro Spirituals	LP	Vogue	LAE1033	1965	£5	£12	
Negro Spirituals	10" LP	Parlophone	PMD1070	1958	£6	£15	

SPIRITUALIZED
Anyway That You Want Me	CD-s	Dedicated	ZD43784	1990	£2.50	£6	
Anyway That You Want Me (Remix)	12"	Dedicated	ZT43784	1990	£3	£8	
Feel So Sad	7"	Fierce	FRIGHT053	1991	£7.50	£15	
Fucked Up Inside	LP	Decicated	DEDLP008	1993	£5	£12	

SPIROGYRA
Bells Boots & Shambles	LP	Polydor	2310246	1973	£150	£250	
Dangerous Dave	7"	Pegasus	PGS3	1972	£5	£10	
Old Boot Wine	LP	Pegasus	PEG13	1972	£40	£80	
St.Radigunds	LP	B&C	CAS1042	1971	£40	£80	sleeve pictured in Guide

SPITFIRE BOYS
British Refugee	7"	RK	RK1001	1977	£2	£5	

SPIVEY, VICTORIA
Treasures Of North American Negro Music No.5	7" EP	Fontana	TFE17264	1960	£5	£10	
Victoria Spivey	LP	XTRA	XTRA1022	1965	£8	£20	
Victoria Spivey	7" EP	HMV	7EG8190	1956	£7.50	£15	

S.P.K.
Dekompositiones	12"	Side Effekts	SER003	1983	£4	£10	
Leichenschrei	LP	Side Effekts	SER002	198-	£5	£12	
Live At The Crypt	LP	Sterile	SRC4	1986	£4	£10	

| Meat Processing Section | | 7" | Industrial | IR0011 | 1980 | £5 | £10 | |

SPLINTER
| untitled - known as 'The White Album' | LP | Dark Horse | DH2 | 1975 | £25 | £50 | demo |

SPLIT KNEE LOONS
| Special Collectors EP | | 7" | Avatar | AAA111 | 1981 | £2 | £5 | |

SPOELSTRA, MARK
5 & 20 Questions	LP	Elektra	EKL283	1965	£6	£15	US
Mark Spoelstra	LP	Columbia	CS9793	1969	£5	£12	US
State Of Mind	LP	Elektra	EKL307	1966	£6	£15	US

SPOKESMEN
Dawn Of Correction	LP	Decca	DL(7)4712	1965	£6	£15	US
Dawn Of Correction	7"	Brunswick	05941	1965	£1.50	£4	
It Ain't Fair	7"	Brunswick	05948	1965	£1.50	£4	
Michelle	7"	Brunswick	05950	1966	£1.50	£4	
Michelle	7" EP	Decca	60003	1966	£5	£10	French
Today's The Day	7"	Brunswick	05958	1966	£1.50	£4	

SPONTANEOUS COMBUSTION
Gay Time Night	7"	Harvest	HAR5060	1972	£4	£8	
Leaving	7"	Harvest	HAR5046	1971	£4	£8	
Sabre Dance	7"	Harvest	HAR5066	1973	£4	£8	
Spontaneous Combustion	LP	Harvest	SHVL801	1972	£10	£25	
Triad	LP	Harvest	SHVL805	1972	£10	£25	

SPONTANEOUS MUSIC ENSEMBLE
Birds Of A Feather	LP	Byg	529023	1972	£8	£20	French
Bobby Bradford And The SME	LP	Freedom	SLP40111	1974	£8	£20	
Challenge	LP	Eyemark	EMPL1002	1966	£25	£50	
For CND For Peace And You To Share	LP	A Records		1970	£15	£30	
Karyobin	LP	Island	ILPS9079	1968	£20	£40	
Oliv	LP	Marmalade	608008	1969	£15	£30	
So What Do You Think	LP	Tangent	TGS118	1971	£8	£20	
Source From & Towards	LP	Tangent	TNGS107	1971	£8	£20	
Spontaneous Music Ensemble	LP	Polydor	2384009	1972	£5	£12	

SPOOKY TOOTH
Ceremony	LP	Island	ILPS9107	1969	£6	£15	with Pierre Henry
It's All About	LP	Island	ILP980/ILPS9080	1968	£8	£20	
Last Puff	LP	Island	ILPS9117	1970	£6	£15	
Love Really Changed Me	7"	Island	WIP6037	1968	£4	£8	
Mirror	LP	Island	ILPS9292	1974	£5	£12	export
Son Of Your Father	7"	Island	WIP6060	1969	£2.50	£6	
Spooky Two	LP	Island	ILPS9098	1969	£8	£20	
Sunshine Help Me	7"	Island	WIP6022	1967	£4	£8	
Weight	7"	Island	WIP6046	1968	£2.50	£6	

SPOTLIGHTERS
| Please Be My Girlfriend | 7" | Vogue | V9130 | 1959 | £60 | £120 | |

SPOTLIGHTS
| Batman And Robin | 7" | Philips | BF1485 | 1966 | £1.50 | £4 | |

SPOTNIKS
The Spotniks were Sweden's answer to the Shadows (and are still playing in fact). The lead guitarist was impressive in a Hank Marvinish sort of way, and the two singles "Orange Blossom Special" and "Rocket Man" (which also turn up on the EP "On The Air" and on the LP "Out-a Space") are as good as anything produced by the English group. The Spotniks also had two gimmicks - they performed wearing rather unserviceable-looking space suits, and they used radio controlled guitars rather than electric leads, although the equipment tended to be somewhat temperamental!

Anna		7"	Oriole	CB1886	1963	£2.50	£6	
Around The World	LP	Swedisc	SWELP42	1966	£8	£20	Swedish
At Home In Gothenberg	LP	Swedisc	SWELP33	1965	£8	£20	Swedish
Back In The Race	LP	Polydor	2379005	1971	£6	£15	Swedish
Bo Winberg And The Spotnicks Today	LP	Polydor	2379060	1973	£6	£15	Swedish
By Request	LP	Swedisc	SWELP67	1968	£8	£20	Swedish
Chart Toppers Recorded 1977	LP	Polydor	231056	1977	£5	£12	German
Donner Wetter	7"	Oriole	CB1981	1964	£2.50	£6	
Feelings	LP	Polydor	2480323	1976	£5	£12	German
Happy Guitar	LP	Polydor	2475639	1982	£4	£10	German
Hava Nagila	7"	Oriole	CB1790	1963	£1.50	£4	chart single
In Acapulco	LP	Swedisc	SWELP60	1967	£8	£20	Swedish
In Paris	LP	Oriole	PS40040	1963	£6	£15	
In Stockholm	LP	Swedisc	SWELP20	1964	£8	£20	Swedish
In The Groove	LP	Swedisc	SWELP63	1968	£8	£20	Swedish
In Tokyo	LP	Swedisc	SWELP38	1966	£8	£20	Swedish
In Winterland	LP	Swedisc	SWELP48	1966	£8	£20	Swedish
Indigo	LP	Polydor	2344138	1979	£5	£12	German
Just Listen To My Heart	7"	Oriole	CB1818	1963	£1.50	£4	chart single
Live In Berlin '74	LP	Polydor	2480201	1974	£6	£15	German
Live In Japan	LP	Swedisc	SWELP53	1966	£8	£20	Swedish
Lovesick Blues	7"	Oriole	CB1953	1964	£2.50	£6	
Never Trust The Robots	LP	Polydor	2344116	1978	£5	£12	German
On The Air	7" EP	Oriole	EP7075	1963	£4	£8	
Orange Blossom Special	7"	Oriole	CB1724	1962	£1.50	£4	chart single
Out-A Space: The Spotnicks In London	LP	Oriole	SPS40037	1963	£10	£25	stereo
Out-a Space/In London	LP	Oriole	PS40036	1962	£5	£12	chart LP
Rocket Man	7"	Oriole	CB1755	1962	£1.50	£4	chart single

Something Like Country	LP	Polydor	2379032	1972	£6	£15	Swedish
Spotnicks At The Olympia Paris	7" EP	Oriole	EP7079	1964	£6	£12	
Spotnicks In Berlin	LP	Oriole	PS40064	1965	£10	£25	
Spotnicks In Paris	7" EP	Oriole	EP7078	1964	£5	£10	
Spotnicks In Spain	LP	Oriole	PS40054	1964	£8	£20	
Twentieth Anniversary Album	LP	Polydor	2344156	1981	£4	£10	German
Valentina	7"	Oriole	CB1844	1963	£1.50	£4	
Volume 1	LP	Swedisc	SWELP50001	1967	£6	£15	Swedish
Volume 2	LP	Swedisc	SWELP50002	1967	£6	£15	Swedish

SPRATT, JACK

Give Me Your Love	7"	Coxsone	CS7100	1969	£5	£10	

SPRIGUNS

Nothing Else To Do	7"	Decca	F13676	1976	£5	£10	
Revel Weird And Wild	LP	Decca	SKL5262	1976	£50	£100	
Rowdy Dowdy Day	cass	private		1974	£8	£20	
Time Will Pass	LP	Decca	SKL5286	1977	£50	£100	
White Witch	7"	Decca	F13739	1977	£5	£10	

SPRIGUNS OF TOLGUS

Jack With A Feather	LP	Alidai Star	ASC7755A	1975	£400	£600	

SPRING

Spring	LP	Neon	NE6	1971	£50	£100	double

SPRINGFIELD, DUSTY

All I See Is You	7"	Philips	BF1510	1966	£1.50	£4	
All I See Is You	7"	Philips	BF1510	1966	£2.50	£6	PS, chart single
Am I The Same Girl	7"	Philips	BF1811	1969	£1.50	£4	chart single
Brand New Me	7"	Philips	BF1826	1969	£1.50	£4	
Cameo	LP	Philips	6308152	1973	£4	£10	
Demain Tu Peux Changer	7" EP	Philips	433570	1963	£10	£20	French
Dusty	7" EP	Philips	BE12564	1964	£5	£10	
Dusty Definitely	LP	Philips	(S)BL7864	1968	£5	£12	chart LP
Dusty In Memphis	LP	Philips	SBL7889	1969	£5	£12	
Dusty In New York	7" EP	Philips	BE12572	1965	£5	£10	
Dusty Springfield	LP	World Record Club	ST848	1968	£5	£12	
Everything Is Coming Up Dusty	LP	Philips	(S)BL1002	1965	£5	£12	chart LP
From Dusty With Love	LP	Philips	SBL7927	1970	£4	£10	chart LP
Girl Called Dusty	LP	Philips	(S)BL7594	1964	£5	£12	chart LP
Give Me Time	7"	Philips	BF1577	1967	£1.50	£4	chart single
Going Back	7"	Philips	BF1502	1966	£1.50	£4	chart single
Hits Of Dusty Springfield	cass-s	Philips	MCP100	1968	£4	£10	
Hits Of The Walker Brothers & Dusty Springfield	cass-s	Philips	MCP1004	1968	£4	£10	
How Can I Be Sure	7"	Philips	6006045	1970	£1.50	£4	chart single
I Close My Eyes And Count To Ten	7"	Philips	BF1682	1968	£1.50	£4	chart single
I Just Don't Know What To Do With Myself	7"	Philips	BF1348	1964	£1.50	£4	chart single
I Only Want To Be With You	7"	Philips	BF1292	1963	£1.50	£4	chart single
I Only Want To Be With You	7" EP	Philips	433664	1963	£6	£12	French
I Only Want To Be With You	7" EP	Philips	BE12560	1964	£5	£10	
I Will Come To You	7"	Philips	BF1706	1968	£1.50	£4	
If You Go Away	7" EP	Philips	BE12605	1968	£5	£10	
I'll Try Anything	7"	Philips	BF1553	1967	£1.50	£4	chart single
In The Middle Of Nowhere	7"	Philips	BF1418	1965	£1.50	£4	chart single
Learn To Say Goodbye	7"	Philips	6006325	1974	£1.50	£4	
Little By Little	7"	Philips	BF1466	1966	£1.50	£4	chart single
Losing You	7"	Philips	BF1369	1964	£1.50	£4	chart single
Mademoiselle Dusty	7" EP	Philips	BE12579	1965	£6	£12	
Morning Please Don't Come	7"	Philips	BF1835	1970	£1.50	£4	with Tom Springfield
Oh Holy Child	7"	Philips	BF1381	1964	£2.50	£6	PS, Springfields B side
Oh Holy Child	7"	Philips	BF1381	1964	£1.50	£4	Springfields B side
See All Her Faces	LP	Philips	6308117	1972	£4	£10	
Sheer Magic	LP	Audio Club	6856020	1972	£4	£10	
Some Of Your Loving	7"	Philips	6006151	1971	£1.50	£4	
Some Of Your Loving	7"	Philips	BF1430	1965	£1.50	£4	chart single
Son Of A Preacher Man	7"	Philips	BF1730	1968	£1.50	£4	chart single
Star Dusty	LP	Audio Club	6850002	1972	£4	£10	
Star Dusty	7" EP	Philips	6850751	1968	£2	£5	
Stay Awhile	7"	Philips	BF1313	1964	£1.50	£4	chart single
Warten Und Hoffen	7"	Philips		1964	£7.50	£15	German
What's It Gonna Be	7"	Philips	6006350	1974	£1.50	£4	
What's It Gonna Be	7"	Philips	BF1608	1967	£5	£10	
Where Am I Going	LP	Philips	(S)BL7820	1967	£5	£12	chart LP
Who Gets Your Love	7"	Philips	6006295	1973	£1.50	£4	
Yesterday When I Was Young	7"	Philips	6006214	1972	£1.50	£4	
You Don't Have To Say You Love Me	7"	Philips	BF1482	1966	£1.50	£4	chart single
Your Hurtin' Kind Of Love	7"	Philips	BF1396	1965	£1.50	£4	chart single

SPRINGFIELD, TOM

Brazilian Shake	7"	Philips	BF1331	1964	£1.50	£4	
Londonderry Air	7"	Philips	BF1294	1963	£1.50	£4	
Love's Philosophy	LP	Decca	LK/SKL5003	1969	£6	£15	
Mogul Theme	7"	Philips	BF1423	1965	£1.50	£4	

SPRINGFIELDS

Bambino	7"	Philips	BF1178	1961	£1.50	£4	chart single

Breakaway	7"	Philips	BF1168	1961	£1.50	£4	chart single
Christmas With The Springfields	7" EP	Woman's Own	P125	1962	£2.50	£6	
Come On Home	7"	Philips	BF1263	1963	£1.50	£4	chart single
Dear John	7"	Philips	BF1145	1961	£1.50	£4	
Folk Songs From The Hills	LP	Philips	632304BL	1963	£4	£10	
Goodnight Irene	7"	Philips	BF1220	1962	£1.50	£4	
Hit Sounds	7" EP	Philips	BE12538	1963	£4	£8	
If I Was Down And Out	7"	Philips	BF1306	1964	£1.50	£4	
Island Of Dreams	7"	Philips	326557BF	1962	£1.50	£4	chart single
Kinda Folksy	LP	Philips	BBL7551/SBBL674	1962	£4	£10	
Kinda Folksy No.1	7" EP	Philips	433622BE	1962	£4	£8	
Kinda Folksy No.2	7" EP	Philips	433623BE	1962	£4	£8	
Kinda Folksy No.3	7" EP	Philips	433624BE	1962	£4	£8	
Say I Won't Be There	7"	Philips	326577BF	1963	£1.50	£4	chart single
Silver Threads And Golden Needles	7"	Philips	BF1241	1962	£1.50	£4	
Sing Again	LP	Fontana	SFL13098	1969	£4	£10	
Springfields	7" EP	Philips	BBE12476	1961	£4	£8	
Springfields	7" EP	Philips	SBBE9068	1961	£7.50	£15	stereo
Springfields Story	LP	Philips	BET606	1964	£5	£12	double
Swahili Papa	7"	Philips	326536BF	1962	£1.50	£4	

SPRINGFIELDS (2)

Sunflower	7"	Sarah	010	1988	£4	£8	with poster

SPRINGSTEEN, BRUCE

As Requested Around The World	LP	Columbia	AS978	1981	£8	£20	US promo sampler
Atlantic City	7"	CBS	A2794	1982	£6	£12	PS
Badlands	7"	CBS	A6532	1978	£2	£5	
Blinded By The Light	7" EP	Columbia	AS45	1973	£75	£150	US, with special sleeve, questionaire, booklet
Born In The USA	LP	CBS	86304	1984	£10	£25	pic disc
Born In The USA	LP	CBS			£12.50	£25	5 track promo
Born In The USA - The 12' Collection	12"	CBS	BRUCE1	1985	£6	£15	4 x 12', 1 x 7', poster, boxed
Born To Run	LP	Columbia	HC43795	1980	£10	£25	US audiophile
Born To Run	LP	Columbia	PC33795	1975	£100	£200	US, cover titles in script
Born To Run	7"	CBS	A3661	1975	£1.50	£4	
Born To Run	7"	CBS	A3661	1975	£10	£20	PS
Born To Run	7"	CBS	A7077	1985	£6	£12	
Born To Run	7"	CBS	BRUCEB2	1987	£4	£8	2 X 7', boxed
Born To Run	7"	CBS	BRUCEBP2	1987	£1.50	£4	with badge
Born To Run	48"	CBS		1975	£37.50	£75	US unplayable promo!
Bruce Springsteen	LP	CBS	66353	1979	£10	£25	3 LPs, boxed
Cadillac Ranch	7"	CBS	A1557	1981	£6	£12	
Circus Song	7" EP	Columbia	AS52	1973	£150	£250	US, with special sleeve, questionaire, booklet
Cover Me	7"	CBS	A4662	1984	£2.50	£6	poster PS
Cover Me	7"	CBS	DA4662	1984	£2.50	£6	double
Cover Me	7"	CBS	WA4662	1984	£7.50	£15	shaped pic disc, stand
Dancing In The Dark	7"	CBS	WA4436	1984	£10	£20	shaped pic disc
Darkness On The Edge Of Town	LP	Columbia	HC45318	1981	£10	£25	US audiophile
Darkness On The Edge Of Town	LP	Columbia	PAL35318	1978	£60	£120	US promo pic disc, pictured in Guide
Greetings From Asbury Park, N.J.	LP	CBS	65480	1973	£5	£12	gatefold sleeve
Hungry Heart	7"	CBS	A9309	1980	£6	£12	PS
I'm On Fire	7"	CBS	A6342	1985	£1.50	£4	with card
I'm On Fire	7"	CBS	WA6342	1985	£5	£10	shaped pic disc
I'm On Fire	12"	CBS	TA6342	1985	£2.50	£6	
Interviews	7"	CBS		1986	£5	£10	2 X 7', boxed
Live 1975-'85	LP	CBS	SAMP1104	1986	£5	£12	promo
Open All Night	7"	CBS	A2969	1982	£6	£12	
Prodigal Son	cass	Dare International		1984	£15	£30	demo
Promised Land	7"	CBS	A6720	1978	£2	£5	
Prove It All Night	7"	CBS	A6424	1978	£1.50	£4	
River	7"	CBS	A1179	1981	£4	£8	
River	12"	CBS	A121179	1981	£3	£8	
Rosalita	7" EP	Columbia	AS66	1973	£75	£150	US, with special sleeve, questionaire, booklet
Sherry Darling	7"	CBS	A9568	1980	£4	£8	
Sherry Darling/Independence Day	7"	CBS	A9568	1980	£25	£50	promo
Sherry Darling/Independence Day	7"	CBS	A9568	1980	£60	£120	promo, PS
Spare Parts	CD-s	CBS	BRUCEB4	1988	£5	£12	in tin
Tenth Avenue Freeze-Out	7"	CBS	A3940	1976	£2	£5	
Tunnel Of Love	CD-s	CBS	6512952	1987	£6	£15	
Tunnel Of Love	12"	CBS	6512955	1987	£3	£8	shaped pic disc
Tunnel Of Love	12"	CBS	6512956	1987	£2.50	£6	with poster
Wild, The Innocent & E Street Shuffle	LP	CBS	65780	1973	£4	£10	yellow sleeve lettering

SPROUD, BILLY & THE ROCK & ROLL SIX

Rock Mister Piper	7"	Columbia	DB3893	1957	£12.50	£25	

SPROUTS
Title		Format	Label	Cat	Year			Notes
Teen Billy Baby		7"	RCA	RCA1031	1958	£15	£30	

SPUD
Happy Handful		LP	Philips	9108003	1975	£5	£12	
Silk Purse		LP	Philips	9108002	1975	£5	£12	
Smoking In The Bog		LP	Sonet	SNTF742	1977	£4	£10	

SPUR
| Spur Of The Moment | | LP | Cinema | | | £25 | £50 | US |

SPYROGYRA
| Morning Dance | | LP | MCA | INF9004 | 1979 | £5 | £12 | US pic disc, 2 B-side designs |

SQUEEZE
Cool For Cats		7"	A&M	AMS7426	1979	£1.50	£4	brilliant pink vinyl
Cool For Cats		7"	A&M	AMS7426	1979	£2.50	£6	red vinyl
Cool For Cats		12"	A&M	AMSP7426	1979	£2.50	£6	pink vinyl
Packet Of Three		12"	Deptford Fun City	01	1977	£3	£8	pink sleeve
Six Squeeze Songs Crammed On To One Ten Inch Record		10" LP	A&M	SP3719	1980	£4	£10	US
UK Squeeze		LP	A&M	SP4687	1978	£4	£10	US red vinyl

SQUIRE
Does Stephanie Know		7"	Hi Lo	LOX1	1985	£2	£5	flexi
Get Ready To Go		7"	Rok	ROKI/II	1979	£1.50	£4	B side by Coming Shortly
Something Old, Something New, Something Borrowed		LP	fan club	L0004	1984	£5	£12	
Young Idea		7"	Squire Fan Club	SFC2	1984	£2.50	£6	

SQUIRES
| Pop The Question | | 7" | Decca | F12226 | 1965 | £1.50 | £4 | |

SQUIRES (2)
The scarce single by the Squires marks the recording debut of Neil Young, who was a member of the group.
| Sultan | | 7" | V | 109 | 1961 | £75 | £150 | US |

SQUIRES, DOROTHY
| Dorothy Squires | | 7" EP | Pye | NEP24036 | 1957 | £6 | £12 | |

SRC
Black Sheep		7"	Capitol	CL15576	1969	£4	£8	
Milestones		LP	Capitol	(S)T134	1969	£15	£30	
SRC		LP	Capitol	(S)T2991	1968	£15	£30	
Traveller's Tale		LP	Capitol	(S)T273	1970	£15	£30	

STACCATOS
| Butchers And Bakers | | 7" | Fontana | TF966 | 1968 | £5 | £10 | |

STACCATOS (2)
| Half Past Midnight | | 7" | Capitol | CL15505 | 1967 | £2.50 | £6 | |
| Let's Run Away | | 7" | Capitol | CL15478 | 1966 | £2.50 | £6 | |

STACCATOS (3)
| Main Line | | 7" | Parlophone | R4828 | 1961 | £4 | £8 | |

STACEY, CLARENCE
| Just Your Love | | 7" | Pye | 7N25025 | 1959 | £2.50 | £6 | |

STACKIE, BOB
| Grab It Hold It Feel It | | 7" | Collins Downbeat | CR009 | 1968 | £2 | £5 | |

STACKRIDGE
| Stackridge | | LP | MCA | MDKS8002 | 1971 | £4 | £10 | |

STACKWADDY
Bugger Off		LP	Dandelion	2310231	1972	£35	£70	
Roadrunner		7"	Dandelion	5119	1970	£4	£8	
Stackwaddy		LP	Dandelion	2310154	1971	£20	£40	
Stackwaddy		LP	Dandelion	DAN8003	1971	£20	£40	
You Really Got Me		7"	Dandelion	2001331	1972	£2	£5	

STACY, JESS
| Jess Stacy | | 10" LP | Brunswick | LA8737 | 1956 | £6 | £15 | |
| Jess Stacy And The Famous Sidemen | | LP | London | LTZK15012 | 1957 | £6 | £15 | |

STAFFORD, JO
American Folk Songs		10" LP	Capitol	LC6500	1950	£8	£20	
As You Desire Me		10" LP	Columbia	33S1024	1954	£8	£20	
Autumn In New York		10" LP	Capitol	H197	195-	£8	£20	US
Ballad Of The Blues		LP	Philips	BBL7327	1959	£5	£12	
Capitol Presents		10" LP	Capitol	LC6575	1953	£6	£15	
Capitol Presents Vol.2		10" LP	Capitol	LC6635	1954	£6	£15	
Chow, Willy		7"	Columbia	SCM5064	1953	£5	£10	with Frankie Laine
Floatin' Down To Cotton Town		10" LP	Philips	BBR8075	1956	£8	£20	with Frankie Laine
Greatest Hits		LP	Columbia	CL1228	1959	£8	£20	US

Title	Format	Label	Cat No	Year	Price	Price	Notes
Happy Holiday	LP	Philips	BBL7100	1956	£6	£15	
I'll Be Seeing You	LP	Philips	BBL7290	1959	£5	£12	
It Is No Secret	7"	Columbia	SCM5012	1953	£4	£8	
Jo & Jazz	LP	Philips	BBL7428/SBBL595	1960	£6	£15	
Jo & Jazz	7" EP	Philips	BBE12459	1961	£2	£5	
Jo Stafford	7" EP	Philips	BBE12014	1955	£6	£12	
Jo Stafford	7" EP	Philips	BBE12141	1957	£2	£5	
Jo Stafford And Nelson Eddy	7" EP	Columbia	SEG7516	1954	£2	£5	with Nelson Eddy
Jo Stafford No.2	7" EP	Philips	BBE12138	1957	£2	£5	
Keep It A Secret	7"	Columbia	SCM5026	1953	£4	£8	
Kiss Me Kate	10" LP	Capitol	LC6515	1951	£5	£12	with Gordon MacRae
Musical Portrait Of New Orleans	LP	Columbia	CL578	195-	£8	£20	US, with Frankie Laine
My Heart's In The Highlands	10" LP	Philips	BBR8011	1954	£6	£15	
On London Bridge	7"	Philips	JK1003	1957	£2	£5	
Once Over Lightly	LP	Philips	BBL7169	1957	£6	£15	
Pine Top's Boogie	7"	Philips	PB935	1959	£2	£5	
Settin' The Woods On Fire	7"	Columbia	SCM5014	1953	£4	£8	
Show Songs	7" EP	Columbia	SEG7548	1954	£2	£5	
Showcase	LP	Philips	BBL7395	1960	£5	£12	
Ski Trails	LP	Philips	BBL7187	1957	£6	£15	
Something To Remember You By	7"	Columbia	SCM5046	1953	£2.50	£6	
Songs Of Scotland	LP	Columbia	CL1043	1957	£8	£20	
Star Of Hope	7"	Columbia	SCM5011	1953	£2.50	£6	
Sunday Evening Songs	10" LP	Capitol	LC6611	1953	£8	£20	with Gordon MacRae
Swingin' Down Broadway	LP	Philips	BBL7243	1958	£6	£15	
TV Series	7" EP	Philips	BBE12214	1958	£4	£8	
Voice Of Your Choice	10" LP	Philips	BBR8076	1956	£6	£15	
With A Little Bit Of Luck	7"	Philips	PB818	1958	£1.50	£4	
You Belong To Me	7"	Columbia	SCM5013	1953	£6	£12	chart single

STAFFORD, TERRY

Title	Format	Label	Cat No	Year	Price	Price	Notes
Follow The Rainbow	7"	London	HLU9923	1964	£2.50	£6	
Heartache On The Way	7"	Stateside	SS225	1963	£2.50	£6	
I'll Touch A Star	7"	London	HLU9902	1964	£1.50	£4	
Suspicion	LP	London	HAU8200	1964	£15	£30	
Suspicion	7"	London	HLU9871	1964	£2.50	£6	chart single
Suspicion	7" EP	London	REU1436	1964	£7.50	£15	

STAMP, TERRY

Title	Format	Label	Cat No	Year	Price	Price	Notes
Eaststicks	LP	A&M	AMLH63329	1975	£6	£15	

STAMPEDE

Title	Format	Label	Cat No	Year	Price	Price	Notes
Days Of Wine And Roses	7"	Polydor	POSP507	1982	£2	£5	
Days Of Wine And Roses	12"	Polydor	POSPX507	1982	£2.50	£6	

STAMPEDERS

Title	Format	Label	Cat No	Year	Price	Price	Notes
From The Fire	LP	Regal Zonophone	SLRZ1039	1974	£6	£15	
Stampeders	LP	Regal Zonophone	SLRZ1032	1972	£6	£15	
Sweet City Woman	LP	Bell	6068	1973	£5	£12	US

STANBACK, JEAN

Title	Format	Label	Cat No	Year	Price	Price	Notes
I Still Love You	7"	Deep Soul	DS9101	1970	£5	£10	

STANDELLS

Title	Format	Label	Cat No	Year	Price	Price	Notes
Dirty Water	LP	Tower	(S)T5027	1966	£15	£30	US
Dirty Water	7"	Capitol	CL15446	1966	£7.50	£15	
Dirty Water	7" EP	Capitol	EAP122009	1966	£25	£50	French
Help Yourself	LP	Liberty	LIB55722	1964	£10	£20	
Hot Ones	LP	Tower	(S)T5049	1966	£10	£25	US
In Person At P.J.'s	LP	Liberty	LBY1243	1965	£15	£30	
In Person At P.J.s	7" EP	Liberty	LEP2211	1964	£25	£50	French
Live & Out Of Sight	LP	Sunset	SUM1186/SUS5186	1966	£8	£20	US
Try It	LP	Tower	(S)T5098	1967	£8	£20	US
Why Pick On Me	LP	Tower	(S)T5044	1966	£10	£25	US

STANG, ARNOLD

Title	Format	Label	Cat No	Year	Price	Price	Notes
Ivy Will Cling	7"	Fontana	H226	1959	£1.50	£4	chart single

STANSFIELD, LISA

Title	Format	Label	Cat No	Year	Price	Price	Notes
I Got A Feeling	7"	Polydor	POSP651	1983	£2	£5	
Listen To Your Heart	7"	Polydor	POSP556	1983	£2	£5	
Only Way	7"	Polydor	POSP521	1982	£2.50	£6	
Your Alibis	7"	Devil	DEV2	1981	£7.50	£15	

STANSHALL, VIV

The former lead singer of the Bonzo Dog Band has made a number of eccentric records since the demise of that group. One recording not listed here is the alternative ending to Mike Oldfield's "Tubular Bells" (included in the four album boxed set of Oldfield's first Virgin recordings) in which Stanshall is the commentator for a drunken guided tour of the Manor recording studio complex. This favourite caricature of a vacuous aristocrat was the inspiration behind Stanshall's classic comedy recording "Sir Henry At Rawlinson End", versions of which were first broadcast on the radio. "Labio-Dental Fricative" would be an unlikely title for a single by anyone but Stanshall, and it seems to have disappeared from all discographies and listings apart from the one here. Were it not for the fact that the author has held a copy in his hand, he would begin to doubt whether the record existed at all! It is one for Eric Clapton completists, incidentally, as the guitarist lends his support to the musical proceedings.

Title	Format	Label	Cat No	Year	Price	Price	Notes
Labio-Dental Fricative	7"	Liberty	LBS15309	1970	£5	£10	with Eric Clapton
Lakanga	7"	Warner Bros	K16424	1974	£1.50	£4	
Men Opening Umbrellas Ahead	LP	Warner Bros	K56052	1974	£6	£15	
Question	7"	Harvest	HAR5114	1976	£1.50	£4	

Sir Henry At Rawlinson End	LP	Charisma	CAS1139	1978	£5	£12	
Suspicion	7"	Fly	BUG4	1970	£2.50	£6	
Teddy Boys Don't Knit	LP	Charisma	CAS1153	1981	£4	£10	
Terry Keeps His Clips On	7"	Charisma	CB373	1980	£1.50	£4	

STAPLE SINGERS

Beatitude/Respect Yourself	LP	Stax	2325069	1970	£4	£10	
City In The Sky	LP	Stax	STX1001	1972	£4	£10	
For What It's Worth	7"	Columbia	DB8292	1967	£4	£8	
For What It's Worth	7"	Soul City	SC117	1969	£4	£8	
Freedom Highway	LP	Columbia	SX6023	1966	£8	£20	
Hammer And Nails	LP	Riverside	RLP3501	1963	£10	£25	
Hammer And Nails	7"	Riverside	106902	1963	£4	£8	
Saviour Is Born	7" EP	Riverside	REP3220	1962	£4	£8	
Soul Folk In Action	LP	Stax	2363011	1971	£4	£10	
Swing Low	LP	Stateside	SL10015	1963	£8	£20	
Uncloudy Day	LP	Fontana	688515ZL	1965	£6	£15	
We'll Get Over	LP	Stax	SXATS1018	1969	£4	£10	

STAPLETON, CYRIL

Blue Star	7"	Decca	F10559	1955	£2	£5	chart single
Come Twistin'	LP	Ace Of Clubs	ACL1114	1962	£6	£15	
Elephant Tango	7"	Decca	F10488	1955	£2	£5	chart single
Fanfare Boogie	7"	Decca	F10470	1955	£1.50	£4	
Forgotten Dreams	7"	Decca	F10912	1957	£1.50	£4	chart single
Happy Whistler	7"	Decca	F10735	1956	£2	£5	chart single
Italian Theme	7"	Decca	F10703	1956	£2	£5	chart single
Presenting	7" EP	Decca	DFE6288	1956	£2.50	£6	
Presenting No.2	7" EP	Decca	DFE6340	1956	£2	£5	

STAPREST

Schooldays	7"	Avatar	AAA103	1981	£5	£10	

STARCASTLE

Citadel	LP	Epic	34935	1978	£5	£12	US pic disc

STARCHER, BUDDY

And His Mountain Guitar Vol.1	7" EP	London	REB1424	1964	£4	£8	
And His Mountain Guitar Vol.2	7" EP	London	REB1425	1964	£4	£8	
And His Mountain Guitar Vol.3	7" EP	London	REB1426	1964	£4	£8	

STARFIRE

Starfire	LP	Crimson	SCAREC1		£8	£20	US

STARFIRES

Starfires Play	LP	Ohio Recording Service	34	1964	£8	£20	US
Teenbeat A Go-Go	LP	La Brea	LS8018	1965	£8	£20	US

STARGAZERS

365 Kisses	7"	Decca	F10379	1954	£1.50	£4	
Close The Door	7"	Decca	F10594	1955	£5	£10	chart single
Crazy Otto Rag	7"	Decca	F10523	1955	£5	£10	chart single
Happy Wanderer	7"	Decca	F10259	1954	£5	£10	chart single
Honky Tonk Song	7"	Decca	F10898	1957	£1.50	£4	
I See The Moon	7"	Decca	F10213	1953	£6	£12	chart single
Presenting The Stargazers	10" LP	Decca	LF1186	1954	£10	£25	
Rocking And Rolling	7"	Decca	F10731	1956	£5	£10	
Rocking And Rolling	7" EP	Decca	DFE6362	1956	£6	£12	
Rose Of The Wildwood	7"	Decca	F10412	1954	£1.50	£4	
She Loves To Rock	7"	Decca	F10775	1956	£5	£10	
Skiffling Dogs	7"	Decca	F10969	1957	£1.50	£4	
Somebody	7"	Decca	F10437	1955	£5	£10	chart single
South Of The Border	LP	Decca	LK4309	1959	£6	£15	
Stargazers	7" EP	Decca	DFE6341	1956	£6	£12	
Tender Trap	7"	Decca	F10668	1956	£1.50	£4	
Twenty Tiny Fingers	7"	Decca	F10626	1955	£5	£10	chart single
Who Is It?	7"	Decca	F10916	1957	£1.50	£4	
You Won't Be Around	7"	Decca	F10867	1957	£1.50	£4	
Zambesi	7"	Decca	F10696	1956	£1.50	£4	

STARK NAKED & THE CAR THIEVES

Stark Naked And The Car Thieves	LP	RCA	SP4592	1971	£5	£12	US

STARK, PETER

Mushroom Country	LP	Montage		1976	£25	£50	US

STARR, CINDY & THE MOPEDS

Way I Do	7"	Columbia	DB110	1968	£4	£8	

STARR, CINDY & THE RUDE BOYS

Pain Of Love	7"	Columbia	DB107	1968	£4	£8	

STARR, EDWIN

25 Miles	LP	Tamla Motown	(S)TML11115	1969	£5	£12	
25 Miles	7"	Tamla Motown	TMG672	1968	£2	£5	chart single
Agent OO-Soul	7"	Tamla Motown	TMG790	1971	£1.50	£4	chart single
Funky Music Sho' Nuff Turns Me On	7"	Tamla Motown	TMG810	1972	£1.50	£4	
Headline News	7"	Polydor	56717	1966	£2.50	£6	chart single
I Am The Man For You Baby	7"	Tamla Motown	TMG646	1968	£5	£10	

I Want My Baby Back	7"	Tamla Motown	TMG630	1967	£6	£12	
It's My Turn Now	7"	Polydor	56726	1967	£7.50	£15	
Soul Master	LP	Tamla Motown	(S)TML11094	1969	£10	£25	
Stop Her On Sight	7"	Polydor	56702	1966	£5	£10	chart single
Stop Her On Sight	7"	Polydor	56753	1968	£1.50	£4	chart single
Stop The War Now	7"	Tamla Motown	TMG764	1971	£1.50	£4	chart single
Time	7"	Tamla Motown	TMG725	1970	£2.50	£6	
War	7"	Tamla Motown	TMG754	1970	£1.50	£4	chart single
Way Over There	7"	Tamla Motown	TMG692	1969	£4	£8	

STARR, EDWIN & BLINKY

Just We Two	LP	Tamla Motown	(S)TML11131	1970	£4	£10	
Oh How Happy	7"	Tamla Motown	TMG720	1969	£50	£100	demo only
Oh How Happy	7"	Tamla Motown	TMG748	1970	£1.50	£4	

STARR, FRANK

| Little Bitty Feeling | 7" | London | HLU9545 | 1962 | £5 | £10 | |

STARR, FREDDIE

Baby Blue	7"	Decca	F11786	1963	£10	£20	
Never Cry On Someone's Shoulder	7"	Decca	F12009	1964	£10	£20	
Who Told You	7"	Decca	F11663	1963	£7.50	£15	

STARR, JIMMY

| It's Only Make Believe | 7" | London | HL8731 | 1958 | £12.50 | £25 | |

STARR, KAY

Am I A Toy Or A Treasure?	7"	Capitol	CL14151	1955	£6	£12	chart single
Blue Starr	LP	RCA	RD27056	1958	£5	£12	
Capitol Presents	10" LP	Capitol	LC6574	1953	£6	£15	
Fool Fool Fool	7"	Capitol	CL14167	1954	£7.50	£15	
Foolin' Around	7"	Capitol	CL15194	1961	£1.50	£4	
Foolishly Yours	7"	HMV	7M307	1955	£4	£8	
Heavenly Kay Starr	7" EP	Top Rank	JKP2042	1960	£4	£8	
Hits Of Kay Starr	10" LP	Capitol	LC6835	1956	£6	£15	
If Anyone Finds This, I Love You	7"	HMV	7M300	1955	£4	£8	
In A Blue Mood	LP	Capitol	T580	1957	£5	£12	
Jamie Boy	7"	HMV	POP357	1957	£2	£5	
Kay Starr	7" EP	Vogue	EPV1014	1955	£5	£10	
Kay Starr	10" LP	Capitol	LC6630	1954	£6	£15	
Kay Stars Again	7" EP	HMV	7EG8184	1956	£2	£5	
Little Loneliness	7"	HMV	POP345	1957	£2	£5	
Moving Pt.1	7" EP	Capitol	EAP11254	1960	£2	£5	
Moving Pt.2	7" EP	Capitol	EAP21254	1960	£2	£5	
Moving Pt.3	7" EP	Capitol	EAP31254	1960	£6	£12	
Riders In The Sky	7"	Capitol	CL15105	1959	£1.50	£4	
Rock And Roll Waltz	7"	HMV	7M371	1956	£7.50	£15	chart single
Rockin' With Kay	LP	RCA	LPM1720	1958	£8	£20	US
Second Fiddle	7"	HMV	7M420	1956	£5	£10	
Stroll Me	7"	RCA	RCA1065	1958	£1.50	£4	
Swinging With The Starr	LP	London	HAU2039	1957	£8	£20	
Well I Ask You	7" EP	Capitol	EAP120210	1962	£2	£5	
What A Star Is Kay	7" EP	HMV	7EG8165	1956	£2	£5	
Wheel Of Fortune	7"	Capitol	CL15137	1960	£1.50	£4	
Wheel Of Fortune	7" EP	Capitol	EAP120063	1961	£5	£10	
Where, What Or When?	7"	HMV	7M315	1955	£4	£8	

STARR, LUCILLE

| French Song | 7" | London | HL9900 | 1964 | £1.50 | £4 | |

STARR, MAXINE

| Wishing Star | 7" | London | HLU9712 | 1963 | £1.50 | £4 | |

STARR, RANDY

After School	7"	London	HL8443	1957	£10	£20	
Count On Me	7"	Felsted	AF106	1958	£4	£8	
Workin' On The Santa Fe	7"	Top Rank	JAR264	1960	£1.50	£4	

STARR, RINGO

The rarest Ringo Starr record typifies the variety of work that Starr has undertaken since the break-up of the Beatles. "Scouse The Mouse" is a children's story produced by Donald Pleasance and dramatised with Ringo Starr playing the title role (and singing eight songs). A projected TV version never happened so that the album failed to attract any attention at the time of its release.

Back Off Boogaloo	7"	Apple	R5944	1972	£2	£5	PS
Beaucoups Of Blues	LP	Apple	PAS10002	1970	£6	£15	
Dose Of Rock'n'Roll	7"	Polydor	2001694	1976	£1.50	£4	
Drowning In A Sea Of Love	7"	Polydor	2001734	1977	£25	£50	
Hey Baby	7"	Polydor	2001699	1976	£1.50	£4	
It Don't Come Easy	7"	Apple	R5898	1971	£2.50	£6	PS
It Don't Come Easy	7"	Old Gold	OG4513	1984	£2	£5	PS
Lipstick Traces	7"	Polydor	2001782	1978	£30	£60	demo
Oh My My	7"	Apple	R6011	1976	£5	£10	
Old Wave	LP	Bellaphon	26016029	1983	£20	£40	German
Only You	7"	Apple	PSR-	1974	£50	£100	interview promo
Only You	7"	Apple	R6000	1974	£2	£5	PS
Photograph	7"	Apple	R5992	1973	£2	£5	PS
Ringo	LP	Apple	SWAL3413	1973	£5	£12	US, with long version of 'Six O'Clock'
Scouse The Mouse	LP	Polydor	2480429	1978	£40	£80	with other artists, sleeve pictured in Guide

Scouse The Mouse	cass ...	Polydor	3194429	1978	£6	£15	with other artists
Sentimental Journey	r-reel .	Apple	TAPMC7101	1970	£8	£20	mono
Sentimental Journey	r-reel .	Apple	TDPCS7101	1970	£6	£15	stereo
Sentimental Journey	LP	Apple	PCS7101	1970	£6	£15	chart LP
Snookeroo	7"	Apple	R6004	1975	£1.50	£4	
Tonight	7"	Polydor	2001795	1978	£20	£40	
You're Sixteen	7"	Apple	R5995	1974	£1.50	£4	PS

STARR, STELLA
Bring Him Back	7"	Piccadilly	7N35366	1967	£12.50	£25

STARR, TONY
Rocket To The Moon	7"	Decca	F11847	1964	£5	£10

STARS OF HEAVEN
Clothes Of Pride	7"	Hotwire	HWS853	1985	£5	£10

STATE OF MICKEY & TOMMY
Frisco Bay	7"	Mercury	MF1009	1967	£20	£40	
Frisco Bay	7" EP.	Mercury	152102	196-	£25	£50	French
With Love From	7" EP.	Mercury	152095	196-	£25	£50	French
With Love From One To Five	7"	Mercury	MF996	1967	£20	£40	

STATESMEN
I've Just Fallen In Love	7"	Fontana	TF432	1964	£2.50	£6
Look Around	7"	Decca	F11687	1963	£2.50	£6

STATIC
When You Went Away	7"	Page One	POF039	1967	£2.50	£6

STATION SKIFFLE GROUP
Station Skiffle Group	7" EP.	Esquire	EP161	1958	£7.50	£15

STATON, CANDI
Love Chain	7"	United Artists ..	UP35823	1975	£1.50	£4

STATON, DAKOTA
Ballads And The Blues	LP	Capitol	(S)T1387	1960	£4	£10
Confessin' The Blues	7"	Capitol	CL14917	1959	£2.50	£6
Crazy He Calls Me	LP	Capitol	T1170	1959	£4	£10
Don't Leave Me Now	7"	Capitol	CL14314	1955	£4	£8
Dynamic Dakota Staton	LP	Capitol	(S)T1054	1959	£4	£10
Dynamic Dakota Staton	7" EP.	Capitol	EAP11054	1959	£2.50	£6
Dynamic Dakota Staton Pt.2	7" EP.	Capitol	EAP21054	1959	£2.50	£6
Dynamic Dakota Staton Pt.3	7" EP.	Capitol	EAP31054	1959	£2.50	£6
I Never Dreamt	7"	Capitol	CL14339	1955	£2	£5
Late, Late Show	LP	Capitol	T876	1958	£4	£10
More Than The Mood	LP	Capitol	(S)T1325	1960	£4	£10
Party's Over	7"	Capitol	CL14870	1958	£1.50	£4
Time To Swing	LP	Capitol	(S)T1421	1961	£4	£10

STATUES
Blue Velvet	7"	London	HLG9192	1960	£5	£10

STATUS QUO

Status Quo are one of the more unlikely success stories of rock music, having stuck with the same Chuck Berry and boogie style ever since first deciding on it some time around 1970. The group's earlier recordings - as the Spectres and Traffic Jam before becoming Status Quo - are more varied in style, but perhaps not very expertly performed. The slightly psychedelic "Pictures Of Matchstick Men" was a considerable hit, of course, but no one bought the accompanying album, which is now extremely scarce. Its awkward title probably did not help its sales when released - "Picturesque Matchstickable Messages". The succeeding "Spare Parts" is also highly sought after today, as is the Marble Arch release "Status Quotations", even though this is only a compilation of singles and tracks from the first LP.

Anniversary Waltz Parts 1 & 2	7"	Vertigo	QUODJ28	1990	£5	£10	promo
Anniversary Waltz Parts 1 & 2	12"	Vertigo	QUO2812	1990	£5	£12	B side plays Little Lady & Paper Plane
Are You Growing Tired Of My Love	7"	Pye	7N17728	1969	£6	£12	chart single
Black Veils Of Melancholy	7"	Pye	7N17497	1968	£6	£12	
Can't Give You More	7"	Vertigo	STATUS30	1991	£6	£12	promo
Caroline	7"	Vertigo	QUOP10	1982	£2.50	£6	pic disc
Caroline (Live)	12"	Vertigo	QUO1012	1982	£2.50	£6	
Down Down Down	7"	Lyntone	LYN3154/5	1976	£4	£8	flexi, PS
Dreamin'	7"	Vertigo	QUOP21	1986	£2.50	£6	with poster
Fakin' The Blues	CD-s .	Vertigo	QUOCD31	1993	£6	£12	no case
Fakin' The Blues	7"	Vertigo	QUO31	1991	£50	£100	
Fakin' The Blues	12"	Vertigo	QUO3112	1991	£60	£120	
File Series	LP	Pye	FILD005	1977	£5	£12	double
From The Makers Of	LP	Vertigo	PROBX1	1982	£8	£20	3 LPs in metal box
Gerdundula	7"	Pye	7N45253	1973	£2	£5	
Hello	LP	Vertigo	6360098	1973	£4	£10	with inner sleeve & poster
Ice In The Sun	7"	Pye	7N17581	1968	£2	£5	chart single
In My Chair	7"	Pye	7N17998	1970	£15	£30	PS
In The Army Now	7"	Vertigo	QUODP20	1986	£2.50	£6	double
In The Army Now	7"	Vertigo	QUOPD20	1986	£10	£20	pic disc
In The Army Now	12"	Vertigo	QUO2012	1986	£4	£10	with poster
Jealousy	7"	Vertigo	QUO9	1982	£25	£50	Irish promo
Just For The Record	LP	Pye	NSPL18607	1979	£6	£15	red vinyl
Make Me Stay A Bit Longer	7"	Pye	7N17665	1969	£7.50	£15	
Marguerita Time	7"	Vertigo	QUOP1414	1983	£6	£12	double Xmas gift pack
Marguerita Time	7"	Vertigo	QUOP14	1983	£5	£10	pic disc
Mess Of Blues	12"	Vertigo	QUO1212	1983	£2.50	£6	

Ol' Rag Blues	12"	Vertigo	QUO1112	1983	£2.50	£6	
Pictures Of Matchstick Men	7"	Pye	7N17449	1968	£4	£8	'75cc
							Minimum' on label
Pictures Of Matchstick Men	7"	Pye	7N17449	1968	£1.50	£4	chart single
Pictures Of Matchstick Men	7"	Pye	FBS2	1979	£2	£5	yellow vinyl
Picturesque Matchstickable Messages	LP	Pye	N(S)PL18220	1968	£25	£50	
Price Of Love	7"	Pye	7N17825	1969	£7.50	£15	
Red Sky	7"	Vertigo	QUOD19	1986	£2.50	£6	double
Red Sky	12"	Vertigo	QUO1912	1986	£4	£10	poster sleeve
Rock Till You Drop	12"	Vertigo	QUO3212	1992	£2.50	£6	2 tracks
Rockin' All Over The World	7"	Vertigo	6059184	1977	£2.50	£6	PS and poster
Rock'n'Roll	7"	Vertigo	QUOJB6	1981	£2	£5	PS and poster
Rollin' Home	7"	Vertigo	QUOP18	1986	£4	£8	shaped pic disc
Spare Parts	LP	Pye	N(S)PL18301	1968	£25	£50	
Status Quotations	LP	Marble Arch	MAL(S)1193	1969	£20	£40	
Technicolour Dreams	7"	Pye	7N17650	1968	£330	£500	
Technicolour Dreams	7"	Pye	7N17650	1968	£75	£150	demo
Tune To The Music	7"	Pye	7N45077	1971	£5	£10	
Wanderer	12"	Vertigo	QUOP16	1984	£6	£15	clear vinyl, pic disc centre

STAVERTON BRIDGE

Staverton Bridge	LP	Saydisc	SDL266	1975	£10	£25	

ST.CHRISTOPHER

Crystal Clear	7"	Bluegrass	GM001	1984	£2.50	£6	
Forevermore Starts Here	7"	Veston	VOD001	1987	£1.50	£4	flexi
Go Ahead Cry	7"	Bluegrass	GM003	1986	£2	£5	

ST.CLAIR, CHERYL

My Heart's Not In It	7"	CBS	202041	1966	£2.50	£6	

STEAMHAMMER

Steamhammer arrived at the tail end of the British blues boom amidst publicity that spoke of them being a next-generation group who would find ways of going beyond the blues. For once, this was no hype, the second LP in particular being a fine example of jazz-rock in which Martin Pugh's fluid guitar playing is ably complemented by Steve Joliffe's flute and saxophone. The long "Another Travelling Tune" shows how improvised rock can be entirely successful when the musicians are as inspired as these.

Autumn Song	7"	CBS	4496	1969	£4	£8	
Junior's Wailing	7"	CBS	4141	1969	£4	£8	
Mountains	LP	B&C	CAS1024	1970	£8	£20	
Speech	LP	Brain	0001009	1972	£10	£25	German
Steamhammer	LP	CBS	63611	1968	£10	£25	
Steamhammer	LP	Reflection	REFL1	1970	£10	£25	
Steamhammer Mark 2	LP	CBS	63694	1969	£10	£25	

STEEL

Rock Out	7"	Neat	NEAT14	1981	£2.50	£6	

STEEL MILL

Bruce Springsteen once led a group called Steel Mill, but the hard rock group who recorded the scarce "Green Eyed God" album has no connection with this.

Get On The Line	7"	Penny Farthing	PEN783	1971	£10	£20	
Green Eyed God	LP	Penny Farthing	PELS549	1975	£60	£120	
Green Eyed God	7"	Penny Farthing	PEN770	1971	£10	£20	
Green Eyed God	7"	Penny Farthing	PEN894	1975	£2	£5	

STEEL RIVER

Better Road	LP	Evolution	Z3006	1971	£5	£12	
Weighing Heavy	LP	Evolution	E2018	1970	£5	£12	

STEELE, BETTE ANN

Barricade	7"	Capitol	CL14315	1955	£2	£5	

STEELE, JAN & JOHN CAGE

Voices & Instruments	LP	Obscure	OBS5	1976	£6	£15	

STEELE, SANDRA & JON

I'm Crazy With Love	7"	Parlophone	MSP6166	1955	£1.50	£4	

STEELE, TOMMY

Boys And Girls	7"	Decca	F11299	1960	£1.50	£4	
Butter Wouldn't Melt In Your Mouth	7"	Decca	F11532	1963	£1.50	£4	
Butterfingers	7"	Decca	F10877	1957	£2.50	£6	chart single
Butterfly	7"	Decca	F10915	1957	£2	£5	with tracks by other artists
Come On Let's Go	7"	Decca	F11072	1958	£1.50	£4	chart single
Come On Let's Go	7" EP	Decca	DFE6551	1958	£5	£10	
Doomsday Rock	7"	Decca	F10808	1956	£7.50	£15	
Dream Maker	7"	Columbia	DB7070	1963	£1.50	£4	
Drunken Guitar	7"	Decca	F11372	1961	£1.50	£4	
Duke Wore Jeans	7" EP	Decca	DFE6472	1958	£5	£10	
Duke Wore Jeans	10" LP	Decca	LF1308	1958	£6	£15	
Flash Bang Wallop	7"	Decca	F11615	1963	£1.50	£4	
Get Happy	LP	Decca	LK4351	1960	£5	£12	
Happy Go Lucky	7"	Decca	F11275	1960	£1.50	£4	
Happy Guitar	7"	Decca	F10976	1958	£1.50	£4	chart single
He's Got Love	7"	Decca	F11551	1962	£1.50	£4	
Hey You	7"	Decca	F10941	1957	£2.50	£6	chart single
Hit Record	7"	Decca	F11479	1962	£1.50	£4	
It's All Happening	7"	Decca	F11026	1958	£1.50	£4	
Knee Deep In The Blues	7"	Decca	F10849	1957	£5	£10	chart single

Little White Bull	7"	Decca	F11177	1959	£1.50	£4	
Little White Bull	7"	Decca	F11177	1959	£2.50	£6	PS
Marriage Type Love	7"	Decca	F11089	1958	£1.50	£4	
My Big Best Shoes	7"	Decca	F11361	1961	£1.50	£4	
Nairobi	7"	Decca	F10991	1958	£1.50	£4	chart single
Only Man On The Island	7"	Decca	F11041	1958	£1.50	£4	chart single
Rock With The Caveman	7"	Decca	F10795	1956	£12.50	£25	chart single
Shiralee	7"	Decca	F10896	1957	£4	£8	chart single
Singing The Blues	7"	Decca	F10819	1956	£6	£12	chart single
Singing The Blues	7" EP	Decca	DFE6389	1956	£7.50	£15	
Tallahassie Lassie	7"	Decca	F11152	1959	£2.50	£6	chart single
Tommy Steele	7" EP	Decca	DFE6592	1959	£5	£10	
Tommy Steele Stage Show	10" LP	Decca	LF1287	1957	£8	£20	
Tommy Steele Story	10" LP	Decca	LF1288	1957	£8	£20	
Tommy Steele Story Vol.1	7" EP	Decca	DFE6398	1957	£7.50	£15	
Tommy Steele Story Vol.2	7" EP	Decca	DFE6424	1957	£7.50	£15	
Tommy The Toreador	7" EP	Decca	DFE6607	1959	£4	£8	
Trial	7"	Decca	F11117	1959	£1.50	£4	
Water Water	7"	Decca	F10923	1957	£2	£5	chart single
What A Mouth	7"	Decca	F11245	1960	£1.50	£4	chart single
What A Mouth	7" EP	Decca	DFE6660	1960	£5	£10	
Young Ideas	7"	Decca	F11162	1959	£1.50	£4	
Young Love	7" EP	Decca	DFE6388	1956	£7.50	£15	

STEELERS
Get It From The Bottom	7"	Direction	584675	1969	£1.50	£4

STEELEYE SPAN
Adam Catched Eve	LP	Boulevard	BD3004	1979	£6	£15	
All Around My Hat	LP	Mobile Fidelity	MFSL1027	1978	£6	£15	US audiophile
Hark The Village Wait	LP	RCA	SF8113	1970	£6	£15	
Live At Last	LP	Chrysalis	CHR1199	1978	£4	£10	
Please To See The King	LP	B&C	CAS1029	1971	£6	£15	chart LP, textured sleeve
Rave On	7"	B&C	CB164	1971	£1.50	£4	
Sails Of Silver	LP	Chrysalis	CHR1304	1980	£5	£12	
Storm Force Ten	LP	Chrysalis	CHR1151	1977	£5	£12	
Ten Man Mop	LP	Pegasus	PEG9	1971	£5	£12	

STEELY DAN
Aja	LP	Mobile Fidelity	MFSL1033	1979	£4	£10	US audiophile
Can't Buy A Thrill	LP	Command	QD40009	1974	£4	£10	US quad
Countdown To Ecstasy	LP	Command	QD40010	1974	£4	£10	US quad
Dallas	7"	ABC	SD1	1978	£2	£5	1 sided promo
Dallas	7"	Probe	PRO562	1972	£2	£5	
Gaucho	LP	MCA	MCA6102	1980	£4	£10	Canadian audiophile
Gold	LP	MCA	MCA16016	1982	£4	£10	audiophile
Katy Lied	LP	Mobile Fidelity	MFSL1007	1978	£8	£20	US audiophile
Pretzel Logic	LP	Command	QD40015	1974	£4	£10	US quad

STEEPLECHASE
Lady Bright	LP	Polydor	2489001	1970	£10	£25

STEGMEYER, BILL
On The Waterfront	7"	London	HL8078	1954	£7.50	£15

STEIG, JEREMY
Wayfaring Stranger	LP	Blue Note	BST84354	1970	£4	£10

STEIN, LOU
Almost Paradise	7"	London	HLZ8419	1957	£5	£10
Who Slammed The Door	7"	Mercury	7MT226	1958	£2	£5

STEINMAN, JIM
Bad For Good	LP	Epic	EPC84361	1981	£4	£10	pic disc

STEPHEN, MIKE
It's Over	7"	Decca	F11702	1963	£1.50	£4

STEPHENS, LEIGH
Cast Of Thousands	LP	Charisma	CAS1040	1971	£6	£15
Red Weather	LP	Philips	SBL7897	1969	£8	£20

STEPPENWOLF
Although their recorded output is quite large, John Kay's Steppenwolf is quite adequately summed up by three great songs - "Magic Carpet Ride", "The Pusher", and especially "Born To Be Wild". Apart from being a glorious rocker, the last song also contains the first use of the phrase "heavy metal". The album "Early Steppenwolf", recorded live at the Matrix, San Francisco in 1967, is best avoided. Long improvisations clearly did not really suit the group, who tend to use random noise as a substitute for genuine inspiration.

At Your Birthday Party	LP	Stateside	(S)SL5011	1969	£4	£10	
Born To Be Wild	7"	RCA	RCA1735	1968	£2.50	£6	
Born To Be Wild	7"	Stateside	SS8017	1969	£1.50	£4	chart single
Early Steppenwolf	LP	Stateside	(S)SL5015	1969	£5	£12	
Hey Lawdy Mama	7"	Stateside	SS8049	1970	£1.50	£4	
Live	LP	Stateside	SSL5029	1970	£4	£10	chart LP
Magic Carpet Ride	7"	Stateside	SS8003	1968	£2.50	£6	
Magic Carpet Ride	7"	Stateside	SS8027	1969	£1.50	£4	
Monster	LP	Stateside	SSL5021	1970	£4	£10	chart LP
Monster	7"	Stateside	SS8035	1970	£1.50	£4	
Pusher	7"	Stateside	SS8038	1970	£2	£5	
Ride With Me	7"	Probe	PRO534	1971	£1.50	£4	
Rock Me	7"	Stateside	SS8013	1969	£1.50	£4	

Title	Format	Label	Cat No	Year	Price1	Price2	Notes
Screaming Night Hog	7"	Stateside	SS8056	1970	£1.50	£4	
Second	LP	Stateside	(S)SL5003	1968	£4	£10	
Snowblind Friend	7"	Probe	PRO525	1970	£1.50	£4	
Sookie Sookie	7"	RCA	RCA1679	1968	£2.50	£6	
Steppenwolf	LP	RCA	RD/SF7974	1968	£5	£12	

STEREOLAB

Title	Format	Label	Cat No	Year	Price1	Price2	Notes
Harmonium	7"	Duophonic	DS4504	1992	£5	£10	amber vinyl
Light (That Will Cease To Fail)	7"	Big Money Inc.	BMI025	1992	£2.50	£6	pink vinyl
Stunning Debut Album	7"	Duophonic	DS4502	1991	£7.50	£15	clear vinyl
Stunning Debut Album	7"	Duophonic	DS4502	1991	£10	£20	multi-coloured vinyl
Super 45	10"	Duophonic	DS4501	1991	£8	£20	
Super 45	10"	Duophonic	DS4501	1991	£15	£30	hand painted PS

STEREOLAB & NURSE WITH WOUND

Title	Format	Label	Cat No	Year	Price1	Price2	Notes
Crumb Duck	10"	Clawfist	20	1993	£6	£15	hand made sleeve

STEREOS

Title	Format	Label	Cat No	Year	Price1	Price2	Notes
Big Knock	7"	MGM	MGM1149	1961	£7.50	£15	
Big Knock	7"	MGM	MGM1328	1966	£2.50	£6	
Please Come Back To Me	7"	MGM	MGM1143	1961	£7.50	£15	

STEREOTYPES

Title	Format	Label	Cat No	Year	Price1	Price2	Notes
Calling All The Shots	7"	Art Theft	AT001	1980	£1.50	£4	

STERLING, LESTER

Title	Format	Label	Cat No	Year	Price1	Price2	Notes
Africkaan Beat	7"	Coxsone	CS7080	1968	£5	£10	Paragons B side
Air Raid Shelter	7"	R&B	JB111	1963	£5	£10	Roy & Annette B side
Bangarang	LP	Pama	SECO15	1969	£15	£30	
Bangarang	7"	Unity	UN502	1968	£2.50	£6	with Stranger Cole
Clean The City	7"	Island	WI121	1963	£5	£10	
Forest Gate Rock	7"	Big Shot	BI507	1968	£4	£8	
Gravy Cool	7"	R&B	JB115	1963	£5	£10	Winston & Bibby B side
Indian Summer	7"	R&B	JB172	1964	£5	£10	Stranger & Patsy B side
Lonesome Feeling	7"	Unity	UN531	1969	£2.50	£6	
Man About Town	7"	Unity	UN518	1969	£2.50	£6	
One Thousand Tons Of Megaton	7"	Unity	UN517	1969	£2.50	£6	King Cannon B side
Reggae In The Wind	7"	Gas	GAS103	1969	£4	£8	Soul Set B side
Regina	7"	Unity	UN512	1969	£2.50	£6	
Sir Collins Special	7"	Collins Downbeat	CR001	1967	£4	£8	
Soul Voyage	7"	Doctor Bird	DB1107	1967	£5	£10	Alva Lewis B side
Spoogy	7"	Unity	UN509	1969	£2.50	£6	Tommy McCook B side
Zigaloo	7"	Blue Cat	BS116	1968	£4	£8	

STEVE & STEVIE

Title	Format	Label	Cat No	Year	Price1	Price2	Notes
Steve And Stevie	LP	Toast	TLP2	1968	£20	£40	

STEVENS, APRIL

Title	Format	Label	Cat No	Year	Price1	Price2	Notes
Coldest Night Of The Year	7"	Atlantic	584048	1966	£1.50	£4	
Falling In Love Again	7"	MGM	MGM1366	1967	£40	£80	
How Could Red Riding Hood	7"	Parlophone	MSP6088	1954	£2.50	£6	
Soft Warm Lips	7"	Parlophone	MSP6060	1953	£2.50	£6	
Teach Me Tiger	LP	Imperial	LP9055/12055	1961	£6	£15	US
Torrid Tunes	LP	Audio Lab	AL1534	1959	£10	£25	US
Wanting You	7"	MGM	2006586	1976	£1.50	£4	

STEVENS, CAT

Title	Format	Label	Cat No	Year	Price1	Price2	Notes
Bad Night	7"	Deram	DM140	1967	£1.50	£4	chart single
Bad Night	7" EP	Deram	15006	1967	£6	£12	French
Buddha And The Chocolate Box	LP	A&M	QU53623	1974	£5	£12	US quad
Catch Bull At Four	LP	A&M	QU54365	1972	£5	£12	US quad
Cats And Dogs	LP	Deram		1967	£15	£30	test pressing
Foreigner	LP	A&M	QU54391	1974	£5	£12	US quad
Greatest Hits	LP	A&M	QU54519	1975	£5	£12	US quad
Here Comes My Wife	7"	Deram	DM211	1968	£1.50	£4	
I Love My Dog	7"	Deram	DM102	1966	£1.50	£4	chart single
I Love My Dog	7" EP	Deram	15000	1966	£6	£12	French
I'm Gonna Get Me A Gun	7"	Deram	DM118	1967	£1.50	£4	chart single
I'm Gonna Get Me A Gun	7" EP	Deram	15003	1967	£6	£12	French
Kitty	7"	Deram	DM156	1967	£1.50	£4	chart single
Lady D'Arbanville	7"	Island	WIP6086	1970	£1.50	£4	chart single
Lovely City	7"	Deram	DM178	1968	£1.50	£4	
Matthew And Son	LP	Deram	DML/SML1004	1967	£5	£12	chart LP
Matthew And Son	7"	Deram	DM110	1966	£1.50	£4	chart single
Mona Bone Jakon	LP	Island	ILPS9118	1970	£4	£10	chart LP, with inner
New Masters	LP	Deram	DML/SML1018	1967	£5	£12	
Saturday Night Live	LP	A&M		1975	£6	£15	US promo
Tea For The Tillerman	LP	A&M	QU54280	1972	£5	£12	US quad
Tea For The Tillerman	LP	Mobile Fidelity	MFSL1035	1979	£5	£12	US audiophile
Tea For The Tillerman	LP	Mobile Fidelity	MFSL1135	1984	£10	£25	US audiophile (UHQR)
Teaser And The Firecat	LP	A&M	QU54313	1972	£5	£12	US quad
Where Are You	7"	Deram	DM260	1969	£1.50	£4	

STEVENS, CHUCK

Title	Format	Label	Cat No	Year	Price1	Price2	Notes
My London	7"	Columbia	DB3938	1957	£1.50	£4	
Take A Walk	7"	Columbia	DB3883	1957	£1.50	£4	

783

STEVENS, CONNIE

And This Is Mine	7"	Warner Bros	WB41	1961	£1.50	£4		
Apollo	7"	Warner Bros	WB25	1960	£1.50	£4		
As Cricket	7" EP	Warner Bros	WEP6007	1960	£2.50	£6		
As Cricket	7" EP	Warner Bros	WSE6007	1962	£5	£10	stereo	
As Cricket No.2	7" EP	Warner Bros	WEP6105	1963	£2.50	£6		
As Cricket No.2	7" EP	Warner Bros	WSE6105	1963	£5	£10	stereo	
As Cricket No.3	7" EP	Warner Bros	WEP6112	1963	£2.50	£6		
As Cricket No.3	7" EP	Warner Bros	WSE6112	1963	£5	£10	stereo	
Conchetta	LP	Warner Bros	W1208	1958	£6	£15	US	
Connie	LP	Warner Bros	WM4061/WS8061	1962	£5	£12		
Connie Stevens From Hawaiian Eye	LP	Warner Bros	W(S)1382	1960	£6	£15	US	
Greenwood Tree	7"	Warner Bros	WB47	1961	£1.50	£4		
Hank Williams Song Book	LP	Warner Bros	WM/WS8111	1963	£4	£10		
Hawaiian Eye	LP	Warner Bros	W(S)1335	1959	£6	£15	US	
Just One Kiss	7"	Warner Bros	WB63	1962	£1.50	£4		
Mr.Songwriter	7"	Warner Bros	WB73	1962	£1.50	£4		
Sixteen Reasons	7"	Warner Bros	WB3	1960	£1.50	£4	chart single	
They're Jealous Of Me	7"	Warner Bros	WB128	1964	£1.50	£4		
Too Young To Go Steady	7"	Warner Bros	WB17	1960	£1.50	£4		

STEVENS, DODIE

Dodie Stevens	LP	Dot	DLP3212/25212	1960	£6	£15	
Don't Send Me Roses	7"	London	HLD9672	1963	£1.50	£4	
I Wore Out The Record	7"	Liberty	LIB83	1964	£1.50	£4	
No	7"	London	HLD9174	1960	£1.50	£4	
Over The Rainbow	LP	Dot	DLP3323/25323	1960	£6	£15	US
Pink Shoe Laces	7"	London	HLD8834	1959	£6	£12	
Pink Shoelaces	LP	Dot	DLP3371/25371	1961	£6	£15	US
Yes I'm Lonesome Tonight	7"	London	HLD9280	1961	£2	£5	

STEVENS, JIMMY

I Love You	7"	Fontana	TF721	1966	£1.50	£4	

STEVENS, JOHN

John Stevens, the erstwhile motivator behind the Spontaneous Music Ensemble (whose music sounds just as the name would suggest it should), began to move into more commercial areas during the seventies. He is the drummer on John Martyn's "Live At Leeds", and for the single "Anni", John Martyn returned the favour - playing guitar and singing on a version of the piece that is quite different from the one found on the LP "John Stevens" Away".

Anni	7"	Vertigo	6059140	1976	£4	£8	with John Martyn
Can't Explain	7"	Vertigo	6059154	1976	£1.50	£4	

STEVENS, KIRK

Once	7"	Decca	F10863	1957	£1.50	£4	

STEVENS, MEIC

Meic Stevens is a major folk-rock artist, whose career is unknown to most collectors apart from the solitary cult favourite album, "Outlander". The obscurity that is Stevens' lot has nothing to do with his output, which is large, but everything to do with the fact that he has chosen to stay true to his Celtic roots and performs almost exclusively in the Welsh language. Most of his early records are much harder to find than their values might suggest - "Did I Dream" will prove near-impossible, although it is an essential item for Led Zeppelin completists, being produced by John Paul Jones. Further Stevens items are listed under Bara Menyn, a folk band of which he was a member. The discographical information included here (together with the other Welsh language items to be found in this Guide) was provided by dealer Andrew Hawkey, who operates a thriving mail order company in Lampeter.

Ballad Of Old Joe Blind	7"	Warner Bros	WB8007	1970	£7.50	£15	
Byw Yn Y Wlad	7" EP	Wren	WRE1107	1971	£7.50	£15	
Can Nana	7"	Theatr Yr Ymylon	YMSP01	1978	£4	£8	
Caneuon Cynnar	LP	TicToc	TTL001	1979	£40	£80	
Did I Dream	7"	Decca	F12174	1965	£15	£30	
Diolch Yn Fawr	7" EP	Sain	SAIN13	1971	£7.50	£15	
Gog	LP	Sain	1065M	1977	£25	£50	
Gwymon	LP	Wren	WRL536	1972	£40	£80	
Lapis Lazuli	LP	Sain	1312M	1983	£6	£15	
Meic Stevens	7" EP	Newyddion Da	ND1	1970	£17.50	£35	
Meic Stevens	7" EP	Wren	WRE1045	1968	£10	£20	
Mwg	7" EP	Wren	WRE1073	1969	£10	£20	
Nid Oes Un Gwydr Ffenestr	7"	Wren	WSP2005	1970	£7.50	£15	
Nos Du Nos Da	LP	Sain	1239M	1982	£8	£20	
Outlander	LP	Warner Bros	WS3005	1970	£60	£120	
Pe Medrwn	7"	Theatr Yr Ymylon	YMSP02	1978	£4	£8	
Rhif 2	7" EP	Wren	WRE1053	1968	£10	£20	
Y Brawd Houdini	7" EP	Sain	SAIN4	1970	£7.50	£15	

STEVENS, RAY

1,837 Seconds Of Humor	LP	Mercury	MG2/SR60732	1962	£4	£10	US
Ahab The Arab	7"	Mercury	AMT1184	1962	£1.50	£4	
Crying Goodbye	7"	Capitol	CL14881	1958	£1.50	£4	
Harry The Hairy Ape	7"	Mercury	AMT1207	1963	£1.50	£4	
Jeremiah Peabody	7"	Mercury	AMT1158	1961	£1.50	£4	

STEVENS, RICKY

Forever	7"	Columbia	DB4778	1962	£1.50	£4	
I Cried For You	7"	Columbia	DB4739	1961	£1.50	£4	chart single
I Cried For You	7" EP	Columbia	SEG8172	1962	£10	£20	
My Mother's Eyes	7"	Columbia	DB4981	1963	£1.50	£4	

STEVENS, SHAKIN'

Bop Won't Stop	LP	Epic	BX86301	1983	£6	£15	LP, cassette, autograph book, boxed

Title	Format	Label	Catalogue	Year	Price	Price	Notes
Cry Just A Little Bit	7"	Epic	WA3774	1983	£2	£5	pic disc
Down On The Farm	7"	Parlophone	R5860	1970	£12.50	£25	
Endless Sleep	7"	Epic	6845	1979	£6	£12	
Honey Honey	7"	Emerald	MD1176	1974	£7.50	£15	
I'm No J.D.	LP	CBS	52901	1971	£20	£40	
It's Late	7"	Epic	WA3565	1983	£2.50	£6	shaped pic disc
It's Raining	7"	Epic	EPCA1643	1981	£2	£5	pic disc
Jungle Rock	7"	Mooncrest	MOON51	1976	£5	£10	
Justine	7"	Track	2094141	1978	£4	£8	
Legend	LP	Parlophone	PCS7112	1970	£25	£50	
Never	7"	Track	2094134	1977	£4	£8	
Somebody Touched Me	7"	Track	2094136	1977	£2	£5	
Somebody Touched Me	7"	Track	2094136	1977	£5	£10	PS
Spooky	7"	Epic	7235	1979	£4	£8	
Sweet Little Rock'n'Roller	7"	Polydor	2058213	1972	£7.50	£15	
Teardrops	7"	Epic	DA4882	1984	£2.50	£6	double
Tiger	7"	Everest	EV10000	1983	£2	£5	pic disc

STEWART, AL

As soon as he achieved a small measure of success, Al Stewart decided that his first LP was not as he would have liked it to be, and managed to persuade CBS to issue a new version, with a slightly different track selection and with the whole album re-mixed. The original "Bed Sitter Images" is now quite scarce. As for the even scarcer "Elf" single, Al Stewart would probably prefer to forget about it altogether!

Title	Format	Label	Catalogue	Year	Price	Price	Notes
Al Stewart Concert	LP	Arista	SP40	1977	£6	£15	US promo
Bedsitter Images	LP	CBS	(S)BPG63087	1967	£25	£50	
Bedsitter Images	LP	CBS	3034	1967	£2	£5	
Electric Los Angeles Sunset	7"	CBS	4843	1970	£1.50	£4	
Elf	7"	Decca	F12467	1966	£30	£60	
First Album (Bedsitter Images)	LP	CBS	64023	1970	£8	£20	
Love Chronicles	LP	CBS	63460	1969	£5	£12	
Orange	LP	CBS	64730	1972	£5	£12	
Year Of The Cat	LP	Mobile Fidelity	MFSL1009	1978	£6	£15	US audiophile
Zero She Flies	LP	CBS	63848	1970	£5	£12	chart LP

STEWART, ANDY

Title	Format	Label	Catalogue	Year	Price	Price	Notes
Donald, Where's Your Troosers?	7"	Top Rank	JAR427	1960	£1.50	£4	

STEWART, BILLY

Title	Format	Label	Catalogue	Year	Price	Price	Notes
Because I Love You	7"	Chess	CRS8028	1966	£5	£10	
Billy Stewart Remembered	LP	Chess	LPS1547	1968	£5	£12	US
Cross My Heart	7"	Chess	CRS8067	1967	£1.50	£4	
I Do Love You	LP	Chess	LP(S)1496	1965	£6	£15	US
I Do Love You	7"	Chess	CRS8009	1965	£4	£8	
I Do Love You	7" EP	Chess	CRE6024	1966	£5	£10	
Love Me	7"	Chess	CRS8038	1966	£2.50	£6	
Ol' Man River	7"	Chess	CRS8050	1966	£1.50	£4	
Reap What You Sow	7"	Pye	7N25164	1962	£4	£8	
Secret Love	7"	Chess	CRS8045	1966	£2.50	£6	
Sitting In The Park	7"	Chess	CRS8017	1965	£4	£8	
Strange Feeling	7"	Pye	7N25222	1963	£2.50	£6	
Summertime	7"	Chess	CRS8040	1966	£2	£5	chart single
Summertime	7"	Chess	CRS8092	1969	£1.50	£6	
Teaches Old Standards New Tricks	LP	Chess	LP(S)1513	1967	£5	£12	US
Unbelievable	LP	Chess	CRL4523	1966	£6	£15	

STEWART, BOB

Title	Format	Label	Catalogue	Year	Price	Price	Notes
Unique Sound Of The Psaltery	LP	Argo	ZDA207	1975	£5	£12	
Up Like The Swallow	LP	Broadside	BRO131	1978	£5	£12	
Wraggle Taggle Gypsies O	LP	Crescent	ARS105	1976	£5	£12	

STEWART, DAVE & BRIAN HARRISON

Title	Format	Label	Catalogue	Year	Price	Price	Notes
Girl	7"	Multicord	MULTSH1	1971	£10	£20	

STEWART, DAVIE

Title	Format	Label	Catalogue	Year	Price	Price	Notes
Davie Stewart	LP	Topic	12T293	1978	£5	£12	

STEWART, DELANO

Title	Format	Label	Catalogue	Year	Price	Price	Notes
Got To Come Back	7"	High Note	HS027	1969	£2.50	£6	
Hallelujah	7"	High Note	HS034	1969	£2	£5	
Let's Have Some Fun	7"	High Note	HS004	1968	£4	£8	
Rocking Sensation	7"	High Note	HS014	1969	£4	£8	Gaytones B side
Stay A Little Bit Longer	LP	Trojan	TBL138	1970	£5	£12	
That's Life	7"	Doctor Bird	DB1138	1968	£5	£10	

STEWART, JOHN

Title	Format	Label	Catalogue	Year	Price	Price	Notes
July, You're A Woman	7"	Capitol	CL15589	1969	£1.50	£4	
Signals Through The Glass	LP	Capitol	(S)T2975	1968	£5	£12	US
Until It's Time For You To Go	7"	CBS	202091	1966	£1.50	£4	

STEWART, RED

Title	Format	Label	Catalogue	Year	Price	Price	Notes
Favorite Old Songs	LP	Audio Lab	AL1528	1959	£10	£25	US

STEWART, REX

Title	Format	Label	Catalogue	Year	Price	Price	Notes
Rendezvous With Rex	LP	Felsted	FAJ7001	1959	£5	£12	
Rex Stewart Orchestra	10" LP	Felsted	EDL87017	1955	£10	£25	

STEWART, ROD

The fact that Rod Stewart often performs indifferent material should not be allowed to obscure the fact that he is one of the great rock singers. His early Vertigo LPs are fine records that successfully blend acoustic and electric styles into a very satisfying whole. Even better is Stewart's powerful blues singing on Jeff Beck's two sixties albums, "Truth" and "Beckola". Before this, Rod Stewart learnt his craft as a member of Long John Baldry's Hoochie Coochie Men and of Steampacket - his first singles come from this period and still hold up well, especially a version of "Shake", backed by Brian Auger's Trinity (who were also a part of Steampacket), which is actually more dynamic than Sam Cooke's original.

Atlantic Crossing	LP	Riva	RVLP4	1975	£4	£10	...blue or orange vinyl
Blondes Have More Fun	LP	Mobile Fidelity	MFSL1054	1981	£4	£10	... US audiophile
Camouflage	LP	Warner Bros	9250951	1984	£6	£15	.... with 1 sided pic disc and cassette
Day Will Come	7"	Columbia	DB7766	1965	£12.50	£25	
Do Ya Think I'm Sexy	12"	Riva	SAM92	1978	£2.50	£6	.... promo
Do Ya Think I'm Sexy	12"	Riva	SAM92	1978	£6	£15	... promo, green or blue vinyl
Gasoline Alley	LP	Vertigo	6360500	1970	£4	£10	.. spiral label, chart LP
Good Morning Little Schoolgirl	7"	Decca	F11996	1964	£15	£30	
Handbags And Gladrags	7"	Mercury	73031	1970	£1.50	£4	
Infatuation	7"	Warner Bros	SAM194	1984	£6	£12	.... 1 sided pic disc with interview tape
It's All Over Now	7"	Vertigo	6086002	1970	£1.50	£4	
Little Miss Understood	7"	Immediate	IM060	1967	£12.50	£25	
Maggie May	7"	Mercury	BRAUN3	197-	£1.50	£4	
Old Raincoat Won't Ever Let You Down	LP	Vertigo	VO4	1970	£4	£10	.... spiral label
Reason To Believe	LP	St.Michael	21020102	1978	£6	£15	
Reason To Believe	7"	Mercury	6052097	1970	£1.50	£4	.. 'Maggie May' on B side, chart single
Sailing	7"	Riva	RIVA9	1977	£15	£30	.........blue vinyl, PS
Shake	7"	Columbia	DB7892	1966	£12.50	£25	
Tonight's The Night/First Cut Is The Deepest	7"	Riva	RIVA3	1977	£2.50	£6	
You're Insane	12"	Riva	DISCO1A	1980	£5	£12	.... promo

STEWART, SANDY

Certain Smile	7"	London	HLE8683	1958	£4	£8	
My Colouring Book	7"	Pye	7N25176	1963	£1.50	£4	

STEWART, WINSTON

All Of My Life	7"	Port-O-Jam	PJ4002	1964	£5	£10	
But I Do	7"	R&B	JB147	1964	£5	£10	

STEWART, WYNN

Wishful Thinking	7"	London	HL7087	1960	£10	£20	..........export

STIDHAM, ARBEE

Tired Of Wandering	LP	Bluesville	BV1021	1961	£8	£20	.... US

STIFF LITTLE FINGERS

Listen	7"	Chrysalis	CHSDJ2580	1982	£2	£5	......juke box issue
Suspect Device	7"	Rigid Digits	SRD1	1978	£5	£10	......red label, hand-made PS
Suspect Device	7"	Rigid Digits	SRD1	1978	£2.50	£6	...... yellow label

STILL LIFE

Still Life	LP	Vertigo	6360026	1971	£40	£80	.... spiral label, sleeve pictured in Guide
What Did We Miss	7"	Columbia	DB8345	1968	£10	£20	

STILLS, STEPHEN

Love The One You're With	7"	Atlantic	2091046	1971	£1.50	£4	........chart single
Stephen Stills	LP	Atlantic	2401004	1970	£5	£12	........chart LP
Stephen Stills 2	LP	Atlantic	2401013	1971	£4	£10	........chart LP

STING

Acoustic Live In Newcastle	CD	A&M	3971712	1991	£10	£25	.... boxed with book
Dream Of The Blue Turtles	LP	A&M	DREMP1	1985	£5	£12	........pic disc
They Dance Alone	10"	A&M	AMX458	1988	£2.50	£6	...... promo

STINKY TOYS

Stinky Toys	LP	Polydor	2393174	1977	£4	£10	

STIRLING, PETER LEE

Big Sam	7"	MCA	MU1093	1969	£1.50	£4	
Everything Will Be Alright	7"	Parlophone	R5198	1964	£1.50	£4	
Goodbye Summer Girl	7"	MCA	MK5027	1970	£1.50	£4	
Goodbye Thimblemill Lane	7"	Decca	F12674	1967	£1.50	£4	
I Could If I Wanted To	7"	Parlophone	R5063	1963	£1.50	£4	
My Heart Commands Me	7"	Columbia	DB4992	1963	£1.50	£4	
Now That I've Found You	7"	Parlophone	R5112	1964	£1.50	£4	
Oh What A Fool	7"	Decca	F22535	1966	£1.50	£4	
Sad, Lonely And Blue	7"	Parlophone	R5158	1964	£1.50	£4	
Sweet And Tender Hold	7"	Decca	F12433	1966	£1.50	£4	
You Don't Live Twice	7"	Decca	F12628	1967	£1.50	£4	

STITES, GARY

Lawdy Miss Clawdy	7"	London	HLL9082	1960	£5	£10	
Lonely For You	LP	Carlton	(ST)LP120	1960	£8	£20	...... US
Lonely For You	7"	London	HLL8881	1959	£5	£10	
Starry Eyed	7"	London	HLL9003	1959	£2.50	£6	

STITT, SONNY

337 Minutes And 48 Seconds	LP	Vogue	LAE12208	1960	£8	£20	
Blows The Blues	LP	HMV	CLP1420/CSD1341	1961	£8	£20	
Kaleidoscope	LP	Esquire	32112	1961	£10	£25	
New York Jazz	LP	Columbia	33CX10114	1958	£20	£40	
Only The Blues	LP	HMV	CLP1280	1959	£8	£20	

Personal Appearance	LP	HMV	CLP1363	1960	£8	£20	
Quartet/Quintet	LP	Vogue	LAE12196	1960	£8	£20	
Sonny Side Up	LP	Columbia	33CX10140	1959	£6	£15	with Dizzy Gillespie & Sonny Rollins
Sonny Stitt-Bud Powell Quartet	10" LP	Esquire	20013	1953	£40	£80	
S.P.J. Jazz	LP	Esquire	32049	1958	£20	£40	with Bud Powell & J.J.Johnson
Stitt's Bits	LP	Esquire	32078	1959	£20	£40	
With The New Yorkers	LP	Vogue	LAE12191	1959	£8	£20	
With The Oscar Peterson Trio	LP	HMV	CLP1384	1960	£8	£20	

STIVELL, ALAN

A L'Olympia	LP	Fontana	6399005	1972	£4	£10	
E Langonned	LP	Fontana	9101500	1975	£4	£10	
From Celtic Roots	LP	Fontana	6325304	1974	£4	£10	
In Dublin	LP	Fontana	9299547	1975	£4	£10	
Reflections	LP	Fontana	6399008	1974	£4	£10	
Renaissance Of The Celtic Harp	LP	Philips	6414406	1971	£4	£10	

ST.JOHN, BARRY

Bread And Butter	7"	Decca	F11975	1964	£2.50	£6	
Come Away Melinda	7"	Columbia	DB7783	1965	£2.50	£6	chart single
Cry Like A Baby	7"	Major Minor	MM587	1969	£2.50	£6	
Everything I Touch Turns To Tears	7"	Columbia	DB7868	1966	£15	£30	
Hey Boy	7"	Decca	F12145	1965	£2	£5	
Little Bit Of Soap	7"	Decca	F11933	1964	£2.50	£6	
Mind How You Go	7"	Decca	F12111	1965	£2	£5	

ST.JOHN, BRIDGET

Ask Me No Questions	LP	Dandelion	63750	1969	£10	£25	
Fly High	7"	Polydor	2001280	1972	£2	£5	PS
If You've Got Money	7"	Warner Bros	WB8019	1970	£1.50	£4	
Jumble Queen	LP	Chrysalis	CHR1062	1974	£5	£12	
Songs For The Gentle Man	LP	Dandelion	DAN8007	1971	£10	£25	
Thank You For	LP	Dandelion	2310193	1972	£10	£25	
To B Without A Hitch	7"	Dandelion	K4404	1970	£1.50	£4	

ST.JOHN, RICH

Thru' His Eyes	LP	Polydor	623034	1966	£8	£20	German

ST.JOHN, TAMMY

Boys	7"	Pye	7N15682	1964	£1.50	£4	
Dark Shadows And Empty Hallways	7"	Pye	7N15948	1965	£1.50	£4	
Nobody Knows What's Goin' On	7"	Pye	7N17042	1966	£7.50	£15	

ST.LOUIS JIMMY

Goin' Down Slow	LP	Bluesville	BV1028	1961	£6	£15	US

ST.LOUIS UNION

Behind The Door	7"	Decca	F12386	1966	£7.50	£15	
East Side Story	7"	Decca	F12508	1966	£7.50	£15	
Girl	7"	Decca	F12318	1966	£1.50	£4	chart single

STOCKER, GREENWOOD & FRIENDS

Billy Plus Nine		Changes	CR1400	1979	£30	£60	

STOCKHAUSEN, KARLHEINZ

Stockhausen has always tended to be the first port of call for those wishing to investigate the classical avant garde, and with good reason, for he pioneered most of it. Amongst his vast output are to be found purely electronic works (try "Telemusik" and "Kontakte" for starters); works that mix electronics with voices and acoustic instruments ("Gesang Der Junglinge" and "Mixtur"); works that experiment with spatial effects ("Carre"); essentially mantric exercises ("Stimmung"); orchestral freak-outs ("Trans"); and free improvisation ("Aus Den Sieben Tagen"). None of it is rock music and yet his ideas have been a considerable influence on many of the more open rock musicians.

Aus Den Sieben Tagen	LP	Deutsche Grammophon		1971	£5	£12	6 separate LPs - price is for each
Ceylon/Bird Of Passage	LP	Chrysalis	CHR1110	1976	£4	£10	
Elektronische Studie I & II	LP	Deutsche Grammophon	LP16133		£5	£12	
Gesang Der Junglinge/Kontakte	LP	Deutsche Grammophon	138811	1962	£5	£12	also a later remixed issue
Gruppen/Carre	LP	Deutsche Grammophon	137002	1968	£5	£12	
Hymnen	LP	Deutsche Grammophon	2707039	19769	£6	£15	double
Klavierstucke 8	LP	Vox	STGBY637	1971	£4	£10	
Klavierstucke 9,11	LP	Philips	6500101	1971	£4	£10	
Klavierstucken	LP	CBS	72591/2		£6	£10	double
Kontakte (piano version)/Refrain	LP	Vox	STGBY638	1970	£4	£10	
Kurzwellen	LP	Deutsche Grammophon	2707045	1971	£6	£15	double
Mantra	LP	Deutsche Grammophon	2530208	1972	£5	£12	
Mikrophonie I and II	LP	Deutsche Grammophon	2530583	197-	£5	£12	
Momente	LP	Deutsche Grammophon	2709055	1976	£8	£20	triple
Momente	LP	Nonesuch	H71157	196-	£4	£10	
Opus 1970	LP	Deutsche Grammophon	139461	197-	£5	£12	
Prozession	LP	Deutsche Grammophon	2530582	197-	£5	£12	

Prozession	LP	Vox	STGBY615	1969	£4	£10	
Solo	LP	Deutsche Grammophon	137005	196-	£5	£12	
Stimmung	LP	Deutsche Grammophon	2543003	1970	£5	£12	
Stop/Ylem	LP	Deutsche Grammophon	2530442	1974	£5	£12	
Telemusik/Mixtur	LP	Deutsche Grammophon	137012	1970	£5	£12	
Trans	LP	Deutsche Grammophon	2530726	1976	£5	£12	
Zyklus	LP	Erato	STU70603		£4	£10	

STOCKTON'S WING

Stockton's Wing	LP	Tara	2004	1978	£5	£12	Irish
Take A Chance	LP	Tara	30041980	1980	£5	£12	Irish

STOICS

Earth, Wind And Fire	7"	RCA	RCA1745	1968	£1.50	£4	

STOKES

Whipped Cream	7"	London	HLU9955	1965	£1.50	£4	

STOLLER, RHET

Bandit	7"	Windsor	PS118	1964	£7.50	£15	demo
Caravan	7"	Windsor	PS119	1964	£5	£10	
Chariot	7"	Decca	F11302	1960	£2.50	£6	chart single
Countdown	7"	Decca	F11738	1963	£2.50	£6	
Ricochet	7"	Windsor	PS130	1964	£5	£10	
Sunshine Anytime	7" EP.	Mosaic	MOSAIC1	196-	£4	£8	
Treble Gold & One	7"	Melodisc	1595	1964	£5	£10	
Uncrowned King	7"	Columbia	DB8013	1966	£7.50	£15	demo
Walk Don't Run	7"	Decca	F11271	1960	£4	£8	

STOLOFF, MORRIS

Moonglow And Theme From Picnic	7"	Brunswick	05553	1956	£1.50	£4	chart single

STOMPERS

Foolish Idea	7"	Fontana	H385	1962	£2.50	£6	

STONE ANGEL

Stone Angel	LP	private	SSLP04	1975	£100	£200	

STONE, CLIFFIE

Cool Cowboy	LP	Capitol	(S)T1230	1959	£5	£12	US
Party's On Me	LP	Capitol	T1080	1959	£5	£12	
Popcorn Song	7"	Capitol	CL14330	1955	£20	£40	

STONE, GEORGE

Hole In The Wall	7"	Stateside	SS479	1965	£2.50	£6	

STONE, KIRBY FOUR

Blue Guitar	7"	Warner Bros	WB118	1963	£1.50	£4	
Honey Hush	7"	Vogue Coral	Q72129	1956	£4	£8	
Honeydripper	7"	Philips	PB1151	1961	£1.50	£4	
Man, I Flipped	LP	London	HAA2164	1959	£5	£12	

STONE, MARK

Stroll	7"	London	HLR8543	1958	£30	£60	

STONE PONEYS

Lead singer with the Stone Poneys was Linda Ronstadt - these are her first recordings.

Different Drum	7"	Capitol	CL15523	1967	£2	£5	
Evergreen	LP	Capitol	ST2763	1967	£4	£10	US
So Fine	7"	Sidewalk	937	1966	£37.50	£75	US
Stone Poneys	LP	Capitol	ST2666	1967	£4	£10	US
Stone Poneys & Friends	LP	Capitol	ST2863	1968	£4	£10	US

STONE, ROLAND

Just A Moment	LP	Ace	LP1018	1961	£6	£15	US

STONE ROSES

Elephant Stone	12"	Silvertone	ORE1T	1988	£2.50	£6	black cat.no. on sleeve
Sally Cinnamon	12"	Black	12REV36	1987	£4	£10	'printed in England' on rear sleeve
So Young	12"	Thin Line	THIN001	1985	£15	£30	

STONE THE CROWS

Continuous Performance	LP	Polydor	2391043	1972	£5	£12	chart LP
Ode To John Law	LP	Polydor	2425042	1970	£5	£12	
Stone The Crows	LP	Polydor	2425017	1970	£5	£12	
Teenage Licks	LP	Polydor	2425071	1971	£5	£12	

STONEFIELD TRAMP

Dreaming Again	LP	Acorn	CF247	1974	£75	£150	

STONEHENGE MEN

Big Feet	7"	HMV	POP981	1962	£10	£20	

STONEHOUSE
Stonehouse Creek .... LP ..... RCA .... SF8197 .... 1971 ... £40 .... £80 ....

STONE'S MASONRY
The recorded evidence is that Martin Stone was one of the great sixties guitarists, even if he seems to have long ago vanished from rock music. The blues instrumental "Flapjacks", which was released on Mike Vernon's pre-Blue Horizon Purdah label, is a good demonstration of his talents. The group folded, before it could record anything else, when Stone joined Savoy Brown - moving from there to Mighty Baby.
Flapjacks .... 7" .... Purdah .... 453504 .... 1966 ... £30 .... £60 ....

STOREY, DAVE & THE HARLEQUINS
Who's Sorry .... 7" .... Parlophone ..... R5365 .... 1965 ... £1.50 .... £4 ....

STOREY SISTERS
Bad Motorcycle .... 7" .... London .... HLU8571 .... 1958 ... £20 .... £40 ....

STORM
.... LP ..... Vampire .... 197- .... £65 .... £130 ....

STORM, BILLY
Billy Storm .... LP ..... Buena Vista ... BV3315 .... 1963 ... £15 .... £30 .... US
Sure As You're Born .... 7" .... London .... HLK9236 .... 1960 ... £2.50 .... £6 ....
This Is The Night .... LP ..... Famous .... F504 .... 1969 ... £6 .... £15 .... US

STORM, DANNY
Honest I Do .... 7" .... Piccadilly .... 7N35025 .... 1962 ... £4 .... £8 .... chart single
I Just Can't Fool My Heart .... 7" .... Piccadilly .... 7N35091 .... 1962 ... £5 .... £10 ....
Just You .... 7" .... Piccadilly .... 7N35053 .... 1962 ... £4 .... £8 ....
Say You Do .... 7" .... Piccadilly .... 7N35143 .... 1963 ... £4 .... £8 ....

STORM, GALE
Dark Moon .... 7" .... London .... HLD8424 .... 1957 ... £5 .... £10 ....
Don't Be That Way .... 7" .... London .... HLD8311 .... 1956 ... £10 .... £20 ....
Farewell To Arms .... 7" .... London .... HLD8570 .... 1958 ... £5 .... £10 ....
Gale Storm .... LP ..... Dot .... DLP3011 .... 1956 ... £10 .... £25 .... US
Heart Without A Sweetheart .... 7" .... London .... HLD8329 .... 1956 ... £7.50 .... £15 ....
Hits .... LP ..... Dot .... DLP3098 .... 1958 ... £10 .... £25 .... US
I Hear You Knocking .... 7" .... London .... HLD8222 .... 1956 ... £12.50 .... £25 ....
Ivory Tower .... 7" .... London .... HLD8283 .... 1956 ... £12.50 .... £25 ....
Lucky Lips .... 7" .... London .... HLD8393 .... 1957 ... £10 .... £20 ....
Memories Are Made Of This .... 7" .... London .... HLD8232 .... 1956 ... £10 .... £20 ....
Orange Blossoms .... 7" .... London .... HLD8413 .... 1957 ... £6 .... £12 ....
Presenting Gale Storm .... 10" LP London .... HBD1056 .... 1956 ... £15 .... £30 ....
Sentimental Me .... LP ..... London .... HAD2104 .... 1958 ... £8 .... £20 ....
Why Do Fools Fall In Love .... 7" .... London .... HL7008 .... 1956 ... £4 .... £8 .... export
Why Do Fools Fall In Love .... 7" .... London .... HLD8286 .... 1956 ... £10 .... £20 ....
You .... 7" .... London .... HLD8632 .... 1958 ... £4 .... £8 ....

STORM, RORY & THE HURRICANES
America .... 7" .... Parlophone ..... R5197 .... 1964 ... £7.50 .... £15 ....
Doctor Feelgood .... 7" .... Oriole .... CB1858 .... 1963 ... £10 .... £20 ....

STORME, ROBB
Bu Bop A Lu Bop A Lie .... 7" .... Piccadilly .... 7N35160 .... 1963 ... £2 .... £5 ....
Earth Angel .... 7" .... Decca .... F11388 .... 1961 ... £2 .... £5 ....
Five Minutes More .... 7" .... Decca .... F11313 .... 1961 ... £2 .... £5 ....
Happens Every Day .... 7" .... Piccadilly .... 7N35133 .... 1963 ... £2 .... £5 ....
Here Today .... 7" .... Columbia .... DB7993 .... 1966 ... £2 .... £5 ....
I Don't Need Your Love Anymore .... 7" .... Decca .... F11282 .... 1960 ... £2 .... £5 ....
Lonely Town .... 7" .... Decca .... F11364 .... 1961 ... £2 .... £5 ....
Pretty Hair And Angel Eyes .... 7" .... Decca .... F11432 .... 1962 ... £2 .... £5 ....
Sixteen Years Ago Tonight .... 7" .... Pye .... 7N15515 .... 1963 ... £2 .... £5 ....
Wheels .... 7" EP.. Decca .... DFE6700 .... 1962 ... £12.50 .... £25 ....
Where Is My Girl .... 7" .... Columbia .... DB7756 .... 1965 ... £2 .... £5 ....

STORMSVILLE SHAKERS
Number One .... 7" EP.. Odeon .... MEO148 .... 1967 ... £7.50 .... £15 .... French

STORYTELLER
Storyteller's blend of poetry and folk song was greeted with ecstatic reviews and the chance of a performance at the Festival Hall while still very much an up-and-coming group. The first track on the "Storyteller" LP is a delightful piece of folk-rock, with a sparkling guitar solo from Peter Frampton, but its companion tracks are not often in the same league. Singer Caroline Attard married the group's producer, Andy Bown (who was formerly a member of the Herd), but her attractive voice has not been heard on record since the early seventies.
More Pages .... LP ..... Transatlantic ... TRA232 .... 1971 ... £6 .... £15 ....
Remarkable .... 7" .... CBS .... 7182 .... 1971 ... £2 .... £5 ....
Storyteller .... LP ..... Transatlantic ... TRA220 .... 1970 ... £8 .... £20 ....

STOUGHTON, DAVID
Transformer .... LP ..... Elektra .... EKS74034 .... 1968 ... £6 .... £15 .... US

STOWAWAYS
Stowaways .... LP ..... Justice .... 196- .... £90 .... £180 .... US

ST.PATRICK, OLIVER
I Want To Be Loved By You .... 7" .... Trojan .... TR005 .... 1967 ... £5 .... £10 ....

ST.PETERS, CRISPIAN
Almost Persuaded .... 7" .... Decca .... F12596 .... 1967 ... £1.50 .... £4 ....
Almost Persuaded .... 7" EP.. Decca .... DFE8678 .... 1967 ... £6 .... £12 ....
At This Moment .... 7" .... Decca .... F12080 .... 1965 ... £1.50 .... £4 ....
But She's Untrue .... 7" .... Decca .... F12525 .... 1966 ... £1.50 .... £4 ....
Carolina .... 7" .... Decca .... F12861 .... 1968 ... £1.50 .... £4 ....

Changes	7″	Decca	F12480	1966	£1.50	£4	
Changes	7″ EP	Decca	457126	1966	£5	£10	French
Follow Me	LP	Decca	LK4805	1966	£6	£15	
Free Spirit	7″	Decca	F12677	1967	£1.50	£4	
No No No	7″	Decca	F12207	1965	£1.50	£4	
Pied Piper	7″	Decca	F12359	1966	£1.50	£4	chart single
Simply	LP	Square	SQA102	1970	£5	£12	
So Long	7″	Decca	F13055	1970	£5	£10	
That's The Time	7″	Decca	F12761	1968	£1.50	£4	
You Were On My Mind	7″	Decca	F12287	1965	£1.50	£4	chart single
You Were On My Mind	7″ EP	Decca	457110	1966	£6	£12	French

STRANGE

Raw Power	LP	Outer Galaxie	1001	1976	£10	£25	US
Translucent World	LP	Outer Galaxie	1000	1973	£15	£30	US

STRANGE, BILLY

Few Dollars More	7″	Vocalion	VP9289	1967	£1.50	£4	
Get Smart	7″	Vocalion	VP9259	1966	£1.50	£4	
Goldfinger	7″	Vocalion	VP9231	1964	£1.50	£4	
James Bond Theme	7″	Vocalion	VP9228	1964	£1.50	£4	
Thunderball	7″	Vocalion	VP9257	1966	£1.50	£4	
Where Your Arms Used To Be	7″	London	HLG9321	1961	£1.50	£4	

STRANGE DAYS

Nine Parts To The Wind	LP	Retreat	RTL6005	1975	£10	£25

STRANGE FRUIT

Cut Across Shorty	7″	Village Thing	VTSX1001	1971	£5	£10

STRANGE, STEVE

In The Year 2525	7″	Palace	1		£12.50	£25	test pressing only
In The Year 2525	7″	Palace	1		£25	£50	test pressing with PS

STRANGELOVES

Cara-Lin	7″	Immediate	IM007	1965	£5	£10	
Cara-Lin	7″	Immediate	IM007	196-	£2.50	£6	pink label
Dansez Le Monkiss	7″ EP	Atlantic	750006	1965	£10	£20	French
Hand Jive	7″	London	HLZ10063	1966	£5	£10	
Honey Do	7″	London	HLK10238	1969	£5	£10	
I Want Candy	LP	Bang	BLP(S)211	1965	£10	£25	US
I Want Candy	7″	London	HLM10481	1975	£1.50	£4	
I Want Candy	7″	Stateside	SS446	1965	£6	£12	
Night Time	7″	London	HLZ10020	1966	£6	£12	

STRANGERS

Do You Or Don't You	7″	Philips	BF1378	1964	£2	£5	
One And One Is Two	7″	Philips	BF1335	1964	£17.50	£35	with Mike Shannon
Ram-Bunk-Shush	7″ EP	President	281	1964	£10	£20	French
Strangers With Mike Shannon	7″ EP	Pathe	EGF795	1964	£12.50	£25	French

STRANGERS (2)

Look Out	7″	Pye	7N17240	1967	£6	£12

STRANGLERS

All Day And All Of The Night	CD-s	Epic	CDVICE1	1988	£4	£10	
All Day And All Of The Night	7″	Epic	VICE1	1988	£4	£8	Monica Couglan sleeve
Bear Cage	12″	United Artists	12BP344	1980	£2.50	£6	no PS
Bear Cage	12″	United Artists	12BP344	1980	£6	£15	PS
Black And White	LP	A&M	SP4706	1978	£6	£15	US, black & white vinyl
Dreamtime	LP	Epic	EPC1126648	1986	£5	£12	pic disc
European Female	7″	Epic	EPCA112893	1983	£2	£5	pic disc
Gospel According To The Men In Black	LP	Liberty	LBG30313	1981	£8	£20	test pressing
N'Emmenes Pas Harry	7″	United Artists		1979	£5	£10	sung in French
Nice In Nice	7″	Epic	EPC6500550	1986	£1.50	£4	shaped pic disc
No Mercy	7″	Epic	WA4921	1984	£1.50	£4	shaped pic disc
No More Heroes	7″	United Artists	FREE8	1977	£10	£20	1 sided promo
Peaches	7″	United Artists	FREE4	1977	£25	£50	promo
Peaches	7″	United Artists	UP36248	1977	£100	£200	PS with newspaper lettering & group pic
Peaches	7″	United Artists	UP36248	1978	£5	£10	mispress, B side plays Buzzcocks
Rattus Norvegicus	LP	United Artists	UAG30045	1977	£5	£12	with 7″ (FREE3)
Raven	LP	United Artists	UAG30262	1979	£5	£12	3-D cover
Something Better Change	7″	A&M	AM1973	1977	£2	£5	US, pink marbled vinyl
Stranglers Singles Collection	LP	Liberty	LBG30353	1982	£4	£10	with original dark cover
Sverge	7″	United Artists	UP36459	1978	£4	£8	sung in Swedish

STRATUS

Throwing Shapes	LP	Steel Trax	STEEL31001	1985	£4	£10

STRAWBERRY ALARM CLOCK

Best Of The Strawberry Alarm Clock	LP	Uni	73074	1970	£8	£20	US
Changes	LP	Vocalion	73915	1971	£8	£20	US
Good Morning Starshine	LP	Uni	73054	1969	£10	£25	US
Good Morning Starshine	7″	MCA	MU1080	1969	£4	£8	

Incense & Peppermints	LP	Pye	N(S)PL28106	1968	£10	£25	
Incense And Peppermints	7"	Pye	7N25436	1967	£6	£12	
Sit With The Guru	7"	Pye	7N25456	1968	£6	£12	
Tomorrow	7"	Pye	7N25446	1968	£6	£12	
Wake Up It's Tomorrow	LP	Uni	73025	1967	£10	£25	US
World In A Sea Shell	LP	Uni	73035	1968	£10	£25	US

STRAWBERRY CHILDREN
Song-writer and producer Jimmy Webb made his first bid for stardom as a performer with the one single released by the Strawberry Children - a trio fronted by Webb himself.

Love Years Coming	7"	Liberty	LBF15012	1967	£5	£10	

STRAWBERRY JAM

Personally	7"	Pye	7N17711	1969	£4	£8	

STRAWBS
The earlier editions of the Price Guide list a Strawbs LP called "Heartbreak Hill", which would be worth a tidy sum if it ever appeared on the market. Alas, the music was recorded in 1979 but never actually committed to vinyl - there are not even any test pressings for collectors to discover. During the eighties, however, Dave Cousins was selling cassettes of the actual music, so that a version of "Heartbreak Hill" does exist, albeit not in a form that is likely to reach any kind of high value.

Benedictus	7"	A&M	AM874	1971	£1.50	£4	
Burning For You	LP	Oyster	2391287	1977	£5	£12	
Bursting At The Seams	LP	A&M	AMLH68144	1973	£5	£12	chart LP
Dead Lines	LP	Arista	SPART1036	1978	£5	£12	
Deep Cuts	LP	Oyster	2391234	1976	£5	£12	
Dragonfly	LP	A&M	AMLS970	1970	£8	£20	
Forever	7"	A&M	AM791	1970	£2	£5	
From The Witchwood	LP	A&M	AMLS64304	1971	£5	£12	chart LP
Ghosts	LP	A&M	AMLH68277	1975	£5	£12	
Grave New World	LP	A&M	AMLH68078	1972	£5	£12	chart LP
Hero And Heroine	LP	A&M	AMLH63607	1974	£5	£12	chart LP
Just A Collection Of Antiques And Curios	LP	A&M	AMLS994	1970	£6	£15	chart LP
King	7"	LO	LO1	197-	£2.50	£6	PS
Man Who Called Himself Jesus	7"	A&M	AM738	1968	£2	£5	
Nomadness	LP	A&M	AMLH68331	1976	£5	£12	
Oh How She Changed	7"	A&M	AM725	1968	£2	£5	
Strawberry Music Sampler No.1	LP	private		1969	£330	£500	
Strawbs	LP	A&M	AMLS936	1969	£8	£20	
Witchwood	7"	A&M	AM837	1971	£2.50	£6	promo

STRAWHEAD

Fortunes Of War	LP	Tradition	TSR032	1978	£4	£10	

STRAY

Hearts Of Fire	LP	Pye	NSPL18512	1976	£4	£10	
Houdini	LP	Pye	NSPL18482	1976	£4	£10	
Move It	LP	Transatlantic	TRA281	1974	£4	£10	
Mudanzas	LP	Transatlantic	TRA268	1973	£4	£10	
Only What You Make It	7"	Transatlantic	PROMO1	1970	£2	£5	promo
Saturday Morning Pictures	LP	Transatlantic	TRA248	1972	£4	£10	
Stand Up & Be Counted	LP	Dawn	DNLS3066	1975	£4	£10	
Stray	LP	Transatlantic	TRA216	1970	£4	£10	
Suicide	LP	Transatlantic	TRA233	1971	£4	£10	

STRAY CATS

She's Sexy And Seventeen	7"	Arista	SCAT6	1983	£5	£10	shaped pic disc

STRAYHORN, BILLY

Cue For Saxophone	LP	Felsted	FAJ7008/SJA2008	1960	£10	£25	

STREAMLINERS & JOANNE

Everybody's Doing The Twist	7"	Columbia	DB4809	1962	£1.50	£4	
Frankfurter Sandwiches	7"	Columbia	DB4689	1961	£1.50	£4	

STREAPLERS

Times They Are A-Changin'	7" EP	Columbia	ESRF1786	1966	£6	£12	French

STREET, GARY & THE FAIRWAYS

Flippedy Flop	7"	Domain	D2	1968	£1.50	£4	

STREET, HILLARD

River Love	7"	Capitol	CL14960	1958	£1.50	£4	

STREET, JOHN & THE INMATES OF NO.12

Keep A Little Love	7"	Deram	DM147	1967	£1.50	£4	

STREETWALKERS

Red Card	LP	Vertigo	9102010	1976	£4	£10	red vinyl

STREISAND, BARBRA

Barbra Joan Streisand	LP	Columbia	PCQ30792	1971	£4	£10	US quad
Barbra Streisand	7" EP	CBS	AGG20054	1964	£2.50	£6	
Butterfly	LP	Columbia	PCQ33005	1974	£4	£10	US quad
Color Me Barbra	LP	Columbia	CL2478	1966	£17.50	£35	US, red vinyl
En Francais	7" EP	CBS	EP6048	1965	£6	£12	
Funny Girl	LP	Columbia	SQ30992	1972	£4	£10	US quad
Funny Lady	LP	Arista	AQ9004	1975	£4	£10	US quad
Greatest Hits Volume 2	LP	Columbia	HC45679	1982	£4	£10	US audiophile
Guilty	LP	Columbia	HC46750	1982	£4	£10	US audiophile
Lazy Afternoon	LP	Columbia	PCQ33815	1975	£4	£10	US quad

Live In Concert At The Forum	LP	Columbia	PCQ31760	1972	£4	£10	US quad
Lover Come Back To Me	7" EP	CBS	AGG20042	1964	£2.50	£6	
Memories	LP	Columbia	HC47678	1982	£4	£10	US audiophile
My Man	7" EP	CBS	EP6068	1966	£2.50	£6	
Second Barbra Streisand Album	LP	Columbia	CS8854	1963	£25	£50	US, blue vinyl
Second Hand Rose	7" EP	CBS	EP6150	1967	£2.50	£6	
Stoney End	LP	Columbia	PCQ30378	1971	£4	£10	US quad
Way We Were	LP	Columbia	PCQ32801	1974	£4	£10	US quad

STRENGTH, TEXAS BILL

Yellow Rose Of Texas	7"	Capitol	CL14357	1955	£7.50	£15	

STRICKLAND, WILLIAM R.

William Strickland was reputed to have made his songs up as he went along and certainly they sound ramshackle enough for him to have done so. At the time, the Deram label was willing to try anything, but in the end, all that can really be said about Mr.Strickland is that he is no Syd Barrett.

Is Only The Name	LP	Deram	DML/SML1041	1969	£5	£12	

STRIDER

Exposed	LP	GM	GML1002	1973	£4	£10	
Misunderstanding	LP	GM	GML1012	1974	£4	£10	

STRING CHEESE

String Cheese	LP	RCA	SF8222	1971	£6	£15	

STRING DRIVEN THING

Another Night	7"	Concord	CON7	1970	£10	£20	
Machine That Cried	LP	Charisma	CAS1070	1973	£5	£12	
String Driven Thing	LP	Charisma	CAS1062	1972	£5	£12	
String Driven Thing	LP	Concord	CON1001	1970	£50	£100	

STRINGALONGS

Brass Buttons	7"	London	HLU9354	1961	£1.50	£4	
Matilda	7"	London	HLD9652	1963	£4	£8	
Mina Bird	7"	London	HLU9452	1961	£2.50	£6	
Should I	7"	London	HLU9394	1961	£1.50	£4	
Spinnin' My Wheels	7"	London	HLD9588	1962	£2	£5	
Stringalong With The Stringalongs	7" EP	London	REU1398	1963	£7.50	£15	

STRING-ALONGS

String-Alongs	LP	London	HAD/SHD8054	1963	£8	£20	

STRINGALONGS

Stringalongs	7" EP	London	REU1322	1961	£7.50	£15	
Stringalongs	7" EP	London	REU1350	1963	£7.50	£15	
Twistwatch	7"	London	HLD9535	1962	£2.50	£6	
Wheels	7"	London	HLU9278	1961	£1.50	£4	chart single

STRIPES OF GLORY

Denial	7"	Vogue	V9194	1962	£6	£12	

STROLLERS

Come On Over	7"	London	HLL9336	1961	£4	£8	
Jumping With Symphony Sid	7"	Vogue	V9113	1958	£7.50	£15	
Little Bitty Pretty One	7"	Vogue	V9124	1958	£7.50	£15	

STROLLERS (2)

Cuckoo	7"	Fontana	TF598	1965	£4	£8	

ST.ROMAIN, KIRBY

Summer's Comin'	7"	Stateside	SS199	1963	£1.50	£4	

STRONG, BARRETT

Money	7"	London	HLU9088	1960	£40	£80	

STRONG, NOLAN & THE DIABLOS

Fortune Of Hits	LP	Fortune	LP8010	1961	£15	£30	US
Fortune Of Hits Vol.2	LP	Fortune	LP8012	1962	£15	£30	US
Mind Over Matter	LP	Fortune	LP8015	1963	£15	£30	US

STUART, CHAD & JEREMY CLYDE

Ark	LP	Columbia	CS9699	1968	£4	£10	US
Before And After	LP	Columbia	CL2374/CS9174	1965	£4	£10	US
Before And After	7"	CBS	201769	1965	£5	£10	
Before And After	7" EP	CBS	6101	1965	£6	£12	French
Best Of Chad And Jeremy	LP	Ember	(ST)NR5036	1967	£4	£10	
Chad Stuart And Jeremy Clyde	7" EP	United Artists	UEP1008	1965	£2	£5	
Distant Shores	LP	Columbia	CL2564/CS9364	1966	£4	£10	US
Distant Shores	7"	CBS	202279	1966	£1.50	£4	
Early In The Morning	7"	Ember	EMBS186	1964	£2	£5	
I Don't Wanna Lose You Baby	LP	Ember	NR5031	1965	£4	£10	
I Don't Want To Lose You	7"	CBS	201814	1965	£1.50	£4	
If I Loved You	7"	Ember	EMBS205	1965	£1.50	£4	
If She Was Mine	7"	United Artists	UP1070	1965	£1.50	£4	
Like I Love You Today	7" EP	Pathe	EGF716	1963	£6	£12	French
More Chad And Jeremy	LP	Capitol	(S)T2546	1966	£4	£10	US
Of Cabbages And Kings	LP	CBS	2671	1967	£4	£10	
Sing For You	LP	Ember	NR5021	1965	£4	£10	
Summer Song	7"	United Artists	UP1062	1964	£1.50	£4	
Summer Song	7" EP	Pathe	EGF775	1964	£6	£12	French
Teenage Failure	7"	CBS	202035	1966	£1.50	£4	

Three In The Attic	LP	Sidewalk	ST5918	1969	£4	£10	US
What Do You Want With Me	7"	Ember	EMBS217	1966	£1.50	£4	
What Do You Want With Me	7" EP.	Pathe	EGF850	1965	£6	£12	French
Yesterday's Gone	LP	World Artists	WAM2002/	1964	£4	£10	US
			WAS3002				
Yesterday's Gone	7"	Ember	EMBS180	1963	£2	£5	chart single
Yesterday's Gone	7" EP.	Ember	EMBEP4543	1964	£2.50	£6	
You Are She	7"	CBS	202397	1966	£1.50	£4	

STUART, MIKE SPAN

Children Of Tomorrow	7"	Jewel	JL01	1968	£30	£60	
Come On Over To Our Place	7"	Columbia	DB8066	1966	£7.50	£15	
Dear	7"	Columbia	DB8206	1967	£7.50	£15	
You Can Understand Me	7"	Fontana	TF959	1968	£4	£8	

STUD

Goodbye Live At Command	LP	BASF	2029117	1973	£8	£20	
September	LP	BASF	2029054	1972	£10	£25	
Stud	LP	Deram	SMLR1084	1971	£10	£25	

STUDIO ONE ALL STARS

| Sherry | 7" | Island | WI3038 | 1967 | £5 | £10 | |

STUDIO SIX

Strawberry Window	7"	Polydor	BM56219	1967	£6	£12	
Times Were When	7"	Polydor	BM56189	1967	£1.50	£4	
When I See My Baby	7"	Polydor	BM56131	1966	£1.50	£4	

STUDIO SWEETHEARTS

| I Believe | 7" | DJM | DJS10915 | 1979 | £2.50 | £6 | PS |

STUPIDS

| Violent Nun | 7" | Children Of | COR3 | 1985 | £5 | £10 | |
| | | The Revolution | | | | | |

STURGES, JEFF & UNIVERSE

| Jeff Sturges And Universe | LP | Mam | MAMAS1002 | 1971 | £4 | £10 | |

ST.VALENTINE'S DAY MASSACRE

| Brother Can You Spare A Dime | 7" | Fontana | TF883 | 1967 | £15 | £30 | |
| Brother Can You Spare A Dime | 7" | Fontana | TF883 | 1967 | £30 | £60 | PS |

STYLE COUNCIL

| It Just Came To Pieces (live) | 7" | Lyntone | LYN15344/5 | 1984 | £2.50 | £6 | flexi |

STYLEMASTERS

| You're A Sweetheart | 7" | Capitol | CL14953 | 1958 | £1.50 | £4 | |

STYLOS

| Head Over Heels | 7" | Liberty | LIB10173 | 1964 | £40 | £80 | |

STYX

Best Of Styx	LP	RCA	3597	1979	£5	£12	Canadian blue vinyl
Collection Of Styx	LP	A&M		1979	£8	£20	promo, 3 LPs, boxed
Cornerstone	LP	A&M	SP3711	1979	£6	£15	US silver vinyl
Cornerstone	LP	Nautilus		198-	£6	£15	US audiophile
Grand Illusion	LP	A&M	SP4637	1977	£5	£12	Canadian gold vinyl
Grand Illusion	LP	Mobile Fidelity	MFSL1026	1978	£6	£15	US audiophile
Paradise Theatre	LP	Nautilus		198-	£6	£15	US audiophile
Pieces Of Eight	LP	A&M	PR4724	1978	£5	£12	US pic disc
Pieces Of Eight	LP	Nautilus		198-	£6	£15	US audiophile
Styx Radio Show	LP	A&M	SP8431	1976	£8	£20	US promo
Styx Radio Special	LP	A&M	SP17053	1977	£8	£20	US promo

SUB

| In Concert | LP | Help | | 197- | £180 | £300 | |

SUBHUMANS

| Incorrect Thoughts | LP | Friends | FR008 | 1980 | £10 | £25 | |
| No Wishes No Prayers | LP | | | | £6 | £15 | Canadian |

SUBJECT ESQ.

| Subject Esq. | LP | Epic | EPC64998 | 1972 | £5 | £12 | German |

SUBOTNICK, MORTON

| Silver Apples Of The Moon | LP | Nonesuch | H71174 | 1967 | £8 | £20 | |
| The Wild Bull | LP | Nonesuch | H71208 | 1968 | £8 | £20 | |

SUBSTITUTE

| One | 7" | Ignition | IR2 | 1979 | £2.50 | £6 | |
| One | 7" | Ignition | IR2 | 1979 | £5 | £10 | PS |

SUDDEN SWAY

Jane's Third Party	7"	Chant	CHANT1	1980	£4	£8	
Spacemate	12"	WEA	BYN8B	1986	£3	£8	double boxed set
Traffic Tax Scheme	12"	Chant	CHANT3	1984	£3	£8	

SUE & MARY

| Traitor In Disguise | 7" | Decca | F11517 | 1962 | £1.50 | £4 | |

SUE & SUNNY

| Every Ounce Of Strength | 7" | Columbia | DB7748 | 1965 | £1.50 | £4 | |

I Like Your Style	7"	Columbia	DB8099	1967	£5	£10
Show Must Go On	7"	CBS	3874	1968	£2	£5
Sue & Sunny	LP	CBS	63740	1970	£4	£10

SUE & SUNSHINE

Little Love	7"	Columbia	DB7409	1964	£1.50	£4
We're In Love	7"	Columbia	DB7533	1965	£1.50	£4

SUEDE

Be My God	12"	RML	RML001	1990	£37.50	£75	test pressing
My Insatiable One	7"	Nude	SUEDE1	1993	£2.50	£6	clear flexi

SUGAR & DANDY

I Want To Be Your Lover	7"	Carnival	CV7029	1965	£2.50	£6	
I'm Into Something Good	7"	Carnival	CV7024	1965	£2.50	£6	
I'm Not Crying Now	7"	Carnival	CV7016	1964	£2.50	£6	
Let's Ska	7"	Carnival	CV7023	1965	£2.50	£6	
Let's Ska	7"	Page One	POF23044	1967	£2.50	£6	
Meditation	7"	Blue Beat	BB367	1965	£5	£10	Jetliners B side
Oh Dear What Can The Matter Be	7"	Carnival	CV7009	1964	£2.50	£6	
One Man Went To Mow	7"	Carnival	CV7006	1963	£2.50	£6	
Ska's The Limit	LP	Page One	FOR006	1967	£8	£20	
Think Of The Good Times	7"	Carnival	CV7027	1965	£2.50	£6	
What A Life	7"	Carnival	CV7015	1964	£2.50	£6	

SUGAR & PEEWEE

One Two Let's Rock	7"	Vogue	V9112	1958	£75	£150

SUGAR & SPICE

Cruel War	7"	London	HLU10259	1969	£2	£5

SUGAR SHOPPE

Skip Along Sam	7"	Capitol	CL15555	1968	£2.50	£6

SUGARBEATS

Alice Designs	7"	Polydor	56120	1966	£2.50	£6
I Just Stand Here	7"	Polydor	56069	1966	£2.50	£6

SUGARCUBES

12.11	12"	One Little Indian	TPBOX1	1990	£22.50	£45	11 x 12', boxed
7.8	7"	One Little Indian	TPBOX2	1990	£12.50	£25	8 x 7', boxed
Birthday	CD-s	One Little Indian	7TP7CD	1987	£2.50	£6	
Birthday	12"	One Little Indian	12TP7	1987	£2.50	£6	
CD.6	CD-s	One Little Indian	TPBOX3	1990	£17.50	£35	6 x CD-s, boxed
Here Today, Tomorrow, Next Week	LP	One Little Indian	TPLP15	1989	£4	£10	silver vinyl

SUGARCUBES (SYKURMOLARNIR)

Einn Mol'a Mann	7"	Smekkleysa	SM3/86	1986	£30	£60	Icelandic
Luftgitar	12"	Smekkleysa	SM7	1987	£15	£30	Icelandic
Skytturnar	12"	Gramm	GRAMM31	1986	£10	£25	Icelandic

SUICIDAL TENDENCIES

Possessed To Skate	12"	Virgin	VS96712	1987	£2.50	£6	pic disc

SUICIDE

23 Minutes In Brussels	LP	Bronze	FRANKIE1	1978	£6	£15	
Alan Vega - Martin Rev	LP	Ze	ILPS7007	1980	£5	£12	
Cheree	7"	Bronze	BRO57	1978	£2	£5	
Dream Baby Dream	12"	Ze	WIP6543	1979	£2.50	£6	
Suicide	LP	Bronze	BRON508	1977	£6	£15	

SUICIDE COMMANDOS

Commandos Commit Suicide Dance Concert	LP	Twintone	TTR7906	1979	£8	£20	US

SULLIVAN, BIG JIM

She Walks Through The Fair	7"	Mercury	MF928	1965	£7.50	£15
Sitar Beat	LP	Mercury	SML30001	1968	£6	£15
You Don't Know What You've Got	7"	Decca	F11387	1961	£2.50	£6

SULLIVAN, IRA

Billy Taylor Introduces Ira Sullivan	LP	HMV	CLP1236	1959	£8	£20

SULLIVAN, JOE

Joe Sullivan	LP	Columbia	33CX10047	1956	£6	£15
Joe Sullivan	LP	London	HAU2011	1956	£6	£15
Joe Sullivan Plays Fats Waller	10" LP	Philips	BBR8091	1956	£8	£20

SULLIVAN, MAXINE

Boogie Woogie Maxine	7"	Parlophone	MSP6086	1954	£1.50	£4

SUMLIN, HUBERT

Across The Board	7"	Blue Horizon	451000	1965	£20	£40

SUMMER, DONNA

Hot Stuff	12"	Casablanca	CANL151	1979	£4	£10	red vinyl

SUMMER SET
Farmer's Daughter	7"	Columbia	DB8004	1966	£4	£8	
It's A Dream	7"	Columbia	DB8215	1967	£15	£30	

SUMMERFIELD, SAFFRON
Fancy Meeting You Here	LP	Mother Earth	MUM1202	1976	£20	£40	
Salisbury Plain	LP	Mother Earth	MUM1001	1974	£20	£40	

SUMMERHILL
Summerhill	LP	Polydor	583746	1969	£15	£30

SUMMERS, BOB
Excitement	7"	Capitol	CL15063	1959	£2	£5
Little Brown Jug	7"	Capitol	CL15130	1960	£2.50	£6

SUMPIN' ELSE
I Can't Get Through To You	7" EP	Liberty	LEP2268	1967	£4	£8	French

SUN ALSO RISES
Sun Also Rises	LP	Village Thing	VTS2	1970	£5	£12

SUN DIAL
Exploding In Your Mind	12"	Tangerine	no number	1991	£20	£40	test pressing
Other Way Out	LP	Tangerine	MM07	1990	£10	£25	

SUN RA
Despite the small number of items listed here, avant garde jazz eccentric Sun Ra's discography is actually huge. Over the years he has issued a large number of albums on his own Saturn label, often in ultra-limited editions with hand-made covers. These are so rare that they hardly ever appear on the market and compiling a list of them is practically impossible. Needless to say, however, all these albums are highly collectable.
Heliocentric Worlds Vol.1	LP	ESP	1014	1966	£6	£15
Heliocentric Worlds Vol.2	LP	ESP	1017	1966	£6	£15
Pictures Of Infinity	LP	Polydor	2460106	1971	£6	£15
Sound Of Joy	LP	Delmark	DL414	1968	£6	£15
Sun Song	LP	Delmark	DL411	1967	£6	£15

SUNDAE TIMES
Baby Don't Cry	7"	President	PT203	1968	£2	£5
Jackboy	7"	President	PT219	1968	£2	£5
Us Coloured Kids	LP	Joy	JOYS159	1969	£5	£12

SUNDANCE
Chuffer	LP	Decca	SKL5183	1974	£5	£12
Rain Steam Speed	LP	Decca	TXS111	1973	£5	£12

SUNDAY AFTERNOON
Sunday Afternoon	LP	Longman			£50	£100

SUNDAYS
Can't Be Sure	12"	Rough Trade	RTTX218	1989	£2.50	£6	export
Reading, Writing And Arithmetic	LP	Rough Trade	ROUGH148P	1990	£4	£10	pic disc

SUNDOWN PLAYBOYS
Saturday Night Special	78	Apple	44	1972	£100	£200	promo, pictured in Guide
Saturday Night Special	7"	Apple	44	1972	£2.50	£6	
Saturday Night Special	7"	Apple	44	1972	£7.50	£15	PS

SUNDOWNERS
Dr.J.Wallace-Browne	7"	Columbia	DB8339	1968	£4	£8
House Of The Rising Sun	7"	Piccadilly	7N35142	1963	£2.50	£6
Shot Of Rhythm And Blues	7"	Piccadilly	7N35162	1964	£2.50	£6
Where Am I	7"	Parlophone	R5243	1965	£2	£5

SUNDRAGON
Blueberry Blue	7"	MGM	MGM1391	1968	£4	£8	
Five White Horses	7"	MGM	MGM1458	1968	£4	£8	
Green Tambourine	LP	MGM	C(S)8090	1968	£15	£30	
Green Tambourine	7"	MGM	MGM1380	1968	£2.50	£6	chart single

SUNFOREST
Sound Of Sunforest	LP	Nova	SDN7	1969	£15	£30

SUNNY & THE HI-JUMPERS
Going To Damascus	7"	Carnival	CV7025	1965	£2.50	£6
Tarry Till You're Better	7"	Carnival	CV7022	1965	£2.50	£6

SUNNY & THE SUNGLOWS
All Night Worker	LP	Tear Drop	2019	196-	£6	£15	US
Peanuts	LP	Sunglow	SLP103	1965	£6	£15	US
Talk To Me	7"	London	HL9792	1963	£6	£12	
Talk To Me/Rags To Riches	LP	Tear Drop	2000	1963	£8	£20	US

SUNNYLAND SLIM
I Done You Wrong	LP	Storyville	SLP169	1965	£6	£15	
Midnight Jump	LP	Blue Horizon	763213	1969	£20	£40	
Portraits In Blues	LP	Storyville	670169	1968	£5	£12	
Slim's Got This Thing Goin' On	LP	Liberty	LBS83237	1969	£15	£30	
Slim's Shout	LP	Bluesville	BV1016	1961	£8	£20	US
Sunnyland Slim	LP	Storyville	616012	1970	£6	£15	

SUNNYSIDERS

Title		Label	Cat No	Year			
Banjo Woogie	7"	London	HLU8180	1955	£10	£20	
Doesn't He Love Me	7"	London	HLU8246	1956	£7.50	£15	
Hey Mister Banjo	7"	London	HL8135	1955	£10	£20	
I Love You Fair Dinkum	7"	London	HLU8202	1955	£7.50	£15	
Oh Me Oh My	7"	London	HL8160	1955	£10	£20	

SUNRAYS

Andrea	LP	Tower	(S)T5017	1966	£5	£12	US
Andrea	7"	Capitol	CL15433	1966	£2	£5	
I Live For The Sun	7"	Capitol	CL15416	1965	£2	£5	

SUNSETS

Cry Of The Wild Goose	7"	Ember	EMBS125	1960	£2.50	£6	
Surfing With The Sunsets	LP	Palace	752	1963	£6	£15	US

SUNSHINE COMPANY

Back On The Street Again	7"	Liberty	LBF15034	1967	£1.50	£4	
Happy Is The Sunshine Company	LP	Imperial	LP12359	1967	£4	£10	US
Look Here Comes The Sun	7"	Liberty	LBF15060	1968	£1.50	£4	
On A Beautiful Day	7"	Liberty	LBF15149	1968	£1.50	£4	
Sunshine & Shadows	LP	Liberty	LBL/LBS83159	1968	£4	£10	
Sunshine Company	LP	Liberty	LBL/LBS83120	1968	£4	£10	

SUNSHINE, MONTY

Carnival	7"	London	HLR9822	1963	£1.50	£4	
Creole Love Call	7"	Columbia	DB4681	1961	£1.50	£4	
Gimme A Pig Foot	7"	Columbia	DB4744	1961	£1.50	£4	
Gonna Build A Mountain	7" EP	London	RER1368	1963	£4	£8	
Hushabye	7"	London	HLR9629	1962	£1.50	£4	
Jacqueline	7"	Columbia	DB4588	1961	£1.50	£4	
Saratoga Shout	7"	Columbia	DB4849	1962	£1.50	£4	
Sunstroke	7"	Polydor	NH66971	1962	£1.50	£4	

SUNSPECS

All I Want	7"	RCA	RCA1413	1964	£1.50	£4	

SUNSPOTS

Paella	7"	Decca	F11672	1963	£1.50	£4	

SUPERBOYS

Ain't That A Shame	7"	Giant	GN22	1968	£4	£8	
You're Hurtin' Me	7"	Giant	GN31	1968	£4	£8	

SUPERFINE DANDELION

Superfine Dandelion	LP	Mainstream	S6102	1968	£6	£15	US

SUPERSISTER

To The Highest Bidder	LP	Dandelion	2310146	1971	£6	£15	

SUPERSONICS

Second Fiddle	LP	Trojan	TRL6	1968	£8	£20	

SUPERSTOCKS

School Is A Drag	LP	Capitol	(S)T2190	1964	£20	£40	US
Surf Route 101	LP	Capitol	(S)T2113	1964	£20	£40	US
Thunder Road	LP	Capitol	(S)T2060	1964	£20	£40	US

SUPERTONES

Freedom Blues	7"	Banana	BA312	1970	£2.50	£6	

SUPERTRAMP

Breakfast In America	LP	Mobile Fidelity	MFSL1045	1980	£4	£10	US audiophile
Crime Of The Century	LP	Mobile Fidelity	MFSL1005	1978	£5	£12	US audiophile
Crime Of The Century	LP	Mobile Fidelity	MFSL1005		£8	£20	US audiophile (UHQR)
Crisis? What Crisis	LP	A&M			£4	£10	audiophile
Even In The Quietest Moments	LP	A&M			£4	£10	audiophile
Famous Last Words	LP	A&M			£4	£10	audiophile
Paris	LP	A&M			£6	£15	audiophile double

SUPREMES

A Go-Go	LP	Tamla Motown	(S)TML11039	1966	£6	£15	chart LP
At The Copa	LP	Tamla Motown	TML11026	1966	£8	£20	
Automatically Sunshine	7"	Tamla Motown	TMG821	1972	£1.50	£4	chart single
Baby Love	7"	Stateside	SS350	1964	£2	£5	chart single
Back In My Arms Again	7"	Tamla Motown	TMG516	1965	£4	£8	chart single
Breathtaking Guy	7"	Motown	1044	1963	£7.50	£15	US
Children's Christmas Song	7"	Motown	1085	1965	£10	£20	US, PS, red vinyl
Come See About Me	7"	Stateside	SS376	1965	£4	£8	
Country,Western & Pop	LP	Tamla Motown	TML11018	1965	£15	£30	
Everybody's Got The Right To Love	7"	Tamla Motown	TMG747	1970	£1.50	£4	
Floy Joy	7"	Tamla Motown	TMG804	1972	£1.50	£4	chart single
Happening	7"	Tamla Motown	TMG607	1967	£2	£5	chart single
I Hear A Symphony	7"	Tamla Motown	TMG543	1965	£2.50	£6	chart single
I Hear A Symphony	LP	Tamla Motown	TML11028	1966	£6	£15	
I Want A Guy	7"	Tamla	1008	1961	£700	£1000	US demo
I Want A Guy	7"	Tamla	T54038	1961	£50	£100	US
L'Amore Verra	7"	Tamla Motown	TM8004	1966	£10	£20	sung in Italian
Let Me Go The Right Way	7"	Motown	1034	1962	£10	£20	US
Little Bit Of Liverpool	LP	Motown	M/S623	1964	£15	£30	US

Title	Format	Label	Cat No	Year	Price1	Price2	Notes
Little Bit Of Liverpool	LP	Stateside	LES501	1965	£50	£100	export
Love Is Here And Now You're Gone	7"	Tamla Motown	TMG597	1967	£2.50	£6	chart single
Love Is Like An Itching In My Heart	7"	Tamla Motown	TMG560	1966	£7.50	£15	
Meet The Supremes	LP	Motown	M/S606	1964	£25	£50	US
Meet The Supremes	LP	Motown	M606	1964	£75	£150	US, group seated on stools on cover
Meet The Supremes	LP	Stateside	SL10109	1964	£8	£20	chart LP
Merry Christmas	LP	Motown	M/S638	1965	£20	£40	US
Moonlight And Kisses	7"	Tamla Motown	GO42625	1967	£10	£20	Dutch, B side sung in French
More Hits	LP	Tamla Motown	TML11020	1965	£8	£20	
My Heart Can't Take It No More	7"	Motown	1040	1963	£7.50	£15	US
My World Is Empty Without You	7"	Tamla Motown	TMG548	1966	£5	£10	
Nathan Jones	7"	Tamla Motown	TMG782	1971	£1.50	£4	chart single
Nothing But Heartaches	7"	Tamla Motown	TMG527	1965	£6	£12	
Run, Run, Run	7"	Motown	1054	1964	£10	£20	US
Shake	7" EP	Tamla Motown	TME2011	1966	£15	£30	
Sing Motown	LP	Tamla Motown	(S)TML11047	1967	£6	£15	chart LP
Sing Rodgers & Hart	LP	Tamla Motown	(S)TML11054	1967	£5	£12	chart LP
Stoned Love	7"	Tamla Motown	TMG760	1971	£1.50	£4	chart single
Stop In The Name Of Love	7"	Tamla Motown	TMG501	1965	£2	£5	chart single
Supremes Hits	7" EP	Tamla Motown	TME2008	1965	£5	£10	
Thank You Darling	7"	Tamla Motown	GO42609	1967	£10	£20	Dutch, B side sung in French
Up The Ladder To The Roof	7"	Tamla Motown	TMG735	1970	£1.50	£4	chart single
We Remember Sam Cooke	LP	Tamla Motown	TML11012	1965	£15	£30	
When The Lovelight Starts Shining	7"	Stateside	SS257	1964	£12.50	£25	
Where Did Our Love Go	LP	Motown	M/S621	1964	£8	£20	US
Where Did Our Love Go	7"	Stateside	SS327	1964	£2	£5	chart single
Who's Loving You	7"	Tamla	T54045	1961	£50	£100	US
With Love From Us To You	LP	Tamla Motown	TML11002	1965	£15	£30	
You Can't Hurry Love	7"	Tamla Motown	TMG575	1966	£2	£5	chart single
You Keep Me Hanging On	7"	Tamla Motown	TMG585	1966	£2	£5	chart single
Your Heart Belongs To Me	7"	Motown	1027	1962	£15	£30	US
Your Heart Belongs To Me	7"	Motown	1027	1962	£100	£200	US, PS

SURFARIS

Title	Format	Label	Cat No	Year	Price1	Price2	Notes
Fun City	LP	Brunswick	LAT8582	1964	£8	£20	
Hit City '64	LP	Brunswick	LAT8567	1964	£8	£20	
Hit City '65	LP	Brunswick	LAT8585	1965	£5	£12	
It Ain't Me Babe	LP	Brunswick	LAT/STA8631	1965	£6	£15	
Point Panic	7"	Brunswick	05894	1963	£1.50	£4	
Scatter Shield	7"	Brunswick	05902	1964	£2	£5	
Surfaris Play	LP	Brunswick	LAT8561	1963	£8	£20	
Wipe Out	LP	Dot	DLP3535	1966	£5	£12	
Wipe Out	LP	London	HAD8110	1963	£10	£25	
Wipe Out	7"	London	HLD9751	1963	£1.50	£4	chart single
Wipe Out	7" EP	Dot	VDEP34019	1963	£10	£20	French
Wipe Out	7" EP	London	RED1405	1963	£10	£20	

SURFERS

Title	Format	Label	Cat No	Year	Price1	Price2	Notes
Mambo Jambo	7"	Vogue	V9147	1959	£4	£8	Alan Kalani B side

SURFRIDERS

Title	Format	Label	Cat No	Year	Price1	Price2	Notes
Surfbeat	LP	Vault	V(S)105	1963	£5	£12	US

SURFSIDE FIVE

Title	Format	Label	Cat No	Year	Price1	Price2	Notes
Recorded Live	LP	Intermountain	153	196-	£37.50	£75	US

SURMAN, JOHN

Title	Format	Label	Cat No	Year	Price1	Price2	Notes
Alors!	LP	Futura	GER12	1970	£25	£50	
How Many Clouds Can You See?	LP	Deram	DMLR/SMLR1045	1969	£20	£40	
John Surman	LP	Deram	DML/SML1030	1968	£20	£40	
Live At Woodstock Town Hall	LP	Daw	DNLS3072	1974	£4	£10	
Obeah Wedding	7"	Deram	DM224	1969	£4	£8	
Tales Of The Algonquin	LP	Deram	SML1094	1971	£20	£40	with John Warren
Westering Home	LP	Island	HELP10	1972	£8	£20	

SURPRISE PACKAGE

Title	Format	Label	Cat No	Year	Price1	Price2	Notes
Free Up	LP	LHI	S12005	1968	£6	£15	US

SURRENDER

Title	Format	Label	Cat No	Year	Price1	Price2	Notes
Surrender	LP	Capitol	11935	1979	£8	£20	US

SURVIVOR

Title	Format	Label	Cat No	Year	Price1	Price2	Notes
Eye Of The Tiger	7"	Scotti Brothers	A2411P	1982	£1.50	£4	pic disc

SURVIVORS

Title	Format	Label	Cat No	Year	Price1	Price2	Notes
Rawhide Ska	7"	Rio	R70	1965	£5	£10	Owen Gray B side
Take Charge	7"	Rio	R55	1965	£5	£10	

SURVIVORS (2)

Not only was the single by the Survivors written and produced by Brian Wilson, but the Survivors themselves were actually the Beach Boys. The group wanted to see if they could have a hit under another name - with the result that a typically classy performance has become the great lost Beach Boys track.

Title	Format	Label	Cat No	Year	Price1	Price2	Notes
Pamela Jean	7"	Capitol	5102	1964	£100	£200	US

SUTCH, SCREAMING LORD

That a small-time rock'n'roll singer who has never had a hit record can still be a celebrity is a tribute to David Sutch's skills at self-publicity. Well known as the leader of the Monster Raving Loony Party, Sutch has also never let it be forgotten that he is also a rock performer. His concerts, however, have always been chaotic affairs. In the wake of his "Lord Sutch And Heavy Friends" LP, expectations were high that he would appear accompanied by some of those same heavy friends - Jeff Beck, Jimmy Page and the rest. People turned up in droves to watch Sutch chase members of an anonymous backing group around the stage with a mop!

Cause I Love You	7"	Atlantic	2091006	1970	£5	£10
Cause I Love You	7"	Atlantic	584321	1970	£6	£12
Cheat	7"	CBS	202080	1966	£7.50	£15
Dracula's Daughter	7"	Oriole	CB1962	1964	£7.50	£15
Election Fever	7"	Atlantic	2091017	1970	£4	£8
Good Golly Miss Molly	7"	HMV	POP953	1961	£6	£12
Gotta Keep A-Rockin'	7"	Atlantic	K10221	1972	£4	£8
Hands Of Jack The Ripper	LP	Atlantic	K40313	1972	£8	£20
Honey Hush	7"	CBS	201767	1965	£12.50	£25
I'm A Hog For You	7"	Decca	F11747	1963	£6	£12
Jack The Ripper	7"	Decca	F11598	1963	£5	£10
Jack The Ripper	7" EP	Decca	457063	1965	£12.50	£25 ... French
Lord Sutch & Heavy Friends	LP	Atlantic	2400008	1970	£8	£20
Screaming Lord Sutch Meets The Meteors	10" LP	Ace	MAD1	1981	£8	£20
She's Fallen In Love With A Monster	7"	Oriole	CB1944	1964	£7.50	£15
Train Kept A-Rollin'	7" EP	CBS	6104	1965	£12.50	£25 ... French

SUTHERLAND, ISABEL

Bank Of Red Roses	7" EP	Collector	JES11	1961	£2	£5
Vagrant Songs Of Scotland	LP	Topic	12T151	1966	£5	£12

SUTTON, RALPH

I Got Rhythm	10" LP	Brunswick	LA8719	1955	£8	£20
Music of Fats Waller	10" LP	Columbia	33S1025	1954	£8	£20
Piano Moods	10" LP	Columbia	33S1018	1954	£8	£20
Ralph Sutton Quartet	LP	Columbia	33CX10061	1956	£5	£12
Stride Piano	10" LP	AF2		1953	£8	£20

SUZI & BIG DEE IRWIN

Ain't That Lovin' You Baby	7"	Polydor	BM65715	1966	£4	£8

SUZUKI, PAT

I Enjoy Being A Girl	7"	RCA	RCA1171	1960	£1.50	£4

SUZY & THE RED STRIPES

Seaside Woman	7"	A&M	AMSP7461	1979	£10	£20 ... yellow vinyl, boxed

SVANTE

Baby I Need Your Loving	7"	United Artists	UP2224	1968	£5	£10

SVENSK

Dream Magazine	7"	Page One	POF036	1967	£5	£10
You	7"	Page One	POF050	1967	£5	£10

SVENSSON, REINHOLD

New Sounds From Sweden Vol.4	10" LP	Esquire	20024	1954	£40	£80 ... with Putte Wickman
Reinhold Svensson Quintet	10" LP	Esquire	20004	1953	£40	£80

SWALLOWS

Roll Roll Pretty Baby	78	Vogue	V2136	1952	£7.50	£15

SWAMP DOGG

Total Destruction To Your Mind	LP	Canyon	LP7706		£5	£12 ... US

SWAN ARCADE

Matchless	LP	Stoof	MU7428	1976	£5	£12
Swan Arcade	LP	Trailer	LER2032	1973	£10	£25

SWANEE RIVER BOYS

Do You Believe	7"	Parlophone	CMSP7	1954	£1.50	£4 ... export

SWANN, BETTYE

Don't Touch Me	7"	Capitol	CL15586	1969	£5	£10
Heading In The Right Direction	7"	Atlantic	K10851	1976	£2.50	£6
Make Me Yours	7"	CBS	2942	1967	£12.50	£25
Today I Started Loving You Again	7"	Atlantic	K10273	1972	£2	£5
Victim Of A Foolish Heart	7"	Atlantic	K10174	1972	£2.50	£6

SWANS

Boy With The Beatle Hair	7"	Cameo Parkway	C302	1964	£4	£8
He's Mine	7"	Stateside	SS224	1963	£4	£8

SWANS (2)

Filth	LP	Zensor	NDO3	1985	£15	£30

SWANSON, BERNICE

Baby I'm Yours	7"	Chess	CRS8008	1965	£10	£20

SWARBRICK, DAVE

Ceilidh Album	LP	Sonet	SNTF764	1978	£5	£12
Rags, Reels And Airs	LP	Bounty	BY6030	1967	£30	£60
Rags, Reels And Airs	LP	Polydor	236514	1967	£30	£60
Selections	LP	Pegasus		1972	£4	£10

Smiddyburn	LP	Logo	1029	1981	£6	£15
Swarbrick	LP	Transatlantic	TRA337	1976	£5	£12
Swarbrick 2	LP	Transatlantic	TRA341	1977	£5	£12

SWARBRICK, DAVE & SIMON NICOL

Close To The Wind	LP	Woodworm	WR006	1984	£5	£12
Live At The White Bear	LP	White Bear	WBR001	1982	£10	£25

SWARBRIGGS

That's What Friends Are For	7"	MCA	MCA179	1975	£1.50	£4

SWEAT, ROSALYN & THE PARAGONS

Blackbird Singing	LP	Horse	HRLP703	1973	£5	£12

SWE-DANES

Swe-Danes	7" EP	Warner Bros	SWEP2017	1961	£4	£8	stereo
Swe-Danes	7" EP	Warner Bros	WEP6017	1961	£2	£5	

SWEENEY, JIM

Midnight Hour	7"	Philips	PB811	1958	£1.50	£4

SWEENEY'S MEN

Rattlin' & Roarin' Willy	LP	Transatlantic	TRA170	1968	£10	£25
Sullivan's John	7"	Transatlantic	TRASP19	1968	£4	£8
Sweeney's Men	LP	Transatlantic	TRASAM37	1976	£6	£15
Tracks Of Sweeney	LP	Transatlantic	TRA200	1969	£10	£25
Tracks Of Sweeney	LP	Transatlantic	TRASAM40	1977	£6	£15
Waxies Dargle	7"	Pye	7N17459	1968	£4	£8

SWEET

Beginning as a teeny-bopper group, the Sweet's music gradually became heavier as it progressed. At the same time, the group aligned itself with the glamour rock movement, and as the only way for anyone to adopt the kind of extravagant image favoured by the likes of Gary Glitter was with his tongue placed firmly in his cheek, so the Sweet became high princes of camp, mocking themselves and their music even while playing it. In the end, of course, this rebounded on them, and the classy "Love Is Like Oxygen" apart, the group failed to convince when they tried to become serious artists.

All You'll Ever Get From Me	7"	Parlophone	R5826	1970	£15	£30	
All You'll Ever Get From Me	7"	Parlophone	R5902	1971	£15	£30	
Ballroom Blitz	7"	RCA	RCA2403	1973	£5	£10	plays slow - matrix 2403-A-1E
Big Apple	7"	Polydor	POSP73	1979	£6	£12	
California Nights	7"	Polydor	POSP5	1978	£10	£20	demo
Call Me	7"	Polydor	POSP36	1979	£1.50	£4	
Cut Above The Rest	LP	Capitol	SO11929	1979	£8	£20	US, different 'Hold Me' & cover
Cut Above The Rest	LP	Polydor	POLD5022	1979	£6	£15	
Desolation Boulevard	LP	RCA	LP15080	1975	£4	£10	
For AOR Radio Only	LP	Capitol		1975	£8	£20	US promo
Fox On The Run	7"	RCA	PE5226	1980	£5	£10	
Funny How Sweet Coco Can Be	LP	RCA	SF8288	1971	£6	£15	
Get On The Line	7"	Parlophone	R5848	1970	£15	£30	
Give The Lady Some Respect	7"	Polydor	POSP131	1980	£1.50	£4	
Give Us A Wink	LP	RCA	RS1036	1976	£4	£10	
Identity Crisis	7"	Polydor	23111179	1982	£8	£20	
It's It's...The Sweet Mix	12"	Anagram	12ANA28	1984	£2.50	£6	
Level Headed	LP	Polydor	POLD5001	1978	£4	£10	
Lollipop Man	7"	Parlophone	R5803	1969	£15	£30	
Off The Record	LP	RCA	PL25072	1977	£5	£12	
Sixties Man/Tall Girls	7"	Polydor	POSP160	1980	£7.50	£15	mispress
Slow Motion	7"	Fontana	TF958	1968	£150	£250	
Stairway To The Stars	7"	RCA	PB5046	1977	£2	£5	
Strung Up	LP	RCA	SPC0001	1975	£5	£12	double
Sweet Fanny Adams	LP	RCA	LP15039	1974	£4	£10	chart LP
Sweet Sixteen	LP	Anagram	PGRAM16	1984	£10	£25	pic disc
Water's Edge	LP	Polydor	POLS1021	1980	£8	£20	

SWEET CHARLES

For Sweet People	LP	People	PE6603	1974	£10	£25	US
For Sweet People	LP	Urban	URBLP9	1988	£5	£12	

SWEET FEELING

All So Long Ago	7"	Columbia	DB8195	1967	£15	£30

SWEET INSPIRATIONS

Brand New Lover	7"	Atlantic	584312	1970	£1.50	£4
Evidence	7"	Atlantic	2091073	1971	£1.50	£4
Let It Be Me	7"	Atlantic	584132	1967	£1.50	£4
Sweet Inspiration	7"	Atlantic	584167	1968	£1.50	£4
Sweets For My Sweet	7"	Atlantic	584279	1969	£1.50	£4
What The World Needs Now Is Love	7"	Atlantic	584233	1968	£1.50	£4
Why Am I Treated So Bad	7"	Atlantic	584117	1967	£1.50	£4

SWEET PAIN

Sweet Pain	LP	Mercury	SMCL20146	1969	£8	£20
Timber Gibbs	7"	United Artists	UP35268	1971	£1.50	£4

SWEET PLUM

Lazy Day	7"	Middle Earth	MDS103	1969	£4	£8
Set The Wheels In Motion	7"	Middle Earth	MDS105	1969	£5	£10

SWEET SAVAGE

Killing Time	7"	Sweet Savage	1980	1981	£5	£10

SWEET SLAG
Tracking With Close Ups .... LP ..... XTRA .... XTRA1112............. 1971 ... £15 ....£30 ....
Tracking With Close-Ups .... LP ..... President .... PTLS1042............. 1971 ... £15 ....£30 ....

SWEET SMOKE
Just A Poke .... LP ..... Catfish .... 5C05424311 .... 1972 ... £6 ....£15 ....Dutch

SWEET THURSDAY
Sweet Thursday .... LP ..... CBS .... 65573 .... 1973 ... £4 ....£10 ....
Sweet Thursday .... LP ..... Polydor .... 2310051................ 1969 ... £6 ....£15 ....

SWEETING, HARRY
From Jamaica With Love .... 7" .... Coxsone .... CS7012 .... 1967 ... £5 ....£10 ....

SWEETSHOP
Barefoot And Tiptoe .... 7" .... Parlophone..... R5707 .... 1968 ... £1.50 ....£4 ....

SWEGAS
Child Of Light .... LP ..... Trend .... 6480002.............. 1971 ... £8 ....£20 ....

SWELL MAPS
Read About Seymour .... 7" .... Rather .... GEAR1 .... 1977 ... £2.50 ....£6 ....
Trip to Marineville .... LP ..... Big Rather....... TROY1 .... 1979 ... £5 ....£12 ....with 7' (GEAR5)
What A Nice Way To Turn Seventeen .... 7" .... Rather .... GEAR17 .... 1984 ... £2.50 ....£6 ....with other artists
No.2
Whatever Happens Next .... LP ..... Rough Trade ... ROUGH21 .... 1981 ... £5 ....£12 ....double

SWETE, ANTHONY
Backfield In Motion .... 7" .... RCA .... RCA1905 .... 1969 ... £1.50 ....£4 ....

SWIFT, TUFTY
How To Make A Bakewell Tart .... LP ..... Free Reed .... FRR017 .... 1977 ... £8 ....£20 ....
You'll Never Die For Love .... LP ..... Shark .... 04....................... 1985 ... £5 ....£12 ....

SWINGERS
Love Makes The World Go Round .... 7" .... Vogue .... V9158 .... 1960 ... £2.50 ....£6 ....

SWINGING BLUE JEANS
Blue Jeans A Swinging .... LP ..... HMV .... CLP1802/CSD1570 1964 ... £25 ....£50 ....
Brand New And Faded .... LP ..... Dart .... BULL1001 .... 1974 ... £5 ....£12 ....
Crazy 'Bout My Baby .... 7" .... HMV .... POP1477 .... 1965 ... £1.50 ....£4 ....
Do You Know .... 7" .... HMV .... POP1206 .... 1963 ... £2 ....£5 ....
Don't Go Out Into The Rain .... 7" .... HMV .... POP1605 .... 1967 ... £1.50 ....£4 ....
Don't Make Me Over .... 7" .... HMV .... POP1501 .... 1966 ... £1.50 ....£4 ....chart single
Good Golly Miss Molly .... 7" .... HMV .... POP1273 .... 1964 ... £1.50 ....£4 ....
Good Golly Miss Molly .... 7" EP.. Pathe .... EGF736 .... 1964 ... £12.50 ..£25 .... French
Hippy Hippy Shake .... LP ..... Imperial .... LP9261/12261 ...... 1964 ... £25 ....£50 .... US
Hippy Hippy Shake .... 7" .... HMV .... POP1242 .... 1963 ... £1.50 ....£4 ....chart single
Hippy Hippy Shake .... 7" EP.. Pathe .... EGF707 .... 1963 ... £12.50 ..£25 .... French
It Isn't There .... 7" .... HMV .... POP1375 .... 1964 ... £1.50 ....£4 ....
It's So Right .... 7" EP.. Pathe .... EGF782 .... 1964 ... £12.50 ..£25 .... French
It's Too Late Now .... 7" .... HMV .... POP1170 .... 1963 ... £1.50 ....£4 ....chart single
Make Me Know You're Mine .... 7" .... HMV .... POP1409 .... 1965 ... £1.50 ....£4 ....
Promise You'll Tell Her .... 7" .... HMV .... POP1327 .... 1964 ... £1.50 ....£4 ....
Rumours, Gossip, Words Untrue .... 7" .... HMV .... POP1564 .... 1966 ... £1.50 ....£4 ....
Rumours, Gossip, Words Untrue .... 7" EP.. Pathe .... EGF950 .... 1966 ... £12.50 ..£25 .... French
Sandy .... 7" .... HMV .... POP1533 .... 1966 ... £1.50 ....£4 ....
Shake With The Swinging Blue Jeans . 7" EP.. HMV .... 7EG8850 .... 1964 ... £7.50 ....£15 ....
Swinging Blue Jeans .... LP ..... MFP .... MFP1163 .... 1967 ... £6 ....£15 ....
Tremblin' .... 7" .... HMV .... POP1596 .... 1967 ... £1.50 ....£4 ....
Tutti Frutti .... 7" .... Regal .... SREG1073............ 1964 ... £10 ....£25 ....export
You're No Good .... 7" .... HMV .... POP1304 .... 1964 ... £1.50 ....£4 ....chart single
You're No Good Miss Molly .... 7" EP.. HMV .... 7EG8868.............. 1964 ... £10 ....£20 ....

SWINGING MEDALLIONS
Double Shot .... LP ..... Smash .... MGS2/SRS67083.. 1966 ... £5 ....£12 .... US
Double Shot Of My Baby's Love .... 7" .... Philips.............. BF1500 .... 1966 ... £2.50 ....£6 ....
She Drives Me Out Of My Mind .... 7" .... Philips.............. BF1515 .... 1966 ... £2 ....£5 ....

SWINGING SOUL MACHINE
Spooky's Day Off .... 7" .... Polydor .... 56760 .... 1969 ... £1.50 ....£4 ....

SWINGING SWEDES
Swinging Swedes .... LP ..... Telefunken ..... LGX66050 .... 1957 ... £8 ....£20 ....

SWINGTONES
Geraldine .... 7" .... HMV .... POP471 .... 1958 ... £50 ....£100 ....

SYDNEY ALL STARS
Return Of Batman .... 7" .... Bullet .... BU436 .... 1970 ... £2 ....£5 ....

SYKES, ERIC & HATTIE JACQUES
Eric, Hattie And Things .... LP ..... Decca .... LK4507 .... 1963 ... £5 ....£12 ....

SYKES, JOHN
Please Don't Leave Me .... 7" .... MCA .... MCA792 .... 1982 ... £12.50 ..£25 ....

SYKES, ROOSEVELT
Back To The Blues .... 7" EP.. Delmark .... DJB2..................... 1966 ... £7.50 ....£15 ....
Big Man Of The Blues .... LP ..... Encore .... ENC183 .... 1959 ... £6 ....£15 ....
Blues From Bar Rooms .... LP ..... 77 .... LEU1250 .... 1967 ... £6 ....£15 ....

Face To Face With The Blues	LP	Columbia	33SX1343	1961	£8	£20
Hard Drivin' Blues	LP	Delmark	DS607	1970	£8	£20
Honeydripper	LP	Columbia	33SX1422	1962	£10	£25
Mr.Sykes Blues 1929-1932	LP	Riverside	RLP8819	1967	£6	£15
Return Of Roosevelt Sykes	LP	Bluesville	BV1006	1960	£10	£25 .... US
Sings The Blues	LP	Ember	EMB3391	196-	£5	£12
Too Hot To Hold	7"	Vogue	V2389	1956	£17.50	£35
Walking This Boogie	7"	Vogue	V2393	1956	£25	£50

SYKO & THE CARIBS

Do The Dog	7"	Blue Beat	BB213	1963	£5	£10
Sugar Baby	7"	Blue Beat	BB223	1963	£5	£10

SYLTE SISTERS

Summer Magic	7"	London	HLU9753	1963	£1.50	£4

SYLVESTER, C.

Going South	7"	Blue Beat	BB206	1963	£5	£10

SYLVESTER, ROLAND

Grandfather's Clock	7"	Carnival	CV7018	1964	£2.50	£6

SYLVIA

I Can't Help It	7"	Soul City	SC103	1968	£2.50	£6

SYLVIAN, DAVID

Red Guitar	7"	Virgin	VSY633	1984	£1.50	£4 .... pic disc
Taking The Veil	7"	Virgin	VSY815	1986	£1.50	£4 .... square pic disc

SYMARIP

Skinhead Moon Stomp	LP	Trojan	TBL102	1968	£8	£20
Skinhead Moon Stomp	7"	Treasure Isle	TI7050	1969	£2.50	£6

SYMBOLS

Best Part Of The Symbols	LP	President	PTL1018	1968	£8	£20
Canadian Sunset	7"	President	PT113	1968	£1.50	£4
One Fine Girl	7"	Columbia	DB7459	1965	£1.50	£4
You're My Girl	7"	Columbia	DB7664	1965	£1.50	£4

SYMON & PI

Got To See The Sunrise	7"	Parlophone	R5719	1968	£2	£5
Sha La La La Lee	7"	Parlophone	R5662	1968	£2	£5

SYMPHONICS

Heaven Must Have Sent You	7"	Polydor	2058341	1972	£2	£5

SYN

The Syndicats eventually metamorphosed into the Syn, none of whose members had been in the original Syndicats line-up. The Yes connection continued, however, for the bass player and guitarist on the Syn's psychedelic singles were Chris Squire and Peter Banks.

Created By Clive	7"	Deram	DM130	1967	£20	£40
Flowerman	7"	Deram	DM145	1967	£20	£40

SYNANTHESIA

Synanthesia	LP	RCA	SF8058	1969	£30	£60

SYNDICATE OF SOUND

Little Girl	LP	Stateside	(S)SL10185	1966	£10	£25
Little Girl	7"	Stateside	SS523	1966	£7.50	£15
Little Girl	7" EP	Columbia	ESRF1794	1966	£12.50	£25 .... French
Rumours	7"	Stateside	SS538	1966	£5	£10

SYNDICATS

The singles made by the Syndicats are collectable on three counts. They are good examples of mid-sixties British R&B; they were produced by legendary producer Joe Meek; and the group's guitarist was Steve Howe, of later Yes fame.

Crawdaddy Simone	7"	Columbia	DB7686	1965	£150	£250
Howlin' For My Baby	7"	Columbia	DB7441	1965	£30	£60
Maybelline	7"	Columbia	DB7238	1964	£30	£60

SYRINX

Long Lost Relatives	LP	True North		1971	£10	£25 .... Canadian
Syrinx	LP	True North		1970	£10	£25 .... Canadian

SYSTEM 7

Miracle	12"	Ten		1990	£4	£10 .... clear vinyl

T

T2
It'll All Work Out In Boomland .... LP ..... Decca .... SKL5050 .... 1970 ... £25 ....£50

TABLETOPPERS
Rocking Mountain Dew .... 7" .... Starlite .... ST45069 .... 1962 ... £4 ....£8

TABOR, CHARLIE
Blue Atlantic .... 7" .... Island .... WI061 .... 1963 ... £5 ....£10

TABOR, JUNE
Airs And Graces .... LP ..... Topic .... 12TS298 .... 1976 ... £4 ....£10
Ashes And Diamonds .... LP ..... Topic .... 12TS360 .... 1977 ... £4 ....£10

TAD & THE SMALL FRY
Checkered Continental Pants .... 7" .... London .... HLU9542 .... 1962 ... £2 ....£5

TAGES
Contrast .... LP ..... EMI .... 1967 ... £10 .....£25 .... Swedish
Crazy 'Bout My Baby .... 7" .... Columbia .... DB8019 .... 1966 ... £2 ....£5
Extra Extra .... LP ..... Platina .... 1966 ... £10 .....£25 .... Swedish
In My Dreams .... 7" EP.. Impact .... 200006 .... 1967 ... £7.50 .....£15 .... French
Lilac Years .... LP ..... Fontana .... 1969 ... £10 .....£25 .... Swedish
So Many Girls .... 7" .... HMV .... POP1515 .... 1966 ... £10 .....£20
Studio .... LP ..... EMI .... 1967 ... £10 .....£25 .... Swedish
Tages .... LP ..... Platina .... 1965 ... £10 .....£25 .... Swedish
There's A Blind Man Playing .... 7" .... Parlophone .... R5702 .... 1968 ... £2 ....£5
Treat Me Like A Lady .... 7" .... Parlophone .... R5640 .... 1967 ... £1.50 .....£4
Two .... LP ..... Platina .... 1966 ... £10 .....£25 .... Swedish

TAGMEMICS
Chimneys .... 7" .... Index................. 003 .... 1980 ... £4 ....£8

TAIEB, JACQUELINE
Tonight I'm Going Home .... 7" .... Fontana .... TF952 .... 1968 ... £15 ....£30

TAITT, LYN
Dial 609 .... 7" .... Ska Beat........... JB264 .... 1967 ... £5 ....£10 .... Tommy
                                                                                                                                              McCook B side
El Casino Royale .... 7" .... Amalgamated . AMG810................. 1968 ... £4 ....£8
Glad Sounds .... LP ..... Big Shot .... BBTL4002.............. 1968 ... £25 ....£50
I Don't Want To Make You Cry .... 7" .... Island .... WI3075 .... 1967 ... £5 ....£10
Napoleon Solo .... 7" .... Island .... WI3139 .... 1968 ... £5 ....£10
Something Stupid .... 7" .... Island .... WI3066 .... 1967 ... £5 ....£10
Soul Food .... 7" .... Pama .... PM723 .... 1968 ... £4 ....£8
Sounds Rock Steady .... LP ..... Island .... ILP969 .... 1968 ... £30 ....£60
Spanish Eyes .... 7" .... Doctor Bird ...... DB1047 .... 1966 ... £5 ....£10 ....with Tommy McCook,
                                                                                                                                        Stranger Cole B side
Vilmas Jump Up .... 7" .... Doctor Bird ...... DB1006................. 1966 ... £5 ....£10 ....Glen Miller B side

TAKE THAT
A valid commercial strategy for a young group is to seek acclaim from an even younger fan-base and to take maximum advantage of that popularity, in the knowledge that it will be short-lived. Groups like the Osmonds, the Bay City Rollers, and New Kids On The Block were enormous in their day, but ceased to sell records as soon as their teenage fans grew old enough to want something different. At the time of writing, Take That are the heirs to this tradition. A handful of collectors' items by the group are included here for form's sake, but it is likely that their values will plummet during the currency of this edition of the Guide.
I Found Heaven .... 7" .... RCA .... 74321108137B .... 1992 ... £4 ....£8 .... pic disc
Once You've Tasted Love .... 12" ..... RCA .... PT45258 .... 1992 ... £8 ....£20 .... pic disc
Promises .... 7" .... RCA .... PB45085P .... 1991 ... £5 ....£10 .... poster PS

TAKERS
If You Don't Come Back .... 7" .... Pye .... 7N15690 .... 1964 ... £5 ....£10

TALBOT BROTHERS
Bloodshot Eyes .... 7" .... Melodisc .... 1507 .... 1959 ... £2 ....£5
She's Got Freckles .... 7" .... Melodisc .... CAL20 .... 1964 ... £2 ....£5

TALENT, ZIGGY
Cheek To Cheek .... 7" .... Brunswick .... 05506 .... 1955 ... £1.50 ....£4

TALES OF JUSTINE
Albert .... 7" .... HMV .... POP1614 .... 1967 ... £7.50 .....£15
Albert .... 7" .... HMV .... POP1614 .... 1967 ... £12.50 .....£25 ....PS

TALISKER
Dreaming Of Glenista .... LP ..... Caroline .... CA1513 .... 1975 ... £4 ....£10

TALISMAN
Primrose Dreams .... LP ..... Argo .... ZFB33 .... 1972 ... £5 ....£12
Stepping Stones .... LP ..... Argo .... ZDA161 .... 1973 ... £5 ....£12

TALISMEN
Masters Of War .... 7" .... Stateside .... SS408 .... 1965 ... £10 ....£20

TALIX
Spuren	LP	Vogue	LDVS17237	1971	£6	£15	German

TALK TALK
Living In Another World	7"	EMI	EMIP5551	1986	£1.50	£4	shaped pic disc
Talk Talk	7"	EMI	EMIP5352	1982	£1.50	£4	pic disc
Talk Talk Demos	7"	EMI	EMID5433	1984	£4	£8	double

TALKING HEADS
Fear Of Music	LP	Sire	K56707	1979	£5	£12	with 'Psycho Killer' 7'
Live At The Roxy	LP	Warner Bros	WBMS104	1979	£10	£25	promo
Love Goes To Building On Fire	7"	Sire	6078604	1977	£1.50	£4	PS
Psycho Killer	12"	Sire	6078610	1977	£3	£8	
Pulled Up	7"	Sire	6078620	1978	£2	£5	PS
Road To Nowhere	7"	EMI	EMIP5530	1985	£1.50	£4	pic disc
Speaking In Tongues	LP	EMI	9238831	1983	£5	£12	clear vinyl
Take Me To The River	7"	Sire	SIR4004	1979	£2.50	£6	double
This Must Be The Place	12"	Sire	W9451T	1984	£2	£5	double

TALL, TOM
Are You Mine	7"	London	HL8150	1955	£10	£20	with Ginny Wright
Country Songs Vol.2	7" EP	London	REU1035	1955	£12.50	£25	with Ginny Wright
Don't You Know	7"	London	HLU8429	1957	£7.50	£15	with Ruckus Taylor
Give Me A Chance	7"	London	HLU8216	1955	£10	£20	
Underway	7"	London	HLU8231	1956	£10	£20	

TALMY/STONE BAND
Madison Time	7"	Decca	F11543	1962	£2.50	£6	
Roses Are Red & Other Hits	LP	Ace Of Clubs	ACL1134	1962	£6	£15	

TALULAH GOSH
Who Needs The Bloody Cartel Anyway	7"	Sha La La	002	1986	£1.50	£4	flexi

TAM, TIM & THE TURN ONS
Wait A Minute	7"	Island	WIP6007	1967	£7.50	£15	

TAMLIN, JAMES
Is There Time	7"	Columbia	DB7438	1965	£4	£8	

TAMPA RED
Don't Jive With Me	LP	Bluesville	BV1043	1962	£6	£15	US
Don't Tampa With The Blues	LP	Bluesville	BV1030	1961	£6	£15	US
R&B Vol.3	7" EP	RCA	RCX7160	1964	£7.50	£15	

TAMPA RED & GEORGIA TOM
Male Blues Vol.2	7" EP	Collector	JEL3	1959	£5	£10	

TAMS
Be Young, Be Foolish, Be Happy	LP	Stateside	SSL10304	1970	£4	£10	
Be Young, Be Foolish, Be Happy	7"	Stateside	SS2123	1969	£2.50	£6	chart single
Concrete Jungle	7"	HMV	POP1464	1965	£4	£8	
Hey Girl Don't Bother Me	LP	ABC	(S)499	1964	£6	£15	US
Hey Girl Don't Bother Me	7"	HMV	POP1331	1964	£15	£30	
Hey Girl Don't Bother Me	7"	Probe	PRO532	1971	£1.50	£4	chart single
It's All Right	7"	HMV	POP1298	1964	£2.50	£6	
Little More Soul	LP	Stateside	(S)SL10258	1968	£4	£10	
Presenting The Tams	LP	ABC	(S)481	1964	£6	£15	US
Too Much Foolin' Around	7"	Capitol	CL15650	1970	£1.50	£4	
Untie Me	7"	Stateside	SS146	1963	£2.50	£6	
What Kind Of Fool	7"	HMV	POP1254	1963	£7.50	£15	

TANDY, SHARON
The reissue specialists, who have turned their attention on to some of the most obscure sixties artists, have nevertheless managed to ignore Sharon Tandy. Her numerous near-miss singles contain many impressive blue-eyed soul performances, which are made even more compelling in some cases by the fiery support of cult favourites, the Fleur De Lys. Tracks like "Hold On" and "Our Day Will Come" emerge as rather fine and distinctive pieces of psychedelic soul.

Fool On The Hill	7"	Atlantic	584166	1968	£2	£5	
Gotta Get Enough Time	7"	Atlantic	584242	1969	£2	£5	
Hold On	7"	Atlantic	584219	1968	£4	£8	
I've Found Love	7"	Pye	7N15939	1965	£1.50	£4	
Love Is Not A Simple Affair	7"	Atlantic	584181	1968	£2	£5	
Love Makes The World Go Round	7"	Mercury	MF898	1965	£1.50	£4	
Now That You've Gone	7"	Pye	7N15806	1965	£1.50	£4	
Our Day Will Come	7"	Atlantic	584137	1967	£4	£8	
Stay With Me	7"	Atlantic	584124	1967	£5	£10	
Toe-Hold	7"	Atlantic	584098	1967	£2	£5	
Way She Looks At You	7"	Atlantic	584214	1968	£2	£5	
You Gotta Believe It	7"	Atlantic	584194	1968	£2	£5	

TANEGA, NORMA
Walking My Cat Named Dog	LP	Stateside	(S)SL10182	1966	£5	£12	
Walking My Cat Named Dog	7"	Stateside	SS496	1966	£1.50	£4	chart single

TANGERINE DREAM
Perhaps it has something to do with the German character, that the rock musicians in that country seized on the newly developed synthesizer, not as a device for creating previously unheard sounds, but as a means for performing mathematically precise patterns of notes. Such is the main approach of Tangerine Dream, as it is of Klaus Schulze and Kraftwerk. "Ultima Thule" is a particularly rare non-album track, and is atypical in style.

Alpha Centauri	LP	Ohr	OMM556012	1971	£5	£12	German
Betrayal	7"	MCA	PSR413	1977	£2	£5	promo

Das Madchen Auf Der Treppe	12″	Virgin	60065213	1982	£2.50	£6	German
Electronic Meditation	LP	Ohr	OMM556004	1970	£6	£15	German
Phaedra	7″	Virgin	PR214	1974	£2.50	£6	promo
Poland - The Warsaw Concert	LP	Jive Electro	HIPX22	1984	£6	£15	double pic disc
Stratosfear	7″	Virgin	VDJ17	1976	£2.50	£6	promo
Thief	LP	Elektra	SE521	1981	£4	£10	US promo pic disc
Ultima Thule	7″	Ohr	OSS7006	1972	£25	£50	German
Warsaw In The Sun	7″	Jive Electro	JIVEP74	1984	£2.50	£6	pic disc

TANGERINE PEEL

Every Christian Lion-Hearted Man Will Show You	7″	United Artists	UP1193	1967	£5	£10	
Move Into My World	7″	RCA	RCA1936	1970	£2	£5	
Never Say Never Again	7″	MGM	MGM1470	1969	£2	£5	
Play Me A Sad Song And I'll Dance	7″	MGM	MGM1487	1969	£2	£5	
Soft Delights	LP	RCA	LSA3002	1970	£8	£20	US
Solid Gold Mountain	7″	CBS	3402	1968	£2	£5	
Talking To No One	7″	CBS	3676	1968	£2	£5	
Thinking Of Me	7″	RCA	RCA1990	1970	£2	£5	
What Am I To Do	7″	RCA	RCA2036	1970	£2	£5	

TANGERINE ZOO

Outside Looking In	LP	Mainstream	S6116	1968	£8	£20	US
Tangerine Zoo	LP	Mainstream	S6107	1968	£8	£20	US

TANNAHILL WEAVERS

Are Ye Sleeping Maggie	LP	Plant Life	PLR001	1976	£5	£12

TANNED LEATHER

Child Of Never Ending Love	LP	Harvest	1C06229440	1972	£4	£10	German

TANNEN, HOLLY & PETE COOPER

Frosty Morning	LP	Plant Life	PLR015	1979	£5	£12

TANSEY, SEAMUS

Masters Of Irish Music	LP	Leader	LEA2005	1970	£5	£12	with Eddie Corcoran
Traditional Music From Sligo	LP	Outlet	SDLP1022	1973	£6	£15	Irish

TANTONES

So Afraid	7″	Vogue	V9085	1957	£100	£200

TAPESTRY

Carnaby Street	7″	London	HLZ10138	1967	£2.50	£6
Heart And Soul	7″	Nems	3964	1969	£2.50	£6
Like The Sun	7″	Nems	3679	1968	£2.50	£6

TAPPI TIKARRASS

Tappi Tikarrass was a band playing in Iceland during 1981-3, whose lead singer was the very youthful Bjork. In addition to the mini album listed here, the band also made an LP called "Miranda", which is still available new.

Bitid Fast I Vitid	LP	Spor	SPOR4	1981	£20	£40

TARA

Happy	7″	Polydor	2066009	1971	£2	£5

TARANTULA

Tarantula	LP	A&M	AMLS959	1970	£4	£10

TARBUCK, JIMMY

Someday	7″	Immediate	IM018	1965	£2	£5

TARGEL, JEM

Lucky Guy	LP	Sheany		1978	£30	£60	US

TARHEEL SLIM & LITTLE ANN

You Make Me Feel So Good	7″	Sue	WI390	1965	£5	£10

TARRIERS

Banana Boat Song	7″	Columbia	DB3891	1957	£1.50	£4	chart single
Dunya	7″	Columbia	DB4025	1957	£1.50	£4	
Hard Travellin'	LP	United Artists	UAL4033/ UAS5033	1959	£5	£12	US
Hard Travellin' Vol.1	7″ EP	London	RET1236	1960	£2	£5	
Hard Travellin' Vol.2	7″ EP	London	RET1237	1960	£2	£5	
Know Where I'm Going	7″	Columbia	DB4148	1958	£1.50	£4	
Lonesome Traveller	7″	London	HLU8600	1958	£4	£8	
Tarriers	10″ LP	Columbia	33S1115	1957	£8	£20	
Tell The World About This	LP	Atlantic	(SD)8042	1960	£5	£12	US
Tom Dooley	7″	Columbia	DB3961	1957	£1.50	£4	

TARTAN HORDE

Bay City Rollers, We Love You	7″	United Artists	UP35891	1975	£1.50	£4

TARTANS

Awake The Town	7″	Caltone	TONE115	1968	£4	£8
Coming On Strong	7″	Caltone	TONE117	1968	£4	£8
Dance All Night	7″	Island	WI3058	1967	£5	£10

TASAVALIAN PRESIDENTTI

Lambertland	LP	Sonet	SNTF636	1973	£6	£15	
Milky Way Moses	LP	Sonet	SNTF658	1974	£6	£15	
Tasavalian Presedentti	LP	Love	LRLP7	1969	£8	£20	Swedish

805

TASSELS
To A Soldier Boy	7"	London	HL8885	1959	£25	£50
To A Young Lover	7"	Top Rank	JAR229	1959	£7.50	£15

TASTE
Guitarist Rory Gallagher began his long career with this trio. The titles issued as singles can be found on the "Taste" LP, but these are re-recordings. The Major Minor originals sound significantly different.
Blister On The Moon	7"	Major Minor	MM560	1968	£4	£8
Born On The Wrong Side Of Time	7"	Major Minor	MM718	197-	£2	£5
Live At The Isle Of Wight	LP	Polydor	2383120	1972	£4	£10
Live Taste	LP	Polydor	2310082	1971	£4	£10
On The Boards	LP	Polydor	583083	1970	£4	£10
Taste	LP	Polydor	583042	1969	£5	£12

TATE, BUDDY
Swinging Like Tate	LP	Felsted	FAJ7004/SJA2004	1958	£6	£15

TATE, ERIC QUINCY
Can't Keep A Good Band Down	LP	EQT		1977	£20	£40	US

TATE, HOWARD
Ain't Nobody Home	7"	Verve	VS541	1966	£2.50	£6
Baby I Love You	7"	Verve	VS555	1967	£2	£5
Get It While You Can	LP	Verve	(S)VLP9179	1967	£6	£15
Get It While You Can	7"	Verve	VS552	1967	£1.50	£4
I Learned It All The Hard Way	7"	Verve	VS556	1967	£1.50	£4
Look At Granny Run Run	7"	Verve	VS549	1967	£4	£8
Look At Granny Run Run	7"	Verve	VS584	1968	£1.50	£4
Night Owl	7"	Verve	VS571	1968	£2.50	£6
Stop	7"	Verve	VS565	1968	£1.50	£4

TATE, PHIL
Tunes For Twisters	7" EP	Oriole	EP7060	1962	£2.50	£6

TATE, TOMMY
Big Blue Diamonds	7"	Columbia	DB8046	1966	£7.50	£15

TATUM, ART
Art	LP	Fontana	FJL904	1967	£4	£10
Art Of Tatum	LP	Brunswick	LAT8358	1961	£6	£15
Art Tatum	LP	Columbia	33CX10115	1958	£8	£20
Art Tatum	LP	XTRA	XTRA1007	1964	£4	£10
Art Tatum	7" EP	Columbia	SEB10003	1955	£2	£5
Art Tatum	7" EP	Columbia	SEG7540	1955	£2	£5
Art Tatum	7" EP	Vogue	EPV1008	1954	£2	£5
Art Tatum	7" EP	Vogue	EPV1212	1957	£2	£5
Art Tatum	10" LP	Capitol	LC6524	1951	£15	£30
Art Tatum No.1	7" EP	Fontana	TFE17235	1960	£2	£5
Art Tatum No.2	7" EP	Fontana	TFE17236	1960	£2	£5
Art Tatum No.3	7" EP	Fontana	TFE17237	1960	£2	£5
Art Tatum Trio	7" EP	Melodisc	EPM7108	195-	£2	£5
Art Tatum Trio	10" LP	Vogue Coral	LRA10011	1955	£10	£25
Art Tatum-Ben Webster Quartet	LP	Columbia	33CX10137	1959	£8	£20
Art Tatum-Buddy De Franco Quartet	7" EP	Columbia	SEB10101	1958	£2	£5
Art Tatum-Buddy De Franco Quartet	7" EP	HMV	7EG8619	1960	£2	£5
Art Tatum-Roy Eldridge-Alvin Stoller-John Simmons Quartet	LP	Columbia	33CX10042	1956	£20	£40
At Hollywood Bowl	7" EP	Columbia	SEB10084	1958	£2	£5
Delicate Touch	7" EP	Columbia	SEB10116	1959	£2	£5
Discoveries	LP	Top Rank	35067	1960	£5	£12
Encores	10" LP	Capitol	LC6638	1954	£10	£25
Genius Of Art Tatum	LP	Columbia	33CX10005	1955	£10	£25
Genius Of Art Tatum No.2	LP	Columbia	33CX10053	1956	£10	£25
Genius Of Art Tatum No.3	10" LP	Columbia	33C9033	1957	£10	£25
Greatest Piano Of Them All	7" EP	HMV	7EG8604	1960	£2	£5
Here's Art Tatum	LP	Vogue Coral	LVA9047	1957	£10	£25
Incomparable Music	7" EP	HMV	7EG8684	1961	£2	£5
Just Jazz	10" LP	Vogue	LDE081	1954	£15	£30
Memories	LP	Ember	EMB3314	1961	£4	£10
Memories	7" EP	Ember	EMBEP4502	1962	£2	£5
Memories Vol.2	LP	Ember	EMB3326	1961	£4	£10
Out Of Nowhere	10" LP	Capitol	LC6625	1953	£15	£30
Presenting The Art Tatum Trio	10" LP	Columbia	33C9039	1957	£10	£25
Tatum-Carter-Bellson Trio	LP	Columbia	SEB10027	1956	£2	£5
Tatum-Carter-Bellson Trio	7" EP	Columbia	SEB10062	1957	£2	£5
Unforgettable Art	7" EP	Philips	BBE12136	1957	£2	£5

TAUPIN, BERNIE
An Interview With Bernie Taupin	LP	RCA		1987	£6	£15	US double promo

TAVERNER, JOHN
Of all the surprising records to have been issued on the Apple label, the pair of works composed by John Taverner are perhaps the most surprising at all. They have nothing to do with rock music at all in themselves, being prime examples of the classical avant-garde, but they were apparently included in the Beatles' release schedule because Ringo Starr liked them. Taverner's more recent work is inspired by his devout religious beliefs and is considerably less way-out than these early works. His tranquil "The Protecting Veil" gained considerable acclaim in some quarters and not a little commercial success during the nineties.
Celtic Requiem	LP	Apple	SAPCOR20	1971	£60	£120
Whale	LP	Apple	SAPCOR15	1970	£20	£40
Whale	LP	Ring O'	2320104	1977	£8	£20

TAVERNERS

Blowing Sand	LP	Trailer	LER2080	1973	£5	£12	
Seldom Sober	LP	Saga	EROS8146	1969	£6	£15	
Times Of Old England	LP	Folk Heritage	FHR062	1974	£4	£10	

TAW FOLK

Devonshire Cream And Cider	LP	Sentinel	SENS1030	1975	£6	£15	

TAWNEY, CYRIL

Down Among The Barley Straw	LP	Trailer	LER2095	1976	£5	£12	
I Will Give My Love	LP	Argo	ZFB87	1973	£5	£12	
In Port	LP	Argo	ZFB28	1972	£6	£15	
Mayflower Garland	LP	Argo	ZFB9	1970	£10	£25	
Outlandish Knight	LP	Polydor	236577	1970	£10	£25	
Sings Children's Songs From Devon And Cornwall	LP	Argo	ZFB4	1970	£10	£25	

TAYLES

Who Are These?	LP	CV		1969	£25	£50		US

TAYLOR, ALLAN

American Album	LP	United Artists	UAG29468	1973	£8	£20	
Lady	LP	United Artists	UAS29275	1972	£8	£20	
Sometimes	LP	Liberty	LBG83483	1971	£10	£25	
Traveller	LP	Rubber	RUB026	1978	£5	£12	

TAYLOR, ART

A.T.'s Delight	LP	Blue Note	BLP/BST84047	196-	£20	£40	

TAYLOR, AUSTIN

Push Push	7"	Top Rank	JAR511	1960	£1.50	£4	

TAYLOR, BILLY

And His Rhythm	10" LP	Felsted	L87001	195-	£20	£40	
At The London House	LP	HMV	CLP1176	1958	£4	£10	
Billy Taylor	7" EP	Esquire	EP115	195-	£2	£5	
Billy Taylor Trio	LP	Esquire	32010	1955	£10	£25	
Billy Taylor Trio	7" EP	Esquire	EP169	1958	£2	£5	
Billy Taylor Trio	10" LP	Esquire	20053	1955	£25	£50	
Evergreens	10" LP	HMV	DLP1171	1958	£4	£10	
Jazz At Storyville	10" LP	Felsted	EDL87009	1954	£20	£40	
My Fair Lady Loves Jazz	10" LP	HMV	DLP1181	1958	£4	£10	with Quincy Jones
New Billy Taylor Trio	LP	HMV	CLP1231	1959	£4	£10	
Taylor Made	10" LP	Esquire	20020	1953	£20	£40	
Taylor Made Piano	LP	Vogue	LAE12192	1960	£4	£10	

TAYLOR, BOBBY

Can't Quit Your Love	7"	Epic	EPC1720	1973	£1.50	£4	
Taylor Made Soul	LP	Tamla Motown	(S)TML11125	1970	£5	£12	

TAYLOR, BOBBY & THE VANCOUVERS

Bobby Taylor & The Vancouvers	LP	Tamla Motown	(S)TML11093	1969	£6	£15	
Does Your Mama Know About Me	7"	Tamla Motown	TMG654	1968	£6	£12	

TAYLOR, BRYAN

Donkey Smile	7"	Piccadilly	7N35018	1961	£6	£12	

TAYLOR, CATHIE

Bobby Boy	7"	Capitol	CL15207	1961	£1.50	£4	

TAYLOR, CECIL

Conquistador	LP	Blue Note	BLP/BST84260	1967	£8	£20	
Innovations	LP	Polydor	2383094	1972	£5	£12	
Looking Ahead	LP	Contemporary	LAC12216	1959	£6	£15	
Nefertiti, The Beautiful One Has Come	LP	Fontana	SFJL926	1969	£5	£12	
Newport Jazz Festival 1957	LP	Columbia	33CX10102	1958	£8	£20	Side 2 by Gigi Gryce & Donald Byrd
Unit Structures	LP	Blue Note	BLP/BST84237	1966	£8	£20	

TAYLOR, CHIP

Here I Am	7"	Warner Bros	WB82	1962	£1.50	£4	

TAYLOR, DEBBIE

Don't Wanna Leave You	7"	Arista	ARIST50	1976	£1.50	£4	

TAYLOR, EARL

Bluegrass Taylor Made	LP	Capitol	(S)T2090	1963	£5	£12		US

TAYLOR, EDDIE & FLOYD JONES

Eddie Taylor & Floyd Jones	7" EP	XX	MIN712	196-	£4	£8	

TAYLOR, ELIZABETH

In London	LP	Colpix	PXL459	1963	£8	£20	

TAYLOR, FELICE

Can Feel Your Love	7"	President	PT193	1968	£1.50	£4	
Feel Love Comin' On	7"	President	PT155	1967	£1.50	£4	chart single

TAYLOR, GLORIA

You Gotta Pay The Price	7"	Polydor	56788	1970	£2	£5	

TAYLOR, HOUND DOG
Christine	7"	Outasite	45504	1966	£12.50	£25	

TAYLOR, JAMES
Carolina In My Mind	7"	Apple	32	1970	£2	£5	
Gorilla	LP	Warner Bros	BS42866	1975	£4	£10	US quad
James Taylor	LP	Apple	APCOR3	1968	£8	£20	mono, black letters
James Taylor	LP	Apple	SAPCOR3	1968	£5	£12	orange lettering
James Taylor	LP	Apple	SAPCOR3	1968	£6	£15	stereo, black letters
One Man Dog	LP	Warner Bros	BS42660	1974	£4	£10	US quad

TAYLOR, JAMES QUARTET
Blow Up	7"	Re-Elect President	FORD1	1987	£1.50	£4	

TAYLOR, JEREMY
Ag Pleez Deddy	7"	Decca	F11502	1962	£1.50	£4	
Always Something New	LP	Decca	LK4731	1966	£8	£20	
His Songs	LP	Fontana	STL5475	1968	£6	£15	
Jobsworth	LP	Canon	CPT3982	1973	£5	£12	
More Of His Songs	LP	Fontana	STL5523	1969	£6	£15	
Piece Of Ground	LP	Galliard	GAL4018	1972	£6	£15	
Red Velvet Steering Wheel	7"	Fontana	TF962	1968	£1.50	£4	
Wait A Minim Songs	7" EP	Decca	DFE8581	1964	£4	£8	

TAYLOR, JOHN
Pause And Think Again	LP	Turtle	TUR302	1971	£25	£50	

TAYLOR, JOHNNIE
Ain't That Loving You	7"	Stax	601003	1967	£1.50	£4	
Friday Night	7"	Stax	STX2025	1968	£2	£5	
I Am Somebody	7"	Stax	STAX156	1970	£1.50	£4	
I Could Never Be President	7"	Stax	STAX129	1969	£1.50	£4	
Looking For Johnnie Taylor	LP	Atco	228008	1969	£5	£12	
Love Bones	7"	Stax	STAX141	1970	£1.50	£4	
Philosophy Continues	LP	Stax	SXATS1024	1969	£5	£12	
Raw Blues	LP	Stax	STS2008	1969	£5	£12	US
Steal Away	7"	Stax	STAX150	1970	£2.50	£6	
Take Care Of Your Homework	7"	Stax	STAX114	1969	£1.50	£4	
Testify	7"	Stax	STAX122	1969	£1.50	£4	
Wanted: One Soul Singer	LP	Stax	589008	1967	£6	£15	
Who's Making Love?	LP	Stax	(S)XATS1006	1969	£5	£12	
Who's Making Love?	7"	Stax	STAX106	1968	£1.50	£4	

TAYLOR, JOSEPH
Unto Brigg Fair	LP	Leader	LEA2050	1972	£10	£25	

TAYLOR, KINGSIZE & THE DOMINOES
Memphis Tennessee	7"	Polydor	NH66990	1963	£6	£12	
Real Gonk Man	LP	Midnight	HLP/HST2101	196-	£20	£40	US
Somebody's Always Trying	7"	Decca	F11935	1964	£6	£12	
Star Club Time	LP	Ariola		1964	£35	£70	German
Stupidity	7"	Decca	F11874	1964	£6	£12	
Teenbeat 2 - Teanbeat From The Star Club Hamburg	7" EP	Decca	DFE8569	1964	£25	£50	
Twist And Shake	7" EP	Polydor	EPH21628	1963	£15	£30	
Twist Time In Star Club	LP	Ariola		1964	£35	£70	German

TAYLOR, KINGSIZE & THE DOMINOS
Thinkin'	7"	Polydor	BM56152	1965	£7.50	£15	

TAYLOR, KOKO
Koko Taylor	LP	Chess	LPS1532	1968	£6	£15	US
Violent Love	7"	Chess	6145018	1972	£1.50	£4	
Wang Dang Doodle	7"	Chess	CRS8035	1966	£4	£8	

TAYLOR, LITTLE JOHNNY
Everybody Knows About My Good Thing	LP	Polydor	2916015	1972	£4	£10	
Little Johnny Taylor	LP	Galaxy	(8)203	1963	£8	£20	US
Little Johnny Taylor	LP	Vocalion	VAP8031	1965	£8	£20	
One More Chance	7"	Vocalion	VF9264	1966	£4	£8	
Part Time Love	7"	Vocalion	VP9234	1965	£4	£8	

TAYLOR MAIDS
Theme From I Am A Camera	7"	Capitol	CL14322	1955	£1.50	£4	

TAYLOR, MICK
If the single by Mick Taylor has aquired any value by reason of its authorship by the future Bluesbreaker and Rolling Stone, then the justification for this is misplaced, for the two Taylor's are not the same.
London Town	7"	CBS	201770	1965	£5	£10	

TAYLOR, MIKE
MIke Taylor showed every sign of developing into a major talent before his premature death in the late sixties. He co-wrote songs for Cream ("Those Were The Days", "Passing The Time") and for Colosseum ("Jumping Off The Sun") and was also a fine jazz pianist. The two rare albums he made have Jack Bruce, Tony Reeves, and Jon Hiseman among the small supporting cast.
Pendulum	LP	Columbia	SX6042	1965	£50	£100	
Trio	LP	Columbia	SX6137	1966	£50	£100	

TAYLOR, NEVILLE
Baby Lay Sleeping	7"	Parlophone	R4493	1958	£2	£5	

Dance With A Dolly	7"	Oriole	CB1546	1960	£2	£5	
First Words Of Love	7"	Parlophone	R4524	1959	£5	£10	
Joshua Fit The Battle Of Jericho	7"	Honey Hit	TB127	196-	£1.50	£4	
Mercy Mercy Percy	7"	Parlophone	R4447	1958	£5	£10	
Tears On My Pillow	7"	Parlophone	R4476	1958	£4	£8	

TAYLOR, PADDY

Boy In The Gap	LP	Claddagh	CC8	1969	£5	£12	Irish

TAYLOR, R.DEAN

Ain't It A Sad Thing	7"	Rare Earth	RES101	1971	£5	£10	TMG786 matrix
Ain't It A Sad Thing	7"	Tamla Motown	TMG786	1971	£20	£40	demo only
Gotta See Jane	7"	Tamla Motown	TMG656	1968	£2	£5	chart single
I Think Therefore I Am	LP	Rare Earth	RS522	1970	£5	£12	US
Indiana Wants Me	LP	Tamla Motown	STML11185	1971	£6	£15	
Indiana Wants Me	7"	Tamla Motown	TMG763	1971	£1.50	£4	chart single

TAYLOR, ROGER

Fun In Space	LP	EMI	EMC3369	1981	£4	£10	
Future Management	7"	EMI	EMI5157	1981	£5	£10	chart single
I Wanna Testify	7"	EMI	EMI2679	1977	£20	£40	
Man On Fire	7"	EMI	EMI5478	1984	£5	£10	
Man On Fire	12"	EMI	EMI125478	1984	£15	£30	
My Country	7"	EMI	EMI5200	1981	£10	£20	
Strange Frontier	LP	EMI	EJ2401371	1984	£5	£12	
Strange Frontier	7"	EMI	EMI5490	1984	£5	£10	
Strange Frontier	12"	EMI	EMI125490	1984	£15	£30	

TAYLOR, SAM

Sam Taylor Orchestra	7" EP	MGM	MGMEP531	1956	£10	£20	

TAYLOR, SAM 'THE MAN'

Please Be Kind	7"	MGM	SP1106	1954	£7.50	£15	

TAYLOR, TED

Cat's Eyes	7"	Oriole	CB1628	1961	£1.50	£4	
Fried Onions	7"	Oriole	CB1574	1961	£1.50	£4	
Haunted Pad	7"	Oriole	CB1630	1961	£2	£5	
Jericho	7"	Oriole	CB1713	1962	£2	£5	
M1	7"	Oriole	CB1573	1961	£1.50	£4	
Son Of Honky Tonk	7"	Oriole	CB1464	1958	£1.50	£4	
Surfrider	7"	Oriole	CB1767	1962	£5	£10	

TAYLOR, TRUE

True Taylor is one of several names tried by Paul Simon during the early years of his recording career.

True Or False	7"	Big	614	1958	£20	£40	US

TAYLOR, VERNON

Mystery Train	7"	London	HLS9025	1960	£25	£50	

TAYLOR, VIC

Does It His Way	LP	Trojan	TRLS38	1971	£5	£12	
Heartaches	7"	Treasure Isle	TI7021	1967	£5	£10	

TAYLOR, VINCE & THE PLAYBOYS

Brand New Cadillac	7"	Parlophone	R4539	1959	£7.50	£15	
Jet Black Machine	7"	Palette	PG9001	1960	£6	£12	
Right Behind You Baby	7"	Parlophone	R4505	1958	£7.50	£15	
Whatcha Gonna Do	7"	Palette	PG9020	1961	£7.50	£15	

T-BONES

I Am Louisiana Red	7" EP	Riviera	231075	1965	£30	£60	French
I'm A Lover	7"	Columbia	DB7401	1964	£12.50	£25	
Won't You Give Me One More Chance	7"	Columbia	DB7489	1965	£7.50	£15	

T-BONES (2)

No Matter What Shape	7" EP	Liberty	LEP2248	1965	£5	£10	French

T.C.ATLANTIC

T.C.Atlantic	LP	Dove	LP4459		£25	£50	US

TEA & SYMPHONY

Asylum For The Musically Insane	LP	Harvest	SHVL761	1969	£30	£60	sleeve pictured in Guide
Boredom	7"	Harvest	HAR5005	1969	£4	£8	
Jo Sago	LP	Harvest	SHVL785	1970	£30	£60	

TEA COMPANY

Come & Have Some Tea	LP	Mercury	SMCL20127	1968	£8	£20	

TEA SET

Join The Tea Set	7"	King	KG1048	1966	£4	£8	

TEACHO & THE STUDENTS

Rocket	7"	Felsted	AF104	1958	£10	£20	

TEAGARDEN, JACK

At The Round Table	LP	Columbia	33SX1235/ SCX3312	1960	£4	£10	
Big T's Jazz	LP	Brunswick	LAT8229	1958	£6	£15	
Jack Teagarden's Dixieland Band	LP	Capitol	T1095	1959	£5	£12	
Jazz Great	LP	London	LTZN15077	1957	£8	£20	

This Is Teagarden	LP	Capitol	T721	1956	£5	£12	

TEAL, J. BAND

Cooks	LP	Mother Cleo		1977	£15	£30	US

TEAR GAS

Tear Gas was a Scottish heavy rock group, whose "Piggy Go Getter" LP received a considerable publicity campaign to little avail. The members' fortunes gained a considerable boost, however, when Tear Gas was taken on entire by singer Alex Harvey, to become The Sensational Alex Harvey Band.

Piggy Go Getter	LP	Famous	SFMA5751	1971	£10	£25	
Tear Gas	LP	Regal Zonophone	SLRZ1021	1971	£70	£140	

TEARDROP EXPLODES

Bouncing Babies	7"	Zoo	CAGE005	1979	£2.50	£6	PS
Ha Ha I'm Drowning	7"	Mercury	TEAR44	1981	£2	£5	double
Ha Ha I'm Drowning	7"	Mercury	TEAR4	1981	£10	£20	PS
Sleeping Gas	7"	Zoo	CAGE003	1979	£2.50	£6	blue PS
Sleeping Gas	7"	Zoo	CAGE003	1979	£4	£8	red PS
Treason	7"	Zoo	CAGE008	1980	£2	£5	

TEARS FOR FEARS

Everybody Wants To Rule The World	7"	Mercury	IDEA99	1985	£1.50	£4	double
Head Over Heels	7"	Mercury	IDEP10	1985	£2	£5	shaped pic disc
Mad World	7"	Mercury	IDEA33	1982	£2	£5	double
Mother's Talk	7"	Mercury	IDEP7	1984	£2.50	£6	pic disc
Pale Shelter	7"	Mercury	IDEAB5	1983	£1.50	£4	blue vinyl
Pale Shelter	7"	Mercury	IDEAG5	1983	£1.50	£4	green vinyl
Pale Shelter	7"	Mercury	IDEAP5	1983	£2.50	£6	pic disc
Pale Shelter	7"	Mercury	IDEAR5	1983	£1.50	£4	red vinyl
Pale Shelter	7"	Mercury	IDEAW5	1983	£1.50	£4	white vinyl
Way You Are	7"	Mercury	IDEAS6	1983	£2	£5	double

TEAZE

Live	LP	Aquarius	AQR520	1978	£6	£15	Canadian
One Night Stands	LP	Capitol	11919	1979	£6	£15	US

TECHNIQUES

Hey Little Girl	7"	Columbia	DB4072	1958	£7.50	£15	

TECHNIQUES (2)

Devoted	7"	Treasure Isle	TI7038	1968	£5	£10	with Tommy McCook
I Wish It Would Rain	7"	Duke	DU1	1968	£4	£8	
It's You I Love	7"	Treasure Isle	TI7040	1968	£5	£10	
Love Is Not A Gamble	7"	Treasure Isle	TI7026	1967	£5	£10	
Man Of My Word	7"	Duke	DU6	1968	£4	£8	
My Girl	7"	Treasure Isle	TI7031	1968	£5	£10	with Tommy McCook
Queen Majesty	7"	Treasure Isle	TI7019	1967	£5	£10	
What Am I To Do	7"	Duke	DU22	1969	£2.50	£6	
Where Were You	7"	Duke	DU60	1969	£2.50	£6	
Who You Gonna Run To	7"	Camel	CA10	1969	£2	£5	
You Don't Care	7"	Treasure Isle	TI7001	1967	£5	£10	Tommy McCook B side

TEDDY & THE PANDAS

Basic Magnetism	LP	Tower	ST5125	1968	£8	£20	US

TEDDY & THE TIGERS

Hold On I'm Coming	7"	Spin	SP2004	1967	£5	£10	

TEDDY & THE TWILIGHTS

I'm Just Your Clown	7"	Stateside	SS167	1963	£2.50	£6	

TEDDY BEARS

Although Phil Spector is famous as a producer - indeed he was the first such to attain fame independently of the artists he produced - he started his career as a singer. He was one third of a group, the Teddybears, whose best known song is remembered as a particularly golden oldie - "To Know Him Is To Love Him".

If Only You Knew	7"	London	HLP8889	1959	£10	£20	
Oh Why	7"	London	HLP8836	1959	£6	£12	
Teddy Bears Sing	LP	Imperial	LP9067	1959	£100	£200	US, mono
Teddy Bears Sing	LP	Imperial	SLP12067	1959	£180	£300	US, stereo
Teddy Bears Sing	LP	London	HAP2183	1959	£75	£150	sleeve pictured in Guide
To Know Him Is To Love Him	7"	London	HLN8733	1958	£4	£8	chart single

TEE SET

Ma Belle Amie	LP	Columbia	SCX6419	1970	£5	£12	
Ma Belle Amie	7"	Major Minor	MM666	1970	£2.50	£6	
Morning Of My Daze	LP	Negram			£10	£25	
What Can I Do	7"	Pye	7N25452	1968	£2.50	£6	

TEE, WILLIE

Thank You John	7"	Atlantic	584116	1967	£7.50	£15	
Walkin' Up A One Way Street	7"	Mojo	2092025	1971	£1.50	£4	

TEEN BEATS

Slop Beat	7"	Top Rank	JAR342	1960	£4	£8	

TEEN KINGS

When reissued as the more common Sun label recording, "Ooby Dooby" was credited to the Teen Kings' lead singer, Roy Orbison.

Ooby Dooby	7"	Jewel	101	1956	£330	£500	US
Ooby Dooby	7"	Jewel	102	1956	£210	£350	US

TEEN QUEENS

Eddie My Love	LP	Crown	CLP5022	1957	£30	£60	US
Eddie My Love	7"	R&B	MRB5000	1965	£10	£20	
Teen Queens	LP	Crown	CLP5373	1963	£10	£25	US

TEENAGE FANCLUB

Ballad Of John And Yoko	7"	Paperhouse	PAPER005	1990	£2	£5	1 side etched
Everything Flows	7"	Paperhouse	PAPER003	1990	£5	£10	
King	LP	Creation	LP096	1991	£5	£12	
King	CD	Creation	CD096	1991	£6	£15	

TEENAGE FILMSTARS

Cloud Over Liverpool	7"	Clockwork	COR002	1979	£5	£10	
Cloud Over Liverpool	7"	Clockwork	COR002	1979	£20	£40	PS
I Helped Patrick McGoohan Escape	7"	Fab Listening	FL1	1980	£2.50	£6	
Odd Man Out	7"	Blueprint	BLU2013	1980	£2.50	£6	PS
Odd Man Out	7"	Wessex	WEX275	1980	£4	£8	no PS

TEENAGERS

Teenagers	7" EP	RCA	RCX102	1957	£7.50	£15	

TEESIDE FETTLERS

Ring Of Iron	LP	Tradition	TSR016	1974	£5	£12	

TELESCOPES

Kick The Wall	7"	Cheree	CHEREE2	1989	£5	£10	2 different PS's

TELEVISION

It is curious how the music of Television, which was conceived as a vehicle for the lengthy display of lead guitar expertise, managed to become considered as part of the seventies punk movement, which generally had no time for such excesses. There was, of course, no denying the freshness and sheer excitement of the "Marquee Moon" album, whose status as a classic recording is never likely to be undermined.

Little Johnny Jewel	7"	Ork	81975	1975	£5	£10	US
Little Johnny Jewel	12"	Ork	NYC1	1979	£3	£8	US

TELEVISION PERSONALITIES

14th Floor	7"	Teen	CUS77089	1978	£15	£30	3 PS's
And Don't The Kids Just Love It	LP	Rough Trade	RT24	1981	£10	£25	with insert
Biff Bang Pow!	7"	Creation/Lyntone	LYN13546	1982	£6	£12	flexi
How I Learned To Love The Bomb	7"	Dreamworld	DREAM10	1986	£5	£10	
How I Learned To Love The Bomb	12"	Dreamworld	DREAM4	1986	£3	£8	
I Know Where Syd Barrett Lives	7"	Rough Trade	RT063	1981	£6	£12	
I Still Believe In Magic	7"	Caff	CAFF5	1989	£7.50	£15	
Mummy You're Not Watching Me	LP	Dreamworld	BIGDREAM4	1986	£5	£12	
Mummy You're Not Watching Me	LP	Whaam!	BIG1	1982	£10	£25	with insert
Painted Word	LP	Illuminated	JAMS37	1984	£10	£25	
Sense Of Belonging	7"	Rough Trade	RT109	1983	£4	£8	
Smashing Time	7"	Rough Trade	RT051	1980	£5	£10	
They Could Have Been Bigger Than The Beatles	LP	Dreamworld	BIGDREAM2	1986	£5	£12	
They Could Have Been Bigger Than The Beatles	LP	Whaam!	BIG5	1982	£10	£25	
Three Wishes	7"	Whaam!	WHAAM4	1982	£4	£8	2 sleeves
Where's Bill Grundy Now	7"	King's Road	LYN5976/7	1978	£5	£10	4 PS's
Where's Bill Grundy Now	7"	Rough Trade	RT033	1979	£2.50	£6	

TELHAM TINKERS

Hot In Alice Springs	LP	Eron	031	1984	£5	£12	

TELLERS

A-Ya-It-Deh	7"	Dragon	DRA1031	1974	£1.50	£4	
Innocent People Cry	7"	Pyramid	PYR7012	1974	£1.50	£4	
No Work No Pay	7"	Pyramid	PYR7011	1974	£1.50	£4	

TELSTARS

I Went Walkin'	7"	Oriole	CB1754	1962	£1.50	£4	

TEMPERANCE SEVEN

Charleston	7"	Parlophone	R4851	1961	£1.50	£4	chart single
Everybody Loves My Baby	7"	Parlophone	R4893	1962	£1.50	£4	
Hard Hearted Hannah	7"	Parlophone	R4823	1961	£1.50	£4	chart single
Letkiss	7"	Parlophone	R5236	1965	£1.50	£4	
Pasadena	7"	Parlophone	R4781	1961	£1.50	£4	chart single
Temperance Seven	LP	Parlophone	PMC1152/PCS3021	1961	£4	£10	chart LP
Temperance Seven Plus One	LP	Argo	RG11	1961	£4	£10	chart LP
You're Driving Me Crazy	7"	Parlophone	R4757	1961	£1.50	£4	chart single

TEMPEST

Living In Fear	LP	Bronze	ILPS9267	1974	£6	£15	
Tempest	LP	Bronze	ILPS9220	1973	£6	£15	

TEMPEST, BOBBY

Love Or Leave	7"	Decca	F11125	1959	£2.50	£6	

TEMPLE, BOB

Vim Vam Vamoose	7"	Parlophone	R4264	1957	£2	£5	

TEMPLE, GERRY

Angel Face	7"	HMV	POP1114	1963	£5	£10	

Title	Format	Label	Catalogue	Year	Price	Price	Notes
Lovin' Up A Storm	7"	RCA	RCA1670	1968	£2.50	£6	
No More Tomorrows	7"	HMV	POP823	1961	£5	£10	
Seventeen Come Sunday	7"	HMV	POP939	1961	£5	£10	

TEMPLE, SHIRLEY

Title	Format	Label	Catalogue	Year	Price	Price	Notes
I Remember	7" EP.	Top Rank	JKR8003	1959	£5	£10	
On The Good Ship Lollipop	7"	Top Rank	JAR139	1959	£1.50	£4	

TEMPLEAIRES

Title	Format	Label	Catalogue	Year	Price	Price	Notes
He Spoke	7"	Vogue	V2421	1970	£2.50	£6	

TEMPO, NINO

Title	Format	Label	Catalogue	Year	Price	Price	Notes
Rock'N'Roll Beach Party	10" LP	London	HBU1075	1957	£30	£60	
Tempo's Tempo	7"	London	HLU8387	1957	£40	£80	

TEMPO, NINO & APRIL STEVENS

Title	Format	Label	Catalogue	Year	Price	Price	Notes
All Strung Out	LP	London	HAU/SHU8314	1967	£6	£15	
All Strung Out	LP	London	HLU10084	1966	£1.50	£4	
All Strung Out	7"	London	HLU10245	1969	£1.50	£4	
Deep Purple	LP	London	HAK8168	1964	£8	£20	
Deep Purple	7"	Atlantic	584151	1968	£1.50	£4	
Deep Purple	7"	London	HLK9782	1963	£1.50	£4	chart single
Deep Purple	7" EP.	London	REK1412	1964	£5	£10	
Great Songs	LP	Atlantic	ATL/STL5006	1964	£6	£15	
Habit Of Lovin' You Baby	7"	London	HLU10106	1967	£1.50	£4	
I'm Confessing	7"	London	HLK9890	1964	£1.50	£4	
Ooh Poo Pah Doo	7"	London	HLU10209	1968	£1.50	£4	
Stardust	7"	London	HLK9859	1964	£1.50	£4	
Sweet And Lovely	7"	London	HLK9580	1962	£2.50	£6	Top Notes B side
Whispering	7"	London	HLK9829	1964	£1.50	£4	chart single

TEMPOS

Title	Format	Label	Catalogue	Year	Price	Price	Notes
See You In September	7"	Pye	7N25026	1959	£5	£10	
Speaking Of The Tempos	LP	Justice	104	1966	£100	£200	US

TEMPREES

Title	Format	Label	Catalogue	Year	Price	Price	Notes
Love Men	LP	Stax	2325083	1972		£12	
Three	LP	Stax	STX1040	1974	£6	£15	

TEMPTATIONS

Title	Format	Label	Catalogue	Year	Price	Price	Notes
Ain't Too Proud To Beg	7"	Tamla Motown	TMG565	1966	£4	£8	chart single
Ain't Too Proud To Beg	7"	Tamla Motown	TMG699	1969	£1.50	£4	
All I Need	7"	Tamla Motown	TMG610	1967	£2.50	£6	
Ball Of Confusion	7"	Tamla Motown	TMG749	1970	£1.50	£4	chart single
Beauty is Only Skin Deep	7"	Tamla Motown	TMG578	1966	£5	£10	chart single
Cloud Nine	LP	Tamla Motown	(S)TML11109	1969	£5	£12	chart LP
Cloud Nine	7"	Tamla Motown	TMG707	1969	£1.50	£4	chart single
Get Ready	7"	Tamla Motown	TMG557	1966	£6	£12	
Get Ready	7"	Tamla Motown	TMG688	1969	£1.50	£4	chart single
Gettin' Ready	LP	Tamla Motown	(S)TML11035	1966	£10	£25	chart LP
Greatest Hits	LP	Tamla Motown	(S)TML11042	1967	£5	£12	chart LP
I Can't Get Next To You	7"	Tamla Motown	TMG722	1970	£1.50	£4	chart single
I Could Never Love Another	7"	Tamla Motown	TMG658	1968	£2	£5	chart single
I Wish It Would Rain	7"	Tamla Motown	TMG641	1968	£2	£5	chart single
I'll Be In Trouble	7"	Stateside	SS319	1964	£12.50	£25	
I'm Losing You	7"	Tamla Motown	TMG587	1966	£4	£8	chart single
In A Mellow Mood	LP	Tamla Motown	(S)TML11068	1968	£5	£12	
It's Growing	7"	Tamla Motown	TMG504	1965	£7.50	£15	chart single
It's The Temptations	7" EP.	Tamla Motown	TME2010	1966	£7.50	£15	
It's You That I Need	7"	Tamla Motown	TMG633	1967	£10	£20	
Just My Imagination	7"	Tamla Motown	TMG773	1971	£1.50	£4	chart single
Live	LP	Tamla Motown	(S)TML11053	1967	£5	£12	chart LP
Live At The Copa	LP	Tamla Motown	(S)TML11104	1969	£4	£10	
Live At The Talk Of The Town	LP	Tamla Motown	(S)TML11141	1970	£5	£12	
Meet The Temptations	LP	Tamla Motown	TML11009	1965	£15	£30	
Memories	7"	Tamla Motown	TMG948	1975	£4	£8	demo, PS
My Baby	7"	Tamla Motown	TMG541	1965	£6	£12	
My Girl	7"	Stateside	SS378	1965	£10	£20	chart single
Papa Was A Rolling Stone	7"	Tamla Motown	TMG839	1973	£1.50	£4	chart single
Psychedelic Shack	LP	Tamla Motown	(S)TML11147	1970	£6	£15	chart LP
Psychedelic Shack	7"	Tamla Motown	TMG741	1970	£1.50	£4	chart single
Puzzle People	LP	Tamla Motown	(S)TML11133	1970	£5	£12	chart LP
Runaway Child Running Wild	7"	Tamla Motown	TMG716	1969	£1.50	£4	
Since I Lost My Baby	7"	Tamla Motown	TMG526	1965	£7.50	£15	
Sing Smokey	LP	Tamla Motown	TML11016	1965	£15	£30	
Superstar	7"	Tamla Motown	TMG800	1972	£1.50	£4	chart single
Take A Look Around	7"	Tamla Motown	TMG808	1972	£1.50	£4	chart single
Temptations	7" EP.	Tamla Motown	TME2004	1965	£7.50	£15	
Temptations Show	LP	Gordy	GS933	1969	£5	£12	US
Temptations Wish It Would Rain	LP	Tamla Motown	(S)TML11079	1968	£6	£15	
Temptin' Temptations	LP	Tamla Motown	TML11023	1966	£15	£30	
Unite The World	7"	Tamla Motown	TMG783	1971	£1.50	£4	
Way You Do The Things You Do	7"	Stateside	SS278	1964	£12.50	£25	
Why Did You Leave Me Darling	7"	Tamla Motown	TMG671	1968	£2	£5	
Why You Wanna Make Me Blue	7"	Stateside	SS348	1964	£17.50	£35	
With A Lot O'Soul	LP	Tamla Motown	(S)TML11057	1967	£6	£15	chart LP
You're My Everything	7"	Tamla Motown	TMG620	1967	£2	£5	chart single

TEMPTATIONS (2)

Title	Format	Label	Catalogue	Year	Price	Price	Notes
Barbara	7"	Top Rank	JAR384	1960	£5	£10	

TEMPUS FUGIT

Come Alive	7"	Philips	BF1802	1969	£7.50	£15	

TEN CC

Greatest Hits	LP	Mercury	HS9102504	1982	£4	£10	audiophile
Original Soundtrack	LP	Mercury	HS9102500	1982	£4	£10	audiophile

TEN FEET

Got Everything But Love	7"	RCA	RCA1544	1966	£7.50	£15	
Shot On Sight	7"	CBS	3045	1966	£7.50	£15	

TEN FEET FIVE

Two members of Ten Feet Five left to join the Troggs soon after the release of the group's only single - guitarist Chris Britton and bass player Pete Staples.

Baby's Back In Town	7"	Fontana	TF578	1965	£10	£20

TEN THOUSAND MANIACS

Can't Ignore The Train	12"	Elektra	EKR11T	1985	£3	£8	
Human Conflict £5	12"	Press	P2010	1984	£10	£25	
Just As The Tide Was A-Flowin'	7"	Elektra	EKR19	1985	£2.50	£6	
My Mother The War	12"	Reflex	12RE1	1984	£5	£12	
Secrets Of The I Ching	LP	private		198-	£20	£40	US

TEN YEARS AFTER

Before Woodstock showed Alvin Lee the mileage he could get from guitar excess, Ten Years After had a light, jazzy sound that made them stand out from the mass of blues bands emerging at the time. "Undead" shows off this quality well - it even includes a lengthy jam on "Woodchopper's Ball", which succeeds in dragging the Woody Herman original into the rock age with its dignity intact. "Stonedhenge" is still impressive too as the work of a band thinking hard and imaginatively of ways in which to break free of the constraints of playing the blues, even if that imagination was largely placed on hold for subsequent recordings.

Cricklewood Green	LP	Deram	SML1065	1970	£4	£10	chart LP
Hear Me Calling	7"	Deram	DM221	1968	£2	£5	
Love Like A Man	7"	Deram	DM299	1970	£1.50	£4	chart single
Portable People	7"	Deram	DM176	1967	£2	£5	
Recorded Live	LP	Chrysalis	CHR1049	1973	£4	£10	chart LP
Rock'n'Roll To The World	LP	Chrysalis	CHR1009	1972	£4	£10	chart LP
Space In Time	LP	Chrysalis	CHR1001	1972	£4	£10	chart LP
Space In Time	LP	Columbia	CQ30801	1972	£5	£12	US quad
Ssssh!	LP	Deram	DML1052	1969	£6	£15	mono
Ssssh!	LP	Deram	SML1052	1969	£6	£12	chart LP
Stonedhenge	LP	Deram	DML1029	1968	£6	£15	mono
Stonedhenge	LP	Deram	SML1029	1968	£6	£12	chart LP
Ten Years After	LP	Deram	DML1015	1967	£8	£20	mono
Ten Years After	LP	Deram	SML1015	1967	£6	£15	
Undead	LP	Deram	DML1023	1968	£6	£15	mono
Undead	LP	Deram	SML1023	1968	£5	£12	chart LP
Watt	LP	Deram	SML1078	1970	£4	£10	chart LP

TENDER SLIM & COUSIN LEROY

Tender Slim & Cousin Leroy	7" EP	XX	MIN702	196-	£4	£8

TENNORS

Another Scorcher	7"	Big Shot	BI517	1969	£2.50	£6	
Copy Me Donkey	7"	Island	WI3140	1968	£5	£10	Romeo Stewart B side
Grampa	7"	Island	WI3156	1968	£5	£10	Romeo Stewart B side
Hopeful Village	7"	Duke Reid	DR2502	1969	£4	£8	Tommy McCook B side
Khaki	7"	Blue Cat	BS127	1968	£4	£8	Leroy Reid B side
Let Go Yah Donkey	7"	Fab	FAB50	1968	£4	£8	Romeo Stewart B side
Massie Massa	7"	Doctor Bird	DB1152	1968	£5	£10	Clive Allstars B side
Pressure And Slide	7"	Coxsone	CS7024	1967	£5	£10	Soul Brothers B side
Ride Your Donkey	7"	Fab	FAB41	1968	£4	£8	
Ride Your Donkey	7"	Island	WI3133	1968	£5	£10	
Sufferer	7"	Doctor Bird	DB1175	1968	£5	£10	
You're No Good	7"	Big Shot	BI514	1969	£2.50	£6	

TERMITES

Every Day Every Day	7"	CBS	201761	1965	£1.50	£4
Tell Me	7"	Oriole	CB1989	1965	£5	£10

TERMITES (2)

Do It Right Now	7"	Coxsone	CS7025	1967	£5	£10	Summertaires B side
Do The Rock Steady	LP	Studio One	SOL9003	1967	£50	£100	
It Takes Two To Make Love	7"	Studio One	SO2029	1967	£6	£12	
Mama Didn't Know	7"	Coxsone	CS7039	1968	£6	£12	
Mercy Mr.Percy	7"	Studio One	SO2006	1967	£6	£12	Soul Brothers B side
Mr.DJ	7"	Studio One	SO2040	1968	£6	£12	
Push It Up	7"	Pama	PM729	1968	£4	£8	
Push Push	7"	Nu Beat	NB017	1968	£4	£8	
Show Me The Way	7"	Pama	PM738	1968	£4	£8	
Sign Up	7"	Coxsone	CS7008	1967	£5	£10	Delroy Wilson B side

TERRACE, PETE

At The Party	7"	Pye	7N25427	1967	£2.50	£6
Boogaloo	LP	Pye	NPL28102	1967	£6	£15
Shotgun Boogaloo	7"	Pye	7N25440	1967	£7.50	£15

TERRELL, LLOYD

Bang Bang Lulu	7"	Pama	PM710	1968	£2.50	£6	Mrs.Miller B side
Birth Control	7"	Pama	PM792	1969	£4	£8	
How Come	7"	Pama	PM740	1968	£2.50	£6	Mrs.Miller B side
Lulu Returns	7"	Pama	PM752	1968	£2.50	£6	Mrs.Miller B side

Title	Format	Label	Cat No	Year	Price	Price	Notes
Mr.Rhya	7"	Nu Beat	NB023	1969	£2.50	£6	

TERRELL, TAMMI
| Come On And See Me | 7" | Tamla Motown | TMG561 | 1966 | £15 | £30 | |
| Irresistible Tammi Terrell | LP | Tamla Motown | (S)TML11103 | 1969 | £8 | £20 | |

TERRY & JERRY
| People Are Doing It Every Day | 7" | R&B | MRB5009 | 1965 | £4 | £8 | |

TERRY, CLARK
Clark Terry	LP	Emarcy	EJL1256	1957	£8	£20	
Duke With A Difference	LP	Riverside	RLP12246	1961	£6	£15	
Gingerbread Men	LP	Fontana	(S)TL5394	1967	£4	£10	with Bob Brookmeyer
It's What's Happenin'	LP	Impulse	MIPL/SIPL507	1968	£4	£10	
Mumbles	LP	Fontana	TL5373	1966	£4	£10	
Power Of Positive Swinging	LP	Fontana	TL5290	1966	£4	£10	with Bob Brookmeyer
Tonight	LP	Fontana	TL5265	1965	£4	£10	with Bob Brookmeyer

TERRY, DEWEY
| Chief | LP | Tumbleweed | TW3502 | 1973 | £5 | £12 | US |

TERRY, GORDON
| Country Clambake | 7" EP | London | REA1098 | 1957 | £7.50 | £15 | |

TERRY SISTERS
| It's The Same Old Jazz | 7" | Parlophone | R4364 | 1957 | £4 | £8 | |
| Sweet Thing | 7" | Parlophone | R4509 | 1958 | £1.50 | £4 | |

TERRY, SONNY
Blind Sonny Terry And Woody Guthrie	LP	Ember	CW136	1969	£4	£10	
Blues	10" LP	Stinson	55		£6	£15	US
Blues And Folk Songs	10" LP	Folkways	2327		£6	£15	US
Blues From Everywhere	LP	XTRA	XTRA1099	1969	£5	£12	
City Blues	10" LP	Vogue	LDE165	1955	£6	£15	
Folk Blues	10" LP	Vogue	LDE137	1955	£6	£15	
Fox Chase	78	Vogue	V2326	1955	£2.50	£6	
Harmonica	10" LP	Folkways	2035		£6	£15	US
Harmonica	10" LP	Folkways	35		£6	£15	US
Harmonica Blues	10" LP	Topic	10T30	1958	£8	£20	
Hooting Blues	7"	Parlophone	MSP6017	1953	£10	£20	
On The Road	LP	XTRA	XTRA1110	1971	£4	£10	
Sonny Is King	LP	Bluesville	BV1059	1963	£6	£15	US
Sonny Terry	LP	Everest	206	196-	£6	£15	US
Sonny Terry	LP	XTRA	XTRA1064	1969	£4	£10	
Sonny Terry	7" EP	Vogue	EPV1095	1956	£5	£10	
Sonny Terry And His Mouth Harp	LP	Riverside	12644		£6	£15	US
Sonny's Story	LP	Bluesville	BV1025	1961	£6	£15	US
Sonny's Story	LP	XTRA	XTRA5025	1966	£5	£12	
Talkin' 'Bout The Blues	LP	Washington	W702	1961	£8	£20	US
Washboard Band	10" LP	Folkways	2006		£6	£15	US
Whoopin' The Blues	10" LP	Melodisc	MLP516	1958	£6	£15	

TERRY, SONNY & BROWNIE MCGHEE
At The Bunk House	LP	Philips	BL7675	1966	£5	£12	US
At The Second Fret	LP	Bluesville	BV1058	1962	£6	£15	US
Back Country Blues	LP	CBS	52165	1963	£6	£15	
Back Country Blues	LP	Savoy	MG14019	195-	£15	£30	US
Blues	LP	Folkways	F63557	1959	£8	£20	US
Blues All Around My Head	LP	Bluesville	BV(S)1020	1961	£6	£15	US
Blues And Folk	LP	Bluesville	BV(S)1005	1960	£6	£15	US
Blues And Shouts	LP	Fantasy	F3317	1962	£6	£15	US
Blues And Shouts	LP	Fantasy	F3317	1962	£15	£30	US, red vinyl
Blues In My Soul	LP	Bluesville	BV(S)1033	1961	£6	£15	US
Blues Is A Story	LP	Vogue	LAE12247	1961	£6	£15	mono
Blues Is A Story	LP	Vogue	SAE5014	1961	£10	£25	stereo
Blues Is My Companion	LP	Columbia	33SX1223	1960	£8	£20	
Brownie McGhee And Sonny Terry	LP	Vogue	LAE552	1964	£6	£15	
Brownie's Blues	LP	Bluesville	BV(S)1042	1962	£6	£15	US
Down Home Blues	LP	Bluesville	BV(S)1002	1960	£6	£15	US
Down South Smmit Meeting	LP	Vogue	LAE12266	1961	£6	£15	
Folk Songs Of Sonny And Brownie	LP	Roulette	R25074	1959	£8	£20	US
Going Down Slow	7"	Oriole	CBA1946	1964	£5	£10	
Guitar Highway	LP	Verve	(S)VLP5010	1966	£5	£12	
Hometown Blues	LP	Ace Of Hearts	(Z)AHT182	1969	£5	£12	
Hometown Blues	LP	Fontana	TL5289	1966	£5	£12	
Hometown Blues	LP	Mainstream	MSL1019	1973	£4	£10	
In London	LP	Nixa	NJL18	1958	£8	£20	
Just A Closer Walk With Thee	LP	Fantasy	F3296	1962	£6	£15	US
Just A Closer Walk With Thee	LP	Fantasy	F3296	1962	£15	£30	US, red vinyl
Key To The Highway	LP	XTRA	XTRA1004	1964	£6	£15	
Livin' With The Blues	LP	Fontana	688006ZL	1965	£5	£12	
Long Way From Home	LP	Stateside	SSL10291	1969	£4	£10	
Me And Sonny	7" EP	Melodisc	EPM783	1958	£5	£10	
Pawn Shop Blues	7" EP	Realm	REP4002	1964	£5	£10	
Penetentiary Blues	LP	Fontana	688007ZL	1965	£6	£15	
R And B From S And B	7" EP	Topic	TOP121	1964	£5	£10	
Rocking And Whooping	7"	Columbia	DB4433	1960	£7.50	£15	
Simply Heavenly	LP	Columbia	OL5240	1957	£8	£20	US
Sonny & Brownie At Sugar Hill	LP	Fantasy	F8091	1962	£6	£15	US
Sonny & Brownie At Sugar Hill	LP	Fantasy	F8091	1962	£15	£30	US, blue vinyl

Title	Format	Label	Cat. No.	Year	Price	Price	Notes
Sonny, Brownie And Chris	10" LP	Pye	NJT515	1958	£8	£20	with Chris Barber
Sonny Terry & Brownie McGhee	LP	Fantasy	F3254	1961	£6	£15	US
Sonny Terry & Brownie McGhee	LP	Fantasy	F3254	1961	£15	£30	US, red vinyl
Sonny Terry & Brownie McGhee	7" EP	Ember	EMBEP4562	1964	£5	£10	
Sonny Terry & Brownie McGhee & Chris Barber	7" EP	Pye	NJE1073	1957	£2.50	£6	
Sonny Terry And Brownie McGhee	LP	Topic	12T29	1958	£8	£20	
Sonny Terry And Brownie McGhee	LP	World Record Club	T7379	1961	£5	£12	
Sonny Terry And Brownie McGhee	7" EP	Vocalion	EPV1274	1963	£5	£10	
Sonny Terry And Brownie McGhee	7" EP	Vocalion	EPVF1279	1964	£5	£10	
Terry & McGhee In London	7" EP	Pye	NJE1074	1957	£4	£8	
Traditional Blues Vol.1	LP	Folkways	F2421	1961	£6	£15	US
Traditional Blues Vol.2	LP	Folkways	F2422	1961	£6	£15	US
Way Down South Summit Meeting	LP	World Pacific	WP(S)1296	1960	£6	£15	US
Where The Blues Began	LP	Fontana	SFJL979	1968	£5	£12	
Whoopin' The Blues	LP	Capitol	T20906	196-	£6	£15	
Work-Play-Faith-Fun Songs	7" EP	Top Rank	JKP3007	1961	£4	£8	

TERRY, SUSAN

Title	Format	Label	Cat. No.	Year	Price	Price	Notes
Looking For A Boy	7"	Piccadilly	7N35026	1962	£1.50	£4	

TEST DEPARTMENT

Title	Format	Label	Cat. No.	Year	Price	Price	Notes
Beating The Retreat	12"	Some Bizarre	TEST2/3	1984	£3	£8	boxed double with inserts
Compulsion	12"	Test	TEST112	1983	£2.50	£6	
Godaddin	12"	Media City	CMC1	1988	£4	£10	

TEST DEPATMENT

Title	Format	Label	Cat. No.	Year	Price	Price	Notes
Ecstasy Under Duress	cass	Pleasantly Surprised	PS5	198-	£5	£12	in bag with inserts

TETRAGON

Title	Format	Label	Cat. No.	Year	Price	Price	Notes
Nature	LP	Soma	SM1	1971	£20	£40	German

TEX, JOE

Title	Format	Label	Cat. No.	Year	Price	Price	Notes
Best Of Joe Tex	LP	London	HAU8334	1967	£8	£20	
Buying A Book	LP	Atlantic	588193	1969	£4	£10	
Go Home And Do It	7"	Atlantic	584212	1968	£1.50	£4	
Greatest Hits	LP	Atlantic	587/588089	1967	£5	£12	
Hold On	LP	Checker	2993	1964	£8	£20	US
Hold On To What You've Got	LP	Atlantic	(SD)8106	1965	£6	£15	US
Hold On To What You've Got	7"	Atlantic	584096	1967	£1.50	£4	
Hold On To What You've Got	7"	Atlantic	AT4015	1965	£2	£5	
I Want To Do Everything	7"	Atlantic	AT4045	1965	£2	£5	
I've Got To Do A Little Better	LP	Atlantic	587053	1967	£5	£12	
Live And Lively	LP	Atlantic	587/588104	1968	£5	£12	
Love You Save	LP	Atlantic	(SD)8124	1966	£6	£15	US
Love You Save	7"	Atlantic	AT4081	1966	£2	£5	
Men Are Getting Scarce	7"	Atlantic	584171	1968	£1.50	£4	
New Boss	LP	Atlantic	587/588059	1967	£5	£12	
New Boss	LP	Atlantic	ATL5043	1965	£8	£20	
Papa Was Too	7"	Atlantic	584068	1967	£1.50	£4	
Show Me	7"	Atlantic	584102	1967	£2.50	£6	
Skinny Legs And All	7"	Atlantic	584144	1967	£1.50	£4	
Soul Country	LP	Atlantic	587/588118	1968	£5	£12	
Sweet Woman Like You	7"	Atlantic	AT4058	1965	£2	£5	
S.Y.S.L.J.F.M.	7"	Atlantic	584016	1966	£1.50	£4	
We Can't Sit Down Now	7"	Atlantic	584296	1969	£1.50	£4	
Woman Can Change A Man	7"	Atlantic	AT4027	1965	£2	£5	
Woman Like That, Yeah	7"	Atlantic	584119	1967	£2	£5	
You Better Believe It Baby	7"	Atlantic	584035	1966	£2.50	£6	
You Better Get It	LP	Atlantic	587/588130	1968	£5	£12	
You Better Get It	7"	Atlantic	AT4021	1965	£4	£8	
You're Alright Ray Charles	7"	Atlantic	584318	1970	£1.50	£4	
Yum Yum Yum	7"	Sue	WI370	1965	£6	£12	

TEXANS

Title	Format	Label	Cat. No.	Year	Price	Price	Notes
Being With You	7"	Columbia	DB7242	1964	£1.50	£4	

TEXAS ALEXANDER

Title	Format	Label	Cat. No.	Year	Price	Price	Notes
Treasures Of North American Negro Music Vol.7	7" EP	Fontana	467136TE	1961	£5	£10	

TEXAS RANGERS

Title	Format	Label	Cat. No.	Year	Price	Price	Notes
Way Out West	7" EP	HMV	7EG8387	1957	£2.50	£6	

TEXTOR SINGERS

Title	Format	Label	Cat. No.	Year	Price	Price	Notes
Sobbin' Women	7"	Capitol	CL14211	1954	£1.50	£4	

THACKER, RUDY & THE STRINGBEANS

Title	Format	Label	Cat. No.	Year	Price	Price	Notes
Ballad Of Johnny Horton	7"	Starlite	ST45087	1962	£5	£10	

THACKRAY, JAKE

Title	Format	Label	Cat. No.	Year	Price	Price	Notes
Jake's Progress	LP	Columbia	SCX6345	1969	£5	£10	
Lah-Di-Dah	7"	Columbia	DB8364	1968	£1.50	£4	
Last Will And Testament	LP	Columbia	SX/SCX6178	1967	£5	£12	
Live Performance	LP	Columbia	SCX6453	1971	£4	£10	

THARPE, SISTER ROSETTA

Title	Format	Label	Cat. No.	Year	Price	Price	Notes
Gospel Train	LP	Mercury	MPL6529	1957	£5	£12	

Title	Format	Label	Cat. No.	Year	Price	Price	Notes
Gospel Truth	LP	Mercury	MMC14057	1961	£4	£10	
If I Can Help Somebody	7"	MGM	MGM1072	1960	£1.50	£4	
Sister Rosetta Tharpe	LP	Brunswick	LAT8290	1959	£5	£12	

THAT PETROL EMOTION

Title	Format	Label	Cat. No.	Year	Price	Price	Notes
Keen	7"	Pink	PINKY4	1985	£2	£5	
V2	7"	Noise A Noise	NAN1	1985	£1.50	£4	
V2	12"	Noise A Noise	NAN1T	1985	£2.50	£6	

THE THE

Title	Format	Label	Cat. No.	Year	Price	Price	Notes
Cold Spell Ahead	7"	Some Bizarre	BZS4	1981	£10	£20	
Controversial Subject	7"	4AD	AD10	1980	£10	£20	
Flesh And Bones	7"	Some Bizarre		1985	£5	£10	1 sided promo
Infected	LP	Epic	26770	1986	£4	£10	torture sleeve, poster
Infected	12"	Epic	TRUTHD3	1986	£2.50	£6	double
Infected	12"	Epic	TRUTHQ3	1986	£4	£10	uncensored PS
Perfect	7"	Epic	EPCA3119	1983	£2	£5	
Perfect	12"	Epic	EPCA133119	1983	£3	£8	
Soul Mining	LP	Epic	25525	1983	£5	£12	with 12'
Sweet Bird Of Truth	12"	Epic	TRUTH1	1986	£2.50	£6	
This Is The Day	7"	Epic	A3710	1983	£1.50	£4	chart single
This Is The Day	7"	Epic	A3710	1983	£6	£12	double
This Is The Day	12"	Epic	TA3710	1983	£3	£8	
Uncertain Smile	7"	Epic	EPCA2787	1982	£2.50	£6	with insert, chart single
Uncertain Smile	12"	Epic	EPC132787	1982	£4	£10	insert
Uncertain Smile	12"	Epic	EPC132787	1982	£10	£25	yellow vinyl, insert

THEATRE OF HATE

Title	Format	Label	Cat. No.	Year	Price	Price	Notes
He Who Dares Wins - Live At The Warehouse Leeds	LP	SS	SSSSS1P	1981	£4	£10	
Original Sin	7"	SS	SS3	1980	£2.50	£6	
Rebel Without A Brain	7"	Burning Rome	BRR1	1981	£1.50	£4	
Wake	7"	Bliss	TOH1EP	1985	£4	£8	with T shirt in 12' pack

THEE

Title	Format	Label	Cat. No.	Year	Price	Price	Notes
Each And Every Day	7"	Decca	F12163	1965	£10	£20	

THEE MIDNIGHTERS

Title	Format	Label	Cat. No.	Year	Price	Price	Notes
Bring You Love Special Delivery	LP	Whittier	W5000	1966	£5	£12	US
Giants	LP	Whittier	WS5002	1967	£5	£12	US
Land Of A Thousand Dances	7" EP	Vogue	EPL8314	1966	£10	£20	French
Thee Midnighters	LP	Chattahoochee	CS1001	1965	£6	£15	US
Unlimited	LP	Whittier	W5001	1966	£5	£12	US

THELWALL, LLANS & THE CELESTIALS

Title	Format	Label	Cat. No.	Year	Price	Price	Notes
Choo Choo Ska	7"	Island	WI262	1966	£5	£10	

THEM

Despite being continually plagued by management and record company problems, Them managed to produce some of the toughest and most enduring of British R&B. Much of the credit for this inevitably goes to the group's lead singer - Van Morrison - already a distinctive and commanding vocalist.

Title	Format	Label	Cat. No.	Year	Price	Price	Notes
Angry Young Them	LP	Decca	LK4700	1965	£15	£30	
Angry Young Them	LP	Decca	LK4700	1969	£5	£12	boxed Decca logo
Baby Please Don't Go	7"	Decca	F12018	1964	£2	£5	chart single
Being Em On In	7" EP	Decca	457108	1966	£12.50	£25	French
Belfast Gypsies	LP	Grand Prix	GP9923	1967	£15	£30	Swedish
Call My Name	7"	Decca	F12355	1966	£4	£8	
Don't Start Crying Now	7"	Decca	F11973	1964	£12.50	£25	
Don't Start Crying Now	7" EP	Decca	457069	1965	£12.50	£25	French
Gloria	7"	Major Minor	MM509	1967	£4	£8	
Gloria	7"	Decca	457073	1965	£10	£20	French
Gloria's Dream	7" EP	Vogue	INT18079	1966	£25	£50	French
Here Comes The Night	7"	Decca	F12094	1965	£1.50	£4	chart single
It Won't Hurt Half As Much	7"	Decca	F12215	1965	£4	£8	
Mystic Eyes	7"	Decca	F12281	1965	£4	£8	
Now & Them	LP	Tower	ST5104	1968	£20	£40	US
One More Time	7"	Decca	F12175	1965	£4	£8	
Portland Town	7" EP	Vogue	INT18135	1967	£25	£50	French
Richard Cory	7"	Decca	F12403	1966	£4	£8	
Story Of Them	7"	Major Minor	MM513	1967	£5	£10	
Them	LP	Happy Tiger	HT1004	1970	£15	£30	US
Them	7" EP	Decca	DFE8612	1965	£15	£30	
Them	7" EP	Decca	DFE8612	1965	£30	£60	export
Them Again	LP	Decca	LK4751	1966	£15	£30	
Them Again	LP	Decca	LK4751	1969	£5	£12	boxed Decca logo
Them In Reality	LP	Happy Tiger	HT1012	1971	£15	£30	US
Time Out, Time In For Them	LP	Tower	ST5116	1968	£15	£30	US
World Of Them	LP	Decca	SPA86	1970	£4	£10	

THEN JERICHO

Title	Format	Label	Cat. No.	Year	Price	Price	Notes
Big Sweep	12"	Immaculate	TJ1	1985	£6	£15	
Fault	12"	London	LONX63	1985	£2.50	£6	

THERAPY

Title	Format	Label	Cat. No.	Year	Price	Price	Notes
Bringing The House Down	LP	Therapy	MAG0009	1975	£5	£12	

THERAPY?

Title	Format	Label	Cat. No.	Year	Price	Price	Notes
Meat Abstract	7"	Multifucking	MFN1	1990	£10	£20	

THERAPY
One Night Stand .... LP ..... Indigo .... IRS5124 .... 1973 ... £8 ....£20 .... Irish

THIELMANS, JEAN 'TOOTS'
Sound .... LP ..... Philips .... BBL7058 .... 1956 ... £6 ....£15

THIN LIZZY
Dublin	7"	Decca	F13208	1972	£40	£80	
Farmer	7"	Parlophone	DIP513	1970	£330	£500	Irish
Hollywood	10"	Vertigo	LIZZY10	1982	£2.50	£6	1 sided
Little Darling	7"	Decca	F13507	1974	£2	£5	
Philomena	7"	Vertigo	6059111	1974	£1.50	£4	
Randolph's Tango	7"	Decca	F13402	1973	£5	£10	2 versions
Rocker	7"	Decca	F13467	1973	£2	£5	
Rosalie	7"	Vertigo	6059124	1975	£1.50	£4	
Shades Of A Blue Orphanage ...	LP	Decca	TXS108	1972	£5	£12	
Thin Lizzy	LP	Decca	SKL5082	1971	£6	£15	
Thunder And Lightning	LP	Vertigo	VERL3	1983	£4	£10	with 12'
Thunder And Lightning	12"	Vertigo	LIZZY1212	1983	£4	£10	with poster
Vagabonds Of The Western World	LP	Decca	SKL5170	1973	£5	£12	with insert
Wild One	7"	Vertigo	6059129	1975	£1.50	£4	

THIRD EAR BAND
Alchemy	LP	Harvest	SHVL756	1969	£6	£15	
Elements	LP	Harvest	SHVL773	1970	£6	£15	chart LP
Experiences	LP	Harvest	SHSM2007	1976	£4	£10	
Music From Macbeth	LP	Harvest	SHSP4019	1972	£6	£15	

THIRD QUADRANT
Seeing Yourself As You Really Are ...... LP ...... Rock Cottage ... no number .... 1982 ... £50 ....£100

THIRD RAIL
Id Music .... LP ...... Epic .... LN24327/BN26327 1967 ... £15 ....£30 .... US
Run Run Run .... 7" ...... Columbia .... DB8274 .... 1967 ... £10 ....£20

THIRD WORLD WAR
Ascension Day .... 7" ...... Fly .... BUG7 .... 1971 ... £2 ....£5 .... PS
Third World War .... LP ...... Fly .... FLY4 .... 1971 ... £5 ....£12
Third World War II .... LP ...... Track .... 2406108 .... 1972 ... £10 ....£25

THIRSTY MOON
Blitz .... LP ...... Brain .... 0001079 .... 1975 ... £4 ....£10 .... German
Thirsty Moon .... LP ...... Brain .... 0001021 .... 1973 ... £4 ....£10 .... German
You'll Never Come Back .... LP ...... Brain .... 0001041 .... 1974 ... £4 ....£10 .... German

13TH FLOOR ELEVATORS
Bull Of The Woods	LP	International Artists	IA9	1969	£15	£30	US
Easter Everywhere	LP	International Artists	IA5	1968	£20	£40	US
Live	LP	International Artists	IA8	1968	£15	£30	US
Psychedelic Sounds	LP	International Artists	LP1	1966	£20	£40	US
Reverberation	7" EP..	Riviera	231240	1966	£180	£300	French

THIRTY SECOND TURN OFF
Thirty Second Turn Off .... LP ...... Jay Boy .... JSL1 .... 1969 ... £15 ....£30

THIRTY-FIRST OF FEBRUARY
Thirty-First Of February .... LP ...... Vanguard .... VSD6503 .... 1969 ... £5 ....£12 .... US

THIS HEAT
This Heat .... LP ...... Piano .... THIS1 .... 1979 ... £4 ....£10

THIS MORTAL COIL
Come Here My Love .... 10" ...... 4AD .... BAD608 .... 1986 ... £2.50 ....£6

THIS 'N' THAT
Get Down With It .... 7" ...... Strike .... JH310 .... 1967 ... £1.50 ....£4
Someday .... 7" ...... Mercury .... MF938 .... 1966 ... £6 ....£12

THOLLOT, JACQUES
Quand Le Son Devient Trop Aigu .... LP ...... Futura .... 24 .... 1971 ... £4 ....£10 .... French

THOMAS, B.J.
B.J.Thomas And The Triumphs ...... LP ...... Pacemaker .... PLP3001 .... 196- ... £8 ....£20 .... US
I'm So Lonesome I Could Cry .... 7" ...... Pye .... 7N25359 .... 1966 ... £1.50 ....£4
Very Best Of B.J.Thomas .... LP ...... Hickory .... LP(S)133 .... 1966 ... £4 ....£10 .... US

THOMAS, CARLA
B-a-b-y	7"	Atlantic	584042	1966	£2	£5	
Best Of Carla Thomas	LP	Atlantic	SD8232	1969	£4	£10	US
Carla	LP	Stax	589004	1967	£6	£15	
Comfort Me	LP	Stax	ST(S)706	1966	£6	£15	US
Comfort Me	7"	Atlantic	AT4074	1966	£2	£5	
Gee Whiz	LP	Atlantic	8057	1961	£15	£30	US
Gee Whiz	7"	London	HLK9310	1961	£4	£8	
I Like What You're Doing To Me ...	7"	Stax	STAX112	1969	£1.50	£4	
I'll Bring It On Home To You	7"	London	HLK9618	1962	£2.50	£6	
I've Got No Time To Lose	7"	Atlantic	AT4005	1964	£2	£5	

Let Me Be Good To You	7"	Atlantic	584011	1966	£1.50	£4	
Love Of My Own	7"	London	HLK9359	1961	£2.50	£6	
Memphis Queen	LP	Stax	SXATS2019	1969	£5	£12	
Pick Up The Pieces	7"	Stax	601032	1968	£1.50	£4	
Queen Alone	LP	Stax	589012	1967	£6	£15	
Something Good	7"	Stax	601002	1967	£2	£5	
When Tomorrow Comes	7"	Stax	601008	1967	£1.50	£4	
Where Do I Go	7"	Stax	STAX103	1968	£1.50	£4	

THOMAS, CLAUDETTE

Roses Are Red My Love	7"	Caltone	TONE116	1968	£4	£8	

THOMAS, CREEPY JOHN

Creepy John Thomas	LP	RCA	SF8061	1969	£20	£40	
Ride A Rainbow	7"	RCA	RCA1912	1970	£5	£10	

THOMAS, DAVID

Didn't Have A Very Good Time	7"	Recommended	REDT7	1983	£1.50	£4	1 sided pic disc

THOMAS, DOC GROUP

The rare LP recorded in Italy by the British Doc Thomas Group achieves its high value by virtue of its connection with Mott The Hoople, whose guitarist Mick Ralphs and bassist Pete (Overend) Watts played in the earlier band. There was, incidentally, no Mr.Thomas.

Doc Thomas Group	LP	Interrecord	ILP280	1966	£60	£120	Italian

THOMAS, DON

Turn Her Around	7"	Polydor	56509	1970	£2	£5	

THOMAS, GENE

Baby's Gone	7"	United Artists	UP1047	1964	£4	£8	

THOMAS, IRMA

Don't Mess With My Man	7"	Sue	WI372	1965	£7.50	£15	
I'm Gonna Cry Till My Tears Run Dry	7"	Liberty	LIB66106	1965	£7.50	£15	
It's A Man's Woman's World	7"	Liberty	LIB66178	1966	£2.50	£6	
Some Things You Never Get Used To	7"	Liberty	LIB66095	1965	£6	£12	
Take A Look	LP	Minit	MLL/MLS40004	1966	£8	£20	
Take A Look	7"	Liberty	LIB66137	1966	£6	£12	
Time Is On My Side	7"	Liberty	LIB66041	1964	£7.50	£15	
Time Is On My Side	7" EP	Liberty	LEP4035	1965	£12.50	£25	
True True Love	7"	Liberty	LIB66080	1965	£4	£8	
Wish Someone Would Care	LP	Imperial	LP9266/12266	1964	£8	£20	US
Wish Someone Would Care	7"	Liberty	LIB66013	1964	£6	£12	

THOMAS, JAMO

I Spy (For The FBI)	7"	Mojo	2092013	1971	£1.50	£4	
I Spy (For The FBI)	7"	Polydor	56709	1966	£7.50	£15	
I Spy (For The FBI)	7"	Polydor	56755	1969	£1.50	£4	chart single
I'll Be Your Fool	7"	Chess	CRS8098	1969	£2	£5	

THOMAS, JIMMY

This Beautiful Night	7"	Parlophone	R5773	1969	£40	£80	
This Beautiful Night	7"	Parlophone	R5773	1969	£30	£60	demo

THOMAS, KID

Victory Walk	LP	77	LA1226	1964	£4	£10	

THOMAS, LEON

Blues And Soulful Truth	LP	Philips	6369417	1973	£5	£12	

THOMAS, NICKY

If I Had A Hammer	7"	Trojan	TR7807	1970	£1.50	£4	
Love Of The Common People	LP	Trojan	TBL143	1970	£5	£12	

THOMAS, RUFUS

Can Your Monkey Do The Dog	7"	London	HLK9850	1964	£2.50	£6	
Did You Hear Me?	LP	Stax	2362028	1972	£6	£15	
Do The Dog	7" EP	Atlantic	AET6001	1964	£7.50	£15	
Doing The Push And Pull	LP	Stax	2362010	1971	£5	£12	
Down To My House	7"	Stax	601028	1968	£1.50	£4	
Funky Chicken	LP	Stax	SXATS1033	1970	£4	£10	
Greasy Spoon	7"	Stax	601013	1967	£1.50	£4	
Jump Back	7"	Atlantic	584089	1967	£2	£5	
Jump Back	7"	Atlantic	AT4009	1964	£4	£8	
Jump Back With Rufus Thomas	7" EP	Atlantic	AET6011	1965	£7.50	£15	
Memphis Train	7"	Stax	601037	1968	£1.50	£4	
Somebody Stole My Dog	7"	London	HLK9884	1964	£2.50	£6	
Walking The Dog	LP	London	HAK8183	1964	£10	£25	
Walking The Dog	7"	London	HLK9799	1963	£5	£12	
Willy Nilly	7"	Atlantic	584029	1966	£2	£5	

THOMAS, TERRY

Sweet Old Fashioned Boy	7"	Decca	F10804	1956	£2	£5	

THOMOPOULOUS, ANDREAS

Born Out Of The Tears Of The Sun	LP	Mushroom	150MR4	1971	£40	£80	
So Long Suzanne	7"	Mushroom		1970	£20	£40	
Songs Of The Street	LP	Mushroom	100MR1	1970	£40	£80	

THOMPSON, BOBBY

That's How Strong My Love Is	7"	Columbia	DB113	1969	£4	£8	
That's How Strong My Love Is	7"	Jolly	JY001	1968	£4	£8	

THOMPSON, CHERYLE

Teardrops	7"	Stateside	SS291	1964	£1.50	£4

THOMPSON, CHRIS

Chris Thompson	LP	Village Thing	VTS21	1973	£6	£15

THOMPSON, EDDIE

His Master's Jazz	LP	Tempo	TAP24	1960	£4	£10

THOMPSON, HANK

Anybody's Girl	7"	Capitol	CL15014	1959	£1.50	£4	
At The Golden Nugget	LP	Capitol	(S)T1632	1962	£5	£12	US
Favorite Waltzes	LP	Capitol	T1111	1959	£5	£12	US
Favourite Waltzes	7" EP	Capitol	EAP11111	1959	£2.50	£6	
Gathering Flowers	7"	Capitol	CL14945	1958	£2	£5	
Golden Country Hits	LP	Capitol	T2089	1965	£4	£10	
Hank	LP	Capitol	T826	1957	£6	£15	US
Hank	7" EP	Capitol	EAP1826	1957	£5	£10	
Hank Thompson Favorites	LP	Capitol	T911	1957	£6	£15	US
Hank Thompson Favorites	10" LP	Capitol	H911	1956	£10	£25	US
Hank Thompson's Dance Ranch	LP	Capitol	T975	1958	£6	£15	US
Honey, Honey Bee Ball	7"	Capitol	CL14517	1956	£4	£8	
I Guess I'm Getting Over You	7"	Capitol	CL15074	1959	£1.50	£4	
I'm Not Mad, Just Hurt	7"	Capitol	CL14668	1956	£2.50	£6	
I've Run Out Of Tomorrows	7"	Capitol	CL14961	1958	£2	£5	
Li'l Liza Jane	7"	Capitol	CL14869	1958	£2.50	£6	
Most Of All	LP	Capitol	(S)T1360	1960	£5	£12	US
New Recordings Of Hank's All-Time Hits	LP	Capitol	T729	1956	£8	£20	US
New Recordings Of Hank's All-Time Hits	10" LP	Capitol	H729	1956	£10	£25	US
North Of The Rio Grande	LP	Capitol	T618	1956	£8	£20	US
North Of The Rio Grande	10" LP	Capitol	H618	1955	£10	£25	US
She's Just A Whole Lot Like You	7"	Capitol	CL15156	1960	£1.50	£4	
Six Pack To Go	7"	Capitol	CL15114	1960	£4	£8	
Songs For Rounders	LP	Capitol	(S)T1246	1959	£5	£12	
Songs Of The Brazos Valley	LP	Capitol	T418	1956	£8	£20	US
Songs Of The Brazos Valley	10" LP	Capitol	H418	1953	£10	£25	US
Songs Of The Brazos Valley No.1	7" EP	Capitol	EAP1028	1956	£5	£10	
This Broken Heart Of Mine	LP	Capitol	(S)T1469	1960	£5	£12	
Wild Side Of Life	7"	Capitol	CL15247	1962	£1.50	£4	
Will We Start It All Over	7"	Capitol	CL15177	1961	£1.50	£4	

THOMPSON, HAYDEN

Here's Hayden Thompson	LP	Kapp	KL1507/KS3507	1966	£5	£12	US

THOMPSON, KAY

Eloise	7"	London	HLA8268	1956	£7.50	£15	
Kay Thompson	LP	MGM	E3146	195-	£6	£15	US

THOMPSON, LUCKY

Lucky Thompson	LP	HMV	CLP1237	1958	£10	£25
Recorded In Paris '56	10" LP	Ducretet-Thomson	D93098	1956	£8	£20
With The Gerard Pochonet Orchestra	LP	Vogue	LAE12022	1956	£8	£20

THOMPSON, MAYO

Corky's Debt To His Father	LP	Texas Revolution	CFS2270	1970	£10	£25	US

THOMPSON, MIKE

Rocksteady Wedding	7"	Island	WI3090	1967	£5	£10

THOMPSON, PAUL & THE NTH DEGREE

For Me It's All Over	7"	Fontana	TF656	1965	£1.50	£4

THOMPSON, RICHARD

Since leaving Fairport Convention, Richard Thompson has matured, not only into a song-writer of particularly fine material, but also into a brilliant and highly individual guitarist. Inevitably, a man who is a major but not especially fashionable talent had trouble in the eighties in finding suitable recording contracts. The relative scarcity of the "Strict Tempo" album is an immediate consequence of this. Happily, Thompson's fortunes have risen in recent years, and following three superb albums for Capitol (it is remarkable enough that any rock musician should make the best music of his career over twenty years after starting it) his profile is higher than it has ever been.

Guitar, Vocal	LP	Island	ICD8	1976	£8	£20	double
Henry The Human Fly	LP	Island	ILPS9197	1972	£6	£15	
Strict Tempo	LP	Elixir	LP1	1981	£4	£10	

THOMPSON, RICHARD & LINDA

Hokey Pokey	LP	Island	ILPS9305	1974	£5	£12
I Want To See The Bright Lights Tonight	LP	Island	ILPS9266	1974	£5	£12
Pour Down Like Silver	LP	Island	ILPS9348	1975	£4	£10

THOMPSON, ROY

Sookie Sookie	7"	Columbia	DB8108	1967	£2.50	£6

THOMPSON, SIR CHARLES

Allstars With Charlie Parker	10" LP	Vogue	LDE032	1953	£30	£60
And His Band Featuring Coleman Hawkins	10" LP	Vanguard	PPT12011	1956	£20	£40
Sir Charles Thompson Quartet	10" LP	Vanguard	PPT12007	1956	£15	£30
Sir Charles Thompson Trio	10" LP	Vanguard	PPT12020	1958	£15	£30

THOMPSON, SONNY

Houseful Of Blues	78	Esquire	10320	1953	£6	£12	
Mellow Blues For The Late Hours	LP	King	655	1959	£20	£40	US
Moody Blues	LP	King	568	1956	£25	£50	US
Real Real Fine	78	Vogue	V2143	1952	£6	£12	
Screamin' Boogie	78	Esquire	10339	1953	£6	£12	
Screaming Boogie	7"	Starlite	ST45008	1960	£50	£100	

THOMPSON, SUE

Bad Boy	7"	Hickory	451255	1964	£2	£5	
Big Daddy	7"	Hickory	451240	1964	£1.50	£4	
Have A Good Time	7"	Polydor	NH66979	1962	£1.50	£4	
I Like Your Kind Of Love	7"	Polydor	NH66989	1963	£2	£5	with Bob Luman
I'm Looking For A World	7"	Hickory	451359	1965	£1.50	£4	
It's Break-Up Time	7"	Hickory	451328	1965	£2	£5	
James	7"	Fontana	267244TF	1962	£2	£5	
Just Kiss Me	7"	Hickory	451340	1965	£1.50	£4	
Norman	7"	Polydor	NH66973	1962	£2	£5	
Paper Tiger	LP	Hickory	LPM102	1964	£6	£15	
Paper Tiger	7"	Hickory	451284	1965	£1.50	£4	chart single
Sad Movies	7"	Polydor	NH66967	1961	£2	£5	chart single
Two Of A Kind	7"	Polydor	NH66976	1962	£1.50	£4	
What Should I Do	7"	Hickory	451381	1965	£1.50	£4	
What's Wrong Billy	7"	Polydor	NH66987	1963	£1.50	£4	
Willie Can	7"	Fontana	267262TF	1963	£1.50	£4	

THOMPSON TWINS

She's In Love With Mystery	7"	Latent	LATE1	1980	£1.50	£4	
Squares And Triangles	7"	Dirty Discs	RANK1	1980	£4	£8	

THORN, GUNILLA

Merry Go Round	7"	HMV	POP1239	1963	£12.50	£25	

THORNE, DAVID

Alley Cat Song	7"	Stateside	SS141	1962	£1.50	£4	chart single
Alley Cat Songster	LP	Stateside	SL10036	1963	£6	£15	
What Will I Tell My Heart	7" EP	Stateside	SE1020	1964	£2	£5	

THORNE, KEN

Legion's Last Patrol	7"	HMV	POP1176	1963	£1.50	£4	chart single

THORNE, WOODY

Sadie Lou	7"	Vogue	V9202	1962	£50	£100	

THORNHILL, CLAUDE

Claude On A Cloud	LP	Brunswick	LAT827-/STA3003	1959	£4	£10	
Dream Music	10" LP	London	HAPB1021	1954	£10	£25	
Goes Modern	7" EP	London	REP1009	1954	£4	£8	
Goes Modern	10" LP	London	HAPB1019	1954	£10	£25	
Pussyfooting	7"	London	HL8042	1954	£10	£20	

THORNTON, EDDIE

Baby Be My Gal	7"	Instant	IN003	1969	£4	£8	

THORNTON, WILLIE MAE (BIG MAMA)

Hound Dog	78	Vogue	V2284	1954	£10	£20	
Mama's Pride	LP	Vanguard	VPC40001	1978	£4	£10	
Stronger Than Dirt	LP	Mercury	SMCL20176	1969	£4	£10	
Tom Cat	7"	Sue	WI345	1964	£15	£30	
Way It Is	LP	Mercury	SRM161249	1970	£4	£10	US

THORPE, BILLY & THE AZTECS

Twilight Time	7"	Parlophone	R5381	1965	£1.50	£4	

THORSON, LINDA

Here I Am	7"	Ember	EMBS257	1968	£2.50	£6	

THORUP, PETER

Thin Slices	LP	Metronome	MLP15635	1978	£4	£10	German

THOUGHTS

All Night Stand	7"	Planet	PLF118	1966	£20	£40	

THOUSAND YARD STARE

Strange	12"	Stifled Aardvark	AARD6T	1991	£3	£8	1 sided
Weatherwatching	12"	Stifled Aardvark	AARD003	1990	£3	£8	with insert

THREADS OF LIFE

Threads Of Life	LP	Alco	ALC530	1972	£250	£400	

THREE BELLS

Cry No More	7"	Columbia	DB7980	1966	£2	£5	

THREE CAPS

It comes as a surprise to many people who remember the Capitols' delightful "Cool Jerk" to find copies credited to The Three Caps. This is the same group, of course, and all the records by the Three Caps are listed in the Guide under The Capitols.

THREE CHUCKLES

Runaround	7"	HMV	7M292	1955	£7.50	£15	

Three Chuckles	LP	Vik	LX1067	1956	£25	£50	US
Times Two, I Love You	7"	HMV	7M333	1955	£6	£12	
We're Gonna Rock Tonight	7"	HMV	POP292	1957	£40	£80	

THREE CITY FOUR

Smoke And Dust	LP	CBS	63039	1967	£50	£100	
Three City Four	LP	Decca	LK4705	1965	£60	£120	

THREE DEGREES

Close Your Eyes	7"	Stateside	SS459	1965	£15	£30	
Gee Baby I'm Sorry	7"	Stateside	SS413	1965	£5	£10	

THREE DOG NIGHT

It Ain't Easy	LP	Dunhill	DS50078	1970	£6	£15	US, nude group on cover

THREE DOLLS

Living End	7"	MGM	MGM958	1957	£1.50	£4	

THREE FLAMES

At The Bon Soir	LP	Mercury	MG20239	1957	£6	£15	US

THREE GOOD REASONS

Build Your Love	7"	Mercury	MF883	1965	£1.50	£4	
Nowhere Man	7"	Mercury	MF899	1966	£2	£5	chart single

THREE JOHNS

English White Boy Engineer	7"	CNT	CNT003	1982	£2	£5	
Pink Headed Bug	7"	CNT	CNT011	1983	£1.50	£4	

THREE MAN ARMY

Mahesha	LP	Polydor	2310241	1974	£20	£40	
Third Of A Lifetime	LP	Pegasus	PEG3	1971	£8	£20	
Three Man Army	LP	Reprise	K44254	1973	£6	£15	
Three Man Army 2	LP	Reprise	K54015	1974	£8	£20	

THREE PEOPLE

Have You Ever Been There	7"	Decca	F12473	1966	£2.50	£6	
Simple Thing Would Be For You	7"	Decca	F12581	1967	£1.50	£4	
Suspicions	7"	Decca	F12514	1966	£1.50	£4	

THREE SOUNDS

Black Orchid	LP	Blue Note	BLP/BST84155	1963	£8	£20	
Coldwater Flat	LP	Blue Note	BST84285	1968	£4	£10	
Elegant Soul	LP	Blue Note	BST84301	1968	£4	£10	
Feelin' Good	LP	Blue Note	BLP/BST84072	1961	£15	£30	
Gene Harris And The Three Sounds	LP	Blue Note	BST84378	1970	£4	£10	
Here We Come	LP	Blue Note	BLP/BST84088	1961	£10	£25	
Hey There!	LP	Blue Note	BLP/BST84102	1962	£10	£25	
It Just Got To Be	LP	Blue Note	BLP/BST84120	1963	£10	£25	
Live At The Lighthouse	LP	Blue Note	BLP/BST84265	1967	£6	£15	
Moods	LP	Blue Note	BLP/BST84044	196-	£10	£25	
Out Of This World	LP	Blue Note	BLP/BST84197	1965	£8	£20	
Soul Symphony	LP	Blue Note	BST84341	1969	£4	£10	
Vibrations	LP	Blue Note	BLP/BST84248	1966	£8	£20	

THREE STOOGES

Sing For Kids	LP	Vocalion	VL73823	1968	£6	£15	US

THREE SUNS

High Fi And Wide	LP	RCA	LPM1249	1956	£6	£15	US
Midnight For Two	LP	RCA	LPM1333	1957	£6	£15	US
Soft And Sweet	LP	RCA	LPM1041	1955	£6	£15	US

THREE TOPS

Do It Right	7"	Treasure Isle	TI7008	1967	£5	£10	
Great Train In '68	7"	Coxsone	CS7051	1968	£5	£10	
It's Raining	7"	Trojan	TR003	1967	£5	£10	
Moving To Progress	7"	Studio One	SO2023	1967	£6	£12	

THREE WISE MEN

Thanks For Christmas	7"	Virgin	VS642	1983	£1.50	£4	

THREE'S A CROWD

Look Around The Corner	7"	Fontana	TF673	1966	£1.50	£4	

THRICE MICE

Thrice Mice	LP	Philips	6305104	1970	£6	£15	German

THRILLINGTON, PERCY 'THRILLS'

Thrillington	LP	Regal Zonophone	EMC3175	1975	£40	£80	
Uncle Albert, Admiral Halsey	7"	EMI	EMI2594	1977	£10	£20	

THRILLS

No One	7"	Capitol	CL15469	1966	£10	£20	

THROBBING GRISTLE

Throbbing Gristle emerged at about the same time as punk, yet their music was more profoundly revolutionary than anything produced by the Sex Pistols or their colleagues. Designed to counterpoint the squalor and cruelty that the group saw in late twentieth century city life, Throbbing Gristle's music consisted of ugly and angry sound, with none of the melodic or rhythmic landmarks that are normally taken for granted. Due to the group's habit of taping all their live performances, the amount of available Throbbing Gristle material is vast and much of it has become very collectable.

Title	Format	Label	Cat No	Year			Notes
24 Hours	cass	Industrial	IRC1-24	198-	£90	£180	26 tapes in case with inserts
Adrenalin	7"	Industrial	IR0015	1980	£2.50	£6	polythene bag, PS
Assume Power Focus	LP	Cause For Concern	POWER FOCUS001	1982	£6	£15	
Best Of Vol.2	cass	Industrial	IR0001	1975	£25	£50	
Boxed Set	LP	Fetish	FX001	1981	£37.50	£75	5 LPs, booklet, badge
Discipline	12"	Fetish	FET006	1981	£4	£10	
D.o.A. The Third And Final Report	LP	Industrial	IR0004	1978	£6	£15	with calendar and postcard
D.o.A. The Third And Final Report	LP	Industrial	IR0004	1979	£5	£12	16 equal length tracks
Editions Frankfurt - Berlin	LP	Svensk Illuminated	SJAMS31	1983	£6	£15	
Fuhrer Der Menscheit	10"	American Phonogram	1JAPSO36	1983	£5	£12	
Fuhrer Der Menscheit	10"	Bundestag	29681	1982	£6	£15	some orange vinyl
Funeral In Berlin	12"	Zensor	ZENSOR01	1981	£6	£15	
Greatest Hits - Entertainment Through Pain	LP	Rough Trade	ROUGHUS23	1981	£4	£10	
Heathen Earth	LP	Industrial	IR0009	1980	£4	£10	
Heathen Earth	LP	Industrial	IR0009	1980	£25	£50	blue vinyl
In The Shadow Of The Sun	LP	Illuminated	JAMS35	1984	£5	£12	
Journey Through A Body	LP	Walter Ulbricht	ST3382	1982	£8	£20	
Mission Is Terminated	LP & 12"	Nice	EX39LY2	1983	£6	£15	with booklet
Music From The Death Factory	LP	Death	01	1982	£50	£100	
Music From The Death Factory	LP	Throbbing Gristle	33033	1982	£8	£20	pic disc
Once Upon A Time	LP	Casual Abandon	CAS1J	1984	£5	£12	
Rafters	LP	Italian	EX23	1981	£5	£12	
Second Annual Report	LP	Fetish	FET2001	1978	£6	£15	with questionnaire, insert
Second Annual Report	LP	Fetish	FET2001	1979	£4	£10	glossy sleeve
Second Annual Report	LP	Fetish	FET2001	1981	£6	£15	backwards version, 2 sleeves
Second Annual Report	LP	Industrial	IR0002	1977	£30	£60	with questionnaire
Special Treatment	LP	Mental Decay	011	1984	£5	£12	
Subhuman	7"	Industrial	IR0013	1980	£2.50	£6	polythene bag, PS
Thee Psychick Sacrifice	LP	Karnage	KILL1	1982	£6	£15	double
Twenty Jazz Funk Greats	LP	Industrial	IR0008	1979	£5	£12	
Twenty Jazz Funk Greats	LP	Industrial	IR0008	1979	£6	£15	with poster
United	7"	Industrial	IR0003	1978	£2	£5	
United	7"	Industrial	IR0003	1980	£5	£10	extended B side, white or clear vinyl
We Hate You Little Girls	7"	Adolescent	ARTT010	1981	£6	£12	US
We Hate You Little Girls	7"	Sordide Sentimentale	SS45001	1979	£25	£50	A4 sleeve, numbered

THUNDER COMPANY (BRIAN BENNETT)

Title	Format	Label	Cat No	Year		
Riding On The Gravy Train	7"	Columbia	DB8706	1970	£10	£20

THUNDER, JOHNNY

Title	Format	Label	Cat No	Year			Notes
Dear John I'm Going To Leave You	7"	Stateside	SS454	1965	£1.50	£4	
Everybody Do The Sloopy	7"	Stateside	SS476	1965	£1.50	£4	
Hey Child	7"	Stateside	SS229	1963	£1.50	£4	
Jailer Bring Me Water	7"	Stateside	SS200	1963	£1.50	£4	
Loop De Loop	LP	Stateside	SL10029	1963	£8	£20	
Loop De Loop	7"	Stateside	SS149	1963	£1.50	£4	
Make Love To Me	7"	Stateside	SS2005	1967	£1.50	£4	with Ruby Winters
More More More Love Love Love	7"	Stateside	SS337	1964	£1.50	£4	
My Prayer	7"	Stateside	SS499	1966	£1.50	£4	
Rock A Bye My Darling	7"	Stateside	SS168	1963	£1.50	£4	
Send Her To Me	7"	Stateside	SS370	1965	£1.50	£4	

THUNDERBIRDS

Title	Format	Label	Cat No	Year			Notes
Ayuh Ayuh	7"	London	HL8146	1955	£12.50	£25	
Meet The Fabulous Thunderbirds	LP	Red Feather	TH1	195-	£50	£100	US

THUNDERBIRDS (2)

Title	Format	Label	Cat No	Year		
New Orleans Beat	7"	Oriole	CB1625	1961	£4	£8
Wild Weekend	7"	Oriole	CB1610	1961	£4	£8

THUNDERBIRDS (3)

Title	Format	Label	Cat No	Year		
Your Ma Said You Cried	7"	Polydor	56710	1966	£12.50	£25

THUNDERBOLTS

Title	Format	Label	Cat No	Year		
Fugitive	7"	Decca	F11522	1962	£2	£5

THUNDERBOYS

Title	Format	Label	Cat No	Year		
Fashion	7"	Recent	EJSP9339	1980	£2	£5

THUNDERCLAP NEWMAN

Accidents	7"	Track	2094001	1970	£1.50	£4	chart single
Hollywood Dream	LP	Track	2406003	1970	£6	£15	
Peter Townshend Talks To, And About, Thunderclap Newman	LP	Track	PR160	1969	£8	£20	US interview promo
Reason	7"	Track	2094003	1970	£1.50	£4	
Something In The Air	7"	Track	604031	1969	£1.50	£4	chart single

THUNDERPUSSY

Documents Of Captivity	LP	MRT		1973	£35	£70	US

THUNDERS, JOHNNY

Dead Or Alive	7"	Real	ARE1	1978	£4	£8	PS
Vintage '77	12"	Jungle	JUNG5	1983	£2.50	£6	
You Can't Put Your Arms Around A Memory	7"	Real	ARE3	1978	£2.50	£6	PS

THUNDERTHUMBS & TOETSENMAN

Freedom	7"	Polydor	POSP480	1982	£5	£10	
Freedom	12"	Polydor	POSPX480	1982	£6	£15	

THUNDERTRAIN

Teenage Suicide	LP	Jelly	JPLP1	1977	£6	£15	

THYRDS

Hide'n'Seek	7"	Decca	F12010	1964	£10	£20	
Hide'n'Seek	7"	Oak	RGJ133	1964	£50	£100	

TIARAS

I'm Gonna Forget You	7"	Warner Bros	WB92	1963	£1.50	£4	

TICH & QUACKERS

Santa Bring Me Ringo	7"	Oriole	CB1980	1965	£1.50	£4	

TICKAWINDA

Rosemary Lane	LP	Pennine	PSS153	1975	£100	£200	

TICKLE

Subway	7"	Regal Zonophone	RZ3004	1967	£40	£80	

TICO & THE TRIUMPHS

The group name hides the identity of the young Paul Simon.

Cards Of Love	7"	Amy	876	1963	£15	£30	US
Cry, Little Boy, Cry	7"	Amy	860	1962	£10	£20	US
Express Train	7"	Amy	845	1962	£10	£20	US
Motorcycle	7"	Amy	835	1962	£10	£20	US
Motorcycle	7"	Madison	169	1961	£10	£20	US

TIDAL WAVE

With Tears In My Eyes	7"	Decca	F22973	1969	£4	£8	

TIDE

Almost Live	LP	Mouth	7237	196-	£8	£20	US

TIEKIN, FREDDIE & THE ROCKERS

By Popular Demand	LP	IT	2301	1957	£8	£20	US
Freddie Tiekin & The Rockers	LP	IT	2304	1958	£8	£20	US

TIERNEY, PETER & THE NIGHTHAWKS

Oh How I Need You	7"	Fontana	TF547	1965	£1.50	£4	

TIERNEY, ROY

Cupid	7"	Philips	PB1159	1961	£1.50	£4	
Just Out Of Reach	7"	Philips	PB1194	1961	£1.50	£4	

TIERNEY'S FUGITIVES

Did You Want To Run Away	7"	Decca	F12247	1965	£4	£8	

TIFFANIES

It's Got To Be A Great Song	7"	Chess	CRS8059	1967	£12.50	£25	

TIFFANY

I Know	7"	Parlophone	R5311	1965	£1.50	£4	

TIFFANY SHADE

Tiffany Shade	LP	Fontana	(S)TL5469	1968	£15	£30	

TIFFANY'S THOUGHTS

Find Out What's Happening	7"	Parlophone	R5439	1966	£7.50	£15	

TIGER

Souls Of Africa	7"	New Beat	NB052	1970	£2.50	£6	

TIGER (2)

Tiger	LP	Retreat	RTL6006	1976	£5	£12	

TIGER LILY

The single by Tiger Lily was the first release by the group that issued all its subsequent records as Ultravox.

Monkey Jive	7"	Gull	GULS12	1975	£4	£8	
Monkey Jive	7"	Gull	GULS12	1975	£10	£20	PS
Monkey Jive	7"	Gull	GULS54	1977	£2.50	£6	PS

823

TIGG, JIMMY & LOUIS
Who Can I Turn To .... 7" ...... Deep Soul .... DS9105 .... 1970 ... £4 .... £8 ....

TIGHT LIKE THAT
Hokum .... LP ..... Village Thing ... VTS12 .... 1972 ... £6 .... £15 ....

TIK & TOK
Intolerance .... LP ..... Survival .... SURLPX8 .... 1984 ... £4 .... £10 .... pic disc

TILLIS, MEL
Mr.Mel .... LP ..... London .... HAR8345 .... 1968 ... £5 .... £12 ....

TILLOTSON, JOHNNY
Alone With You	LP	MGM	C972	1964	**1964**	**£8**	£20
Angel	7"	MGM	MGM1266	1964	£1.50	£4	
Cabaret	7"	MGM	MGM1393	1968	£1.50	£4	
Dreamy Eyes	7"	London	HLA9514	1962	£1.50	£4	
Earth Angel	7"	London	HLA9101	1960	£7.50	£15	
Funny How Time Slips Away	7"	London	HLA9811	1963	£1.50	£4	
Heartaches By The Number	7"	MGM	MGM1281	1965	£1.50	£4	
Hello Enemy	7"	MGM	MGM1300	1966	£1.50	£4	
I Can't Help It	7"	London	HLA9642	1962	£1.50	£4	chart single
I'm Watching My Watch	7"	MGM	MGM1235	1963	£1.50	£4	
It Keeps Right On A-Hurtin'	LP	London	HAA8019	1962	£15	£30	
It Keeps Right On A-Hurtin'	7"	London	HLA9550	1962	£1.50	£4	chart single
Jimmy's Girl	7"	London	HLA9275	1961	£1.50	£4	chart single
Johnny Tillotson	7" EP..	London	REA1345	1962	£7.50	£15	
Johnny Tillotson	7" EP..	MGM	MGMEP788	1963	£7.50	£15	
Johnny Tillotson's Best	LP	London	HAA2431	1961	£20	£40	
Johnny Tillotson's Hit Parade ...	7" EP..	MGM	MGMEP790	1964	£7.50	£15	
J.T.	7" EP..	London	REA1388	1963	£7.50	£15	
Me Myself And I	7"	MGM	MGM1311	1966	£1.50	£4	
No Love At All	LP	MGM	C(S)8025	1966	£6	£15	
No Love At All	7"	MGM	MGM1319	1966	£1.50	£4	
Our World	7"	MGM	MGM1290	1965	£1.50	£4	
Out Of My Mind	7"	London	HLA9695	1963	£1.50	£4	chart single
Poetry In Motion	7"	London	HLA9231	1960	£1.50	£4	chart single
Send Me The Pillow You Dream On ..	7"	London	HLA9598	1962	£1.50	£4	chart single
She Understands Me	7"	MGM	MGM1252	1964	£1.50	£4	
Sings Our World	LP	MGM	C(S)8005	1965	£6	£15	
Suffering From A Heartache	7"	MGM	MGM1247	1964	£1.50	£4	
Talk Back Trembling Lips	7"	MGM	MGM1214	1963	£1.50	£4	
Then I'll Count Again	7"	MGM	MGM1275	1965	£1.50	£4	
True True Happiness	7"	London	HLA8930	1959	£15	£30	
Why Do I Love You So	7"	London	HLA9048	1960	£7.50	£15	
Without You	7"	London	HLA9412	1961	£1.50	£4	
Worried Guy	7"	MGM	MGM1225	1963	£1.50	£4	
You Can Never Stop Me Loving You	LP	Cadence	CLP3067/25067	1963	£10	£25	US

TILSLEY ORCHESTRA
Thunderbirds Theme .... 7" ...... Fontana .... TF783 .... 1966 ... £2.50 ... £6 ....
Top TV Themes .... LP ..... Fontana .... (S)TL5411 .... 1967 ... £5 .... £12 ....

TILSTON, STEVE
Acoustic Confusion .... LP ..... Village Thing ... VTS5 .... 1971 ... £10 .... £25 ....
Collection .... LP ..... Transatlantic ... TRA252 .... 1972 ... £5 .... £12 ....
Songs From The Dress Rehearsal .... LP ..... Cornucopia ...... CR1 .... 1977 ... £6 .... £15 ....

TIME
First Time I Saw The Sunshine .... 7" ...... Pye .... 7N17146 .... 1966 ... £6 .... £12 ....
Take A Bit Of Notice .... 7" ...... Pye .... 7N17019 .... 1965 ... £10 .... £20 ....

T.I.M.E.
Smooth Ball .... LP ..... Liberty .... LBS83232 .... 1969 ... £8 .... £20 ....
Take Me Along .... 7" ...... Liberty .... LBF15082 .... 1969 ... £1.50 ... £4 ....
T.I.M.E. .... LP ..... Liberty .... LST7558 .... 1968 ... £8 .... £20 .... US

TIME
Time .... LP ..... Buk .... BULP2005 .... 1975 ... £37.50 ... £75 ....

TIMEBOX
Timebox were an interesting soul-inflected group, several of whose songs employ touches of psychedelia to worthwhile effect. In the seventies, the group became Patto.
Baked Jam Roll In Your Eye .... 7" ...... Deram .... DM246 .... 1969 ... £4 .... £8 ....
Beggin' .... 7" ...... Deram .... DM194 .... 1968 ... £4 .... £8 .... chart single
Don't Make Promises .... 7" ...... Deram .... DM153 .... 1967 ... £5 .... £10 ....
Girl Don't You Make Me Wait .... 7" ...... Deram .... DM219 .... 1968 ... £4 .... £8 ....
I'll Always Love You .... 7" ...... Piccadilly .... 7N35369 .... 1967 ... £7.50 ... £15 ....
Original Moose On The Loose .... LP ..... Cosmos .... CCLPS9016 .... 1977 ... £8 .... £20 .... US
Soul Sauce .... 7" ...... Piccadilly .... 7N35379 .... 1967 ... £10 .... £20 ....
Yellow Van .... 7" ...... Deram .... DM271 .... 1969 ... £4 .... £8 ....

TIMELORDS
Doctorin' The Tardis .... CDV ... KLF .... KLFCD003 .... 1988 ... £2.50 ... £6 ....
Doctorin' The Tardis .... 7" ...... KLF .... KLF003P .... 1988 ... £2 .... £5 .... shaped pic disc
Gary Glitter Joins The Jams .... 12" .... KLF .... KLF003R .... 1988 ... £4 .... £10 ....
Gary In The Tardis .... 7" ...... KLF .... KLF003GG .... 1988 ... £6 .... £12 .... promo with
Gary Glitter

TIMERS
Brian Wilson performs on the A side of this single by the Timers.

No-Go Showboat .... 7" ...... Reprise .... 231 .... 1963 ... £25 ....£50 .... US

TIMES
Boys About Town	7"	Artpop	43DOZ	1985	£2.50	£6	
Boys Brigade	7"	Artpop	POP46	1984	£1.50	£4	
Hello Europe	LP	Artpop	ART17	1984	£4	£10	
Here Comes The Holidays	7"	Artpop	POP50	1982	£4	£8	
I Helped Patrick McGoohan Escape	7"	Artpop	POP49	1983	£4	£8	
I Helped Patrick McGoohan Escape	12"	Artpop	No1	1983	£4	£10	
Pop Goes Art	LP	Artpop	ART20	1984	£5	£12	
Pop Goes Art	LP	Whaam!	WHAAMLP1	1982	£8	£20	
Red With Purple Flashes	7"	Whaam!	WHAAM002	1981	£10	£20	

TIMES (2)
Love We Knew	7"	Columbia	DB7904	1966	£6	£12	
Ooh Wee	7" EP	Columbia	7ES24	1965	£20	£40	demo, no PS
Think About The Times	7"	Columbia	DB7804	1966	£6	£12	

TIMMONS, BOBBY
Easy Does It	LP	Riverside	RLP363	1961	£6	£15
In Person	LP	Riverside	RLP(9)391	1961	£6	£15
Moanin'	7"	Riverside	3204	1967	£1.50	£4
Soul Time	LP	Riverside	RLP334	1960	£6	£15
This Here Is Bobby Timmons	LP	Riverside	RLP12317	1960	£6	£15

TIMON
Bitter Thoughts Of Little Jane	7"	Pye	7N17451	1968	£10	£20	
I'm Just A Travelling Man	7"	Threshold	TH3	1970	£1.50	£4	

TIMONEERS
Roasted Live .... LP ..... WHM .... 1976 ... £8 ....£20 ....

TIMOTHY, AL
Gruntin' Blues .... 7" .... Decca .... F10558 .... 1955 ... £1.50 ....£4 ....

TIN MACHINE
Prisoner Of Love .... 7" ..... EMI .... MTPD76 .... 1989 ... £1.50 ....£4 ....shaped pic disc

TIN TIN
Come On Over Again	7"	Polydor	2058076	1970	£1.50	£4
Is That The Way	7"	Polydor	2058114	1971	£1.50	£4
Toast And Marmalade For Tea	7"	Polydor	2058023	1970	£2	£5

TINKERBELL'S FAIRYDUST
The records made by this obscure group are typical of the slightly psychedelic late sixties pop that is still sought after by enthusiasts looking for that elusive lost "masterpiece" of the period. The album is a recent discovery - at the time of writing only one copy of a demo in a finished sleeve is known to have surfaced, but others must presumably exist.

In My Magic Garden	7"	Decca	F12705	1967	£10	£20	
Sheila's Back In Town	7"	Decca	F12865	1969	£12.50	£25	
Tinkerbell's Fairydust	LP	Decca	LK5028	1969	£530	£800	demo only
Twenty Ten	7"	Decca	F12778	1968	£10	£20	

TINKERS
Spring Rain	LP	Argo	ZFB35	1970	£6	£15
Til The Wild Birds	LP	Fontana	6438020	1970	£6	£15

TINO, BABS
Forgive Me	7"	London	HLR9589	1962	£5	£10
Forgive Me	7" EP	London	RER1377	1963	£15	£30

TINTERN ABBEY
Beeside .... 7" ...... Deram .... DM164 .... 1967 ... £50 ....£100 ....

TINY TIM
Bring Back Those Rockabye Baby Days	7"	Reprise	RS20760	1968	£1.50	£4	
For All My Little Friends	LP	Reprise	6351	1969	£5	£12	US
God Bless Tiny Tim	LP	Reprise	RSLP6292	1968	£5	£12	
Great Balls Of Fire	7"	Reprise	R20802	1968	£1.50	£4	chart single
Hello Hello	7"	Reprise	R20769	1968	£1.50	£4	
Mickey The Monkey	7"	Reprise	R20855	1969	£1.50	£4	
Second Album	LP	Reprise	RSLP6323	1968	£5	£12	
There'll Always Be An England	78	Reprise	RS27004	1969	£5	£10	
Tip Toe Thru The Tulips	7"	Reprise	R23258	1968	£1.50	£4	

TIP TOPS
Oo-Kook-A-Boo .... 7" ...... Cameo
 Parkway .... P868 .... 1963 ... £5 ....£10 ....

TIPPETT, JULIE
Sunset Glow	LP	Utopia	UTS601	1976	£6	£15
Voice	LP	Ogun	OG110	1974	£6	£15

TIPPETT, KEITH
Blue Print	LP	RCA	SF8290	1972	£15	£30	
Dedicated To You But You Weren't Listening	LP	Vertigo	6360024	1971	£10	£25	spiral label
Frames	LP	Ogun	OGD003/4	1978	£6	£15	double
T'N'T	LP	Steam	SJ104	1976	£6	£15	with Stan Tracey
Warm Spirits Cool Spirits	LP	Vinyl	VS101	1977	£6	£15	
You Are Here I Am There	LP	Polydor	2384004	1969	£25	£50	

TIPPI & THE CLOVERS
My Heart Said .... 7" .... Stateside .... SS160 .... 1963 ... £4 .... £8 ....

TIPTON, LESTER
This Won't Change .... 7" .... Grapevine .... GRP138 .... 1979 ... £2 .... £5 . Masqueraders B side

TIR NA NOG
Strong In The Sun .... LP ..... Chrysalis .... CHR1047 .... 1973 ... £4 .... £10
Tear And A Smile .... LP ..... Chrysalis .... CHR1006 .... 1972 ... £5 .... £12
Tir Na Nog .... LP ..... Chrysalis .... ILPS9153 .... 1971 ... £5 .... £12

TITANS
Don't You Just Know It .... 7" .... London .... HLU8609 .... 1958 ... £22.50 .. £45 ....
Today's Teen Beat .... LP ..... MGM .... (S)E3992 .... 1961 ... £6 .... £15 .... US

TITUS GROAN
Titus Groan .... LP ..... Dawn .... DNLS3012 .... 1970 ... £25 .... £50

TITUS OATS
Jungle Lady .... LP .... 1971 ... £60 .... £120 .... US

TJADER, CAL
Best Of Cal Tjader .... LP ..... Verve .... (S)VLP9192 .... 1968 ... £4 .... £10
Cal Tjader Group/Don Elliott Group ... LP ..... London .... LTZC15050 .... 1957 ... £6 .... £15
Hip Vibrations .... LP ..... Verve .... (S)VLP9215 .... 1968 ... £4 .... £10
Solar Heat .... LP ..... Fontana .... STL5527 .... 1969 ... £4 .... £10
Soul Sauce .... 7" ..... Verve .... VS529 .... 1965 ... £12.50 .. £25

TOAD
Dreams .... LP ..... Frog .... 1975 ... £40 .... £80 .... Italian
Toad .... LP ..... RCA .... SF8241 .... 1972 ... £65 .... £130
Tomorrow Blue .... LP ..... Hallelujah .... X626 .... 1973 ... £40 .... £80 .... Swiss

TOAD THE WET SPROCKET
Pete's Punk Song .... 7" ..... Sprocket .... 1979 ... £5 .... £10
Reaching For The Sky .... 7" ..... Sprockets .... BRS008 .... 1980 ... £2.50 .... £6

TOADS
Toads .... LP ..... Wiggins .... 64021 .... 1964 ... £50 .... £100 .... US

TOBY JUG
Greasy Quiff .... LP ..... private .... 1969 ... £330 ..... £500

TODD, ART & DOTTIE
Chanson D'Amour .... 7" ..... London .... HLB8620 .... 1958 ... £5 .... £10
Straight As An Arrow .... 7" ..... London .... HLN8838 .... 1959 ... £5 .... £10

TODD, DIANE
It's A Wonderful Thing To Be Loved ..... 7" ..... Decca .... F10993 .... 1958 ... £1.50 .... £4

TODD, NICK
At The Hop .... 7" ..... London .... HLD8537 .... 1958 ... £6 .... £12
Plaything .... 7" ..... London .... HLD8500 .... 1957 ... £12.50 .. £25
Tiger .... 7" ..... London .... HLD8902 .... 1959 ... £7.50 .. £15

TODD, PATSY
We Were Lovers .... 7" ..... High Note .... HS012 .... 1968 ... £2.50 .... £6

TODD, SHARKEY & THE MONSTERS
Cool Ghoul .... 7" ..... Parlophone .... R4536 .... 1959 ... £2.50 .... £6

TODD, WILF
He Took Her Away .... 7" ..... Blue Beat .... BB240 .... 1963 ... £5 .... £10

TOEFAT
Toefat's LP is most notable for its unsettling cover, showing human figures with enormous toes replacing their heads. The group was one of Cliff Bennett's attempts to revive his career after the demise of the Rebel Rousers - on this occasion he effectively took over a pre-existing band, the Gods.
Bad Side Of The Road .... 7" ..... Parlophone .... R5829 .... 1970 ... £4 .... £8
Brand New Band .... 7" ..... Chapter One .... CH175 .... 1972 ... £2.50 .... £6
Toefat .... LP ..... Parlophone .... PCS7097 .... 1970 ... £15 .... £30
Toefat II .... LP ..... Regal .... SLRZ1015 .... 1971 ... £20 .... £40
                                              Zonophone......

TOGETHER
Henry's Coming Home .... 7" .... Columbia .... DB8491 .... 1968 ... £15 .... £30

TOGGERY FIVE
I'd Much Rather Be With The Boys ...... 7" ..... Parlophone .... R5249 .... 1965 ... £12.50 .. £25
I'm Gonna Jump .... 7" ..... Parlophone .... R5175 .... 1964 ... £10 .... £20

TOKENS
B'wa Nina .... 7" EP.. RCA .... 75701 .... 1962 ... £5 .... £10 .... French
B'wna Nina .... 7" ..... RCA .... RCA1279 .... 1962 ... £1.50 .... £4
December 5th .... LP ..... B.T.Puppy .... BTPS1014 .... 1971 ... £5 .... £12 .... US
Greatest Moments .... LP ..... B.T.Puppy .... BTPS1012 .... 1970 ... £5 .... £12 .... US
Green Plant .... 7" ..... Stateside .... SS598 .... 1967 ... £1.50 .... £4
He's In Town .... 7" ..... Fontana .... TF500 .... 1964 ... £1.50 .... £4
I Hear Trumpets Blow .... LP ..... B.T.Puppy .... BTLP(S)1000 .... 1966 ... £5 .... £12 .... US
I Hear Trumpets Blow .... 7" ..... Fontana .... TF683 .... 1966 ... £1.50 .... £4
I'll Do My Crying Tomorrow .... 7" ..... RCA .... RCA1313 .... 1962 ... £1.50 .... £4
It's A Happening World .... 7" ..... Warner Bros .... WB7056 .... 1967 ... £1.50 .... £4

Title	Format	Label	Catalogue	Year			Notes
It's A Happening World	7" EP	Warner Bros	WEP1457	1967	£5	£10	French
Lion Sleeps Tonight	LP	RCA	RD27256/SF5128	1962	£8	£20	
Lion Sleeps Tonight	7"	RCA	RCA1263	1961	£1.50	£4	chart single
Lion Sleeps Tonight	7" EP	RCA	75688	1962	£5	£10	French
Portrait Of My Love	7"	Warner Bros	WB5900	1967	£1.50	£4	
She Lets Her Hair Down	7"	Buddah	201069	1969	£1.50	£4	
She Lets Her Hair Down	7"	Buddah	201076	1969	£1.50	£4	
Till	7"	Warner Bros	WB7169	1968	£1.50	£4	
Tokens Again	LP	RCA	LPM/LSP3685	1966	£5	£12	US
Tokens Of Gold	LP	B.T.Puppy	BTPS1006	1969	£5	£12	US
Tonight I Fell In Love	7"	Parlophone	R4790	1961	£1.50	£4	
We Sing Folk	LP	RCA	SF7535	1962	£5	£12	
Wheels	LP	RCA	LPM/LST2886	1964	£5	£12	US
Wishing	7"	RCA	RCA1322	1962	£1.50	£4	

TOM & JERRY

The Tom and Jerry who made the single "Baby Talk" were Tom Graph and Jerry Landis, otherwise known (in the reverse order) as Simon and Garfunkel.

Title	Format	Label	Catalogue	Year			Notes
Baby Talk	7"	Bell	120	1971	£6	£12	US
Baby Talk	7"	Big	621	1958	£20	£40	US
Baby Talk	7"	Gala	GSP806	196-	£10	£20	
Hey Schoolgirl	7"	Big	613	1957	£15	£30	US
Hey Schoolgirl	7"	King	5167	1957	£15	£30	US
I'll Drown In My Tears	7"	Mercury	71930	1961	£15	£30	US
I'm Lonesome	7"	Ember	1094	1959	£15	£30	US
I'm Lonesome	7"	Pye	7N25202	1963	£15	£30	US
Our Song	7"	Big	616	1958	£15	£30	US
Surrender, Please Surrender	7"	Paramount	10363	1962	£10	£20	US
That's My Story	7"	Big	618	1958	£15	£30	US
That's My Story	7"	Hunt	319	1958	£15	£30	US
That's My Story	7"	Paramount	10788	1966	£5	£10	US

TOM & JERRY (2)

Title	Format	Label	Catalogue	Year		
Johann Mouse	7" EP	MGM	MGMEP688	1958	£6	£12

TOM & JERRYO

Title	Format	Label	Catalogue	Year		
Boogaloo	7"	HMV	POP1435	1965	£7.50	£15

TOM CATS

Title	Format	Label	Catalogue	Year		
Tom Tom Cat	7"	Starlite	ST45054	1961	£7.50	£15

TOMLIN, LEE

Title	Format	Label	Catalogue	Year		
Sweet Sweet Lovin'	7"	CBS	202455	1966	£4	£8

TOMLINSON, ALBERT

Title	Format	Label	Catalogue	Year			Notes
Don't Wait For Me	7"	Giant	GN28	1968	£4	£8	Lloyd Evans B side

TOMLINSON, ROY

Title	Format	Label	Catalogue	Year			Notes
I Stand For I	7"	Coxsone	CS7056	1968	£5	£10	Martin B side

TOMORROW

Tomorrow are usually held up as the classic psychedelic group, but this reputation derives less from their album, which is very uneven in quality, as from the two wonderful singles, "My White Bicycle" and "Revolution". The chaotic, anarchist streak within the group (Twink) carried through into the Pink Fairies; the musically inventive part (Steve Howe) joined the group Yes.

Title	Format	Label	Catalogue	Year		
My White Bicycle	7"	Parlophone	R5597	1967	£7.50	£15
My White Bicycle	7"	Parlophone	R5813	1969	£7.50	£15
Revolution	7"	Parlophone	R5627	1967	£7.50	£15
Tomorrow	LP	Harvest	SHSM2010	1976	£5	£12
Tomorrow	LP	Parlophone	PMC/PCS7042	1968	£25	£50

TOMORROW COME SOMEDAY (ITHACA)

Title	Format	Label	Catalogue	Year		
Tomorrow Come Someday	LP	private	SNP97	1969	£400	£600

TOMORROW'S CHILDREN

Title	Format	Label	Catalogue	Year		
Bang Bang Rock Steady	7"	Island	WI3073	1967	£5	£10

TOMORROW'S GIFT

Title	Format	Label	Catalogue	Year			Notes
Goodbye Future	LP	Amok		1973	£8	£20	German
Tomorrow's Gift	LP	Plus		1970	£15	£30	German double

TON STEINE SCHERBEN

Title	Format	Label	Catalogue	Year			Notes
Keine Macht Fur Niemand	LP	Volksmund	TSS2	1972	£5	£12	German double
Warum Geht Es Mir So Dreckig	LP	Volksmund	TSS13	1971	£5	£12	German
Wenn Die Nacht Am Tiefsten	LP	Volksmund	TSS3	1975	£5	£12	German double

TONER, ELEANOR

Title	Format	Label	Catalogue	Year		
All Cried Out	7"	Decca	F12119	1965	£2	£5
Will You Still Love Me Tomorrow	7"	Decca	F12192	1965	£2	£5

TONES ON TAIL

Title	Format	Label	Catalogue	Year			Notes
Bigger Splash	12"	4AD	BAD203	1982	£3	£6	
Lions	12"	Beggars Banquet	BEGT109	1984	£2.50	£6	red vinyl
There's Only One	12"	Beggars Banquet	BEG85T	1982	£2.50	£6	

TONETTES

Title	Format	Label	Catalogue	Year		
Love That Is Real	7"	Island	WI064	1962	£5	£10

TONEY JR., OSCAR

Title	Format	Label	Catalogue	Year		
Down In Texas	7"	Bell	BLL1057	1969	£1.50	£4
For Your Precious Love	LP	Stateside	(S)SL10211	1967	£5	£12

For Your Precious Love	7"	Stateside	SS2033	1967	£4	£8	
No Sad Songs	7"	Bell	BLL1011	1968	£1.50	£4	
Turn On Your Lovelight	7"	Stateside	SS2046	1967	£2	£5	
Without Love There Is Nothing	7"	Bell	BLL1003	1968	£1.50	£4	
You Can Lead Your Woman To The Altar	7"	Stateside	SS2061	1967	£2	£5	

TONGUE & GROOVE
Tongue & Groove	LP	Fontana	STL5528	1969	£8	£20	

TONIK, TERRY
Just A Little Mod	7"	Posh	TOFF1	1980	£7.50	£15	

TONTON MACOUTE
Tonton Macoute	LP	Neon	NE4	1971	£25	£50	

TONTO'S EXPANDING HEADBAND
Tonto is an instrument (The Original New Timbral Orchestra) - a huge synthesizer - played by Robert Margouleff and Malcolm Cecil. These two are among the more imaginative electronic keyboard performers and "Zero Time" is a good example of what can be achieved. They take advantage of the possibilities afforded to them, by such stratagems as using a ten note, equally tempered scale (impossible on conventional instruments) and yet the music still manages to be as accessible as it is interesting. Margouleff and Cecil also worked as advisers to Stevie Wonder and their sounds can be heard on many of his records.
It's About Time	LP	Polydor	2383308	1974	£4	£10	
Zero Time	LP	Atlantic	2400150	1971	£6	£15	
Zero Time	LP	Atlantic	K40251	1971	£5	£12	

TONY & DENNIS
Folk Song	7"	Trojan	TR002	1967	£4	£8	Tommy McCook B side

TONY & JOE
Freeze	7"	London	HLN8694	1958	£12.50	£25	

TONY & LOUISE
Ups And Downs	7"	Island	WI059	1962	£5	£10	

TONY & TANDY
Two Can Make It Together	7"	Atlantic	2091075	1971	£2.50	£6	
Two Can Make It Together	7"	Atlantic	584262	1969	£5	£10	

TONY & THE GRADUATES
Statue	7"	Hit	HIT13	196-	£15	£30	

TONY & THE VELVETS
Sunday	7"	Decca	F11637	1963	£1.50	£4	

TONY'S DEFENDERS
Since I Lost My Baby	7"	Columbia	DB7996	1966	£6	£12	
Yes I Do	7"	Columbia	DB7850	1966	£7.50	£15	

TOOMORROW
Toomorrow was a group put together, Monkees-style, for the purpose of making a rather silly film. This was the flop it deserved to be, but the group's lead singer, Olivia Newton-John, persevered with her musical career.
I Could Never Live Without Your Love	7"	Decca	F13070	1970	£12.50	£25	
Toomorrow	LP	RCA	LSA3008	1970	£35	£70	
You're My Baby Now	7"	RCA	RCA1978	1970	£12.50	£25	

TOOP, DAVID
New And Rediscovered Musical Instruments	LP	Obscure	OBS4	1976	£4	£10	

TOOTS
Do You Like It	7"	Upsetter	US327	1970	£2	£5	Upsetters B side

TOP DRAWER
Solid Oak	LP	Wishbone		1969	£100	£200	US

TOPHAM, TOP
Ascension Heights	LP	Blue Horizon	763857	1970	£30	£60	sleeve pictured in Guide
Christmas Cracker	7"	Blue Horizon	573167	1969	£7.50	£15	

TOPICS
The Topics shortly afterwards changed their name to the Four Seasons.
Girl In My Dreams	7"	Perri	1007	1961	£37.50	£75	US

TOPSY, TINY & THE CHARMS
After Marriage Blues	7"	Pye	7N25104	1961	£10	£20	
Come On Come On Come On	7"	Parlophone	R4397	1958	£12.50	£25	
You Shocked Me	7"	Parlophone	R4427	1958	£12.50	£25	

TORA TORA
Red Sun Setting	7"	Mancunian Metal	TT5000	1980	£2.50	£6	

TORME, BERNIE
I'm Not Ready	7"	Jet	JET126	1978	£2	£5	orange vinyl

TORME, MEL
All Of You	7"	Vogue Coral	Q72202	1956	£1.50	£4	
And The Marty Paich Dektette	LP	London	LTZN15009	1956	£6	£15	
At The Crescendo	LP	Parlophone	PMC1096	1959	£5	£12	

At The Crescendo	LP	Vogue Coral	LVA9004	1955	£6	£15	
At The Red Hill	LP	London	HAK/SHK8021	1963	£5	£12	
Back In Town	7"	HMV	CLP1382	1960	£6	£15	
Blue Moon	7"	Vogue Coral	Q72159	1956	£2.50	£6	
California Suite	LP	Bethlehem	BCP6016	1958	£8	£20	US
Comin' Home Baby	LP	London	HAK8065	1963	£5	£12	
Comin' Home Baby	7"	London	HLK9643	1962	£4	£8	chart single
I Can't Give You Anything But Love	7"	MGM	MGM922	1956	£1.50	£4	
It's A Blue World	LP	London	HAN2016	1956	£6	£15	
Love Is Here To Stay	7"	Vogue Coral	Q72185	1956	£1.50	£4	
Lullaby Of Birdland	7"	London	HLN8322	1956	£5	£10	
Lulu's Back In Town	7"	London	HLN8305	1956	£5	£10	
Magic Of Mel	7" EP	London	REK1372	1963	£4	£8	
Meet The British	LP	Philips	BBL7205	1957	£15	£30	
Meets The British	7" EP	Philips	BBE12181	1958	£4	£8	
Mel Torme	LP	Bethlehem	BCP52	1956	£8	£20	US
Mel Torme	LP	HMV	CLP1238	1958	£4	£10	
Mountain Greenery	7"	Vogue Coral	Q72150	1956	£2	£5	chart single
Musical Sounds	LP	Coral	CRL57044	1954	£8	£20	US
Musical Sounds Are The Best Songs	LP	Vogue Coral	LVA9032	1956	£6	£15	
My Kind Of Music	LP	HMV	CLP1584/CSD1442	1962	£5	£12	
My Rosemarie	7"	Vogue Coral	Q72217	1957	£1.50	£4	
Ole Torme	LP	HMV	CLP1315	1960	£4	£10	
Sings At The Crescendo Pt.1	7" EP	Coral	FEP2026	1959	£2.50	£6	
Sings At The Crescendo Pt.2	7" EP	Coral	FEP2027	1959	£2.50	£6	
Sings At The Crescendo Pt.3	7" EP	Coral	FEP2028	1959	£2.50	£6	
Sings Fred Astaire	LP	London	LTZN15076	1957	£5	£12	
Sings Fred Astaire Pt.1	7" EP	London	EZN19027	1958	£2	£5	
Sings Fred Astaire Pt.2	7" EP	London	EZN19028	1958	£2	£5	
Sings Fred Astaire Pt.3	7" EP	London	EZN19039	1958	£2	£5	
Songs	10" LP	MGM	552	1952	£10	£25	US
Songs For Any Taste	LP	Parlophone	PMC1114	1959	£6	£15	
Sunday In New York	LP	Atlantic	(SD)8091	1963	£5	£12	US
Swingin' On The Moon	LP	HMV	CLP1449/CSD1349	1961	£6	£15	
Swings Schubert Alley	LP	HMV	CLP1405/CSD1330	1960	£6	£15	
Torme	LP	Verve	V2105	1958	£5	£12	US
Voice In Velvet	7" EP	MGM	MGMEP562	1956	£4	£8	
Voice In Velvet No.2	7" EP	MGM	MGMEP591	1957	£4	£8	
Walkin' Shoes	7"	Decca	F10800	1956	£1.50	£4	
Walkin' Shoes	7" EP	Decca	DFE6384	1956	£2.50	£6	

TORNADOES

| Bustin' Surfboards | LP | Josie | 4005 | 1963 | £25 | £50 | US |

TORNADOS

Away From It All	LP	Decca	LK4552	1963	£10	£25	
Dragonfly	7"	Decca	F11745	1963	£1.50	£4	chart single
Earlybird	7"	Columbia	DB7589	1965	£5	£10	
Exodus	7"	Decca	F11946	1964	£4	£8	
Globetrotter	7"	Decca	F11562	1963	£1.50	£4	chart single
Granada	7"	Columbia	DB7455	1965	£5	£10	
Hot Pot	7"	Decca	F11838	1964	£1.50	£4	
Ice Cream Man	7"	Decca	F11662	1963	£1.50	£4	chart single
Is That A Ship I Hear	7"	Columbia	DB7984	1966	£7.50	£15	
Love And Fury	7"	Decca	F11449	1962	£4	£8	
Monte Carlo	7"	Decca	F11889	1964	£4	£8	
More Sounds From The Tornados	7" EP	Decca	DFE8521	1963	£7.50	£15	
Pop Art Goes Mozart	7"	Columbia	DB7856	1966	£7.50	£15	
Robot	7"	Decca	F11606	1963	£1.50	£4	chart single
Sounds Of The Tornados	LP	London	LL3293	1963	£8	£20	US
Sounds Of The Tornados	7" EP	Decca	DFE8510	1962	£5	£10	
Stingray	7"	Columbia	DB7687	1965	£7.50	£15	
Telstar	LP	London	LL3279	1962	£10	£25	US
Telstar	CD	Decca		1988	£25	£50	
Telstar	7"	Decca	F11494	1962	£1.50	£4	chart single
Telstar	7" EP	Decca	DFE8511	1962	£5	£10	
Tornado Rock	7" EP	Decca	DFE8533	1963	£7.50	£15	
World Of The Tornados	LP	Decca	SPA253	1972	£4	£8	

TOROK, MITCHELL

Caribbean	LP	London	HAW2279	1960	£15	£30	
Caribbean	7"	London	HL8004	1954	£10	£20	
Drink Up And Go Home	7"	Brunswick	05642	1957	£5	£10	
Haunting Waterfall	7"	London	HL8083	1954	£12.50	£25	
Havana Huddle	7"	Brunswick	05626	1956	£7.50	£15	
Hootchy Coochy	7"	London	HL8048	1954	£12.50	£25	
Louisiana Hayride	7" EP	London	REP1014	1954	£12.50	£25	
Pink Chiffon	7"	London	HLW9130	1960	£2	£5	
Pledge Of Love	7"	Brunswick	05657	1957	£4	£8	
Two Words	7"	Brunswick	05718	1957	£2.50	£6	
When Mexico Gave Up The Rhumba	7"	Brunswick	05586	1956	£6	£12	chart single
World Keeps Turning Around	7"	Brunswick	05423	1955	£6	£12	

TORQUES

| Live | LP | Lemco | 604 | 196- | £25 | £50 | US |
| Zoom! | LP | Wiggins | 64010 | 1964 | £37.50 | £75 | US |

TORRENCE, GEORGE & THE NATURALS

| Lickin' Stick | 7" | London | HLZ10181 | 1968 | £4 | £8 | |

TORTILLA
Little Heroes	LP	Catfish	5C05624381	1971	£25	£50		Dutch

TORTILLA FLAT
Fur Eine 3/4 Stunden	LP		TF0175	1974	£15	£30	German

TOSH, PETER
Bush Doctor	LP	Rolling Stones	CUN39109	1978	£4	£10	with scratch & sniff sticker
Crimson Pirate	7"	Jackpot	JP706	1969	£5	£10	
Hoot Nanny Hoot	7"	Island	WI211	1965	£12.50	£25	
I Am The Toughest	7"	Island	WI3042	1967	£10	£20	Marcia Griffiths B side
Maga Dog	7"	Bullet	BU486	1971	£5	£10	Third & Fourth Generation B side
Return Of Al Capone	7"	Unity	UN525	1969	£4	£8	Lennox Brown B side
Rudies Medley	7"	Punch	PH91	1972	£2.50	£6	
Selassie Serenade	7"	Bullet	BU414	1971	£2.50	£6	Glen Adams B side
Sun Valley	7"	Unity	UN529	1969	£4	£8	Hedley Bennett B side
Them A Fi Get A Beatin'	7"	Pressure Beat	PB5509	1972	£5	£10	Third & Fourth Generation B side

TOTNAMITES
Danny Boy	7"	Oriole	CB1615	1961	£1.50	£4

TOTO
Africa	7"	CBS	A2510	1982	£1.50	£4	shaped pic disc
Rosanna	7"	CBS	A2079	1982	£1.50	£4	shaped pic disc
Toto	LP	Epic	PJC35317	1978	£5	£12	French pic disc

TOTTERDELL, DAVE
Whitby Bells	LP	Cottage	COT711	1977	£5	£12

TOUCH
Miss Teach	7"	Deram	DM243	1969	£4	£8	
This Is Touch	LP	Deram	DML/SML1033	1969	£10	£25	with poster

TOUCH (2)
Don't You Know What Love Is	7"	Ariola	ARO243	1980	£2.50	£6
Touch	LP	Ariola	ARL5036	1980	£5	£12
When The Spirit Moves You	7"	Ariola	ARO209	1980	£2	£5

TOUFF, CY
Having A Ball	LP	Vogue	LAE12040	1957	£6	£15

TOURISTS
Blind Among The Flowers	7"	Logo	GOD350	1979	£1.50	£4	double
Loneliest Man In The World	7"	Logo	GOP360	1979	£2	£5	pic disc
Luminous Basement	LP	RCA	RCALP5001	1980	£4	£10	with yellow vinyl 7'

TOUSAN, AL
Naomi	7"	London	HLU9291	1961	£2.50	£6

TOUSSAINT, ALLEN
Southern Nights	LP	Reprise	K54021	1975	£4	£10	
We The People	7"	Soul City	SC119	1969	£4	£8	
Wild Sound Of New Orleans	LP	RCA	LPM1767	1958	£20	£40	US

TOVEY, ROBERTA
Who's Who	7"	Polydor	56021	1965	£1.50	£4

TOWER OF POWER
Back To Oakland	LP	Warner Bros	K46282	1974	£4	£10	
Bump City	LP	Warner Bros	K46167	1972	£4	£10	
East Bay Grease	LP	San Francisco	SD204	1970	£5	£12	US
Tower Of Power	LP	Warner Bros	K46223	1974	£4	£10	
Urban Renewal	LP	Warner Bros	K56093	1975	£4	£10	

TOWERS
To Know Him Is To Love Him	7"	Capitol	CL14944	1958	£1.50	£4

TOWNSEL SISTERS
Will I Ever	7"	Polydor	NH66954	1960	£2.50	£6

TOWNSEND, ED
Ed Townsend	7" EP	Capitol	EAP11091	1959	£2	£5

TOWNSEND, HENRY
Tired Of Bein' Mistreated	LP	Bluesville	BV1041	1962	£5	£12	US

TOWNSHEND, PETE
Pete's Listening Time	LP	Atco	SAM150	1982	£6	£15	interview promo
Pete's Listening Time	LP	Atco	SAM150	1982	£10	£25	interview promo, autographed
Townshend Tapes	LP	Atco	SAM121/2	1980	£10	£25	double interview promo
Townshend Tapes	LP	Atco	SAM121/2	1980	£15	£30	double interview promo, autographed
Uniforms	12"	Atco	K11751PT	1982	£2.50	£6	pic disc
Who Came First	LP	Track	2408201	1972	£4	£10	chart LP

TOWNSHEND, PETE & JOHN WILLIAMS
Won't Get Fooled Again	7"	Island	SPB1	1981	£2.50	£6	1 sided promo

TOWNSHEND, PETE & MEHER BABA
All Time Star...	LP	Universal S.L.	MBO1	1975	£15	£30	reissue of USL001
Happy Birthday	LP	Universal S.L.	USL001	1970	£32.50	£65	
I Am	LP	Universal S.L.	MBO2	1975	£15	£30	
I Am	LP	Universal S.L.	USL002	1973	£32.50	£65	
With Love	LP	Universal S.L.	USL003	1974	£32.50	£65	

TOXIC REASONS
Ghost Town	7"	Risky		1981	£10	£20
War Hero	7"	Banit		1981	£10	£20

TOY DOLLS
Everybody Jitterbug	7"	Zonophone	Z31	1982	£2.50	£6	
Nellie The Elephant	7"	Volume	VOL3	1983	£2	£5	
Tommy Kowie's Car	7"	GBH	GRC104	1981	£5	£10	
Tommy Kowie's Car	7"	GBH	SSM005	1981	£7.50	£15	no PS

TOY DOLLS (2)
Little Tin Soldier	7"	London	HLN9647	1963	£1.50	£4

TOY FACTORY
Toy Factory	LP	Avco			£8	£20	US

TOYS
Attack	7"	Stateside	SS483	1966	£2	£5	chart single
Baby Toys	7"	Stateside	SS539	1966	£2	£5	
Ciao Baby	7"	Philips	BF1563	1967	£1.50	£4	
Lover's Concert/Attack	LP	Stateside	(S)SL10175	1966	£8	£20	
Lover's Concerto	7"	Bell	BLL1053	1969	£1.50	£4	
Lover's Concerto	7"	Stateside	SS460	1965	£2	£5	chart single
May My Heart Be Cast To Stone	7"	Stateside	SS502	1966	£2	£5	
My Lover's Sonata	7"	Philips	BF1581	1967	£2.50	£6	
Silver Spoon	7"	Stateside	SS519	1966	£2	£5	

TRACEY, GRANT & THE SUNSETS
Everybody Shake	7"	Decca	F11741	1963	£2.50	£6
Love Me	7"	Ember	EMBS130	1961	£4	£8
Please Baby Please	7"	Ember	EMBS126	1961	£5	£10
Taming Tigers	7"	Ember	EMBS155	1962	£4	£8
Tears Came Rolling Down	7"	Ember	EMBS148	1962	£4	£8
Teenbeat	LP	Ember	EMB3352	1964	£6	£15

TRACEY, MARK
Caravan Of Lonely Men	7"	Parlophone	R4944	1962	£1.50	£4

TRACEY, STAN
Alice In Jazzland	LP	Columbia	SX/SCX6051	1966	£10	£25	
Free An' One	LP	Columbia	SCX6385	1970	£10	£25	
In Person	LP	Columbia	SX/SCX6124	1967	£10	£25	
Jazz Suite	LP	Columbia	33SX1774/ SCX3589	1965	£10	£25	
Latin American Caper	LP	Columbia	SCX6358	1969	£10	£25	
Little Klunk	LP	Ace Of Clubs	ACL1259	1969	£6	£15	
Little Klunk	LP	Vogue	VA160155	1959	£15	£30	
Original	LP	Cadillac	SAC1002	197-	£10	£25	with Mike Osborne
Perspectives	LP	Columbia	SCX6485	1971	£10	£25	
Seven Ages Of Man	LP	Columbia	SCX6413	1970	£10	£25	
Showcase	LP	Vogue	VA160130	1958	£15	£30	
We Love You Madly	LP	Columbia	SX/SCX6320	1969	£10	£25	
With Love From Jazz	LP	Columbia	SX/SCX6205	1968	£10	£25	

TRACEY, WENDALL
Who's To Know	7"	London	HLM8664	1958	£7.50	£15

TRACEY, ZEN
Two By Two	7"	Decca	F11492	1962	£1.50	£4

TRACK
Why Do Fools Fall In Love	7"	Columbia	DB7987	1966	£4	£8

TRACTOR
No More Rock And Roll	7"	Cargo	CRS002	1977	£2.50	£6
Stone Glory	7"	Polydor	2001282	1972	£4	£8
Tractor	LP	Dandelion	2310217	1972	£40	£80

TRADE WINDS
Crossroads	7"	RCA	RCA1141	1959	£4	£8

TRADE WINDS (2)
Excursions	LP	Kama Sutra	KLP(S)8057	1967	£6	£15	US
Mind Excursion	7"	Kama Sutra	KAS202	1966	£2	£5	
Mind Excursion	7" EP	Kama Sutra	617104	1966	£5	£10	French
New York's A Lonely Town	7"	Red Bird	RB10020	1965	£2.50	£6	

TRADER HORNE
Trader Horne was a folky group formed by Jackie McAuley, who had played keyboards with Them for a while, and Judy Dyble, who was the original lead singer with Fairport Convention. Their one album was followed by a Jackie McAuley solo LP in a similar style, but neither was sufficiently distinctive to make much head-way in the market place.

Here Comes The Rain	7"	Dawn	DNS1003	1970	£2.50	£6	
Morning Way	LP	Dawn	DNLS3004	1970	£30	£60	
Sheena	7"	Pye	7N17846	1969	£4	£8	

TRAFFIC

The first two albums made by Traffic are near-perfect examples of why so many rock music collectors view the sixties through rose-coloured glasses. Presenting a blend of inspirational song-writing, ever-imaginative arranging, and skilful playing, these qualities emerging relatively undiminished by the passing of time, the albums are far more satisfying than any number of more expensive "progressive" rarities. (Sadly, the reformed 1994 model of Traffic is not the same at all - some of the sound is the same, but the white heat of inspiration has cooled to charcoal).

Best Of Traffic	LP	Island	ILPS9112	1969	£5	£12	
Empty Pages	7"	Island		1974	£1.50	£4	promo
Feelin' Alright	7"	Island	WIP6041	1968	£1.50	£4	
Gimme Some Lovin'	7"	Island		1971	£2.50	£6	promo
Heaven Is In Your Mind	LP	United Artists	UAS6651	1968	£6	£15	US
Here We Go Round The Mulberry Bush	7"	Island	WIP6025	1967	£2	£5	chart single
Here We Go Round The Mulberry Bush	7"	Island	WIP6025	1967	£2.50	£6	PS
Hole In My Shoe	7"	Island	IEP7	1978	£2.50	£6	pic disc
Hole In My Shoe	7"	Island	WIP6017	1967	£2	£5	chart single
Hole In My Shoe	7"	Island	WIP6017	1967	£4	£8	PS
Hole In My Shoe/Paper Sun	7"	Island	IEP7JB	1978	£1.50	£4	juke box issue
John Barleycorn Must Die	LP	Island	ILPS9116	1970	£4	£10	chart LP
Last Exit	LP	Island	ILPS9097	1969	£5	£12	
Live At The Fillmore	LP	Island	ILPS9124	1970	£50	£100	demo only
Medicated Goo	7"	Island	WIP6050	1968	£1.50	£4	
Mr.Fantasy	LP	Island	ILP961	1967	£6	£15	mono, chart LP
Mr.Fantasy	LP	Island	ILPS9061	1967	£5	£12	stereo, chart LP
No Face,No Name,No Number	7"	Island	WIP6030	1968	£1.50	£4	
Paper Sun	7"	Island	WIP6002	1967	£2	£5	chart single
Paper Sun	7"	Island	WIP6002	1967	£5	£10	PS
Traffic	LP	Island	ILP981	1968	£6	£15	mono
Traffic	LP	Island	ILPS9081	1968	£5	£12	stereo
Walking In The Wind	7"	Island	WIP6207	1974	£1.50	£4	
Welcome To The Canteen	LP	Island	ILPS9166	1971	£4	£10	
You Can All Join In	7"	Island	WIP6041	1968	£5	£10	demo only

TRAFFIC JAM

The Spectres changed their name to Traffic Jam for one single, before deciding that the possible confusion with Steve Winwood's new group, Traffic, was not helping their career. Accordingly, they changed names yet again, this time to Status Quo.

Almost But Not Quite There	7"	Piccadilly	7N35386	1967	£75	£150	

TRAINER, PHIL

Phil Trainer	LP	BASF		1973	£10	£25

TRAITS

Harlem Shuffle	7"	Pye	7N25404	1967	£4	£8

TRAMLINE

Moves Of Vegetable Centuries	LP	Island	ILPS9095	1969	£15	£30
Somewhere Down The Line	LP	Island	ILPS9088	1968	£15	£30

TRAMMELL, BOBBY LEE

Arkansas Twist	LP	Atlantic	LPM1503	1962	£17.50	£35	US
New Dance In France	7"	Sue	WI326	1964	£6	£12	

TRAMP

Each Day	7"	Youngblood	SBY4	1969	£1.50	£4
Put A Record On	LP	Spark	SRLP112	1974	£15	£30
Put A Record On	7"	Spark	SRL1107	1974	£1.50	£4
Tramp	LP	Music Man	SMLS603	1969	£50	£100
Tramp	LP	Spark	SRLM2001	1973	£15	£30

TRANSATLANTICS

Don't Fight It	7"	Mercury	MF948	1965	£7.50	£15
Many Things From Your Window	7"	Fontana	TF593	1965	£2.50	£6
Run For Your Life	7"	King	KG1033	1965	£2.50	£6
Stand Up And Fight Like A Man	7"	Fontana	TF638	1965	£2.50	£6

TRANSVISION VAMP

Tell That Girl To Shut Up	CD-s	MCA	DVVT2	1988	£2.50	£6	pic disc

TRAPEZE

Coast To Coast	7"	Threshold	TH11	1972	£1.50	£4
Final Swing	LP	Threshold	THS11	1974	£8	£20
Hot Wire	LP	Warner Bros	K56064	1974	£5	£12
Medusa	LP	Threshold	THS4	1970	£8	£20
Send Me No More Letters	7"	Threshold	TH2	1969	£1.50	£4
Trapeze	LP	Threshold	THS2	1970	£8	£20
Trapeze	LP	Warner Bros	K56165	1975	£5	£12
You Are The Music	LP	Threshold	THS8	1972	£8	£20

TRAPEZE (2)

Don't Ask Me How I Know	7"	Aura	AUS114	1979	£2	£5
Running Away	7"	Aura	AUS116	1980	£2	£5

TRASH

Golden Slumbers	7"	Apple	17	1969	£6	£12	chart single

TRASHMEN

Bad News	7" EP	Columbia	ESRF1564	1964	£15	£30	French
Bird Dance Beat	7"	Stateside	SS276	1964	£7.50	£15	
Surfin' Bird	LP	Garrett	GA(S)200	1964	£25	£50	US
Surfin' Bird	7"	Stateside	SS255	1964	£10	£20	
Surfin' Bird	7" EP	Columbia	ESRF1491	1964	£15	£30	French
Whoa Dad	7" EP	Columbia	ESRF1627	1964	£25	£50	French

TRAUM, HAPPY

Relax Your Mind	LP	Kicking Mule	SNKF111	1976	£5	£12

TRAUM, HAPPY & ARTIE

Doubleback	LP	Capitol	ST799	1971	£5	£12
Happy & Artie Traum	LP	Capitol	ST586	1969	£5	£12
Mud Acres	LP	Matchbox	239	1972	£5	£12

TRAVELING WILBURYS

Handle With Care	7"	Warner Bros	W7732	1988	£1.50	£4	gatefold PS
Wilbury Twist	7"	Warner Bros	W0018W	1991	£1.50	£4	with cards

TRAVELLING STEWARTS

Travelling Stewarts	LP	Topic	12T179	1968	£10	£25

TRAVIS & BOB

Tell Him No	7"	Pye	7N25018	1959	£1.50	£4

TRAVIS, MERLE

Back Home	LP	Capitol	T891	1957	£8	£20	
Back Home	7" EP	Capitol	EAP1891	1957	£5	£10	
Merle Travis And Joe Maphis	LP	Capitol	T2102	1965	£4	£10	
Merle Travis Guitar	LP	Capitol	T650	1956	£10	£25	US
Merle Travis Guitar No.1	7" EP	Capitol	EAP1032	1956	£7.50	£15	
Merle Travis Guitar No.2	7" EP	Capitol	EAP2650	1956	£5	£10	
Travis	LP	Capitol	(S)T1664	1963	£4	£10	
Walkin' The Strings	LP	Capitol	T1391	1960	£6	£15	US
Walkin' The Strings	7" EP	Capitol	EAP41391	1960	£5	£10	

TRAVIS, NICK

Panic Is On	LP	HMV	CLP1036	1955	£10	£25

TREASURE ISLE BOYS

Love Is A Treasure	7"	Trojan	TR010	1967	£5	£10	Tommy McCook B side

TREBLETONES

In Real Life	7"	Oriole	CB1838	1963	£1.50	£4

TREE, VIRGINIA (SHIRLEY KENT)

Fresh Out	LP	Minstrel	0001	1975	£15	£30

TREES

Garden Of Jane Delawney	LP	CBS	63837	1970	£35	£70
Nothing Special	7"	CBS	5078	1970	£6	£12
On The Shore	LP	CBS	64168	1970	£35	£70
On The Shore	LP	Decal	LIK12	1987	£5	£12

TREETOPS

Without The One You Love	7"	Columbia	DB8799	1971	£4	£8

TREETOPS (2)

California My Way	7"	Parlophone	R5669	1968	£4	£8
Don't Worry Baby	7"	Parlophone	R5628	1967	£4	£8

TREKKAS

Please Go	7"	Planet	PLF105	1965	£12.50	£25

TREMELOES

58/68 World Explosion	LP	CBS	BN26388	1968	£4	£10	US
Be Mine	7"	CBS	3043	1967	£1.50	£4	
Blessed	7"	Decca	F12423	1966	£1.50	£4	
By The Way	7"	CBS	4815	1970	£1.50	£4	chart single
Call Me Number One	7"	CBS	4582	1969	£1.50	£4	chart single
Chip, Rick, Alan And Dave	LP	CBS	(S)BPG63138	1967	£4	£10	
Even The Bad Times Are Good	7"	CBS	2930	1967	£1.50	£4	chart single
Good Day Sunshine	7"	CBS	202242	1966	£1.50	£4	
Hello Buddy	7"	CBS	7294	1971	£1.50	£4	chart single
Hello World	7"	CBS	4065	1969	£1.50	£4	chart single
Helule Helule	7"	CBS	2889	1967	£1.50	£4	chart single
Here Come The Tremeloes	LP	CBS	(S)BPG63017	1967	£4	£10	chart LP
Here Comes My Baby	7"	CBS	202519	1967	£1.50	£4	chart single
I Like It That Way	7"	CBS	8048	1972	£1.50	£4	
I Shall Be Released	7"	CBS	3873	1968	£1.50	£4	chart single
Live In Cabaret	LP	CBS	63547	1969	£4	£10	
Master	LP	CBS	64242	1970	£4	£10	
Me And My Life	7"	CBS	5139	1970	£1.50	£4	chart single
My Little Lady	7"	CBS	3443	1968	£1.50	£4	chart single
My Little Lady	7" EP	CBS	EP6402	1968	£4	£8	
Once On A Sunday Morning	7"	CBS	4313	1969	£1.50	£4	
Right Wheel Left Hammer Sham	7"	CBS	5429	1971	£1.50	£4	
Silence Is Golden	7"	CBS	2723	1967	£1.50	£4	chart single
Suddenly You Love Me	7"	CBS	3234	1968	£1.50	£4	chart single

Too Late	7"	CBS	7579	1971	£1.50	£4	

TREND
Shot On Sight	7"	Page One	POF004	1966	£6	£12	

TRENDS
All My Loving	7"	Piccadilly	7N35171	1964	£2.50	£6	
Way You Do The Things You Do	7"	Pye	7N15644	1964	£2.50	£6	

TRENDSETTERS
At The Hotel De France	7" EP.	Oak	RGJ999	196-	£10	£20	
You Don't Care	7"	Silver Phoenix.	1001	1964	£10	£20	

TRENDSETTERS LTD.
The roots of King Crimson lie in the four unprepossessing singles made by Trendsetters Ltd., which feature the early work of Michael and Peter Giles.
Funny Way Of Showing Your Love	7"	Parlophone.	R5324	1965	£2.50	£6	
Go Away	7"	Parlophone.	R5191	1964	£4	£8	
Hello Josephine	7"	Parlophone.	R5161	1964	£5	£10	
In A Big Way	7"	Parlophone.	R5118	1964	£4	£8	

TRENIERS
	10" LP			195-	£75	£150	
Go Go Go	7"	Fontana	H137	1958	£30	£60	
Ooh La La	7"	Coral	Q72319	1958	£7.50	£15	
Souvenir Album	LP	Dot	DLP3257	1960	£10	£25	US
Treniers On TV	LP	Epic	LG3125	195-	£20	£40	US
When Your Hair Has Turned Silver	7"	London	HLD8858	1959	£10	£20	

TRENT, JACKIE
Autumn Leaves	7"	Pye	7N15649	1964	£1.50	£4	
How Soon	7"	Pye	7N15742	1964	£1.50	£4	
If You Ever Leave Me	7"	Pye	7N17158	1966	£1.50	£4	
If You Love Me	7"	Piccadilly	7N35165	1964	£1.50	£4	
It's All In The Way You Look At Life	7"	Pye	7N15949	1965	£1.50	£4	
Love Is Me Love Is You	7"	Pye	7N17082	1966	£1.50	£4	
Magic Of Jackie Trent	LP	Pye	NPL18125	1965	£4	£10	
Melancholy Me	7"	Piccadilly	7N35121	1963	£1.50	£4	
One Who Really Loves You	7"	Oriole	CB1749	1962	£1.50	£4	
Pick Up The Pieces	7"	CBS	201776	1965	£1.50	£4	
Pick Up The Pieces	7"	Oriole	CB1711	1962	£1.50	£4	
Somewhere In The World	7"	Pye	7N15692	1964	£1.50	£4	
When The Summertime Is Over	7"	Pye	7N15865	1965	£1.50	£4	chart single
Where Are You Now	7"	Pye	7N15776	1965	£1.50	£4	chart single
Where Are You Now	7" EP.	Pye	NEP24225	1965	£4	£8	
You Baby	7"	Pye	7N17047	1966	£4	£8	

TRESPASS
Bright Lights	7"	Trial	CASE3	1982	£4	£8	
Jealousy	7"	Trial	CASE2	1980	£4	£8	
One Of These Days	7"	Trial	CASE1	1979	£5	£10	

TREVOR
Down In Virginia	7"	Blue Beat	BB228	1963	£5	£10	
Everyday Like A Holiday	7"	Blue Cat	BS153	1969	£4	£8	with The Maytones

TRIANA
Hyos Del Agobio	LP	Movie Play.	1709079	1977	£8	£20	Spanish
Sombra Y Luz	LP	Movie Play.	1714394	1979	£8	£20	Spanish
Triana	LP	Movie Play.	1706787	1975	£8	£20	Spanish
Un Encuentro	LP	Movie Play.	5506785	1980	£8	£20	Spanish

TRIBAN
Rainmaker	LP	Cambrian		1972	£8	£20	
Triban	LP	Cambrian	MCT592	1969	£8	£20	

TRIBE
Gamma Goochi	7"	Planet	PLF108	1966	£12.50	£25	
Love Is A Beautiful Thing	7"	RCA	RCA1592	1967	£5	£10	

TRIBE (2)
Dancin' To The Beat Of My Heart	7"	Polydor	56510	1970	£5	£10	

TRIBE, TONY
Red Red Wine	7"	Down Town	DT419	1969	£2.50	£6	Rico B side

TRIFFIDS
Lonely Boy	7"	Columbia	DB7177	1963	£2.50	£6	
Lookin' Around	7"	Columbia	DB7084	1963	£4	£8	
So Shy	7"	Columbia	DB7251	1964	£2.50	£6	

TRIFFIDS (2)
Are Really Folk	LP	Fontana	TL5231	1965	£4	£10	

TRIFLE
First Meeting	LP	Dawn	DNLS3017	1971	£8	£20	

TRIKHA, PANDIT KANWAR SAIN
Three Sitar Pieces	LP	Mushroom	100MR7	1970	£20	£40	

TRILOGY
I'm Beginning To Feel It	LP	Mercury	6338034	1970	£5	£12	

TRIO
Trio		LP	London	LTZC15017	1956	£15	£30	
Trio With Guests		LP	London	LTZC15046	1957	£10	£25	

TRIO (2)
In the heady days of the early seventies, the Trio (John Surman, Barre Phillips, and Stu Martin) achieved the remarkable feat of playing uncompromising avant-garde jazz, while gaining a record contract with one of the major record companies. The group even managed a tour of rock venues on the strength of this, yet actually managed to sell very few records, as their scarcity today testifies.

Conflagration		LP	Dawn	DNLS3022	1971	£15	£30	
Trio		LP	Dawn	DNLS3006	1970	£20	£40	double

TRIOS, CHUCK & AMAZING MAZE
Call On You		7"	Action	ACT4517	1968	£2.50	£6	

TRIP
Atlantide		LP	RCA		1972	£30	£60	

TRIPPERS
Dance With Me		7"	Pye	7N25388	1966	£4	£8	

TRIPSICHORD MUSIC BOX
Tripsichord Music Box		LP	Janus		1971	£20	£40	US

TRISTANO, LENNIE
Bebop		LP	Mercury	SMWL21028	1969	£4	£10	with tracks by Red Rodney
Lennie Tristano		LP	London	LTZK15033	1957	£15	£30	
Lines		LP	Atlantic	590031	1969	£4	£10	
New Tristano		LP	Atlantic	590017	1968	£5	£12	

TRISTRAM SHANDY
Tristram Shandy		LP	Silvermore	SIL0001	1979	£5	£12	

TRIUMPH
Rock'n'Roll Machine		LP	Attic	LATX1036	1977	£6	£15	Canadian, vinyl & metal

TRIXIE'S BIG RED MOTORBIKE
Norman And Narcissus		7"	Lobby Ludd	L100001	1984	£2.50	£6	
Splash Of Red		7"	Chew	CH9271	1982	£2.50	£6	
Splash Of Red		7"	Lobby Ludd	L100002	1984	£2	£5	
Trixie's Big Red Motorbike EP		7"	Chew	RAM510	1982	£2.50	£6	
Trixie's Big Red Motorbike EP		7"	Lobby Ludd	L100003	1984	£2	£5	

TRO, MARCUS
Tell Me		7"	Ember	EMBS203	1965	£2	£5	

TROGGS
When the Trogg's "Wild Thing", with its novelty ocarina solo offsetting the Louie Louie riff, climbed to the top of the charts, Jonathan King offered to treat the group to a slap-up meal if they were still in the charts three years later. He lost his bet - but only just. The Trogg's simple hard(ish) rock bordered on the inept, but they had managed to create a considerable affection in the minds of the record collecting public. All the Trogg's original recordings are becoming increasingly sought after, especially the LP "Mixed Bag", which includes the group's over-the-top attempts at psychedelia.

Anyway That You Want Me		7"	Page One	POF010	1966	£1.50	£4	chart single
Anyway That You Want Me		7" EP	Fontana	460987	1966	£10	£20	French
Best Of Vol.1		LP	Page One	FOR001	1967	£8	£20	chart LP
Best Of Vol.2		LP	Page One	FOR002	1967	£8	£20	
Cellophane		LP	Page One	POL003	1967	£15	£30	
Contrasts		LP	DJM	DJML009	1970	£6	£15	
Easy Livin'		7"	Page One	POF164	1970	£1.50	£4	
Every Little Thing		7"	10	TENY21	1984	£1.50	£4	pic disc
Everything's Funny		7"	Pye	7N45147	1970	£1.50	£4	
Evil Woman		7"	Page One	POF114	1969	£1.50	£4	
Feeling For Love		LP	Penny Farthing	PEN929	1977	£1.50	£4	
From Nowhere		LP	Fontana	(S)TL5355	1966	£8	£20	chart LP
Give It To Me		7"	Page One	POF015	1967	£1.50	£4	chart single
Give It To Me		7" EP	Fontana	460203	1967	£10	£20	French
Good Vibrations		7"	Penny Farthing	PEN861	1975	£1.50	£4	
Hi Hi Hazel		7"	Page One	POF030	1967	£1.50	£4	chart single
Hip Hip Hooray		7"	Page One	POF092	1968	£1.50	£4	
I Can't Control Myself		7"	Page One	POF001	1966	£1.50	£4	chart single
I Can't Control Myself		7" EP	Fontana	460981	1966	£10	£20	French
I'll Buy You An Island		7"	Penny Farthing	PEN919	1976	£1.50	£4	
Just A Little Too Much		7"	Raw	RAW25	1978	£2.50	£6	
Lazy Weekend		7"	DJM	DJS248	1971	£1.50	£4	
Listen To The Man		7"	Pye	7N45244	1973	£1.50	£4	
Little Girl		7"	Page One	POF056	1968	£1.50	£4	chart single
Lost Girl		7"	CBS	202038	1966	£7.50	£15	
Love Is All Around		7"	Page One	POF040	1967	£1.50	£4	chart single
Lover		7"	Page One	POF171	1970	£1.50	£4	
Mixed Bag		LP	Page One	POLS012	1968	£40	£80	
My Lady		7"	Page One	POF022	1967	£12.50	£25	
Night Of The Long Grass		7"	Page One	POF022	1967	£1.50	£4	chart single
Night Of The Long Grass		7" EP	Fontana	460212	1967	£10	£20	French
Raver		7"	Page One	POF182	1970	£1.50	£4	
Satisfaction		7"	Penny Farthing	PEN901	1975	£1.50	£4	
Strange Movies		7"	Pye	7N45295	1973	£1.50	£4	
Summertime		7"	Penny Farthing	PEN889	1975	£1.50	£4	
Surprise Surprise		7"	Page One	POF064	1968	£1.50	£4	
Trogg Tapes		LP	Penny Farthing	PELS551	1976	£4	£10	
Trogg Tops Vol.1		7" EP	Page One	POE001	1967	£5	£10	

Trogg Tops Vol.2	7" EP	Page One	POE002	1967	£10	£20	
Trogglodynamite	LP	Page One	POL001	1966	£8	£20	chart LP
Trogglomania	LP	Page One	POS602	1969	£8	£20	
Troggs	LP	Penny Farthing	PEN543	1975	£4	£10	
Troggs Tapes	7"	DJM	DJS6	1981	£5	£10	double
Wild Thing	LP	Fontana	SRF27556	1966	£8	£20	
Wild Thing	7"	Fontana	TF689	1966	£2	£5	chart single
Wild Thing	7" EP	Fontana	460974	1966	£10	£20	French
Wild Thing (Reggae Version)	7"	Penny Farthing	PEN884	1975	£1.50	£4	
With a Girl Like You	7"	Fontana	TF717	1966	£1.50	£4	chart single
With A Girl Like You	7" EP	Fontana	465321	1966	£10	£20	French
You Can Cry If You Want To	7"	Page One	POF082	1968	£1.50	£4	

TROJANS
Man I'm Gonna Be	7"	Decca	F11065	1958	£6	£12	

TROLL
Animated Music	LP	Smash		1968	£8	£20	US

TROLL BROTHERS
You Turn Me On	7"	SRT	SRT733316	197-	£2.50	£6	

TROMBONES INC.
Trombones Inc.	LP	Warner Bros	WM4023/WS8023	1961	£5	£12	

TRONICS
Cantina	7"	Fontana	H348	1961	£4	£8	

TROOPERS
Get Out	7"	Vogue	V9087	1957	£70	£140	

TROTT, ARCHIBALD
Get Together	7"	Black Swan	WI407	1964	£5	£10	

TROTTO
Trotto	LP	Free Reed	FRR005	1976	£5	£12	

TROUBADOURS
Fascination	7"	London	HLR8469	1957	£2.50	£6	
In Spain	LP	London	HAR2095	1958	£4	£10	
Lights Of Paris	7"	London	HLR8541	1958	£2.50	£6	
Troubadours	7" EP	London	RER1135	1958	£2.50	£6	

TROUP, BOBBY
Bobby Troup	7" EP	Capitol	EAP1484	1955	£2.50	£6	
Bobby Troup	10" LP	Capitol	LC6660	1954	£5	£12	
Julie Is Her Name	7"	Capitol	CL14219	1954	£1.50	£4	

TROW, BOB
Soft Squeeze Baby	7"	London	HL8082	1954	£10	£20	

TROWER, ROBIN
Bridge Of Sighs	LP	Chrysalis	CHR1057	1974	£4	£10	
For Earth Below	LP	Chrysalis	CHR1073	1975	£4	£10	
Twice Removed From Yesterday	LP	Chrysalis	CHR1039	1973	£4	£10	

TROY & THE T-BIRDS
Twistle	7"	London	HL9476	1961	£2	£5	

TROY, DORIS
Ain't That Cute	7"	Apple	24	1970	£2.50	£6	
Ain't That Cute	7"	Apple	24	1970	£5	£10	PS
Doris Troy	LP	Apple	SAPCOR13	1970	£8	£20	
Heartaches	7"	Atlantic	AT4032	1965	£2.50	£6	
I'll Do Anything	7"	Cameo Parkway	C101	1962	£20	£40	
I'll Do Anything	7"	Toast	TT507	1968	£2.50	£6	
Jacob's Ladder	7"	Apple	28	1970	£2.50	£6	
Just One Look	LP	Atlantic	(SD)8088	1964	£8	£20	US
Just One Look	7"	Atlantic	584148	1968	£2	£5	
Just One Look	7"	London	HLK9749	1963	£4	£8	
One More Chance	7"	Atlantic	AT4020	1965	£2.50	£6	
Rainbow Testament	LP	Polydor	2956001	1972	£4	£10	
Whatcha Gonna Do About It	7"	Atlantic	AT4011	1964	£4	£8	chart single
Whatcha Gonna Do About It	7" EP	Atlantic	AET6007	1965	£10	£20	

TRUBROT
Undir Ahrifum	LP	Parlophone		1970	£30	£60	Danish

TRUMPETEERS
Milky White Way	LP	Score	4021	1960	£25	£50	US

TRUTH
Baby Don't You Know	7"	Pye	7N15923	1965	£4	£8	
Girl	7"	Pye	7N17035	1966	£2	£5	chart single
I Go To Sleep	7"	Pye	7N17095	1966	£7.50	£15	
Jingle Jangle	7"	Deram	DM105	1966	£10	£20	
Seuno	7"	Decca	F12764	1968	£4	£8	
Walk Away Renee	7"	Decca	F12582	1967	£2.50	£6	
Who's Wrong	7"	Pye	7N15998	1965	£5	£10	

TRUTH & JANEY

Title	Format	Label	Cat. No.	Year			Notes
No Rest For The Wicked	LP	Montrose		1976	£25	£50	US

TRUTH (2)

Title	Format	Label	Cat. No.	Year			Notes
Truth	LP	People		1970	£8	£20	US

TRUTH OF TRUTHS

Title	Format	Label	Cat. No.	Year			Notes
Truth Of Truths	LP	Oak	OR1001	1971	£10	£25	double

TUBB, ERNEST

Title	Format	Label	Cat. No.	Year			Notes
All Time Hits	LP	Decca	DL(7)4046	1961	£5	£12	US
Daddy Of 'Em All	LP	Brunswick	LAT8260	1958	£6	£15	
Daddy Of 'Em All	LP	Decca	DL8553	1956	£8	£20	US
Daddy Of 'Em All Pt.1	7" EP	Brunswick	OE9372	1958	£5	£10	
Daddy Of 'Em All Pt.2	7" EP	Brunswick	OE9373	1958	£5	£10	
Daddy Of 'Em All Pt.3	7" EP	Brunswick	OE9374	1958	£5	£10	
Ernest Tubb Record Shop	LP	Brunswick	LAT8349	1960	£6	£15	
Ernest Tubb Story Vol.1	LP	Brunswick	LAT8313	1959	£5	£12	
Ernest Tubb Story Vol.2	LP	Brunswick	LAT8314	1960	£5	£12	
Favorites	LP	Decca	DL8291	1956	£8	£20	US
Favorites	10" LP	Decca	DL5301	1951	£10	£25	US
Favourites	LP	Brunswick	LAT8161	1957	£6	£15	
Golden Favorites	LP	Decca	DL(7)4118	1961	£5	£12	US
Importance Of Being Ernest	LP	Brunswick	LAT8292	1959	£6	£15	
Jimmie Rodgers Songs	10" LP	Decca	LA8736	1956	£8	£20	
Jimmie Rodgers Songs	10" LP	Decca	DL5336	1951	£10	£25	US
Just Call Me Lonesome	LP	Decca	DL(7)4385	1964	£5	£12	US
Midnight Jamboree	LP	Decca	DL(7)4045	1960	£5	£12	US
Old Rugged Cross	10" LP	Decca	DL5334	1951	£10	£25	US
On Tour	LP	Decca	DL(7)4321	1962	£5	£12	US
Sing A Song Of Christmas	10" LP	Decca	DL5497	1954	£10	£25	US
So Doggone Lonesome	7"	Brunswick	05587	1956	£6	£12	
Thirty Days	7"	Brunswick	05527	1956	£15	£30	
What Am I Living For	7"	Decca	BM31214	195-	£4	£8	export

TUBB, JUSTIN

Title	Format	Label	Cat. No.	Year			Notes
Star Of The Grand Ole Opry	LP	Ember	CW100	1963	£4	£10	
Take A Letter Miss Gray	7" EP	RCA	RCX7133	1964	£7.50	£15	

TUBES

Title	Format	Label	Cat. No.	Year			Notes
Prime Time	7"	A&M	AMS7423	1979	£15	£30	7 x coloured vinyl 7' & pic disc, boxed, promo
Remote Control	LP	A&M	AMLH9964751	1979	£4	£10	Dutch pic disc
Tubes First Clean Album	LP	A&M	SP17012	1978	£6	£15	US promo

TUBEWAY ARMY

Title	Format	Label	Cat. No.	Year			Notes
Are 'Friends' Electric?	7"	Beggars Banquet	BEG18P	1979	£2.50	£6	pic disc, insert
Are 'Friends' Electric?	12"	Intercord	INT126501	1979	£4	£10	German
Bombers	7"	Beggars Banquet	BEG8	1978	£2	£5	
Down In The Park	12"	Beggars Banquet	BEG17T	1979	£5	£12	
That's Too Bad	7"	Beggars Banquet	BEG5	1978	£2	£5	
This Is My Life	7"	Beggars Banquet	TUB1	1985	£12.50	£25	promo
Tubeway Army	LP	Beggars Banquet	BEGA4	1978	£17.50	£35	blue vinyl
Tubeway Army '78-'79 Vol.2	12"	Beggars Banquet	BEG123E	1984	£2.50	£6	red vinyl
Tubeway Army '78-'79 Vol.3	12"	Beggars Banquet	BEG124E	1984	£2.50	£6	blue vinyl

TUCKER, BESSIE

Title	Format	Label	Cat. No.	Year			Notes
Blues By Bessie	7" EP	HMV	7EG8085	1955	£7.50	£15	

TUCKER, BILLY JOE

Title	Format	Label	Cat. No.	Year			Notes
Boogie Woogie Bill	7"	London	HLD9455	1961	£20	£40	

TUCKER, CY

Title	Format	Label	Cat. No.	Year			Notes
Apologise	7"	Fontana	TF470	1964	£1.50	£4	
My Prayer	7"	Fontana	TF424	1963	£1.50	£4	

TUCKER, MAUREEN

Title	Format	Label	Cat. No.	Year			Notes
Playin' Possum	LP	Trash	TLP1001	1981	£5	£12	US

TUCKER, SOPHIE

Title	Format	Label	Cat. No.	Year			Notes
Bigger And Better Than Ever	LP	Mercury	MPL6513	1957	£4	£10	
Cabaret Days	LP	Mercury	MG20046	1954	£5	£12	
Cabaret Days	LP	Mercury	MPL65033	1956	£4	£10	
Great Sophie Tucker	LP	Brunswick	LAT8144	1956	£4	£10	
Latest And Greatest Spicy Saucy Songs	LP	Mercury	MPL6000	1954	£4	£10	
My Dream	LP	Mercury	MG20035	1954	£5	£12	

TUCKER, TOMMY

Title	Format	Label	Cat. No.	Year			Notes
Hi Heel Sneakers	LP	Checker	2990	1964	£10	£25	US
Hi Heel Sneakers	7"	Chess	CRS8086	1969	£2.50	£6	
Hi Heel Sneakers	7"	Pye	7N25238	1964	£4	£8	chart single

Hi Heel Sneakers	7" EP	Pye	NEP44027	1964	£6	£12	
Long Tall Shorty	7"	Pye	7N25246	1964	£4	£8	
Oh What A Feeling	7"	London	HLU9932	1964	£7.50	£15	

TUCKY BUZZARD

Alright On The Night	LP	Purple	TPSA7510	1973	£4	£10	
Buzzard	LP	Purple	TPSA7512	1973	£4	£10	
Coming On Again	LP	Capitol	864	1971	£5	£12	US
Warm Slash	LP	Capitol	EST864	1969	£6	£15	

TUDOR LODGE

Lady's Changing Home	7"	Vertigo	6059044	1971	£7.50	£15	
Tudor Lodge	LP	Vertigo	6360043	1971	£80	£160	

TUDOR MINSTRELS

Family Way	7"	Decca	F12536	1966	£4	£8	

TUESDAY'S CHILDREN

Baby's Gone	7"	Pye	7N17406	1967	£2.50	£6	
High On A Hill	7"	Columbia	DB8018	1966	£5	£10	
In The Valley Of The Shadow Of Love	7"	Pye	7N17474	1968	£1.50	£4	
Strange Light From The East	7"	King	KG1051	1967	£5	£10	
When You Walk In The Sun	7"	Columbia	DB7978	1966	£4	£8	

TULLY, LEE

Around The World With Elwood Pretzel	7"	London	HL8363	1957	£20	£40	gold label

TUNDRA

Kentish Garland	LP	Sweet Folk	SFA078	1978	£5	£12	

TUNEROCKERS

Green Mosquito	7"	London	HLT8717	1958	£10	£20	

TUNETOPPERS

At The Madison Dance Party	LP	Amy	A1	1960	£8	£20	US

TUNEWEAVERS

Happy Happy Birthday Baby	7"	London	HL8503	1957	£30	£60	B side by Paul Gayter

TUNNEY, PADDY

Flowery Vale	LP	Topic	12TS289	1976	£5	£12	
Ireland Her Own	LP	Topic	12T153	1966	£5	£12	with other artists
Irish Edge	LP	Topic	12T165	1966	£8	£20	
Wild Bees Nest	LP	Topic	12T139	1965	£8	£20	

TURNER, BRUCE

Bruce Turner	10" LP	Polygon	JTL2	1955	£15	£30	

TURNER, DENNIS

Lover Please	7"	London	HL9537	1962	£1.50	£4	

TURNER, GORDON

Meditation	LP	Charisma	CAS1009	1969	£8	£20	

TURNER, IKE & TINA

Anything I Wasn't Born With	7"	HMV	POP1544	1966	£6	£12	
Come Together	7"	Liberty	LBF15303	1970	£1.50	£4	
Crazy 'Bout You Baby	7"	Liberty	LIB15233	1969	£2.50	£6	
Dance With Ike & Tina Turner	LP	Sue	LP2003	1962	£15	£30	US
Don't Play Me Cheap	LP	Sue	LP2005	1963	£15	£30	US
Dynamite	LP	Sue	LP2004	1963	£15	£30	US
Finger Poppin'	7"	Warner Bros	WB153	1965	£2.50	£6	
Fool In Love	7"	London	HLU9226	1960	£4	£8	
Goodbye So Long	7"	Stateside	SS551	1966	£2	£5	
Greatest Hits	LP	London	HAC8248	1965	£6	£15	
Greatest Hits	LP	Sue	LP1038	1965	£10	£25	US
Hunter	LP	Harvest	SHSP4001	1970	£10	£25	
Hunter	7"	Harvest	HAR5018	1970	£2.50	£6	
I Can't Believe What You Say	7"	Sue	WI350	1964	£6	£12	
I Want To Take You Higher	7"	Liberty	LBF15367	1970	£1.50	£4	
Ike & Tina Turner Revue	LP	Ember	EMB3368	1966	£4	£10	
Ike & Tina Turner Show II	LP	Warner Bros	WB5904	1967	£4	£10	
Ike & Tina Turner Show Vol.1	7" EP	Warner Bros	WEP619	1965	£10	£20	
Ike And Tina Turner Show	LP	Warner Bros	W1579	1966	£4	£10	
Ike And Tina Turner Show	LP	Warner Bros	WM8170	1965	£6	£15	
I'll Never Need More Than This	7"	London	HLU10155	1967	£1.50	£4	
I'm Gonna Do All I Can	7"	Minit	MLF11016	1969	£4	£8	
I'm Hooked	7"	HMV	POP1583	1967	£7.50	£15	
In Person	LP	Minit	MLS40014	1969	£5	£12	
It's Gonna Work Out Fine	LP	Sue	LP2007	1963	£15	£30	US
It's Gonna Work Out Fine	7"	London	HL9451	1961	£5	£10	
It's Gonna Work Out Fine	7"	Sue	WI306	1964	£5	£10	
Love Like Yours	7"	London	HLU10083	1966	£1.50	£4	chart singl
Make Em Wait	7"	A&M	AMS783	1970	£4	£8	
Please Please Please	7"	Sue	WI376	1965	£5	£10	
Poor Fool	7"	Sue	WI322	1964	£5	£10	
Proud Mary	7"	Liberty	LBF15432	1970	£1.50	£4	chart L
River Deep & Mountain High	LP	London	HAU/SHU8298	1966	£6	£15	
River Deep & Mountain High	LP	Philles	PHLP4011	1966	£840	£1200	US, no cove
River Deep Mountain High	7"	A&M	AMS829	1971	£1.50	£4	

River Deep Mountain High	7"	London	HLU10046	1966	£2	£5	chart single
So Fine	LP	London	HAU/SHU8370	1969	£4	£10	
So Fine	7"	London	HLU10189	1968	£1.50	£4	
Somebody	7"	Warner Bros	WB5766	1966	£6	£12	
Somebody Needs You	7" EP	Warner Bros	WEP620	1966	£10	£20	
Soul Of Ike & Tina Turner	7" EP	Sue	IEP706	1966	£40	£80	
Sound Of Ike & Tina Turner	LP	Sue	LP2001	1961	£20	£40	US
Tell Her I'm Not At Home	7"	Warner Bros	WB5753	1966	£1.50	£4	chart single
We Need An Understanding	7"	London	HLU10217	1968	£1.50	£4	

TURNER, JESSE LEE
Do I Worry	7"	Top Rank	JAR516	1960	£5	£10	
I'm The Little Space Girl's Father	7"	London	HLP9108	1960	£7.50	£15	
Shake Baby Shake	7"	London	HLL8785	1959	£20	£40	
Teenage Misery	7"	Top Rank	JAR303	1960	£6	£12	
Voice Changing Song	7"	Vogue	V9201	1962	£5	£10	

TURNER, JOE
Best Of Joe Turner	LP	Atlantic	8081	1963	£10	£25	US
Big Joe Is Here	LP	London	HAE2231	1960	£25	£50	
Big Joe Rides Again	LP	London	LTZK15205/SAHK6123	1960	£30	£60	
Boogie Woogie Country Girl	7"	London	HLE8332	1956	£180	£300	
Boss Of The Blues	LP	Atlantic	590006	1967	£4	£10	
Boss Of The Blues	LP	London	LTZK15053/SAHK6019	1957/1959	£30	£60	
Careless Love	LP	Savoy	MG14106	1963	£8	£20	US
Corrine Corrina	7"	London	HLE8301	1956	£100	£200	
Honey Hush	7"	London	HLE9055	1960	£15	£30	
Joe Turner	LP	Atlantic	8005	1957	£30	£60	US
Joe Turner & Pete Johnson	LP	EmArcy	36014	1955	£30	£60	US
Joe Turner & Pete Johnson Group	7" EP	Emarcy	ERE1500	1956	£15	£30	
Joe Turner & The Blues	LP	Savoy	MG14012	1962	£8	£20	US
Jumpin' The Blues	LP	Fontana	688802ZL	1965	£5	£12	
Kansas City Jazz	LP	Atlantic	1243	1956	£30	£60	US
Lipstick Powder And Paint	7"	London	HLE8357	1957	£180	£300	gold label
Mardi Gras Boogie	78	MGM	MGM253	1949	£6	£12	
Midnight Cannonball	7"	Atlantic	AT4026	1965	£6	£12	
My Little Honeydripper	7"	London	HLK9119	1960	£15	£30	
Presenting Joe Turner	7" EP	London	REE1111	1957	£25	£50	tri-centre
Rockin' The Blues	LP	London	HAE2173	1959	£30	£60	
Singing The Blues	LP	Stateside	(S)SL10226	1967	£5	£12	
Stride By Stride	LP	77	LEU1232	1964	£6	£15	double

TURNER, MEL
Doing The Ton	7"	Columbia	DB7076	1963	£1.50	£4	
Don't Cry	7"	Columbia	DB4963	1963	£2	£5	
Let Me Hold Your Hand	7"	Melodisc	1580	1964	£1.50	£4	
Mohican Crawl	7"	Carnival	CV7003	1963	£1.50	£4	
Swing Low Sweet Chariot	7"	Columbia	DB4791	1962	£2	£5	
Welcome Home Little Darlin'	7"	Island	WI276	1966	£4	£8	
What's The Matter With Me	7"	Carnival	CV7005	1963	£1.50	£4	

TURNER, NIK
Maximum Effect	LP	Avatar	AALP5004	1982	£4	£10	
New Anatomy	LP	Demi Monde	DM001	1985	£4	£10	
Pass Out	LP	Riddle	RID002	1980	£6	£15	
President's Tapes	LP	Flicknife	SHARP031	1985	£4	£10	
Punkadelia	LP	Flicknife	SHARP103	1982	£4	£10	
Xitintoday	LP	Charisma	CDS4011	1978	£4	£10	
Xitintoday	LP	Charisma	CDS4011	1978	£8	£20	with booklet

TURNER, NIK & ROBERT CALVERT
Ersatz	LP	Pompadour	POMP001	1982	£8	£20	

TURNER, SAMMY
Always	7"	London	HLX8963	1959	£4	£8	chart single
Lavender Blue	7"	London	HLX8918	1959	£5	£10	
Lavender Blue Moods	LP	London	HAX2246	1960	£17.50	£35	
Paradise	7"	London	HLX9062	1960	£2.50	£6	
Raincoat In The River	7"	London	HLX9488	1962	£6	£12	

TURNER, SPYDER
Stand By Me	LP	MGM	(S)E4450	1967	£6	£15	US
Stand By Me	7"	MGM	MGM1332	1967	£6	£12	

TURNER, TINA
Break Every Rule	7"	Capitol	CLP452	1987	£1.50	£4	pic disc
Help	7"	Capitol	CLP325	1984	£1.50	£4	pic disc
We Don't Need Another Hero	7"	Capitol	CLP364	1985	£1.50	£4	pic disc

TURNER, TITUS
Miss Rubberneck Jones	7"	Blue Beat	BB32	1961	£5	£10	
Tony Train	7"	Oriole	CB1611	1961	£6	£12	
Sound Off	LP	Jamie	JLP(70)3018	1961	£10	£25	US
Sound Off	7"	Parlophone	R4746	1961	£7.50	£15	
We Told You Not To Marry	7"	London	HLU9024	1960	£7.50	£15	

TURNQUIST REMEDY
Turnquist Remedy	LP	Pentagram			£8	£20	US

TURNSTILE

Don't Think We Can Make It	7"	Pye	7N45605	1976	£25	£50
Once More From The Top	7"	Pye	7N46056	1978	£25	£50
Riding A Wave	7"	Pye	7N17653	1968	£25	£50

TURQUOISE

53 Summer Street	7"	Decca	F12756	1968	£10	£20
Woodstock	7"	Decca	F12842	1968	£10	£20

TURRENTINE, STANLEY

Always Something There	LP	Blue Note	BST84298	1968	£5	£12
Another Story	LP	Blue Note	BST84336	1970	£5	£12
Blue Hour	LP	Blue Note	BLP/BST84057	1964	£15	£30
Chip Off The Old Block	LP	Blue Note	BLP/BST84150	1965	£10	£25
Common Touch	LP	Blue Note	BST84315	1969	£5	£12
Dearly Beloved	LP	Blue Note	BLP/BST84081	1964	£10	£25
Easy Walker	LP	Blue Note	BLP/BST84268	1967	£8	£20
Hustlin'	LP	Blue Note	BLP/BST84162	1965	£10	£25
Joyride	LP	Blue Note	BLP/BST84201	1966	£8	£20
Look Of Love	LP	Blue Note	BST84286	1968	£5	£12
Look Out!	LP	Blue Note	BLP/BST84039	1961	£15	£30
Never Let Me Go	LP	Blue Note	BLP/BST84129	1964	£10	£25
Never Let Me Go	7"	Blue Note	451894	1964	£2	£5
Rough 'n Tumble	LP	Blue Note	BLP/BST84240	1966	£8	£20
Spoiler	LP	Blue Note	BLP/BST84256	1967	£6	£15
That's Where It's At	LP	Blue Note	BLP/BST84096	1962	£10	£25
Tiger Tail	LP	Fontana	TL5300	1966	£5	£12
Up At Minton's	LP	Blue Note	BLP/BST84069	1962	£15	£30
Up At Minton's Part 2	LP	Blue Note	BLP/BST84070	1964	£15	£30

TURTLES

Battle Of The Bands	LP	London	HAU/SHU8376	1968	£5	£12	
Can I Get To Know You Better	7"	London	HLU10095	1966	£1.50	£4	
Elenore	7"	London	HLU10223	1968	£1.50	£4	chart single
Golden Hits	LP	White Whale	(S7)115	1967	£5	£12	US
Happy Together	LP	London	HAU8330	1967	£6	£15	chart LP
Happy Together	7"	London	HLU10115	1967	£1.50	£4	chart single
Happy Together	7" EP	London	REU10185	1966	£6	£12	French
It Ain't Me Babe	LP	White Whale	(S7)111	1965	£6	£15	US
It Ain't Me Babe	7"	Pye	7N25320	1965	£2	£5	
It Ain't Me Babe	7" EP	Polydor	27770	1965	£6	£12	French
It Ain't Me Babe	7" EP	Pye	NEP44089	1967	£6	£12	
Let Me Be	7"	Pye	7N25341	1966	£2	£5	
Let Me Be	7"	Pye	7N25421	1967	£1.50	£4	
Let Me Be	7" EP	Polydor	27780	1966	£6	£12	French
Love In The City	7"	London	HLU10291	1969	£1.50	£4	
More Golden Hits	LP	White Whale	WW7127	1970	£4	£10	US
She'd Rather Be With Me	7"	London	HLU10135	1967	£1.50	£4	chart single
She'd Rather Be With Me	7" EP	London	REU10189	1966	£6	£12	French
She's My Girl	7"	London	HLU10168	1967	£1.50	£4	
Sound Asleep	7"	London	HLU10184	1968	£1.50	£4	
Story Of Rock And Roll	7"	London	HLU10207	1968	£1.50	£4	
Turtle Soup	LP	White Whale	S7124	1969	£5	£12	US
Wooden Head	LP	White Whale	WW7133	1971	£5	£12	US
You Baby	LP	White Whale	(S7)112	1966	£6	£15	US
You Baby	7"	Immediate	IM031	1966	£4	£8	
You Don't Have To Walk In The Rain	7"	London	HLU10279	1969	£1.50	£4	
You Know What I Mean	7"	London	HLU10153	1967	£1.50	£4	
You Showed Me	7"	London	HLU10251	1969	£1.50	£4	

TUSHINGHAM, RITA & LYNN REDGRAVE

Smashing Time	7"	Stateside	SS2081	1968	£1.50	£4

TU-TONES

Still In Love With You	7"	London	HLW8904	1959	£30	£60

TUTTLE, WESLEY & MARILYN

Jim, Johnny And Jonas	7"	Capitol	CL14291	1955	£1.50	£4

T.V. & THE TRIBESMEN

Barefootin'	7"	Pye	7N25375	1966	£6	£12

TV 21

Ambition	7"	Powbeat	AAARGH!2	1980	£5	£10
Playing With Fire	7"	Powbeat	AAARGH!1	1980	£4	£8

TV PRODUCT

Nowhere's Safe	7"	Limited Edition	TAKE3	1979	£2	£5 ... B side by the Pratt

TWARDZIK, RICHARD

Last Set	LP	Vogue	LAE12117	1959	£8	£20 ... with track by Russ Freeman

TWELFTH NIGHT

First 7' Album	7"	Twelfth Night	TN001	1980	£2.50	£6
Live At The Target	LP	Twelfth Night	TN002	1981	£4	£10

TWENTIETH CENTURY ZOO

Thunder On A Clear Day	LP	Vault		1965	£8	£20 ... US

TWENTY SEVEN DOLLAR SNAP ON FACE
Heterodyne State Hospital	LP	Heterodyne		1977	£15	£30	US, blue vinyl

TWENTY SIXTY-SIX AND THEN
Reflections Of The Future	LP	United Artists	UAS29314	1972	£50	£100	

TWENTY-FIVE RIFLES
World War Three	12"	25 Rifles	TFR1	1979	£2.50	£6	

TWENTY-THIRD TURNOFF
Michael Angelo	7"	Deram	DM150	1967	£15	£30	

23 SKIDOO
Ethics	7"	Pineapple	PULP23	1981	£2	£5	
Last Words	7"	Fetish	FE10	1981	£2	£5	no PS

TWICE AS MUCH
Crystal Ball	7"	Immediate	IM042	1967	£4	£8	
Own Up	LP	Immediate	IMLP/IMSP007	1966	£6	£15	
Sittin' On A Fence	7"	Immediate	IM033	1966	£2	£5	chart single
Step Out Of Line	7"	Immediate	IM036	1966	£2	£5	
That's All	LP	Immediate	IMSP013	1968	£6	£15	
True Story	7"	Immediate	IM039	1966	£2.50	£6	
True Story	7" EP	Columbia	ESRF1818	1966	£10	£20	French

TWIGGY
Beautiful Dreams	7"	Ember	EMBS239	1966	£4	£8	
Beautiful Dreams	7"	Ember	EMBS239	1966	£6	£12	PS
Beautiful Dreams	7" EP	Pathe	EGF966	1966	£7.50	£15	French

TWIGGY & ANNIE
Some Do, Some Don't	7"	Columbia	DB7799	1966	£1.50	£4	

TWILIGHT ZONERZ
Zero Zero One EP	7"	Zip/Dining Out.	ZEROZERO1	1979	£2.50	£6	many different sleeves

TWILIGHTS
Cathy Come Home	7"	Columbia	DB8396	1968	£6	£12	
Needle In A Haystack	7"	Columbia	DB8065	1966	£6	£12	
What's Wrong With The Way	7"	Columbia	DB8125	1967	£4	£8	

TWILIGHTS (2)
Take What I Got	7"	London	HLU9992	1965	£5	£10	

TWIN TONES
Jo Ann	7"	RCA	RCA1040	1958	£12.50	£25	

TWIN TUNES QUINTET
Baby Lover	7"	RCA	RCA1046	1958	£2	£5	

TWINK
Think Pink	LP	Polydor	2343032	1970	£30	£60	
Think Pink	LP	Polydor	2343032	1970	£35	£70	pink vinyl

TWINKLE
End Of The World	7"	Decca	F12305	1965	£1.50	£4	
Golden Lights	7"	Decca	F12076	1965	£1.50	£4	chart single
Golden Lights	7" EP	Decca	457059	1965	£7.50	£15	French
Lonely Singing Doll	7" EP	Decca	457077	1965	£7.50	£15	French
Lonely Singing Doll	7" EP	Decca	DFE8621	1965	£7.50	£15	
Micky	7"	Instant	IN005	1969	£2.50	£6	
Poor Old Johnny	7"	Decca	F12219	1965	£1.50	£4	
Terry	7"	Decca	F12013	1964	£2	£5	chart single
Tommy	7"	Decca	F12139	1965	£2	£5	
What Am I Doing Here With You	7"	Decca	F12464	1966	£1.50	£4	

TWINS
Teenagers Love The Twins	LP	RCA	LPM1708	1958	£8	£20	US

TWINSET
Tremblin'	7"	Decca	F12629	1967	£4	£8	

TWIRL, TOBY
Harry Faversham	7"	Decca	F12728	1968	£7.50	£15	
Movin' In	7"	Decca	F12867	1969	£6	£12	
Toffee Apple Sunday	7"	Decca	F12804	1968	£10	£20	

TWIST
This Is Your Life	LP	Polydor	2383552	1979	£6	£15	

TWISTED ACE
Firebird	7"	Heavy Metal	HEAVY9	1981	£4	£8	

TWISTED SISTER
Come Out And Play	LP	Atlantic	7812751P	1985	£4	£10	pic disc
Kids Are Back	7"	Atlantic	A9827P	1983	£2	£5	shaped pic disc
Ruff Cuts	12"	Secret	SHH13712	1982	£2.50	£6	

TWISTERS
Doin' The Twist	LP	Treasure	TLP890	1962	£6	£15	US
Peppermint Twist Time	7"	Windsor	PSA106	1962	£2.50	£6	

Turn The Page	7"	Capitol	CL15167	1960	£1.50	£4	

TWISTIN' KINGS

The Twistin' Kings are not a well-known name, and their music is not in the label's usual house style, but "Twistin' The World Around" just happens to be the first album release on the Motown label.

Twistin' The World Around	LP	Motown	MLP601	1960	£50	£100	US, sleeve pictured in Guide

TWITTY, CONWAY

C'Est Si Bon	7"	MGM	MGM1118	1961	£1.50	£4	chart single
Comfy 'n' Cozy	7"	MGM	MGM1170	1962	£2	£5	
Conway Twitty Sings	LP	MGM	C781	1959	£20	£40	
Conway Twitty Touch	LP	MGM	(S)E3943	1961	£15	£30	US
Darling You Know I Wouldn't Lie	LP	MCA	MUPS386	1969	£4	£10	
Go On And Cry	7"	HMV	POP1258	1963	£1.50	£4	
Greatest Hits	LP	MGM	(S)E3849	1960	£10	£25	US
Greatest Hits	LP	MGM	(S)E3849	1960	£25	£50	US, with poster
Handy Man	7"	MGM	MGM1201	1963	£2.50	£6	
Here's Conway Twitty	LP	MCA	MUP(S)342	1968	£5	£12	
Hey Little Lucy	7"	MGM	MGM1016	1959	£1.50	£4	
Hey Little Lucy	7" EP	MGM	MGMEP698	1959	£15	£30	
Hit The Road	LP	MGM	(S)E4217	1964	£6	£15	US
Hurt In My Heart	7"	MGM	MGM1066	1960	£1.50	£4	
I Love You More Today	LP	MCA	MUPS404	1970	£4	£10	
I Need Your Lovin'	7" EP	Mercury	ZEP10069	1960	£45	£90	
Is A Bluebird Blue	7"	MGM	MGM1082	1960	£1.50	£4	chart single
Is A Bluebird Blue	7" EP	MGM	MGMEP738	1960	£12.50	£25	
It's Drivin' Me Wild	7"	MGM	MGM1137	1961	£2	£5	
It's Only Make Believe	7"	MGM	MGM992	1958	£1.50	£4	chart single
It's Only Make Believe	7" EP	MGM	MGMEP684	1958	£15	£30	
Lonely Blue Boy	LP	MGM	C829	1960	£20	£40	
Lonely Blue Boy	7"	MGM	MGM1056	1960	£2	£5	
Mona Lisa	7"	MGM	MGM1029	1959	£1.50	£4	chart single
Next In Line	LP	MCA	MUPS363	1969	£5	£12	
Next Kiss	7"	MGM	MGM1129	1961	£1.50	£4	
Pick-Up	7"	MGM	MGM1187	1962	£2.50	£6	
Portrait Of A Fool	LP	MGM	(S)E4019	1962	£8	£20	US
R & B '63	LP	MGM	C950	1963	£10	£25	
Rock And Roll Story	LP	MGM	(S)E3907	1961	£10	£25	US
Rock And Roll Story	LP	MGM	C(S)8100	1968	£8	£20	
Rock And Roll Story	7" EP	MGM	MGMEP752	1961	£15	£30	
Rosaleena	7"	MGM	MGM1047	1959	£1.50	£4	
Saturday Night With Conway	LP	MGM	C801	1959	£20	£40	
Saturday Night With Conway	7" EP	MGM	MGMEP719	1960	£15	£30	
Shake It Up	78	Mercury	MT173	1957	£15	£30	
She Ain't No Angel	7"	MGM	MGM1209	1963	£2.50	£6	
Story Of My Love	7"	MGM	MGM1003	1959	£1.50	£4	chart single
Tell Me One More Time	7"	MGM	MGM1095	1960	£1.50	£4	
To See My Angel Cry	LP	MCA	MUPS412	1970	£4	£10	
Tower Of Tears	7"	MGM	MGM1152	1962	£2	£5	
Whole Lotta Shakin' Goin' On	7"	MGM	MGM1108	1960	£2.50	£6	

TWO AND A HALF

I Don't Need To Tell You	7"	Decca	F22715	1967	£5	£10	
Suburban Early Morning Station	7"	Decca	F22672	1967	£6	£12	

TWO KINGS

Hit You Let You Feel It	7"	Island	WI249	1965	£5	£10	
Rolling Stone	7"	Island	WI240	1965	£5	£10	

TWO MUCH

It's A Hip Hip Hippy World	7"	Fontana	TF900	1968	£1.50	£4	
Wonderland Of Love	7"	Fontana	TF858	1967	£1.50	£4	

TWO NINETEEN SKIFFLE GROUP

Two Nineteen Skiffle Group	7" EP	Esquire	EP126	1957	£6	£12	
Two Nineteen Skiffle Group	7" EP	Esquire	EP146	1957	£6	£12	
Two Nineteen Skiffle Group	7" EP	Esquire	EP176	1958	£6	£12	
Two Nineteen Skiffle Group	7" EP	Esquire	EP196	1958	£10	£20	

TWO OF CLUBS

Angel Must Have Made You	7"	Columbia	DB7371	1964	£1.50	£4	
Walk Tall	7"	President	PT124	1968	£1.50	£4	

TWO OF EACH

Every Single Day	7"	Decca	F12626	1967	£1.50	£4	

TWO SMITH BROTHERS

Cherry Wine	7"	Decca	F11578	1963	£1.50	£4	

TYE, ARLYNE

Universe	7"	London	HLL8825	1959	£5	£10	

TYLER, BIG T

King Kong	7"	Vogue	V9079	1957	£60	£120	

TYLER, FRANKIE

This was a pseudonym used by Frankie Valli, lead singer with the Four Lovers - later the Four Seasons.

I Go Ape	7"	OKeh	7103	1958	£30	£60	US

TYLER, JIMMY
Fool 'Em Devil .... 7" ...... Parlophone..... MSP6215.............. 1956 ... £4 ....£8 ....

TYLER, RED
Junk Village .... 7" ...... Top Rank .... JAR306.............. 1960 ... £4 ....£8 ....
Rockin' And Rollin' .... LP ...... Ace .... LP1006.............. 1960 ... £10 ....£25 .... US

TYLER, TERRY
Thousand Feet Below .... 7" ...... Pye...... 7N25119.............. 1961 ... £1.50 ....£4 ....

TYLER, T.TEXAS
Country Round Up .... 7" EP.. Parlophone.. GEP8788 .... 1959 ... £7.50 ....£15 ....
Deck Of Cards .... LP ...... Sound .... 607.............. 1958 ... £10 ....£25 .... US
Great Texan .... LP ...... King .... 686.............. 1960 ... £8 ....£20 .... US
Man With A Million Friends ...... LP ...... London ...... HAB8322 .... 1967 ... £5 ....£12 ....
Songs Along The Way .... LP ...... King .... 734.............. 1961 ... £8 ....£20 .... US
T.Texas Tyler .... LP ...... King .... 664.............. 1959 ... £8 ....£20 .... US
T.Texas Tyler .... LP ...... King .... 721.............. 1961 ... £8 ....£20 .... US

TYMES
Come With Me To The Sea .... 7" ...... Cameo Parkway P884 .... 1963 ... £2 ....£5 ....
Come With Me To The Sea .... 7" ...... Cameo Parkway P884 .... 1963 ... £6 ....£12 .... PS
Here She Comes .... 7" ...... Cameo Parkway P924 .... 1964 ... £25 ....£50 ....
If You Love Me Baby .... 7" ...... Direction 584450 .... 1969 ... £1.50 ....£4 ....
Magic Of Our Summer Love ...... 7" ...... Cameo Parkway P919 .... 1964 ... £2 ....£5 ....
People .... 7" ...... Direction 583903 .... 1968 ... £1.50 ....£4 ....
So Much In Love .... LP ...... Cameo P7032 .... 1963 ... £8 ....£20 ....
So Much In Love .... 7" ...... Cameo Parkway P871 .... 1963 ... £2 ....£5 ....chart single
Somewhere .... LP ...... Parkway P7039 .... 1964 ... £6 ....£15 .... US
Somewhere .... 7" ...... Cameo Parkway P891 .... 1964 ... £2 ....£5 ....
Sound Of Wonderful Tymes .... LP ...... Parkway P7038 .... 1963 ... £6 ....£15 .... US
To Each His Own .... 7" ...... Cameo Parkway P908 .... 1964 ... £2 ....£5 ....
Twelfth Of Never .... 7" ...... Cameo Parkway P933 .... 1964 ... £4 ....£8 ....

TYNER, MCCOY
Expansions .... LP ...... Blue Note....... BST84338.............. 1969 ... £5 ....£12 ....
Inception .... LP ...... HMV .... CLP1638.............. 1962 ... £5 ....£12 ....
Real McCoy .... LP ...... Blue Note....... BLP/BST84264 ...... 1967 ... £6 ....£15 ....
Tender Moments .... LP ...... Blue Note....... BST84275.............. 1968 ... £5 ....£12 ....
Time For Tyner .... LP ...... Blue Note....... BST84307.............. 1969 ... £5 ....£12 ....

TYNER, ROBIN & THE RODS
Till The Night Is Gone .... 7" ...... Island .... WIP6418.............. 1977 ... £1.50 ....£4 ....

TYPHOONS
Needles And Pins .... 7" EP.. Festival .... FX451384 ...... 196- .... £6 ....£12 ....French

TYRANNOSAURUS REX
Tyrannosaurus Rex was originally a duo consisting of Marc Bolan on vocals and acoustic guitar, and Steve Peregrine Took on bongos - the style of their acoustic music being determined less by a burning desire to create modern folk music than by the fact that they had all their electric equipment stolen just as they were starting out. The duo did have a very distinctive sound, although this became considerably diluted once they began to expand the line-up and switched the electricity back on.
Beard Of Stars .... LP ...... Regal Zonophone SLRZ1013.............. 1970 ... £15 ....£30 ... with insert, chart LP
By The Light Of A Magical Moon ...... 7" ...... Regal Zonophone RZ3025 .... 1970 ... £15 ....£30 ....
Debora .... 7" ...... Magnifly ECHO102.............. 1972 £2.50 ....£6 .... PS
Debora .... 7" ...... Regal Zonophone RZ3008 .... 1968 ... £10 ....£20 ....
Debora .... 7" ...... Regal Zonophone RZ3008 .... 1968 ... £150 .....£250 .... PS
King Of The Rumbling Spires ...... 7" ...... Regal Zonophone RZ3022 .... 1969 ... £15 ....£30 ....
King Of The Rumbling Spires ...... 7" ...... Regal Zonophone RZ3022 .... 1969 ... £150 .....£250 .... PS
My People Were Fair... .... LP ...... Regal Zonophone LRZ1003 .... 1968 ... £17.50 ....£35 ....with insert, mono
My People Were Fair... .... LP ...... Regal Zonophone SLRZ1003.............. 1968 ... £15 ....£30 ....with insert, chart LP, Sleeve Pictured in Guide
My People Were Fair.../Prophets, Seers... ...... LP ...... Cube TOOFA3/4 ...... 1972 ... £6 ....£15 ... double, chart LP
One Inch Rock .... 7" ...... Regal Zonophone RZ3011 .... 1968 ... £12.50 ....£25 ....
One Inch Rock .... 7" ...... Regal Zonophone RZ3011 .... 1968 ... £150 .....£250 .... PS
Pewter Suitor .... 7" ...... Regal Zonophone RZ3016 .... 1969 ... £15 ....£30 ....
Prophets, Seers And Sages ...... LP ...... Regal Zonophone LRZ1005 .... 1968 ... £17.50 ....£35 ....mono, with insert

843

Prophets,Seers,and Sages	LP	Regal Zonophone	SLRZ1005	1968	£15	£30	stereo, with insert
Unicorn	LP	Regal Zonophone	LRZ1007	1969	£17.50	£35	mono
Unicorn	LP	Regal Zonophone	SLRZ1007	1969	£15	£30	stereo, chart LP
Unicorn/Beard Of Stars	LP	Cube	TOOFA9/10	1972	£6	£15	double

TYTAN

Blind Men And Fools	7"	Kamaflage	KAM6	1982	£1.50	£4	
Blind Men And Fools	12"	Kamaflage	KAMA6	1982	£2.50	£6	

TZUKE & PAXO

Tzuke and Paxo are Judie Tzuke and her writing partner, Mike Paxman.

These Are The Laws	7"	Good Earth	GD12	1976	£15	£30	

TZUKE, JUDIE

Stay With Me Till Dawn	7"	Rocket	XPRES17	1979	£2.50	£6	PS

U

U2

Title	Format	Label	Cat. No.	Year	Price	Price	Notes
11 O'Clock Tick Tock	7"	CBS	8687	1980	£15	£30	Irish, yellow vinyl
11 O'Clock Tick Tock	7"	Island	WIP6601	1980	£4	£8	
4 U2 Play	7"	CBS	PAC1	1982	£20	£40	Irish, 4-pack
4 U2 Play	7"	CBS	PAC1	1982	£75	£150	Irish, 4-pack, coloured vinyl
All I Want Is You	Island		IS422	1989	£1.50	£4	in tin box
Another Day	7"	CBS	8306	1980	£12.50	£25	Irish
Another Day	7"	CBS	8306	1980	£15	£30	Irish, yellow or orange vinyl
Another Day	7"	CBS	8306	1980	£25	£50	white vinyl
Celebration	7"	Island	WIP6770	1982	£7.50	£15	chart single
Day Without Me	7"	Island	WIP6630	1980	£5	£10	
Fire	7"	Island	UWIP6679	1981	£6	£12	double
Fire	7"	Island	WIP6679	1981	£1.50	£4	chart single
Gloria	7"	Island	WIP6733	1981	£2	£5	chart single
I Still Haven't Found What I'm Looking For	CD-s	Island	CID328	1987	£10	£25	
I Will Follow	7"	CBS	9065	1980	£12.50	£25	Irish, yellow vinyl
I Will Follow	7"	Island	9065	1980	£15	£30	Irish, white vinyl
I Will Follow	7"	Island	WIP6656	1980	£5	£10	
Joshua Tree	7"	Island		1987	£25	£50	box set, 5 x 7'
Lemon	12"	Island		199-	£30	£60	promo double
New Year's Day	7"	Island	UWIP6848	1983	£2.50	£6	double
New Year's Day	7"	Island	WIP6848	1983	£2.50	£6	B side plays Martha Reeves
Night And Day	12"	Island	RHB1	1985	£30	£60	promo
Out Of Control (U2:3)	cass	CBS	40-7951	1985	£3	£8	Irish
Out Of Control (U2:3)	7"	CBS	7951	1979	£7.50	£15	Irish
Out Of Control (U2:3)	7"	CBS	7951	1979	£50	£100	Irish, brown vinyl
Out Of Control (U2:3)	7"	CBS	7951	1979	£15	£30	Irish, orange vinyl
Out Of Control (U2:3)	7"	CBS	7951	1979	£25	£50	Irish, white vinyl
Out Of Control (U2:3)	7"	CBS	7951	1979	£15	£30	Irish, yellow vinyl
Out Of Control (U2:3)	12"	CBS	127951	1979	£6	£15	Irish
Out Of Control (U2:3)	12"	CBS	127951	1979	£50	£100	Irish, numbered
PAC2	7"	CBS	PAC2		£12.50	£25	Irish, 4-pack
PAC3	7"	CBS	PAC3		£10	£20	Irish, 4-pack
Pride	cass-s	Island	CIS202	1984	£2.50	£6	
Pride	7"	Island	ISD202	1984	£2	£5	double
Pride	7"	Island	ISP202	1984	£7.50	£15	pic disc
Pride	12"	Island	ISX202	1984	£4	£10	5 tracks
Rattle And Hum	LP	Island	U27	1988	£50	£100	studio versions of 2 live tracks
Salome	12"	Island		199-	£25	£50	promo
Two Hearts Beat As One	7"	Island	ISD109	1983	£2.50	£6	double
Two Sides Live	LP	Warner Bros		1981	£50	£100	US promo
Under A Blood Red Sky	LP	Island	IMA3	1983	£25	£50	red vinyl
Under A Blood Red Sky	LP	Island	US1PR	1983	£10	£25	promo with interviews
Unforgettable Fire	7"	Island	ISD220	1985	£2	£5	double
Unforgettable Fire	7"	Island	ISP220	1985	£10	£20	shaped pic disc
War	LP	Island	ILPS9733	1983	£25	£50	pic disc
Where The Streets Have No Name	CD-s	Island	CID340	1987	£2.50	£6	
With Or Without You	CD-s	Island	CID319	1987	£2.50	£6	
Zoo Station	12"	Island		1992	£40	£80	promo pic disc

UB40

Title	Format	Label	Cat. No.	Year	Price	Price	Notes
UB44	LP	Dep International	LPDEP3	1982	£4	£10	hologram sleeve

UFO

Title	Format	Label	Cat. No.	Year	Price	Price	Notes
Boogie For George	7"	Beacon	BEA172	1971	£2.50	£6	
Come Away Melinda	7"	Beacon	BEA165	1971	£2.50	£6	
Flying	LP	Beacon	BES19	1972	£5	£12	
Prince Kajuki	7"	Beacon	BEA181	1971	£2.50	£6	
Shake It About	7"	Beacon	BEA161	1970	£2.50	£6	
UFO	LP	Beacon	BEAS12	1971	£6	£15	

UGLY CUSTARD

Title	Format	Label	Cat. No.	Year	Price	Price	Notes
Ugly Custard	LP	Kaleidoscope	KAL100	1970	£25	£50	

UGLY DUCKLINGS

Title	Format	Label	Cat. No.	Year	Price	Price	Notes
Off The Wall	LP	Razor		1968	£6	£15	Canadian
Somewhere Outside	LP	Yorktown		1966	£40	£80	Canadian

UGLYS

Title	Format	Label	Cat. No.	Year	Price	Price	Notes
End Of The Season	7"	Pye	7N17178	1966	£7.50	£15	
Good Idea	7"	Pye	7N17027	1966	£7.50	£15	
I See The Light	7"	MGM	MGM1465	1969	£100	£200	demo
It's Alright	7"	Pye	7N15968	1965	£6	£12	

Squire Blew His Horn	7"	CBS	2933	1967	£10	£20	
Wake Up My Mind	7"	Pye	7N15858	1965	£7.50	£15	

UK BONDS
Anything You Do Is Alright	7"	Polydor	56112	1966	£1.50	£4	
World Is Watching Us	7"	Polydor	56061	1965	£1.50	£4	

UK DECAY
UK Decay	7"	Plastic	PLAS001	1979	£7.50	£15	B side by Pneumania

UK SUBS
C.I.D.	7"	City	NIK5	1978	£1.50	£4	various coloured vinyls
Crash Course	LP	Gem	GEMLP111	1980	£5	£12	purple vinyl, with 12' (GEMEP1)
Party In Paris	7"	Ramkup	CAC2	1981	£10	£20	1 sided, no PS

U.K.'S
Ever Faithful Ever True	7"	HMV	POP1310	1964	£4	£8	
I Will Never Let You Go	7"	HMV	POP1357	1964	£6	£12	

ULTIMATE SPINACH
Behold And See	LP	MGM	C8094	1968	£8	£20	
Ultimate Spinach	LP	MGM	C8071	1968	£10	£25	
Ultimate Spinach	LP	MGM	SE4600	1969	£8	£20	US

ULTRA VIVID SCENE
Mercy Seat	12"	4AD	BAD906	1989	£6	£15	
Something To Eat	7"	4AD	AD908	1989	£2	£5	

ULTRAFUNK
Ultrafunk	LP	Contempo	CLP509	1975	£5	£12	

ULTRAVOX
Ha! Ha! Ha!	LP	Island	ILPS9505	1977	£4	£10	with 7' (WIP6417)

ULVAEUS, BJORN & BENNY ANDERSSON
Lycka	LP	Polar	POLL113	1970	£6	£15	Swedish, mono
Lycka	LP	Polar	POLS226	1970	£5	£12	Swedish, stereo

UMPS AND DUMPS
Moon's In A Fit	LP	Topic	12TS416	1980	£5	£12	

UNBEATABLES
Live At Palisades Park	LP	Fawn	LP5050	1964	£17.50	£35	US

UNDER THE SUN
Under The Sun	LP	Redball			£35	£70	

UNDERGROUND SET
Underground Set	LP	Pan	PAN6302	1970	£10	£25	

UNDERGROUND SUNSHINE
Birthday	7"	Fontana	TF1049	1969	£2.50	£6	
Let There Be Light	LP	Intrepid	IT4003	1969	£6	£15	US

UNDERGROUNDS
Psychedelic Visions	LP	Mercury	MG/SR16337	1967	£6	£15	US

UNDERNEATH
Imp Of The Perverse	7"	El	GPO17	1986	£2	£5	
Imp Of The Perverse	12"	El	GPO17T	1986	£2.50	£6	
Lunatic Dawn Of The Dismantler	7"	Acme	ACME9	1986	£5	£10	

UNDERNEATH WHAT?
Land For Your World	12"	11th Hour	SRT6KL961	1988	£2.50	£6	

UNDERTAKERS
Everybody Loves A Lover	7"	Pye	7N15543	1963	£5	£10	
Just A Little Bit	7"	Pye	7N15607	1964	£5	£10	chart single
What About Us	7"	Pye	7N15562	1963	£5	£10	

UNDERTONES
Get Over You	7"	Sire	SIR4010	1979	£1.50	£4	chart single
Sin Of Pride	LP	Ardeck	ARD104	1983	£8	£20	with tracks Bittersweet and Stand So Close
Teenage Kicks	7"	Good Vibrations	GOT4	1978	£2.50	£6	poster sleeve

UNDISPUTED TRUTH
Best Of The Undisputed Truth	LP	Tamla Motown	STML8029	1977	£5	£12	
Cosmic Truth	LP	Tamla Motown	STMA8023	1975	£4	£10	
Higher Than High	LP	Tamla Motown	STML12009	1975	£4	£10	
Law Of The Land	LP	Tamla Motown	STML11240	1973	£4	£10	
Method To The Madness	LP	Whitfield	K56289	1977	£4	£10	
Save My Love For A Rainy Day	7"	Parlophone	TMG776	1971	£4	£8	mispressed label
Save My Love For A Rainy Day	7"	Tamla Motown	TMG776	1971	£1.50	£4	
Smiling Face Sometimes	7"	Tamla Motown	TMG789	1971	£1.50	£4	
Superstar	7"	Tamla Motown	TMG818	1972	£1.50	£4	
Undisputed Truth	LP	Tamla Motown	STML11197	1972	£4	£10	

UNFOLDING
How To Blow Your Mind .... LP ..... Audio Fidelity .. 6184 .... 196- ... £8 .... £20 .... US

UNFOLDING BOOK OF LIFE
Vol.1 .... LP ..... Island .... ILPS9093 .... 1969 ... £8 ....£20
Vol.2 .... LP ..... Island .... ILPS9094 .... 1969 ... £8 ....£20

UNICORN
Going Home .... 7" ...... Hollick & .... HT1258 .... 196- ... £10 ....£20
                                                                 Taylor ....

UNIFICS
Court Of Love .... 7" ...... London .... HLZ10231 .... 1968 ... £2.50 ....£6

UNION GAP
Lady Willpower .... 7" ...... CBS .... 3551 .... 1968 ... £1.50 ....£4
Woman Woman .... 7" ...... CBS .... 3100 .... 1967 ... £1.50 ....£4
Young Girl .... 7" ...... CBS .... 3365 .... 1968 ... £1.50 ....£4

UNIQUES
Absolutely The Uniques .... LP ..... Trojan .... TRL15 .... 1969 ... £8 ....£20
A-Yuh .... 7" ...... Trojan .... TR645 .... 1968 ... £4 ....£8
Beatitude .... 7" ...... Island .... WI3123 .... 1967 ... £5 ....£10 ..... Keith Blake B side
Beatitude .... 7" ...... Unity .... UN527 .... 1969 ... £2.50 ....£6
Build My World Around You .... 7" ...... Island .... WI3114 .... 1967 ... £5 ....£10 ..... Lloyd Clarke B side
Crimson And Clover .... 7" ...... Nu Beat .... NB034 .... 1969 ... £2.50 ....£6
Dry The Water .... 7" ...... Collins .... CR002 .... 1967 ... £4 ....£8
                                                                 Downbeat ....
Girl Of My Dreams .... 7" ...... Island .... WI3145 .... 1968 ... £5 ....£10 .....Lester Stirling B side
Gypsy Woman .... 7" ...... Island .... WI3084 .... 1967 ... £5 ....£10 .....Ken Ross B side
I'll Make You Love Me .... 7" ...... Nu Beat .... NB037 .... 1969 ... £2.50 ....£6
Lesson Of Love .... 7" ...... Island .... WI3107 .... 1967 ... £5 ....£10 . Delroy Wilson B side
Let Me Go Girl .... 7" ...... Island .... WI3086 .... 1967 ... £5 ....£10 ...... Soulettes B side
More Love .... 7" ...... Island .... WI3117 .... 1967 ... £5 ....£10 .....Val Bennett B side
More Love .... 7" ...... Trojan .... TR610 .... 1968 ... £4 ....£8 ...... Race Dans B side
My Conversation .... 7" ...... Island .... WI3122 .... 1967 ... £5 ....£10 ..... Slim Smith B side
Never Let Me Go .... 7" ...... Island .... WI3087 .... 1967 ... £5 ....£10 ...Don Tony Lee B side
People Rock Steady .... 7" ...... Island .... WI3070 .... 1967 ... £5 ....£10
Speak No Evil .... 7" ...... Island .... WI3106 .... 1967 ... £5 ....£10 ..... Glen Adams B side
Too Proud To Beg .... 7" ...... Gas .... GAS117 .... 1969 ... £4 ....£8

UNIQUES (2)
Fast Way Of Living .... 7" ...... Pye .... 7N25303 .... 1965 ... £37.50 .....£75
Uniquely Yours .... LP ..... Pye .... NPL28094 .... 1966 ... £25 ....£50

UNIT FOUR PLUS TWO
Baby Never Say Goodbye .... 7" ...... Decca .... F12333 .... 1966 ... £2 ....£5 ....chart single
Butterfly .... 7" ...... Fontana .... TF840 .... 1967 ... £2.50 ....£6
Concrete And Clay .... 7" ...... Decca .... F12071 .... 1965 ... £1.50 ....£4 ....chart single
Concrete And Clay .... 7" EP. Decca .... 457070 .... 1965 ... £7.50 ....£15 .... French
For A Moment .... 7" ...... Decca .... F12398 .... 1966 ... £2 ....£5
Green Fields .... 7" ...... Decca .... F11821 .... 1964 ... £4 ....£8 ....chart single
Hark .... 7" ...... Decca .... F12211 .... 1965 ... £2 ....£5
I Was Only Playing Games .... 7" ...... Decca .... F12509 .... 1966 ... £2 ....£5
Loving Takes A Little Understanding ... 7" ...... Fontana .... TF891 .... 1967 ... £2.50 ....£6
Sorrow And Pain .... 7" ...... Decca .... F11994 .... 1964 ... £2.50 ....£6
Three Thirty .... 7" ...... Fontana .... TF990 .... 1969 ... £7.50 ....£15
Too Fast, Too Slow .... 7" ...... Fontana .... TF834 .... 1967 ... £5 ....£10
Unit Four Plus Two .... LP ..... Decca .... LK4697 .... 1965 ... £20 ....£40
Unit Four Plus Two .... LP ..... Fontana .... SFL13123 .... 1969 ... £8 ....£20
Unit Four Plus Two .... 7" EP. Decca .... DFE8619 .... 1966 ... £6 ....£12
You Ain't Goin' Nowhere .... 7" ...... Fontana .... TF931 .... 1968 ... £4 ....£8
You've Got To Be Cruel To Be Kind ..... 7" ...... Decca .... F12299 .... 1965 ... £2 ....£5
You've Never Been In Love Like This ... 7" ...... Decca .... F12144 .... 1965 ... £1.50 ....£4 ....chart single
Before
You've Never Been In Love Like This ... 7" EP.. Decca .... 457087 .... 1965 ... £7.50 ....£15 .... French
Before

UNITED STATES DOUBLE QUARTET
Life Is Groovy .... LP ..... B.T.Puppy .... BTPS1005 .... 1969 ... £6 ....£15 .... US
Life Is Groovy .... 7" ...... Stateside .... SS590 .... 1967 ... £2.50 ....£6

UNITED STATES OF AMERICA
Garden Of Earthly Delights .... 7" ...... CBS .... 3745 .... 1968 ... £4 ....£8
United States Of America .... LP ..... CBS .... 63340 .... 1968 ... £8 ....£20

UNIVERSALS
Green Veined Orchid .... 7" ...... Page One .... POF049 .... 1967 ... £5 ....£10
I Can't Find You .... 7" ...... Page One .... POF032 .... 1967 ... £7.50 ....£15

UNTAMED
Daddy Longlegs .... 7" ...... Planet .... PLF113 .... 1966 ... £15 ....£30 ....as Lindsay
                                                                                                                                        Muir's Untamed
I'll Go Crazy .... 7" ...... Stateside .... SS431 .... 1965 ... £15 ....£30
It's Not True .... 7" ...... Planet .... PLF103 .... 1966 ... £15 ....£30
Once Upon A Time .... 7" ...... Parlophone ...... R5258 .... 1965 ... £20 ....£40
So Long .... 7" ...... Decca .... F12045 .... 1964 ... £10 ....£20

UNTOUCHABLES
Prisoner In Love .... 7" ...... Blue Cat .... BS137 .... 1968 ... £4 ....£8
Tighten Up .... 7" ...... Trojan .... TR613 .... 1968 ... £4 ....£8

UNUSUAL WE
Unusual We	LP	Pulsar	10608	1969	£5	£12	US

UNWANTED
Memory Man	7"	Raw	RAW30	1978	£4	£8	
Secret Police	7"	Raw	RAW15	1978	£2	£5	
Withdrawal	7"	Raw	RAW6	1977	£5	£10	PS
Withdrawal	7"	Raw	RAWT6	1978	£4	£8	

UNWIN, STANLEY
Rotatety Diskers	LP	Pye	NPL18062	1961	£5	£12	

UPBEATS
Keep Cool Crazy Heart	7"	Pye	7N25016	1959	£2	£5	
My Foolish Heart	7"	London	HLJ8688	1958	£5	£10	
Teeny Weeny Bikini	7"	Pye	7N25028	1959	£2	£5	

UPCHURCH, PHIL
Darkness, Darkness	LP	Blue Thumb	ILPS9219	1972	£4	£10	
Feeling Blue	LP	Milestone	9010	1968	£5	£12	US
Nothing But Soul	7"	Sue	WI4017	1966	£5	£10	
Twist The Big Hit Dances	LP	United Artists	6175	1960	£5	£12	US
Upchurch	LP	Cadet	826	1969	£4	£10	US
Way I Feel	LP	Cadet	840	1969	£4	£10	US
You Can't Sit Down	LP	Boyd	398	1960	£6	£15	US
You Can't Sit Down	7"	HMV	POP899	1961	£7.50	£15	chart single
You Can't Sit Down	7"	Sue	WI4005	1966	£5	£12	
You Can't Sit Down II	LP	United Artists	6162	1960	£5	£12	US

UPSETTERS
Africa's Blood	LP	Trojan	TBL166	1971	£6	£15	
Battle Axe	LP	Trojan	TBL167	1971	£6	£15	
Clint Eastwood	LP	Pama	PSP1014	1969	£10	£25	
Clint Eastwood	7"	Punch	PH21	1969	£2	£5	
Cold Sweat	7"	Upsetter	US315	1969	£2	£5	
Double Seven	LP	Trojan	TRLS70	1974	£6	£15	
Dry Acid	7"	Punch	PH19	1970	£2	£5	Reggae Boys B side
Eastwood Rides Again	LP	Trojan	TBL125	1970	£6	£15	
Eight For Eight	7"	Duke	DU11	1969	£2.50	£6	
Eight For Eight	7"	Upsetter	US300	1969	£2.50	£6	
Good, The Bad And The Upsetters	LP	Trojan	TBL119	1970	£8	£20	
Kiddyo	7"	Upsetter	US309	1969	£2	£5	
Live Injection	7"	Upsetter	US313	1969	£2	£5	Bleechers B side
Man From MI5	7"	Upsetter	US310	1969	£2	£5	West Indians B side
Many Moods Of The Upsetters	LP	Pama	SECO24	1970	£15	£30	
Night Doctor	7"	Upsetter	US307	1969	£2	£5	Termites B side
Prisoner	LP	Trojan	TBL127	1970	£6	£15	
Return Of Django	LP	Trojan	TRL19	1969	£6	£15	
Return Of Django	7"	Upsetter	US301	1969	£2	£5	chart single
Return Of The Ugly	7"	Punch	PH18	1969	£2	£5	
Stranger On The Shore	7"	Upsetter	US321	1969	£2.50	£6	
Taste Of Killing	7"	Camel	CA13	1969	£2	£5	
Ten To Twelve	7"	Upsetter	US303	1969	£2.50	£6	
Three In One	7"	Island	WIP6328	1976	£2	£5	
Vampire	7"	Upsetter	US317	1969	£2	£5	Bleechers B side
Walk Down The Aisle	7"	Rio	R70	1965	£5	£10	
Wildcat	7"	Doctor Bird	DB1034	1966	£5	£10	

UPTOWNERS
If'n	7"	London	HLU9877	1964	£1.50	£4	

URCHIN
Black Leather Fantasy	7"	DJM	DJS10776	1977	£15	£30	
She's A Roller	7"	DJM	DJS10850	1978	£12.50	£25	

URIAH HEEP
Demons And Wizards	LP	Island	ILPS9193	1972	£6	£15	
Lady In Black	7"	Vertigo	6059037	1971	£2.50	£6	
Look At Yourself	LP	Bronze	ILPS9169	1971	£4	£10	chart LP
Salisbury	LP	Bronze	ILPS9152	1971	£4	£10	
Salisbury	LP	Island	ILPS9152	1971	£6	£15	
Salisbury	LP	Vertigo	6360028	1971	£5	£12	spiral label
Very 'Umble, Very 'Eavy	LP	Bronze	ILPS9142	1971	£5	£12	
Very 'Umble, Very 'Eavy	LP	Vertigo	6360006	1970	£6	£15	spiral label

URSO, PHIL
Phil Urso	10" LP	London	LZC14016	1955	£15	£30	

U.S. T-BONES
No Matter What Shape	7"	Liberty	LIB55836	1965	£1.50	£4	
Proper Thing To Do	7"	Liberty	LIB55951	1967	£1.50	£4	
Sippin' And Chippin'	7"	Liberty	LIB55867	1966	£1.50	£4	

USERS
Sick Of You	7"	Raw	RAW1	1977	£2	£5	numbered PS
Sick Of You	12"	Raw	RAWT1	1978	£2.50	£6	

UTOPIA
Utopia	LP	United Artists	UAG29438	1973	£4	£10	

UTOPIA (2)
Utopia .... LP ...... Kent .... 1967 ... £8 ....£20 .... US

UV POP
Just A Game .... 7" .... Pax .... PAX9 .... 1982 ... £2 ....£5 ....

V

V2

Title	Format	Label	Cat#	Year			Notes
Speed Freak	7"	Bent	SMALLBENT1	1978	£2	£5	red or black vinyl

VACELS

Title	Format	Label	Cat#	Year			
Can You Please Crawl Out Of Your Window	7"	Pye	7N25330	1965	£4	£8	

VAGABONDS

Title	Format	Label	Cat#	Year			
Presenting The Fabulous Vagabonds	LP	Island	ILP916	1964	£20	£40	
Ska Time	LP	Decca	LK4617	1964	£8	£20	

VAGINA DENTATA ORGAN

Title	Format	Label	Cat#	Year			Notes
Cold Meat	12"		WSNS004		£6	£15	pic disc
Music For Hashasins	LP	Temple	TOPY012	1987	£8	£20	

VAGRANTS

Title	Format	Label	Cat#	Year			
I Can't Make A Friend	7"	Fontana	TF703	1966	£15	£30	

VALADIERS

Title	Format	Label	Cat#	Year			
I Found A Girl	7"	Oriole	CBA1809	1963	£250	£400	

VALANCE, RICKY

Title	Format	Label	Cat#	Year			Notes
Bobby	7"	Columbia	DB4680	1961	£1.50	£4	
Don't Play Number Nine	7"	Columbia	DB4864	1962	£1.50	£4	
I Never Had A Chance	7"	Columbia	DB4725	1961	£1.50	£4	
Jimmy's Girl	7"	Columbia	DB4586	1961	£1.50	£4	
Lipstick On Your Lips	7"	Columbia	DB4543	1960	£1.50	£4	
Six Boys	7"	Decca	F12129	1965	£1.50	£4	
Tell Laura I Love Her	7"	Columbia	DB4493	1960	£2	£5	chart single
Try To Forget Her	7"	Columbia	DB4787	1962	£1.50	£4	
Why Can't We	7"	Columbia	DB4592	1961	£1.50	£4	

VALE, RICKY & HIS SURFERS

Title	Format	Label	Cat#	Year			Notes
Everybody's Surfin'	LP	Strand	SL(S)1104	1963	£6	£15	US

VALENS, RITCHIE

Title	Format	Label	Cat#	Year			Notes
C'mon Let's Go	7"	Pye	7N25000	1958	£30	£60	
Donna	7"	London	HL7068	1959	£4	£8	
Donna	7"	London	HL8803	1959	£7.50	£15	chart single
Donna	7"	President	PT126	1967	£1.50	£4	
Greatest Hits	LP	London	HA8196	1964	£15	£30	
Greatest Hits Vol.2	LP	Del-Fi	1247	1965	£15	£30	US
I Remember Ritchie Valens	LP	President	PTL1001	1967	£5	£12	
In Concert At Pacoima Jr.High	LP	Del-Fi	1214	1960	£30	£60	US
La Bamba	7"	London	HL9494	1962	£6	£12	
La Bamba	7"	Sue	WI4011	1966	£15	£30	demo
Ritchie	LP	London	HA2390	1961	£25	£50	
Ritchie Valens	LP	Del-Fi	1201	1959	£25	£50	US
Ritchie Valens	LP	London	HAR8535	1979	£5	£12	
Ritchie Valens	LP	MGM	GAS117	1970	£5	£12	US
Ritchie Valens	7" EP.	London	RE1232	1959	£30	£60	tri centre
Rock Li'l Darlin'	LP	Joy	JOYS264	1973	£4	£10	
That's My Little Suzie	7"	London	HL8886	1959	£7.50	£15	

VALENTE, CATERINA

Title	Format	Label	Cat#	Year			
Bravo Caterina	7" EP.	Polydor	EPH20282	1963	£2	£5	
Breeze And I	7"	Polydor	NH66953	1960	£2	£5	
Caterina Cherie	LP	Polydor	LPHM46310	1961	£5	£12	
Caterina Valente	7" EP.	Polydor	EPH20106	1963	£2	£5	
Caterina Valente	7" EP.	Polydor	EPH20501	1963	£2.50	£6	
Caterina Valente	7" EP.	Polydor	EPH21613	1963	£2	£5	
Caterina Valente No.2	7" EP.	Polydor	EPH20528	1963	£2	£5	
Caterina Valente No.3	7" EP.	Polydor	EPH20545	1963	£2	£5	
Cosmopolitan Lady	LP	Polydor	LPHM46065	1960	£5	£12	
De Paris A Grenade	7" EP.	Polydor	EPH20547	1963	£2	£5	
Frenesi	7" EP.	London	GEB7001	1962	£2.50	£6	
Great Continental Hits	LP	Decca	LK/SKL4508	1962	£4	£10	
Haiti Cherie	7" EP.	Polydor	EPH20516	1963	£2	£5	
I Happen To Like New York	LP	Decca	LK/SKL4630	1964	£5	£12	
La Malaguena	7"	Polydor	NH66914	1960	£2.50	£6	
My Hawaiian Melody	7" EP.	Decca	DFE8544	1963	£5	£12	
Rendezvous With Caterina	LP	Decca	LK4350	1960	£5	£12	
Sombreros Y Guitarras	7" EP.	Polydor	EPH20596	1963	£2	£5	
Superfonics	LP	RCA	RD27216/SF5099	1961	£5	£12	
Valente And Violins	LP	Decca	LK/SKL4646	1965	£5	£12	
Valente In Swingtime	LP	Decca	LK/SKL4537	1963	£4	£10	
Valente On TV	LP	Decca	LK4604	1964	£4	£10	

VALENTE, DINO

Title	Format	Label	Cat#	Year			
Dino	LP	CBS	65715	1968	£6	£15	
Dino Valente	LP	CBS	63443	1968	£15	£30	

VALENTINE, BILLY

It's A Sin	7"	Capitol	CL14320	1955	£4	£8

VALENTINE, DICKIE

Belonging To Someone	7" EP	Decca	DFE6549	1958	£2	£5	
Blossom Fell	7"	Decca	F10430	1955	£5	£10	chart single
Chapel Of The Roses	7"	Decca	F10874	1957	£1.50	£4	
Christmas Alphabet	7"	Decca	F10628	1955	£10	£20	chart single
Christmas Island	7"	Decca	F10798	1956	£4	£8	chart single
Day Dreams	7"	Decca	F10766	1956	£2	£5	
Dickie Goes Dixie	7" EP	Decca	DFE6427	1957	£2.50	£6	
Dickie Valentine's Rock'n'Roll Party	7"	Decca	F10820	1956	£2.50	£6	
Dreams Can Tell A Lie	7"	Decca	F10667	1956	£2	£5	
Endless	7"	Decca	F10346	1954	£5	£10	chart single
Finger Of Suspicion Points At You	7"	Decca	F10394	1954	£7.50	£15	chart single
Hello Mrs.Jones	7"	Decca	F10517	1955	£2.50	£6	
Here Is Dickie Valentine	10" LP	Decca	LF1211	1955	£6	£15	
Hit Parade	7" EP	Pye	NEP24120	1959	£2	£5	
I Wonder	7"	Decca	F10493	1955	£4	£8	chart single
Long Before I Knew You	7"	Decca	F10949	1957	£1.50	£4	
Love Me Again	7"	Decca	F11005	1958	£1.50	£4	
Ma Cherie Amie	7"	Decca	F10484	1955	£4	£8	
Mister Sandman	7"	Decca	F10415	1954	£10	£20	chart single
My Impossible Castle	7"	Decca	F10753	1956	£1.50	£4	
No Such Luck	7"	Decca	F10549	1955	£2.50	£6	
Old Pianna Rag	7"	Decca	F10645	1955	£4	£8	chart single
Only For You	7" EP	Decca	DFE6363	1956	£2.50	£6	
Over My Shoulder	10" LP	Decca	LF1257	1956	£6	£15	
Presenting	7" EP	Decca	DFE6279	1956	£6	£12	
Presenting Dickie Valentine	10" LP	Decca	LF1163	1954	£6	£15	
Puttin' On The Style	7"	Decca	F10906	1957	£1.50	£4	
Snowbound For Christmas	7"	Decca	F10950	1957	£2	£5	chart single
Swing Along	7" EP	Decca	DFE6236	1955	£2.50	£6	
Venus	7"	Pye	7N15192	1959	£1.50	£4	chart single
Voice	7"	Decca	F10714	1956	£2	£5	
With Vocal Refrain By...	LP	Decca	LK4269	1958	£4	£10	
With Vocal Refrain By...	7" EP	Decca	DFE6529	1958	£2.50	£6	

VALENTINE, HILTON

All In Your Head	LP	Capitol	ST330	1969	£25	£50	US, Sleeve pictured in Guide

VALENTINES

Hey Baby	7"	Ember	EMBS123	1960	£10	£20
Till Then	7"	Decca	F11711	1963	£1.50	£4

VALENTINO

I Was Born This Way	7"	Gaiee	GAE101	1975	£1.50	£4

VALENTINO, ANNA

Calypso Joe	7"	London	HLD8421	1957	£5	£10

VALENTINO, DANNY

Biology	7"	MGM	MGM1067	1960	£4	£8
Pictures	7"	MGM	MGM1109	1960	£2	£5
Stampede	7"	MGM	MGM1049	1959	£7.50	£15

VALENTINO, MARK

Do It	7"	Stateside	SS186	1963	£1.50	£4	
Jiving At The Drive In	7"	Stateside	SS233	1963	£5	£10	
Mark Valentino	LP	Swan	LP508	1963	£6	£15	US
Push And Kick	7"	Stateside	SS148	1963	£1.50	£4	

VALENTINOS

It's All Over Now	7"	Soul City	SC106	1968	£2.50	£6
Raise Your Hand In Anger	7"	Polydor	2058090	1971	£1.50	£4
Tired Of Being Nobody	7"	Stateside	SS2137	1969	£2	£5

VALENTINOS & SIMS TWINS

Valentinos/The Sims Twins	LP	Soul City	SCM001	1969	£8	£20

VALERIE & THE ROCK & ROLL YOUNGSTERS

Tonight You Belong To Me	7"	Columbia	DB3832	1956	£4	£8

VALERY, DANA

I Wake Up Crying	7"	Decca	F11977	1964	£1.50	£4
She Doesn't Love You	7"	Decca	F12134	1965	£1.50	£4
This Is My Prayer	7"	Decca	F11881	1964	£1.50	£4

VALINO, JOE

Garden Of Eden	7"	HMV	POP283	1957	£2	£5	chart single
God's Little Acre	7"	London	HLT8705	1958	£2.50	£6	

VALKYRIES

Rip It Up	7"	Parlophone	R5123	1964	£5	£10

VALLADARES, DIORIS

Authentic Merengue	7" EP	Sue	IEP703	1966	£5	£10

VALLEY, JIM

Harpo	LP	Panorama	104	1969	£8	£20	US

VALLI, FRANKIE
My Mother's Eye	7"	Corona	1234	1953	£330	£500	US
Please Take A Chance	7"	Decca	30994	1959	£37.50	£75	US
Proud One	7"	Philips	BF1529	1966	£1.50	£4	
Real	7"	Cindy	3012	1959	£37.50	£75	US
Somebody Else Took Her Home	7"	Mercury	70381	1954	£37.50	£75	US
You're Gonna Hurt Yourself	7"	Philips	BF1467	1966	£4	£8	
You're Ready Now	7"	Philips	BF1512	1966	£5	£10	

VALLI, FRANKIE & THE FOUR SEASONS
Night	7"	Mowest	MW3002	1972	£2	£5
Walk On, Don't Look Back	7"	Mowest	MW3003	1973	£1.50	£4
You're A Song	7"	Tamla Motown	TMG819	1972	£1.50	£4

VALLI, JUNE
Anonymous Letter	7"	Mercury	AMT1048	1959	£1.50	£4
Answer To A Maiden's Prayer	7"	Mercury	AMT1034	1959	£1.50	£4
Apple Green	7"	Mercury	AMT1091	1960	£1.50	£4
I Understand	7"	HMV	7M245	1954	£4	£8
Por Favor	7"	HMV	7M347	1956	£2.50	£6
Tell Me, Tell Me	7"	HMV	7M259	1954	£4	£8
Wrong, Wrong, Wrong	7"	HMV	7M284	1955	£2.50	£6

VALUES
Return To Me	7"	Ember	EMBS211	1966	£4	£8

VAMP
Floatin'	7"	Atlantic	584213	1968	£20	£40	
Green Pea	7"	Atlantic	584263	1969	£5	£10	demo

VAMPIRES
Do You Wanna Dance	7"	Pye	7N17553	1968	£2	£5

VAMPIRES (2)
Swinging Ghosts	7"	Parlophone	R4599	1959	£2.50	£6

VAMPIRE'S SOUND INCORPORATION
Psychedelic Dance Party	LP	Mercury	MCY134615	1969	£20	£40	German

VAN DAMME, ART
Art Van Damme Quintet	10" LP	Capitol	LC6622	1954	£5	£12

VAN DER GRAAF GENERATOR
Peter Hammill's complicated songs, each incorporating several melodic themes and intricate instrumental passages, are well served by Van Der Graaf Generator's musicians. Hugh Banton, in particular, shines as one of the very few organ players in rock to have made a serious attempt to fully explore the potential of the electronic instrument. Peter Hammill's voice too has some of the characteristics of an instrument, as he varies its tonal qualities considerably from moment to moment - sometimes with a little electronic assistance. It is the combination of instrumental bravado and compositional depth that arguably makes these albums, by a short head, the most durable of all the progressive rock canon. With regard to the group's rare singles, meanwhile, it should be noted that "Refugees" is a different version to that found on "The Least We Can Do Is Wave To Each Other". "Firebrand" - the rarest Van Der Graaf release of all - is actually the B side of the single, but this is always the named title to appear on dealers' or collectors' wants lists, due to it being the more experimental and dynamic side.

Aerosol Grey Machine	LP	Fontana	6430083	1975	£6	£15	
Aerosol Grey Machine	LP	Mercury	SR61238	1968	£10	£25	US
Firebrand	7"	Polydor	56758	1968	£75	£150	
H To He Who Am The Only One	LP	Charisma	CAS1027	1970	£5	£12	
Least We Can Do Is Wave	LP	Charisma	CAS1007	1969	£15	£30	with poster
Least We Can Do Is Wave To Each Other	LP	Charisma	CAS1007	1969	£6	£15	chart LP
Long Hello	LP	no label	no number	1973	£8	£20	
Pawn Hearts	LP	Buddah		1971	£6	£15	US, with 'Theme One'
Pawn Hearts	LP	Charisma	CAS1051	1971	£5	£12	
Refugees	7"	Charisma	CB122	1970	£17.50	£35	
Theme One	7"	Charisma	CB175	1972	£12.50	£25	PS
Wondering	7"	Charisma	CB297	1976	£4	£8	

VAN DOREN, MAMIE
Something To Dream About	7"	Capitol	CL14850	1958	£1.50	£4

VAN DYKE & THE BAMBIS
Doin' The Mod	7"	Piccadilly	7N35180	1964	£2	£5

VAN DYKE, EARL
All For You	7"	Tamla Motown	TMG506	1965	£25	£50	
Earl Of Funk	LP	Soul	SS715	1970	£8	£20	US
Can't Help Myself	7"	Tamla Motown	TMG814	1972	£1.50	£4	
Six By Six	7"	Tamla Motown	TMG759	1970	£1.50	£4	
Soul Stomp	7"	Stateside	SS357	1964	£30	£60	
That Motown Sound	LP	Tamla Motown	TML11014	1965	£30	£60	

VAN DYKE, LEROY
Big Man In A Big House	7"	Mercury	AMT1173	1962	£1.50	£4	chart single
Broken Promise	7"	Mercury	AMT1183	1962	£1.50	£4	
It's All Over Now, Baby Blue	7"	Warner Bros	WB5650	1965	£1.50	£4	
Movin'	LP	Mercury	MMC14118	1963	£8	£20	
Walk On By	LP	Mercury	MMC14101	1961	£8	£20	
Walk On By	7"	Mercury	AMT1166	1961	£1.50	£4	chart single

VAN DYKES
I've Gotta Go On Without You	7"	Stateside	SS530	1966	£4	£8	
No Man Is An Island	7"	Stateside	SS504	1966	£2	£5	
Tellin' It Like It Is	LP	Bell	6004	1967	£6	£15	US

VAN EATON, LON & DERREK
Brother	LP	Apple	SAPCOR25	1973	£6	£15	
Warm Woman	7"	Apple	46	1973	£1.50	£4	
Warm Woman	7"	Apple	46	1973	£10	£20	PS

VAN HALEN
Dance The Night Away	7"	Warner Bros	K17371	1979	£1.50	£4	
Dance The Night Away	7"	Warner Bros	K17371	1979	£2.50	£6	pic disc
Dreams	7"	Warner Bros	W8642P	1986	£2.50	£6	shaped pic disc, plinth
Why Can't This Be Love	7"	Warner Bros	W8740P	1986	£2	£5	shaped pic disc, plinth

VAN RONK, DAVE
Ballads And Blues And Spirituals	LP	Folkways	F3818	1959	£6	£15	US

VAN ZANDT, TOWNES
For The Sake Of A Song	LP	Poppy	PYS40001	1968	£4	£10	US

VANCE, TOMMY
Off The Hook	7"	Columbia	DB8062	1966	£4	£8	
You Must Be The One	7"	Columbia	DB7999	1966	£2	£5	

VANGELIS
Chariots Of Fire	LP	Polydor	BOX1	1983	£4	£10	boxed set

VANILLA FUDGE
Beat Goes On	LP	Atlantic	587/588100	1968	£4	£10	
Eleanor Rigby	7"	Atlantic	584139	1967	£4	£8	
Renaissance	LP	Atlantic	587/588110	1968	£4	£10	
Shotgun	7"	Atlantic	584257	1969	£2	£5	
Some Velvet Morning	7"	Atlantic	584276	1969	£1.50	£4	
Vanilla Fudge	LP	Atlantic	587/588086	1967	£5	£12	chart LP
Where Is My Mind	7"	Atlantic	584179	1968	£2.50	£6	
You Keep Me Hanging On	7"	Atlantic	584123	1967	£1.50	£4	chart single

VANITY FARE
Sun, The Wind And Other Things	LP	Page One	POLS010	1968	£5	£12	

VANN, TEDDY
Cindy	7"	London	HLU9097	1960	£4	£8	

VARDAS, PETER
He Threw A Stone	7"	Top Rank	JAR173	1959	£1.50	£4	

VARDIS
If I Were King	7"	Castle	QUEL2/100	1980	£2.50	£6	
Let's Go	7"	Logo	VAR1	1980	£1.50	£4	double

VARIATIONS
Man With All The Toys	7"	Immediate	IM019	1965	£5	£10	

VARICOSE VEINS
Geographical Problem	7"	Warped	WARP1	1978	£7.50	£15	

VARIOUS

Various Artist albums can become collectable for a number of reasons. Some contain tracks that are only available on that particular record. The most valuable of this sort is the "Glastonbury Fayre" triple album, which within its extravagant packing and multiple inserts contains material by artists like David Bowie, Marc Bolan, and the Grateful Dead, none of which has been released anywhere else. Other albums are or labels that are themselves collectable, like the various Tamla Motown anthologies, or the United Dairies compilation. Others simply seem to epitomise an area or era of music particularly well - the classic example here being the "Nuggets" double, which gathers together a number of the American groups whose music represents what was meant by "punk rock" in the sixties. For jazz collectors, various artist compilations are not popular, and the large number of such albums from the fifties and sixties do not, in general, appear in these listings, even when they feature artists who do have substantial collectors' discographies to their names.

	LP	Treasure Isle	TI101	1966	£30	£60	
	7"	Tamla Motown	TMG956-975,1000	1975	£50	£100	boxed set of demos
	7" EP	Track	2094011	1970	£40	£80	blue sleeve
	7" EP	Track	2094011	1970	£2.50	£6	maroon & gold sleeve
	7" EP	Track	2094011	1970	£20	£40	red & white sleeve, press pack
1968 Memphis Country Music Festival	LP	Blue Horizon	763210	1968	£17.50	£35	
49 Greek Street	LP	RCA	SF8118	1970	£5	£12	
50 Minutes & 24 Seconds Of Recorded Dynamite	LP	Sue	ILP920	1965	£15	£30	
Abbey Tavern Traditional Music And Song	LP	Abbey Tavern	ATP101	1970	£10	£25	Irish
Action Packed Soul	LP	Action	ACLP6005	1969	£6	£15	
African Melody	LP	Pama	PMP2004	1970	£5	£12	
Album Full Of Soul	LP	Stateside	SL10172	1966	£8	£20	
Alive!	LP	Key	KL002	1969	£10	£25	
Alive In The Living Room	LP	Creation	CRELP001	1984	£4	£10	
All For Art...And Art For All	LP	Wham!	BIG8	1984	£8	£20	
All Good Clean Fun	LP	United Artists	UDX201/2	1971	£5	£12	
All Star Hit Parade	LP	Decca	F10752	1956	£4	£8	chart single
All Star Hit Parade	7" EP	Pye	NEP24168	1963	£2	£5	
All Star Hit Parade Vol.2	7" EP	Pye	NEP24172	1964	£2	£5	
All This And World War Two	LP	Riva	RVLP2	1977	£5	£12	dble
American Country Jubilee No.1	7" EP	Decca	DFE8571	1964	£4	£8	
American Folk Blues Festival	LP	Polydor	LPHM46397/ SLPHM237597	1963	£5	£12	
American Folk Blues Festival 1963	LP	Fontana	TL5204	1964	£5	£12	
American Folk Blues Festival 1964	LP	Fontana	TL5225	1965	£5	£12	
American Folk Blues Festival 1965	LP	Fontana	TL5286	1966	£5	£12	

Title	Format	Label	Catalogue	Year			Notes
American Folk Blues Festival 1966	LP	Fontana	(S)TL5389	1966	£6	£15	
Angola Prisoners' Blues	LP	Collector	JGN1003	1960	£6	£15	
Anthology Of British Blues Vol.1	LP	Immediate	IMAL03/04	1969	£6	£15	double
Anthology Of British Blues Vol.2	LP	Immediate	IMAL05/06	1969	£6	£15	double
Apollo Saturday Night	LP	London	HAK/SHK8174	1964	£10	£25	
At The Cavern	LP	Decca	LK4597	1964	£10	£25	
Atlantic Discotheque	LP	Atlantic	ATL5020	1965	£5	£12	
Atlantic Is Soul	LP	Atlantic	AP2	196-	£4	£10	
Atlanticclassics	LP	Atlantic	AC3	196-	£20	£40	
Authentic Rhythm And Blues	LP	Stateside	SL10068	1964	£8	£20	
Authentic Ska	LP	Stateside	SL10107	1964	£8	£20	
Backwoods Blues	10" LP	London	AL3535	1954	£10	£25	
Ballin'	LP	Fontana	688200ZL	1962	£4	£10	
Bang Bang Lulu	LP	Pama	PMLP4	1968	£8	£20	
Barrelhouse, Boogie Woogie, And Blues	10" LP	Fontana	TFR6018	1959	£6	£15	
Barrelhouse Piano	10" LP	Vogue Coral	LRA10022	1955	£6	£15	
Barrelhouse Piano Vol.2	10" LP	Vogue Coral	LRA10023	1955	£6	£15	
Battle Of The Bands	10" LP	Capitol	LC6510	1951	£6	£15	
Battle Of The Giants	LP	Melodisc	12192	196-	£4	£10	
Bebop Era	LP	RCA	RD7909	1967	£4	£10	
Bells Are Ringing	7" EP	Philips	BBE12148	1957	£2	£5	
Best Of American Folk Music	LP	XTRA	XTRA1032	1965	£4	£10	
Best Of Bluegrass	7" EP	Melodisc	EPM7115	195-	£4	£8	
Best Of British Folk Music	LP	XTRA	XTRA1031	1965	£4	£10	
Best Of Camel	LP	Pama	SECO18	1969	£6	£15	
Best Wishes For Christmas	7" EP	Philips	BBE12225	1958	£2	£5	
Big Beat	LP	Fontana	TFL5080	1959	£20	£40	
Big D Jamboree	LP	London	HAB8199	1964	£4	£10	
Big Four	7" EP	Fontana	TE17469	1966	£4	£8	
Big Four	7" EP	Philips	BBE12021	1956	£5	£10	
Big Four	7" EP	Philips	BE12593	1966	£2	£5	
Big Four No.10	7" EP	Philips	BBE12190	1958	£4	£8	
Big Four No.11	7" EP	Philips	BBE12288	1959	£2.50	£6	
Big Four No.12	7" EP	Philips	BBE12336	1959	£2.50	£6	
Big Four No.2	7" EP	Philips	BBE12040	1956	£5	£10	
Big Four No.3	7" EP	Philips	BBE12088	1956	£2.50	£6	
Big Four No.4	7" EP	Philips	BBE12091	1956	£4	£8	
Big Four No.5	7" EP	Philips	BBE12114	1957	£2.50	£6	
Big Four No.6	7" EP	Philips	BBE12139	1957	£2.50	£6	
Big Four No.7	7" EP	Philips	BBE12145	1957	£4	£8	
Big Four No.8	7" EP	Philips	BBE12158	1957	£2.50	£6	
Big Four No.9	7" EP	Philips	BBE12165	1957	£4	£8	
Big One	LP	Minit	MML40007E	1969	£4	£10	
Birth Control	LP	Pama	SECO32	1970	£6	£15	
Bitter End Years	LP	Roxbury	RX3300	1976	£10	£25	US triple
Black Country Night Out	LP	Broadside	BRO120	1976	£5	£12	
Black Country Night Out Vol.2	LP	Broadside	BRO122	1977	£5	£12	
Black Diamond Express To Hell	LP	Matchbox	SDX207/8	1970	£5	£12	double
Black Slacks And Bobby Socks	LP	HMV	CLP1167	1958	£8	£20	
Black, Whites And Blues	LP	CBS	52796	1970	£4	£10	
Blackpool Nights	LP	Columbia	33SX1244	1960	£6	£15	
Blue Beat Special	LP	Coxsone	CSP1	1968	£30	£60	
Blue Ridge Mountain Field Trip	LP	Leader	LEA4012	1970	£5	£12	
Bluebird Blues	LP	RCA	RD7786	1966	£4	£10	
Bluegrass	7" EP	Range	JRE7005	196-	£2	£5	
Blues	LP	Chess	CRL4003	1964	£4	£10	
Blues	LP	Columbia	33SX1417	1962	£8	£20	
Blues Anytime Vol.1	LP	Immediate	IMLP014	1968	£5	£12	chart LP
Blues Anytime Vol.2	LP	Immediate	IMLP015	1968	£5	£12	
Blues Anytime Vol.3	LP	Immediate	IMLP019	1968	£5	£12	
Blues Are Alive And Well	LP	XTRA	XTRA1105	1971	£4	£10	
Blues At Newport	LP	Vanguard	VSD79145	1965	£5	£12	US
Blues Came Down From Memphis	LP	London	HAS8265	1966	£10	£25	
Blues Fell This Morning	LP	Philips	BBL7369	1960	£15	£30	
Blues Festival	7" EP	Pye	NEP44038	1964	£7.50	£15	
Blues From Big Bill's Copa Cabana	LP	Chess	CRLS4558	1970	£5	£12	
Blues From Chicago	LP	Python	PLP6	1969	£8	£20	
Blues From Chicago Vol.2	LP	Python	PLP9	1970	£8	£20	
Blues From Chicago Vol.3	LP	Python	PLP15	1970	£8	£20	
Blues From Maxwell Street	LP	Heritage	1004	196-	£8	£20	
Blues From The Bayou	LP	Pye	NPL28142	1971	£5	£12	
Blues From The Windy City	LP	Python	PLP21	1971	£8	£20	
Blues Is My Companion	LP	Sunflower		196-	£6	£15	
Blues Keep Falling	LP	Sunflower		196-	£6	£15	
Blues Leftovers	LP	Immediate	IMLP024	1969	£4	£10	
Blues Like Showers Of Rain	LP	Matchbox	SDM142	1967	£25	£50	
Blues Like Showers Of Rain Vol.2	LP	Saydisc	SDM167	1968	£20	£40	
Blues Now	LP	Decca	LK4681	1965	£10	£25	
Blues Obscurities Vol.1	LP	Blues Obscurities		1972	£8	£20	
Blues Obscurities Vol.1	LP	London	HAU8454	1974	£4	£10	
Blues Obscurities Vol.10	LP	Blues Obscurities		1972	£8	£20	
Blues Obscurities Vol.2	LP	Blues Obscurities		1972	£8	£20	
Blues Obscurities Vol.2	LP	London	HAU8455	1974	£4	£10	
Blues Obscurities Vol.3	LP	Blues Obscurities		1972	£8	£20	
Blues Obscurities Vol.3	LP	London	HAU8456	1974	£4	£10	

Title	Format	Label	Cat. No.	Year			Notes
Blues Obscurities Vol.4	LP	Blues Obscurities		1972	£8	£20	
Blues Obscurities Vol.5	LP	Blues Obscurities		1972	£8	£20	
Blues Obscurities Vol.6	LP	Blues Obscurities		1972	£8	£20	
Blues Obscurities Vol.7	LP	Blues Obscurities		1972	£8	£20	
Blues Obscurities Vol.8	LP	Blues Obscurities		1972	£8	£20	
Blues Obscurities Vol.9	LP	Blues Obscurities		1972	£8	£20	
Blues On Parade No.1	7" EP	Columbia	SEG8226	1963	£5	£10	
Blues People	LP	Highway 51	H102	1969	£20	£40	
Blues Piano - Chicago Plus	LP	Atlantic	K40404	1972	£5	£12	
Blues Potpourri	LP	Kokomo	K1001	1968	£20	£40	
Blues Rarities Vol.1	LP	Rarities		1971	£6	£15	double
Blues Roll On	LP	Atlantic	590019	1969	£4	£10	
Blues Roots Vol.1	LP	Poppy		197-	£5	£12	
Blues Southside Chicago	LP	Decca	LK4748	1966	£8	£20	
Blues Today - Southern Style	LP	Python	PLP16	1971	£8	£20	
Blues Vol.1	LP	Pye	NPL28030	1964	£5	£12	chart LP
Blues Vol.1	7" EP	Pye	NEP44029	1964	£6	£12	
Blues Vol.1 Pt.2	7" EP	Pye	NEP44035	1964	£5	£10	
Blues Vol.2	LP	Pye	NPL28035	1964	£5	£12	chart LP
Blues Vol.2 Part 1	7" EP	Chess	CRE6011	1966	£6	£12	
Blues Vol.3	LP	Pye	NPL28045	1964	£5	£12	
Bluescene USA Vol.1	LP	Storyville	SLP176	1965	£5	£12	
Bluescene USA Vol.2	LP	Storyville	SLP177	1965	£5	£12	
Bluescene USA Vol.3	LP	Storyville	SLP181	1965	£5	£12	
Bluescene USA Vol.4	LP	Storyville	SLP189	1967	£5	£12	
Bocastle Breakdown	LP	Topic	12TS240	1974	£5	£12	
Bonnie Lass Come O'er The Burn	LP	Topic	12T128	1965	£10	£25	
Bonny North Tyne	LP	Topic	12TS239	1974	£5	£12	
Boogie Woogie Rarities	LP	Milestone	MLP2009	197-	£4	£10	
Boogie Woogie With The Blues	10" LP	London	AL3544	1955	£6	£15	
Boss Reggae	LP	Pama	SECO17	1969	£15	£30	
Both Sides Of The Downs	LP	Eron	002	1974	£6	£15	
Bothy Ballads	LP	Tangent	TNGM109	1971	£5	£12	
Bouquet Of Steel	LP	Aardvark	STEAL2	1980	£4	£10	blue vinyl
Brave Plough Boy	LP	XTRA	XTRA1150	1975	£10	£25	
Breeze From Erin	LP	Topic	12T184	1969	£5	£12	
Bristol Recorder Vol.2	LP	Bristol Recorder	BR002	1981	£5	£12	
British Blue-Eyed Soul	LP	Island	ILP966/ILPS9066	1968	£15	£30	
British Motown Chartbusters	LP	Tamla Motown	(S)TML11055	1967	£4	£10	chart LP
Broadside Ballads Vol.1	LP	Broadside	BR301	1964	£6	£15	US
Brum Beat - Live At The Barrel Organ	LP	Big Bear	BRUM1	1979	£5	£12	double
Brumbeat	LP	Dial	DLP1	1964	£25	£50	
Brunswick Hit Parade Vol.2	7" EP	Brunswick	OE9450	1959	£2	£5	
Bumper Bundle - 16 Hits	LP	Decca	LK4734	1965	£6	£15	
Buskers	LP	Columbia	SX/SCX6356	1969	£10	£25	
Busted At Oz	LP	Autumn	AU2	1981	£6	£15	
Buttons And Bows Vol.1	LP	Dambusters	DAM003	1984	£10	£25	double
Buttons And Bows Vol.2	LP	Dambusters	DAM006	1985	£8	£20	double
Bye Bye Birdie	7" EP	Pye	NEP24142	1961	£2	£5	
Cabaret Night In London	LP	Columbia	SX1481	1963	£6	£15	
Cabaret Night In Paris	7" EP	Columbia	33S1083	1956	£2.50	£6	
Cabaret Night In Paris No.4	7" EP	Columbia	33S1099	1957	£2.50	£6	
Cabaret Night In Paris No.5	7" EP	Columbia	33S1105	1957	£2.50	£6	
Calypso Time	7" EP	Melodisc	EPM767	1956	£2.50	£6	
Cameo Big Four	7" EP	Cameo Parkway	CPE552	1963	£5	£10	
Canny Newcassel	LP	Topic	12TS219	1972	£10	£25	
Carolina Country Blues	LP	Flyright	LP505	1973	£4	£10	
Cerne Box Set	LP	Cerne	CERNE123	198-	£15	£30	3 LPs, boxed
Chaplin Revue	LP	Brunswick	LAT8345	1960	£8	£20	
Charge Of The Light Brigade	LP	United Artists	UAS5177	1968	£5	£12	US
Chicago - The Blues Today	LP	Fontana	TFL6068	1966	£8	£20	
Chicago - The Blues Today Vol.1	LP	Vanguard	SVRL19020	1969	£8	£20	
Chicago - The Blues Today Vol.2	LP	Fontana	TFL6069	1966	£8	£20	
Chicago - The Blues Today Vol.2	LP	Vanguard	SVRL19021	1969	£8	£20	
Chicago - The Blues Today Vol.3	LP	Fontana	TFL6070	1966	£8	£20	
Chicago - The Blues Today Vol.3	LP	Vanguard	SVRL19022	1969	£8	£20	
Chicago House Bands	LP	Sunflower	ET1401	1968	£6	£15	
Chicago Sessions Vol.1	LP	Kokomo	K1005	1969	£15	£30	
Chicken Stuff	LP	Flyright	LP4700	1970	£4	£10	
Christmas	10" LP	Philips	BBR8112	1957	£4	£10	
Christmas Dedication	LP	Chess	CRLS4541	1968	£4	£10	
Christmas Reggae	7" EP	Coxsone	SCE1	1967	£20	£40	
Classic Rhythm And Blues	LP	Atlantic	587167	1969	£5	£12	
Classic Scots Ballads	LP	Tangent	TNGM199D	1975	£8	£20	double
Classics Of Irish Traditional Music	LP	Morning Star	45001	1973	£6	£15	US
Club Folk Vol.1	LP	Pegasus	PS2	1972	£5	£12	
Club Folk Vol.2	LP	Pegasus	PS3	1972	£5	£12	
Club Reggae Vol.1	LP	Trojan	TBL159	1970	£4	£10	
Club Reggae Vol.2	LP	Trojan	TBL164	1971	£4	£10	
Club Reggae Vol.3	LP	Trojan	TBL178	1971	£4	£10	
Club Reggae Vol.4	LP	Trojan	TBL188	1972	£4	£10	
Club Rock Steady	LP	Trojan	TTL54	1970	£8	£20	

Title	Format	Label	Catalogue	Year	Price	Price	Notes
Club Rock Steady '68	LP	Island	ILP965	1968	£30	£60	
Club Ska '67	LP	Island	ILP948	1967	£20	£40	chart LP
Club Ska '67 Vol.2	LP	Island	ILP956	1967	£30	£60	
Club Ska Vol.1	LP	Trojan	TTL48	1970	£8	£20	
Club Ska Vol.2	LP	Trojan	TTL51	1970	£8	£20	
Club Soul	LP	Island	ILP964	1968	£10	£25	
Collection Of 16 Big Hits Vol.6	LP	Tamla Motown	(S)TML11074	1968	£6	£15	chart LP
Collection Of 16 Original Big Hits Vol.4	LP	Tamla Motown	TML11043	1967	£8	£20	chart LP
Collection Of 16 Original Big Hits Vol.5	LP	Tamla Motown	TML11050	1967	£6	£15	chart LP
Collection Of 16 Tamla Motown Hits	LP	Tamla Motown	TML11001	1965	£15	£30	chart LP
Collection Of Big Hits Vol.7	LP	Tamla Motown	(S)TML11092	1969	£5	£12	
Collectors Blues Series Vol.1	LP	Chicago	202	1975	£6	£15	
Collectors Blues Series Vol.2	LP	Chicago	205	1975	£6	£15	
Collectors Blues Series Vol.3	LP	Chicago	210	1975	£6	£15	
Collectors Blues Series Vol.4	LP	Chicago	212	1975	£6	£15	
Collectors Blues Series Vol.5	LP	Chicago	213	1975	£6	£15	
Collectors Items Vol.1	10" LP	London	AL3514	1954	£4	£10	
Collectors Items Vol.2	10" LP	London	AL3533	1954	£4	£10	
Collectors Items Vol.3	10" LP	London	AL3550	1956	£4	£10	
Columbia Cavalcade	7"	Columbia	SCD2008	1953	£1.50	£4	
Come Fly With Me	LP	Blue Beat	BBLP803	1964	£50	£100	
Cool Music For A Hot Night	LP	Tempo	TAP10	1957	£6	£15	
Country & Western Hits Vol.1	7" EP	CBS	AGG20033	1963	£2	£5	
Country & Western Hits Vol.2	7" EP	CBS	AGG20041	1964	£2	£5	
Country And Western	7" EP	Range	JRE7001	196-	£2	£5	
Country And Western	7" EP	Range	JRE7004	196-	£2	£5	
Country And Western Express Vol.1	7" EP	Top Rank	JKP2055	1960	£2	£5	
Country And Western Express Vol.4	7" EP	Top Rank	JKP2063	1960	£2	£5	
Country And Western Express Vol.6	7" EP	Top Rank	JKP2065	1960	£5	£10	
Country And Western Golden Hit Parade Vol.1	LP	London	HAB8145	1964	£4	£10	
Country And Western Golden Hit Parade Vol.2	LP	London	HAB8145	1964	£4	£10	
Country And Western Showcase Vol.2	7" EP	Hickory	LPE1505	1965	£2	£5	
Country And Western Spectacular	7" EP	Philips	BBE12149	1957	£5	£10	
Country And Western Trail Blazers No.1	7" EP	Mercury	ZEP10038	1959	£4	£8	
Country Blues	LP	RBF	RF1	1961	£6	£15	
Country Blues	7" EP	Heritage	105	196-	£7.50	£15	
Country Blues Vol.2	LP	RBF	RBF9	1964	£6	£15	
Country Favourites Vol.1	10" LP	Brunswick	LA8729	1956	£4	£10	
Country Guitar Hall Of Fame	LP	London	HAB8243	1965	£4	£10	
Country Guitar Vol.1	7" EP	RCA	RCX107	1958	£2	£5	
Country Guitar Vol.10	7" EP	RCA	RCX176	1959	£4	£8	
Country Guitar Vol.11	7" EP	RCA	RCX177	1959	£2	£5	
Country Guitar Vol.12	7" EP	RCA	RCX185	1960	£2	£5	
Country Guitar Vol.2	7" EP	RCA	RCX110	1958	£4	£8	
Country Guitar Vol.5	7" EP	RCA	RCX127	1959	£2	£5	
Country Guitar Vol.6	7" EP	RCA	RCX141	1959	£2	£5	
Country Guitar Vol.8	7" EP	RCA	RCX147	1959	£2	£5	
Country Guitar Vol.9	7" EP	RCA	RCX159	1959	£4	£8	
Country Jubilee Vol.1	7" EP	Decca	DFE8522	1963	£2	£5	
Country Jubilee Vol.2	7" EP	Decca	DFE8523	1963	£2	£5	
Crab - Biggest Hits	LP	Pama	ECO2	1969	£8	£20	
Damn Yankees	7" EP	Mercury	MEP9509	1956	£2	£5	
Dance Craze	7" EP	Capitol	EAP1518	1955	£4	£8	
Dancing Down Orange Street	LP	Big Shot	BSLP5002	1968	£20	£40	
Dandelion Sampler	7"	Dandelion	DS7001	1971	£2	£5	
Dark Horse Records '76	LP	Dark Horse	DH1	1976	£8	£20	promo
Dark Muddy Bottom	7" EP	XX	MIN706	196-	£4	£8	
Decade Of The Blues - The 1950's	LP	Highway 51	H100	1966	£20	£40	
Decade Of The Blues - The 1950's Vol.2	LP	Highway 51	H104	1966	£15	£30	
Decca Showcase Vol.5	10" LP	Decca	LF1265	1955	£4	£10	
Deep In My Heart	7" EP	MGM	MGMEP652	1958	£2	£5	
Depression Blues	7" EP	Poydras	102	195-	£5	£10	
Devastate To Liberate	LP	YANGKI	1	1985	£4	£10	
Ding Dong Dollar Anti-Polaris And Scottish Republican Songs	LP	Folkways	FD5444	1962	£10	£25	US
Dingles Regatta	LP	Dingles	DIN301	1976	£5	£12	
Dirt Blues	LP	Minit	MLL/MLS40005	1969	£6	£15	
Disc A Dawn	LP	BBC	REC65M	1970	£6	£15	
Discs A Go Go	7" EP	Decca	DFE8520	1962	£7.50	£15	
Doctor Soul	LP	Island	ILP943	1967	£15	£30	
Down Home Blues - Sixties Style	7" EP	Jan & Dil	JR450	196-	£5	£10	
Down In Hogan's Alley	LP	Flyright	LP4703	1971	£4	£10	
Downhome Blues	LP	Python		1970	£8	£20	
Downhome Blues Vol.2	LP	Python	PLP14	1970	£8	£20	
Downhome Blues Vol.3	LP	Python	PLP22	1971	£8	£20	
Downhome Harp	7" EP	XX	MIN709	196-	£2.50	£6	
Dr.Kitch	LP	Island	ILP954	1967	£30	£60	
Drumbeat	LP	Parlophone	PMC1101	1959	£10	£25	
Drumbeat	7" EP	Fontana	TFE17146	1959	£7.50	£15	
Duke And The Peacock	LP	Island	ILP976	1968	£30	£60	
Duke Reid's Golden Hits	LP	Trojan	TTL8	1969	£8	£20	
Duke Reid's Rock Steady	LP	Island	ILP958	1967	£30	£60	
Duke Reid's Rock Steady	LP	Trojan	TTL53	1970	£15	£30	
Dulcimer Players	LP	Transatlantic	LTRA502	1978	£5	£12	
Dungeon Folk	LP	BBC	REC355	1969	£6	£15	
Earcom 2	12"	Fast	EARCOM2	1979	£4	£10	
Early Blues Vol.1	LP	Saydisc	SDR199	1970	£4	£10	

Title	Format	Label	Catalogue	Year	Price	Price	Notes
Early Blues Vol.2	LP	Saydisc	SDR206	1970	£4	£10	
Earthed	LP	Middle Earth	MDLS20	1970	£25	£50	
East	LP	Dead Good	GOOD1	1980	£5	£12	
East Vernon Blues	LP	Southern Sound	SD200	1973	£8	£20	
Easy Rider	LP	Stateside	SSL5018	1969	£4	£10	
Edinburgh Folk Festival	LP	Decca	LK4546	1963	£25	£50	
Edinburgh Folk Festival Vol.2	LP	Decca	LK4563	1964	£35	£70	
Edinburgh Students Charity Appeal	7" EP	E.S.C.	ESC02	1965	£10	£20	
Edinburgh Students Charity Appeal	7" EP	E.S.C.	ESC03	1966	£10	£20	
Electric Blues	LP	Chess	109597/8/9	1969	£10	£25	German, 3 LPs in metal box
Electric Muse	LP	Island/Transatlantic	FOLK1001	1975	£20	£40	4 LP set
English Country Music	LP	Topic	12T296	1976	£5	£12	
English Country Music From East Anglia	LP	Topic	12TS229	1973	£5	£12	
English Melodeon Players	LP	Plant Life	PLR073	1986	£5	£12	
Esquire's Jazz	LP	RCA	RD7904	1967	£4	£10	
European Song Cup 1963	7" EP	Decca	DFE8534	1963	£2.50	£6	
Every Day I Have The Blues	LP	Speciality	SPE6601	1967	£4	£10	
Excello Story	LP	Blue Horizon	2683007	1972	£30	£60	double
Explosive Rocksteady	LP	Amalgamated	AMGLP2002	1968	£25	£50	
Extracts From Stiff's Greatest Hits	7"	Stiff	FREEBIE2	1978	£2.50	£6	
Ey Up Mi Duck! A Celebration Of Derbyshire	LP	RAM	1	1978	£5	£12	
Fantastic Folk	LP	Elektra	EUK259	1968	£4	£10	
Farewell Nancy	LP	Topic	12T110	1964	£8	£20	
Fashioned To A Device Behind A Tree	LP	Come Organisation	WDC881021	198-	£30	£60	
Feast Of Irish Folk	LP	Polydor	2475605	1977	£5	£12	Irish
Festival Of British Jazz	LP	Decca	LK4180	1957	£6	£15	
Festival Of The Blues Vol.1	7" EP	Pye	NEP44030	1964	£5	£10	
Fifteen Oldies But Goodies	LP	Melodisc	MS4	196-	£4	£10	
Fillmore Last Days	LP	Warner Bros	K66013	1972	£17.50	£35	boxed set, with booklet, ticket, poster
Fillmore Last Days	LP	Warner Bros	K66013	1972	£25	£50	promo boxed set with interview single
Fingers On Fire	LP	London	HAB8205	1965	£4	£10	
Fings Ain't Wot They Used To Be	LP	HMV	CLP1358/CSD1298	1960	£6	£15	
Firepoint	LP	Spark	SRLM2003	1969	£8	£20	
First Lame Bunny Album	LP	Spaceward	3S1/EDENLP53	1973	£8	£20	
First National Skiffle Contest	10" LP	Esquire	20089	1957	£10	£25	
First O T'Sort	LP	Transatlantic	LTRA505	1978	£5	£12	
First Rock'n'Roll Party	10" LP	Mercury	MPT7512	1956	£6	£15	
Fleadh Ceoil 1975	LP	Dolphin	DOLM5013	1975	£6	£15	Irish
Folk At The Black Horse	LP	Eron	012	1976	£5	£12	
Folk Box	LP	Elektra	EUK251/2	1966	£6	£15	double
Folk Festival	LP	Transatlantic	TRAD324	1976	£6	£15	double
Folk Festival	LP	World Record Club	ST890	1964	£10	£25	
Folk Festival At Newport 1959 Vol.1	LP	Top Rank	35070	1960	£8	£20	
Folk Festival At Newport 1959 Vol.2	LP	Top Rank	35071	1960	£8	£20	
Folk Festival At Newport 1959 Vol.3	LP	Top Rank	35072	1960	£8	£20	
Folk Festival At Newport Vol.1	LP	Fontana	TFL6000	1962	£8	£20	
Folk Festival At Newport Vol.2	LP	Fontana	TFL6004	1962	£8	£20	
Folk Festival At Newport Vol.3	LP	Fontana	TFL6009	1962	£8	£20	
Folk Festival Of The Blues	LP	Pye	NPL28033	1964	£6	£15	chart LP
Folk From McTavish's Kitchen	LP	Counterpoint	CPT3994	1973	£6	£15	
Folk Now	LP	Decca	LK4683	1965	£10	£25	
Folk On Friday	LP	BBC	REC955	1970	£10	£25	
Folk Song Today	10" LP	HMV	DLP1143	1957	£20	£40	
Folk Songs Of Britain Vol.1	LP	Topic	12T157	1966	£6	£15	
Folk Songs Of Britain Vol.10	LP	Topic	12T198	1969	£6	£15	
Folk Songs Of Britain Vol.2	LP	Topic	12T158	1966	£6	£15	
Folk Songs Of Britain Vol.3	LP	Topic	12T159	1966	£6	£15	
Folk Songs Of Britain Vol.4	LP	Topic	12T160	1966	£6	£15	
Folk Songs Of Britain Vol.5	LP	Topic	12T161	1966	£6	£15	
Folk Songs Of Britain Vol.6	LP	Topic	12T194	1969	£6	£15	
Folk Songs Of Britain Vol.7	LP	Topic	12T195	1969	£6	£15	
Folk Songs Of Britain Vol.8	LP	Topic	12T196	1969	£6	£15	
Folk Songs Of Britain Vol.9	LP	Topic	12T197	1969	£6	£15	
Folk Sound Of Britain	LP	HMV	CLP1910	1965	£8	£20	
Folk Trailer	LP	Trailer	LER2019	1970	£6	£15	
Four Bob Dylan Songs	7" EP	Riviera	231160	1966	£12.50	£25	French
Four Great Movie Themes	7" EP	Philips	BBE12140	1957	£4	£8	
Four Of The Tops	7" EP	Pye	NEP24300	1968	£2	£5	
Fourteen	LP	Decca	LK4695	1965	£6	£15	
Freedom Sounds	LP	Bamboo	BLP205	1970	£15	£30	
Fresh From The Can	LP	Polydor	2675004	1970	£10	£25	German, 3 LPs in metal box
From Bam Bam To Cherry Oh Baby	LP	Trojan	TRL51	1972	£4	£10	
From Torture To Conscience	LP	New European	BADVC666	198-	£5	£12	
Funky Chicken	LP	Trojan	TBL137	1970	£6	£15	
Funky Reggae	LP	Bamboo	BLP206	1970	£15	£30	
Fylde Acoustic	LP	Trailer	LER2105	1977	£10	£25	
Gas - Greatest Hits	LP	Pama	ECO4	1969	£8	£20	
Gayfeet	LP	Doctor Bird	DLM5001	1966	£40	£80	
Gene Norman's Just Jazz	LP	Vogue	LAE12001	1955	£8	£20	
Genesis - Memphis To Chicago	LP	Chess	6641125	1973	£20	£40	4 LPs, boxed

Title	Format	Label	Catalogue	Year	Price	Price	Notes
Genesis - Sweet Home Chicago	LP	Chess	6641174	1975	£20	£40	4 LPs, boxed
Genesis - The Beginnings Of Rock	LP	Chess	6641047	1972	£20	£40	4 LPs, boxed
Georgia Guitars 1927-1938	LP	Kokomo	K1004	1969	£15	£30	
Get Ready Rock Steady	LP	Coxsone	CSL8007	1967	£50	£100	
Giants Of Modern Jazz	LP	Concert Hall	BJ1204	1955	£5	£12	
Gift From Pama	LP	Pama	SECO20	1970	£8	£20	
Girls And More Girls	7" EP	MGM	MGMEP703	1959	£2.50	£6	
Glastonbury Fayre	LP	Revelation	REV1	1974	£45	£90	triple, 4 inserts
Go	LP	Columbia	SX6062	1966	£15	£30	
Goin' Away Walkin'	LP	Flyright	LP103	1972	£4	£10	
Goin' Back To Chicago	LP	Python	LP1	1970	£8	£20	
Goin' Up The Country	LP	Decca	LK4931	1968	£4	£10	
Going To California	LP	Heritage	1003	196-	£8	£20	
Gold	LP	Mother	MO4001	1972	£20	£40	
Golden Hits	LP	Philips	BBL7331	1959	£5	£12	
Golden Hits Vol.2	LP	Philips	BBL7422	1960	£4	£10	
Golden Hits Vol.3	LP	Philips	BBL7581	1961	£5	£12	
Gonks Go Beat	LP	Decca	LK4673	1965	£25	£50	
Good Folk Of Kent	LP	Eron	004	197-	£25	£50	
Good Time Music	LP	Elektra	EUK/EUKS7260	1967	£8	£20	
Gospel Sound	LP	CBS	67234	1972	£6	£15	double
Grand Airs Of Connemara	LP	Topic	12T177	1968	£5	£12	
Grand Old Fifties	LP	Atlantic	ATL5004	1964	£8	£20	
Greasy Truckers Live At Dingwalls	LP	Greasy Truckers	GT4997	1973	£6	£15	double
Greasy Truckers Party	LP	United Artists	UDX203/4	1974	£8	£20	double
Great Blues Singers	LP	Riverside	RLP12121	196-	£5	£12	
Great Blues Singers	10" LP	London	AL3530	1954	£8	£20	
Great Country And Western Hits	7" EP	Philips	BBE12318	1959	£4	£8	
Great White Dap	7" EP	Village Thing	VTSX1000	1970	£7.50	£15	
Greater Jamaica	LP	Trojan	TBL111	1970	£8	£20	
Greatest Jamaican Beat	LP	Doctor Bird	DLM5009	1967	£40	£80	
Greatest On Stage	7" EP	Pye	NEP44054	1966	£4	£8	
Grooving With Bamboo	LP	Bamboo	BDLP215	1971	£15	£30	
Groovy Baby	LP	Direction	863452	1968	£5	£12	
Group Beat '63	LP	Realm	RM149	1963	£8	£20	
Group Of Goodies	LP	London	HAU8086	1963	£6	£15	
Group Of Goodies	7" EP	London	REU1393	1963	£5	£10	
Groups Galore	7" EP	Mercury	ZEP10010	1959	£30	£60	
Gulf Coast Blues	LP	Sunnyland	KS102	1971	£6	£15	
Guns Of Navarone	LP	Trojan	TTL16	1969	£8	£20	
Guy Stevens' Testament Of Rock'n'Roll	LP	Island	ILP977	1968	£8	£20	
Guys And Dolls	7" EP	Philips	BBE12077	1956	£2	£5	
Hallucinations Off 2 - Psychedelic Underground	LP	Elektra/ Metronome	KMLP310	1969	£8	£20	German pic disc
Harlem Piano Roll	10" LP	London	AL3553	1956	£6	£15	
Harvest Sampler	LP	Harvest	HARSPSLP118	1969	£30	£60	promo
Havin' A Good Time - Chicago Blues Anthology	LP	Sunnyland	KS101	1971	£6	£15	
Headline News	LP	Polydor	582701	1966	£5	£12	
Heads Together, First Round	LP	Vertigo	6360045	1971	£5	£12	double, spiral label
Heather And Glen	LP	Tradition	TLP1047	1963	£6	£15	US
Here Come The Girls	LP	Pye	NPL18122	1965	£5	£12	
Here Comes The Duke	LP	Trojan	TRL6	1968	£15	£30	
Hey Boy Hey Girl	LP	Pama	PSP1002	1969	£8	£20	
Hickory Showcase Vol.1	7" EP	Hickory	LPE1500	1964	£2	£5	
Highway To Heaven	LP	Parlophone	PMC1085	1959	£6	£15	
History Of Jazz Part 1	10" LP	Capitol	LC6507	1951	£6	£15	
History Of Jazz Part 2	10" LP	Capitol	LC6508	1951	£6	£15	
History Of R&B Vol.1	LP	Atlantic	587094	1968	£4	£10	
History Of R&B Vol.2	LP	Atlantic	587095	1968	£4	£10	
History Of R&B Vol.3	LP	Atlantic	587096	1968	£4	£10	
History Of R&B Vol.4	LP	Atlantic	587097	1968	£4	£10	
History Of R&B Vol.5	LP	Atlantic	587140	1968	£4	£10	
History Of R&B Vol.6	LP	Atlantic	587141	1968	£4	£10	
History Of Ska Vol.1	LP	Bamboo	BDLP203	1969	£20	£40	
Hit Makers	LP	Pye	NPL18108	1964	£4	£10	
Hit Parade	7" EP	Brunswick	OE9340	1957	£2	£5	
Hit Parade Of 1956	10" LP	Pye	NPT19015	1957	£5	£12	
Hit Parade Vol.1	7" EP	Mercury	MEP9003	1956	£7.50	£15	
Hit Parade Vol.2	7" EP	Mercury	MEP9510	1956	£7.50	£15	
Hit The Road Stax	LP	Stax	589005	1967	£6	£15	chart LP
Hitmakers	7" EP	Piccadilly	NEP34100	1966	£2	£5	
Hitmakers International	7" EP	Pye	NEP44065	1966	£2.50	£6	
Hitmakers No.1	7" EP	Pye	NEP24213	1965	£2.50	£6	
Hitmakers No.2	7" EP	Pye	NEP24214	1965	£5	£10	
Hitmakers No.3	7" EP	Pye	NEP24215	1965	£2.50	£6	
Hitmakers Vol.1	7" EP	Pye	NEP24241	1966	£2.50	£6	
Hitmakers Vol.2	7" EP	Pye	NEP24242	1966	£4	£8	
Hitmakers Vol.3	7" EP	Pye	NEP24243	1966	£2.50	£6	
Hits From Can Can	7" EP	Capitol	EAP1482	1955	£2	£5	
Hits Vol.1	7" EP	Decca	DFE8648	1965	£2.50	£6	
Hits Vol.2	7" EP	Decca	DFE8649	1965	£4	£8	
Hits Vol.3	7" EP	Decca	DFE8653	1965	£4	£8	
Hits Vol.4	7" EP	Decca	DFE8662	1966	£4	£8	
Hits Vol.5	7" EP	Decca	DFE8663	1966	£5	£10	
Hits Vol.6	7" EP	Decca	DFE8667	1966	£4	£8	
Hits Vol.7	7" EP	Decca	DFER8675	1967	£2.50	£6	
Hitsville	7" EP	Mercury	ZEP10133	1962	£7.50	£15	

Title	Format	Label	Catalogue	Year	Price	Price	Notes
Hitsville USA	LP	Tamla Motown	TML11019	1965	£15	£30	
Hitsville USA No.1	7" EP	Tamla Motown	TME2001	1965	£20	£40	
Hitsville Vol.1	7" EP	Coral	FEP2034	1959	£15	£30	
Hitsville Vol.2	7" EP	Coral	FEP2035	1959	£6	£12	
Hobos And Drifters	7" EP	Postwar Blues	100	1966	£6	£12	
Hoisting The Black Flag	LP	United Dairies	UD06	1981	£30	£60	
Honeys	LP	Melodisc	12216	196-	£4	£10	
Honky Tonk Train	LP	Riverside	RLP8806	196-	£6	£15	
Hootenanny In London	LP	Decca	LK4544	1963	£10	£25	
Hootenanny New York City	7" EP	Topic	TOP37	1959	£5	£10	
Hot Calypsos	7" EP	Capitol	EAP1852	1957	£4	£8	
Hot Numbers	LP	Pama	PMP2006	1971	£6	£15	
Hot Numbers Vol.2	LP	Pama	PMP2009	1971	£6	£15	
Hot Shots Of Reggae	LP	Trojan	TBL128	1970	£6	£15	
House That Track Built	LP	Track	613016	1969	£5	£12	
Houston Jump	7" EP	Solid Sender	SEP100	1975	£2	£5	
How Blue Can We Get?	LP	Blue Horizon	PR45/46	1970	£10	£25	double
I'm Your Country Man	LP	Highway 51	H104	1970	£10	£25	
In Crowd	LP	CBS		1966	£6	£15	
In Crowd	7" EP	Chess	CRE6010	1966	£7.50	£15	
In Fractured Silence	LP	United Dairies	UD015	198-	£10	£25	
In Loving Memory	LP	Tamla Motown	(S)TML11124	1969	£20	£40	
In Our Own Way/Oldies But Goodies	LP	Blue Horizon	PR37	1969	£6	£15	
Independent Jamaica	LP	Trojan	TTL15	1969	£8	£20	
Industrial Records Story	LP	Illuminated	JAMS39	1984	£6	£15	
International Artists	7"	Radar	SAM88	1978	£2	£5	
Irish Folk Night	LP	Decca	LK4633	1964	£6	£15	
Irish Music In London Pubs	LP	Folkways	FG3575	1965	£10	£25	US
Irish Music In London Pubs	LP	XTRA	XTRA1090	1969	£6	£15	
Irish Pipering	LP	Claddagh	CC11	1971	£6	£15	Irish
Irish Reels, Jigs, Hornpipes And Airs	LP	Kicking Mule	SNKF153	1979	£5	£12	
Irish Traditional Concertina Styles	LP	Free Reed	FRS506	1977	£5	£12	
Iron Muse	LP	Topic	12T86	1963	£10	£25	
Isle Of Wight/Atlanta Festival	LP	CBS	66311	1971	£10	£25	triple
Items From Guys And Dolls	7" EP	Mercury	MEP9503	1956	£4	£8	
It's All Happening	LP	Columbia	SCX3486	1963	£5	£12	
It's Cha Cha Time	7" EP	Mercury	ZEP10001	1959	£5	£10	
It's Great To Be Young	7" EP	Columbia	SEG7639	1956	£4	£8	
It's Trad Dad	LP	Columbia	33SX1412	1962	£8	£20	chart LP
Jack Good's Oh Boy!	LP	Parlophone	PMC1072	1958	£15	£30	chart LP
Jackpot Of Hits	LP	Amalgamated	CSP3	1969	£30	£60	
Jamaica Ska	LP	Atlantic	587075	1968	£20	£40	
Jamaican Blues	LP	Blue Beat	BBLP801	1961	£50	£100	
Jamaican Memories	LP	Blue Cat	BCL1	1968	£25	£50	
Jamaica's Greatest Hits	LP	Melodisc	MLP12158	197-	£6	£15	
Jambalaya On The Bayou Vol.1	LP	Flyright	LP3502	1968	£6	£15	
Jambalaya On The Bayou Vol.2	LP	Flyright	LP3503	1968	£6	£15	
James Bond Collection	LP	United Artists	UAS60027/8	1972	£6	£15	double
Jazz Explosion	LP	Columbia	SLJS1	1969	£4	£10	
Jazz Juice	LP	Streetsounds	MUSIC1	1984	£8	£20	
Jazz Juice	LP	Streetsounds	SOUND1	1985	£6	£15	
Jazz Juice 2	LP	Streetsounds	SOUND4	1986	£5	£12	
Jazz Juice 4	LP	Streetsounds	SOUND5	1986	£5	£12	
Jazz Juice 5	LP	Streetsounds	SOUND6	1986	£5	£12	
Jazz Juice 6	LP	Streetsounds	SOUND8	1987	£5	£12	
Jazz Juice 7	LP	Streetsounds	SOUND9	1987	£5	£12	
Jazz Juice 8	LP	Streetsounds	SOUND10	1988	£5	£12	
Jazz Juice 9	LP	Streetsounds	SOUND11	1988	£4	£10	
	LP	Streetsounds	SOUND12	1988	£4	£10	
Joe Meek Story	LP	Decca	DPA3035/6	1977	£5	£12	double
John Peel Presents Top Gear	LP	BBC	REC52S	1969	£10	£25	
Jug Bands Vol.1	7" EP	Natchez	NEP701	1967	£6	£12	
Jug Of Punch	LP	HMV	CLP1327	1960	£10	£25	
Jug Of Punch	LP	HMV	XLP50003	1960	£25	£50	
Jugs And Washboards	LP	Ace Of Hearts	AH163	1967	£5	£12	
Jugs, Washboards And Kazoos	LP	RCA	RD7893	1967	£5	£12	
Jump Jamaica Jump	LP	R&B	JBL1111	1964	£50	£100	
Jumping At The Go Go	LP	RCA	RS1066	1976	£5	£12	
Just For Fun	LP	Decca	LK4524	1963	£10	£25	chart LP
Just For Kicks	LP	CBS			£6	£15	Irish
King Size Reggae	LP	Trojan	TBL140	1970	£8	£20	
Kings Of Memphis Town 1927-1930	LP	Saydisc	RL333	196-	£4	£10	
Kings Of The Blues Vol.1	7" EP	RCA	RCX202	1961	£2	£5	
Kings Of The Blues Vol.2	7" EP	RCA	RCX203	1961	£5	£10	
Kings Of The Blues Vol.3	7" EP	RCA	RCX204	1961	£5	£10	
Kings Of The Twelve String Guitar	LP	Flyright	LP101	1974	£5	£12	
Kings Of The Twelve String Guitar	LP	Gryphon	13159	196-	£5	£12	
Kinney Collection	LP	Kinney	KC1	1971	£5	£12	
Label - Sofa	LP	The Label	TRLP002S	1979	£17.50	£35	pic disc
Lark In The Morning	LP	Tradition	TLP1004	1955	£10	£25	US
Last Thing On My Mind	7" EP	Holyground	HG111	1966	£12.50	£25	
Let Me Tell You About The Blues	LP	Blue Horizon	LP2	1966	£150	£250	
Let's Go	7" EP	Top Rank	JKR8008	1959	£4	£8	
Let's Go Down South	LP	Neshoba	N11	1966	£10	£25	
Let's Go Vol.2	7" EP	Top Rank	JKR8012	1959	£5	£10	
Let's Have A Party	LP	Brunswick	LAT8271	1958	£4	£10	
Liberty/United Artists Sampler	LP	United Artists	REP102	1971	£10	£25	promo
Live At The Vortex	LP	NEMS	NEL6013	1977	£4	£10	
Live It Up	LP	Big Shot	BBTL4000	1968	£30	£60	
Liverpool Beat	LP	Embassy	WLP6065	1964	£6	£15	

Title	Format	Label	Cat No	Year	Price 1	Price 2	Notes
Lleisiau	LP	private	ADF1	1975	£30	£60	
Loch Ness Monster	LP	Trojan	TBL135	1970	£6	£15	
London Boys	7"	Decca	FR13864	1979	£1.50	£4	
London Hit Parade Vol.1	7" EP	London	RED1075	1957	£5	£10	
London Hit Parade Vol.2	7" EP	London	REP1096	1957	£15	£30	
London Hit Parade Vol.3	7" EP	London	RED1097	1958	£5	£10	
London Hit Parade Vol.4	7" EP	London	RED1130	1958	£5	£10	
London Hit Parade Vol.5	7" EP	London	RED1145	1958	£5	£10	
Lonely Is An Eyesore	CD/vid/cass	4AD	CADX703	1987	£75	£150	wooden box, etching, screen print
Lovely Dozen	LP	Pama	PSP1001	1969	£10	£25	
Man From Carolina	LP	Trojan	TBL129	1970	£6	£15	
Marmalade 100% Proof	LP	Marmalade	643314	1969	£4	£10	
Matchbox Days	LP	Village Thing	VTSAM16	1972	£8	£20	
Memories Are Made Of Hits Vol.1	LP	London	HA8129	1964	£5	£12	
Memories Are Made Of Hits Vol.2	LP	London	HA8130	1964	£5	£12	
Memories Are Made Of Hits Vol.3	LP	London	HA8131	1964	£5	£12	
Memories Are Made Of Hits Vol.4	LP	London	HA8138	1964	£5	£12	
Memories Are Made Of Hits Vol.5	LP	London	HA8148	1964	£5	£12	
Memories Are Made Of Hits Vol.6	LP	London	HA8171	1964	£5	£12	
Memories Are Made Of Hits Vol.7	LP	London	HA8189	1964	£5	£12	
Memories Are Made Of Hits Vol.8	LP	London	HA8213	1965	£5	£12	
Memphis Gold	LP	Stax	589001	1967	£5	£12	
Merry Christmas	7" EP	Decca	DFE6408	1957	£4	£8	
MGM Evergreens	7" EP	MGM	MGMEP749	1960	£4	£8	
Midnight Soul	LP	Atlantic	587021	1966	£5	£12	chart LP
Midnight Special	LP	Storyville	616009	1969	£5	£12	
Mill Valley Jam Session	LP	Polydor		1972	£6	£15	
Million-Airs	LP	Coral	LVA9126	1960	£6	£15	
Miniatures	LP	Pipe	PIPE2	1980	£4	£10	
Miss Labba Labba Reggae	LP	Trojan	TBL174	1971	£6	£15	
Modern Chicago Blues	LP	Bounty	BY6025	1966	£8	£20	
Modern Chicago Blues	LP	Polydor	545031	1967	£4	£10	
Month's Best From The Country And West	7" EP	RCA	RCX7159	1964	£2	£5	
Month's Best From The Country And West Vol.2	7" EP	RCA	RCX7162	1964	£2	£5	
Month's Best From The Country And West Vol.3	7" EP	RCA	RCX7171	1964	£2	£5	
Month's Best From The Country And West Vol.4	7" EP	RCA	RCX7172	1965	£2	£5	
Month's Best From The Country And West Vol.5	7" EP	RCA	RCX7178	1965	£2	£5	
Month's Best From The Country And West Vol.6	7" EP	RCA	RCX7181	1965	£2	£5	
Month's Best From The Country And West Vol.7	7" EP	RCA	RCX7186	1967	£2	£5	
Moonlight Groover	LP	Trojan	TTL31	1970	£8	£20	
More American Graffiti	LP	MCA		1979	£6	£15	US, promo pic disc, 4 different B sides
More Down Home Blues	7" EP	Jan & Dil	JR451	196-	£4	£8	
More Music From Mud Acres Woodstock Mountains	LP	Sonet	SNTF767	1978	£5	£12	
Morpeth Rant Northumbrian Country Music	LP	Topic	12TS267	1975	£5	£12	chart LP
Morris On	LP	Island	HELP5	1972	£5	£12	
Most Happy Fella	7" EP	Philips	BBE12348	1960	£2	£5	
Motortown Revue	LP	Tamla Motown	TML11007	1965	£20	£40	
Motortown Revue Live In Paris	LP	Tamla Motown	TML11027	1966	£20	£40	
Motown Magic	LP	Tamla Motown	TML11030	1966	£15	£30	
Motown Memories	LP	Tamla Motown	TML11064	1968	£10	£25	chart LP
Motown Memories Vol.2	LP	Tamla Motown	TML11077	1968	£8	£20	
Motown Memories Vol.3	LP	Tamla Motown	STML11143	1970	£8	£20	
Motown Story	LP	Tamla Motown	TMSP1130	1972	£8	£20	boxed set, chart LP
Motown Story - The First 25 Years	LP	Tamla Motown	TMSP6019	1983	£6	£15	boxed set
Mrs.Ackroyd Superstar!	LP	Free Reed	FRR015	1977	£6	£15	
Murderer's Home	LP	Pye	NJL11	1957	£6	£15	
Murderer's Home part 1	7" EP	Pye	NJE1062	1957	£4	£8	
Murderer's Home part 2	7" EP	Pye	NJE1063	1957	£4	£8	
Murderer's Home part 3	7" EP	Pye	NJE1064	1957	£4	£8	
Murderer's Home part 4	7" EP	Pye	NJE1065	1957	£4	£8	
Mushroom Folk Sampler	LP	Mushroom	100MR16	1971	£25	£50	
Music For The Boy Friend	LP	Brunswick	LAT8201	1957	£8	£20	
Music From The Twisted Nerve & Les Bicyclettes De Belsize	LP	Polydor	583728	1969	£20	£40	
Music House	LP	Trojan	TBL170	1971	£4	£10	
Music House Vol.2	LP	Trojan	TBL177	1971	£4	£10	
Na Ceirnini 78	LP	Gael Linn	CEF075	1978	£5	£12	Irish
Napton Folk Club	7" EP	Eden		1971	£20	£40	
Natural Reggae Vol.1	LP	Bamboo	BLP201	1969	£15	£30	
Natural Reggae Vol.2	LP	Bamboo	BLP204	1970	£15	£30	
Natures Mortes - Still Lives	LP	4AD	CAD117	1981	£25	£50	export
Negro Folklore From Texas State Prison	LP	Bounty	BY6012	1966	£6	£15	
Negro Spirituals	LP	Vogue	LAE12033	1957	£6	£15	
Negro Spirituals	7" EP	Vogue	EPV1106	1956	£5	£10	
Negro Spirituals	7" EP	Vogue	EPV1271	1962	£5	£10	
Negro Spirituals	7" EP	Vogue	EPV1276	1962	£5	£10	
New Faces From Hitsville	7" EP	Tamla Motown	TME2014	1966	£40	£80	

Title	Format	Label	Cat. No.	Year	Price	Price	Notes
New Orleans R&B Vol.1	LP	Flyright	LP4708	1974	£4	£10	
New Orleans R&B Vol.2	LP	Flyright	LP4709	1974	£4	£10	
New Sounds In Folk	7" EP.	Halcyon	HAL1	196-	£15	£30	
New Sounds In Folk	7" EP.	Harlequin	HW349	196-	£15	£30	
New Voices From Scotland	LP	Topic	12T133	1965	£15	£30	
New York City Blues	LP	Flyright	LP4706	1972	£4	£10	
New York Rhythm And Blues	LP	Flyright	LP4707	1972	£4	£10	
Newport Broadside	LP	Fontana	TFL6038	1965	£8	£20	
Newport Folk Festival Evening Concert Vol.1	LP	Fontana	TFL6041	1965	£8	£20	
Newport Folk Festival Vol.1	LP	Fontana	TFL6050	1965	£6	£15	
Newport Spiritual Stars	LP	London	LTZC15155	1959	£6	£15	
Night At The Apollo	LP	Vanguard	PPL11004	1957	£5	£12	
Nixa Hit Parade No.1	7" EP.	Pye	NEP24052	1957	£4	£8	
Nixa Hit Parade No.2	7" EP.	Pye	NEP24064	1958	£5	£10	
Nixa Hit Parade No.3	7" EP.	Pye	NEP24071	1958	£4	£8	
Nixa Hit Parade No.4	7" EP.	Pye	NEP24078	1958	£2.50	£6	
Nixa Hit Parade No.5	7" EP.	Pye	NEP24082	1958	£2	£5	
Nixa Hit Parade No.6	7" EP.	Pye	NEP24090	1958	£2	£5	
Nixa Hit Parade No.7	7" EP.	Pye	NEP24100	1959	£2	£5	
No Introduction	LP	Spark	SRLM107	1968	£6	£15	
No More Heartaches	LP	Trojan	TTL14	1969	£6	£15	
No Wave	LP	A&M	PR4738	1978	£6	£15	US, pic disc
No-one's Gonna Change Our World	LP	Starline	SRS5013	1970	£4	£10	
Norman Granz Jazz Concert No.1	LP	Columbia	33CX10059	1956	£8	£20	
Norman Granz Jazz Concert No.2	LP	Columbia	33CX10060	1956	£8	£20	
Northumbrian Minstrelry	LP	Concert Hall	AM2339	1964	£20	£40	
Nothin' But The Blues	LP	Fontana	TFL5123	1960	£5	£12	
Nothing But The Blues	LP	CBS	66278	1971	£8	£20	double
Nova Sampler	LP	Nova/Decca	SPA72	1970	£4	£10	
Nubeat - Greatest Hits	LP	Pama	ECO6	1969	£8	£20	
Nuggets	LP	Elektra	K62012	1972	£15	£30	double
Nuggets	LP	Sire	SASH37162	1976	£6	£15	US double
Oakland Blues	LP	Liberty	LBS83234	1969	£5	£12	
Oh No It's More From Raw	LP	Raw	RAWLP2	1978	£4	£10	
Old Original Tennessee Blues	LP	Revival	RVS1008	1971	£5	£12	
Oldies R&B	LP	Stateside	SL10094	1964	£6	£15	
On Stage	LP	Stateside	SL10065	1963	£25	£50	
On The Road Again	LP	XTRA	XTRA1133	1973	£6	£15	
On The Scene	LP	Columbia	33SX1662	1964	£20	£40	
On The Scene	7" EP.	Columbia	SEG8413	1965	£10	£20	
Once A Week's Enough	LP	private	C2005	1977	£10	£25	
Once More	LP	Big Shot	BBTL4001	1968	£30	£60	
One Night Stand	LP	Columbia	33SX1536	1963	£10	£25	
Original Cool Jamaican Ska	LP	Rio	RLP1	1964	£30	£60	
Original Golden Oldies Vol.2	LP	Prince Buster	PB10	1973	£8	£20	
Original Hits	LP	London	HAG2308	1960	£10	£25	
Original Hits	7" EP.	London	REK1390	1963	£4	£8	
Original Hits	7" EP.	MGM	MGMEP787	1963	£7.50	£15	
Original Hits Vol.2	LP	London	HAG2339	1961	£10	£25	
Original Hits Vol.2	7" EP.	Atlantic	AET6006	1965	£5	£10	
Original Rhythm And Blues Hits	7" EP.	Ember	EMBEP4522	1962	£10	£20	
Ossiach Live	LP	BASF	49211193	1971	£10	£25	German
Our Choice	7" EP.	Columbia	SEG7669	1957	£2.50	£6	
Our Significant Hits	LP	London	HAU2404	1962	£10	£25	
Out Came The Blues	LP	Ace Of Hearts	AH72	1964	£4	£10	
Out Came The Blues Vol.2	LP	Ace Of Hearts	AH158	1967	£4	£10	
Out Of Sight	LP	Decca	DL(7)4751	1966	£4	£10	US
Out Of Sight	LP	Design	DLP269	1968	£8	£20	US
Owdham Edge Popular Song And Verse From Lancashire	LP	Topic	12T204	1970	£5	£12	
Package Tour	LP	Golden Guinea	GGL0268	1963	£6	£15	
Paddy In The Smoke	LP	Topic	12T176	1968	£5	£12	
Pain In My Belly	LP	Blue Beat	BBLP804	1965	£50	£100	
Pajama Game	7" EP.	London	REA1036	1955	£2	£5	
Pakistani Soul Session	LP	Island	ILP945	1967	£8	£20	
Parade Of The Pops	LP	Parlophone	PMC1134	1961	£4	£10	
Party Time In Jamaica	LP	Studio One	SOL9009	1968	£50	£100	
Piano Blues 1927-1933	LP	Riverside	RLP8809	1967	£5	£12	
Picnic	LP	Harvest	SHSS1/2	1970	£5	£12	double
Piedmont Blues	LP	Flyright	LP104	1972	£5	£12	
Pinch Of Salt	LP	HMV	CLP1362	1960	£10	£25	
Pinch Of Salt	LP	HMV	XLP50004	1960	£25	£50	
Pioneers Of Boogie Woogie	10" LP	London	AL3506	1953	£10	£25	
Pioneers Of Boogie Woogie Vol.2	10" LP	London	AL3537	1954	£10	£25	
Pipeline	LP	Trojan	TBL203	1973	£6	£15	
Pop Parade Vol.1	10" LP	Mercury		1956	£4	£10	
Pop Parade Vol.2	10" LP	Mercury		1956	£4	£10	
Pop Parade Vol.3	10" LP	Mercury	MPT7519	1957	£4	£10	
Pop Parade Vol.4	10" LP	Mercury	MPT7523	1957	£4	£10	
Pop Parade Vol.5	10" LP	Mercury	MPT7525	1957	£4	£10	
Pops Go Stereo	7" EP.	Pye	NSEP85000	1958	£2.50	£6	
Post War Blues: Chicago	LP	Post War Blues	PWB1	1965	£8	£20	
Post War Blues: Detroit	LP	Post War Blues	PWB5	1968	£8	£20	
Post War Blues: Eastern And Gulf Coast States	LP	Post War Blues	PWB3	1967	£8	£20	
Post War Blues: Memphis On Down	LP	Post War Blues	PWB2	1966	£8	£20	
Post War Blues: Texas	LP	Post War Blues	PWB4	1968	£8	£20	
Post War Blues: The Deep South	LP	Post War Blues	PWB7	1969	£8	£20	
Post War Blues: West Coast	LP	Post War Blues	PWB6	1969	£8	£20	

Title	Format	Label	Catalogue	Year	Price	Price	Notes
Post War Collector Series Vol.1	LP	Python	PWBC1	1969	£8	£20	
Preachin' The Blues	LP	Stateside	SL10046	1963	£5	£12	
Presages	LP	4AD	BAD11	1980	£4	£10	
Pre-War Texas Blues	LP	Kokomo	K1006	1970	£15	£30	
Primitive Piano	LP	Jazz Collector	ABC1	1959	£8	£20	
Psilotripitaka	LP	United Dairies	UD134	198-	£30	£60	4 LP set
Psilotripitaka	LP	United Dairies	UD134	198-	£60	£120	4 LP set, leather bag
Psilotripitaka	CD	United Dairies	UD134CD	198-	£30	£60	4 CD set
Psilotripitaka	CD	United Dairies	UD134CD	198-	£60	£120	4 CD set, leather bag
Pure Blues Vol.1	LP	Sue	ILP919	1965	£8	£20	
Put It On, It's Rock Steady	LP	Island	ILP978	1968	£30	£60	
Pye Sales Sampler	LP	Pye	PSA6	1971	£6	£15	promo
Quartet Of Soul	LP	Stateside	(S)SL10209	1968	£4	£10	
Queen Of The World	LP	Trojan	TBL136	1970	£6	£15	
Ragtime Piano Roll	10" LP	London	AL3515	1954	£6	£15	
Ragtime Piano Roll Vol.2	10" LP	London	AL3523	1954	£6	£15	
Ragtime Piano Roll Vol.3	10" LP	London	AL3542	1955	£6	£15	
Ragtime Piano Roll Vol.4	10" LP	London	AL3563	1957	£6	£15	
Raw Blues	LP	Ace Of Clubs	ACL/SCL1220	1967	£6	£15	
R&B Chartmakers	7" EP	Stateside	SE1009	1964	£15	£30	
R&B Chartmakers No.2	7" EP	Stateside	SE1018	1964	£15	£30	
R&B Chartmakers No.3	7" EP	Stateside	SE1022	1964	£15	£30	
R&B Chartmakers No.4	7" EP	Stateside	SE1025	1964	£15	£30	
R&B Greats Vol.1	LP	Realm	RM101	1963	£6	£15	
R&B Greats Vol.2	LP	Realm	RM105	1964	£6	£15	
R&B Party	LP	Mercury	MCL20019	1964	£6	£15	
Ready Steady Go	LP	Decca	LK4577	1964	£8	£20	chart LP
Ready Steady Go Rocksteady	LP	Pama	PMLP3	1968	£15	£30	
Ready Steady Win	LP	Decca	LK4634	1964	£10	£25	
Real R&B	LP	Stateside	SL10112	1965	£4	£10	
Recommended Records Sampler	7"	Recommended	RR89	1982	£2	£5	1 sided, clear vinyl
Recording The Blues	LP	CBS	52797	1970	£5	£12	
Red Bird Goldies	LP	Red Bird	RB20102	1965	£15	£30	
Red, Red Wine Vol.1	LP	Trojan	TTL11	1969	£6	£15	
Red, Red Wine Vol.1	LP	Trojan	TTL11	1969	£20	£40	pink Island label
Red, Red Wine Vol.2	LP	Trojan	TBL116	1970	£6	£15	
Reggae Chartbusters	LP	Trojan	TBL105	1970	£5	£12	
Reggae Chartbusters Vol.2	LP	Trojan	TBL147	1970	£5	£12	
Reggae Chartbusters Vol.3	LP	Trojan	TBL169	1971	£5	£12	
Reggae Flight 404	LP	Trojan	TBL115	1970	£6	£15	
Reggae Girl	LP	Big Shot	BIL3000	1968	£20	£40	
Reggae Hit The Town	LP	Pama	PTP1001	1969	£8	£20	
Reggae Hits '69 Vol.1	LP	Pama	ECO3	1969	£8	£20	
Reggae Hits '69 Vol.2	LP	Pama	ECO11	1969	£8	£20	
Reggae In The Grass	LP	Studio One	SOL9007	1968	£50	£100	
Reggae Jamaica	LP	Trojan	TBL181	1971	£6	£15	
Reggae Movement	LP	Trojan	TBL144	1970	£6	£15	
Reggae Power	LP	Trojan	TBL189	1972	£5	£12	
Reggae Reggae Reggae	LP	Trojan	TBL130	1970	£6	£15	
Reggae Reggae Reggae Vol.2	LP	Trojan	TBL176	1971	£6	£15	
Reggae Special	LP	Coxsone	CSP2	1969	£20	£40	
Reggae Steady Go	LP	Trojan	TBL151	1970	£6	£15	
Reggae Time	LP	Ashanti	ANB201	1972	£5	£12	
Reggae Time	LP	Coxsone	CSL8017	1968	£50	£100	
Reggae To Reggae	LP	Pama	PMP2012	1971	£10	£25	
Reggae To UK With Love	LP	Pama	PSP1004	1969	£8	£20	
Reggaematic Sounds	LP	Bamboo	BDLP208	1971	£15	£30	
Revolution	LP	United Artists	UAS29069	1969	£6	£15	
Rhythm & Blues	LP	Decca	LK4616	1964	£15	£30	
Rhythm & Blues	LP	Golden Guinea	GGL0280	1963	£4	£10	
Rhythm & Blues	LP	Golden Guinea	GGL0351	1965	£4	£10	
Rhythm & Blues All Stars	LP	Golden Guinea	GGL0293	1963	£4	£10	
Rhythm & Blues Showcase Vol.1	7" EP	Pye	NEP44021	1964	£5	£10	
Rhythm & Blues Showcase Vol.2	7" EP	Pye	NEP44022	1964	£5	£10	
Rhythm And Blues Classics Vol.1	LP	Minit	MLS40008	1969	£6	£15	
Rhythm And Blues Classics Vol.2	LP	Minit	MLS40009	1969	£6	£15	
Rhythm And Blues Party	LP	Philips	6436028	1976	£4	£10	
Rhythm And Blues Vol.1	LP	Liberty	LBL83216	1969	£5	£12	
Rhythm And Blues Vol.2	LP	Liberty	LBL83328	1969	£5	£12	
Ric Tic Relics	LP	Tamla Motown	STML11232	1973	£8	£15	
Ride Me Donkey	LP	Coxsone	CSL8015	1968	£50	£100	
Ride Your Donkey	LP	Trojan	TTL18	1969	£8	£20	
Rivertown Blues	LP	London	SHU8245	1971	£4	£10	
Rock And Roll	7" EP	Vogue	VE170111	1958	£30	£60	
Rock, Rock, Rock	LP	Chess	LP1425	1957	£25	£50	US
Rock-A-Hits	LP	London	HAA2338	1961	£15	£30	
Rocket Along	10" LP	HMV	DLP1204	1960	£10	£25	
Rockin' At The 2 I's	10" LP	Decca	LF1300	1958	£15	£30	
Rockin' Together	LP	London	HAE2167	1959	£17.50	£35	
Rock'n'Roll Forever	10" LP	London	HBC1067	1956	£15	£30	
Rock'n'Roll	LP	London	HAE2180	1959	£20	£40	
Rocksteady Cool	LP	Pama	PMLP7	1969	£15	£30	
Rocksteady Coxsone Style	LP	Coxsone	CSL8013	1968	£50	£100	
Round Up	7" EP	Capitol	EAP120197	1962	£5	£10	
Rural Blues	LP	XTRA	XTRA1035	1969	£6	£15	double
Rural Blues Vol.1	LP	Liberty	LBL83213	1969	£6	£15	
Rural Blues Vol.2	LP	Liberty	LBL83214	1969	£6	£15	
Rural Blues Vol.3	LP	Liberty	LBL83329	1969	£6	£15	
Sandy Bell's Ceilidh	LP	Alba	MAR056	1979	£6	£15	
Saturday Club	LP	Decca	LK4583	1964	£8	£20	

Title	Format	Label	Cat. No.	Year			Notes
Saturday Club	LP	Parlophone	PMC1130	1960	£15	£30	
Saturday Night At The Apollo	LP	Atlantic	590007	1966	£4	£10	
Saturday Night At The Uptown	LP	Atlantic	ATL5018	1964	£6	£15	
Scene '65	LP	Columbia	33SX1730	1965	£17.50	£35	
Scorcha From Bamboo	LP	Bamboo	BDLP202	1969	£20	£40	
Scotia Folk	LP	Fontana	6438021	1970	£10	£25	
Screening The Blues	LP	CBS	66208	1968	£6	£15	double
Sea Shanties	LP	Topic	12TS234	1974	£5	£12	
Second Coming	LP	Come Organisation ...	WDC881008	1980	£25	£50	
Second Folk Review Record	LP	Folksound	FS107	1976	£15	£30	
Secret Policeman's Other Ball	10"	Springtime	RARA1001	1981	£4	£10	promo sampler
Select Elektra	LP	Elektra	EUK261/ EUKS7261	1968	£4	£10	
Seoda Ceoil 2	LP	Gael Linn	CEF002	1969	£5	£12	Irish
Shades Of Gospel Soul	LP	Motown	M/S701	1969	£6	£15	US
Shake, Rattle And Roll	LP	Atlantic	587109	1968	£4	£10	
Shepway Folk	LP	Eron	003	1974	£6	£15	
Short Circuit - Live At The Electric Circus	10" LP	Virgin	VCL5003	1978	£5	£12	blue vinyl
Short Circuit - Live At The Electric Circus	10" LP	Virgin	VCL5003	1978	£37.50	£75	orange vinyl
Short Circuit - Live At The Electric Circus	10" LP	Virgin	VCL5003	1978	£10	£25	yellow vinyl
Sing A Song Of Soul	LP	Chess	CRL4519	1966	£5	£12	
Singer Songwriter	LP	Elektra	EKL/EKS7299	1965	£15	£30	US
Singing In The Rain	7" EP.	MGM	MGMEP671	1958	£2.50	£6	
Singing The Blues	7" EP.	London	REP1403	1963	£7.50	£15	
Six Five Special	LP	Parlophone	PMC1047	1957	£15	£30	
Six Five Special	7" EP.	Decca	DFE6485	1958	£5	£10	
Sixteen Dynamic Reggae Hits	LP	Pama	PMP2015	1971	£6	£15	
Sixteen Dynamic Reggae Hits	LP	Trojan	TBL191	1972	£5	£12	
Ska at The Jamaican Playboy Club	LP	Island	ILP930	1966	£30	£60	
Ska To Rocksteady	LP	Studio One	SOL9000	1967	£50	£100	
Skiffle	LP	Ace Of Clubs	ACL1250	1967	£8	£20	
Solid Gold	LP	Bamboo	BDLP212	1971	£15	£30	
Solid Gold Soul	LP	Atlantic	ATL5048	1966	£5	£12	chart LP
Solid Gold Soul Vol.2	LP	Atlantic	587058	1967	£4	£10	
Solid On Soul	LP	United Artists	LBR1001	197-	£6	£15	
Some Cleveland And Dales Folk Vol.1	LP	Pied Piper	MIK1001	1976	£6	£15	
Some Cold Rainy Day	LP	Flyright	LP114	1975	£4	£10	
Some Cold Rainy Day	LP	Southern Preservation...	SPR1	1972	£6	£15	
Something Sweet From The Lady	LP	Pama	PMP2003	1970	£6	£15	
Songs And Ballads Of The Industrial North West	LP	Topic	12T188	1969	£5	£12	
Songs From Washington Davy Lamp Folksong Club	LP	DLFC	110	1974	£25	£50	
Soul '66	LP	Sue	ILP934	1966	£15	£30	
Soul Food	LP	Minit	MLL40011E	1968	£6	£15	
Soul From The City	LP	Soul City	SCB001	1969	£6	£15	
Soul Of Jamaica	LP	Trojan	TRL3	1968	£15	£30	
Soul Sauce From Pama	LP	Pama	PMLP8	1969	£6	£15	
Soul Seller	LP	Polydor	236554	1969	£4	£10	
Soul Sixteen	LP	Stateside	SL10186	1966	£5	£12	
Soul Sounds Of The Sixties	LP	HMV	CLP3617	1967	£6	£15	
Soul Supply	LP	Stateside	SL10203	1967	£6	£15	
Soulful Reggae	LP	Trojan	TRL65	1974	£4	£10	
Sound Of The Grapevine	LP	Grapevine	GRAL1001	197-	£6	£12	
Sound Of The R&B Hits	LP	Stateside	SL10077	1964	£25	£50	sleeve pictured in Guide
Sound Of The Stars	7"	Lyntone	LYN995	1966	£7.50	£15	Disc And Music Echo flexi
Sounds Of Savile	7" EP.	Lyntone	LYN951/2	1965	£20	£40	
Soundsville	LP	Design	DLP187	1965	£25	£50	US
Southern Sanctified Singers	LP	Saydisc	RL328	196-	£4	£10	
Southside Chicago	LP	Python	PLP10	1971	£8	£20	
Speak Low - More Music In The Modern Manner	LP	Tempo	TAP17	1958	£6	£15	
Spin With The Stars No.2	10" LP	Pye	NPT19019	1957	£5	£12	
Spin With The Stars No.3	10" LP	Pye	NPT19021	1957	£5	£12	
Spree '73	LP	Key	KL021	1973	£5	£12	
Star Parade	7" EP.	Decca	DFE6147	1955	£4	£8	
Star Souvenir Greetings	7"	208 Radio Luxembourg ...		196-	£6	£12	flexi
Stars Of Liberty	LP	Liberty	LBY1001	1960	£8	£20	
Stars Of the 6.5 Special	10" LP	Decca	LF1299	1957	£15	£30	
Statik Compilation One	LP	Statik	POL274	1985	£6	£15	double
Stax/Volt Tour In London Vol.1	LP	Stax	589010	1967	£6	£15	
Stax/Volt Tour In London Vol.2	LP	Stax	589011	1967	£6	£15	
Steam Ballads	LP	Broadside	BRO121	1977	£6	£15	
Stiff Box Set No.1	7"	Stiff	BUY1-10	1979	£15	£30	10 x 7', boxed
Story Of The Blues	LP	CBS	66218	1969	£5	£12	double
Story Of The Blues Vol.2	LP	CBS	66232	1970	£6	£15	double
Straighten Up	LP	Pama	PMP2002	1970	£6	£15	
Straighten Up Vol.2	LP	Pama	PMP2007	1971	£6	£15	
Straighten Up Vol.3	LP	Pama	PMP2014	1971	£6	£15	
Straighten Up Vol.4	LP	Pama	PMP2017	1972	£6	£15	
Street To Street - A Liverpool Compilation	LP	Open Eye	OELP501	1979	£5	£12	

Title	Format	Label	Cat. No.	Year	Price	Price	Notes
Sue Story	LP	London	HAC8239	1965	£10	£25	different to Sue LP
Sue Story	LP	Sue	ILP925	1965	£15	£30	
Sue Story Vol.2	LP	Sue	ILP933	1966	£15	£30	
Sue Story Vol.3	LP	Sue	ILP938	1966	£10	£25	
Super Duper Blues	LP	Blue Horizon	PR31	1969	£5	£12	
Super Soul	LP	Pye	NPL28107	1968	£4	£10	
Swamp Blues	LP	Blue Horizon	766263	1970	£17.50	£35	double
Sweet Beat	7" EP	Top Rank	JKR8007	1959	£7.50	£15	
Sweet Home Chicago	LP	Delmark	DS618	1970	£6	£15	
Sweet Soul Sounds	LP	Stateside	(S)SL10243	1968	£6	£15	
Swing Easy	LP	Coxsone	CSL8018	1968	£50	£100	
Swingin' Set	LP	MGM	C8012	1966	£8	£20	
Swingin' The Blues	LP	Tempo	TAP21	1958	£6	£15	
Swinging Saga	LP	Saga	FID2136	1968	£4	£10	
Take Off Your Head And Listen	LP	Rubber	LP001	1971	£5	£12	
Take Six	7" EP	Oriole	EP7080	1964	£12.50	£25	
Talk Of THe Grapevine	LP	Grapevine	GRAL1000	197-	£4	£10	
Tear It Up	7" EP	Mercury	ZEP10015	1959	£30	£60	
Teen Scene '64	7" EP	Ember	EMBEP4540	1964	£7.50	£15	
Teenage Rock	LP	Capitol	T1009	1958	£15	£30	
Teenage Rock	7" EP	Mercury	MEP9522	1957	£25	£50	
Teenage Tops	7" EP	RCA	RCX111	1958	£10	£20	
Texas Blues	LP	Fountain	FV205	197-	£4	£10	
Texas-Louisiana Blues	LP	Highway 51	H103	1969	£20	£40	
Thank Your Lucky Stars	LP	Ace Of Clubs	ACL1108	1962	£10	£25	
Thank Your Lucky Stars Vol.2	LP	Decca	LK4554	1963	£8	£20	
That's Underground	LP	CBS	SPR23	1970	£6	£15	German, multi-coloured vinyl
Themes From James Bond Films	7" EP	CBS	WEP1126	1967	£2.50	£6	
There Is Some Fun Going Forward	LP	Dandelion	2485021	1972	£8	£20	with poster
These Kind Of Blues Vol.1	LP	Action	ACLP6009	1969	£6	£15	
They Sold A Million No.10	7" EP	Brunswick	OE9426	1959	£2.50	£6	
They Sold A Million No.11	7" EP	Brunswick	OE9427	1959	£6	£12	
They Sold A Million No.12	7" EP	Brunswick	OE9428	1959	£2	£5	
They Sold A Million No.13	7" EP	Brunswick	OE9429	1959	£2	£5	
They Sold A Million No.4	7" EP	Brunswick	OE9420	1959	£2	£5	
They Sold A Million No.9	7" EP	Brunswick	OE9425	1959	£7.50	£15	
Third Irish Folk Festival In Concert	LP	Intercord	INT181008	1976	£15	£30	German double
This Is Blue Beat	LP	Island	ILP910	1964	£50	£100	test pressing
This Is Blues	LP	Island	IWP5	1970	£8	£20	pink label
This Is Merseybeat Vol.1	LP	Oriole	PS40047	1963	£25	£50	chart LP
This Is Merseybeat Vol.2	LP	Oriole	PS40048	1963	£25	£50	
This Is Northern Soul	LP	Grapevine	GRAL1002	197-	£6	£15	
This Is Reggae	LP	Pama	PSP1003	1969	£8	£20	
This Is Reggae Vol.2	LP	Pama	PMP2005	1971	£6	£15	
This Is Reggae Vol.3	LP	Pama	PMP2008	1971	£6	£15	
This Is Reggae Vol.4	LP	Pama	PMP2016	1972	£6	£15	
This Is Sue!	LP	Island	IWP3	1969	£6	£15	pink label
Those Cakewalkin' Babies From Home	LP	Saydisc	SDR182	1970	£4	£10	
Tighten Up	LP	Trojan	TBL120	1969	£6	£15	
Tighten Up	LP	Trojan	TTL1	1969	£5	£12	
Tighten Up Vol.2	LP	Trojan	TBL131	1970	£4	£10	
Tighten Up Vol.2	LP	Trojan	TTL7	1969	£5	£12	
Tighten Up Vol.2	LP	Trojan	TTL7	1969	£20	£40	pink Island label
Tighten Up Vol.3	LP	Trojan	TBL145	1970	£4	£10	
Tighten Up Vol.4	LP	Trojan	TBL163	1971	£4	£10	
Tighten Up Vol.5	LP	Trojan	TBL165	1971	£4	£10	
Tighten Up Vol.6	LP	Trojan	TBL185	1972	£4	£10	
To The Shores Of Lake Placid	LP	Zoo	ZOO4	1982	£4	£10	
Top Teen Dances	7" EP	Stateside	SE1004	1963	£5	£10	
Top TV Themes	7" EP	Pye	NEP24276	1967	£2.50	£6	
Topic Sampler No.1	LP	Topic	TPS114	1964	£6	£15	
Topic Sampler No.2	LP	Topic	TPS145	1965	£6	£15	
Topic Sampler No.3	LP	Topic	TPS166	1966	£5	£12	
Topic Sampler No.4	LP	Topic	TPS168	1966	£5	£12	
Topic Sampler No.5	LP	Topic	TPS169	1967	£5	£12	
Topic Sampler No.6	LP	Topic	TPS201	1968	£5	£12	
Topic Sampler No.7	LP	Topic	TPS205	1969	£5	£12	
Topic Sampler No.8	LP	Topic	TPS221	1972	£6	£15	
Tops In Pops No.1	7" EP	Decca	DFE6411	1957	£4	£8	
Tops In Pops No.3	7" EP	Decca	DFE6467	1958	£2.50	£6	
Tops In Pops No.7	7" EP	Decca	DFE6583	1959	£2	£5	
Traditional Music Of Ireland Vol.1	LP	Folkways	FW8781	1963	£8	£20	US
Traditional Music Of Ireland Vol.2	LP	Folkways	FW8782	1963	£8	£20	US
Treasures Of North American Negro Music Vol.6	7" EP	Fontana	TFE17265	1960	£4	£8	
Treasury Of Field Recordings	LP	77	LA122	1960	£6	£15	
Treasury Of Field Recordings Vol.2	LP	77	LA123	1960	£6	£15	
Tribute To Michael Holliday	LP	Columbia	33SX1635	1964	£8	£20	
Triple Treat	LP	Parlophone	PMC1139	1961	£5	£12	
Trojan Reggae Party	LP	Trojan	TBL172	1971	£4	£10	
Trojan's Greatest Hits	LP	Trojan	TBL180	1971	£4	£10	
Trojan's Greatest Hits Vol.2	LP	Trojan	TBL190	1972	£4	£10	
Troublemakers	LP	Warner Bros	PROA857	1981	£10	£25	promo double
Tub Jug Washboard Bands	LP	Riverside	RLP8802	1967	£6	£15	
TV Themes	7" EP	Decca	DFE8585	1964	£15	£30	
TV Themes 1966	7" EP	Pye	NEP24244	1966	£4	£8	
Twelve Big Hits	LP	Melodisc	12193	196-	£4	£10	
Twelve Carat Gold	LP	Melodisc	12217	196-	£4	£10	
Twist At The Star Club	LP	Philips	BL7578	1963	£8	£20	

Title		Label	Cat No	Year			Notes
Twist Off	7" EP..	Starlite	STEP31	1962	£20	£40	
Twist On	7" EP..	Starlite	STEP29	1962	£25	£50	
Twrw Tanllyd	LP	Sain	1201M	1981	£5	£12	
Ulster's Flowery Vale	LP	BBC	REC28M	1968	£10	£25	
Unholy Montage	7"	Fierce	FRIGHT38	198-	£10	£20	
Unity's Great Reggae Hits	LP	Pama	ECO7	1969	£8	£20	
Urban Blues Vol.1	LP	Liberty	LBL83215	1969	£5	£12	
Urban Blues Vol.2	LP	Liberty	LBL83327	1969	£5	£12	
Vaudeville Blues	LP	VJM	VLP30	1970	£4	£10	
Version Galore Vol.2	LP	Trojan	TBL175	1971	£6	£15	
Version Galore Vol.3	LP	Trojan	TBL200	1973	£6	£15	
Version To Version	LP	Trojan	TBL182	1972	£6	£15	
Version To Version Vol.3	LP	Trojan	TBL206	1973	£6	£15	
Vertigo Annual 1970	LP	Vertigo	6499407/8	1970	£5	£12	double
Vogue Surprise Partie	7" EP..	Vogue	VRE5002	1965	£2	£5	
Voices Record One	LP	Argo	PLP1112	1968	£15	£30	
Voices Record Two	LP	Argo	PLP1115	1968	£8	£20	
Wagon Train	7" EP..	RCA	RCX128	1959	£2	£5	
Wakey Wakey	LP	Columbia	33SX1385	1962	£6	£15	
Walking By Myself	LP	Pye	NPL28041	1964	£8	£20	
Walking The Blues	LP	Pye	NPL28044	1964	£6	£15	
Walls Ice Cream Presents	7" EP..	Apple	CT1	1969	£20	£40	
Washboard Rhythm	LP	Ace Of Hearts ..	AH55	1963	£4	£10	
We Like Girls	LP	Coral	LVA9096	1959	£5	£12	
We Like Guys	LP	Coral	LVA9098	1959	£5	£12	
We Love You Beatles	7" EP..	CBS	5649	1965	£12.50	£25	French
We Sing The Blues	LP	Liberty	LBY3051	1965	£6	£15	
We Sing The Blues	LP	London	HAP8061	1963	£10	£25	
We Sing The Blues	LP	Sue	ILP921	1965	£10	£25	
We Sing The Blues	7" EP..	Liberty	LEP4036	1965	£5	£10	
West Side Chicago	7" EP..	Solid Sender	SEP101	1975	£2.50	£6	
We've Moved	LP	MPL	MPL1	197-	£30	£60	promo
What Am I Do	LP	Trojan	TTL34	1970	£6	£15	
What's Shakin'	LP	Elektra	EKS7304	1968	£6	£15	
Wild Beach Weekend	7" EP..	RCA	86466	1964	£6	£12	French
Women Of The Blues	LP	RCA	RD7840	1967	£6	£15	
Woodstock	LP	Atlantic	2663001	1970	£6	£15	triple
Woodstock 2	LP	Atlantic	2400130/1	1971	£6	£15	double
World Of Blues	LP	London	HAP8099	1963	£10	£25	
World Of Blues Power Vol.3	LP	Decca	SPA263	1973	£5	£12	
World Of Bullet	LP	Pama	SECO19	1969	£6	£15	
World Of Folk	LP	Argo	SPA132	1971	£6	£15	
Yes L.A.	LP	Dangerhouse	EW79	1979	£8	£20	..1 sided clear pic disc
You Can't Wine	LP	Trojan	TBL142	1970	£6	£15	
You Left Me Standing	LP	Trojan	TTL9	1969	£8	£20	
Your Chess Requests	7" EP..	Chess	CRE6026	1968	£5	£10	
Your Choice	7" EP..	Mercury	MEP9525	1957	£6	£12	
Your Choice No.2	7" EP..	Mercury	MEP9532	1958	£6	£12	
Your Jamaican Girl	LP	Bamboo	BDLP211	1971	£15	£30	
You're Either On The Train....	LP	Stiff	DEAL1	1978	£6	£15	promo

VASELINES

Title		Label	Cat No	Year			Notes
Dum Dum	LP	53rd And 3rd	AGAS7	1990	£5	£12	
Dying For It	12"	53rd And 3rd	AGARR17T	1988	£2.50	£6	
Son Of A Gun	7"	53rd & 3rd	AGARR10	1987	£4	£8	

VASHTI

Title		Label	Cat No	Year			Notes
Some Things Just Stick In Your Mind ..	7"	Decca	F12157	1965	£5	£10	
Train Song	7"	Columbia	DB7917	1966	£2	£5	

VASSY, KIN

Title		Label	Cat No	Year			Notes
That's The Bag I'm In	7"	Uni	UN506	1969	£1.50	£4	

VAUGHAN, FRANKIE

Title		Label	Cat No	Year			Notes
Cuff Of My Shirt	7"	HMV	7M182	1954	£2.50	£6	
Frankie Vaughan	7" EP..	Philips	BBE12022	1956	£2	£5	
Frankie Vaughan	7" EP..	Philips	BBE12071	1956	£2	£5	
Frankie Vaughan	7" EP..	Philips	BBE12111	1957	£2	£5	
Frankie Vaughan	7" EP..	Philips	BBE12220	1958	£2	£5	
Garden Of Eden	7"	Philips	JK1002	1957	£4	£8	chart single
Give Me The Moonlight	7"	Philips	PB423	1955	£2.50	£6	
Gotta Have Something In The Bank, Frank	7"	Philips	JK1030	1957	£2.50	£6	chart single
Happy Days And Lonely Nights	7"	HMV	7M270	1954	£2.50	£6	chart single
Happy Go Lucky	LP	Philips	BBL7198	1957	£4	£10	
Happy Go Lucky	7" EP..	Philips	BBE12171	1958	£2	£5	
Heart Of A Man	7" EP..	Philips	BBE12299	1959	£2	£5	
Istanbul	7"	HMV	7M167	1953	£5	£10	chart single
It's Frankie	7" EP..	Philips	BBE12157	1957	£2	£5	
Kisses Sweeter Than Wine	7"	Philips	JK1035	1957	£4	£8	chart single
Lady Is A Square	7" EP..	Philips	BBE12247	1959	£2	£5	
Let Me Sing & I'm Happy	7" EP..	Philips	BBE12484	1961	£4	£8	
Let Me Sing & I'm Happy	7" EP..	Philips	SBBE9071	1961	£4	£8	stereo
Let Me Sing & I'm Happy No.2	7" EP..	Philips	BBE12485	1961	£4	£8	
Let Me Sing & I'm Happy No.2	7" EP..	Philips	SBBE9072	1961	£4	£8	stereo
Let Me Sing & I'm Happy No.3	7" EP..	Philips	BBE12486	1961	£4	£8	
Let Me Sing & I'm Happy No.3	7" EP..	Philips	SBBE9073	1961	£4	£8	stereo
Mister Elegant	7" EP..	HMV	7EG8245	1957	£2.50	£6	
My Son, My Son	7"	HMV	7M252	1954	£2.50	£6	
Showcase	LP	Philips	BBL7233	1958	£4	£10	

These Dangerous Years	7"	Philips	JK1022	1957	£2.50	£6	
Too Many Heartaches	7"	HMV	7M298	1955	£2.50	£6	
What's Behind That Strange Door	7"	Philips	JK1014	1957	£2.50	£6	

VAUGHAN, MALCOLM

Chapel Of The Roses	7"	HMV	POP325	1957	£1.50	£4	chart single
Hello	LP	HMV	CLP1284	1959	£4	£10	
Hello No.1	7" EP	HMV	GES5785	1959	£2	£5	stereo
Hello No.2	7" EP	HMV	GES5793	1959	£2	£5	stereo
More Than A Millionaire	7"	HMV	7M317	1955	£1.50	£4	
My Special Angel	7"	HMV	POP419	1957	£1.50	£4	chart single
Only You	7"	HMV	7M389	1956	£1.50	£4	
Requests	7" EP	HMV	GES5799	1959	£2	£5	stereo
Sincerity In Song	7" EP	HMV	7EG8272	1957	£4	£8	
Sincerity In Song No.2	7" EP	HMV	7EG8377	1957	£2	£5	
Sincerity In Song No.3	7" EP	HMV	7EG8453	1957	£2	£5	
St.Therese Of The Roses	7"	HMV	POP250	1956	£1.50	£4	chart single
With Your Love	7"	HMV	7M338	1955	£2	£5	chart single
World Is Mine	7"	HMV	POP303	1957	£1.50	£4	chart single

VAUGHAN, SARAH

After Hours At The London House	LP	Mercury	MMC14001	1959	£5	£12	
At Mister Kelly's	LP	Mercury	MPL6542	1958	£4	£10	
Best Of Berlin Vol.1	7" EP	Mercury	SEZ19016	1961	£2	£5	stereo
Broken-Hearted Melody	7"	Mercury	AMT1057	1959	£1.50	£4	
Close To You	LP	Mercury	CMS18040	1961	£4	£10	stereo
Count Basie - Sarah Vaughan	LP	Columbia	SCX3403	1962	£4	£10	stereo
Divine One	LP	Columbia	SCX3390	1962	£4	£10	stereo
Dreamy	LP	Columbia	SCX3324	1960	£4	£10	stereo
Great Songs From Hit Shows Part 1	LP	Mercury	CMS18019	1960	£4	£10	stereo
Great Songs From Hit Shows Part 2	LP	Mercury	CMS18023	1960	£4	£10	stereo
Hit Parade	7" EP	Mercury	MEP9511	1956	£2	£5	
Images	10" LP	Mercury	MG26005	1955	£5	£12	
Images	10" LP	Mercury	MPT7518	1957	£4	£10	
In Romantic Mood	LP	Mercury	MPL6540	1958	£4	£10	
In The Land Of Hi Fi	10" LP	Emarcy	EJL100	1956	£5	£12	
Linger Awhile	LP	Philips	BBL7165	1957	£4	£10	
Live For Love	7" EP	Mercury	SEZ19006	1961	£2.50	£6	stereo
Make Yourself Comfortable	10" LP	Mercury	MPT7503	1956	£5	£12	
Sarah Vaughan	LP	Philips	BBL7082	1956	£4	£10	
Sarah Vaughan	7" EP	London	REU1065	1956	£2	£5	
Sassy	LP	Emarcy	EJL1258	1957	£4	£10	
Sings	10" LP	London	HBU1049	1956	£6	£15	
Sings George Gershwin Vol.1	LP	Mercury	CMS18011	1959	£5	£12	stereo
Sings George Gershwin Vol.1	LP	Mercury	MPL6525	1957	£4	£10	
Sings George Gershwin Vol.2	LP	Mercury	CMS18012	1959	£5	£12	stereo
Sings George Gershwin Vol.2	LP	Mercury	MPL6527	1957	£4	£10	
Sings Great Songs From Hit Shows Part 1	LP	Mercury	MPL6522	1957	£4	£10	
Sings Great Songs From Hit Shows Part 2	LP	Mercury	MPL6523	1957	£4	£10	
Swingin' Easy	LP	Emarcy	EJL1273	1958	£4	£10	
Vaughan And Violins	LP	Mercury	CMS18003	1959	£4	£10	stereo
Wonderful Sarah	LP	Mercury	MPL6532	1958	£4	£10	

VAUGHN, BILLY

All Nite Long	7"	London	HLD8920	1959	£1.50	£4	
Billy Vaughn	7" EP	London	RED1285	1961	£2	£5	
Blue Hawaii	7"	London	HLD8797	1959	£1.50	£4	
Cimarron	7"	London	HLD8772	1958	£1.50	£4	
Golden Instrumentals	LP	London	HAD2025	1957	£5	£12	
Golden Instrumentals	LP	London	SAHD6018	1959	£8	£20	
Golden Instrumentals No.1	7" EP	London	RED1083	1957	£2.50	£6	
Golden Instrumentals No.2	7" EP	London	RED1084	1957	£2.50	£6	
It's No Sin	7"	London	HLD8996	1959	£1.50	£4	
Johnny Tremain	7"	London	HLD8511	1957	£2	£5	
La Paloma	7"	London	HLD8703	1958	£1.50	£4	
Look For A Star	7"	London	HLD9152	1960	£1.50	£4	
Melodies Of Love	10" LP	London	HBD1048	1956	£5	£12	
Melody Of Love	7"	London	HL8112	1955	£10	£20	gold label
Morgen	7"	London	HLD8952	1959	£1.50	£4	
Petticoats Of Portugal	7"	London	HLD8342	1956	£5	£10	gold label
Plays The Million Sellers	LP	London	SAHD6003	1958	£5	£12	stereo
Raunchy	7"	London	HLD8522	1957	£2	£5	
Sail Along Silvery Moon	LP	London	SAHD6037	1958	£5	£12	stereo
Sail Along Silvery Moon	7"	London	HLD8680	1958	£1.50	£4	
Sail Along Silvery Moon	7" EP	London	RED1189	1959	£2	£5	
Swingin' Safari	7" EP	London	RED1352	1963	£2	£5	
Theme From The Threepenny Opera	7"	London	HLD8238	1956	£5	£10	chart single, gold label
Tumbling Tumbleweeds	7"	London	HLD8612	1958	£1.50	£4	
When The Lilac Blooms Again	7"	London	HLD8319	1956	£5	£10	gold label
Your Cheatin' Heart	7"	London	HLD8859	1959	£1.50	£4	

VAUGHT, BOB & THE RENAGADES

Surf Crazy	LP	GNP-Crescendo	(S)83	1963	£6	£15	US

VEDDAR, CHUCK

Spanky Boy	7"	London	HLU8951	1959	£7.50	£15	

VEE, BOBBY

Title	Format	Label	Catalogue	Year	Price	Price	Notes
Bobby Tomorrow	7"	Liberty	LIB55530	1963	£1.50	£4	chart single
Bobby Vee	LP	London	HAG2352	1961	£10	£25	
Bobby Vee Meets The Crickets	7" EP	Liberty	LEP2116	1963	£7.50	£15	
Bobby Vee Meets The Crickets	7" EP	Liberty	SLEP2116	1963	£10	£20	stereo
Bobby Vee Meets The Crickets Vol.2	7" EP	Liberty	LEP2149	1963	£7.50	£15	
Bobby Vee No.1	7" EP	London	REG1278	1961	£7.50	£15	
Bobby Vee No.2	7" EP	London	REG1299	1961	£7.50	£15	
Bobby Vee No.3	7" EP	London	REG1308	1961	£7.50	£15	
Bobby Vee No.4	7" EP	London	REG1323	1961	£7.50	£15	
Bobby Vee's Biggest Hits	7" EP	Liberty	LEP2102	1963	£6	£12	
Bobby Vee's Biggest Hits	7" EP	Liberty	SLEP2102	1963	£10	£20	stereo
Buddy's Song	7"	Liberty	LIB10141	1963	£2.50	£6	
Come Back When You Grow Up	7"	Liberty	LBF15016	1967	£1.50	£4	
Devil Or Angel	7"	London	HLG9179	1960	£7.50	£15	
Do What You Gotta Do	LP	Liberty	LBL/LBS83130	1968	£5	£12	
Electric Trains And You	7"	Liberty	LBF15305	1970	£1.50	£4	
Forever Kind Of Love	7"	Liberty	LIB10046	1962	£1.50	£4	chart single
Forever Kind Of Love	7" EP	Liberty	LEP2089	1963	£6	£12	
Golden Greats	LP	Liberty	(S)LBY1112	1962	£8	£20	chart LP
Hickory, Dick And Dock	7"	Liberty	LIB55700	1964	£2	£5	
Hits Of The Rockin' Fifties	LP	London	HAG2406/SAHG6206	1961	£15	£30	chart LP
Hits Of The Rockin' Fifties	7" EP	London	REG1324	1961	£7.50	£15	
How Many Tears	7"	London	HLG9389	1961	£2	£5	chart single
I Remember Buddy Holly	LP	Liberty	(S)LBY1188	1963	£8	£20	
I'm Gonna Make It Up To You	7"	Liberty	LBF15234	1969	£1.50	£4	
I'm Looking For Someone To Love	7"	Liberty	LBF15178	1969	£1.50	£4	
Just For Fun	7" EP	Liberty	LEP2084	1963	£6	£12	with The Crickets
Just Today	LP	Liberty	LBL/LBS83112	1968	£5	£12	
Keep On Trying	7"	Liberty	LIB10197	1965	£1.50	£4	
Like You've Never Known Before	7"	Liberty	LIB10272	1967	£2	£5	
Live On Tour	LP	Liberty	(S)LBY1263	1965	£6	£15	
Look At Me Girl	LP	Liberty	(S)LBY1341	1966	£6	£15	
Look At Me Girl	7"	Liberty	LIB55877	1966	£2	£5	
Love's Made A Fool Of You	7"	London	HLG9459	1961	£4	£8	
Maybe Just Today	7"	Liberty	LBF15058	1968	£1.50	£4	
Meets The Crickets	LP	Liberty	(S)LBY1086	1962	£5	£12	chart LP
Meets The Ventures	LP	Liberty	(S)LBY1147	1963	£8	£20	
Meets The Ventures	7" EP	Liberty	LEP2212	1965	£7.50	£15	
Merry Christmas From Bobby Vee	LP	Liberty	LRP3267/LST7267	1962	£8	£20	US
More Than I Can Say	7"	London	HLG9316	1961	£1.50	£4	chart single
New Sound From England	LP	Liberty	LRP3352/LST7352	1964	£8	£20	US
New Sounds	7" EP	Liberty	LEP2181	1964	£7.50	£15	
Night Has A Thousand Eyes	LP	Liberty	(S)LBY1139	1963	£8	£20	chart LP
Night Has A Thousand Eyes	7"	Liberty	LIB10069	1963	£1.50	£4	chart single
Please Don't Ask About Barbara	7"	Liberty	LIB55419	1962	£1.50	£4	chart single
Recording Session	LP	Liberty	(S)LBY1084	1962	£8	£20	chart LP
Rubber Ball	7"	London	HLG9255	1961	£2.50	£6	chart single
Run Like The Devil	7"	Liberty	LIB55828	1965	£2.50	£6	
Run To Him	7"	Liberty	LIB55388	1962	£1.50	£4	
Run To Him	7"	London	HLG9470	1961	£2	£5	chart single
Sharing You	7"	Liberty	LIB55451	1962	£1.50	£4	chart single
Sincerely	7" EP	Liberty	LEP2053	1962	£6	£12	
Sings Your Favourites	LP	London	HAG2320	1961	£15	£30	
Stranger In Your Arms	7"	Liberty	LIB10124	1963	£1.50	£4	
Suzie Baby	7"	Liberty	55208	1959	£10	£20	US
Suzie Baby	7"	Soma	1110	1959	£20	£40	US
Sweet Sweetheart	7"	Liberty	LBF15420	1970	£1.50	£4	
Take Good Care Of My Baby	LP	Liberty	(S)LBY1004	1961	£6	£15	
Take Good Care Of My Baby	LP	London	HAG2428/SAHG6224	1961	£10	£25	chart LP
Take Good Care Of My Baby	7"	Liberty	LBF15096	1968	£1.50	£4	
Take Good Care Of My Baby	7"	London	HLG7111	1961	£2.50	£6	export
Take Good Care Of My Baby	7"	London	HLG9438	1961	£2	£5	chart single
Thirty Big Hits From The 60s	LP	Liberty	LRP3385/LST7385	1964	£8	£20	US
True Love Never Runs Smooth	7"	Liberty	LIB10213	1965	£2	£5	
What Do You Want?	7"	Liberty	55234	1960	£10	£20	US
With Strings And Things	LP	London	HAG2374/SAHG6174	1961	£15	£30	
Woman In My Life	7"	Liberty	LBF15370	1970	£1.50	£4	

VEGA, SUZANNE

Title	Format	Label	Catalogue	Year	Price	Price	Notes
Left Of Center	CD-s	A&M	CDQ320	1986	£3	£8	
Small Blue Thing	7"	A&M	AM294	1985	£1.50	£4	double

VEGAS, PAT & LOLLY

Title	Format	Label	Catalogue	Year	Price	Price	Notes
At The Haunted House	LP	Mercury	MG2/SR61059	1966	£6	£15	US

VEJTABLES

Title	Format	Label	Catalogue	Year	Price	Price	Notes
I Still Love You	7"	Pye	7N25339	1965	£4	£8	
I Still Love You	7" EP	Vogue	INT18051	1965	£12.50	£25	French

VELEZ, MARTHA

Title	Format	Label	Catalogue	Year	Price	Price	Notes
Boogie Kitchen	7"	Blue Horizon	2096010	1972	£4	£8	
Fiends And Angels	LP	London	HAK/SHK8395	1969	£6	£15	
Fiends And Angels Again	LP	Blue Horizon	763867	1970	£10	£25	
It Takes A Lot To Laugh	7"	London	HLK10266	1969	£2	£5	
Tell Mama	7"	London	HLK10280	1969	£2	£5	

MUSIC MASTER PRICE GUIDE

VELOURS
Title	Fmt	Label	Cat	Year			Notes
I'm Gonna Change	7"	MGM	2006603	1977	£1.50	£4	

VELVELETTES
Title	Fmt	Label	Cat	Year			Notes
He Was Really Sayin' Something	7"	Stateside	SS387	1965	£15	£30	
Lonely Lonely Girl Am I	7"	Tamla Motown	TMG521	1965	£30	£60	
Needle In A Haystack	7"	Stateside	SS361	1964	£10	£20	
Needle In A Haystack	7"	Tamla Motown	TMG595	1967	£4	£8	
Needle In A Haystack	7"	Tamla Motown	TMG806	1972	£1.50	£4	
These Things Will Keep Me Loving You	7"	Tamla Motown	TMG580	1966	£7.50	£15	
These Things Will Keep Me Loving You	7"	Tamla Motown	TMG780	1971	£1.50	£4	chart single

VELVET FOGG
Title	Fmt	Label	Cat	Year			Notes
Telstar '69	7"	Pye	7N17673	1969	£10	£20	
Velvet Fogg	LP	Pye	NSPL18272	1967	£35	£70	

VELVET HUSH
Title	Fmt	Label	Cat	Year			Notes
Broken Heart	7"	Oak	RGJ648	1968	£40	£80	

VELVET OPERA
Title	Fmt	Label	Cat	Year			Notes
Anna Dance Square	7"	CBS	4189	1969	£2	£5	
Black Jack Davy	7"	CBS	4802	1970	£1.50	£4	
Ride A Hustler's Dream	LP	CBS	63692	1969	£20	£40	

VELVET UNDERGROUND
Title	Fmt	Label	Cat	Year			Notes
All Tomorrow's Parties	7"	Verve	10427	1966	£75	£150	US
Candy Says	7"	MGM	2006283	1973	£4	£8	
Index Cardboard Picture Disc	7"	Index		1966	£50	£100	US
Loaded	LP	Atlantic	2400111	1970	£5	£12	
Loop	7"	Aspen		1966	£50	£100	US flexi
Radio Spot	7"	MGM	VU1	1969	£100	£200	US promo
Squeeze	LP	Polydor	2383180	1972	£4	£10	
Sunday Morning	7"	Verve	10466	1966	£60	£120	US
Sweet Jane	7"	Atlantic	K10339	1973	£4	£8	
Velvet Underground	LP	MGM	CS8108	1969	£10	£25	
Velvet Underground And Nico	LP	MGM	2315056	1971	£5	£12	
Velvet Underground And Nico	LP	Verve	VLP9184	1967	£20	£40	mono
Velvet Underground With Nico	LP	MGM	2315056	1971	£20	£40	with US peelable banana cover
Velvet Underground With Nico	LP	Verve	SVLP9184	1967	£15	£30	
Velvet Underground With Nico	LP	Verve	V5008	1967	£30	£60	US, peelable banana cover, male torso airbrushed out, mono
Velvet Underground With Nico	LP	Verve	V5008	1967	£50	£100	US, peelable banana cover, male torso frames group photo, mono
Velvet Underground With Nico	LP	Verve	V5008	1967	£37.50	£75	US, peelable banana cover, sticker covers group photo, mono
Velvet Underground With Nico	LP	Verve	V65008	1967	£20	£40	US, peelable banana cover, male torso airbrushed out, stereo
Velvet Underground With Nico	LP	Verve	V65008	1967	£37.50	£75	US, peelable banana cover, male torso frames group photo, stereo
Velvet Underground With Nico	LP	Verve	V65008	1967	£25	£50	US, peelable banana cover, sticker covers group photo, stereo
What Goes On?	7"	MGM	14057	1969	£25	£50	US promo
White Light, White Heat	7"	Verve	10560	1968	£25	£50	US promo, 2 different B sides
White Light/White Heat	LP	Verve	SVLP9201	1967	£15	£30	
White Light/White Heat	LP	Verve	VLP9201	1968	£17.50	£35	mono
Who Loves The Sun	7"	Atlantic	2091088	1971	£7.50	£15	
Who Loves The Sun	7"	Cotillion	44107	1971	£15	£30	US promo

VELVETS
Title	Fmt	Label	Cat	Year			Notes
Laugh	7"	London	HLU9444	1961	£7.50	£15	
That Lucky Old Sun	7"	London	HLU9328	1961	£7.50	£15	chart single
Tonight	7"	London	HLU9372	1961	£7.50	£15	chart single
Velvets	7" EP	London	REU1297	1961	£20	£40	

VELVETTES
Title	Fmt	Label	Cat	Year			Notes
He's The One I Want	7"	Mercury	MF802	1964	£2	£5	
He's The One I Want	7"	Mercury	MF802	1964	£5	£10	PS

VENDORS
Title	Fmt	Label	Cat	Year			Notes
Peace Pipe	7"	private		1964	£150	£250	demo

VENGERS
Title	Fmt	Label	Cat	Year			Notes
Shake And Clap	7"	Oriole	CB1879	1963	£1.50	£4	

VENOM
Title	Fmt	Label	Cat	Year			Notes
Blood Lust	7"	Neat	NEAT13	1982	£1.50	£4	
Die Hard	7"	Neat	NEAT027	1983	£4	£8	export pic disc
In League With Satan	7"	Neat	NEAT08	1982	£1.50	£4	
Manitou	7"	Neat	NEATSHAPE43	1985	£1.50	£4	shaped pic disc

Nightmare	12"	Neat	NEATSP4712	1985	£2.50	£6	pic disc

VENTURA, CHARLIE

Concert	LP	Brunswick	LAT8023	1953	£15	£30	
Gene Norman Concert Recordings	10" LP	Vogue	LDE107	1954	£15	£30	

VENTURA, TOBY

If My Heart Were A Story Book	7"	Decca	F11581	1963	£7.50	£15	

VENTURAS

Here They Are	LP	Drum Boy	DB(S)1003	1964	£10	£25	US

VENTURES

The Ventures are the American equivalent of the Shadows, maintaining a long and still buoyant career by playing melodic guitar instrumentals regardless of the prevailing musical fashions. The size of the Ventures" output is astonishing - they have released far more albums than are listed here, including many that have been issued only in Japan. Despite this, the group still found it necessary to issue an album on their own label in 1964, thereby producing the only real rarity in their catalogue.

A Go-Go	LP	Liberty	LBY1274	1965	£4	£10	
Another Smash	LP	London	HAG2376/	1961	£8	£20	
			SAHG6176				
Another Smash	7" EP.	London	REG1326	1961	£7.50	£15	
Batman Theme	LP	Dolton	BLP2042/BST8042	1966	£6	£15	US
Beach Party	LP	Dolton	BLP2016/BST8016	1963	£6	£15	US
Blue Moon	7"	London	HLG9465	1961	£2	£5	
Christmas Album	LP	Liberty	LBY1285	1965	£6	£15	
Colourful Ventures	LP	London	HAG2409/	1961	£8	£20	
			SAHG6209				
Colourful Ventures	7" EP.	London	REG1328	1961	£6	£12	
Dance!	LP	Dolton	BLP2010/BST8010	1963	£6	£15	US
Dance Party	LP	Liberty	(S)LBY1110	1962	£6	£15	
Dance With The Ventures	LP	Dolton	BLP2014/BST8014	1963	£6	£15	US
Diamond Head	7"	Liberty	LIB303	1965	£1.50	£4	
El Cumbanchero	7"	Liberty	LIB68	1964	£1.50	£4	
Fabulous Ventures	LP	Dolton	BLP2029/BST8029	1964	£6	£15	US
Flights Of Fantasy	7"	Liberty	LBF15075	1968	£1.50	£4	
Go With The Ventures	LP	Liberty	LBY1323	1966	£5	£12	
Guitar Freakout	LP	Liberty	LBY1345	1967	£5	£12	
Hawaii Five-O	7"	Liberty	LBF15221	1969	£1.50	£4	
In Space	LP	Liberty	(S)LBY1189	1964	£6	£15	
Journey To The Stars	7"	Liberty	LIB91	1964	£1.50	£4	
Knock Me Out	LP	Liberty	(S)LBY1252	1965	£5	£12	
Lady Of Spain	7"	London	HLG7113	1961	£7.50	£15	export
Let's Go	LP	Liberty	LBY1169	1963	£5	£12	
Lolita Ya Ya	7"	Liberty	LIB60	1964	£1.50	£4	
Lullaby Of The Leaves	7"	London	HLG9344	1961	£1.50	£4	chart single
Mashed Potatoes And Gravy	LP	Dolton	BLP2016/BST8016	1962	£8	£20	US
Ninth Wave	7"	Liberty	LIB78	1964	£1.50	£4	
On Stage	LP	Liberty	LBY1270	1965	£5	£12	
Penetration	7"	Liberty	LIB10142	1964	£1.50	£4	
Perfidia	7"	London	HLG9232	1960	£2	£5	chart single
Perfidia	7" EP.	London	REG1279	1960	£7.50	£15	
Play Guitar With The Ventures	LP	Dolton	BLP16501	1965	£6	£15	US
Play Guitar With The Ventures Vol.2	LP	Dolton	BLP16502	1966	£6	£15	US
Play Guitar With The Ventures Vol.3	LP	Dolton	BLP16503	1966	£6	£15	US
Play Guitar With The Ventures Vol.4	LP	Dolton	BLP16504	1966	£6	£15	US
Ram Bunk Shush	7"	London	HLG9292	1961	£1.50	£4	chart single
Ram Bunk Shush	7" EP.	London	REG1288	1961	£7.50	£15	
Real McCoy	7"	Blue Horizon	100	1960	£12.50	£25	US
Secret Agent Man	7"	Liberty	LIB316	1966	£1.50	£4	
Secret Agent Man	7" EP.	Liberty	LEP2250	1966	£7.50	£15	
Slaughter On Tenth Avenue	7"	Liberty	LIB300	1965	£1.50	£4	
Sleigh Ride	7"	Liberty	LIB10210	1965	£1.50	£4	
Smash Hits	7" EP.	Liberty	LEP2131	1963	£6	£12	
Stranger	7"	Liberty	LIB308	1965	£1.50	£4	
Strawberry Fields Forever	7"	Liberty	LIB55967	1967	£1.50	£4	
Super Psychedelics	LP	Liberty	LBL/LBS83033	1968	£4	£10	
Super Psychedelics	LP	Liberty	LBY1372	1967	£5	£12	
Surfing	LP	Liberty	LBY1150	1963	£6	£15	
Swingin' Creeper	7"	Liberty	LIB306	1965	£1.50	£4	
Telstar, The Lonely Bull	LP	Dolton	BLP2019/BST8019	1963	£8	£20	US
Tenth Anniversary Album	LP	Liberty	LST35000	1970	£5	£12	US
Theme From Silver City	7"	London	HLG9411	1961	£2	£5	
Theme From The Wild Angels	7"	Liberty	LIB10266	1967	£1.50	£4	
Twist Party	LP	Liberty	LBY1072	1962	£6	£15	
Twist With The Ventures	LP	London	HAG2429/	1962	£8	£20	
			SAHG6225				
Twist With The Ventures	7" EP.	Liberty	LEP2058	1962	£6	£12	
Two Thousand Pound Bee	7"	Liberty	LIB67	1964	£1.50	£4	
Ventures	LP	Dolton	BLP2042/BST8042	1966	£6	£15	US
Ventures	LP	London	HAG2340	1961	£10	£25	
Ventures	LP	London	SAHG6143	1961	£15	£30	stereo
Ventures	LP	Ventures	BG101	1964	£25	£50	US
Ventures Play Country Greats	7" EP.	Liberty	LEP2174	1964	£7.50	£15	
Ventures Play Telstar & Lonely Bull	7" EP.	Liberty	LEP2104	1963	£6	£12	
Ventures Play The Country Classics	LP	Dolton	BLP2023/BST8023	1963	£8	£20	US
Versatile Ventures	LP	Liberty	SCR5	1966	£6	£15	US
Walk Don't Run	LP	Liberty	LBY1002	1960	£6	£15	
Walk Don't Run	7"	Blue Horizon	101	1960	£12.50	£25	US
Walk Don't Run	7"	Top Rank	JAR417	1960	£2	£5	chart single
Walk Don't Run '64	7"	Liberty	LIB96	1964	£1.50	£4	

Walk Don't Run Vol.2	LP	Liberty	LBY1228	1964	£6	£15	
Where The Action Is	LP	Liberty	LBY1297	1966	£5	£12	
Wild Things	LP	Dolton	BLP2047/BST8047	1966	£6	£15	US

VENUS IN FURS

| Momento Mori | 7" | Backs | PNCH105 | 1985 | £2 | £5 | pic disc |
| Momento Mori | 7" | Movement | MOO1 | 1984 | £2 | £5 | |

VENUTI, JOE

| Joe Venuti | 10" LP | Brunswick | LA8522 | 1951 | £10 | £25 | |

VERA, BILLY

| With Pen In Hand | 7" | Atlantic | 584196 | 1968 | £1.50 | £4 | |

VERA, BILLY & JUDY CLAY

Country Girl, City Man	7"	Atlantic	584169	1968	£1.50	£4	
Reaching For The Moon	7"	Atlantic	584293	1969	£1.50	£4	
Storybook Children	7"	Atlantic	584164	1968	£1.50	£4	

VERNE, LARRY

Mr.Custer	7"	London	HLN9194	1960	£2	£5	
Mr.Larry Verne	LP	Era	EL104	1961	£6	£15	US
Mr.Livingston	7"	London	HLN9263	1961	£2	£5	

VERNON, MIKE

Although he has made the occasional record himself, both under his own name and as a member of the Olympic Runners, Mike Vernon is best known as a producer and as the proprietor of Blue Horizon records. As the producer of John Mayall's pivotal "Bluesbreakers" and "Hard Road" albums, Vernon was ideally placed to take a major role within the development of British blues, and he went on to work with most of the significant talents within the genre, including Fleetwood Mac, Chicken Shack, Savoy Brown, and the Groundhogs. Every record on his Blue Horizon label is now a collectors' item, as indeed are the handful of singles issued by the label's predecessor, Purdah.

Bring It Back Home	LP	Blue Horizon	2931003	1971	£30	£60	
Let's Try It Again	7"	Blue Horizon	2096007	1971	£4	£8	
Moment Of Madness	LP	Sire	SAS7410	1973	£6	£15	US

VERNONS GIRLS

Do The Bird	7"	Decca	F11629	1963	£1.50	£4	chart single
Don't Look Now	7"	Parlophone	R4596	1959	£1.50	£4	
Funny All Over	7"	Decca	F11549	1962	£1.50	£4	chart single
He'll Never Come Back	7"	Decca	F11685	1963	£1.50	£4	
It's A Sin To Tell A Lie	7"	Decca	F12021	1964	£1.50	£4	
Jealous Heart	7"	Parlophone	R4532	1959	£2	£5	
Let's Get Together	7"	Parlophone	R4832	1961	£1.50	£4	
Locomotion	7"	Decca	F11495	1962	£1.50	£4	chart single
Lover Please	7"	Decca	F11450	1962	£1.50	£4	chart single
Madison Time	7"	Parlophone	R4654	1960	£1.50	£4	
Only You Can Do It	7"	Decca	F11887	1964	£1.50	£4	
Ten Little Lonely Boys	7"	Parlophone	R4734	1961	£1.50	£4	
Tomorrow Is Another Day	7"	Decca	F11781	1963	£1.50	£4	
Vernons Girls	LP	Parlophone	PMC1052	1958	£25	£50	
Vernons Girls	7" EP	Decca	DFE8506	1962	£5	£10	
We Like Boys	7"	Parlophone	R4624	1960	£1.50	£4	
We Love The Beatles	7"	Decca	F11807	1964	£1.50	£4	
White Bucks And Saddle Shoes	7"	Parlophone	R4497	1958	£5	£10	

VERONICA

Veronica Bennett was the lead singer of the Ronettes and, not long after these solo releases, became Mrs.Phil Spector.

| So Young | 7" | Phil Spector | 1 | 1964 | £20 | £40 | US |
| Why Don't They Let Us Fall In Love? | 7" | Phil Spector | 2 | 1964 | £20 | £40 | US |

VERSATILE NEWTS

| Newtrition | 7" | Shanghai | No.2 | 1980 | £7.50 | £15 | |

VERSATILES

Children Get Ready	7"	Crab	CRAB1	1968	£4	£8	
Just Can't Win	7"	Amalgamated	AMG802	1968	£4	£8	Leaders B side
Lu Lu Bell	7"	Amalgamated	AMG854	1969	£4	£8	
Spread Your Bed	7"	Crab	CRAB5	1969	£2.50	£6	
Teardrops Falling	7"	Island	WI3142	1968	£5	£10	
Worries A Yard	7"	Big Shot	BI520	1969	£2.50	£6	Val Bennett B side

VERSATONES

| Versatones | LP | RCA | LPM1538 | 1957 | £8 | £20 | US |

VERTO

| Krig/Volubilis | LP | Tapioca | 10007 | 1976 | £5 | £12 | French |
| Reel 19/36 | LP | Fleau | FL7004 | 1978 | £4 | £10 | French |

VETERANS

| Administration | LP | | | 1968 | £10 | £25 | US |

VETTES

| Rev-up | LP | MGM | (S)E4193 | 1963 | £5 | £12 | US |

VIAN, PATRICK

| Bruits Et Temps Analogues | LP | Egg | 900541 | 1978 | £4 | £10 | French |

VIBRATIONS

Canadian Sunset	7"	Columbia	DB7895	1966	£2.50	£6	
Greatest Hits	LP	Direction	863644	1969	£6	£15	
Love In Them There Hills	7"	Direction	583511	1968	£2	£5	
Misty	LP	OKeh	OKM4112/OKS14112	1966	£6	£15	US

My Girl Sloopy	7"	London	HLK9875	1964	£4	£8	
New Vibrations	LP	Columbia	SX6106	1966	£6	£15	
One Mint Julep	7"	Columbia	DB8319	1967	£2	£5	
Pick Me	7"	Columbia	DB8175	1967	£5	£10	
Shout	LP	OKeh	OKM4111/	1965	£8	£20	US
			OKS14111				
Talkin' 'Bout Love	7"	Columbia	DB8318	1967	£4	£8	
Watusi	LP	Checker	2978	1961	£10	£25	US
Watusi	7"	Pye	7N25107	1961	£5	£10	

VIBRATORS (2)
| Sloop John B | 7" | Doctor Bird | DB1036 | 1966 | £5 | £10 | |

VICE VERSA
| Music 4 | 7" | Neutron | NT001 | 1980 | £2 | £5 | |

VICEROYS
Fat Fish	7"	Blue Cat	BS121	1968	£4	£8	Octaves B side
Jump In A Fire	7"	Punch	PH3	1969	£2	£5	
Last Night	7"	Studio One	SO2064	1968	£6	£12	
Lips And Tongue	7"	Island	WI3095	1967	£5	£10	Dawn Penn B side
Lose And Gain	7"	Studio One	SO2016	1967	£6	£12	Soul Brothers B side
Try Hard To Leave	7"	Coxsone	CS7036	1968	£5	£10	
Work It	7"	Crab	CRAB12	1969	£1.50	£4	

VICEROYS (2)
| At Granny's Pad | LP | Bolo | BLP8000 | 1963 | £8 | £20 | US |

VICIOUS PINK PHENOMENA
| My Private Tokyo | 7" | Mobile Suit Corp. | CORP1 | 1982 | £2 | £5 | |
| My Private Tokyo | 12" | Mobile Suit Corp. | CORP12 | 1982 | £3 | £8 | |

VICK, HAROLD
| Steppin' Out | LP | Blue Note | BLP/BST84138 | 1963 | £20 | £40 | |

VICKERS, MIKE
Air On A G String	7"	Columbia	DB8171	1967	£2.50	£6	
Captain Scarlet And The Mysterons	7"	Columbia	DB8281	1967	£5	£10	
Eleventy One	7"	Columbia	DB7825	1966	£2.50	£6	
I Wish I Were A Group Again	LP	Columbia	SX/SCX6180	1968	£6	£15	
Morgan	7"	Columbia	DB7906	1966	£2.50	£6	
Puff Adder	7"	Columbia	DB7657	1965	£12.50	£25	

VICKERS, SUE
| Loving You The Way I Do | 7" | Threshold | TH8 | 1972 | £1.50 | £4 | |

VICKY
| Colours Of Love | 7" | Philips | B1565 | 1967 | £4 | £8 | |

VICKY & JERRY
| Don't Cry | 7" | HMV | POP715 | 1960 | £4 | £8 | |

VICTIMS OF CHANCE
| Victims Of Chance | LP | Stable | SLE8004 | 1969 | £10 | £25 | |

VICTIMS OF PLEASURE
| When You're Young | 7" | PAM | VOP1 | 1980 | £1.50 | £4 | |

VICTOR, TONY
Dear One	7"	Decca	F11459	1962	£4	£8	
Hokey Cokey	7"	Decca	F11626	1963	£1.50	£4	
In The Still Of The Night	7"	Decca	F11708	1963	£1.50	£4	

VICTORS
| Things Come Up To Bump | 7" | Studio One | SO2077 | 1969 | £6 | £12 | Lyrics B side |

VIDELS
| Mister Lonely | 7" | London | HLI9153 | 1960 | £10 | £20 | |

VIGILANTES
| Eclipse | 7" | Pye | 7N25082 | 1961 | £4 | £8 | |

VIKINGS
Come Into The Parlour	7"	Black Swan	WI430	1964	£5	£10	
Daddy	7"	Island	WI167	1965	£5	£10	
Down By The Riverside	7"	Black Swan	WI423	1964	£5	£10	
Fever	7"	Island	WI117	1963	£5	£10	
Get Ready	7"	Island	WI122	1963	£5	£10	Don Drummond B side
Hallelujah	7"	Island	WI065	1962	£5	£10	
Just Got To Be	7"	Island	WI107	1963	£5	£10	
Maggie Don't Leave Me	7"	Island	WI035	1962	£5	£10	
Never Grow Old	7"	Island	WI101	1963	£5	£10	
Six And Seven Books Of Moses	7"	Island	WI075	1963	£5	£10	
Treat Me Bad	7"	Black Swan	WI428	1964	£5	£10	

VIKINGS (2)
| Bad News Feeling | 7" | Alp | 595011 | 1966 | £5 | £10 | |

VILLAGE

Title	Format	Label	Cat#	Year	Low	High	Notes
Man In The Moon	7"	Head	HDS4002	1969	£10	£20	

VILLAGE SOUL

Title	Format	Label	Cat#	Year	Low	High	Notes
Cat Walk	7"	Direction	584969	1970	£1.50	£4	

VILLAGE STOMPERS

Title	Format	Label	Cat#	Year	Low	High	Notes
Washington Square	7"	Columbia	DB7123	1963	£2	£5	

VILLAGE VOICES

This is the same group as shortly afterwards began recording as the Four Seasons.

Title	Format	Label	Cat#	Year	Low	High	Notes
Red Lips	7"	Topix	6000	1960	£25	£50	US

VINCENT, GENE

Title	Format	Label	Cat#	Year	Low	High	Notes
Anna Annabelle	7"	Capitol	CL15169	1960	£6	£12	
B I Bickey Bi Bo Bo Go	7"	Capitol	CL14722	1957	£25	£50	
Baby Blue	7"	Capitol	CL14868	1958	£10	£20	
Baby Don't Believe Him	7"	Capitol	CL15243	1962	£6	£12	
Be Bop A Lula	7"	Capitol	CL14599	1956	£10	£20	chart single
Be Bop A Lula	7"	Dandelion	4596	1969	£2	£5	
Be Bop A Lula '62	7"	Capitol	CL15264	1962	£6	£12	
Best Of Gene Vincent	LP	Capitol	T20957	1967	£5	£12	
Best Of Gene Vincent Vol.2	LP	Capitol	(S)T21144	1969	£6	£15	
Bird Doggin'	7"	London	HLH10079	1966	£6	£12	
Bluejean Bop	LP	Capitol	T764	1957	£20	£40	
Bluejean Bop	LP	Capitol	T764	1957	£100	£200	US
Bluejean Bop	7"	Capitol	CL14637	1956	£20	£40	chart single
Crazy Beat	7"	Capitol	CL15307	1963	£7.50	£15	
Crazy Beat Of Gene Vincent	LP	Capitol	T20453	1963	£15	£30	
Crazy Beat Of Gene Vincent Pt.1	7" EP	Capitol	EAP120453	1963	£12.50	£25	
Crazy Beat Of Gene Vincent Pt.2	7" EP	Capitol	EAP220453	1964	£12.50	£25	
Crazy Beat Of Gene Vincent Pt.3	7" EP	Capitol	EAP320453	1964	£12.50	£25	
Crazy Legs	7"	Capitol	CL14693	1957	£25	£50	
Crazy Times	LP	Capitol	ST1342	1960	£25	£50	stereo, sleeve pictured in Guide
Crazy Times	LP	Capitol	T1342	1960	£15	£30	chart LP
Crazy Times	LP	Capitol	T1342	1960	£75	£150	US
Crazy Times	LP	MFP	MFP1053	1965	£5	£12	
Dance To The Bop	7"	Capitol	CL14808	1957	£12.50	£25	
Day The World Turned Blue	LP	Kama Sutra	2316005	1971	£4	£10	
Day The World Turned Blue	LP	Kama Sutra	KSBS2027	1971	£6	£15	
Day The World Turned Blue	7"	Kama Sutra	2013018	1971	£2	£5	
Gene Vincent	LP	Kama Sutra	KSBS2019	1970	£6	£15	
Gene Vincent	LP	London	HAH8333	1967	£10	£25	
Gene Vincent & The Blue Caps	LP	Capitol	T811	1957	£20	£40	
Gene Vincent & The Blue Caps	LP	Capitol	T811	1957	£100	£200	US
Gene Vincent Record Date	LP	Capitol	T1059	1958	£15	£30	
Gene Vincent Record Date	LP	Capitol	T1059	1958	£100	£200	US
Gene Vincent Record Date Pt.1	7" EP	Capitol	EAP11059	1959	£12.50	£25	
Gene Vincent Record Date Pt.2	7" EP	Capitol	EAP21059	1959	£30	£60	
Gene Vincent Record Date Pt.3	7" EP	Capitol	EAP31059	1960	£12.50	£25	
Gene Vincent Rocks & The Blue Caps Roll	LP	Capitol	T970	1958	£20	£40	
Gene Vincent Rocks & The Blue Caps Roll	LP	Capitol	T970	1958	£100	£200	US
Git It	7"	Capitol	CL14935	1958	£10	£20	
Held For Questioning	7"	Capitol	CL15290	1963	£6	£12	
Hot Rod Gang	7" EP	Capitol	EAP1985	1958	£15	£30	
Humpity Dumpity	7"	Columbia	DB7218	1964	£5	£10	
I Got A Baby	7"	Capitol	CL14830	1958	£10	£20	
If You Could Only See Me Today	LP	Buddah	2361009	1972	£5	£12	
If You Want My Loving	7"	Capitol	CL15185	1961	£6	£12	
If You Want My Loving	7" EP	Capitol	EAP120173	1961	£15	£30	
I'm Back & I'm Proud	7"	Dandelion	63754	1969	£8	£20	
I'm Going Home	7"	Capitol	CL15215	1961	£5	£10	chart single
Jumps Giggles And Shouts	7"	Capitol	CL14681	1957	£30	£60	
La Den Da Den Da Da	7"	Columbia	DB7293	1964	£5	£10	
Live And Rockin'	7" EP	Emidisc/fan club	no number	1968	£75	£150	
Lonely Street	7"	London	HLH10099	1966	£5	£10	
Maybe	7"	Capitol	CL15179	1961	£6	£12	
My Heart	7"	Capitol	CL15115	1960	£6	£12	chart single
Over The Rainbow	7"	Capitol	CL15000	1959	£6	£12	
Pistol Packing Mama	7"	Capitol	CL15136	1960	£5	£10	chart single
Private Detective	7"	Columbia	DB7343	1964	£5	£10	
Race With The Devil	7"	Capitol	CL14628	1956	£25	£50	chart single
Race With The Devil	7" EP	Capitol	EAP120354	1962	£15	£30	
Rainy Day Sunshine	7"	Rollin' Danny	RD1	1979	£5	£10	
Rainy Day Sunshine	7" EP	Magnum Force	MFEP003	1981	£2.50	£6	
Right Now	7"	Capitol	CL15053	1959	£6	£12	
Rip It Up	7"	Capitol	CL15307	1963	£60	£120	demo
Rocky Road Blues	7"	Capitol	CL14908	1958	£10	£20	
Roll Over Beethoven	7"	BBC	BEEB001	1974	£1.50	£4	
Say Mama	7"	Capitol	CL14974	1959	£7.50	£15	
Say Mama	7"	Capitol	CL15546	1968	£2	£5	
Say Mama	7"	Capitol	CL15906	1977	£1.50	£4	
Shakin' Up A Storm	LP	Columbia	33SX1646	1964	£10	£25	
She She Little Sheila	7"	Capitol	CL15202	1961	£5	£10	chart single
Sounds Like Gene Vincent	LP	Capitol	T1207	1959	£17.50	£35	
Sounds Like Gene Vincent	LP	Capitol	T1207	1959	£75	£150	US

Summertime	7"	Capitol	CL15035	1959	£6	£12	
Temptation Baby	7"	Columbia	DB7174	1963	£4	£8	
True To You	7" EP.	Capitol	EAP120461	1963	£12.50	£25	
Unchained Melody	7"	Capitol	CL15231	1961	£6	£12	
Wear My Ring	7"	Capitol	CL14763	1957	£12.50	£25	
White Lightning	7"	Dandelion	4974	1970	£2	£5	
Wild Cat	7"	Capitol	CL15099	1959	£6	£12	chart single

VINE, JOEY
Down And Out	7"	Immediate	IM017	1965	£6	£12	

VINEGAR
Vinegar	LP	Phonofoly	WP710101	1971	£45	£90	German

VINEGAR JOE
Rock'n'Roll Gypsies	LP	Island	ILPS9214	1972	£5	£12	
Six Star General	LP	Island	ILPS9262	1973	£5	£12	
Vinegar Joe	LP	Island	ILPS9183	1972	£6	£15	

VINNEGAR, LEROY
Leroy Walks	LP	Contemporary.	LAC12136	1959	£8	£20	

VINSON, EDDIE 'CLEANHEAD'
Backdoor Blues	LP	Riverside	3502	196-	£6	£15	US
Cherry Red	LP	BluesWay	BL(S)6007	1967	£5	£12	US
Eddie Cleanhead Vinson Sings	LP	Aamco	312	196-	£5	£12	US
Eddie Cleanhead Vinson Sings	LP	Bethlehem	BCP5005	196-	£6	£15	US
Jump And Grunt	78	Vogue	V2023	1951	£5	£10	

VINSON, EDDIE 'CLEANHEAD' & JIMMY WITHERSPOON
Battle Of The Blues Vol.3	LP	King	634	1959	£180	£300	US

VINSTRICK, V.
Love Is Not A Game	7"	Doctor Bird	DB1167	1968	£5	£10	Cinderella B side

VINTON, BOBBY
Blue On Blue	LP	Columbia	33SX1566	1963	£5	£12	
Blue On Blue	7"	Columbia	DB7052	1963	£1.50	£4	
Blue Velvet	7"	Columbia	DB7110	1963	£2	£5	
Clinging Vine	7"	Columbia	DB7348	1964	£1.50	£4	
Coming Home Soldier	7"	Columbia	DB8114	1967	£1.50	£4	
Corrine Corrina	7"	Fontana	H307	1961	£1.50	£4	
Dancing At The Hop	LP	Epic	LN3727/LN579	1960	£6	£15	US
Don't Go Away Mad	7"	Columbia	DB7628	1965	£1.50	£4	
Dum De Da	7"	Columbia	DB7922	1966	£1.50	£4	
Greatest Hits Of The Greatest Groups	LP	Epic	LN24049/BN26049	1963	£6	£15	US
Halfway To Paradise	LP	CBS	3636	1968	£1.50	£4	
I Love The Way You Are	7"	London	HLU9592	1962	£1.50	£4	
Just As Much As Ever	7"	Columbia	DB8346	1968	£1.50	£4	
Long Lonely Nights	7"	Columbia	DB7514	1965	£1.50	£4	
Mr.Lonely	7"	Columbia	DB7422	1964	£1.50	£4	
My Heart Belongs To Only You	7"	Columbia	DB7240	1964	£1.50	£4	
Over The Mountain	7"	Columbia	DB7015	1963	£1.50	£4	
Please Love Me Forever	7"	Columbia	DB8319	1967	£1.50	£4	
Rain Rain Go Away	7"	Columbia	DB4900	1962	£1.50	£4	
Roses Are Red	7"	Columbia	DB4878	1962	£1.50	£4	chart single
Satin Pillows	7"	Columbia	DB7808	1966	£1.50	£4	
Sings The Big Ones	LP	Columbia	33SX1517	1963	£5	£12	
Songs Of Christmas	7" EP.	Columbia	SEG8363	1964	£7.50	£15	
Tell Me Why	LP	Columbia	33SX1649	1965	£5	£12	
Tell Me Why	7"	Columbia	DB7303	1964	£1.50	£4	chart single
There I've Said It Again	7"	Columbia	DB7179	1963	£1.50	£4	
Trouble Is My Middle Name	7"	Columbia	DB4961	1963	£1.50	£4	
What Colour Is A Man	7"	Columbia	DB7731	1965	£1.50	£4	
Young In Heart	7" EP.	Columbia	SEG8212	1962	£5	£10	
Young Man With A Big Band	LP	Epic	LN3780/LN597	1961	£6	£15	US

VINYL, MATT
Useless Tasks	7"	Housewife's Choice		1977	£2	£5	

VIOLATORS
NY Ripper	7"	Violators	FRS0022	1980	£2	£5	

VIOLENT THIMBLE
Gentle People	7"	Polydor	56217	1967	£1.50	£4	

VIOLENTS
Ghia	7"	HMV	POP1130	1963	£1.50	£4	

VIPERS SKIFFLE GROUP
Coffee Bar Session	10" LP	Parlophone	PMD1050	1957	£15	£30	sleeve pictured in Guide
Cumberland Gap	7"	Parlophone	R4289	1957	£4	£8	chart single
Don't You Rock Me Daddyo	7"	Parlophone	R4261	1957	£5	£10	chart single
Homing Bird	7"	Parlophone	R4351	1957	£4	£8	
Jim Dandy	7"	Parlophone	R4286	1957	£5	£10	
Make Ready For Love	7"	Parlophone	R4435	1958	£2.50	£6	
No Other Baby	7"	Parlophone	R4393	1958	£2.50	£6	
Pick A Bale Of Cotton	7"	Parlophone	R4238	1956	£5	£10	
Skiffle Music Vol.1	7" EP.	Parlophone	GEP8615	1957	£7.50	£15	

Skiffle Music Vol.2	7" EP..	Parlophone......	GEP8626	1957	£7.50	£15	
Skiffle Party	7".....	Parlophone......	R4371	1957	£2.50	£6	
Skiffling Along With The Vipers	7" EP..	Parlophone......	GEP8655	1957	£7.50	£15	
Streamline Train	7".....	Parlophone......	R4308	1957	£4	£8	...............chart single
Summertime Blues	7".....	Parlophone......	R4484	1958	£7.50	£15	

VIPPS
Wintertime	7".....	CBS..............	202031	1966	£10	£20	

V.I.P.'S
I Wanna Be Free	7".....	Island............	WI3003	1966	£10	£20	
I Wanna Be Free	7" EP..	Fontana.........	460982	1966	£25	£50	...............French
Mercy Mercy	7".....	Philips...........	40387	1966	£12.50	£25	...............US
Stagger Lee	7" EP..	Fontana.........	460219	1967	£25	£50	...............French
Straight Down To The Bottom	7".....	Island............	WIP6005	1967	£10	£20	
Straight Down To The Bottom	7" EP..	Fontana.........	460996	1967	£25	£50	...............French
What's That Sound	7" EP..	Fontana.........	460238	1968	£25	£50	...............French

V.I.P.'S (2)
Don't Keep Shouting At Me	7".....	RCA..............	RCA1427	1964	£17.50	£35	

V.I.P.'S (3)
Music For Funsters	7".....	Bust..............	SOL3	1978	£1.50	£4	

VIRGIL BROTHERS
Good Love	7".....	Parlophone......	R5802	1969	£1.50	£4	
Temptation 'Bout To Get Me	7".....	Parlophone......	R5787	1969	£4	£8	

VIRGIN PRUNES
Baby Turns Blue	7".....	Rough Trade ...	RT119	1982	£1.50	£4	
Heresie	10"...	Baby.............	BABY011	1987	£2	£5	...............double
Heresie	10"...	Baby.............	BABY011	1987	£3	£8	.....double, clear vinyl
Heresie	10"...	Suicide...........		1982	£8	£20	...............boxed set
In The Grey Light	7".....	Rough Trade ...	RT072	1981	£4	£8	...............blue PS
In The Grey Light	7".....	Rough Trade ...	RT072	1981	£1.50	£4	.... green PS
New Form Of Beauty	7"/ 10"/ 12".....	Rough Trade ...	RT089-91	1981	£10	£20	... 3 records, boxed
New Form Of Beauty Part One	7".....	Rough Trade ...	RT089	1981	£2	£5	
Pagan Love Song	7".....	Rough Trade ...	RT106	1982	£2.50	£6	
Twenty Tens	7".....	Baby.............	BABY001	1981	£5	£10	

VIRGIN SLEEP
Love	7".....	Deram............	DM146	1967	£10	£20	
Secret	7".....	Deram............	DM173	1968	£10	£20	

VIRGINIA WOLVES
Stay	7".....	Stateside......	SS563	1966	£10	£20	

VIRGINIANS
Limbo Baby	7".....	Pye..............	7N25175	1963	£1.50	£4	

VIRTUES
Guitar Boogie Shuffle	LP.....	Strand............	SL1061	1960	£8	£20	...............US
Guitar Boogie Shuffle	LP.....	Wynne............	WLP111	1960	£8	£20	...............US
Guitar Boogie Shuffle	LP.....	HMV.............	POP621	1959	£4	£8	
Shuffling Along	7".....	HMV.............	POP637	1959	£5	£10	

VIRTUES (2)
High Tide	7".....	Doctor Bird	DB1164	1968	£5	£10	
Your Wife And Your Mother	7".....	Island............	WI196	1965	£5	£10	

VIRTUOSA, FRANK
Rollin' And Rockin'	7".....	Melodisc.........	1386	1958	£7.50	£15	

VIRUS
Revelation	LP.....	BASF..............	CRC015	1971	£8	£20	...............German
Thoughts	LP.....	Pilz...............	20211029	1971	£8	£20	...............German

VISAGE
Pleasure Boys	12"...	Polydor	POSPX523	1982	£3	£8	

VISCOUNTS
The Viscounts were a vocal trio, whose easy harmonies were typical of the kind of thing the Beatles blew away. One of the group, however, was Gordon Mills, who later made himself a very comfortable living as manager of both Tom Jones and Engelbert Humperdinck.

Chug A Lug	7".....	Top Rank	JAR388	1960	£2.50	£6	
Harlem Nocturne	LP.....	Amy.............	(S)8008	1965	£8	£20	...............US
Harlem Nocturne	7".....	Stateside........	SS468	1965	£2	£5	
Harlem Nocturne	7".....	Top Rank	JAR254	1959	£2	£5	
Night Train	7".....	Top Rank	JAR502	1960	£2	£5	
Viscounts	LP.....	Madison	1001	1960	£20	£40	...............US
Viscounts' Rock	7" EP..	Top Rank	JKP3005	1961	£15	£30	

VISCOUNTS (2)
Banned In Boston	7".....	Pye..............	7N15344	1961	£1.50	£4	
Don't Let Me Cross Over	7".....	Pye..............	7N15510	1963	£1.50	£4	
Everybody's Got A Ya Ya	7".....	Pye..............	7N15445	1962	£1.50	£4	
I Don't Care What People Say	7".....	Columbia	DB7146	1963	£1.50	£4	
It's You	7".....	Pye..............	7N15536	1963	£1.50	£4	
Joe Sweeney	7".....	Pye..............	7N15356	1961	£1.50	£4	
Mama's Doin' The Twist	7".....	Pye..............	7N15414	1962	£1.50	£4	

Money Is The Root Of All Evil	7"	Pye	7N15323	1961	£1.50	£4
One Of The Guys	7"	Pye	7N15431	1962	£1.50	£4
Rockin' Little Angel	7"	Pye	7N15249	1960	£2	£5
Shortnin' Bread	7"	Pye	7N15287	1960	£1.50	£4	chart single
Viscounts' Hit Parade	7" EP	Pye	NEP24132	1960	£6	£12
Who Put The Bomp	7"	Pye	7N15379	1961	£1.50	£4	chart single

VISION
Lucifer's Friend ... 7" ... MVM ... 2885 ... 1983 ... £2 ... £5

VISITORS
Empty Rooms ... 7" ... Departure ... RAPTURE1 ... 1980 ... £1.50 ... £4

VOGUES
Magic Town ... 7" ... King ... KG1035 ... 1966 ... £2.50 ... £6
Younger Girl ... 7" ... Columbia ... DB7985 ... 1966 ... £4 ... £8

VOGUES (2)
Five O'Clock World	LP	Co&Ce	1230	1966	£6	£15	US
Five O'Clock World	7"	London	HLG10247	1969	£1.50	£4
Five O'Clock World	7"	London	HLU10014	1966	£2	£5
Five O'Clock World	7" EP	London	RE10176	1966	£6	£12	French
Meet The Vogues	LP	Co&Ce	1229	1965	£6	£15	US
My Special Angel	7"	Reprise	RS20766	1968	£1.50	£4
Please Mr.Sun	7" EP	Vogue	INT18104	1966	£6	£12	French
Turn Around Look At Me	7"	Reprise	RS20686	1968	£1.50	£4
You're The One	7"	London	HLU9996	1965	£2	£5

VOICE
Train To Disaster ... 7" ... Mercury ... MF905 ... 1965 ... £30 ... £60

VOICES
Rock & Roll Hit Parade ... 7" ... Beltona ... BL2667 ... 1956 ... £2.50 ... £6

VOIDS
Come On Out ... 7" ... Polydor ... BM56073 ... 1966 ... £10 ... £20

VOIGHT, WES
I'm Moving In ... 7" ... Parlophone ... R4586 ... 1959 ... £20 ... £40

VOKES, HOWARD COUNTRY BOYS
Howard Vokes Country Boys ... 7" EP ... Starlite ... GRK508 ... 1966 ... £4 ... £8
Howard Vokes Country Boys ... 7" EP ... Starlite ... STEP27 ... 1962 ... £6 ... £12
Mountain Guitar ... 7" EP ... Starlite ... STEP37 ... 1963 ... £6 ... £12

VOLCANOES
Polaris ... 7" ... Philips ... BF1246 ... 1963 ... £4 ... £8
Ruby Duby Du ... 7" ... Philips ... PB1098 ... 1961 ... £4 ... £8
Tightrope ... 7" ... Philips ... PB1113 ... 1961 ... £4 ... £8
Volcanoes ... 7" EP ... Philips ... BBE12432 ... 1960 ... £12.50 ... £25

VOLUMES
Dreams ... 7" ... Fontana ... 270109TF ... 1962 ... £10 ... £20
I Just Can't Help Myself ... 7" ... Pama ... PM755 ... 1968 ... £150 ... £250 ... test pressing
Sandra ... 7" ... London ... HL9733 ... 1963 ... £7.50 ... £15

VON SCHMIDT, ERIC
Eric Von Schmidt ... LP ... Prestige ... PR7384 ... 1969 ... £5 ... £12

VON TRAPP FAMILY
Brand New Thrill ... 7" ... Woronzow ... WOO1 ... 1980 ... £10 ... £20

VONTASTICS
Day Tripper ... 7" ... Chess ... CRS8043 ... 1966 ... £4 ... £8
Lady Love ... 7" ... Stateside ... SS2002 ... 1967 ... £7.50 ... £15

VOOMINS
If You Don't Come Back ... 7" ... Polydor ... 56001 ... 1965 ... £4 ... £8

VOXPOPPERS
Last Drag ... 7" ... Mercury ... 7MT202 ... 1958 ... £12.50 ... £25
Voxpoppers ... 7" EP ... Mercury ... MEP9533 ... 1958 ... £25 ... £50

VULCANS
Star Trek ... LP ... Trojan ... TRLS53 ... 1971 ... £6 ... £15

VULCAN'S HAMMER
True Hearts And Sound Bottoms ... LP ... Brown ... BVH1 ... 1973 ... £100 ... £200

W

W. GIMMICS
Hot Rods	7" EP..	Polydor	EPH27125	1965	£5	£10	

WACKERS
Girl Who Wanted Fame	7"	Piccadilly	7N35210	1964	£2.50	£6	
I Wonder Why	7"	Oriole	CB1902	1964	£4	£8	
Love Or Money	7"	Piccadilly	7N35195	1964	£2.50	£6	

WADE, ADAM
Adam And Evening	LP	Coed	LPC(S)903	1961	£5	£12	US
Adam And Evening	LP	HMV	CLP1451	1961	£5	£12	
And Then Came Adam	LP	Coed	LPC902	1960	£6	£15	US
And Then Came Adam	7" EP.	HMV	7EG8620	1960	£4	£8	
As If I Didn't Know	7"	HMV	POP913	1961	£1.50	£4	
Does Goodnight Mean Goodbye	7"	Columbia	DB7165	1963	£1.50	£4	
Don't Let Me Cross Over	7"	Columbia	DB4986	1963	£1.50	£4	
For The Want Of Your Love	7"	HMV	POP807	1960	£1.50	£4	
Four Film Songs	7" EP.	Columbia	SEG8316	1964	£4	£8	
I Had The Craziest Dream	7"	HMV	POP764	1960	£1.50	£4	
I'm Climbing	7"	Columbia	DB4891	1962	£1.50	£4	
Irma La Douce	7"	Columbia	DB7213	1964	£1.50	£4	
Preview Of Paradise	7"	HMV	POP966	1962	£1.50	£4	
Prisoner's Song	7"	HMV	POP996	1962	£1.50	£4	
Ruby	7"	Top Rank	JAR370	1960	£1.50	£4	
Speaking Of Her	7"	HMV	POP787	1960	£1.50	£4	
Take Good Care Of Her	7"	HMV	POP843	1961	£1.50	£4	chart single
Tell Her For Me	7"	Top Rank	JAR296	1960	£1.50	£4	
There'll Be No Teardrops Tonight	7"	Columbia	DB4962	1963	£1.50	£4	
Tonight I Won't Be There	7"	HMV	POP942	1961	£1.50	£4	
Why Do We Have To Wait So Long	7"	Columbia	DB7045	1963	£1.50	£4	
Writing On The Wall	7"	HMV	POP896	1961	£1.50	£4	

WADE, WELLINGTON
Let's Turkey Trot	7"	Oriole	CB1857	1963	£2.50	£6	

WAGNER, ADRIAN
Distance Between Us	LP	Atlantic	K50082	1974	£5	£12	

WAGNER, ROBERT
Almost Eighteen	7"	London	HLU8491	1957	£5	£10	

WAGONER, PORTER
Blue Grass Story	LP	RCA	RD7693	1965	£5	£12	
Little Slice Of Life	7" EP.	RCA	RCX7157	1964	£5	£10	
Old Log Cabin For Sale	LP	Camden	CDN5128	1965	£4	£10	
Satisfied Mind	LP	RCA	LPM1358	1956	£8	£20	US
Y'All Come	7" EP.	RCA	RCX7158	1964	£4	£8	

WAILERS
And I Love Her	7"	Ska Beat	JB230	1966	£12.50	£25	
Bend Down Low	7"	Island	WI3043	1967	£12.50	£25	
Concrete Jungle	7"	Island	WIP6164	1973	£1.50	£4	
Dancing Shoes	7"	Rio	R116	1967	£12.50	£25	
Donna	7"	Island	WI216	1965	£12.50	£25	
Down Presser	7"	Punch	PH77	1971	£5	£10	Junior Byles B side
Dreamland	7"	Upsetter	US371	1971	£5	£10	Upsetters B side
Get Up Stand Up	7"	Island	WIP6167	1973	£1.50	£4	
Good Good Rudie	7"	Doctor Bird	DB1021	1966	£12.50	£25	City Slickers B side
He Who Feels It Knows It	7"	Island	WI3001	1966	£12.50	£25	
I Made A Mistake	7"	Ska Beat	JB226	1965	£15	£30	Soul Brothers B side
I Need You	7"	Island	WI3035	1967	£12.50	£25	Ken Boothe B side
I Stand Predominant	7"	Studio One	SO2024	1967	£10	£20	Norma Frazer B side
It Hurts To Be Alone	7"	Island	WI188	1965	£15	£30	
Jailhouse	7"	Bamboo	BAM55	1970	£5	£10	John Holt B side
Jumbie Jamboree	7"	Island	WI260	1966	£12.50	£25	Skatalites B side
Let Him Go	7"	Island	WI3009	1966	£12.50	£25	
Lonesome Feelings	7"	Ska Beat	JB211	1965	£15	£30	
Lonesome Track	7"	Ska Beat	JB249	1966	£12.50	£25	
Love And Affection	7"	Ska Beat	JB228	1965	£15	£30	
Maga Dog	7"	Island	WI212	1965	£12.50	£25	
Mr.Chatterbox	7"	Jackpot	JP730	1970	£10	£20	Doreen Shaeffer B side
Nice Time	7"	Doctor Bird	DB1091	1967	£12.50	£25	
Playboy	7"	Island	WI206	1965	£12.50	£25	
Put It On	7"	Island	WI268	1966	£12.50	£25	
Rasta Put It On	7"	Doctor Bird	DB1039	1966	£12.50	£25	Roland Alphonso B side
Reggae On Broadway	7"	CBS	8144	1972	£6	£12	
Rude Boy	7"	Doctor Bird	DB1013	1966	£12.50	£25	Roland Alphonso B side
Shame And Scandal	7"	Island	WI215	1965	£12.50	£25	

Simmer Down	7"	Ska Beat	JB186	1965	£15	£30	
Stop The Train	7"	Summit	SUM8526	1972	£5	£10	
Version Of Cup	7"	Upsetter	US342	1970	£5	£10	Upsetters B side
What's New Pussycat	7"	Island	WI254	1965	£12.50	£25	

WAILERS (2)

At The Castle	LP	Etiquette	ALB01	1962	£8	£20	US
Fabulous Wailers	LP	Golden Crest	CR3075	1959	£10	£25	US
Mau Mau	7"	London	HL8994	1959	£30	£60	
Out Of Our Tree	LP	Etiquette	ALB026	1966	£6	£15	US
Outburst	LP	United Artists	UAL3557/ UAS6557	1966	£6	£15	US
Tall Cool One	LP	Imperial	LP9262/12262	1964	£6	£15	US
Tall Cool One	7"	London	HL8958	1959	£6	£12	
Tall Cool One	7"	London	HL9892	1964	£4	£8	
Wailers And Company	LP	Etiquette	ALB022	1963	£8	£20	US
Wailers Wailers Everywhere	LP	Etiquette	ALB023	1965	£6	£15	US
Walk Thru The People	LP	Bell	6016	1968	£5	£12	US

WAILING SOULS

Back Out	7"	Banana	BA307	1970	£1.50	£4	
Row Fisherman Row	7"	Banana	BA321	1970	£1.50	£4	
Walk Walk Walk	7"	Banana	BA335	1971	£1.50	£4	King Sporty B side

WAINER, CHERRY

Cherry Wainer	7" EP	Pye	NEP24099	1959	£6	£12	
I Walk The Line	7"	Top Rank	JAR253	1959	£1.50	£4	
Itchy Twitchy Feeling	7"	Pye	7N15161	1958	£2.50	£6	
Money	7"	Columbia	DB4528	1960	£6	£12	
Sleepwalk	7"	Honey Hit	TB128	1963	£1.50	£4	
Waltzes In Springtime	LP	Top Rank	BUY042	1960	£4	£10	

WAINMAN, PHIL

Hear Me A Drummer Man	7"	Columbia	DB7615	1965	£4	£8	

WAITING FOR THE SUN

Waiting For The Sun	LP	Profile	GMOR167	1978	£50	£100	sleeve pictured in Guide

WAKE

23.59	LP	Carnaby	CNLS6005	1970	£50	£100	
Angelina	7"	Pye	7N17813	1969	£6	£12	
Linda	7"	Carnaby	6151001		£6	£12	
Live Today Little Girl	7"	Carnaby	CNS4010	1970	£6	£12	
Noah	7"	Carnaby	CNS4016	1971	£6	£12	

WAKE (2)

On Our Honeymoon	7"	Scanlist	SCN1	1982	£5	£10	

WAKELY, JIMMY

Are You Mine	7"	Vogue Coral	Q72125	1956	£4	£8	
Are You Satisfied	7"	Brunswick	05542	1956	£5	£10	
Christmas On The Range	10" LP	Capitol	H9004	195-	£8	£20	US
Country Million Sellers	LP	Shasta	SHLP501	1959	£5	£12	US
Enter And Rest And Pray	LP	Decca	DL8680	1957	£6	£15	US
Folsom Prison Blues	7"	Brunswick	05563	1956	£6	£12	US
Jimmy Wakely Sings	LP	Shasta	SHLP505	1960	£5	£12	US
Merry Christmas	LP	Shasta	SHLP502	1959	£5	£12	US
Santa Fe Trail	LP	Brunswick	LAT8179	1957	£6	£15	US
Songs Of The West	10" LP	Capitol	H4008	195-	£8	£20	US

WAKEMAN, RICK

Those critics who dismiss Rick Wakeman's music as no more than musak will be delighted if they hear the scarce "Piano Vibrations", as this really is a musak LP. Nevertheless, the modest value achieved by this rarity reflects not its paucity of musical imagination, but Rick Wakeman's limited status as a collectable artist. Many records as bland as this do attain high values!

Journey To The Centre Of The Earth	LP	A&M	QU53621	1975	£4	£10	US quad
Myths And Legends Of King Arthur	LP	A&M	QU54515	1975	£4	£10	US quad
Piano Vibrations	LP	Polydor	2460135	1971	£5	£12	
Six Wives Of Henry VIII	LP	A&M	QU54361	1973	£4	£10	US quad

WALDRON, MAL

Quest	LP	XTRA	XTRA5006	1966	£6	£15	

WALHAM GREEN EAST WAPPING C.C.R.B.E. ASSOCIATION

Sorry Mr.Green	7"	Columbia	DB8426	1968	£12.50	£25	

WALKER, BILLY

Certain Girl	7"	Columbia	DB7724	1965	£2.50	£6	
Forever	7"	Philips	PB1001	1960	£1.50	£4	
My Heart Cries For You	7"	Decca	F11917	1964	£1.50	£4	

WALKER BROTHERS

Scott Engel, John Morse, and Gary Leeds were not called Walker and were not brothers. Gary Leeds did not even seem to do very much - he had no voice to match the rich tones of the other two, and so he sat behind a drum kit and pretended (very unconvincingly) that drumming was a vital ingredient in the group's music. The cult interest in Scott Walker's solo music has extended only slightly towards the Walker Brothers, whose music was too popular to ever acquire the attraction of exclusivity and which has none of the disturbing quality of Scott's best work.

Another Tear Falls	7"	Philips	BF1514	1966	£1.50	£4	chart single
But I Do	7" EP	Philips	434560	1965	£5	£10	French
Deadlier Than The Male	7"	Philips	BF1537	1966	£1.50	£4	chart single
I Need You	7" EP	Philips	BE12596	1966	£4	£8	

Images	LP	Philips	(S)BL7770	1967	£4	£10	chart LP
Love Her	7"	Philips	BF1409	1965	£1.50	£4	chart single
Make It Easy On Yourself	7"	Philips	BF1428	1965	£1.50	£4	chart single
My Ship Is Coming In	7"	Philips	BF1454	1965	£1.50	£4	chart single
My Ship Is Coming In	7" EP	Philips	434564	1965	£5	£10	French
Portrait	LP	Philips	BL7732	1966	£4	£10	chart LP
Pretty Girls Everywhere	7"	Philips	BF1401	1965	£1.50	£4	
Stay With Me Baby	7"	Philips	BF1548	1967	£1.50	£4	chart single
Story	LP	Philips	DBL002	1967	£5	£12	double
Sun Ain't Gonna Shine Anymore	7"	Philips	BF1473	1966	£1.50	£4	
Sun Ain't Gonna Shine Anymore	7" EP	Philips	434567	1966	£5	£10	French
Take It Easy	LP	Philips	BL7691	1965	£4	£10	chart LP
Walker Brothers	7" EP	Philips	BE12603	1967	£12.50	£25	demo
Walking In The Rain	7"	Philips	BF1576	1967	£1.50	£4	chart single
You Don't Have To Tell Me	7"	Philips	BF1497	1966	£1.50	£4	chart single

WALKER, CLINT

Inspiration	7" EP	Warner Bros	WEP6006/ WSEP2006	1960	£5	£10	

WALKER, DAVID

Ring The Changes	7"	RCA	RCA1664	1968	£7.50	£15	

WALKER, GARY

Come In You'll Get Pneumonia	7"	Philips	BF1740	1968	£10	£20	
Here's Gary	7" EP	CBS	EP5742	1966	£4	£8	
Spooky	7"	Polydor	56237	1968	£2.50	£6	
Twinkie Lee	7"	CBS	202081	1966	£2	£5	chart single
You Don't Love Me	7"	CBS	202036	1966	£2.50	£6	chart single

WALKER, JACKIE

Oh Lonesome Me	7"	London	HLP8588	1958	£50	£100	

WALKER, JERRY JEFF

Driftin' Way Of Life	LP	Vanguard	SVRL19049	1969	£5	£12	
Jerry Jeff Walker	LP	Atco	SD33297	1969	£5	£12	US
Mr.Bojangles	LP	Atco	SD33259	1968	£5	£12	US
Mr.Bojangles	7"	Atlantic	584200	1968	£1.50	£4	

WALKER, JOHN

Annabella	7"	Philips	BF1593	1967	£1.50	£4	chart single
Cottonfields	7"	Carnaby	CNS4012	1970	£1.50	£4	
Everywhere Under The Sun	7"	Carnaby	CNS4004	1969	£1.50	£4	
If I Promise	7"	Philips	BF1612	1967	£1.50	£4	
If You Go Away	LP	Philips	(S)BL7829	1967	£8	£20	
I'll Be Your Baby Tonight	7"	Philips	BF1655	1968	£1.50	£4	
Kentucky Woman	7"	Philips	BF1676	1968	£1.50	£4	
Over And Over Again	7"	Carnaby	CNS4017	1971	£1.50	£4	
This Is John Walker	LP	Carnaby	CNLS6001	1969	£8	£20	
True Grit	7"	Carnaby	CNS4009	1969	£1.50	£4	
Woman	7"	Philips	BF1724	1968	£1.50	£4	
Yesterday's Sunshine	7"	Philips	BF1758	1969	£1.50	£4	

WALKER, JOHN & SCOTT

Solo John - Solo Scott	7" EP	Philips	BE12597	1966	£6	£12	

WALKER, JUNIOR & THE ALL STARS

Cleo's Mood	7"	Tamla Motown	TMG550	1966	£6	£12	
Come See About Me	7"	Tamla Motown	TMG637	1968	£2	£5	
Do The Boomerang	7"	Tamla Motown	TMG520	1965	£20	£40	
Do You See My Love	7"	Tamla Motown	TMG750	1970	£1.50	£4	
Gasss	LP	Tamla Motown	STML11167	1970	£4	£10	
Hip City	7"	Tamla Motown	TMG667	1968	£2	£5	
Home Cookin'	LP	Tamla Motown	(S)TML11097	1969	£5	£12	
Home Cookin'	7"	Tamla Motown	TMG682	1969	£2	£5	
How Sweet It Is	7"	Tamla Motown	TMG571	1966	£4	£8	chart single
Live	LP	Tamla Motown	STML11152	1970	£6	£15	
Money	7"	Tamla Motown	TMG586	1966	£4	£8	
Pucker Up Buttercup	7"	Tamla Motown	TMG596	1967	£5	£10	
Road Runner	LP	Tamla Motown	(S)TML11038	1966	£6	£15	
Road Runner	7"	Tamla Motown	TMG559	1966	£5	£10	
Road Runner	7"	Tamla Motown	TMG691	1969	£1.50	£4	chart single
Shake & Fingerpop	7" EP	Tamla Motown	TME2013	1966	£7.50	£15	
Shake And Fingerpop	7"	Tamla Motown	TMG529	1965	£6	£12	
Shotgun	LP	Tamla Motown	TML11017	1965	£15	£30	
Shotgun	7"	Tamla Motown	TMG509	1965	£6	£12	
Soul Session	LP	Tamla Motown	TML11029	1966	£15	£30	
These Eyes	7"	Tamla Motown	TMG727	1970	£1.50	£4	
Walk In The Night	7"	Tamla Motown	TMG824	1972	£1.50	£4	chart single
What Does It Take To Win Your Love	7"	Tamla Motown	TMG712	1969	£1.50	£4	chart single

WALKER, LUCILLE

Best Of Lucille Walker	LP	Checker	1428	1957	£8	£20	US

WALKER, RONNIE

It's A Good Feeling	7"	Stateside	SS2151	1969	£2.50	£6	

WALKER, SCOTT

Scott Walker has followed an unusual musical course. He has the voice and the musical inclinations of a cabaret singer, yet he writes much of his own material in a style which is too unsettling and too idiosyncratic to fit comfortably into a cabaret setting. His tendency towards hermit-like behaviour has added to his enigma and created a climate within which his cult following is steadily increasing. As a result, the LPs he made in the years following the demise of the Walker Brothers are becoming more and more collectable.

Title	Format	Label	Cat. No.	Year	Price	Price	Notes
Any Day Now	LP	Philips	6308148	1973	£10	£25	
Best Of Scott Vol.1	LP	Philips	SBL7910	1969	£4	£10	
Delta Dawn	7"	CBS	2521	1974	£1.50	£4	
Fire Escape In The Sky	LP	Zoo	ZOO2	1981	£8	£20	
Great Scott	cass	Philips	MCP1006	1967	£8	£20	
I Still See You	7"	Philips	6006168	1972	£1.50	£4	
Jackie	7"	Philips	BF1628	1967	£1.50	£4	chart single
Joanna	7"	Philips	BF1662	1968	£1.50	£4	chart single
Lights Of Cincinnati	7"	Philips	BF1793	1969	£1.50	£4	chart single
Looking Back With Scott Walker	LP	Ember	EMB3393	1968	£8	£20	
Mathilde	7" EP.	Philips	438402	1967	£6	£12	French
Me I Never Knew	7"	Philips	6006311	1971	£1.50	£4	
Moviegoer	LP	Philips	6308127	1972	£10	£25	
Romantic Scott Walker	LP	Philips	6850013	197-	£10	£25	
Scott	LP	Philips	BL7816	1967	£6	£15	chart LP
Scott	LP	Philips	SBL7816	1967	£8	£20	stereo
Scott 2	LP	Philips	BL7840	1968	£6	£15	chart LP
Scott 2	LP	Philips	BL7840	1968	£8	£20	with picture insert
Scott 2	LP	Philips	SBL7840	1968	£8	£20	stereo
Scott 2	LP	Philips	SBL7840	1968	£10	£25	with picture insert, stereo
Scott 3	LP	Philips	SBL7882	1969	£15	£30	chart LP
Scott 4	LP	Philips	SBL7913	1969	£25	£50	
Sings Songs From His TV Series	LP	Philips	SBL7900	1969	£5	£12	chart LP
Spotlight On Scott Walker	LP	Philips	6625017	1976	£8	£20	double
Stretch	LP	CBS	65725	1973	£8	£20	
Terrific	LP	Philips	6856022	197-	£10	£25	
Till The Band Comes In	LP	Philips	6308035	1970	£20	£40	
We Had It All	LP	CBS	80254	1974	£8	£20	
Woman Left Lonely	7"	CBS	1795	1973	£1.50	£4	

WALKER, T-BONE

Title	Format	Label	Cat. No.	Year	Price	Price	Notes
Blue Rocks	LP	Bluestime	29010	1968	£5	£12	US
Blues Of T-Bone Walker	LP	MFP	MFP1043	1965	£6	£15	
Classics In Jazz	LP	Capitol	T370	1956	£25	£50	US
Classics In Jazz	10" LP	Capitol	H370	1953	£37.50	£75	US
Classics In Jazz	10" LP	Capitol	LC6681	1954	£25	£50	
Funky Town	LP	Stateside	(S)SL10265	1969	£5	£12	
Hustle Is On	78	London	HL8087	1954	£7.50	£15	
I Get So Weary	LP	Imperial	9146	1961	£10	£25	US
I Want A Little Girl	LP	Delmark	DS633	197-	£4	£10	
Party Girl	7"	Liberty	LIB12018	1965	£5	£10	
Singing The Blues	LP	Imperial	9116	1960	£10	£25	US
Sings The Blues	LP	Imperial	9098	1959	£10	£25	US
Stormy Monday Blues	LP	Stateside	(S)SL10223	1968	£5	£12	
T B Walker	LP	Capitol	T1958	1963	£6	£15	
T-Bone Blues	LP	Atlantic	SD8020	1959	£17.50	£35	US, black label
T-Bone Blues	LP	Atlantic	SD8020	196-	£6	£15	US, red label
T-Bone Blues	LP	Atlantic	SD8256	1970	£4	£10	US
Travellin' Blues	7" EP.	London	REP1404	1963	£7.50	£15	
Truth	LP	MCA	MUPS331	1968	£5	£12	

WALKER, WENDY

Title	Format	Label	Cat. No.	Year	Price	Price	Notes
Boys Will Be Boys	7"	Decca	F11671	1963	£1.50	£4	
There Ain't A Boy In The World	7"	Decca	F11573	1963	£1.50	£4	

WALKIE TALKIES

Title	Format	Label	Cat. No.	Year	Price	Price	Notes
Rich And Nasty	7"	Sire	SIR4023	1979	£1.50	£4	

WALKS, DENNIS

Title	Format	Label	Cat. No.	Year	Price	Price	Notes
Billy Lick	7"	Blue Cat	BS144	1968	£4	£8	Drumbago B side
Having A Party	7"	Amalgamated	AMG816	1968	£4	£8	Groovers B side

WALLACE BROTHERS

Title	Format	Label	Cat. No.	Year	Price	Price	Notes
I'll Step Aside	7"	Sue	WI4036	1967	£6	£12	
Lover's Prayer	7"	Sue	WI355	1965	£6	£12	
Precious Words	7"	Sue	WI334	1964	£5	£10	
Soul Connection	LP	Sue	ILP950	1967	£50	£100	

WALLACE COLLECTION

Title	Format	Label	Cat. No.	Year	Price	Price	Notes
Daydream	7"	Parlophone	R5764	1969	£2	£5	
First Collection	LP	Parlophone	PMC/PCS7076	1969	£4	£10	
Fly Me To The Earth	7"	Parlophone	R5793	1969	£2	£5	
Walk On Out	7"	Parlophone	R5844	1970	£2	£5	
Wallace Collection	LP	Parlophone	PMC/PCS7099	1970	£4	£10	

WALLACE, GIG

Title	Format	Label	Cat. No.	Year	Price	Price	Notes
Rockin' On The Railroad	7"	Philips	PB981	1960	£2	£5	

WALLACE, JERRY

Title	Format	Label	Cat. No.	Year	Price	Price	Notes
Little Coco Palm	7"	London	HLH9040	1960	£1.50	£4	
Primrose Lane	7"	London	HLH8943	1959	£1.50	£4	
Shutters And Boards	7"	London	HLH9630	1962	£1.50	£4	
Swingin' Down The Lane	7"	London	HLH9177	1960	£1.50	£4	
With This Ring	7"	London	HL8719	1958	£4	£8	

With This Ring	7"	Philips	HL7062	1958	£1.50	£4	export
You're Singing Our Love Song	7"	London	HLH9110	1960	£1.50	£4	chart single

WALLACE, SIPPIE

Sings The Blues	LP	Storyville	671198	1967	£5	£12	

WALLENSTEIN

Blitzkrieg	LP	Pilz	20290646	1971	£8	£20	German
Blue Eyed Boys	LP	RCA	PL30061	1979	£4	£10	German
Charline	LP	RCA	PL30045	1978	£4	£10	German
Cosmic Century	LP	Komische	KM58006	1973	£5	£12	German
Frauleins	LP	Harvest	06445932	1980	£4	£10	German
Mother Universe	LP	Pilz	20291138	1972	£8	£20	German
No More Love	LP	RCA	PL30010	1977	£4	£10	German
SSSSS...Top	LP	RCA	06446307	1981	£4	£10	German
Stories, Songs And Symphonies	LP	Komische	KM58014	1975	£5	£12	German

WALLER, FATS

By The Light Of The Silvery Moon	7"	HMV	7M244	1954	£2.50	£6	
Fats 1935-1937	LP	RCA	RD27047	1957	£8	£20	
Fats 1938-1942	10" LP	RCA	RC24004	1958	£8	£20	
Fats At The Organ	10" LP	London	AL3521	1954	£20	£40	
Fats Waller	7" EP	HMV	7EG8098	1955	£2	£5	
Fats Waller	7" EP	HMV	7EG8212	1957	£2	£5	
Fats Waller	7" EP	RCA	RCX1010	1959	£2	£5	
Fats Waller And His Rhythm	7" EP	HMV	7EG8022	1954	£2	£5	
Fats Waller And His Rhythm	7" EP	HMV	7EG8042	1954	£2	£5	
Fats Waller And His Rhythm	7" EP	HMV	7EG8054	1954	£2	£5	
Fats Waller And His Rhythm	7" EP	HMV	7EG8078	1955	£2	£5	
Fats Waller And His Rhythm	7" EP	HMV	7EG8148	1956	£2	£5	
Fats Waller And His Rhythm	7" EP	HMV	7EG8242	1957	£2	£5	
Fats Waller And His Rhythm	7" EP	HMV	7EG8255	1957	£2	£5	
Favourites	10" LP	HMV	DLP1008	1953	£20	£40	
Favourites No.2	10" LP	HMV	DLP1118	1956	£15	£30	
Fun With Fats	10" LP	HMV	DLP1082	1955	£20	£40	
Good Man Is Hard To Find	7"	HMV	7M157	1953	£1.50	£4	
Handful Of Keys	LP	RCA	RD27185	1960	£6	£15	
Honey Hush	7"	HMV	7M142	1953	£2	£5	
In London No.1	7" EP	HMV	7EG8304	1958	£2	£5	
In London No.2	7" EP	HMV	7EG8341	1958	£2	£5	
In London No.3	7" EP	HMV	7EG8602	1960	£2	£5	
Jivin' With Fats	10" LP	London	AL3522	1954	£20	£40	
My Very Good Friend The Milkman	7"	HMV	7M128	1953	£2	£5	
Plays And Sings	10" LP	HMV	DLP1017	1953	£20	£40	
Real Fats Waller	LP	RCA	CDN131	1959	£5	£12	
Rediscovered Solos	10" LP	London	AL3507	1953	£20	£40	
Rhythm And Romance	10" LP	HMV	DLP1056	1954	£20	£40	
Spreadin' Rhythm Around	10" LP	HMV	DLP1138	1957	£15	£30	
Swinging At The Organ	7" EP	HMV	7EG8191	1956	£2	£5	
Thomas Fats Waller No.1	LP	HMV	CLP1035	1955	£8	£20	
Thomas Fats Waller No.2	LP	HMV	CLP1042	1955	£8	£20	
Young Fats Waller	10" LP	HMV	DLP1111	1956	£15	£30	
Your Feet's Too Big	7" EP	RCA	RCX1053	1959	£2	£5	
You've Been Taking Lessons In Love	7"	HMV	7M208	1954	£1.50	£4	

WALLER, GORDON

Every Day	7"	Columbia	DB8440	1968	£2	£5	
Gordon	LP	Vertigo	6360069	1972	£60	£120	spiral label
I Was A Boy When You Needed A Man	7"	Bell	BLL1059	1969	£1.50	£4	
Rosecrans Boulevard	7"	Columbia	DB8337	1968	£4	£8	
Weeping Analeah	7"	Columbia	DB8518	1968	£2	£5	
You're Gonna Hurt Yourself	7"	Bell	BLL1106	1970	£1.50	£4	

WALLER, JIM & THE DELTAS

Surfin' Wild	LP	Arvee	A(S)432	1963	£6	£15	US

WALLINGTON, GEORGE

George Wallington	10" LP	Esquire	20025	1954	£25	£50	
George Wallington Trio	10" LP	Esquire	20076	1956	£15	£30	
Jazz For The Carriage Trade	LP	Esquire	32032	1957	£50	£100	
New Sounds From Europe Vol.5	10" LP	Vogue	LDE059	1954	£25	£50	
Workshop	10" LP	Columbia	33C9035	1957	£15	£30	

WALLIS, BOB

Everybody Loves Saturday Night	LP	Top Rank	BUY023	1960	£4	£10	
Ole Man River	LP	Pye	NJL27	1961	£4	£10	
Travellin' Blues	LP	Pye	NJL30	1961	£4	£10	
Wallis Collection	LP	Pye	NJL41	1962	£4	£10	

WALPURGIS

Queen Of Sheba	LP	Ohr	OMM556023	1972	£6	£15	German

WALRUS

Walrus	LP	Deram	SML1072	1971	£8	£20	

WALSH, JOE

Smoker You Drink The Player You Get	LP	ABC	COQ40016	1974	£4	£10	US quad

WALSH, JOHNNY

Girl Machine	7"	Warner Bros	WB40	1961	£1.50	£4	

WALSH, SHEILA & CLIFF RICHARD

Drifting	7"	DJM	SHEIL100	1983	£2	£5		pic disc
Drifting	12"	DJM	SHEILT100	1983	£2.50	£6		pic disc

WALTON, DAVE

After You There Can Be Nothing	7"	CBS	202508	1967	£4	£8	
Every Window In The City	7"	CBS	202098	1966	£1.50	£4	
Love Ain't What It Used To Be	7"	CBS	202057	1966	£10	£20	

WAMMACK, TRAVIS

Scratchy	7"	Atlantic	AT4017	1965	£7.50	£15	

WANDERERS

As Time Goes By	7"	MGM	MGM1169	1961	£6	£12	
I Could Make You Mine	7"	MGM	MGM1102	1960	£7.50	£15	
Run Run Senorita	7"	United Artists	UP1020	1964	£6	£12	

WANDERERS (2)

Wiggle Waggle	7"	Trojan	TR7721	1969	£1.50	£4	

WANSEL, DEXTER

Voyager	LP	Philadelphia	PIR82786	1978	£8	£20	

WAR

All Day Music	LP	United Artists	UAS29269	1972	£4	£10	
War	LP	Liberty	LBG83478	1971	£4	£10	

WARD, BILLY & THE DOMINOES

Billy Ward & His Dominoes	LP	Decca	DL8621	1958	£50	£100	US
Billy Ward & His Dominoes	LP	Federal	395548	1956	£250	£400	US
Billy Ward & His Dominoes	LP	King	LP548	1956	£100	£200	US
Billy Ward & His Dominoes	10" LP	Federal	29594	1954	£530	£800	US
Billy Ward & His Dominoes Feat. Clyde McPhatter & Jackie Wilson	LP	King	LP733	1961	£50	£100	US
Billy Ward & The Dominoes	7" EP	London	REU1114	1958	£50	£100	
Billy Ward & The Dominoes	10" LP	Parlophone	PMD1061	1958	£250	£400	
Clyde McPhatter With Billy Ward	LP	Federal	395559	1957	£250	£400	US
Clyde McPhatter With Billy Ward	LP	King	LP559	1956	£100	£200	US
Deep Purple	7"	London	HLU8502	1957	£7.50	£15	chart single
Don't Thank Me	78	Parlophone	R3789	1953	£10	£20	
Evermore	7"	Brunswick	05656	1957	£10	£20	
Have Mercy Baby	78	Vogue	V2135	1952	£6	£12	
Jennie Lee	7"	London	HLU8634	1958	£7.50	£15	
Pagan Love Song	LP	Liberty	LRP3113/LST7113	1959	£20	£40	US
Please Don't Say No	7"	London	HLU8883	1959	£6	£12	
Sea Of Glass	LP	Liberty	LRP3056	1959	£20	£40	US
Sixty Minute Man	78	Vogue	V9012	1951	£10	£20	
Stardust	7"	London	HLU8465	1957	£7.50	£15	chart single
St.Theresa Of The Roses	7"	Brunswick	05599	1956	£10	£20	
Three Coins In A Fountain	7"	Parlophone	MSP6112	1954	£37.50	£75	
Twenty-Four Songs	LP	King	LP952	1966	£15	£30	US
Yours Forever	LP	London	HAU2116	1958	£25	£50	

WARD, BURT

Burt Ward was the Boy Wonder (Robin in Batman), of course - this record is a Frank Zappa creation.

Boy Wonder, I Love You	7"	MGM	13632	1967	£25	£50	US

WARD, CHRISTINE

Face Of Empty Me	7"	Decca	F12339	1966	£5	£10	

WARD, CLARA

Gonna Build A Mountain	7"	Stateside	SS474	1965	£1.50	£4	

WARD, DALE

Letter from Shirley	7"	London	HLD9835	1964	£2	£5	

WARD, ROBIN

Wonderful Summer	LP	Dot	DLP3555/2555	1963	£8	£20	US
Wonderful Summer	7"	London	HLD9821	1963	£2	£5	

WARD SINGERS

Famous Ward Singers	10" LP	London	LZC14013	1955	£5	£12	

WARDS OF COURT

All Night Girl	7"	Deram	DM127	1967	£4	£8	

WARE, LEON

Musical Massage	LP	Tamla Motown	STML12050	1977	£5	£12	

WARHORSE

Red Sea	LP	Vertigo	6360066	1972	£20	£40	spiral label
St.Louis	7"	Vertigo	6059027	1970	£5	£10	
Warhorse	LP	Vertigo	6360015	1970	£15	£30	spiral label

WARLEIGH, RAY

First Album	LP	Philips	SBL781	1969	£10	£25	

WARLOCK, OZZIE & THE WIZARDS

Juke Box Fury	7"	HMV	POP635	1959	£2.50	£6	

WARM

Demo Tapes	7"	Warm	SMS001	1978	£2.50	£6	double

WARM DUST

And It Came To Pass	LP	Trend	TNLS700	1970	£8	£20	
It's A Beautiful Day	7"	Trend	6099002	1970	£1.50	£4	
Peace For Our Time	LP	Trend	6480001	1971	£6	£15	

WARM EXPRESSION

Let No Man Put Asunder	7"	Columbia	DB8672	1970	£4	£8	

WARM SOUNDS

Birds And Bees	7"	Deram	DM120	1967	£2.50	£6	chart single
Nite Is A-Comin'	7"	Deram	DM174	1968	£7.50	£15	
Sticks And Stones	7"	Immediate	IM058	1967	£6	£12	

WARNING, GALE

Rock Those Crazy Skins	78	Oriole	CB1349	1956	£2	£5	

WARPIG

Warpig	LP	Fonthill	NAS13528	1971	£40	£80	Canadian

WARREN, ALMA

Stealin'	7"	Parlophone	MSP6200	1956	£1.50	£4	

WARREN OF GHANA, GUY

Africa Speaks - America Answers	LP	Brunswick	LAT8237	1958	£15	£30	
African Soundz	LP	Regal Zonophone	SLRZ1031	1972	£15	£30	
Afro-Jazz	LP	Columbia	SCX6340	1969	£15	£30	
Monkeys And Butterflies	7"	Brunswick	05791	1959	£2	£5	

WARRIOR

Breakout	7"	Warrior	W002	1984	£2.50	£6	
For Europe Only	LP	Warrior	W001	1983	£4	£10	

WARRIORS

The collectability of the Warriors" single derives from the fact that the group's singer was Jon Anderson. The drummer, meanwhile, was Ian Wallace, who has played on numerous records since, most notably LPs made by King Crimson and Bob Dylan.

You Came Along	7"	Decca	F11926	1964	£25	£50	

WARSAW PAKT

Needletime	LP	Island	ILPS9515	1977	£6	£15	
Safe And Warm	7"	Island	PAKT1	1978	£2.50	£6	
Safe And Warm	7"	Island	PAKT1	1978	£10	£20	PS

WARWICK, DEE DEE

Cold Night In Georgia	7"	Atlantic	2091057	1971	£1.50	£4	
Dee Dee Warwick	LP	Mercury	SR61221	1969	£4	£10	US
Do It With All Your Heart	7"	Mercury	MF860	1965	£1.50	£4	
Foolish Fool	7"	Mercury	MF1084	1969	£1.50	£4	
Gotta Get A Hold Of Myself	7"	Mercury	MF890	1965	£1.50	£4	
I Want To Be With You	LP	Mercury	MG2/SR61100	1967	£4	£10	US
I Want To Be With You	7"	Mercury	MF937	1965	£1.50	£4	
If This Was The Last Song	7"	Atlantic	2091037	1970	£1.50	£4	
I'll Be Better Off	7"	Mercury	MF1061	1968	£4	£8	
I'm Gonna Make You Love Me	7"	Mercury	MF953	1965	£1.50	£4	
Lover's Chant	7"	Mercury	MF909	1966	£7.50	£15	
She Didn't Know	7"	Atlantic	2091011	1970	£1.50	£4	
We're Doing Fine	7"	Mercury	MF867	1965	£1.50	£4	
We're Doing Fine	7" EP	Mercury	10036MCE	1966	£5	£10	
When Love Slips Away	7"	Mercury	MF974	1967	£1.50	£4	

WARWICK, DIONNE

Alfie	7"	Pye	7N25424	1967	£1.50	£4	
Always Something There To Remind Me	7"	Pye	7N25474	1968	£1.50	£4	
Another Night	7"	Pye	7N25395	1966	£1.50	£4	
Anyone Who Had A Heart	7"	Pye	7N25234	1964	£1.50	£4	chart single
Are You There	7"	Pye	7N25338	1965	£1.50	£4	
Dionne	7" EP	Pye	NEP44044	1965	£2.50	£6	
Do You Know The Way To San Jose	7"	Pye	7N25457	1968	£1.50	£4	chart single
Do You Know The Way To San Jose	7" EP	Pye	NEP44090	1968	£2	£5	
Don't Make Me Over	7"	Stateside	SS157	1963	£4	£8	
Don't Make Me Over	7" EP	Pye	NEP44026	1964	£2	£5	
Forever My Love	7" EP	Pye	NEP44046	1965	£2	£5	
Here I Am	7"	Pye	7N25316	1965	£1.50	£4	
Here I Am	7" EP	Pye	NEP44051	1966	£2	£5	
I Just Don't Know What To Do With Myself	7" EP	Pye	NEP44077	1966	£2.50	£6	
I Love Paris	7" EP	Pye	NEP44083	1967	£2	£5	
I Say A Little Prayer	7"	Pye	7N25436	1967	£1.50	£4	
In Between The Heartaches	7"	Pye	7N25357	1966	£1.50	£4	
It's Love That Really Counts	7" EP	Pye	NEP44044	1964	£2	£5	
Looking With My Eyes	7"	Pye	7N25310	1965	£1.50	£4	
Make The Music Play	7"	Pye	7N25223	1963	£1.50	£4	
Make The Music Play	7"	Stateside	SS222	1963	£4	£8	demo only
Message To Michael	7"	Pye	7N25368	1966	£1.50	£4	
Message To Michael	7" EP	Pye	NEP44067	1966	£2.50	£6	
Odds And Ends	7"	Pye	7N25497	1969	£1.50	£4	
People Got To Be Free	7"	Pye	7N25491	1969	£1.50	£4	

Presenting	LP	Pye	NPL28037	1964	£4	£10	chart LP
Promises Promises	7"	Pye	7N25496	1969	£1.50	£4	
Reach Out For Me	7"	Pye	7N25265	1964	£1.50	£4	chart single
Take It From Me	7"	Warner Bros	WB16530	1963	£1.50	£4	
This Girl's In Love With You	7"	Pye	7N25484	1969	£1.50	£4	
Trains And Boats And Planes	7"	Pye	7N25378	1966	£1.50	£4	
Valley Of The Dolls	7"	Pye	7N25445	1968	£1.50	£4	chart single
Walk On By	7"	Pye	7N25241	1964	£1.50	£4	chart single
Who Can I Turn To	7"	Pye	7N25302	1965	£1.50	£4	
Who Can I Turn To	7" EP	Pye	NEP44049	1965	£2	£5	
Window Wishing	7" EP	Pye	NEP44073	1966	£2	£5	
Windows Of The World	7"	Pye	7N25428	1967	£1.50	£4	
Wishin' And Hopin'	7"	Stateside	SS191	1963	£2.50	£6	
Wishin' And Hopin'	7" EP	Pye	NEP44039	1965	£2	£5	
You Can Have Him	7"	Pye	7N25290	1965	£1.50	£4	chart single
You'll Never Get To Heaven	7"	Pye	7N25256	1964	£1.50	£4	chart single
You've Lost That Lovin' Feelin'	7"	Pye	7N25505	1969	£1.50	£4	

WASHBOARD RHYTHM KINGS

Washboard Rhythm Kings	7" EP	HMV	7EG8101	1955	£4	£8	
Washboard Rhythm Kings	7" EP	HMV	7EG8126	1955	£4	£8	

WASHBOARD SAM

Feeling Lowdown	LP	RCA	RD8274	1972	£5	£12	

WASHINGTON, ALBERT & THE KINGS

Turn On THe Bright Lights	7"	President	PT242	1969	£1.50	£4	
Woman Love	7"	President	PT227	1969	£1.50	£4	

WASHINGTON, BABY

Breakfast In Bed	7"	Atlantic	584316	1970	£1.50	£4	
Get A Hold Of Yourself	7"	United Artists	UP2247	1968	£6	£12	
I Can't Wait Until I See My Baby	7"	Sue	WI321	1964	£10	£20	
I Don't Know	7"	Atlantic	584299	1969	£2	£5	
Only Those In Love	LP	London	HAC8292	1966	£6	£15	
Only Those In Love	7"	London	HLC9987	1965	£2.50	£6	
That's How Heartaches Are Made	LP	London	HAC8260	1963	£8	£20	
That's How Heartaches Are Made	7"	Sue	WI302	1963	£7.50	£15	
With You In Mind	LP	Veep	16528	1968	£5	£12	US

WASHINGTON DC'S

I've Done It All Wrong	7"	Domain	D9	1969	£2.50	£6	
Kisses Sweeter Than Wine	7"	Ember	EMBS190	1964	£2	£5	
Kisses Sweeter Than Wine	7" EP	Pathe	EGF761	1964	£6	£12	French
Seek And Find	7"	CBS	202464	1967	£10	£20	
Seek And Find	7"	CBS	202464	1967	£20	£40	PS
Thirty-Second Floor	7"	CBS	202226	1966	£5	£10	

WASHINGTON, DINAH

After Hours With Miss D.	10" LP	Emarcy	EJT501	1956	£6	£15	
Blues	LP	Top Rank	RX3006	1959	£4	£10	with tracks by Betty Roche
Dinah	LP	Emarcy	EJL1255	1957	£5	£12	
I Concentrate On You	LP	Mercury	MMC14063/ CMS18043	1961	£4	£10	
I Wouldn't Know	7"	Columbia	DB4911	1962	£1.50	£4	
Sings The Best In Blues	LP	Mercury	MPL6519	1957	£4	£10	
Unforgettable	LP	Mercury	MMC14048	1960	£4	£10	
What A Difference A Day Made	LP	Mercury	MMC14030	1960	£4	£10	
What A Difference A Day Made	7"	Mercury	AMT1051	1959	£1.50	£4	

WASHINGTON, ELLA

He Called Me Baby	7"	Monument	MON1030	1969	£1.50	£4	

WASHINGTON, GENO & THE RAM JAM BAND

Alison Please	7"	Pye	7N45019	1970	£1.50	£4	
Different Strokes	7"	Pye	7N17425	1967	£1.50	£4	
Different Strokes	7" EP	Pye	NEP24293	1968	£4	£8	
Hand Clappin', Foot Stompin'	LP	Piccadilly	NPL38026	1966	£6	£15	chart LP
Hi	7" EP	Piccadilly	NEP34054	1966	£4	£8	
Hi Hi Hazel	7"	Piccadilly	7N35329	1966	£1.50	£4	chart single
Hipsters And Flipsters	LP	Piccadilly	N(S)PL38032	1967	£5	£12	chart LP
I Can't Let You Go	7"	Pye	7N17649	1968	£2	£5	
I Can't Quit Her	7"	Pye	7N17570	1968	£1.50	£4	
Michael	7"	Piccadilly	7N35359	1967	£2	£5	chart single
Que Sera Sera	7"	Piccadilly	7N35346	1966	£1.50	£4	chart single
Running Wild	LP	Pye	N(S)PL18029	1968	£4	£10	
Shake A Tail Feather	LP	Piccadilly	N(S)PL38029	1968	£4	£10	
She Shot A Hole In My Soul	7"	Piccadilly	7N35392	1967	£2	£5	
Small Package Of Hipsters	7" EP	Pye	NEP24302	1968	£5	£10	
Tell It Like It Is	7"	Piccadilly	7N35403	1967	£1.50	£4	
Tell It Like It Is	7" EP	Pye	PNV24198	1967	£5	£10	French
Water	7"	Piccadilly	7N35312	1966	£1.50	£4	chart single
Water	7" EP	Pye	PNV24178	1966	£5	£10	French

WASHINGTON, GROVER

All The King's Horses	LP	Kudu	KUL5	1973	£4	£10	
Inner City Blues	LP	Kudu	KUL1	1973	£4	£10	

WASHINGTON, JUSTINE

Only Those In Love	LP	Sue	(S)1042	1965	£5	£12	US

WASHINGTON, KENNETH
If I Had A Ticket	7"	CBS	202494	1967	£4	£8	with Chris Barber

WASHINGTON, NORMAN T.
Jumping Jack Flash	7"	Pama	PM749	1968	£1.50	£4
Tiptoe	7"	Pama	PM741	1968	£2.50	£6
You've Been Cheating	7"	Pama	PM730	1968	£2	£5

WASHINGTON, SHERI
I Got Plenty	7"	Vogue	V9070	1957	£40	£80

WASHINGTON, SISTER ERNESTINE
Sister Ernestine Washington	7" EP	Melodisc	EPM752	1955	£4	£8

WASHINGTON, TONY
But I Do	7"	Black Swan	WI459	1965	£5	£10
Dilly Dilly	7"	Black Swan	WI460	1965	£5	£10
Show Me How	7"	Sue	WI327	1964	£5	£10
Surely You Love Me	7"	Fontana	TF478	1964	£1.50	£4

WASHINGTON, TYRONE
Natural Essence	LP	Blue Note	BST84274	1968	£6	£15

W.A.S.P.
9.5 N.A.S.T.Y.	7"	Capitol	CLP432	1986	£1.50	£4	pic disc
Animal	7"	Music For Nations	PKUT109	1984	£4	£8	shaped pic disc, 2 different designs
Animal	12"	Music For Nations	12KUT109	1984	£4	£10	white vinyl
I Wanna Be Somebody	12"	Capitol	12CLP336	1984	£2.50	£6	pic disc

WASP (BRIAN BENNETT)
Melissa	7"	EMI	EMI2253	1975	£5	£10

WASPS
Can't Wait Till '78	7"	NEMS	NES115	1977	£2	£5	Mean Street B side

WASTELAND
Friends, Romans, Countrymen	7"	Invicta	INV014	1979	£5	£10
Want Not	7"	Ellie Jay	EJSP9261	1979	£5	£10

WATCH COMMITTEE
Throw Another Penny In The Well	7"	Philips	BF1695	1968	£2	£5

WATER INTO WINE BAND
Harvest Time	LP	private	CJT002	1976	£100	£200	
Hill Climbing For Beginners	LP	Myrrh	MYR1004	197-	£40	£80	white cover, re-recorded tracks
Hill Climbing For Beginners	LP	Myrrh	MYR1004	1973	£25	£50	brown cover

WATERBOYS
Big Music	12"	Ensign	12ENY508	1984	£3	£8
December	12"	Ensign	12ENY506	1984	£3	£8
Girl Called Johnny	7"	Chicken Jazz	CJ1	1983	£1.50	£4
Girl Called Johnny	12"	Chicken Jazz	CJT1	1983	£3	£8
Whole Of The Moon	7"	Ensign	ENY520	1985	£2.50	£6
Whole Of The Moon	12"	Ensign	12ENY520	1985	£3	£8

WATERFALL
Beneath The Stars	LP	Gun Dog	LP003	1981	£20	£40
Flight Of The Day	LP	Bob	FRR001	198-	£20	£40

WATERPROOF CANDLE
Electronically Heated Child	7"	RCA	RCA1717	1968	£5	£10

WATERS, MUDDY
After The Rain	LP	Chess	CRL4553	1969	£6	£15	
At Newport	LP	Chess	CRL4513	1965	£8	£20	
At Newport	LP	Pye	NJL34	1961	£8	£20	
Back In The Good Old Days	LP	Syndicate	001	1970	£8	£20	double
Best Of Muddy Waters	LP	London	LTZM15152	1959	£15	£30	
Blues From Big Bill's Copacabana	LP	Chess	LP(S)1533	1968	£6	£15	US
Blues Man	LP	Polydor	236574	1969	£5	£12	
Can't Get No Grindin'	LP	Chess	6310129	1973	£4	£10	
Country Boy	7"	Python	P04	1969	£10	£20	
Down On Stovall's Plantation	LP	Bounty	BY6031	1968	£6	£15	
Electric Mud	LP	Chess	CRL4542	1968	£6	£15	
Fathers And Sons	LP	Chess	CRL4556	1969	£6	£15	
Folk Singer	LP	Pye	NPL28038	1964	£8	£20	
Good News	LP	Syndicate	002	1970	£6	£15	
Honey Bee	78	Vogue	V2372	1956	£10	£20	
I Got A Rich Man's Woman	7"	Chess	CRS8019	1965	£4	£8	
I'm Ready	7" EP	Chess	CRE6006	1965	£7.50	£15	
Let's Spend The Night Together	7"	Chess	CRS8083	1969	£2.50	£6	
London Sessions	LP	Chess	6310121	1972	£4	£10	
Long Distance Call	78	Vogue	V2273	1954	£10	£20	
McKinley Morganfield AKA Muddy Waters	LP	Chess	6671001	1971	£5	£12	
Mississippi Blues	7" EP	London	REU1060	1956	£30	£60	gold label
More Real Folk Blues	LP	Chess	LP(S)1511	1966	£8	£20	US
Muddy Sings Big Bill	LP	Marble Arch	MAL723	1967	£4	£10	

Muddy Waters	LP	Pye	NPL28040	1964	£10	£25	
Muddy Waters	LP	Python	PLP12	1969	£8	£20	
Muddy Waters	7" EP	Pye	NEP44010	1963	£6	£12	
Muddy Waters Live	LP	Chess	CH50012	1972	£4	£10	US
Muddy Waters Vol.2	LP	Python	PLP18	1969	£8	£20	
Muddy Waters Vol.3	LP	Python	PLP19	1969	£8	£20	
Muddy Waters With Little Walter	7" EP	Vogue	EPV1046	1955	£30	£60	
Muddy,Brass,& The Blues	LP	Chess	CRL4525	1967	£6	£15	
My John The Conqueror Root	7"	Chess	CRS8001	1965	£5	£10	
Rare Live Recordings Vol.1	LP	Black Bear	LP901	1972	£6	£15	
Rare Live Recordings Vol.2	LP	Black Bear	LP902	1972	£6	£15	
Rare Live Recordings Vol.3	LP	Black Bear	LP903	1972	£6	£15	
Real Folk Blues	LP	Chess	CRL4515	1966	£8	£20	
Real Folk Blues Vol.4	7" EP	Chess	CRE6022	1966	£7.50	£15	
Rollin' Stone	78	Vogue	V2101	1952	£10	£20	
Sail On	LP	Chess	LPS1539	1969	£5	£12	US
Sings Big Bill Broonzy	LP	Pye	NPL28048	1964	£8	£20	
They Call Me Muddy Waters	LP	Chess	LPS1553	1971	£4	£10	US
They Call Me Muddy Waters	7"	Chess	6145011	1972	£1.50	£4	
Vintage Mud	LP	Sunnyland	KS100	1969	£6	£15	

WATERS, MUDDY, BO DIDDLEY, HOWLIN' WOLF

Super Super Blues Band	LP	Chess	CRL4537	1968	£6	£15	

WATERS, MUDDY, BO DIDDLEY, LITTLE WALTER

Super Blues	LP	Chess	CRL4529	1967	£6	£15	

WATERS, ROGER

5:06 am (Every Stranger's Eyes)	7"	Harvest	HAR5230	1984	£2.50	£6	
Pros And Cons Of Hitch-Hiking	LP	Harvest	SHVL2401051	1984	£5	£12	banded promo
Radio K.A.O.S.	LP	EMI	KAOSDJ1	1987	£6	£15	banded promo, no dialogue
Radio Waves	CD-s	EMI	CDEM6	1987	£2.50	£6	
Sunset Strip	7"	EMI	EM20	1987	£2.50	£6	

WATERSON, MIKE

Mike Waterson	LP	Topic	12TS332	1977	£5	£12	

WATERSONS

Bright Phoebus	LP	Trailer	LES2076	1972	£6	£15	
Frost And Fire	LP	Topic	12T136	1965	£6	£15	
Watersons	LP	Topic	12T142	1966	£6	£15	
Yorkshire Garland	LP	Topic	12T167	1966	£6	£15	

WATERSONS, HARRY BOARDMAN, MAUREEN CRAIK

New Voices	LP	Topic	12T125	1965	£15	£30	

WATSON, DOC

Doc Watson Family	LP	XTRA	XTRA1082	1969	£4	£10	
Home Again	LP	Fontana	STFI6083	1968	£5	£12	

WATSON, JOHN L.

Mother's Love	7"	Deram	DM285	1970	£2.50	£6	
White Hot Blue Black	LP	Deram	SMLR1061	1970	£6	£15	

WATSON, JOHNNY GUITAR

Bad	LP	OKeh	OKM4118/ OKS14118	1967	£6	£15	US
Blues Soul	LP	Chess	1490	1965	£10	£25	US
I Cried For You	LP	Cadet	LP4056	1967	£5	£12	US
In The Fats Bag	LP	OKeh	OKM4124/ OKS14124	1967	£6	£15	US
Johnny Guitar Watson	LP	King	LP857	1963	£25	£50	US

WATT, TOMMY

It Might As Well Be Swing	LP	Parlophone	PMC1068	1959	£6	£15	
Watt's Cooking	LP	Parlophone	PMC1107	1959	£6	£15	

WATTERS, LU

Dixieland Jamboree	10" LP	Columbia	33C9036	1957	£6	£15	
Lu Watters 1947	10" LP	London	HBU1061	1956	£6	£15	
Lu Watters And His Jazz Band	10" LP	Vogue	LDE009	1952	£8	£20	
Lu Watters And The Yerba Buena Jazz Band	LP	Good Time Jazz	LAG12030	1956	£5	£12	
Lu Watters Jazz Band	LP	Good Time Jazz	LAG12025	1956	£5	£12	
Lu Watters Jazz Band Vol.1	10" LP	Good Time Jazz	LDG038	1954	£8	£20	
Lu Watters Yerba Buena Band	10" LP	Columbia	33C9004	1955	£8	£20	
Lu Watters Yerba Buena Band Vol.1	10" LP	Good Time Jazz	LP8	1953	£8	£20	
Lu Watters' Yerba Buena Jazz Band	LP	Good Time Jazz	LAG12123	1958	£5	£12	

WATTS 103RD STREET RHYTHM BAND

Cornbread And Grits	LP	Warner Bros	WS1741	1967	£5	£12	US
Do Your Thing	7"	Warner Bros	WB7250	1969	£1.50	£4	
Express Yourself	LP	Warner Bros	1864	1970	£6	£15	US
Express Yourself	7"	Warner Bros	WB7417	1970	£1.50	£4	
In The Jungle Babe	LP	Warner Bros	WS1801	1969	£4	£10	US
Love Land	7"	Warner Bros	WB7365	1970	£1.50	£4	

Spreadin' Honey	7"	Jay Boy	BOY71	1973	£2	£5	
Till You Get Enough	7"	Warner Bros	WB7298	1969	£1.50	£4	
You're So Beautiful	LP	Warner Bros	1904	1970	£4	£10	US

WATTS, NOBLE THIN MAN

Hard Times	7"	London	HLU8627	1958	£15	£30	
Noble Thin Man Watts & Wild Jimmy Spurrill	7" EP	XX	MIN717	196-	£4	£8	
Noble's Theme	7"	Sue	WI347	1964	£7.50	£15	June Bateman B side

WATUSI WARRIORS

Wa-chi-bam-ba	7"	London	HL8866	1959	£4	£8	

WAVE CRESTS

Surftime USA	LP	Viking	VKS6606	1963	£6	£15	US

WAY, DARRYL & WOLF

Canis Lupus	LP	Deram	SDL14	1973	£5	£12	
Saturation Point	LP	Deram	SML1104	1973	£5	£12	

WAY WE LIVE

Candle For Judith	LP	Dandelion	DAN8004	1971	£50	£100	sleeve pictured in Guide

WAYBURN, NANCY

World Goes On Without Me	7"	Warner Bros	WB5646	1965	£4	£8	

WAYNE, ALVIS

Don't Mean Maybe Baby	7"	Starlite	ST45104	1963	£100	£200	

WAYNE, BOBBY

Ballad Of A Teenage Queen	7"	Pye	7N25315	1965	£2.50	£6	

WAYNE, CARL

Carl Wayne	LP	RCA	SF8239	1971	£5	£12	
Take My Hand For A While	7"	RCA	RCA2257	1972	£1.50	£4	

WAYNE, CARL & THE VIKINGS

This Is Love	7"	Pye	7N15824	1965	£10	£20	
What's A Matter Baby	7"	Pye	7N15702	1964	£10	£20	

WAYNE, CHUCK

Chuck Wayne Quintet	10" LP	London	LZC14014	1955	£20	£40	

WAYNE, FRANCES

Frances Wayne	LP	Brunswick	BL54022	1957	£5	£12	US
Songs For My Man	LP	Epic	LN3222	195-	£5	£12	US
Warm Sound Of Frances Wayne	LP	Atlantic	1263	1956	£6	£15	US

WAYNE, JEFF

War Of The Worlds	LP	CBS	WOW100	1979	£8	£20	Double LP, 12', book, poster, boxed

WAYNE, JERRY

Half Hearted Love	7"	Vogue	V9169	1960	£6	£12	

WAYNE, PAT & THE BEACHCOMBERS

Brand New Man	7"	Columbia	DB7417	1964	£2.50	£6	
Bye Bye Johnny	7"	Columbia	DB7262	1964	£4	£8	
Come Dance With Me	7"	Columbia	DB7603	1965	£2	£5	
Jambalaya	7"	Columbia	DB7121	1963	£4	£8	
My Friend	7"	Columbia	DB7739	1965	£1.50	£4	
Night Is Over	7"	Columbia	DB7944	1966	£2	£5	
Roll Over Beethoven	7"	Columbia	DB7182	1963	£4	£8	
Roll Over Beethoven	7" EP	Columbia	ESRF1502	1964	£12.50	£25	French

WAYNE, RICKY

Chick A Roo	7"	Top Rank	JAR432	1960	£7.50	£15	demo
Chick A Roo	7"	Triumph	RGM1009	1960	£12.50	£25	
In My Imagination	7"	CBS	201764	1965	£1.50	£4	
Make Way Baby	7"	Pye	7N15289	1960	£4	£8	
Say You're Gonna Be My Own	7"	Oriole	CB306	1965	£2	£5	

WAYNE, TERRY

All Mama's Children	7"	Columbia	DB4067	1958	£6	£12	
Matchbox	7"	Columbia	DB4002	1957	£7.50	£15	
Oh Lonesome Me	7"	Columbia	DB4112	1958	£4	£8	
She's Mine	7"	Columbia	DB4312	1959	£2.50	£6	
Slim Jim Tie	7"	Columbia	DB4035	1957	£6	£12	
Terrific	7" EP	Columbia	SEG7758	1958	£25	£50	
Where My Baby Goes	7"	Columbia	DB4205	1958	£2.50	£6	

WAYNE, THOMAS

Tragedy	7"	London	HL7075	1959	£5	£10	
Tragedy	7"	London	HLU8846	1959	£12.50	£25	

WAYNE, WEE WILLIE

Travellin' Mood	LP	Imperial	LP9144	1961	£17.50	£35	US

WAYS AND MEANS

Little Deuce Coupe	7"	Columbia	DB7907	1966	£2.50	£6	
Sea Of Faces	7"	Pye	7N17217	1966	£6	£12	

WE FIVE
Let's Get Together	7"	Pye	7N25346	1966	£1.50	£4	
Let's Get Together	7" EP	Pye	NEP44056	1966	£2	£5	
You Were On My Mind	7"	Pye	7N25314	1965	£1.50	£4	

WE THE PEOPLE
He Doesn't Go About It Right	7"	London	HLH10089	1966	£30	£60	
St.John's Shop	7" EP	London	RE10184	1966	£100	£200	French
You Burn Me Up And Down	7" EP	London	RE10191	1966	£100	£200	French

WEASELS
Liverpool Beat	LP	Wing	MGW/SRW12282	1964	£5	£12	US

WEATHER REPORT
When the time comes to assess the major innovators of late twentieth century music, then the name of Weather Report is likely to loom large. Marketed as jazz, Weather Report's music is of equal appeal to progressive rock fans for the way in which it blends improvisation with composed passages, setting up frequently elaborate structures in which the textures and timbres available to electronic instruments are exploited to the full. Under Josef Zawinul's fingers, the synthesiser begins to achieve some of the potential of which it is obviously capable, but which is so seldom realised. The double Japan-only release "Live In Tokyo" contains the complete concert that was presented in excerpt on the UK album "I Sing The Body Electric".

Live In Tokyo	LP	CBS Sony	40AP942-3	1972	£10	£25	Japanese double

WEAVERS
At Home	LP	Top Rank	RX3008	1959	£5	£12	
At The Carnegie Hall	LP	Vanguard	PPL11006	1957	£4	£10	
Best Of The Weavers	LP	Brunswick	LAT8357	1961	£4	£10	
Best Of The Weavers	LP	Decca	DL8893	1959	£5	£12	US
Best Of The Weavers	LP	Decca	DX(S)B(7)173	1963	£5	£12	US
Folk Songs Around The World	LP	Decca	DL8909	1959	£5	£12	US
On Tour	LP	Vanguard	PPL11011	1958	£5	£12	
Reunion At Carnegie Hall	LP	Fontana	TFL6032	1963	£4	£10	

WEB
Baby Won't You Leave Me Alone	7"	Deram	DM217	1968	£4	£8	
Fully Interlocking	LP	Deram	SML1025	1968	£8	£20	
Hatton Mill Morning	7"	Deram	DM201	1968	£4	£8	
Monday To Friday	7"	Deram	DM253	1969	£4	£8	
Theraphosa Blondi	LP	Deram	SML1058	1970	£8	£20	

WEB (2)
I Spider	LP	Polydor	2383024	1970	£50	£100

WEBB, DEAN
Hey Miss Fanny	7"	Parlophone	R4549	1959	£6	£12
Streamline Baby	7"	Parlophone	R4587	1959	£6	£12

WEBB, DON
Little Ditty Baby	7"	Coral	Q72385	1960	£40	£80

WEBB, GEORGE
George Webb Dixielanders	7" EP	Melodisc	WPM770	195-	£2.50	£6

WEBB, JIMMY
Jimmy Webb is a songwriter of genius - "By The Time I Get To Phoenix", "Didn't We", "MacArthur Park", and "Wichita Lineman" are early landmarks in his career. His own records reveal him to be a limited but effective singer, with "Land's End" containing some particularly fine material.

And So On	LP	Reprise	K44134	1971	£5	£12	
I Keep It Hid	7"	CBS	3672	1968	£5	£10	B side Shane Martin
Jim Webb Sings Jim Webb	LP	CBS	63335	1968	£8	£20	
Land's End	LP	Asylum	SYL9014	1974	£5	£12	
Letters	LP	Reprise	K44173	1972	£5	£12	
Words And Music	LP	Reprise	RSLP6421	1970	£5	£12	

WEBB, JOHNNY
Dig	7"	Columbia	DB3805	1956	£1.50	£4

WEBB, PETTA
I Have Wandered In Exile	LP	Topic	12TS223	1973	£10	£25

WEBB, PETTA & PETE COOPER
Heart Is True	LP	Heart	HR001	1986	£5	£12

WEBB, ROGER TRIO
All My Loving	7"	Parlophone	R5176	1964	£1.50	£4

WEBB, SKEETER
Was It A Bad Dream	7"	Parlophone	CMSP32	1955	£2	£5	export

WEBB, SONNY & THE CASCADES
You've Got Everything	7"	Oriole	CB1873	1963	£6	£12
You've Got Everything	7"	Polydor	NH52158	1963	£2.50	£6

WEBBER SISTERS
My World	7"	Island	WI3109	1967	£5	£10	Alva Lewis B side

WEBS
This Thing Called Love	7"	London	HLU10188	1968	£2.50	£6

WEBSTER, BEN
Ben Webster	10" LP	Vogue Coral	LRA10021	1955	£30	£60	
Ben Webster And Associates	LP	HMV	CLP1336	1960	£6	£15	
Ben Webster Meets Oscar Peterson	LP	HMV	CLP1412/CSD1336	1960	£6	£15	

Title	Format	Label	Cat No	Year			Notes
Ben Webster With Strings	LP	Columbia	33CX10014	1955	£8	£20	
Soulville	LP	Columbia	33CX10122	1958	£8	£20	

WEBSTER, DEENA
| Scarborough Fair | 7" | Parlophone | R5738 | 1968 | £1.50 | £4 | |
| You're Losing | 7" | Parlophone | R5699 | 1968 | £2.50 | £6 | |

WEDDING PRESENT
Blue Eyes	7"	RCA	PB45185	1992	£5	£10	.. No.1 of 1992 singles
Boing	7"	RCA	PB10117	1992	£1.50	£4	.. No.8 of 1992 singles
Brassneck	7"	RCA	PB43403	1990	£4	£8	handpainted cover
California	7"	RCA	PB45315	1992	£1.50	£4	.. No.6 of 1992 singles
Come Play With Me	7"	RCA	PB45313	1992	£2	£5	.. No.5 of 1992 singles
Don't Try And Stop Me Mother	12"	Reception	REC002/12	1986	£4	£10	
Flying Saucer	7"	RCA	PB10115	1992	£1.50	£4	.. No.7 of 1992 singles
George Best	LP	Reception	LEEDS1	1987	£5	£12	with 7' (REC005)
Go Go Dancer	7"	RCA	PB45183	1992	£4	£8	.. No.2 of 1992 singles
Go Out And Get 'Em Boy!	7"	City Slang	CSL001	1985	£12.50	£25	
Go Out And Get 'Em Boy!	7"	Reception	REC001	1985	£20	£40	
Katrusyu	7"	RCA		1989	£5	£10	promo only
Loveslave	7"	RCA	PB10116	1992	£1.50	£4	.. No.9 of 1992 singles
Million Miles	7"	Reception		1987	£10	£20	promo only
My Favourite Dress	7"	Reception	REC005	1987	£4	£8	white vinyl
No Christmas	7"	RCA	PB11693	1992	£1.50	£4	No.12 of 1992 singles
Once More	7"	Reception	REC002	1986	£7.50	£15	
Queen Of Outer Space	7"	RCA	PB11692	1992	£1.50	£4	No.11 of 1992 singles
Silver Shorts	7"	RCA	PB45311	1992	£2	£5	.. No.4 of 1992 singles
Sticky	7"	RCA	PB11691	1992	£1.50	£4	No.10 of 1992 singles
This Boy Can Wait	7"	Reception	REC003	1986	£2.50	£6	
This Boy Can Wait	12"	Reception	REC003/12	1986	£3	£8	
Three	7"	RCA	PB45181	1992	£2	£5	.. No.3 of 1992 singles
Tommy	LP	Reception	LEEDS2	1988	£6	£15	signed, with poster
Ukrainski Vistupi V Johna Peela	10" LP	Reception	REC010	1988	£4	£10	

WEDGE
| No One Left But Me | LP | private | | 197- | £20 | £40 | US |

WEDGES
| Hang Ten | LP | Time | (S)T2090 | 1963 | £5 | £12 | US |

WEDGEWOODS
| Gone Gone Away | 7" | Pye | 7N15642 | 1964 | £1.50 | £4 | |
| Peace | 7" | Pye | 7N15826 | 1965 | £1.50 | £4 | |

WEE WILLIE & THE WINNERS
| Get Some | 7" | Action | ACT4624 | 1974 | £2 | £5 | |

WEED
| Weed | LP | Philips | 6305096 | 1971 | £50 | £100 | German |

WEED, BUDDY
| Kent Song | 7" | Vogue | V9075 | 1957 | £7.50 | £15 | |

WEEDON, BERT
$64,000 Question	7"	Parlophone	R4256	1957	£4	£8	
Apache	7"	Top Rank	JAR415	1960	£1.50	£4	chart single
Big Beat Boogie	7"	Top Rank	JAR300	1960	£1.50	£4	chart single
Big Note Blues	7"	Parlophone	R4446	1958	£2.50	£6	
Boy With The Magic Guitar	7"	Parlophone	MSP6242	1956	£5	£10	
China Doll	7"	HMV	POP946	1961	£1.50	£4	
Dark Eyes	7"	HMV	POP1216	1963	£1.50	£4	
Demonstration Record With David Gell	7" EP	Selmer		1959	£4	£8	
Fifi	7"	Saga	SAG2906	1959	£4	£8	
Ghost Train	7"	Top Rank	JAR582	1961	£1.50	£4	
Gin Mill Guitar	7"	HMV	POP1302	1964	£1.50	£4	
Ginchy	7"	Top Rank	JAR537	1961	£1.50	£4	chart single
Guitar Boogie Shuffle	7"	Top Rank	JAR117	1959	£2	£5	chart single
Guitar Man	7" EP	HMV	7EG8856	1964	£4	£8	
High Steppin'	7"	HMV	POP1485	1965	£1.50	£4	
Honky Tonk Guitar	LP	Top Rank	35101	1961	£8	£20	
It Happened In Monterey	7"	HMV	POP1248	1964	£1.50	£4	
Jealousy	7"	Top Rank	JAR210	1959	£1.50	£4	
Kick Off	7"	HMV	POP1535	1966	£1.50	£4	
King Size Guitar	LP	Top Rank	BUY026	1960	£10	£25	chart LP
Lady Is A Tramp	7"	Top Rank	JAR121	1959	£1.50	£4	
Mr.Guitar	7"	Top Rank	JAR559	1961	£1.50	£4	chart single
Nashville Boogie	7"	Top Rank	JAR221	1959	£1.50	£4	chart single
Night Cry	7"	HMV	POP1141	1963	£4	£8	
Petite Fleur	7"	Top Rank	JAR122	1959	£1.50	£4	
Play That Big Guitar	7"	Parlophone	R4381	1957	£2.50	£6	
Rockin' At The Roundhouse	7"	Fontana	6007012	1970	£1.50	£4	
Roulette	7" EP	Top Rank	TR5004	1959	£2.50	£6	with other artists
Soho Fair	7"	Parlophone	R4315	1957	£4	£8	
Some Other Love	7"	HMV	POP1043	1962	£1.50	£4	
Sorry Robbie	7"	Top Rank	JAR517	1960	£1.50	£4	chart single
South Of The Border	7"	HMV	POP1077	1962	£1.50	£4	
Stardust	7"	Top Rank	JAR211	1959	£1.50	£4	
Stranger Than Fiction	7"	HMV	POP1592	1967	£1.50	£4	
Teenage Guitar	7"	Top Rank	JAR136	1959	£1.50	£4	
Time To Say Goodnight	7"	Top Rank	JAR123	1959	£1.50	£4	

Tokyo Melody	7"	HMV	POP1355	1964	£1.50	£4
Tune For Two	7"	HMV	POP1039	1962	£5	£10	demo onl
Twelfth Street Rag	7"	Top Rank	JAR360	1960	£1.50	£4	chart singl
Twelve String Shuffle	7"	HMV	POP1387	1965	£1.50	£4
Twist A Napoli	7"	HMV	POP989	1962	£1.50	£4
Watch Your Step	7"	Grosvenor	GRS1015	196-	£1.50	£4
Waxing The Winners	7" EP.	Esquire	EP56	1956	£5	£10
Weedon Winners	7" EP.	Top Rank	JKP3008	1961	£5	£10

WEGMULLER, WALTER

Tarot	LP	Kosmische	KM58003	1973	£10	£25	German doubl

WEIR, BOB

Ace	LP	Warner Bros	K46165	1972	£5	£12

WEIR, FRANK ORCHESTRA

Theme From Journey Into Space	7"	Decca	F10435	1955	£1.50	£4

WEIRD STRINGS

Criminal Cage	7"	Ace	ACE009	1980	£2	£5
Oscar Mobile	7"	Velvet Moon	VM1	1980	£2.50	£6

WEIRDOS

We Got The Neutron Bomb	7"	Dangerhouse	SP1063	1978	£5	£10

WEISSBERG, ERIC

Duelling Banjos	LP	Warner Bros	K46214	1973	£4	£10

WELCH, BOB

French Kiss	LP	Capitol	EST11663	1977	£6	£15	US pic dis

WELCH, BRUCE

Please Mr., Please	7"	EMI	EMI2141	1974	£30	£60

WELCH, ELIZABETH

Stormy Weather	7"	Industrial	IR002	1980	£2.50	£6

WELCH, LENNY

Are You Sincere	7"	London	HLA9810	1963	£1.50	£4
Breaking Up Is Hard To Do	7"	Major Minor	MM707	1970	£1.50	£4
Darling Take Me Back	7"	London	HLR9981	1965	£2	£5
Ebb Tide	7"	London	HLA9880	1964	£1.50	£4
If You See My Love	7"	London	HLA9910	1964	£1.50	£4
Rags To Riches	7"	London	HLR10031	1966	£1.50	£4
Run To My Lovin' Arms	7"	London	HLR10010	1965	£2.50	£6
Since I Fell For You	LP	Cadence	CLP5068/25068	1963	£5	£12	US
Taste Of Honey	7"	London	HLA9601	1962	£1.50	£4
Two Different Worlds	7"	London	HLR9991	1965	£1.50	£4
When There's No Such Thing As Love	7"	Mainstream	MSS307	1975	£1.50	£4
You Don't Know Me	7"	London	HLA9094	1960	£1.50	£4

WELCH, TIM

Weak In The Knees	7"	Columbia	DB4529	1960	£1.50	£4

WELLINGTON, WADE

Let's Turkey Trot	7"	Oriole	CB1857	1963	£1.50	£4

WELLS, BOBBY

Let's Cop A Groove	7"	Beacon	3102	1968	£1.50	£4	white coloured labe
Let's Coppa Groove	7"	Beacon	3102	1968	£2	£5	yellow labe

WELLS, DICKY

Bones For The King	LP	Felsted	FAJ7006	1959	£5	£12
Trombone Four-In-Hand	LP	Felsted	FAJ7009/SJA2009	1960	£5	£12

WELLS, HOUSTON

Anna Marie	7"	Parlophone	R5099	1964	£4	£8
Blowing Wild	7"	Parlophone	R5069	1963	£4	£8
Blue Of The Night	7"	Parlophone	R5226	1965	£2	£5
Just For You	7" EP.	Parlophone	GEP8878	1963	£10	£20
Livin' Alone	7"	Parlophone	R5141	1964	£4	£8
Only The Heartaches	7"	Parlophone	R5031	1963	£4	£8	chart single
Ramona	7" EP.	Parlophone	GEP8914	1964	£12.50	£25
Shutters And Boards	7"	Parlophone	R4980	1962	£4	£8
This Song Is Just For You	7"	Parlophone	R4955	1962	£4	£8
Western Style	LP	Parlophone	PMC1215	1963	£25	£50	sleeve
							pictured in Guid

WELLS, JEAN

After Loving You	7"	Mojo	2092023	1971	£7.50	£15

WELLS, JOHNNY

Lonely Moon	7"	Columbia	DB4377	1959	£2.50	£6
Wondering Why	7"	Parlophone	R5559	1967	£1.50	£4

WELLS, JUNIOR

Blues Hit Big Town	LP	Delmark	640	1969	£4	£10	US
Blues With A Beat	7" EP.	Delmark	DJB1	1966	£7.50	£15
Coming At You	LP	Vanguard	SVRL19011	1968	£6	£15
Girl You Lit My Fire	7"	Mercury	MF1056	1968	£1.50	£4
Hoodoo Man Blues	LP	Delmark	612	1966	£6	£15	US
It's My Life Baby	LP	Fontana	(S)TFL6084	1966	£6	£15

t's My Life Baby	LP	Vanguard	SVRL19028	1968	£4	£10	
Junior Wells	7" EP	XX	MIN715	196-	£5	£10	
On Tap	LP	Delmark	DS635	197-	£4	£10	
Southside Blues Jam	LP	Delmark	628	1967	£4	£10	US
You're Tuff Enough	LP	Mercury	SMCL20130	1968	£5	£12	

WELLS, KITTY

After Dark	LP	Decca	DL8888	1959	£5	£12	US
Country Hit Parade	LP	Decca	DL8293	1956	£6	£15	US
Dust On The Bible	LP	Decca	DL8858	1959	£5	£12	US
Gave My Wedding Dress Away	7"	Brunswick	05920	1964	£1.50	£4	
Kitty Sings	7" EP	Brunswick	OE9149	1955	£6	£12	
Kitty Wells Story	LP	Decca	DX(S)B(7)174	1963	£4	£10	US, with booklet
Kitty's Choice	LP	Brunswick	LAT8361	1961	£5	£12	
Winner Of Your Heart	LP	Decca	DL8552	1956	£6	£15	US

WELLS, MARY

Ain't It The Truth	7"	Stateside	SS372	1965	£7.50	£15	
Bye Bye Baby	7"	Oriole	PS40051	1963	£25	£50	
Dear Lover	7"	Atlantic	AT4067	1966	£6	£12	
Dig The Way I Feel	7"	Direction	584816	1970	£2	£5	
Doctor	7"	Stateside	SS2111	1968	£4	£8	
Greatest Hits	LP	Motown	616	1964	£10	£25	US
Greatest Hits	LP	Tamla Motown	TML11032	1966	£6	£15	
He's A Lover	7"	Stateside	SS439	1965	£6	£12	
Laughing Boy	7"	Oriole	CBA1829	1963	£25	£50	
Live On Stage	LP	Motown	611	1963	£20	£40	US
Love Songs To The Beatles	LP	Stateside	(S)SL10171	1966	£8	£20	
Mary Wells	LP	Stateside	SL10133	1965	£6	£15	
Mary Wells	7" EP	Tamla Motown	TME2007	1965	£10	£20	
Me And My Baby	7"	Atlantic	584054	1966	£2.50	£6	
Me Without You	7"	Stateside	SS463	1965	£6	£12	
My Baby Just Cares For Me	LP	Tamla Motown	TML11006	1965	£15	£30	
My Guy	LP	Stateside	SL10095	1964	£25	£50	
My Guy	7"	Stateside	SS288	1964	£4	£8	chart single
Never Never Leave Me	7"	Stateside	SS415	1965	£6	£12	
Nothing But A Man	LP	Motown	(MS)630	1965	£10	£25	US
One Who Really Loves You	LP	Motown	605	1962	£30	£60	US
Ooh	LP	Movietone	71010/72010	1966	£6	£15	US
Servin' Up Some Soul	LP	Stateside	(S)SL10266	1968	£5	£12	
Set My Soul On Fire	7"	Atlantic	584104	1967	£2	£5	
Two Lovers	LP	Oriole	PS40045	1963	£25	£50	
Two Lovers	7"	Oriole	CBA1796	1963	£25	£50	
Two Sides Of Mary Wells	LP	Atlantic	587049	1966	£4	£10	
Use Your Head	7"	Stateside	SS396	1965	£6	£12	
Vintage Stock	7"	Motown	653	1966	£10	£25	US
You Beat Me To The Punch	7"	Oriole	CBA1762	1962	£25	£50	
You Lost The Sweetest Boy	7"	Stateside	SS242	1963	£10	£20	
Your Old Standby	7"	Oriole	CBA1847	1963	£25	£50	

WELLSTOOD, DICK

Dick Wellstood	10" LP	London	HBU1059	1956	£6	£15	

WELSH, ALEX

Alex Welsh And His Band	10" LP	Nixa	NJT507	1957	£6	£15	
It's Right Here For You	LP	Columbia	33SX1322/ SCX3377	1961	£4	£10	
Melrose Folio	10" LP	Nixa	NJT516	1958	£8	£20	
Music Of The Mauve Decade	LP	Columbia	33SX1219	1960	£5	£12	

WERLWINDS

Winding It Up	7"	Columbia	DB4650	1961	£4	£8	

WESLEY, FRED

House Party	7"	RSO	RSO67	1980	£2	£5	
House Party	12"	RSO	RSO67	1980	£5	£12	

WESS, FRANK

Frank Wess Quintet	10" LP	Atlantic	ATLLP1	195-	£20	£40	

WEST, ADAM & BURT WARD

Batman	LP	Twentieth Century	TF(S)4180	1966	£20	£40	US

WEST, BRUCE & LAING

The connection between Mountain and Cream was made even tighter when Mountain's bass player, Felix Pappalardi, left to be replaced by Jack Bruce. Unfortunately, the newly constituted West, Bruce, & Laing chose to concentrate on the more bombastic elements of Cream's style and their records are much less interesting than those of either of the group's predecessors.

Live And Kicking	LP	RSO	2394128	1974	£4	£10	
Whatever Turns You On	LP	RSO	2394107	1973	£4	£10	
Why Don'tcha	LP	CBS	65314	1972	£4	£10	

WEST COAST CONSORTIUM

Colour Sergeant Lillywhite	7"	Pye	7N17482	1968	£6	£12	
Some Other Someday	7"	Pye	7N17352	1967	£1.50	£4	

WEST COAST DELEGATION

Reach The Top	7"	Deram	DM113	1967	£2.50	£6	

WEST COAST KNACK

I'm Aware	7"	Capitol	CL15497	1967	£5	£10	

WEST COAST POP ART EXPERIMENTAL BAND

Child's Guide To Good & Evil	LP	Reprise	RSLP6298	1968	£15	£30	
Help I'm A Rock	7" EP.	Reprise	RVEP60104	1966	£15	£30	Frenc
Part One	LP	Reprise	R(S)6247	1967	£15	£30	U!
Volume 2	LP	Reprise	R(S)6270	1967	£15	£30	U!
West Coast Pop Art Experimental Band	LP	Fifo	M101	1966	£180	£300	U!
Where's My Daddy	LP	Amos	AAS7004	1969	£10	£25	U!

WEST, DODIE

Going Out Of My Head	7"	Decca	F12046	1964	£1.50	£4	chart singl
In The Deep Of The Night	7"	Piccadilly	7N35239	1965	£1.50	£4	

WEST FIVE

But If It Doesn't Work Out	7"	HMV	POP1513	1966	£4	£8
Congratulations	7"	HMV	POP1396	1965	£7.50	£15
Just Like Romeo And Juliet	7"	HMV	POP1428	1965	£6	£12

WEST, HEDY

Old Times And Hard Times	LP	Topic	12T117	1965	£15	£30

WEST INDIANS

Falling In Love	7"	Doctor Bird	DB1127	1968	£5	£10	
Right On Time	7"	Doctor Bird	DB1121	1968	£5	£10	
Strange Whisperings	7"	Camel	CA16	1969	£1.50	£4	Carl Dawkins B sid

WEST, KEITH

Keith West was the singer with Tomorrow, and his solo singles featured at least some of the members of that group. Certainly guitarist Stev Howe can be heard on West's hit, "Excerpt From A Teenage Opera". The opera from which this song was supposedly taken never did appea if indeed it ever existed in the first place. The single works brilliantly in any case as a tantalising glimpse of something much larger, bu invisible.

Excerpt From A Teenage Opera	7"	Parlophone	R5623	1967	£1.50	£4	chart singl
On A Saturday	7"	Parlophone	R5713	1968	£10	£20	
Sam	7"	Parlophone	R5651	1967	£2.50	£6	chart singl

WEST, LESLIE

Great Fatsby	LP	RCA	RS1009	1975	£4	£10	U!
Leslie West Band	LP	Phantom	701	1975	£4	£10	U!
Mountain	LP	Bell	SBLL126	1969	£8	£20	

WEST, MAE

Fabulous Mae West	LP	Brunswick	LAT8082	1956	£6	£15
Great Balls Of Fire	7"	MGM	2006203	1973	£1.50	£4
Twist And Shout	7"	Stateside	SS2021	1967	£5	£10
Way Out West	LP	Stateside	(S)SL10197	1967	£5	£12

WEST POINT SUPERNATURAL

Time Will Tell	7"	Reaction	591013	1967	£4	£8

WEST, SPEEDY

Guitar Spectacular	LP	Capitol	(S)T1835	1962	£6	£15	U!
Steel Guitar	LP	Capitol	(S)T1341	1960	£8	£20	U!
West Of Hawaii	LP	Capitol	T956	1958	£10	£25	U!

WEST, SPEEDY & JIMMY BRYANT

Capitol Presents	10" LP	Capitol	LC6619	1953	£8	£20	
Two Guitars Country Style	LP	Capitol	T520	1956	£20	£40	U!
Two Guitars Country Style	10" LP	Capitol	H520	1954	£37.50	£75	U!
Two Guitars Country Style	10" LP	Capitol	LC6694	1955	£20	£40	
Two Guitars Country Style Part 1	7" EP.	Capitol	EAP1520	1955	£6	£12	
Two Guitars Country Style Part 2	7" EP.	Capitol	EAP2520	1955	£6	£12	

WESTBROOK, MIKE

Celebration	LP	Deram	DML/SML1013	1967	£25	£50	
Citadel/Room 315	LP	RCA	SF8433	1975	£6	£15	
For The Record	LP	Transatlantic	TRA312	1975	£15	£30	
Life Of Its Own	7"	Deram	DM234	1969	£4	£8	
Live	LP	Cadillac	SGC1001	1972	£8	£20	
Love, Dream And Variations	LP	Transatlantic	TRA323	1975	£8	£20	
Love Songs	LP	Deram	SML1069	1970	£20	£40	
Marching Song Vol.1	LP	Deram	DML/SML1047	1969	£25	£50	
Marching Song Vol.2	LP	Deram	DML/SML1048	1969	£25	£50	
Metropolis	LP	Neon	NE10	1971	£15	£30	
Metropolis/Citadel/Room 315	LP	RCA		1979	£8	£20	doubl
Original Peter	7"	Deram	DM311	1970	£4	£8	
Release	LP	Deram	DML/SML1031	1968	£25	£50	sleev
							pictured in Guid
Requiem	7"	Deram	DM286	1970	£4	£8	
Tyger	LP	RCA	SER5612	1971	£15	£30	

WESTFAUSTER

In A King's Dream	LP	Nasco		1970	£10	£25	U!

WESTLAKE, CLIVE

Hundred Days	7"	Fontana	TF940	1968	£1.50	£4

WESTLAKE, KEVIN

Stars Fade	LP	Utopia	1388	1976	£5	£12	U!

WESTMINSTER FIVE

Railroad Blues	7"	Carnival	CV7017	1964	£4	£8

ticks And Stones	7″	Carnival	CV7019	1965	£2.50	£6	

WESTON, KIM

anger Heartbreak Dead Ahead	7″	Major Minor	MM683	1970	£2	£5	
or The First Time	LP	MGM	C(S)8055	1967	£10	£25	
elpless	7″	Tamla Motown	TMG554	1966	£15	£30	
Got What You Need	7″	MGM	MGM1338	1967	£4	£8	
m Still Loving You	7″	Tamla Motown	TMG511	1965	£30	£60	
im Weston	7″ EP.	Tamla Motown	TME2005	1965	£25	£50	
ittle More Love	7″	Stateside	SS359	1964	£25	£50	
lobody	7″	MGM	MGM1382	1968	£5	£10	
ock Me A Little While	7″ EP.	Tamla Motown	TME2015	1966	£40	£80	
ake Me In Your Arms	7″	Tamla Motown	TMG538	1965	£12.50	£25	
hat's Groovy	7″	MGM	MGM1357	1967	£2.50	£6	

WESTON, RANDY

ole Porter In Modern Mood	10″ LP	London	HAPB1040	1955	£15	£30	
andy Weston Trio	LP	London	HAU2018	1956	£8	£20	
andy Weston Trio	10″ LP	London	HBU1046	1956	£15	£30	

WESTWIND

ove Is	LP	Penny Farthing	PELS505	1970	£40	£80	

WET WET WET

Can Give You Everything	7″	Lyntone		1990	£2.50	£6	flexi
Remember	7″	Precious	JEWEL5	1987	£2.50	£6	
Remember	12″	Precious	JEWEL512	1987	£4	£10	
weet Little Mystery	7″	Precious	JWLS4	1987	£2	£5	shaped pic disc
weet Little Mystery	12″	Precious	JEWEL412	1987	£4	£10	'wet' cover
Vishing I Was Lucky	12″	Precious	JWLD3	1987	£5	£12	double

WETTLING, GEORGE

eorge Wettling Jazz Band	10″ LP	Columbia	33S1019	1954	£5	£12	

WHALEFEATHERS

Vhalefeathers	LP	Blue Horizon	2431009	1971	£10	£25	
Vhalefeathers Declare	LP	Nasco	9003	1969	£10	£25	US

WHAM!

ad Boys	7″	Innervision	IVL3143	1983	£5	£10	pic disc
ad Boys	7″	Innervision	IVL3143	1983	£2	£5	poster PS
lub Tropicana	7″	Innervision	IVL3613	1983	£5	£10	pic disc
inal	LP	Epic	WHAM2	1986	£6	£15	2 gold vinyl discs, inserts, boxed
reedom	7″	Epic	QA4743	1984	£5	£10	shaped pic disc
reedom	7″	Epic	WA4743	1984	£6	£12	shaped pic disc
ast Christmas	7″	Epic	GA4949	1984	£1.50	£4	gatefold sleeve
Vake Me Up Before You Go-Go	12″	Epic	TA4440	1984	£4	£10	poster sleeve
Vham Rap	12″	Innervision	IVLA122442	1982	£4	£10	

WHAT'S NEW

arly Morning Rain	7″ EP.	Number One	LOU2013	196-	£4	£8	French
et Away	7″ EP.	Number One	LOU2014	196-	£4	£8	French

WHEATSTRAW, PEETIE

evil's Son In Law	LP	Saydisc	SDR191	1969	£5	£12	
igh Sheriff From Hell	LP	Saydisc	SDR192	1969	£5	£12	

WHEELER, BILLY ED

de To The Little Brown Shack	7″	London	HLR9950	1965	£1.50	£4	
n THe Outside	7″	London	HLR9920	1964	£1.50	£4	

WHEELER, KENNY

Vindmill Tilter	LP	Fontana	STL5494	1968	£20	£40	with Johnny Dankworth

WHEELS

erbie Armstrong has enjoyed a lengthy and varied career - gaining chart hits as a member of Fox and of Yellow Dog, playing on several Van Morrison LPs, and doing much other session work besides. His roots, however, go back to Belfast and an R&B group called Wheels. The group nade two singles, then changed its name to Wheels-A-Way for a third.

ad Little Woman/Call My Name	7″	Columbia	DB7827	1966	£30	£60	
ad Little Woman/Road Block	7″	Columbia	DB7827	1966	£70	£140	
iloria	7″	Columbia	DB7682	1965	£37.50	£75	
icks	7″	Columbia	DB7981	1966	£37.50	£75	

WHEELS OF TIME

984	7″	Spin	62008	1967	£12.50	£25	

WHICHWHAT

Wanna Be Free	7″	Beacon	BEA144	1969	£2	£5	
n The Year 2525	7″	Beacon	BEA133	1969	£2	£5	
ietnam Rose	7″	Beacon	BEA169	1971	£2	£5	
Vhichwhat's First	LP	Beacon	BEAS14	1970	£15	£30	
Jhy Do Lovers Break Each Other's earts	7″	Beacon	BEA131	1969	£2	£5	

WHIRLWINDS

he Whirlwinds were led by Graham Gouldman, of later song-writing and Ten cc fame.

ook At Me	7″	HMV	POP1301	1964	£10	£20	

WHISKEY, NANCY

lancy Whiskey	8″ EP.	Topic	T7	195-	£8	£20	

WHISKEY, NANCY & CHAS MCDEVITT
Intoxicating Miss Whiskey	LP	Mercury	MG10018	1957	£10	£25	

WHISKEY, NANCY & THE SKIFFLERS
Bowling Green	7"	Fontana	TF612	1965	£1.50	£4	
He's Solid Gone	7"	Oriole	CB1394	1957	£2	£5	
Hillside In Scotland	7"	Oriole	CB1452	1958	£1.50	£4	
Old Grey Goose	7"	Oriole	CB1485	1959	£1.50	£4	

WHISPERS OF TRUTH
Whispers Of Truth	LP	Key			£15	£30

WHISTLER
Ho-Hum	LP	Deram	SML1083	1971	£8	£20

WHITCOMB, IAN
Good Hard Rock	7"	Capitol	CL15431	1966	£1.50	£4	
Good Hard Rock	7" EP	Capitol	EAP122008	1966	£6	£12	Frenc
Nervous	7" EP	Capitol	EAP122004	1965	£6	£12	Frenc
N-N-Nervous	7"	Capitol	CL15418	1965	£1.50	£4	
Sporting Life	7" EP	Capitol	EAP160002	1965	£6	£12	Frenc
This Sporting Life	7"	Capitol	CL15382	1965	£1.50	£4	
You Turn Me On	LP	Ember	NR5065	1967	£6	£15	
You Turn Me On	7"	Capitol	CL15395	1965	£2.50	£6	

WHITE, BUKKA
Blues Masters Vol.4	LP	Blue Horizon	4604	1972	£5	£12	U
Bukka White	LP	CBS	52629	1969	£20	£40	
Memphis Hot Shots	LP	Blue Horizon	763229	1969	£20	£40	
Sic 'Em Dogs	LP	Herwin	201	1965	£8	£20	U
Sky Songs	LP	Fontana	688804ZL	1966	£5	£12	

WHITE, DANNY
Keep My Woman Home	7"	Sue	WI4031	1967	£7.50	£15

WHITE, DUKE
It's Over	7"	Island	WI084	1963	£5	£10
Sow Good Seeds	7"	Black Swan	WI444	1965	£5	£10

WHITE, GEORGIA
Was I Drunk?	78	Vocalion	V1038	1954	£6	£12

WHITE, IAN
Ian White	LP	private		1970	£8	£20

WHITE, JAY
Faraway Places	7" EP	London	REF1045	1956	£2	£5

WHITE, JEANETTE
Music	7"	A&M	AMS761	1969	£10	£20

WHITE, JOE
Downtown Girl	7"	Island	WI166	1965	£5	£10	Do
							Drummond B sid
Hog In A Coco	7"	Island	WI159	1964	£5	£10	Rolan
							Alphonso B sid
I Need A Woman	7"	Doctor Bird	DB1090	1967	£5	£10	
If It Don't Work Out	7"	Gayfeet	GS202	1973	£2	£5	
Irene	7"	Island	WI201	1965	£5	£10	
Lonely Nights	7"	Doctor Bird	DB1080	1967	£5	£10	
My Love For You	7"	Doctor Bird	DB1024	1966	£5	£10	Sammy Ismay B sic
Punch You Down	7"	Ska Beat	JB180	1965	£5	£10	Tomm
							McCook B sid
Rudies All Around	7"	Doctor Bird	DB1069	1966	£5	£10	
Since The Other Day	LP	Magnet	MGT006	197-	£6	£15	
Sinners	7"	R&B	JB137	1964	£5	£10	Rolan
							Alphonso B sid
Try A Little Tenderness	7"	Blue Cat	BS119	1968	£4	£8	Lyn Taitt B sid
Way Of Life	7"	Blue Cat	BS108	1968	£4	£8	
When You Are Young	7"	Island	WI145	1964	£5	£10	

WHITE, JOHN & GAVIN BRYARS
Machine Music	LP	Obscure	OBS8	1978	£4	£10

WHITE, JOSH
At The Town Hall	LP	Mercury	MMC14102	1962	£4	£10	
Ballads And Blues	10" LP	Brunswick	LA8562	1953	£8	£20	
Ballads And Blues Vol.2	10" LP	Brunswick	LA8653	1954	£8	£20	
Beginning	LP	Mercury	20039MCL	1964	£5	£12	
Blues And Josh White	LP	Nixa	NJL2	1957	£6	£15	
Blues And... Pt.1	7" EP	Pye	NJE1057	1957	£2.50	£6	
Blues And... Pt.2	7" EP	Pye	NJE1058	1957	£2.50	£6	
Blues And... Pt.3	7" EP	Pye	NJE1059	1957	£2.50	£6	
John Henry, Ballads, Blues And Other Songs	LP	Storyville	SLP123	1964	£4	£10	
Josh	LP	Elektra	EKL114	195-	£4	£10	U
Josh At Midnight	LP	Elektra	EKL102	195-	£4	£10	U
Josh Comes A-Visitin'	10" LP	London	HAPB1038	1955	£8	£20	
Josh White	LP	Decca	DL8665	1957	£6	£15	U
Josh White	7" EP	Mercury	10006MCE	1964	£2.50	£6	
Josh White	10" LP	London	338	195-	£6	£15	U

osh White Program	10" LP	London	HAPB1005	1951	£8	£20	
osh White's Blues	LP	Mercury	MG20203	1956	£5	£12	US
ive!	LP	HMV	CLP1588	1962	£4	£10	
ings Vol.2	10" LP	London	HAPB1032	1954	£8	£20	
ongs By Josh White	10" LP	Mercury	MG25014	1954	£6	£15	
outhern Blues	7" EP	Mercury	YEP9504	1956	£2.50	£6	
tories Vol.1	LP	HMV	CLP1159	1958	£5	£12	
tories Vol.2	LP	HMV	CLP1175	1958	£5	£12	
toryville Blues Anthology Vol.8	7" EP	Storyville	SEP388	1964	£4	£8	
wenty-Fifth Anniversary Album	LP	Elektra	EKL123	195-	£4	£10	US

VHITE, JOSH & BEVERLY

everly And Josh White Jnr.	7" EP	Realm	REP4003	1964	£2.50	£6	

VHITE, JOSH & BIG BILL BROONZY

osh White & Big Bill Broonzy	LP	Period	1209	196-	£5	£12	US

VHITE, KITTY & DAVID HOWARD

esse James	7"	London	HL8102	1954	£10	£20	

VHITE LIGHT

Vhite Light	LP	Century	39955	196-	£35	£70	US

VHITE, LOUISIANA JANE

When the Battle Is Over	7"	Philips	BF1810	1969	£2	£5	

VHITE NOISE

lectric Storm	LP	Island	ILPS9099	1969	£5	£12	

VHITE PLAINS

Vhen You Are A King	LP	Deram	SML1092	1971	£5	£12	
Vhite Plains	LP	Deram	SML1067	1970	£5	£12	

VHITE SPIRIT

Midnight Chaser	7"	MCA	MCA638	1981	£2.50	£6	

VHITE, TAM

irl Watcher	7"	Decca	F12849	1968	£2	£5	
ewis Carroll	7"	Middle Earth	MDS104	1970	£1.50	£4	
am White	LP	Middle Earth	MDLS304	1970	£8	£20	
hat Old Sweet Roll	7"	Deram	DM261	1969	£1.50	£4	

VHITE, TERRY

ock Around The Mailbag	7"	Decca	F11133	1959	£10	£20	

VHITE, TONY JOE

est Of Tony Joe White	LP	Warner Bros	K56149	1973	£4	£10	
lack And White	LP	Monument	SMO5027	1968	£6	£15	
ontinued	LP	Monument	SMO5035	1969	£6	£15	
roupie Girl	7"	Monument	MON1043	1970	£1.50	£4	chart single
ome-Made Ice Cream	LP	Warner Bros	K46229	1973	£5	£12	
ve Got A Thing About You Baby	7"	Warner Bros	K16411	1974	£1.50	£4	
olk Salad Annie	7"	Monument	MON1031	1969	£2	£5	
oosevelt And Ira Lee	7"	Monument	MON1040	1969	£1.50	£4	
ave Your Sugar For Me	7"	Monument	MON1048	1970	£1.50	£4	
oul Francisco	7"	Monument	MON1024	1968	£1.50	£4	
ony Joe	LP	Monument	SMO5043	1970	£6	£15	chart LP
ony Joe White	LP	Warner Bros	K46068	1971	£6	£15	
rain I'm On	LP	Warner Bros	K46147	1972	£6	£15	
Villie And Laura	7"	Monument	MON1036	1969	£1.50	£4	

VHITE TRASH

oad To Nowhere	7"	Apple	6	1969	£6	£12	

VHITEHORN, GEOFF

Vhitehorn	LP	Stateside	ISS80164	1974	£6	£15	Japanese

VHITEHOUSE

irthdeath Experience	LP	Come Organisation	WDC881004	1980	£40	£80	
uchenwald	LP	Come Organisation	WDC881013	1981	£25	£50	
edicated To Peter Kurten	LP	Come Organisation	WDC881010	1981	£30	£60	
rector	LP	Come Organisation	WDC881007	1980	£30	£60	
reat White Death	LP	Come Organisation		1981	£25	£50	
ive Action 1	cass	Come Organisation	WDC881020	1982	£5	£12	
ive Action 2	cass	Come Organisation	WDC881022	1982	£5	£12	
ew Britain	LP	Come Organisation	WDC881017	1982	£50	£100	
ne Hundred And Fifty Murderous assions	LP	Come Organisation		198-	£20	£40	
sychopathia Sexualis	LP	Come Organisation	WDC881027	198-	£50	£100	clear or black vinyl
ight To Kill	LP	Come Organisation	WDC881033	198-	£25	£50	

895

Total Sex	LP	Come Organisation ...	WDC881005	1980	£40	£80	

WHITESNAKE

Bloody Mary	7"	EMI	INEP751	1978	£2	£5	PS, white vin
Fool For Your Loving	7"	United Artists ..	BP352	1980	£2	£5	luminous sleev
Give Me All Your Love	12"	EMI	12EM23	1988	£2.50	£6	white vin
Give Me All Your Love	12"	EMI	12EMP23	1988	£2.50	£6	pic dis
Guilty Of Love	7"	Liberty	BP420	1983	£2	£5	pic dis
Here I Go Again	7"	Liberty	BP416	1982	£2	£5	pic dis
Here I Go Again	10"	EMI	10EMI35	1987	£2.50	£6	white vin
Is This Love	7"	EMI	EMP3	1987	£1.50	£4	shaped pic dis
Live At Hammersmith	LP	Polydor	MPF1288	1980	£5	£12	Japanes
Now You're Gone	7"	EMI	EMPD150	1990	£1.50	£4	shaped pic disc, plint
Slide It In	LP	Liberty	LBGP2400000	1984	£4	£10	pic dis
Standing In The Shadow	7"	Liberty	BPP423	1984	£1.50	£4	pic dis
Still Of The Night	7"	EMI	EMIW5606	1987	£2.50	£6	whit vinyl, with poste
Still Of The Night	12"	EMI	12EMIP5606	1987	£2.50	£6	pic dis
Take Me With You	12"	Liberty		1982	£2.50	£6	1 sided prom
Trouble	LP	Sunburst..	INS3022	1978	£4	£10	
Victim Of Love	7"	Liberty	BP418	1982	£7.50	£15	
Whitesnake 1987	LP	EMI	EMC3528	1987	£4	£10	pic dis

WHITFIELD, DAVID

Adoration Waltz	7"	Decca	F10833	1957	£2	£5	chart sing
Alone	7" EP	Decca	STO158	1962	£2	£5	stere
Beyond The Stars	7"	Decca	F10458	1955	£4	£8	chart sing
Book	7"	Decca	F10242	1954	£5	£10	chart sing
Cara Mia	7"	Decca	F10327	1954	£5	£10	chart sing
Cara Mia	7" EP	Decca	DFE6225	1955	£5	£10	
David Whitfield No.1	7" EP..	Decca	DFE6342	1956	£2	£5	
David Whitfield No.2	7" EP..	Decca	DFE6400	1957	£2	£5	
David Whitfield No.3	7" EP..	Decca	DFE6434	1957	£2	£5	
Everywhere	7"	Decca	F10515	1955	£4	£8	chart sing
From David With Love	LP	Decca	LK4270	1958	£4	£10	
I'll Find You	7"	Decca	F10864	1957	£2	£5	chart sing
I'll Never Stop Loving You	7"	Decca	F10596	1955	£1.50	£4	
Lady	7"	Decca	F10562	1955	£1.50	£4	
My September Love	7"	Decca	F10690	1956	£2	£5	chart sing
My Son John	7"	Decca	F10769	1956	£2	£5	chart sing
Santo Natale	7"	Decca	F10399	1954	£2.50	£5	chart sing
Smile	7"	Decca	F10355	1954	£2	£5	chart sing
When You Lose The One You Love	7"	Decca	F10627	1955	£2	£5	chart sing
Whitfield Favourites	LP	Decca	LK4242	1958	£4	£10	
Yours From The Heart	10" LP	Decca	LF1165	1954	£6	£15	

WHITFIELD, WILBUR & THE PLEASERS

Heart To Heart	7"	Vogue	V9097	1958	£50	£100	
P.B.Baby	7"	Vogue	V9078	1957	£50	£100	
Plaything	7"	Vogue	V9091	1957	£50	£100	

WHITING, LEONARD

Piper	7"	Pye	7N15943	1965	£4	£8	

WHITING, MARGARET

Capitol Presents	10" LP	Capitol	LC6585	1953	£5	£12	
Goin' Places	LP	London	HAD2109	1958	£5	£12	
Heat Wave	7"	Capitol	CL14242	1955	£2	£5	
Hot Spell	7"	London	HLD8662	1958	£2	£5	
I Can't Help It	7"	London	HLD8562	1958	£2	£5	
I Love A Mystery	7"	Capitol	CL14527	1956	£1.50	£4	
Just A Dream	LP	London	HAD2321	1961	£5	£12	
Just Like A Man	7"	London	HLD10114	1967	£1.50	£4	
Kill Me With Kisses	7"	London	HLD8451	1957	£2	£5	
Lover Lover	7"	Capitol	CL14375	1955	£2	£5	
Maggie Isn't Margaret Anymore	LP	London	HAU8332	1967	£5	£12	
Man	7"	Capitol	CL14348	1955	£2	£5	
Margaret Whiting	10" LP	Capitol	LC6811	1956	£5	£12	
My Own True Love	7"	Capitol	CL14213	1954	£2	£5	
Nothing Lasts Forever	7"	London	HLU10078	1966	£2	£5	
Stowaway	7"	Capitol	CL14307	1955	£2	£5	
Wheel Of Hurt	LP	London	HAU/SHU8317	1967	£5	£12	

WHITLEY, RAY

I've Been Hurt	7"	HMV	POP1473	1965	£37.50	£75	

WHITMAN, SLIM

All Time Favorites	LP	Imperial	LP9252	1964	£4	£10	U
America's Favorite Folk Artist	10" LP	Imperial	LP3004	1954	£15	£30	U
And His Singing Guitar	7" EP..	London	REP1006	1954	£6	£12	gold lab
And His Singing Guitar	10" LP	London	HAPB1015	1954	£17.50	£35	gold lab
And His Singing Guitar Vol.2	LP	London	HAU2015	1956	£10	£25	
And His Singing Guitar Vol.2 Pt.1	7" EP..	London	REU1064	1956	£5	£10	gold lab
And His Singing Guitar Vol.2 Pt.2	7" EP..	London	REU1070	1956	£5	£10	gold lab
And His Singing Guitar Vol.2 Pt.3	7" EP..	London	REU1100	1957	£5	£10	gold lab
Annie Laurie	LP	Imperial	LP9077	1959	£6	£15	U
Beautiful Dreamer	7"	London	HL8080	1954	£10	£20	gold lab
Candy Kisses	7"	London	HLP8642	1958	£4	£8	
Cool Water	7"	Liberty	LIB15066	1968	£1.50	£4	
Curtain Of Tears	7"	London	HLP8416	1957	£5	£10	

Title	Format	Label	Catalogue	Year			Notes
Dear Mary	7"	London	HLU8327	1956	£10	£20	gold label
Favorites	LP	Imperial	LP9003	1956	£10	£25	US
First Visit To Britain	LP	Imperial	LP9135	1960	£5	£12	US
Gone	7"	London	HLP8420	1957	£10	£20	gold label
Haunted Hungry Heart	7"	London	HL8141	1955	£10	£20	gold label
Heart Songs And Love Songs	LP	London	HAP8059	1963	£6	£15	
I Never See Maggie Alone	7"	London	HLP8835	1959	£2	£5	
I'll Hold You In My Heart	7"	Liberty	LIB66040	1964	£1.50	£4	
I'll Never Stop Loving You	7"	London	HLU8167	1955	£10	£20	gold label
I'll Take You Home Again Kathleen	7"	London	HLP8403	1957	£6	£12	chart single, gold label
I'll Walk With God	LP	Imperial	LP9088	1960	£5	£12	US
I'm A Fool	7"	London	HLU8252	1956	£7.50	£15	chart single, gold label
I'm A Lonely Wanderer	LP	London	HAP8093	1963	£6	£15	
I'm Casting My Lasso	7"	London	HLU8350	1956	£7.50	£15	gold label
Indian Love Call	7"	London	HL1149	1954	£7.50	£15	gold label
Indian Love Call	7"	London	L1149	1954	£12.50	£25	chart single, gold label
Irish Songs The Slim Whitman Way	7" EP	Liberty	LEP4018	1964	£2.50	£6	
Irish Songs The Whitman Way	LP	Imperial	LP9245	1963	£5	£12	US
Just Call Me Lonesome	LP	London	HAP2392	1961	£6	£15	
Lovesick Blues	7"	London	HLP8459	1957	£5	£10	
Many Times	7"	London	HLP8434	1957	£5	£10	
Million Record Hits	LP	Imperial	LP9102	1960	£5	£12	US
More Than Yesterday	7"	Liberty	LIB12020	1965	£1.50	£4	
My Happiness	7"	Liberty	LIB15198	1969	£1.50	£4	
North Wind	7"	London	HL1226	1954	£12.50	£25	gold label
North Wind	7"	London	L1226	1954	£15	£30	gold label
Once In A Lifetime	LP	Imperial	LP9156	1961	£5	£12	US
One Dream	7"	Liberty	LIB66212	1966	£1.50	£4	
Remember Me	7"	Liberty	LIB12013	1965	£1.50	£4	
Reminiscing	7"	Liberty	LIB66103	1965	£1.50	£4	
Roll River Roll	7"	London	HLP9103	1960	£1.50	£4	
Rose Marie	7"	London	HL8061	1954	£7.50	£15	chart single, gold label
Satisfied Man	7" EP	Liberty	LEP4046	1966	£4	£8	
Secret Love	7"	London	HL8039	1954	£12.50	£25	gold label
Serenade	7"	London	HLU8287	1956	£7.50	£15	chart single, gold label
Singing Hills	7"	London	HL8091	1954	£10	£20	gold label
Sings	LP	Imperial	LP9064	1959	£6	£15	US
Slim Whitman	LP	Imperial	LP9056	1958	£6	£15	US
Slim Whitman	LP	London	HAP2343	1961	£6	£15	
Slim Whitman Sings	LP	Imperial	LP9026	1957	£10	£25	US
Slim Whitman Sings	LP	London	HAP2139	1959	£6	£15	
Slim Whitman Sings	7" EP	London	REP1199	1959	£5	£10	tri-centre
Slim Whitman Sings And Yodels	10" LP	RCA	LPM3217	1954	£15	£30	US
Slim Whitman Sings More Irish Songs	7" EP	Liberty	LEP4027	1965	£2.50	£6	
Slim Whitman Sings No.2	7" EP	London	REP1258	1960	£5	£10	
Slim Whitman Sings Vol.2	LP	London	HAP2199	1959	£6	£15	
Slim Whitman Sings Vol.3	LP	London	HAP2443	1962	£6	£15	
Slim Whitman Sings Vol.3	LP	London	SAHP6232	1962	£8	£20	stereo
Slim Whitman Sings Vol.4	LP	London	HAP8013	1962	£6	£15	
Song Of The Wild	7"	London	HLU8196	1955	£10	£20	gold label
Song Of The Wild	7" EP	London	REP1042	1955	£6	£12	gold label
Stairway To Heaven	7"	London	HL8018	1954	£17.50	£35	gold label
Stranger On The Shore	7"	Liberty	LIB15220	1969	£1.50	£4	
There's A Rainbow In Every Teardrop	7"	London	HL1214	1954	£10	£20	gold label
There's A Rainbow In Every Teardrop	7"	London	L1214	1954	£12.50	£25	gold label
Travellin' Man	7"	Liberty	LIB66181	1966	£1.50	£4	
Tumbling Tumbleweeds	7"	London	HLU8230	1956	£7.50	£15	chart single, gold label
Unchain My Heart	7"	London	HLP8518	1957	£5	£10	
Vaya Con Dios	7"	London	HLP9302	1961	£1.50	£4	
Very Precious Love	7"	London	HLP8590	1958	£5	£10	
Wayward Wind	7" EP	London	REP1360	1963	£6	£12	
What's The World A-Comin' To	7"	Liberty	LIB66226	1967	£1.50	£4	
When I Grow Too Old To Dream	7"	London	HL8125	1955	£10	£20	gold label
Wherever You Are	7"	London	HLP8708	1958	£4	£8	

WHITNEY, MARVA

Title	Format	Label	Catalogue	Year			Notes
Daddy Don't Know About The Sugar Beat	7"	Mojo	2092041	1972	£2	£5	
I Sing Soul	LP	King	K1053	1969	£25	£50	US
It's My Thing	LP	Polydor	583767	1969	£50	£100	US
Live And Lowdown At The Apollo	LP	King	K1079	1970	£25	£50	US
This Girl's In Love With You	7"	Polydor	2001036	1970	£6	£12	

WHITSETT, TIM

Title	Format	Label	Catalogue	Year			Notes
Macks By The Tracks	7"	Sue	WI318	1964	£6	£12	

WHITSETT, TIM & STICKS HERMAN

Title	Format	Label	Catalogue	Year			Notes
Rhythm And Blues	7" EP	Range	JRE7002	196-	£6	£12	

WHITTLE, TOMMY

Title	Format	Label	Catalogue	Year			Notes
New Horizons	LP	Tempo	TAP27	1960	£6	£15	
Tommy Whittle	10" LP	Esquire	20048	1955	£8	£20	
Tommy Whittle Orchestra	10" LP	Esquire	20061	1956	£4	£10	
Tommy Whittle Quartet	10" LP	Esquire	20068	1956	£4	£10	

Waxing With Whittle	10" LP	Esquire	20028	1954	£8	£20	

WHO

The Who's status as one of the world's most popular rock groups has inevitably led to a considerable interest in their early recordings, which fetch respectable prices even where they were chart hits. The three different B sides for the original issues of "Substitute" are the result of a dispute between Brunswick and Reaction as to the ownership of the track "Circles". "Instant Party" is the same track, whose change of title did not fool anyone, but "Waltz For A Pig", credited to the Who Orchestra, is actually a Graham Bond Organisation instrumental. The 1976 reissue of "Substitute" has the distinction of being the first twelve inch single ever made. Meanwhile, the most expensive rarities include a withdrawn mail order compilation, "Who Did It", and scarce picture sleeves for the singles "Anyway,Anyhow,Anywhere" and "My Generation".

Title	Format	Label	Cat No	Year	Price	Price	Notes
Acid Queen	7"	Track	PRO3	1969	£15	£30	promo
Anyway,Anyhow,Anywhere	7"	Brunswick	05935	1965	£5	£10	chart single
Anyway,Anyhow,Anywhere	7"	Brunswick	05935	1965	£50	£100	PS
Athena/Why Did I Fall For That	12"	Polydor	WHOPX6	1982	£4	£10	pic disc
Christmas	7"	Track	PRO4	1969	£15	£30	promo
Circles	7"	Brunswick	05951	1966	£50	£100	demo
Direct Hits	LP	Track	612/613006	1969	£8	£20	
Dogs	7"	Track	604023	1968	£2.50	£6	chart single
Excerpts From Tommy	7" EP.	Track	2252001	1970	£5	£10	
Face Dances	LP	Mobile Fidelity	MFSL1115	1984	£5	£12	US audiophile
Filling In The Gaps	LP	Polydor	WHOT1	1981	£15	£30	double interview promo
Go To The Mirror	7"	Track	PRO2	1969	£15	£30	promo
Happy Jack	LP	Decca	DL(7)4892	1967	£8	£20	US
Happy Jack	7"	Reaction	591010	1966	£2	£5	chart single
Happy Jack	7" EP.	Polydor	27799	1966	£12.50	£25	French
I Can See For Miles	7"	Track	604011	1967	£2	£5	chart single
I Can't Explain	7"	Brunswick	05926	1965	£4	£8	chart single
I Can't Explain	7" EP.	Brunswick	10668	1965	£25	£50	French
I'm A Boy	7"	Reaction	591004	1966	£2	£5	chart single
I'm A Boy	7" EP.	Polydor	27789	1966	£12.50	£25	French
I'm Free	7"	Track	PRO1	1969	£15	£30	promo
It's Hard	LP	Warner Bros	237311	1982	£8	£20	US audiophile promo
Join Together	7"	Polydor	2094102	1972	£7.50	£15	export, PS
Join Together	7"	Track	2094102	1972	£1.50	£4	chart single
Kids Are Alright	7"	Brunswick	05956	1966	£12.50	£25	
Kids Are Alright	7"	Brunswick	05965	1966	£6	£12	chart single
Kids Are Alright	7" EP.	Decca	60008	1966	£12.50	£25	French
La La La Lies	7"	Brunswick	05968	1966	£10	£20	
Legal Matter	7"	Brunswick	05956	1966	£5	£10	chart single
Legal Matter	7"	Brunswick	05956	1966	£50	£100	export with Scandinavian PS
Legal Matter	7"	Decca	AD1002	1968	£17.50	£35	export
Let's See Action	7"	Track	2094012	1971	£1.50	£4	chart single
Live At Leeds	7"	Track	2406001	1970	£4	£10	12 inserts, chart LP
Long Live Rock	7"	MCA	41053	1979	£10	£20	US pic disc, 6 different backs
Magic Bus	LP	Decca	DL75064	1968	£8	£20	US
Magic Bus	7"	Track	604024	1968	£2	£5	chart single
Making Of Tommy	LP	Polydor	SA010	1975	£10	£25	US interview promo
My Generation	LP	Brunswick	LAT8616	1965	£17.50	£35	chart LP
My Generation	LP	Decca	DL(7)4664	1966	£10	£25	US
My Generation	7"	Brunswick	05944	1965	£2.50	£6	chart single
My Generation	7"	Brunswick	05944	1965	£75	£150	PS
My Generation	7"	Decca	AD1001	1968	£20	£40	export
My Generation	7"	Decca	AD1001	1968	£50	£100	export, PS
My Generation	7" EP.	Decca	10671	1965	£12.50	£25	French
My Generation	7" EP.	Decca	60002	1965	£12.50	£25	French
Out In The Street	7" EP.	Decca	60004	1966	£12.50	£25	French
Pictures Of Lily	7"	Track	604002	1967	£2	£5	chart single
Pictures Of Lily	7" EP.	Polydor	27805	1967	£12.50	£25	French
Pinball Wizard	7"	Track	604027	1969	£1.50	£4	chart single
Quadrophenia	LP	Track	2657013	1973	£5	£12	double
Quick One	LP	Reaction	593002	1966	£8	£20	chart LP
Ready Steady Who	7" EP.	Polydor	27801	1966	£20	£40	French
Ready Steady Who	7" EP.	Reaction	592001	1966	£15	£30	
Ready Steady Who	7" EP.	Reaction	WHO7	1983	£1.50	£4	
Roger Daltrey & Pete Townshend Talk About Quadrophenia	LP	Polydor	PRO114	1979	£8	£20	US interview promo
See Me Feel Me	7"	Track	2094004	1970	£5	£10	
Seeker	7"	Track	604036	1970	£1.50	£4	chart single
Substitute	12"	Polydor	2058803	1976	£2.50	£6	no PS
Substitute/Circles	7"	Reaction	591001	1966	£5	£10	
Substitute/Instant Party	7"	Reaction	591001	1966	£5	£10	
Substitute/Waltz For A Pig	7"	Reaction	591001	1966	£4	£8	chart single
Summertime Blues	7"	Track	2094002	1970	£1.50	£4	chart single
Tommy	LP	Track	613013/014	1969	£6	£15	double, book, chart LP
Tommy Part 1	LP	Track	2406007	1970	£4	£10	
Tommy Part 2	LP	Track	2406008	1970	£4	£10	
Under My Thumb	7"	Track	604006	1967	£10	£20	
Who Are You	LP	MCA		1978	£6	£15	US interview promo
Who Are You	LP	MCA	P14950	1978	£4	£10	US pic disc
Who Are You	LP	Superdisk	SD166108	1981	£6	£15	US audiophile
Who Did It	LP	Track	2856001	1971	£150	£250	sleeve pictured in Guide
Who Sell Out	LP	Track	612002	1967	£15	£30	mono, chart LP
Who Sell Out	LP	Track	613002	1967	£8	£20	stereo, chart LP
Won't Get Fooled Again	7"	Track	2094009	1971	£4	£8	PS
Won't Get Fooled Again	7"	Track	A4112	1971	£5	£10	1 sided promo

WHO & STRAWBERRY ALARM CLOCK
Who/Strawberry Alarm Clock .... LP ...... Decca .... DL734568 .... 1969 ... £15 ....£30 .... US

WHYTON, WALLY
All Over This World .... 7" ...... Parlophone..... R4630 .... 1960 ... £1.50 ....£4 ....
Don't Tell Me Your Troubles .... 7" ...... Parlophone..... R4585 .... 1959 ... £2.50 ....£6 ....
It's A Rat Race .... 7" ...... Pye .... 7N15304 .... 1960 ... £1.50 ....£4 ....
Little Red Pony .... 7" ...... Piccadilly .... 7N35089 .... 1961 ... £1.50 ....£4 ....

WIG
Live At The Jade Room .... LP ...... Texas Archive . ... 1982 ... £10 ....£25 .... US

WIGGINS, GERALD
Music FRom Around The World In 80   LP ...... London .... LTZU15109 .... 1958 ... £6 ....£15 ....
Days ....

WIGGINS, PERCY
Book Of Memories .... 7" .... Atlantic .... 584113.................... 1967 ... £4 ....£8 ....

WIGGINS, SPENCER
I'm A Poor Man's Son .... 7" ...... Pama................ PM794 .... 1969 ... £4 ....£8 ....
Uptight Good Woman .... 7" ...... Stateside .... SS2024 .... 1967 ... £4 ....£8 ....

WIGGONS
Rock Baby .... 7" .... Blue Beat .... BB29.................... 1961 ... £5 ....£10 ....

WIGWAM
Being .... LP ...... Love .... LRLP92 .... 1974 ... £8 ....£20 .... Swedish
Dark Album .... LP ...... Love .... LRLP227 .... 1978 ... £8 ....£20 .... Swedish
Fairyport .... LP ...... Love .... LRLP44/55 .... 1971 ... £15 ....£30 ...... Swedish double
Hard And Horny .... LP ...... Love .... LRLP9 .... 1969 ... £8 ....£20 .... Swedish
Live From The Twilight Zone .... LP ...... Love .... LXPS517/8 .... 1975 ... £10 ....£25 ...... Swedish double
Lucky Golden Stripes And Starpose .... LP ...... Virgin .... V2051 .... 1976 ... £4 ....£10 ....
Rumours On The Rebound .... LP ...... Virgin .... VD3503.............. 1979 ... £6 ....£15 .... double
Tombstone Valentine .... LP ...... Love .... LRLP19 .... 1970 ... £8 ....£20 .... Swedish
Wicked Ivory .... LP ...... Love .... LRLP52 .... 1972 ... £8 ....£20 .... Swedish
Wigwam .... LP ...... Love .... LRLP511 .... 1972 ... £8 ....£20 .... Swedish

WILBURN BROTHERS
Livin' In God's Country .... LP ...... Decca .... DL(7)8959.............. 1959 ... £4 ....£10 .... US
Side By Side .... LP ...... Brunswick....... LAT8291.............. 1958 ... £4 ....£10 ....
Silver Haired Daddy Of Mine .... 7" ...... Brunswick....... 05799.................. 1959 ... £2 ....£5 ....
Wilburn Brothers .... LP ...... Decca .... DL8576.............. 1957 ... £5 ....£12 .... US
Wonderful Wilburn Brothers .... LP ...... King .... 746.................... 1961 ... £8 ....£20 .... US

WILD & WANDERING
2000 Light Ales From Home .... 12" ..... Iguana............ VYK14 .... 1986 ... £15 ....£30 ....

WILD ANGELS
Buzz Buzz .... 7" ...... B&C................ CB114 .... 1970 ... £2 ....£5 ....
Nervous Breakdown .... 7" ...... Major Minor ... MM569 .... 1968 ... £4 ....£8 ....
Sally Ann .... 7" ...... B&C................ CB123 .... 1970 ... £1.50 ....£4 ....

WILD FLOWERS
Melt Like Ice .... 7" ...... No Future ...... FS11 .... 1984 ... £2 ....£5 ....
Things Have Changed .... 7" ...... Reflex............ RE2 .... 1984 ... £1.50 ....£4 ....

WILD GEESE
Flight Two .... LP ...... Joke .... JLP207 .... 1979 ... £6 ....£15 .... German

WILD MAGNOLIAS
They Call Us Wild .... LP ...... Barclay............ XBLY90033 .... 1975 ... £8 ....£20 .... French
They Call Us Wild .... 7" ...... Barclay............ BAR34 .... 1975 ... £2 ....£5 ....
Wild Magnolias .... LP ...... Barclay............ 80529.............. 1975 ... £8 ....£20 .... French

WILD OATS
Wild Oats .... 7" EP.. Oak................ RGJ117 .... 1963 ... £250 ....£400 ....

WILD OATS (2)
Wild Oats .... LP ...... Westwood ...... WRS032 .... 1973 ... £5 ....£12 ....

WILD ONES
Bowie Man .... 7" ...... Fontana .... TF468 .... 1964 ... £12.50 ....£25 ....

WILD SILK
Help Me .... 7" ...... Columbia......... DB8611 .... 1969 ... £4 ....£8 ....
Plaster Sky .... 7" ...... Columbia........ DB8534 .... 1969 ... £4 ....£8 ....
Poor Man .... 7" ...... Polydor .... 56256 .... 1968 ... £1.50 ....£4 ....

WILD SWANS
Revolutionary Spirit .... 7" ...... Zoo................ CAGE009............ 1982 ... £7.50 ....£15 .... test pressing
Revolutionary Spirit .... 12" ..... Zoo................ CAGE009............ 1981 ... £6 ....£15 ....PS with
                                                                                                                                  'Lament For Icarus'
Revolutionary Spirit .... 12" ..... Zoo................ CAGE009............ 1982 ... £2.50 ....£6 ....

WILD THING
Old Lady .... 7" ...... Elektra............ EKSN45076 .... 1969 ... £1.50 ....£4 ....
Partyin' .... LP ...... Polydor .... 2410003 .... 1971 ... £6 ....£15 ....

WILD THYME
Plays Fallibroome .... LP ...... Saydisc .... SDL339.................. 1983 ... £5 ....£12 ....

WILD TURKEY

Battle Hymn	LP	Chrysalis	CHR1002	1971	£4	£10	
Turkey	LP	Chrysalis	CHR1010	1972	£4	£10	

WILD UNCERTAINTY

Man With Money	7"	Planet	PLF120	1966	£10	£20	

WILDCATS

Bandstand Record Hop	LP	United Artists	UAL3031	1958	£8	£20	US
Gazachstahagen	7"	London	HLT8787	1959	£4	£8	

WILDE, KIM

Dancing In The Dark	12"	Rak	12RAK365	1983	£3	£8	with poster
Hey Mr.Heartache	CD-s	MCA	DKIM7	1988	£2.50	£6	
Love In The Natural Way	CD-s	MCA	DKIM11	1989	£2.50	£6	pic disc
Rage To Love	7"	MCA	KIMP3	1985	£4	£8	shaped pic disc
Second Time	7"	MCA	KIMP1	1984	£5	£10	pic disc
Touch	7"	MCA	KIMP2	1984	£4	£8	shaped pic disc
You Came	CD-s	MCA	DKIM8	1988	£2.50	£6	

WILDE, MARTY

Abergavenny	7"	Philips	BF1669	1968	£1.50	£4	
All Night Girl	7"	Magnet	MAG11	1974	£1.50	£4	
All The Love I Have	7"	Philips	BF1753	1969	£1.50	£4	
Bad Boy	LP	Epic	LN3686	1960	£15	£30	US
Bad Boy	7"	Philips	PB972	1959	£2	£5	chart single
Busker	7"	Philips	6006126	1971	£1.50	£4	
By The Time I Get To Phoenix	7"	Philips	BF1632	1968	£1.50	£4	
Bye Bye Birdie	LP	Philips	SBL3383	196-	£6	£15	
Bye Bye Birdie	7" EP	Philips	BBE12472	1961	£4	£8	
Bye Bye Birdie No.2	7" EP	Philips	BBE12473	1961	£4	£8	
Bye Bye Birdie No.3	7" EP	Philips	BBE12474	1961	£4	£8	
Bye Bye Birdie No.4	7" EP	Philips	BBE12475	1961	£4	£8	
Come Running	7"	Philips	BF1206	1961	£2	£5	
Come Running	7" EP	Philips	BBE12517	1962	£6	£12	
Diversions	LP	Philips	SBL7877	1968	£5	£12	
Donna	7"	Philips	PB902	1959	£2.50	£6	chart single
Endless Sleep	7"	Philips	BF1783	1969	£1.50	£4	chart single
Endless Sleep	7"	Philips	PB835	1958	£2.50	£6	
Ever Since You Said Goodbye	7"	Philips	326546BF	1962	£2	£5	chart single
Fight	7"	Philips	BF1022	1960	£2	£5	chart single
Hide And Seek	7"	Philips	PB1161	1961	£2	£5	
Honeycomb	7"	Philips	JK1028	1958	£15	£30	
I Love You	7"	Magnet	MAG15	1974	£1.50	£4	
I Wanna Be Loved By You	7"	Philips	BF1037	1960	£2	£4	
I've Got So Used To Loving You	7"	Philips	BF1490	1966	£1.50	£4	
Jezebel	7"	Philips	PB1240	1962	£2	£5	chart single
Johnny Rocco	7"	Philips	PB1002	1960	£2	£5	chart single
Kiss Me	7"	Columbia	DB7285	1964	£2	£5	
Little Girl	7"	Philips	BF1078	1960	£2	£5	chart single
Lonely Avenue	7"	Columbia	DB4980	1963	£2	£5	
Love Bug Crawl	78	Philips	PB781	1958	£2	£5	
Marty	7" EP	Philips	433638BE	1963	£6	£12	
Marty Wilde Favourites	7" EP	Philips	BBE12422	1960	£7.50	£15	
Mexican Boy	7"	Decca	F11979	1964	£2	£5	
More Of Marty	7" EP	Philips	BBE12200	1958	£7.50	£15	
My Lucky Love	7"	Philips	PB850	1958	£2.50	£6	
No! Dance With Me	7"	Philips	326579BF	1963	£2	£5	
No One Knows	7"	Philips	PB875	1958	£2.50	£6	
No Trams To Lime Street	7"	Philips	BF1839	1970	£1.50	£4	
Oh Oh I'm Falling In Love Again	7"	Philips	PB804	1958	£10	£20	
Presenting Marty Wilde	7" EP	Philips	BBE12164	1957	£15	£30	
Rock And Roll Crazy	7"	Magnet	MAG2	1973	£1.50	£4	
Rubber Ball	7"	Philips	PB1101	1961	£2	£5	chart single
Save Your Love For Me	7"	Columbia	DB7145	1963	£2	£5	chart single
Sea Of Love	7"	Philips	PB959	1959	£2	£5	chart single
Sea Of Love	7" EP	Philips	BBE12327	1959	£7.50	£15	
Shelley	7"	Philips	BF1815	1969	£1.50	£4	
Showcase	LP	Philips	BBL7380	1960	£10	£25	
Teenager In Love	7"	Philips	PB926	1959	£2	£5	chart single
Tomorrow's Clown	7"	Philips	BF1191	1961	£2	£5	chart single
Versatile Mr.Wilde	LP	Philips	BBL7385	1960	£10	£25	
Versatile Mr.Wilde	LP	Philips	SBBL570	1960	£15	£30	stereo
Versatile Mr.Wilde	7" EP	Philips	BBE12385	1960	£7.50	£15	
When Does It Get To Be Love	7"	Philips	PB1121	1961	£2	£5	
Wilde About Marty	LP	Philips	BBL7342	1960	£15	£30	

WILDE THREE

I Cried	7"	Decca	F12232	1965	£12.50	£25	
Since You've Gone	7"	Decca	F12131	1965	£7.50	£15	

WILDER BROTHERS

I Want You	7"	HMV	POP365	1957	£30	£60	

WILDER, JOE

Jazz From Peter Gunn	LP	Philips	BBL7321	1959	£6	£15	
Joe Wilder	LP	London	LTZC15027	1957	£6	£15	

WILDWEEDS

It Was Fun While It Lasted	7"	Chess	CRS8065	1967	£2	£5	

WILEY, LEE

Title	Format	Label	Catalog	Year			Notes
Touch Of The Blues	LP	RCA	SF5003	1958	£5	£12	stereo

WILFRED & MILLIE

Title	Format	Label	Catalog	Year			Notes
Vow	7"	Island	WI190	1965	£5	£10	

WILHELM, MIKE

Title	Format	Label	Catalog	Year		
Mike Wilhelm	LP	United Artists	ZZ1	1976	£6	£15

WILKERSON, DON

Title	Format	Label	Catalog	Year		
Elder Don	LP	Blue Note	BLP/BST84121	1963	£20	£40
Preach, Brother!	LP	Blue Note	BLP/BST84107	1962	£20	£40
Shoutin'	LP	Blue Note	BLP/BST84145	1963	£20	£40

WILKINS, ERNIE

Title	Format	Label	Catalog	Year		
Top Brass	LP	London	LTZC15013	1956	£6	£15
Trumpets All Out	LP	London	LTZC15093	1957	£6	£15

WILKINS, ROBERT

Title	Format	Label	Catalog	Year		
Rev.Robert Wilkins	LP	Piedmont	PLP13162	196-	£8	£20

WILKINS, ROGER

Title	Format	Label	Catalog	Year		
Before The Reverence	LP	Spokane	SPL1002	1970	£15	£30

WILKINSON, ARTHUR

Title	Format	Label	Catalog	Year		
Beatle Cracker Suite	7" EP	HMV	7EG8919	1965	£2	£5

WILLETT FAMILY

Title	Format	Label	Catalog	Year		
Roving Journeyman	LP	Topic	12T84	1962	£8	£20

WILLETT, SLIM

Title	Format	Label	Catalog	Year			Notes
Slim Willett	LP	Audio Lab	AL1542	1961	£10	£25	US

WILLETTE, BABY FACE

Title	Format	Label	Catalog	Year		
Face To Face	LP	Blue Note	BLP/BST84068	1961	£30	£60
Stop And Listen	LP	Blue Note	BLP/BST84084	1961	£25	£50

WILLIAMS, AL

Title	Format	Label	Catalog	Year		
I Am Nothing	7"	Grapevine	GRP136	1979	£1.50	£4

WILLIAMS, ANDY

Title	Format	Label	Catalog	Year			Notes
Andy Williams' Best	LP	London	HAA8005	1962	£4	£10	
Are You Sincere	7"	London	HLA8587	1958	£2.50	£6	
Baby Doll	7"	London	HLA8360	1956	£6	£12	gold label
Best	7" EP	London	REA1394	1963	£4	£8	
Big Hits	7" EP	London	REA1088	1957	£5	£10	
Big Hits No.2	7" EP	London	REA1102	1957	£5	£10	
Butterfly	7"	London	HLA8399	1957	£5	£10	chart single
Canadian Sunset	7"	London	HL7013	1956	£1.50	£4	export
Canadian Sunset	7"	London	HLA8315	1956	£6	£12	gold label
Can't Get Used To Losing You	7"	CBS	AAG138	1963	£1.50	£4	chart single
House Of Bamboo	7"	London	HLA8784	1959	£2.50	£6	
I Like Your Kind Of Love	7"	London	HLA8437	1957	£5	£10	chart single
Lips Of Wine	7"	London	HLA8487	1957	£4	£8	
Lonely Street	LP	London	HAA2238	1960	£5	£12	
Lonely Street	7"	London	HLA8957	1959	£2	£5	
Promise Me, Love	7"	London	HLA8710	1958	£4	£8	
Sings Rodgers And Hammerstein	LP	London	HAA2113	1958	£5	£12	
Sings Steve Allen	LP	London	HAA2054	1957	£6	£15	
Two Time Winners	LP	London	HAA2203	1959	£5	£12	
Village Of St.Bernadette	7"	London	HLA9018	1959	£1.50	£4	
Wake Me When It's Over	7"	London	HLA9099	1960	£1.50	£4	
Walk Hand In Hand	7"	London	HLA8284	1956	£6	£12	gold label

WILLIAMS, AUDREY

Title	Format	Label	Catalog	Year		
Living It Up	7"	MGM	SP1179	1956	£4	£8

WILLIAMS, BIG JOE

Title	Format	Label	Catalog	Year			Notes
Back To The Country	LP	Bounty	BY6018	1966	£6	£15	
Big Joe Williams	LP	Storyville	616011	1970	£5	£12	
Big Joe Williams	LP	World Pacific	21897	1969	£4	£10	US
Big Joe Williams	LP	XTRA	XTRA1033	1966	£6	£15	
Big Joe Williams	7" EP	XX	MIN700	196-	£4	£8	
Blues For Nine Strings	LP	Bluesville	BV1056	1963	£6	£15	US
Blues On Highway 49	LP	Delmark	D604	1962	£6	£15	US
Blues On Highway 51	LP	Esquire	32191	1963	£10	£25	
Classic Delta Blues	LP	CBS	BPG63813	1964	£6	£15	
Crawlin' King Snake	LP	RCA	INTS1087	1970	£5	£12	
Hand Me Down My Old Walking Stick	LP	Liberty	LBL/LBS83207	1968	£6	£15	
Hell Bound And Heaven Sent	LP	Folkways	31004	1967	£6	£15	US
Live At Folk City	LP	XTRA	XTRA5059	1968	£4	£10	
Mississippi's Big Joe Williams	LP	Folkways	F(S)3820	1962	£6	£15	US
On The Highway	7" EP	Delmark	DJB4	1966	£6	£15	
Piney Woods Blues	LP	77	LA1219	1963	£6	£15	
Portraits In Blues Vol.4	LP	Storyville	SLP158	1964	£5	£12	
Portraits In Blues Vol.7	LP	Storyville	SLP163	1964	£5	£12	
Starvin' Chain Blues	LP	Delmark	(S)D609	1966	£5	£12	US
Studio Blues	LP	Bluesville	BV1083	1964	£6	£15	US
Tough Times	LP	Fontana	688800ZL	1965	£5	£12	

WILLIAMS, BILLY

Begin The Beguine	7"	Coral	Q72414	1960	£1.50	£4	
Billy Williams	LP	Coral	LVA9092	1958	£6	£15	
Billy Williams Quartet	LP	MGM	E3400	1957	£8	£20	US
Billy Williams Revue	LP	Coral	LVA9139	1961	£6	£15	
Billy Williams Singing Oh Yeah	LP	Mercury	MG20317	1958	£8	£20	US
Butterfly	7"	Vogue Coral	Q72241	1957	£4	£8	
Crazy Little Palace	7"	Vogue Coral	Q72149	1956	£5	£10	
Don't Let Go	7"	Coral	Q72303	1958	£2.50	£6	
Follow Me	7"	Vogue Coral	Q72222	1957	£4	£8	
Goodnight Irene	7"	Coral	Q72369	1959	£1.50	£4	
Got A Date With An Angel	7"	Vogue Coral	Q72295	1957	£2.50	£6	
Half Sweet, Half Beat	LP	Coral	LVA9120	1960	£6	£15	
I Cried For You	7"	Coral	Q72402	1960	£1.50	£4	
I'll Get By	7"	Coral	Q72331	1958	£1.50	£4	
I'm Gonna Sit Right Down	7"	Vogue Coral	Q72266	1957	£6	£12	chart single
Love Me	7"	Vogue Coral	Q2039	1954	£5	£10	
Nola	7"	Coral	Q72359	1959	£1.50	£4	
Pray	7"	Vogue Coral	Q72180	1956	£2.50	£6	
Steppin' Out Tonight	7"	Coral	Q72316	1958	£12.50	£25	
Telephone Conversation	7"	Coral	Q72377	1959	£2.50	£6	
Vote For Billy Williams	LP	Wing	MGW12131	1959	£8	£20	US

WILLIAMS, BOBBY

Baby I Need Your Love	7"	Action	ACT4509	1968	£5	£10	
Let's Jam	7"	Contempo	C17	1973	£2.50	£6	

WILLIAMS, CHRIS & HIS MONSTERS

Monster	7"	Columbia	DB4383	1959	£5	£10	

WILLIAMS, CLARENCE

Back Room Special	10" LP	Columbia	33S1067	1955	£10	£25	
Clarence Williams And His Orchestra	10" LP	London	AL3526	1954	£10	£25	
Clarence Williams And His Orchestra Vol.2	10" LP	London	AL3561	1957	£10	£25	
Clarence Williams Vol.1	LP	Philips	BBL7521	1962	£6	£15	
Clarence Williams' Washboard Band	7" EP	Parlophone	GEP8733	1959	£2.50	£6	
High Society	7"	Columbia	SCM5134	1954	£5	£10	
Jazz Originators	7" EP	Collector	JEL18	1964	£2.50	£6	
Sidney Bechet Memorial	LP	Fontana	TFL5087	1960	£6	£15	
Treasures Of North American Music Vol.3	7" EP	Fontana	TFE17053	1958	£2.50	£6	

WILLIAMS, DAN

Donkey City	7"	London	CAY110	1955	£2.50	£6	

WILLIAMS, DANNY

Danny Williams	LP	HMV	CLP1458/CSD1369	1961	£5	£12	
Days Of Wine And Roses	7" EP	HMV	7EG8800	1963	£2	£5	
Everybody Needs Somebody	7"	Deram	DM199	1968	£1.50	£4	
Forget Her, Forget Her	7"	HMV	POP1372	1964	£1.50	£4	
Go Away	7"	HMV	POP1410	1965	£1.50	£4	
Hits	7" EP	HMV	7EG8748	1962	£2	£5	
Moon River	LP	HMV	CLP1521	1961	£4	£10	
Moon River	7"	HMV	POP932	1961	£1.50	£4	chart single
Never My Love	7"	Deram	DM149	1967	£1.50	£4	
Rain	7"	HMV	POP1560	1966	£1.50	£4	
So High - So Low	7"	HMV	POP655	1959	£1.50	£4	
Swings With Tony Osborne	7" EP	HMV	7EG8763	1962	£2	£5	
Tall Tree	7"	HMV	POP624	1959	£1.50	£4	
White On White	7"	HMV	POP1263	1963	£1.50	£4	
Wonderful World Of The Young	7"	HMV	POP1002	1962	£1.50	£4	chart single
Youthful Years	7"	HMV	POP703	1959	£1.50	£4	

WILLIAMS, EDDIE & LITTLE SONNY WILLIS

Going To California	7" EP	XX	MIN707	196-	£4	£8	

WILLIAMS, GRANVILLE ORCHESTRA

Hi-Life	LP	Island	ILP971	1968	£30	£60	
Hi-Life	7"	Island	WI3062	1967	£5	£10	

WILLIAMS, HANK

Authentic Sound Of The Country Hits	7" EP	MGM	MGMEP770	1963	£5	£10	
Beyond The Sunset	LP	MGM	E4138	1961	£5	£12	US
Blue Love	7"	MGM	MGM931	1956	£6	£12	
Cold Cold Heart	78	MGM	MGM459	1951	£3	£8	
Crazy Heart	7"	MGM	SP1085	1954	£6	£12	
Dear John	78	MGM	MGM405	1951	£3	£8	
First, Last And Always	LP	MGM	E3928	1961	£6	£15	US
Greatest Hits	LP	MGM	E3918	1961	£5	£12	US
Half As Much	78	MGM	MGM527	1952	£3	£8	
Hank Williams	7" EP	MGM	MGMEP551	1956	£7.50	£15	
Hank Williams & His Drifting Cowboys	7" EP	MGM	MGMEP512	1954	£6	£12	
Hank Williams Favorites	7" EP	MGM	MGMEP757	1961	£5	£10	
Hank Williams Sings	10" LP	MGM	D105	1952	£15	£30	
Hank Williams Story	LP	MGM	E4267	1966	£8	£20	US
Hank's Laments	7" EP	MGM	MGMEP675	1958	£5	£10	
Hey Good Lookin'	78	MGM	MGM454	1951	£3	£8	
Honky Tonk Blues	78	MGM	MGM505	1952	£3	£8	
Honky Tonk Blues	7" EP	MGM	MGMEP614	1957	£6	£12	

Honky Tonkin'	LP	MGM	E3412	1957	£15	£30	US
Honky Tonkin'	7" EP.	MGM	MGMEP582	1957	£6	£12	
Honky Tonkin'	10" LP	MGM	E242	1954	£17.50	£35	US
I Ain't Got Nothing But Time	7"	MGM	SP1102	1954	£6	£12	
I Can't Help It	78	MGM	MGM471	1952	£3	£8	
I Saw The Light	LP	MGM	E3331	1956	£15	£30	US
I Saw The Light	78	MGM	MGM630	1953	£3	£8	
I Saw The Light	10" LP	MGM	E243	1954	£17.50	£35	US
I Saw The Light No.1	7" EP.	MGM	MGMEP569	1956	£6	£12	
I Saw The Light No.2	7" EP.	MGM	MGMEP608	1957	£6	£12	
I Wish I Had A Nickel	7"	MGM	MGM921	1956	£6	£12	
I Won't Be Home No More	LP	MGM	C(S)8057	1968	£4	£10	
I'll Never Get Out Of This World Alive	7"	MGM	SP1016	1953	£7.50	£15	
I'm Blue Inside	LP	MGM	C8021	1966	£5	£12	
I'm Blue Inside	LP	MGM	E3926	1961	£5	£12	US
I'm Gonna Sing	78	MGM	MGM799	1955	£3	£8	
I'm So Lonesome I Could Cry	7"	MGM	MGM1309	1966	£4	£8	
Immortal Hank Williams	LP	MGM	E3605	1958	£8	£20	US
Immortal Hank Williams	10" LP	MGM	D154	1958	£10	£25	
In Memory Of Hank Williams	LP	MGM	C8020	1966	£5	£12	
Jambalaya	78	MGM	MGM566	1952	£3	£8	
Jambalaya	7"	MGM	2006106	1972	£1.50	£4	
Kaw Liga	7"	MGM	SP1034	1953	£7.50	£15	
Kaw-Liga	7"	MGM	MGM1322	1966	£2.50	£6	
Leave Me Alone With The Blues	7"	MGM	MGM966	1957	£5	£10	
Legend Lives Anew	LP	MGM	C(S)8031	1967	£4	£10	
Let Me Sing A Blue Song	LP	MGM	E3924	1961	£5	£12	US
Lives Again	LP	MGM	E3923	1961	£5	£12	US
Lonesome Sound Of Hank Williams	LP	MGM	C811	1960	£8	£20	
Love Songs,Comedy & Hymns	LP	MGM	C8040	1967	£5	£12	
Lovesick Blues	78	MGM	MGM269	1950	£3	£8	
Low Down Blues	7"	MGM	MGM942	1957	£6	£12	
Luke The Drifter	LP	MGM	C8022	1966	£5	£12	
Luke The Drifter	LP	MGM	E3267	1955	£17.50	£35	US
Luke The Drifter	10" LP	MGM	D119	1953	£15	£30	
Many Moods Of Hank Williams	LP	MGM	C8023	1966	£5	£12	
May You Never Be Alone	LP	MGM	C8019	1966	£5	£12	
Memorial Album	LP	MGM	E3272	1955	£15	£30	US
Memorial Album	10" LP	MGM	D137	1955	£10	£25	
Mind Your Own Business	78	MGM	MGM553	1952	£3	£8	
Moanin' The Blues	LP	MGM	E3330	1956	£15	£30	US
Moanin' The Blues	78	MGM	MGM381	1951	£3	£8	
Moanin' The Blues	10" LP	MGM	D144	1956	£15	£30	
More Greatest Hits	LP	MGM	E4040	1961	£5	£12	US
More Greatest Hits Vol.3	LP	MGM	E4140	1962	£5	£12	US
More Hank Williams & Strings	LP	MGM	C(S)8038	1967	£4	£10	
My Bucket's Got A Hole In It	7"	MGM	SP1048	1953	£7.50	£15	
On Stage Recorded Live	LP	MGM	C893	1962	£8	£20	
Ramblin' Man	LP	MGM	E3219	1955	£15	£30	US
Ramblin' Man	7"	MGM	SP1049	1954	£7.50	£15	
Ramblin' Man	10" LP	MGM	E291	1954	£17.50	£35	US
Rootie Tootie	7"	MGM	MGM957	1957	£6	£12	
Sing Me A Blue Song	LP	MGM	E3560	1958	£8	£20	US
Sing Me A Blue Song	10" LP	MGM	D150	1958	£10	£25	
Someday You'll Call My Name	7"	MGM	SP1163	1956	£6	£12	
Songs For A Broken Heart	7" EP.	MGM	MGMEP639	1958	£6	£12	
Songs For A Broken Heart No.2	7" EP.	MGM	MGMEP649	1958	£6	£12	
Spirit Of Hank Williams	LP	MGM	C956	1963	£6	£15	
Thirty-Six Greatest Hits	LP	MGM	3E2	1957	£25	£50	US, triple
Thirty-Six More Greatest Hits	LP	MGM	3E4	1958	£25	£50	US, triple
Unforgettable Hank Williams	LP	MGM	C784	1959	£8	£20	
Unforgettable Hank Williams	7" EP.	MGM	MGMEP710	1960	£5	£10	
Unforgettable Hank Williams No.2	7" EP.	MGM	MGMEP726	1960	£5	£10	
Unforgettable Hank Williams No.3	7" EP.	MGM	MGMEP732	1960	£5	£10	
Wait For The Light To Shine	LP	MGM	C834	1960	£6	£15	
Wanderin' Around	LP	MGM	E3925	1961	£5	£12	US
Weary Blues	7"	MGM	SP1067	1954	£7.50	£15	
Why Don't You Love Me	78	MGM	MGM483	1952	£3	£8	
Window Shopping	78	MGM	MGM678	1953	£3	£8	
Your Cheatin' Heart	78	MGM	MGM896	1956	£3	£8	

WILLIAMS, HANK & HANK WILLIAMS JR.

Singing Together	LP	MGM	C1008	1965	£5	£12

WILLIAMS, HANK JR.

Long Gone Lonesome Blues	7"	MGM	MGM1223	1963	£1.50	£4
Your Cheatin' Heart	LP	MGM	C996	1964	£4	£10

WILLIAMS, JEANETTE

Hound Dog	7"	Action	ACT4557	1969	£5	£10
Stuff	7"	Action	ACT4534	1969	£5	£10

WILLIAMS, JIMMY

Walking On Air	7"	Atlantic	AT4042	1965	£4	£8

WILLIAMS, JOE

Ballad And Blues	7" EP.	Columbia	SEG7984	1960	£2	£5
Everyday I Have The Blues	7" EP.	Columbia	SEG8001	1960	£4	£8
Greatest	LP	HMV	CLP1109	1957	£6	£15
Groovy Joe Williams	7" EP.	Columbia	SEB10110	1959	£2	£5

Joe Sings The Blues	7" EP.	Columbia	SEG8016	1960	£4	£8	
Joe Williams & Count Basie's Orchestra	7" EP.	Columbia	SEG7810	1958	£2	£5	
Man Ain't Supposed To Cry	LP	Columbia	33SX1087	1958	£6	£15	
Sings	10" LP	London	HBC1065	1956	£5	£12	
Sings About You	LP	Columbia	33SX1229/ SCX3308	1960	£6	£15	

WILLIAMS, JOHN

Can't Find Time For Anything Now	7"	Columbia	DB8251	1967	£1.50	£4	
John Williams	LP	Columbia	SX6169	1967	£20	£40	
She's That Kind Of Woman	7"	Columbia	DB8128	1967	£1.50	£4	

WILLIAMS, KENNETH

Ballad Of The Woggler's Moulie	7"	Parlophone	R5638	1967	£1.50	£4	credited to Rambling Syd Rumpo
Extracts From Pieces Of Eight	7" EP.	Decca	DFE8548	1963	£2.50	£6	
In Season	7" EP.	Decca	DFE8671	1966	£2.50	£6	
On Pleasure Bent	LP	Decca	LK4856	1967	£4	£10	
Rambling Syd Rumpo In Concert No.1	7" EP.	Parlophone	GEP8965	1967	£2.50	£6	
Rambling Syd Rumpo In Concert No.2	7" EP.	Parlophone	GEP8966	1967	£2.50	£6	

WILLIAMS, LARRY

Baby Baby	7"	London	HLM9053	1960	£7.50	£15	
Bony Moronie	7"	London	HLU8532	1958	£10	£20	chart single
Dizzy Miss Lizzy	7"	London	HLU8604	1958	£12.50	£25	
Greatest Hits	LP	OKeh	OKM2123/ OKS12123	1967	£5	£12	US
Here's Larry Williams	LP	Speciality	SP2109	1959	£30	£60	US
I Can't Stop Loving You	7"	London	HLU8911	1960	£7.50	£15	
Larry Williams	7" EP.	London	REU1213	1959	£20	£40	
Larry Williams Show	LP	Decca	LK4691	1965	£10	£25	with Johnny Guitar Watson
On Stage	LP	Sue	ILP922	1965	£20	£40	
Shake Your Body Girl	7"	MGM	MGM1447	1968	£2.50	£6	
She Said Yeah	7"	London	HLU8844	1959	£7.50	£15	
Short Fat Fannie	7"	London	HLN8472	1957	£12.50	£25	chart single
Strange	7"	Sue	WI371	1965	£6	£12	
Turn On Your Lovelight	7"	Sue	WI381	1965	£6	£12	

WILLIAMS, LARRY & JOHNNY GUITAR WATSON

Mercy Mercy Mercy	7"	Columbia	DB8140	1967	£12.50	£25	
Sweet Little Baby	7"	Decca	F12151	1965	£6	£12	
Too Late	7"	Epic	EPC4421	1976	£2.50	£6	
Two For The Price Of One	LP	OKeh	OKM4122/ OKS14122	1967	£6	£15	US

WILLIAMS, LITTLE JERRY

Baby You're My Everything	7"	Cameo Parkway	C100	1962	£7.50	£15	

WILLIAMS, LLOYD

Funky Beat	7"	Treasure Isle	TI7029	1968	£5	£10	
Sad World	7"	Doctor Bird	DB1051	1966	£5	£10	Tommy McCook B side
Wonderful World	7"	Doctor Bird	DB1135	1968	£5	£10	Tommy McCook B side

WILLIAMS, LORETTA

Baby Cakes	7"	Atlantic	584032	1966	£7.50	£15	

WILLIAMS, MARY LOU

At The Piano	7" EP.	Parlophone	GEP8567	1956	£2	£5	
Chug A Lug Jug	7"	Sue	WI311	1964	£6	£12	
Don Carlos Meets Mary Lou Williams	7" EP.	Vogue	EPV1042	1955	£2.50	£6	
In Paris	10" LP	Felsted	EDL87012	1955	£15	£30	
Mary Lou Williams	7" EP.	Columbia	SEG7608	1956	£2	£5	
Mary Lou Williams Quartet	7" EP.	Esquire	EP66	195-	£2.50	£6	
Piano Panorama	10" LP	Esquire	20026	1954	£20	£40	
Plays In London	10" LP	Vogue	LDE022	1953	£20	£40	

WILLIAMS, MASON

Classical Gas	7"	Warner Bros	WB7190	1968	£1.50	£4	chart single

WILLIAMS, MAURICE & THE ZODIACS

At The Beach	LP	Snyder	5586	196-	£10	£25	US
Come Along	7"	Top Rank	JAR563	1961	£5	£10	
I Remember	7"	Top Rank	JAR550	1961	£2.50	£6	
Stay	LP	Herald	HLP1014	1961	£30	£60	US
Stay	LP	Sphere Sound	SSR7007	1964	£8	£20	US
Stay	7"	Top Rank	JAR526	1960	£2.50	£6	chart single
Stay	7" EP.	Top Rank	JKP3006	1961	£15	£30	

WILLIAMS, MEL & JOHNNY OTIS

All Through The Night	LP	Dig	103	1955	£25	£50	US

WILLIAMS, MIKE

Lonely Soldier	7"	Atlantic	584027	1966	£5	£10	

WILLIAMS, OTIS & THE CHARMS

Hearts Of Stone	7"	Parlophone	MSP6155	1955	£60	£120	
I'm Waiting Just For You	7"	Parlophone	R4293	1957	£40	£80	
It's All Over Now	7"	Parlophone	R4210	1956	£50	£100	
Ivory Tower	7"	Parlophone	CMSP36	1955	£40	£80	export
Ivory Tower	7"	Parlophone	MSP6239	1956	£50	£100	
Secret	7"	Parlophone	R4495	1958	£20	£40	
Their All Time Hits	LP	Deluxe	750	1957	£75	£150	US
Their All Time Hits	LP	King	560	1957	£30	£60	US
This Is Otis Williams And The Charms	LP	King	614	1959	£30	£60	US
Two Hearts	7"	Parlophone	R4860	1961	£15	£30	

WILLIAMS, PAUL

Gin House	7"	Columbia	DB7421	1964	£6	£12	
Many Faces Of Love	7"	Columbia	DB7768	1965	£6	£12	with Zoot Money
My Sly Sadie	7"	Decca	F12844	1968	£2.50	£6	

WILLIAMS, PAUL (2)

Delta Blues Singer	LP	Sonet	SNTF654	1973	£5	£12	
In Memory Of Robert Johnson	LP	Intercord	28754	1973	£5	£12	German

WILLIAMS, POOR JOE

Man Sings The Blues	7" EP	Collector	JEN3	1960	£5	£10	
Man Sings The Blues Vol.2	7" EP	Collector	JEN4	1960	£5	£10	

WILLIAMS, ROBERT PETE

Legacy Of The Blues	LP	Sonet	SNTF649	1973	£4	£10	
Robert Pete Williams	LP	Saydisc	AMS2002	1972	£5	£12	
Sugar Farm	LP	Blues Beacon	1932101ST	197-	£5	£12	
Those Prison Blues	LP	77	LA1217	1963	£6	£15	

WILLIAMS, ROGER

Almost Paradise	7"	London	HLR8422	1957	£2	£5	
Anastasia	7"	London	HLU8379	1957	£4	£8	
Arrivederci Roma	7"	London	HLR8572	1958	£1.50	£4	
Autumn Leaves	7"	London	HLU8214	1955	£5	£10	
Songs Of The Fabulous Fifties Vol.1	LP	London	HAR2057	1957	£5	£12	
Songs Of The Fabulous Fifties Vol.2	LP	London	HAR2058	1957	£5	£12	
Till	7"	London	HLR8516	1957	£1.50	£4	
Two Different Worlds	7"	London	HLU8341	1956	£6	£12	with Jane Morgan

WILLIAMS, SMITTY

Cure	7"	MGM	MGM1167	1962	£1.50	£4	

WILLIAMS, SONNY

Bye Bye Baby Goodbye	7"	London	HLD8931	1959	£5	£10	

WILLIAMS, TEX

All Time Greats	7" EP	Brunswick	OE9147	1955	£5	£10	
Be Sure You're Right	7"	Brunswick	05516	1956	£1.50	£4	
Country Music Time	LP	Decca	DL4295	1962	£5	£12	US
Dance-O-Rama	LP	Decca	DL5565	1955	£15	£30	US
Keeper Of Boot Hill	7"	Top Rank	JAR330	1960	£2.50	£6	
Money	7"	Brunswick	05393	1955	£4	£8	
River Of No Return	7"	Brunswick	05327	1954	£5	£10	
Smoke! Smoke! Smoke!	LP	Capitol	(S)T1463	1960	£5	£12	
Talking To The Blues	7"	Brunswick	05684	1957	£5	£10	
Tex Williams' Best	LP	Camden	CAL363	1958	£5	£12	US
This Ole House	7"	Brunswick	05341	1954	£5	£10	with Rex Allen

WILLIAMS, TONY

Girl Is A Girl Is A Girl	LP	Mercury	MMC14027	1960	£5	£12	
How Come	7"	Philips	BF1282	1962	£10	£20	
Life Time	LP	Blue Note	BLP/BST84180	1964	£8	£20	
Spring	LP	Blue Note	BLP/BST84216	1965	£8	£20	

WILLIAMSON, CLAUDE

Claude Williamson Trio	10" LP	Capitol	KPL103	1955	£8	£20	
Claude Williamson Trio	10" LP	Capitol	LC6804	1956	£8	£20	

WILLIAMSON, DUDLEY

Coming On The Scene	7"	Doctor Bird	DB1117	1967	£5	£10	

WILLIAMSON, ROBIN

Myrrh	LP	Island	HELP2	1972	£6	£15	

WILLIAMSON, SONNY BOY

It has long been a matter of some confusion that there were two Sonny Boy Williamsons. John Lee "Sonny Boy" Williamson was a successful blues harmonica player who recorded in the thirties and forties, but who was murdered in 1948 at the age of 34. Sonny Boy Williamson II was christened Alec Ford, but later adopted the surname of his stepfather and the nickname Rice. At the beginning of the forties, Rice Miller began calling himself Sonny Boy Williamson in a deliberate attempt to gain some success on the back of the man who was, at the time, the better known artist. Ironically, Miller, who was actually the older man by some seventeen years, went on to achieve considerably more success than his namesake - and not because of the name confusion, but because he was himself a fine and innovative harmonica player. During the early sixties, he spent some time in the UK, touring and recording with several of the up and coming British R&B groups.

Blues Of Sonny Boy Williamson	LP	Storyville	SLP170	1965	£6	£15	
Bring It On Home	7"	Chess	CRS8030	1966	£5	£10	
Bummer Road	LP	Chess	1536	1969	£5	£12	US
Down And Out Blues	LP	Marble Arch	MAL662	1967	£4	£10	
Down And Out Blues	LP	Pye	NPL28036	1964	£8	£20	chart LP
From The Bottom	7"	Blue Horizon	451008	1966	£17.50	£35	
Help Me	7"	Pye	7N25191	1963	£4	£8	

Title	Format	Label	Catalogue	Year			Notes
Help Me	7" EP	Chess	CRE6001	1965	£7.50	£15	
In Memoriam	LP	Chess	CRL4510	1965	£6	£15	
In Memoriam	7" EP	Chess	CRE6013	1966	£7.50	£15	
Last Sessions	LP	Rarity	RLP1	1974	£8	£20	
Lonesome Cabin	7"	Pye	7N25268	1964	£4	£8	
More Real Folk Blues	LP	Chess	1509	1966	£8	£20	US
No Nights By Myself	7"	Sue	WI365	1965	£6	£12	
Portraits In Blues	LP	Fontana	670158	1966	£6	£15	
Real Folk Blues	LP	Chess	1503	1966	£8	£20	US
Real Folk Blues Vol.2	7" EP	Chess	CRE6018	1966	£6	£12	
Sonny Boy Williamson	LP	Checker	1437	1959	£25	£50	US
Sonny Boy Williamson	7" EP	Pye	NEP44037	1964	£6	£12	

WILLIAMSON, SONNY BOY I

Title	Format	Label	Catalogue	Year			Notes
Bluebird Blues	LP	RCA	INTS1088	1970	£4	£10	
Sonny Boy And His Pals	LP	Saydisc	SDR169	1969	£5	£12	

WILLIAMSON, STU

Title	Format	Label	Catalogue	Year			Notes
Sapphire	10" LP	London	LZN14030	1956	£20	£40	
Stu Williamson	LP	London	LTZN15123	1958	£8	£20	

WILLIE & THE RED RUBBER BAND

Title	Format	Label	Catalogue	Year			Notes
We're Coming Up	LP	RCA	LSP4193	1969	£6	£15	US
Willie & The Red Rubber Band	LP	RCA	LSP4074	1968	£6	£15	US

WILLING, FOY & THE RIDERS OF THE PURPLE SAGE

Title	Format	Label	Catalogue	Year			Notes
Cowboy	LP	Roulette	R25035	1958	£6	£12	US
Cowboy No.1	7" EP	Columbia	SEG7834	1958	£2	£5	
Cowboy No.2	7" EP	Columbia	SEG7855	1958	£2	£5	

WILLINGHAM, DORIS

Title	Format	Label	Catalogue	Year			Notes
You Can't Do That	7"	Jay Boy	BOY1	1969	£2.50	£6	

WILLIS, CHUCK

Title	Format	Label	Catalogue	Year			Notes
Betty And Dupree	7"	London	HLE8595	1958	£12.50	£25	
C.C.Rider	7"	London	HLE8444	1957	£15	£30	
Chuck Willis Wails The Blues	LP	Epic	LN3425	1958	£50	£100	US
I Remember Chuck Willis	LP	Atlantic	(SD)8079	1963	£10	£25	US
I Remember Chuck Willis	LP	Atlantic	588145	1968	£5	£12	
King Of The Stroll	LP	Atlantic	8018	1958	£50	£100	US, black label
King Of The Stroll	LP	Atlantic	8018	1959	£20	£40	US, red label
My Life	7"	London	HLE8818	1959	£12.50	£25	
That Train Has Gone	7"	London	HLE8489	1957	£15	£30	
Tribute To Chuck Willis	LP	Epic	LN3728	1960	£30	£60	US
What Am I Living For	7"	London	HLE8635	1958	£12.50	£25	
Willis Wails The Blues	7" EP	Fontana	TFE17138	1959	£75	£150	

WILLIS, RALPH

Title	Format	Label	Catalogue	Year			Notes
Goodbye Blues	78	Esquire	10370	1954	£6	£12	
Old Home Blues	78	Esquire	10380	1954	£6	£12	
Ralph Willis	7" EP	Esquire	EP241	1961	£7.50	£15	
Ralph Willis	7" EP	XX	MIN703	196-	£5	£10	
Ralph Willis	7" EP	XX	MIN711	196-	£5	£10	

WILLIS, SLIM

Title	Format	Label	Catalogue	Year			Notes
Running Around	7"	R&B	MRB5004	1965	£5	£10	

WILLOWS

Title	Format	Label	Catalogue	Year			Notes
Church Bells May Ring	7"	London	HLL8290	1956	£330	£500	

WILLS, BOB

Title	Format	Label	Catalogue	Year			Notes
Best Of Bob Wills	LP	Harmony	HL7304	1963	£6	£15	US
Bob Wills And His Texas Playboys	LP	Decca	DL8727	1957	£20	£40	US
Bob Wills And Tommy Duncan	LP	Liberty	LRX/LSX1912	1961	£6	£15	US
Bob Wills Sings And Plays	LP	Liberty	LRP3303/LST7303	1963	£6	£15	US
Bob Wills Special	LP	Harmony	HL7036	1957	£8	£20	US
Dance-O-Rama	10" LP	Decca	DL5562	1955	£30	£60	US
Great Bob Wills	LP	Harmony	HL7345	1965	£6	£15	US
Heart To Heart Talk	7"	London	HL7102	1960	£5	£10	export, with Tommy Duncan
Keepsake Album £1	LP	Longhorn	LP001	1965	£15	£30	US
Living Legend	LP	Liberty	LRP3182/LST7182	1961	£6	£15	US
Mr.Words And Music	LP	Liberty	LRP3194/LST7194	1961	£6	£15	US
Old Time Favorites	10" LP	Antones	LP6000	195-	£30	£60	US
Old Time Favorites	10" LP	Antones	LP6010	195-	£30	£60	US
Ranch House Favorites	LP	MGM	E3352	1956	£30	£60	US
Ranch House Favorites	10" LP	MGM	E91	1951	£30	£60	US
Round Up	10" LP	Columbia	HL9003	195-	£30	£60	US
San Antonio Rose	LP	Starday	SLP375	1965	£6	£15	US
Together Again	LP	Liberty	LRP3173/LST7173	1960	£5	£12	US, with Tommy Duncan
Western Swing Band	LP	Vocalion	VL(7)3735	1965	£6	£15	US

WILLS, TOMMY & HARRY LEWIS

Title	Format	Label	Catalogue	Year			Notes
Rhythm And Blues	7" EP	Range	JRE7006	196-	£2	£5	

WILLS, VIOLA

Title	Format	Label	Catalogue	Year			Notes
Lost Without The Love Of My Guy	7"	President	PT108	1968	£1.50	£4	

WILMER & THE DUKES

Title	Format	Label	Catalogue	Year			Notes
Give Me One More Chance	7"	Action	ACT4500	1968	£2	£5	

Wilmer & The Dukes	LP	Aphrodisiac	6001	1969	£5	£12		US

WILSON, ADA
In The Quiet Of My Room	7"	Ellie Jay	EJSP9288	1979	£2.50	£6	

WILSON, AL
Do What You Gotta Do	7"	Liberty	LBF15044	1968	£5	£10	
Lodi	7"	Liberty	LBF15257	1969	£1.50	£4	
Searching For The Dolphins	LP	Liberty	LBS83173	1969	£6	£15	
Searching For The Dolphins	LP	Soul City	SCS92006	1970	£6	£15	
Shake Me, Wake Me	7"	Liberty	LBF15236	1969	£2	£5	
Snake	7"	Liberty	LIB15121	1968	£6	£12	

WILSON, ANN & THE DAYBREAKS
This is the same Ann Wilson as the later co-leader of Heart.
Standin' Watchin' You	7"	Topaz	1311	1967	£25	£50	US
Through Eyes And Glass	7"	Topaz	1312	1967	£25	£50	US

WILSON, BRIAN
Caroline No	7"	Capitol	CL15438	1966	£5	£10	
Words And Music	LP	Warner Bros	WBWM154	1988	£6	£15	US promo

WILSON, BRIAN & MIKE LOVE
Gettin' Hungry	7"	Capitol	CL15513	1967	£7.50	£15

WILSON, CLIVE
Mango Tree	7"	R&B	JB144	1964	£5	£10

WILSON, DELROY
1-2-3	7"	Island	WI103	1963	£5	£10	
Better Must Come	LP	Trojan	TRLS44	1972	£6	£15	
Captivity	LP	Big Shot	BILP102	197-	£6	£15	
Come Down From Your Palms And Pray	7"	R&B	JB132	1963	£5	£10	
Dancing Mood	7"	Island	WI3013	1966	£5	£10	Soul Brothers B side
Easy Snappin'	7"	Studio One	SO2074	1969	£6	£12	Webber Sisters B side
Feel Good All Over	7"	Studio One	SO2057	1968	£6	£12	
Get Ready	7"	Island	WI3050	1967	£5	£10	Roy Richards B side
Give Me A Chance	7"	Doctor Bird	DB1022	1966	£5	£10	
Good All Over	LP	Coxsone	CSL8016	1968	£50	£100	
Goodbye	7"	Black Swan	WI420	1964	£5	£10	
I Am Not A King	7"	Studio One	SO2031	1967	£6	£12	Heptones B side
I Shall Not Remove	LP	R&B	JBL1112	1964	£50	£100	
I Shall Not Remove	7"	Island	WI097	1963	£5	£10	
I'm The One Who Loves You	7"	High Note	HS015	1969	£2.50	£6	Afrotones B side
Lion Of Judah	7"	R&B	JB108	1963	£5	£10	
Lover Mouth	7"	R&B	JB148	1964	£5	£10	
Never Conquer	7"	Studio One	SO2019	1967	£6	£12	
Once Upon A Time	7"	Island	WI3127	1967	£5	£10	
Pick Up The Pieces	7"	Island	WI205	1965	£5	£10	
Prince Pharoah	7"	R&B	JB128	1963	£5	£10	
Put Yourself In My Place	7"	High Note	HS011	1968	£2.50	£6	
Rain From The Skies	7"	Studio One	SO2046	1968	£6	£12	
Riding For A Fall	7"	Island	WI3033	1967	£5	£10	
Sad Mood	7"	Camel	CA15	1969	£1.50	£4	Stranger Cole B side
Sammy Dead	7"	R&B	JB168	1964	£5	£10	Cynthia & Archie B side
Spit In The Sky	7"	Black Swan	WI405	1964	£5	£10	
Spit In The Sky	7"	Blue Beat	BB172	1963	£5	£10	
This Heart Of Mine	7"	Island	WI3099	1967	£5	£10	Glen Adams B side
True Believer	7"	Coxsone	CS7064	1968	£5	£10	Marshall Williams B side
Won't You Come Home Baby	7"	Studio One	SO2009	1967	£6	£12	Peter & Hortense B side
You Bend My Love	7"	Island	WI116	1963	£5	£10	
Your Number One	7"	High Note	HS022	1969	£2.50	£6	

WILSON, DENNIS
Sound Of Free	7"	Stateside	SS2184	1970	£15	£30

WILSON, DOYLE
Hey Hey	7"	Vogue	V9117	1958	£60	£120

WILSON, EDDIE
Get Out On The Street	7"	Action	ACT4555	1969	£1.50	£4
Shing A Ling A Stroll	7"	Action	ACT4536	1969	£4	£8

WILSON, EDITH
With Johnny Dunn's Jazzhounds	LP	Fountain	FB302	196-	£6	£15

WILSON, ERNEST
If I Were A Carpenter	7"	Studio One	SO2058	1968	£6	£12	Soul Vendors B side
Money Worries	7"	Studio One	SO2032	1967	£6	£12	Soul Vendors B side
Storybook Children	7"	Coxsone	CS7044	1968	£5	£10	Little Freddie B side
Undying Love	7"	Coxsone	CS7059	1968	£5	£10	Soul Vendors B side

WILSON, FRANK
Last Kiss	LP	Josie	JS4006	1964	£8	£20	US
Last Kiss	7"	Fontana	TF505	1964	£2	£5	

WILSON, FRANK (2)

Do I Love You	7"	Motown	TMG1170	1979	£12.50	£25	demo, PS

WILSON, JACK

Easterly Winds	LP	Blue Note	BST84270	1968	£15	£30	
Jack Wilson Quartet	LP	London	HAK/SHK8170	1964	£6	£15	
Something Personal	LP	Blue Note	BLP/BST84251	1967	£10	£25	
Song For My Daughter	LP	Blue Note	BST84328	1969	£5	£12	

WILSON, JACKIE

The dynamic singer with big hits in four decades (the tour de force vocal gymnastics of "Reet Petite" in the fifties; "Higher And Higher" in the sixties; "I Get The Sweetest Feeling" in the seventies; and a reissued "Reet Petite" in the eighties - when a memorable animated video helped propel the song to number one in the UK) is sadly perhaps best remembered for having died in 1984 after spending nearly nine years in a coma. Apart from some of his joyous performances, he should be remembered as the man who indirectly got the Tamla Motown company going. For Wilson's earliest hits were written by the young Berry Gordy, who was able to use the resulting windfall to start his own label.

All My Love	7"	Coral	Q72407	1960	£2.50	£6	chart single
Alone At Last	7"	Coral	Q72412	1960	£4	£8	chart single
At The Copa	LP	Coral	LVA9209	1962	£10	£25	mono
At The Copa	LP	Coral	SVL9209	1962	£15	£30	stereo
Baby Workout	LP	Brunswick	BL(7)54110	1963	£10	£25	US
Baby Workout	7"	Coral	Q72460	1963	£2.50	£6	
Beautiful Day	7"	Brunswick	BR3	1973	£1.50	£4	
Big Boss Line	7"	Coral	Q72474	1964	£2.50	£6	
Body And Soul	LP	Coral	LVA9202	1962	£10	£25	
By Special Request	LP	Coral	LVA9151	1962	£17.50	£35	mono
By Special Request	LP	Coral	SVL3018	1962	£22.50	£45	stereo
Do Your Thing	LP	MCA	MUPS405	1970	£6	£15	
Dogging Around	7"	Coral	Q72393	1960	£4	£8	
Dynamic Jackie Wilson	7" EP	Coral	FEP2043	1960	£12.50	£25	export
For Your Precious Love	7"	Decca	AD1008	1968	£5	£10	
For Your Precious Love	7"	MCA	MU1014	1968	£1.50	£4	with Count Basie
Greatest Hurt	7"	Coral	Q72450	1962	£2.50	£6	
Helpless	7"	MCA	MU1105	1969	£1.50	£4	
He's So Fine	LP	Coral	LVA9087	1958	£30	£60	
Higher And Higher	LP	MCA	MUP(S)304	1967	£4	£10	
Higher And Higher	7"	Coral	Q72493	1967	£5	£10	
Higher And Higher	7"	MCA	BAG2	1969	£1.50	£4	chart single
Higher And Higher	7"	MCA	MU1131	1970	£1.50	£4	
I Get The Sweetest Feeling	LP	MCA	MUPS361	1969	£4	£10	
I Get The Sweetest Feeling	7"	MCA	MU1160	1972	£1.50	£4	chart single
I Just Can't Help It	7"	Coral	Q72454	1962	£2.50	£6	
I'll Be Satisfied	7"	Coral	Q72372	1959	£4	£8	
I'm Comin' On Back To You	7"	Coral	Q72434	1961	£2.50	£6	
I'm Wandering	7"	Coral	Q72332	1958	£5	£10	
It Only Happens When I Look At You	7"	Brunswick	BR43	1977	£1.50	£4	
Jackie Sings The Blues	LP	Coral	LVA9130	1960	£25	£50	
Lonely Teardrops	LP	Coral	LVA9108	1959	£30	£60	
Lonely Teardrops	7"	Coral	Q72347	1958	£6	£12	
Lonely Teardrops	7"	Coral	Q72482	1965	£4	£8	
Lonely Teardrops	7" EP	Coral	FEP2016	1959	£15	£30	
Merry Christmas	LP	Brunswick	BL(7)54112	1963	£10	£25	US
My Golden Favorites Vol.2	LP	Brunswick	BL(7)54115	1964	£10	£25	US
My Golden Favourites	LP	Coral	LVA9135	1960	£17.50	£35	
My Heart Belongs To Only You	7"	Coral	Q72444	1961	£2.50	£6	
New Breed	7"	Coral	Q72467	1963	£2.50	£6	
No Pity In The Naked City	7"	Coral	Q72481	1965	£4	£8	
Please Tell Me Why	7"	Coral	Q72430	1961	£2.50	£6	
Reet Petite	7"	Coral	Q72290	1957	£4	£8	
Reet Petite	7"	Vogue Coral	Q72290	1957	£7.50	£15	chart single
Shake A Hand	LP	Brunswick	BL(7)54113	1963	£10	£25	US
Shake A Hand	7"	Coral	Q72464	1963	£2.50	£6	with Linda Hopkins
Shake Shake Shake	7"	Coral	Q72465	1963	£2.50	£6	
Since You Showed Me How To Be Happy	7"	Coral	Q72496	1967	£5	£10	
Since You Showed Me How To Be Happy	7"	MCA	BAG7	1969	£1.50	£4	
Since You Showed Me How To Be Happy	7"	MCA	MU1104	1969	£1.50	£4	
Sing	7"	Coral	Q72453	1962	£2.50	£6	
So Much	LP	Coral	LVA9121	1960	£25	£50	
Somethin' Else	LP	Brunswick	BL(7)54117	1964	£10	£25	US
Soul Galore	LP	Coral	LVA9232	1966	£10	£25	mono
Soul Galore	LP	Coral	SVL9232	1966	£15	£30	stereo
Soul Time	LP	Brunswick	BL(7)54118	1965	£10	£25	US
Spotlight On Jackie Wilson	LP	Coral	LVA9231	1965	£10	£25	
Squeeze Her, Tease Her	7"	Coral	Q72476	1964	£2.50	£6	
Talk That Talk	7"	Coral	Q72453	1959	£4	£8	
Tear Of The Year	7"	Coral	Q72421	1961	£7.50	£15	demo
Tear Of The Year	7"	Coral	Q72424	1961	£2.50	£6	
Tenderly	7"	Ember	JBS705	1962	£75	£150	Clyde McPhatter B side
That's Why	7"	Coral	Q72366	1959	£4	£8	
To Be Loved	7"	Coral	Q72306	1958	£5	£10	chart single
To Make A Big Man Cry	7"	Coral	Q72484	1966	£4	£8	
Two Much	LP	MCA	MUP(S)333	1968	£4	£10	with Count Basie
Very Best Of Jackie Wilson	LP	Brunswick	BRLS3016	1975	£4	£10	
We Have Love	7"	Coral	Q72338	1958	£5	£10	
Whispers	LP	Coral	LVA9235	1967	£10	£25	
Whispers Gettin' Louder	7"	Coral	Q72487	1966	£5	£10	
Woman,A Lover,A Friend	LP	Coral	LVA9144	1961	£25	£50	

World's Greatest Melodies	LP	Coral	LVA9214	1962	£10	£25	mono
World's Greatest Melodies	LP	Coral	SVL9214	1962	£15	£30	stereo
Years From Now	7"	Coral	Q72439	1961	£2.50	£6	
Yes Indeed	7"	Coral	Q72480	1965	£2.50	£6	
You Ain't Heard Nothing Yet	LP	Coral	LVA9148	1961	£17.50	£35	
You Better Know	7"	Coral	Q72380	1959	£2.50	£6	
You Got Me Walkin'	LP	Brunswick	BRLS3001	1973	£4	£10	

WILSON, JOE

Sweetness	7"	Pye	7N25550	1971	£1.50	£4	

WILSON, JOE LEE

Blues For Mister Charlie	7"	Stateside	SS404	1965	£2	£5	

WILSON, MARTY & THE STRATOLITES

Hey Eula	7"	Brunswick	05750	1958	£5	£10	

WILSON, MAYNELL

Crazy Baby	7"	Carnival	CV7002	1963	£2.50	£6	
Hey Hey Johnny	7"	Carnival	CV7014	1964	£2.50	£6	
Motown Feeling	7"	CBM	001	1967	£2.50	£6	

WILSON, MURRY

At least John Lennon's father only got to make a single: they let the father of the Beach Boys make a whole album! The result consists of light instrumental music that would be of marginal interest were it not for Mr.Wilson's superstar connections.

Many Moods Of Murry Wilson	LP	Capitol	(S)T2819	1967	£5	£12	
Plumber's Tune	7"	Capitol	CL15525	1967	£2	£5	

WILSON, NANCY

Best Is Yet To Come	7"	Capitol	CL15330	1964	£1.50	£4	
Don't Come Running Back To Me	7"	Capitol	CL15378	1965	£2	£5	
Don't Look Over Your Shoulder	7"	Capitol	CL15508	1967	£2.50	£6	
Face It Girl It's Over	7"	Capitol	CL15547	1968	£7.50	£15	
How Glad I Am	7"	Capitol	CL15352	1964	£2.50	£6	
My Foolish Heart	7"	Capitol	CL15205	1961	£1.50	£4	
Power Of Love	7"	Capitol	CL15443	1966	£1.50	£4	
That's What I Want For Christmas	7"	Capitol	CL15343	1964	£1.50	£4	
Uptight	7"	Capitol	CL15466	1966	£5	£10	
Welcome, Welcome	7"	Capitol	CL15396	1965	£1.50	£4	
Where Does That Leave Me	7"	Capitol	CL15412	1965	£2.50	£6	
You Don't Know Me	7"	Capitol	CL15536	1968	£1.50	£4	

WILSON, PEANUTS

Cast Iron Arm	7"	Coral	Q72302	1958	£100	£200	

WILSON, PHIL

Better Days	7"	Caff	CAFF3	1989	£1.50	£4	

WILSON, REUBEN

Blue Mode	LP	Blue Note	BST84343	1970	£4	£10	
Cisco Kid	LP	People	PLEO1	1973	£5	£12	
Got To Get Your Own	7"	Chess	6078700	1976	£2.50	£6	
Groovy Situation	LP	Blue Note	BST84365	1970	£4	£10	
I'll Take You There	LP	People	PEO109	1974	£1.50	£4	
Love Bug	LP	Blue Note	BST84317	1969	£5	£12	
On Broadway	LP	Blue Note	BST84295	1968	£5	£12	
Set Us Free	LP	Blue Note	BST84377	1970	£4	£10	
Sweet Life	LP	People	PLEO20	1974	£5	£12	

WILSON, SMILEY

Running Bear	7"	London	HLG9066	1960	£15	£30	

WILSON, TEDDY

For Quiet Lovers	10" LP	HMV	DLP1162	1957	£10	£25	
I Got Rhythm	LP	HMV	CLP1230	1958	£8	£20	
Mr.Wilson And Mr.Gershwin	LP	Philips	BBL7344	1960	£4	£10	
Newport Jazz Festival 1957	LP	Columbia	33CX10107	1958	£6	£15	...with Gerry Mulligan
Teddy Wilson	10" LP	Columbia	33C9019	1956	£15	£30	
Teddy Wilson	10" LP	Columbia	33S1066	1955	£20	£40	
Teddy Wilson	10" LP	Philips	BBR8065	1955	£20	£40	
Teddy Wilson Orchestra With Billie Holiday	10" LP	Philips	BBR8061	1955	£20	£40	
Teddy Wilson Trio	10" LP	Esquire	20009	1953	£25	£50	

WILSON, TIMOTHY

Phoney People	7"	Decca	F13432	1973	£2	£5	

WILSON, TREVOR

You Couldn't Believe	7"	Ska Beat	JB207	1965	£5	£10	

WILTSHIRE, JOHNNY

If The Shoe Fits	7"	Oriole	CB1494	1959	£7.50	£15	

WIMPLE WINCH

Rumble On Mersey Square South	7"	Fontana	TF781	1967	£35	£70	
Rumble On Mersey Square South/ Atmospheres	7"	Fontana	TF781	1967	£75	£150	
Save My Soul	7"	Fontana	TF718	1966	£40	£80	
What's Been Done	7"	Fontana	TF686	1966	£40	£80	

WINCHESTER, JESSE
Jesse Winchester .... LP ...... Ampex .... A10104 .... 1970 ... £4 ....£10 .... US

WIND
Morning .... LP ...... CBS .... £35 ....£70 ....German
Seasons .... LP ...... Plus .... 1971 ... £35 ....£70 ....German

WIND IN THE WILLOWS
*Lead singer with the Wind In The Willows was Debbie Harry. The folky music played by the group is as different from that of Blondie as is
Debbie Harry's own hippy appearance from that of the blonde bombshell she decided to become.*
Moments Spent .... 7" ...... Capitol .... CL15561 .... 1968 ... £7.50 ..£15
Wind In The Willows .... LP ...... Capitol .... SKAO2956 .... 1968 ... £8 ....£20 .... US, gatefold

WINDING, KAI
Comin' Home Baby .... 7" ...... Verve .... VS512 .... 1965 ... £1.50 ...£4
East Coast Jazz No.7 .... LP ...... London .... LTZN15003 .... 1956 ... £8 ....£20
Swingin' States .... LP ...... Philips .... BBL7316/SBBL509 1959 ... £8 ....£20
Trombone Panorama .... LP ...... Philips .... BBL7275 .... 1959 ... £8 ....£20
Trombone Sound .... LP ...... Philips .... BBL7150 .... 1957 ... £8 ....£20

WINSOR, MARTIN & REDD SULLIVAN
Hosts Of The Troubadour .... LP ...... Deacon .... DEA1045 .... 1971 ... £5 ....£12

WINSTON & ERROL
Fay Is Gone .... 7" ...... Blue Beat .... BB272 .... 1964 ... £5 ....£10

WINSTON & GEORGE
Keep The Pressure On .... 7" ...... Pyramid .... PYR6002 .... 1966 ... £4 ....£8

WINSTON & PAT
Pony Ride .... 7" ...... Trojan .... TR605 .... 1968 ... £2.50 ...£6

WINSTON & ROY
Babylon Gone .... 7" ...... Blue Beat .... BB80 .... 1961 ... £5 ....£10

WINSTON, JIMMY
*Jimmy Winston was the original organist with the Small Faces and plays on their first single. His own singles, however, recorded as
Winston's Fumbs and as Jimmy Winston & his Reflections, were not at all successful.*
Sorry She's Mine .... 7" ...... Decca .... F12410 .... 1966 ... £25 ....£50

WINSTONE, ERIC
Dr.Who Theme .... 7" ...... Pye .... 7N15603 .... 1964 ... £2.50 ...£6

WINSTONE, NORMA
Edge Of Time .... LP ...... Argo .... ZDA148 .... 1971 ... £25 ....£50

WINSTONS
Colour Him Father .... 7" ...... Pye .... 7N25493 .... 1969 ... £2.50 ...£6
Love Of The Common People .... 7" ...... Pye .... 7N25500 .... 1969 ... £1.50 ...£4

WINSTON'S FUMBS
Real Crazy Appartment .... 7" ...... RCA .... RCA1612 .... 1967 ... £50 ....£100

WINTER CONSORT
Winter Consort .... LP ...... A&M .... AMLS942 .... 1969 ... £5 ....£12

WINTER, EDGAR
Jasmine Nightdreams .... LP ...... Blue Sky .... PZQ33483 .... 1975 ... £4 ....£10 ....US quad
Shock Treatment .... LP ...... Epic .... PEQ32461 .... 1974 ... £4 ....£10 ....US quad
They Only Come Out At Night .... LP ...... Epic .... EQ31584 .... 1973 ... £4 ....£10 ....US quad
With Rick Derringer .... LP ...... Blue Sky .... PZQ33798 .... 1975 ... £4 ....£10 ....US quad

WINTER, JOHNNY
About Blues .... LP ...... Janus .... 3008 .... 1969 ... £4 ....£10 ....US
Before The Storm .... LP ...... Janus .... 3056 .... 1970 ... £4 ....£10 ....US
First Winter .... LP ...... Buddah .... 2359011 .... 1970 ... £4 ....£10
I'm Yours And I'm Hers .... 7" ...... CBS .... 4386 .... 1969 ... £1.50 ...£4
John Dawson Winter III .... LP ...... Blue Sky .... PZQ33292 .... 1974 ... £5 ....£12 ....US quad
Johnny Winter .... LP ...... CBS .... 63619 .... 1969 ... £5 ....£12
Johnny Winter And... .... LP ...... CBS .... 64117 .... 1971 ... £4 ....£10 ....chart LP
Johnny Winter And...Live .... LP ...... CBS .... 64289 .... 1971 ... £4 ....£10 ....chart LP
Progressive Blues Experiment .... LP ...... Liberty .... LBS83240 .... 1969 ... £4 ....£10
Saints And Sinners .... LP ...... Columbia .... CQ32715 .... 1974 ... £5 ....£12 ....US quad
Second Winter .... LP ...... CBS .... 66231 .... 1970 ... £5 ....£12 ...... 3 sides, chart LP
Still Alive And Well .... LP ...... Columbia .... CQ32188 .... 1973 ... £5 ....£12 ....US quad

WINTERHALTER, HUGO ORCHESTRA
Canadian Sunset .... 7" ...... HMV .... POP241 .... 1956 ... £1.50 ...£4

WINTERS, DON
Someday Baby .... 7" ...... Brunswick .... 05827 .... 1960 ... £5 ....£10

WINTERS, LIZ & BOB CORT
Liz Winters & Bob Cort .... 7" EP.. Decca .... DFE6409 .... 1957 ... £7.50 ...£15
Love Is Strange .... 7" ...... Decca .... F10878 .... 1957 ... £4 ....£8
Maggie May .... 7" ...... Decca .... F10899 .... 1957 ... £2.50 ...£6

WINTERS, LOIS
Japanese Farewell Song .... 7" ...... London .... HLD8266 .... 1956 ... £7.50 ...£15

WINTERS, MIKE & BERNIE
How Do You Do? .... 7" ...... Parlophone ...... R4384 .... 1957 ... £4 ....£8

WINTERS, RUBY

Title	Format	Label	Cat#	Year	Price	Price	Notes
Baby Lay Down	7″	Creole	CR171	1979	£1.50	£4	
Back To Love	7″	Creole	CR174	1979	£1.50	£4	
I Want Action	7″	Stateside	SS2090	1968	£7.50	£15	

WINWOOD, STEVE

Title	Format	Label	Cat#	Year	Price	Price	Notes
Conversation With Steve Winwood	LP	Island	SWCLP1	1986	£6	£15	promo
Time Is Running Out	12″	Island		1977	£2.50	£6	promo, no PS
Winwood	LP	United Artists	UAS9950	1971	£5	£12	US, with booklet

WIPERS

Title	Format	Label	Cat#	Year	Price	Price	Notes
Better Off Dead	7″	Trap	810X44	1978	£10	£20	
Is This Real	LP	Park Avenue		1979	£6	£15	US
Youth Of America	LP	Park Avenue	PA82802	1981	£6	£15	US

WIRE

Title	Format	Label	Cat#	Year	Price	Price	Notes
154	LP	Harvest	SHSP4105	1979	£4	£10	with 7′ (PSR444)
Document And Eyewitness	LP	Rough Trade	ROUGH29	1984	£5	£12	with 12′ (ROUGH2912)
Dot Dash	7″	Harvest	HAR5161	1978	£2	£5	PS
Eardrum Buzz	7″	Mute	MUTE87	1989	£4	£8	PS, clear vinyl
I Am The Fly	7″	Harvest	HAR5151	1978	£2	£5	PS
Mannequin	7″	Harvest	HAR5144	1977	£4	£8	PS
Outdoor Miner	7″	Harvest	HAR5172	1979	£2	£5	PS, white vinyl
Question Of Degree	7″	Harvest	HAR5187	1979	£2	£5	PS

WIRTZ, MARK *(e See Mood Mosaic)*

Title	Format	Label	Cat#	Year	Price	Price	Notes
Caroline	7″	CBS	4539	1969	£2	£5	
He's Our Dear Old Weatherman	7″	Parlophone	R5668	1968	£4	£8	
Mrs.Raven	7″	Parlophone	R5683	1968	£2.50	£6	

WISDOM, NORMAN

Title	Format	Label	Cat#	Year	Price	Price	Notes
Follow A Star	7″	Top Rank	JAR246	1959	£1.50	£4	
Narcissus	7″	Columbia	SCD2160	1961	£2.50	£6	
Norman And Ruby	7″ EP	Columbia	SEG7687	1957	£2	£5	with Ruby Murray
Norman Wisdom	7″ EP	Columbia	SEG7612	1956	£5	£10	
Two Rivers	7″	Columbia	SCM5222	1956	£4	£8	
Up In The World	7″	Columbia	DB3864	1957	£4	£8	
Where's Charly?	LP	Columbia	33SX1085	1958	£4	£10	
Wisdom Of A Fool	7″	Columbia	DB3903	1957	£2	£5	chart single

WISE BOYS

Title	Format	Label	Cat#	Year	Price	Price	Notes
Why Why Why	7″	Parlophone	R4693	1960	£2	£5	

WISE GUYS

Title	Format	Label	Cat#	Year	Price	Price	Notes
Big Noise	7″	Top Rank	JAR271	1960	£1.50	£4	

WISEMAN, MAC

Title	Format	Label	Cat#	Year	Price	Price	Notes
Beside The Still Waters	LP	Dot	DLP3135/DLP25135	1959	£8	£20	US
Fireball Mail	LP	Dot	DLP3408	1961	£8	£20	US
Fireball Mail	7″	London	HLD8259	1956	£15	£30	
Great Folk Ballads	LP	London	HAD2217	1960	£15	£30	
Jimmy Brown The Newsboy	7″	London	HL7084	1959	£10	£20	export
Keep On The Sunny Side	LP	Dot	DLP3336	1960	£8	£20	US
Kentuckian Song	7″	London	HLD8174	1955	£15	£30	
My Little Home In Tennessee	7″	London	HLD8226	1956	£12.50	£25	
Songs From The Hills	7″ EP	London	RED1056	1956	£7.50	£15	
Songs From The Hills	10″ LP	London	HBD1052	1956	£15	£30	
Songs From The Hills Vol.2	7″ EP	London	RED1147	1958	£7.50	£15	
Songs From The Hills Vol.3	7″ EP	London	RED1242	1960	£7.50	£15	
Step It Up And Go	7″	London	HLD8412	1957	£60	£120	
Tis Sweet To Be Remembered	LP	Dot	DLP3084	1958	£8	£20	US

WISHBONE ASH

Title	Format	Label	Cat#	Year	Price	Price	Notes
Evening Program With Wishbone Ash	LP	Decca		1972	£6	£15	US promo
Live Dates Vol.2	LP	MCA	MCG4012	1980	£5	£12	with bonus LP
LIve From Memphis	LP	MCA	L331922	1974	£8	£20	US promo
Pilgrimage	LP	MCA	MDKS8004	1971	£4	£10	
Raw To The Bone	LP	Neat	NEAT1027	1985	£6	£15	
Raw To The Bone	LP	Neat	NEATP1027	1985	£10	£25	pic disc
Wishbone Ash	LP	MCA	MKPS2014	1970	£5	£12	chart LP

WISHFUL THINKING

Title	Format	Label	Cat#	Year	Price	Price	Notes
Alone	7″	Decca	F22742	1968	£4	£8	
Count To Ten	7″	Decca	F12598	1967	£2	£5	
Hiroshima	LP	B&C	CAS1038	1971	£6	£15	
It's So Easy	7″	Decca	F12760	1968	£1.50	£4	
Live Vol.1	LP	Decca	SKL4900	1967	£8	£20	
Meet The Sun	7″	Decca	F22673	1967	£4	£8	
Peanuts	7″	Decca	F12627	1967	£2	£5	
Step By Step	7″	Decca	F12499	1966	£1.50	£4	
Turning Round	7″	Decca	F12438	1966	£2.50	£5	

WITCHFINDER GENERAL

Title	Format	Label	Cat#	Year	Price	Price	Notes
Burning A Sinner	7″	Heavy Metal	HEAVY6	1981	£2	£5	
Death Penalty	LP	Heavy Metal	HMRLP8	1982	£4	£10	red vinyl
Death Penalty	LP	Heavy Metal	HMRPD8	1982	£4	£10	pic disc
Music	7″	Heavy Metal	HEAVY21	1983	£1.50	£4	
Music	7″	Heavy Metal	HMPD21	1983	£2	£5	pic disc
Soviet Invasion	12″	Heavy Metal	12HM17	1982	£4	£10	

911

WITCHFYNDE
I'd Rather Go Wild	7"	Expulsion	ABOUT1	1983	£4	£8		

WITHERS, BILL
Live At Carnegie Hall	LP	A&M	AMLD3001	1973	£6	£15	double
Still Bill	LP	A&M	AMLH68107	1972	£4	£10	

WITHERSPOON, JIMMY
All That's Good	7"	Vogue	V2420	1964	£7.50	£15	
At The Monterey Jazz Festival	LP	Hi Fi	421	1959	£8	£20	US
At The Renaissance	LP	Vogue	LAE12253	1961	£6	£15	
Back Door Blues	LP	Polydor	623256	1969	£5	£12	
Blue Point Of View	LP	Verve	(S)VLP9156	1967	£5	£12	
Blue Spoon	LP	Stateside	SL10139	1965	£6	£15	
Blues Around The Clock	LP	Stateside	SL10105	1965	£8	£20	
Blues For Easy Livers	LP	Transatlantic	PR7475	1968	£5	£12	
Blues Is Now	LP	Verve	(S)VLP9181	1968	£5	£12	
Blues Singer	LP	Stateside	(S)SL10289	1969	£5	£12	
Come And Walk With Me	7"	Stateside	SS429	1965	£4	£8	
Evenin' Blues	LP	Stateside	SL10088	1964	£6	£15	
Evenin' Blues	LP	Transatlantic	PR7300	1967	£4	£10	
Falling By Degrees	78	Vogue	V2261	1955	£6	£12	
Feelin' The Spirit	LP	Hi Fi	422	1959	£8	£20	US
Feeling The Spirit Vol.1	7" EP	Vocalion	VEH170158	1964	£6	£12	
Feeling The Spirit Vol.2	7" EP	Vocalion	VEH170159	1964	£6	£12	
Goin' To Kansas City Blues	LP	RCA	LPM1639	1958	£8	£20	US
Hey Mrs.Jones	LP	Reprise	R(9)6012	1962	£6	£15	US
Highway To Happiness	7"	Parlophone	MSP6125	1954	£10	£20	
I Done Told You	7"	Parlophone	MSP6142	1954	£12.50	£25	
I Never Will Marry	7"	Stateside	SS325	1964	£4	£8	
If There Wasn't Any You	7"	Stateside	SS503	1966	£4	£8	
In Person	LP	Vogue	VRL3005	1965	£6	£15	
It's All Over But The Crying	7"	Verve	VS538	1966	£2	£5	
Jimmy Witherspoon	LP	Ember	EMB3369	1966	£5	£12	
Jimmy Witherspoon	7" EP	Vocalion	EPVH1278	1964	£6	£12	
Jimmy Witherspoon At Monterey No.1	7" EP	Vocalion	EPV1269	1962	£10	£20	
Jimmy Witherspoon At Monterey No.2	7" EP	Vocalion	EPV1270	1962	£10	£20	
Jump Children	78	Vogue	V2356	1956	£6	£12	
Live	LP	Stateside	(S)SL10232	1968	£6	£15	
Love Me Right	7"	Stateside	SS461	1965	£4	£8	
Money Is Getting Cheaper	7"	Stateside	SS304	1964	£4	£8	
New Orleans Blues	LP	Atlantic	1266	1956	£15	£30	US
New Orleans Blues	LP	London	LTZK15150	1959	£6	£15	
No Rolling Blues	7"	Vogue	V2060	1956	£7.50	£15	
Outskirts Of Town	7" EP	Vocalion	EPVH1284	1965	£6	£12	
Past Forty Blues	7"	Verve	VS553	1967	£1.50	£4	
Roots	LP	Reprise	R(9)6059	1962	£6	£15	US
Singin' The Blues	LP	Vogue	LAE12218	1960	£6	£15	
Sings The Blues At The Renaissance	LP	Ember	CJS820	1969	£4	£10	
Some Of My Best Friends Are The Blues	LP	Stateside	SL10114	1965	£8	£20	
Some Of My Best Friends Are The Blues	LP	Transatlantic	PR7356	1968	£4	£10	
Spoon	LP	Reprise	R(9)2008	1961	£6	£15	US
Spoon In London	LP	Transatlantic	PR7418	1968	£5	£12	
Spoon Sings And Swings	LP	Fontana	(S)TL5382	1967	£8	£20	
Spoonful Of Soul	LP	Verve	(S)VLP9216	1968	£5	£12	
Take This Hammer	LP	Constellation	M1422	1964	£6	£15	US
There's Good Rockin' Tonight	LP	Fontana	688005ZL	1965	£5	£12	
Who's Been Jivin' With You	78	Vogue	V2295	1954	£6	£12	
You're Next	7"	Stateside	SS362	1964	£4	£8	

WITTHUSER & WESTRUPP
Bauer Plath	LP	Pilz	20291154	1972	£5	£12	German
Der Jesuspilz	LP	Pilz	20210987	1971	£5	£12	German
Lieder Von Vampiren, Nonnen Und Toten	LP	Ohr	OMM56002	1970	£6	£15	German
Live 68-73	LP	Komische	KM258004	1973	£6	£15	German double
Trips Und Traume	LP	Ohr	OMM56016	1971	£5	£12	German

WIZARD
Original Wizard	LP	Peon	1069	1971	£25	£50	US

WIZARD'S CONVENTION
Wizard's Convention	LP	RCA	RS1085	1976	£4	£10	

WIZARDS FROM KANSAS
Wizards From Kansas	LP	Mercury	SR61309	1970	£8	£20	US

WIZZARD
I Wish It Could Be Christmas Every Day	7"	Warner Bros	K16336	1973	£2.50	£6	gatefold PS

WOLF
Head Contact	12"	Chrysalis	CHS122592	1982	£3	£8	

WOLFE, CHARLES
Dance Dance Dance	7"	NEMS	563675	1968	£1.50	£4	

WOLFE TONES

Belt Of The Celts	LP	Triskel	TRL1003	1978	£5	£12	Irish
James Connelly	7"	Fontana	TF945	1968	£1.50	£4	
Let The People Sing	LP	Dolphin	DOL1004	1972	£5	£12	Irish
Live Alive Oh!	LP	Triskel	TRL1005	1980	£6	£15	Irish double
Man From Mullingar	7"	Fontana	TF743	1966	£1.50	£4	
Spanish Lady	7"	Fontana	TF565	1965	£1.50	£4	
Teddy Bear's Head	LP	Dolphin	DOLM5005	1976	£5	£12	Irish
This Town Is Not Our Own	7"	Fontana	TF804	1967	£1.50	£4	
Till Ireland A Nation	LP	Dolphin	DOL1006	1974	£5	£12	Irish

WOLFGANG PRESS

Scarecrow	12"	4AD	BAD409	1984	£3	£8	
Water	12"	4AD	BAD502	1985	£2.50	£6	

WOLFMAN JACK

And The Wolf Pack	LP	Bread		1963	£15	£30	US
Fun And Romance	LP	Columbia		1975	£6	£15	US

WOLVES

At The Club	7"	Pye	7N17013	1965	£6	£12	
Journey Into Dreams	7"	Pye	7N15676	1964	£4	£8	
Lust For Life	7"	Parlophone	R5511	1966	£15	£30	
Now	7"	Pye	7N15733	1964	£7.50	£15	

WOMACK, BOBBY

Across 110th Street	LP	United Artists	UAS29451	1973	£6	£15	
Across 110th Street	7"	United Artists	UP35512	1973	£1.50	£4	
Broadway Talk	7"	Minit	MLF11001	1968	£5	£10	
California Dreamin'	7"	Minit	MLF11012	1969	£2	£5	
Check It Out	7"	United Artists	UP35859	1975	£1.50	£4	
Communication	LP	United Artists	UAS29306	1973	£6	£15	
Daylight	7"	United Artists	UP36098	1976	£1.50	£4	
Facts Of Life	LP	United Artists	UAG29456	1973	£6	£15	
Fly Me To The Moon	7"	Minit	MLF11010	1968	£2	£5	
Harry Hippie	7"	United Artists	UP35456	1973	£1.50	£4	
I Can Understand It	7"	United Artists	UAS29715	1975	£5	£12	
I Don't Know What The World Is Coming To	LP	United Artists	UAG29762	1975	£5	£12	
Lookin' For A Love	7"	United Artists	UP35644	1974	£1.50	£4	
Lookin' For A Love Again	LP	United Artists	UAS29574	1974	£5	£12	
Nobody Wants You When You're Down And Out	7"	United Artists	UP35565	1973	£1.50	£4	
Roads Of Life	LP	Arista	ARTY165	1979	£10	£25	
Safety Zone	LP	United Artists	UAG29907	1976	£5	£12	
That's The Way I Feel About 'Cha	7"	United Artists	UP35339	1972	£1.50	£4	
Understanding	LP	United Artists	UAS29365	1972	£6	£15	
What Is This	7"	Jayboy	BOY75	1974	£2	£5	
What Is This	7"	Minit	MLF11005	1968	£2.50	£6	
Where There's A Will There's A Way	7"	United Artists	UP36042	1976	£1.50	£4	
Woman's Got To Have It	7"	United Artists	UP35375	1972	£1.50	£4	

WOMEGA

Quick Step	LP	Skruup	162210751	1975	£5	£12	Belgian

WONDER, STEVIE

Blowin' In The Wind	7"	Tamla Motown	TMG570	1966	£5	£10	chart single
Castles In The Sand	7"	Stateside	SS285	1964	£10	£20	
Down To Earth	LP	Tamla Motown	(S)TML11045	1967	£8	£20	
Eivets Rednow	LP	Gordy	GS932	1968	£6	£15	US
Fingertips	7"	Oriole	CBA1853	1963	£25	£50	
For Once In My Life	LP	Tamla Motown	(S)TML11098	1969	£4	£10	
For Once In My Life	7"	Tamla Motown	TMG679	1968	£2	£5	chart single
Heaven Help Us All	7"	Tamla Motown	TMG757	1970	£1.50	£4	chart single
Hey Harmonica Man	LP	Stateside	SL10108	1965	£30	£60	
Hey Harmonica Man	7"	Stateside	SS323	1964	£10	£20	
Hi Heel Sneakers	7"	Tamla Motown	TMG532	1965	£6	£12	
I Call It Pretty Music	7" EP	Stateside	SE1014	1964	£10	£20	
I Was Made To Love Her	LP	Tamla Motown	(S)TML11059	1968	£6	£15	
I Was Made To Love Her	7"	Tamla Motown	TMG613	1967	£2	£5	chart single
I'm Wondering	7"	Tamla Motown	TMG626	1967	£2	£5	chart single
Jazz Soul Of Little Stevie	LP	Stateside	SL10078	1964	£25	£50	
Kiss Me Baby	7"	Tamla Motown	TMG505	1965	£7.50	£15	
Live	LP	Tamla Motown	(S)TML11150	1970	£4	£10	
Live At The Talk Of The Town	LP	Tamla Motown	STML11164	1970	£4	£10	
My Cherie Amour	7"	Tamla Motown	TMG690	1969	£1.50	£4	chart single
Never Dreamed You'd Leave Me In Summer	7"	Tamla Motown	TMG779	1971	£1.50	£4	
Never Had A Dream Come True	7"	Tamla Motown	TMG731	1970	£1.50	£4	chart single
Nothing's Too Good For My Baby	7"	Tamla Motown	TMG558	1966	£7.50	£15	
Place In The Sun	7"	Tamla Motown	TMG588	1966	£5	£10	chart single
Shoo-Be-Doo-Be-Doo-Da-Day	7"	Tamla Motown	TMG653	1968	£1.50	£4	chart single
Signed Sealed Delivered I'm Yours	7"	Tamla Motown	TMG744	1970	£1.50	£4	chart single
Someday At Christmas	LP	Tamla Motown	(S)TML11085	1969	£8	£20	
Stevie Wonder	7" EP	Tamla Motown	TME2006	1965	£10	£20	
Talking Book	LP	EMI	5CP06293880	1979	£6	£15	Dutch pic disc
Travelling Man	7"	Tamla Motown	TMG602	1967	£2.50	£6	
Tribute To Uncle Ray	LP	Oriole	PS40049	1963	£25	£50	
Twelve Year Old Genius	LP	Oriole	PS40050	1963	£25	£50	
Uptight	LP	Tamla Motown	(S)TML11036	1966	£6	£15	

Title	Format	Label	Cat No	Year	Price	Price	Notes
Uptight	7"	Tamla Motown	TMG545	1966	£5	£10	chart single
We Can Work It Out	7"	Tamla Motown	TMG772	1971	£1.50	£4	chart single
We Can Work It Out	7"	Tamla Motown	TMG772	1971	£4	£8	PS
With A Song In My Heart	LP	Tamla	T250	1964	£25	£50	US
Workout Stevie Workout	7"	Stateside	SS238	1963	£12.50	£25	
Workout Stevie, Workout	LP	Tamla	TS248	1963	£25	£50	US
Yester-me,Yester-you,Yesterday	7"	Tamla Motown	TMG717	1969	£1.50	£4	chart single
You Met Your Match	7"	Tamla Motown	TMG666	1968	£1.50	£4	

WONDER STUFF

Title	Format	Label	Cat No	Year	Price	Price	Notes
Don't Let Me Down Gently	12"	Polydor	GONEX7	1989	£2.50	£6	with inner
Give Give Give Me More More More	CD-s	Polydor	GONECD3	1988	£4	£10	
Give Give Give Me More More More	7"	Polydor	GONE3	1988	£2.50	£6	
Give Give Give Me More More More	12"	Polydor	GONEX3	1988	£4	£10	
It's Yer Money I'm After Baby	CD-s	Polydor	GONCD5	1988	£2.50	£6	
It's Yer Money I'm After Baby	12"	Polydor	GONEX5	1988	£2.50	£6	with inner
Unbearable	7"	Far Out	GONE002	1987	£2	£5	no PS
Unbearable	7"	Farout	GONE002	1987	£7.50	£15	
Waffle And Maple Syrup	LP	Polydor	STUFF1		£8	£20	promo
Who Wants To Be The Disco King?	12"	Polydor	GONEX6	1989	£2.50	£6	with inner
Wish Away	CD-s	Polydor	GONECD4	1988	£3	£8	
Wish Away	12"	Polydor	GONEX4	1988	£3	£8	
Wonderful Day	7"	Farout	GONE ONE	1987	£25	£50	

WONDER WHO

The Wonder Who were the Four Seasons, recording under a pseudonym to see if they could still sell records. With a voice as distinctive as Frankie Valli's, however, they did not succeed in fooling anyone for very long.

Title	Format	Label	Cat No	Year	Price	Price
Don't Think Twice It's Alright	7"	Philips	BF1440	1965	£2.50	£6
Lonesome Road	7"	Philips	BF1600	1967	£2.50	£6
On The Good Ship Lollipop	7"	Philips	BF1504	1966	£2.50	£6

WONDERLAND

Title	Format	Label	Cat No	Year	Price	Price
Poochy	7"	Polydor	56539	1968	£2	£5

WONDERLAND, ALICE

Title	Format	Label	Cat No	Year	Price	Price
He's Mine	7"	London	HLU9783	1963	£1.50	£4

WONDERLAND BAND

Title	Format	Label	Cat No	Year	Price	Price	Notes
Best Of The Wonderland Band	LP	Karussell	2415078	1973	£8	£20	German
No.1	LP	Polydor	2371125	1971	£10	£25	German

WONG, ROYCE

Title	Format	Label	Cat No	Year	Price	Price
Everything's Gonna Be Alright	7"	Blue Beat	BB301	1964	£5	£10

WOOD, ANITA

Title	Format	Label	Cat No	Year	Price	Price
Dream Baby	7"	Sue	WI328	1964	£5	£10
I'll Wait Forever	7"	London	HLS9585	1962	£7.50	£15

WOOD, BOBBY

Title	Format	Label	Cat No	Year	Price	Price
I'm A Fool For Loving You	7"	Pye	7N25264	1964	£2	£5

WOOD, BRENTON

Title	Format	Label	Cat No	Year	Price	Price	Notes
Baby You Got It	LP	Double Shot	1003/5003	1967	£4	£10	US
Baby You Got It	7"	Liberty	LBF15065	1968	£1.50	£4	
Gimme Little Sign	LP	Liberty	LBL/LBS83088E	1967	£4	£10	
Gimme Little Sign	7"	Liberty	LBF15021	1967	£1.50	£4	chart single
Oogum Boogum Song	7"	Philips	BF1579	1967	£1.50	£4	
Some Got It, Some Don't	7"	Liberty	LBF15103	1968	£1.50	£4	

WOOD, CHUCK

Title	Format	Label	Cat No	Year	Price	Price
I've Got My Lovelight Shining	7"	Transatlantic	BIG107	1968	£1.50	£4
Seven Days Too Long	7"	Mojo	2092010	1971	£1.50	£4
Seven Days Too Long	7"	Transatlantic	BIG104	1967	£2.50	£6

WOOD, DEL

Title	Format	Label	Cat No	Year	Price	Price
Ragtime Annie	7"	London	HL8036	1954	£10	£20
Ragtime Piano	7" EP	London	REP1007	1954	£4	£8

WOOD, ROBERT

Title	Format	Label	Cat No	Year	Price	Price	Notes
Sonabular	LP	Edici	ED6103	1973	£4	£10	French
Tarot	LP	Edici	ED6102	1972	£5	£12	French
Vibrarock	LP	Polydor	2393137	1976	£4	£10	French

WOOD, ROY

Title	Format	Label	Cat No	Year	Price	Price	Notes
Roy Wood Story	LP	Harvest	SHDW408	1976	£5	£12	double

WOOD, ROY & ANNIE HASLAM

Title	Format	Label	Cat No	Year	Price	Price
I Never Believed In Love	7"	Warner Bros	K17028	1977	£2	£5

WOOD, ROYSTON & HEATHER

Title	Format	Label	Cat No	Year	Price	Price
No Relation	LP	Transatlantic	TRA342	1977	£25	£50

WOODEN HORSE

Title	Format	Label	Cat No	Year	Price	Price
Pick Up The Pieces	7"	York	SYK526	1972	£2	£5
Wooden Horse	LP	York	FYK403	1972	£30	£60
Wooden Horse II	LP	York	FYK413	1973	£60	£120
Wooden Horses	7"	York	SYK543	1973	£2	£5

WOODEN O

Title	Format	Label	Cat No	Year	Price	Price	Notes
Handful Of Pleasant Delites	LP	Middle Earth	MDLS301	1969	£30	£60	sleeve pictured in Guide

WOODMAN, KEN & HIS PICCADILLY BRASS
That's Nice	LP	Strike	JLH101	1966	£6	£15

WOODPECKERS
Hey Little Girl	7"	Oriole	CB311	1965	£2	£5
Woodpecker	7"	Decca	F11835	1964	£1.50	£4

WOODS, DANNY
Everybody's Trippin'	7"	Invictus	INV532	1973	£1.50	£4

WOODS, DONALD
Memories Of An Angel	7"	Vogue	V9107	1958	£60	£120

WOODS, GAY & TERRY
Backwoods	LP	Polydor	2383322	1975	£25	£50	
Renowned	LP	Polydor	2383406	1976	£25	£50	
Tenderhooks	LP	Rockburgh	ROC104	1978	£6	£15	
Time Is Right	LP	Polydor	2383375	1976	£15	£30	
Woods Band	LP	Greenwich	GSLP1004	1971	£25	£50	
Woods Band	LP	Mulligan	LUN015	1977	£8	£20	Different cover to 1971 issue
Woods Band	LP	Rockburgh	CREST29	1977	£10	£25	

WOODS, NICK
Ballad Of Billy Bud	7"	London	HLU9621	1962	£1.50	£4

WOODS, PHIL
New Jazz Quintet	10" LP	Esquire	20055	1955	£25	£50
Phil Woods Quartet	LP	Esquire	32020	1957	£15	£30
Phil Woods Septet	LP	Esquire	32026	1957	£15	£30

WOODWARD, MAGGIE
Ali Bama	7"	Vogue	V9148	1959	£2.50	£6

WOOFERS
Dragsville	LP	Wyncote	9001	196-	£8	£20	US

WOOLEY, SHEB
Blue Guitar	7"	MGM	MGM1263	1965	£1.50	£4	
Hootenanny Hoot	7"	MGM	MGM1257	1965	£1.50	£4	
I Flipped	7"	MGM	SP1130	1955	£5	£10	
Jest Plain, Wild And Wooley	7" EP	MGM	MGMEP540	1956	£15	£30	
Laughing The Blues	7"	MGM	SP1162	1956	£4	£8	
Luke The Spook	7"	MGM	MGM1081	1960	£2.50	£5	
Meet Mr.Lonely	7"	MGM	MGM1147	1961	£2	£5	
More	7"	MGM	MGM1017	1959	£2	£5	
Purple People Eater	7"	MGM	MGM981	1958	£4	£8	2 different B sides, chart single
Santa & The Purple People Eater	7"	MGM	MGM997	1958	£2	£5	
Sheb Wooley	LP	MGM	E3299	1956	£10	£25	US
Songs From The Day Of Rawhide	LP	MGM	C859	1961	£4	£10	
Spoofing The Big Ones	LP	MGM	C945	1963	£4	£10	
Tales Of How The West Was Won	LP	MGM	C955	1963	£5	£12	
That's My Ma & That's My Pa	LP	MGM	C903	1962	£4	£10	
Wayward Wind	7"	MGM	MGM1132	1961	£2	£5	

WOOLIES
Basic Rock	LP	Split	96452001	1970	£5	£12	US
Live At Lizard's	LP	Split		1973	£8	£20	US
Who Do You Love?	7"	RCA	RCA1602	1967	£10	£20	

WORK, JIMMY
Country Songs	7" EP	London	RED1039	1955	£12.50	£25
When She Said You All	7"	London	HLD8270	1956	£30	£60
You've Got A Heart Like A Merry-Go-Round	7"	London	HLD8308	1956	£12.50	£25

WORLD
Angelina	7"	Liberty	LBF15402	1970	£2	£5
Lucky Planet	LP	Liberty	LBS83419	1970	£8	£20

WORLD DOMINATION ENTERPRISES
Asbestos Lead Asbestos	7"	Karbon	KAR008	1985	£2	£5

WORLD OF OZ
King Croesus	7"	Deram	DM205	1968	£4	£8
Muffin Man	7"	Deram	DM187	1968	£4	£8
Willow's Harp	7"	Deram	DM233	1969	£5	£10
World Of Oz	LP	Deram	DML/SML1034	1969	£15	£30

WORRYING KYNDE
Call Out The Name	7"	Piccadilly	7N35370	1967	£10	£20

WORTH, JOHNNY
Just Because	7"	Columbia	DB3962	1957	£2	£5
Nightmare	7"	Oriole	CB1545	1960	£1.50	£4
You Know What I Mean	7"	Columbia	DB4811	1962	£1.50	£4

WORTH, MARION
Are You Willing, Willie	7"	London	HL7089	1960	£2.50	£6	export
That's My Kind Of Love	7"	London	HL7097	1960	£2.50	£6	export

WORTH SCHOOL CHOIR
Worth School Choir	LP	Nova	SDN23	1971	£6	£15	

WRANGLERS
Liza Jane	7"	Parlophone	R5163	1964	£20	£40	

WRAY, LINK
Batman Theme	7"	Chiswick	NS32	1978	£5	£10	demo
Fire And Brimstone	7"	Polydor	2066120	1971	£1.50	£4	
Good Rockin' Tonight	7"	Stateside	SS397	1965	£5	£10	
Great Guitar Hits	LP	Vermillion	1924	196-	£10	£25	US
Jack The Ripper	LP	Swan	SLP510	1963	£10	£25	US
Jack The Ripper	7"	Stateside	SS217	1963	£5	£10	
Link Wray	LP	Polydor	2489029	1971	£4	£10	
Link Wray And The Wraymen	LP	Epic	LN3661	1960	£15	£30	US
Link Wray Sings And Plays Guitar	LP	Vermillion	1925	196-	£10	£25	US
Mr.Guitar	7" EP.	Stateside	SE1015	1964	£12.50	£25	
Rumble	7"	London	HLA8623	1958	£10	£20	
Sweeper	7"	Stateside	SS256	1964	£5	£10	
There's Good Rockin' Tonight	LP	Union Pacific	UP002	1971	£6	£15	
Yesterday And Today	LP	Record Factory	1929	196-	£5	£12	US

WRAY, RAY QUARTET
When You Lover Has Gone	7"	Salvo	SLO1808	1962	£4	£8	

WRAY, VERNON & LINK WRAY
Wasted	LP	Vermillion	1972	196-	£6	£15	US

WREN, JENNY
Chasing My Dreams All Over Town	7"	Fontana	TF672	1966	£12.50	£25	

WRIGGLERS
Cooler	7"	Giant	GN26	1968	£4	£8	
Get Right	7"	Blue Cat	BS106	1968	£4	£8	

WRIGHT, BETTY
Girls Can't Do What The Guys Do	7"	Atlantic	584216	1968	£1.50	£4	

WRIGHT, DALE
She's Neat	7"	London	HLH8573	1958	£50	£100	
That's Show Biz	7"	Pye	7N25022	1959	£10	£20	

WRIGHT, EARL
Thumb A Ride	7"	Capitol	CL15825	1975	£1.50	£4	

WRIGHT, GARY
Extraction	LP	A&M	AMLS2004	1970	£4	£10	
Foot Print	LP	A&M	AMLS64296	1971	£4	£10	

WRIGHT, GINNY
Indian Moon	7"	London	HL8119	1955	£12.50	£25	

WRIGHT, GINNY & TOMMY CUTRER
Wonderful World	7"	London	HL8093	1954	£12.50	£25	

WRIGHT, NAT
Anything	7"	HMV	POP629	1959	£10	£20	

WRIGHT, OTIS
It Will Soon Be Done	LP	Doctor Bird	DLM5006	1967	£40	£80	
Over In Gloryland	LP	Coxsone	TLP1001	196-	£50	£100	
Peace Perfect Peace	LP	Doctor Bird	DLM5005	1967	£40	£80	

WRIGHT, O.V.
8 Men 4 Women	7"	London	HLZ10137	1967	£2	£5	
8 Men, 4 Women	LP	Island	ILP975	1968	£15	£30	
Gone For Good	7"	Vocalion	VP9272	1966	£4	£8	
I Want Everyone To Know	7"	Action	ACT4527	1969	£2.50	£6	
If It's Only For Tonight	LP	Back Beat	61	1965	£6	£15	US
Nucleus Of Soul	LP	Back Beat	67	1969	£5	£12	US
Oh Baby Mine	7"	Action	ACT4505	1968	£5	£10	
O.V.Wright	7" EP.	Vocalion	VEP170165	1965	£12.50	£25	
Poor Boy	7"	Vocalion	VP9255	1966	£2.50	£6	
What About You	7"	Sue	WI4043	1968	£6	£12	
You're Gonna Make Me Cry	7"	Vocalion	VP9249	1965	£4	£8	

WRIGHT, RITA
I Can't Give Back The Love	7"	Tamla Motown	TMG643	1968	£4	£8	
I Can't Give Back The Love I Feel For You	7"	Tamla Motown	TMG791	1971	£5	£10	
Love Is All You Need	7"	Jet	UP36382	1978	£4	£8	

WRIGHT, RUBEN
Hey Girl	7"	Capitol	CL15460	1966	£6	£12	

WRIGHT, RUBY
Bimbo	7"	Parlophone	MSP6073	1954	£7.50	£15	chart single
I Fall In Love With You Every Day	7"	Parlophone	MSP6209	1956	£4	£8	
Santa's Little Sleigh Bells	7"	Parlophone	MSP6133	1954	£5	£10	
Three Stars	7"	Parlophone	R4556	1959	£4	£8	chart single
Three Stars Girl	7" EP.	Parlophone	GEP8785	1959	£10	£20	

Till I Waltz Again With You	7"	Parlophone	MSP6025	1953	£7.50	£15	
What Have They Told You?	7"	Parlophone	MSP6150	1955	£4	£8	
You're Just A Flower From An Old Bouquet	7"	Parlophone	R4589	1959	£2	£5	

WRIGHT, STEVE

Wild Wild Women	7"	London	HLW8991	1959	£40	£80	

WRIGHT, WINSTON

Five Miles High	7"	Doctor Bird	DB1308	1969	£5	£10	

WRIGHT, ZACHARIAH

Lumumba Limbo	7"	Bamboo	BAM403	197-	£2	£5	

WRIT

Did You Ever Have To Make Up Your Mind	7"	Decca	F12385	1966	£1.50	£4	

WRITING ON THE WALL

Child On A Crossing	7"	Middle Earth	MDS101	1969	£7.50	£15	
Power Of The Picts	LP	Middle Earth	MDLS303	1969	£65	£130	sleeve pictured in Guide

WYATT, JOHNNY

This Thing Called Love	7"	President	PT109	1968	£4	£8	

WYATT, ROBERT

End Of An Ear	LP	CBS	64189	1970	£5	£12	

WYLIE, RICHARD

Brand New Man	7"	Columbia	DB7012	1963	£7.50	£15	
Funky Rubber Band	7"	Tamla Motown	TMG932	1975	£1.50	£4	

WYMAN, BILL

Monkey Grip	LP	Rolling Stones	QD79100	1974	£4	£10	US quad
Stone Alone	LP	Rolling Stones	QD79103	1976	£4	£10	US quad

WYNDHAM-READ, MARTIN

Ballad Singer	LP	Autogram	ALLP218	1977	£10	£25	German
Harry The Hawker Is Dead	LP	Argo	ZFB82	1973	£15	£30	
Martin Wyndham-Read	LP	Trailer	LER2028	1971	£10	£25	
Ned Kelly And That Gang	LP	Trailer	LER2009	1970	£8	£20	
Rose From The Bush	LP	Greenwich Village	GVR222	1984	£6	£15	
Andy's Gone	LP	Broadside	BRO134	1979	£10	£25	

WYNDHAM-READ, MARTIN & THE DRUIDS

Songs And Music Of The Redcoats	LP	Argo	ZDA147	1971	£25	£50	

WYNDHAM-READ, MARTIN & GEOFF & PENNIE HARRIS

Maypoles To Mistletoe	LP	Trailer	LER2092	1975	£10	£25	

WYNGARDE, PETER

Peter Wyngarde	LP	RCA	SF8087	1970	£8	£20	

WYNNE, PETER

Twilight Time	7"	Parlophone	R4597	1959	£1.50	£4	

WYNNS, SANDY

Touch Of Venus	7"	Fontana	TF550	1965	£150	£250	

WYNTER, MARK

Aladdin's Lamp	7"	Pye	7N15511	1963	£1.50	£4	
Answer Me	7"	Pye	7N15658	1964	£1.50	£4	
Babe I'm Gonna Leave You	7"	Pye	7N15994	1965	£1.50	£4	
Before Your Time	7"	Pye	7N17051	1966	£1.50	£4	
Boy You're Kissing	7"	Pye	7N15595	1964	£1.50	£4	
Can I Get To Know You Better	7"	Pye	7N15771	1965	£1.50	£4	
Dream Girl	7"	Decca	F11323	1961	£1.50	£4	chart single
Exclusively Yours	7"	Decca	F11354	1961	£1.50	£4	chart single
Forever And A Day	7"	Pye	7N15716	1964	£1.50	£4	
Girl For Everyday	7"	Decca	F11380	1961	£1.50	£4	
Go Away Little Girl	7"	Pye	7N15492	1962	£1.50	£4	chart single
Heaven's Plan	7"	Decca	F11434	1962	£1.50	£4	
I Love Her Still	7"	Decca	F11467	1962	£1.50	£4	
Image Of A Girl	7"	Decca	F11263	1960	£1.50	£4	chart single
It's Almost Tomorrow	7"	Pye	7N15577	1963	£1.50	£4	chart single
It's Mark Time	7" EP	Pye	NEP24176	1962	£6	£12	
Kickin' Up The Leaves	7"	Decca	F11279	1960	£1.50	£4	chart single
Love Hurts	7"	Pye	7N15685	1964	£1.50	£4	
Mark Time	7" EP	Decca	DFE6674	1960	£7.50	£15	
Mark Wynter	LP	Ace Of Clubs	ACL1141	1962	£8	£20	
Mark Wynter	LP	Golden Guinea	GGL0250	1963	£6	£15	
Mark Wynter	LP	Marble Arch	MAL647	1967	£4	£10	
Only You	7"	Pye	7N15604	1964	£1.50	£4	
Please Love Me Tender	7"	Pye	7N17438	1968	£1.50	£4	
Running To You	7"	Pye	7N15554	1963	£1.50	£4	
She's A Woman	7"	Pye	7N17651	1968	£1.50	£4	
Shy Girl	7"	Pye	7N15525	1963	£1.50	£4	chart single
Someday	7"	Pye	7N15861	1965	£1.50	£4	
Venus In Blue Jeans	7"	Pye	7N15466	1962	£1.50	£4	chart single

MUSIC MASTER PRICE GUIDE

Warmth Of Wynter	LP	Decca	LK4409	1961	£10	£25
We'll Sing In The Sunshine	7″	Pye	7N17122	1966	£1.50	£4
Wynter Time	7″ EP	Pye	NEP24185	1964	£6	£12
You Made Me What I Am	7″	Pye	7N17214	1966	£1.50	£4

X

X
Adult Books	7"	Dangerhouse	D88	1978	£10 ..... £20	
White Girl	7"	Slash	SRS106	1981	£1.50 ..... £4	

X MEN
Ghosts	7"	Creation	CRE006	1984	£2.50 ..... £6	
Spiral Girl	7"	Creation	CRE014	1985	£2 ..... £5	

XERO
Oh Baby	7"	Brickyard	XERO1	1983	£1.50 ..... £4	
Oh Baby	12"	Brickyard	XERO1T	1983	£4 ..... £10	

XHOL
Electrip	LP	Hansa	80099	1969	£20 ..... £40	German
Hauruk	LP	Ohr	OMM56014	1970	£6 ..... £15	German
Motherfuckers GmbH And Co Kg	LP	Ohr	OMM56024	1972	£6 ..... £15	German

XL5
XL5	7"	HMV	POP1148	1963	£4 ..... £8	

XMAL DEUTSCHLAND
Incubus Succubus II	7"	4AD	AD311	1983	£1.50 ..... £4	

X-RAY SPEX
Day The World Turned Day-Glo	7"	EMI	INT553	1978	£1.50 ..... £4	orange vinyl
Germ Free Adolescents	LP	EMI	INS3023	1978	£6 ..... £15	chart LP
Highly Inflammable	7"	EMI	INT583	1979	£1.50 ..... £4	red vinyl
Identity	7"	EMI	INT563	1978	£1.50 ..... £4	pink vinyl
Oh Bondage, Up Yours	7"	Virgin	VS189	1977	£5 ..... £10	PS

X-RAYS
Out Of Control	7"	London	HLR8805	1959	£10 ..... £20	

XS ENERGY
Eighteen	7"	World	WRECK1	1978	£2.50 ..... £6	

XTC
3D EP (Science Friction)	7"	Virgin	VS188	1977	£100 ..... £200	
Drums And Wires	LP	Virgin	V2129	1979	£4 ..... £10	with 7" (VDJ30)
Go 2	LP	Virgin	V2108	1978	£4 ..... £10	with Go& 12'
Love On A Farmboy's Wages	7"	Virgin	VS613	1983	£1.50 ..... £4	double

XTRAVERTS
Blank Generation	7"	Spike	SRTSSP001	198-	£5 ..... £10	no PS

XXX
Live	LP	private			£40 ..... £80	US

Y

Y & T
Yesterday & Today .... LP ...... London .... PS677 .... 1976 ... £8 ....£20 .... US

Y BLEW
Maes B .... 7" ...... Qualiton........... QSP7001 .... 1967 ... £4 ....£8 ....PS

Y TRWYNAU COCH
Merched Dan 15 .... 7" ...... Recordian   RSROC002 .... 1978 ... £2 ....£5
    Sqwar ....
Rhedeg Rhag Y Torpidos .... LP ..... Recordian   OCHR2198 .... 198- ... £6 ....£15
    Coch................
Wastod Ar Y Tu Fas .... 7" .... 197- ... £2 ....£5

YA HO WA
Golden Sunrise .... LP ..... Psycho .... PSYCHO2 .... 1983 ... £20 ....£40
I'm Gonna Take You Home .... LP ..... Higher Key...... 3309 .... 1974 ... £50 ....£100 .... US
Penetration .... LP ..... Higher Key...... .... 1974 ... £20 ....£40 .... US
Savage Sons Of Ya Ho Wa .... LP ..... Higher Key...... 3306 .... 1974 ... £50 ....£100 .... US
To The Principles For The Children ...... LP ..... Higher Key...... .... 197- ... £330 ....£500 .... US
Ya Ho Wa .... LP ..... Higher Key...... .... 1974 ... £25 ....£50 .... US
Ya Ho Wa .... LP ..... Higher Key...... .... 1974 ... £150 .....£250 .... US, sheep
    shag cover, double
Ya Ho Wa 2 .... LP ..... Higher Key...... .... 197- ... £50 ....£100 .... US
Yod Ship Suite .... LP ..... Father .... 1975 ... £50 ....£100 .... US

YAKS
Yakety Yak .... 7" ...... Decca .... F12115 .... 1965 ... £4 ....£8

YAMASH'TA, STOMU
Japanese percussionist Stomu Yamash'ta came to Britain during the early seventies and amazed the classical music world with his virtuosity. The two LPs listed here contain works by some of the leading contemporary classical composers which allow Yamash'ta to show off his formidable technique - the L'Oiseau Lyre record has percussion as the only instrumentation. Interestingly, Yamash'ta discovered progressive rock and completely changed his musical policy with a number of jazz-rock albums. Perhaps he realised that this was where the most vital musical developments were taking place, although the cynic might argue that he merely realised that there was more money to be made out of rock music.
Henze/Takemitsu/Maxwell Davies .... LP ..... L'Oiseau Lyre .. DSLO1 .... 1972 ... £5 ....£12
Takemitsu Ishii .... LP ..... EMI.................. EMD5508 .... 1973 ... £5 ....£12

YANA
Climb Up The Wall .... 7" ...... HMV .... POP252 .... 1956 ... £4 ....£8
I Miss You Mama .... 7" ...... HMV .... POP481 .... 1958 ... £2 ....£5
Mr.Wonderful .... 7" ...... HMV .... POP340 .... 1957 ... £2.50 ......£6
Papa And Mama .... 7" ...... HMV .... POP546 .... 1958 ... £1.50 ......£4

YANCEY, JIMMY
Jimmy And Mama Yancey .... LP ..... Gannet .... 5137 .... 195- ... £5 ....£12
Jimmy And Mama Yancey .... 10" LP Atlantic .... 130 .... 195- ... £15 ....£30 .... US
Jimmy And Mama Yancey .... 10" LP Atlantic .... 134 .... 195- ... £15 ....£30 .... US
Jimmy Yancey .... 7" EP. HMV .... 7EG8062 .... 1954 ... £5 ....£10
Jimmy Yancey .... 7" EP.. Vogue .... EPV1203 .... 1958 ... £5 ....£10
Jimmy Yancey .... 10" LP Vogue .... LDE166 .... 1956 ... £8 ....£20
Lost Recording Date .... 10" LP London .... AL3525 .... 1954 ... £8 ....£20
Lowdown Dirty Blues .... LP ..... Atlantic .... 590018.................. 1968 ... £5 ....£12
Pure Blues .... LP ..... Atlantic .... 1231 .... 1956 ... £10 ....£25 .... US
Yancey Special .... 10" LP Atlantic .... 103 .... 195- ... £15 ....£30 .... US
Yancey's Piano .... 7" EP.. HMV .... 7EG8083 .... 1955 ... £5 ....£10

YANCEY, MAMA & DON EWELL
Mama Yancey And Don Ewell .... 10" LP Tempo .... LAP7 .... 1957 ... £8 ....£20

YANKEE DOLLAR
Yankee Dollar .... LP ..... Dot .... DLP25874 .... 1968 ... £6 ....£15 .... US

YANOVSKY, ZALMAN
Alive & Well In Argentina .... LP ..... Buddah .... BDS5019 .... 1968 ... £5 ....£12 .... US
Alive & Well In Argentina .... LP ..... Kama Sutra ..... 2316003 .... 1971 ... £4 ....£10
As Long As You're Here .... 7" ...... Pye .... 7N25438................ 1967 ... £1.50 ......£4

YARDBIRDS
All of the Yardbirds' innovative original records are now collectable - even the chart hits - although the rarest come from right at the start of the group's career, and right at the end. The single "Goodnight Sweet Josephine" definitely does exist, despite occasional murmerings to the contrary, although possibly only as a demo. Meanwhile, the LP "Live Yardbirds", ruined, according to the group, by the engineers miking Jimmy Page's monitor speaker rather than the real thing, and also by its extravagant over-dubbed applause, was given two releases and rapidly withdrawn each time. Counterfeits exist, but these have black and white covers, rather than the colour of the originals.
Evil Hearted You .... 7" ...... Columbia .... DB7706.................. 1965 ... £2 ....£5 ....chart single
Face And Place .... LP ..... Direction .... 1964 ... £25 ....£50 .... New Zealand
Five Live Yardbirds .... LP ..... Columbia .... 33SX1677 .... 1964 ... £15 ....£30
Five Live Yardbirds .... LP ..... Columbia .... 33SX1677 .... 1969 ... £4 ....£10 . black and white label
Five Yardbirds .... 7" EP. Columbia .... SEG8421 .... 1965 ... £15 ....£30
For Your Love .... LP ..... Epic .... LN24167/BN26167 1965 ... £15 ....£30 .... US
For Your Love .... 7" ...... Columbia .... DB7499.................. 1965 ... £2 ....£5 ....chart single

Title	Format	Label	Catalogue	Year	Price	Price	Notes
For Your Love	7" EP	Riviera	231074	1965	£15	£30	French
Good Morning Little Schoolgirl	7"	Columbia	DB7391	1964	£4	£8	chart single
Goodnight Sweet Josephine	7"	Columbia	DB8368	1968	£75	£150	demo
Greatest Hits	LP	Epic	LN24246/BN26246	1966	£8	£20	US
Happening Ten Years Time Ago	7"	Columbia	DB8024	1966	£7.50	£15	chart single
Happening Ten Years Time Ago	7" EP	Riviera	231220	1966	£15	£30	French
Having A Rave Up	LP	Columbia	SCXC28	1966	£25	£50	export
Having A Rave Up	LP	Epic	LN24177/BN26177	1965	£10	£25	US
Heart Full Of Sound	7"	Columbia	DB7594	1965	£2	£5	chart single
Heart Full Of Sound	7" EP	Riviera	231099	1965	£15	£30	French
I Wish You Would	7"	Columbia	DB7283	1964	£5	£10	
Little Games	LP	Epic	LN24313/BN26313	1967	£15	£30	US
Little Games	7"	Columbia	DB8165	1967	£10	£20	
Little Games	7" EP	Riviera	231242	1967	£25	£50	French
Live Featuring Jimmy Page	LP	Columbia	P13311	1972	£15	£30	US, colour cover
Live Featuring Jimmy Page	LP	Epic	KE30615	1971	£20	£40	US, colour cover
Over Under Sideways Down	LP	Epic	LN24210/BN26210	1966	£10	£25	US
Over Under Sideways Down	7"	Columbia	DB7928	1966	£4	£8	chart single
Over Under Sideways Down	7" EP	Riviera	231196	1966	£15	£30	French
Paf Bum	7"	Ricordi International	SIR20010	1966	£10	£20	Italian
Shapes Of Things	7"	Columbia	DB7848	1966	£2	£5	chart single
Shapes Of Things	7" EP	Riviera	231170	1966	£15	£30	French
Still I'm Sad	7" EP	Riviera	231131	1965	£15	£30	French
With Sonny Boy Williamson	LP	Fontana	SFJL960	1968	£8	£20	
With Sonny Boy Williamson	LP	Fontana	TL5277	1964	£30	£60	
With Sonny Boy Williamson	LP	Philips	6435011	1971	£5	£12	
Yardbirds	LP	Columbia	SX/SCX6063	1966	£15	£30	chart LP
Yardbirds	LP	Epic	EG30135	1970	£8	£20	US
Yardbirds	LP	Epic	HE38455	1983	£8	£20	US audiophile
Yardbirds	7" EP	Columbia	SEG8521	1966	£70	£140	

YARDBIRDS & HERBIE HANCOCK

Title	Format	Label	Catalogue	Year	Price	Price	Notes
Blow-Up	LP	MGM	C8039	1967	£10	£25	

YATES, CHRIS

Title	Format	Label	Catalogue	Year	Price	Price	Notes
New Born	LP	ILSM		1977	£30	£60	US

YATES, TOM

Title	Format	Label	Catalogue	Year	Price	Price	Notes
Love Comes Well Armed	LP	President	PTLS1053	1972	£6	£15	
Second City Spiritual	LP	CBS	BPG63094	1967	£10	£25	
Song Of The Shimmering Way	LP	Satril	SATL4007	1977	£6	£15	

YATHA SIDHRA

Title	Format	Label	Catalogue	Year	Price	Price	Notes
Meditation Mass	LP	Brain	0001045	1974	£10	£25	German

YAZOO

Title	Format	Label	Catalogue	Year	Price	Price	Notes
Upstairs At Eric's	LP	Mute	STUMM7	1983	£6	£15	inner sleeve with happy faces/sad faces

YEAR ONE

Title	Format	Label	Catalogue	Year	Price	Price	Notes
Eli's Comin'	7"	Major Minor	MM660	1969	£2	£5	

YELLO

Title	Format	Label	Catalogue	Year	Price	Price	Notes
Goldrush	12"	Mercury	MERXD218	1986	£2.50	£6	double
Rhythm Divine	12"	Mercury	MERXR253	1987	£8	£20	
Tied Up In Life	12"	Mercury	YELLR212	1988	£2.50	£6	

YELLOW BALLOON

Title	Format	Label	Catalogue	Year	Price	Price	Notes
Stained Glass Window	7"	Stateside	SS2124	1968	£2	£5	
Yellow Balloon	LP	Canterbury	CLPM/CLPS1502	1967	£6	£15	US
Yellow Balloon	7"	Stateside	SS2008	1967	£4	£8	

YELLOW BELLOW ROOM BOOM

Title	Format	Label	Catalogue	Year	Price	Price	Notes
Seeing Things Green	7"	CBS	3205	1968	£5	£10	

YELLOW PAGES

Title	Format	Label	Catalogue	Year	Price	Price	Notes
Here Comes Jane	7"	Page One	POF090	1968	£2	£5	

YELLOW PAYGES

Title	Format	Label	Catalogue	Year	Price	Price	Notes
Little Woman	7"	UNI	UNS516	1970	£1.50	£4	
Volume One	LP	UNI	73045	1969	£5	£12	US

YELLOWSTONE & VOICE

Title	Format	Label	Catalogue	Year	Price	Price	Notes
Yellowstone & Voice	LP	Regal Zonophone	SRZA8511	1972	£5	£12	

YEMM AND YEMEN

Title	Format	Label	Catalogue	Year	Price	Price	Notes
Black Is The Night	7"	Columbia	DB8022	1966	£5	£10	

YES

Title	Format	Label	Catalogue	Year	Price	Price	Notes
Classic Yes	LP	Atlantic	K50842	1980	£10	£25	test pressing, different sleeve
Close To The Edge	LP	Mobile Fidelity	MFSL1077	1980	£6	£15	US audiophile
Fragile	LP	Atlantic	2401019	1971	£4	£10	
Going For The One	LP	Atlantic	DSK50379	1977	£5	£12	3 x 12', boxed
Interview	7"	Atlantic	SAM7	1972	£5	£10	promo
Interview/Five Songs	7"	Lyntone	LYN2536	197-	£5	£10	
Looking Around	7"	Atlantic	584298	1969	£25	£50	
Sweet Dreams	7"	Atlantic	2091004	1970	£10	£20	

Title	Format	Label	Catalogue	Year			Notes
Sweetness	7"	Atlantic	584280	1969	£15	£30	
Time And A Word	LP	Atlantic	2400006	1970	£4	£10	lyric sheet, chart LP
Time And A Word	7"	Atlantic	584323	1970	£10	£20	
Yes	LP	Atlantic	588190	1969	£4	£10	lyric sheet
Yes Album	LP	Atlantic	2400101	1971	£4	£10	
Yes Solos	LP	Atlantic	PR260	1976	£8	£20	US promo compilation

YESTERDAY'S CHILDREN
Title	Format	Label	Catalogue	Year			Notes
To Be Or Not To Be	7" EP	DiscAZ	1101	1967	£6	£12	French

YETTIES
Title	Format	Label	Catalogue	Year			Notes
Dorset Is Beautiful	LP	Argo	ZFB38	1972	£5	£12	
Fifty Stone Of Loveliness	LP	Acorn	CF203	1969	£6	£15	

YOGI, MAHARISHI MAHESH
Title	Format	Label	Catalogue	Year			Notes
Maharishi Mahesh Yogi	LP	Liberty	LBS83075E	1967	£5	£12	

YOLANDA
Title	Format	Label	Catalogue	Year			Notes
With This Kiss	7"	Triumph	RGM1007	1960	£7.50	£15	

YORK BROTHERS
Title	Format	Label	Catalogue	Year			Notes
Country And Western	7" EP	Parlophone	GEP8736	1958	£5	£10	
Country And Western No.2	7" EP	Parlophone	GEP8753	1958	£6	£12	
Sixteen Great Country & Western Hits	LP	King	820	1963	£5	£12	US
Strange Town	7"	Parlophone	CMSP22	1954	£2	£5	export
Why Don't You Open The Door	7"	Parlophone	CMSP5	1954	£2	£5	export
York Brothers	LP	King	586	1958	£6	£15	US
York Brothers Vol.2	LP	King	591	1958	£6	£15	US

YORK, NOLA
Title	Format	Label	Catalogue	Year			Notes
Here I Stand	7"	HMV	POP1326	1964	£1.50	£4	

YORK, PETE
Title	Format	Label	Catalogue	Year			Notes
Pete York Percussion Band	LP	Decca	TXS109	1972	£5	£12	

YORK POP MUSIC PROJECT
Title	Format	Label	Catalogue	Year			Notes
All Day	LP	private		1973	£50	£100	

YORK, RUSTY
Title	Format	Label	Catalogue	Year			Notes
Peggy Sue	7"	Parlophone	R4398	1958	£180	£300	demo only

YOU KNOW WHO GROUP
Title	Format	Label	Catalogue	Year			Notes
My Love	7" EP	Kapp	KEV13016	1965	£5	£10	French, B side by Angelo & Initials
Roses Are Red My Love	7"	London	HLR9947	1965	£2	£5	
You Know Who Group	LP	International Allied	420	1965	£15	£30	US

YOULDEN, CHRIS
Title	Format	Label	Catalogue	Year			Notes
City Child	LP	Deram	SML1112	1974	£5	£12	
Nowhere Road	LP	Deram	SML1099	1973	£5	£12	

YOUNG & MOODY BAND
Title	Format	Label	Catalogue	Year			Notes
Don't Do That	7"	Bronze	BRO130	1981	£1.50	£4	

YOUNG BLOOD
Title	Format	Label	Catalogue	Year			Notes
Continuing Story Of Bungalow Bill	7"	Pye	7N17696	1969	£2	£5	
Green Light	7"	Pye	7N17495	1968	£2.50	£6	
I Can't Stop	7"	Pye	7N17627	1968	£2.50	£6	
Just How Loud	7"	Pye	7N17588	1968	£2	£5	

YOUNG, BRETT
Title	Format	Label	Catalogue	Year			Notes
Guess What	7"	Pye	7N15578	1963	£2	£5	
You Can't Fool Me	7"	Pye	7N15641	1964	£2	£5	

YOUNG BROTHERS
Title	Format	Label	Catalogue	Year			Notes
High Energy Rock	LP	GDM		1978	£10	£25	US, gold vinyl

YOUNG, CECIL
Title	Format	Label	Catalogue	Year			Notes
Cool Jazz	10" LP	Vogue	LDE003	1953	£8	£20	

YOUNG, DARREN
Title	Format	Label	Catalogue	Year			Notes
My Tears Will Turn To Laughter	7"	Parlophone	R4919	1963	£4	£8	

YOUNG, FARON
Title	Format	Label	Catalogue	Year			Notes
Country Dance Favourites	LP	Mercury	20025MCL	1964	£4	£10	
Every Time I'm Kissing You	7"	Capitol	CL14891	1958	£2	£5	
Five Dollars And It's Saturday Night	7"	Capitol	CL14655	1956	£5	£10	
Hello Walls	7" EP	Capitol	EAP11549	1961	£4	£8	
I Can't Dance	7"	Capitol	CL14860	1958	£5	£10	
I Hate Myself	7"	Capitol	CL14930	1958	£1.50	£4	
I Hear You Talkin'	7"	Capitol	CL15050	1959	£1.50	£4	
If You Ain't Lovin'	7"	Capitol	CL14754	1956	£5	£10	
Live Fast, Love Hard, Die Young	7"	Capitol	CL14336	1955	£7.50	£15	
Long Time Ago	7"	Capitol	CL14975	1959	£1.50	£4	
Memory Lane	LP	Capitol	(S)T2037	1965	£4	£10	
Moonlight Mountain	7"	Capitol	CL14762	1957	£2	£5	
Object Of My Affection	LP	Capitol	T1004	1958	£5	£12	
Shrine Of St.Cecilia	7"	Capitol	CL14735	1957	£2.50	£6	
Snowball	7"	Capitol	CL14822	1958	£2	£5	
Story Songs For Country Folk	LP	Mercury	20026MCL	1964	£4	£10	

Sweethearts Or Strangers	LP	Capitol	T778	1957	£6	£15	US
Sweethearts Or Strangers Pt.1	7″ EP.	Capitol	EAP1778	1957	£4	£8	
Sweethearts Or Strangers Pt.2	7″ EP.	Capitol	EAP2778	1957	£4	£8	
Sweethearts Or Strangers Pt.3	7″ EP.	Capitol	EAP3778	1957	£4	£8	
That's The Way It's Gotta Be	7″	Capitol	CL15004	1959	£1.50	£4	
This Is Faron Young	LP	Capitol	T1096	1963	£5	£12	
Vacation's Over	7″	Capitol	CL14793	1957	£4	£8	

YOUNG FLOWERS

Blomsterpistolen	LP	Sonet		1968	£40	£80	
Volume 2	LP	Polydor		1969	£40	£80	

YOUNG, GEORGIE

Nine More Miles	7″	London	HLU8748	1958	£4	£8	

YOUNG GROWLER

Amy The Sunbather	7″	Columbia	DB7870	1966	£1.50	£4	
V For Victory	7″	Columbia	DB7958	1966	£1.50	£4	
V For Victory	7″ EP.	Columbia	SEG8502	1966	£2	£5	

YOUNG, HARRY

Show Me The Way	7″	Dot	DS16756	1965	£4	£8	

YOUNG IDEA

Gotta Get Out The Mess	7″	Columbia	DB8067	1966	£1.50	£4	
Mr.Lovin' Luggage Man	7″	Columbia	DB8284	1967	£1.50	£4	
Peculiar Situation	7″	Columbia	DB8132	1967	£1.50	£4	
With A Little Help From My Friends	LP	MFP	MFP1225	1968	£4	£10	
With A Little Help From My Friends	7″	Columbia	DB8205	1967	£1.50	£4	chart single
World's Been Good To Me	7″	Columbia	DB7961	1966	£2	£5	

YOUNG, JESSE COLIN

Soul Of A City Boy	LP	Capitol	(S)T2070	1964	£6	£15	US
Youngblood	LP	Mercury	MG2/SR61005	1965	£6	£15	US

YOUNG JESSIE

Shuffle In The Gravel	7″	London	HLE8544	1958	£75	£150	

YOUNG, JIMMY

Baby Cried	7″	Decca	F10232	1954	£2.50	£6	
Chain Gang	7″	Decca	F10694	1956	£4	£8	chart single
Deep Blue Sea	7″	Decca	F10948	1957	£1.50	£4	
Give Me Your Word	7″	Decca	F10406	1954	£2.50	£6	
If Anyone Finds This	7″	Decca	F10483	1955	£2	£5	
Jimmy Young	7″ EP.	Decca	DFE6404	1957	£2	£5	
Jimmy Young Sings	7″ EP.	Pye	NEP24004	1955	£2	£5	
Lovin' Baby	7″	Decca	F10842	1957	£2	£5	
Man From Laramie	7″	Decca	F10597	1955	£5	£10	chart single
Man On Fire	7″	Decca	F10925	1957	£1.50	£4	
More	7″	Decca	F10774	1956	£4	£8	chart single
Presenting Jimmy Young	7″ EP.	Decca	DFE6277	1956	£2	£5	
Rich Man Poor Man	7″	Decca	F10736	1956	£2.50	£6	chart single
Round And Round	7″	Decca	F10875	1957	£1.50	£4	chart single
Someone On Your Mind	7″	Decca	F10640	1955	£4	£8	chart single
These Are The Things We'll Share	7″	Decca	F10444	1955	£2	£5	
Unchained Melody	7″	Decca	F10502	1955	£5	£10	chart single

YOUNG, JOHNNY

Fat Mandolin	LP	Blue Horizon	763852	1970	£15	£30	
Step Back	7″	Decca	F22548	1967	£2.50	£6	

YOUNG, KAREN

Are You Kidding	7″	Mercury	MF943	1965	£2	£5	
Me And My Mini Skirt	7″ EP.	Fontana	460979	1966	£5	£10	French
Too Much Of A Good Thing	7″	Major Minor	MM584	1968	£2.50	£6	
We'll Start The Party Again	7″	Pye	7N15956	1965	£2.50	£6	

YOUNG, KATHY & THE INNOCENTS

Happy Birthday Blues	7″	Top Rank	JAR554	1961	£4	£8	
Innocently Yours	LP	Indigo	503	1961	£25	£50	US
Sound Of Kathy Young	LP	Indigo	504	1961	£25	£50	US
Thousand Stars	7″	Top Rank	JAR534	1961	£7.50	£15	

YOUNG, LAMONTE

Theatre Of Eternal Music	LP	Shandar	8350	1973	£6	£15	French

YOUNG, LARRY

Contrasts	LP	Blue Note	BLP/BST84266	1967	£15	£30	
Heaven On Earth	LP	Blue Note	BST84304	1968	£10	£25	
Into Somethin'	LP	Blue Note	BLP/BST84187	1964	£25	£50	
Of Love And Peace	LP	Blue Note	BLP/BST84242	1966	£15	£30	
Unity	LP	Blue Note	BLP/BST84221	1965	£20	£40	

YOUNG, LEON STRINGS

Glad All Over	7″	Pye	7N15646	1964	£5	£10	

YOUNG, LESTER

Battle Of THe Saxes	10″ LP	Felsted	EDL87014	1955	£25	£50	
Blue Lester	LP	London	LTZC15132	1958	£15	£30	
Greatest	LP	Vogue	LAE12194	1960	£8	£20	
Jazz Giants '56	LP	Columbia	33CX10054	1956	£20	£40	

Leaps Again	LP	Fontana	FJL128	1966	£4	£10	
Lester Young	LP	Vogue	LAE12016	1956	£15	£30	
Lester Young	7" EP	Vogue	EPV1127	1956	£2.50	£6	
Lester Young	10" LP	Columbia	33C9015	1956	£25	£50	
Lester Young And His Tenor Sax	LP	Liberty	LBY3048	1965	£4	£10	
Lester Young And The Kansas City Five	LP	Stateside	SL10002	1962	£5	£12	
Memorial Album Vol.1	LP	Fontana	TFL5064	1959	£8	£20	
Memorial Album Vol.2	LP	Fontana	TFL5065	1960	£8	£20	
Pres	LP	Columbia	33CX10070	1957	£20	£40	
Pres And Teddy	LP	HMV	CLP1302	1959	£10	£25	with Teddy Wilson
President	LP	Columbia	33CX10031	1956	£25	£50	
Prez	LP	Columbia	TL5260	1965	£5	£12	
With The Oscar Peterson Trio	10" LP	Columbia	33C9001	1955	£25	£50	

YOUNG, MIGHTY JOE

Legacy Of The Blues Vol.4	LP	Sonet	SNTF633	1972	£4	£10	
Why Don't You Follow Me	7"	Parlophone	R5794	1969	£5	£10	

YOUNG, NEIL

Neil Young's blend of electric guitar overkill and acoustic folkiness was established quite early in his long career. It seems extraordinary, therefore, how his reputation among modern critics has become transformed in recent years. The man who was once dismissed as a "boring old fart" is now extravagantly lauded for music that is hardly distinguishable from that which earned the condemnation. This critic finds Young's electric music to be frequently exhilarating, is bored by much of the acoustic stuff, but is glad that Neil Young is still around to show that a rock attitude and rock creativity do not have to be the exclusive preserve of youth.

After The Goldrush	LP	Reprise	RSLP6383	1970	£4	£10	chart LP
Conversation With Neil Young	LP	Warner Bros		1980	£8	£20	US promo
Don't Be Denied	7"	Reprise	SAM15	197-	£2.50	£6	1 sided promo
Down By The River	7"	Reprise	RS23462	1969	£4	£8	
Everybody Knows This Is Nowhere	LP	Reprise	RSLP6349	1969	£5	£12	
Everybody Knows This Is Nowhere	7"	Reprise	0819	1969	£25	£50	US promo, alternate version
Everybody's Rockin'	LP	Geffen		1983	£8	£20	US audiophile promo
Harvest	LP	Nautilus		1981	£15	£15	US audiophile
Loner	7"	Reprise	RS23405	1969	£4	£8	
Neil Young	LP	Reprise	RSLP6317	1969	£5	£12	
Neil Young	LP	Reprise	RSLP6317	1969	£6	£15	No name on front cover
Oh Lonesome Me	7"	Reprise	RS20861	1970	£2.50	£6	
Only Love Can Break Your Heart	7"	Reprise	RS20958	1970	£1.50	£4	
Trans	LP	Geffen	GHS2018	1982	£8	£20	US audiophile promo
When You Dance I Can Really Love	7"	Reprise	RS23488	1971	£1.50	£4	

YOUNG ONES

Baby That's It	7"	Decca	F11705	1963	£4	£8	

YOUNG, RALPH

Bible Tells Me So	7"	Brunswick	05466	1955	£2.50	£6	
Bring Me A Bluebird	7"	Brunswick	05500	1955	£1.50	£4	
Legend Of Wyatt Earp	7"	Brunswick	05605	1956	£1.50	£4	

YOUNG, ROGER

Sweet Sweet Morning	7"	Columbia	DB7869	1966	£2	£5	

YOUNG, ROY

Big Fat Mamma	7"	Fontana	H200	1959	£6	£12	
Four And Twenty Thousand Kisses	7"	Ember	EMBS128	1961	£2.50	£6	
Granny's Got A Painted Leg	7"	RCA	RCA2031	1970	£1.50	£4	
Hey Little Girl	7"	Fontana	H215	1959	£4	£8	
I Hardly Know It	7"	Fontana	H237	1960	£5	£10	
I'm In Love	7"	Fontana	H247	1960	£2.50	£6	
Plenty Of Love	7"	Fontana	H290	1961	£4	£8	
Roy Young Band	LP	RCA	SF8161	1971	£4	£10	

YOUNG SISTERS

Cassanova Brown	7"	London	HLU9610	1962	£1.50	£4	

YOUNG SOULS

Why Did You Leave	7"	Amalgamated	AMG844	1969	£4	£8	

YOUNG, STEVE

Rock Salt And Nails	LP	A&M	4177	1969	£8	£20	US

YOUNG, TERRY

Joe's Been A Gittin' There	7"	Pye	7N15416	1962	£1.50	£4	
Maverick	7"	Pye	7N15321	1961	£1.50	£4	
Now, Forever And A Day	7"	Pye	7N15353	1961	£1.50	£4	

YOUNG TRADITION

Boar's Head Carol	7"	Argo	AFW115	1974	£1.50	£4	
Chicken On A Raft	7" EP	Transatlantic	TRAEP164	1968	£10	£20	
Galleries	LP	Transatlantic	TRA172	1968	£8	£20	
Galleries Revisited	LP	Transatlantic	TRASAM30	1973	£5	£12	
So Cheerfully Round	LP	Transatlantic	TRA155	1967	£10	£25	
Young Tradition	LP	Transatlantic	TRA142	1966	£8	£20	
Young Tradition Sampler	LP	Transatlantic	TRASAM13	1969	£5	£12	

YOUNG, VICKI

Bye Bye Just For A While	7"	Capitol	CL14528	1956	£2	£5	
Hearts Of Stone	7"	Capitol	CL14228	1955	£6	£12	
Live Fast Love Hard Die Young	7"	Capitol	CL14281	1955	£5	£10	

Spanish Main	7"	Capitol	CL14653	1956	£2.50	£6
Vicki Young	7" EP	Capitol	EAP1593	1956	£7.50	£15

YOUNG, VICTOR
Cherry Pink And Apple Blossom White	7"	Brunswick	05448	1955	£1.50	£4

YOUNG WORLD SINGERS
Ringo For President	7"	Brunswick	05916	1964	£2	£5

YOUNGBLOODS
Darkness Darkness	7"	RCA	RCA1821	1969	£1.50	£4	
Earth Music	LP	RCA	LPM/LSP3865	1967	£4	£10	US
Elephant Mountain	LP	RCA	SF8026	1969	£4	£10	
Get Together	7"	RCA	RCA1877	1969	£1.50	£4	
Ride The Wind	LP	Warner Bros	K46100	1971	£4	£10	
Rock Festival	LP	Warner Bros	WS1878	1970	£4	£10	
Sunlight	LP	RCA	SF8218	1971	£4	£10	
Two Trips	LP	Mercury	6338019	1970	£4	£10	
Youngbloods	LP	RCA	LPM/LSP3724	1967	£4	£10	US

YOUNGFOLK
Lonely Girl	7"	President	PT136	1968	£2.50	£6

YOUNG-HOLT TRIO
Wack Wack	7"	Coral	Q72489	1967	£2.50	£6

YOUNG-HOLT UNLIMITED
Country Slicker Joe	7"	MCA	MU1053	1969	£2.50	£6
Soulful Strut	LP	MCA	MUPS368	1969	£6	£15

YOUTH
As Long As There Is Your Love	7"	Polydor	56121	1966	£4	£8

YOUTH (2)
At The Diorama	LP	Illuminated	JAMS41	1985	£4	£10
Empty Quarter	LP	Illuminated	JAMS36	1984	£6	£15

YOUTH BRIGADE
Youth Brigade EP	7"	Dischord	6	1981	£20	£40

YURO, TIMI
Amazing Timi Yuro	LP	Mercury	MG2/SR60963	1964	£5	£12	US
Amazing Yuro	LP	Mercury	20032MCL	1964	£4	£10	
As Long As There Is You	7"	Liberty	LIB15182	1969	£75	£150	
Best Of Timi Yuro	LP	Liberty	(S)LBY1290	1963	£5	£12	
Get Out Of My Life	7"	Mercury	MF859	1965	£10	£20	
Gotta Travel On	7"	Liberty	LIB55634	1963	£1.50	£4	
Great Performances	LP	Liberty	LBL/LBS83115	1968	£4	£10	
Hurt	LP	Liberty	LBY1247	1965	£6	£15	
Hurt	7"	Liberty	LIB10177	1964	£1.50	£4	
Hurt	7"	London	HLG9403	1961	£2.50	£6	
I Ain't Gonna Cry No More	7"	Liberty	LIB55519	1963	£5	£10	
I Must Have Been Out Of My Mind	7"	Liberty	LBF15142	1968	£5	£10	
If	7"	Mercury	MF826	1964	£1.50	£4	
In The Beginning	LP	Liberty	LBL/LBS83128	1968	£4	£10	
Let Me Call You Sweetheart	LP	Liberty	(S)LBY1275	1962	£5	£12	
Make The World Go Away	LP	Liberty	LBY1192	1963	£5	£12	
Make The World Go Away	7"	Liberty	LIB55587	1963	£2	£5	
Make The World Go Away	7" EP	Liberty	LEP2252	1966	£5	£10	
Once A Day	7"	Mercury	MF903	1965	£1.50	£4	
Satan Never Sleeps	7"	Liberty	LIB55410	1962	£1.50	£4	
Something Bad On My Mind	LP	Liberty	LBL/LBS83198	1968	£8	£20	
Soul	LP	Liberty	LBY1042	1962	£6	£15	
Soul	7" EP	Liberty	LEP2214	1965	£5	£10	
Talented	LP	Mercury	SMWL21019	1969	£4	£10	
Timi Yuro	LP	London	HAG2415	1962	£6	£15	
Timi Yuro	LP	Sunset	SUM1107/ SUS5107	1966	£4	£10	US
Turn The World Around The Other Way	7"	Mercury	MF949	1965	£1.50	£4	
What's A Matter Baby	LP	Liberty	(S)LBY1154	1963	£5	£12	
What's A Matter Baby	7"	Liberty	LIB55469	1962	£6	£12	
You Can Have Him	7"	Mercury	MF848	1965	£1.50	£4	

Z

Z, ROMEO
Come Back Baby Come Back	7"	CBS	202645	1967	£1.50	£4	

ZACHERLEY, JOHN
Dinner With Drac	7"	London	HLU8599	1958	£7.50	£15	
Monster Mash	LP	Parkway	P7018	1962	£8	£20	US
Scary Tales	LP	Parkway	P7023	1963	£8	£20	US
Spook Along With Zacherley	LP	Elektra	EKL/EKS7190	1960	£8	£20	US
Zacherley's Monster Gallery	LP	Crestview	CR(S7)803	1963	£8	£20	US

ZAGER & EVANS
In The Year 2525	7"	RCA	RCA1860	1969	£1.50	£4	chart single

ZAKARRIAS
Zakarrias	LP	Deram	SML1091	1971	£100	£200	

ZANG, TOMMY
Break The Chain	7"	HMV	POP611	1959	£1.50	£4	
Hey, Good Lookin'	7"	Polydor	NH66957	1962	£1.50	£4	
I Can't Hold Your Letters	7"	Polydor	NH66977	1962	£1.50	£4	
I'm Gonna Slip You Offa My Mind	7"	Polydor	NH66955	1962	£1.50	£4	
Just Call My Name	7"	Polydor	NH66980	1962	£1.50	£4	
Take These Chains From My Heart	7"	Polydor	NH66960	1962	£1.50	£4	

ZAPPA, FRANK

Critics have never known quite what to make of Frank Zappa. He was such a vastly talented musician and produced such a variety of material that they have tended to focus on just one of the things that he did (usually his satire) and then criticise the rest of his output for failing to measure up in this one area. The fact that Zappa was inclined to hide his art behind a smokescreen of vulgarity does not help, of course, nor does the fact that he was quite self-deprecating about works that are actually little short of being masterpieces. In ages past, many composers were virtuoso instrumentalists who wrote music which would enable them to display their prowess in public performance. Frank Zappa continued this tradition, and because he was working in the rock age and in America, his instrument was the electric guitar and the music he played is easily categorised as rock music. His best work, however, (and much of his output qualifies) transcends all the usual categories, emerging as a classical music for our time that is far more relevant, and probably far more durable, than most of what is actually produced under that name. The proof is as close as a copy of "Studio Tan", or "Uncle Meat", or "Ship Arriving Too Late To Save A Drowning Witch", or "The Perfect Stranger", or "The Grand Wazoo", or "Make A Jazz Noise Here", or... Frank Zappa will be much missed.

200 Motels	LP	United Artists	UDF50003	1971	£8	£20	with booklet
Absolutely Free	LP	Verve	(S)VLP9174	1967	£15	£30	
Absolutely Free	LP	Verve	2317035	1971	£8	£20	
Apostrophe	LP	Discreet	K59201	1973	£4	£10	
Apostrophe	LP	Discreet	MS42175	1973	£8	£20	US quad
Baby Snakes	LP	Barking Pumpkin	BPR1115	1983	£8	£20	pic disc
Baby Take Your Teeth Out	7"	EMI	EMI5499	1984	£1.50	£4	
Big Leg Emma	7"	Verve	VS557	1967	£15	£30	US
Bongo Fury	LP	Discreet	DS2234	1975	£5	£12	
Bongo Fury	LP	Discreet	K59209	1975	£35	£70	test pressing only
Burnt Weeny Sandwich	LP	Reprise	K44083	1971	£5	£12	
Burnt Weeny Sandwich	LP	Reprise	RSLP6370	1969	£6	£15	chart LP
Burnt Weeny Sandwich/Weasels Ripped My Flesh	LP	Reprise	K64024	1979	£6	£15	double
Chunga's Revenge	LP	Reprise	K44020	1971	£5	£12	
Chunga's Revenge	LP	Reprise	RSLP2030	1970	£6	£15	green cover
Chunga's Revenge	LP	Reprise	RSLP2030	1970	£5	£12	red cover, chart LP
Clean Cuts From Sheik Yerbouti	LP	Zappa	MK78	1980	£8	£20	US promo
Clean Cuts From Tinseltown Rebellion	LP	Barking Pumpkin	AS995	1981	£8	£20	US promo
Clean Cuts From You Are What You Is	LP	Barking Pumpkin	AS1294	1981	£8	£20	US promo
Cosmic Debris	7"	Discreet	K19201	1973	£5	£10	
Dancin' Fool	7"	CBS	7261	1979	£1.50	£4	
Don't Eat The Yellow Snow	7"	Discreet	K19205	1973	£5	£10	
Drafted	7"	CBS	8625	1980	£2	£5	
Fillmore East 1971	LP	Reprise	K44150	1971	£5	£12	
Frank Zappa & The Mothers Of Invention	LP	Verve	2352057	1975	£6	£15	
Freak Out	LP	Verve	(S)VLP9154	1966	£17.50	£35	
Freak Out	LP	Verve	2683004	1971	£10	£25	double
Freak Out	LP	Verve	V(6)5005	1966	£25	£50	US, with map insert
Grand Wazoo	LP	Reprise	K44209	1972	£5	£12	
Hot Rats	LP	Reprise	K44078	1971	£4	£10	
Hot Rats	LP	Reprise	RSLP6356	1969	£6	£15	chart LP
Hot Rats	LP	Reprise	RSLP6356	1969	£30	£60	with Zappa/Beefheart argument
It Can't Happen Here	7"	Verve	VS545	1966	£20	£40	
Joe's Garage	7"	CBS	7950	1980	£7.50	£15	mispress with Bob Dylan B side
Joe's Garage Act 1	LP	CBS	86101	1979	£5	£12	with lyric sheet, chart LP
Joe's Garage Acts 2/3	LP	CBS	88475	1979	£6	£15	double, lyric sheets, chart LP

Title	Format	Label	Catalogue	Year	Price	Price	Notes
Just Another Band From L.A.	LP	Reprise	K44179	1972	£5	£12	
Lather	LP	Columbia	41500	1976	£700	£1000	4 LPs, test pressings
Lumpy Gravy	LP	Verve	(S)VLP9223	1968	£15	£30	
Lumpy Gravy	LP	Verve	2317046	1971	£8	£20	
Man From Utopia	LP	CBS	25251	1983	£4	£10	with lyric sheet, chart LP
Man From Utopia	7"	CBS	XPS180	1983	£5	£10	promo only
Mothermania	LP	Verve	(S)VLP9239	1969	£10	£25	
Mothermania	LP	Verve	2317047	1971	£8	£20	
Mothers Of Invention	LP	MGM	GAS112	1970	£8	£20	US
One Size Fits All	LP	Discreet	K59207	1974	£5	£12	
Orchestral Favourites	LP	Discreet	K59212	1979	£4	£10	
Overnight Sensation	LP	Discreet	K41000	1973	£5	£12	
Overnight Sensation	LP	Discreet	MS42149	1973	£8	£20	US quad
Roxy And Elsewhere	LP	Discreet	K69201	1974	£6	£15	double
Ruben And The Jets	LP	Verve	(S)VLP9327	1968	£15	£30	
Ruben And The Jets	LP	Verve	2317069	1971	£8	£20	
Ruben And The Jets	LP	Verve	V65055	1968	£25	£50	US, with three inserts
Sheik Yerbouti	LP	CBS	88339	1979	£5	£12	double, chart LP
Ship Arriving Too Late....Sampler	LP	Barking Pumpkin	AS1569	1982	£5	£12	US promo
Shut Up And Play Your Guitar	LP	CBS	66368	1981	£10	£25	triple
Shut Up And Play Your Guitar	7"	CBS	XPS147	1981	£2.50	£6	
Sleep Dirt	LP	Discreet	K59211	1978	£4	£10	
Studio Tan	LP	Discreet	K59210	1978	£4	£10	
Tears Began To Fall	7"	Reprise	K14100	1971	£10	£20	
Tears Began To Fall	7"	Reprise	K14120	1971	£2	£5	
Thingfish	LP	EMI	2402943	1985	£10	£25	with libretto
Uncle Meat	LP	Bizarre	MS2024	1969	£6	£15	double
Uncle Meat	LP	Transatlantic	TRA197	1969	£10	£25	double
Uncle Meat	LP	Transatlantic	TRA197	1969	£15	£30	double, booklet
Valley Girl	7"	CBS	A2412	1982	£1.50	£4	
Waka Jawaka	LP	Reprise	K44203	1972	£5	£12	
Weasels Ripped My Flesh	LP	Reprise	K44019	1971	£4	£10	
Weasels Ripped My Flesh	LP	Reprise	RSLP2028	1970	£5	£12	chart LP
Welcome To Joe's Garage	LP	Zappa	MK129	1981	£8	£20	US promo
We're Only In It For The Money	LP	Verve	(S)VLP9199	1967	£15	£30	chart LP
We're Only In It For The Money	LP	Verve	(S)VLP9199	1967	£17.50	£35	with insert
We're Only In It For The Money	LP	Verve	2317034	1971	£8	£20	
What Will This Evening..	7"	United Artists	UP35319	1971	£10	£20	
Worst Of The Mothers	LP	MGM	SE4754	1971	£8	£20	US
XXXX Of The Mothers Of Invention	LP	Verve	V65074	1969	£8	£20	US
You Are What You Is	7"	CBS	1622	1981	£2	£5	
You Are What You Is	12"	CBS	A121622	1981	£3	£8	pic disc
Zappa In New York	LP	Discreet	K69204	1977	£6	£15	double, chart LP
Zappa In New York	LP	Discreet	K69204	1977	£20	£40	double, with 'Punky's Whips'
Zapped	LP	Warner Bros	PRO368	1969	£10	£25	US, collage cover
Zapped	LP	Warner Bros	PRO368	1969	£6	£15	US, photo cover
Zoot Allures	LP	Warner Bros	K56298	1976	£5	£12	

ZARATHUSTRA

Title	Format	Label	Catalogue	Year	Price	Price	Notes
Zarathustra	LP	Metronome		1971	£25	£50	

ZEAR, PETE

Title	Format	Label	Catalogue	Year	Price	Price	Notes
Tomorrow's World	7"		22-1	1984	£2.50	£6	

ZENITH SIX

Title	Format	Label	Catalogue	Year	Price	Price	Notes
At The Royal Festival Hall	7" EP	Decca	DFE6255	1956	£4	£8	
Zenith Six	7" EP	Tempo	EXA42	1957	£4	£8	
Zenith Six	7" EP	Tempo	EXA58	1957	£4	£8	

ZEPHYR

Title	Format	Label	Catalogue	Year	Price	Price	Notes
Going Back To Colorado	LP	Warner Bros	BS1897	1971	£8	£20	US
Sunset Ride	LP	Warner Bros	BS2603	1972	£8	£20	US
Zephyr	LP	Probe	SPB1006	1970	£10	£25	

ZEPHYRS

Title	Format	Label	Catalogue	Year	Price	Price	Notes
I Just Can't Take It	7"	Columbia	DB7571	1965	£5	£10	
Little Bit Of Soap	7"	Columbia	DB7324	1964	£5	£10	
She's Lost You	7"	Columbia	DB7481	1965	£5	£10	chart single
Sweet Little Baby	7"	Columbia	DB7199	1964	£5	£10	
What's All That About	7"	Decca	F11647	1963	£7.50	£15	
Wonder What I'm Gonna Do	7"	Columbia	DB7410	1964	£5	£10	

ZERO BOYS

Title	Format	Label	Catalogue	Year	Price	Price	Notes
Living In The 80's	7"	Z Disc	6	1981	£35	£70	
Vicious Circle	LP	Nimrod		1982	£10	£25	

ZERO FIVE

Title	Format	Label	Catalogue	Year	Price	Price	Notes
Dusty	7"	Columbia	DB7751	1965	£2	£5	

ZEVON, WARREN

Title	Format	Label	Catalogue	Year	Price	Price	Notes
Wanted Dead Or Alive	LP	Imperial	LP12456	1969	£6	£15	US
Werewolves Of London	12"	Asylum	AS11386	1978	£4	£10	US pic disc

ZIMMERMAN, TUCKER

Title	Format	Label	Catalogue	Year	Price	Price	Notes
Red Wind	7"	Regal Zonophone	RZ3020	1969	£1.50	£4	
Ten Songs By Tucker Zimmerman	LP	Regal Zonophone	SLRZ1010	1969	£6	£15	

Tucker Zimmerman	LP	Village Thing	VTS13	1972	£5	£12	

ZIOR
Cat's Eyes	7"	Nepentha	6129003	1973	£4	£8	
Za Za Za Zilda	7"	Nepentha	6129002	1971	£2.50	£6	
Zior	LP	Nepentha	6437005	1971	£15	£30	

ZIP CODES
Mustang	LP	Liberty	LRP3367/LST7367	1964	£6	£15	US

ZIPPER
Zipper	LP	Whizeagle		1975	£8	£20	US

ZITRO
Zitro	LP	ESP		1967	£8	£20	US

ZODIAC MOTEL
Story Of Roland Flagg	7"	Swordfish	SWF1	198-	£5	£10	1 sided promo
Sunshine Miner	7"	Swordfish	SWF004	1987	£2.50	£6	

ZOMBIES
With sixties rock music keenly seeking wider credibility within the arts generally, much used to be made of the Zombies" educational qualifications. In fact, the Zombies brand of pop-R&B was particularly distinctive, but this had rather more to do with Rod Argent's skilfull keyboard playing and Colin Blunstone's attractive, breathy singing than with any qualifications. "Odessey and Oracle" (the mis-spelling is on the record), recorded as the group was breaking up, is something of a pop masterpiece, inspired by the Beatles no doubt, but nevertheless retaining the Zombies stamp.

Begin Here	LP	Decca	LK4679	1965	£30	£60	
Bunny Lake A Disparu	7" EP	RCA	86507	1965	£15	£30	French
Bunny Lake Is Missing	LP	RCA	RD7791	1965	£15	£30	
Care Of Cell 44	7"	CBS	3087	1967	£4	£8	
Friends Of Mine	7"	CBS	2960	1967	£4	£8	
Goin' Out Of My Head	7"	Decca	F12584	1967	£4	£8	
Gotta Get A Hold Of Myself	7"	Decca	F12495	1966	£2.50	£6	
I Love You	7"	Decca	F12798	1968	£2.50	£6	
Indication	7"	Decca	F12426	1966	£4	£8	
Is This The Dream	7"	Decca	F12296	1965	£2.50	£6	
Is This The Dream	7" EP	Decca	457100	1966	£15	£30	French
Kind Of Girl	7" EP	Decca	457083	1965	£15	£30	French
Leave Me Be	7"	Decca	F12004	1964	£2.50	£6	
Odessey And Oracle	LP	CBS	(S)BPG63280	1968	£15	£30	Sleeve pictured in Guide
Remember You	7"	Decca	F12322	1966	£2.50	£6	
She's Coming Home	7"	Decca	F12125	1965	£2.50	£6	
She's Not There	7"	Decca	F11940	1964	£1.50	£4	chart single
She's Not There	7" EP	Decca	457051	1964	£15	£30	French
Tell Her No	7"	Decca	F12072	1965	£2	£5	chart single
Time Of The Season	7"	CBS	3380	1968	£4	£8	
Time Of The Zombies	LP	Epic	EPC65727	1973	£8	£20	double
What More Can I Do	7" EP	Decca	457075	1965	£15	£30	French
Whenever You're Ready	7"	Decca	F12225	1965	£2.50	£6	
Zombies	7" EP	Decca	DFE8598	1965	£15	£30	

ZOO
I Shall Be Free	LP	Riviera	521147	1971	£5	£12	
Zoo	LP	Barclay	521172	1971	£5	£12	
Zoo	LP	Major Minor	SMLP74	1970	£6	£15	

ZOO (2)
Zoo Presents The Chocolate Mouse	LP	Sunburst	7500	1968	£6	£15	US

ZOROASTER
Ahriman	LP				£330	£500	

ZOSKIA
Be Like Me	12"	Temple	TOPY005	1985	£4	£10	clear vinyl
J.G.	7"	Temple	TOPY021	1987	£2	£5	test pressing

ZOUNDS
La Vache Qui Rit	7"	Not So Brave	NSB001	1982	£1.50	£4	
Manege	7"	Recommended	RR1415	198-	£2	£5	

ZUIDERZEE
Peace Of Mind	7"	CBS	202235	1966	£1.50	£4	

ZWEISTEIN
Trip, Flipout, Meditation	LP	Philips	6630002	1970	£20	£40	German triple

ZYGOAT
Zygoat	LP	Polydor	2383270	1974	£5	£12	

ZZ TOP
Arrested For Driving While Blind	7"	London	HLU10547	1977	£4	£8	
Arrested For Driving While Blind	7"	London	HLU10547	1977	£5	£10	mispress with Ray Charles B side
Beer Drinkers And Hell Raisers	7"	London	HLU10458	1974	£4	£8	
Cheap Sunglasses (Live)	12"	Warner Bros	PRO887	1980	£4	£10	promo
Eliminator	LP	Warner Bros	W3774P	1985	£4	£10	pic disc
Francene	7"	London	HLU10376	1972	£4	£8	
Gimme All Your Lovin'	7"	Warner Bros	W9693P	1983	£6	£12	shaped pic disc
It's Only Love	7"	London	HLU10538	1976	£2.50	£6	
La Grange	7"	London	HLU10475	1975	£4	£8	

Legs (Dance)	12"	Warner Bros	PRO2146	1983	£3	£8	promo
Legs (Extended)	12"	Warner Bros	PRO2127	1983	£3	£8	promo
Rough Boy	7"	Warner Bros	W2003FP	1986	£2	£5	interlocking shaped pic disc
Sleeping Bag	7"	Warner Bros	W2001DP	1985	£2.50	£6	shaped pic disc
Sleeping Bag	7"	Warner Bros	W2001P	1985	£2	£5	interlocking shaped pic disc
Sleeping Bag	7"	Warner Bros	W2001P	1985	£4	£8	shaped pic disc
Stages	7"	Warner Bros	W2002BP	1986	£2	£5	interlocking shaped pic disc
Tejas	LP	London	LDU1	1976	£4	£10	
Tush	7"	London	HLU10495	1975	£2.50	£6	

THE AUTHOR

Nick Hamlyn

Nick Hamlyn is the proprietor of Pied Piper Records, the well-known collectors' record shop in Northampton. He has been a record collector himself for over thirty years and a dealer for over twelve. He has contributed to various rock magazines and record collecting features on the radio, and is to be found giving specialist valuation advice at various record fairs across the country. In his spare time, Nick plays lead guitar for local bands Spindizzy and Six Bop Drop.

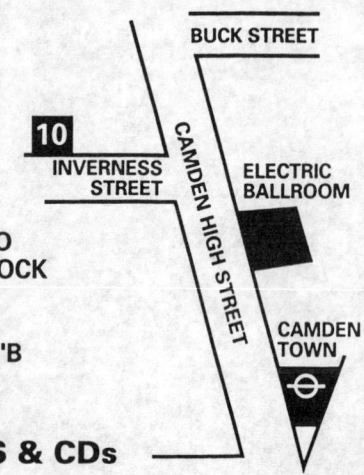